Houghton Mifflin
Math
North Carolina

fraction

radius

angle

Teacher's Edition

Grade 5

Volume 2

 HOUGHTON MIFFLIN BOSTON

Printed in the U.S.A.

ISBN: 0-618-40320-5

3 4 5 6 7 8 9 B 09 08 07 06 05

An Introduction to
Houghton Mifflin
Math
North Carolina

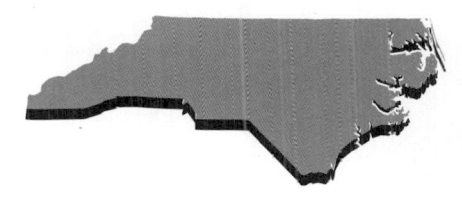

Your Teacher's Edition is a key component for effective and easy teaching of mathematics. This section will give you an overview of *Houghton Mifflin Math.* You will learn about how the exciting features of the program can help you meet the needs of all your students, prepare students for high-stakes testing, and make lessons fun and engaging for your students and you.

Program Authors & Consultants

Authors

Dr. Carole Greenes

Professor of Mathematics Education

Boston University
Boston, Massachusetts

Dr. Matt Larson

Curriculum Specialist for Mathematics

Lincoln Public Schools
Lincoln, Nebraska

Dr. Miriam A. Leiva

Distinguished Professor of Mathematics Emerita

University of North Carolina
Charlotte, North Carolina

Dr. Jean M. Shaw

Professor Emerita of Curriculum and Instruction

University of Mississippi
Oxford, Mississippi

Dr. Lee Stiff

Professor of Mathematics Education

North Carolina State University
Raleigh, North Carolina

Dr. Bruce R. Vogeli

Clifford Brewster Upton Professor of Mathematics

Teachers College, Columbia University
New York, New York

Dr. Karol Yeatts

Associate Professor

Barry University
Miami, Florida

Consultants

Strategic Consultant

Dr. Liping Ma

Senior Scholar

Carnegie Foundation for the Advancement of Technology
Palo Alto, California

Language and Vocabulary Consultant

Dr. David Chard

Professor of Reading

University of Oregon
Eugene, Oregon

North Carolina Teacher Advisory Panel Members

Stephanie McDaniel
Grade 1
B. Everett Jordan Elementary School
Graham, NC

Yvette Smith
Grade 1
Northeast Elementary School
Pikeville, NC

Caroline Annas
Grade 2
Shepherd Elementary School
Moorsville, NC

Del Daniels
Grade 2
Meadow Lane Elementary School
Goldsboro, NC

Tracy McKeel
Grade 3
Rosewood Elementary School
Goldsboro, NC

Fran Coleman
Grade 3
Rosenwald Elementary School
Fairmont, NC

Janet Lee Blue
Grade 4
Rosenwald Elementary School
Fairmont, NC

Lynnetta Burton
Grade 4
Pleasant Grove Elementary School
Burlington, NC

Amy Janning
Grade 5
Spring Creek Elementary School
Goldsboro, NC

Brenda Sharts
Elementary Director
Cleveland County Schools
Shelby, NC

Teacher Reviewers

KINDERGARTEN

Karen Sue Hinton
Washington Elementary School
Ponca City, OK

Hilda Kendrick
W. E. Wilson Elementary School
Jefferson, IN

Debby Nagel
Assumption Elementary School
Cincinnati, OH

GRADE 1

Stephanie McDaniel
B. Everett Jordan Elementary School
Graham, NC

Juan Melgar
Lowrie Elementary School
Elgin, IL

Sharon O'Brien
Echo Mountain School
Phoenix, AZ

GRADE 2

Sally Bales
Akron Elementary School
Akron, IN

Rose Marie Bruno
Mawbey Street Elementary School
Woodbridge, NJ

Megan Burton
Valley Elementary School
Pelham, AL

GRADE 3

Jenny Chang
North Elementary School
Waukegan, IL

Patricia Heintz
PS 92
Harry T. Stewart Elementary School
Corona, NY

Allison White
Kingsley Elementary School
Naperville, IL

GRADE 4

Kathy Curtis
Hoxsie School
Warwick, RI

Lynn Fox
Kendall-Whittier Elementary School
Tulsa, OK

Barbara O'Hanlon
Maurice & Everett Haines
Elementary School
Medford, NJ

Connie Rapp
Oakland Elementary School
Bloomington, IL

Pam Rettig
Solheim Elementary Schoo
Bismarck, ND

Tracy Smith
Carstens Elementary School
Detroit, MI

GRADE 5

Jim Archer
Maplewood Elementary School
Indianapolis, IN

Linda Carlson
Van Buren Elementary School
Oklahoma City, OK

Maggie Dunning
Horizon Elementary School
Hanover Park, IL

Mike Intoccia
McNichols Plaza
Scranton, PA

Jennifer LaBelle
Washington Elementary School
Waukegan, IL

Peg McCann
Warwick Neck School
Warwick, RI

GRADE 6

Robin Akers
Sonoran Sky Elementary School
Scottsdale, AZ

Ellen Greenman
Daniel Webster Middle School
Waukegan, IL

Angela McCray
Abbott Middle School
West Bloomfield, MI

Houghton Mifflin
Math

Reaching All Learners, All Of The Time.

HOUGHTON MIFFLIN

Houghton Mifflin Math A+

Time-Tested Approaches Ensure Proven Results

Houghton Mifflin Math really works! Here's why:

★ It's proven with scientifically based research.

★ It's based on more than 30 years of studies on how students learn best.

★ It incorporates models and strategies from high-performing classrooms.

★ It meets the needs of all learners.

A Complete System of Intervention and Challenge Means Success for All Learners

With a variety of specialized, focused teaching support, you can effectively manage instruction to meet the diverse needs of all students in your classroom.

Reaching All Learners

Practical point-of-use support is built into each lesson so that your English learners, gifted and talented students, early finishers, and struggling students can all reach their goals.

 **MathTracks MP3 Audio CD**

Our unique audio tutor on audio CD reteaches lessons just as you would to students who have missed instruction or who need a little extra support in mastering content and building confidence.

Ways to Success Intervention CD-ROM

Built into every lesson, this special safety net of support ensures that students stay on track with diagnostic reteaching and plenty of practice.

Chapter Challenges

Encourage advanced students to put their skills to the test and expand their thinking with challenging activities and projects linked to each chapter.

Lesson Planner

Customize daily instruction with this powerful CD-ROM to meet your state standards and school calendar, then personalize the lessons to match your teaching style, the needs of your students, and the materials you have on hand.

Activity

Or use Intervention CD-ROM Lesson 5.3

Lesson Intervention
Using Counters to Model Equations

| 👤👤👤 Small Group | ⏱ 5–10 minutes | Tactile, Visual |

1. Provide two-color counters. Have students make stacks of four counters each. Guide them to see that the stacks are equal because each has the same number of counters.
2. Have students add a counter to one pile. **Are the stacks equal now?** (No.) **How can they be made equal again?** (Either add a counter to the shorter stack or take away the fifth counter from the taller stack.)
3. Repeat and vary this procedure for other size stacks to help students see the distinction [between equal and] unequal values.

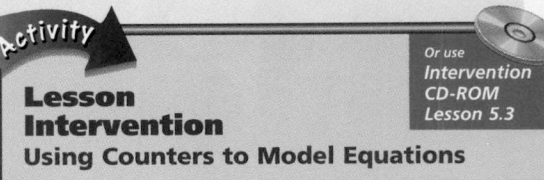

Houghton Mifflin Math

CHAPTER Challenges

• For mathematically promising students
• Opportunities to explore, extend, and connect mathematical ideas

GRADE 5

Houghton Mifflin Math

Lesson Planner

CD-ROM

PLUS, a wide selection of leveled resources for Practice, Reteach, Enrichment, Problem Solving, Homework, and English Learners Links to each lesson for your convenience!

Compelling Literature and Real-World Connections Give Immediate Meaning to Math

With engaging literature plus strong connections, our program reinforces math concepts and demonstrates the value of mathematics in everyday life, for every student.

- Authentic literature selections enable young learners to connect mathematics to their own world.

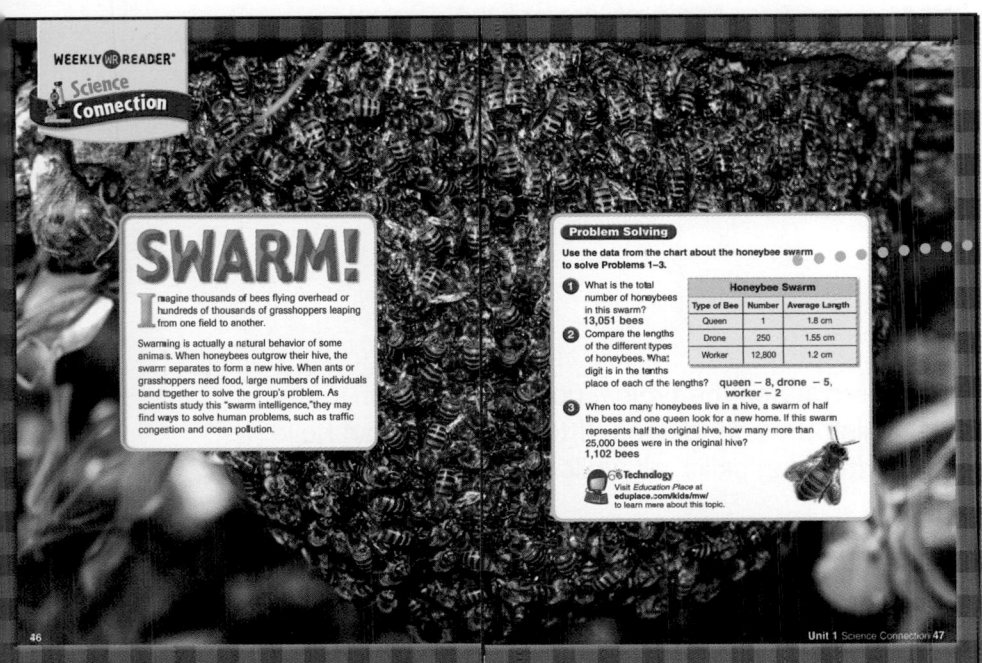

- A special partnership with *Weekly Reader®* makes our real-world and curriculum connections dynamic, relevant, and just right for your students.

A Plan for Test-Taking Success Builds Skills and Confidence

With a four-tiered plan that systematically builds critical skills, your students are sure to perform well on standardized tests, every time.

1 Using a series of guided questions, students effectively build the reasoning and thinking skills necessary for test-taking achievement.

2 With daily exposure to typical test content and questions, plus instruction on critical test-taking strategies, students feel more comfortable and focused on test days.

3 Powerful practice in listening, reading, and problem-solving strategies prepares students for the challenges of test taking.

4 With authentic practice that replicates the typical content, question format, materials, and administrative conditions of test day, you can build students' confidence and test-taking skills, all while ensuring success.

And, our comprehensive, daily vocabulary plan reinforces the mathematical language included on state tests.

Technology Solutions Help You Manage the Big Jobs of Your Classroom

A wealth of technology on CD-ROM and the Web provides everything you need to make your job easier and builds motivation and skill in your students.

Just for Students

eMathBook

With content identical to the student books, an eGlossary, and printable homework masters, our eMathBook—available on CD-ROM and via the Web—makes math readily accessible to students on the go.

Especially for Teachers

Ways to Success Intervention CD-ROM

Developed to engage students and offer self-help and extra support, our easy-to-use CD-ROM features diagnostic and prescriptive reteaching, focused practice, plus background-building opportunities for customized intervention that links to each lesson.

Ways to Assess CD-ROM (Test and Spiral Review Generator)

Create, print, and administer customized assessments in print or online form for all lessons in *Houghton Mifflin Math*. With ready-made Chapter and Unit tests, plus multiple-choice, fill-in-the-blank, and free-response question formats, you can easily choose which tests best fit your classroom. And you can instantly generate spiral reviews based on specific lesson objectives, student needs, and your own teaching sequence.

For Students, Teachers, Parents, and Caregivers

Education Place®

Packed with an array of FREE materials and support for the lessons in *Houghton Mifflin Math*, including a Math Vocabulary Glossary, Games, Brain Teasers, Extra Practice, Homework Help, Teaching Models, Manipulatives, Family Letters, and so much more, our award-winning Web site has it all!

Visit **www.eduplace.com/math/mw** today.

Technology that gets you and your students ready for success!

Components

	K	1	2	3	4	5	6
Student Book	●	●	●	●	●	●	●
Student Book, Multi-Volume Sets	●	●	●				
Big Book	●						
Teacher's Edition	●	●	●	●	●	●	●
Read-Aloud Anthologies, Volumes 1–4	●	●	●				
Trade Book Literature Library	●	●	●	●	●	●	●
Unit Resource Folders	●	●	●	●	●	●	●
Reteach/Practice/Enrichment	●	●	●	●	●	●	●
Problem Solving/Homework/English Learners		●	●	●	●	●	●
Assessments/Learning Tools	●	●	●	●	●	●	●
Practice Workbook	●	●	●	●	●	●	●
Homework Workbook		●	●	●	●	●	●
English Learners Handbook	●	●	●	●	●	●	●
Building Vocabulary Kit	●	●	●	●	●	●	●
Test Prep Blackline Masters		●	●	●	●	●	●
Chapter Challenges	●	●	●	●	●	●	●
Combination Classroom Planning Guide	●	●	●	●	●	●	●
Kindergarten Kit	●						
Busy Bear Puppet	●						
Math Songs for Young Learners	●						
Student Manipulatives Kit	●	●	●	●	●	●	●
Custom Manipulatives Kits	●	●	●	●	●	●	●
Overhead Manipulatives Kit	●	●	●	●	●	●	●
Math Center	●	●	●	●	●	●	●
Lesson Transparencies	●	●	●	●	●	●	●
Daily Routines Flip Chart	●	●	●	●	●	●	●
Teaching Transparencies	●	●	●	●	●	●	●
Test Prep Transparencies		●	●	●	●	●	●
Lesson Planner CD-ROM	●	●	●	●	●	●	●
Ways to Success Intervention CD-ROM		●	●	●	●	●	●
Chapter Intervention Blackline Masters		●	●	●	●	●	●
eMathBook (Student Book on CD-ROM)	●	●	●	●	●	●	●
Ways to Assess CD-ROM (test and spiral review generator)		●	●	●	●	●	●
MathTracks MP3 Audio CD		●	●	●	●	●	●
Learner Profile		●	●	●	●	●	●
Education Place Web site	●	●	●	●	●	●	●

Manipulatives

Program Manipulatives	Suggested Alternatives	K	1	2	3	4	5	6
Algebra Tiles	Bars and squares made from grid paper or construction paper						●	●
Attribute Blocks	Seashells, pasta, buttons	●	●	●				
Balance Scales	Ruler, paper cups, and string	●	●	●	●	●	●	●
Bill Set	Bills made from construction paper and markers	●	●	●	●	●	●	●
Blank Number Cubes with Labels	Number cards, spinners	●	●	●	●	●	●	●
Coin Set	Real coins, buttons	●	●	●	●	●	●	●
Connecting Cubes	Paper clips, string and beads or pasta	●	●	●	●	●	●	●
Counting Chips	Buttons, coins, beans	●						
Demonstration Clock	Clockface with two lengths of string fastened to the center for the hands	●	●	●	●	●	●	●
Fraction Strips	Bars and squares made from grid paper or construction paper				●	●	●	●
Geometric Solids	Cans, boxes, balls, cones, modeling clay shapes	●	●	●	●	●	●	●
Geotool Compass							●	●
Pattern Blocks	Shapes cut out of different-colored construction paper or cardboard	●	●	●	●	●	●	●
Place-Value Blocks/ Base Ten Blocks	Grid paper cutouts	●	●	●	●	●	●	●
Protractor						●	●	●
Ruler, inch and centimeter	One-inch or one-centimeter grid paper strips					●	●	●	●
Transparent Spinner	Construction paper, paper clip, and pencil	●	●	●	●	●	●	●
Two-Color Counters	Coins, washers, or beans with one side painted	●	●	●	●	●	●	●

Scope and Sequence

In the Program...

Number and Operations

KEY: Teach and Apply ●   Practice and Apply ▲   Teacher's Edition Lesson ★

Addition

	K	1	2	3	4	5	6
Adding decimals				●	●	▲	▲
Adding fractions				●	●	▲	▲
Adding integers and rational numbers					●	●	▲
Adding measurements						●	▲
Adding mixed numbers					●	▲	▲
Adding money	●	●	●	●	▲	▲	●
Adding multi-digit numbers	●	●	●	▲	▲	▲	▲
Adding whole numbers	●	●	▲	▲	▲	▲	▲
Basic facts	●	●	▲				
Equations						●	▲
Estimating sums		●	●	▲	▲	▲	▲
Expressions					●	●	▲
Inverse operations					●	▲	▲
Mental math		●	●	●	●	▲	▲
Missing addends	●	●	●	▲	▲		
Number sentences	●	●	●	▲	▲		
Problem-solving applications	●	●	●	▲	▲	▲	▲
Properties of addition		●	●	▲	▲	▲	▲
Regrouping to add		●	●	●	▲	▲	▲
Strategies for adding	●	●	●	▲	▲		
Three or more addends		●	▲				

Comparing and Ordering Numbers

	K	1	2	3	4	5	6
Decimals				●	●	▲	▲
Decimals and fractions				●	●	●	▲
Decimals, fractions, and percents						●	▲
Fractions			●	●	●	▲	▲
Integers					●	▲	▲
Money amounts	●	●	●	▲			
Percents						●	●
Rational numbers						●	●
Using <, >, and = symbols		●	●	●	▲	▲	▲
Whole numbers	●	●	●	▲	▲	▲	▲

Counting, Reading, Writing Numbers

	K	1	2	3	4	5	6
Decimals				●	●	●	▲
Fractions		●	●	●	▲	▲	▲
Integers						●	▲
Mixed numbers				●	●	▲	▲
Money	●	●	▲	▲			
Ordinal Numbers	●	●	●	▲			
Percent						●	●
Powers and exponents						●	●
Rational numbers						●	●
Roman and other numerals			●	●	●	▲	▲
Scientific notation						●	●
Square numbers				●	●	●	●
Square roots							●
Whole numbers	●	●	●	●	●	▲	▲

KEY   Teach and Apply ●   Practice and Apply ▲   Teacher's Edition Lesson ★

In Level 5...

Number and Operations

Addition

adding decimals 282–285
adding fractions
  like denominators 258–259
  unlike denominators 260–261
  writing sums in simplest form 260–261
adding integers 592–595, 598–601
adding measurements 164–165
adding mixed numbers 258–259, 262–264
adding money 282–285
adding whole numbers 34–36, 38–39
  estimating sums 32–33
addition equations 40–41
addition expressions 28–30
estimating sums
  of decimals 290–291
  of fractions 256–257
  of whole numbers 32–33
inverse operations 568–570
mental math 32–33, 256–257, 290–291
order of operations 124–126
properties of addition
  Associative Property 28–30
  Commutative Property 28–30
  Zero Property 28–30

Comparing

decimals
  comparing digits 20–22
  different number of places 20–22, 248–250
  with fractions 248–250
decimals, fractions, and percents 510–513
fractions
  with decimals 248–250
  with unlike denominators 248–250
integers 588–591
measurements 152–154, 160–162
mixed numbers and decimals 248–250
rational numbers 591
using <, >, and = symbols 10–12, 20–22, 46–47, 158–159, 161–162, 248–250, 484–485, 588–590, 591
whole numbers 10–12

Ordering

decimals 20–22, 248–250
fractions 248–250
integers 588–591
mixed numbers, fractions, and decimals 248–250
rational numbers 591
whole numbers 10–12

Counting, Reading, Writing Numbers

decimals 14–15
fractions 237–238
integers 586–590
mixed numbers 237–238
percent 506–507, 513, 519
powers and exponents 6–9, 125–127, 156, 225–227, 343, 356–357, 571
rational numbers 591
Roman numerals 23
scientific notation 343
square numbers 571
whole numbers 4–5, 6–7, 8–9, 10–12

In the Program...

Number and Operations

In Level 5...

Number and Operations

Decimals

	K	1	2	3	4	5	6
Adding decimals				●	●	▲	▲
Comparing decimals				●	●	▲	▲
Decimal notation			●	●	▲	▲	▲
Decimals and fractions				●	●	▲	▲
Decimals and mixed numbers				●	●	▲	▲
Decimals and percents						●	▲
Dividing decimals						●	▲
Estimating decimals					●	●	▲
Modeling decimals				●	▲		
Multiplying decimals						●	▲
Ordering decimals				●	●	▲	▲
Place value of decimals				●	●	▲	▲
Reading decimals			●	●	●	▲	▲
Repeating and terminating						●	●
Rounding decimals					●	▲	▲
Subtracting decimals				●	●	▲	▲
Writing decimals			●	●	▲	▲	▲

Division

	K	1	2	3	4	5	6
Basic facts			●	●	▲		
Checking division with multiplication				●	▲	▲	▲
Dividing decimals						●	▲
Dividing fractions						●	▲
Dividing integers and rational numbers							●
Dividing mixed numbers						●	▲
Dividing money				●	●	▲	▲
Dividing whole numbers			●	●	●	▲	▲
Division as equal groups			●	▲	▲		
Equations						●	▲
Estimating the quotient				●	●	▲	▲
Expressions					●	▲	▲
Fact families				●	▲		
Missing factors				●	▲	▲	▲
Number sentences				●	▲		
Problem-solving applications			●	●	▲	▲	▲
Relating multiplication and division				●	▲	▲	▲
Relating subtraction and division				●	▲		
Remainders				●	●	▲	
Strategies for dividing			●	●	▲		

Decimals

adding decimals 282–285
comparing decimals 20–22, 248–250
  with fractions 248–250
  with fractions and percents 510–513
decimal patterns 16–18
decimals as fractions 508–509
decimals as mixed numbers 248–250
decimals as percents 508–509
dividing decimals 352–353, 356–360, 362–364, 368–369
estimating 290–291, 338–339, 354–355
fractions as decimals 508–509
measurement and decimals 283, 287–291, 342, 355, 357, 360, 364, 369
mixed numbers as decimals 248–250
money and decimals 79, 282–285, 372, 337
multiplying decimals 334–342
multiplying money in decimal notation 337
number lines 20–22
ordering decimals 20–22, 248–250
ordering decimals, fractions, and mixed numbers 248–250
place-value chart 14
place value of decimals 14–15
reading decimals 14–15
repeating decimals 366–367
rounding decimals 20–22, 290–291
subtracting decimals 286–288
writing decimals 14–15

Division

checking division with multiplication 88–89
dividing by powers of ten 156–158, 356–357
dividing decimals 352–360, 362–364, 368–369
dividing fractions 320–323
dividing mixed numbers 324–326
dividing money amounts 372
dividing whole numbers
  by a fraction 320–321
  by multiples of ten 110–111
  one-digit divisors 86–105
  two-digit divisors 112–113, 120–122
  zeros in the quotient 96–97
divisibility rules 92–94
division equations 102–104
division expressions 359
estimating quotients 86–87, 118–119, 354–355
order of operations 124–126
remainder 88–89, 370–372
short division 127
using repeated subtraction 127

KEY Teach and Apply ● Practice and Apply ▲ Teacher's Edition Lesson ★

Scope and Sequence

Number and Operations

	K	1	2	3	4	5	6
Estimating							
Benchmarks		●	●	●	▲	▲	▲
Estimated or Exact Answer?				●	●	●	●
Estimating decimals				●	●	●	▲
Estimating differences				●	●	▲	▲
Estimating fractions					●	▲	▲
Estimating measures	●	●	●	▲	▲	▲	▲
Estimating money			●	●	●	▲	
Estimating products				●	●	▲	▲
Estimating quotients				●	●	▲	▲
Estimating sums		●	●	▲	▲	▲	▲
For reasonableness of answer				●	▲	▲	▲
Quantities	●	▲					
Using a referent	●	●	▲	▲			
Using strategies		●	●	●	●	▲	▲
Fractions							
Adding fractions				●	●	▲	▲
Comparing fractions			●	●	●	▲	▲
Decimals and fractions				●	●	▲	▲
Decimals and percents						●	▲
Dividing fractions						●	▲
Equivalent fractions				●	●	▲	▲
Improper fractions			●	●	▲	▲	▲
Meaning of fractions	●	●	●	●	▲	▲	▲
Measurement and fractions				●	▲	▲	▲
Mixed numbers				●	▲	▲	▲
Modeling fractions	●	●	●	▲	▲	▲	▲
Multiplying fractions						●	▲
Ordering fractions			●	▲	▲	▲	▲
Ratios and fractions						●	▲
Reciprocals						●	●
Simplifying fractions					●	●	▲
Subtracting fractions				●	●	●	▲
Integers and Rational Numbers							
Absolute value						●	▲
Adding and subtracting integers					●	●	▲
Comparing and ordering					●	●	▲
Graphing on the number line					●	●	▲
Meaning					●	●	▲
Multiplicative inverse							●
Multiplying and dividing integers							●
Negative numbers on a thermometer				●	●	▲	▲
Operations with rational numbers							●
Opposites						●	●
Scientific notation						●	●

KEY Teach and Apply ●   Practice and Apply ▲   Teacher's Edition Lesson ★

Number and Operations

Estimation
adjusting the quotient 118–119
benchmarks (fractions) 256–257
differences 32–33, 256–257, 290–291
Estimated or Exact Answer? 500
for reasonableness of answers 34, 262, 346–347
measurement 148–149, 163
products 74–75, 338–339
quotients 86–87, 118-119, 354–355
sums 32–33, 256–257, 290–291
using strategies
  clustering 290–291
  compatible numbers 86–87, 88, 110–111, 112
  front-end estimation 290–291
  rounding 32–33, 74–75, 86–87, 338–339, 354–355

Fractions
adding fractions 258–261
changing fractions to mixed numbers 236–239
comparing fractions
  with decimals 248–250
  with decimals and percents 510–513
  with fractions 248–250
decimal equivalent 248–250
dividing 320–323
equivalent fractions
  dividing to find 240–241
  in simplest form 240–241
  meaning of equivalent fraction 240–241
  mixed numbers and equivalent fractions 236–239
  multiplying to find 240–241
estimating fraction sums and differences 256–257
expressing a remainder as a fraction 370–371
fractional parts
  of a region 236–239
  of an inch 148–151
improper fractions 237–238
least common denominator 268–269
meaning of fractions 236–238, 239
measurement and fractions 148–151
multiplying fractions 310–315
ordering fractions 248–250
ordering fractions, decimals, and mixed numbers 248–250
percent 508–509
probability and fractions 532–535, 540–547
ratio and fractions 484–485
reciprocals 322–323
simplifying 240–241
subtracting fractions 268–269

Integers and Rational Numbers
absolute value and 586–587
adding 598–604
comparing and ordering 588–590
multiplicative inverses (reciprocals) 322
opposites 586, 598
rational numbers 591
scientific notation 343
subtracting 596–604
using to solve problems 602–604

Number and Operations

Mental Math

	K	1	2	3	4	5	6
Addition		●	●	●	●	▲	▲
Division				●	▲	▲	▲
Multiples and powers of 10		●	●	●	▲	▲	▲
Multiplication				●	▲	▲	▲
Patterns	●	●	▲	▲	▲	▲	▲
Problem-solving applications			●	▲	▲	▲	▲
Subtraction		●	●	▲	▲	▲	▲
Use properties		●	●	●	●	▲	▲

Mixed Numbers

	K	1	2	3	4	5	6
Adding mixed numbers					●	▲	▲
Decimals and mixed numbers				●	●	▲	▲
Dividing mixed numbers						●	▲
Meaning of mixed numbers				●	▲	▲	▲
Multiplying mixed numbers						●	▲
Subtracting mixed numbers					●	▲	▲
Using a number line with mixed numbers				●	▲	▲	▲
Writing mixed numbers				●	▲	▲	▲

Multiplication

	K	1	2	3	4	5	6
Arrays			●	▲			
Basic facts		●	●	●	▲		
Concrete/pictorial representations	●	●	●	▲			
Drawing a picture to multiply		●	●	▲			
Equations						●	▲
Estimating products				●	●	▲	▲
Expressions					●	▲	▲
Horizontal and vertical forms				●	▲		
Mental math				●	▲	▲	▲
Missing factors					●	▲	▲
Multiplication as equal groups	●	●	●	▲			
Multiplying decimals						●	▲
Multiplying fractions						●	▲
Multiplying integers and rational numbers							●
Multiplying mixed numbers						●	▲
Multiplying money				●	●	▲	▲
Multiplying three factors				●	▲	▲	▲
Multiplying whole numbers		●	●	▲	▲	▲	▲
Number sentences			●	●	▲		
Problem-solving applications			●	▲	▲	▲	▲
Properties of multiplication			●	●	▲	▲	▲
Related facts			●	●	▲		
Related to other operations			●	●	▲	▲	▲
Skip-counting to multiply	●	●	●	●	▲		
Square numbers				●	▲	▲	▲
Strategies			●	●	▲		

KEY Teach and Apply ●   Practice and Apply ▲   Teacher's Edition Lesson ★

Number and Operations

Mental Math

adding 258, 290–291
dividing 110–111, 356–357
multiplying 72–73, 338–339, 356–357
problem solving with equations 40–41, 102–104
subtracting 275, 290–291
using patterns in multiplication 72–73
use properties 60–61, 68–69
  breaking apart numbers 62–63, 139
  properties of zero and one 28–30, 60–61

Mixed Numbers

adding mixed numbers 258–259, 262–264
comparing to decimals 248–250
dividing 324–326
mixed numbers as decimals 248–250
mixed numbers as fractions 236–239
multiplying mixed numbers 316–318
simplest form 266–267, 274–276
subtracting mixed numbers
  with like denominators 266–267
  with unlike denominators 274–276
using a number line with mixed numbers 246–247
writing mixed numbers 236–239

Multiplication

composite numbers 224–225
equations 102–104
estimating products 74–75, 338–339
exponents 343, 571
expressions 60–61
multiples
  common multiples 232–234
  least common multiple 232–235
multiplying decimals
  by a decimal 334–335, 340–342
  by a whole number 336–337
  zeros in the product 344–345
multiplying fractions
  by a fraction 310–315
  by a whole number 310–315
multiplying mixed numbers 316–318
multiplying money amounts 79, 337
multiplying to check division 88–89
multiplying whole numbers
  multiplying by one-digit numbers
    three, four or five digits 68–70
  multiplying by two-digit numbers
    three or four digits 76–78
prime factorization 226–227
prime numbers 224–225
properties
  Associative Property 60–61
  Commutative Property 60–61
  Distributive Property 60–61
  Identity Property 60–61
  Zero Property 60–61
square numbers 571

Scope and Sequence

In the Program...

Number and Operations

	K	1	2	3	4	5	6
Number Theory							
Even and odd numbers	●	●	●	▲	▲	▲	▲
Factor trees				●		▲	▲
Factors			●	●	▲	▲	▲
Figurate numbers						▲	▲
Greatest common factor						●	▲
Least common denominator						●	▲
Least common multiple						●	▲
Multiples				●	●	●	▲
Prime factorization						●	▲
Prime and composite numbers					●	●	▲
Reciprocals						●	▲
Rules for divisibility						●	▲
Place Value							
Decimals				●	●	▲	▲
Expanded form			●	▲	▲	▲	▲
Millions and billions					●	▲	▲
Money				●	●	▲	▲
Standard form	●	●	●	▲	▲	▲	▲
Using a place-value chart		●	●	●	▲	▲	▲
Whole numbers	●	●	●	▲	▲	▲	▲
Ratio, Proportion, and Percent							
Estimation with percents						●	●
Finding a percent of a number						●	●
Meaning of percents				●	●	●	●
Percents related to circle graphs						●	●
Percents related to fractions and/or decimals				●	●	●	●
Rates					●	▲	▲
Reading and writing ratios						●	●
Writing and solving proportions						●	●
Subtraction							
Basic facts	●	●	●	▲			
Checking subtraction		●	●	●	▲	▲	▲
Equations						●	▲
Estimating differences				●	●	▲	▲
Expressions						●	▲
Mental math		●	●	●	▲	▲	▲
Number sentences	●	●	●	▲	▲	▲	▲
Problem-solving applications	●	●	▲	▲	▲	▲	▲
Properties of subtraction				●	▲	▲	▲
Regrouping to subtract				●	▲	▲	▲
Strategies for subtracting	●		●	▲	▲	▲	
Subtracting decimals					●	●	▲
Subtracting fractions					●	●	▲
Subtracting integers						●	▲
Subtracting mixed numbers					●	▲	▲
Subtracting measurements						●	▲
Subtracting money	●	●	●	●	▲	▲	▲
Subtracting whole numbers	●	●	▲	▲	▲	▲	▲
Subtracting with zeros				●	●	▲	▲

KEY   Teach and Apply ●   Practice and Apply ▲   Teacher's Edition Lesson ★

In Level 5...

Number and Operations

Number Theory
common multiples 232–234
composite numbers 224–225
divisibility rules 92–94
exponents 343, 571
factor tree 226–227
factors 224–225
  greatest common factor (GCF) 228–230
greatest common divisor (GCD) 228–230
multiples 232–235
  least common multiple (LCM) 232–235
prime numbers 224–225
reciprocals 322–323

Place Value
chart 4–5
comma and periods 4–5
decimals 14–15
expanded form 4–9
exponent form of a number 6–7
hundred thousands 4–5
millions, billions, trillions 8–12, 38–39
short word form 8–9
standard form 4–9
whole numbers 4–5
word form 8–9

Ratio, Proportion, and Percent
estimation with percents 514–515, 519
finding a percent of a number 514–515, 516–518
meaning of percents 506–507, 513, 519
meaning of ratio 484–485, 486–487, 519
percents related to circle graphs 520–521
percents related to fractions and decimals 508–509, 510–512, 523
rates 488–490, 491
reading and writing ratios 484–485
writing and solving proportions 492–494

Subtraction
checking subtraction with addition 35–36
estimating differences 32–33
  of decimals 290–291
  of fractions 256–257
  of whole numbers 32–33
inverse operations 568–570
money amounts 286–288
subtracting decimals 286–288
subtracting fractions
  with like denominators 266–267
  with unlike denominators 268–269
subtracting integers 596–601
subtracting measurements 164–165
subtracting mixed numbers 266–267, 274–276
subtracting whole numbers
  subtracting across zeros 34–36
  subtracting four-digit and five-digit numbers 34–36
  subtracting six–digit and seven–digit numbers 38–39
subtraction equations 40–41, 566-567
subtraction expressions 28–30

Algebra

	K	1	2	3	4	5	6
Readiness and Applications							
Addition and subtraction number sentences	●	●	●	▲	▲		
Analyze change	●	●	●	▲	▲	▲	▲
Fact families		●	●	●	▲		
Inverse operations		●	●	●	▲	▲	▲
Meaning of equality				●	●	▲	▲
Missing addends	●	●	●	▲	▲		
Missing digits			▲	▲	▲	▲	▲
Missing factors			●	●	▲	▲	▲
Missing measurements and units			●	●	●	▲	▲
Missing operations	●	●	●	●	▲	▲	▲
Multiplication and division number sentences			●	●	▲	▲	▲
Proportional reasoning	●	●	●	●	▲	▲	▲
Symbols showing relations	●	●	●	▲	▲	▲	▲
Variables			●	●	●	▲	▲
Venn diagrams		●	●	●	●	▲	▲
Writing and solving number sentences or equations	●	●	●	●	●	●	●
Coordinate Graphs							
Graphing ordered pairs			●	●	▲	▲	▲
Ordered pairs			●	●	▲	▲	▲
Equations and Inequalities							
Equations with more than one variable						●	●
Graphing an equation						●	▲
Linear equations						●	▲
Modeling equations		●	●	●	▲	▲	▲
Formulas					●	●	▲
Solving addition and subtraction equations						●	▲
Solving equations by using inverse operations						●	▲
Solving multiplication and division equations						●	▲
Writing an equation or number sentence				●	●	▲	▲
Writing and solving proportions						●	▲
Writing and solving percent equations						●	▲

Algebra

Readiness and Applications

analyze change
   changing one variable produces a change in another variable 576–581
   identify, compare and describe changes 37, 404–406, 622–625
classifying and sorting 242, 394, 396–397, 400–401
fact families 102–104
equations
   reading, writing, and evaluating
      addition 40–41, 566–577
      division 102–104, 566–577
      multiplication 102–104, 566–577
      subtraction 40–41, 566–577
      using inverse operations to solve 568–570
inequality 10–12, 20–22, 248–250, 588–591
integers
   absolute value 586–587
   adding 592–595, 598–601
   comparing and ordering 588–591
   opposite 586–587
   subtracting 596–601
inverse operations 568–570
meaning of equality 40–41
missing addends, 35, 40–41
missing digits 12, 22, 70, 97
missing factors 60–61, 70
missing measurements and units 150–153, 157–158, 160–161
multiplication and division number sentences 102–104
proportional reasoning
   better buy 162
   equivalences in measurement and money 150–154, 156–162, 164–166
   equivalent fractions 240–241
   map scales/scale drawings 496–498, 499
   probabilities 530–531, 532–534, 540–542, 552–553
symbols showing relations 10–12, 20–22, 40–41
variables 28–30
Venn diagrams 242

Coordinate Graphs

function table 576–581, 614–618
graphing a function 616–618
graphing a line 616–618
integers 610–612
ordered pairs
   graphing 178–180, 610–612
   locating on a grid 610–612
plotting points 610–612
quadrants 610–612
transformations 622–625
x–coordinate 610–612
y–coordinate 610–612

Equations and Inequalities

reading, writing, and evaluating
   addition 40–41, 566–577
   division 102–104, 566–577
   multiplication 102–104, 566–577
   subtraction 40–41, 566–577
   using inverse operations to solve 568–570

KEY Teach and Apply ●   Practice and Apply ▲   Teacher's Edition Lesson ★

In the Program...
Algebra

In Level 5...
Algebra

	K	1	2	3	4	5	6
Expressions							
Evaluate by substitution					●	●	▲
Evaluate by using order of operations					●	●	▲
Exploring expressions		●	●	●	▲		
Expressions with exponents						●	▲
Inverse relationship of addition and subtraction		●	●	▲	▲	▲	▲
Inverse relationship of multiplication and division				●	▲	▲	▲
Order of operations					●	▲	▲
Pi as a ratio						●	▲
Writing expressions				●	●	●	▲
Patterns and Functions							
Continuing patterns	●	●	●	●	▲	▲	▲
Describing patterns	●	●	●	●	▲	▲	▲
Function tables						●	●
Input/output tables		●	▲	▲	▲	▲	▲
Measurement patterns			●	●	▲	▲	▲
Numerical patterns		●	●	▲	▲	▲	▲
Patterns in the coordinate plane						●	●
Special patterns and sequences		●	●	▲	▲	▲	▲
Tessellations			●	●	▲	▲	▲
Using patterns to solve problems	●	●	●	▲	▲	▲	▲
Visual patterns	●	●	●	▲	▲	▲	▲
Properties							
Associative Property		●	●	●	▲	▲	▲
Commutative Property		●	●	▲	▲	▲	▲
Distributive Property					●	●	▲
Equality Property							●
Identity Property				●	▲	▲	▲
Inverse Property							●
Zero Property		●	●	●	▲	▲	▲

Equations and Inequalities (continued)
formulas
  area 428–433
  circumference 438–441
  perimeter 422–423
  surface area 452–455
  volume 460–463
graphing a function 616–618
inverse operations
  using inverse operations to solve equations 568–570
proportion
  equivalent ratio and proportion 492–495
  percent 519
  using cross products 492–495

Expressions
reading, writing, and evaluating
  addition 28–30
  division 359
  multiplication 60–61
  subtraction 28–30
Order of operations 124–126
ratio
  equivalent ratios 486–487, 492–495
  in simplest form 486–487
  reading and writing 484–485
  scale drawing and ratios 496–499

Patterns and Functions
function table
  integers 614–618
  whole numbers 576–581
patterns
  continuing patterns 16–18
  describing patterns 16–18
  geometric patterns 417, 424–426
  number patterns 16–18, 71–73, 605
special patterns and sequences
  Sieve of Eratosthenes 231
  tessellations 417
using patterns 16–18, 72–73, 110–111, 424–426

Properties
Associative Property 28–30
Commutative Property 28–30
Distributive Property 62–63
Identity Property 28–30, 60–61
Zero Property 60–61

KEY   Teach and Apply ●   Practice and Apply ▲   Teacher's Edition Lesson ★

Geometry

Geometry

	K	1	2	3	4	5	6
Basic Figures							
Attributes of plane figures		●	●	●	▲	▲	▲
Basic figures: square, rectangle, triangle, and circle	●	●	●	▲	▲	▲	▲
Classifying and sorting figures and shapes	●	●	●	●	▲	▲	▲
Geometric patterns	●	●	●	▲	▲	▲	▲
Pattern blocks: triangle, square, rhombus, trapezoid, hexagon	●	●	●	●	▲	▲	▲
Real-life objects	●	●	▲	▲	▲	▲	▲
Sides, corners, square corners		●	●	▲			
Plane Figures and Spatial Sense							
Angles			●	●	▲	▲	▲
Circles	●	●	●	●	▲	▲	▲
Circumference						●	▲
Comparing angles				●	●	▲	▲
Complex figures		●	●	▲	▲	▲	▲
Constructing angles						●	▲
Constructing circles, using a compass						●	▲
Classifying polygons				●	●	▲	▲
Congruent figures		●	●	●	▲	▲	▲
Intersecting lines				●	●	▲	▲
Line of symmetry	●	●	●	▲	▲	▲	▲
Line segments				●	▲	▲	▲
Lines				●	▲	▲	▲
Making and drawing polygons		●	●	▲	▲	▲	▲
Making and drawing quadrilaterals		●	●	▲	▲	▲	▲
Measuring angles, using a protractor					●	▲	▲
Orientations						●	▲
Parallel lines				●	▲	▲	▲
Perpendicular lines				●	▲	▲	▲
Polygons				●	▲	▲	▲
Points				●	▲	▲	▲
Pythagorean Theorem							●
Quadrilaterals				●	▲	▲	▲
Radius, diameter, chord					●	●	▲
Rays				●	▲	▲	▲
Relating solid and plane figures	●	●	▲	▲	▲	▲	▲
Right angles				●	▲	▲	▲
Sides, angles, and diagonals of polygons				●	●	●	▲
Similar figures				●	▲	▲	▲
Symmetry	●	●	●	▲	▲	▲	▲
Subdividing and combining		●	●	▲	▲	▲	▲
Tesselations and tangrams			●	●	▲	▲	▲
Vertex			●	▲	▲	▲	▲
Visual Thinking	●	●	●	▲	▲	▲	▲

Plane Figures and Spatial Sense

angles
  acute angle 392–395
  classifying angles 392–395
  degree 392–395
  drawing angles 392–395
  measuring angles 392–395
  obtuse angle 392–395
  right angle 392–395
  straight angle 392–395
  sum of angles of quadrilaterals 403
  triangles 396–397
circles
  center 412–413
  central angle 412–413
  chord 412–413
  circumference 438–441
  diameter 412–413
  point 412–413
  radius 412–413
classifying
  polygons 396-397, 400–403
  quadrilaterals 400–403
  triangles 396–397
complex figures 434–436
congruent figures 398–399
constructions
  angle 392–395
  circle 412–413
  perpendicular lines 395
diagonal 400–403
endpoint 390–391
lines
  intersecting 390–391
  line segment 390–391
  parallel 390–391
  perpendicular 390–391
plane 390–391
point 390–391
polygons
  identifying, classifying, and describing polygons 400–403
  irregular polygons 400–403
  regular polygons 400–403
quadrilaterals 400–403
ray 390–391
relating space figures and plane figures 450–451
similar figures 496–499
symmetry
  line symmetry 414–416
  rotational symmetry 412–413
triangles
  classify and find missing angle measures 396–397
two-dimensional views of irregular solid figures 448–449
using visual thinking, spatial reasoning, and geometric modeling to solve problems 408–410, 566–567

KEY Teach and Apply ●   Practice and Apply ▲   Teacher's Edition Lesson ★

Scope and Sequence

In the Program...

Geometry

	K	1	2	3	4	5	6
Solid Figures (3-dimensional objects)							
Complex figures				●		●	▲
Cone	●	●	●	▲	▲	▲	▲
Cube	●	●	●	▲	▲	▲	▲
Cylinder	●	●	●	▲	▲	▲	▲
Face, edge, vertex			●	▲	▲	▲	▲
Identifying, classifying, and describing solid figures		●	▲	▲	▲	▲	▲
Nets			●	●	●	▲	
Prisms	●	●	●	▲	▲	▲	▲
Pyramids		●	●	▲	▲	▲	▲
Sphere	●	●	●	▲			
Transformations							
Constructions, using a compass to draw arcs						●	▲
Degrees turned						●	▲
Flips (Reflections)	●	●	●	●	●	▲	▲
Slides (Translations)	●	●	●	●	●	▲	▲
Transformations in the coordinate plane						●	●
Turns (Rotations)	●	●	●	●	●	▲	▲

Measurement

Area and Perimeter

	K	1	2	3	4	5	6
Complex figures					●	●	▲
Estimating area, using square units			●	▲			
Finding area, using a formula					●	●	▲
Finding area, using square units			●	▲			
Finding circumference						●	●
Finding perimeter			●	●	▲	▲	▲
Finding perimeter, using a formula					●	●	▲
Meaning of area			●	▲	▲	▲	▲
Meaning of perimeter			●	▲			
Problem-solving applications			●	●	▲	▲	▲
Pythagorean theorem						●	●
Relating area and perimeter				●	●	▲	▲
Surface area						●	▲
Surface area, using a formula					●	●	▲

Capacity

	K	1	2	3	4	5	6
Conversion table			●	●	●	▲	▲
Customary system		●	●	●	▲	▲	▲
Equivalent units		●	●	●	▲	▲	▲
Estimating capacity		●	●	●	▲	▲	▲
Measuring capacity	●	●	●	▲	▲	▲	▲
Metric system		●	●	●	▲	▲	▲
Problem-solving applications	●	●	●	▲	▲	▲	▲

In Level 5...

Geometry

Solid Figures (3-dimensional objects)

base, face, edge, vertex 446–447
cone 446–447
cube 446–447, 450–451
cylinder 446–447, 450–451
nets
  cube 450–451
  cylinder 450–451
  pentagonal prism 450–451
  pentagonal pyramid 450–451
  rectangular prism 450–451
  square pyramid 450–451
  triangular prism 450–451
  triangular pyramid 450–451
pentagonal prism 446–447, 450–451
pentagonal pyramid 446–447
rectangular prism 446–447, 450–451
sphere 446–447
square pyramid 446–447, 450–451
triangular prism 446–447, 450–451
triangular pyramid 446–447, 450–451

Transformations

in the coordinate plane 622–625
reflections and translations 404–406
rotations
  degrees turned 404–406

Measurement

Area and Perimeter

area
  complex figures 434–436
  exploring area of a circle 441
  finding area 428–430, 432–433
  formula, 428-433
  parallelogram 428–430
  Pythagorean theorem 478
  rectangle 428–430
  right triangle 432–433
  surface area 452–455
perimeter
  circumference of a circle 438–440
  complex figures 434–437
  formula 422–423
  problem solving 422-423

Capacity

choosing the unit
  customary 152–154
  metric 160–162
comparing capacity
  customary 152–154
  metric 160–162
converting capacity
  customary system 152–154
  metric system 160–162
customary system 152–154
measuring 163
metric system 160–161
problem solving 166–167, 464-467

KEY   Teach and Apply ●   Practice and Apply ▲   Teacher's Edition Lesson ★

Measurement

Length

	K	1	2	3	4	5	6
Centimeter		●	●	▲	▲	▲	▲
Choosing appropriate unit		●	●	●	▲	▲	▲
Conversion table			●	●	▲	▲	▲
Customary measurement		●	●	▲	▲	▲	▲
Distance formula							●
Equivalent units			●	●	▲	▲	▲
Estimating length	●	●	●	▲	▲	▲	▲
Fractions and measurement			●	●	▲	▲	▲
Foot, yard			●	●	▲	▲	▲
Inch	●	●	▲	▲	▲	▲	▲
Indirect measurement					●	●	●
Kilometer					●	▲	▲
Measuring instruments		●	●	▲	▲	▲	▲
Measuring length	●	●	●	▲	▲	▲	▲
Meter		●	●	●	▲	▲	▲
Metric measurement		●	●	●	▲	▲	▲
Mile				●	▲	▲	▲
Problem-solving applications	●	●	●	●	▲	▲	▲

Money

	K	1	2	3	4	5	6
Adding and subtracting money		●	●	●	▲		▲
Comparing amounts			●	●	▲	▲	▲
Consumer applications	●	●	●	▲	▲	▲	▲
Counting coins and bills	●	●	▲	▲	▲		
Counting on with money	●	●	▲	▲			
Decimals, fractions, and money				●	▲		
Equivalent amounts	●	●	▲	▲	▲		
Estimating money				●	●	▲	
Identifying coins and bills	●	●	▲	▲			
Making change				●	▲	▲	▲
Multiplying and dividing money					●	●	▲
Place value					●	▲	▲
Problem-solving applications	●	●	●	●	▲	▲	▲
Rounding money					●	▲	
Symbolic notation	●	●	●	▲	▲	▲	▲

Temperature

	K	1	2	3	4	5	6
Celsius scale			●	▲	▲	▲	▲
Estimating temperature				●	▲		
Fahrenheit scale		●	●	▲	▲	▲	▲
Interpreting a thermometer		●	●	▲	▲		
Negative numbers					●	▲	▲
Relating Celsius scale to Fahrenheit scale						●	●
Writing temperature			●	●	▲	▲	▲

KEY Teach and Apply ●   Practice and Apply ▲   Teacher's Edition Lesson ★

Measurement

Length

centimeter, millimeter, decimeter
  choosing the unit 156–158
  equivalencies 156–158
foot, yard, mile
  equivalencies 148–151
inch
  equivalencies 148–151
  estimating 148–151
indirect measurement—map scales 499
measuring 148–151, 156–158, 163
meter, kilometer
  choosing the unit 156–158
  equivalencies 156–158
problem solving 166–167

Money

adding money 282–285
dividing money 372
multiplying money 79, 337
subtracting money 286–288
problem solving applications 79

Temperature

Celsius 319, 586
  converting to degrees Fahrenheit 319
Fahrenheit 319

Scope and Sequence

In the Program...

Measurement

In Level 5...

Measurement

Time

	K	1	2	3	4	5	6
A.M. and P.M.			●	●	▲		
Analog clock	●	●	●	▲			
Calendar concepts	●	●	▲	▲			
Digital clock	●	●	●	▲			
Elapsed time		●	●	▲	▲	▲	▲
Equivalent units			●	▲			
Estimating time	●	●	▲	▲			
Ordinal numbers	●	●	▲	▲			
Problem-solving applications	●	●	●	▲	▲	▲	▲
Schedules		●	●	▲	▲		
Sequencing events	●	●	▲				
Telling time	●	●	●	▲	▲		
Time line				●	●	▲	▲
Time zones				●	●	●	▲

Volume

	K	1	2	3	4	5	6
Estimating volume				●	▲	▲	▲
Finding volume, counting cubic units				●	▲	▲	▲
Finding volume, using a formula					●	●	▲
Meaning of volume				●	●	▲	▲
Problem-solving applications				●	●	●	▲

Weight and Mass

	K	1	2	3	4	5	6
Conversion table				●	●	▲	▲
Equivalent units				●	●	▲	▲
Estimating weight and mass	●	●	●	●	▲	▲	▲
Finding weight and mass			●	●	▲	▲	▲
Gram and kilogram		●	●	●	▲	▲	▲
Ounce				●	●	▲	▲
Pound		●	●	▲	▲	▲	▲
Problem-solving applications	●	●	●	●	▲	▲	▲
Ton					●	●	▲

Time

adding time 37, 164–165
elapsed 166–167
schedules 65, 166
subtracting time 37, 164–165
time line 26, 108
time zone 37

Volume

cube 460–463
rectangular prism 460–463
triangular prism 460–463
problem solving 463, 464–467

Weight and Mass

mass
  choosing the unit 160–162
  comparing 160–162
  equivalencies 160–162
  measuring 163
weight
  choosing the unit 152–154
  comparing 152–154
  converting 152–154
  equivalencies 152–154
  measuring 163
problem solving 166–167

KEY Teach and Apply Practice and Apply ● Teacher's Edition Lesson ▲

Data Analysis and Probability

Data Analysis

	K	1	2	3	4	5	6
Analyzing and interpreting data	●	●	●	●	▲	▲	▲
Average				●	▲	▲	▲
Bar graphs	●	●	●	▲	▲	▲	▲
Box-and-whisker plots							●
Choosing an appropriate display				●	●	▲	▲
Circle graph			●	●	●	●	▲
Cluster						●	●
Collecting, organizing, and displaying data	●	●	●	●	▲	▲	▲
Double bar graphs					●	▲	▲
Double line graphs						●	▲
Frequency tables/tally charts	●	●	●	●	●	▲	▲
Gap						●	▲
Histogram					●	●	▲
Line graphs		●			●	▲	▲
Line plots		●	●	●	▲	▲	▲
Making tables and charts	●	●	●	▲	▲	▲	▲
Mean				●	▲	▲	▲
Measures of central tendency			●	●	▲	▲	▲
Median				●	▲	▲	▲
Misleading data or graphs						●	▲
Mode			●	●	▲	▲	▲
Organized lists			●	●	●	●	●
Outliers					●	●	▲
Pictographs	●	●	●	▲	▲	▲	▲
Problem-solving applications	●	●	●	▲	▲	▲	▲
Quartiles							●
Range			●	●	▲	▲	▲
Reading tables and charts	●	●	●	▲	▲	▲	▲
Sampling techniques						●	●
Scatter plot							●
Stem-and-leaf plots					●	●	▲
Surveys	●	●	●	●	▲	▲	▲

Probability

	K	1	2	3	4	5	6
Calculating probability of simple event					●	●	▲
Compound events					●	▲	▲
Developing and analyzing predictions and inferences	●	●	●	●	▲	▲	▲
Fair or unfair			●	▲			
Fundamental Counting Principle							●
Likelihood of an event	●	●	●	▲	▲	▲	▲
Permutations and combinations							●
Possible outcomes				●	●	▲	▲
Probability experiments	●	●	●	●	▲	▲	▲
Problem-solving applications	●	●	●	●	▲	▲	▲
Recording outcomes	●	●	●	●	▲	▲	▲
Representing likelihood as a number from 0 to 1					●	●	▲
Theoretical probability						●	▲
Using a tree diagram or grid					●	▲	▲
Using coins, cubes, or spinners	●	●	●	▲	▲	▲	▲

KEY Teach and Apply ● Practice and Apply ▲ Teacher's Edition Lesson ★

Data Analysis and Probability

Data Analysis

analyze data
  cluster 194–196
  gap 194–196
  mean 194–199
  median 194–199
  misleading data 184–185
  mode 194–199
  range 194–199
choosing an appropriate graph 182–183
cluster or gap 194–196
data
  collecting data 172–180, 194–196, 198–199
  comparing ways of representing data 182–183
  reading and interpreting data
    in graphs 172–175, 178–180, 194–199, 520–522
    in tables or charts 200–201
  recording and organizing data
    in graphs 172–180, 194–199
    in tables or charts 200–201
formulate questions
  designing investigations to address a question 192–193
  representing categorical and numerical data 192–193
frequency tables 176–177, 546–547
graphs
  circle graph 520–522
  double bar graph 172–175
  histogram 176–177
  line and double line graph 178–180
  line plot 194–196
  stem-and-leaf plots 198–199
mean, median, mode 194–199
misleading data/graphs 184–185
organized lists 536–538
predicting from data 532–534
predicting probability 540–543
range 194–196
representative samples 207
statistics
  measures of central tendency
    mean 194–199
    median 194–199
    mode 194–199
survey 192–193

Probability

as a fraction 532–535, 540–547
certain, impossible 530–531
combinations 528–529
compound events 544–545
develop and analyze predictions and inferences 204–206, 532–534, 546–548
experimental 540–543
outcomes
  certain, impossible 530–531
  meaning of outcome 532–534
possible outcomes 532–534
representing likelihood as a number from 0 to 1 530–531
theoretical 532–534
using a grid 528–529
using a tree diagram 225–227, 528–529
using coins 544
using cubes 533–534, 540–542, 544
using spinners 530–533, 545

Scope and Sequence

Problem Solving

Applications / Decisions

	K	1	2	3	4	5	6
Addition applications	●	●	●	▲	▲	▲	▲
Building new knowledge	●	●	●	●	●	●	●
Choosing a computation method		●	●	●	●	▲	▲
Choosing an operation	●	●	●	▲	▲	▲	▲
Curriculum connections	●	●	●	●	●	●	●
Data applications	●	●	●	▲	▲	▲	▲
Decimal applications					●	▲	▲
Division applications				●	●	▲	▲
Estimated or exact answers			●	●	●	▲	▲
Fraction applications	●	●	●	●	●	▲	▲
Geometry applications	●	●	●	●	●	▲	▲
Integer applications						●	▲
Interpreting remainders				●	●	▲	▲
Measurement applications	●	●	●	▲	▲	▲	▲
Money applications	●	●	●	▲	▲	▲	▲
Multiplication applications			●	▲	▲	▲	▲
Number and operations	●	●	●	●	▲	▲	▲
Percent applications						●	▲
Place-value applications		●	●	●	▲	▲	▲
Probability applications	●	●	●	▲	▲	▲	▲
Ratio applications						●	▲
Solving multi-step problems		●	●	●	●	▲	▲
Subtraction applications	●	●	●	▲	▲	▲	▲
Time applications	●	●	●	●	▲	▲	▲
Too much information or too little information		●	●	▲	▲	▲	▲
Using a bar graph		●	●	▲	▲	▲	▲
Using a diagram					●	▲	▲
Using a formula					●	●	▲
Using a number sentence	●	●	●	▲	▲		
Using a pattern	●	●	●	▲	▲	▲	▲
Using a pictograph	●	●	●	▲	▲	▲	▲
Using a picture, graph, or map	●	●	●	▲	▲	▲	▲
Using a table or chart	●	●	●	▲	▲	▲	▲
Using an equation						●	▲
Using estimation			●	●	●	▲	
Using functions and graphs					●	●	●

Strategies

	K	1	2	3	4	5	6
Act it out with models	●	●	●	●	▲	▲	▲
Choose a method		●	●	●	▲	▲	▲
Draw a picture or diagram	●	●	●	●	●	▲	▲
Find a pattern	●	●	●	▲	▲	▲	▲
Guess and check	●	●	●	●	▲	▲	▲
Make a model	●	●	●	●	●	●	▲
Make a table or chart	●	●	●	●	▲	▲	▲
Make an organized list				●	●	▲	▲
Monitor and reflect on the process	●	●	●	●	●	▲	▲
Solve a simpler problem				●	●	▲	▲
Use logical reasoning	●	●	●	●	▲	▲	▲
Work backward				●	●	▲	▲
Write a number sentence or equation	●	●	●	●	●	▲	▲

KEY Teach and Apply ● Practice and Apply ▲ Teacher's Edition Lesson ★

In Level 5...

Problem Solving

Applications/Decisions

addition applications 30, 36, 39
building new knowledge 38–39, 120–122,164–165, 256–257, 260–261, 268–269, 282–285, 310–318, 320–326, 334–335, 340–343, 368–369, 592–601
choosing a computation method 39, 78, 122, 272, 276, 292, 326, 342, 372, 466, 518, 522, 548, 604
choosing an operation 90–91, 328
curriculum connections 23, 37, 167, 207, 251, 319, 329, 431, 499, 581, 619
data applications 192–206
decimal applications 292–293, 346–347
division applications 115–116, 128–130
estimated or exact answers 500–501
fraction applications 270–272, 328
geometry applications 408–410, 424–426, 464–467
integer applications 602–603
interpreting remainders 128–130, 370–372
measurement applications 166–167
money applications 79
multiplication applications 64–66, 78–81
number and operations applications 5, 7, 9, 12, 15–19, 22, 242–244
percent applications 520–522
place-value applications 16–18
probability applications528–548
ratio applications 485, 489–490, 498
real-world applications 501, 513, 581
solving multi-step problems 166–167
statistics applications 194–202
subtraction applications 30, 36, 39
time applications 37
too much or too little information 42–43, 186–187
using a diagram 270–271
using an equation 40–41, 102–104, 568–570, 572–574
using an estimate 33, 75
using a formula 464–467
using a pattern 16–18
using a picture, graph, or map 620–621
using charts or tables 200–201
using estimation 33, 75
using graphs 620–621

Strategies

choose a strategy 202, 272, 604
conjecture and verify 98–100
draw a picture or diagram 41–43, 270–271
find a pattern 16–18, 424–426
logical thinking 64–66, 242–244
make a chart or table 200–201
make a graph 620–621
make a model 408–410
make an organized list 528–529, 536–538
monitor and reflect upon the process 80–81, 346–347
solve a simpler problem 456–458
solve multi-step problems 166–167
too much or not enough information 42–43, 186–187
use formulas 464–467
use logical thinking 64–66, 242–244
use mental math 318
use models 62-63, 408-410, 566-567
work backward 114–116
write an equation 40–41, 102–104, 568–570, 572–574

In the Program...

Reasoning and Proof

Reasoning and Proof

Analyzing

	K	1	2	3	4	5	6
Algebraic Thinking				▲	▲	▲	▲
Analyzing	●	●	●	●	▲	▲	▲
Checking reasonableness of answers		●	●	●	▲	▲	▲
Classifying	●	●	●	●	●	▲	▲
Creating and solving problems	●	●	●	●	●	●	●
Developing arguments and proof	●	●	●	●	●	▲	▲
Drawing conclusions	●	●	●	●	●	▲	▲
Explaining reasoning	●	●	●	●	●	▲	▲
Generalizing	●	●	●	●	●	▲	▲
Identifying relationships					●	●	▲
Identifying relevant information		●	●	▲	▲	▲	▲
Logical thinking	●	●	●	●	▲	▲	▲
Making and investigating conjectures	●	●	●	●	▲	▲	▲
Making decisions	●	●	●	●	▲	▲	▲
Making predictions	●	●	●	●	▲	▲	▲
Number relationships	●	●	●	●	●	▲	▲
Reading mathematics	●	●	●	●	●	▲	▲
Reasonableness of method and solution		●	●	●	●	▲	▲
Using logic	●	●	●	●	●	▲	▲
Using strategies to find solutions	●	●	●	●	●	▲	▲
Visual thinking	●	●	●	▲	▲	▲	▲

Communication

Analyzing and Evaluating Strategies

	K	1	2	3	4	5	6
Act it out with models	●	●	●	●	▲	●	
Choose a method		●	●	●	●	▲	▲
Choose an operation	●	●	●	▲	▲	▲	▲
Draw a picture or diagram	●	●	●	●	●	▲	▲
Find a pattern	●	●	●	▲	▲	▲	▲
Guess and check	●	●	●	●	▲	▲	▲
Make a table or chart	●	●	●	●	●	▲	▲
Make an organized list			●	●	●	▲	▲
Monitor and reflect on the process	●	●	●	●	▲	▲	
Solve a simpler problem				●	●	▲	▲
Use logical reasoning	●	●	●	▲	▲	▲	▲
Work backward					●	●	▲
Write a number sentence or equation	●	●	●	●	●	▲	▲

Analyzing

algebraic reasoning 30, 41
Algebraic Thinking 105, 403, 605
analyzing 5, 30, 33, 116, 122
checking reasonableness of answers 346–347
classifying 392–397, 400–403
creating and solving problems 192–193
developing arguments and proof 392–397, 400–403
drawing conclusions 204–205
evaluating reasonableness 346–347
explaining reasoning 80–81
formulating and solving problems 192–193
generalizing 392–397, 400–403
identifying relationships 148–154 156–162, 236–241, 246–250,
 322–323, 396–397, 404–406, 450–451, 496–499, 510–513, 586–587,
 622–625
identifying relevant information 42–43, 186–187
interpreting remainders 128–130, 370–372
justifying thinking 80–81
logical thinking 64–66, 242–244
making and investigating conjectures 98–100
making decisions
 choosing a graph 182–183
 choosing a method 292–293
 choosing a strategy 202, 272, 604
 choosing an operation 90–91, 328
 determining reasonableness of an answer 346–347
 estimated or exact answer 500–501
 too much or too little information 42–43, 186–187
making predictions 204–205, 546–548
number relationships 236–241, 246–250, 322–323, 510–513, 586–587
reading mathematics 81, 549
reasonableness of method and solution 346–347
solving a simpler problem 456–458
using logic 64–66, 242–244
using strategies to find solutions 202, 272, 604
visual thinking 43, 408–410, 566–567

Analyzing and Evaluating Strategies

choose a method 292–293
choose an operation 90–91, 328
draw a picture or diagram 41–43, 270–271
find a pattern 16–18, 424–426
guess and check 98–100
make a table or chart 200–201
make an organized list 528–529, 536–538
monitor and reflect on the process 80–81, 346–347
solve a simpler problem 456–458
use logical reasoning 64–66, 242–244
use models 62–63, 408–410, 566–567
work backward 114–116
write an equation 40–41, 102–104, 568–570, 572–574

KEY Teach and Apply ●   Practice and Apply ▲   Teacher's Edition Lesson ★

Scope and Sequence

▼ (Level 5 marker)

In the Program...

Communication

KEY Teach and Apply ●   Practice and Apply ▲   Teacher's Edition Lesson ★

Analyzing and Evaluating Thinking

	K	1	2	3	4	5	6
Determining reasonableness of an answer		●	●	●	▲	▲	▲
Estimating or exact answer			●	●	●	▲	▲
Explaining reasoning	●	●	●	●	▲	▲	▲
Identifying relevant information		●	●	▲	▲	▲	▲
Justifying thinking	●	●	●	●	▲	▲	▲
Making predictions	●	●	●	●	▲	▲	▲
Too much or too little information		●	●	▲	▲	▲	▲

Communicating Mathematical Thinking

	K	1	2	3	4	5	6
Clarifying understanding	●	●	●	●	●	▲	▲
Drawing a picture or diagram	●	●	●	●	●	▲	▲
Using manipulatives	●	●	●	●	▲	▲	▲
Talk About It/Write About It		▲	▲	▲	▲	▲	▲

Organizing and Consolidating Thinking

	K	1	2	3	4	5	6
Classifying	●	●	●	●	●	▲	▲
Drawing conclusions		●	●	●	●	▲	▲
Generalizing	●	●	●	●	●	▲	▲

Using Mathematical Language

	K	1	2	3	4	5	6
Creating and solving problems	●	●	●	●	●	●	●
Describing problems and solutions	●	●	●	●	▲	▲	▲
Vocabulary		▲	▲	▲	▲	▲	▲

Connections

Building Upon Prior Knowledge

	K	1	2	3	4	5	6
Adding	●	●	●	▲	▲	▲	▲
Dividing			●	●	▲	▲	▲
Multiplying		●	●	●	▲	▲	▲
Subtracting	●	●	●	▲	▲	▲	▲
Using money	●	●	●	●	▲	▲	

Recognizing and Applying Mathematics in Context

	K	1	2	3	4	5	6
Curriculum connections	●	●	●	●	●	●	●
Real-life applications	●	●	●	●	●	●	●

Recognizing and Using Connections

	K	1	2	3	4	5	6
Decimals, fractions, and mixed numbers				●	●	▲	▲
Drawing conclusions		●	●	●	▲	▲	
Generalizing	●	●	●	●	●	▲	▲
Measurement and time	●	●	●	▲	▲	▲	▲
Money	●	●	●	▲			
Patterns	●	●	●	▲	▲	▲	▲
Related facts	●	●	●	●	▲		

KEY Teach and Apply ●   Practice and Apply ▲   Teacher's Edition Lesson ★

In Level 5...

Communication

Analyzing and Evaluating Thinking

determining reasonableness of an answer 346–347
estimating or exact answer 500–501
explaining reasoning 80–81
identifying relevant information 42–43, 186–187
justifying thinking 80–81
making predictions 204–205, 546–548
too much or too little information 42–43, 186–187

Communicating Mathematical Thinking

clarifying understanding See Explain Your Thinking in lessons
drawing a picture or diagram 41–43, 270–271
Talk About It/Write About It 55, 63, 143, 149, 193, 219, 225, 247, 305, 313, 321, 385, 395, 407, 413, 436, 440, 449, 479, 507, 542, 561, 567, 594, 597, 637
using manipulatives 62–63, 408–410, 566–567

Organizing and Consolidating Thinking

classifying 392–397, 400–403
drawing conclusions 204–205
generalizing 392–397, 400–403

Using Mathematical Language

Building Vocabulary xxx–1, 56–57, 144–145, 220–221, 306–307, 386–387, 480–481, 562–563
creating and solving problems 192–193
describing problems and solutions 148–162, 194–199, 392–395, 400–406, 412–413, 446–447, 450–451, 530–531, 540–543
Vocabulary Wrap-Up 55, 143, 219, 305, 385, 479, 561, 637

Connections

Building Upon Prior Knowledge

adding 38–39, 256–257, 260–261, 282–285, 592–595, 598–601
dividing 120–122, 320–326, 368–369
multiplying 310–318, 334–335, 340–343, 571
subtracting 164–165, 256–257, 268–269, 596–601
using money 79

Recognizing and Applying Mathematics in Context

curriculum connections 1, 23, 37, 46–47, 57, 81, 134-135, 145, 167, 207, 221, 251, 307, 319, 329, 376–377, 387, 417, 431, 467, 470 –471, 481, 499, 549, 552–553, 563, 581, 619, 628–629, 638–649
real-life applications 210–211, 296–297, 501, 513, 581

Recognizing and Using Connections

decimals, fractions, and mixed numbers 246–247
drawing conclusions 204–205
generalizing 392–397, 400–403
measurement 148–154, 156–158, 160–162
patterns 16–18, 51, 424–426

In the Program...

Representation

	K	1	2	3	4	5	6

Organizing, Recording, and Communicating Ideas

	K	1	2	3	4	5	6
Making a list			●	●	●	▲	▲
Using a bar graph	●	●	●	▲	▲	▲	▲
Using a circle graph			●	●	●	▲	▲
Using a double bar graph				●	●	▲	▲
Using a double line graph						●	▲
Using a line graph					●	▲	▲
Using a line plot		●	●	●	▲	▲	▲
Using a pictograph	●	●	●	▲	▲		
Using a picture or diagram			●		●	▲	▲
Using a stem-and-leaf plot					●	●	▲
Using a table or chart	●	●	●	▲	▲	▲	▲
Using measurement	●	●	●	●	▲	▲	▲
Using probability	●	●	●	▲	▲	▲	▲
Using symbols	●	●	●	▲	▲	▲	▲

Selecting, Applying, and Translating Among Representations

	K	1	2	3	4	5	6
In decimals, fractions, and money				●	▲		
In geometry	●	●	●	●	▲	▲	▲
In measurement	●	●	●	●	▲	▲	▲
In percent						●	▲
In time		●	●	▲	▲	▲	

Using Representations to Model and Interpret Mathematics

	K	1	2	3	4	5	6
Algebraic equations	●	●		●	●	▲	▲
Arrays			●	●	●	▲	▲
Counters, connecting cubes	●	●	●	●	●	▲	▲
Data	●	●	●	▲	▲	▲	▲
Decimal models				●	●	●	▲
Fraction models		●	●	●	▲	▲	▲
Geoboard/dot or grid paper		●	●	●	●	▲	▲
Geometric tools (compass, protractor, straightedge)					●	●	●
Hundreds chart	●	●	●	▲	▲	▲	▲
Integer models				●	●	●	▲
Make a model (act it out)	●	●	●	●	●	●	●
Manipulatives or models	●	●	●	●	▲	▲	▲
Modeling solids	●	●	●	●	▲	●	●
Money and coins	●	●	▲	▲	▲	▲	▲
Multiplication table				●	▲		
Number lines	●	●	●	●	●	▲	▲
Part/part whole models			●	●	●	▲	▲
Pattern blocks	●	●	▲	▲	▲	▲	▲
Percent models				●	●	●	●
Pictures/diagrams	●	●	●	▲	▲	▲	▲
Place-value models		●	●	▲	▲	▲	▲
Symbols	●	●	●	●	▲	▲	▲
Technology	▲	▲	▲	▲	▲	▲	▲

KEY Teach and Apply ● Practice and Apply ▲ Teacher's Edition Lesson ★

In Level 5...

Representation

Organizing Recording and Communicating Ideas

making a list 528–529, 536–538
using a circle graph 520–522
using a double bar graph 172–175
using a graph 620–621
using a line or double line graph 178–180
using a line plot 194–196
using models 62–63, 408–410, 566–567
using a picture or diagram 41–43, 270–271
using a stem-and-leaf plot 198–199
using a table or chart 200–201
using mathematical language 148–162, 194–199, 392–395, 400–406, 412–413, 446–447, 450–451, 530–531, 540–543
using measurement 148–158, 160–162, 428–433, 452–455, 460–463
using probability 528–548
using symbols 10–12, 14–15, 20–22, 28–30, 40–41, 102–104, 568–570, 572–574

Selecting Applying and Translating Among Representations

in decimals, fractions, mixed numbers, or percents 248–250, 508–509
in geometry 392–397, 400–403
in measurement 148–154, 156–158, 160–162

Using Representations to Model and Interpret Mathematics

algebraic expressions, equations, and number sentences 28–30, 40–41, 60–61, 102–104, 566–567
arrays 57, 62–63
counters 566, 592–594, 596–598
data 172–187
decimal models 20–22, 247, 282, 286–287, 334–335, 338, 352–353
fraction models 236–238, 249, 256, 258, 266, 270–272, 310–313, 314, 320–321
geoboard/dot or grid paper 51, 404–406, 422, 428, 434–436
geometric tools (compass, protractor, straightedge) 392–395, 396, 412–413
hundreds chart 105
integer models 586, 592–593, 596–597, 600, 602
make a model 408–410
modeling solids 447, 449–449, 450–451
money and coins 173, 293
number cards 123, 293, 327
number cubes 197, 540
number lines
   adding and subtracting 258, 266, 598–600, 602
   line plot 194–196, 204, 205, 209
   modeling absolute value 586
   to compare 20, 338, 511, 588, 590, 591
   to round numbers 21, 256
   to show likelihood 530, 532
part/part whole bar model 35, 40–41, 42, 102–103, 286–287, 514–516
pattern blocks 293, 408–409
percent models 506–508, 510–511, 514–515, 516
pictures/diagrams 41–43, 270–271
place-value (base ten) blocks 1
real-world objects 438
spinners 530–533, 535, 542, 544–545
symbols 10–12, 14–15, 20–22, 28–30, 40–41, 102–104, 568–570, 572–574
tangrams 407
technology 34–36, 38–39, 71, 95, 277, 371, 523, 571
thermometers 586
Venn diagrams 242

Test-Taking Tips

You can do well on a math test if you know how to think about the math and how to take a test.

Your book helps you learn the math and practice the strategies you need to take tests. Look for these special signs on the pages.

 TEST TIPS are ways you can think about math when you take a test or solve any problem.

 TEST PREP provides practice for answering the kinds of questions you will find on tests.

Cumulative Test Prep Practice

has practice in answering multiple-choice, open-response, and other test questions.

TWO Important Things You Can Do Before A Test
- Get plenty of sleep the night before.
- Eat a good breakfast in the morning.

xxii Student Handbook

Use Reading Strategies to Think About Math

What you learn during reading class can help you understand how to solve word problems.

Understand What the Question Is
Read the problem once to be sure it makes sense to you. Ask yourself the question in your own words. Picture the situation and make a drawing if it helps.

Think About the Words
As you read, pay attention to the vocabulary words. If you don't understand a word, try to decide what it means by looking at the words around it.

Be Sure You Have Enough Information
Identify the information. Look at tables or graphs as well as the words. Think about what you already know that may help.

Plan What You Will Do
Think about the problem-solving plan and strategies. Decide what computation method is needed. Then make a plan and follow it.

Evaluate Your Work
Look back at what the question asked, and check that your answer really answers that question. Be sure you have labeled your answer.

Student Handbook **xxiii**

Strategies for Taking Tests

You need to think differently about how to answer various kinds of questions.

All Questions
If you can't answer a question, go on to the next question. You can return to it if there is time.

Always check your computation.

Multiple-Choice Questions
Estimate the answer. This can help eliminate any unreasonable choices.

On bubble sheets, be sure you mark the bubble for the right question and for the right letter.

Short-Answer Questions
Follow the directions carefully. You may need to show your work, write an explanation, or make a drawing.

If you can't give a complete answer, show what you do know. You may get credit for part of an answer.

Long-Answer Questions
Take time to think about these questions because you often need to explain your answer.

When you finish, reread the question and answer to be sure you have answered the question correctly.

Student Scoring Rubric
Your teacher may use a scoring rubric to evaluate your work. An example is on the next page. Not all rubrics are the same, so your teacher may use a different one.

xxiv Student Handbook

Scoring Rubric

Rating	My work on this problem
Exemplary (full credit)	• has no errors, has the correct answer, and shows that I checked my answer • is explained carefully and completely • shows all needed diagrams, tables, or graphs
Proficient (some credit)	• has small errors, has a close answer, and shows that I checked only the math • is explained but may have missing parts • shows most needed diagrams, tables, or graphs
Acceptable (little credit)	• has some errors, has an answer, and shows that I did not check my answer • is not explained carefully and completely • shows few needed diagrams, tables, or graphs
Limited (very little credit)	• has many errors and may not have an answer • is not explained at all • shows no needed diagrams, tables, or graphs

More Test Prep Help in Your Book

TEST TIPS help you think about the math and how to answer a question.

 TEST PREP gives you practice with questions like those that will be on tests.

Daily Review **Test Prep**
helps you review key concepts and practice the lesson skill the way you will see it on a test.

Problem-Solving for Tests helps you review problem-solving strategies as you learn what tests are like.

Cumulative Review
gives you more test practice as you review the math that may be on the test.

Test Prep on the Net is another way to practice test-taking skills. Go to **eduplace.com/math/kids/mw/**.

Student Handbook **xxv**

Your Plan For Problem Solving!

Follow this four-part plan and you'll become a problem solving superstar!

- Understand
- Plan
- Solve
- Look Back

Remember!
Always START at the "Understand" step and move on. But if you can't get an answer, don't give up. Just go back and start again.

UNDERSTAND

Always be sure you know what the question means! Here are some hints to help you:

- Read the problem twice.
- Replace any hard names you can't read with easier ones.
- Ignore extra information you don't need to solve the problem.
- Look for words that help you decide whether to add, subtract, multiply, or divide.
- Identify what the question is asking.

PLAN

Start by making a plan! Ask yourself:

- Do I have too much or too little information?
- Should I do more than one step?
- Which operation should I use?
- Should I use paper and pencil, mental math, or a calculator?
- What strategy should I use?

PROBLEM-SOLVING Strategies
- Draw a Picture
- Find a Pattern
- Guess and Check
- Make an Organized List
- Make a Table
- Solve a Simpler Problem
- Use Logical Reasoning
- Work Backward
- Write an Equation

SOLVE

Finally! Now you're ready to solve the problem!

- Carry out your plan.
- Test your method and strategy.
- Adjust your plan if needed.
- Check your calculations.

LOOK BACK

Congratulations! You've solved the problem. But is it correct? Once you have an answer, ask:

- Is my answer reasonable?
- Is my answer labeled correctly?
- Did I answer the question that was asked?
- Do I need to explain how I found the answer?

Study Skills

Knowing how to study math will help you do well in math class.

To be a good math student, you need to learn
- ★ How to listen when your teacher is teaching
- ★ How to work alone and with others
- ★ How to plan your time

Listen carefully when your teacher is showing the class how to do something new. Try to understand what is being taught as well as how to do each step.

If you don't understand what your teacher is showing the class, ask a question. Try to let your teacher know what you don't understand.

Listening carefully will also help you be ready to answer any questions your teacher may ask. Or you may be able to help another student.

Working Alone and With Others

When you work alone, try to connect the math you are learning to math you already know. Knowing how parts of math fit together helps you remember and understand the math.

When you work with others, help as much as you can. Cooperating is another word for working together. When people cooperate, they often learn more because they share ideas.

Planning Your Time

Doing your homework on time is part of being a good math student. Make sure that you take the assignment home with you.

Have a place at home to do your homework—it could be in your room or at the kitchen table or anywhere that works for your family.

Get extra help if you are having trouble. Write questions about what you don't understand. This will help your teacher give you the extra help you need.

Pacing Guide

Grade Five

Houghton Mifflin Math encourages you to customize instruction to meet the needs of your students. As a guide, we have identified lessons as review, core, or extend for typical fifth-grade level content. As these categories may vary based on you local curriculum, consider this chart as a guide to help you plan your teaching year.

Unit	Chapter	Review Lessons	Number of Days	Core Lessons	Number of Days	Extend Lessons	Number of Days	Days to Assess
1	1	1	1	2–7	6			1
	2	1	1	2–6	5			2
2	3	1	1	2–8	7			1
	4	1	1	2–7	6			1
	5	1	1	2–4, 6–7	5	5	1	2
3	6	1	1	2–7	6			1
	7	1	1	2–6	5			1
	8			1–5	5			2
4	9			1–7, 9	8	8	1	1
	10	1	1	2–8	7			1
	11	1–2	2	3–5	3			2
5	12			1–3, 7	4	4–6	3	1
	13			1–6	6			1
	14					1–8	8	2
6	15	1	1	2–9	8			1
	16			1–6	6			1
	17			1–3, 5–7	6	4	1	2
7	18	1	1	2–4, 6	4	5	1	1
	19	1	1	2–4, 6	4	5	1	1
	20			1–5, 7	6	6	1	2
8	21			1–5	5			1
	22			1–6	6			1
	23			1–5	5			2
Totals		Review	13	Core	123	Extend	17	31

Table of Contents

As you read through the Table of Contents (it begins on the next page), you will see that *Houghton Mifflin Math* is organized into 8 units. Each unit consists of 2–4 chapters related to the big mathematical idea of the unit. Chapters have from 5 through 9 lessons, one or two Quick Checks, and a Chapter Review/Test. At the end of each unit is a Unit Test.

This unit/chapter organization promotes the kind of effective teaching and assessment that will help you reach all the learners in your class. Daily Lesson Quizzes make you aware of which students may be in need of help and which have mastered the material. Quick Checks and Chapter and Unit Tests are all linked to immediate and focused remediation and intervention tools—*Reteach* resources and the *Ways to Success Intervention* CD-ROM. *Enrichment* resources and *Chapter Challenges* are available for those students who are ready for some extra challenge. If algebra is an important element in your mathematics curriculum, you will find special support for this teaching in those lessons with an Algebra label.

Be sure to look for the *Weekly Reader Connection* icons—these indicate activities for which students can find additional information by visiting the Weekly Reader link at Houghton Mifflin's Education Place Web site (**www.eduplace.com/kids/mw/**).

Place Value/Addition and Subtraction
STARTING THE UNIT

1 Place Value of Whole Numbers and Decimals

Algebra Indicates lessons that include algebra instruction.

2 Add and Subtract Whole Numbers

FINISHING THE UNIT

Unit 1 Literature Connection
The Most Amazing Sights in Nature
page T51

Technology

Ways to Assess Customized Spiral Review and Test Generator CD

Lesson Planner CD-ROM

Ways to Success Intervention CD-ROM

MathTracks CD-ROM

Education Place: www.eduplace.com/math/mw

Houghton Mifflin Math eBook CD-ROM

eManipulatives

eGames

ⓌⓇ Indicates  **WEEKLY** ⓌⓇ **READER**® **Connection**

Multiplication, Division, and Algebra
STARTING THE UNIT

3 Multiply Whole Numbers

4 Divide by One-Digit Numbers

Algebra Indicates lessons that include algebra instruction.

5 Divide by Two-Digit Numbers

FINISHING THE UNIT

Unit 2
Literature Connection
Ready for Anything
page T52

Technology

Ways to Assess Customized
Spiral Review and Test
Generator CD

Lesson Planner CD-ROM

Ways to Success Intervention
CD-ROM

MathTracks CD-ROM

Education Place:
www.eduplace.com/math/mw

Houghton Mifflin Math eBook
CD-ROM

eManipulatives

eGames

 Indicates **WEEKLY WR READER® Connection**

Measurement/Data and Graphing

STARTING THE UNIT

Algebra Indicates lessons that include algebra instruction.

8 Data and Statistics

FINISHING THE UNIT

Unit 3 Literature Connection
Ships of the Desert
page T52

Technology

Ways to Assess Customized Spiral Review and Test Generator CD

Lesson Planner CD-ROM

Ways to Success Intervention CD-ROM

MathTracks CD-ROM

Education Place: www.eduplace.com/math/mw

Houghton Mifflin Math eBook CD-ROM

eManipulatives

eGames

(WR) Indicates **WEEKLY WR READER® Connection**

Addition and Subtraction of Fractions and Decimals

STARTING THE UNIT

9 Number Theory and Fraction Concepts

10 Add and Subtract Fractions

Algebra Indicates lessons that include algebra instruction.

11 Add and Subtract Decimals

FINISHING THE UNIT

Unit 4
Literature Connection
The Fruitomatic
page T53

Technology

Ways to Assess Customized
Spiral Review and Test
Generator CD

Lesson Planner CD-ROM

Ways to Success Intervention
CD-ROM

MathTracks CD-ROM

Education Place:
www.eduplace.com/math/mw

Houghton Mifflin Math eBook
CD-ROM

eManipulatives

eGames

WR Indicates  **WEEKLY** WR **READER** **Connection**

Multiplication and Division of Fractions and Decimals

STARTING THE UNIT

12 Multiply and Divide Fractions

13 Multiply Decimals

Algebra Indicates lessons that include algebra instruction.

14 Divide Decimals

Unit 5
Literature Connection
The World's Largest Trees
page T54

FINISHING THE UNIT

👩‍💻 Technology

Ways to Assess Customized Spiral Review and Test Generator CD

Lesson Planner CD-ROM

Ways to Success Intervention CD-ROM

MathTracks CD-ROM

Education Place: www.eduplace.com/math/mw

Houghton Mifflin Math eBook CD-ROM

eManipulatives

eGames

WR Indicates  **Connection**

Geometry and Measurement
STARTING THE UNIT

15 Plane Figures and Geometric Concepts

16 Perimeter, Area, and Circumference

Algebra Indicates lessons that include algebra instruction.

17 Solid Figures, Surface Area, and Volume

FINISHING THE UNIT

Unit 6
Literature Connection
No Place to Go
page T55

Technology

Ways to Assess Customized Spiral Review and Test Generator CD

Lesson Planner CD-ROM

Ways to Success Intervention CD-ROM

MathTracks CD-ROM

Education Place: www.eduplace.com/math/mw

Houghton Mifflin Math eBook CD-ROM

eManipulatives

eGames

 Indicates **WEEKLY WR READER Connection**

Ratio, Proportion, Percent, and Probability

STARTING THE UNIT

18 Ratio and Proportion

19 Percent

Algebra Indicates lessons that include algebra instruction.

20 Probability

FINISHING THE UNIT

Unit 7
Literature Connection
Numbers
page T55

📡 Technology

Ways to Assess Customized Spiral Review and Test Generator CD

Lesson Planner CD-ROM

Ways to Success Intervention CD-ROM

MathTracks CD-ROM

Education Place: www.eduplace.com/math/mw

Houghton Mifflin Math eBook CD-ROM

eManipulatives

eGames

 Indicates  **WEEKLY WR READER' Connection**

Algebra, Integers, and Coordinate Graphing
STARTING THE UNIT

21 Equations and Functions

22 Integers

Algebra Indicates lessons that include algebra instruction.

23 Coordinate Graphing

FINISHING THE UNIT

Unit 8
Literature Connection
Treasure Hunt
page T56

END OF BOOK RESOURCES

🖥 Technology

Ways to Assess Customized Spiral Review and Test Generator CD

Lesson Planner CD-ROM

Ways to Success Intervention CD-ROM

MathTracks CD-ROM

Education Place: www.eduplace.com/math/mw

Houghton Mifflin Math eBook CD-ROM

eManipulatives

eGames

 Indicates  Connection

Multiplication and Division of Fractions and Decimals

Unit at a Glance

Assessment System

Assess Prior Knowledge

Check whether students understand the prerequisite concepts and skills.

- **REVIEWING VOCABULARY:** Unit Opener
- **CHAPTER PRETESTS:** PE pp. 309, 333, 351 (Unit Resource Folder or *Ways to Success* CD-ROM)
- **WARM-UP ACTIVITY:** Found on the third page of every TE lesson.

Ongoing Assessment

Monitor whether students are acquiring new concepts and skills.

- **PROBLEM OF THE DAY:** First page of every TE lesson
- **QUICK REVIEW:** First page of every TE lesson
- **LESSON QUIZ:** First page of every TE lesson
- **COMMON ERROR:** TE Lessons 12.2–12.3, 12.6, 13.1–13.5, 14.1–14.7
- **QUICK CHECK:** PE pp. 319, 329, 343, 347, 361, 373
- **DAILY REVIEW • TEST PREP:** PE pp. 315, 323, 326, 335, 337, 339, 345, 353, 355, 357, 364, 367, 369

 Test Prep and Practice

Help students prepare for state and standardized tests.

- **DAILY REVIEW • TEST PREP:** PE pp. 315, 323, 326, 335, 337, 339, 345, 353, 355, 357, 364, 367, 369
- **DAILY TEST PREP:** TE Lessons 12.1–12.7, 13.1–13.6, and 14.1–14.8
- **PROBLEM SOLVING TEST PREP:** PE pp. 245, 273
- **CUMULATIVE TEST PREP:** PE pp. 382–383
- **READING TEST QUESTIONS: UNIT OPENER:** PE p. 307
- **TEST PREP ON THE NET:** eduplace.com/kids/mw
- **TEST TAKING STRATEGIES:** eduplace.com/math/mw

Summary Assessment

Assess student mastery of new concepts and skills.

- **CHAPTER TEST:**
  - ✔ PE pp. 330, 348, 374
  - ✔ Unit Resource Folder
- **UNIT TEST:**
  - ✔ PE pp. 378–379
  - ✔ Form A, Unit Resource Folder
  - ✔ Form B, Unit Resource Folder

Student Self-Assessment

Allow students to evaluate their own understanding.

- **EXPLAIN YOUR THINKING:** PE pp. 315, 317, 323, 325, 335, 336, 339, 341, 344, 353, 355, 357, 359, 363, 367, 369
- **VOCABULARY WRAP UP:** PE p. 385

Performance Assessment

Evaluate students' ability to use mathematics in real-world situations.

- **PERFORMANCE ASSESSMENT:** PE p. 380
- **WRITE ABOUT IT • TALK ABOUT IT:** in all Hands-On lessons
- **DECISION MAKING** End of Unit Test

 Technology Options

Use computer-based assessment to make testing and reporting easier.

- **WAYS TO ASSESS** (CD-ROM, LAN, or Web spiral review and test creation, administration, scoring, and report generation)
- **LEARNER PROFILE** (observations, evaluations, and reports from your handheld or desktop computer)

Reaching All Learners

Resources	On Level Students	Extra Support Students	English Learners	Inclusion/ Special Needs	Advanced Learners	Mathematically Promising
Student Editions						
Building Vocabulary	●	●	●	●	●	●
Different Ways Instruction *	●	●	●	●	●	●
Guided Practice *	●	●	●	●	○	○
MathTracks MP3 Audio CD	●	●	●	●	○	○
Teacher's Editions						
Building Vocabulary Strategies	●	●	●	●	●	○
Teacher Support	●	●	●	●	●	●
Intervention Activities	○	●	●	●	○	○
Other Resources						
Chapter Challenges	○				●	●
Combination Classroom Guide	●	●	●	●	●	●
English Learners Handbook	○	○	●	○		
Ways to Success CD-ROM	○	●	●	●		

KEY   ● **Highly Appropriate**   ○ **Appropriate**   * **Scaffolded Instruction**

Documenting Adequate Yearly Progress

National Test Correlation

UNIT 5 Objectives		ITBS	Terra Nova (CTBS)	CAT	SAT	MAT
5A	Multiply and divide with fractions and mixed numbers.		●	●	●	●
5B	Estimate decimal products and quotients.	●	●	●	●	●
5C	Multiply and divide with decimals.	●	●	●	●	●
5D	Solve problems, using skills and strategies.	●	●	●	●	●

Chapter Planner

Lesson	Objective	Vocabulary	Materials	✔ NCTM Standards
12.1 Hands-On: Model Multiplication p. 310A	Use area to find the product of two fractions.			**Number and Operations:** Develop and use strategies to estimate computations involving fractions and decimals in situations relevant to students' experience.
12.2 Multiply Fractions p. 314A	Find the product of two fractions.			**Number and Operations:** Develop understanding of fractions as parts of unit wholes, as parts of a collection, as locations on number lines, and as divisions of whole numbers.
12.3 Multiply with Mixed Numbers p. 316A	Find products of fractions and mixed numbers.	mixed number improper fraction	Mixed Numbers Transparency	**Number and Operations:** Understand various meanings of multiplication and division.
12.4 Hands-On: Model Division p. 320A	Use models to divide with fractions.	unit fraction	grid paper, fraction strips	**Number and Operations:** Develop understanding of fractions as parts of unit wholes, as parts of a collection, as locations on number lines, and as divisions of whole numbers.
12.5 Divide Fractions p. 322A	Use the reciprocal to divide fractions.	reciprocal		**Number and Operations:** Develop understanding of fractions as parts of unit wholes, as parts of a collection, as locations on number lines, and as divisions of whole numbers.
12.6 Divide Mixed Numbers p. 324A	Divide with mixed numbers.	mixed number	two-copies of Learning Tool 42, 4 sets of number cards numbered 1 to 10	**Number and Operations:** Compute fluently and make reasonable estimates.
12.7 Problem Solving Decision: Choose the Operation p. 328A	Review how to choose the operation that will help you solve a problem.		Problem Solving: Four Step Process Transparency	**Problem Solving:** Solve problems that arise in mathematics and inother contexts.

Resources For Reaching All Learners

LESSON RESOURCES: Reteach, Practice, Enrichment, Problem Solving, Homework, English Learners, Daily Routines, Transparencies, Math Center.

ADDITIONAL RESOURCES FROM HOUGHTON MIFFLIN: Combination Classroom Planning Guide, Chapter Challenges, Every Day Counts, Math at Hand (student handbook)

Every Day Counts

The **Measurement** activities in **Every Day Counts** support the math in this chapter.

Assessing Prior Knowledge

Before beginning the chapter, you can assess student understandings in order to assist you in differentiating instruction.

Complete Chapter Pretest in Unit Resource Folder

Use this test to assess both prerequisite skills (**Are You Ready?** — one page) and chapter content (**Check What You Know** — two pages).

Chapter 12 Prerequisite Skills Pretest

Chapter 12 New Content Pretest

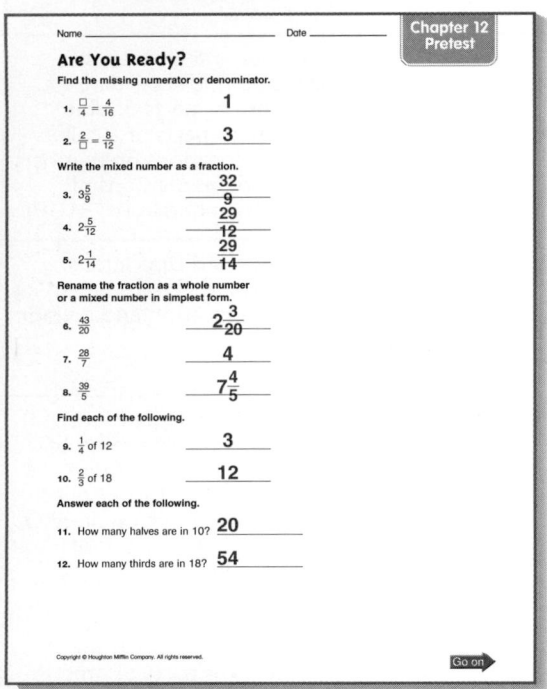

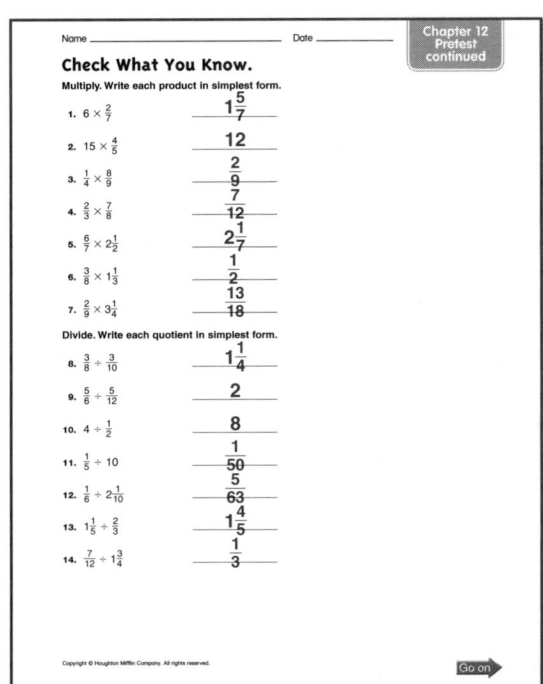

Customizing Instruction

For Students Having Difficulty

Items	Prerequisites	Ways to Success
1–6	Multiply with fractions	Skillsheet: 95
7–12	Divide with fractions	Skillsheet: 96

Ways to Success: Intervention for every concept and skill (CD-ROM or Chapter Intervention Skillsheets).

Consider using **Knowing Mathematics** with any students who are working two or more years below grade level.

For Students Having Success

Items	Objectives	Resources
1–7	**12A** Multiply with fractions, mixed numbers, and whole numbers.	Enrichment 12.1, 12.2, 12.3
8–14	**12B** Divide with fractions, mixed numbers, and whole numbers.	Enrichment 12.4, 12.5, 12.6
15–20	**12C** Analyze and solve problems by deciding which operation to choose.	Enrichment 10.5, 10.6, 10.8

Use **Chapter Challenges** with any students who have success with all new chapter content.

Other Pretest Options

Informal Pretest in Student Book

The student book pretest assesses vocabulary and prerequisite skills needed for success in this chapter.

Ways to Success CD-ROM

The *Ways to Success* chapter pretest has automatic assignment of appropriate review lessons.

Chapter Resources

Assessing Prior Knowledge

Partner Up (mixed numbers, improper fractions, factors)

- Have each student in a pair write five mixed numbers. Ask the students to exchange papers and write each mixed number as an improper fraction.
- Continue in a similar fashion to have students list the factors of five numbers.

Ongoing Skill Activity

Dancing Fractions (multiply and divide fractions)

- Have students "choreograph" dances using 3 different "moves" to cross the stage: a slide, which takes $\frac{1}{2}$ minute; a jump, which takes $\frac{1}{3}$ minute; and a gallop, which takes $\frac{1}{6}$ minute.
- After appropriate lessons, ask questions such as these: "How long is a dance in which you jump across 16 times? ($16 \times \frac{1}{3} = 5\frac{1}{3}$ minutes) "How many times can you slide across the stage in a 3-minute dance?" ($3 \div \frac{1}{2} = 6$ times) Have students use all three dance moves in various lengths.

Connecting to the Unit Project

- You may wish to enlist the help of the school music teacher as you work through this project. Have available music books for students to use as reference materials.
- Have students write word problems about music that involve some of the following fractions: $\frac{2}{4}$, $\frac{3}{4}$, and $\frac{6}{8}$. These are among the most commonly used time signatures in music.

Teacher Support

Professional Resources Handbook

Research, Mathematics Content, and Language Intervention

Research-Based Teaching

Newstead and Murray (1998) explored children's understanding of operations with fractions in the intermediate grades. Children's understandings clearly reflected the way they had been taught in school. Children relied on a fixed approach rather than exhibiting flexibility. The results of this study indicate that "after their first few years of school limited and limiting understandings of fractions persist." Using manipulatives or visual models add to students' flexibility and ability in interpreting and using fractions. See Professional Resources Handbook, Grade 5, Unit 5.

For more ideas relating to Unit 5, see the Teacher Support Handbook at the back of this Teacher's Edition.

Language Intervention

When new vocabulary words (for example, reciprocal, mixed number) are introduced in a lesson, have students write their own definitions. Have students share their definitions with the class and have other students help you critique the quality of the definitions and help make improvements.

 **Time Saving Technology Support**

Ways to Assess Customized Spiral Review and Test Generator CD-ROM
Lesson Planner CD-ROM
Ways to Success Intervention CD-ROM
Math Tracks CD-ROM
Education Place: **www.eduplace.com/math/mw/**
Houghton Mifflin Math eBook CD-ROM
eManipulatives
eGames

Starting Chapter 12
Multiply and Divide Fractions

Chapter Objectives

12A Multiply with fractions, mixed numbers, and whole numbers.

12B Divide with fractions, mixed numbers, and whole numbers.

12C Analyze and solve problems by deciding which operation to choose.

Math Background

Multiplying Fractions

Many real-life situations require one to multiply a whole number by a fraction. For instance, finding out how many feet are in one-half mile.

The algorithm of fraction multiplication is fairly simple, however, it is important for students to have a sense of how it works, not just use it. Using models will prevent some students from confusing the algorithms or settling into manipulation of symbols by rote to get the right answer. Students also need to realize that the product of two proper fractions is less than each factor. The concept that the product of two numbers is not always bigger than either or both numbers is difficult and important for students to understand.

Dividing Fractions

To avoid students settling into manipulation of symbols by rote, it is important to go back to the meaning of division with whole numbers. There are two meanings, partition and measurement.

The division algorithm is to multiply by the reciprocal of the second fraction. A product of a fraction and its reciprocal is 1. Multiplication and division are inverse operations, hence multiplying by a reciprocal of a fraction is the same as diving by the fraction.

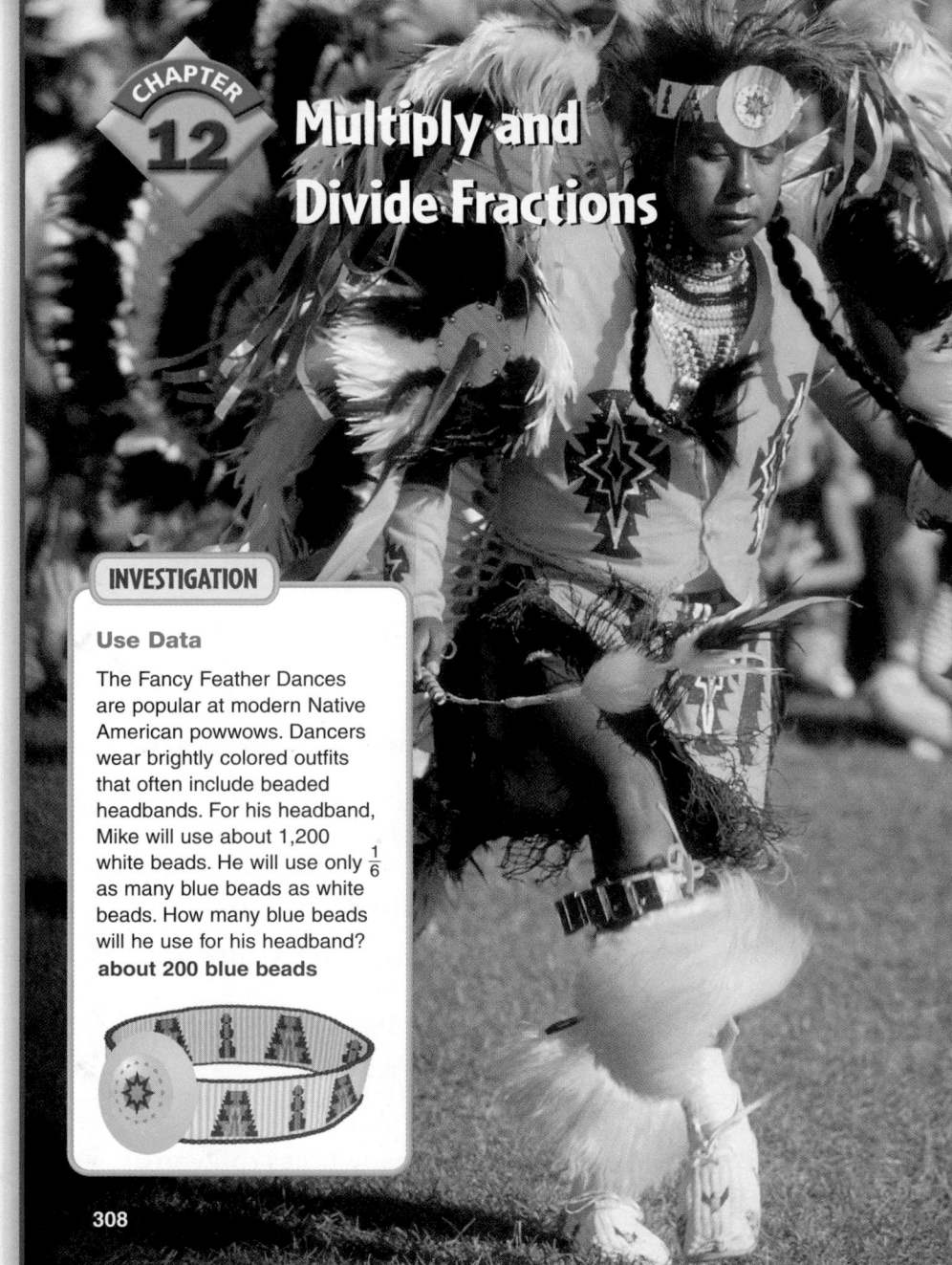

CHAPTER 12 Multiply and Divide Fractions

INVESTIGATION

Use Data

The Fancy Feather Dances are popular at modern Native American powwows. Dancers wear brightly colored outfits that often include beaded headbands. For his headband, Mike will use about 1,200 white beads. He will use only $\frac{1}{6}$ as many blue beads as white beads. How many blue beads will he use for his headband?
about 200 blue beads

308

Using the Investigation

Have students work in small groups to answer the question posed on page 308.

To extend the investigation, have students do the following activity.

* Research more about Native Americans. Use the information you find to write three word problems that can be solved by using multiplication or division of fractions.

For more information about projects and investigations, visit **Education Place**. www.eduplace.com/math/mw/

Activities for Reaching All Learners

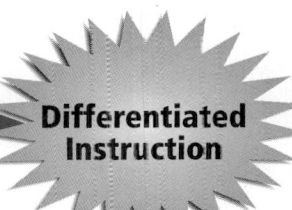

Polishing Prerequisite Skills

Materials: fraction cards, mixed number cards no greater than 3, bag

Emphasize to students that this is a multiplication game. Place the cards in a bag and shake. Each player draws 2 cards from the bag and places them face up. Each player finds the product of his or her 2 numbers. Students check each other's work. The player with the highest product wins the round. Play continues for 4 rounds.

Repeatable Unit Game

Materials: 40 decimal cards through thousandths

Students play in small groups. Place the cards in a pile facedown in the middle of the table. Each player draws 2 decimal cards. Players choose to multiply or divide. The player who has the product or quotient of the least amount scores 1 point. Game continues until one student scores 5 points.

Home School Activity

Materials: 12 decimal (price) cards, 12 whole (2–100) number cards

Write the prices of 12 household items on individual cards. Include a multiplication or division sign after the price. Shuffle the price cards and distribute to players facedown. Then shuffle and distribute numbers cards face down. Each player turns over the top two cards and finds the product or quotient. Repeat until all the cards are gone. Each player finds the sum of his or her results. The player with the highest sum wins.

Unit Vocabulary Activity

Materials: 12 vocabulary cards, and 2 examples of each vocabulary word on 24 separate cards

Display the 24 cards, with examples on them, face up in the center of the table. Distribute the vocabulary word cards face down among the players. One player turns over a card, reads the word, and tries to match it to an example on the table. The player "claims" the card if it is a correct match. Player with the most "claimed" cards after 5 rounds wins the game.

Remediation

Lessons with MathTracks Audio Support:
12.3, 12.5, 12.6, 13.4, 13.6, 14.2, 14.5, 14.7 (Tracks 2/1, 2/3–2/8)

Use the MathTracks CD-ROM to help children who need a quick review or extra support for the lesson, to provide children who were absent with a complete lesson presentation, or to assist children with reading difficulties.

Intervention

Ways to Success CD-ROM

Use the *Ways to Success* CD-ROM to help children who need extra help with lessons. This software is designed to reteach the lesson objective, provide extra guided and independent practice, and if needed, reteach a key prerequisite skill.

Starting Unit 5

Building Vocabulary

Use the Building Vocabulary pages to be sure that students have adequate understanding and fluency with the unit vocabulary. This provides the key foundation for developing the unit concepts and skills.

Reviewing Vocabulary

- Review factor, common factor, and prime factor by having students create problems that demonstrate the differences between these terms.
- Have the students label the parts of the problems in the previous activity.
- Give students 30 seconds to write as many examples of fractions in as many equivalent forms as possible, starting with the simplest form ($\frac{1}{4}$, $\frac{2}{8}$, $\frac{4}{16}$, $\frac{8}{32}$, etc).

Reading Words and Symbols

- Have students use the "Pizza Principle" to demonstrate the examples in the chart. 1. Sam brought $\frac{3}{4}$ of a pizza. Jane brought $\frac{1}{4}$ of a pizza. Together this makes 1 whole pizza. 2. Sam took $\frac{3}{4}$ of the pizza from the whole. That left $\frac{1}{4}$ of a pizza.
- Have the students repeat the "Pizza Principle" exercise using decimals.
- Have the students create Pizza Problems in fractions (such as $1 - \frac{1}{2} = \frac{1}{2}$) with matching problems in decimals ($1.00 - 0.5 = 0.5$).

Building Vocabulary

Reviewing Vocabulary

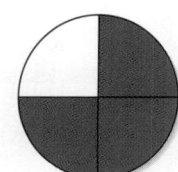

Here are some math vocabulary words that you should know.

factor	one of two or more numbers that are multiplied to give a product
common factor	a factor of two or more numbers
prime factor	a prime number that is a factor of a composite number
unit fraction	a fraction that has 1 as the numerator
simplest form	a fraction whose numerator and denominator have 1 as their only common factor

Reading Words and Symbols

Sometimes a model can be used to illustrate more than one idea in mathematics.

The model at the right can be used to show that each of the following statements is true:

Words and Symbols	Symbols Only
The sum of $\frac{3}{4}$ and $\frac{1}{4}$ is 1.	$\frac{3}{4} + \frac{1}{4} = 1$
Subtracting $\frac{3}{4}$ from 1 leaves $\frac{1}{4}$.	$1 - \frac{3}{4} = \frac{1}{4}$

Use words and symbols to answer the questions.

1. How many equal sections are in the model above? What fraction represents each section? **4; $\frac{1}{4}$**

2. What decimal represents the purple portion of the model? What decimal represents $\frac{1}{3}$ of the purple portion? **0.75; 0.25**

306

Unit Project

- Explain that music and mathematics are closely linked. At the beginning of a piece of music, the time signature indicates the meter or the beat of the piece.
- Divide students into groups. Explain that they are to research time signatures in music and how these are related to mathematics. They are also going to research a time–keeping machine called a metronome.
- Explain that the groups are to make visuals that show the time values of various musical notes based on time signatures.
- Explain that the visuals and research will be used to create a "Big Book of Music".
- Use the activity found on p. 385 to wrap-up the Unit Project.

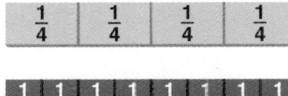

Choose the correct answer for each.

3. Using the fraction strips, find the number of eighths there are in $\frac{3}{4}$.

   a. 5   c. 7

   (b.) 6   d. 8

Fraction strips are models used to show fraction equivalents. These are sometimes called fraction bars.

| $\frac{1}{4}$ | $\frac{1}{4}$ | $\frac{1}{4}$ | $\frac{1}{4}$ |

| $\frac{1}{8}$ | $\frac{1}{8}$ | $\frac{1}{8}$ | $\frac{1}{8}$ | $\frac{1}{8}$ | $\frac{1}{8}$ | $\frac{1}{8}$ | $\frac{1}{8}$ |

4. What is the sum of $\frac{5}{8}$ and $\frac{1}{8}$? Express your answer in lowest terms.

   a. $\frac{6}{16}$ c. $\frac{6}{8}$

   b. $\frac{4}{8}$ (d.) $\frac{3}{4}$

When you express a fraction in lowest terms, you express it in simplest form.

5. Find $\frac{7}{8} - \frac{5}{8}$. Be sure to reduce your answer.

   (a.) $\frac{1}{4}$ c. $1\frac{1}{2}$

   b. $\frac{2}{8}$ d. 2

To reduce an answer means to express it in lowest terms or in simplest form.

Learning Vocabulary

 Watch for these new words in this unit. Write their definitions in your journal.

   reciprocal

   compatible numbers

   power of 10

   exponent

   repeating decimal

Vocabulary
e • Glossary
e • WordGame

Literature Connection

Read "The World's Largest Trees" on pages 644–645. Then work with a partner to answer the questions about the story.

Reading Test Questions

- Before having students look at item 3, write the following problem: Find the number of eighths in $\frac{3}{4}$. Ask students if they think the problem is easy, somewhat hard, or difficult. Next, have the students look at the item in the book. Discuss how the model helps make the problem easier.

- There are two parts in each of items 4 and 5. Have the students practice completing the first part before completing the second part of each item.

Learning Vocabulary

Go over the list of new words with the class. Help students to pronounce the words correctly and explain that they will learn about these words as they work on this unit. If students are keeping Math Journals, be sure that they enter the words and their definitions as they find them in the unit.

Home-School Connection

To foster home-school communication, *Houghton Mifflin Math* has a Family Letter for every unit. The letters include vocabulary words, worked-out examples, home activities, and literature suggestions.

Each Family Letter is in the Unit Resource Folder. Go to **eduplace.com/math/mw/** to download the letters in English, Spanish, and other languages.

In the Student Book

Literature Connection

Student Book List Selection

You may use the literature connection (Student Book page 644–645, Teachers Edition page T54) at any time during this unit.

Other Literature Connections

The I Hate Mathematics! Book (a Brown Paper School book)
By Marilyn Burns
Illustrated by Martha Weston

The Everything Kids' Math Puzzles Book (Everything Kids Series)
By Meg Clemens, et al

The Grapes of Math: Mind Stretching Math Riddles
By Greg Tang
Illustrated by Harry Briggs

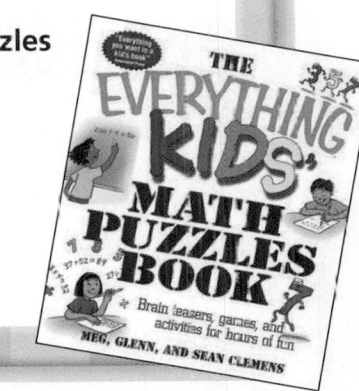

See also the **Math and Literature Bibliography** in the Teacher Support Handbook at the back of this Teacher's Edition.

Lesson By Lesson Overview
Multiply and Divide Fractions

Lesson 1

- Students use area models to visualize finding the product of two fractions and to multiply a whole number by a fraction and a fraction by a mixed number.

Lesson 2

- Students multiply two fractions and a fraction by a whole number.
- Students practice algebraic expressions that involve multiplying fractions.

Lesson 3

- Students find products of fractions and mixed numbers
- Students use fraction multiplication and interpret a data table to solve real-life problems.

Lesson 4

- Students use models to explore dividing with fractions.
- Students connect division by a fraction to multiplication by the reciprocal of the divisor.

Lesson 5

- Students learn how to use the reciprocal of the divisor when dividing with fractions.
- Students work with function tables where the rule involves division.

Lesson 6

- Students divide with mixed numbers.
- Students rewrite division expressions as fractions in simplest form.

Lesson 7

- Students review choosing an operation to solve real-life problems.

SKILLS TRACE: MULTIPLICATION AND DIVISION WITH FRACTIONS		
Grade 4	**Grade 5**	**Grade 6**
	• multiply with fractions, mixed numbers, and whole numbers	• estimate fraction products and quotients (ch. 6)
	• divide with fractions, mixed numbers, and whole numbers	• multiply and divide fractions and mixed numbers (ch. 6)
		• evaluate expressions with fractions and mixed numbers (ch. 6)

 **Chapter Pretest**

Use this page to review and remember
what you need to know for this chapter.

VOCABULARY

Choose the best word to complete each sentence.
improper fraction

Vocabulary
greatest common factor
improper fraction
least common denominator
simplest form

1. You can always rename a mixed number as a(n) ____.

2. A(n) ____ is the largest number that divides evenly into two or more numbers. **greatest common factor**

3. You can use the greatest common factor of the numerator and denominator to find the ____ of a fraction. **simplest form**

CONCEPTS AND SKILLS

Use the numbers listed to answer each question.

$\frac{1}{3}$ $\frac{4}{2}$ 2 $\frac{1}{6}$ $\frac{4}{10}$

4. Which two name the same number? $\frac{4}{2}$, **2**

5. Which two fractions have an LCD of 6? $\frac{1}{3}, \frac{1}{6}$ **or** $\frac{1}{6}, \frac{4}{2}$

6. Which fractions are not in simplest form? $\frac{4}{10}, \frac{4}{2}$

7. Which is a counting number? **2**

Rename each mixed number as an improper fraction.

8. $6\frac{2}{9}$ $\frac{56}{9}$ 9. $11\frac{4}{5}$ $\frac{59}{5}$ 10. $4\frac{3}{7}$ $\frac{31}{7}$

Rename each improper fraction as a mixed number.

11. $\frac{301}{3}$ $100\frac{1}{3}$ 12. $\frac{23}{8}$ $2\frac{7}{8}$ 13. $\frac{38}{5}$ $7\frac{3}{5}$

Find the GCF of each pair.

14. 15, 27 **3**   15. 12, 32 **4**   16. 10, 25 **5**

17. 14, 35 **7**   18. 72, 144 **72**   19. 81, 108 **27**

20. *Possible answer:* You can multiply both the numerator and the denominator by the same number to find an equivalent fraction.

Write About It

20. How can you use multiplication to find an equivalent fraction for $\frac{2}{5}$?

Test Prep on the Net
Visit *Education Place* at
eduplace.com/kids/mw/
for more review.

 Chapter Pretest

Prerequisite Skills

Items	Skill
1–3	Vocabulary needed for this chapter
4–7	Understanding fraction concepts
8–10	Renaming mixed numbers as improper fractions
11–13	Renaming improper fractions as mixed numbers
14–19	Finding the greatest common factor
20	Equivalent fractions

Chapter Challenges

Explore: Fraction Products, page 67, after Lesson 1

Extend: Use Fractions to Compare, page 69, after Lesson 3

Connect: Fraction Division, page 71, after Lesson 5

Using The Chapter Pretest

This page will help students review some of the prerequisite skills needed for this chapter. The chart above indicates which skills are covered on the pretest. If students need more help with these prerequisite skills use **Ways to Success,** Houghton Mifflin's intervention program.

Students who need more review can visit **Education Place,** Houghton Mifflin's award-winning website.

NSF **Children's Math Worlds**

Build stronger conceptual understanding of fractions with *Children's Math Worlds* lessons. The most effective approach is to use the *Children's Math Worlds* lessons along with the lessons in the chapter.

Hands-On: Model Multiplication

PLANNING THE LESSON

MATHEMATICS OBJECTIVE
Use area to find the product of two fractions.

Use Lesson Planner CD-ROM for Lesson 12.1.

Daily Routines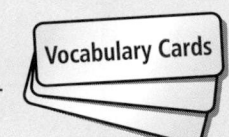

Vocabulary
Review the terms *fraction, numerator,* and *denominator* in preparation for this hands-on lesson.

Vocabulary Cards

Meeting North Carolina's Standards
Prepare for Grade 6 Objective **1.04** Develop fluency in addition, subtraction, multiplication, and division of nonnegative rational numbers.

Lesson Transparency 12.1

Problem of the Day
What are the next two fractions in this pattern? Describe the pattern. $\frac{5}{12}, \frac{1}{2}, \frac{7}{12}, \frac{2}{3}, \ldots$? $(\frac{3}{4}, \frac{5}{6};$ add $\frac{1}{12})$

Quick Check
Simplify.

1. $\frac{3}{5} + \frac{1}{5} = ?$ $(\frac{4}{5})$

2. $\frac{1}{2} + \frac{1}{2} = ?$ (1)

3. $\frac{4}{9} + \frac{2}{9} = ?$ $(\frac{2}{3})$

4. $\frac{8}{12} + \frac{3}{12} = ?$ $(\frac{11}{12})$

5. $\frac{1}{8} + \frac{5}{8} = ?$ $(\frac{3}{4})$

6. $\frac{7}{10} + \frac{13}{10} = ?$ (2)

Lesson Quiz
Use models to find each product.

1. $\frac{3}{4} \times \frac{2}{5}$ $(\frac{3}{10})$

2. $\frac{2}{3} \times \frac{3}{4}$ $(\frac{1}{2})$

3. $\frac{1}{3} \times \frac{1}{6}$ $(\frac{1}{18})$

4. $2 \times \frac{1}{3}$ $(\frac{2}{3})$

5. $3 \times 1\frac{3}{8}$ $(4\frac{1}{8})$

LEVELED PRACTICE

RETEACH 12.1
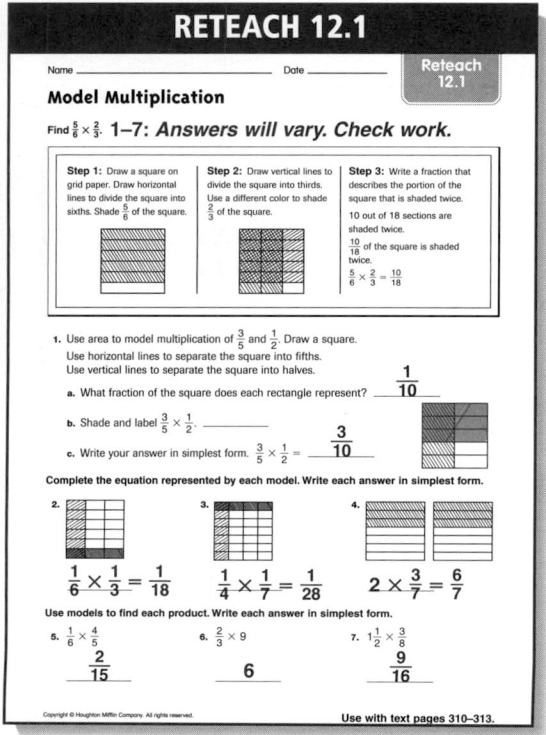

PRACTICE 12.1
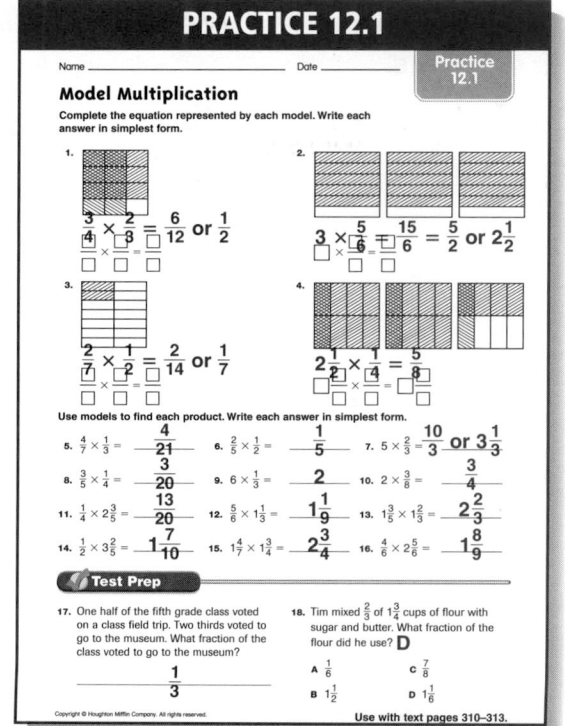

Practice Workbook Page 76

ENRICHMENT 12.1
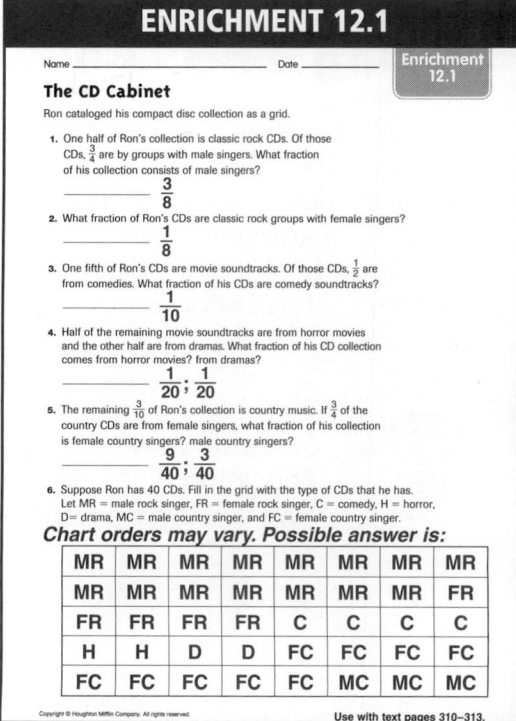

Reaching All Learners
Differentiated Instruction

English Learners

Use Worksheet 12.1 to help students understand the term *model* and to illustrate how models help make math problems easier to visualize.

Special Needs
VISUAL, KINESTHETIC

Draw a large square. Below it write: $\frac{2}{3} \times \frac{1}{5}$.

- **The first fraction is in thirds.** Divide the square horizontally into thirds. Shade 2 of the thirds.

- **What is the denominator of the second fraction?** (5) Divide the square vertically into fifths. **To represent $\frac{1}{5}$, how many vertical rectangles do we shade?** (1) **There are 15 equal rectangles. How many are double-shaded?** (2) **What is $\frac{2}{3} \times \frac{1}{5}$?** ($\frac{2}{15}$)

Early Finishers
VISUAL, KINESTHETIC

- Have students draw three models for multiplying fractions: multiplying a fraction by a fraction; multiplying a whole number by a fraction; multiplying a fraction by a mixed number.

- Have them exchange models and write the multiplication statement represented by each model. Have students share their work.

TECHNOLOGY

Spiral Review

Using the *Ways to Assess* CD–ROM, you can create **customized** spiral review worksheets covering any lessons you choose.

Lesson Planner

Use the Lesson Planner CD-ROM to see how lesson objectives for this chapter are correlated to standards.

Manipulatives

Interactive Fraction Models are available on the *Ways to Success* CD.

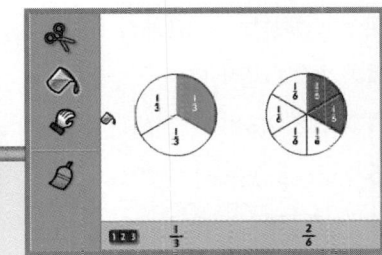

Language Arts Connection

Describe the Process

- Have students describe and illustrate the process of using a square grid to model multiplying a fraction by a fraction.

- Ask them to describe using a model for multiplying fourths by fifths, fifths by sixths, or fourths by eighths. Tell them they may also choose their own multiplication problem.

- Display their work.

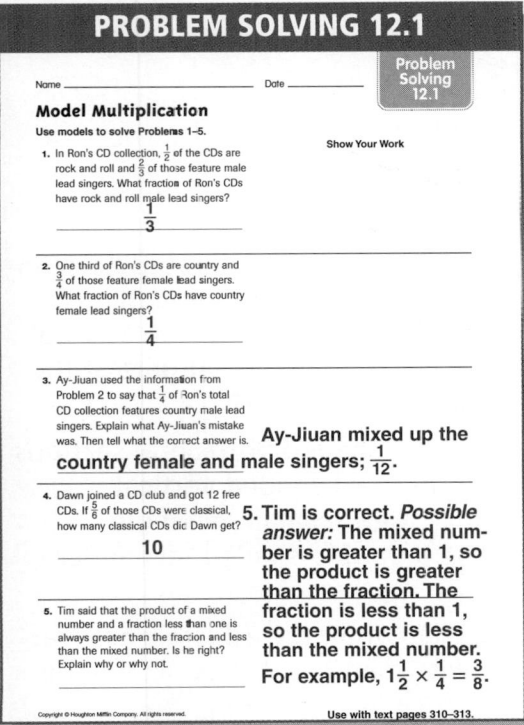

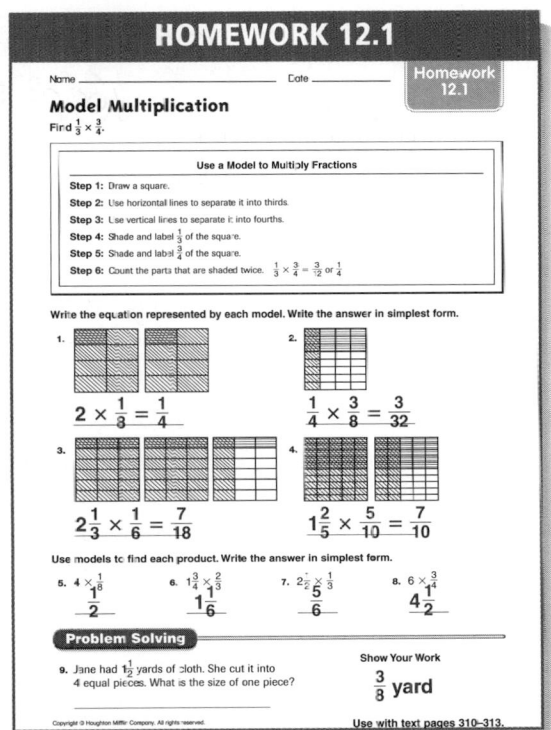

Homework Workbook Page 76

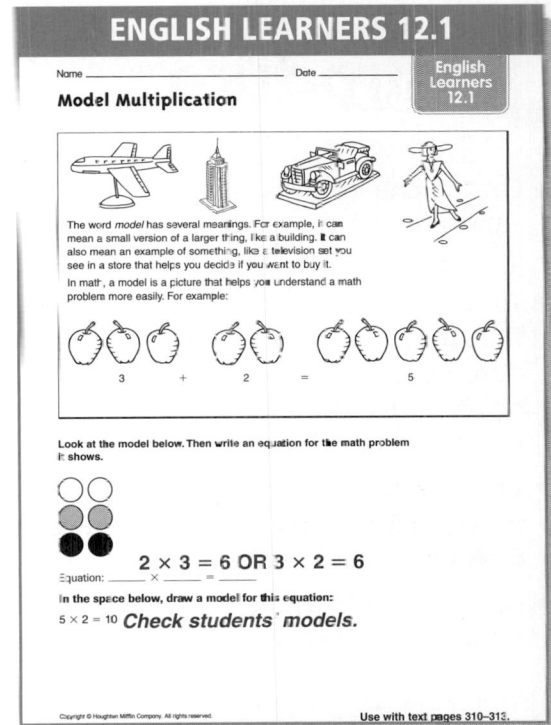

TEACHING LESSON 12.1

LESSON ORGANIZER

Objective Use area to find the product of two fractions.

Resources Reteach, Practice, Enrichment, Problem Solving, Homework, English Learners, Transparencies, Math Center

Materials None

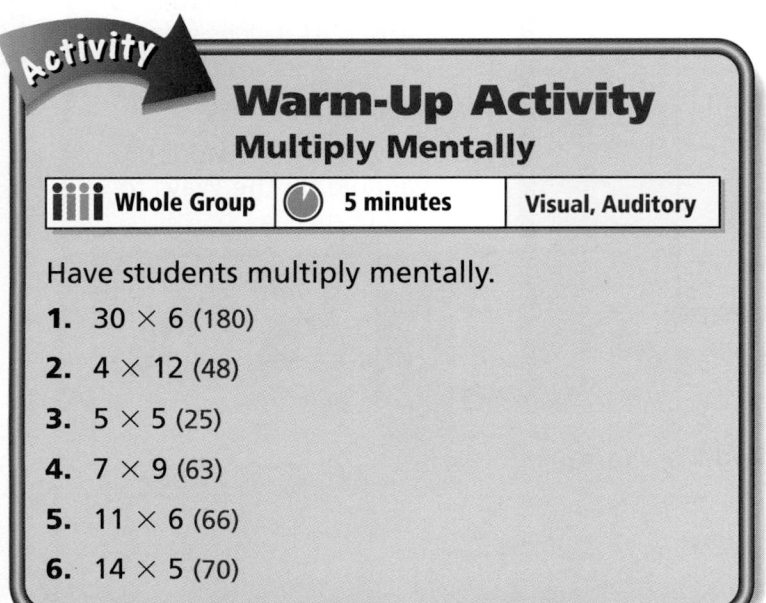

Warm-Up Activity
Multiply Mentally

👥 Whole Group	⏱ 5 minutes	Visual, Auditory

Have students multiply mentally.

1. 30×6 (180)
2. 4×12 (48)
3. 5×5 (25)
4. 7×9 (63)
5. 11×6 (66)
6. 14×5 (70)

Lesson 1 Hands-On
Model Multiplication

Objective Use area to find the product of two fractions.

Work Together

You can use an area model to multiply two fractions.

Find $\frac{2}{3} \times \frac{4}{5}$.

STEP 1 Draw a 5×3 square.

Use horizontal lines to separate the square into thirds. Label each third.

Use vertical lines to separate the square into fifths. Label each fifth.

- How many rectangles have you separated the large square into? **15**

- What fraction of the square does each rectangle represent? $\frac{1}{15}$

STEP 2 Shade part of the square to show $\frac{2}{3} \times \frac{4}{5}$ by doing the following:

Shade $\frac{2}{3}$ of the square red.

Shade $\frac{4}{5}$ of the square blue.

- Identify the part that is shaded twice. That part shows $\frac{2}{3} \times \frac{4}{5}$.

- Complete: $\frac{2}{3} \times \frac{4}{5} = \dfrac{\blacksquare}{\blacksquare}$ ← number of rectangles shaded twice
  ← total number of rectangles
  $= \frac{8}{15}$

Check your answer.

You are multiplying $\frac{2}{3}$ and $\frac{4}{5}$.

You know that you can multiply any number by 1 to get the same number again.

$\frac{2}{3} \times 1 = \frac{2}{3}$, so $\frac{2}{3} \times \frac{4}{5} < \frac{2}{3}$ and $\frac{4}{5} \times \frac{2}{3} < \frac{4}{5}$.

Is your answer less than either factor?

310

---

1 Introduce

- On the chalkboard, write: $\frac{3}{4} \times \frac{1}{6}$. Then draw a large square. Have students work at their seats as you demonstrate.

- To use an area model for multiplying two fractions, the first thing to do is look at each denominator. **What is the denominator of the first fraction?** (4) As you divide the square into four equal rectangles with 3 horizontal lines, explain what you are doing.

- **What is the denominator of the second fraction?** (6) By drawing 5 vertical lines, we can separate the area into 6 equal vertical rectangles.

- Have students count the small sections. **Into how many small rectangles is the square area separated?** (24)

2 Develop

Guide students through the steps of the *Work Together* section.

- **Look at Step 1. Why is the square first separated horizontally into 3 equal sections?** (The first fraction is in thirds.) **Why is the square then separated vertically into 5 equal sections?** (The second fraction is in fifths.) **What part of the area does each small rectangle represent?** ($\frac{1}{15}$)

- **Look at Step 2. What do the 2 shaded horizontal sections represent?** (2 thirds) **What do the 4 shaded vertical sections represent?** (4 fifths) **If each small rectangle represents $\frac{1}{15}$, what do the 8 double-shaded rectangles represent?** (8 fifteenths)

- Be sure they understand that when the 2 factors are fractions greater than 0 and less than 1, the product will be less than either factor.

▶ You can use models to multiply a fraction and a counting number.

Find $2 \times \frac{3}{4}$.

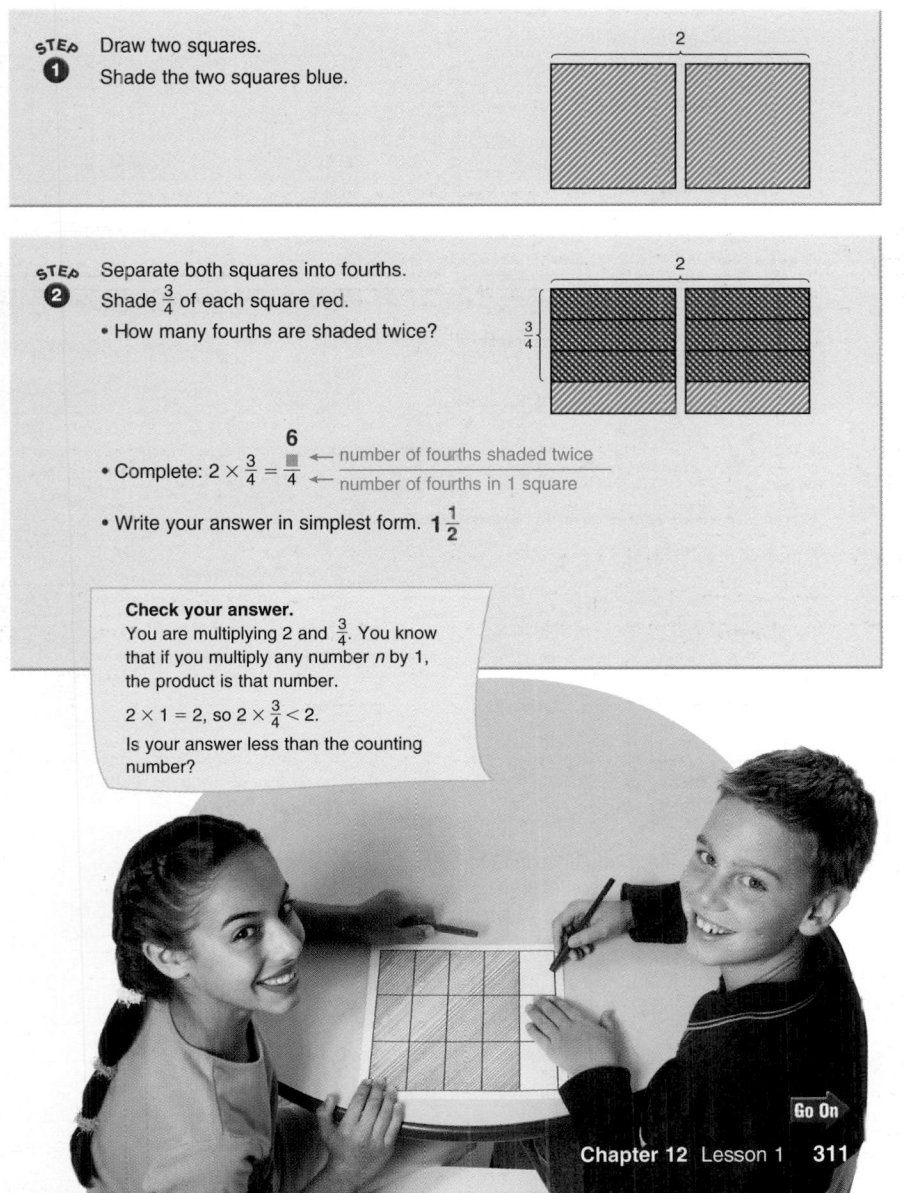

STEP 1 Draw two squares.
Shade the two squares blue.

STEP 2 Separate both squares into fourths.
Shade $\frac{3}{4}$ of each square red.
• How many fourths are shaded twice?

• Complete: $2 \times \frac{3}{4} = \dfrac{6}{4}$ ← number of fourths shaded twice
 ← number of fourths in 1 square

• Write your answer in simplest form. $1\frac{1}{2}$

Check your answer.
You are multiplying 2 and $\frac{3}{4}$. You know that if you multiply any number n by 1, the product is that number.
$2 \times 1 = 2$, so $2 \times \frac{3}{4} < 2$.
Is your answer less than the counting number?

Go On

ACHIEVING Mathematical Proficiency

Understanding Our Number System

Research indicates that many American middle school students have difficulty computing with rational numbers. This difficulty arises from the fact that students **often fail to see the meaning behind the procedures** they use when computing with rational numbers.

One way to give meaning to rational numbers is to present them in ways in which students are encouraged to apply informal, intuitive knowledge to gain understanding. Activities which help students in this way include drawing pictures of the computation method, describing solution strategies, and explaining the appropriateness of answers.

When students **understand the meaning behind rational numbers and the computation methods used with them,** they build a foundation for approaching higher mathematics.

• Work through the second example with students, in which a fraction is multiplied by a whole number.

• **Look at Step 1. Why are 2 squares needed?** (because one of the factors is the whole number 2)

• **Look at Step 2. Why are both squares separated into fourths?** (The second factor is a fraction in fourths.) **How many fourths have been shaded in all in the two squares?** (6)

Technology Connection

Use Computer Models to Multiply Fractions

Students use the one-color counter manipulatives on <u>eduplace.com/kids/mw/</u> to multiply fractions.

Have students follow the directions to find $\frac{3}{4} \times \frac{5}{6}$.

- In **Workmat** mode click **Choose Counter**. Pick red. Click **Place**. Make a 4 row by 6 column array.

- Change counters to blue. Click on 3 of the 4 rows to show $\frac{3}{4}$. Then change to yellow and click on 5 of the 6 columns to show $\frac{5}{6}$ of the blue set.

- The product is the yellow subset over the entire set, or, $\frac{15}{24}$. Have students write this in simplest form.

Have students use the counters to solve.

1. $\frac{1}{2} \times \frac{7}{8} \left(\frac{7}{16}\right)$
2. $\frac{1}{4} \times \frac{3}{5} \left(\frac{3}{20}\right)$
3. $\frac{2}{5} \times \frac{3}{4} \left(\frac{3}{10}\right)$
4. $\frac{3}{7} \times \frac{2}{3} \left(\frac{2}{7}\right)$
5. $\frac{4}{5} \times \frac{2}{7} \left(\frac{8}{35}\right)$
6. $\frac{5}{6} \times \frac{1}{3} \left(\frac{5}{18}\right)$

▶ You can use models to multiply with mixed numbers.

Find $\frac{1}{2} \times 2\frac{1}{4}$.

STEP 1 Draw three squares.
Separate the squares into fourths.
Shade and label $2\frac{1}{4}$ of the three squares.
- How many fourths are in $2\frac{1}{4}$? **9**

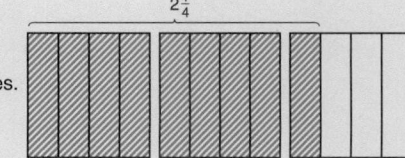

STEP 2 Separate the squares into halves.
Notice that each square is now separated into eighths.
- Shade and label $\frac{1}{2}$ of the three squares.
- How many eighths did you shade twice? **9**
- Complete: $\frac{1}{2} \times 2\frac{1}{4} = \frac{\blacksquare}{8}$ **9** ← number of eighths shaded twice
  ← number of eighths in 1 square
- Write your answer in simplest form.
  $\frac{9}{8} = 1\frac{1}{8}$

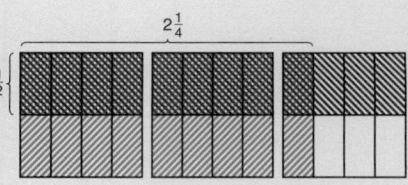

> **Check your answer.**
> Another way to estimate products is to round fractions to 0, $\frac{1}{2}$, or 1.
> $\frac{1}{2}$ rounds to $\frac{1}{2}$ and $2\frac{1}{4}$ rounds to 2.
> $\frac{1}{2} \times 2\frac{1}{4} \approx \frac{1}{2} \times 2$
> $\frac{1}{2} \times 2 = 1$
> The product of $\frac{1}{2}$ and $2\frac{1}{4}$ is about 1.

On Your Own

1. Use area to model multiplication of $\frac{2}{5}$ and $\frac{3}{4}$. Draw a unit square. Use horizontal lines to separate the square into fifths. Use vertical lines to separate the square into fourths. **Check students' work.**

   a. What fraction of the square does each small rectangle represent? $\frac{1}{20}$

   b. Shade and label $\frac{2}{5} \times \frac{3}{4}$. **Check students' work.**

   c. Write your answer in simplest form. $\frac{2}{5} \times \frac{3}{4} = \blacksquare$ $\frac{6}{20}$ or $\frac{3}{10}$

312

- Work through the third example with students.

- **Look at Step 1. Why are three squares needed?** (The second factor is greater than 2.) **Why is each of the three squares separated into fourths?** (The mixed number includes a fraction in fourths.)

- **Look at Step 2. Why are the squares divided into halves?** (The denominator of the first factor is in halves.) **Into how many sections have each of the three squares been separated?** (8)

3 Practice

Assign **Exercises 1–16** of *On Your Own* as independent work.

- *Problem Solving for Problems 1–4* Have students compare their answers.

Complete the equation represented by each model.
Write each answer in simplest form.

2.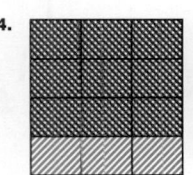

$\frac{2}{3} \times \frac{1}{2} = \blacksquare \quad \frac{2}{3} \times \frac{1}{2} = \frac{2}{6} \text{ or } \frac{1}{3}$

3.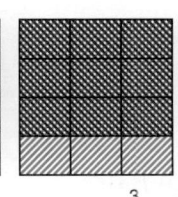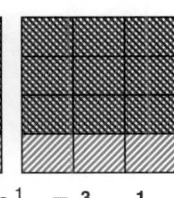

$2 \times \frac{3}{8} = \blacksquare \quad 2 \times \frac{3}{8} = \frac{3}{4}$

4.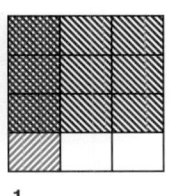

$\frac{3}{4} \times 3\frac{1}{3} = \blacksquare \quad \frac{3}{4} \times 3\frac{1}{3} = 2\frac{1}{2}$

Use models to find each product.
Write each product in simplest form.

5. $\frac{1}{2} \times \frac{1}{3} = \blacksquare \quad \frac{1}{6}$ **6.** $\frac{1}{3} \times \frac{3}{4} = \blacksquare \quad \frac{1}{4}$ **7.** $4 \times \frac{1}{2} = \blacksquare \quad 2$ **8.** $\frac{3}{4} \times \frac{4}{5} = \blacksquare \quad \frac{3}{5}$

9. $3 \times \frac{2}{3} = \blacksquare \quad 2$ **10.** $5 \times \frac{3}{5} = \blacksquare \quad 3$ **11.** $\frac{3}{4} \times 4\frac{1}{2} = \blacksquare \quad 3\frac{3}{8}$ **12.** $1\frac{2}{5} \times 2\frac{1}{2} = \blacksquare \quad 3\frac{1}{2}$

13. $2 \times \frac{1}{6} = \blacksquare \quad \frac{1}{3}$ **14.** $\frac{1}{4} \times \frac{3}{5} = \blacksquare \quad \frac{3}{20}$ **15.** $\frac{2}{3} \times 1\frac{2}{3} = \blacksquare \quad 1\frac{1}{9}$ **16.** $3\frac{1}{3} \times 2\frac{1}{8} = \blacksquare \quad 7\frac{1}{12}$

Talk About It • Write About It

You have learned how to use models to multiply with fractions and mixed numbers. *See Additional Answers on Page 331.*

17. When you multiply two fractions that are both less than one, will the product be less than or greater than either factor? Use words, pictures, and numbers to justify your answer.

18. When you multiply a counting number by a fraction less than one, will the product be a counting number all of the time, some of the time, or none of the time? Explain how you know.

Test Prep Transparency 12.1

DAILY TEST PREP

Which multiplication does the model show? (D)

A. $4 \times \frac{3}{2}$ C. $\frac{3}{4} \times \frac{1}{2}$

B. $\frac{3}{8} \times \frac{1}{2}$ D. $\frac{3}{4} \times \frac{1}{3}$

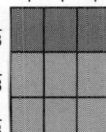

Activity

Lesson Intervention

Or use Intervention CD-ROM Lesson 12.1

Model Multiplication

👤👤👤 Small Group	🕐 5–10 minutes	Tactile, Kinesthetic

- Draw a large square to model $\frac{1}{2} \times \frac{3}{5}$.
- **How can we model halves?** (by drawing a horizontal line across the square halfway down the side) **How can we model $\frac{1}{2}$?** (shade one of the halves)
- **How can we can show fifths?** (by drawing 4 vertical lines to separate the square into 5 equal parts) **How can we model $\frac{3}{5}$?** (shade 3 of the 5 vertical sections)
- **How many small rectangles are there in the square?** (10) **Each one represents $\frac{1}{10}$ of the whole. How many double-shaded sections are there?** (3)
- **What fractional part of the square do they represent?** ($\frac{3}{10}$) **What multiplication does the model show?** ($\frac{1}{2} \times \frac{3}{5}$) **What is the product?** ($\frac{3}{10}$)

---

4 Assess and Close

Assign **Exercises 17 and 18** of the *Talk About It • Write About It* section. Have volunteers explain their work.

Assign the **LESSON QUIZ** on Transparency 12.1 to further assess student understanding.

 **Keeping a Journal**

Have students write a few sentences explaining how to use models to multiply two fractions, a fraction and a counting number, or a fraction and a mixed number.

Lesson 12.2

Multiply Fractions

PLANNING THE LESSON

MATHEMATICS OBJECTIVE
Find the product of two fractions.

Use Lesson Planner CD-ROM for Lesson 12.2.

Daily Routines

Vocabulary

Remind students that a *factor* is one of two or more numbers that are multiplied. The *product* is the number that results from multiplying the factors.

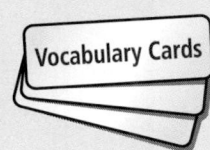

Vocabulary Cards

Meeting North Carolina's Standards

Prepare for Grade 6 Objective **1.04** Develop fluency in addition, subtraction, multiplication, and division of nonnegative rational numbers.

Lesson Transparency **12.2**

Problem of the Day

Troy spent one half hour studying math and one third of an hour studying spelling. How many minutes did he study in all? (50 minutes)

Quick Review
Multiply.
1. 5×9 (45)
2. 8×7 (56)
3. 4×9 (36)
4. 7×9 (63)
5. 9×9 (81)

Lesson Quiz
Multiply. Write your answer in simplest form.
1. $\frac{1}{3} \times \frac{3}{8}$ $\left(\frac{1}{8}\right)$
2. $\frac{3}{4} \times \frac{4}{9}$ $\left(\frac{1}{3}\right)$
3. $\frac{5}{6} \times \frac{1}{3}$ $\left(\frac{5}{18}\right)$
4. $4 \times \frac{5}{8}$ $\left(2\frac{1}{2}\right)$
5. $3 \times \frac{1}{6}$ $\left(\frac{1}{2}\right)$

LEVELED PRACTICE

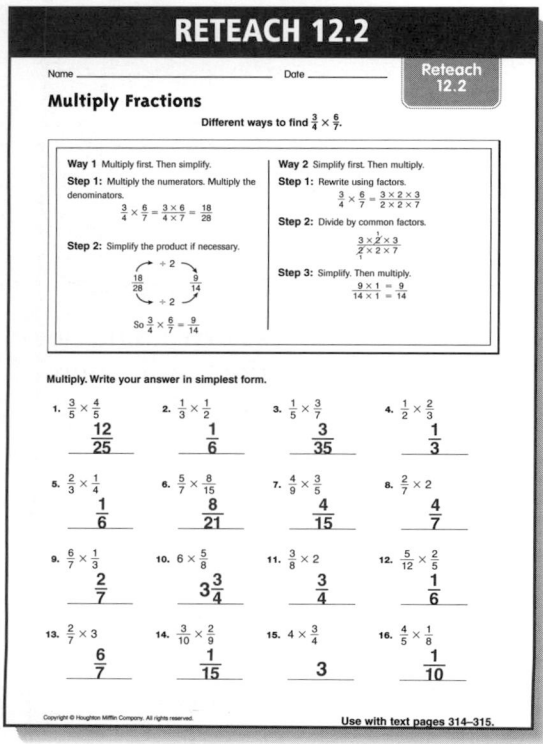

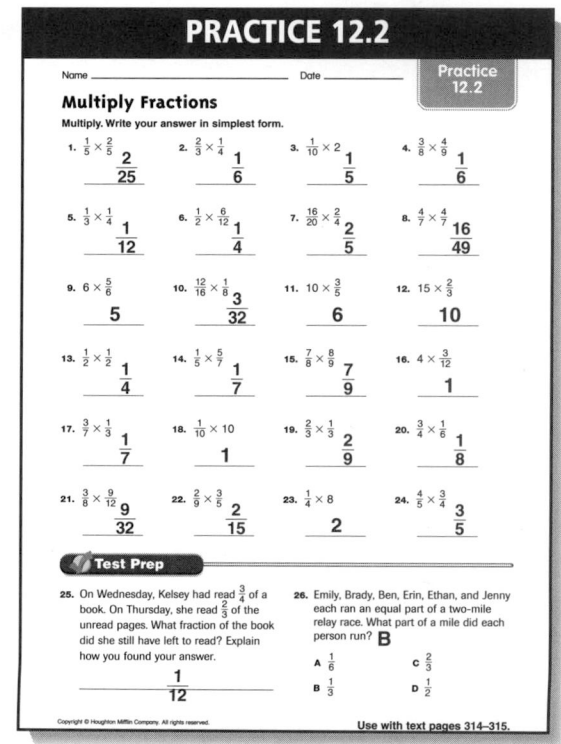

Practice Workbook Page 77

Reaching All Learners

Differentiated Instruction

English Learners

Use Worksheet 12.2 to give students practice translating numbers in word form to numerical form when solving word problems.

Inclusion
VISUAL, AUDITORY

- **What equation do we write to find $\frac{3}{5}$ of $\frac{5}{6}$?** ($\frac{3}{5} \times \frac{5}{6} = n$)
- **Multiply the numerators and denominators.** Write: $\frac{3}{5} \times \frac{5}{6} = \frac{(3 \times 5)}{(5 \times 6)}$.
- **What is the product?** ($\frac{15}{30}$) **How can we simplify that fraction?** (Find the GCF and divide the numerator and denominator by that number.) **What is the GCF of 15 and 30?** (15) **What is $\frac{15}{30}$ in simplest form?** ($\frac{1}{2}$) **What is $\frac{3}{5} \times \frac{5}{6}$?** ($\frac{1}{2}$)

Gifted and Talented
VISUAL, AUDITORY

- Ask students to create a fraction model for $\frac{1}{3} \times \frac{3}{4}$. (Possible answer: Model $\frac{3}{4}$ as $\frac{1}{4} + \frac{1}{4} + \frac{1}{4}$. Then remove 2 of the fourths, leaving 1 fourth.)
- Ask students to model $\frac{1}{2} \times \frac{5}{6}$ in the same way. (Possible answer: Since 5 is not divisible by 2, model $\frac{5}{6}$ as $\frac{10}{12}$. One half of $\frac{10}{12}$ is $\frac{5}{12}$.)
- Have students create models for two similar multiplication problems of their own.

TECHNOLOGY

Spiral Review

To reinforce skills on lessons taught earlier, create **customized** spiral review worksheets using the *Ways to Assess* CD-ROM.

Tool Software

Use *Easy Sheet* or another spreadsheet to explore this lesson more fully.

Education Place

Encourage students to visit Education Place at <u>eduplace/kids/mw/</u> for more student activities.

Music Connection

Voice Parts

Give students this problem: There are four voice parts in a school choir. Girl's parts are alto (low) and soprano (high). Boy's parts are baritone (low) and tenor (high). Suppose there is an equal number of girls and boys in a choir of 72 students. You need twice as many altos as sopranos, and twice as many baritones as tenors. How many of each voice type should there be? Use a model to represent the problem. (12 sopranos, 24 altos; 12 tenors, 24 baritones)

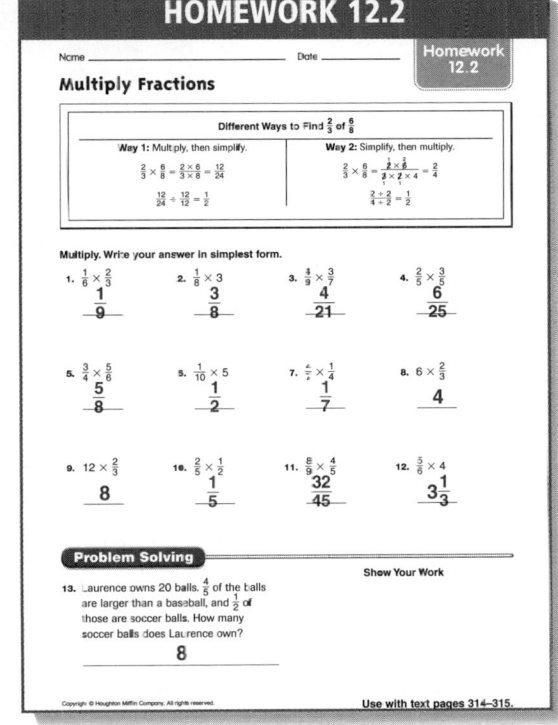

PROBLEM SOLVING 12.2

Multiply Fractions

HOMEWORK 12.2

Multiply Fractions

ENGLISH LEARNERS 12.2

Multiply Fractions

Homework Workbook Page 77

TEACHING LESSON 12.2

LESSON ORGANIZER

Objective Find the product of two fractions.

Resources Reteach, Practice, Enrichment, Problem Solving, Homework, English Learners, Transparencies, Math Center

Materials None

Activity

Warm-Up Activity
Writing Equivalent Fractions

Whole Group	5 minutes	Visual, Auditory

Write an equivalent fraction for the given fraction. (Possible answers are given.)

1. $\frac{4}{8}$ $\left(\frac{1}{2}\right)$

2. $\frac{3}{12}$ $\left(\frac{1}{4}\right)$

3. $\frac{10}{30}$ $\left(\frac{1}{3}\right)$

4. $\frac{3}{15}$ $\left(\frac{1}{5}\right)$

5. $\frac{36}{48}$ $\left(\frac{3}{4}\right)$

Lesson 2

Multiply Fractions

Objective Find the product of two fractions.

Learn About It

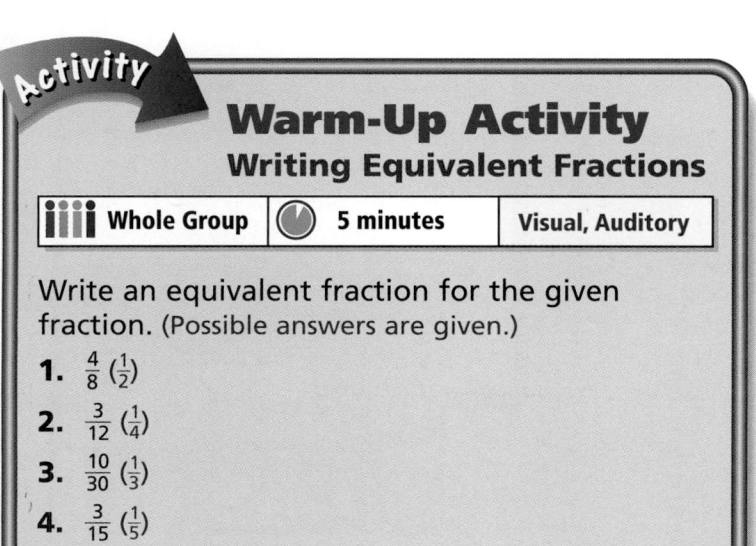

To find a fraction of a fraction, you need to find the product of the fractions. You know how to use models to multiply fractions. Here are some other ways to find products of fractions.

Find $\frac{5}{6}$ of $\frac{3}{4}$.

Different Ways to Find $\frac{5}{6}$ of $\frac{3}{4}$

Way ❶ You can multiply first, then simplify.

STEP 1 Multiply the numerators. Multiply the denominators.

$$\frac{5}{6} \times \frac{3}{4} = \frac{5 \times 3}{6 \times 4} = \frac{15}{24}$$

STEP 2 Simplify the product if necessary.

$$\frac{15}{24} \overset{\div 3}{\underset{\div 3}{=}} \frac{5}{8}$$

Way ❷ You can simplify first, then multiply.

STEP 1 Rewrite using factors.

$$\frac{5}{6} \times \frac{3}{4} = \frac{5 \times 3}{2 \times 3 \times 4}$$

STEP 2 Divide by common factors.

$$\frac{5}{6} \times \frac{3}{4} = \frac{5 \times \overset{1}{\cancel{3}}}{2 \times \underset{1}{\cancel{3}} \times 4}$$

STEP 3 Multiply.

$$\frac{5 \times 1}{1 \times 2 \times 4} = \frac{5}{8}$$

Solution: $\frac{5}{6}$ of $\frac{3}{4}$ is $\frac{5}{8}$.

Other Examples

A. Prime Factorization

$$\frac{9}{10} \times \frac{2}{3} = \frac{9 \times 2}{10 \times 3}$$

$$= \frac{3 \times 3 \times 2}{2 \times 5 \times 3}$$

$$= \frac{3}{5} \times \frac{3}{3} \times \frac{2}{2}$$

$$= \frac{3}{5}$$

Notice that $\frac{2}{2} = 1$ and $\frac{3}{3} = 1$. The product of 1 and any number is that number.

B. Fraction and Whole Number

$$\frac{1}{5} \times 4 = \frac{1}{5} \times \frac{4}{1}$$

$$= \frac{1 \times 4}{5 \times 1}$$

$$= \frac{4}{5}$$

314

---

❶ Introduce

- Write $\frac{1}{3} \times \frac{3}{8}$ on the chalkboard. **Model the product by shading the fractions on a square. Another way to multiply two fractions is to multiply the numerators and the denominators to get a new fraction. What will that fraction be?** $\left(\frac{3}{24}\right)$

- **How can we write that fraction in simplest form?** (Divide numerator and denominator by their GCF, 3.) **What do we get?** $\left(\frac{1}{8}\right)$

- Explain that another way is to simplify the factors first before multiplying. Write $\frac{1}{3} \times \frac{3}{8} = \frac{(1 \times 3)}{(3 \times 8)}$.

- **What factor is common to both the numerator and denominator?** (3) **If we divide each by 3, what fraction results?** $\left(\frac{1}{8}\right)$

❷ Develop

Guide students through the *Learn About It* portion of the lesson.

- Review the steps in Way 1. Make sure that students understand that they first multiply numerators and denominators and then divide each by their GCF.

- Review the steps in Way 2. In Step 1, make sure students understand that the numerator and denominator have been written in factored form.

- Work through the other examples with students. In *Other Examples A*, be sure students understand how to write a prime factorization.

Guided Practice

Have students complete **Exercises 1–6** as you observe. Remind them to use the *Ask Yourself* questions to help. Give students the opportunity to talk about the question in *Explain Your Thinking*.

Ask Yourself

- Can I use prime factorization?
- Did I write my answer in simplest form?

Multiply. Write your answer in simplest form.

1. $\frac{2}{3} \times \frac{3}{5}$ $\frac{2}{5}$ 2. $\frac{3}{8} \times \frac{4}{5}$ $\frac{3}{10}$ 3. $\frac{5}{6} \times \frac{3}{10}$ $\frac{1}{4}$

4. $8 \times \frac{3}{4}$ 6   5. $6 \times \frac{2}{5}$ $2\frac{2}{5}$ 6. $\frac{4}{7} \times 4$ $2\frac{2}{7}$

Explain Your Thinking ▶ Why can you divide by common factors in the numerator and denominator to simplify a fraction? **Common factors in the numerator and denominator are equivalent to 1 and multiplying and dividing a number by 1 does not change its value.**

Practice and Problem Solving

Multiply. Write your answer in simplest form.

7. $\frac{1}{5} \times \frac{5}{8}$ $\frac{1}{8}$ 8. $\frac{2}{5} \times \frac{5}{8}$ $\frac{1}{4}$ 9. $\frac{3}{5} \times \frac{5}{9}$ $\frac{1}{3}$ 10. $\frac{4}{5} \times \frac{5}{12}$ $\frac{1}{3}$ 11. $\frac{1}{6} \times \frac{2}{3}$ $\frac{1}{9}$

12. $\frac{1}{8} \times 6$ $\frac{3}{4}$ 13. $\frac{3}{8} \times 4$ $1\frac{1}{2}$ 14. $9 \times \frac{5}{8}$ $5\frac{5}{8}$ 15. $8 \times \frac{1}{6}$ $1\frac{1}{3}$ 16. $2 \times \frac{3}{4}$ $1\frac{1}{2}$

✗ Algebra • Expressions Multiply. Write each answer in simplest form.

17. $\frac{a}{6} \cdot \frac{2}{b}$ $\frac{a}{3b}$ 18. $2 \cdot \frac{2}{n}$ $\frac{4}{n}$ 19. $\frac{p}{q} \cdot \frac{q}{p}$ 1

20. $3 \cdot \frac{6}{y}$ $\frac{18}{y}$ 21. $\frac{x}{8} \cdot \frac{2}{y}$ $\frac{1x}{4y}$ 22. $\frac{a}{x} \cdot \frac{b}{y}$ $\frac{ab}{xy}$

The multiplication dot is used to avoid confusion between the multiplication symbol (x) and the variable x.

Solve.

23. Two fifths of a class is in the drama club. Only $\frac{1}{4}$ of them have parts in a play. What fraction of that class has parts in the play? $\frac{1}{10}$ **of the class**

24. The middle school has 135 students. Two thirds of them are girls. How many of the students are girls? How many are boys? **90 girls; 45 boys**

25. **Write About It** How could you use two-color counters or coins to model $\frac{3}{4} \times \frac{1}{2}$? **25–26. See Additional Answers on Page 331.**

26. **Explain** A bottle of water contains $\frac{7}{8}$ liter. Annette buys 12 bottles. How many liters does she buy? Explain.

| **Daily Review** | **Test Prep** |

Find the product. (Ch.3, Lesson 7)

27. 24×32 **768**   28. 18×43 **774**

29. 15×16 **240**   30. 92×87 **8,004**

31. 42×27 **1,134**   32. 83×13 **1,079**

33. John memorized $\frac{2}{3}$ of his lines for the school play. Then he memorized $\frac{1}{3}$ of what was left on Sunday. What fraction of his lines did he memorize on Sunday?

(A) $\frac{1}{9}$ B $\frac{1}{3}$ C $\frac{1}{2}$ D 1

Extra Practice See page 331, Set A.

DAILY TEST PREP

Marta read $\frac{3}{5}$ of a play in one evening. In study period, she read $\frac{1}{2}$ of what was left. What fraction did she read in study period? $(\frac{1}{5})$

Activity

Or use Intervention CD-ROM 12.2

Lesson Intervention

Dividing by Common Factors

👥 Small Group   ⏱ 5–10 minutes   Visual, Auditory

- Display: $\frac{5}{6} \times \frac{3}{7}$. Have students copy the steps as you demonstrate.
- First multiply the numerators and denominators. Write: $\frac{(5 \times 3)}{(6 \times 7)}$.
- We can't factor the numerator any further, but look at the denominator. We can factor 6. What are the factors of 6? Write: $6 \times 7 = 3 \times 2 \times 7$
- Write the new fraction: $\frac{(5 \times 3)}{(3 \times 2 \times 7)}$.
- Do the numerator and denominator have any factors in common? (yes, 3)
- Divide the numerator and denominator by 3. Strike through each 3.
- Write the resulting numerator and denominator: $\frac{5}{(2 \times 7)} = \frac{5}{14}$. What is $\frac{5}{6} \times \frac{3}{7}$? $(\frac{5}{14})$

---

3 Practice

Assign **Exercises 7–33** as independent work

- **Exercises 7–16** Have students discuss their answers.
- **Algebra • Expressions for Exercises 17–22** Have students discuss their methods as well as their answers.
- **Problem Solving for Problems 23–26** For Problem 26, have students discuss their method of solution.

Common Error

Not dividing by the greatest common factors When simplifying the product, students should make sure they have divided both parts of the fraction by the GCF.

4 Assess and Close

- **What are three ways to find the product of two fractions?** (shading, rectangles; multiply first, then simplify; simplify first, then multiply.)

Assign the **LESSON QUIZ** on Transparency 12.2 to further assess student understanding.

Keeping a Journal

Have students write two problems and illustrate the three ways of multiplying a fraction by a fraction.

Multiply With Mixed Numbers

PLANNING THE LESSON

MATHEMATICS OBJECTIVE
Find products of fractions and mixed numbers.

Use Lesson Planner CD-ROM for Lesson 12.3.

Daily Routines

Vocabulary

Explain that a *mixed number* is the sum of a whole number and a fraction. Give examples, such as $3\frac{1}{2}$ and $1\frac{2}{3}$. Then explain that an *improper fraction* is a fraction that is greater than or equal to 1. **The numerator in an improper fraction is greater than or equal to the denominator.** Point out that $\frac{11}{3}$, $\frac{8}{8}$, and $\frac{8}{1}$ are all improper fractions.

Meeting North Carolina's Standards

Prepare for Grade 6 Objective **1.04** Develop fluency in addition, subtraction, multiplication, and division of nonnegative rational numbers.

Vocabulary Cards

Lesson
Transparency
12.3

Problem of the Day

Linus has $\frac{1}{3}$ of $\frac{3}{4}$ of a dollar. Fiona has $\frac{3}{5}$ of $\frac{1}{2}$ of a dollar. Who has more money? Explain. (Fiona; $\frac{1}{4}$ of a dollar, or 25 cents, is less than $\frac{3}{10}$ of a dollar, or 30 cents.)

Quick Review

Write each improper fraction as a mixed number.

1. $\frac{11}{4}$ ($2\frac{3}{4}$)
2. $\frac{8}{5}$ ($1\frac{3}{5}$)
3. $\frac{9}{3}$ (3)
4. $\frac{17}{4}$ ($4\frac{1}{4}$)
5. $\frac{22}{3}$ ($7\frac{1}{3}$)

Lesson Quiz

Multiply. Write each product in simplest form.

1. $\frac{3}{5} \times 1\frac{1}{4}$ ($\frac{3}{4}$)
2. $3 \times 2\frac{1}{3}$ (7)
3. $4 \times 1\frac{2}{5}$ ($\frac{28}{5}$ or $5\frac{3}{5}$)
4. $1\frac{1}{2} \times 2\frac{1}{6}$ ($\frac{13}{4}$ or $3\frac{1}{4}$)
5. $1\frac{4}{5} \times 1\frac{2}{3}$ (3)

LEVELED PRACTICE

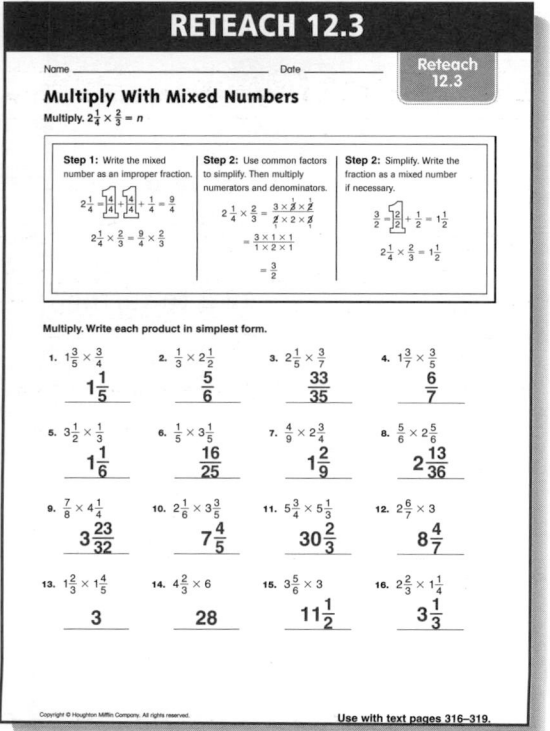

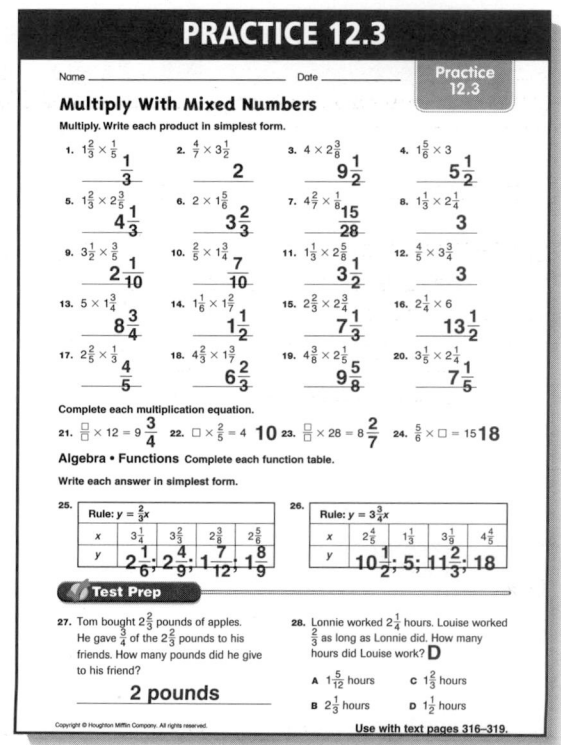

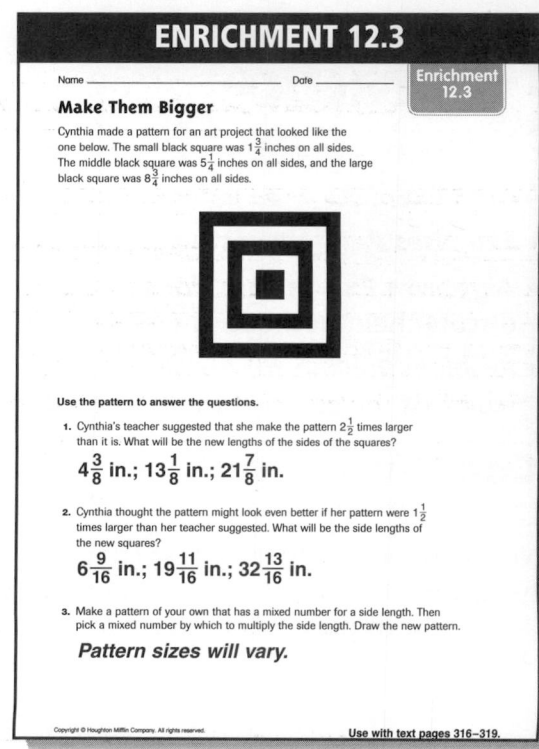

Practice Workbook Page 78

Reaching All Learners
Differentiated Instruction

English Learners

Worksheet 12.3 instructs students on using context clues to determine the meanings of unfamiliar words or phrases in word problems.

Special Needs
VISUAL, AUDITORY

Materials: *Mixed Numbers Transparency*

- Arrange nine $\frac{1}{4}$-circle pieces to show 2 full circles plus a $\frac{1}{4}$-circle piece.

- **How many whole circles are there?** (2) Write *2* above the circles. Point to the $\frac{1}{4}$-circle piece. **What fraction names this part of a circle?** ($\frac{1}{4}$) Write $\frac{1}{4}$ next to the 2.

- **How many $\frac{1}{4}$-pieces are there in all?** (9) Write $= \frac{9}{4}$ after $2\frac{1}{4}$.

Early Finishers
VISUAL, TACTILE

Materials: *Calculators*

- Give students this problem. **Which of the following mixed numbers, when multiplied by themselves, come closest to, but are less than, 2?** $1\frac{1}{4}$, $1\frac{3}{8}$, $1\frac{2}{5}$, $1\frac{1}{2}$. ($(1\frac{1}{4})^2 = 1\frac{9}{16}$; $(1\frac{3}{8})^2 = 1\frac{57}{64}$; $(1\frac{2}{5})^2 = 1\frac{24}{25}$; $(1\frac{1}{2})^2 = 2\frac{1}{4}$; $(1\frac{2}{5})^2$ or $1\frac{24}{25}$ is closer to 2 than the others.)

- Help them use a calculator to check answer.

TECHNOLOGY

Spiral Review

Help students remember skills they learned earlier by creating **customized** spiral review worksheets using the *Ways to Assess* CD-ROM.

eBook

eMathbook allows students to review lessons and do homework without carrying their textbooks home.

Lesson Planner

You can use the Lesson Planner CD-ROM to create a report of the lessons and standards you have taught.

Science Connection

Cooking Fractions
Materials: *Cookbooks*

- Have students look up recipes for muffins or cupcakes that serve 24, or give them a recipe to discuss with the class.

- Suppose you have a tin that makes 6 muffins, and you want to make only 1 tin. How could you reduce the recipe? (Multiply the measurements of the ingredients by $\frac{6}{24}$, or $\frac{1}{4}$.)

- Have students use the recipes to write a fraction multiplication problem. Discuss.

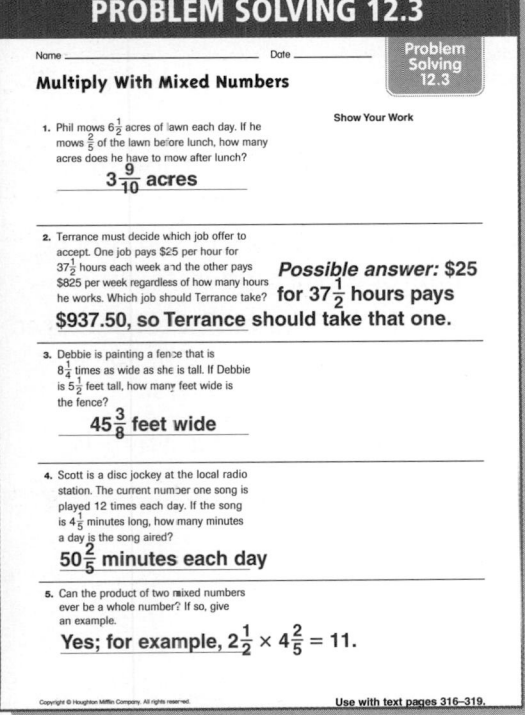

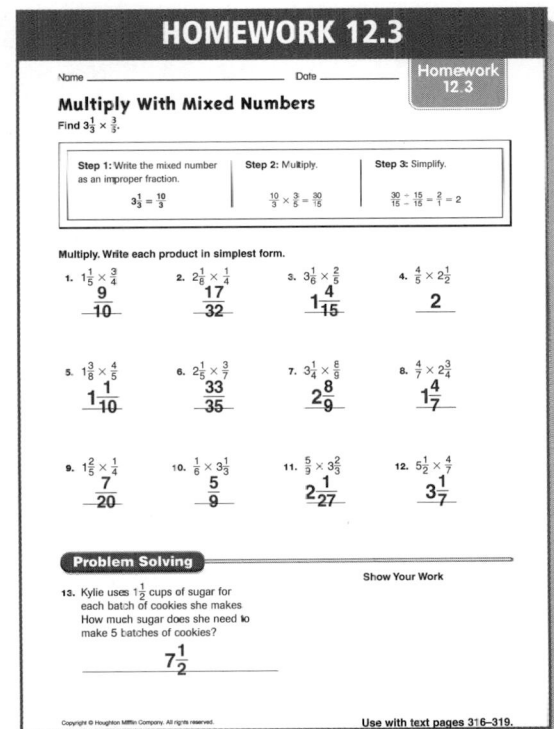

Homework Workbook Page 78

TEACHING LESSON 12.3

LESSON ORGANIZER

Objective Find products of fractions and mixed numbers.

Resources Reteach, Practice, Enrichment, Problem Solving, Homework, English Learners, Transparencies, Math Center

Materials None

Warm-Up Activity

Find the Product

iiii Whole Group	⏱ 5 minutes	Visual, Auditory

Have students find the products of the following proper fractions.

1. $\frac{3}{8} \times \frac{4}{5}$ ($\frac{3}{10}$)

2. $\frac{2}{3} \times \frac{6}{8}$ ($\frac{1}{2}$)

3. $\frac{6}{7} \times \frac{5}{12}$ ($\frac{5}{14}$)

4. $\frac{2}{5} \times \frac{7}{10}$ ($\frac{7}{25}$)

5. $\frac{2}{9} \times \frac{3}{5}$ ($\frac{2}{15}$)

All of the factors in the exercises are greater than zero and less than one. How can you check to see if your answers are too big? (The product should be less than either factor.)

Lesson 3 — Multiply With Mixed Numbers

Objective Find products of fractions and mixed numbers.

 **Learn About It** 💿 MathTracks 2/1 Listen and Understand

You can multiply with a **mixed number**, like $2\frac{3}{4}$, or an **improper fraction**, like $\frac{11}{4}$.

Max is a clown who juggles and does yo-yo tricks for parties. He has been hired for a party that will last $1\frac{3}{4}$ hours. Max plans to spend $\frac{2}{3}$ of that time juggling. How long will Max's juggling last?

Multiply. $\frac{2}{3} \times 1\frac{3}{4} = n$

You can write the mixed number as an improper fraction and multiply.

STEP 1 Write the mixed number as an improper fraction.

$1\frac{3}{4} = \frac{4}{4} + \frac{3}{4} = \frac{7}{4}$

$\frac{2}{3} \times 1\frac{3}{4} = \frac{2}{3} \times \frac{7}{4}$

STEP 2 Use common factors to simplify. Then multiply.

$\frac{2}{3} \times \frac{\overset{1}{7}}{4} = \frac{2 \times 7}{3 \times 2 \times 2}$

$= \frac{1 \times 7}{3 \times 2}$

$= \frac{7}{6}$

STEP 3 Simplify. Write the fraction as a mixed number if necessary.

$\frac{7}{6} = \frac{6}{6} + \frac{1}{6} = 1\frac{1}{6}$

$\frac{2}{3} \times 1\frac{3}{4} = 1\frac{1}{6}$

Solution: Max will juggle for $1\frac{1}{6}$ hours.

Other Examples

A. Two Mixed Numbers

$1\frac{2}{3} \times 3\frac{1}{4} = \frac{5}{3} \times \frac{13}{4}$

$= \frac{5 \times 13}{3 \times 4}$

$= \frac{65}{12}$  $65 \div 12 = \blacksquare$

$= 5\frac{5}{12}$

B. Mixed Number and Whole Number

$2\frac{1}{8} \times 4 = \frac{17}{8} \times \frac{4}{1}$

$= \frac{17 \times \overset{1}{2} \times \overset{1}{2}}{2 \times 2 \times 2}$

$= \frac{17}{2}$

$= 8\frac{1}{2}$

316

---

1 Introduce

- When you multiply a fraction by a mixed number, the mixed number must be written as an improper fraction. For example, suppose we want to write $2\frac{1}{2}$ as an improper fraction. What denominator should we use? (2, since 2 is the denominator of the fractional part.) **How many halves are there in 2?** (4) Write: $4(\frac{1}{2}) = \frac{4}{2}$. **How many halves will there be in $2\frac{1}{2}$?** (4 + 1 = 5)

- **What improper fraction can we write for $2\frac{1}{2}$?** ($2\frac{1}{2} = 2 + \frac{1}{2} = \frac{4}{2} + \frac{1}{2} = \frac{5}{2}$)

2 Develop

Guide students through the *Learn About It* portion of the lesson.

- **Look at Step 1.** Be sure students understand the process of converting $1\frac{3}{4}$ into an improper fraction in fourths.

- **Look at Step 2.** Why is the 4 in the denominator factored as 2 × 2? (In order to make the common factor 2 visible in the denominator.)

- **Look at Step 3.** Be sure students understand why $\frac{7}{6}$ is written as $\frac{6}{6} + \frac{1}{6}$.

Ask Yourself
- Did I use improper fractions?
- Did I write my answer in simplest form?

TEST TIPS

Multiply. Write each product in simplest form.

1. $\frac{4}{5} \times 1\frac{2}{3}$ $1\frac{1}{3}$ 2. $2\frac{3}{4} \times 1\frac{1}{2}$ $4\frac{1}{8}$ 3. $1\frac{3}{8} \times 4$ $5\frac{1}{2}$

4. $6 \times 2\frac{3}{4}$ $16\frac{1}{2}$ 5. $1\frac{2}{3} \times \frac{2}{5}$ $\frac{2}{3}$ 6. $1\frac{1}{4} \times 3\frac{2}{5}$ $4\frac{1}{4}$

TEST TIPS **Explain Your Thinking** ▶ How is multiplying with mixed numbers similar to multiplying with fractions?

See Additional Answers on Page 331.

Practice and Problem Solving

Multiply. Write each product in simplest form.

7. $1\frac{5}{6} \times \frac{1}{3}$ $\frac{11}{18}$ 8. $\frac{3}{4} \times 2\frac{1}{3}$ $1\frac{3}{4}$ 9. $1\frac{7}{9} \times 2$ $3\frac{5}{9}$ 10. $5 \times 4\frac{1}{5}$ 21

11. $2\frac{1}{3} \times 3\frac{3}{4}$ $8\frac{3}{4}$ 12. $3\frac{1}{2} \times \frac{2}{5}$ $1\frac{2}{5}$ 13. $3 \times 4\frac{1}{6}$ $12\frac{1}{2}$ 14. $2\frac{5}{6} \times 2\frac{1}{4}$ $6\frac{3}{8}$

15. $\frac{3}{8} \times 1\frac{1}{4}$ $\frac{15}{32}$ 16. $3\frac{5}{8} \times 2\frac{1}{2}$ $9\frac{1}{16}$ 17. $1\frac{7}{9} \times \frac{1}{12}$ $\frac{4}{27}$ 18. $2\frac{3}{4} \times \frac{5}{6}$ $2\frac{7}{24}$

19. $3\frac{1}{8} \times 4$ $12\frac{1}{2}$ 20. $2\frac{1}{5} \times \frac{2}{3}$ $1\frac{7}{15}$ 21. $3 \times 2\frac{2}{3}$ 8   22. $4\frac{5}{8} \times 2\frac{2}{3}$ $12\frac{1}{3}$

23. $9 \times 2\frac{1}{3}$ 21   24. $\frac{5}{8} \times 1\frac{3}{5}$ 1   25. $2\frac{1}{4} \times 3\frac{1}{9}$ 7   26. $3\frac{5}{6} \times 2\frac{3}{8}$ $9\frac{5}{48}$

Complete each multiplication equation.

27. $\frac{1}{6} \times \blacksquare = \frac{5}{6}$ 5   28. $\blacksquare \times 32 = 8$ $\frac{1}{4}$ 29. $\blacksquare \times 4 = 3$ $\frac{3}{4}$ 30. $\frac{2}{3} \times \blacksquare = 10$ 15

31. $\frac{3}{4} \times \blacksquare = 6$ 8   32. $\blacksquare \times 24 = 3$ $\frac{1}{8}$ 33. $\blacksquare \times \frac{6}{7} = 36$ 42   34. $45 \times \blacksquare = 10$ $\frac{2}{9}$

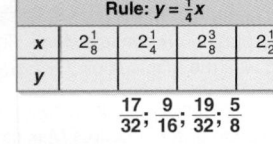 **Algebra** • **Functions** Complete each function table. Write each answer in simplest form.

35.

Rule: $y = \frac{1}{4}x$			
x	$2\frac{1}{8}$	$2\frac{1}{4}$	$2\frac{3}{8}$	$2\frac{1}{2}$
y				

$\frac{17}{32}, \frac{9}{16}, \frac{19}{32}, \frac{5}{8}$

36.

Rule: $y = 8x$			
x	$3\frac{3}{4}$	4	$4\frac{1}{4}$	$4\frac{1}{2}$
y				

30, 32, 34, 36

37.

Rule: $y = 1\frac{1}{4}x$			
x	$\frac{4}{5}$	$1\frac{3}{5}$	$3\frac{1}{3}$	$6\frac{2}{3}$
y				

$1, 2, 4\frac{1}{6}, 8\frac{1}{3}$

38.

Rule: $y = 3\frac{1}{3}x$			
x	$1\frac{1}{8}$	$2\frac{1}{8}$	$3\frac{1}{8}$	$4\frac{1}{8}$
y				

$3\frac{3}{4}; 7\frac{1}{12}; 10\frac{5}{12}; 13\frac{3}{4}$

 **Go On**

 **Quick Check Options**

The following activities will help students prepare for the Quick Check or may be used as an alternative assessment.

Vocabulary Review (individual, small group, or whole class)

Have students review the following vocabulary words by giving an example of how each term is used in this chapter.

- mixed number
- factor
- improper fraction
- product

Math Conversations (small group or whole class)

Have students discuss what they have learned about multiplying with mixed numbers in this chapter. Encourage students to ask each other questions to clarify their understanding.

Writing Prompt (individual or partners)

To solidify student understanding of vocabulary and concepts, have each student complete the following sentence:

The thing I found most difficult about multiplying with mixed numbers is _____.

---

3 Practice

- Work through the *Other Examples* with students. In Example A, have students note in particular that when a fraction such as $\frac{65}{12}$ cannot be simplified, the only way to find the mixed number equivalent is to divide the numerator by the denominator and write the remainder as a fraction.

Guided Practice

Have students complete **Exercises 1–6** as you observe. Remind them to use the *Ask Yourself* questions to help. Give students the opportunity to talk about the question in *Explain Your Thinking*.

Assign **Problems 7–47** as independent work.

- *Exercises 7–34* Have students discuss their work.
- *Algebra • Functions for Exercises 35–38* Have students compare answers and discuss their work.

DAILY TEST PREP

Rudy uses $2\frac{2}{3}$ cups of flour to make 2 pizzas. How much flour should he use if he wants to make only 1 pizza? (B)

A. $1\frac{1}{5}$ B. $1\frac{1}{3}$ C. $1\frac{1}{6}$ D. $1\frac{1}{4}$

Activity

Lesson Intervention

Or use Intervention CD-ROM Lesson 12.3

Write Improper Fractions as Mixed Numbers

| Small Group | 5–10 minutes | Visual, Kinesthetic |

- **How do we write mixed numbers when multiplying by a fraction or another mixed number?** (as improper fractions)

- Display $2\frac{1}{3}$. **Notice that the fractional part of the number is in thirds. The denominator of the improper fraction will be 3.**

- Draw two circles under 2. Draw $\frac{1}{3}$ of a circle under $\frac{1}{3}$. Then divide each circle into thirds.

- **Each part of a circle is $\frac{1}{3}$ of the whole. How many thirds are in 1 whole circle?** (3) **in 2 whole circles?** (6)

- Write $\frac{6}{3}$. **Six thirds represent 2 circles. There is one more third. How many thirds in all?** (7) **What fraction can we write for $2\frac{1}{3}$?** $(\frac{7}{3})$

Solve.

39. For the yo-yo trick "Rock the Baby," Max places his fingers halfway down the string. The string is $2\frac{3}{4}$ feet long. How long is each half? **$1\frac{3}{8}$ ft**

40. Vicki bought a yo-yo with a string that was $\frac{5}{8}$ of her height. How long was the string on Vicki's yo-yo? **3 ft**

41. **Measurement** For the trick "Tidal Wave," Max placed a finger under the yo-yo string about 4 inches from the end of its $2\frac{3}{4}$-foot length. How long is the rest of the string? **29 in.**

42. **Mental Math** For one job, Max earned $8 for each hour he worked. How much did he earn if he worked $1\frac{1}{2}$ hours? **$12**

43. Of the 40 jobs Max has worked so far this year, $\frac{5}{8}$ of them were from repeat customers. How many of his jobs were from new customers? **15 jobs**

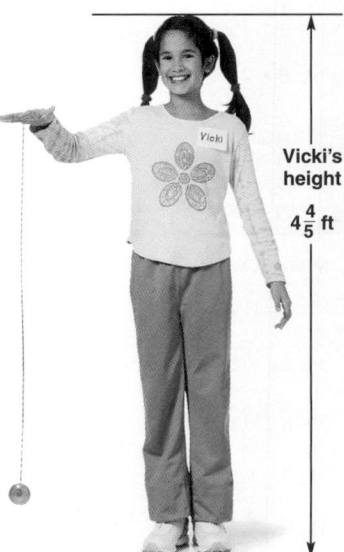

Vicki's height
$4\frac{4}{5}$ ft

Data Use the table for Problems 44–47.

The table shows the number of hours Max worked at various jobs this week and the amount he was paid for each job.

Jobs		
Event	**Hours Worked**	**Amount Earned**
Mall Opening	$6\frac{1}{2}$	$65
Rosa's Party	$3\frac{3}{4}$	$40
Graduation	$1\frac{1}{3}$	$15
Josh's Party	$2\frac{1}{4}$	$20
Town Picnic	$5\frac{2}{3}$	$60

44. Max sets aside $\frac{1}{4}$ of his earnings to put into savings. How much did he save from the five jobs shown in the table? **$50**

45. Max spent half of his time at Rosa's party putting on a magic show. How long was the magic show? **$1\frac{7}{8}$ hours**

46. **Analyze** Find the mean, median, mode, and range of the amounts Max earned at his jobs this week. **See below.**

47. **Create and Solve** Write your own problem that uses data from the table. Solve your problem. ***Check students' problems.***

46. mean: $40; median: $40; there is no mode; range: $50

Extra Practice See page 331, Set B.

---

4 Assess and Close

- *Problem Solving for Problems 39–43* Have students explain the methods they used. For Problem 43, students will need to perform two operations.

- *Problem Solving for Problems 44–47* Have students share their work. For Problem 46, have students discuss the methods they used to compute these statistical measures.

Common Error

Not writing fractions in simplest form Suggest that students write the prime factors of the numerator and denominator to be sure they can tell if there are common factors.

- Have volunteers come up to the chalkboard and give examples of how to write mixed numbers as improper fractions, and how to write improper fractions as mixed numbers.

- Then have other volunteers show the steps for multiplying two of the improper fractions.

Assign the **LESSON QUIZ** on Transparency 12.3 to further assess student understanding.

Quick Check

Check your understanding for Lessons 1–3.

Multiply. Write your answer in simplest form. (Lessons 1 and 2)

1.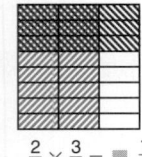

$$\frac{2}{3} \times \frac{3}{8} = \blacksquare \quad \frac{1}{4}$$

2.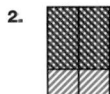

$$\frac{3}{4} \times \frac{1}{2} = \blacksquare \quad \frac{3}{8}$$

3. $\frac{4}{5} \times \frac{5}{6}$ **2/3**
4. $\frac{1}{3} \times \frac{5}{8}$ **5/24**
5. $\frac{7}{8} \times 6$ **5 1/4**
6. $8 \times \frac{3}{4}$ **6**

Multiply. Write each product in simplest form. (Lesson 3)

7. $2\frac{7}{8} \times 8$ **23**
8. $1\frac{3}{5} \times 2\frac{1}{2}$ **4**
9. $4 \times 5\frac{3}{4}$ **23**
10. $2\frac{1}{3} \times 5\frac{1}{7}$ **12**

Quick Check

Purpose: The Quick Check allows you to assess the students' understanding of the concepts presented in Lessons 1–3.

Items	Objectives Tested	Pages	Intervention
1–6	Use area to find the product of two fractions. Find the product of two fractions.	310–313 314–315	Reteach Resource 12.1–12.2 *Ways to Success* 12.1–12.2
7–10	Find products of fractions and mixed numbers.	316–318	Reteach Resource 12.3 *Ways to Success* 12.3

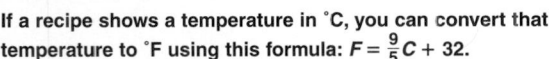

WEEKLY WR READER® eduplace.com/kids/mw/

How Hot Is It?

Science Connection

If a recipe shows a temperature in °C, you can convert that temperature to °F using this formula: $F = \frac{9}{5}C + 32$.

Here's how to change 200°C to °F.

STEP 1 Substitute values in the formula.

$F = \frac{9}{5}C + 32$

$= \left(\frac{9}{5} \times 200\right) + 32$

STEP 2 Multiply first.

$F = \left(\frac{9}{5} \times 200\right) + 32$

$= \left(\frac{9}{5} \times \frac{\overset{40}{200}}{1}\right) + 32$

$= 360 + 32$

STEP 3 Then add.

$F = 360 + 32$

$F = 392$

The temperature 200°C is the same as the temperature 392°F.

Change these temperatures to °F.

1. 190°C **374°F**
2. 150°C **302°F**
3. 235°C **455°F**
4. 100°C **212°F**

Keeping a Journal

Have students illustrate and write a few sentences explaining how to multiply a mixed number by a fraction.

Science Connection

How Hot Is It?

- Go over Step 1 of the process, the substitution of the Celsius temperature in the formula. Make sure students know that C stands for Celsius; F stands for Fahrenheit.

- Go over Steps 2 and 3. **How is 200 written as an improper fraction?** ($\frac{200}{1}$) Have a volunteer check Step 2 by multiplying first, then simplifying the fraction. ($(9 \times 200) \div (5 \times 1) = 1800 \div 5 = 360$)

Lesson
12.4

Hands-On: Model Division

PLANNING THE LESSON

MATHEMATICS OBJECTIVE
Use models to divide with fractions.

Use Lesson Planner CD-ROM for Lesson 12.4.

Daily Routines

Vocabulary

Call attention to the fact that a *unit fraction* is a fraction in which the numerator is 1. Ask students to give some examples of unit fractions.

Vocabulary Cards

Meeting North Carolina's Standards

Prepare for Grade 6 Objective **1.04** Develop fluency in addition, subtraction, multiplication, and division of nonnegative rational numbers.

Lesson
Transparency

12.4

Problem of the Day

I am an improper fraction. The two digits in my numerator are the same as the two digits in my denominator, but in reverse order. As a mixed number in simplest form, I am $1\frac{3}{4}$. What fraction am I? $\left(\frac{21}{12}\right)$

Quick Review

Find the product.

1. $2 \times \frac{1}{2}$ $\left(\frac{2}{2}$ or $1\right)$
2. $5 \times \frac{1}{5}$ $\left(\frac{5}{5}$ or $1\right)$
3. $7 \times \frac{1}{7}$ $\left(\frac{7}{7}$ or $1\right)$
4. $8 \times \frac{1}{8}$ $\left(\frac{8}{8}$ or $1\right)$
5. $9 \times \frac{1}{9}$ $\left(\frac{9}{9}$ or $1\right)$

Lesson Quiz

Divide. Check your answers.

1. $\frac{2}{3} \div \frac{1}{3}$ (2)
2. $\frac{5}{8} \div \frac{1}{8}$ (5)
3. $4 \div \frac{1}{4}$ (16)
4. $3 \div \frac{1}{4}$ (12)
5. $2 \div \frac{1}{6}$ (12)

LEVELED PRACTICE

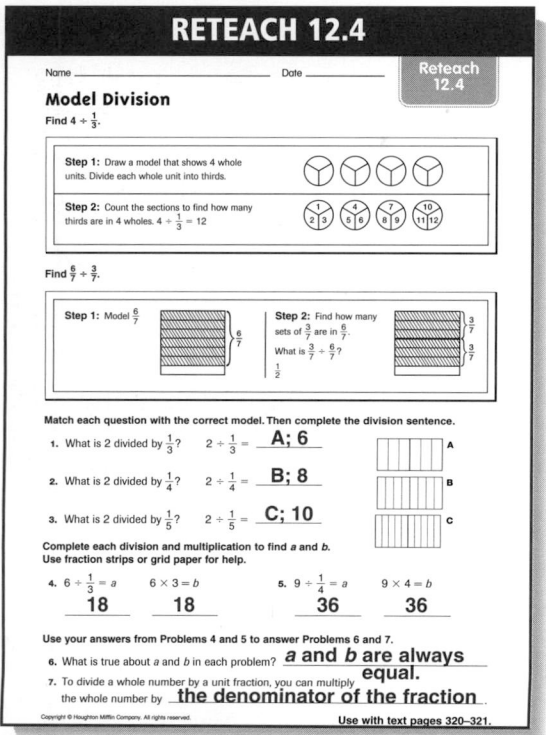

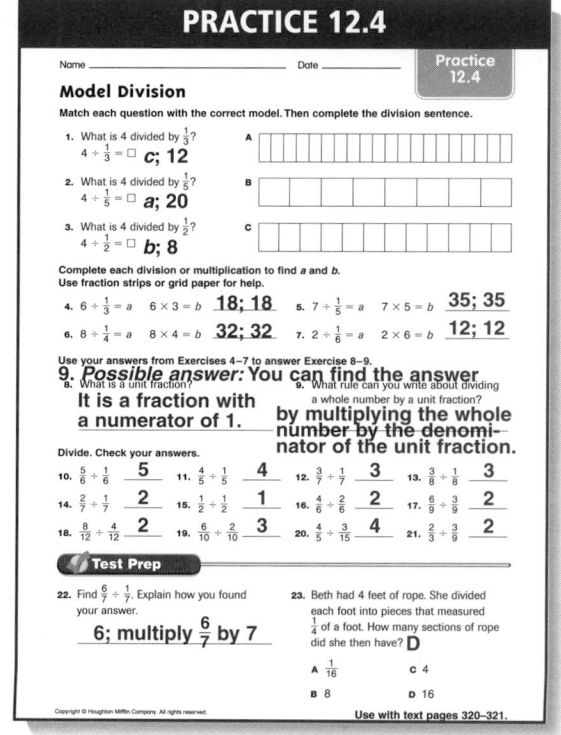

RETEACH 12.4 / **PRACTICE 12.4** / **ENRICHMENT 12.4**

Practice Workbook Page 79

Reaching All Learners
Differentiated Instruction

English Learners

Use Worksheet 12.4 to help familiarize students with the rules for forming plural nouns. The irregular plural *halves* appears in Lesson 4.

Inclusion
VISUAL, KINESTHETIC

Materials: *blank transparency, cut-outs from Mixed Numbers Transparency*

- Arrange 4 cut-out $\frac{1}{4}$-circle pieces to form a circle. **How many whole circles do you see?** (1)
- Separate each of the 4 pieces so that there is a thin open space between each quarter.
- **How many $\frac{1}{4}$ pieces are there?** (4) Write $1 \div \frac{1}{4} = 4$ above the circle.

Gifted and Talented
VISUAL, KINESTHETIC

- Have students model division by a unit fraction by creating models. They can use either drawn circles or fraction strips. Ask students to model three different division problems.
- Have them exchange models and write the division that is modeled. Students discuss their answers.

TECHNOLOGY

Spiral Review

You can prepare students for standardized tests with **customized** spiral review on key skills using the *Ways to Assess* CD-ROM.

Education Place

You can visit Education Place at eduplace.com/math/mw/ for teacher support materials.

Manipulatives

Interactive Fraction Models are available on the *Ways to Success* CD.

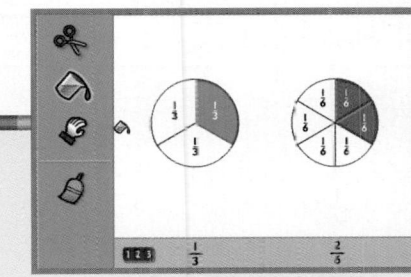

Music Connection

Time Signatures
- Have students who read music explain time signatures such as $\frac{4}{4}$.
- Have them use a music staff line broken into measures. Each measure equals 1 whole time unit. For $\frac{4}{4}$ time, show one measure with a whole note (equal to 4 beats), one with 2 half-notes (each equal to 2 beats), one with four quarter-notes (1 beat each), and one with eighth-notes.
- Ask them to write a division sentence for each measure: $1 \div 1 = 1$ whole note; $1 \div \frac{1}{2} = 2$ half notes, and so on.

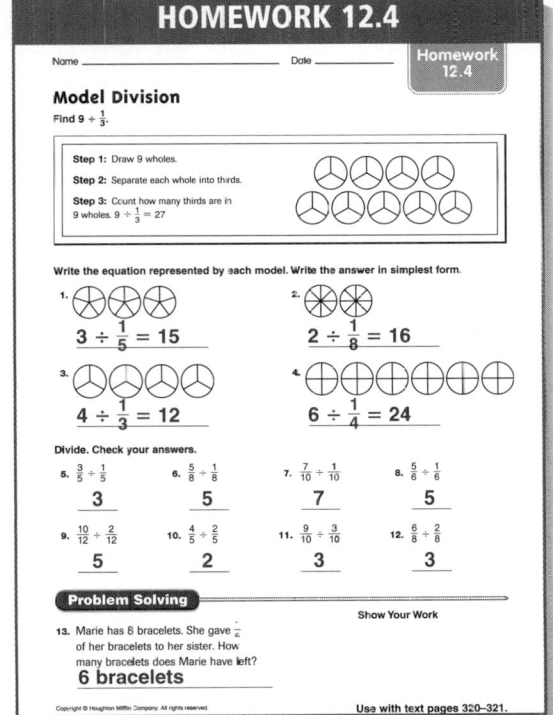

PROBLEM SOLVING 12.4

Name _____ Date _____ Problem Solving 12.4

Model Division

Use models to solve Problems 1–5.

Show Your Work

1. One period in a hockey game is 20 minutes. Each period makes up $\frac{1}{3}$ of the game. How many minutes long is the game?

   60 minutes

2. Twenty minutes of playing time makes up $\frac{1}{2}$ of a NCAA women's basketball game. How many minutes long is a game?

   40 minutes

3. If you divide $\frac{1}{4}$ of a dollar into parts that are $\frac{1}{20}$ of a dollar, how many parts are there? What are they called?

   5 parts; nickels

4. Manny said that $8 \div \frac{1}{4}$ is equal to $\frac{1}{8} \times 4$. Explain what Manny's mistake was. Then tell the correct answer.

   Possible answer: Manny probably meant to say that $8 \div \frac{1}{4}$ is equal to 8×4; 32

5. Can the quotient of two fractions be less than 1? Explain and include an example.

   Yes; *Possible answer:* If the dividend is less than the divisor, the quotient of two fractions will be less than 1, for example, $\frac{1}{4} \div \frac{1}{2} = \frac{1}{2}$.

Copyright © Houghton Mifflin Company. All rights reserved.
Use with text pages 320–321.

HOMEWORK 12.4

Name _____ Date _____ Homework 12.4

Model Division

Find $9 \div \frac{1}{3}$.

| Step 1: Draw 9 wholes. |
| Step 2: Separate each whole into thirds. |
| Step 3: Count how many are in 9 wholes. $9 \div \frac{1}{3} = 27$ |

Write the equation represented by each model. Write the answer in simplest form.

1. $3 \div \frac{1}{5} = 15$

2. $2 \div \frac{1}{8} = 16$

3. $4 \div \frac{1}{3} = 12$

4. $6 \div \frac{1}{4} = 24$

Divide. Check your answers.

5. $\frac{3}{5} \div \frac{1}{5}$ → 3
6. $\frac{5}{8} \div \frac{1}{8}$ → 5
7. $\frac{7}{10} \div \frac{1}{10}$ → 7
8. $\frac{5}{6} \div \frac{1}{6}$ → 5
9. $\frac{10}{12} \div \frac{2}{12}$ → 5
10. $\frac{4}{5} \div \frac{2}{5}$ → 2
11. $\frac{9}{10} \div \frac{3}{10}$ → 3
12. $\frac{6}{8} \div \frac{2}{8}$ → 3

Problem Solving

Show Your Work

13. Marie has 8 bracelets. She gave $\frac{1}{4}$ of her bracelets to her sister. How many bracelets does Marie have left?

   6 bracelets

Copyright © Houghton Mifflin Company. All rights reserved.
Use with text pages 320–321.

ENGLISH LEARNERS 12.4

Name _____ Date _____ English Learners 12.4

Model Division

A noun is a word that describes a person, place, thing, or idea. **Plural nouns** describe more than one person, place, thing, or idea.

dog   dogs

Many plural nouns are made by adding -s to the end of a noun. Look at the pictures above. The first picture shows 1 dog. The second picture shows 2 dogs. Here are a few more examples:

boat + s = boats   stamp + s = stamps   snake + s = snakes

Some plural nouns are made by adding -es to the end of a noun. Nouns that end in ch, sh, s, ss, x, and z are made plural by adding -es.

lunch + es = lunches   dish + es = dishes   glass + es = glasses

Other plural nouns are not made by adding -s or -es to the noun. They follow special rules. Notice how the spelling changes in these plural nouns:

penny + s = pennies   wolf + es = wolves   quiz + es = quizzes

Make each noun below plural. Use the examples above to guide you.

1. story _____ **stories**
2. wish _____ **wishes**
3. half _____ **halves**
4. trick _____ **tricks**
5. bus _____ **buses**

Copyright © Houghton Mifflin Company. All rights reserved.
Use with text pages 320–321.

Homework Workbook Page 79

TEACHING LESSON 12.4

LESSON ORGANIZER

Objective Use models to divide with fractions.

Resources Reteach, Practice, Enrichment, Problem Solving, Homework, English Learners, Transparencies, Math Center

Materials grid paper, fraction strips

Activity

Warm-Up Activity
Multiply Mentally

👥 Whole Group	🕐 5 minutes	Visual, Auditory

Have students multiply mentally.

1. $3 \times \frac{1}{6}$ $(\frac{1}{2})$
2. $4 \times \frac{1}{2}$ (2)
3. $5 \times \frac{1}{5}$ (1)
4. $6 \times \frac{1}{2}$ (3)
5. $12 \times \frac{1}{6}$ (2)

Model Division

Objective Use models to divide with fractions.

Materials
grid paper
fraction strips

Work Together

A **unit fraction** is a fraction in which the numerator is 1. You can use models to divide a counting number by a unit fraction.

Work with a partner to find $6 \div \frac{1}{2}$.

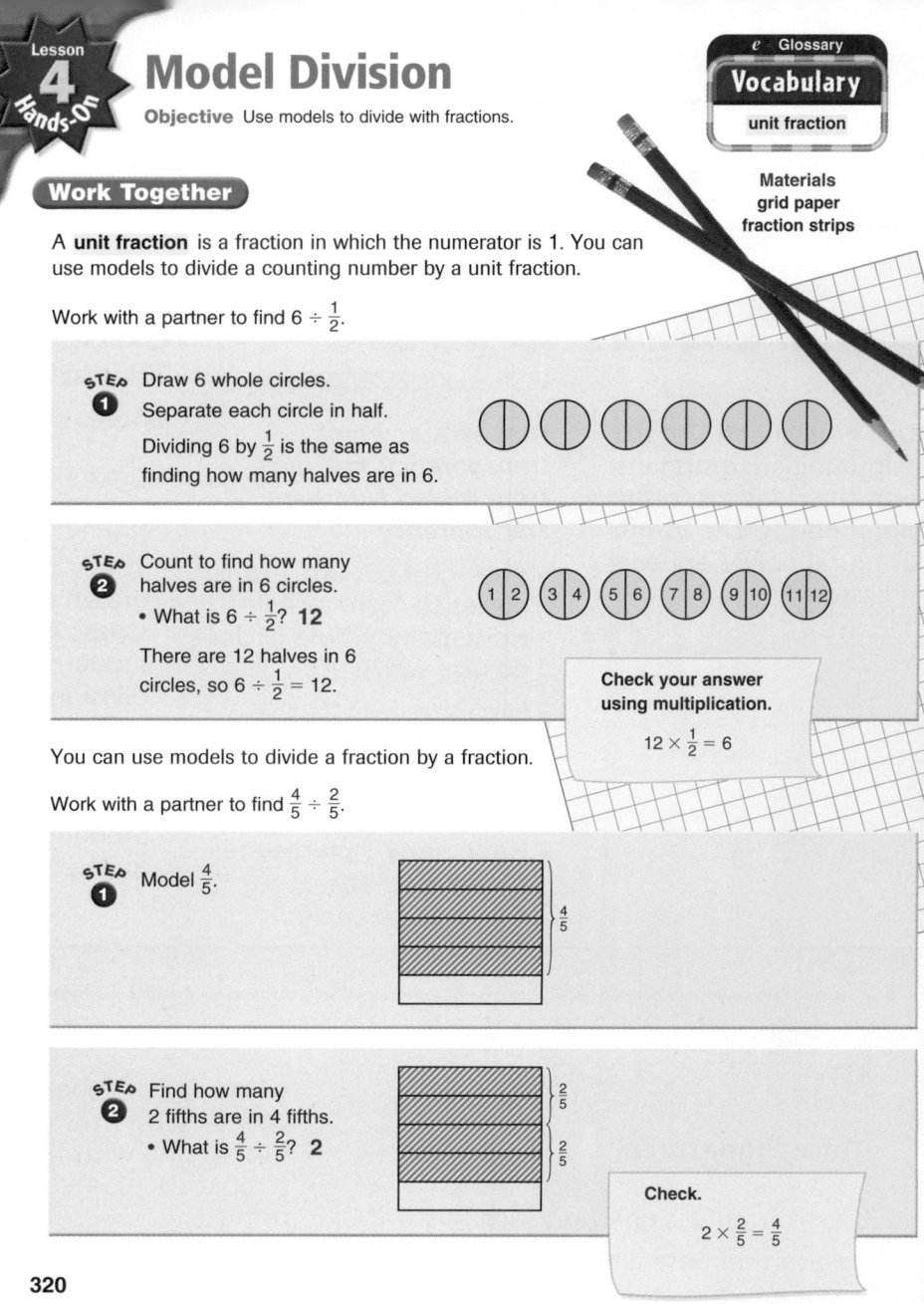

STEP 1 Draw 6 whole circles.
Separate each circle in half.
Dividing 6 by $\frac{1}{2}$ is the same as finding how many halves are in 6.

STEP 2 Count to find how many halves are in 6 circles.
• What is $6 \div \frac{1}{2}$? **12**
There are 12 halves in 6 circles, so $6 \div \frac{1}{2} = 12$.

Check your answer using multiplication.
$12 \times \frac{1}{2} = 6$

You can use models to divide a fraction by a fraction.

Work with a partner to find $\frac{4}{5} \div \frac{2}{5}$.

STEP 1 Model $\frac{4}{5}$.

$\frac{4}{5}$

STEP 2 Find how many 2 fifths are in 4 fifths.
• What is $\frac{4}{5} \div \frac{2}{5}$? **2**

$\frac{2}{5}$
$\frac{2}{5}$

Check.
$2 \times \frac{2}{5} = \frac{4}{5}$

320

---

① Introduce

• On the chalkboard, write the division expression $1 \div \frac{1}{2}$. Then draw one circle.

• **How many whole circles are there?** (1) **How could we show dividing the circles by $\frac{1}{2}$?** (draw a diameter through the center of the circle) **How many halves are there in one circle?** (2) **What is $1 \div \frac{1}{2}$?** (2)

• Now write the expression $4 \div \frac{1}{2}$. Draw 4 circles below the expression. **How many whole circles are there?** (4) **How could we show dividing the 4 circles by $\frac{1}{2}$?** (draw a diameter in each circle) **How many halves are there in 4 circles?** (8) **What is $4 \div \frac{1}{2}$?** (8)

• Continue with $1 \div \frac{1}{3}$. Make connections between the divisor ($\frac{1}{3}$) and the quotient (3).

② Develop

Guide students through the steps of the *Work Together* section.

• **Look at Step 1. Why are the 6 circles divided into two halves?** (to model dividing each by $\frac{1}{2}$)

• **Look at Step 2. How many halves are there in each circle?** (2) **How many are there in 6 circles altogether?** (12)

• For the second example, be sure students understand dividing the grid paper into fifths. For Step 2, be sure they see that $\frac{4}{5} \div \frac{2}{5} = 2$.

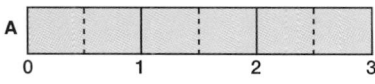

On Your Own

**Match each question with the correct model.
Then complete the division sentence.**

1. What is 3 divided by $\frac{1}{4}$?
   $3 \div \frac{1}{4} = \blacksquare$ **C; $3 \div \frac{1}{4} = 12$**

A
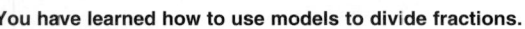

2. What is 3 divided by $\frac{1}{2}$?
   $3 \div \frac{1}{2} = \blacksquare$ **A; $3 \div \frac{1}{2} = 6$**

B

3. What is 3 divided by $\frac{1}{6}$?
   $3 \div \frac{1}{6} = \blacksquare$ **B; $3 \div \frac{1}{6} = 18$**

C

**Complete each division and multiplication to find a and b.
Use fraction strips or grid paper for help.**

4. $4 \div \frac{1}{2} = a$ $4 \times 2 = b$ **8; 8**   5. $5 \div \frac{1}{3} = a$ $5 \times 3 = b$ **15; 15**

6. $6 \div \frac{1}{5} = a$ $6 \times 5 = b$ **30; 30**   7. $9 \div \frac{1}{2} = a$ $9 \times 2 = b$ **18; 18**

Use your answers from Exercises 4–7 to answer Exercises 8–9.

8. What is true about a and b in each exercise? **a and b are equal**

9. To divide a whole number by a unit fraction, by what can
   you multiply the whole number? **the denominator of the unit fraction**

Divide. Check your answers.

10. $\frac{3}{4} \div \frac{1}{4}$ **3**   11. $\frac{2}{3} \div \frac{1}{3}$ **2**   12. $\frac{4}{5} \div \frac{1}{5}$ **4**   13. $\frac{2}{3} \div \frac{1}{3}$ **2**

14. $\frac{6}{8} \div \frac{2}{8}$ **3**   15. $\frac{9}{12} \div \frac{3}{12}$ **3**   16. $\frac{8}{10} \div \frac{2}{10}$ **4**   17. $\frac{4}{6} \div \frac{2}{6}$ **2**

Talk About It • Write About It

You have learned how to use models to divide fractions.

18. How would you explain to another student how to divide a
    fraction by a unit fraction? *Possible answer:* **you can multiply the fraction
    by the denominator of the unit fraction.**
19. Explain how you found the answers to Exercises 16 and 17.
    Possible answer: **Use mental math; $8 \div 2 = 4$, so there are
    $4 \times \frac{2}{10}$ in $\frac{8}{10}$; $4 \div 2 = 2$, so there are $2 \times \frac{2}{6}$ in $\frac{4}{6}$.**

DAILY TEST PREP

What is $5 \div \frac{1}{4}$? (B)

A. $1\frac{1}{4}$ C. $\frac{9}{4}$

B. 20   D. $\frac{1}{9}$

Activity

*Or use
Intervention
CD-ROM
Lesson 12.4*

Lesson Intervention
Division Circles

|  Small Group | 5–10 minutes | Visual, Kinesthetic |

- Explain that you are going to use a model to
  illustrate the division $1 \div \frac{1}{2}$.
- Begin by drawing 1 circle on the chalkboard.
  How can we divide 1 circle into halves? (draw a
  line through the center of the circle, both ends of
  which are on the circle) Ask a volunteer to do that.
- **How many halves do you see?** (2) **What is
  $1 \div \frac{1}{2}$?** (2)
- Now illustrate the division $3 \div \frac{1}{2}$. Draw 3 circles.
  How can we divide 3 circles into halves? (draw
  a line through the center of each circle) Ask a
  volunteer to do that.
- **How many halves do you see in the 3 circles?**
  (6) **What is $3 \div \frac{1}{2}$?** (6)

 **Practice**

Assign **Exercises 1–17** of *On Your Own* as independent
work.

- *Exercises 1–3* Have students discuss their answers.
- *Exercises 4–9* Have students discuss their answers to
  Exercises 8 and 9.

4 **Assess and Close**

Assign **Exercises 18 and 19** of the *Talk About It • Write
About It* section. Have volunteers explain their work.

Assign the **LESSON QUIZ** on Transparency 12.4 to further
assess student understanding.

 **Keeping a Journal**

Have students write a few sentences explaining
how to use models to divide with fractions.

Lesson 12.5

Divide Fractions

PLANNING THE LESSON

MATHEMATICS OBJECTIVE
Use the reciprocal to divide fractions.

Use Lesson Planner CD-ROM for Lesson 12.5.

Daily Routines

Vocabulary

Have students look up the words *reciprocate*, *reciprocity*, and **reciprocal** in the dictionary. Discuss the similarities in meaning. Explain that in multiplication and division of fractions, the term *reciprocal* refers to the inverse of a fraction. Give several examples.

Vocabulary Cards

Meeting North Carolina's Standards

Prepare for Grade 6 Objective **1.04** Develop fluency in addition, subtraction, multiplication, and division of nonnegative rational numbers.

Lesson Transparency 12.5

Problem of the Day

Megan is deciding on an outfit to wear. She can choose between black, tan, or grey pants; a red or blue shirt, and brown or black shoes. How many different combinations can she choose from? (12 combinations)

Quick Review

Write the value of *n*.

1. $\frac{3}{n} \times 4 = 3$ ($n = 4$)
2. $\frac{n}{3} \times 6 = 4$ ($n = 2$)
3. $\frac{1}{2} \times n = 6$ ($n = 12$)
4. $\frac{5}{n} \times 10 = 10$ ($n = 5$)

Lesson Quiz

Divide. Write each answer in simplest form.

1. $2 \div \frac{1}{7}$ (14)
2. $\frac{3}{4} \div 6$ ($\frac{1}{8}$)
3. $\frac{5}{6} \div 10$ ($\frac{1}{12}$)
4. $\frac{4}{5} \div 8$ ($\frac{1}{10}$)
5. $\frac{2}{3} \div \frac{1}{4}$ ($2\frac{2}{3}$)

LEVELED PRACTICE

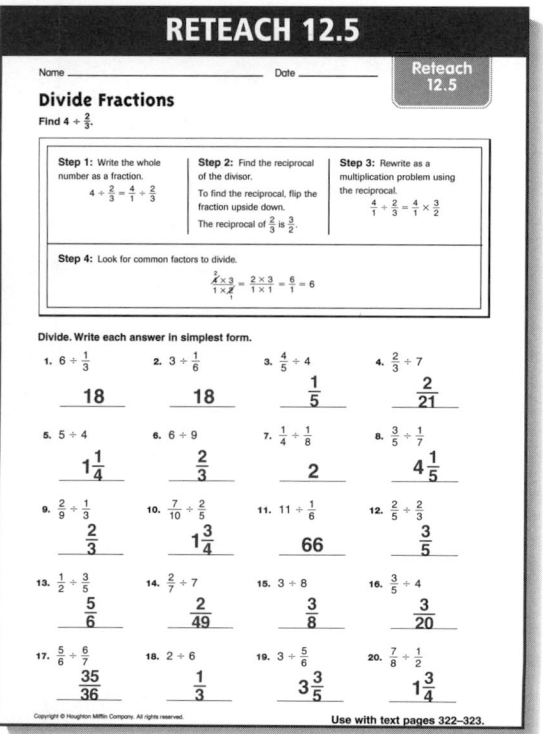

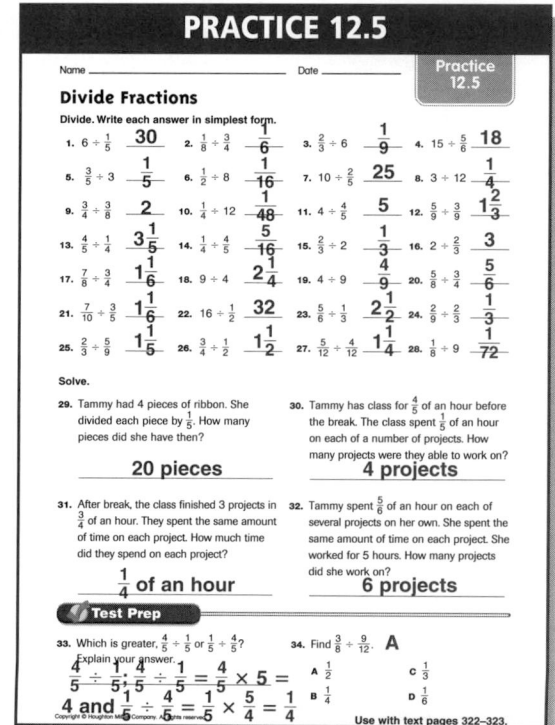

ENRICHMENT 12.5

Division Dilemma

Play Division Dilemma with a partner. Start at GO and move clockwise around the board. Use a number cube to see how many spaces you move. When you land on a problem, solve it and add the quotient to your score.

If you land on a corner box, subtract from your score. If the corner number is more than your score, your score goes to 0. Cross out problems once solved. If you land on GO or on a solved problem, move forward to the next available box. The corner boxes do not get crossed out.

1. Play until all the boxes are crossed out. High score wins.

Answers to the problems going clockwise starting from GO:
Top row: 4; 9; $\frac{1}{8}$; $1\frac{1}{4}$; $\frac{1}{2}$; 32
Right column: $\frac{7}{64}$; $13\frac{3}{4}$; $\frac{9}{50}$; 35; 2; 54
Bottom row: 12; $\frac{5}{36}$; $\frac{1}{40}$; 24; 8; $1\frac{17}{18}$
Left column: $2\frac{2}{3}$; $2\frac{3}{4}$; $\frac{1}{27}$; 36; $\frac{7}{32}$; 4

2. Was it easier to have the fraction as the dividend or the divisor? Explain.
***Possible answer:* It was easier to have the fraction as the divisor, since the reciprocal of a fraction is a whole number or a mixed number.**

3. On a separate sheet of paper, make a new gameboard. Use the same fractions, but switch them so that what had been the dividend is now the divisor, and what had been the divisor is now the dividend. Play again. Which game was harder? Explain.
Answers will vary.

Use with text pages 322–323.

Practice Workbook Page 80

Reaching All Learners
Differentiated Instruction

English Learners

Worksheet 12.5 provides step-by-step instruction to help students understand how to complete an Algebra function table.

Special Needs
VISUAL, AUDITORY

- Explain that the reciprocal of a fraction is the fraction with numerator and divisor inverted.
- **To divide a whole number by a fraction, multiply it by the reciprocal of the fraction.**
- Display: $6 \div \frac{3}{4}$. **What is the reciprocal of $\frac{3}{4}$?** ($\frac{4}{3}$) **So, $6 \div \frac{3}{4} = 6 \times \frac{4}{3}$.**
- **Multiply $\frac{6}{1} \times \frac{4}{3}$.** ($\frac{24}{3}$) **How many times does 3 go into 24?** (8) **What is $\frac{24}{3}$ in simplest form?** (8)

Early Finishers
VISUAL, AUDITORY

- Challenge students to show why dividing by a fraction is the same as multiplying by the reciprocal. Write $\frac{8}{\frac{2}{3}}$. **Simplify the fraction.**
- **Hint:** You want to write the fraction with 1 in the denominator.

$$\frac{8 \times \frac{3}{2}}{\frac{2}{3} \times \frac{3}{2}} = \frac{\frac{24}{2}}{1} = \frac{24}{2} = 12$$

Social Studies Connection

Recipes and Fractions
Materials: *international cookbook*

- Tell students that knowing how to divide by fractions is useful when you need to find out how many batches of a recipe you can make, given the amounts of ingredients you have.

- Suppose a recipe for Irish soda bread calls for 3/4 pints of buttermilk. How many batches of Irish soda bread could you make if you have 3 pints of buttermilk? (4)

- Have students use international recipes to write problems involving division by fractions. Have them trade problems with their classmates and solve.

TECHNOLOGY

Spiral Review

Create **customized** spiral review worksheets for individual students using the *Ways to Assess* CD-ROM.

Tool Software

Use *Easy Street* or another spreadsheet to explore this lesson more fully.

Lesson Planner

You can customize your teaching plan to meet your curriculum requirements with the Lesson Planner CD-ROM.

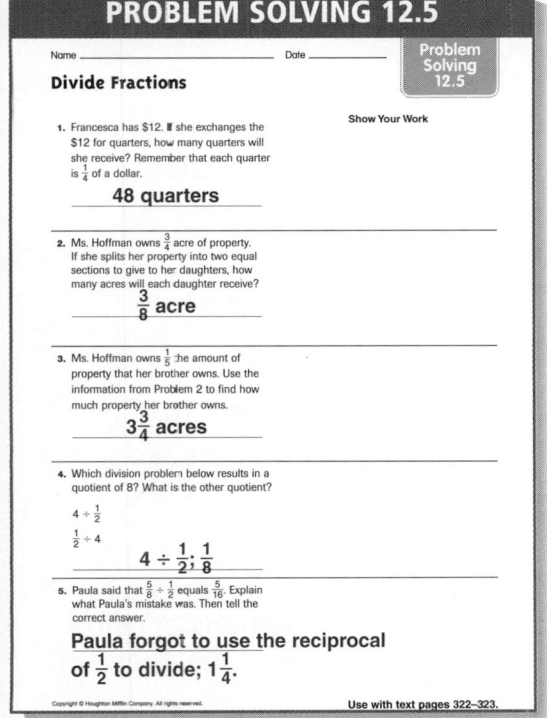

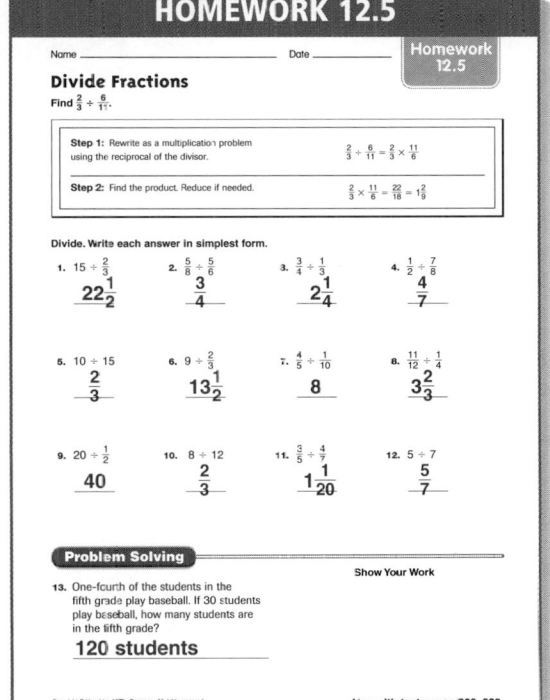

Homework Workbook Page 80

TEACHING LESSON 12.5

LESSON ORGANIZER

Objective Use the reciprocal to divide fractions.

Resources Reteach, Practice, Enrichment, Problem Solving, Homework, English Learners, Transparencies, Math Center

Materials None

Activity

Warm-Up Activity
Multiply Fractions

| iiii Whole Group | ⏱ 5 minutes | Visual, Auditory |

Have students complete these exercises.

1. $\frac{1}{4} \times \frac{4}{5}$ $\left(\frac{1}{5}\right)$
2. $\frac{3}{11} \times \frac{22}{36}$ $\left(\frac{1}{6}\right)$
3. $\frac{8}{9} \times \frac{18}{24}$ $\left(\frac{2}{3}\right)$
4. $\frac{3}{14} \times \frac{7}{18}$ $\left(\frac{1}{12}\right)$
5. $\frac{3}{8} \times 2\frac{1}{6}$ $\left(\frac{13}{16}\right)$

Lesson 5

Divide Fractions

Objective Use the reciprocal to divide fractions.

glossary**Vocabulary**
reciprocal

Learn About It  MathTracks 2/2 Listen and Understand

If a fraction is not equal to 0, then its **reciprocal** is obtained by interchanging the numerator and the denominator. For example, the fraction $\frac{4}{3}$ is the reciprocal of $\frac{3}{4}$. If neither a nor b is zero, then the fraction $\frac{b}{a}$ is the reciprocal of $\frac{a}{b}$.

The product of a fraction and its reciprocal is always 1.

$$\frac{3}{4} \times \frac{4}{3} = \frac{\overset{1}{3} \times \overset{1}{4}}{\underset{1}{4} \times \underset{1}{3}} = \frac{a}{b} \times \frac{b}{a} = 1$$

A concert lasted for 4 hours. The concert was divided into acts. Each act was different and lasted $\frac{2}{5}$ hour. How many acts performed at the concert?

Find $4 \div \frac{2}{5}$.

STEP 1 Rewrite the division as a multiplication by the reciprocal of the divisor.

$$4 \div \frac{2}{5} = \frac{4}{1} \times \frac{5}{2}$$

STEP 2 Look for common factors to cancel.

$$= \frac{\overset{2}{4} \times 5}{1 \times \underset{1}{2}} = 10$$

Check your work.

$$10 \times \frac{2}{5} = \frac{\overset{2}{10} \times 2}{\underset{1}{5}} = 2 \times 2 = 4$$

Solution: Ten acts performed.

Other Examples

A. Divide by Counting Number

Find $\frac{9}{10} \div 3$.

$$\frac{9}{10} \div 3 = \frac{9}{10} \times \frac{1}{3}$$
$$= \frac{9}{30}$$
$$= \frac{3}{10}$$

B. Divide Counting Numbers

Find $3 \div 6$.

$$3 \div 6 = 3 \times \frac{1}{6}$$
$$= \frac{3}{6}$$
$$= \frac{1}{2}$$

C. Divide Fractions

Find $\frac{3}{4} \div \frac{5}{8}$.

$$\frac{3}{4} \div \frac{5}{8} = \frac{3}{4} \times \frac{8}{5}$$
$$= \frac{3 \times \overset{2}{8}}{\underset{1}{4} \times 5} = \frac{6}{5}$$
$$= 1\frac{1}{5}$$

322

---

1 Introduce

- Write the following on the chalkboard:

$$\frac{3}{4} \times \frac{4}{3} =$$
$$\frac{3 \times 4}{4 \times 3} = \frac{3 \times 4}{3 \times 4}$$
$$\frac{12}{12} = 1$$

- Give several examples of multiplying fractions by their reciprocals and have students solve the problems at the chalkboard. **What is the product of all these problems?** (1)

- Write $\frac{a}{b} \times \frac{b}{a} = 1$ on the chalkboard. **The product of a fraction and its reciprocal is always 1, as long as the fraction is not equal to zero.**

2 Develop

Guide students through the *Learn About It* section.

- **To divide a number by a fraction, you multiply the number by the reciprocal of the fraction.**

- **Look at Step 1. To divide 4 by $\frac{2}{5}$, multiply 4 by the reciprocal of $\frac{2}{5}$. What is the reciprocal of $\frac{2}{5}$?** $\left(\frac{5}{2}\right)$ We can also write 4 as $\frac{4}{1}$.

- **Look at Step 2. What is the common factor?** (2)

- In *Other Examples A* and *B*, point out that the reciprocal of a whole number is a unit fraction.

Guided Practice

Have students complete **Exercises 1–6** as you observe. Remind them to use the *Ask Yourself* questions to help. Give students the opportunity to talk about the question in *Explain Your Thinking*.

322 CHAPTER 12 Lesson 5

Ask Yourself
• Did I multiply by the reciprocal of the divisor?
• Did I divide by common factors to simplify?

TEST TIPS

Divide. Write each answer in simplest form.

1. $3 \div \frac{1}{2}$ **6**
2. $\frac{1}{2} \div \frac{7}{12}$ **$\frac{6}{7}$**
3. $\frac{1}{2} \div 7$ **$\frac{1}{14}$**
4. $6 \div 8$ **$\frac{3}{4}$**
5. $\frac{2}{3} \div 12$ **$\frac{1}{18}$**
6. $\frac{5}{12} \div \frac{1}{4}$ **$1\frac{2}{3}$**

TEST TIPS **Explain Your Thinking ▶** Why does multiplying by 2 give the same result as dividing by $\frac{1}{2}$?

When you divide by $\frac{1}{2}$, there are two parts for every whole in the dividend, which has the same effect as multiplying by 2.

Practice and Problem Solving

Divide. Write each answer in simplest form.

7. $8 \div \frac{1}{4}$ **32**
8. $\frac{4}{5} \div 8$ **$\frac{1}{10}$**
9. $\frac{1}{4} \div \frac{2}{3}$ **$\frac{3}{8}$**
10. $\frac{5}{6} \div \frac{5}{12}$ **2**
11. $12 \div \frac{2}{3}$ **18**
12. $\frac{3}{4} \div \frac{1}{3}$ **$2\frac{1}{4}$**
13. $\frac{3}{8} \div 2$ **$\frac{3}{16}$**
14. $\frac{1}{3} \div 6$ **$\frac{1}{18}$**
15. $5 \div 15$ **$\frac{1}{3}$**
16. $\frac{4}{7} \div 2$ **$\frac{2}{7}$**
17. $9 \div 12$ **$\frac{3}{4}$**
18. $12 \div 9$ **$1\frac{1}{3}$**
19. $\frac{9}{10} \div \frac{7}{10}$ **$1\frac{2}{7}$**
20. $\frac{7}{8} \div \frac{3}{4}$ **$1\frac{1}{6}$**
21. $\frac{3}{10} \div \frac{4}{5}$ **$\frac{3}{8}$**

✗ Algebra • **Functions** Complete each function table. Write each answer in simplest form.

22.

Rule: $y = x \div 8$			
x	$1\frac{1}{4}$	2	$2\frac{3}{4}$	$3\frac{1}{2}$
y				

23.   1, 2, 3, 4

Rule: $y = x \div \frac{4}{5}$			
x	$\frac{4}{5}$	$1\frac{3}{5}$	$2\frac{2}{5}$	$3\frac{1}{5}$
y				

Solve.
$\frac{5}{32}, \frac{1}{4}, \frac{11}{32}, \frac{7}{16}$

24. A band played for $\frac{1}{2}$ hour on stage. Each song lasted $\frac{1}{10}$ hour. How many songs did they perform? **5 songs**

25. One band played 4 audience requests in 15 minutes. What was the average length of each song they played?
$3\frac{3}{4}$ minutes

26. A band took 3 breaks during a 4-hour concert. Each break was $\frac{1}{6}$ hour. How many minutes of breaks were there?
Three breaks; $\frac{1}{6}$ of an hour is $\frac{3}{6}$, or $\frac{1}{2}$ hour.

27. During a $\frac{1}{4}$-hour act, the band performs 3 songs. Each song is the same length. How long is each song? **$\frac{1}{12}$ hr**

Daily Review **Test Prep** ✏

Divide. (Ch. 4, Lesson 2)

28. $674 \div 3$ **224 R2**
29. $984 \div 8$ **123**
30. $742 \div 9$ **82R4**
31. $102 \div 5$ **20R2**

✓ 32. **Free Response** During a 2 hour meeting, each person spoke for $\frac{1}{6}$ hour. How many speakers were there? Explain how you got your answer.

Extra Practice See page 331, Set C.
See Additional Answers on Page 331.

DAILY TEST PREP

To find $36 \div \frac{3}{4}$, you would multiply 36 by (D)

A. $\frac{36}{4}$
B. $\frac{36}{3}$
C. $\frac{3}{4}$
D. $\frac{4}{3}$

Activity →

Lesson Intervention

Or use Intervention CD-ROM Lesson 12.5

Writing Reciprocals

👤👤👤 Small Group	🕐 5–10 minutes	Visual, Auditory

• Point out that the reciprocal of a fraction is the fraction inverted, or turned upside down.
• What is the reciprocal of $\frac{2}{3}$? ($\frac{3}{2}$)
• What is the reciprocal of $\frac{7}{10}$? ($\frac{10}{7}$)
• How can you write the whole number 5 as a fraction? ($\frac{5}{1}$) What is the reciprocal of 5? ($\frac{1}{5}$)
• To divide a number by a fraction, you multiply it by the reciprocal of the divisor. Use what you know about reciprocals to find $5 \div \frac{5}{6}$.
($5 \div \frac{5}{6} = \frac{5}{1} \times \frac{6}{5} = 5 \times \frac{6}{5} = 6$)

---

3 Practice

Assign **Exercises 7–32** as independent work.

• *Exercises 7–21* Have students discuss their answers.
• *Algebra • Functions for Exercises 22–23* Have students discuss their methods as well as their answers.
• *Problem Solving for Problems 24–27* For Problem 26, have students discuss their methods.

Common Error

Incorrect reciprocal Be sure that students write the reciprocal of the divisor, not the reciprocal of the dividend. They can check to see that the product of the divisor and its reciprocal is 1.

4 Assess and Close

• **Explain how to find $\frac{3}{8} \div \frac{3}{5}$.** (Multiply $\frac{3}{8}$ by $\frac{5}{3}$ to get $\frac{5}{8}$)
• **Explain how to find $6 \div 12$ using reciprocals.** (Multiply 6 by $\frac{1}{12}$ to get $\frac{1}{2}$.)

Assign the **LESSON QUIZ** on Transparency 12.5 to further assess student understanding.

Keeping a Journal

Have students write two problems: one showing how to divide a whole number by a fraction; one showing how to divide a fraction by a fraction.

Lesson 12.6

Divide Mixed Numbers

PLANNING THE LESSON

MATHEMATICS OBJECTIVE
Divide with mixed numbers.

Use Lesson Planner CD-ROM for Lesson 12.6.

Daily Routines

Vocabulary
Review the meanings of a *mixed number*, a number that is the sum of a whole number and a fraction, and an *improper fraction*, a fraction that is greater than or equal to 1.

Vocabulary Cards

Meeting North Carolina's Standards
Prepare for Grade 6 Objective **1.04** Develop fluency in addition, subtraction, multiplication, and division of nonnegative rational numbers.

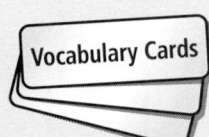

Lesson Transparency **12.6**

Problem of the Day
I am a mixed number in simplest form. My reciprocal is $\frac{2}{9}$. $(4\frac{1}{2})$

Quick Review
Write the GCF of each pair of numbers.
1. 9, 27 (9)
2. 11, 17 (1)
3. 12, 36 (12)
4. 18, 21 (3)
5. 25, 30 (5)

Lesson Quiz
Write each quotient in simplest form.
1. $1\frac{3}{5} \div 2\frac{2}{5}$ $(\frac{2}{3})$
2. $3\frac{1}{8} \div 1\frac{1}{4}$ $(2\frac{1}{2})$
3. $14 \div 1\frac{2}{5}$ (10)
4. $1\frac{1}{3} \div 2\frac{1}{6}$ $(\frac{8}{13})$
5. $8\frac{2}{5} \div 4\frac{1}{5}$ (2)

LEVELED PRACTICE

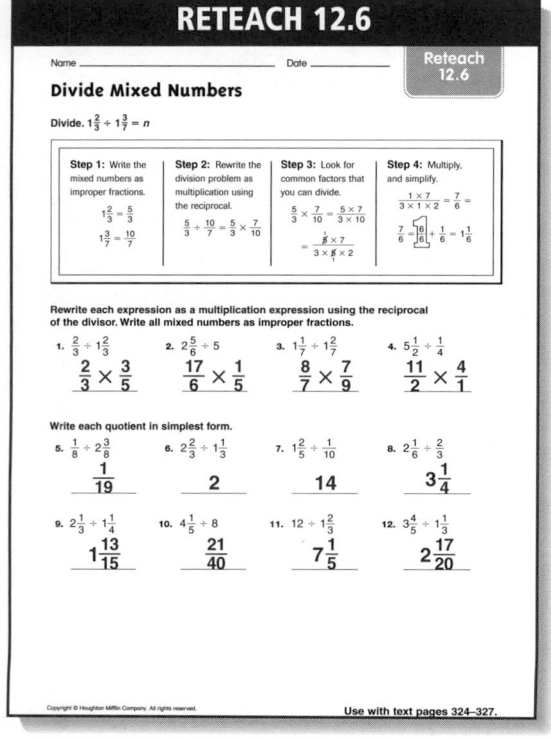

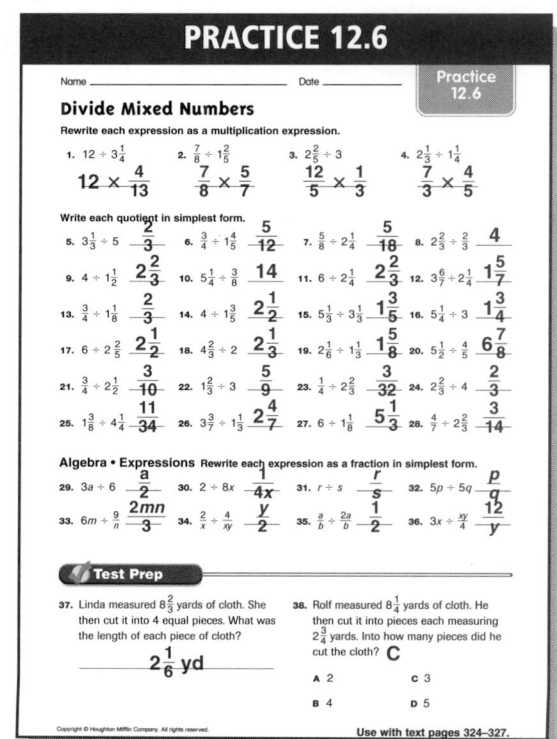

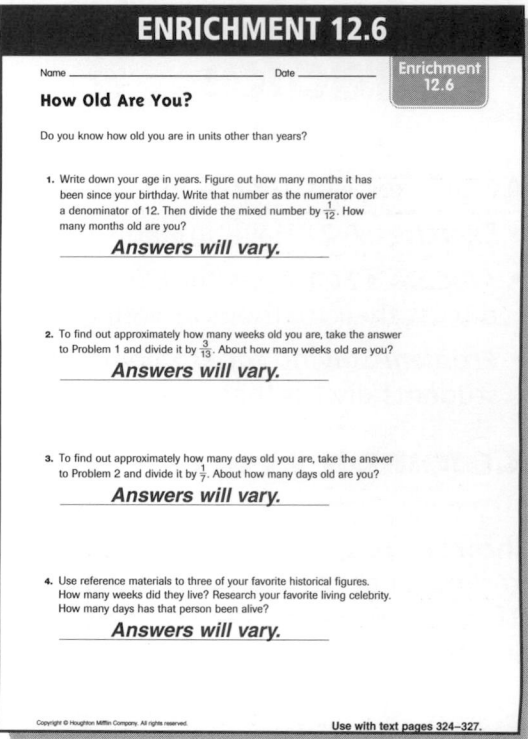

Practice Workbook Page 81

Reaching All Learners
Differentiated Instruction

English Learners

Use Worksheet 12.6 to familiarize English learners with the dance vocabulary they will encounter in the lesson.

Inclusion
VISUAL, AUDITORY

Write: $3\frac{1}{3} \div 1\frac{2}{3}$.

- **To divide with mixed numbers, each number must be expressed as an improper fraction. How do we change $3\frac{1}{3}$ to an improper fraction?**
  (express 3 as $\frac{9}{3}$; $\frac{9}{3} + \frac{1}{3} = \frac{10}{3}$)

- **How do we write $1\frac{2}{3}$ as an improper fraction?**
  (express 1 as $\frac{3}{3}$; $\frac{3}{3} + \frac{2}{3} = \frac{5}{3}$)

- **What do we do when the divisor is a fraction?**
  (invert it and multiply)

- **Write: $\frac{10}{3} \div \frac{5}{3} = \frac{10}{3} \times \frac{3}{5}$. What is the quotient?**
  ($\frac{30}{15} = 2$)

Early Finishers
VISUAL, TACTILE

- Give students these problems:

- Donnie saws a board $7\frac{1}{2}$ feet long into 5 equal lengths. How long is each section?
  ($1\frac{1}{2}$ feet long)

- Carita has a piece of cloth 18 yards long. How many scarves can she make if each one is to be $4\frac{1}{2}$ feet long?
  (12 scarves)

- Have students write and share similar problems.

TECHNOLOGY

Spiral Review

Using the *Ways to Assess* CD-ROM, you can create **customized** spiral review worksheets covering any lessons you choose.

Game

Students can practice their skills using the Rock Hopper math game, available on the *Ways to Success* CD.

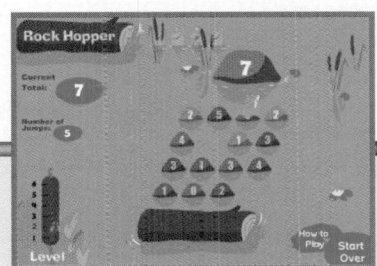

Literature Connection

Suggest that students read *Cool Math* by Christy Maganzini (Putnam Publishing Co, 1997). The book contains games, quizzes, and amazing facts about mathematics and its history that help to reinforce math skills in all areas.

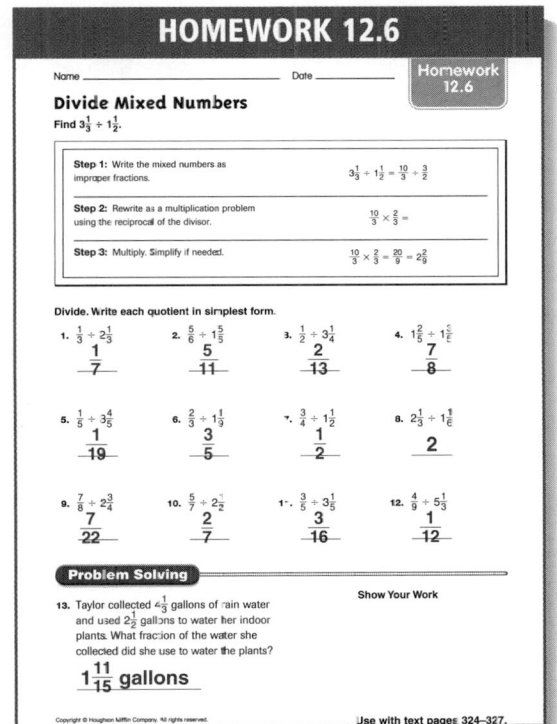

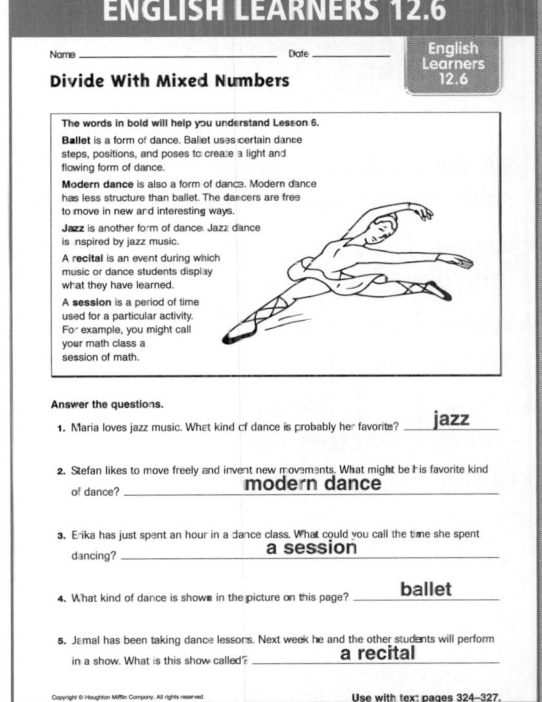

TEACHING LESSON 12.6

LESSON ORGANIZER

Objective Divide with mixed numbers.

Resources Reteach, Practice, Enrichment, Problem Solving, Homework, English Learners, Transparencies, Math Center

Materials Two sets of Learning Tool 42, 4 sets of number cards numbered 1–10

Warm-Up Activity
Divide with Fractions

| 👤👤👤👤 Whole Group | ⏱ 5 minutes | Visual, Auditory |

Have students find the product for the following exercises:

1. $\frac{4}{5} \div \frac{2}{5}$ (2)

2. $\frac{3}{8} \div \frac{5}{12}$ $\left(\frac{9}{10}\right)$

3. $\frac{7}{10} \div \frac{7}{15}$ $\left(1\frac{1}{2}\right)$

4. $\frac{3}{5} \div \frac{7}{20}$ $\left(1\frac{5}{7}\right)$

5. $\frac{5}{9} \div \frac{3}{4}$ $\left(\frac{20}{27}\right)$

Divide Mixed Numbers

Objective Divide with mixed numbers.

 **Vocabulary** mixed number

Learn About It 🔊 MathTracks 2/3 Listen and Understand

A dance teacher has scheduled $3\frac{1}{2}$ hours of practice before the spring recital. Today's practice lasted $1\frac{1}{4}$ hours. What fraction of the practice time is that? You can write each **mixed number** as an improper fraction to divide.

Divide. $1\frac{1}{4} \div 3\frac{1}{2} = n$

STEP 1 Write the mixed numbers as improper fractions.

$$1\frac{1}{4} \div 3\frac{1}{2} = \frac{5}{4} \div \frac{7}{2}$$

STEP 2 Rewrite as a multiplication problem using the reciprocal of the divisor.

$$\frac{5}{4} \div \frac{7}{2} = \frac{5}{4} \times \frac{2}{7}$$

STEP 3 Look for common factors.

$$\frac{5}{4} \times \frac{2}{7} = \frac{5 \times 2}{4 \times 7}$$
$$= \frac{5 \times \overset{1}{2}}{2 \times \underset{1}{2} \times 7}$$

STEP 4 Multiply. Be sure the answer is in simplest form.

$$\frac{5 \times 1}{2 \times 1 \times 7} = \frac{5}{14}$$

Check your work.
$$\frac{5}{14} \times 3\frac{1}{2} = \frac{5}{14} \times \frac{7}{2}$$
$$= \frac{5 \times \overset{1}{7}}{2 \times \underset{1}{7} \times 2}$$
$$= \frac{5}{4}, \text{ or } 1\frac{1}{4}$$

Solution: $1\frac{1}{4} \div 3\frac{1}{2} = \frac{5}{14}$

Other Examples

A. Dividend is Counting Number

Find $9 \div 2\frac{1}{4}$.

$9 \div 2\frac{1}{4} = \frac{9}{1} \div \frac{9}{4}$

$= \frac{9}{1} \times \frac{4}{9}$

$= \frac{\overset{1}{9} \times 4}{1 \times \underset{1}{9}}$

$= \frac{4}{1} = 4$

B. Divisor is Fraction

Find $2\frac{1}{4} \div \frac{3}{4}$.

$2\frac{1}{4} \div \frac{3}{4} = 2\frac{1}{4} \times \frac{4}{3}$

$= \frac{9}{4} \times \frac{4}{3}$

$= \frac{9 \times \overset{1}{4}}{\underset{1}{4} \times 3}$

$= \frac{9}{3} = 3$

C. Dividend is Fraction

Find $\frac{5}{8} \div 1\frac{2}{3}$.

$\frac{5}{8} \div 1\frac{2}{3} = \frac{5}{8} \div \frac{5}{3}$

$= \frac{5}{8} \times \frac{3}{5}$

$= \frac{\overset{1}{5} \times 3}{8 \times \underset{1}{5}}$

$= \frac{3}{8}$

---

1 Introduce

- **When a division involves mixed numbers, you must write each mixed number as an improper fraction.**

- Write: $1\frac{1}{6} \div 2\frac{1}{3}$. Ask volunteers to convert $1\frac{1}{6}$ and $2\frac{1}{3}$ to improper fractions. ($\frac{7}{6}$ and $\frac{7}{3}$)

- Write the division as $\frac{7}{6} \div \frac{7}{3}$. **How can we divide by $\frac{7}{3}$?** (multiply by the reciprocal of $\frac{7}{3}$, which is $\frac{3}{7}$)

- Write: $\frac{7}{6} \times \frac{3}{7}$. **We can write this division as $\frac{(7 \times 3)}{(6 \times 7)}$. What common factors can be divided out?** (7 and 3) **What is the quotient?** ($\frac{1}{2}$)

2 Develop

Guide students through the *Learn About It* portion of the lesson.

- **Look at Step 1.** Be sure students know that the first thing to do is to write each mixed number as an improper fraction.

- **Look at Step 2.** Emphasize the necessity of rewriting the division as a multiplication using the reciprocal of the divisor.

- **Look at Step 3.** Point out that there is only one common factor, 2, in the denominator and numerator.

- **Look at Step 4.** Multiplying and simplifying the result is the final step.

Guided Practice

Ask Yourself
- Did I invert the divisor to form the reciprocal?
- Did I cancel common factors?
- Did I write the quotient in simplest form?

TEST TIPS

Rewrite each division as a multiplication. Write all mixed numbers as improper fractions. $\frac{26}{3} \times \frac{2}{25}$

1. $\frac{2}{3} \div 4\frac{2}{5}$ 2. $11 \div 1\frac{1}{2}$ 3. $8\frac{2}{3} \div 12\frac{1}{2}$

4. $2\frac{1}{3} \div 4$ 5. $1\frac{3}{4} \div \frac{1}{2}$ 6. $5\frac{5}{8} \div 1\frac{3}{4}$

Write each quotient in simplest form.

7. $\frac{1}{4} \div 1\frac{1}{4}$ **$\frac{1}{5}$**   8. $4\frac{7}{8} \div 2$ **$2\frac{7}{16}$**   9. $8\frac{5}{8} \div 2\frac{7}{8}$ **3**   10. $6 \div 1\frac{1}{2}$ **4**

TEST TIPS **Explain Your Thinking ▶** How are the reciprocals of unit fractions and counting numbers related? *See Additional Answers on Page 331.*

Practice and Problem Solving

Rewrite each each division as a multiplication.

11. $\frac{3}{4} \div 1\frac{2}{3}$ **$\frac{3}{4} \times \frac{3}{5}$**   12. $10 \div 3\frac{1}{5}$ **$\frac{10}{1} \times \frac{5}{16}$** 13. $7\frac{3}{4} \div 4$ 14. $1\frac{1}{5} \div 3\frac{7}{8}$

Write each quotient in simplest form.

15. $\frac{4}{5} \div 1\frac{1}{2}$ **$\frac{8}{15}$**   16. $4\frac{1}{4} \div 3$ **$1\frac{5}{12}$**   17. $\frac{2}{3} \div 1\frac{1}{3}$ **$\frac{1}{2}$**   18. $3\frac{2}{3} \div \frac{1}{3}$ **11**

19. $2\frac{1}{8} \div \frac{1}{2}$ **$4\frac{1}{4}$**   20. $4\frac{1}{2} \div \frac{3}{8}$ **12**   21. $3 \div 1\frac{1}{2}$ **2**   22. $6 \div 3\frac{1}{3}$ **$1\frac{4}{5}$**

23. $3\frac{1}{4} \div \frac{2}{3}$ **$4\frac{7}{8}$**   24. $\frac{3}{4} \div 2\frac{1}{2}$ **$\frac{3}{10}$**   25. $1\frac{1}{4} \div 2\frac{1}{2}$ **$\frac{1}{2}$**   26. $4 \div 1\frac{3}{4}$ **$2\frac{2}{7}$**

27. $6 \div 1\frac{3}{4}$ **$3\frac{3}{7}$**   28. $6\frac{1}{2} \div \frac{3}{4}$ **$8\frac{2}{3}$**   29. $5\frac{1}{8} \div 3$ **$1\frac{17}{24}$**   30. $\frac{2}{3} \div 2\frac{2}{3}$ **$\frac{1}{4}$**

Algebra • Expressions Rewrite each expression as a fraction in simplest form. No variable equals 0.

31. $n \div 2$ **$\frac{n}{2}$**   32. $2 \div n$ **$\frac{2}{n}$**   33. $4a \div \frac{4}{b}$ **ab**   34. $b \div a$ **$\frac{b}{a}$**

35. $3n \div 3m$ **$\frac{n}{m}$**   36. $6xy \div 3x$ **$2y$**   37. $\frac{1}{a} \div \frac{1}{a}$ **1**   38. $5ab \div \frac{a}{2}$ **$10b$**

Compare Write >, <, or = for each ⬤.

39. $6\frac{3}{4} \div 2\frac{1}{4}$ **<** ⬤ $6\frac{1}{3} \div 2$ 40. $5 \div 1\frac{1}{2}$ **<** ⬤ $2 \div \frac{1}{2}$

41. $\frac{1}{2} \div \frac{1}{3}$ ⬤ $\frac{5}{8} \div \frac{2}{3}$ 42. $3\frac{3}{4} \div \frac{1}{2}$ **=** ⬤ $1\frac{7}{8} \div \frac{1}{4}$

Go On ▶

Reaching All Learners

Number Sense

Reciprocals Two numbers are reciprocals of each other when their product is 1.

$\frac{2}{3}$ and $1\frac{1}{2}$ are reciprocals because

$1\frac{1}{2} = \frac{3}{2}$ and $\frac{2}{3} \times \frac{3}{2} = 1$

Have students write the reciprocal of each number.

1. $2\frac{4}{5}$ 2. $6\frac{1}{8}$ 3. $\frac{7}{3}$ 4. 2 5. $7\frac{2}{3}$

Have students complete each sentence. Have them write the answers in simplest form.

6. ⬛ $\times \frac{5}{2} = 1$ 7. $\frac{6}{8} \times$ ⬛ $= 1$

8. $3\frac{3}{5} \times$ ⬛ $= 1$ 9. ⬛ $\times 2\frac{1}{3} = 1$

10. ⬛ $\times 4\frac{2}{3} = 1$ 11. ⬛ $\times 10\frac{1}{5} = 1$

Answers

1. $\frac{5}{14}$ 2. $\frac{8}{49}$ 3. $\frac{3}{7}$ 4. $\frac{1}{2}$

5. $\frac{3}{23}$ 6. $\frac{2}{5}$ 7. $1\frac{1}{3}$ 8. $\frac{5}{18}$

9. $\frac{3}{7}$ 10. $\frac{3}{14}$ 11. $\frac{5}{51}$

Differentiated Assignments		
At Risk	**Average**	**Advanced**
Exercise 1–5	Exercise 2–8	Exercise 4–11

---

③ Practice

- Work through the *Other Examples* with students. Make sure that students see in Example A that a whole number is expressed as an improper fraction with a denominator of 1.

Guided Practice

Have students complete **Exercises 1–10** as you observe. Remind them to use the *Ask Yourself* questions to help. Give students the opportunity to talk about the question in *Explain Your Thinking*.

Assign **Problems 11–57** as independent work.

- *Exercises 11–30* Have students discuss their work.
- *Algebra • Expressions for Exercises 31–38* Have students compare answers and discuss their work.
- *Exercises 39–42* Have students compare and discuss their answers.

DAILY TEST PREP

Martin spends 6 hours on Saturdays taking classes at the music conservatory. If each class is $1\frac{1}{2}$ hours, how many classes does he take? (4 classes)

Activity

Lesson Intervention
Using Reciprocals

Or use Intervention CD-ROM Lesson 12.6

👥 Small Group	🕐 5–10 minutes	Visual, Kinesthetic

- Explain that to divide a mixed number by a fraction or another mixed number, the mixed numbers must be written as improper fractions.

- Write: $1\frac{1}{4} \div 1\frac{1}{2}$. Point to $1\frac{1}{4}$. **How do we find the improper fraction equivalent to $1\frac{1}{4}$?** (Multiply the whole number 1 by the denominator 4 to get 4 and add the numerator of the fraction, 1 and keep 4 as the denominator of the improper fraction.) **What fraction do we get?** ($\frac{5}{4}$)

- Follow a similar procedure for $1\frac{1}{2}$ to get $\frac{3}{2}$.

- Write the new problem: $\frac{5}{4} \div \frac{3}{2}$. **We can't divide by a fraction. How do we proceed?** (We can multiply $\frac{5}{4}$ by the reciprocal of $\frac{3}{2}$.) Write the multiplication $\frac{5}{4} \times \frac{2}{3}$. **What is the product?** ($\frac{10}{12}$) **Can we simplify this?** (Yes; divide numerator and denominator by 2 to get $\frac{5}{6}$.)

Choose a Computation Method

Mental Math • Estimation • Paper and Pencil • Calculator

Data Use the schedule for Problems 43–46.

Beth is studying at a ballet school. The schedule at the right shows her Monday classes and their times.

$\frac{5}{16}$ of his Monday schedule

43. What fraction of Beth's Monday class schedule does ballet represent?

44. Last Monday, Beth was late for her Jazz class. She missed $\frac{1}{3}$ of the class. How much time is that? $\frac{5}{12}$ **or 25 minutes**

Beth's Monday Schedule	
Class	**Number of Hours**
Modern Dance	2
Ballet	$2\frac{1}{2}$
Jazz	$1\frac{1}{4}$
Character	$1\frac{1}{2}$
Strength Training	$\frac{3}{4}$

45. Analyze One of Beth's teachers divides each hour of class into thirds. She uses those six sessions to work with different groups. Which class is this? **modern dance**

46. Reasoning Beth's Tuesday schedule is like Monday's, except ballet class is half as long, and jazz class is twice as long. Does her total time change? **See Additional Answers on Page 331.**

47. Measurement Draw a line segment that is $3\frac{1}{8}$ inches long. If you divide the line segment into five equal lengths, how long will each piece be? Show it on your line. $\frac{5}{8}$ **in.; check drawings.**

48. Glennis drew a line segment that was $9\frac{3}{5}$ inches long. Then she divided it into line segments that were each $1\frac{1}{5}$ inches long. How many line segments did she make? **8 pieces**

49. Write About It When dividing by a fraction greater than one, is the quotient less than or greater than the dividend? Support your conclusion. **See Additional Answers on Page 331.**

50. Patrick plans to study for $3\frac{3}{4}$ hours. He wants to spend $\frac{3}{4}$ hour on each subject. How many subjects will Patrick be able to study? **5 subjects**

Daily Review   Test Prep ✔

Write the prime factorization. Use exponents if possible. (Ch. 9, Lesson 2)

51. 36 $2^2 \times 3^2$ **52.** 42 $2 \times 3 \times 7$

53. 25 5^2 **54.** 9 3^2

55. 56 $2^3 \times 7$ **56.** 72 $2^3 \times 3^2$

57. Lance did homework for $2\frac{1}{4}$ hours. He spent the same amount of time on each of 3 subjects. How long did he spend on each subject?

A $\frac{1}{4}$ hour   C $1\frac{1}{3}$ hours

B $\frac{3}{4}$ hour   D $6\frac{3}{4}$ hours

Extra Practice See page 331, Set D.

---

④ Assess and Close

Choose a Computation Method

- **Problem Solving for Problems 43–50** Have students explain the methods they used. For Problem 43, students will need to perform more than one computation. Have students discuss their answers to Problem 49.

Common Error

Writing an incorrect improper fraction Remind students that the denominator of an improper fraction is the same as the denominator of the fraction part of a mixed number. To find the numerator for an improper fraction, multiply the whole number by the denominator, and then add the numerator of the fraction part.

Have volunteers demonstrate at the chalkboard.

- **Give an example of how to divide a mixed number by a mixed number.**

- **Give an example of how to divide a fraction by a mixed number.**

Assign the **LESSON QUIZ** on Transparency 12.6 to further assess student understanding.

Division Scramble

2 players

What You'll Need • two copies of Learning Tool 42 or 2 game boards; 4 sets of number cards, numbered 1 to 10

How to Play

1 Shuffle the number cards and place them on the table facedown in a stack. Give each player a game board. The goal of the game is to create a division example that will have a greater quotient than your opponent's example has.

2 In turn each player takes one card from the stack and places that card face up on his or her game board. Once placed, a card cannot be moved.

3 The game continues until each player has four cards showing on his or her game board.

4 Each player then divides the fractions displayed on the game board. The player whose example has the greater quotient wins.

5 Shuffle the number cards and play again. This time the player whose example has the lesser quotient wins.

Chapter 12 Lesson 6 **327**

Division Scramble

• Go over the steps with students. Remind students that placing the number cards is important. It will take 4 cards to make two fractions.

• If the divisor is a fraction that is less than the dividend, the quotient will be larger than either of the two fractions.

Keeping a Journal

Have students write a few sentences explaining how to divide a fraction or a mixed number by a mixed number.

Problem-Solving Decision: Choose the Operation

PLANNING THE LESSON

MATHEMATICS OBJECTIVE
Review how to choose the operation that will help you solve a problem.

Use Lesson Planner CD-ROM for Lesson 12.7.

Daily Routines

Vocabulary

What *operations* do you use to solve problems? (addition, subtraction, multiplication, division) **When choosing the operation, remember to read the question closely.** Remind students that in order to solve a word problem, they need to decide which operation to use and to translate the problem from English to mathematical symbols.

Vocabulary Cards

Meeting North Carolina's Standards

1.03 Develop flexibility in solving problems by selecting strategies and using mental computation, estimation, calculators or computers, and paper and pencil.

Lesson Transparency **12.7**

Problem of the Day
Toni drew three line segments. The red segment is $\frac{3}{16}$ in. shorter than the green one and $\frac{2}{3}$ as long as the yellow segment. The yellow segment is $\frac{3}{4}$ in. long. How long is the green segment? ($\frac{11}{16}$ in.)

Quick Review
Find the product or quotient.

1. $5 \times \frac{4}{5}$ (4)
2. $36 \div \frac{3}{8}$ (96)
3. $48 \div \frac{3}{4}$ (64)
4. $\frac{1}{4} \times \frac{12}{18}$ ($\frac{1}{6}$)
5. $2\frac{1}{4} \div \frac{3}{5}$ ($3\frac{3}{4}$)

Lesson Quiz
Solve.

Gina spends $\frac{3}{8}$ of her monthly salary on transportation and food. She spends $\frac{1}{2}$ of it on housing expenses. If her salary is $2,400 a month, how much does she spend on these expenses? How much does she have left? ($900; $1,200; $300)

LEVELED PRACTICE

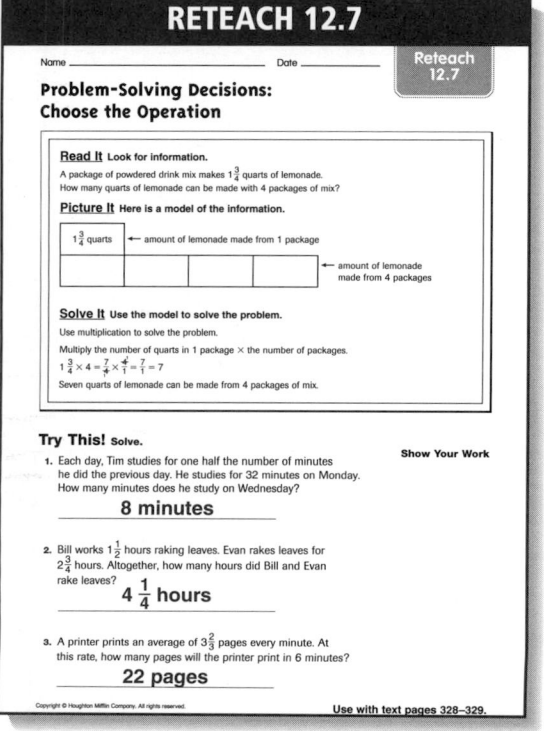

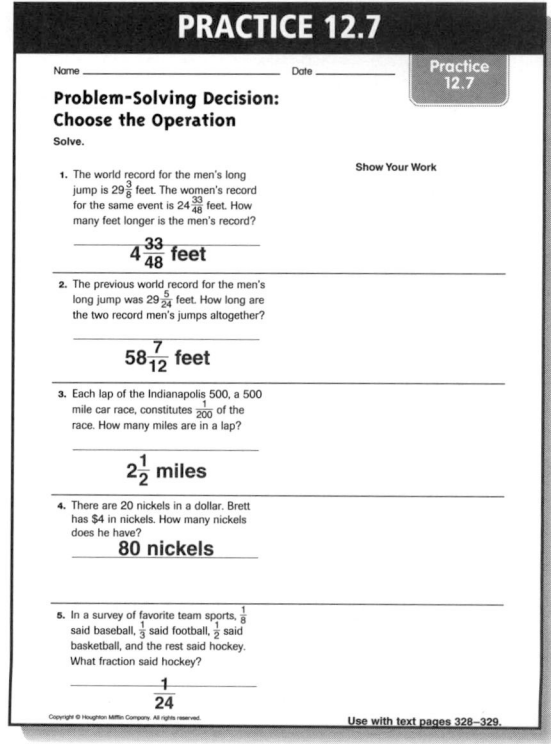

Practice Workbook Page 82

Reaching All Learners

Differentiated Instruction

English Learners

Worksheet 12.7 introduces musical terms students will encounter in Lesson 7.

Special Needs
VISUAL, AUDITORY

- Give students this problem: A garden with an area of 320 square feet is to be separated equally into 5 plots. How many square feet will be in each? (64)
- **What does the problem ask?** (How many square feet will be in each of the 5 plots?)
- **What operation means "separate equally"?** (division)
- **What is 320 ÷ 5?** (64 square feet)

Gifted and Talented
VISUAL, AUDITORY

- Have students create two or three problems similar to those in *Try These* on page 328.
- Have students exchange problems, solve them, and discuss the operation they chose to solve them.

TECHNOLOGY

Spiral Review

To reinforce skills on lessons taught earlier, create **customized** spiral review worksheets using the *Ways to Assess* CD-ROM.

Education Place

Recommend that parents visit Education Place at eduplace.com/parents/mw/ for parent support activities.

Intervention

Use the *Ways to Success* intervention software to support students who need more help in understanding the concepts and skills taught in this chapter.

Ways to Success

Social Studies Connection

House Representatives

- Extend the Social Studies Connection in the student edition on page 329 by having students look up the number of House Representatives from several states.

- Have students look up the populations of the corresponding states.
- Have students write multiplication and division problems using these data.

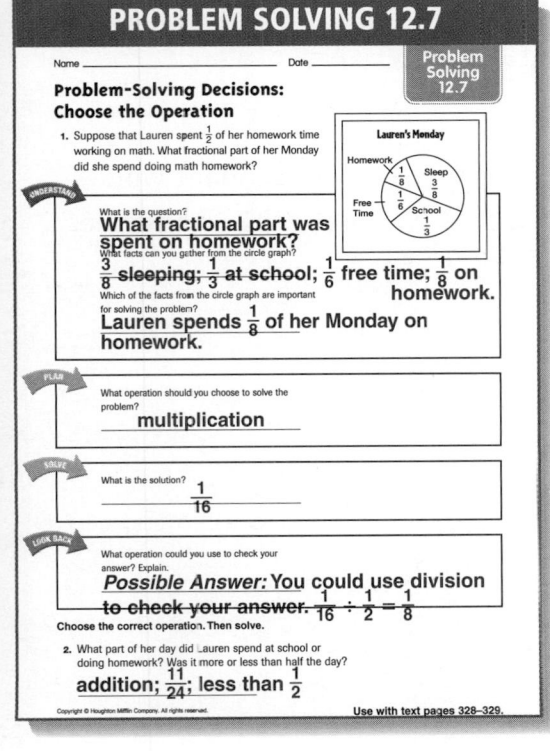

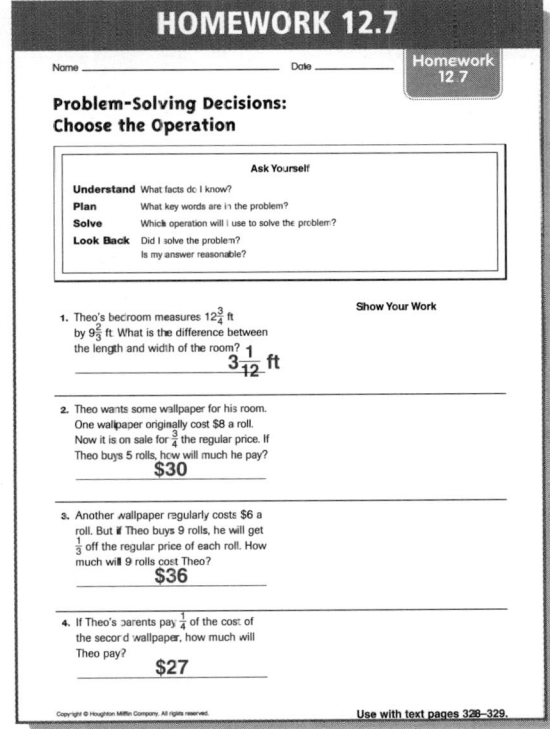

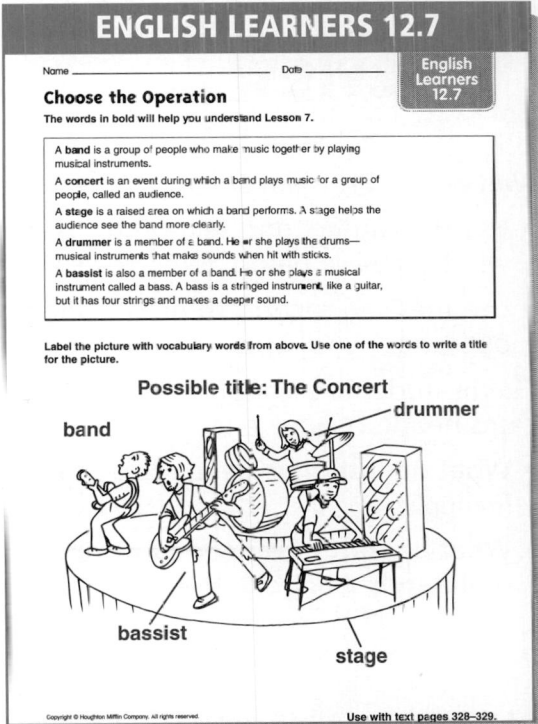

Homework Workbook Page 79

TEACHING LESSON 12.7

Warm-Up Activity
Multiplying and Dividing with Fractions

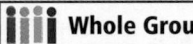 Whole Group 5 minutes | Visual, Auditory

Have students review multiplying and dividing with fractions with the following exercises.

1. $80 \times \frac{3}{5}$ (48)

2. $68 \div \frac{4}{5}$ (85)

3. $\frac{7}{16} \times 144$ (63)

4. $80 \div \frac{5}{8}$ (128)

5. $120 \times \frac{5}{6}$ (100)

 Lesson 7

Problem-Solving Decision
Choose the Operation

Objective Review how to choose the operation that will help you solve a problem.

When solving problems you must decide which operation to use.

Problem The area of the gym floor is 610 square feet. Five eighths of the floor will be used as the stage for a "battle of the bands" concert. The stage will be separated equally into four sections—one for each of the four bands. How much space is given to each band?

Find the area of the gym floor to be used as the stage.	Find how much of the stage each band will have.
Multiply to find a fraction of a number.	**Divide to separate a number equally.**
$610 \times \frac{5}{8} = 381\frac{1}{4}$	$381\frac{1}{4} \div 4 = 95\frac{5}{16}$

Solution: Each band is given $95\frac{5}{16}$ square feet of space.

Try These

Solve.

1. Look back at the problem above. The remaining $\frac{3}{8}$ of the gym floor was separated equally into 5 sections for seating. How large was each section? **$45\frac{3}{4}$ square feet**

2. Tickets for the concert cost $5.00 at the door. Students could buy tickets in advance for $\frac{3}{4}$ of the door price. How much did advance tickets cost? **$3.75**

3. The drummer needs $29\frac{1}{4}$ square feet. The bassist needs $10\frac{1}{2}$ square feet of space. How much more space does the drummer need? How much space do they need combined?
$18\frac{3}{4}$ square feet; $39\frac{3}{4}$ square feet

4. The 320 people in the audience each cast one vote for their favorite band. If $\frac{5}{16}$ of the audience voted for Band 1, $\frac{1}{8}$ for Band 2, $\frac{3}{16}$ for Band 3, and $\frac{3}{8}$ for Band 4, how many votes did each band get?
Band 1: 100 votes; Band 2: 40 votes; Band 3: 60 votes; Band 4: 120 votes

328

---

1 Review

Materials: Problem Solving: Four-Step Process Transparency

- Use the Understand section to help students determine what they are being asked to find.

- Use the Plan section to help students determine which operation would be necessary to solve the probelm.

Guide students through the problem and the two operations needed to solve it.

- **What operation is needed to find $\frac{5}{8}$ of 610 square feet?** (multiplication)

- **What operation is needed to find how much space each of 4 bands will get?** (division)

2 Practice

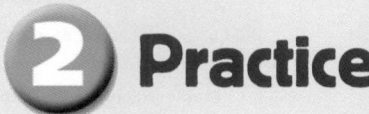

Assign **Exercises 1–4** of *Try These* as independent work.

Assign the **LESSON QUIZ** on Transparency 12.6 to further assess student understanding.

Quick Check

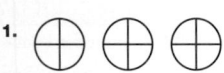

Check your understanding for Lessons 4–7.

Use the models to divide. Write each quotient in simplest form. (Lessons 4–6)

1.

$3 \div \frac{1}{4} = \blacksquare \quad \frac{12}{1}$

2.

$\frac{9}{10} \div \frac{3}{10} = \blacksquare \quad \frac{3}{1}$

3. $6 \div \frac{3}{5}$ **10**   4. $\frac{7}{9} \div \frac{5}{6}$ **$\frac{14}{15}$**   5. $8 \div 3$ **$2\frac{2}{3}$**   6. $\frac{7}{12} \div \frac{3}{4}$ **$\frac{7}{9}$**   7. $2\frac{2}{3} \div 1\frac{1}{3}$ **2**   8. $2\frac{1}{2} \div \frac{3}{5}$ **$4\frac{1}{6}$**

Name the operation(s) you chose to solve. Write each answer in simplest form. (Lesson 7)

9. A recipe makes two and one half dozen cookies. How many dozen cookies can Sarah make if she used three times the original recipe? **multiplication; $7\frac{1}{2}$ dozen**

10. Rachael's garden has 134 square feet. She wants to separate the space equally into 6 parts. What will be the size of each part? **division; $22\frac{1}{3}$ square feet**

WEEKLY WR READER eduplace.com/kids/mw/

Social Studies Connection

United States Congress

The United States Congress is made up of the House of Representatives and the Senate. The House of Representatives has 435 members and the Senate has 100 members. To pass a bill, a majority of the members (one half of the members plus 1) of each house must vote to pass the bill.

Problem To pass a bill, how many members of the Senate must vote for the bill? **51**

Now solve the problem. Look back. Does your answer make sense?

1. How many members of the House of Representatives are needed for a majority?
219 members

2. It takes $\frac{2}{3}$ of the House of Representatives and $\frac{2}{3}$ of the Senate to vote to override a veto. How many members of each house is that?
290 members of the House of Representatives and 67 members of the Senate

Chapter 12 Lesson 7   329

Quick Check

Purpose: The Quick Check allows you to assess the students' understanding of the concepts presented in Lessons 4–7.

Items	Objectives Tested	Pages	Intervention
1–8	Use models to divide fractions. Use the reciprocal to divide fractions.	320–321 322–323	Reteach Resource 12.4–12.5 *Ways to Success* CD-ROM 12.4–12.5
7–8	Divide with mixed numbers.	324–327	Reteach Resource 12.6 *Ways to Success* CD-ROM12.6
9–10	Review how to choose the operation that will help you solve a problem.	328–329	Reteach Resource 12.7 *Ways to Success* CD-ROM 12.7

Test Prep Transparency
12.7

DAILY TEST PREP

In a survey of 400 students, $\frac{3}{8}$ are taking Spanish. How many students are not taking Spanish? (250 students)

Keeping a Journal

Have students write an original problem that requires two different operations to solve. Have students write a few sentences explaining how to solve their problem.

Social Studies Connection

United States Congress

- **What operations are needed to solve the problem in the text?** (multiplication and addition)

- For Problem 1, $\frac{1}{2}$ plus 1 of the members of the House will not be a whole number.

- For Problem 2, $\frac{2}{3}$ of the members of the Senate is not a whole number. Ask students how they solved this problem.

Purpose: This test provides an informal assessment of the Chapter 12 objectives.

Chapter Test Items 1–25

To assign a numerical grade for this Chapter Test, use 4 points for each test item.

Check Understanding

You can use the **Write About It** question to assess student understanding of a key chapter concept.

Customizing Your Instruction

For students who have not yet mastered these objectives, you can use the Reteaching Resources listed in the chart below.

 ## Assessment Options

A summary test for this chapter is also provided in the Unit Resource Folder.

 ## Adequate Yearly Progress

Use the End of Grade Test Prep Assessment Guide to help familiarize your students with the format of standardized tests.

 **Chapter Review/Test**

Write About It: *Possible answer:* 3 ÷ 6 means 3 units divided into 6 equal parts of $\frac{1}{2}$ each. 2 is the answer to 6 ÷ 3, or 6 units divided into 3 equal parts of 2 each.

VOCABULARY

1. The product of a number and its ____ is always 1. **reciprocal**

2. A(n) ____ is a fraction in which the numerator is 1. **unit fraction**

3. A(n) ____ has a numerator that is greater than or equal to the denominator. **improper fraction**

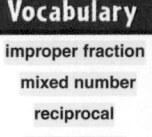
Vocabulary
improper fraction
mixed number
reciprocal
unit fraction

CONCEPTS AND SKILLS

Draw a model to show how you find each product. *Check students' models.*
Write your answer in simplest form. (Lesson 1, pp. 310–313)

4. $\frac{1}{2} \times \frac{2}{3}$ **$\frac{1}{3}$**   5. $\frac{1}{6} \times 3$ **$\frac{1}{2}$**

Multiply. Write your answers in simplest form. (Lessons 2–3, pp. 314–319)

6. $\frac{3}{7} \times 21$ **9**   7. $\frac{5}{8} \times \frac{1}{3}$ **$\frac{5}{24}$**   8. $\frac{5}{8} \times \frac{4}{25}$ **$\frac{1}{10}$**   9. $6 \times 2\frac{5}{6}$ **17**

10. $\frac{3}{8} \times \frac{4}{7}$ **$\frac{3}{14}$**   11. $2\frac{3}{5} \times 5$ **13**   12. $9\frac{1}{5} \times 1\frac{1}{2}$ **$13\frac{4}{5}$**   13. $2\frac{1}{4} \times 3\frac{1}{3}$ **$7\frac{1}{2}$**

Use the models to divide. Write each answer in simplest form. (Lesson 4, pp. 320–321)

14. $2 \div \frac{1}{6} = $ ■ **12**   15. $4 \div \frac{1}{4} = $ ■ **16**

Divide. Write each answer in simplest form. (Lessons 5–6, pp. 322–327)

16. $\frac{3}{4} \div \frac{1}{2}$ **$1\frac{1}{2}$**   17. $\frac{7}{9} \div \frac{2}{3}$ **$1\frac{1}{6}$**   18. $\frac{5}{8} \div \frac{5}{6}$ **$\frac{3}{4}$**   19. $8 \div 20$ **$\frac{2}{5}$**

20. $\frac{3}{5} \div 9$ **$\frac{1}{15}$**   21. $9 \div \frac{3}{5}$ **15**   22. $2\frac{1}{4} \div 1\frac{1}{2}$ **$1\frac{1}{2}$**   23. $3\frac{3}{5} \div 1\frac{1}{7}$ **$2\frac{4}{5}$**

PROBLEM SOLVING

Solve and name the operation(s) you chose. (Lesson 7, pp. 328–329)

24. The string section is $\frac{3}{5}$ of the school orchestra. 50 students are in the orchestra. How many of them are string players? **multiplication; 30 students**

25. Marianne practices her violin $7\frac{1}{2}$ hours each week. If she practices $1\frac{1}{4}$ hours each day, how many days does she practice each week? **division; 6 days**

Write About It

Show You Understand

Why is 3 ÷ 6 equal to $\frac{1}{2}$ and not 2? Explain, using pictures, symbols, or words. *See above.*

Reteaching Support

Chapter Test Items	Summary Test Items	Chapter Objectives Tested	TE Pages	Use These Reteaching Resources
4–13	4–7	**12A** Multiply with fractions, mixed numbers, and whole numbers.	310A–319	Reteach Resource 12.1–12.3 Ways to Success CD: 12.1–12.3 Skillsheet 97, 98
14–23	8–14	**12B** Divide with fractions, mixed numbers, and whole numbers.	320A–327	Reteach Resource 12.4–12.6 Ways to Success CD: 12.4–12.6 Skillsheet 99, 100
24, 25	15–20	**12C** Analyze and solve problems by deciding which operation to choose.	328A–329	Reteach Resource 12.7 Ways to Success CD: 12.7 Skillsheet 101

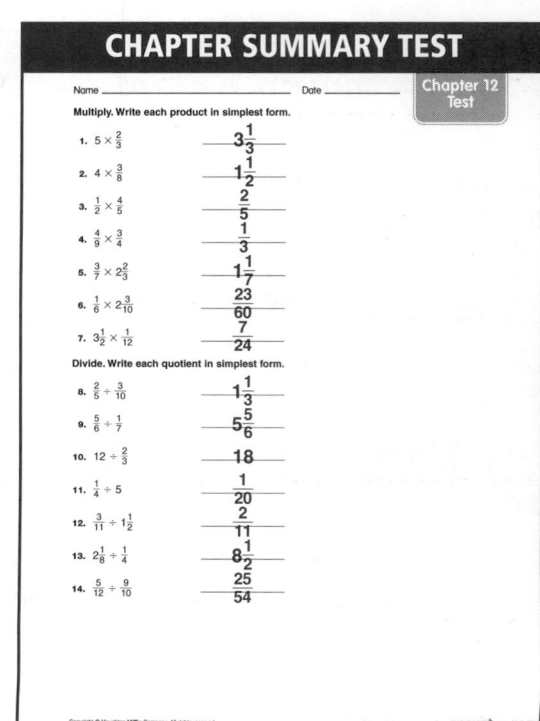

CHAPTER SUMMARY TEST

Name ____ Date ____   Chapter 12 Test

Multiply. Write each product in simplest form.

1. $5 \times \frac{2}{3}$ $3\frac{1}{3}$
2. $4 \times \frac{3}{8}$ $1\frac{1}{2}$
3. $\frac{1}{2} \times \frac{4}{5}$ $\frac{2}{5}$
4. $\frac{4}{9} \times \frac{3}{4}$ $\frac{1}{3}$
5. $\frac{3}{7} \times 2\frac{2}{3}$ $1\frac{1}{7}$
6. $\frac{1}{6} \times 2\frac{3}{10}$ $\frac{23}{60}$
7. $3\frac{1}{2} \times \frac{1}{12}$ $\frac{7}{24}$

Divide. Write each quotient in simplest form.

8. $\frac{2}{5} \div \frac{3}{10}$ $1\frac{1}{3}$
9. $\frac{5}{6} \div \frac{1}{7}$ $5\frac{5}{6}$
10. $12 \div \frac{2}{3}$ 18
11. $\frac{1}{4} \div 5$ $\frac{1}{20}$
12. $\frac{3}{11} \div 1\frac{1}{2}$ $\frac{2}{11}$
13. $2\frac{1}{8} \div \frac{1}{4}$ $8\frac{1}{2}$
14. $\frac{5}{12} \div \frac{9}{10}$ $\frac{25}{54}$

Go on

Extra Practice

Set A (Lessons 1–2, pp. 310–315)

Multiply. Write your answer in simplest form.

1. $\frac{1}{3} \times \frac{1}{6}$ $\frac{1}{18}$
2. $8 \times \frac{3}{5}$ $4\frac{4}{5}$
3. $\frac{5}{9} \times \frac{2}{3}$ $\frac{10}{27}$
4. $\frac{3}{4} \times 4$ 3
5. $\frac{2}{5} \times 3$ $1\frac{1}{5}$
6. $\frac{5}{8} \times \frac{1}{3}$ $\frac{5}{24}$
7. $5 \times \frac{3}{4}$ $3\frac{3}{4}$
8. $\frac{5}{6} \times 6$ 5
9. $\frac{1}{4} \times \frac{8}{9}$ $\frac{2}{9}$
10. $\frac{7}{8} \times \frac{6}{7}$ $\frac{3}{4}$
11. $\frac{5}{6} \times \frac{9}{10}$ $\frac{3}{4}$
12. $\frac{4}{7} \times \frac{5}{4}$ $1\frac{3}{7}$
13. $\frac{2}{3} \times \frac{1}{12}$ $\frac{1}{18}$
14. $\frac{10}{13} \times \frac{1}{10}$ $\frac{1}{13}$
15. $\frac{3}{10} \times \frac{7}{9}$ $\frac{7}{30}$
16. $\frac{1}{5} \times \frac{10}{11}$ $\frac{2}{11}$

Set B (Lesson 3, pp. 316–319)

Multiply. Write each product in simplest form.

1. $1\frac{4}{5} \times \frac{5}{6}$ $1\frac{1}{2}$
2. $\frac{1}{3} \times 1\frac{1}{3}$ $\frac{4}{9}$
3. $3\frac{1}{4} \times \frac{4}{9}$ $1\frac{4}{9}$
4. $\frac{4}{9} \times 1\frac{3}{4}$ $\frac{7}{9}$
5. $1\frac{1}{8} \times \frac{4}{7}$ $\frac{9}{14}$
6. $2\frac{2}{5} \times \frac{5}{7}$ $1\frac{5}{7}$
7. $2\frac{1}{4} \times \frac{8}{9}$ 2
8. $4 \times 3\frac{1}{8}$ $12\frac{1}{2}$
9. $1\frac{2}{3} \times 3\frac{3}{7}$ $6\frac{3}{7}$
10. $2\frac{7}{8} \times 2$ $5\frac{3}{4}$
11. $1\frac{12}{13} \times \frac{1}{5}$ $\frac{5}{13}$
12. $2\frac{4}{7} \times \frac{5}{9}$ $1\frac{3}{7}$
13. $3\frac{3}{8} \times \frac{7}{9}$ $2\frac{5}{8}$
14. $\frac{3}{4} \times 4\frac{4}{5}$ $3\frac{9}{20}$
15. $3\frac{1}{5} \times 2\frac{5}{8}$ $8\frac{2}{5}$
16. $2\frac{1}{2} \times 1\frac{3}{5}$ 4

Set C (Lessons 4–5, pp. 320–323)

Divide. Write each answer in simplest form.

1. $4 \div \frac{1}{5}$ 20
2. $\frac{5}{6} \div \frac{3}{4}$ $1\frac{1}{9}$
3. $\frac{1}{6} \div 2$ $\frac{1}{12}$
4. $10 \div \frac{1}{10}$ 100
5. $3 \div \frac{1}{4}$ 12
6. $\frac{4}{5} \div \frac{2}{3}$ $1\frac{1}{5}$
7. $4 \div 6$ $\frac{2}{3}$
8. $\frac{1}{2} \div 16$ $\frac{1}{32}$
9. $\frac{1}{4} \div \frac{7}{8}$ $\frac{2}{7}$
10. $5 \div \frac{1}{3}$ 15
11. $\frac{1}{6} \div \frac{1}{2}$ $\frac{1}{3}$
12. $\frac{2}{5} \div 10$ $\frac{1}{25}$
13. $\frac{7}{8} \div \frac{5}{9}$ $1\frac{23}{40}$
14. $12 \div 8$ $1\frac{1}{2}$
15. $\frac{5}{7} \div \frac{1}{4}$ $2\frac{6}{7}$
16. $\frac{6}{7} \div \frac{1}{4}$ $3\frac{3}{7}$

Set D (Lesson 6, pp. 324–327)

Write each quotient in simplest form.

1. $\frac{2}{5} \div 1\frac{1}{5}$ $\frac{1}{3}$
2. $\frac{2}{3} \div 6$ $\frac{1}{9}$
3. $2\frac{1}{4} \div \frac{3}{8}$ 6
4. $\frac{3}{4} \div 2\frac{5}{8}$ $\frac{2}{7}$
5. $2\frac{5}{6} \div 1\frac{7}{9}$ $1\frac{19}{32}$
6. $\frac{5}{9} \div 3$ $\frac{5}{27}$
7. $\frac{5}{8} \div 2\frac{3}{4}$ $\frac{5}{22}$
8. $1\frac{3}{4} \div \frac{1}{8}$ 14
9. $10 \div 3\frac{1}{5}$ $3\frac{1}{8}$
10. $2\frac{4}{5} \div 1\frac{2}{3}$ $1\frac{17}{25}$
11. $1\frac{3}{4} \div 1\frac{3}{8}$ $1\frac{3}{11}$
12. $\frac{2}{5} \div 1\frac{3}{5}$ $\frac{1}{4}$
13. $4 \div 2\frac{1}{4}$ $1\frac{7}{9}$
14. $11 \div 3\frac{2}{3}$ 3
15. $1\frac{1}{8} \div 4$ $\frac{9}{32}$
16. $3\frac{1}{3} \div \frac{2}{9}$ 15

Chapter 12 Extra Practice **331**

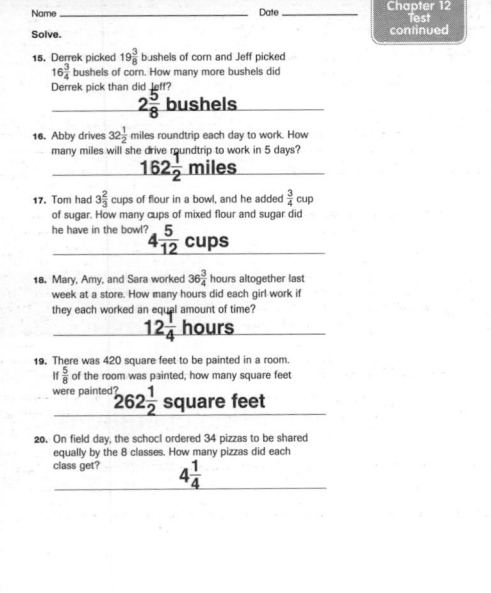

CHAPTER SUMMARY TEST

Chapter 12

Lesson 1, pp. 310–313

17. Less than either factor. Possible explanation: Since any number times one is that number, then any number times a number less than one must be less than that number.

18. Some of the time. Possible explanation: $\frac{1}{2} \times 5 = 2\frac{1}{2}$, $\frac{1}{2} \times 4 = 2$, $\frac{1}{2} \times 1 = \frac{1}{2}$.

Lesson 2, pp. 314–315

25. *Possible answer:* Make two sets with 4 chips in each. To show $\frac{3}{4}$, turn 3 of the chips in each set so they show the same color. Turn the fourth chip in each set to a side with a different color. Separate the sets into two piles so you have half of the $\frac{3}{4}$.

26. $10\frac{1}{2}$ liters; 12 bottles $\times \frac{7}{8}$ in each bottle.

Lesson 3, pp. 316–319

Explain Your Thinking: Multiplying with mixed numbers is similar to multiplying with fractions because you can write the mixed numbers as fractions, then multiply as you would with fractions.

Lesson 5, pp. 322–323

32. 12 speakers; $\frac{1}{6}$ of an hour is 10 minutes. There are 12 sets of 10 minutes in 2 hours.

Lesson 6, pp. 324–327

Explain Your Thinking: The reciprocal of a unit fraction is a counting number equal to the denominator. The reciprocal of a counting number is a unit fraction with the counting number as the denominator.

46. No, it does not change, because $\frac{1}{2}$ of $2\frac{1}{2}$ is $1\frac{1}{4}$ and $2 \times 1\frac{1}{4} = 2\frac{1}{2}$, so halving one is the same as doubling the other.

49. *Possible answer:* When you divide by a divisor that is a fraction greater than 1, you "break apart" the dividend into parts that are greater than 1. You have fewer parts than you began with, so the quotient is less than the dividend. For example: $4 \div 2\frac{1}{4} = 1\frac{7}{9}$; $1\frac{7}{9} < 4$.

Lesson By Lesson Overview
Multiply Decimals

Lesson 1

- Students use models and prior knowledge about multiplying fractions and mixed numbers to practice multiplication with decimals.

Lesson 2

- Students multiply decimals by whole numbers, including money amounts.
- Students practice placing the decimal point so that the number of decimal places in the product equals the sum of the decimal places in the factors.

Lesson 3

- Students practice rounding to estimate products of whole numbers and decimals.
- Students estimate and analyze data from a table of cellular phone costs.

Lesson 4

- Students find the product of two decimals.
- Students choose a value for each variable in an expression that will yield a given product.
- Students use data from a table and choose a computation method to solve problems.

Lesson 5

- Students write zeros in the product in order to place the decimal point correctly.
- Students use data from a sales tax table to solve problems.

Lesson 6

- Students decide whether an answer to a problem is reasonable.

SKILLS TRACE: MULTIPLICATION WITH DECIMALS		
Grade 4	**Grade 5**	**Grade 6**
	• relate fraction and decimal multiplication	• link decimal to fraction operations (ch. 7)
	• estimate decimal products	• multiply decimals and powers of ten (ch. 7)
	• multiply with decimals and whole numbers	

Chapter Planner

Lesson	Objective	Vocabulary	Materials	✔ NCTM Standards
13.1 **Explore Multiplication** p. 334A	Use models to explore multiplication with decimals.		Centimeter Grid Transparency, grid paper, red and blue pencils	**Number and Operations:** Recognize and generate equivalent forms of commonly used fractions, decimals, and percents.
13.2 **Multiply Whole Numbers and Decimals** p. 336A	Find the product of a whole number and a decimal.	estimate product		**Number and Operations:** Develop and use strategies to estimate computations involving fractions and decimals in situations relevant to students' experience.
13.3 **Estimate Products** p. 338A	Use rounding to estimate products of decimals.			**Number and Operations:** Develop and use strategies to estimate computations involving fractions and decimals in situations relevant to students' experience.
13.4 **Multiply Decimals** p. 340A	Find the product of two decimals.		Centimeter Grid Transparency, grid paper, two colored markers	**Problem Solving:** Apply and adapt a variety of appropriate strategies to solve problems
13.5 **Zeros in the Product** p. 344A	Decide when to write zeros in the products of decimal factors.	factor		**Number and Operations:** Understand various meanings of multiplication and division.
13.6 **Problem Solving Decision: Reasonable Answers** p. 346A	Review how to decide if the answer to a problem is reasonable.		Problem Solving: Four-Step Process Transparency	**Number and Operations:** Develop and use strategies to estimate the results of whole-number computations and to judge the reasonableness of such results.

Resources For Reaching All Learners

LESSON RESOURCES: Reteach, Practice, Enrichment, Problem Solving, Homework, English Learners, Daily Routines, Transparencies, Math Center.

ADDITIONAL RESOURCES FROM HOUGHTON MIFFLIN: Combination Classroom Planning Guide, Chapter Challenges, Every Day Counts, Math at Hand (student handbook)

Every Day Counts
The **Daily Decimal** activities in **Every Day Counts** support the math in this chapter.

Assessing Prior Knowledge

Before beginning the chapter, you can assess student's understandings in order to assist you in differentiating instruction.

Complete Chapter Pretest in Unit Resource Folder

Use this test to assess both prerequisite skills (**Are You Ready?** — one page) and chapter content (**Check What You Know** — two pages).

Chapter 13 Prerequisite Skills Pretest

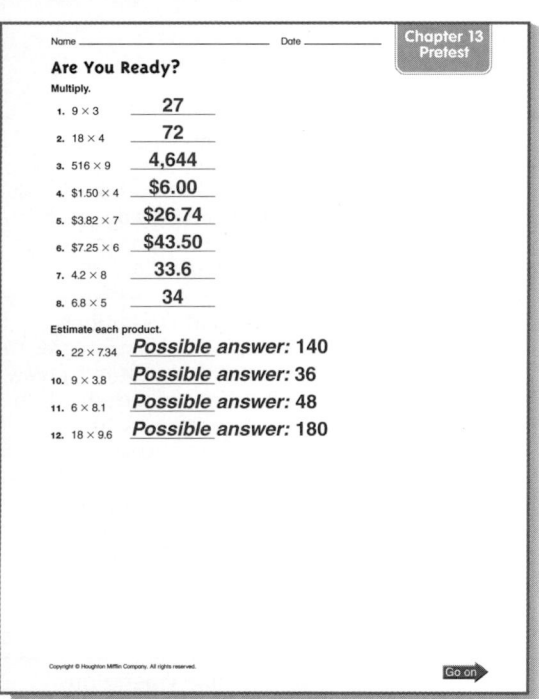

Chapter 13 New Content Pretest

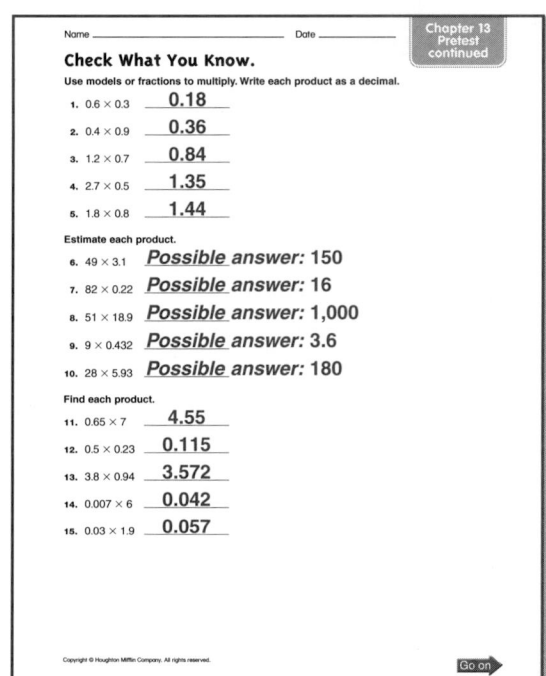

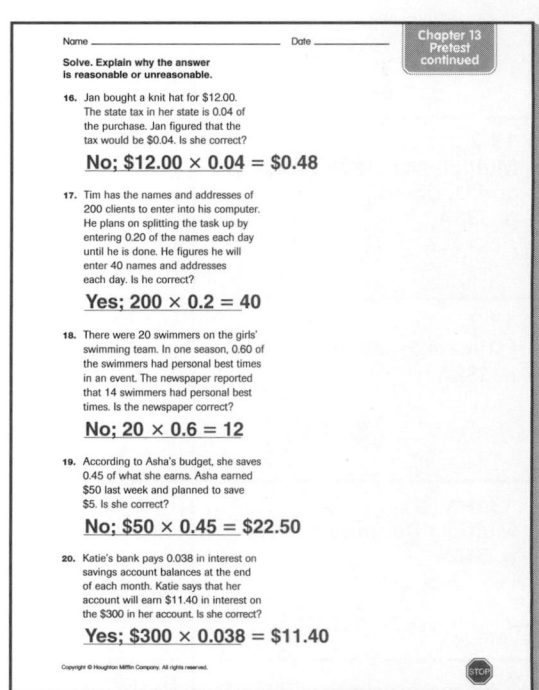

Customizing Instruction

For Students Having Difficulty

Items	Prerequisites	Ways to Success
1–8	Multiply by one-digit numbers.	CD: 13a Skillsheet: 102
9–12	Estimate products by rounding decimals.	CD: 13c Skillsheet: 103

Ways to Success: Intervention for every concept and skill (CD-ROM or Chapter Intervention Skillsheets).

Consider using **Knowing Mathematics** with any students who are working two or more years below grade level.

For Students Having Success

Items	Objectives	Resources
1–5	**13A** Relate multiplication of fractions to multiplication of decimals	Enrichment 13.1
6–10	**13B** Estimate decimal products.	Enrichment 13.3
11–15	**13C** Multiply with decimals and whole numbers.	Enrichment 13.2, 13.4, 13.5
16–20	**13D** Decide whether the solution to a problem is reasonable.	Enrichment 13.6

Use **Chapter Challenges** with any students who have success with all new chapter content.

Other Pretest Options

Informal Pretest in Student Book

The student book pretest assesses vocabulary and prerequisite skills needed for success in this chapter.

Ways to Success CD-ROM

The *Ways to Success* chapter pretest has automatic assignment of appropriate review lessons.

Chapter Resources

Assessing Prior Knowledge

Multiplying Decimals

- Read aloud five multiplication exercises involving multiplying by a one- or two-digit whole number.
- Have students write down each exercise as you read it. First have them estimate each product, then have them find each product.

Ongoing Skill Activity

Spinning to Multiply

- Use a spinner divided into equal regions numbered 0–9 to generate multiplication exercises using decimals.
- After Lesson 2, have students spin once for a whole number and then either once or twice more for decimals to the tenths or hundredths places.
- After Lessons 3 and 5, have them spin up to three times to generate each decimal factor. For Lesson 3, students should estimate the products; for Lesson 5, they can both estimate and compute the products.

Connecting to the Unit Project

- Have students work with their group to make a table to show how many of each kind of note (half, quarter, eighth, and sixteenth) there are in one measure of music with the following time signatures: $\frac{4}{4}$ and $\frac{2}{4}$.
- Have students discuss and display their tables.

Teacher Support

Professional Resources Handbook

Research, Mathematics Content, and Language Intervention

Research-Based Teaching

Research suggests the relationship of decimals to fractions can be utilized to develop multiplication of decimals. Such development helps students enhance their number sense, or feeling for numbers, rather than simply learning a rule about placing the decimal point in the product. Students also need practice deciding when to use mental math, estimation, paper and pencil, or a calculator when solving problems. See *Professional Resources Handbook, Grade 5,* Unit 5.

For more ideas relating to Unit 5, see the Teacher Support Handbook at the back of this Teacher's Edition.

Language Intervention

Be sure students are using correct mathematical language when they read decimals. The correct way to read 3.2 is "three and two tenths," not "three point two."

Time Saving Technology Support

Ways to Assess Customized Spiral Review and Test Generator CD-ROM
Lesson Planner CD-ROM
Ways to Success Intervention CD-ROM
Math Tracks CD-ROM
Education Place: **www.eduplace.com/math/mw/**
Houghton Mifflin Math eBook CD-ROM
eManipulatives
eGames

Starting Chapter 13
Multiply Decimals

Chapter Objectives

13A Relate multiplication of fractions to multiplication of decimals.

13B Estimate decimal products.

13C Multiply with decimals and whole numbers.

13D Decide whether the solution to a problem is reasonable.

INVESTIGATION

Use Data

Lin makes $5.50 per hour babysitting during the summer. Her weekly schedule is shown at the right. How much does Lin make each week she babysits? **$145.75**

Lin's Schedule	
Monday	11 A.M. - 5 P.M.
Tuesday	2 P.M. - 6 P.M.
Wednesday	11 A.M. - 5 P.M.
Thursday	2 P.M. - 6 P.M.
Friday	11 A.M. - 5:30 P.M.

332

Math Background

Multiply Decimals

It is important for students to understand that when they multiply decimals they should multiply them as whole numbers and afterwards put the decimal point in the right place. To correctly place the decimal point, first count the total number of decimal places in the factors. Then place the decimal point that many places from the right in the product.

The placement of the decimal point can also be explained by using fractions. For instance:

$$3.5 \times 4.25 = \frac{35}{10} \times \frac{425}{100} = \frac{14,875}{1,000}$$

$$= 14\frac{875}{1,000}$$

$$= 14.875$$

Notice that in the above example, the product of the fractions is not written in simplest form. The denominator should be kept as a multiple of ten. It is a good idea to go back to concepts students feel comfortable with and use them to explain new ideas.

Multiplication of a decimal by 10 simply moves the decimal point one place to the right. Multiplication by 10^n moves the decimal point n places to the right, when n is positive.

Using the Investigation

Have students work in small groups to answer the question posed on page 332.

To extend the investigation, have students do the following activity.

• Suppose you wanted to earn $100. Write a paragraph about how you would do it. Include jobs you could do, how much you would charge, and how long it would take you to earn the total amount.

For more information about projects and investigations, visit **Education Place**. **www.eduplace.com/math/mw/**

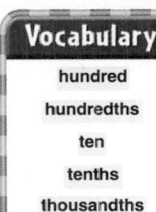 **Chapter Pretest**

Use this page to review and remember
what you need to know for this chapter.

VOCABULARY

Choose the best word to complete each sentence.

Vocabulary
hundred
hundredths
ten
tenths
thousandths

hundredths
1. In the decimal 0.095, the 9 is in the ____ place.

tenths
2. The six in the decimal 0.62 is in the ____ place.

thousandths
3. The decimal 0.002 is read as "two ____."

ten
4. The decimal 10.02 is read as ____ and two hundredths.

CONCEPTS AND SKILLS

Write each fraction as a decimal.

5. $\frac{8}{10}$ 0.8   6. $\frac{32}{100}$ 0.32   7. $\frac{1}{4}$ 0.25   8. $\frac{1}{2}$ 0.50, or 0.5

Write these numbers from least to greatest.

9. 60.05, 6.5, 6.005
   6.005, 6.5, 60.05

10. 74.3, 79.02, 54.85, 54.58
    54.58, 54.85, 74.3, 79.02

11. 1.1, 9.11, 3.4, 1.101
    1.1, 1.101, 3.4, 9.11

Write >, <, or = for each ●.

12. 27.1 **>** 27.01   13. 6.102 **>** 6.021   14. 13.20 **=** 13.2

Multiply.

15.	16.	17.	18.	19.
31	49	52	22	93
× 23	× 17	× 36	× 45	× 90
713	833	1,872	990	8,370

 **Write About It**

20. Adventure videos cost $7.49, and comedies
are on sale at 3 for $20. If you could afford
to buy three videos, which kind of movie
would cost you less? Explain.

 Test Prep on the Net
Visit *Education Place* at
eduplace.com/kids/mw/
for more review.

Possible answer: 3 comedies; 3 adventure videos at $7.49 would cost
3 × $7.49, or $22.47, which is $2.47 more than the three comedies for $20.

 **Chapter Pretest**

Prerequisite Skills

Items	Skill
1–4	Vocabulary needed for this chapter
5–8	Remaining fractions as decimals
9–11	Ordering decimals
12–14	Comparing decimals
15–19	Multiplying whole numbers
20	Understanding multiplication with decimals

Chapter Challenges

For Mathematically Promising Students

Use Chapter Challenges resource book.

Explore: Relate Multiplication and
Division, page 73, after Lesson 1

Extend: Converting Measurements,
page 75, after Lesson 3

Connect: Decimal Movement, page 77, after
Lesson 5

Using The Chapter Pretest

This page will help students review some of the
prerequisite skills needed for this chapter. The chart
above indicates which skills are covered on the
pretest. If students need more help with these
prerequisite skills use *Ways to Success,* Houghton
Mifflin's intervention program.

Students who need more review can visit
Education Place, Houghton Mifflin's
award-winning website.

NSF Children's Math Worlds

Children's Math Worlds focuses on the use of
models to represent mathematical situations. Thus,
using a *Children's Math Worlds* lesson helps
students develop a general facility with drawing
models to support their thinking that will transfer
to all their mathematical work.

Explore Multiplication

PLANNING THE LESSON

MATHEMATICS OBJECTIVE
Use models to explore multiplication with decimals.

Use Lesson Planner CD-ROM for Lesson 13.1.

Daily Routines

Vocabulary

Ask students to name the parts of a division problem. (*divisor, dividend, quotient*) Ask students how they would check a division problem to see if it is correct. (*Multiply the divisor by the quotient to arrive at the dividend.*) **The two numbers that are multiplied together are called *factors*. The result of the multiplication is called the *product*.**

Vocabulary Cards

Meeting North Carolina's Standards

Prepare for Grade 6 Objective **1.04** Develop fluency in addition, subtraction, multiplication, and division of nonnegative rational numbers.

Lesson Transparency 13.1

Problem of the Day

Rhea saved up $35. She spent $\frac{1}{5}$ of that amount on a gift. How much did she spend? Sam said that the money she spent was equivalent to $\frac{1}{4}$ of his savings. How much does Sam have in savings? ($7; $28)

Quick Review

Multiply.
1. 50×9 (450)
2. 50×10 (500)
3. 50×11 (550)
4. 50×12 (600)

Lesson Quiz

Use models or fractions to multiply. Write each product as a decimal.
1. 0.2×0.6 (0.12)
2. 0.3×0.7 (0.21)
3. 0.6×0.7 (0.42)
4. 0.8×0.4 (0.32)

LEVELED PRACTICE

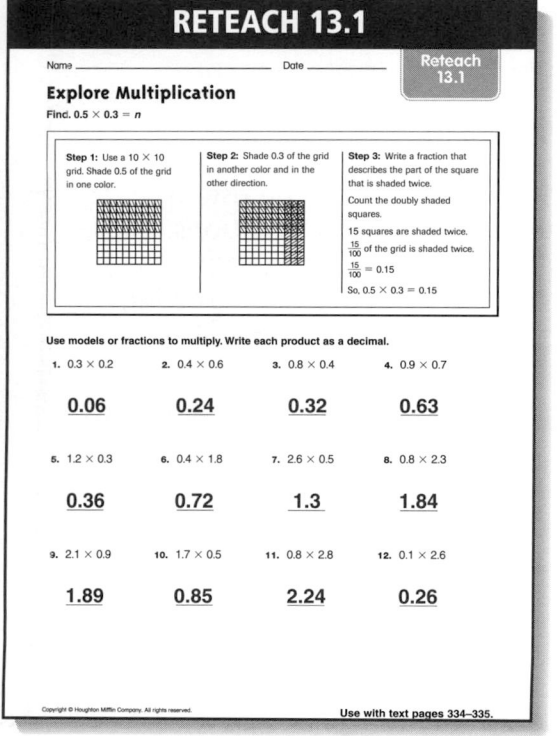

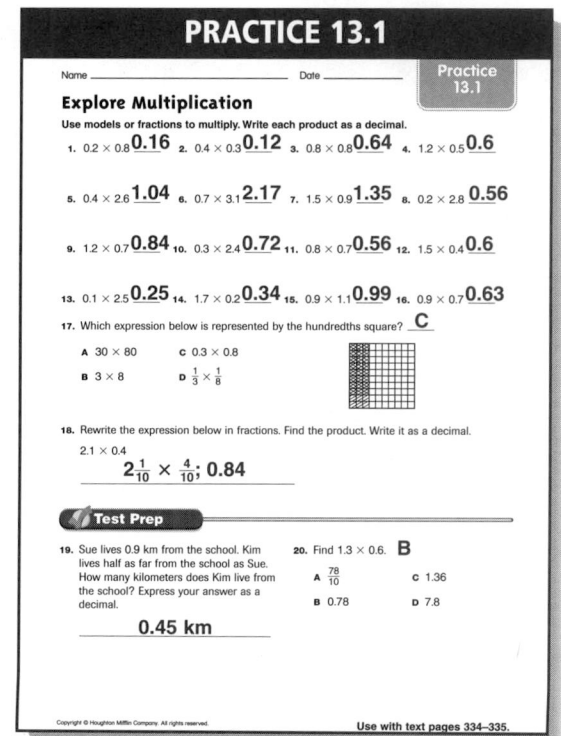

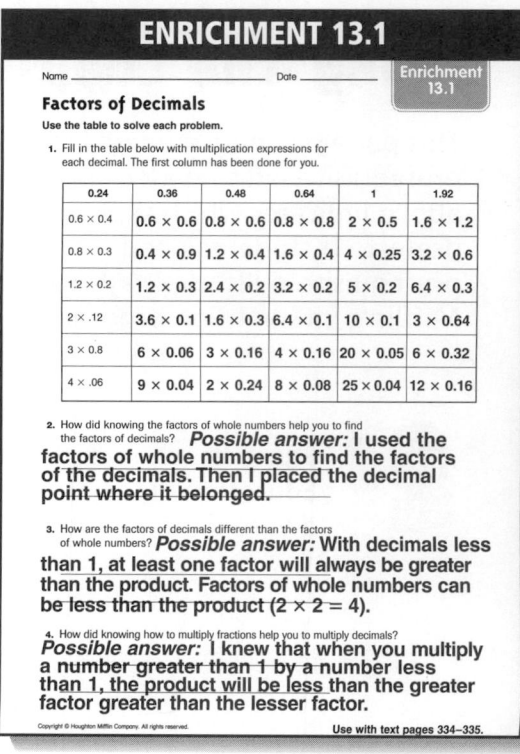

Practice Workbook Page 83

Reaching All Learners
Differentiated Instruction

English Learners

Worksheet 13.1 reviews the concept of a model and shows students how to use a visual model to solve a multiplication problem with fractions.

Special Needs
VISUAL, AUDITORY

- Write *0.4 × 0.8* on the chalkboard. **We can rewrite the decimals as fractions.** Write this equivalence:

$$0.4 \times 0.8 = \frac{4}{10} \times \frac{8}{10}$$

- **To multiply fractions, we multiply numerators and denominators.** Write:

$$\frac{4}{10} \times \frac{8}{10} = \frac{(4 \times 8)}{(10 \times 10)} = \frac{32}{100}$$

What decimal is equal to $\frac{32}{100}$? (0.32) Continue with other examples.

Gifted and Talented
VISUAL, KINESTHETIC

Materials: *half-centimeter grid paper*

- Have students draw a 10 × 10 grid on the grid paper. Have them shade in squares to model a multiplication problem using decimals, such as 0.2 × 0.9 or 0.6 × 0.7.

- Have them exchange grids and write multiplication problems based on the grid models.

Social Studies Connection

How Fast Did They Run?
Materials: *almanac or other sports reference materials*

Have students look up the running times of track medalists from three different Olympics. Have students choose a year in the early, mid-, and late 20th century. For each medalist, have students write the track speeds in decimals and fractions. Have students compare and discuss speeds from each era.

TECHNOLOGY

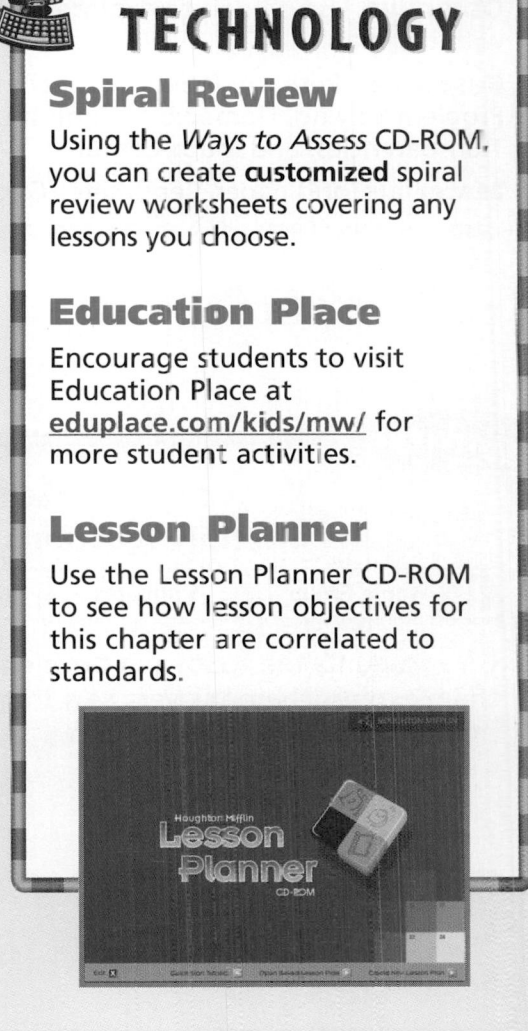

Spiral Review

Using the *Ways to Assess* CD-ROM, you can create **customized** spiral review worksheets covering any lessons you choose.

Education Place

Encourage students to visit Education Place at eduplace.com/kids/mw/ for more student activities.

Lesson Planner

Use the Lesson Planner CD-ROM to see how lesson objectives for this chapter are correlated to standards.

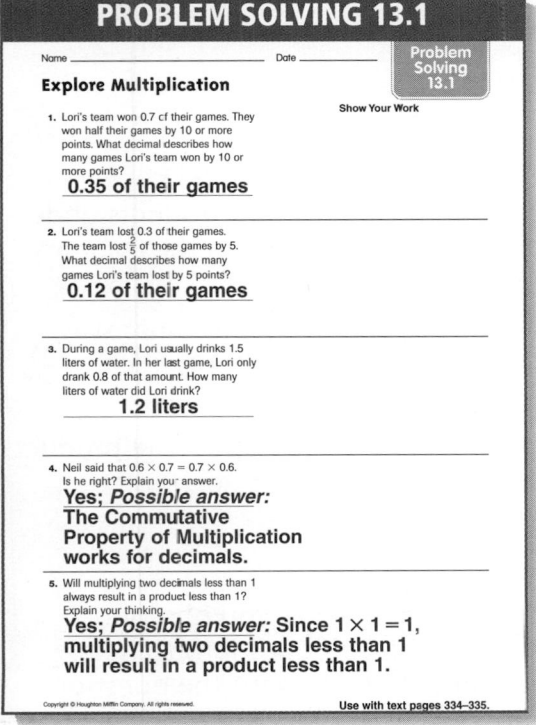

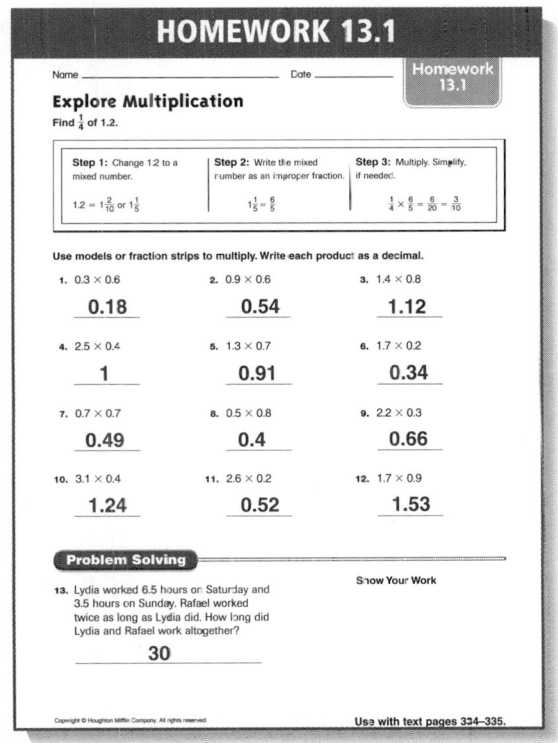

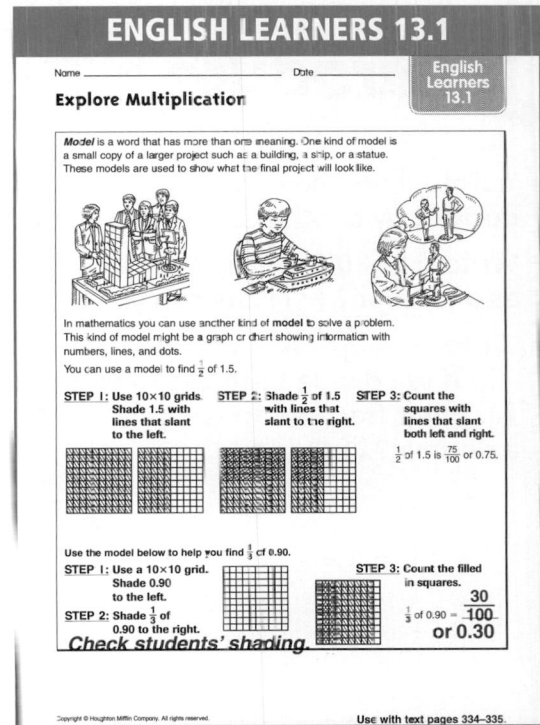

Homework Workbook Page 83

TEACHING LESSON 13.1

Activity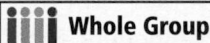

Warm-Up Activity
Multiply Fractions

| Whole Group | 5 minutes | Visual, Auditory |

Give students the following problems. Have them express their answers as a fraction or mixed number in simplest form.

1. $\frac{3}{10} \times \frac{3}{4}$ $\left(\frac{9}{40}\right)$

2. $\frac{5}{8} \times \frac{1}{3}$ $\left(\frac{5}{24}\right)$

3. $8 \times \frac{2}{3}$ $\left(5\frac{1}{3}\right)$

4. $3 \times \frac{3}{10}$ $\left(\frac{9}{10}\right)$

5. $5 \times \frac{4}{5}$ (4)

Lesson 1

Explore Multiplication

Objective Use models to explore multiplication with decimals.

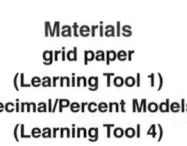

Learn About It

How many more liters of juice does the larger container of Just Juice hold?

You need to find $\frac{1}{5}$ of 1.5.

Materials
grid paper
(Learning Tool 1)
Decimal/Percent Models
(Learning Tool 4)

Different Ways to Find $\frac{1}{5}$ of 1.5

Way 1 You can use models to find $\frac{1}{5}$ of 1.5.

STEP 1 Use 10 × 10 grids. Shade 1.5 in blue.

STEP 2 Shade $\frac{1}{5}$ of 1.5 in red.

STEP 3 Count the purple squares.

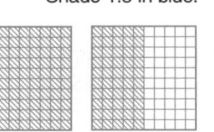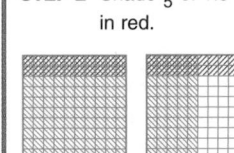

$\frac{1}{5}$ of 1.5 is $\frac{30}{100}$, or 0.30, or 0.3.

Way 2 You can use what you know about multiplication of fractions and mixed numbers to find $\frac{1}{5}$ of 1.5.

STEP 1 Change 1.5 to a mixed number.

$1.5 = 1\frac{5}{10}$, or $1\frac{1}{2}$

STEP 2 Multiply.

$1\frac{1}{2} \times \frac{1}{5} = \frac{3}{2} \times \frac{1}{5}$

$= \frac{3}{10}$, or 0.3

Solution: The larger container of Just Juice holds 0.3 liter more.

Another Example Find 0.18 × 3.

Use fractions.

$\frac{18}{100} \times \frac{3}{1} = \frac{54}{100}$

$= 0.54$

Use models.

54 of 100 squares, or 0.54 is shaded.

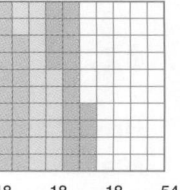

$\frac{18}{100} + \frac{18}{100} + \frac{18}{100} = \frac{54}{100}$

334

---

1 Introduce

- Tell students they are going to explore multiplying one decimal by another, using fractions.

- Write *0.5 × 0.8* on the chalkboard. **How can we write 0.5 as a fraction?** $\left(\frac{5}{10}\right)$ **How can we write 0.8 as a fraction?** $\left(\frac{8}{10}\right)$

- Write $\frac{5}{10} \times \frac{8}{10}$. Ask a volunteer to give you the product. $\left(\frac{40}{100}\right)$ **If we divide both the numerator and denominator by 10. What fraction do we get?** $\left(\frac{4}{10}\right)$ **How can we write $\frac{4}{10}$ as a decimal?** (0.4)

2 Develop

Guide students through the *Learn About It* section.

- Review the steps in Way 1. Make sure that students understand how the number of squares shaded in the columns and rows in Steps 1–3 relate to the problem $\frac{1}{5} \times 1.5$.

- Review the steps in Way 2. Point out that another way would be to write 1.5 as $\frac{15}{10}$ and then multiply: $\frac{15}{10} \times \frac{1}{5} = \frac{15}{50}$, which is $\frac{3}{10}$ in simplest form.

- Go over *Another Example*. **Would you expect the product to be more or less than 3?** (less than 3, because 3 is being multiplied by a number less than 3)

Guided Practice

Have students complete **Exercises 1–6** as you observe. Remind them to use the *Ask Yourself* questions to help. Give students the opportunity to talk about the question in *Explain Your Thinking*.

Use models or fractions to multiply. Write each product as a decimal.

1. 0.6×0.2
0.12
2. 0.5×0.8
0.40
3. 0.7×2.6
1.82
4. 1.5×0.4
0.60
5. 0.8×0.9
0.72
6. 0.6×1.4
0.84

Ask Yourself
- Did I model the multiplication correctly?
- Did I multiply correctly?
- Did I write the product as a decimal?

Explain Your Thinking ▶ Is $\frac{1}{2} \times 0.4$ equal to $\frac{2}{5} \times 0.5$? Explain why or why not. **Yes; $\frac{1}{2} = 0.5$, and $0.4 = \frac{2}{5}$.**

Practice and Problem Solving

Use models or fractions to multiply. Write each product as a decimal.

7. 0.6×0.5
0.30
8. 0.4×0.8
0.32
9. 1.5×0.5
0.75
10. 0.5×2.8
1.4
11. 2.1×0.5
1.05
12. 1.7×0.3
0.51
13. 0.9×0.9
0.81
14. 0.3×0.3
0.09
15. 1.3×0.8
1.04
16. 1.2×0.2
0.24

Solve.

17. Miguel works at a juice bar 8.5 hours each week. Kim works half as many hours. How many hours does Kim work in a week? **4.25 hours, or $4\frac{1}{4}$ hours**

18. **Mental Math** A manufacturer puts a bonus coupon on 0.1 of its juice bottles. In a case with 20 bottles, how many juice bottles will have the coupon?
2 bottles

19. **Create and Solve** Write a problem that can be solved using the model at the right. Solve your problem. Then give it to a partner to solve. **Check problems and solutions.**

20. **Analyze** Look back at page 334. Suppose the advertisement read, "New size holds 0.2 liter more!" How many liters would the new container hold?
The new container would hold 1.7 liters. $1.5 + 0.2 = 1.7$.

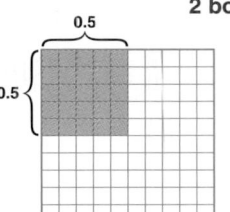

Daily Review   Test Prep

Subtract. (Ch. 11, Lesson 3)

21. $23.2 - 7.5$
15.7
22. $107.26 - 27.05$
80.21
23. $\begin{array}{r} 222.22 \\ -\ 78.51 \\ \hline 143.71 \end{array}$
24. $\begin{array}{r} 79.305 \\ -\ 12.047 \\ \hline 67.258 \end{array}$

25. Use models or fractions to find $\frac{2}{3}$ of 0.6.

A 0.2
B 0.5
C 0.4
D 0.9

Extra Practice See page 349, Set A.

Chapter 13 Lesson 1   **335**

DAILY TEST PREP

Arlene spent $0.80 for two oranges. Marian spent 0.6 as much. How much did Marian spend? **($0.48)**

 **Activity**

Lesson Intervention

Using a Model to Multiply

Or use Intervention CD-ROM Lesson 13.1

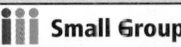 Small Group   5–10 minutes   Visual, Auditory

Materials: *Centimeter Grid Transparency, red and blue pencils*

- Put the Centimeter Grid Transparency on the overhead. Tell students they are going to model 0.7×0.3. How can we rewrite the problem using fractions instead of decimals? ($\frac{7}{10} \times \frac{3}{10}$)

- We can model $\frac{7}{10}$ by shading 7 tenths vertically in red. How can we model $\frac{3}{10}$? (Shade 3 tenths horizontally in blue.) **To find the product of 0.7×0.3, what do we do?** (Count the squares that are shaded in red and blue.)

- **How many squares are shaded?** (21) **Since each square represents 1 hundredth, what fraction of 100 squares have we shaded?** ($\frac{21}{100}$) **How can we write that fraction as a decimal?** (0.21)

---

3 Practice

Assign **Exercises 7–25** as independent work.

- *Problem Solving for Problems 17–20* For Problems 17–18, have students discuss their answers. For Problem 20, have students discuss and share their answers.

Common Error

Not expressing fractions in simplest form When a problem involves rewriting a decimal as a fraction or mixed number, students should be sure either to write the factor in simplest form, or to write the product in simplest form.

4 Assess and Close

What are two ways of multiplying a decimal by a whole number or by another decimal? (Use a 10 × 10 grid to model the problem or rewrite the factors as fractions before multiplying.)

Assign the **LESSON QUIZ** on Transparency 13.1 to further assess student understanding.

 **Keeping a Journal**

Have students explain how to multiply a decimal by another decimal, and how to multiply a decimal by a whole number.

Multiply Whole Numbers and Decimals

PLANNING THE LESSON

MATHEMATICS OBJECTIVE

Find the product of a whole number and a decimal.

Use Lesson Planner CD-ROM for Lesson 13.2.

Daily Routines

Vocabulary

Discuss rounding numbers. Explain that an *estimate* is a number that is close to an exact amount. Remind students that a *product* is the result of multiplication.

Vocabulary Cards

Meeting North Carolina's Standards

Prepare for Grade 6 Objective **1.04** Develop fluency in addition, subtraction, multiplication, and division of nonnegative rational numbers.

Lesson Transparency

13.2

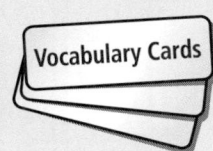

Problem of the Day

Amanda has followed a pattern for saving money each week for one year. In Week 1, she saved $1.00; in Week 2, $1.60; in Week 3, $2.20, and in Week 4, $2.80. During which weeks will she save $6.40; $8.80? (Week 10, Week 14)

Quick Review

Multiply mentally.

1. $2 \times 5 \times 7$ (70)
2. $5 \times 18 \times 0$ (0)
3. $10 \times 1 \times 4$ (40)
4. $5 \times 4 \times 8$ (160)
5. $25 \times 6 \times 4$ (600)

Lesson Quiz

Find each product.

1. 2×2.5 (5)
2. 3×3.5 (10.5)
3. 6×2.48 (14.88)
4. 8×9.145 (73.16)
5. 4×3.561 (14.244)

LEVELED PRACTICE

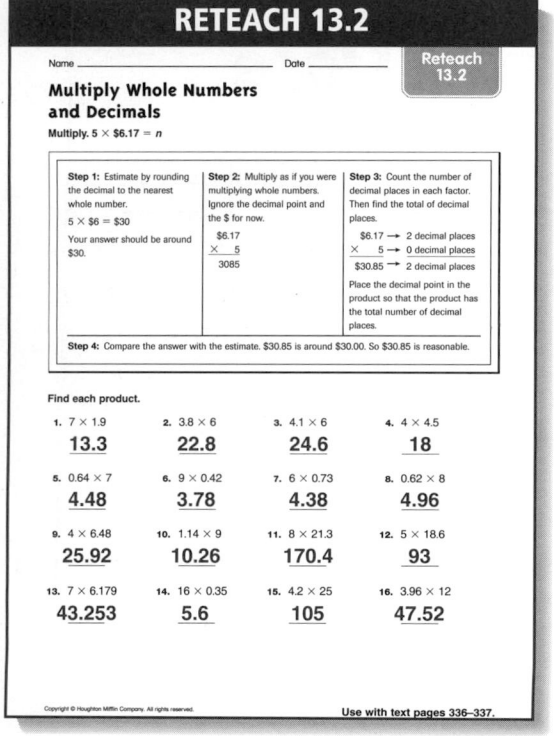

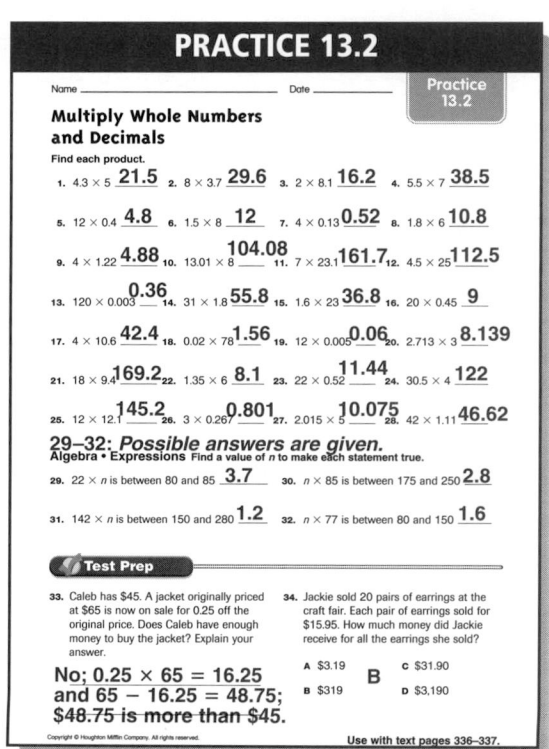

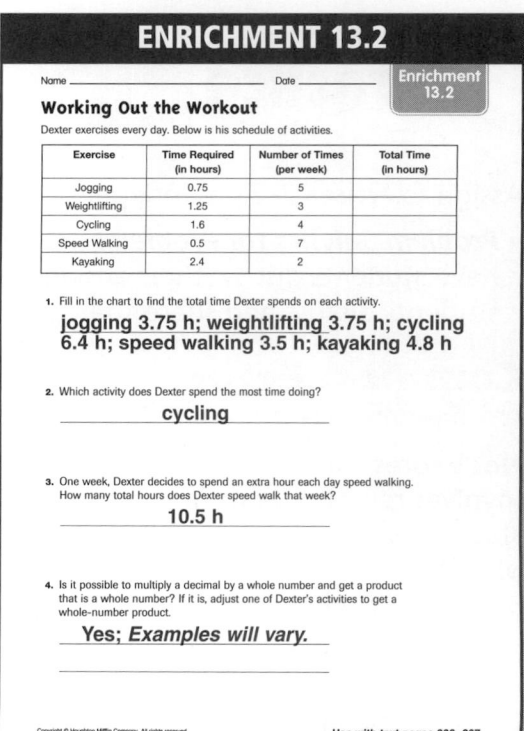

Practice Workbook Page 84

Reaching All Learners
Differentiated Instruction

English Learners

Worksheet 13.2 introduces students to content vocabulary they will encounter in word problems in Lesson 2.

Inclusion
VISUAL, AUDITORY

- Display: 3×4.8. Explain to students that it is a good idea to estimate a product before multiplying.
- **How can we round 4.8?** (Since the tenths digit is 8, we can round 4 up to 5.) **What is 3×5?** (15)
- Repeat the procedure for these problems: 4×8.4; 6×7.6; 3×10.7

Early Finishers
VISUAL, AUDITORY

- Have students complete this pattern.

  $2 \times 1.75 = 3.5$

  $3 \times 1.75 = ?$ (5.25)

  $4 \times 1.75 = ?$ (7)

  $5 \times 1.75 = ?$ (8.75)

  $6 \times 1.75 = ?$ (10.5)

- In pairs, have them discuss and describe the pattern.

TECHNOLOGY

Spiral Review

To reinforce skills on lessons taught earlier, create **customized** spiral review worksheets using the *Ways to Assess* CD-ROM.

Tool Software

Use *Easy Sheet* or another spreadsheet to explore this lesson more fully.

Education Place

Encourage students to visit Education Place at **eduplace.com/kids/mw/** for more student activities.

Social Studies Connection

Making Stock Portfolios
Materials: *current newspaper*

- Have students look up stock prices in the newspaper. Have them choose 5 companies for their portfolios, and "buy" 10 shares of each.
- Guide students in looking up the abbreviations for their companies and finding the "Last" share price.

- Have them calculate the values of their portfolios.
- Challenge them to track the changing value of their stock shares over several days. Then have them find the amount of money and percentage of total value their portfolio gained or lost.

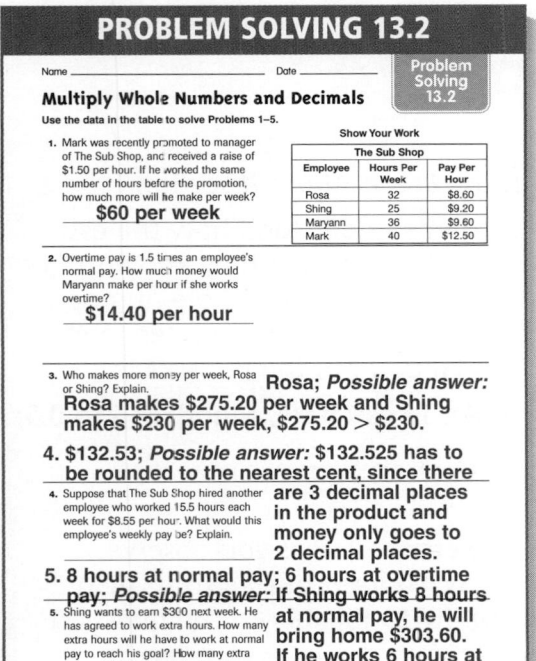

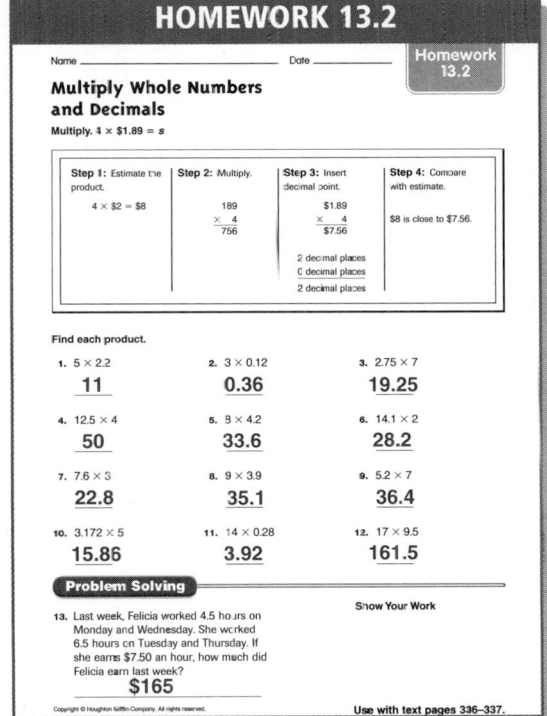

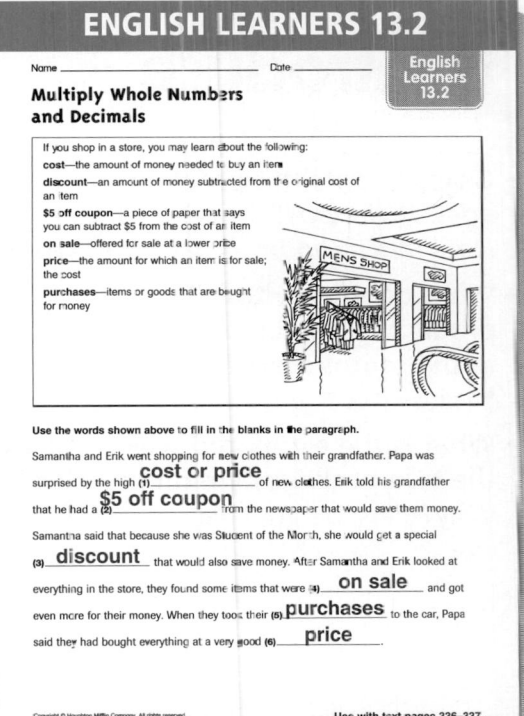

Homework Workbook Page 84

TEACHING LESSON 13.2

LESSON ORGANIZER

Objective Find the product of a whole number and a decimal.

Resources Reteach, Practice, Enrichment, Problem-Solving, Homework, English Learners, Transparencies, and Math Center

Materials None

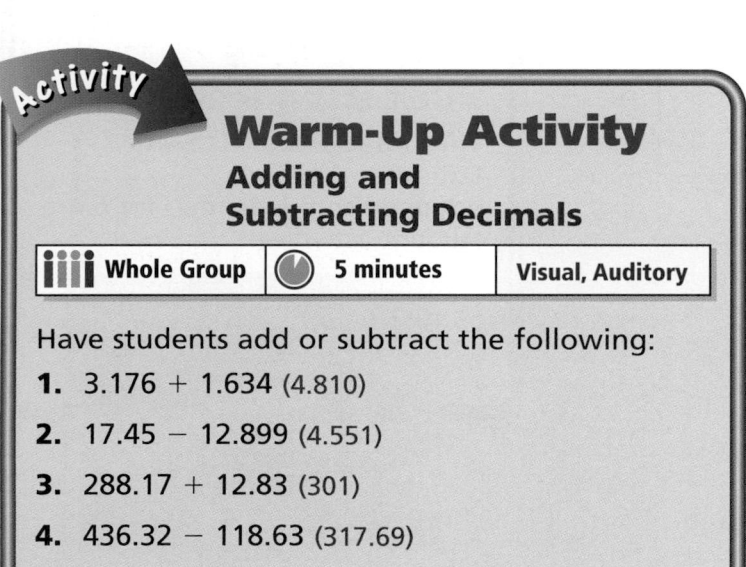

Warm-Up Activity
Adding and Subtracting Decimals

👥 Whole Group	🕐 5 minutes	Visual, Auditory

Have students add or subtract the following:

1. 3.176 + 1.634 (4.810)
2. 17.45 − 12.899 (4.551)
3. 288.17 + 12.83 (301)
4. 436.32 − 118.63 (317.69)
5. 1009.1 − 840.26 (168.84)

Multiply Whole Numbers and Decimals

Objective Find the product of a whole number and a decimal.

Vocabulary
estimate
product

Learn About It

Lian bought 3 caps that were on sale. How much did Lian pay for the caps?

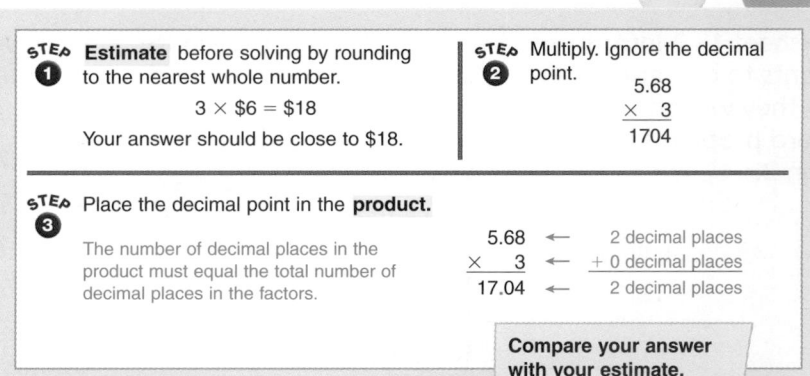
CAPS ON SALE!
$5.68 each

Multiply. 3 × $5.68 = *c*

STEP 1 Estimate before solving by rounding to the nearest whole number.

3 × $6 = $18

Your answer should be close to $18.

STEP 2 Multiply. Ignore the decimal point.

$$\begin{array}{r} 5.68 \\ \times\ \ 3 \\ \hline 1704 \end{array}$$

STEP 3 Place the decimal point in the **product.**

The number of decimal places in the product must equal the total number of decimal places in the factors.

$$\begin{array}{r} 5.68 \\ \times\ \ \ 3 \\ \hline 17.04 \end{array}$$ ← 2 decimal places
← + 0 decimal places
← 2 decimal places

Compare your answer with your estimate.

$18 is close to $17.04.

An answer of $17.04 is a reasonable answer.

Solution: Lian paid $17.04 for the caps.

Another Example

Find 14 × 0.45.

$$\begin{array}{r} 0.45 \\ \times\ \ 14 \\ \hline 180 \\ 450 \\ \hline 6.30 \end{array}$$ ← 2 decimal places
← + 0 decimal places

← 2 decimal places

Guided Practice

Find each product.

1. 4 × 1.3
   5.2
2. 2.6 × 5
   13
3. 0.59 × 8
   4.72
4. 6 × 1.82
   10.92
5. 3.25 × 16
   52
6. 0.515 × 7
   3.605

Ask Yourself
- Did I estimate first?
- Did I use the correct number of decimal places in my answer?

Explain Your Thinking ▶ Why does it help to estimate before you find the exact answer? **Estimating before you solve helps you know what to expect when you find the exact answer.**

---

1 Introduce

- Give students this problem: *Ivan was mailing two packages at the post office. Each one weighed 3.7 pounds. How much did both packages weigh?*

- **What do we multiply?** (3.7 × 2) **How can we estimate the product?** (Round to the nearest full pound.) **What is the digit in the tenths place?** (7) **Do we round up? Why?** (yes, because it is 5 or greater)

- **What is the estimated weight of each package?** (4 lb) **Will the two packages weigh more or less than 8 pounds? Why?** (less, because we rounded up)

2 Develop

Guide students through the *Learn About It* section.

- In Step 1, make sure students understand how the estimate was derived. In Step 2, make sure they know to first multiply the two factors as if they were whole numbers: 3 × 568 = 1704. In Step 3, make sure they understand where to place the decimal point in the product.

- Go over *Another Example.* **To estimate, round 0.45 to 0.5; 14 × 5 = 70.**

Guided Practice

Have students complete **Exercises 1–6** as you observe. Remind them to use the *Ask Yourself* questions to help. Give students the opportunity to talk about the question in *Explain Your Thinking.*

Find each product.

7. 6 × 2.4 **14.4**	**8.** 3.8 × 2 **7.6**	**9.** 9.6 × 8 **76.8**	**10.** 9 × 5.6 **50.4**	**11.** 0.13 × 5 **0.65**
12. 3 × 3.4 **10.2**	**13.** 9 × 0.18 **1.62**	**14.** 0.1 × 13 **1.3**	**15.** 8 × 10.8 **86.4**	**16.** 3 × 31.44 **94.32**
17. 7 × 7.7 **53.9**	**18.** 20.5 × 4 **82**	**19.** 0.9 × 11 **9.9**	**20.** 50.2 × 6 **301.2**	**21.** 4.412 × 8 **35.296**
22. 6 × 9.8 **58.8**	**23.** 12 × 0.56 **6.72**	**24.** 23 × 2.1 **48.3**	**25.** 16 × 9.5 **152**	**26.** 35 × 0.86 **30.1**

X Algebra • **Expressions** Find a value of *n* to make each statement true. *Ex. 27–30: Possible answers are given.*

27. 13 × *n* is between 55 and 65. **4.5**

28. *n* × 138 is between 200 and 250. **1.8**

29. *n* × 11 is between 135 and 140. **12.5**

30. *n* × 25 is between 40 and 45. **1.7**

Solve.

31. Kayla works 8 hours one week and earns $48. If 0.08 of that amount is for taxes, how much money does Kayla have to spend that week? **$44.16**

32. John's cost for a sweater is $21 after his discount of 0.7. Is the price of the sweater before the discount more or less than $42? Explain.
See Additional Answers on Page 349.

33. Sierra worked 3.5 hours on Saturday morning and 2.5 hours on Sunday afternoon. If Sierra earns $9.80 per hour, how much did she earn on Saturday and Sunday? **$58.80**

$20

34. **Analyze** Because his father works at the store, Gavin pays only 0.7 of the marked price on clothing. Wayne has a coupon for $5 off any jacket. Who will pay the least for the jacket at the right? Explain how you decided.
Gavin. Gavin pays 0.7 × 20 = $14 while Wayne pays 20 − 5 = $15. 14 < 15

Daily Review	**Test Prep**
Add. (Ch. 11, Lesson 2)	**43.** **Free Response** Grant's purchases at the grocery store come to $130. He saves 0.2 of this by using coupons. How much does Grant pay after using the coupons? **$104**
35. 1.8 + 3.246 **5.046** **36.** 4.01 + 5.07 **9.08**	
37. 3.02 + 4.08 **7.1** **38.** 5.02 + 2.88 **7.9**	
39. 8.6 + 3.4 **12** **40.** 3.21 + 3.22 **6.43**	Explain how you got your answer.
41. 6.90 + 1.1 **8** **42.** 0.35 + 0.07 **0.42**	

Extra Practice See page 349, Set B.

DAILY TEST PREP

Which is the product of 12 and 3.45? (B)

A. 414   C. 4.14

B. 41.4   D. 0.414

Activity

Lesson Intervention

Where's the Point?

Or use Intervention CD-ROM Lesson 13.2

👤👤👤 Small Group	🕐 5–10 minutes	Visual, Auditory

- Put these three problems on the chalkboard in vertical form: *3 × 125, 3 × 12.5, 3 × 1.25.*

- Multiply to find the first product, 375. **Where is the decimal point in this product?** (after the 5, because 3 and 125 are whole numbers)

- Write the same digits as the product of the second multiplication. **How many decimal places are in the second factor?** (1) **How many decimal places should there be in the product?** (1) **How do you know where to put it?** (Count back 1 place from the right of the 5.)

- Follow a similar procedure for the third multiplication.

- Point out that the digits in each product are the same, but the decimal goes in a different place.

---

3 Practice

Assign **Exercises 7–43** as independent work.

- *Exercises 7–26* Have students discuss their answers.

- *Algebra • Expressions for Exercises 27–30* Have students explain their method of finding a value for *n*.

- *Problem Solving for Problems 31–34* Have students discuss and share their answers.

Common Error

Misplaced decimal point in the product Suggest that students compare their answer with their estimate as a guide to locating the decimal point in the product.

4 Assess and Close

- **How do you place the decimal point in the product when you multiply a whole number and a decimal?** (number of places in product is same as total number of places in factors)

- **Why estimate the product?** (It helps to place the decimal point in the exact product, to see if answer is reasonable.)

Assign the **LESSON QUIZ** on Transparency 13.2 to further assess student understanding.

Keeping a Journal

Have students write a few sentences explaining how to multiply a decimal and a whole number, and why estimating the product is useful.

Estimate Products

PLANNING THE LESSON

MATHEMATICS OBJECTIVE
Use rounding to estimate products of decimals.

Use Lesson Planner CD-ROM for Lesson 13.3.

Daily Routines

Vocabulary
Remind students how to ***round down*** and ***round up***.

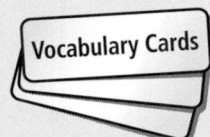
Vocabulary Cards

Meeting North Carolina's Standards
Prepare for Grade 6 Objective **1.04** Develop fluency in addition, subtraction, multiplication, and division of nonnegative rational numbers.

Lesson Transparency
13.3

Problem of the Day
A number is doubled and then increased by 300. Then 50 is subtracted from the result. The final number is 404. Find the original number. (77)

Quick Review
Estimate the product.
1. 61×44 (2,400)
2. 619×8 (4,800)
3. 240×12 (2,400)
4. 41×58 (2,400)
5. 82×29 (2,400)

Lesson Quiz
Estimate each product.
1. 0.41×27 (12)
2. 9×0.221 (1.8)
3. 6×6.55 (42)
4. 52×4.145 (200)
5. 40×7.41 (280)

LEVELED PRACTICE

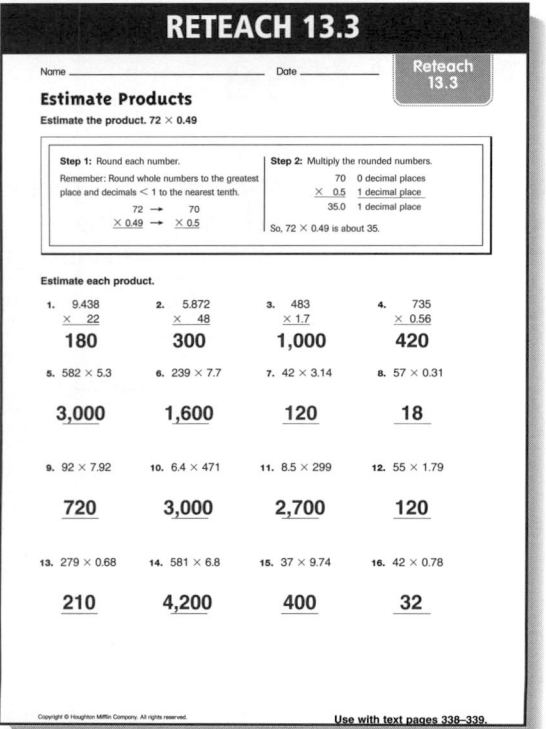

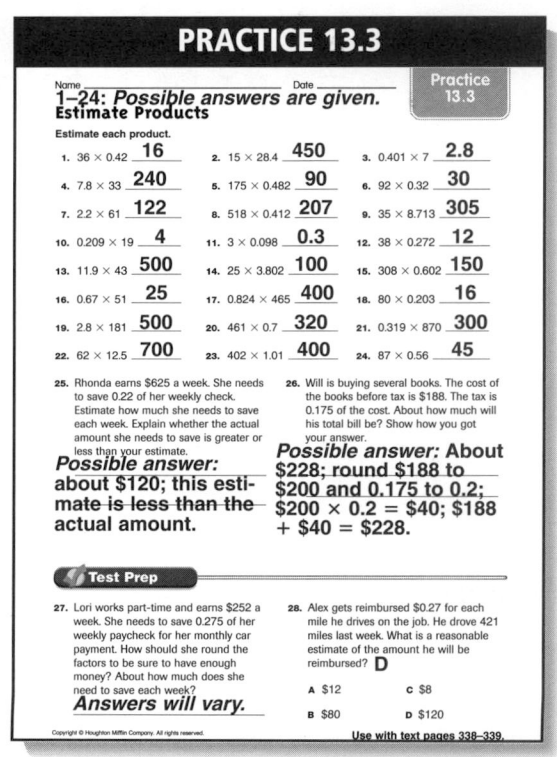

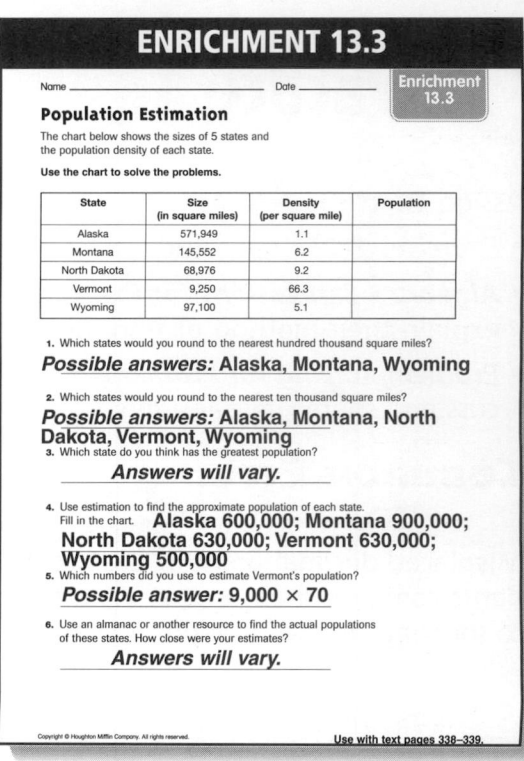

Practice Workbook Page 85

Reaching All Learners
Differentiated Instruction

English Learners

Worksheet 13.3 uses antonym pairs to teach students vocabulary they will use as they estimate products.

Special Needs
VISUAL, AUDITORY

- Display: *1.6*. Review the rule for rounding numbers. Explain that if the digit to the right of the number is less than 5, round down; 5 or more, round up. **How do we round 1.6?** (Digit to the right of whole number is more than 5, so round up.) **What is 1.6 rounded up to the nearest whole number?** (2) Repeat with 1.9, 1.3.

Early Finishers
VISUAL, AUDITORY

- On a sheet of paper, have students write two examples of 4-place decimal numbers to be rounded first to the nearest hundredth, then to the nearest tenth, and then to the nearest whole number.
- Have students exchange examples with partners and round each other's numbers.

TECHNOLOGY

Spiral Review

You can prepare students for standardized tests with **customized** spiral review on key skills using the *Ways to Assess* CD-ROM.

Lesson Planner

You can use the Lesson Planner CD-ROM to create a report of the lessons and standards you have taught.

eBook

eMathbook allows students to review lessons and do homework without carrying their textbooks home.

Houghton Mifflin
Math

e MathBook

Science Connection

Rounding Liquid Measures

- Explain to students that most scientists use the metric system to measure fluids; however, before the metric system was adopted, fluid measures were often in fluid ounces, liquid pints, and gallons. Display the following: 16 ounces = 1 pint;

8 pints = 1 gallon

- Have students round to the nearest hundredth: How many ml are in 1 fluid ounce? (exact: 29.576; rounded 29.58) How many mL are in 1 pint? (exact: 473.216; rounded 473.22) How many ml are in 1 gallon? (exact: 3,785.728; rounded: 3,785.73)

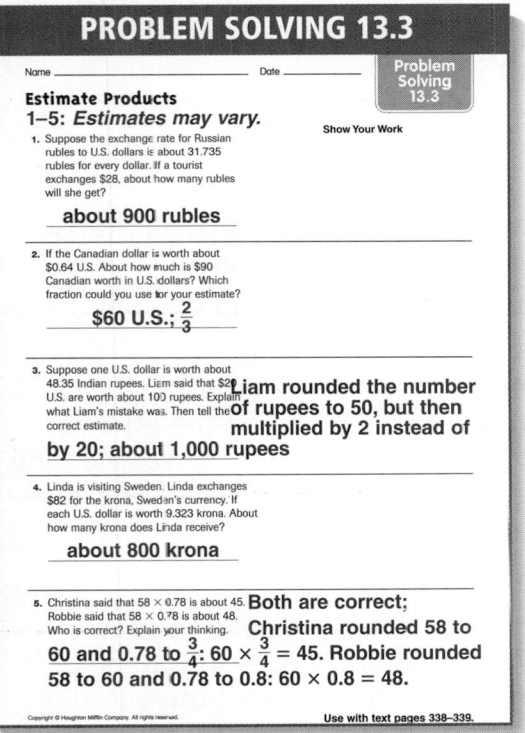

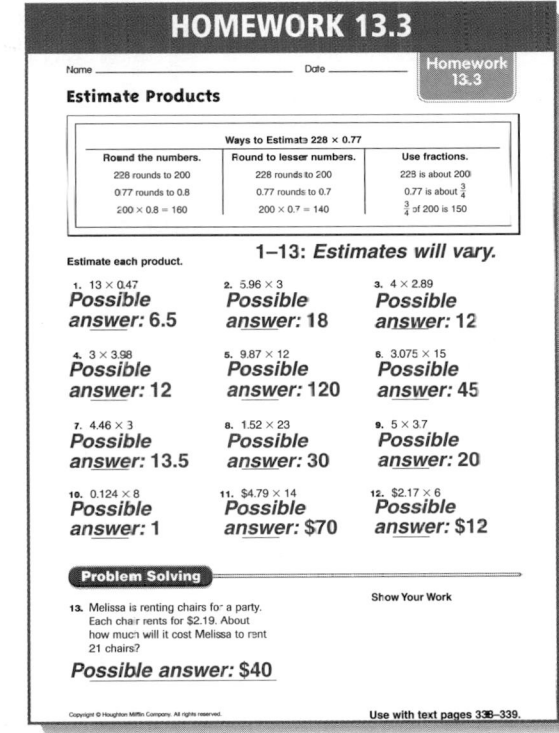

TEACHING LESSON 13.3

LESSON ORGANIZER

Objective Use rounding to estimate products of decimals.

Resources Reteach, Practice, Enrichment, Problem-Solving, Homework, English Learners, Transparencies, and Math Center

Materials None

Warm-Up Activity
Rounding Up or Down?

|  Small Group | 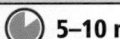 5–10 minutes | Visual, Auditory |

- Tell students they are going to estimate the product 4 × 3.3. **Should we round 3.3 down or up? Why?** (down, because the tenths digit is 3) **What should we round it to?** (3.0) **What is 4 × 3?** (12)

- Now ask students to round 4 × 3.6. **Do we round 3.6 up or down? Why?** (up, because the tenths digit is 6) **What should we round 3.6 to?** (4) **What is 4 × 4?** (16)

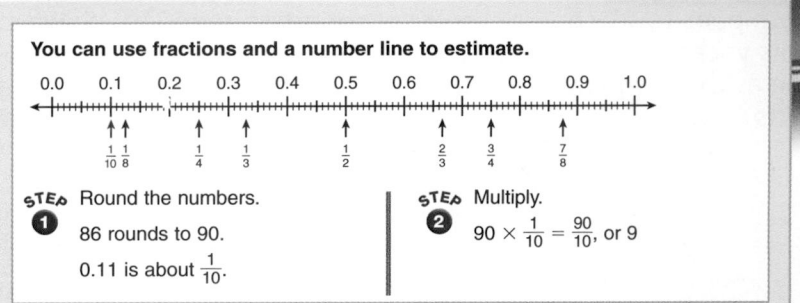

Lesson 3
Estimate Products

Objective Use rounding to estimate products of decimals.

Learn About It

When Isaac's father makes a call on his cell phone, it costs 11 cents for each minute the call lasts. About how much did it cost Isaac to talk on his father's cell phone for 86 minutes after school?

Estimate the product. 86 × $0.11

You can use fractions and a number line to estimate.

```
0.0   0.1   0.2   0.3   0.4   0.5   0.6   0.7   0.8   0.9   1.0
 |     |     |     |     |     |     |     |     |     |     |
      1/10 1/8      1/4  1/3       1/2       2/3  3/4       7/8
```

STEP 1 Round the numbers.

86 rounds to 90.

0.11 is about $\frac{1}{10}$.

STEP 2 Multiply.

$90 \times \frac{1}{10} = \frac{90}{10}$, or 9

Solution: It cost about $9 for Isaac's phone call.

You can round each factor to a greater or lesser number, depending on whether you want a high or a low estimate.

Other Examples

A. Lesser Numbers

Estimate 328 × 0.62.

$$\begin{array}{rcl} 328 & \to & 300 \\ \times\ 0.62 & \to & \times\ 0.6 \\ & \to & 180 \end{array}$$

Since both factors were rounded to a lesser number, the actual product must be greater than 180.

B. Greater and Lesser Numbers

Estimate 0.34 × 359.

$0.34 \approx \frac{1}{3}$

$359 \approx 360$

$\frac{1}{3} \times \overset{120}{\cancel{360}} \approx 120$

338

---

1 Introduce

- On the chalkboard, write the problem: *60 × 0.34*. **What is 0.34 rounded to the nearest tenth?** (0.3) **What is 60 × 0.3?** (18) **Is that a high or a low estimate?** (low, because 0.34 was rounded down to 0.3) **Will the actual product be greater or less than 18?** (greater, because we rounded down.)

- Now write *60 × 0.38*. **Should we round down or up? Why?** (up, because 8 is greater than 5) **Will the actual product be greater or less than 24? Explain.** (less, because we rounded up.)

2 Develop

Guide students through the *Learn About It* section.

- **Look at Step 1.** Make sure students understand that 86 was rounded up and 0.11 was rounded down.

- **Look at Step 2.** Point out it can be helpful to write decimals as fractions.

- Go over *Other Examples*. In the first example, point out that both factors were rounded down, so the estimate will be lower than the actual product. In the second, one factor was rounded down and the other, up. The actual product may be greater or less than 120.

Guided Practice

Have students complete **Exercises 1–6** as you observe. Remind them to use the *Ask Yourself* questions to help. Give students the opportunity to talk about the question in *Explain Your Thinking.*

Guided Practice

Estimate each product.

Ask Yourself
• How can I round each number?
• Can I easily use fractions?

1. 6.572
   × 18 **140**

2. 122
   × 0.24 **30**

3. 532
   × 1.7 **1,000**

4. 87 × 3.12 **270**

5. 32 × 0.48 **16**

6. 2.5 × 351 **1,200**

Explain Your Thinking ▶ How does your estimated product in Exercise 6 compare with the actual product? Explain. *Possible answer: The actual product is less than the estimated product because both factors were rounded up.*

Practice and Problem Solving

Estimate each product. Ex. 7–14: *Possible answers are given.*

7. 0.23 × 41 **10**

8. 8 × 0.119 **0.8**

9. 12.7 × 32 **300**

10. 209 × 0.467 **100**

11. 6.6 × 27 **210**

12. 0.45 × 80 **40**

13. 3.5 × 58 **240**

14. 25 × 7.92 **200**

Data Use the table for Problems 15–19.

The table shows the current cellular phone plan Mr. Henry uses and two alternate plans to which he may consider switching.

Plan	Peak Minute Cost	Off-Peak Minute Cost
Current Plan	$0.350	$0.055
Alternate 1	$0.700	Free
Alternate 2	$0.125	$0.125

15. **Estimate** Last month, Mr. Henry's cellular phone bill included 135 peak minutes and 240 off-peak minutes. About how much was this bill? *Possible answer: $64*

16. **Explain** If a person uses 100 peak and 100 off-peak minutes each month, which plan is least expensive to use? *See Additional Answers on Page 349.*

17. Which calling plan has the greatest difference between peak and off-peak charges? How much is the difference? **Alternate 1: $0.70/min.**

18. **Calculator** A customer with Alternate 1 plan has a bill of $35. The customer used the same number of peak and off-peak minutes each month. How many minutes each was that? **50 minutes each**

19. Mr. Henry's average bill includes 98 peak minutes and 516 off-peak minutes. Should he switch plans or stay with the one he has? Explain your reasoning. *See Additional Answers on Page 349.*

Daily Review   Test Prep

Write each sum or difference in simplest form. (Ch. 10, Lessons 2 and 5)

20. $\frac{1}{4} + \frac{1}{4}$ **$\frac{1}{2}$**

21. $\frac{3}{7} + \frac{2}{7}$ **$\frac{5}{7}$**

22. $\frac{7}{8} - \frac{3}{8}$ **$\frac{1}{2}$**

23. $\frac{5}{9} - \frac{2}{9}$ **$\frac{1}{3}$**

24. $\frac{3}{5} + \frac{7}{5}$ **2**

25. $\frac{6}{3} - \frac{3}{3}$ **1**

26. A box of crackers costs $0.296 per ounce. Which is a reasonable estimate for the cost of a 12-ounce box of those crackers?

   A $2.00   **C** $4.00

   B $6.00   D $12.00

Extra Practice See page 349, Set C.

Test Prep Transparency 13.3

DAILY TEST PREP

What is a reasonable estimate for the cost of a 16-ounce package of spaghetti, if the unit price is $0.047 per ounce? ($0.80)

Activity

Lesson Intervention
Rounding Decimals

Or use Intervention CD-ROM Lesson 13.3

| Whole Group | 5–10 minutes | Visual, Auditory |

• Display 2.163. Underline the hundredths place. Round to the nearest hundredth.

• Circle the place you have to look in order to round to the nearest hundredth. (thousandth place–3) Do we round up or down? (down) Why? (3 is less than 5) Write the number rounded to the nearest hundredth. (2.160)

• Repeat for rounding to the nearest tenth and whole number. (2.20; 2.0)

③ Practice

Assign **Exercises 7–26** as independent work.

• *Exercises 7–14* Have students discuss their answers.

• *Problem Solving for Problems 15–19* For Problems 15–16, have students explain and discuss their answers. For Problems 17–19, have students discuss and share their reasons for their answers.

Common Error

Misplaced decimal point Sometimes the estimated product may be a whole number. Students may forget to place a decimal point in the product. Remind them to make sure to place a decimal point in the product.

④ Assess and Close

When will the actual product be less than the estimated product? (when one or both factors have been rounded up)

When would it be difficult to know whether the actual product is greater or lesser than the estimate? (when one factor is rounded up and the other is rounded down)

Assign the **LESSON QUIZ** on Transparency 13.3 to further assess student understanding.

Keeping a Journal

Have students write a few sentences explaining the difference between an estimated and an actual product in these cases: rounding one or both factors up; down; rounding one up, one down.

Multiply Decimals

PLANNING THE LESSON

MATHEMATICS OBJECTIVE
Find the product of two decimals.

Use Lesson Planner CD-ROM for Lesson 13.4.

Daily Routines

Vocabulary

Explain to students that when an approximate answer is called for, it is expressed with the symbol that stands for **about equal to**. Write the symbol on the chalkboard: ≈. Explain that the symbol can also be defined as *approximately*. When you see this symbol, the answer given is an estimated value.

Vocabulary Cards

Meeting North Carolina's Standards

Prepare for Grade 6 Objective **1.04** Develop fluency in addition, subtraction, multiplication, and division of nonnegative rational numbers.

Lesson Transparency **13.4**

Problem of the Day

The sum of four decimals is 9. Each decimal is 0.5 greater than the previous decimal. What are the decimals? (1.5, 2.0, 2.5, 3.0)

Quick Review

Add mentally.

1. $20 + 40 + 80$ (140)
2. $50 + 60 + 40$ (150)
3. $60 + 90 + 40$ (190)
4. $90 + 900 + 3,000$ (3,990)
5. $500 + 4,000 + 500$ (5,000)

Lesson Quiz

Multiply.

1. 0.5×0.6 (0.3)
2. 0.8×0.2 (0.16)
3. 0.32×0.4 (0.128)
4. 4.7×2.1 (9.87)
5. 1.75×7.2 (12.6)

LEVELED PRACTICE

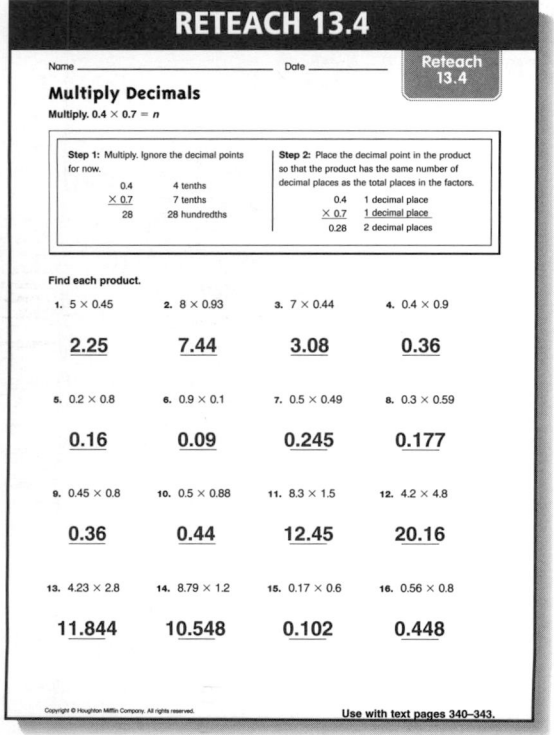

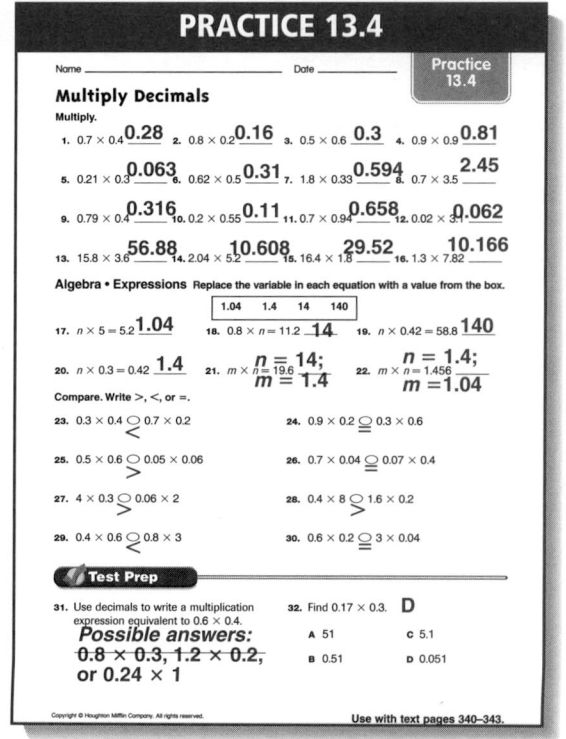

RETEACH 13.4

Multiply Decimals
Multiply. $0.4 \times 0.7 = n$

Step 1: Multiply. Ignore the decimal points for now.	Step 2: Place the decimal point in the product so that the product has the same number of decimal places as the total places in the factors.
0.4 4 tenths × 0.7 7 tenths 28 28 hundredths	0.4 1 decimal place × 0.7 1 decimal place 0.28 2 decimal places

Find each product.

1. 5×0.45 **2.25**
2. 8×0.93 **7.44**
3. 7×0.44 **3.08**
4. 0.4×0.9 **0.36**
5. 0.2×0.8 **0.16**
6. 0.9×0.1 **0.09**
7. 0.5×0.49 **0.245**
8. 0.3×0.59 **0.177**
9. 0.45×0.8 **0.36**
10. 0.5×0.88 **0.44**
11. 8.3×1.5 **12.45**
12. 4.2×4.8 **20.16**
13. 4.23×2.8 **11.844**
14. 8.79×1.2 **10.548**
15. 0.17×0.6 **0.102**
16. 0.56×0.8 **0.448**

Use with text pages 340–343.

PRACTICE 13.4

Multiply Decimals
Multiply.

1. 0.7×0.4 **0.28**
2. 0.8×0.2 **0.16**
3. 0.5×0.6 **0.3**
4. 0.9×0.9 **0.81**
5. 0.21×0.3 **0.063**
6. 0.62×0.5 **0.31**
7. 1.8×0.33 **0.594**
8. 0.7×3.5 **2.45**
9. 0.79×0.4 **0.316**
10. 0.2×0.55 **0.11**
11. 0.7×0.94 **0.658**
12. 0.02×3 **0.062**
13. 15.8×3.6 **56.88**
14. 2.04×5.2 **10.608**
15. 16.4×1.8 **29.52**
16. 1.3×7.82 **10.166**

Algebra • Expressions Replace the variable in each equation with a value from the box.

| 1.04 | 1.4 | 14 | 140 |

17. $n \times 5 = 5.2$ **1.04**
18. $0.8 \times n = 11.2$ **14**
19. $n \times 0.42 = 58.8$ **140**
20. $n \times 0.3 = 0.42$ **1.4**
21. $m \times n = 19.6$ **n = 14; m = 1.4**
22. $m \times n = 1.456$ **n = 1.4; m = 1.04**

Compare. Write >, <, or =.

23. 0.3×0.4 ◯ 0.7×0.2 **<**
24. 0.9×0.2 ◯ 0.3×0.6
25. 0.5×0.6 ◯ 0.05×0.06 **>**
26. 0.7×0.04 ◯ 0.07×0.4
27. 4×0.3 ◯ 0.06×2 **>**
28. 0.4×8 ◯ 1.6×0.2
29. 0.4×0.6 ◯ 0.8×3
30. 0.6×0.2 ◯ 3×0.04

Test Prep

31. Use decimals to write a multiplication expression equivalent to 0.6×0.4.
Possible answers:
0.8×0.3, 1.2×0.2, or 0.24×1

32. Find 0.17×0.3. **D**
A 51   C 5.1
B 0.51   D 0.051

Use with text pages 340–343.

ENRICHMENT 13.4

How Much Land?
Mr. Rodriguez bought land to give to his family. He wants to give his wife 0.45 of the land, his daughter 0.25 of the land, and to each of his two nephews he wants to give 0.15 of the land.

1. Mr. Rodriguez bought his family 1.75 acres in Florida. How many decimal places will there be in each product?
4

2. How much of the land will each family member receive?
wife 0.7875 acre; daughter 0.4375 acre, each nephew 0.2625 acre

3. Suppose Mr. Rodriguez decides to add to his daughter's gift the land he had designated for his nephews. How much of the 1.75 acres will she now receive?
0.9625 acre

4. In New York, Mr. Rodriguez purchased a house on a 0.8-acre lot. How much of that land will each family member receive?
wife 0.36 acre, daughter 0.2 acre, each nephew 0.12 acre

5. Mr. Rodriguez purchased 2.3 times as much land in California than he did in Florida. How much land did he purchase in California?
4.025 acres

6. Mr. Rodriguez gives his family the land in California. How many decimal places are there in each portion of land received by his family? Explain how you know.
5; Possible answer: The land in California goes to 3 decimal places. Family members get land to 2 decimal places, and $3 + 2 = 5$.

Use with text pages 340–343.

Practice Workbook Page 86

Reaching All Learners

Differentiated Instruction

English Learners

Worksheet 13.4 introduces students to content vocabulary they will encounter in Lesson 4.

Inclusion

VISUAL, TACTILE

- Write vertically on the chalkboard: *0.8 × 0.4.* **Multiply 8 and 4 as if they were whole numbers. What is 8 × 4?** (32) Write *32* as the product.
- **How many decimal places are in 0.8?** (1) **How many in 0.4?** (1) **How many decimal places altogether?** (2)
- **Where does the decimal point go?** (Count two places to the left from the end of the product.)
- Place the point. **What is 0.8 × 0.4?** (0.32 or 32 hundredths)

Gifted and Talented

VISUAL, AUDITORY

- Have students write 8 problems in which a decimal is multiplied by a decimal, then use pairs of problems to write 4 comparisons of products. Tell them to leave a blank for the <, >, or = sign, for example: *0.2 × 0.8 _____ 0.3 × 0.8.*
- Ask students to exchange problems. Have them write the sign that should go in each problem and discuss.

TECHNOLOGY

Spiral Review

You can prepare students for standardized tests with **customized** spiral review on key skills using the *Ways to Assess* CD-ROM.

Education Place

You can visit Education Place at eduplace.com/math/mw/ for teacher support materials.

Literature Connection

The Largest Numbers

- Discuss a book on large numbers such as *On Beyond a Million: An Amazing Math Journey* by David M. Schwartz (Bantam Doubleday Dell Books for Young Readers, 1999).
- Explain that it presents very large numbers and explores expressing them as powers of ten.

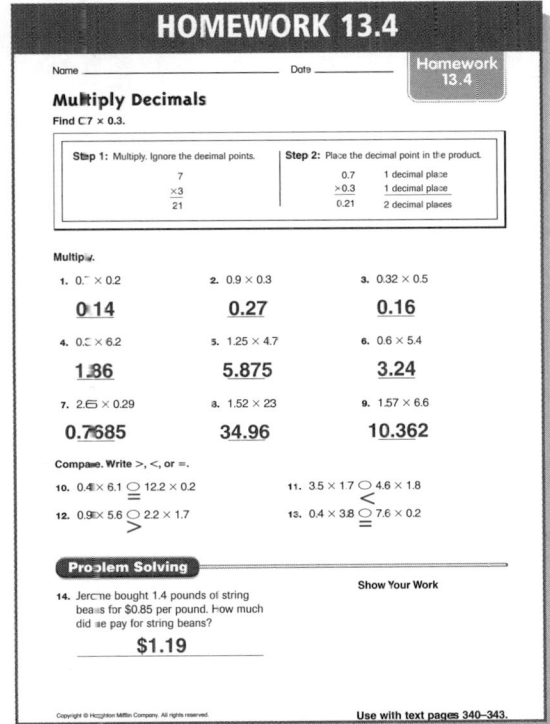

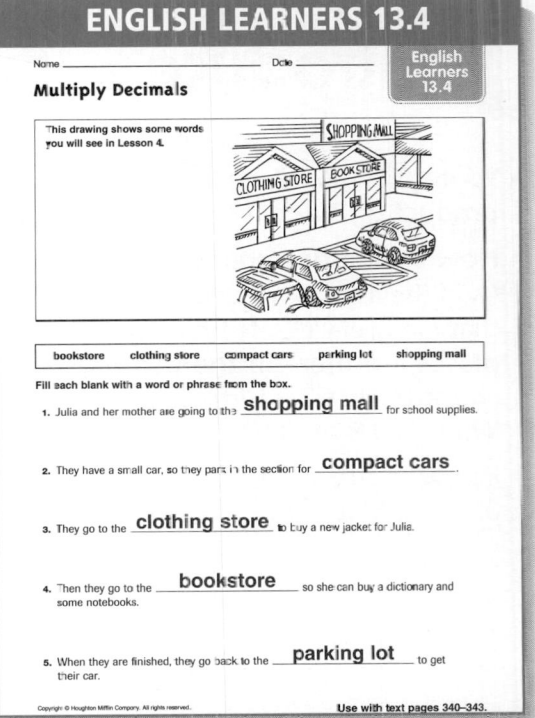

Homework Workbook Page 86

TEACHING LESSON 13.4

LESSON ORGANIZER

Objective Find the product of two decimals.

Resources Reteach, Practice, Enrichment, Problem-Solving, Homework, English Learners, Transparencies, and Math Center

Materials Centimeter Grid Transparency, two colored markers

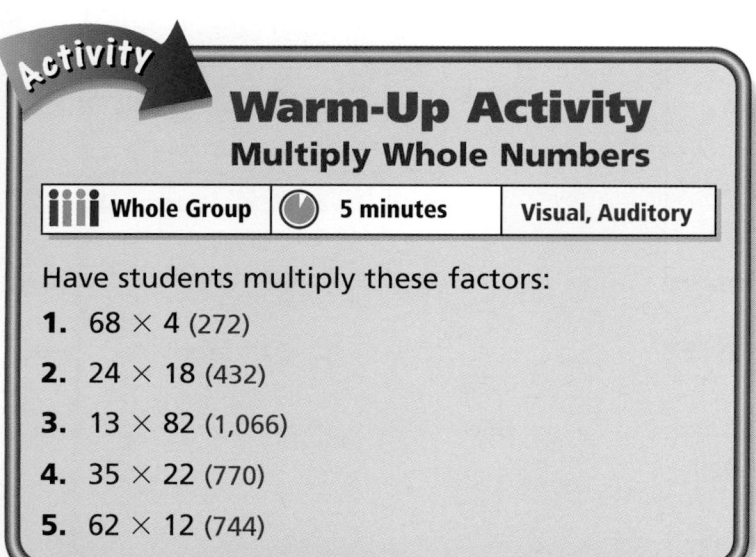

Warm-Up Activity
Multiply Whole Numbers

Whole Group	5 minutes	Visual, Auditory

Have students multiply these factors:

1. 68 × 4 (272)
2. 24 × 18 (432)
3. 13 × 82 (1,066)
4. 35 × 22 (770)
5. 62 × 12 (744)

Multiply Decimals

Objective Find the product of two decimals.

Learn About It MathTracks 2/4 Listen and Understand

The parking lot at the shopping mall covers 0.9 acre. Three tenths of the parking lot is reserved for compact cars. How large is the area reserved for compact cars?

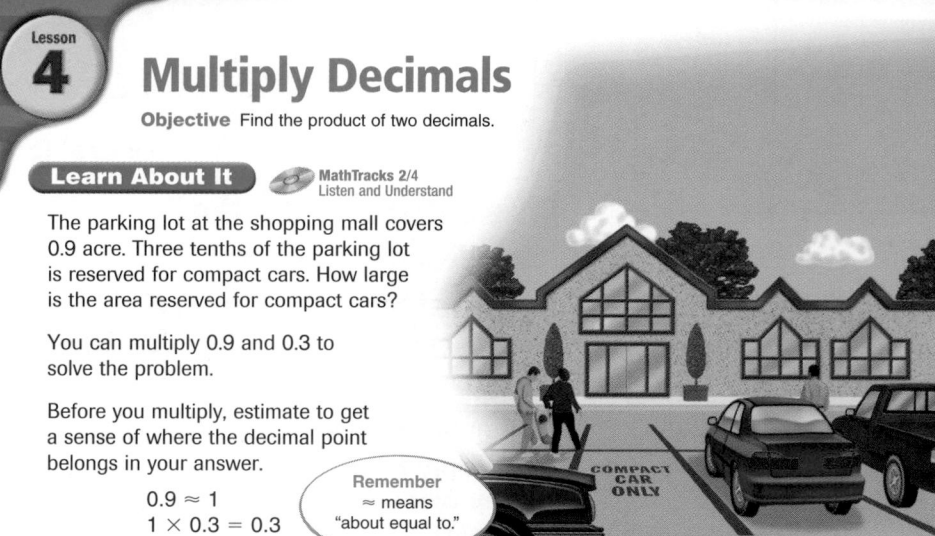

You can multiply 0.9 and 0.3 to solve the problem.

Before you multiply, estimate to get a sense of where the decimal point belongs in your answer.

$$0.9 \approx 1$$
$$1 \times 0.3 = 0.3$$

Remember ≈ means "about equal to."

The answer should be a little less than 0.3.

Multiply. $0.9 \times 0.3 = n$

Multiply and then place the decimal point.

STEP 1 Multiply. Ignore the decimal points.

$$\begin{array}{r} 3 \\ \times\ 9 \\ \hline 27 \end{array}$$

STEP 2 Place the decimal point in the product.

$$\begin{array}{r} 0.3 \leftarrow \quad \text{1 decimal place} \\ \times\ 0.9 \leftarrow +\ \text{1 decimal place} \\ \hline 0.27 \leftarrow \quad \text{2 decimal places} \end{array}$$

Use fractions to check.
$$\frac{3}{10} \times \frac{9}{10} = \frac{3 \times 9}{10 \times 10}$$
$$= \frac{27}{100}, \text{ or } 0.27$$

Solution: In the parking lot, 0.27 acre is reserved for compact cars.

Other Examples

A. Factor in Hundredths

$$\begin{array}{r} 0.71 \leftarrow \quad \text{2 decimal places} \\ \times\ 0.9 \leftarrow +\ \text{1 decimal place} \\ \hline 0.639 \leftarrow \quad \text{3 decimal places} \end{array}$$

B. Factors Greater Than 1

$$\begin{array}{r} 1.43 \leftarrow \quad \text{2 decimal places} \\ \times\ 3.2 \leftarrow +\ \text{1 decimal place} \\ \hline 286 \\ 4290 \\ \hline 4.576 \leftarrow \quad \text{3 decimal places} \end{array}$$

340

---

1 Introduce

• Write *0.8 × 0.02* vertically on the chalkboard. **What is the product of 8 and 2?** (16) Write *16* below the problem.

• **How do we determine where to place the decimal point?** (Add the number of decimal places in the factors and count that many places left from the 6 in 16.) **How many decimal places are there in the factors?** (3) Have the students count back 1-2-3 with you as you move left from the 6. **What is 0.8 × 0.02?** (0.016)

• Follow a similar procedure for 0.7 × 0.02 (0.014) and 0.6 × 0.03 (0.018)

2 Develop

Guide students through the *Learn About It* section.

• Be sure students understand that the problem asks to find three tenths of 0.9, or 0.3 × 0.9.

• **Look at Step 1. What is the first thing to do?** (Multiply 9 and 3.)

• **Look at Step 2. How do you know where to put the decimal point in 27?** (Add the number of decimal places in each factor and count that many places left from the 7.)

Ask Yourself
- Did I count the number of decimal places in the product correctly?

TEST TIPS

Multiply.

1.	0.6 $\times\ 0.4$ 0.24	2.	0.6 $\times\ 5$ 3	3.	0.46 $\times\ 2$ 0.92

4. 0.8×0.34 **0.272** 5. 4.28×1.2 **5.136** 6. 0.23×0.7 **0.161**

TEST TIPS **Explain Your Thinking** ▶ Look back at Exercise 1. Why would 24 be an unreasonable answer to 0.6×0.4? **Since there are two decimal places in the two factors the answer could not be a whole number.**

 **Practice and Problem Solving**

Multiply.

7.	0.5 $\times\ 0.5$ 0.25	8.	0.9 $\times\ 0.2$ 0.18	9.	0.4 $\times\ 0.7$ 0.28	10.	0.7 $\times\ 0.3$ 0.21	11.	0.6 $\times\ 0.9$ 0.54
12.	1.6 $\times\ 0.8$ 1.28	13.	4.5 $\times\ 0.7$ 3.15	14.	0.47 $\times\ 0.3$ 0.141	15.	1.34 $\times\ 0.2$ 0.268	16.	9.53 $\times\ 0.6$ 5.718

17. 0.8×0.22 **0.176** 18. 0.68×0.5 **0.34** 19. 0.4×0.44 **0.176** 20. 0.8×0.62 **0.496**

21. 0.92×0.3 **0.276** 22. 8.34×4.7 **39.198** 23. 12.3×5.4 **66.42** 24. 1.66×2.2 **3.652**

X Algebra • **Expressions** Choose the value for the variables from the box that makes each equation true.

25. $n \times 4 = 0.08$ **0.02** 26. $n \times 0.1 = 0.2$ **2**

27. $16 \times n = 35.2$ **2.2** 28. $n^2 = 4.84$ **2.2**

2		2.2
0.02	0.2	

29. $n \times 8 = 1.6$ **0.2** 30. $n \times 0.5 = 0.1$ **0.2**

31. $a \times b = 4.4$ **2; 2.2** 32. $a \times b = 0.4$ **2; 0.2**

Compare. Write >, <, or =.

33. 0.4×0.5 0.2×0.6 **>** 34. 0.8×0.4 ⬤ 0.7×0.5 **<**

35. 4×0.9 ⬤ 6×0.6 **=** 36. 0.2×7 ⬤ 0.7×2 **=**

37. 6×0.05 ⬤ 0.7×0.6 **<** 38. 8×0.1 ⬤ 0.4×2 **=**

Go On ▶

Quick Check Options

The following activities will help students prepare for the Quick Check or may be used as an alternative assessment.

Vocabulary Review *(individual, small group, or whole class)*

Have students review the following vocabulary words by giving an example of how each term is used in this chapter.

- estimate
- product
- factor
- round
- mixed number

Math Conversations *(small group or whole class)*

Have students discuss what they have learned about multiplying decimals in this chapter. Encourage students to ask each other questions to clarify their understanding.

Writing Prompt *(individual or partners)*

To solidify student understanding of vocabulary and concepts, have each student complete the following sentence:

The thing I found easiest about multiplying decimals is _____.

---

3 Practice

Go over *Other Examples*.

- In the first example, point out that both factors are less than 1, and the product is less than 1.
- In the second example, point out that both factors are greater than 1. Remind students that when both factors are greater than 1, the product will be greater than either factor.

Guided Practice

Have students complete **Exercises 1–6** as you observe. Remind them to use the *Ask Yourself* question to help. Give students the opportunity to talk about the question in *Explain Your Thinking.*

Assign **Exercises 7–48** as independent work. Have students discuss their work.

- *Algebra • Expressions for Exercises 25–32* Have students discuss their methods and reasoning.

DAILY TEST PREP

Omar gets an allowance of $15 per week. He saves 0.2 of it. How much does Omar have left to spend? (D)

A. $3   B. $0.30   C. $9   D. $12

Activity

Lesson Intervention
Modeling Products

Or use Intervention CD-ROM Lesson 13.4

| 👤👤👤 Small Group | ⏱ 5–10 minutes | Visual, Kinesthetic |

Materials: *Centimeter Grid Transparency, two colored markers, grid paper*

• Display the transparency. Outline a 10 × 10 grid. Have students copy it onto grid paper. **How many squares are in the grid?** (100)

• Write *0.3 × 0.9* above it. **We can show 0.9 on the grid by shading.** Shade 9 tenths of the grid vertically to represent 0.9. **How can we represent 0.3 of the grid?** (Shade 3 tenths of the grid horizontally to represent 0.3.) Do this as students do the same.

• **How many squares did we shade?** (27) **Since each square represents** $\frac{1}{100}$ **of the 10 × 10 grid, how much do 27 squares represent?** (27 hundredths) **Now write that amount as a decimal.** (0.27)

Solve.

39. A new parking lot at the city swimming pool will cover 0.7 acre. The planners want to use two tenths of the parking lot for handicapped parking. How large is the handicapped parking area? **0.14 acre**

40. At a bookstore, *The World Almanac for Kids* costs $11.95. If you bought that book at the school book sale, you would pay 0.4 of that amount. How much does the book cost at the book sale? **$4.78**

41. Shane walks 1.2 miles to school. Michael's home is 0.6 of the way between Shane's home and school. How far has Shane walked when he reaches Michael's on the way to school? **0.72 miles**

42. Look back at Problem 41. Emma's home is 0.4 of the way between Shane's home and Michael's home. How far is Emma's from Shane's? How far is Emma's from school?
0.288 miles; 1.2 − 0.288 = 0.912 miles from school

Choose a Computation Method ✓

Mental Math • Estimation • Paper and Pencil • Calculator

📊 Data Use the table for Problems 43–46.

43. Last year, Ursula's allowance was $10 a week. The table shows how she spent her money. How much did she spend each week on clothing? **$3**

44. Ursula earned $24.50 from doing yard work. According to her budget, how much of that should she save? **$2.45**

Ursula is keeping the same budget this year. Her allowance is now $17.50 a week.

45. This year, how much should Ursula save in 4 weeks? **$7**

46. How much more will she spend each week on clothes than on food? **$1.75**

Ursula's Budget From Last Year	
Food	$\frac{2}{10}$
Entertainment	$\frac{4}{10}$
Savings	$\frac{1}{10}$
Clothing	$\frac{3}{10}$

48. When you multiply two decimals less than 1, the product is always less than 1.

47. Measurement Draw a line that is 8.6 cm long. Draw a second line that is 0.5 of that length. Draw a third line that is 0.5 the length of the second line. How long is the third line? *Check drawings*; **2.15 cm**

48. Write About It Jennifer multiplied two decimals less than one and got an answer greater than one. Explain to Jennifer why her answer cannot be correct. Use words, examples, and drawings to explain.
See above.

Extra Practice See page 349, Set D.

342

Practice *continued*

Choose a Computation Method

• **Problem Solving for Problems 43–46** Have students share their solutions.

Common Error

Misplaced decimal point in product Have students underline each digit to the right of the decimal point in each factor and count the underlined digits before placing the decimal point in the product.

④ Assess and Close

How do you determine where to place the decimal point in a product when one or more factors are decimals? (Add the number of decimal places in the factors and count left from the last digit in the answer the total number of places.)

Assign the **LESSON QUIZ** on Transparency 13.4 to further assess student understanding.

Quick Check

Check your understanding of Lessons 1–4.

Use models or fractions to multiply. Write each product as a decimal. (Lesson 1)

1. 0.5×0.8 **0.40**
2. 0.2×0.3 **0.06**

Estimate each product. (Lesson 3) **3–4. Possible answers are given.**

3. 0.83×6 **6**
4. 5.22×4.79 **25**

Find each product. (Lessons 2 and 4)

5. 7×0.2 **1.4**
6. 0.4×5 **2**
7. 5.28×7 **36.96**
8. 1.6×0.05 **0.08**
9. 0.9×0.6 **0.54**
10. 0.7×0.7 **0.49**

Number Sense

Math Reasoning

Far, Far Away

You can use scientific notation to write very large numbers.
The mean distance from the Sun to Pluto is about 5 billion, 900 million km.

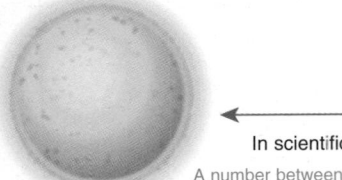

Pluto

←————— 5,900,000,000 km —————→

In scientific notation: 5.9×10^9

A number between 1 and 10 ↗   ↖ A power of 10

Earth is only about 150,000,000 km from the Sun. Try writing that number in scientific notation.

(Hint) $150,000,000 = 1.5 \times 10 \times 10 \times 10 \times 10 \times 10 \times 10 \times 10 \times 10.$

The Andromeda Galaxy is the nearest spiral galaxy to our own galaxy. It is about 21 quintillion km away. That is 21,000,000,000,000,000,000 km. How would you write that distance in scientific notation?

1.5×10^8; 2.1×10^{19} km

Chapter 13 Lesson 4 **343**

Quick Check

Purpose: The Quick Check allows you to assess the students' understanding of the concepts presented in Lessons 1–4.

Items	Objectives Tested	Pages	Intervention
1–2	Use models to explore multiplication with decimals.	334–335	Reteach Resource 13.1 *Ways to Success* 13.1
5–7	Find the product of a whole number and a decimal.	336–337	Reteach Resource 13.2 *Ways to Success* 13.2
3–4	Use rounding to estimate products of decimals.	338–339	Reteach Resource 13.3 *Ways to Success* 13.3
8–10	Find the product of two decimals.	340–342	Reteach Resource 13.4 *Ways to Success* 13.4

Keeping a Journal

Have students write a word problem based on a real-life situation that would involve multiplying decimals. Have students explain how to solve their problem.

Number Sense

Math Reasoning

Far, Far Away

- Have students explain how to represent large numbers in scientific notation. (using the product of a number between 1 and 10 and a power of 10)

- Go over the example of 150,000,000. Then give another example, such as 20,000. (2×10^4) **How can you tell what exponent to use?** (Count the number of places the decimal point was moved to make the first number that is greater than 1 and less than 10.) Discuss the final example.

Zeros in the Product

PLANNING THE LESSON

MATHEMATICS OBJECTIVE
Decide when to write zeros in the products of decimal factors.

Use Lesson Planner CD-ROM for Lesson 13.5.

Daily Routines

Vocabulary

Make sure that students do not confuse the terms *factor* and *product*. Two or more numbers that are multiplied are *factors*. The result of the multiplication is the *product*.

Vocabulary Cards

Meeting North Carolina's Standards
Prepare for Grade 6 Objective **1.04** Develop fluency in addition, subtraction, multiplication, and division of nonnegative rational numbers.

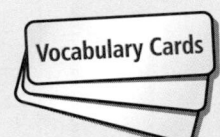
Lesson Transparency
13.5

Problem of the Day
The product of 0.4 and another decimal is greater than 0.3 but less than 0.4. What are the least and greatest decimals, to the nearest hundredth, for the other factor? (0.76, 0.99)

Quick Review
Estimate the product.
1. 6.1×4.2 (24)
2. 1.9×8 (16)
3. 0.24×8 (2)
4. 5.1×5.8 (30)
5. 0.49×0.29 (0.15)

Lesson Quiz
Multiply.
1. 0.4×0.2 (0.08)
2. 0.5×0.5 (0.25)
3. 0.9×0.2 (0.18)
4. 0.03×0.3 (0.009)
5. 0.04×0.03 (0.0012)
6. 40×7.51 (300.4)

LEVELED PRACTICE

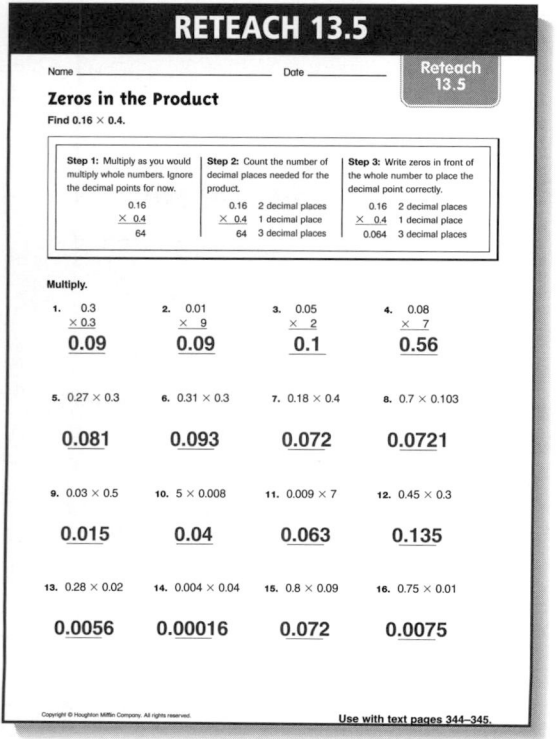

RETEACH 13.5

Name _____ Date _____
Reteach 13.5

Zeros in the Product
Find 0.16×0.4.

Step 1: Multiply as you would multiply whole numbers. Ignore the decimal points for now.	Step 2: Count the number of decimal places needed for the product.	Step 3: Write zeros in front of the whole number to place the decimal point correctly.
0.16 ×0.4 ———— 64	0.16 2 decimal places ×0.4 1 decimal place ———— 64 3 decimal places	0.16 2 decimal places ×0.4 1 decimal place ———— 0.064 3 decimal places

Multiply.

1. 0.3 ×0.3 = **0.09**
2. 0.01 ×9 = **0.09**
3. 0.05 ×2 = **0.1**
4. 0.08 ×7 = **0.56**

5. 0.27×0.3 = **0.081**
6. 0.31×0.3 = **0.093**
7. 0.18×0.4 = **0.072**
8. 0.7×0.103 = **0.0721**

9. 0.03×0.5 = **0.015**
10. 5×0.008 = **0.04**
11. 0.009×7 = **0.063**
12. 0.45×0.3 = **0.135**

13. 0.28×0.02 = **0.0056**
14. 0.004×0.04 = **0.00016**
15. 0.8×0.09 = **0.072**
16. 0.75×0.01 = **0.0075**

Use with text pages 344–345.

PRACTICE 13.5

Name _____ Date _____
Practice 13.5

Zeros in the Product
Multiply.

1. 0.04 ×0.5 = **0.020**
2. 0.002 ×6 = **0.012**
3. 0.14 ×0.06 = **0.0084**
4. 0.025 ×0.3 = **0.0075**

5. 0.08 ×0.09 = **0.0072**
6. 0.9 ×0.06 = **0.054**
7. 0.42 ×0.07 = **0.0294**
8. 0.12 ×0.09 = **0.0108**

9. 0.52 ×0.03 = **0.0156**
10. 0.77 ×0.03 = **0.0231**
11. 0.007 ×5 = **0.035**
12. 0.085 ×4 = **0.340**

13. 0.7 ×0.7 = **0.49**
14. 0.16 ×3 = **0.48**
15. 0.17 ×0.06 = **0.0102**
16. 0.15 ×0.2 = **0.030**

17. 0.22 ×0.07 = **0.0154**
18. 0.19 ×0.09 = **0.0171**
19. 0.26 ×0.03 = **0.0078**
20. 4 ×0.03 = **0.12**

21. 0.08×0.02 = **0.0016**
22. 0.7×0.004 = **0.0028**
23. 5×0.007 = **0.035**

24. 0.06×0.06 = **0.0036**
25. 0.08×0.09 = **0.0072**
26. 0.04×0.9 = **0.036**

27. 0.08×0.25 = **0.0200**
28. 0.16×0.2 = **0.032**
29. 0.15×0.03 = **0.0045**

Test Prep

30. A cowboy hat costs $41.95 in Texas. The sales tax there is 0.0625. With tax, what does the hat cost? **$44.57**

31. Find 6.1×0.03. **C**
   A 18.3
   B 0.83
   C 0.183
   D 0.0183

Use with text pages 344–345.

ENRICHMENT 13.5

Name _____ Date _____
Enrichment 13.5

Five-In-a-Row

With a partner, take turns tossing 2 number cubes. However, instead of using the numbers on the cube, use these numbers:

Let 1 be 0.3.   Let 3 be 0.7.   Let 5 be 0.06.
Let 2 be 0.04.   Let 4 be 0.08.   Let 6 be 0.9.

Roll the cubes and multiply the two numbers. Then find the product on the game board and cross it out using either X or O. You may mark a box that your partner has already marked. The winner is the first one to mark five boxes in a row across, down, or diagonally.

0.49	FREE	0.018	0.056	0.042
0.012	0.09	0.0032	0.0016	FREE
0.0064	0.81	0.0036	0.024	0.072
0.036	0.21	FREE	0.054	0.0048
FREE	0.028	0.27	0.0024	0.63

1. Was it easier or harder to multiply a decimal with 1 place or with 2 places?
   Answers will vary.

2. Which factors made the greatest product? the least product?
   0.7×0.9; 0.04×0.06

3. What would happen if you played the game with 3 number cubes?
   Possible answer: **The products of multiplying 3 cubes would all be less than the numbers on the game board.**

Use with text pages 344–345.

Practice Workbook Page 87

Reaching All Learners

Differentiated Instruction

English Learners

Worksheet 13.5 introduces the concept of sales tax and prepares students to solve word problems that involve calculating sales tax.

Special Needs
VISUAL, AUDITORY

- Display vertically: 0.02×0.5. **What is 2×5?** (10) Write *10*.
- **How many decimal places are there altogether in the 2 factors?** (3) **How many digits are in 10?** (2) **What do we add in front of the 10 to get 3 places?** (0) Write *0.010*.
- Repeat for 0.1×0.1, 0.3×0.02.

Early Finishers
VISUAL, AUDITORY

- Have students solve these problems:
  0.4×0.4 (0.16)
  0.18×0.03 (0.0054)
  0.002×0.6 (0.0012)
  0.012×0.02 (0.00024)
- Have students exchange problems and discuss and share their answers.
- Have students write and solve their own examples using decimals.

Literature Connection

Discount to Decimal to Price
Materials: *catalog or newspaper advertisements*

- Have students find sales advertisements. Have them find the discounts and then compute sale prices for several items.

- Suggest that students design ads for five sale items, such as sweaters, shoes, skates, bicycles, or computers. Tell them to draw the items and include their computed sales prices in the ad.

TECHNOLOGY

Spiral Review

Create **customized** spiral review worksheets for individual students using the *Ways to Assess* CD-ROM.

Tool Software

Use *Easy Sheet* or another spreadsheet to explore this lesson more fully.

Lesson Planner

You can customize your teaching plan to meet your curriculum requirements with the Lesson Planner CD-ROM.

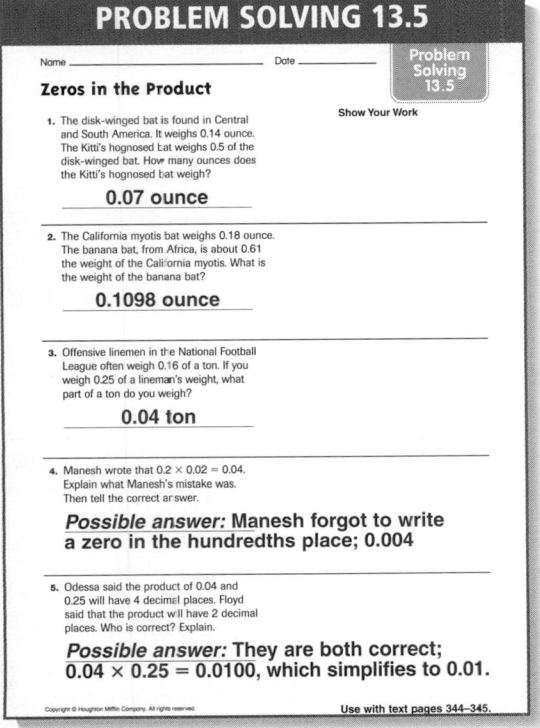

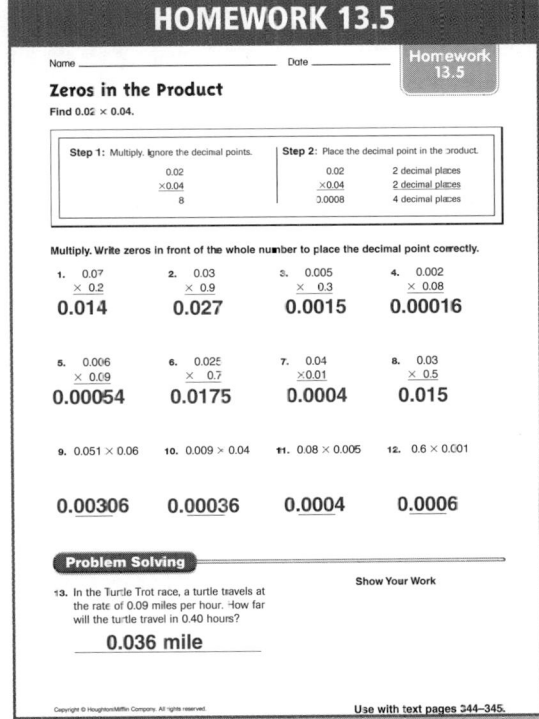

Homework Workbook Page 87

TEACHING LESSON 13.5

Activity

Warm-Up Activity
Multiplying Decimals

👥 Whole Group	🕐 5 minutes	Visual, Auditory

Have students multiply the following:

1. 1.2×6 (7.2)
2. 7.0×4.1 (28.7)
3. 2.4×9 (21.6)
4. 0.32×1.3 (0.416)
5. 1.8×0.52 (0.936)

Zeros in the Product

Vocabulary factor

Objective Decide when to write zeros in the products of decimal factors.

Learn About It

Sylvia bought a pencil for $0.40. Where Sylvia lives, a sales tax of $0.05 for every dollar spent is added to all purchases. How much will the sales tax be on the pencil Sylvia bought?

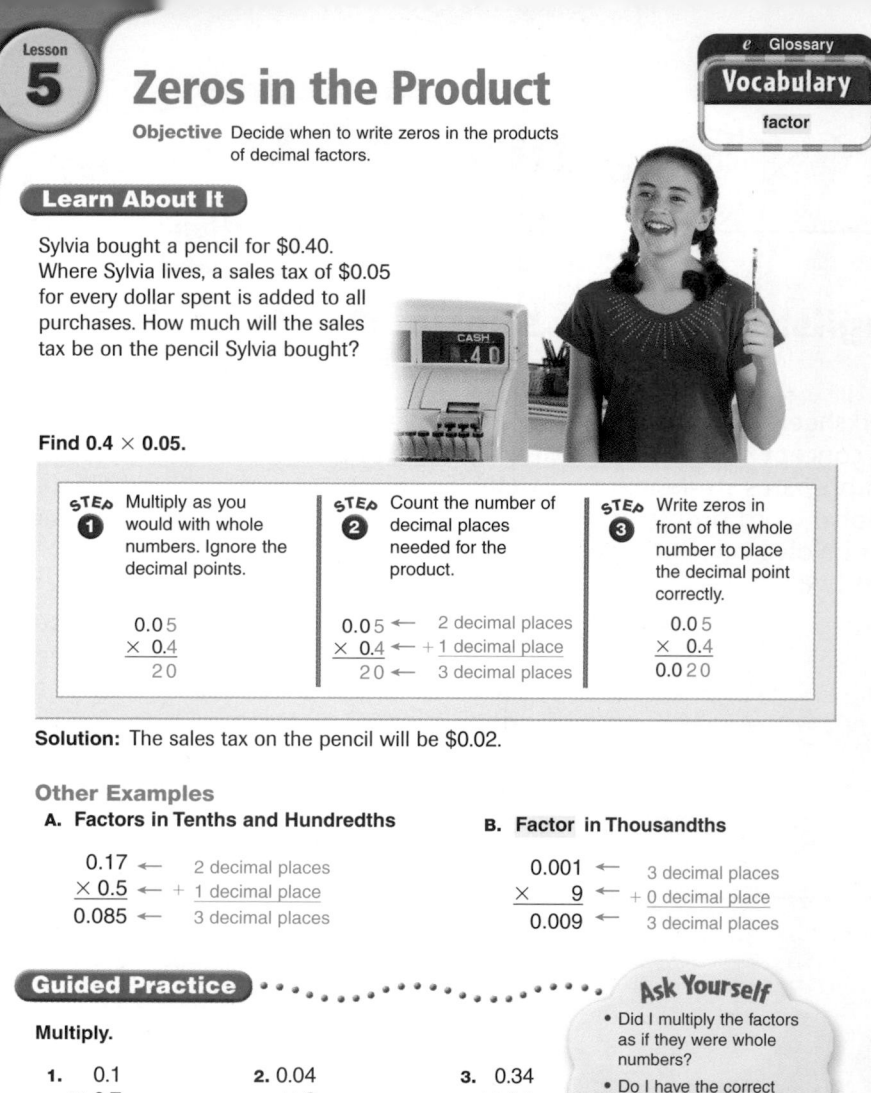

Find 0.4×0.05.

STEP 1 Multiply as you would with whole numbers. Ignore the decimal points.	**STEP 2** Count the number of decimal places needed for the product.	**STEP 3** Write zeros in front of the whole number to place the decimal point correctly.
$\begin{array}{r} 0.05 \\ \times\ 0.4 \\ \hline 20 \end{array}$	$\begin{array}{r} 0.05 \leftarrow 2\ \text{decimal places} \\ \times\ 0.4 \leftarrow +\ 1\ \text{decimal place} \\ \hline 20 \leftarrow 3\ \text{decimal places} \end{array}$	$\begin{array}{r} 0.05 \\ \times\ 0.4 \\ \hline 0.020 \end{array}$

Solution: The sales tax on the pencil will be $0.02.

Other Examples

A. Factors in Tenths and Hundredths

$\begin{array}{r} 0.17 \leftarrow 2\ \text{decimal places} \\ \times\ 0.5 \leftarrow +\ 1\ \text{decimal place} \\ \hline 0.085 \leftarrow 3\ \text{decimal places} \end{array}$

B. Factor in Thousandths

$\begin{array}{r} 0.001 \leftarrow 3\ \text{decimal places} \\ \times\ \ \ 9 \leftarrow +\ 0\ \text{decimal place} \\ \hline 0.009 \leftarrow 3\ \text{decimal places} \end{array}$

Guided Practice

Ask Yourself
- Did I multiply the factors as if they were whole numbers?
- Do I have the correct number of decimal places in my answer?

Multiply.

1. $\begin{array}{r} 0.1 \\ \times\ 0.7 \\ \hline 0.07 \end{array}$
2. $\begin{array}{r} 0.04 \\ \times\ 2 \\ \hline 0.08 \end{array}$
3. $\begin{array}{r} 0.34 \\ \times\ 0.1 \\ \hline 0.034 \end{array}$

4. 0.06×1.3 0.078
5. 0.3×0.02 0.006
6. 0.004×3 0.012

TEST TIPS

TEST TIPS Explain Your Thinking ▶ Why can 0.020 be written as 0.02?
$0.020 = \frac{20}{1000} = \frac{2}{100}; 0.02 = \frac{2}{100}$

---

1 Introduce

- On the chalkboard, write: *0.1 × 0.1*. **Will the product be more or less than 0.1? Why?** (Less, because the product of two decimals is always less than either decimal.) **Let's multiply the counting numbers first. What is 1 × 1?** (1)

- **How many decimal places are there in the factors?** (2) **There is only one number in the answer. How can we get 2 places to the left?** (Add a zero in front of the 1.) Write the answer *0.01*. **Is this less than 0.1? How do you know?** (Yes, 1 hundredth is less than one tenth.) **Why do we put a zero in front of the decimal point?** (to make sure that the number is read as a decimal)

2 Develop

Guide students through the *Learn About It* section.

- **Look at Step 1.** Make sure students understand to multiply the counting numbers first.

- **Look at Step 2. How many decimal places are there in the two factors?** (3)

- **Look at Step 3. Where do we begin to count places in the product?** (Begin with the last digit and count back left.)

- Go over *Other Examples*. Point out that only one example has a factor in thousandths. The products of both examples, however, have 3 decimal places. Discuss.

Guided Practice

Have students complete **Exercises 1–6** as you observe. Remind them to use the *Ask Yourself* questions to help. Give students the opportunity to talk about the question in *Explain Your Thinking*.

Multiply.

7.	8.	9.	10.	11.
3 × 0.3 **0.9**	0.3 × 0.3 **0.09**	0.03 × 0.3 **0.009**	0.03 × 3 **0.09**	7 × 0.2 **1.4**

12.	13.	14.	15.	16.
0.7 × 0.2 **0.14**	0.7 × 0.02 **0.014**	0.07 × 0.2 **0.014**	0.2 × 0.06 **0.012**	0.5 × 0.06 **0.030**

17. 0.04 × 0.6 **0.024**
18. 0.6 × 0.25 **0.150**
19. 0.8 × 0.1 **0.08**
20. 0.03 × 0.7 **0.021**
21. 0.5 × 0.3 **0.15**
22. 0.01 × 0.9 **0.009**
23. 0.09 × 0.5 **0.045**
24. 0.7 × 0.06 **0.042**
25. 0.02 × 0.4 **0.008**
26. 0.04 × 0.04 **0.0016**
27. 0.05 × 0.8 **0.040**
28. 0.002 × 6 **0.012**

 Data Use the table for Problems 29–34.

The table shows sales tax per dollar for some states in 2002.

State	Sales Tax per Dollar (2002)
Texas	0.0625
New Jersey	0.06
Maryland	0.05
Georgia	0.04
Colorado	0.029

29. A shirt is priced at $11.95. With sales tax, what will that shirt cost in Colorado? in Texas? **$12.30; $12.70**

30. A jacket costs $25. How much will the sales tax be on this jacket if it is sold in Maryland? **$1.25**

31. **Calculator** You are in Georgia and you buy items that cost $4.79, $5.99, and $9 before tax. All you have in your wallet is $20. Do you have enough money? Explain. *See Additional Answers on Page 349.*

32. Suppose a city government in Maryland decides to add on a local sales tax that is 0.5 of the state sales tax. What would the combined sales tax be in that city? **0.075**

33. What is the mean, median, and range of the sales taxes for the states listed in the table? **mean: 0.0483; median: 0.05; range: 0.0335**

34. **Create and Solve** Use the information in the table to write and solve a problem. *Check problems and solutions.*

Daily Review	**Test Prep**

Find the mean, median, mode, and range of each set of data. (Ch. 8, Lesson 2)

35. 78°F, 74°F, 75°F, 68°F, 75°F

36. 6°C, 8°C, 8°C, 8°C, 4°C, 6°C, 7°C, 9°C

37. 85, 85, 85, 80, 84, 85

38. **Free Response** What is the sales tax on $5, if a state charges 6.5¢ sales tax on every dollar you spend? Explain how you found your answer. **33¢; multiply 5 and 0.065 and round to the nearest hundredth.**

Extra Practice See page 349, Set E.

See Additional Answers on Page 349.

Chapter 13 Lesson 5 **345**

DAILY TEST PREP

Which is the correct product of 0.18 and 0.05? (□)

A 0.09
B 0.9
C 9.0
D 0.009

 **Activity**

Or use Intervention CD-ROM Lesson 13.5

Lesson Intervention

Where Does the Decimal Point Go?

iii Small Group	⏱ 5–10 minutes	Visual, Auditory

- Write *0.04 × 0.4* vertically on the chalkboard. **What is the product of 4 × 4?** (16) Write *16* below the problem.

- **To place the decimal point in the answer, we have to count the decimal places in the two factors. How many places are there in the first factor?** (2) **in the second factor?** (1) **How many in all?** (3)

- Ask students to count back with you three places, starting with the 6. When you get to the second place, ask: **What do we have to do now to get three places?** (Add a zero to make the third place.)

- Add the zero and the decimal point. **How do we read 0.016?** (16 thousandths)

---

3 Practice

Assign **Exercises 7–38** as independent work.

- *Exercises 7–28* Have students discuss their answers.

- *Problem Solving for Problems 29–34* Have students discuss and share their answers.

Common Error

Adding an incorrect number of zeros Students may forget to add a zero, or may add an incorrect number of zeros to the product of two decimals. Make sure students understand how to count decimal places to make the number of decimal places in the product the same as the sum of the places in the factors.

4 Assess and Close

- **When will the product be less than either factor?** (when one or both factors are decimals less than 1)

- **Explain where to add zeros in the product.** (Add them to the left of the leftmost counting number.)

Assign the **LESSON QUIZ** on Transparency 13.5 to further assess student understanding.

 **Keeping a Journal**

Have students write a few sentences explaining when and where to add zeros to the products of decimal factors. Have them give an example.

Problem Solving Decision: Reasonable Answers

PLANNING THE LESSON

MATHEMATICS OBJECTIVE
Review how to decide if the answer to a problem is reasonable.

Use Lesson Planner CD-ROM for Lesson 13.6.

Daily Routines

Vocabulary
Make sure that students understand that a **reasonable** answer is one that makes sense, given the facts and the numbers in the problem.

Vocabulary Cards

Meeting North Carolina's Standards
1.03 Develop flexibility in solving problems by selecting strategies and using mental computation, estimation, calculators or computers, and paper and pencil.

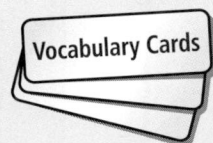

Lesson Transparency **13.6**

Problem of the Day
The product of two whole numbers is 40. If 12 is added to the first and 8 is added to the second, the new product is 260. What are the two numbers? (8 and 5)

Quick Review
Find the product.
1. 0.5×0.4 (0.20)
2. 0.04×0.8 (0.032)
3. 0.24×0.3 (0.072)
4. 14×0.4 (5.6)
5. 0.6×6 (3.6)

Lesson Quiz
Solve. Explain why the answer is reasonable or unreasonable.

Nia earns $48. She plans to save 0.4 of it. She says that means she can save $1.92. Is this reasonable? (unreasonable; she would save $19.20, because $0.4 \times 48 = 19.2$.)

LEVELED PRACTICE

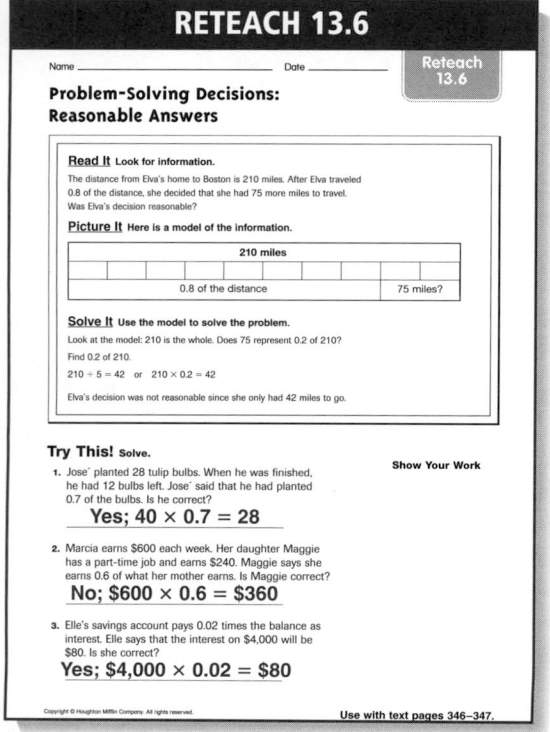

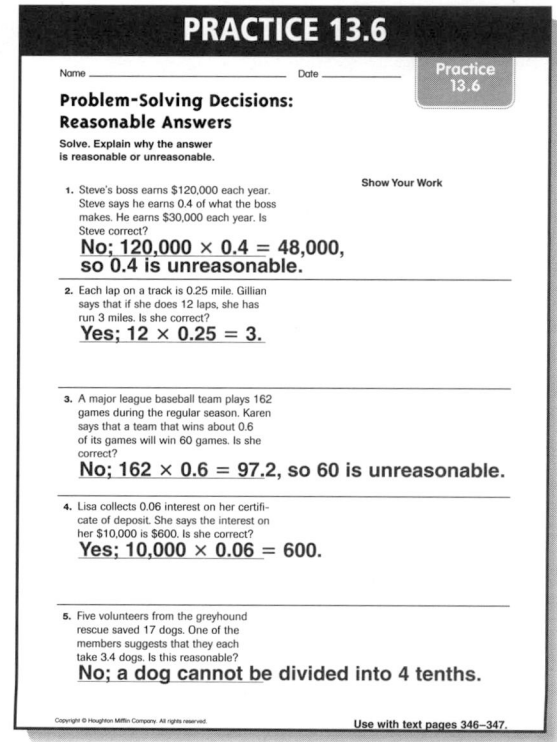

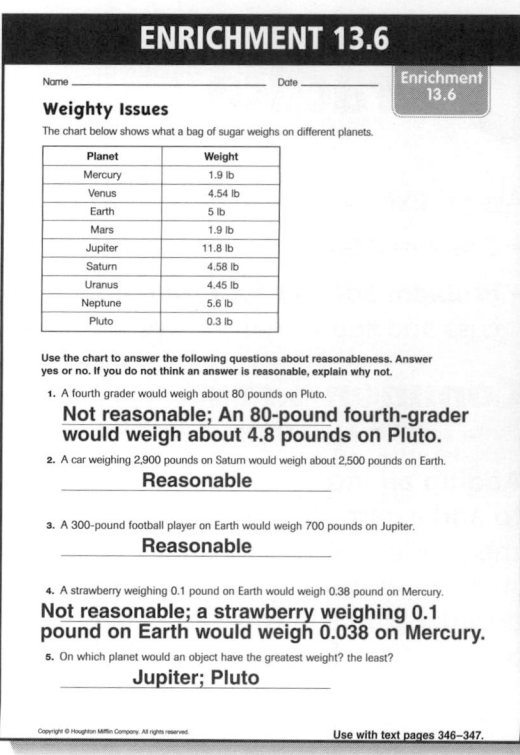

Practice Workbook Page 88

Reaching All Learners
Differentiated Instruction

English Learners

Worksheet 13.6 teaches students about prefixes using words from Lesson 6.

Inclusion
VISUAL, AUDITORY

Display: *Ed lent Joe $300 and charged 0.02 interest. Joe says he owes Ed $.060 in interest. Is Joe right?*

Multiply 300 × 2. (600) **Where do we put the decimal point?** (There are 2 decimal places in the factors, so count 2 places from the last zero.) **How much is that?** ($6.00) **Was Joe right?** (No; he has to pay $6.00 in interest, not $0.60.)

Gifted and Talented
VISUAL, AUDITORY

Have students make up a problem and find a solution that is incorrect or unreasonable because of an error in reading or in computation. Then have them write a few sentences explaining what part of the reasoning is incorrect. Have them provide the correct answer.

TECHNOLOGY

Spiral Review

Using the *Ways to Assess* CD-ROM, you can create **customized** spiral review worksheets covering any lessons you choose.

Intervention

Use the *Ways to Success* intervention software to support students who need more help in understanding the concepts and skills taught in this chapter.

Science Connection

A Sure Thing, Taxes

- Explain to students that there are many kinds of taxes. Federal, state, and city income tax, sales tax, restaurant tax, and entertainment tax are a few to mention.
- The table shows the Gasoline Excise Tax Rates for four states as of January 1, 2003.

State	Tax per dollar
California	0.18
Florida	0.04
Alabama	0.16
Alaska	0.08

- Ask students to find how much tax would be paid on $19 worth of gasoline for each state listed. ($3.42, $0.76, $3.04, $1.52)

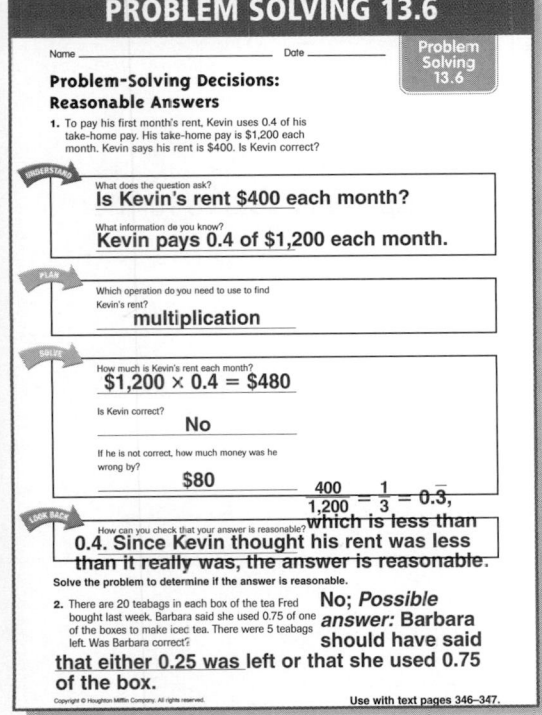

PROBLEM SOLVING 13.6

Problem-Solving Decisions: Reasonable Answers

1. To pay his first month's rent, Kevin uses 0.4 of his take-home pay. His take-home pay is $1,200 each month. Kevin says his rent is $400. Is Kevin correct?

UNDERSTAND
What does the question ask?
Is Kevin's rent $400 each month?

What information do you know?
Kevin pays 0.4 of $1,200 each month.

PLAN
Which operation do you need to use to find Kevin's rent?
multiplication

SOLVE
How much is Kevin's rent each month?
$1,200 × 0.4 = $480

Is Kevin correct?
No

If he is not correct, how much money was he wrong by?
$80

LOOK BACK
How can you check that your answer is reasonable?
$\frac{400}{1,200} = \frac{1}{3} = 0.3$, which is less than 0.4. Since Kevin thought his rent was less than it really was, the answer is reasonable.

Solve the problem to determine if the answer is reasonable.

2. There are 20 teabags in each box of the tea Fred bought last week. Barbara said she used 0.75 of one of the boxes to make iced tea. There were 5 teabags left. Was Barbara correct?
No; *Possible answer:* Barbara should have said that either 0.25 was left or that she used 0.75 of the box.

Use with text pages 346–347.

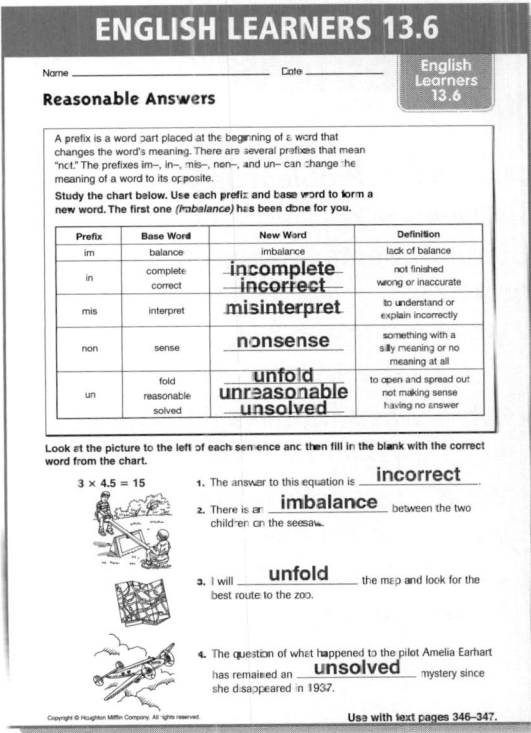

HOMEWORK 13.6

Problem-Solving Decisions: Reasonable Answers

Ask Yourself

Understand What is the problem?
What facts do I know?

Plan Which operation will I use to solve the problem?

Solve Are my calculations correct?

Look Back Did I solve the problem?
Is my answer reasonable?

Solve. Explain why the answer is reasonable or unreasonable.

Show Your Work

1. Alvin earns $80. He plans to put 0.4 of that money in the bank and give his mother 0.2 of it. Alvin figures he will have $55 left over. Is he correct?
No; 0.4 + 0.2 = 0.6; 0.6 > 0.5; 0.5 × $80 = $40; He will have less than $40 left. Alvin will actually have $32.

2. Alvin wants to buy a new video game system that costs $299. He plans to save $28.50 a week for the system. Alvin rounded the numbers to estimate how long it will take him to buy the system. He says he will have enough money after 10 weeks. Is he correct?
No; Alvin did correctly round the numbers. However, since both were rounded up, his estimate is greater than the actual savings. It will take him 11 weeks to save enough money to buy the system.

Use with text pages 346–347.

ENGLISH LEARNERS 13.6

Reasonable Answers

A prefix is a word part placed at the beginning of a word that changes the word's meaning. There are several prefixes that mean "not." The prefixes im–, in–, mis–, non–, and un– can change the meaning of a word to its opposite.

Study the chart below. Use each prefix and base word to form a new word. The first one (*imbalance*) has been done for you.

Prefix	Base Word	New Word	Definition
im	balance	imbalance	lack of balance
in	complete	incomplete	not finished
	correct	incorrect	wrong or inaccurate
mis	interpret	misinterpret	to understand or explain incorrectly
non	sense	nonsense	something with a silly meaning or no meaning at all
un	fold	unfold	to open and spread out
	reasonable	unreasonable	not making sense
	solved	unsolved	having no answer

Look at the picture to the left of each sentence and then fill in the blank with the correct word from the chart.

3 × 4.5 = 15
1. The answer to this equation is **incorrect**

2. There is an **imbalance** between the two children on the seesaw.

3. I will **unfold** the map and look for the best route to the zoo.

4. The question of what happened to the pilot Amelia Earhart has remained an **unsolved** mystery since she disappeared in 1937.

Use with text pages 346–347.

Homework Workbook Page 88

TEACHING LESSON 13.6

LESSON ORGANIZER

Objective Review how to decide if the answer to a problem is reasonable.

Resources Reteach, Practice, Enrichment, Problem-Solving, Homework, English Learners, Transparencies, and Math Center

Materials Problem Solving: Four-Step Process Tranparency

Activity

Warm-Up Activity
Zero in the Product

👤👤👤👤 Whole Group	⏱ 5 minutes	Visual, Auditory

Have students multiply the following:

1. 0.02×0.6 (0.012)
2. 7×0.22 (1.54)
3. 2.5×0.09 (0.225)
4. 0.3×3.3 (0.99)
5. 1.8×0.05 (0.09)

Problem-Solving Decision

Reasonable Answers

Objective Review how to decide if the answer to a problem is reasonable.

After you have solved a problem, look back at the problem and decide if the answer is reasonable.

Problem Ishana's dad tells her she must save 0.6 of the money she earns. Ishana earns $15 one week. She figures that her savings must be $6. Is this reasonable?

Here are the responses from three students:

Hannah	Antonio	Sora
No, Ishana's answer should be $15.60.	No, Ishana's answer should be $15.	No, Ishana needs to multiply.
$15 + $0.60 is $15.60	$0.6 \approx 1$ $1 \times $15 = 15	$0.6 \times $15 = 0.90
The problem may be misinterpreted.	**An answer may not make sense.**	**The calculations may be incorrect.**
To find the amount Ishana must save, you have to multiply, not add.	$15 is the total amount Ishana earned. She is only saving part of her money, not all of it.	Check that you have the correct number of decimal places in the product.
$0.6 \times 15		$\begin{array}{r} 15 \leftarrow \text{0 decimal places} \\ \times\ 0.6 \leftarrow \text{+1 decimal place} \\ \hline 9.0 \leftarrow \text{1 decimal place} \end{array}$

Solution: Ishana's answer is not reasonable. Ishana should save $0.6 \times 15, or $9.

Try These

Solve. Explain why the answer is reasonable or unreasonable.

1. Each month Dan's savings account pays 0.03 of the balance as interest. Dan says that the interest on his $200 will be $0.03. Is he correct?
   no; $0.03 \times $200 = 6

2. Ella's credit card balance is $325. Interest charges are 0.06 of the balance. Ella thinks the interest would be $1.95. Is Ella correct?
   no; $0.06 \times $325 = 19.50

3. Linda earns $40. She plans to put 0.5 of that money into savings and 0.5 of what is left toward a new bike. She says she'll have $10 left. Is she correct?
   yes; $0.5 \times $40 = $20; 0.5 \times $20 = $10; $40 - ($20 + $10) = 10

4. Clarice has $2 and she wants to buy a fruit drink for $1.80. The sales tax on the drink is 0.05. Clarice says she has enough money. Is she right?
   yes; $1.80 + ($1.80 \times 0.05) = 1.89

MathTracks 2/5
Listen and Understand

---

1 Review

Materials: *Problem Solving: Four-Step Process Transparency*

Guide students through the problem and the three responses.

- **What did Hannah do wrong?** (She forgot to multiply and mistook the decimal amount for cents.)

- **What was Antonio's mistake?** (0.6 of 15 cannot be 15; it has to be less than 15. His rounding doesn't make sense.)

- **What was Sora's mistake?** (She calculated 6×15 correctly, but put the decimal point in the wrong place.)

- Use the Problem Solving: Four Step Process Transparency to help students find this correct response to the poblem.

2 Practice

Assign **Exercises 1–4** as independent work.

Assign the **Lesson Quiz** on Transparency 13.6 to further assess student understanding.

Quick Check

Check your understanding of Lessons 5–6.

Multiply. (Lesson 5)

1.	0.04	2.	0.008	3.	0.3	4.	0.009
	× 0.6		× 4		× 0.1		× 4
	0.024		**0.032**		**0.03**		**0.036**

5. 0.003×7 **0.021**   6. 2.1×0.05 **0.105**   7. 4×0.016 **0.064**   8. 0.02×0.8 **0.016**

Solve. Explain why the answer is reasonable or unreasonable. (Lesson 6)

9. Jason plans to save 0.25 of his earnings for a gift for his mom. He earns $50 this week. He thinks he needs to put $25 of that money away toward his mom's gift. Is this reasonable?
no; 0.25 × $50 = $12.50.

10. In one district, 0.8 of the students ride a bus to school. Of those students, 0.03 of them need wheelchair vans. Terry says that 1.1 of the students need wheelchair vans. Is he right?
no; 0.03 × 0.8 = 0.024.

It Goes On and On and On—or Does It?

Number Sense

Math Reasoning

Start with a sheet of paper that is 10 inches by 10 inches. Think about folding the paper exactly in half. Then folding it in half again and then again.

1. **Calculator** Copy and complete the table to show mathematically what will happen to the area that the folded paper covers. Round answers to the nearest tenth.
See Additional Answers on Page 349.

2. Try the experiment. Measure to check your results with your table. What happened? ***Answers will vary.***

3. Try the experiment again with a piece of paper that is 2 or 4 times as big as the 10 by 10 square. What happened this time? ***Answers will vary.***

Number of Folds	Area Covered	
1	50 in.²	← 100 × 0.5
2	25 in.²	← 50 × 0.5
3	12.5 in.²	← 25 × 0.5
4	■	**6.3 in.²**
5	■	**3.2 in.²**
6	■	**1.6 in.²**
7	■	**0.8 in.²**
8	■	**0.4 in.²**
9	■	**0.2 in.²**
10	■	**0.1 in.²**

Chapter 13 Lesson 6 347

 **Quick Check**

Purpose: The Quick Check allows you to assess the students' understanding of the concepts presented in Lessons 5–6.

Items	Objectives Tested	Pages	Intervention
1–8	Decide when to write zeros in the products of decimal factors.	344–345	Reteach Resource 13.5 *Ways to Success 13.5*
9–10	Review how to decide if the answer to a problem is reasonable.	346	Reteach Resource 13.6 *Ways to Success 13.6*

Test Prep Transparency

13.6

DAILY TEST PREP

Round 4.719 to the nearest hundredth. (C)

A. 4.71   C. 4.72

B. 4.79   D. 4.719

Keeping a Journal

Have students write a few sentences explaining how to read and represent a word problem in mathematics.

Number Sense

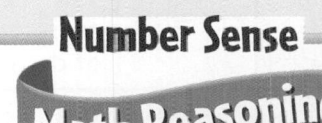

Math Reasoning

It Goes On and On and On—or Does It?

- Point out that the values can be calculated indefinitely to many decimal places, but that folding the paper many times over eventually becomes physically impossible.

- Have students predict the results of the experiment before doing step 3. Then have them do the experiment and discuss the results.

Monitoring Student Progress

 Chapter Review/Test

Purpose: This test provides an informal assessment of the Chapter 13 objectives.

Chapter Test Items 1–25

To assign a numerical grade for this Chapter Test, use 4 points for each test item.

Check Understanding

You can use the **Write About It** question to assess student understanding of a key chapter concept.

Customizing Your Instruction

For students who have not yet mastered these objectives, you can use the Reteaching Resources listed in the chart below.

 ## Assessment Options

A summary test for this chapter is also provided in the Unit Resource Folder.

Adequate Yearly Progress

Use the End of Grade Test Prep Assessment Guide to help familiarize your students with the format of standardized tests.

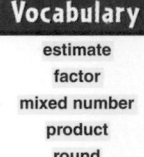

Chapter Review/Test

VOCABULARY

1. To ____ is to find an approximate rather than an exact answer. **estimate**
2. When you ____ a number, you express it to the nearest hundredth, tenth, and so on. **round**
3. A ____ is made up of a whole number and a fraction. **mixed number**

Vocabulary
estimate
factor
mixed number
product
round

CONCEPTS AND SKILLS

Use models or fractions to multiply. Write each product as a decimal. (Lesson 1, pp. 334–335)

4. 0.9×0.5 **0.45**   5. 0.3×1.7 **0.51**   6. 0.2×2.4 **0.48**   7. 1.9×0.6 **1.14**

Estimate each product. (Lesson 3, pp. 338–339)   *Possible estimates are given.*

8. 0.85×7 **6.3**   9. 3.82×5 **20**   10. 8.36×61 **480**   11. 4.72×4.9 **25**

Multiply. (Lessons 2, 4, pp. 336–337, 340–343)

12. 7×6.2 **43.4**   13. 7.25×0.4 **2.9**   14. 8.3×6.5 **53.95**   15. 2.6×4 **10.4**

16. 9.12×4.7 **42.864**   17. 0.96×0.8 **0.768**   18. 3.15×7.4 **23.31**   19. 0.7×0.77 **0.539**

Multiply. Write zeros in front of the whole number to place the decimal point correctly. (Lesson 5, pp. 344–345)

20. 0.8×0.007 **0.0056**   21. 0.4×0.012 **0.0048**   22. 0.06×0.4 **0.024**   23. 4×0.0008 **0.0032**

PROBLEM SOLVING

Solve. (Lesson 6, pp. 346–347)

24. Yes; $0.24 \times 0.4 = 0.096$, so approximately 0.1 of the girls are involved in sports.

25. No; $40 is over half of $65, and 0.33 is less than one half.

24. At Franklin Middle School, 0.24 of the students are involved in a school sport. Of these students, 0.4 of them are girls. Janet says this means about 0.1 of girls are involved in sports. Is she correct? *See above.*

25. Trisha makes $65 dollars a month babysitting. She makes $40 of this babysitting for Mrs. Ramirez. She thinks this is about 0.33 of her income. Is this reasonable? *See above.*

Write About It

Show You Understand

Look at how Sasha multiplied.

$$\begin{array}{r} 0.2 \\ \times\ 0.007 \\ \hline 0.014 \end{array}$$

Explain what Sasha did wrong.

Sasha miscounted the decimal places when placing the decimal point.

348   Chapter 13 Chapter Review/Test

Reteaching Support

Chapter Test Items	Summary Test Items	Chapter Objectives Tested	TE Pages	Use These Reteaching Resources
3–7	1–5	**13A** Relate multiplication of fractions to multiplication of decimals.	334A–335	Reteach Resource 13.1 Ways to Success CD: 13.1 Skillsheet 104
1, 2, 8–11	6–10	**13B** Estimate decimal products.	338A–339	Reteach Resource 13.3 Ways to Success CD: 13.3 Skillsheet 105
12–23	11–15	**13C** Multiply with decimals and whole numbers.	336A–337, 340A–345	Reteach Resource 13.2, 13.4, 13.5 Ways to Success CD: 13.2, 13.4, 13.5 Skillsheet 106, 107, 108
24, 25	16–20	**13D** Decide whether the solution to a problem is reasonable.	346A–347	Reteach Resource 13.6 Ways to Success CD: 13.6 Skillsheet 109

CHAPTER SUMMARY TEST

Name _____ Date _____   Chapter 13 Test

Use models or fractions to multiply. Write each product as a decimal.

1. 0.2×0.8 **0.16**
2. 0.6×0.9 **0.54**
3. 1.7×0.4 **0.68**
4. 2.5×0.5 **1.25**
5. 2.3×0.6 **1.38**

Estimate each product.

6. 31×5.9 *Possible answer:* **180**
7. 68×21.3 *Possible answer:* **1,400**
8. 49×0.52 *Possible answer:* **25**
9. 5×0.319 *Possible answer:* **1.5**
10. 33×4.95 *Possible answer:* **150**

Find each product.

11. 0.78×9 **7.02**
12. 0.6×0.37 **0.222**
13. 8.4×0.44 **3.696**
14. 0.06×0.02 **0.0012**
15. 0.005×1.8 **0.009**

Go on ▶

Set A (Lesson 1, pp. 334–335)

Use models or fractions to multiply. Write each product as a decimal.

1. 0.7×0.3 **0.21** 2. 0.6×0.9 **0.54** 3. 0.4×1.3 **0.52** 4. 0.3×0.6 **0.18** 5. 1.7×0.5 **0.85**

6. 0.5×1.8 **0.90** 7. 0.9×2.1 **1.89** 8. 1.2×0.8 **0.96** 9. 0.7×0.9 **0.63** 10. 3.2×0.2 **0.64**

Set B (Lesson 2, pp. 336–337)

Find each product.

1. 6×0.2 **1.2** 2. 9×0.5 **4.5** 3. 8×0.61 **4.88** 4. 5×0.82 **4.1** 5. 2×5.47 **10.94**

6. 8×4.17 **33.36** 7. 6×7.08 **42.48** 8. 3×4.98 **14.94** 9. 6.5×4.2 **27.3** 10. 7.4×17 **125.8**

Set C (Lesson 3, pp. 338–339)

Estimate each product. *Possible estimates are given.*

1. 0.17×4 **0.8** 2. 3.97×6 **24** 3. 7.22×7 **49** 4. 11.79×3 **36** 5. 82×0.58 **48**

6. 21×4.07 **84** 7. 48×9.39 **450** 8. 4×10.77 **44** 9. 0.42×300 **120** 10. 4.25×6 **24**

Set D (Lesson 4, pp. 340–343)

Multiply.

1. 0.6×0.3 **0.18** 2. 0.5×0.7 **0.35** 3. 0.8×0.8 **0.64** 4. 0.5×0.8 **0.40** 5. 0.18×0.8 **0.144**

6. 5.75×0.5 **2.875** 7. 3.6×1.3 **4.68** 8. 6.14×3.5 **21.49** 9. 0.83×0.7 **0.581** 10. 5.16×6.1 **31.476**

Compare. Write >, <, or =.

11. 0.3×0.5 **<** 0.4×0.4 12. 0.9×0.3 **<** 0.7×0.4 13. 0.7×0.7 **>** 0.6×0.8

Set E (Lesson 5, pp. 344–345)

Multiply. Write zeros in front of the whole number to place the decimal point correctly.

1.	2.	3.	4.	5.
0.6	0.4	0.4	0.9	0.09
$\times\ 4$	$\times\ 0.6$	$\times\ 0.06$	$\times\ 0.09$	$\times\ 0.08$
2.4	**0.24**	**0.024**	**0.081**	**0.0072**

6. 0.5×7 **3.5** 7. 0.5×0.7 **0.35** 8. 0.5×0.07 **0.035** 9. 0.05×0.07 **0.0035** 10. 0.5×0.04 **0.02**

Additional Answers

Chapter 13

Lesson 2, pp. 336–337

32. The price of the sweater before the discount is more than $42, because 0.7, or $\frac{7}{10}$, is greater than 0.5, or $\frac{5}{10}$ or $\frac{1}{2}$.

Lesson 3, pp. 338–339

16. Alternate 2; Possible answer: Current plan costs about $40 ($30 + $10); Alternate 1 costs $70 ($70 + $0); Alternate 2 costs about $20 ($10 + $10).

19. He should stay with his current plan. He now pays $62.68; Alternate 1 would be $68.60; Alternate 2 would be $76.75.

Lesson 5, pp. 344–345

31. No, you will be $0.57 short: $4.79 + $5.99 + $9 = $19.78; $19.78 × 0.04 = $0.7912 which rounds to $0.79; $19.78 + $0.79 = $20.57.

35. mean: 74°F; median: 75°F; mode: 75°F; range: 10°F

36. mean: 7°C; median: 7.5°C; mode: 8°C; range: 5°C

37. mean: 84; median: 85; mode: 85; range: 5

Lesson 6, pp. 346–347

Number Sense

A table showing the number of folds and area. Data should be: 4, 6.3 in.²; 5, 3.2 in.²; 6, 1.6 in.²; 7, 0.8 in.²; 8, 0.4 in.²; 9, 0.2 in.²; 10, 0.1 in.².

CHAPTER SUMMARY TEST

Name _____ Date _____

Chapter 13
Test
continued

Solve. Explain why the answer is reasonable or unreasonable.

16. Tom earned $60 last week at his part-time job. He has a plan to save 0.75 of his earnings. Tom put $52.50 in his savings account. Is he correct?

No; $60 × 0.75 = $45.00

17. Melanie had $100 in her savings account at the end of the month. Her bank pays 0.025 in interest on the savings account balance. Melanie figured the interest on $100 would be $2.50. Is she correct?

Yes; $100 × 0.025 = $2.50

18. Rosa had a CD wallet that held 30 CDs. She wanted to have 0.1 of the CDs in the wallet to be computer games. She figured that would be 1 CD. Is she correct?

No; 30 × 0.1 = 3

19. Micah and Jim bought some sports equipment for $80. The state sales tax is 0.05 of the purchase. Micah thought the sales tax would be $5.00, and Jim thought the sales tax would be $4.00. Who was correct?

Jim; $80 × 0.05 = $4.00

20. The cooks in the school cafeteria made 40 pizzas for the first lunch. A cook told Maggie that 0.7 of the pizzas had meat toppings. Maggie figured that 33 of the pizzas had meat toppings. Was she correct?

No; 40 × 0.7 = 28

Lesson By Lesson Overview
Divide Decimals

Lesson 1

- Students use models to explore the relationship between dividing fractions and dividing decimals.

Lesson 2

- Students use compatible numbers to estimate quotients with decimals and whole numbers.

Lesson 3

- Students multiply and divide a decimal by a power of 10.
- Students solve algebra equations that involve multiplying or dividing by powers of 10.

Lesson 4

- Students divide decimals by one-digit whole numbers.
- Students evaluate algebraic expressions by using substitution and completing function tables.

Lesson 5

- Students add one or more zeros to the dividend to help solve division problems.

Lesson 6

- Students review using division to change a fraction to a decimal.
- Students learn that some calculators round the last digit of a repeating decimal.

Lesson 7

- Students divide one decimal by another.
- Students divide to a specified place.

Lesson 8

- Students decide how to write the quotient to solve a problem.
- Students practice choosing a computation method and using data from a table to solve problems.

SKILLS TRACE: DIVISION WITH DECIMALS		
Grade 4	**Grade 5**	**Grade 6**
	• relate fraction and decimal division	• link decimal to fraction operations (ch. 7)
	• estimate decimal quotients	• divide decimals and powers of 10 (ch. 7)
	• divide with decimals and whole numbers	
	• use division to find repeating decimals	

Chapter Planner

Lesson	Objective	Vocabulary	Materials	✔ NCTM Standards
14.1 **Explore Division with Decimals** p. 352A	Use models to show the relationship between dividing fractions and decimals.			**Number and Operations:** Develop understanding of fractions as parts of unit wholes, as parts of a collection, as locations on number lines, and as divisions of whole numbers.
14.2 **Estimate Quotients** p. 354A	Estimate decimal quotients using compatible numbers.			**Number and Operations:** Develop and use strategies to estimate computations involving fractions and decimals in situations relevant to students' experience.
14.3 **Multiply and Divide by Powers of 10** p. 356A	Use patterns to multiply and divide by powers of 10.	power of 10 exponent		**Number and Operations:** Understand various meanings of multiplication and division.
14.4 **Divide a Decimal by a Whole Number** p. 358A	Divide a decimal by a whole number.			**Number and Operations:** Develop fluency in adding, subtracting, multiplying, and dividing whole numbers.
14.5 **Write Zeros in the Dividend** p. 362A	Write one or more zeros in the dividend to help solve division problems.			**Number and Operations:** Understand numbers, ways of representing numbers, relationships among numbers, and number systems.
14.6 **Repeating Decimals** p. 366A	Change a fraction to a decimal using division.	repeating decimal		**Number and Operations:** Recognize equivalent representations for the same number and generate them by decomposing and composing numbers.
14.7 **Divide a Decimal by a Decimal** p. 368A	Divide one decimal by another.			**Number and Operations:** Understand the effects of multiplying and dividing whole numbers.
14.8 **Problem-Solving Application: Decide How to Write the Quotient** p. 370A	Decide how to write the quotient to solve a problem.		50 counters Problem Solving: Four Step Process Transparency	**Number and Operations:** Understand meanings of operations and how they relate to one another.

Resources For Reaching All Learners

LESSON RESOURCES: Reteach, Practice, Enrichment, Problem Solving, Homework, English Learners, Daily Routines, Transparencies, Math Center.

ADDITIONAL RESOURCES FROM HOUGHTON MIFFLIN: Combination Classroom Planning Guide, Chapter Challenges, Every Day Counts, Math at Hand (student handbook)

Every Day Counts
The **Daily Decimal** activities in **Every Day Counts** support the math in this chapter.

Assessing Prior Knowledge

Before beginning the chapter, you can assess student understandings in order to assist you in differentiating instruction.

Complete Chapter Pretest in Unit Resource Folder

Use this test to assess both prerequisite skills (**Are You Ready?** — one page) and chapter content (**Check What You Know** — two pages).

Chapter 14 Prerequisite Skills Pretest

Chapter 14 New Content Pretest

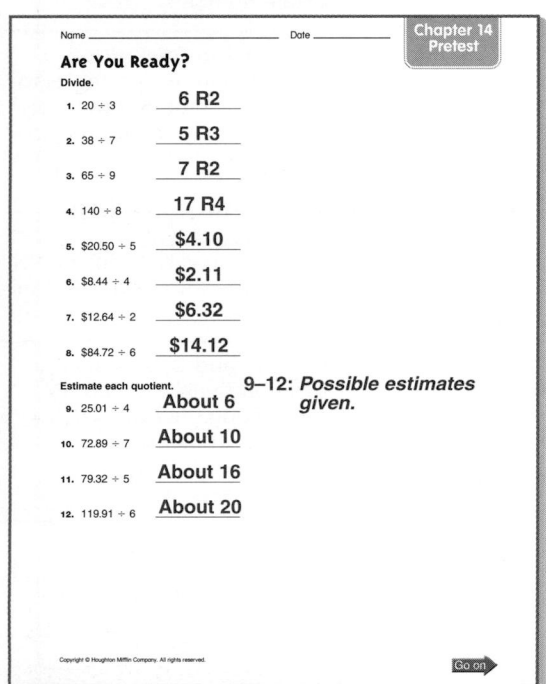

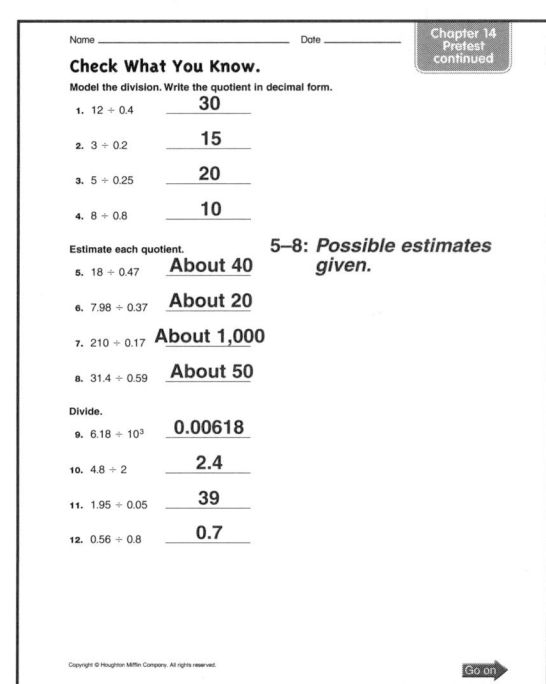

Customizing Instruction

For Students Having Difficulty

Items	Prerequisites	Ways to Success
1–4	Divide two- and three-digit dividends with one- and two-digit quotients	CD: 14c Skillsheet: 110
5–8	Divide money	Skillsheet: 111
9–12	Estimate quotients	CD: 14b Skillsheet: 110

Ways to Success: Intervention for every concept and skill (CD-ROM or Chapter Intervention Skillsheet).

Consider using **Knowing Mathematics** with any students who are working two or more years below grade level.

For Students Having Success

Items	Objectives	Resources
1–4	**14A** Relate division of fractions to division of decimals.	Enrichment 14.1
5–8	**14B** Estimate decimal quotients.	Enrichment 14.2
9–12	**14C** Divide with decimals and whole numbers.	Enrichment 14.3, 14.4, 14.5, 14.7
13–16	**14D** Use division to find repeating decimals.	Enrichment 14.6
17–20	**14E** Decide how to write a quotient when a quotient is the solution to a problem.	Enrichment 14.8

Other Pretest Options

Informal Pretest in Student Book

The student book pretest assesses vocabulary and prerequisite skills needed for success in this chapter.

Ways to Success CD-ROM

The *Ways to Success* chapter pretest has automatic assignment of appropriate review lessons.

Use **Chapter Challenges** with any students who have success with all new chapter content.

Chapter Resources

Assessing Prior Knowledge

Buying in Multiples (multiply decimals)

- Have students look through ads to identify four items they would like to buy. Have them list the items and each item's unit price, which should involve dollars and cents.
- Ask students to determine how many of each item they would like to buy, and to find the total cost.

Ongoing Skill Activity

Use Division to Relate Decimals to Fractions (divide decimals)

- As appropriate, relate the skill taught in a given lesson to the analogous skill using fractions.
- For example, after Lesson 1, relate the division model for decimals to the one used for fractions.
- After Lesson 2, have students make comparisons between rounding fractions and rounding decimals when estimating quotients.
- For Lesson 7, have students use equivalents to show the relationship between dividing a fraction by a fraction and dividing a decimal by a decimal.

Connecting to the Unit Project

- Have students add to the tables they began in Chapter 13 by using quarter, eighth, and sixteenth notes and these time signatures: $\frac{3}{4}$ and $\frac{6}{8}$. Remind them that each measure should contain only one note type.
- Have students discuss and display their tables.

Professional Resources Handbook

Research, Mathematics Content, and Language Intervention

Research-Based Teaching

The National Council of Teachers of Mathematics (NCTM, 2000) continues to encourage equal emphasis upon operations with fractions and with decimals. By the fifth-grade level, children should understand that fractions and decimals are just different notational systems for recording rational numbers. See *Professional Resources Handbook, Grade 5,* Unit 5.

For more ideas relating to Unit 5, see the Teacher Support Handbook at the back of this Teacher's Edition.

Language Intervention

When students are asked to explain their thinking, have them write a written response. This will help them organize their thoughts. Then have students share their responses orally with other members of their group or with the whole class. This will help students to improve their communication skills and their mathematics vocabulary. It will also help all students to better understand the mathematical topic being discussed.

 **Time Saving Technology Support**

Ways to Assess Customized Spiral Review and Test Generator CD-ROM
Lesson Planner CD-ROM
Ways to Success Intervention CD-ROM
Math Tracks CD-ROM
Education Place: **www.eduplace.com/math/mw/**
Houghton Mifflin Math eBook CD-ROM
eManipulatives
eGames

Starting Chapter 14
Divide Decimals

Chapter Objectives

14A Relate division of fractions to division of decimals.

14B Estimate decimal quotients.

14C Divide with decimals and whole numbers.

14D Use division to find repeating decimals.

14E Decide how to write a quotient when a quotient is the solution to a problem.

Math Background

Dividing Decimals

The division algorithm for dividing a decimal by a whole number is similar to the division algorithm for whole numbers. An example of dividing money can be used to illustrate this.

If a divisor and dividend are multiplied by the same number, the quotient remains the same.

$$\frac{57}{0.3} = \frac{57 \times 10}{0.3 \times 10} = \frac{570}{3}$$

This is a principle used when dividing by a decimal. Use multiples of 10 to convert the division by a decimal into a problem of dividing by a whole number. The quotient of two decimals can always be written as a quotient of two whole numbers.

Dividing a decimal by 10 simply moves the decimal point one place to the left. Division by 10^n moves the decimal point n places to the left, when n is positive.

Divide Decimals

INVESTIGATION

Use Data

The side of the wave that surfers ride is called the face. The face of the wave that Carli just rode on was 2.5 meters high. An expert surfer may ride a big wave with a face 18 meters high. How many times higher is an 18-meter wave than the wave Carli just rode? **7.2 times higher**

face of wave

350

Using the Investigation

Have students work in small groups to answer the question posed on page 350.

To extend the investigation, have students do the following activity.

- Research surfboards. Write an ad for a surfboard. Use as many decimal numbers in your ad as you can. Circle each decimal number.

For more information about projects and investigations, visit **Education Place.** eduplace.com/math/mw

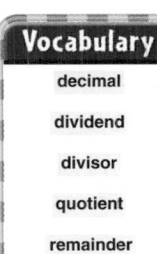 **Chapter Pretest**

Use this page to review and remember
what you need to know for this chapter.

✓ VOCABULARY

Choose the best word to complete each sentence.

Vocabulary
- decimal
- dividend
- divisor
- quotient
- remainder

1. The **quotient** ___ is the result of dividing one number by another.

2. In the expression 24 ÷ 6, 24 is the **dividend** ___.

3. In the expression 63 ÷ 9, the **divisor** ___ is 9.

✓ CONCEPTS AND SKILLS

Write a fraction in simplest form for each decimal.

4. 0.2 $\frac{1}{5}$ 5. 0.5 $\frac{1}{2}$ 6. 0.75 $\frac{3}{4}$ 7. 0.6 $\frac{3}{5}$

Estimate using compatible numbers. *Ex. 8–11. Possible estimates given.*

8. 92 ÷ 28 **3**   9. 403 ÷ 17 **20**   10. 2,361 ÷ 74 **30**   11. 589 ÷ 28 **20**

Multiply.

12. $\frac{8}{10} \times \frac{1}{6}$ $\frac{2}{15}$ 13. $\frac{45}{10} \times \frac{1}{5}$ $\frac{9}{10}$

14. $\frac{36}{10} \times \frac{1}{4}$ $\frac{9}{10}$ 15. $\frac{16}{10} \times \frac{1}{9}$ $\frac{8}{45}$

Divide.

16. $22\overline{)451}$ **20 R11**   17. 738 ÷ 17 **43 R7**

18. $65 ÷ 13 **$5**   19. 9,802 ÷ 34 **288 R10**

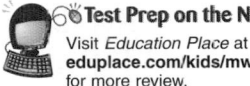 **Write About It**

20. Amelia computed 237 ÷ 18 and got a quotient of 13 R3. Explain how you could check to see whether her answer is correct.

Possible answer: Multiply 13 and 18 and add the remainder of 3 to see whether this equals the original dividend of 237.

 **Test Prep on the Net**
Visit *Education Place* at
eduplace.com/kids/mw/
for more review.

 **Chapter Pretest**

Prerequisite Skills

Items	Skill
1–3	Vocabulary needed for this chapter
4–7	Writing decimals as fractions in simplest form
8–11	Estimating quotients
12–15	Multiplying fractions
16–19	Dividing by two-digit Numbers
20	Understanding how to check division

Chapter Challenges

For Mathematically Promising Students

Use *Chapter Challenges* resource book.

Explore: Divisor/Quotient Relationships, page 79, after Lesson 1

Extend: Powers of 10, page 81, after Lesson 3

Connect: Decimal Division, page 83, after Lesson 5

Using The Chapter Pretest

This page will help students review some of the prerequisite skills needed for this chapter. The chart above indicates which skills are covered on the pretest. If students need more help with these prerequisite skills use **Ways to Success,** Houghton Mifflin's intervention program.

Students who need more review can visit **Education Place,** Houghton Mifflin's award-winning website.

NSF Children's Math Worlds

Using *Children's Math Worlds* helps develop student communication skills because of the daily work with Math Talk, a teaching practice that can be used with all lessons. The emphasis on building a helping community will also enhance student participation in all classroom discussion.

Explore Division With Decimals

PLANNING THE LESSON

MATHEMATICS OBJECTIVE
Use models to show the relationship between dividing fractions and decimals.

Use Lesson Planner CD-ROM for Lesson 14.1.

Daily Routines

Vocabulary
Discuss the meaning of *dividend, divisor,* and the fact that the *quotient* is the result of the division.

Vocabulary Cards

Meeting North Carolina's Standards
Prepare for Grade 6 Objective **1.04** Develop fluency in addition, subtraction, multiplication, and division of nonnegative rational numbers.

Lesson Transparency **14.1**

Problem of the Day
Phoebe has a savings plan. She wants to save $2.00 more each week than she saved the previous week. She saved $2 the first week. How much will she save in the fifth week if she continues with her plan? How much will she have saved in all after 5 weeks? ($10 after 5 weeks; $30)

Quick Review
Multiply.
1. 0.5×80 (40)
2. 0.8×1.2 (0.96)
3. 0.4×88 (35.2)
4. 0.7×2.4 (1.68)

Lesson Quiz
Model the division. Write the quotient in decimal form.
1. $10 \div 0.5$ (20)
2. $8 \div 0.25$ (32)
3. $6 \div 0.6$ (10)
4. $9 \div 0.3$ (30)
5. $10 \div 0.4$ (25)

LEVELED PRACTICE

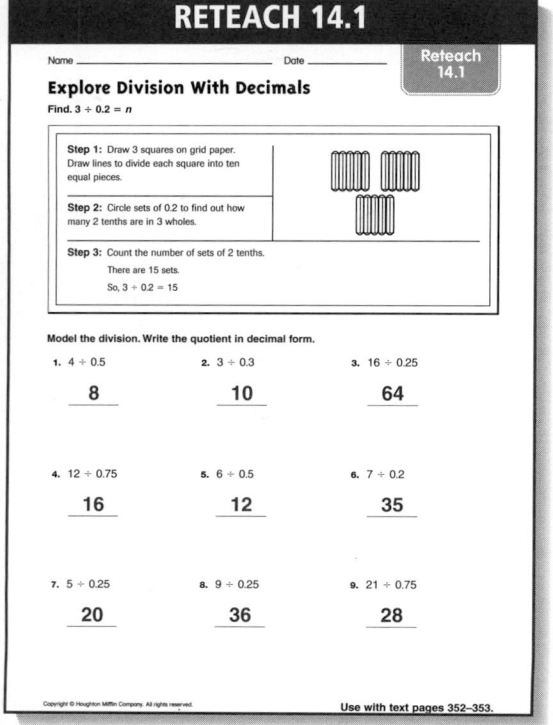

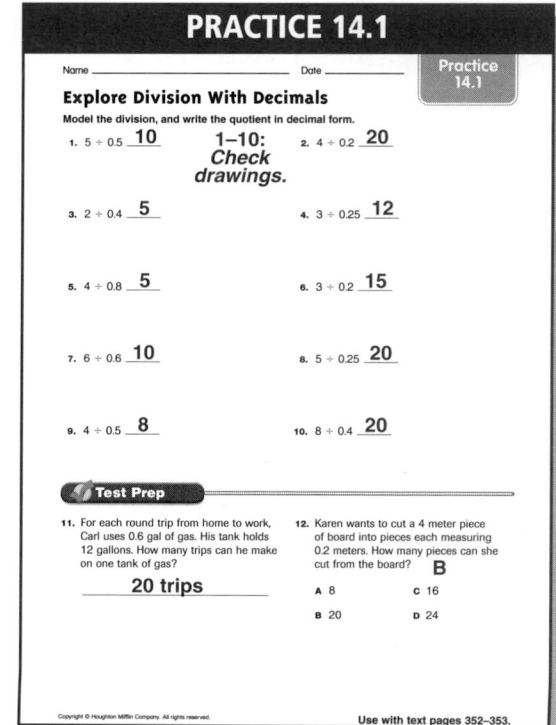

ENRICHMENT 14.1

Name _____ Date _____   Enrichment 14.1

Breaking It Down

Distances in sports are not always round numbers like the Indianapolis 500. Many of the distances are parts of larger units and can be given as decimals.

1. Many tracks in track and field are a 0.25 mile oval. How many laps is 2 miles?

   8 laps

2. The marathon is a 26-mile, 385-yard race that tests a runner's endurance. If in the first 26 miles of the race there are water stops every 0.2 mile, how many water stops are there?

   130 water stops

3. In the National Basketball Association, games last 48 minutes. Suppose that in one game, two teams average a shot every 0.3 minutes. How many shots are taken in that game?

   160 shots

4. A lap in an Olympic-sized swimming pool is 0.1 kilometer. How many laps are there in the 800-meter freestyle? Remember that 800 meters is equal to 0.8 kilometer.

   8 laps

5. A round in a boxing match is 0.05 hour. If a match lasts 0.6 hour, how many rounds is the match?

   12 rounds

Use with text pages 352–353.

Practice Workbook Page 89

Reaching All Learners

Differentiated Instruction

English Learners

Worksheet 14.1 includes diagrams and sentence frames to help students understand and complete *Explain Your Thinking*.

Special Needs
VISUAL, AUDITORY

- Display $5 \div 0.5$. **We can rewrite the decimal as a fraction.** Write $0.5 = \frac{5}{10}$. **What is $\frac{5}{10}$ in simplest form?** ($\frac{1}{2}$)

- **We can use a model for the division.** Draw 5 circles and divide them in half. **Since 0.5 is equal to $\frac{1}{2}$, how many halves are there in each circle?** (2) **in 5 circles?** (10) **What is $5 \div 0.5$?** (10)

- Follow a similar procedure for $12 \div 0.5$.

Gifted and Talented
VISUAL, AUDITORY

- Give students these problems in which the divisors are decimals greater than 1. Have them find a fractional equivalent for each divisor and then solve.
  1. $30 \div 1.2$ (25)
  2. $70 \div 1.4$ (50)
  3. $120 \div 1.6$ (75)
  4. $85 \div 1.7$ (50)
  5. $126 \div 1.8$ (70)

TECHNOLOGY

Spiral Review

Using the *Ways to Assess* CD-ROM, you can create **customized** spiral review worksheets covering any lessons you choose.

Education Place

Encourage students to visit Education Place at <u>eduplace.com/kids/mw/</u> for more student activities.

Lesson Planner

Use the Lesson Planner CD-ROM to see how lesson objectives for this chapter are correlated to standards.

Social Studies Connection

Materials: *reference materials*

- Have students research and report to the class about situations in which rationing of food was necessary, for example: World War II, bread lines in the former U.S.S.R., or the famine in Ethiopia. Suggest that students start by interviewing family members to gather oral histories.

- Then have students write problems that use division of whole numbers by decimals to represent the situations, for example: If a family can live on 0.75 pound of rice and there are 900 pounds of rice, how many families can eat? (1,200)

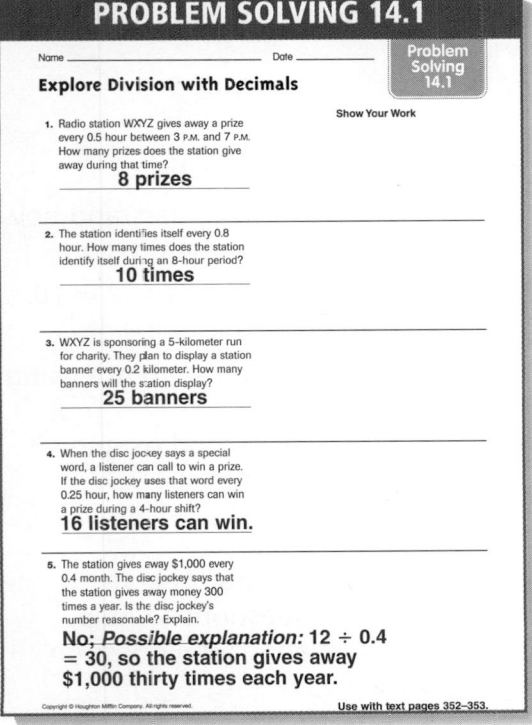

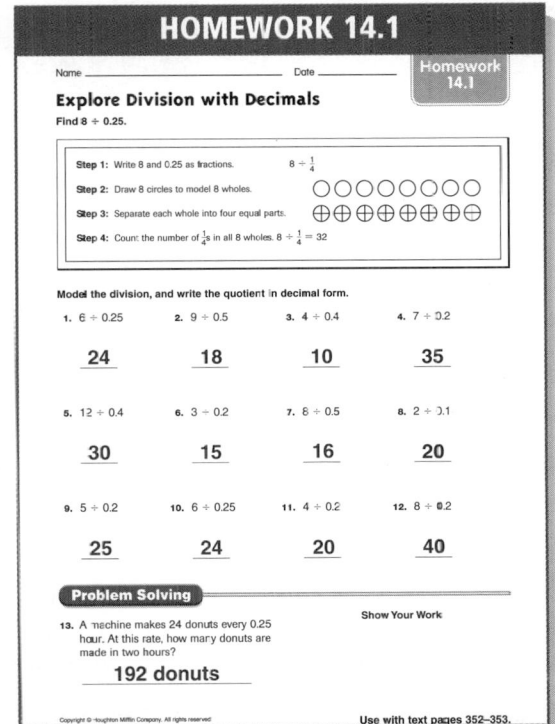

Homework Workbook Page 89

TEACHING LESSON 14.1

LESSON ORGANIZER

Objective Use models to show the relationship between dividing fractions and decimals.

Resources Reteach, Practice, Enrichment, Problem Solving, Homework, English Learners, Transparencies, Math Center

Materials None

Warm-Up Activity
Multiplying and Dividing with Fractions

| 👥 Whole Group | ⏱ 5 minutes | Visual, Auditory |

Write the following problems on the board for students to solve.

1. $12 \div \frac{1}{4}$ (48)
2. $8 \div \frac{1}{3}$ (24)
3. $6 \div \frac{3}{4}$ (8)
4. $10 \times \frac{3}{2}$ (15)
5. $10 \times \frac{8}{5}$ (16)

Explore Division With Decimals

Objective Use models to show the relationship between dividing fractions and decimals.

Learn About It

Melissa is training for a 5-kilometer race. Her coach has separated the course into 0.5-kilometer sections. How many sections is that for a 5-kilometer course?

Find $5 \div 0.5 = n$.

You can use models and what you know about fractions to find $5 \div 0.5$. Try changing the decimals to fractions and then modeling the division.

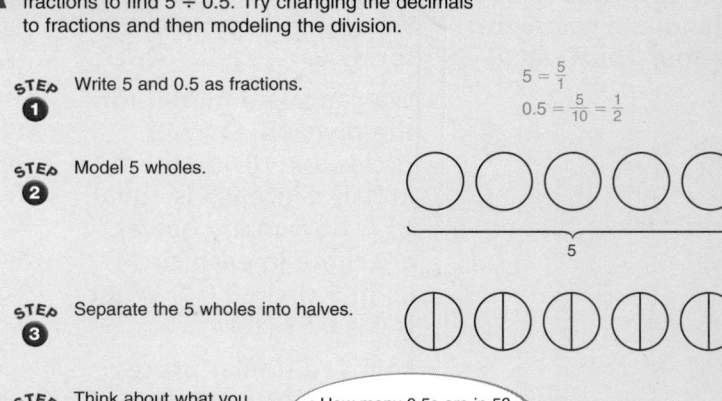

STEP 1 Write 5 and 0.5 as fractions.

$$5 = \frac{5}{1}$$
$$0.5 = \frac{5}{10} = \frac{1}{2}$$

STEP 2 Model 5 wholes.

STEP 3 Separate the 5 wholes into halves.

STEP 4 Think about what you are asked to find.
- How many 0.5s are in 5?
- How many $\frac{1}{2}$s are in 5?

STEP 5 Count to find the number of $\frac{1}{2}$s in 5?

Write a multiplication sentence that shows the answer to $5 \div \frac{1}{2}$.

There are 10 halves in 5 wholes.

$$5 \div \frac{1}{2} = 5 \times 2 = 10.$$

There are two $\frac{1}{2}$s in each whole. Multiplying 2 times 5 shows that there are 10 halves in 5 wholes.

Solution: Since $5 \div \frac{1}{2} = 10$, then $5 \div 0.5 = 10$.

---

1 Introduce

- Tell students they are going to use a model to explore dividing a whole number by a decimal.
- Write $6 \div 0.5$ on the chalkboard. **How can we write 0.5 as a fraction?** ($\frac{5}{10}$) **What is that fraction in simplest form?** ($\frac{1}{2}$)
- Draw 6 circles on the chalkboard. **We can divide each circle into halves. If there are two halves in each circle, how many halves are there in the 6 circles?** (12) **What is $6 \div 0.5$?** (12)

2 Develop

Guide students through the *Learn About It* section.

- Review the steps. Make sure that students understand how the number of halves in 5 circles relates to the division.
- **Look at the last step.** Write: $5 \div \frac{1}{2} = 5 \times \frac{2}{1} = 5 \times 2 = 10$. **Why is $5 \div \frac{1}{2}$ the same as 5×2?** (2 is the reciprocal of $\frac{1}{2}$)
- Go over the *Other Examples*. **What division sentence using a fraction can we write for the first example?** ($2 \div \frac{4}{10}$ or $2 \div \frac{2}{5}$) **What is the quotient?** (5) **for the second example?** ($6 \div \frac{2}{10}$ or $6 \div \frac{1}{5}$) **What is the quotient?** (30)

Guided Practice

Have students complete **Exercises 1–6** as you observe. Remind them to use the *Ask Yourself* questions to help. Give students the opportunity to talk about the question in *Explain Your Thinking*.

Other Examples

A. Use a Model

Find $2 \div 0.4$.

You can use models to show how many groups of 4 tenths there are in 2.

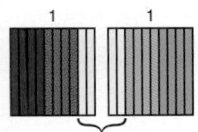

0.4 0.4 0.4 0.4 0.4

There are 5 groups of 4 tenths in 2,
$2 \div 0.4 = 5$

B. Use Number Sense

Find $6 \div 0.2$.

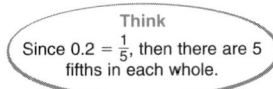
Think
Since $0.2 = \frac{1}{5}$, then there are 5 fifths in each whole.

So, in 6 wholes, there are 6×5, or 30 fifths.

$6 \div 0.2 = 30$

1–6. Check students' drawings.

Guided Practice

Model the division. Write the quotient in decimal form.

1. $6 \div 0.5$ **12**
2. $4 \div 0.4$ **10**
3. $12 \div 0.25$ **48**
4. $10 \div 0.25$ **40**
5. $8 \div 0.5$ **16**
6. $9 \div 0.2$ **45**

Ask Yourself
- Did I change the decimal to a fraction?
- Did I think about the number of parts in each whole?

TEST TIPS

TEST TIPS **Explain Your Thinking ▶** Explain how you could use number sense to find the quotient for Exercise 6.

Think about 0.2 as a fraction: $\frac{1}{5}$. There are 5 fifths in 1 whole, so there are 5×9 or 45 fifths in 9.

Practice and Problem Solving

Model the division and write the quotient in decimal form. *Check students' drawings.*

7. $3 \div 0.5$ **6**
8. $4 \div 0.5$ **8**
9. $8 \div 0.4$ **20**
10. $2 \div 0.25$ **8**
11. $3 \div 0.25$ **12**
12. $4 \div 0.25$ **16**
13. $3 \div 0.6$ **5**
14. $4 \div 0.8$ **5**
15. $5 \div 0.2$ **25**
16. $10 \div 0.2$ **50**

17. **Mental Math** As Melita trains, she checks her heart rate every 0.25 kilometer. How many times does she check it in 1 kilometer? **4 times**

18. **Represent** Cameron speed walks 2 miles in 0.5 hour. At this pace, how far can he speed walk in 1 hour? Draw a model to show your solution. **4 miles**

Daily Review	Test Prep

Compare. Write <, >, or = for each ●.
(Ch. 9, Lessons 8 and 9)

19. 0.5 **>** ● $\frac{1}{3}$

20. $1\frac{3}{4}$ **>** ● 1.6

21. 2.6 **=** ● $2\frac{3}{5}$

22. 0.125 **=** ● $\frac{1}{8}$

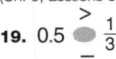 23. Each runner's number bib uses 0.2 meter of cloth. How many bibs can be made from 3 meters of cloth?

A 0.2   **C** 6

B 1.5   **(D)** 15

Extra Practice See page 375, Set A.

Chapter 14 Lesson 1 **353**

A team is having a post-game celebration. They buy 10 pizzas. If the committee expects that each member will eat 0.5 of a pizza, how many team members are on the team? (20)

Activity

Or use Intervention CD-ROM Lesson 14.1

Lesson Intervention
Using a Model to Divide by a Decimal

👥 Small Group	🕐 5–10 minutes	Visual, Auditory

- Write $8 \div 0.5$ on the chalkboard. **This division asks us to find how many times five tenths divides into 8. It will help if we express the decimal as a fraction. What fraction is equivalent to 0.5?** $\left(\frac{5}{10}\right)$ **How can we write $\frac{5}{10}$ in simplest form?** (divide the numerator and the denominator by 5) **What fraction do we get?** $\left(\frac{1}{2}\right)$

- **To solve the problem, we need to find out how many halves there are in 8. We can use a model to help.**

- **Draw 8 circles on the chalkboard. Ask a volunteer to come to the board and divide each circle into halves. How many halves are there in 1 circle?** (2) **in 8 circles?** (16) **What is $8 \div 0.5$?** (16)

---

③ Practice

Assign **Exercises 7–23** as independent work.

- ***Problem Solving for Problems 17–18*** For Problems 17–18, have students discuss their answers.

Common Error

Not multiplying by the reciprocal of the fraction divisor
When rewriting a decimal divisor as a fraction, students should be sure to use the reciprocal of the divisor when rewriting the division as a multiplication.

④ Assess and Close

- **What is the advantage of expressing a decimal divisor as a fraction when you divide a whole number by a decimal?** (Expressing a decimal divisor as a fraction may allow an application of number sense: simplifying the problem by dividing by common factors of the divisor and dividend.)

Assign the **LESSON QUIZ** on Transparency 14.1 to further assess student understanding.

 **Keeping a Journal**

Have students write a problem involving dividing a whole number by a decimal. Have students illustrate their problem with a model. Have them explain how to use a fraction equivalent for the decimal divisor.

Lesson 14.2

Estimate Quotients

PLANNING THE LESSON

MATHEMATICS OBJECTIVE
Estimate decimal quotients using compatible numbers.

Use Lesson Planner CD-ROM for Lesson 14.2.

Daily Routines

Vocabulary

When we say people are *compatible*, we mean they get along well together. Sometimes we say that objects, such as computers, are compatible. What does that mean? (They can work together.) Explain that *compatible numbers* are numbers that are easy to work with, and that you can easily compute with mentally. They are especially useful in estimating quotients.

Vocabulary Cards

Meeting North Carolina's Standards

Prepare for Grade 6 Objective **1.04** Develop fluency in addition, subtraction, multiplication, and division of nonnegative rational numbers.

Lesson Transparency 14.2

Problem of the Day

A number is divided by 4 and then increased by 160. Then 40 is subtracted from the result. The final number is 320. Find the original number. (800)

Quick Review

Estimate the quotient.

1. $61 \div 18$ (3)
2. $615 \div 9$ (60)
3. $242 \div 12$ (20)
4. $482 \div 6$ (80)
5. $886 \div 29$ (30)

Lesson Quiz

Estimate the quotient by using compatible numbers.

1. $58 \div 0.47$ (120)
2. $95 \div 0.241$ (400)
3. $8 \div 0.19$ (40)
4. $52 \div 0.54$ (100)
5. $4.9 \div 0.22$ (25)

LEVELED PRACTICE

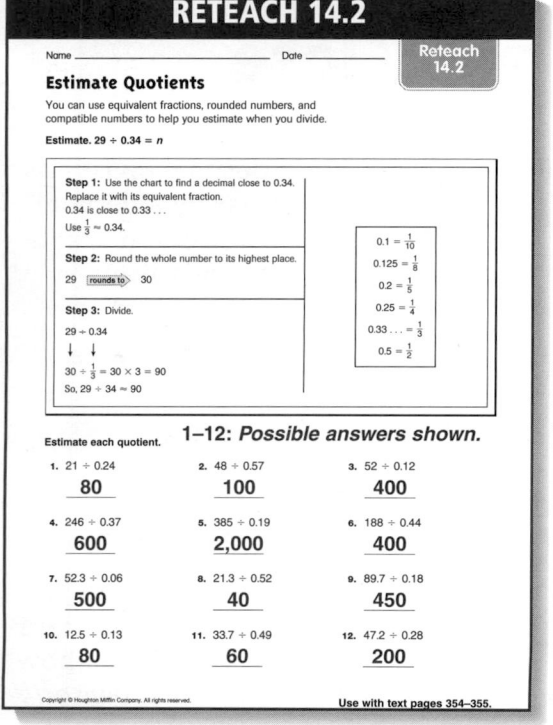

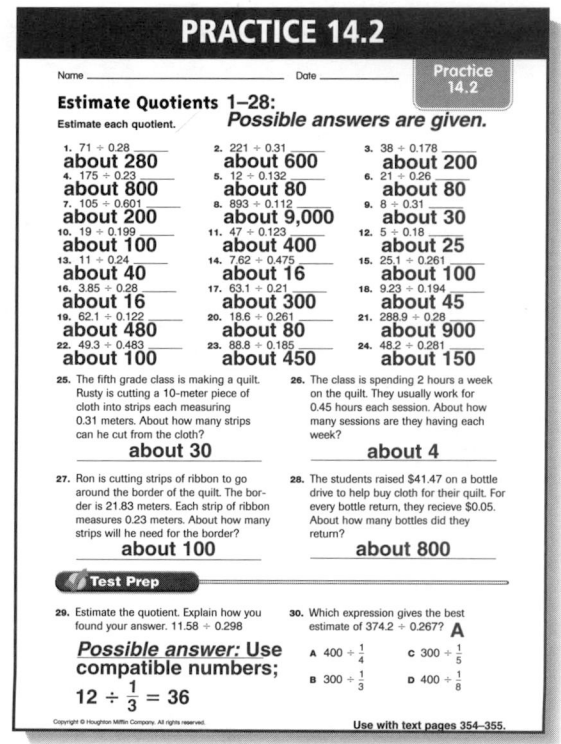

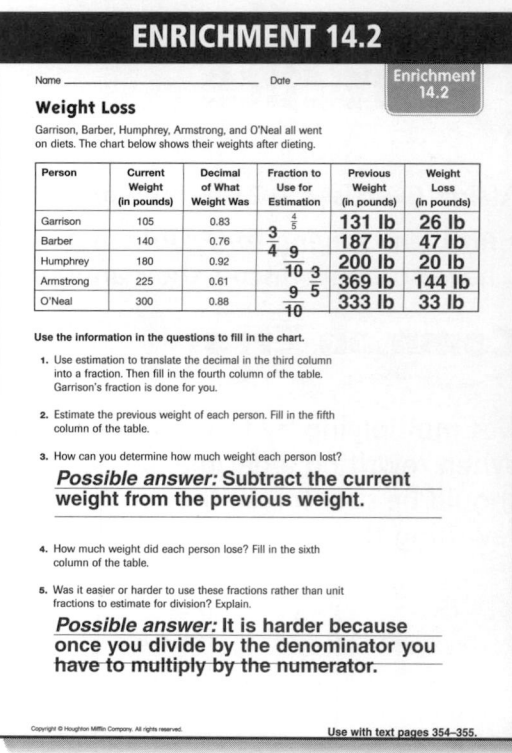

Practice Workbook Page 90

Reaching All Learners
Differentiated Instruction

English Learners

Use Worksheet 14.2 to help students understand the meaning of *compatible* and apply it in a math context. Exposure to compatible numbers will enable them to work through the activities in the lesson.

Inclusion
VISUAL, AUDITORY

- Display: *22 ÷ 0.47*. **We can estimate quotients using compatible numbers. What is 22 close to?** (20) **0.4?** (0.50) **Write a fraction for 0.5.** ($\frac{5}{10}$) **What equals $\frac{5}{10}$?** ($\frac{1}{2}$)

- Display: *20 ÷ $\frac{1}{2}$*. Ask if there are 2 halves in 1, how many are in 20? (2 × 20 or 40) **What is the estimated quotient of 22 ÷ 0.47?** (40)

Early Finishers
VISUAL, AUDITORY

- Give students these 5 problems and ask them to estimate the quotients:
  1. 18 ÷ 0.217 (100)
  2. 57.3 ÷ 0.18 (300)
  3. 413 ÷ 0.47 (800)
  4. 97.4 ÷ 0.24 (400)
  5. 146 ÷ 0.124 (1200)

- Have students exchange problems with partners and discuss the compatible numbers and unit fractions they used to solve each problem.

TECHNOLOGY

Spiral Review

To reinforce skills on lessons taught earlier, create **customized** spiral review worksheets using the *Ways to Assess* CD-ROM.

Tool Software

Use *Easy Sheet* or another spreadsheet to explore this lesson more fully.

Education Place

Recommend that parents visit Education Place at **eduplace.com/parents/mw/** for parent support activities.

Social Studies Connection

Egypt

- Explain to students that the Egyptians had a way of writing $\frac{1}{2}$, $\frac{2}{3}$, and $\frac{3}{4}$, but expressed all other fractions as sums of unit fractions. Where we might write $\frac{3}{5} = \frac{1}{5} + \frac{1}{5} + \frac{1}{5}$, the Egyptians wrote $\frac{3}{5} = \frac{1}{2} + \frac{1}{10}$.

- Likewise, a fraction as cumbersome as $\frac{47}{60}$, they wrote as $\frac{1}{3} + \frac{1}{4} + \frac{1}{5}$. And for $\frac{63}{64}$, they wrote: $\frac{1}{2} + \frac{1}{4} + \frac{1}{8} + \frac{1}{16} + \frac{1}{32} + \frac{1}{64}$.

- Have students check the common denominators the Egyptians used and then check to see that the fractions are added correctly.

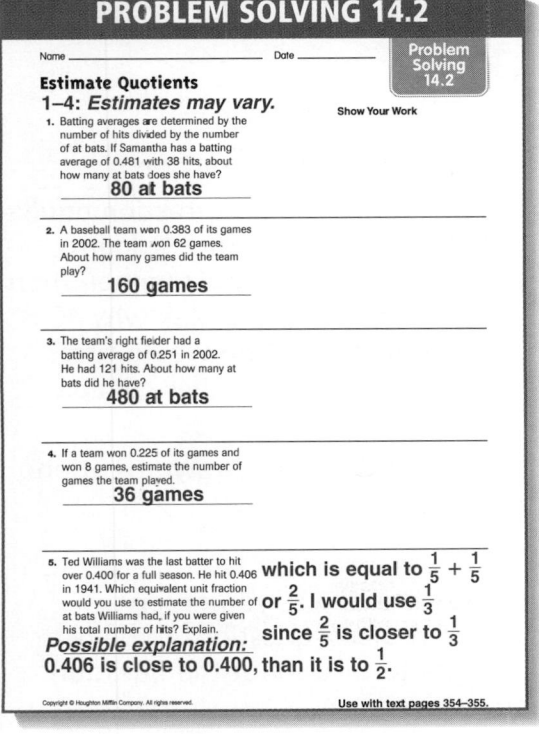

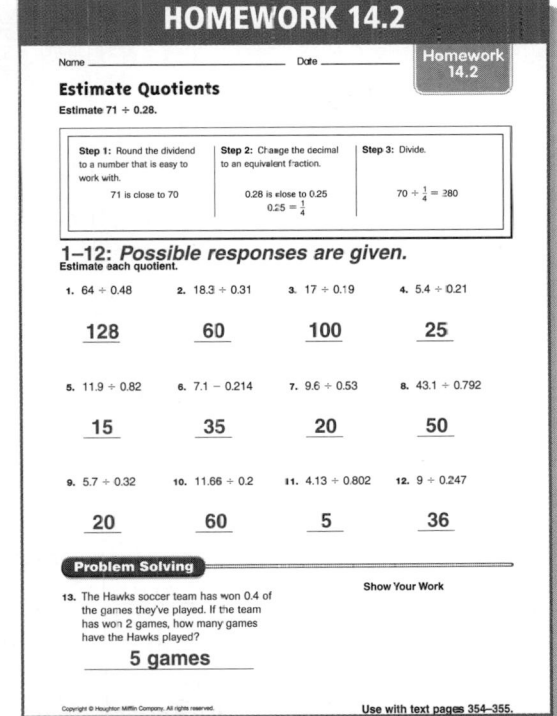

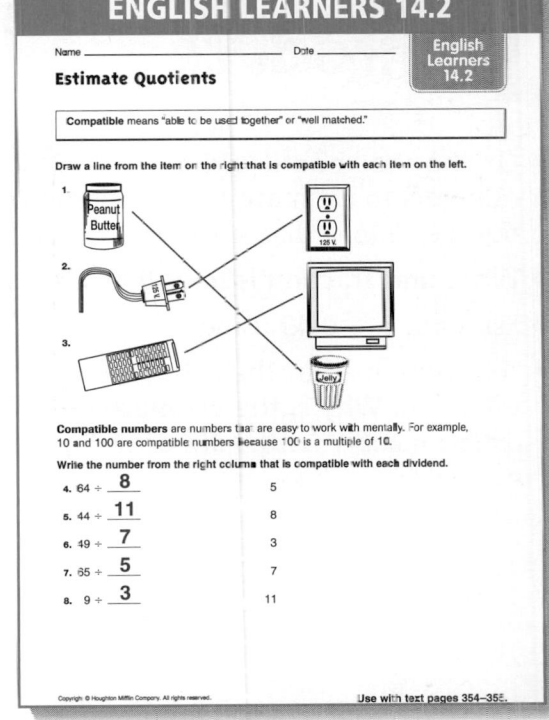

Homework Workbook Page 90

TEACHING LESSON 14.2

LESSON ORGANIZER

Objective Estimate decimal quotients using compatible numbers.

Resources Reteach, Practice, Enrichment, Problem Solving, Homework, English Learners, Transparencies, Math Center

Materials None

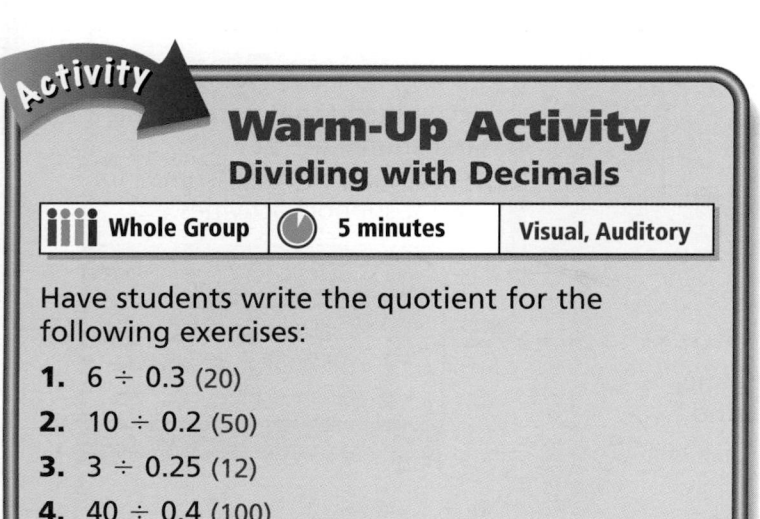

Warm-Up Activity
Dividing with Decimals

Whole Group	5 minutes	Visual, Auditory

Have students write the quotient for the following exercises:

1. $6 \div 0.3$ (20)
2. $10 \div 0.2$ (50)
3. $3 \div 0.25$ (12)
4. $40 \div 0.4$ (100)
5. $18 \div 0.6$ (30)

Estimate Quotients

Objective Estimate decimal quotients using compatible numbers.

Learn About It  MathTracks 2/6 Listen and Understand

During its history, one team's win ratio has been 0.23. They have won 38 games. To find about how many games they have played in all, divide 38 by 0.23.

You can use fractions, rounded decimals, and compatible numbers to estimate a quotient. Using equivalent unit fractions for decimals makes estimation easier.

$0.1 = \frac{1}{10}$	$0.25 = \frac{1}{4}$
$0.125 = \frac{1}{8}$	$0.33... = \frac{1}{3}$
$0.2 = \frac{1}{5}$	$0.5 = \frac{1}{2}$

Estimate. $38 \div 0.23 = n$

STEP 1 Change the decimal to an equivalent unit fraction.
$$0.23 \approx 0.25$$
$$0.25 = \frac{1}{4}$$

STEP 2 Change the dividend to a compatible number.
$$38 \approx 40$$
40 is easy to work with.

STEP 3 Estimate the number of fourths in 40.
There are 160 fourths in 40.
The quotient will be about 160.
$$38 \div 0.23 \approx 160$$

> **Think**
> There are 4 fourths in 1. 40 has 4×40 fourths, or 160 fourths.

Solution: The team has played about 160 games.

Another Example

Dividend and Divisor Are Decimals

Estimate. $54.8 \div 0.13 = n$

$54.8 \approx 50$, $0.13 \approx 0.125$ and $0.125 = \frac{1}{8}$

$54.8 \div 0.13 \approx 50 \div \frac{1}{8}$

$54.8 \div 0.13 \approx 400$

> **Think**
> There are 8 eighths in 1, so there are 50×8 or 400 eighths in 50.

354

---

1 Introduce

- On the chalkboard, write $6 \div 0.49$. We can use compatible numbers to estimate the quotient. **What are compatible numbers?** (one that is easy to work with mentally)

- **What unit fraction is near 0.49 and compatible with 6?** ($\frac{1}{2}$)

- Estimate $6 \div 0.49$ using $6 \div \frac{1}{2}$. (12)

- Tell students that the actual quotient is 12.3, to the nearest tenth. **Why is the estimated quotient less?** (The compatible number for the divisor was greater than the original number.)

2 Develop

Guide students through the *Learn About It* section.

- Have students copy and memorize the unit fraction equivalents in the table. **Look at Step 1.** Make sure students understand that they first find a compatible number, then an equivalent unit fraction. **Look at Step 2.** Ask why 40 is a good estimate for 38. **In Step 3, what do we do first? second?** (Find out how many fourths are in 1, then multiply that number by 40.)

- Have students look at *Another Example.* Draw attention to the compatible numbers that were chosen.

Guided Practice

Have students complete **Exercises 1–6** as you observe. Remind them to use the *Ask Yourself* questions to help. Give students the opportunity to talk about the question in *Explain Your Thinking.*

Estimate each quotient. *Possible estimates given.*

1. 127 ÷ 0.19
   about 625
2. 57 ÷ 0.32
   about 180
3. 190 ÷ 0.49
   about 380
4. 17.6 ÷ 0.09
   about 200
5. 48.4 ÷ 0.27
   about 200
6. 57.6 ÷ 0.11
   about 600

Ask Yourself
- Did I change the decimal to an equivalent unit fraction?
- Is my new dividend easy to work with?

Explain Your Thinking ▶ Explain how you chose the numbers you used to estimate the quotient in Exercise 1.

Possible answer: 127 is close to 125, and 0.19 is close to 0.2, which is $\frac{1}{5}$. 5 × 125 = 625

Practice and Problem Solving

Estimate each quotient. Ex. 7–18: *Possible estimates given.*

7. 47 ÷ 0.53
   about 100
8. 152 ÷ 0.29
   about 450
9. 408 ÷ 0.18
   about 2,000
10. 36 ÷ 0.54
    about 80
11. 8 ÷ 0.236
    about 32
12. 19 ÷ 0.179
    about 100
13. 5 ÷ 0.475
    about 10
14. 47 ÷ 0.345
    about 150
15. 8.38 ÷ 0.24
    about 32
16. 6.97 ÷ 0.341
    about 21
17. 52.1 ÷ 0.18
    about 250
18. 17.6 ÷ 0.26
    about 80

Solve.

19. **Estimate** A newspaper finds the field hockey team's winning ratio by dividing the number of games won by the number of games played. The team has won 6 games and has a winning ratio of 0.33. About how many games has the team played?

19–21. See Additional Answers on Page 375.

20. **You Decide** Decide on a win ratio for a team and the number of games it has won. Use the data you create to figure out the number of games the team has lost.

21. **Write About It** How does thinking about an equivalent fraction for a decimal help you estimate quotients?

Field Hockey Team Gets 6TH Win

In the last ten minutes of hectic play and two turn-arounds, our team surprised the fans with the final goal against the Panthers.

22. In field hockey the goal cage takes up $\frac{1}{5}$ of the 60-yard goal line. How many feet long is the goal cage? **12 feet**

Daily Review | Test Prep

Add or subtract. Write your answer in simplest form. (Ch. 10, Lessons 4 and 8)

23. $2\frac{3}{5} + 1\frac{7}{10}$ $4\frac{3}{10}$
24. $5\frac{3}{4} + 2\frac{1}{3}$ $8\frac{1}{12}$
25. $4\frac{2}{3} - 3\frac{5}{6}$ $\frac{5}{6}$
26. $7\frac{1}{8} - \frac{9}{10}$ $6\frac{9}{40}$

27. **Free Response** For fifth-graders, field hockey games last an average of 0.55 hour. About how many games can be played during a 4-hour tournament? **about 7 games**

Extra Practice See page 375, Set B.

DAILY TEST PREP

Test Prep Transparency **14.2**

It takes about 0.71 minute to sprint from one end of the gym to the other and back. About how many track students could do that one after another in a 15-minute period of time? (3)

A. 15
C. 12
E. 20
D. 7

Activity

Lesson Intervention
Rounding to find Compatible Numbers

Or use Intervention CD-ROM Lesson 14.2

| 👥 Small Group | 🕐 10–15 minutes | Visual, Auditory |

- On the chalkboard, write *33 ÷ 0.23.*
- Since 33 and 0.23 are not easy to work with, we can use compatible numbers to estimate the quotient of this problem. We can round to find compatible numbers. What is 0.23 rounded to the greatest place? (0.2) What is 33 rounded to the greatest place? (30) Write *30 ÷ 0.2*
- Compatible numbers for decimals should convert easily into fractions. What is the fraction equivalent of 0.2? $(\frac{2}{10} = \frac{1}{5})$
- How many fifths are there in 1? (5) How many fifths are there in 30? (150)

---

3 Practice

Assign **Exercises 7–27** as independent work. For Exercises 7–18, have students discuss their answers.

- *Problem Solving for Problems 19–22* For Problem 19, have students explain how they set up and solved the problem. For Problem 20, have students discuss and share their problems and the data they created.

Common Error

Choosing numbers that are not compatible Make sure students understand that they should choose numbers that make the dividend easily divisible by the divisor.

4 Assess and Close

- **Explain how to choose compatible numbers to estimate a quotient. Give one or two examples.** (The numbers should be easy to work with and the decimal should equal a fraction that divides easily into the dividend.)

Assign the **LESSON QUIZ** on Transparency 14.2 to further assess student understanding.

Keeping a Journal

Have students write a few sentences explaining the advantage of using compatible numbers to estimate quotients. Have students write about a possible disadvantage of using this process.

Mental Math: Multiply and Divide by Powers of 10

PLANNING THE LESSON

MATHEMATICS OBJECTIVE
Use patterns to multiply and divide by powers of 10.

Use Lesson Planner CD-ROM for Lesson 14.3.

Daily Routines

Vocabulary

Explain that a *power* is a number that can be expressed by using an *exponent.* For example, 4 can be expressed as a power of 2: 2^2. Explain that the expression 10^n is called a power of 10, where *n* is the exponent, the number that tells how many times 10 is used as a *factor.* In 10^3, 10 is a factor 3 times. $10^3 = 10 \times 10 \times 10 = 1,000$.

Vocabulary Cards

Meeting North Carolina's Standards

Prepare for Grade 6 Objective **1.04** Develop fluency in addition, subtraction, multiplication, and division of nonnegative rational numbers.

Lesson Transparency 14.3

Problem of the Day
Without using exponents, what is the greatest number you can make using two different operations, and the numbers 5, 20, and 30? $(30 \times (20 + 5) = 750)$

Quick Review
Choose the greater product.
1. 52×10 or $5.2 \times 1,000$ $(5.2 \times 1,000)$
2. $0.6 \times 1,000$ or 60×100 (60×100)
3. 380×0.1 or $3,800 \times 0.01$ (The numbers are equal.)
4. $6,400 \times 0.1$ or $6.4 \times 1,000$ $(6.4 \times 1,000)$

Lesson Quiz
Multiply or divide by using patterns.
1. 6.88×10^1 (68.8)
2. 9.32×10^2 (932)
3. 8.5×10^3 (8,500)
4. $3.5 \div 10^1$ (0.35)
5. $76 \div 10^2$ (0.76)

LEVELED PRACTICE

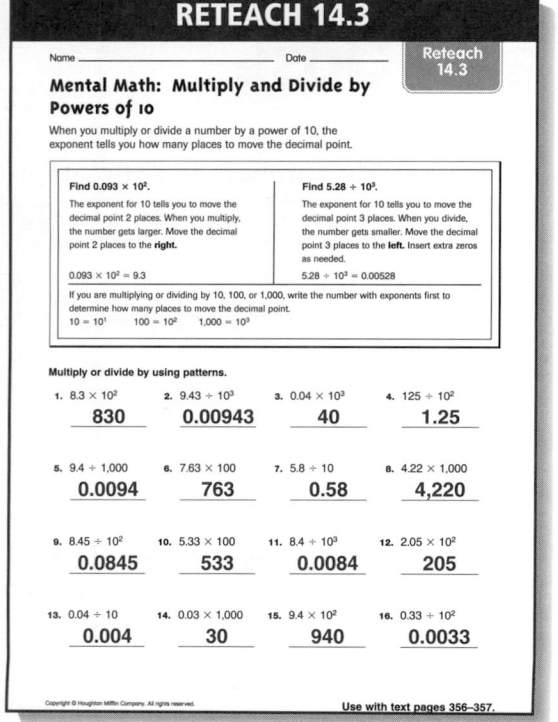

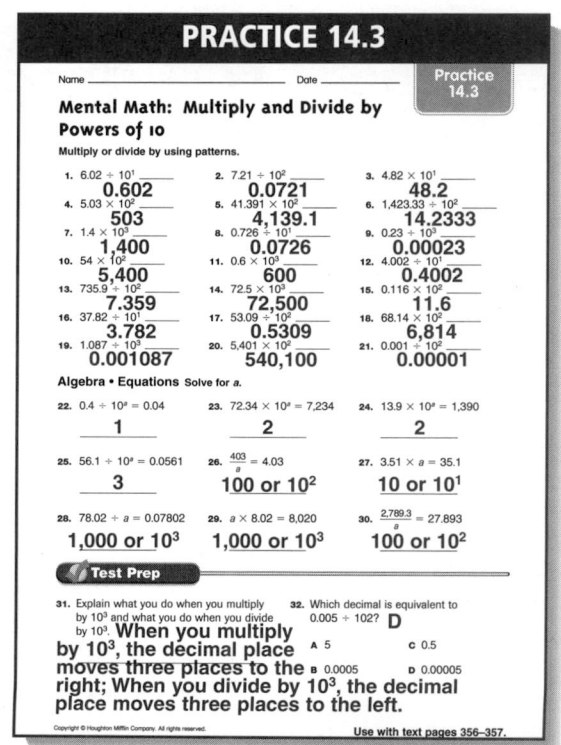

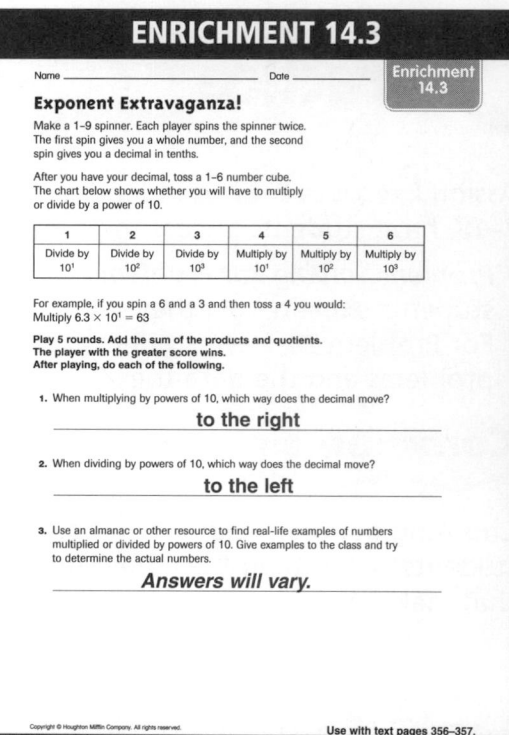

Practice Workbook Page 91

Reaching All Learners
Differentiated Instruction

English Learners

Use Worksheet 14.3 to help students see the relationship between the number of places a decimal point moves when a number is divided or multiplied by a power of 10 and the exponent of 10. This will help students complete the activities in the lesson.

Special Needs
VISUAL, AUDITORY

- Display:
$0.003 \times 10^1 = 0.03$
$0.003 \times 10^2 = 0.3$
$0.003 \times 10^3 = 3$

- The pattern shows that multiplying a decimal by a power of 10 moves the decimal point to the right the same number of places as the number of the exponent. Review examples to help students understand.

Early Finishers
VISUAL, AUDITORY

- Give students these problems. Tell them to use the rule for dividing a decimal by a power of 10 to find each quotient.
  1. $18 \div 10^2$ (0.18)
  2. $57.3 \div 10^3$ (0.0573)
  3. $97.4 \div 10^4$ (0.0097.4)

- Have students create their own examples, using exponents from 1 to 5. Have them exchange and solve.

TECHNOLOGY

Spiral Review

Help students remember skills they learned earlier by creating **customized** spiral review worksheets using the *Ways to Assess* CD-ROM.

Lesson Planner

You can use the Lesson Planner CD-ROM to create a report of the lessons and standards you have taught.

eBook

eMathBook allows students to review lessons and do homework without carrying their textbooks home.

Houghton Mifflin
Math

e MathBook

Science Connection

- Display the masses, given in scientific notation, of these six planets:

Planet	Mass (kg)
Mercury	3.30×10^{23}
Venus	4.87×10^{24}
Earth	5.97×10^{24}
Mars	6.42×10^{23}
Jupiter	1.90×10^{27}
Saturn	5.69×10^{26}

- **How do we write the masses in standard form instead of in scientific notation?** Ask how many places the decimal point moves. Call for a volunteer to come to the chalkboard and write the mass of Venus in standard form.
(4,870,000,000,000,000,000,000,000 kg)
Have students write the masses for other planets.

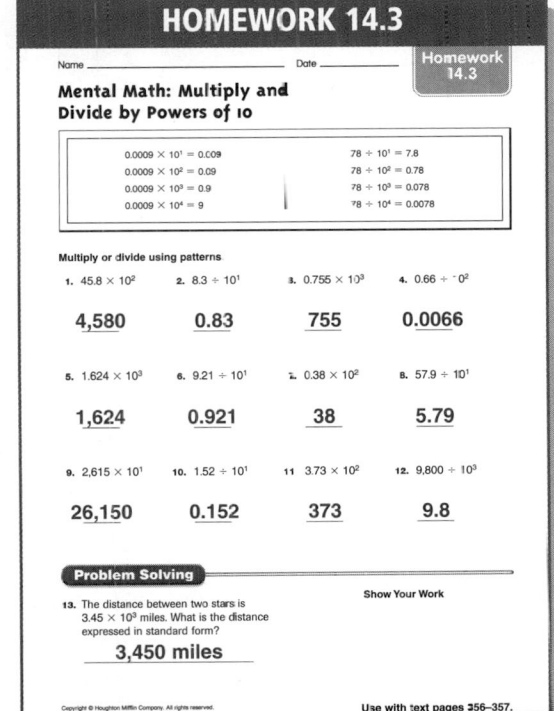

PROBLEM SOLVING 14.3

Name _____ Date _____

Problem Solving 14.3

Mental Math: Multiply and Divide by Powers of 10

Show Your Work

1. New York's Verrazano Narrows Bridge is the longest suspension bridge in the United States. It is 4.26×10^3 feet long. How long is it?
4,260 feet

2. The George Washington Bridge that connects New York and New Jersey is 7.6×10^2 feet shorter than the Verrazano Narrows Bridge. Use the information in Problem 1 to find the length of the George Washington Bridge.
3,500 feet

3. New York's Arthur Kill Bridge is the longest drawbridge in the United States. The bridge is $5,580 \div 10^1$ feet long. How long is the bridge?
558 feet

4. The Golden Gate Bridge in San Francisco is 1,280 meters long. To find its length in kilometers, should you multiply by 10^3 or divide by 10^3? Explain. ***Possible answer:*** divide by 10^3; divide to change smaller units into larger units: 1,000 meters = 1 kilometer

5. The Greater New Orleans Bridge is the longest cantilever bridge in the United States. Its length is 1,575 feet. Write a question about the bridge and use a power of 10 in the answer.
Possible explanation: How can you use a power of 10 to describe how long the Greater New Orleans Bridge is in feet?
1.575×10^3

Use with text pages 356–357.

HOMEWORK 14.3

Name _____ Date _____

Homework 14.3

Mental Math: Multiply and Divide by Powers of 10

$0.0009 \times 10^1 = 0.009$	$78 \div 10^1 = 7.8$
$0.0009 \times 10^2 = 0.09$	$78 \div 10^2 = 0.78$
$0.0009 \times 10^3 = 0.9$	$78 \div 10^3 = 0.078$
$0.0009 \times 10^4 = 9$	$78 \div 10^4 = 0.0078$

Multiply or divide using patterns

1. 45.8×10^2	2. 8.3×10^1	3. 0.755×10^3	4. $0.66 \div 10^2$
4,580	**0.83**	**755**	**0.0066**

5. 1.624×10^3	6. $9.21 \div 10^1$	7. 0.38×10^2	8. $57.9 \div 10^1$
1,624	**0.921**	**38**	**5.79**

9. $2,615 \times 10^1$	10. $1.52 \div 10^1$	11. 3.73×10^2	12. $9,800 \div 10^3$
26,150	**0.152**	**373**	**9.8**

Problem Solving

13. The distance between two stars is 3.45×10^3 miles. What is the distance expressed in standard form?
Show Your Work
3,450 miles

Use with text pages 356–357.

ENGLISH LEARNERS 14.3

Name _____ Date _____

English Learners 14.3

Multiply and Divide by Powers of 10

Look at the multiplication examples. Complete the statements.

1. $0.8387 \times 10^1 = 8.387$
The exponent of 10 is **1**. The decimal point moved **1** place(s) to the right.

2. $0.8387 \times 10^2 = 83.87$
The exponent of 10 is **2**. The decimal point moved **2** place(s) to the right.

3. $0.8387 \times 10^3 = 838.7$
The exponent of 10 is **3**. The decimal point moved **3** place(s) to the right.

Look at the division examples. Complete the statements.

4. $0.8387 \div 10^1 = 0.08387$
The exponent of 10 is **1**. The decimal point moved **1** place(s) to the left.

5. $0.8387 \div 10^2 = 0.008387$
The exponent of 10 is **2**. The decimal point moved **2** place(s) to the left.

6. $0.8387 \div 10^3 = 0.0008387$
The exponent of 10 is **3**. The decimal point moved **3** place(s) to the left.

Find the pattern.

7. When a number is multiplied by a power of 10, the decimal point moves a number of place(s) to the **right** that is equal to the **exponent or power** of 10.

8. When a number is divided by a power of 10, a decimal moves a number of places to the **left** that is equal to the **exponent or power** of 10.

Use with text pages 356–357.

Homework Workbook Page 91

TEACHING LESSON 14.3

LESSON ORGANIZER

Objective Use patterns to multiply and divide by powers of 10.

Resources Reteach, Practice, Enrichment, Problem Solving, Homework, English Learners, Transparencies, Math Center

Materials None

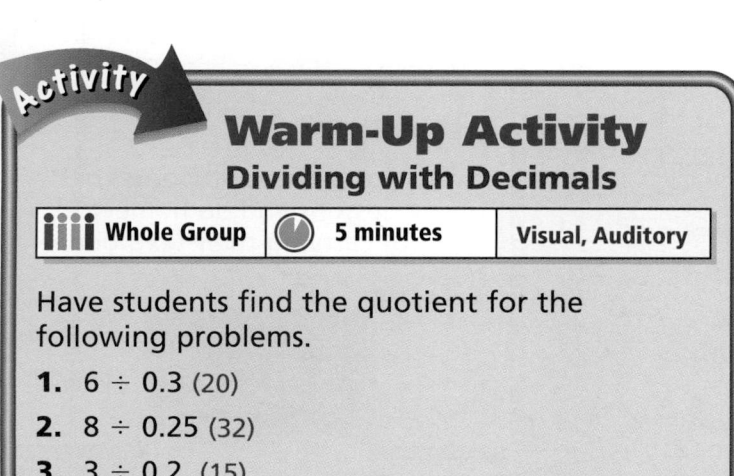

Warm-Up Activity
Dividing with Decimals

𝗂𝗂𝗂𝗂 Whole Group	⏱ 5 minutes	Visual, Auditory

Have students find the quotient for the following problems.

1. $6 \div 0.3$ (20)

2. $8 \div 0.25$ (32)

3. $3 \div 0.2.$ (15)

4. $4 \div 0.5$ (8)

5. $9 \div 0.3$ (30)

Mental Math
Multiply and Divide by Powers of 10

Objective Use patterns to multiply and divide by powers of 10.

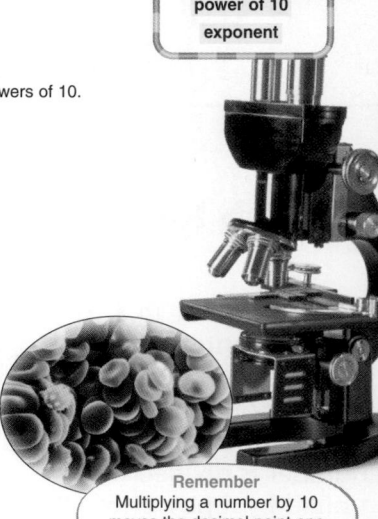

e Glossary
Vocabulary
power of 10
exponent

Learn About It

When you multiply a number by 10^n, or a **power of 10**, you are using 10 as a factor n times. In 10^n, n is called the **exponent.**

A researcher might need to examine blood cells. The diameter of a red blood cell is 0.008 millimeter. Microscopes can make objects appear 10^1 times, 10^2 times, or 10^3 times larger.

How large would a red blood cell appear at each magnification level?

Multiply 0.008 mm by 10^1, 10^2, and 10^3.

10^1 level	10^2 level	10^3 level
0.008×10^1	0.008×10^2	0.008×10^3
$\begin{array}{r} 0.008 \\ \times\ 10 \\ \hline 0.080 \text{ or } 0.08 \end{array}$	$\begin{array}{r} 0.008 \\ \times\ 100 \\ \hline 0.800 \text{ or } 0.8 \end{array}$	$\begin{array}{r} 0.008 \\ \times\ 1,000 \\ \hline 8.000 \text{ or } 8 \end{array}$
The diameter of the cell appears to be 0.08 mm.	The diameter of the cell appears to be 0.8 mm.	The diameter of the cell appears to be 8 mm.

Solution: A red blood cell can be enlarged so its diameter appears to be 0.08 millimeter, 0.8 millimeter, or 8 millimeters.

Remember
Multiplying a number by 10 moves the decimal point one place to the right.

Other Examples

A. Use Patterns

$6.5 \div 10^1 = 0.65$

The decimal point moves one place to the left.

B. Divide by 10^2

$6.5 \div 10^2 = 0.065$

The decimal point moves two places to the left.

Remember
Dividing a number by 10 moves the decimal point one place to the left.

356

---

① Introduce

- Write these equations on the chalkboard:
  $10^1 = 10$
  $10^2 = 10 \times 10 = 100$

- Then write these sentences:
  $0.005 \times 10^1 = 0.05$
  $0.005 \times 10^2 = 0.5$
  $0.005 \times 10^3 = 5$

- **How many places does the decimal point move when 0.005 is multiplied by 10^1 or 10?** (1) **In which direction?** (to the right) **What is the power of 10?** (1st)

- **How many places does the decimal point move to the right when 0.005 is multiplied by 10^2?** (2) **What is the power of 10?** (2nd)

② Develop

Guide students through the *Learn About It* section.

- Look at each of the three examples. Make sure students see the pattern illustrated by the examples: **When a decimal is multiplied by a positive power of 10, the decimal point moves to the right the same number of places as the number of the exponent.**

- Have students look at the *Other Examples*. What is the pattern? (When a decimal is divided by a power of 10, the decimal point moves *left* the same number of places as the exponent.)

Guided Practice

Have students complete **Exercises 1–6** as you observe. Remind them to use the *Ask Yourself* question to help. Give students the opportunity to talk about the question in *Explain Your Thinking.*

Ask Yourself
- Do I move the decimal point to the right or to the left?

Multiply or divide by using patterns.

1. 0.5×10^2 **50**
2. $0.2 \div 10$ **0.02**
3. 3.8×100 **380**
4. $159 \div 10^3$ **0.159**
5. 0.04×10^3 **40**
6. $6.1 \div 10^2$ **0.061**

TEST TIPS

Explain Your Thinking ▶ Why is the expression 4.2×10^3 equal to the expression 42×10^2? **When simplified, both expressions are equal to 4,200.**

Practice and Problem Solving

Multiply or divide by using patterns.

7. 5.34×10^1 **53.4**
8. 5.34×10^2 **534**
9. $5.34 \div 10^1$ **0.534**
10. $5.34 \div 10^2$ **0.0534**
11. 2.0×10^3 **2,000**
12. $75 \div 10^2$ **0.75**
13. 0.68×10^3 **680**
14. $4.72 \div 10^1$ **0.472**

✗ Algebra • Equations Solve for a.

15. $100 = 10^a$ **2**
16. $1,000 = 10^a$ **3**
17. $10 = 10^a$ **1**
18. $10.000 = 10^a$ **4**
19. $0.01a = 12$ **1,200**
20. $0.001a = 12$ **12,000**
21. $\frac{a}{10} = 15$ **150**
22. $\frac{a}{100} = 15$ **1,500**

Solve.

23. One type of cell is 0.005 mm across. It is put under a microscope so it appears to be 10^3 larger. How large would that cell seem under that microscope? **5 mm**

24. **Represent** Draw a line segment to show how large the cell in Problem 23 would appear under the microscope.
Check students' drawings.

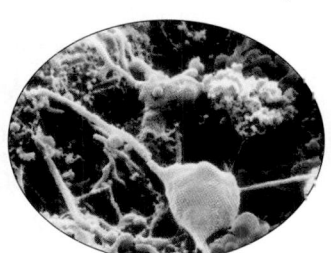

Daily Review	Test Prep ✓
Multiply. Write each product in simplest form. (Ch. 12, Lessons 2 and 3)	**29.** A sports photographer's telephoto lens keeps the shutter open for only $1.0 \div 10^3$ seconds. Which fraction shows how long that is?
25. $\frac{4}{5} \times \frac{1}{3}$ $\frac{4}{15}$ 26. $3\frac{1}{2} \times \frac{5}{7}$ $2\frac{1}{2}$	**A** $\frac{10}{1}$ **B** $\frac{1}{10}$ **C** $\frac{1}{100}$ **(D)** $\frac{1}{1,000}$
27. $\frac{3}{4} \times 1\frac{5}{9}$ $1\frac{1}{6}$ 28. $5\frac{1}{3} \times 1\frac{1}{2}$ **8**	

Extra Practice See page 375, Set C.

Chapter 14 Lesson 3 **357**

Test Prep Transparency

14.3

A cell is 0.003 millimeters in diameter. What would the measure of the diameter appear to be under a microscope with a magnifying power of 10^3? (3 millimeters)

Activity

Or use Intervention CD-ROM Lesson 14.3

Lesson Intervention
Multiplying by a Power of 10

👤👤👤 Small Group	🕐 5–10 minutes	Visual, Auditory

- Tell students they are going to explore powers of 10. 10^2 means that 10 is a factor 2 times. The 2, the exponent, tells how many times 10 is going to be a factor. So, $10^2 = 10 \times 10 = 100$.

- **What does 10^3 mean?** (that 10 is a factor 3 times; $10^3 = 10 \times 10 \times 10 = 1,000$) **What do you think 10^1 means?** (10 is a factor once; so $10^1 = 10$.)

- On the chalkboard write:

$$\begin{array}{r} 0.5 \\ \times\ 10 \\ \hline 050 \end{array}$$

There is one decimal place in 0.5. So we count back from the right of the product's ones place. So there will be one decimal place in the product. So the product is 5.0, or 5.

- Now write 0.5×10^2 We know that $0.5 \times 10 = 5$. What would the product be if we multiplied 5 by 10 again? (50)

---

3 Practice

Assign **Exercises 7–29** as independent work. For Exercises 7–14, have students discuss their answers.

- *Algebra • Equations for Exercises 15–22* For Exercises 15–18, students must first express the number on the left as a power of 10. For Exercises 19–22, have students discuss their methods and answers.

- *Problem Solving for Problems 23–24* For Problem 24, have students share their drawings with the class.

Common Error

Moving the decimal point incorrectly Have students note the exponent of the power of 10 and count carefully. They might also use a pencil to draw arrows right or left to show the movement, place by place.

4 Assess and Close

- **Explain how to multiply a decimal by a positive power of 10. Give two examples.**

- **Explain how to divide a decimal by a positive power of 10. Give two examples.**

Assign the **LESSON QUIZ** on Transparency 14.3 to further assess student understanding.

Keeping a Journal

Have students write a few sentences explaining how to multiply by positive powers of 10 using patterns

Lesson 14.4

Divide a Decimal by a Whole Number

PLANNING THE LESSON

MATHEMATICS OBJECTIVE
Divide a decimal by a whole number.

Use Lesson Planner CD-ROM for Lesson 14.4.

Daily Routines

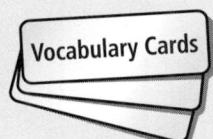

Vocabulary

Review the meaning of *reciprocal.* Ask students to give examples of when a reciprocal of a number is used.

Vocabulary Cards

Meeting North Carolina's Standards

Prepare for Grade 6 Objective **1.04** Develop fluency in addition, subtraction, multiplication, and division of nonnegative rational numbers.

Lesson Transparency **14.4**

Problem of the Day

What are the next two numbers in the sequence? Describe the pattern of the sequence.

1, 4, 2, 8, 4, 16, 8, ?, ?, . . .

(32, 16; multiply by 4, divide by 2)

Quick Review

Divide.

1. 350 ÷ 10 (35)
2. 625 ÷ 25 (25)
3. 480 ÷ 12 (40)
4. 1,600 ÷ 20 (80)
5. 228 ÷ 4 (57)

Lesson Quiz

Divide and check.

1. 7)8.4 (1.2)
2. 6)5.4 (0.9)
3. 3)34.2 (11.4)
4. 11)78.1 (7.1)
5. 6)10.8 (1.8)

LEVELED PRACTICE

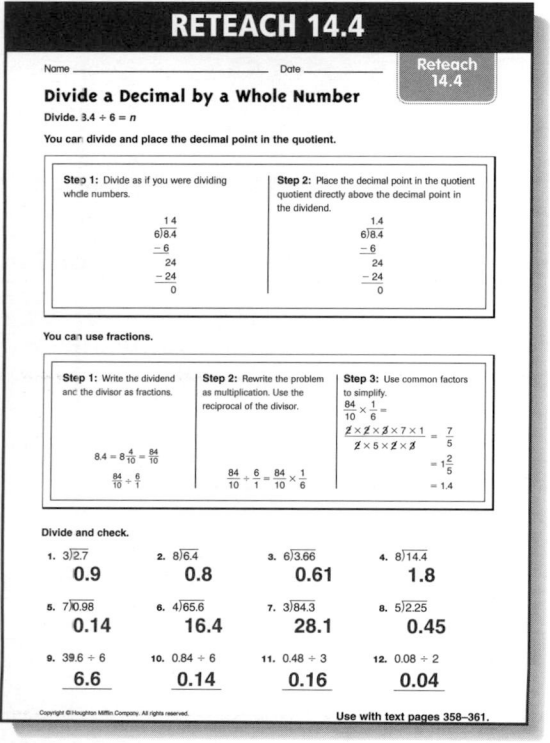

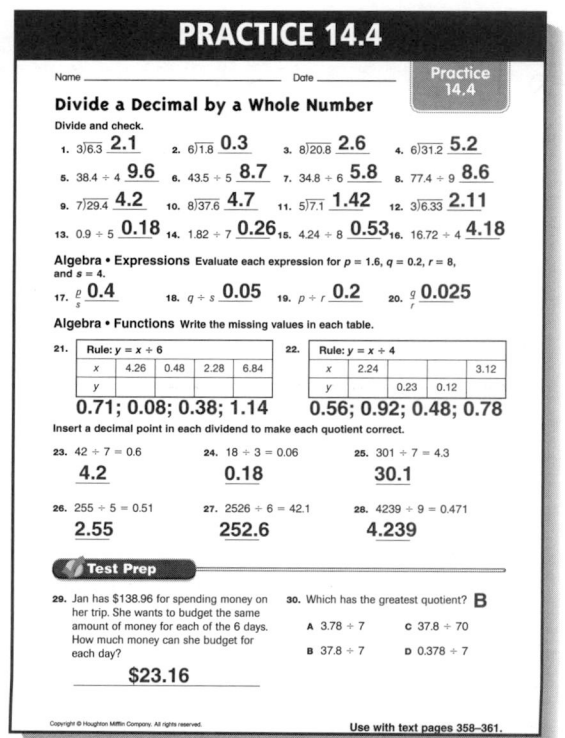

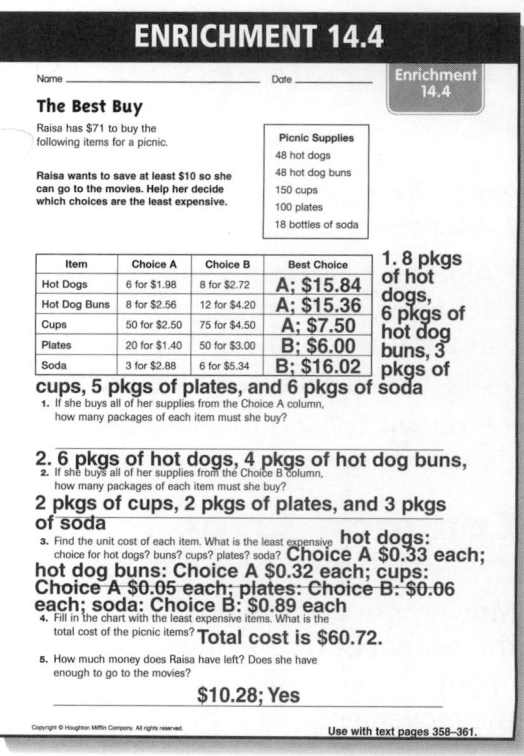

Practice Workbook Page 92

358A   CHAPTER 14   Lesson 4

Reaching All Learners
Differentiated Instruction

English Learners

English-language learners may be unfamiliar with BMX racing. Use Worksheet 14.4 to give students an introduction to the sport and to show them diagrams of a racer and a track. This background will help students understand the example problem as well as Problems 41–45.

Inclusion
VISUAL, AUDITORY

- Write $3.2 \div 0.4$. To divide a decimal by a whole number, you can express both numbers as fractions.
- Write $\frac{32}{10} \div \frac{4}{10}$. How can we write this division as multiplication? (Multiply the first factor by the reciprocal of the divisor.) What is the reciprocal of $\frac{4}{10}$? ($\frac{10}{4}$) Write $\frac{32}{10} \times \frac{10}{4}$. What is the product? ($\frac{320}{40} = 8$)

Gifted and Talented
VISUAL, TACTILE

- Have students write problems in which a decimal with one or two decimal places is divided by a whole number.
- Have students exchange problems with partners and solve one another's problems.

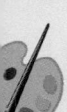

Art Connection

Materials: *cardstock, fabric scraps, scissors, stapler, centimeter ruler*

- Ask students to make a design by weaving together equal-width strips of cloth.
- Have students make a frame out of cardstock by cutting a 9.6 cm × 9.6 cm square out of the center.

- Help each student to decide the number of fabric strips to staple across the top and along the side of the frame. Explain to students that they will need to divide 9.6 by that number in order to find the width they will need to measure each strip. For example, if they want to use four strips, each will measure 9.6 cm ÷ 4 = 2.4 cm.
- Help them make their frames.

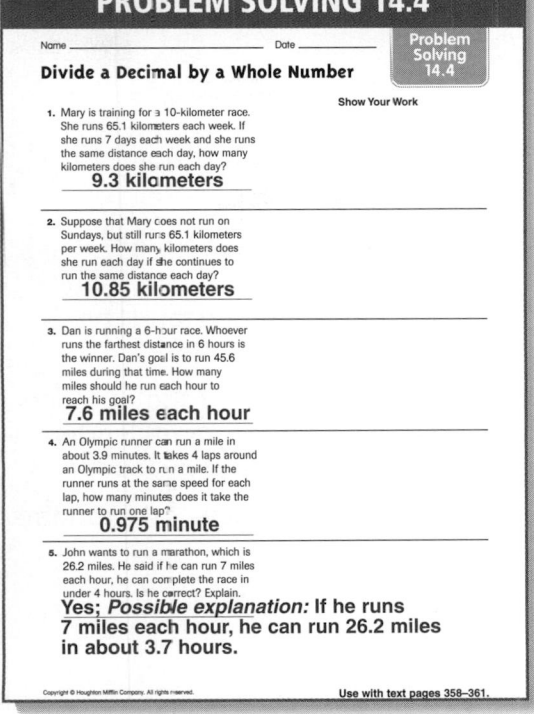

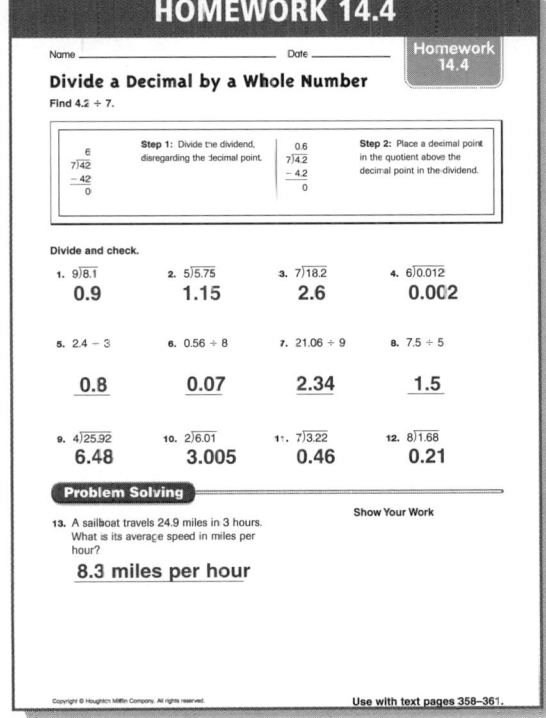

ENGLISH LEARNERS 14.4

Name _____ Date _____

Multiply and Divide by Powers of 10

Look at the multiplication examples. Complete the statements.

1. $0.8387 \times 10^1 = 8.387$

   The exponent of 10 is **1**. The decimal point moved **1** place(s) to the right.

2. $0.8387 \times 10^2 = 83.87$

   The exponent of 10 is **2**. The decimal point moved **2** place(s) to the right.

3. $0.8387 \times 10^3 = 838.7$

   The exponent of 10 is **3**. The decimal point moved **3** place(s) to the right.

Look at the division examples. Complete the statements.

4. $0.8387 \div 10^1 = 0.08387$

   The exponent of 10 is **1**. The decimal point moved **1** place(s) to the left.

5. $0.8387 \div 10^2 = 0.008387$

   The exponent of 10 is **2**. The decimal point moved **2** place(s) to the left.

6. $0.8387 \div 10^3 = 0.0008387$

   The exponent of 10 is **3**. The decimal point moved **3** place(s) to the left.

Find the pattern.

7. When a number is multiplied by a power of 10, the decimal point moves a number of place(s) to the **right** that is equal to the **exponent or power** of 10.

8. When a number is divided by a power of 10, a decimal moves a number of places to the **left** that is equal to the **exponent or power** of 10.

Use with text pages 356–357.

Homework Workbook Page 92

TEACHING LESSON 14.4

LESSON ORGANIZER

Objective Divide a decimal by a whole number.

Resources Reteach, Practice, Enrichment, Problem Solving, Homework, English Learners, Transparencies, Math Center

Materials None

Warm-Up Activity
Estimating Quotients with Compatible Numbers

Whole Group	5 minutes	Visual, Auditory

Have students estimate the quotients for the following problems by using compatible numbers.

1. $8 \div 0.42$ (20)
2. $4.2 \div 0.86$ (5)
3. $72 \div 0.42$ (175)
4. $37 \div 0.47$ (80)
5. $52 \div 0.23$ (200 or 250)

Lesson **4**

Divide a Decimal by a Whole Number

Objective Divide a decimal by a whole number.

Learn About It

The starting section for a BMX race is 7.2 meters wide. It is divided into equal-width lanes for 8 riders. How wide is each rider's lane?

Divide. $7.2 \div 8 = n$

Different Ways to Divide 7.2 by 8

Way ❶ You can use fractions.

STEP 1 Write the dividend and the divisor as fractions.

$$\frac{72}{10} \div \frac{8}{1}$$

$$7.2 = 7\frac{2}{10} = \frac{72}{10}$$

STEP 2 Multiply the dividend by the reciprocal of the divisor.

$$\frac{72}{10} \times \frac{1}{8} = \frac{72}{80}$$

STEP 3 Write the quotient as a decimal.

$$\frac{72}{80} = \frac{9}{10} = 0.9$$

Way ❷ You can divide and place the decimal point in the quotient.

STEP 1 Divide as though the dividend were a whole number.

$$\begin{array}{r} 9 \\ 8\overline{)72} \\ -72 \\ \hline 0 \end{array}$$

STEP 2 Place a decimal point in the quotient directly above the decimal point in the dividend.

$$\begin{array}{r} 0.9 \\ 8\overline{)7.2} \\ -7\ 2 \\ \hline 0 \end{array}$$

Estimate to check.
Since 7.2 m is a little less than 8 m, each of the 8 lanes would be a little less than 1 m wide. So 0.9 m is a reasonable answer.

Solution: Each lane is 0.9 meter wide.

358

---

1 Introduce

- On the chalkboard write $\frac{45}{10} \div 3$. **How do you write 3 as a fraction?** $\left(\frac{3}{1}\right)$ Write $\frac{45}{10} \div \frac{3}{1}$. **What do we do when the divisor is a fraction?** (Rewrite the division as a multiplication by the reciprocal of the original divisor.)

- **What is the equivalent multiplication sentence?** $\left(\frac{45}{10} \times \frac{1}{3}\right)$ Ask a volunteer to tell you the product. $\left(\frac{45}{30}\right)$ **How can we simplify this fraction?** (divide both numbers by 3) **What is the result?** $\left(\frac{15}{10}\right)$

- **How can we rewrite $\frac{45}{10}$ and $\frac{15}{10}$ as decimals?** (4.5, 1.5) **Now rewrite the original problem in decimal form and include the quotient.** ($4.5 \div 3 = 1.5$)

- **How can we check?** (multiply: $1.5 \times 3 = 4.5$)

2 Develop

Guide students through the *Learn About It* portion of the lesson.

- Be sure students understand that the task is to find $7.2 \div 8$.

- **Look at Way 1.** Be sure that students understand the process of rewriting the problem using fractions.

- **Look at Way 2.** Step 1 involves dividing as if the numbers were whole numbers. In Step 2, be sure students understand how to place the decimal point in the quotient.

- After finishing the discussion of the two ways, ask students which method they prefer and why.

Other Examples

A. Quotient Less Than 1

$$\begin{array}{r} 0.92 \\ 7\overline{)6.44} \\ -63 \\ \hline 14 \\ -14 \\ \hline 0 \end{array}$$

Estimate to check.

$6.44 \approx 7$
$7 \div 7 = 1$
$0.92 \approx 1$

B. Quotient Is in Dollars and Cents

$$\begin{array}{r} \$0.15 \\ 5\overline{)\$0.75} \\ -5\downarrow \\ \hline 25 \\ -25 \\ \hline 0 \end{array}$$

Multiply to check.

$$\begin{array}{r} \$0.15 \\ \times\ 5 \\ \hline \$0.75 \end{array}$$

Guided Practice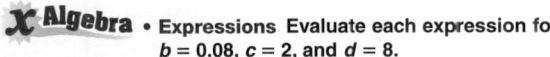

Ask Yourself
- Would it help me to use fractions?
- Did I place the decimal point correctly?

Divide and check.

1. $2\overline{)16.2}$ **8.1**   2. $5\overline{)9.75}$ **1.95**   3. $6\overline{)5.4}$ **0.9**

4. $22.8 \div 4$ **5.7**   5. $58.1 \div 7$ **8.3**   6. $0.03 \div 3$ **0.01**

TEST TIPS **Explain Your Thinking ▶** Why is it important to align the quotient and the dividend correctly when you divide with decimals?
To make sure that the decimal point appears in the correct place in the answer.

Practice and Problem Solving

Divide and check.

7. $6\overline{)7.2}$ **1.2**   8. $7\overline{)41.3}$ **5.9**   9. $3\overline{)16.2}$ **5.4**   10. $7\overline{)11.9}$ **1.7**   11. $4\overline{)0.08}$ **0.02**

12. $5.5 \div 5$ **1.1**   13. $8.4 \div 4$ **2.1**   14. $0.8 \div 2$ **0.4**   15. $20.7 \div 3$ **6.9**   16. $75.6 \div 9$ **8.4**

17. $8\overline{)2.80}$ **0.35**   18. $2\overline{)3.46}$ **1.73**   19. $6\overline{)1.44}$ **0.24**   20. $7\overline{)26.25}$ **3.75**   21. $9\overline{)45.27}$ **5.03**

22. $42.8 \div 4$ **10.7**   23. $3.87 \div 9$ **0.43**   24. $9.75 \div 3$ **3.25**   25. $6.32 \div 8$ **0.79**   26. $0.84 \div 2$ **0.42**

Insert a decimal point in each dividend to make each quotient correct.

27. $24 \div 6 = 0.4$
   2.4

28. $35 \div 7 = 0.5$
   3.5

29. $129 \div 3 = 0.43$
   1.29

30. $196 \div 4 = 4.9$
   19.6

31. $3252 \div 4 = 0.813$
   3.252

32. $5327 \div 7 = 7.61$
   53.27

✗ Algebra • **Expressions** Evaluate each expression for $a = 3.2$, $b = 0.08$, $c = 2$, and $d = 8$.

33. $a \div c$ **1.6**   34. $\dfrac{b}{c}$ **0.04**   35. $a \div d$ **0.4**   36. $b \div d$ **0.01**

Go On ➡

 Quick Check Options

The following activities will help students prepare for the Quick Check or may be used as an alternative assessment.

Vocabulary Review *(individual, small group, or whole class)*

Have students review the following vocabulary words by giving an example of how each term is used in this chapter.

- power of 10
- reciprocal
- exponent

Math Conversations *(small group or whole class)*

Have students discuss what they have learned about dividing decimals in this chapter. Encourage students to ask each other questions to clarify their understanding.

Writing Prompt *(individual or partners)*

To solidify student understanding of vocabulary and concepts, have each student complete the following sentence:

The thing I found most difficult about dividing decimals is _____.

---

❸ Practice

- Discuss how making an estimate can also be a way of checking whether the answer, 0.9, is reasonable.
- Work through the *Other Examples* with students, as well as the methods used to check their answers. The examples give students another chance to see how both methods are used. Remind them to check division by multiplying.

Guided Practice

Have students complete **Exercises 1–6** as you observe. Remind them to use the *Ask Yourself* questions to help. Give students the opportunity to talk about the question in *Explain Your Thinking*.

Assign **Problems 7–48** as independent work.

- *Exercises 7–32* Have students discuss their work.
- *Algebra • Expressions for Exercises 33–36* Have students discuss their methods and solutions.

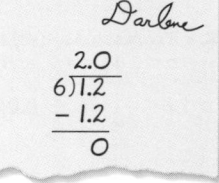

DAILY TEST PREP

Rhonda bought 12 items for $14.40. Each item cost the same amount. What was the cost of each item? (C)

A. $ 0.12   C. $1.20

B. $12   D. $120

Activity

Lesson Intervention

Or use Intervention CD-ROM Lesson 14.4

Placing the Decimal Point in the Quotient

👥 Small Group	⏱ 5–10 minutes	Visual, Kinesthetic

- **When you divide a decimal by a whole number, you can use long division. Suppose we have this problem.** Write $6)\overline{9.6}$ on the chalkboard.

- **First divide as if there were only whole numbers.** Review each step of solving the division problem as you write it on the chalkboard. **What is the quotient?** (16)

- **Notice where the decimal point is in the dividend. Where do we place the decimal point in the quotient?** (directly above the point in the dividend) **Where should the decimal point go?** (beween the 1 and the 6) **What is the quotient of 9.6 ÷ 6?** (1.6)

Write the missing values in each table.

37.

	Rule: $b = a \div 3$			
a	0.96	1.29	6.33	6.78
b				

0.32; 0.43; 2.11; 2.26

38.

	Rule: $b = a \div 5$			
a	0.65	1.5	2.25	2.75
b				

0.13; 0.3; 0.45; 0.55

39.

	Rule: $b = a \div 6$			
a	0.72		0.90	
b		0.13	0.14	

0.12; 0.78; 0.84; 0.15

40.

	Rule: $b = a \div 9$			
a		6.3	4.68	
b	0.75			0.91

6.75; 0.7; 0.52; 8.19

Solve.

41. One third of the entry fee for each rider in the BMX race shown at the right goes to pay taxes and other fees. If 150 riders enter a race, how much goes for taxes and other fees? **$675**

42. A BMX track is made up of 0.8 part clay and 0.2 part sand for every 1 part of soil. There are 3,500 cubic yards of soil on the track. How many cubic yards of clay are there? of sand? **2,800 cubic yards clay; 700 cubic yards sand**

43. Estimate The maximum length of a BMX track is 454 meters. The minimum length is 0.66 of that. Estimate the minimum length. **about 300 meters**

44. Analyze Tony and Jan are training for a bike race. Tony rode his bike 4.5 km in 9 minutes. Jan rode her bike 3.6 km in 6 minutes. Who rides farther in 1 minute? How much farther? **Jan; 0.1 km**

46. Represent A city bought a 20-acre section of land for recreational use. The land was split into 0.5-acre pieces. Draw a model to show the number of 0.5-acre pieces that can be made from that 20 acres. **See students' models; 40 pieces**

48. Write About It How is dividing a decimal by a whole number the same or different from dividing a whole number by a whole number? **See Additional Answers on page 375.**

BMX Race
Entry Fee
$13.50

47. Possible answer: Darlene should have placed 2 in the tenths place in the quotient

45. Explain Which will be greater: the quotient 6.56 ÷ 8, or the quotient 656 ÷ 80? Explain how you can tell without dividing. *See Additional Answers on Page 375.*

47. What's Wrong? Darlene divided 1.2 by 6. Her work is shown below. Explain why Darlene's method is not correct. *See above.*

Darlene

$$\begin{array}{r} 2.0 \\ 6)\overline{1.2} \\ -1.2 \\ \hline 0 \end{array}$$

Extra Practice See page 375, Set D.

Practice *continued*

- *Problem Solving for Problems 41–48* For Problems 41–48, have students explain and discuss the methods they used.

Common Error

Misplacing decimal point in quotient Suggest that students highlight the decimal point in the dividend and immediately place a decimal point in the quotient above it.

---

④ Assess and Close

- **What are two ways to divide a decimal by a whole number?** (Use fractions; use long division and place the decimal point in the quotient.)

- **How do you determine where to place the decimal point in the quotient?** (Place it directly above the decimal point in the dividend.)

Assign the **LESSON QUIZ** on Transparency 14.4 to further assess student understanding.

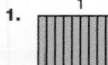

Quick Check

Check your understanding of Lessons 1–4.

Use models to divide. Write the quotients. (Lesson 1)

1.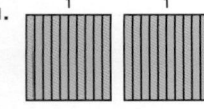

2 ÷ 0.2 **10**

2.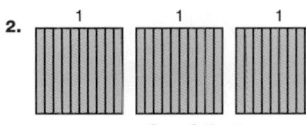

3 ÷ 0.5 **6**

3. 5 ÷ 0.2 **25**   4. 2 ÷ 0.5 **4**

Estimate each quotient. (Lesson 2)

5. 28 ÷ 0.34   6. 57.9 ÷ 0.46

Possible answer: about 90   *Possible answer: about 120*

Multiply or divide. (Lessons 3 and 4)

7. 52.3 × 10² **5,230** 8. 53.2 ÷ 10² **0.532** 9. 0.84 ÷ 7 **0.12**   10. 16.05 ÷ 3 **5.35**

Math Challenge

Use What You Know

You know how to divide whole numbers with two-digit divisors. You also know how to divide decimals with one-digit divisors. You can use what you know to divide decimals by two-digit divisors.

STEP **1** Divide the dividend by the divisor as if both are whole numbers.	STEP **2** Place a decimal point in the quotient directly above the decimal point in the dividend.
604 24)14.496 − 144↓↓ 096 − 96 0	0.604 24)14.496 − 144↓↓ 096 − 96 0

Divide. Show your work.

1. 37.5 ÷ 15   2. 157.44 ÷ 32   3. 64.05 ÷ 21   4. 0.406 ÷ 14
    2.5   **4.92**   **3.05**   **0.029**

Chapter 14 Lesson 4 **361**

Quick Check

Purpose: The Quick Check allows you to assess the students' understanding of the concepts presented in Lessons 1–4.

Items	Objectives Tested	Pages	Intervention
1–4	Use models to show the relationship between dividing fractions and decimals.	352–353	Reteach Resource 14.1 *Ways to Success* 14.1
5–6	Estimate decimal quotients using compatible numbers.	354–355	Reteach Resource 14.2 *Ways to Success* 14.2
7–8	Use patterns to multiply and divide by powers of 10.	356–357	Reteach Resource 14.3 *Ways to Success* 14.3
9–10	Divide a decimal by a whole number.	358–360	Reteach Resource 14.4 *Ways to Success* 14.4

Keeping a Journal

Have students write a few sentences explaining the two methods of dividing a decimal by a whole number.

Math Challenge

Use What You Know

• Go over **Step 1**. Review each step in the process.

• Go over **Step 2**. **Why is there a 0 in the hundredths place in the quotient?** (24 does not divide into 9.) **What do you notice about the number of decimal places in the dividend and in the quotient?** (They are the same.)

Lesson 14.5

Write Zeros in the Dividend

PLANNING THE LESSON

MATHEMATICS OBJECTIVE

Write one or more zeros in the dividend to help solve division problems.

Use Lesson Planner CD-ROM for Lesson 14.5.

Daily Routines

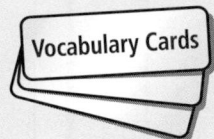

Vocabulary

Review the meanings of the decimal places to the right of the decimal point: *tenths, hundredths, thousandths.*

Vocabulary Cards

Meeting North Carolina's Standards

Prepare for Grade 6 Objective **1.04** Develop fluency in addition, subtraction, multiplication, and division of nonnegative rational numbers.

Lesson Transparency **14.5**

Problem of the Day

Four students are waiting in line in the cafeteria. Maria is directly behind Brad. Kevin is not first in line but is directly in front of Aretha. In which order are the four students standing in line? (Brad, Maria, Kevin, Aretha)

Quick Review

Estimate the quotients to the nearest ten or hundred. (Possible answers are given.)

1. $3\overline{)899}$ (300)
2. $4\overline{)218}$ (50)
3. $7\overline{)1,350}$ (200)
4. $6\overline{)2,990}$ (500)
5. $5\overline{)4,625}$ (900)

Lesson Quiz

Divide. Check using a calculator or estimation.

1. $5\overline{)3.6}$ (0.72)
2. $4\overline{)6.5}$ (1.625)
3. $6\overline{)43.2}$ (7.2)
4. $8\overline{)6.8}$ (0.85)
5. $5\overline{)28.15}$ (5.63)

LEVELED PRACTICE

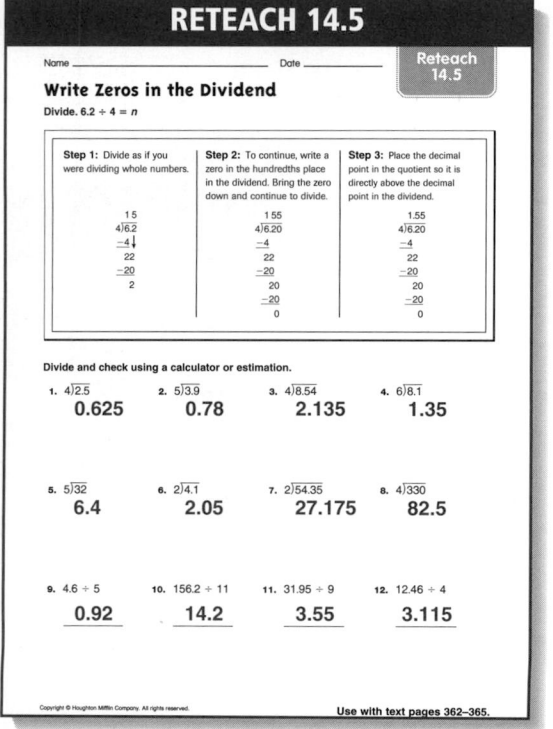

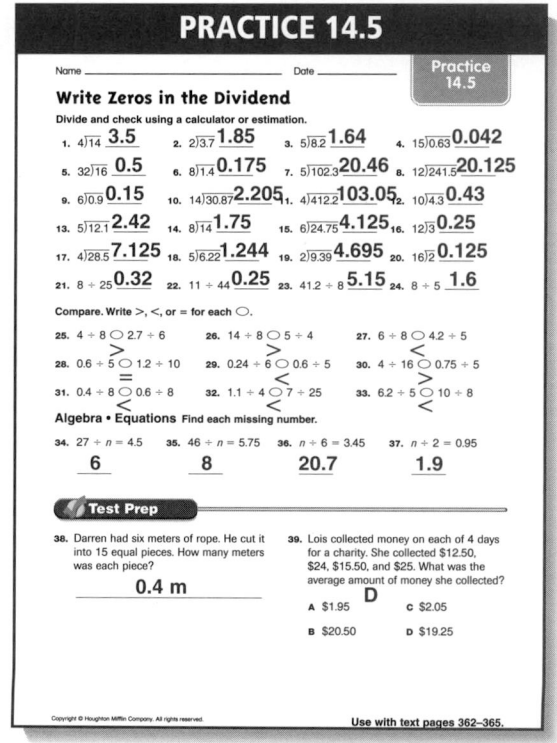

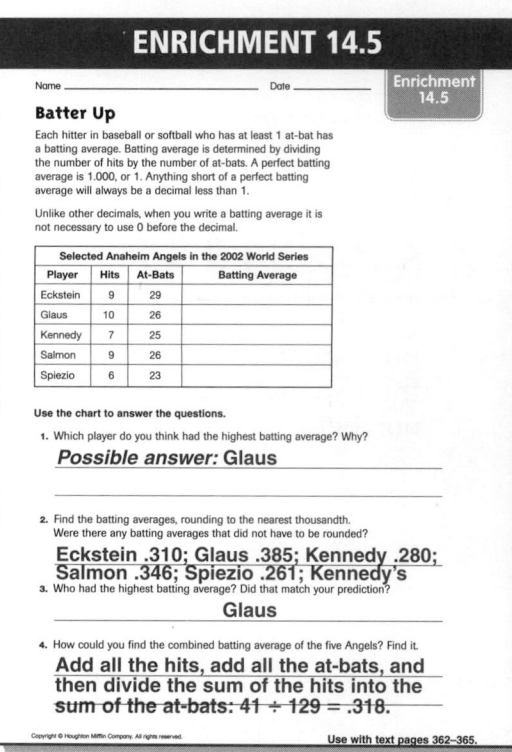

Practice Workbook Page 93

Reaching All Learners
Differentiated Instruction

English Learners

Use Worksheet 14.5 to help students understand the related word forms *long/length* and the definition of *short*, as well as related language structures that will help them complete Problems 46 and 49.

Special Needs
VISUAL, AUDITORY

Materials: *grid paper*

- Display *1.4 ÷ 2*. To model 1.4, shade the squares on a hundredths grid. **How many are shaded?** (140) **Divide into 2 equal parts. How many are in each?** (70)
- Model and solve the problem using long division. **How does adding zero to the dividend relate to your models? Explain.**

Early Finishers
VISUAL, AUDITORY

- In the Fall season, 50 pairs of track shoes cost $1,809. Find the per-pair cost. ($36.18) A bus rented for 50 riders is $169. Find the per-rider cost. ($3.38) Event admission is $2.25 each. Find the total cost per person. ($41.81)
- Have students invent and share similar problems.

TECHNOLOGY

Spiral Review

Create **customized** spiral review worksheets for individual students using the *Ways to Assess* CD-ROM.

Lesson Planner

You can use the Lesson Planner CD-ROM to create a report of the lessons and standards you have taught.

Game

Students can practice their skills using the Rock Hopper math game, available on the *Ways to Success* CD

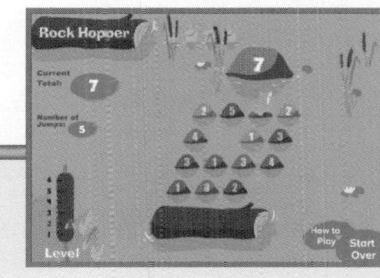

Science Connection

Materials: *The Internet or almanacs*

- Have students look up the annual precipitation in inches for a location in their state. Use sources such as *The World Almanac* that express the figures in decimal form. **How would you find the mean inches of rainfall per month?** (Divide by 12.)
- Then have students look up the monthly precipitation for the same location and find the highest and lowest numbers for the year. How do these figures compare to the mean inches of rainfall per month?

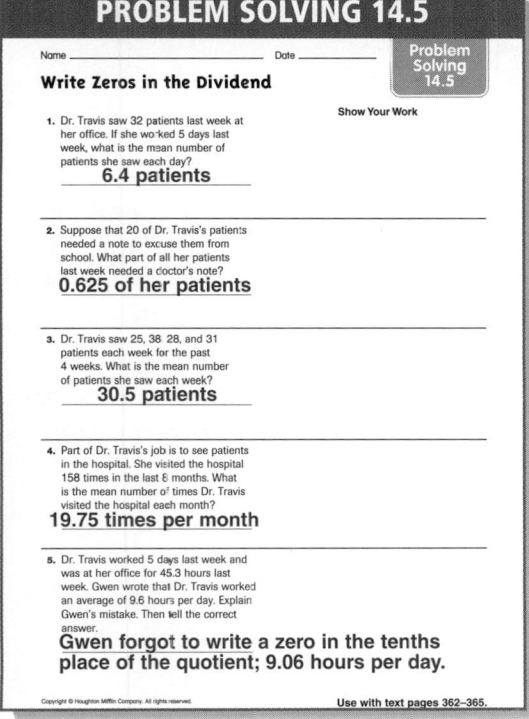

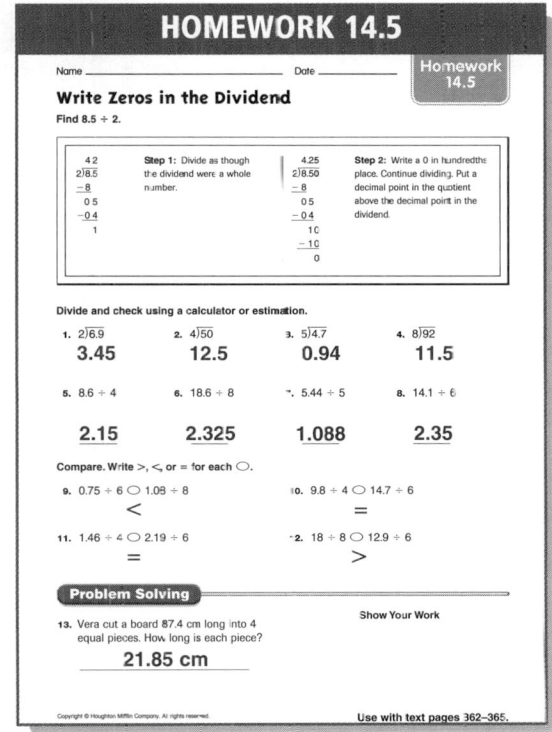

Homework Workbook Page 93

TEACHING LESSON 14.5

LESSON ORGANIZER

Objective Write one or more zeros in the dividend to help solve division problems.

Resources Reteach, Practice, Enrichment, Problem Solving, Homework, English Learners, Transparencies, Math Center

Materials None

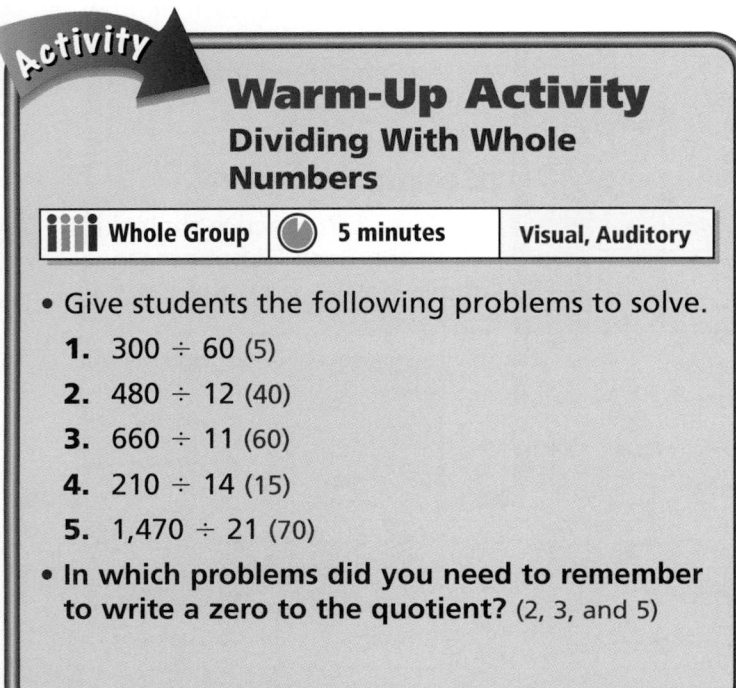

Activity

Warm-Up Activity
Dividing With Whole Numbers

👥 Whole Group	⏱ 5 minutes	Visual, Auditory

- Give students the following problems to solve.
  1. 300 ÷ 60 (5)
  2. 480 ÷ 12 (40)
  3. 660 ÷ 11 (60)
  4. 210 ÷ 14 (15)
  5. 1,470 ÷ 21 (70)

- **In which problems did you need to remember to write a zero to the quotient?** (2, 3, and 5)

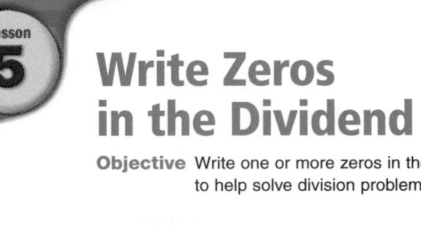

Write Zeros in the Dividend

Objective Write one or more zeros in the dividend to help solve division problems.

Learn About It  MathTracks 2/7 Listen and Understand

Billie's first long jump was 4.5 meters. Her second long jump was 6 meters. What part of her second long jump was Billie's first attempt?

Divide. 4.5 ÷ 6 = n

Different Ways to Divide 4.5 by 6

Way 1 You can use the pencil-and-paper method.

STEP 1 Divide as though the dividend were a whole number.

$$\begin{array}{r} 7 \\ 6\overline{)4.5} \\ -4\,2 \\ \hline 3 \end{array}$$

Think 45 ÷ 6 is about 7.

STEP 2 To continue, write a 0 in the hundredths place.

$$\begin{array}{r} 75 \\ 6\overline{)4.50} \\ -4\,2\downarrow \\ \hline 30 \\ -30 \\ \hline 0 \end{array}$$

Bring down the 0. Continue dividing.

STEP 3 Place the decimal point in the quotient above the decimal point in the dividend.

$$\begin{array}{r} 0.75 \\ 6\overline{)4.50} \\ -4\,2\downarrow \\ \hline 30 \\ -30 \\ \hline 0 \end{array}$$

Write 0 in the ones place.

Way 2 You can divide decimals using a calculator.

STEP 1 Press the calculator keys to enter the division. Press the equals sign to calculate the quotient.

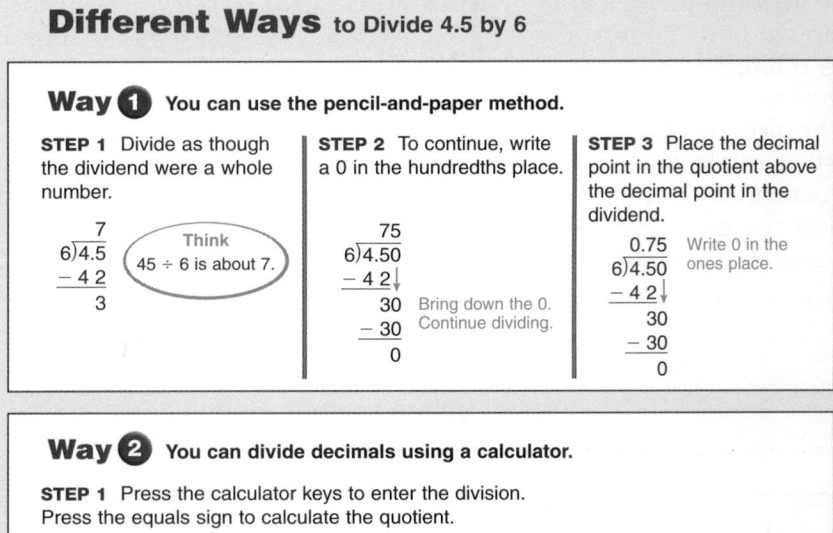

4 . 5 ÷ 6 Enter = → 0.75

Check that the quotient is reasonable.
Think How many 6s are in 4.5?
6 × 1 = 6
There is less than one 6 in 4.5.
0.75 is a reasonable answer.

Solution: Billie's first long jump was 0.75 of her second long jump.

362

---

1 Introduce

- Remind students that they have written zeros in the dividend before, when dividing a whole number by a whole number. Write this problem on the chalkboard: 8)30.

$$\begin{array}{r} 3.75 \\ 8\overline{)30.00} \\ 24 \\ \hline 6\,0 \\ 5\,6 \\ \hline 40 \\ 40 \\ \hline 0 \end{array}$$

- Have them work with you as you do the division. Continue until the remainder is zero. What is 30 ÷ 8? (3.75)

2 Develop

Guide students through the *Learn About It* section.

- **Look at Way 1.** Go over Steps 1 and 2 in Way 1, making sure that students understand the division. **How do you know you have to write a zero in the hundredths place of the dividend?** (There is a remainder after the first step in the division.)

- **Look at Way 2.** In Step 1, carefully go through the calculator steps required. Make sure the answer given is the same as that from the calculations in Way 1.

Another Example

Divide Whole Numbers

When dividing whole numbers, you
can add zeros after the decimal
point to get a decimal answer.

Find 42 ÷ 8.

```
      5.25
  8)42.00
   − 40↓
      20
    − 16↓
      40
    − 40
       0
```

Guided Practice ••••••••••••••••••••••••

Ask Yourself

- Did I place the first digit of the quotient correctly?
- Did I write zeros in the dividend until there was no remainder?

Divide. Check using a calculator or estimation.

1. 5)2.7 **0.54**
2. 5)24 **4.8**
3. 4)3.5 **0.875**
4. 6)0.75 **0.125**
5. 8)51 **6.375**
6. 2)39.77 **19.885**

7. 6.11 ÷ 2 **3.055**   8. 9.6 ÷ 5 **1.92**   9. 2.7 ÷ 4 **0.675**

TEST TIPS

TEST TIPS **Explain Your Thinking** ▶ Why does writing zeros to the right of
the least-place digit in a decimal not
change the value of that number?
Possible answer: Writing zeros to the right of the least
place after the decimal point in a decimal does not
change the value of that number because the zeros
have a value of 0 tenths, 0 hundredths,
0 thousandths, and so on.

Practice and Problem Solving

Divide. Check using a calculator or estimation.

10. 2)9 **4.5**
11. 8)5.2 **0.65**
12. 4)19 **4.75**
13. 16)12.4 **0.775**
14. 18)0.9 **0.05**

15. 46)16.1 **0.35**
16. 10)6.24 **0.624**
17. 5)24.72 **4.944**
18. 6)106.5 **17.75**
19. 8)474.8 **59.35**

20. 8)19 **2.375**
21. 24)15 **0.625**
22. 12)4.2 **0.35**
23. 6)8.67 **1.445**
24. 4)28.18 **7.045**

25. 33 ÷ 22 **1.5**   26. 9 ÷ 5 **1.8**   27. 15 ÷ 8 **1.875**   28. 32.6 ÷ 4 **8.15**   29. 37 ÷ 10 **3.7**

Compare. Write >, <, or = for each ●.

30. 2.5 ÷ 4 **=** 5 ÷ 8
31. 3.6 ÷ 8 **>** 1 ÷ 4
32. 12 ÷ 5 **>** 9 ÷ 4

33. 2 ÷ 4 **>** 0.8 ÷ 2
34. 0.4 ÷ 2 **>** 0.2 ÷ 4
35. 0.35 ÷ 7 **<** 3 ÷ 12

36. 3.2 ÷ 8 **<** 8 ÷ 2
37. 0.4 ÷ 4 **=** 0.2 ÷ 2
38. 5.25 ÷ 3 **=** 14 ÷ 8

Go On

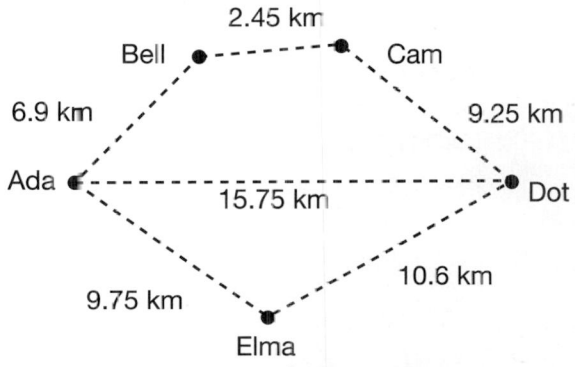

Reaching All Learners

Number Sense Copy the diagram.

Bell — 2.45 km — Cam

6.9 km   9.25 km

Ada   Dot

15.75 km

9.75 km   10.6 km

Elma

1. Have students find the least distance
   between these cities.

   a. Ada to Cam   **b.** Bell to Dot

2. How much farther is it from Ada to Dot
   through Elma than through Bell?

3. Find the mean distance between adjacent
   cities to the nearest hundredth of a kilometer.

Answers

1. **a.** 9.35 km   **b.** 11.7 km
2. 1.75 km   3. 9.12 km

Differentiated Assignments		
At Risk	**Average**	**Advanced**
Exercise 1	Exercises 1–2	Exercises 1–3

---

3 Practice

- Go over how to check the quotient by reviewing the
  questions listed.
- Work through the *Other Example* with students. Each
  time a zero is added, make sure students understand why.

Guided Practice

Have students complete **Exercises 1–9** as you observe.
Remind them to use the *Ask Yourself* questions to help.
Give students the opportunity to talk about the question
in *Explain Your Thinking*.

Assign **Problems 10–56** as independent work.

- For Exercises 10–33, have students discuss their work.

DAILY TEST PREP

Which is the quotient of $5\overline{)4.75}$? (D)

A. 0.095   C. 95

B. 9.5   D. 0.95

Activity

Or use Intervention CD-ROM Lesson 14.5

Lesson Intervention

Adding Zeros in the Dividend

| Small Group | 5–10 minutes | Visual, Kinesthetic |

• Give students these division problems to solve using a calculator:

1. 45 ÷ 9 (5)   **2.** 64 ÷ 4 (16)

3. 72 ÷ 8 (9)   **4.** 81 ÷ 9 (9)

Be sure students know that the dividend is entered first, the operation second, and the divisor last.

• **How can you use the calculator to check the quotient?** (Multiply the quotient by the divisor.)

• Then give these problems:

1. 30 ÷ 4 (7.5)   **2.** 3.85 ÷ 7 (0.55)

3. 5.20 ÷ 8 (0.65)   **4.** 10.5 ÷ 6 (1.75)

X Algebra • Equations Find each missing value for *n*.

39. $19 \div n = 4.75$ **4**   **40.** $n \div 4 = 0.525$ **2.1**   **41.** $n \div 5 = 3.44$ **17.2**   **42.** $15 \div n = 7.5$ **2**

 **Data**   Use the chart below to solve Problems 43–47.

The chart shows two jumps each member of a track team made during a recent meet.

43. What part of her second jump is Sarah's first jump? **0.95**

44. What is the mean of the distances of Lita's jumps? Remember, to find the mean, you divide the sum of the distances by the number of jumps. **5.15 m**

 45. **Calculator** What is the mean distance of the jumps made by this team? **4.275 m**

46. Which team member had the greatest range in her jumps? How much difference was there between her longest and shortest jumps? **Elisa; 0.6 m**

 47. **Measurement** To convert from meters to feet, multiply the number of meters by 3.281. Who had a first jump of about 15 feet? **Elisa**

JUMPING CHART		
Name	Jump 1	Jump 2
Sarah	3.8 meters	4 meters
Lita	5.3 meters	5 meters
Sue	3.5 meters	4 meters
Elisa	4.6 meters	4 meters

Test Prep
Add all the temperatures and divide the sum by 5, the number of days

48. **Write About It** When you are dividing 63 by 4, how can you tell whether or not you need to write zeros in the dividend? **See Additional Answers on Page 375.**

49. In the 2000 Olympics, second place in the long jump was a jump of 6.92 m. The winning jump was 7 cm longer. How long was the winning jump? **6.927 m**

Daily Review   **Test Prep**

Multiply. Write your answer in simplest form. (Ch. 12, Lessons 2 and 3)

50. $\frac{2}{3} \times \frac{3}{5}$ **$\frac{2}{5}$**   **51.** $\frac{3}{4} \times \frac{8}{9}$ **$\frac{2}{3}$**

52. $1\frac{5}{6} \times 2\frac{3}{4}$ **$5\frac{1}{24}$**   **53.** $4\frac{2}{5} \times 3\frac{1}{4}$ **$14\frac{3}{10}$**

54. $1\frac{2}{3} \times 1\frac{3}{5}$ **$2\frac{2}{3}$**   **55.** $7\frac{1}{5} \times 3\frac{3}{2}$ **$26\frac{2}{5}$**

56. **Free Response** The following temperatures were recorded in Antarctica: 27.2°F, 24.6°F, 29°F, 22.1°F, and 28.1°F. What was the mean daily temperature for these five days? **26.2°F**

Explain your thinking. **See above.**

Extra Practice See page 375, Set E.

Practice *continued*

• *Algebra • Equations For Exercises 39–42* Have students discuss their methods for deriving the expression equal to *n* and their answers. Exercises 39 and 42 require two steps.

• *Problem Solving for Problems 43–49* Have students explain the methods they used.

Common Error

Misplacing or forgetting to write a decimal point Remind students that the decimal point in the quotient goes directly above the decimal point in the dividend.

4 Assess and Close

When do you need to write zeros in the dividend? (When the divisor divided the dividend and there was a nonzero remainder, write a zero in the next decimal place in the dividend until the remainder is 0.)

Assign the **LESSON QUIZ** on Transparency 14.5 to further assess student understanding.

Flying Measures

In the 1920s, the Frisbie Baking Company sold pies to students at Yale University. The students discovered that the empty pie tins made great flying discs. Adding a spin to their toss kept the pie tins aloft for great distances.

In 1948, a California building inspector and carpenter made the first plastic flying disc. Since that time, these discs have gained in popularity.

Four results for outdoor distance throwing are shown below. Convert the results to feet using 1 m ≈ 3.281 ft. Round your answer to the nearest hundredth.

1. Boys under 11: 82.3 m **270.03 ft**
2. Girls under 11: 70.2 m **230.33 ft**
3. Boys under 12: 101.5 m **333.02 ft**
4. Girls under 12: 97.74 m **320.68 ft**

Money Power

Businesses circulate coupons on the Internet. One Web site offers a coupon worth $3.25. If the value of the coupons that have been downloaded so far totals $32,500, how many coupons have been downloaded so far? **10,000 coupons**

Brain Teaser

| 1 | 2 | 3 | 4 | 5 |

Use each of these digits once to create a decimal division expression whose quotient is about 2.

Possible answer: 45.1 ÷ 23

 Technology
Visit *Education Place* at **eduplace.com/kids/mw/** to try more brain teasers.

Flying Measures

What operation do you use to convert meters into feet in these problems? (Multiply each measurement in meters by 3.281.)

Money Power

- **What division sentence did you write to find the answer?** (32,500 ÷ 3.25 = 10,000 coupons)

Brain Teaser

- Ask students to share their answers. Point out that several answers are possible, for example, 32.5 ÷ 14.

Keeping a Journal

Have students write a few sentences explaining why it is sometimes necessary to write additional zeros in the dividend.

Lesson 14.6 Repeating Decimals

PLANNING THE LESSON

MATHEMATICS OBJECTIVE

Change a fraction to a decimal using division.

Use Lesson Planner CD-ROM for Lesson 14.6.

Daily Routines

Vocabulary

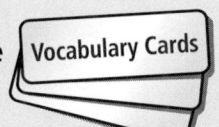

Vocabulary Cards

When a digit or digits repeat infinitely to the right of a decimal point of a number, the number is called a *repeating decimal.*

Write 59.0979797… on the chalkboard. **If the number is a repeating decimal, what would you expect the next two digits to be?** (9 then 7) To indicate a number is a repeating decimal, a line is drawn over the digit or digits that repeat.

Meeting North Carolina's Standards

Prepare for Grade 6 Objective **1.04** Develop fluency in addition, subtraction, multiplication, and division of nonnegative rational numbers.

Lesson Transparency 14.6

Problem of the Day

Four friends buy a pizza for $13 and divide the cost equally. How many one-dollar bills and quarters can each friend use to pay for the pizza? (Each friend pays with 3 one-dollar bill and one quarter.)

Quick Review

Multiply mentally.

1. 35×10^3 (35,000)
2. 0.3×10^2 (30)
3. 75.9×10 (759)
4. 0.08×10^3 (80)
5. 0.0462×10^3 (46.2)

Lesson Quiz

Change each fraction to decimal form.

1. $\frac{1}{9}$ ($0.\overline{1}$)
2. $\frac{4}{11}$ ($0.\overline{36}$)
3. $\frac{2}{15}$ ($0.1\overline{3}$)
4. $\frac{5}{6}$ ($0.8\overline{3}$)
5. $\frac{5}{18}$ ($0.2\overline{7}$)

LEVELED PRACTICE

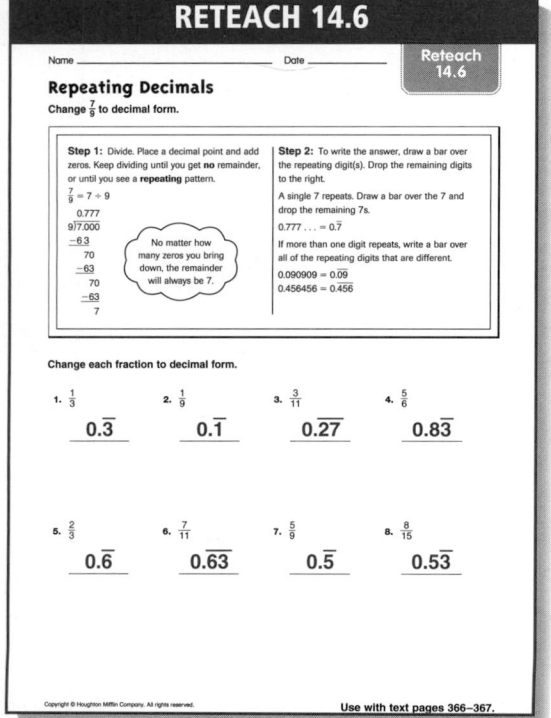

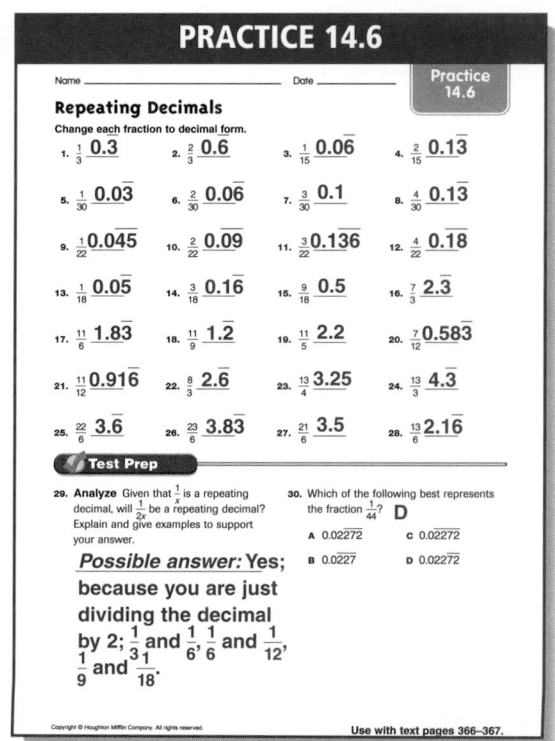

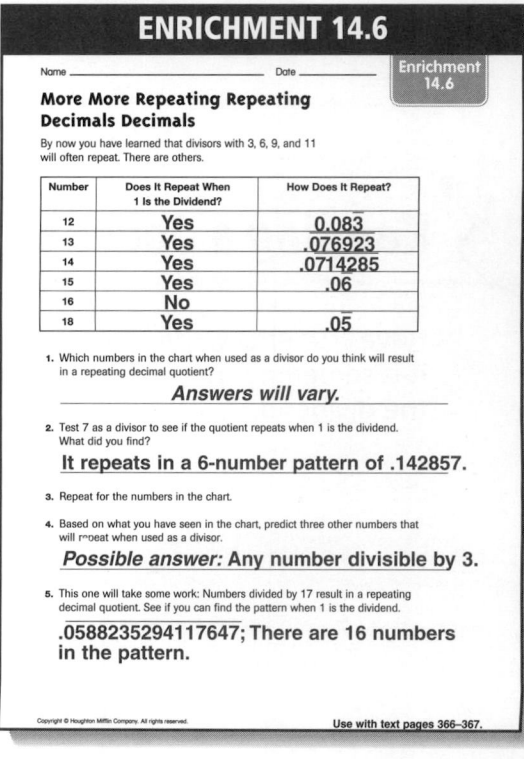

Practice Workbook Page 94

Reaching All Learners
Differentiated Instruction

English Learners

Worksheet 14.6 helps students to understand the meaning of *repeat* and apply it to decimals in preparation for following the major concept in the lesson.

Inclusion
VISUAL, AUDITORY

- Write this fraction on the chalkboard: $\frac{1}{9}$. **How can we find the decimal value of a fraction?** (Divide the denominator into the numerator.)
- Then write $9\overline{)1}$ on the chalkboard and do the division to four or six decimal places. (0.1111 . . .)
- **What do you notice about this decimal?** (It has a repeating digit.) Point out that this kind of decimal is called a repeating decimal.

Gifted and Talented
VISUAL, AUDITORY

- Have students find the decimal equivalent for each of these fractions:
  1. $\frac{1}{11}$ $(0.\overline{09})$
  2. $\frac{2}{11}$ $(0.\overline{18})$
  3. $\frac{3}{11}$ $(0.\overline{27})$
- Then have students predict the value of these fractions: $\frac{4}{11}$ $(0.\overline{36})$, $\frac{5}{11}$ $(0.\overline{45})$, $\frac{5}{11}$ $(0.\overline{54})$, $\frac{7}{11}$ $(0.\overline{63})$, $\frac{8}{11}$ $(0.\overline{72})$, $\frac{9}{11}$ $(0.\overline{81})$, $\frac{10}{11}$ $(0.\overline{90})$
- Have students use their calculators to check their predictions.

TECHNOLOGY

Spiral Review

Using the *Ways to Assess* CD-ROM, you can create **customized** spiral review worksheets covering any lessons you choose.

eBook

eMathbook allows students to review lessons and do homework without carrying their textbooks home.

Houghton Mifflin
Math

e MathBook

Social Studies Connection

Sports Statistics
Materials: *newspapers, reference books*

- Have students research sports in which decimals are used to express players' scores or ratings.
- Ask them to talk about the meanings of such decimal ratings and report their findings to the class.

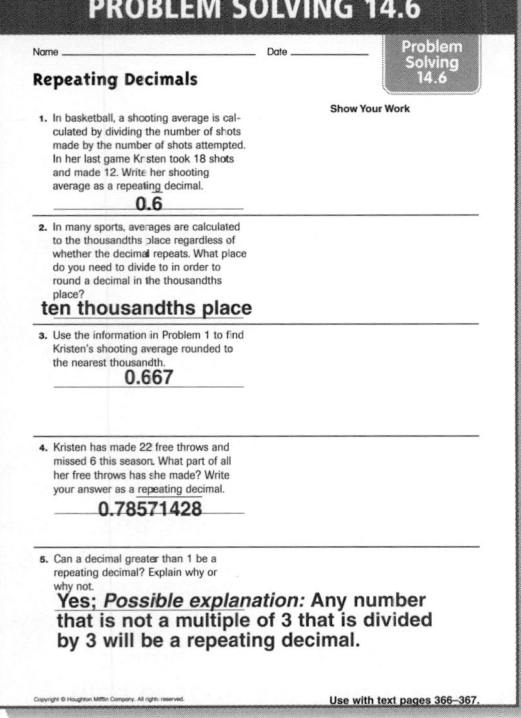

Homework Workbook Page 94

TEACHING LESSON 14.6

LESSON ORGANIZER

Objective Change a fraction to a decimal using division.

Resources Reteach, Practice, Enrichment, Problem Solving, Homework, English Learners, Transparencies, Math Center

Materials None

 **Activity**

Warm-Up Activity
Converting Fractions to Decimals

| Whole Group | 5 minutes | Visual, Auditory |

Review with students the fact that converting a fraction into a decimal means dividing the numerator by the denominator. Have students find the decimal that is equivalent to each fraction.

1. $\frac{3}{20}$ (0.15)

2. $\frac{4}{5}$ (0.8)

3. $\frac{5}{8}$ (0.625)

4. $\frac{1}{16}$ (0.0625)

5. $\frac{9}{25}$ (0.36)

Repeating Decimals

Objective Change a fraction to a decimal using division.

Learn About It

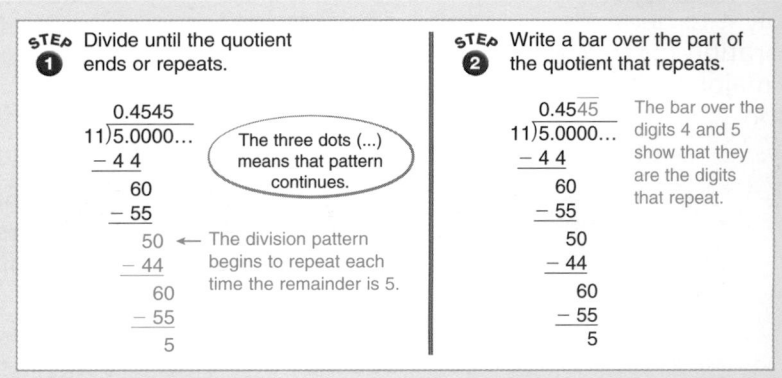

Mack had 5 hits out of 11 times at bat. His batting average is $\frac{5}{11}$. What is his batting average in decimal form?

To change a fraction to a decimal, divide the numerator by the denominator. Sometimes the remainder is not 0. If the division continues indefinitely, the quotient will be a **repeating decimal.**

Find 5 ÷ 11.

STEP 1 Divide until the quotient ends or repeats.

```
    0.4545
11)5.0000...
  − 4 4
     60
   − 55
     50  ← The division pattern
   − 44     begins to repeat each
     60     time the remainder is 5.
   − 55
      5
```

The three dots (...) means that pattern continues.

STEP 2 Write a bar over the part of the quotient that repeats.

```
    0.4545
11)5.0000...
  − 4 4
     60
   − 55
     50
   − 44
     60
   − 55
      5
```

The bar over the digits 4 and 5 show that they are the digits that repeat.

Solution: Mack's batting average is $0.\overline{45}$.

Other Examples

A. Single Repeating Digit

Change $\frac{1}{3}$ to decimal form.

```
   0.33...
3)1.0...
 − 9
   10
  − 0
    1
```

The decimal form of $\frac{1}{3}$ is $0.\overline{3}$.

B. Calculator

Some calculators round the last digit of a repeating decimal. Check how your calculator displays repeating decimals.

```
5 ÷ 9 =
0.5555555556
```

366

---

① Introduce

- Ask students to find the decimal equivalent of $\frac{1}{8}$. Have students do the long division for 1 ÷ 8. **What decimal quotient do you get?** (0.125) **Decimals like 0.125 are called *terminating decimals*, because the divisor divides evenly into the dividend, and the remainder is 0.**

- **Sometimes when you convert fractions to decimals, however, you don't get an even answer, or terminating decimal.** Give students the fraction $\frac{1}{11}$. Ask them to find the decimal equivalent. **What decimal quotient do you get?** (0.0909 . . .) Explain that this is a *repeating decimal*.

② Develop

Guide students through the *Learn About It* section.

- Go over the problem with students. Make sure they understand that computing the batting average involves finding a decimal equivalent.

- **Look at Step 1.** Point out that if the division were continued beyond four decimal places, the digits 45 would repeat endlessly.

- **Look at Step 2.** Explain that a repeating decimal may be written as 0.4545..., or as $0.\overline{45}$.

- Work through the *Other Examples* with students. Be sure students understand the keystrokes for division given in part B.

Guided Practice

Have students complete **Exercises 1–6** as you observe. Remind them to use the *Ask Yourself* questions to help. Give students the opportunity to talk about the question in *Explain Your Thinking.*

Ask Yourself
- Does the decimal terminate or not?
- Do one or more digits repeat?

Change each fraction to decimal form.

1. $\frac{1}{6}$ $0.1\overline{6}$ 2. $\frac{2}{6}$ $0.\overline{3}$ 3. $\frac{5}{6}$ $0.8\overline{3}$

4. $\frac{7}{15}$ $0.4\overline{6}$ 5. $\frac{4}{9}$ $0.\overline{4}$ 6. $\frac{1}{11}$ $0.\overline{09}$

TEST TIPS

TEST TIPS Explain Your Thinking ▶ If you know the decimal for $\frac{1}{3}$, how can you find the decimal for $\frac{2}{3}$? Double it; $\frac{1}{3} = 0.\overline{3}$, so $\frac{2}{3} = 2 \times 0.\overline{3} = 0.\overline{6}$.

Practice and Problem Solving

Change each fraction to decimal form.

7. $\frac{1}{12}$ $0.083\overline{3}$ 8. $\frac{2}{12}$ $0.1\overline{6}$ 9. $\frac{3}{12}$ 0.25 10. $\frac{4}{12}$ $0.\overline{3}$ 11. $\frac{5}{12}$ $0.416\overline{6}$

12. $\frac{2}{11}$ $0.\overline{18}$ 13. $\frac{3}{11}$ $0.\overline{27}$ 14. $\frac{4}{11}$ $0.\overline{36}$ 15. $\frac{5}{11}$ $0.\overline{45}$ 16. $\frac{6}{11}$ $0.\overline{54}$

17. $\frac{10}{4}$ 2.5 18. $\frac{10}{11}$ $0.\overline{90}$ 19. $\frac{1}{5}$ 0.2 20. $\frac{1}{15}$ $0.0\overline{6}$ 21. $\frac{1}{30}$ $0.03\overline{3}$

Solve.

22. The number of ones changes but the repeating digits in the decimal places are the same (142857).

22. Calculator Compare the quotients of $\frac{8}{7}$ and $\frac{22}{7}$. How are they alike? How are they different?

23. Ed has had 5 hits in his last 8 at bats. How much more or less than a 0.500 batting average does he have? **0.125 more**

24. Analyze Look at the denominators of the fractions below. Which denominators always result in a repeating decimal? Give examples.

$$\frac{1}{5} \quad \frac{1}{6} \quad \frac{1}{9} \quad \frac{1}{10} \quad \frac{1}{11}$$

9, 11; *Check students' examples.*

25. Predict Look at the decimal values for the fractions below.

$$\frac{1}{9} = 0.\overline{1} \quad \frac{2}{9} = 0.\overline{2} \quad \frac{3}{9} = 0.\overline{3}$$

Without dividing, predict the quotients of $\frac{5}{9}$, $\frac{7}{9}$, and $\frac{8}{9}$. $0.\overline{5}$; $0.\overline{7}$; $0.\overline{8}$

Daily Review	Test Prep

Write each pair of numbers as fractions with common denominators. Then write >, <, or = for each ●. (Ch. 9, Lessons 8 and 9)

26. $\frac{8}{5}$ ● 1.3   27. $\frac{16}{7}$ ● $\frac{7}{3}$

28. $5\frac{1}{4}$ ● 5.25   29. 3.02 ● $\frac{16}{5}$

See Additional Answers on Page 375.

30. Lionel's batting average is $\frac{7}{11}$. Which of the following best represents his batting average in decimal form?

A 0.6   C $0.6\overline{3}$

B 0.63   **D** 0.636

DAILY TEST PREP

Melanie hits 11 out of 30 times at bat. What is her batting average as a decimal? ($0.3\overline{6}$)

Activity

Lesson Intervention

Or use Intervention CD-ROM Lesson 14.6

Recognizing a Repeating Decimal

👥 Small Group	⏱ 5–10 minutes	Visual, Auditory

- Ask students to explain the difference between a terminating decimal and a repeating decimal.

- Ask students to find the decimal equivalent for $\frac{2}{15}$. **What do we have to do to find this decimal?** (Divide the numerator 2 by the denominator 15.) Have students copy and follow this division step by step as you do it on the chalkboard:

```
     0.13333
15)2.00000
   1 5
     5 0
     4 5
       50
       45   divide 2 more places
```

- **What do you notice about the quotient?** (It has a repeating digit.) **Will the division ever end?** (No, because the same digits will repeat.)

---

3 Practice

Assign **Exercises 7–30** as independent work. For Exercises 7–21, have students discuss their answers.

- *Problem Solving for Problems 22–25* For Problems 24 and 25, have students share their results.

Common Error

Subtracting incorrectly in long division Students should be sure to align digits correctly in order to subtract correctly at each step of the division.

4 Assess and Close

In a division problem, how can you determine that the quotient is a repeating decimal? (A decimal quotient whose last digit or block of digits repeat without end.)

Assign the **LESSON QUIZ** on Transparency 14.6 to further assess student understanding.

Keeping a Journal

Have students write a few sentences explaining how to convert a fraction to a decimal. Have students explain why fractions sometimes convert to repeating decimals.

Divide a Decimal by a Decimal

PLANNING THE LESSON

MATHEMATICS OBJECTIVE
Divide one decimal by another.

Use Lesson Planner CD-ROM for Lesson 14.7.

Daily Routines

Vocabulary
Review the relationship between *kilometers* and *meters*.

Vocabulary Cards

Meeting North Carolina's Standards
Prepare for Grade 6 Objective **1.04** Develop fluency in addition, subtraction, multiplication, and division of nonnegative rational numbers.

Lesson Transparency
14.7

Problem of the Day
Jason had scores of 75, 88, 96, 75, and 92 on his science tests this semester. What are the range, mode, median, and mean of these scores? (range, 21; mode, 75; median, 88; mean, 85.2)

Quick Review
Divide mentally.
1. $560 \div 70$ (8)
2. $72,000 \div 8$ (9,000)
3. $81,000 \div 90$ (900)
4. $6,300 \div 90$ (70)
5. $40,000 \div 800$ (50)

Lesson Quiz
Divide. Check that your answers are reasonable.
1. $0.4\overline{)1.6}$ (4)
2. $0.4\overline{)0.24}$ (0.6)
3. $0.5\overline{)43.5}$ (87)
4. $0.5\overline{)4.35}$ (8.7)
5. $4.5\overline{)35.1}$ (7.8)

LEVELED PRACTICE

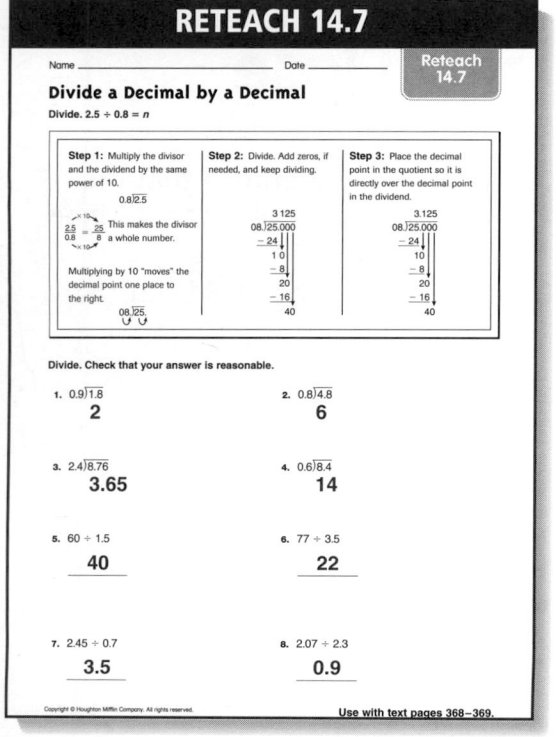

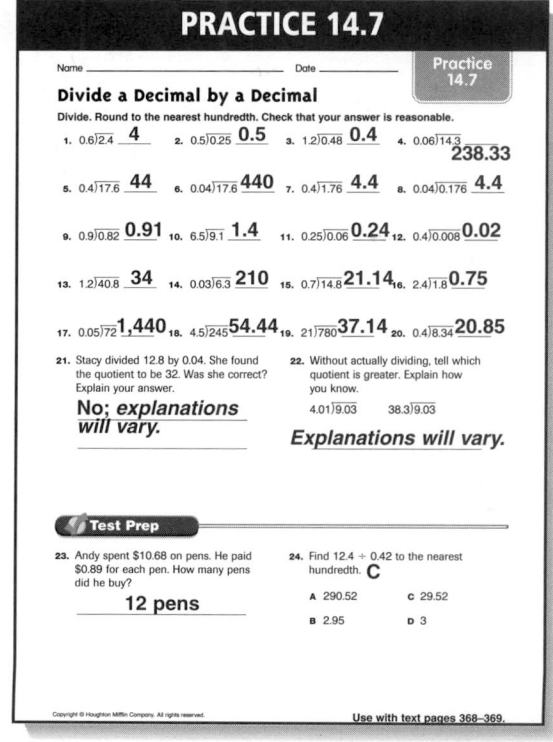

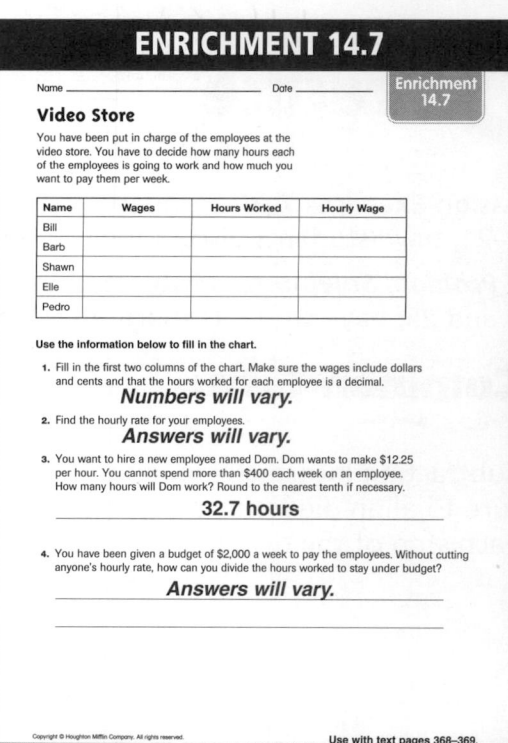

Practice Workbook Page 95

Reaching All Learners

Differentiated Instruction

English Learners

Worksheet 14.7 introduces students to the prefixes *tri-* and *kilo-* to help them understand the content of the example problem and Problems 22 and 23 more clearly. Additional words with these prefixes are included to broaden students' range of vocabulary.

Special Needs
VISUAL, AUDITORY

- Display $0.8\overline{)3.6}$. **Let's write this division expression as a fraction. What is the numerator?** (3.6) **denominator?** (0.8)
- Display $\frac{3.6}{0.8}$. Guide students through the process of multiplying by $\frac{10}{10}$ to get a whole number. **What is the new fraction?** ($\frac{36}{8}$) **the quotient?** (4.5)

Early Finishers
VISUAL, AUDITORY

- Assign these exercises.
  1. $56 \div 7$ (8)
  2. $56 \div 0.7$ (80)
  3. $56 \div 0.07$ (800)
- **Do you see a pattern?** (as the divisor decreases by a power of 10, the quotient increases by a power of 10.)
- Have students write and solve the next 3 problems in the sequence.

Language Arts Connection

Dewey Decimal System

- **How do you find a book in the stacks of the library after you have looked it up in a card catalogue or on the computer?** (Answers will vary. Encourage all responses.)
- Explain to students that American librarian Melvil Dewey (1851–1931) created the system used by librarians to classify and order books.
- Have students research the Dewey decimal system. Have them explain how the "point" is used and what the numbers to its right and left really mean.

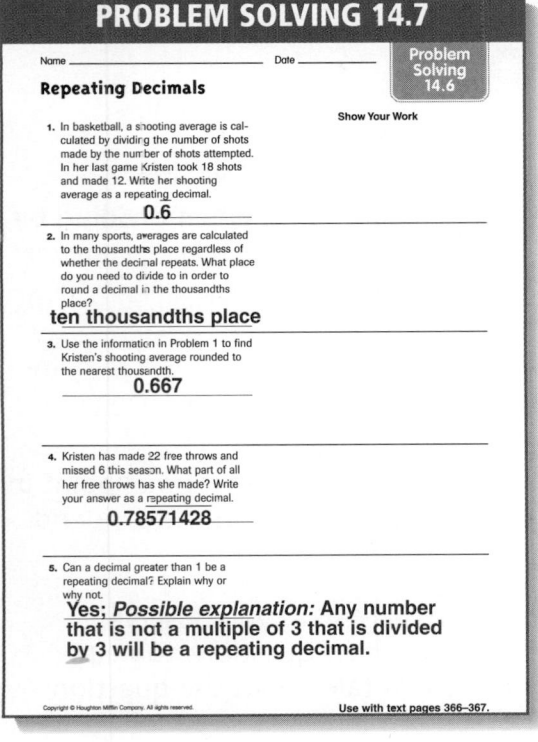

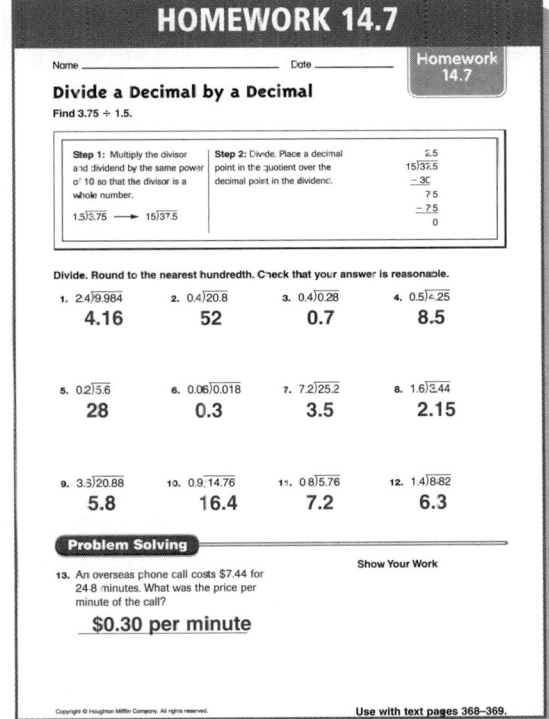

Homework Workbook Page 95

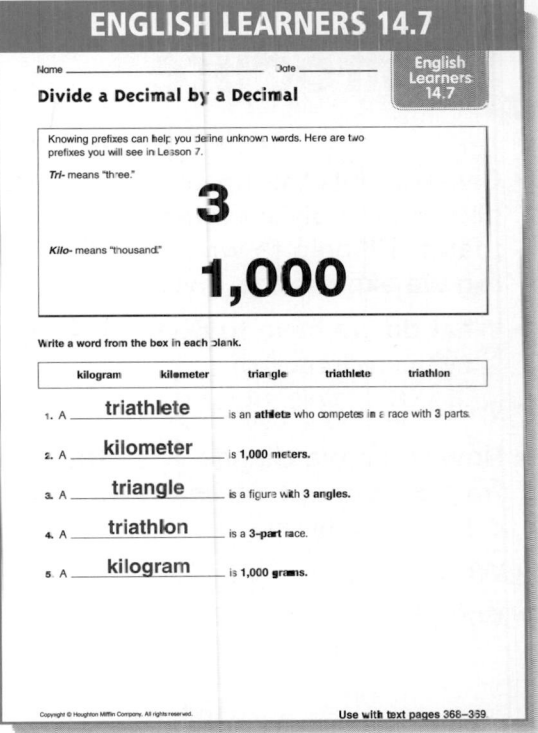

TEACHING LESSON 14.7

LESSON ORGANIZER

Objective Divide one decimal by another.

Resources Reteach, Practice, Enrichment, Problem Solving, Homework, English Learners, Transparencies, Math Center

Materials None

Warm-Up Activity
Changing Fractions into Decimals

👥 Whole Group	🕐 5 minutes	Visual, Auditory

Have students find the decimal equivalent of each fraction, and identify any repeating decimals.

1. $\frac{3}{50}$ (0.06)

2. $\frac{1}{15}$ (0.0$\overline{6}$, repeating)

3. $\frac{6}{20}$ (0.3)

4. $\frac{1}{3}$ (0.$\overline{3}$, repeating)

5. $\frac{1}{20}$ (0.05)

6. $\frac{1}{18}$ (0.05$\overline{5}$, repeating)

Divide a Decimal by a Decimal

Objective Divide one decimal by another.

Learn About It 💿 MathTracks 2/8 Listen and Understand

In a triathlon, athletes swim 1.5 km, bike for 40 km, and then run 10 km. A winning triathlete completed the swimming portion of a race in 0.4 hour. How fast did he swim in kilometers per hour?

Divide. 1.5 ÷ 0.4 = n

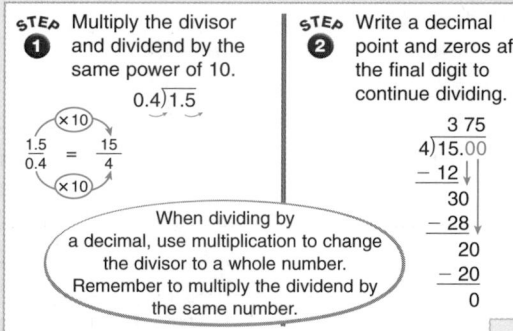

STEP 1 Multiply the divisor and dividend by the same power of 10.

$$0.4\overline{)1.5}$$

$$\frac{1.5}{0.4} = \frac{15}{4}$$ (×10)

STEP 2 Write a decimal point and zeros after the final digit to continue dividing.

```
    3 75
4)15.00
  -12↓
    30
  -28↓
    20
  -20
     0
```

When dividing by a decimal, use multiplication to change the divisor to a whole number. Remember to multiply the dividend by the same number.

STEP 3 Place a decimal point in the quotient over the decimal point in the dividend.

```
    3.75
4)15.00
  -12↓
    30
  -28↓
    20
  -20
     0
```

Estimate to check.
0.4 ≈ 0.5 and 1.5 ≈ 2.
2 ÷ 0.5 = 4
A quotient of 3.75 is reasonable.

Solution: The triathlete swam at an average speed of 3.75 kilometers per hour.

Another Example

Divide to a Specified Place

Divide 1.5 ÷ 0.45 to the nearest hundredth.

To find a quotient to the nearest hundredth, divide to the nearest thousandth and round the quotient to the nearest hundredth.

```
              3.333
0.45)1.50000
    -1 35↓
       150
     -135↓
        150
      -135↓
         150
       -135
          15
```

3 < 5 so round down.
1.5 ÷ 0.45 = 3.33 to the nearest hundredth

---

1 Introduce

- Give students this problem: *1.5 ÷ 0.2*. Point out that in division, the divisor must be a whole number. Tell students that it will help to write the division as a fraction. **How can we express this division using fractions?** ($\frac{15}{10} ÷ \frac{2}{10}$)

- **What do we have to do to perform the division?** (Multiply $\frac{15}{10}$ by the reciprocal of $\frac{2}{10}$.)

- Write: $\frac{15}{10} \times \frac{10}{2} = \frac{150}{20} = \frac{15}{2}$

- **How could we change $\frac{1.5}{0.2}$ so that we would have a fraction without decimals?** (Multiply both numerator and denominator by 10.)

- Write: $\frac{1.5}{0.2} \times \frac{10}{10} = \frac{15}{2}$?

- **What is $\frac{15}{2}$?** (7.5)

2 Develop

Guide students through the *Learn About It* section.

- **Look at Step 1. What must you do first when dividing by a decimal?** (Change the divisor to a whole number by multiplying it by a positive power of 10. Multiply the dividend by the same power of ten.)

- **Look at Step 2. What do you do when there is a remainder?** (Write zeros in the dividend and continue dividing until the remainder is zero or the quotient repeats.)

- **Look at Step 3.** Remind students that the decimal point in the divisor goes above the decimal point in the dividend.

Guided Practice

Have students complete **Exercises 1–6** as you observe. Remind them to use the *Ask Yourself* questions to help. Give students the opportunity to talk about the question in *Explain Your Thinking*.

Guided Practice

Divide. Check that your answer is reasonable.

1. $0.8\overline{)1.6}$ **2**   2. $0.4\overline{)1.84}$ **4.6**   3. $0.2\overline{)0.101}$ **0.505**

4. $9 \div 0.8$ **11.25**   5. $30 \div 1.5$ **20**   6. $1.44 \div 1.2$ **1.2**

Ask Yourself
- Do I need to write any zeros after the dividend?
- Did I place the decimal point correctly?

TEST TIPS **Explain Your Thinking** ▶ How do you decide which power of 10 to use for multiplying when simplifying division by a decimal?
Possible answer: Use whatever power of 10 is needed to make the divisor a whole number.

Practice and Problem Solving

Divide. Round to the nearest hundredth if necessary. Check that your answer is reasonable.

7. $0.3\overline{)1.8}$ **6**   8. $0.3\overline{)0.18}$ **0.6**   9. $0.5\overline{)38.5}$ **77**   10. $0.5\overline{)3.85}$ **7.7**   11. $0.05\overline{)0.385}$ **7.7**

12. $6.1\overline{)32}$ **5.25**   13. $3.5\overline{)17.5}$ **5**   14. $0.35\overline{)17.5}$ **50**   15. $0.8\overline{)1.12}$ **1.4**   16. $0.08\overline{)11.2}$ **140**

  60 86 236.09 107.5 0.24

17. $0.7\overline{)42}$ 18. $4.5\overline{)387}$ 19. $0.23\overline{)54.3}$ 20. $0.04\overline{)4.3}$ 21. $1.4\overline{)0.342}$

Solve.

22. A triathlete averaged 33.3 kilometers per hour for a 40-kilometer portion of a bike race. To the nearest tenth, how long did this portion of the race take? **1.2 hours**

24. Catherine ran the 10-kilometer race portion of a triathlon in 0.91 hour. To the nearest tenth, what was her average speed in kilometers per hour?
11.0 kilometers per hour

23. **Explain** You know that $4 \div 8 = 0.5$. Use patterns below to explain how to complete divisions involving small numbers. Then complete the next division problem in each pattern.

a. $4 \div 8 = 0.5$
$4 \div 0.8 = 5$
$4 \div 0.08 = 50$
$4 \div 0.008 =$ ■ **500**

b. $4 \div 8 = 0.5$
$0.4 \div 8 = 0.05$
$0.04 \div 8 = 0.005$
$0.004 \div 8 =$ ■ **0.0005**

Daily Review   Test Prep

Add or subtract. Write your answers in simplest form. (Chapter 10, Lessons 4 and 8)

25. $3\frac{3}{4} + 2\frac{5}{8}$ **$6\frac{3}{8}$**   26. $7\frac{1}{6} + 1\frac{1}{5}$ **$8\frac{11}{30}$**

27. $4\frac{3}{4} - 2\frac{1}{8}$ **$2\frac{5}{8}$**   28. $6\frac{1}{4} - 4\frac{2}{3}$ **$1\frac{7}{12}$**

29. **Free Response** A triathlete swims the 1.5-kilometer course in 0.5 hour. What is the athlete's average speed in kilometers per hour? **3 kilometers per hour**

Extra Practice See page 375, Set G.

Chapter 14   Lesson 7   **369**

Test Prep Transparency **14.7**

DAILY TEST PREP

What is the quotient of $5.23 \div 0.05$? (104.6)

Activity

Lesson Intervention
Whole-Number Divisors

Or use Intervention CD-ROM Lesson 14.7

| Small Group | 5–10 minutes | Visual, Auditory |

- On the chalkboard write: $1.4\overline{)4.2}$. How can we write this division expression as a fraction? ($\frac{4.2}{1.4}$)
- Explain that in dividing, the divisor must always be a whole number. The denominator is the divisor, and it is a decimal, 1.4. **What can we do to 1.4 to make it a whole number?** (Multiply it by 10.)
- Explain that if you multiply the denominator by 10, you have to do the same to the numerator because you don't want to change the value of the fraction. Since $\frac{10}{10} = 1$, multiplying by $\frac{10}{10}$ won't change the value of the fraction. Write the equivalence: $\frac{4.2}{1.4} = \frac{42}{14}$
- So 4.2 divided by 1.4 is equivalent to 42 divided by 14. Write the division: $14\overline{)42}$.
- **What is 42 divided by 14?** (3) **What is 4.2 divided by 1.4?** (3)

③ Practice

Assign **Exercises 7–29** as independent work.

- *Exercises 7–21* Have students discuss their answers.
- *Problem Solving for Problems 22–24* For Problem 24, have students share their results and discuss the pattern.

Common Error

Aligning digits incorrectly in long division Students should be sure to align digits correctly in order to subtract correctly at each step of the long division. Have students use lined paper turned sideways to do division in columns.

④ Assess and Close

- **What should you do when there is a remainder at any step in the division?** (Write zeros in dividend to continue dividing until remainder is zero or quotient repeats.)
- **Why is it helpful to rewrite the division as a fraction when the divisor is a decimal?** (You can see that you must multiply both denominator and numerator by the same power of 10 in order not to change the value of the fraction.)

Assign the **LESSON QUIZ** on Transparency 14.7 to further assess student understanding.

 **Keeping a Journal**

Have students write a few sentences explaining the process of dividing a decimal by a decimal.

CHAPTER 14   Lesson 7   **369**

Problem-Solving Application: Decide How to Write the Quotient

PLANNING THE LESSON

MATHEMATICS OBJECTIVE
Decide how to write the quotient to solve a problem.

Use Lesson Planner CD-ROM for Lesson 14.8.

Daily Routines

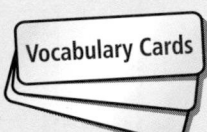

Vocabulary
Remind students that the *remainder* is the number that is left over after one whole number is divided by another, and the divisor is not a *factor* of the dividend.

Vocabulary Cards

Meeting North Carolina's Standards
Prepare for Grade 6 Objective **1.04** Develop fluency in addition, subtraction, multiplication, and division of nonnegative rational numbers.

Lesson Transparency 14.8

Problem of the Day
Frannie speedwalks 0.3 miles every day. Alma speedwalks $\frac{3}{8}$ miles every day. Who speedwalks the greater distance? How much greater? (Alma; 0.075 miles)

Quick Review
Find the quotient.
1. $16.25 \div 5$ (3.25)
2. $3.32 \div 0.8$ (4.15)
3. $50.85 \div 9$ (5.65)
4. $118.5 \div 15$ (7.9)
5. $91.875 \div 10.5$ (8.75)

Lesson Quiz
Solve.
1. The Youth Center orders 18 basketballs. The basketballs are shipped 8 to a carton. How many cartons will be needed for the shipment? (3 cartons)
2. A team orders 9 pairs of shorts. The cost is $67.50. What does each pair cost? ($7.50)

LEVELED PRACTICE

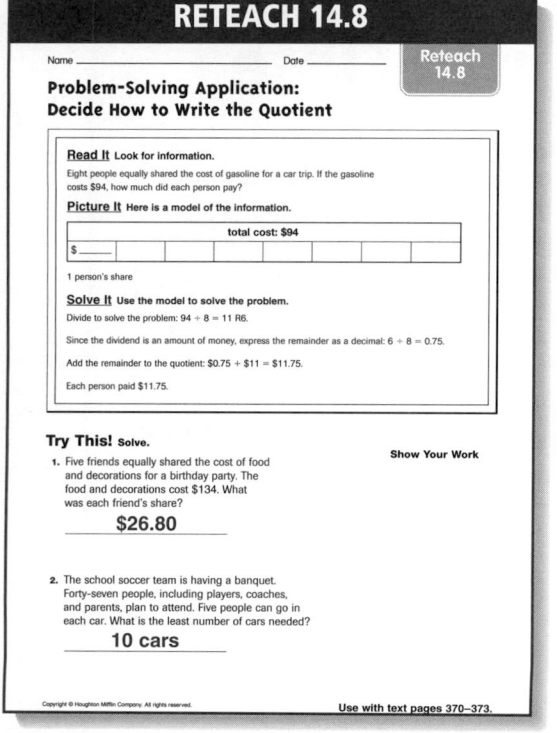

RETEACH 14.8

Problem-Solving Application: Decide How to Write the Quotient

Read It Look for information.
Eight people equally shared the cost of gasoline for a car trip. If the gasoline costs $94, how much did each person pay?

Picture It Here is a model of the information.

| total cost: $94 |
| $ |

1 person's share

Solve It Use the model to solve the problem.
Divide to solve the problem. $94 \div 8 = 11$ R6.
Since the dividend is an amount of money, express the remainder as a decimal: $6 \div 8 = 0.75$.
Add the remainder to the quotient: $0.75 \div 11 = 11.75$.
Each person paid $11.75.

Try This! Solve.
1. Five friends equally shared the cost of food and decorations for a birthday party. The food and decorations cost $134. What was each friend's share? **$26.80**
2. The school soccer team is having a banquet. Forty-seven people, including players, coaches, and parents, plan to attend. Five people can go in each car. What is the least number of cars needed? **10 cars**

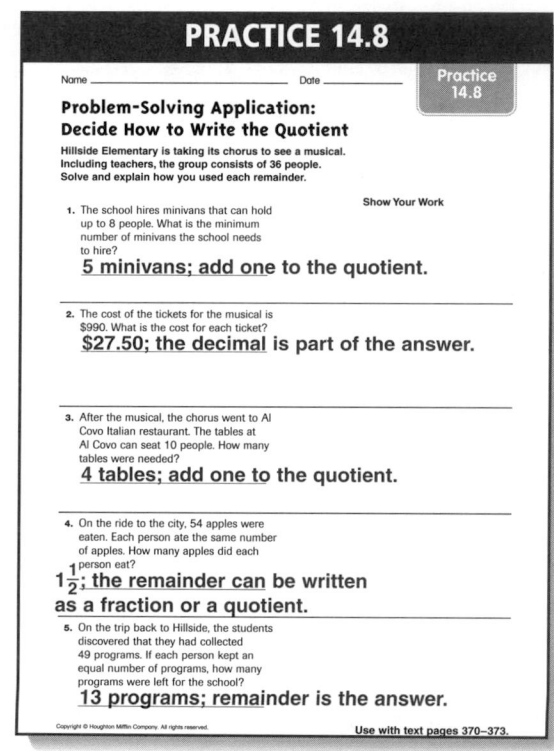

PRACTICE 14.8

Problem-Solving Application: Decide How to Write the Quotient
Hillside Elementary is taking its chorus to see a musical. Including teachers, the group consists of 36 people. Solve and explain how you used each remainder.

1. The school hires minivans that can hold up to 8 people. What is the minimum number of minivans the school needs to hire? **5 minivans; add one to the quotient.**
2. The cost of the tickets for the musical is $990. What is the cost for each ticket? **$27.50; the decimal is part of the answer.**
3. After the musical, the chorus went to Al Covo Italian restaurant. The tables at Al Covo can seat 10 people. How many tables were needed? **4 tables; add one to the quotient.**
4. On the ride to the city, 54 apples were eaten. Each person ate the same number of apples. How many apples did each person eat? **$1\frac{1}{2}$; the remainder can be written as a fraction or a quotient.**
5. On the trip back to Hillside, the students discovered that they had collected 49 programs. If each person kept an equal number of programs, how many programs were left for the school? **13 programs; remainder is the answer.**

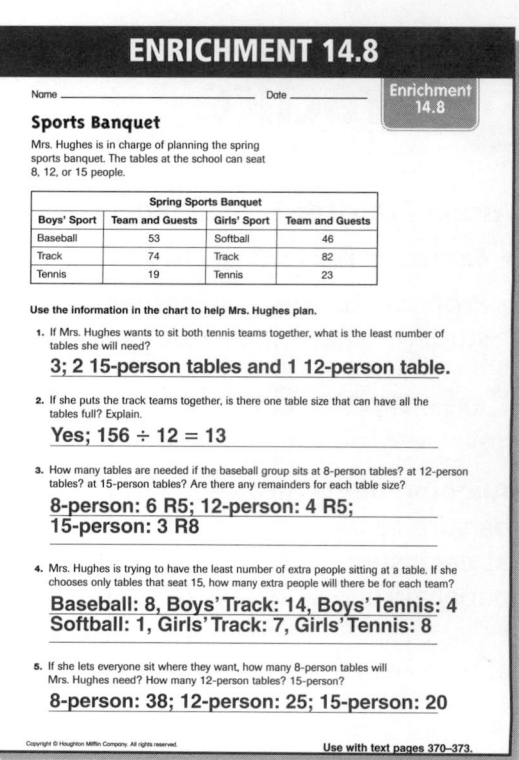

ENRICHMENT 14.8

Sports Banquet
Mrs. Hughes is in charge of planning the spring sports banquet. The tables at the school can seat 8, 12, or 15 people.

| Spring Spring Banquet | | | |
Boys' Sport	Team and Guests	Girls' Sport	Team and Guests
Baseball	53	Softball	46
Track	74	Track	82
Tennis	19	Tennis	23

Use the information in the chart to help Mrs. Hughes plan.
1. If Mrs. Hughes wants to sit both tennis teams together, what is the least number of tables she will need? **3; 2 15-person tables and 1 12-person table.**
2. If she puts the track teams together, is there one table size that can have all the tables full? Explain. **Yes; $156 \div 12 = 13$**
3. How many tables are needed if the baseball group sits at 8-person tables? at 12-person tables? at 15-person tables? Are there any remainders for each table size? **8-person: 6 R5; 12-person: 4 R5; 15-person: 3 R8**
4. Mrs. Hughes is trying to have the least number of extra people sitting at a table. If she chooses only tables that sit 15, how many extra people will there be for each team? **Baseball: 8, Boys' Track: 14, Boys' Tennis: 4 Softball: 1, Girls' Track: 7, Girls' Tennis: 8**
5. If she lets everyone sit where they want, how many 8-person tables will Mrs. Hughes need? How many 12-person tables? 15-person? **8-person: 38; 12-person: 25; 15-person: 20**

Practice Workbook Page 96

Reaching All Learners
Differentiated Instruction

English Learners

Use Worksheet 14.8 to explore with students the various ways that remainders enter into the solutions of word problems in preparation for completing Problems 1–7.

Inclusion
VISUAL, KINESTHETIC

Materials: *28 counters*

- 1 box holds 6 hats. How many boxes are needed for 28 hats?
- How many groups of 6 in 28? (4 R4) Show with counters. **How many hats go into 4 boxes?** (24) **Where do the rest go?** (fifth box) Restate problem. (5 boxes: 4 with 6 hats, 1 with 4)

Gifted and Talented
VISUAL, AUDITORY

A record label ships 12 CDs per box and will ship a partly-full box only if it has 8 or more CDs. Store A orders 100 CDs. Store B orders 176. Which store will not receive its full order? Why? (Store A; $100 \div 12 = 8$ R4, so 4 CDs will not be shipped)

TECHNOLOGY

Spiral Review

Help students remember skills they learned earlier by creating **customized** spiral review worksheets using the *Ways to Assess* CD-ROM.

Intervention

Use the *Ways to Success* intervention software to support students who need more help in understanding the concepts and skills taught in this chapter.

Music Connection

Rounds
- **Does anyone know a round in four lines?** Choose a suggestion from students that is easy to learn and write the lyrics on the chalkboard.
- **How many groups of singers should there be if a new group starts each time a line is finished, and no two groups can sing a line at the same time?** (4)
- Suppose you are teaching the round to a group of 22 second-graders. How many children would be in each group? (5 with 2 left over)
- If the remaining 2 children form a fifth group, when would they start singing? (when the first group gets to the beginning of the song)

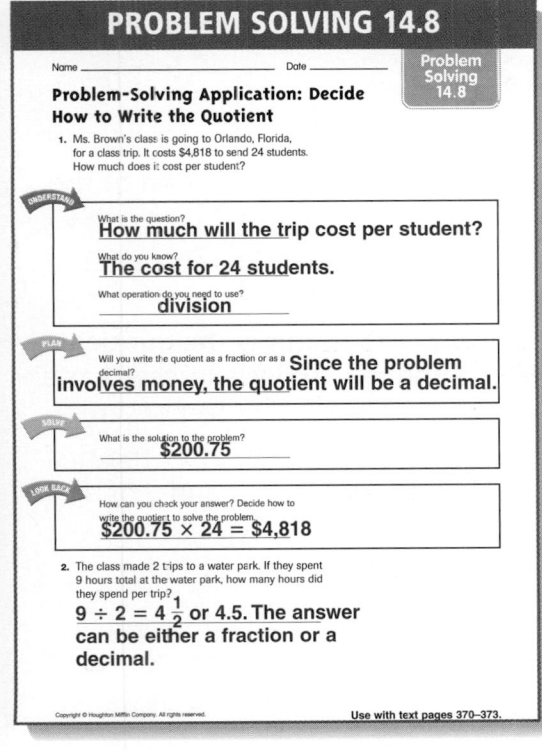

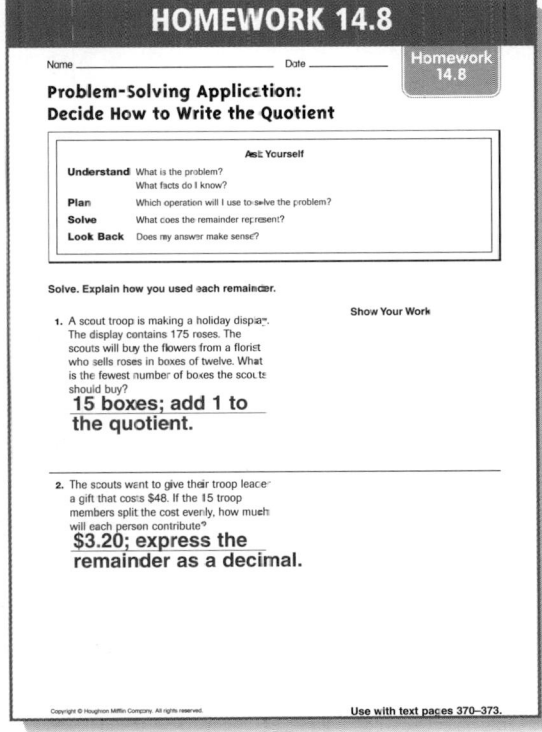

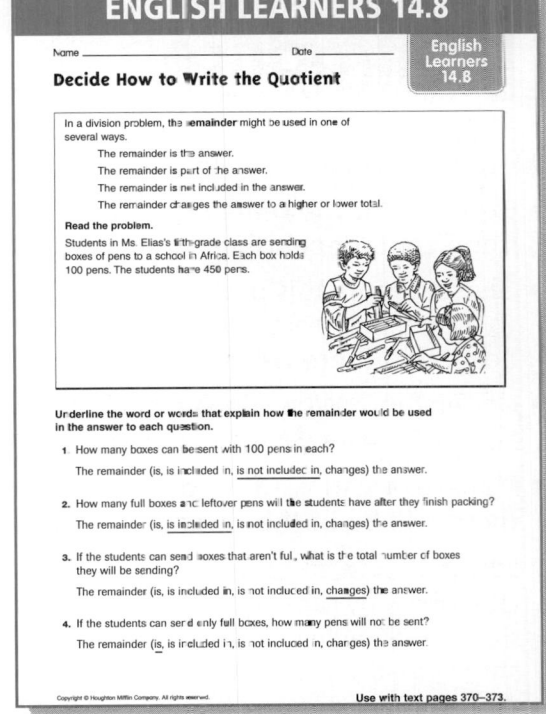

TEACHING LESSON 14.8

LESSON ORGANIZER

Objective Decide how to write the quotient to solve a problem.

Resources Reteach, Practice, Enrichment, Problem Solving, Homework, English Learners, Transparencies, Math Center

Materials 50 counters, Problem Solving: Four Step Process Transparency

Warm-Up Activity
Express Remainders as Fractions

| 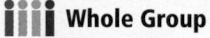 Whole Group | 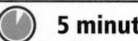 5 minutes | Visual, Auditory |

Give students the following problems. Have them express any remainder as a fraction.

1. $15\overline{)1,260}$ (84)
2. $12\overline{)456}$ (38)
3. $28\overline{)1,183}$ ($42\frac{1}{4}$)
4. $18\overline{)402}$ ($22\frac{1}{3}$)
5. $70\overline{)854}$ ($12\frac{1}{5}$)

Lesson 8

Problem-Solving Application
Decide How to Write the Quotient

Objective Decide how to write the quotient to solve a problem.

When you solve a division problem, sometimes you need to decide how to interpret the remainder.

▶ **Sometimes you use the remainder to decide on the answer.**

A store received boxes containing 19 jackets. Only 5 jackets fit in each box. How many boxes did they receive?

There are 3 full boxes. Another box is needed for the extra 4 jackets.

$$\begin{array}{r} 3 \text{ R4} \\ 5\overline{)19} \\ -15 \\ \hline 4 \end{array}$$

Solution: They received 4 boxes in all.

▶ **Sometimes you write the remainder as a fraction.**

A group makes sweatshirts. They use 18 feet of material to make 4 sweatshirts. How much material does each sweatshirt require?

$$\begin{array}{r} 4 \text{ R2} = 4\frac{2}{4} = 4\frac{1}{2} \\ 4\overline{)18} \\ -16 \\ \hline 2 \end{array}$$

Solution: Each sweatshirt requires $4\frac{1}{2}$ feet of material.

▶ **Sometimes you write the quotient as a decimal.**

Liang buys 8 identical T-shirts at the sports center store. If he spends $30 in all, how much does each shirt cost?

$$\begin{array}{r} 3.75 \\ 8\overline{)30.00} \\ -24\downarrow \\ \hline 60 \\ -56\downarrow \\ \hline 40 \\ -40 \\ \hline 0 \end{array}$$

Solution: Each T-shirt costs $3.75.

Look Back How does thinking about the question in each situation help you decide what to do with the remainder?

370

---

1 Introduce

Materials: Problem Solving: Four Step Process Transparency

- Explain that the remainder of a quotient may be significant, depending on the situation.

- Give students this problem: A company ships jeans 7 pairs to a box. If a store orders 38 pairs of jeans, how many boxes will there be in the shipment?

- Understand: **What do we need to find out?** (How many boxes of 7 jeans will be in the shipment?)

- Plan: **How can we find out how many boxes of 7 jeans there will be in the shipment?** (Divide 38 by 7.)

- Solve: 38 ÷ 7 = 5 R3 **Why is the remainder significant?** (The company can ship 35 pairs in 5 boxes, but they must also ship the remaining 3.) **How many boxes will be needed to ship the 38 pairs of jeans?** (6 boxes in all)

- Check: **Does this solution make sense?**

370   **CHAPTER 14   Lesson 8**

2 Develop

Guide students through the *Learn About It* portion of the lesson.

- **Look at the first example.** Discuss how the remainder in this situation is important in the solution.

- **Look at the second example. What unit is the quotient expressed in?** (feet) **Why is the remainder expressed as a fraction?** (Material is measured in fractions of feet or yards.)

- **Look at the third example.** Point out that, after the first step, the remainder would be $\frac{6}{8}$, which is $\frac{3}{4}$, and $\frac{3}{4}$ of a dollar is 75 cents.

Use the Ask Yourself questions to help you solve each problem.

 **Ask Yourself**
- What does the question ask me to find?
- What does the remainder represent?
- Does my answer make sense?

TEST
TIPS

1. Each pair of sweatpants requires 2 yards of fabric. How many pairs of sweatpants can be made with 7 yards of fabric? **3 pair**

   (Hint) Can you make part of a pair of sweatpants?

2. It cost 8 runners a total of $42.00 to enter a local race. How much was each runner's entry fee? **$5.25**

Independent Practice

Solve. Explain how you used each remainder.

3. During a parade, 46 award winners from the Youth Sports Center rode in automobiles. If only 6 winners could fit in each automobile, how many automobiles did they need for all the winners?
See Additional Answers on Page 375.

5. Pedro is making a 7-foot banner for Awards Night. Pedro needs to find the center of the banner so he can space the lettering correctly. How far from the end of the banner is its center?
See Additional Answers on Page 375.

6. The Youth Sports Center will have pizzas at their Awards Night. Each pizza is cut into 8 slices. If 150 people plan to attend and each eats 3 slices of pizza, what is the fewest number of pizzas they should order?
See Additional Answers on Page 375.

7. **Write Your Own** Write a word problem in which the quotient must be used to decide the answer.
Check students' problems.

8. **Create and Solve** Write a word problem in which the quotient must be written as a decimal.
Check students' problems.

4. At the car wash shown in the picture below, $434 was raised for the Youth Sports Center. Of that, $107 was from donations. The rest was from washing cars. How many cars did they wash?
109 cars

SHINE EXIT

CAR WASH
$3.00

CENTER

Go On

Chapter 14 Lesson 8   371

 **Quick Check Options**

The following activities will help students prepare for the Quick Check or may be used as an alternative assessment.

Vocabulary Review (individual, small group, or whole class)

Have students review the following vocabulary words by giving an example of how each term is used in this chapter.
- repeating decimal

Math Conversations (small group or whole class)

Have students discuss what they have learned about deciding how to write a quotient in this chapter. Encourage students to ask each other questions to clarify their understanding.

Writing Prompt (individual or partners)

To solidify student understanding of vocabulary and concepts, have each student complete the following sentence:

The thing I found easiest about deciding how to write a quotient is _____.

---

③ Practice

Guided Practice

Have students complete **Exercises 1 and 2** as you observe. Remind them to use the *Ask Yourself* questions to help.

Assign **Problems 3–16** as independent work. Have students share and discuss their work.

Problem-Solving Reminders

Have students review their answers to make sure they have done the following:
- expressed the solution clearly
- used appropriate mathematical notation and terms
- supported their solutions with verbal and symbolic work
- determined the reasonableness of the solution in the context of the original problem.

DAILY TEST PREP

A store orders 600 gift boxes from a company. If one carton will hold 45 boxes, how many cartons will be needed to ship the gift boxes? [C]

A. 12   B. 13   C. 14   D. 15

Activity

Lesson Intervention

Or use Intervention CD-ROM Lesson 14.8

Seating Arrangements

| 👤👤👤 Small Group | 🕐 5–10 minutes | Visual, Kinesthetic |

Materials: *50 counters*

- A charity is giving a dinner to honor people who have given money to support young athletes. If each table seats 6 people, how many tables will be needed for 50 guests?

- Use a group of counters to simulate groups of 6 guests. Have students help or follow as you make groups of 6 counters. Have students add the groups of 6 as they go until you get to 48.

- **How many groups of 6 do we have?** (8) **How many guests is that?** (48) **How many tables will seat those groups?** (8 tables) Point to the 2 counters left over. **How many counters are left over?** (2) **What do we do to seat them?** (add another table) **How many tables in all now?** (9)

Choose a Computation Method

Mental Math • Estimation • Paper and Pencil • Calculator

Solve each problem. Name the computation method you used.
Ex. 8–12: Computation methods may vary. Possible methods are given.

8. The room for the Youth Sports Center's Awards Night has tables that seat 4 people. If 146 people attend the Awards Night, how many tables are needed?
37 tables; pencil and paper

9. Val donated four times as much money to the equipment fund as Gary did. Together they donated $150. How much did each person donate?
Val: $120; Gary $30; mental math

10. The board at the Youth Sports Center got an estimate of $15,450 to redo the basketball courts. They've raised $\frac{2}{3}$ of the amount they need. About how much do they still have to raise?
About $5,000; estimation

11. To decorate for a party, a youth group needed 750 feet of ribbon. The ribbon is sold on rolls of 8 yards each. No partial rolls are sold. How many rolls of ribbon will they need? **32 rolls**

12. The sports club members made refrigerator magnets for a fundraiser. On Monday they made 20 magnets, 2 more than on Sunday. On Sunday they made 4 fewer than on Saturday. On Saturday they made twice as many as on Friday. How many did they make in all?
71 magnets; pencil and paper

Data Use the table for Problems 13–16.

13. Each soccer team has 11 players. What is the greatest number of soccer games that these players could have going on at the same time?
6 games

14. About 0.6 of the people who participate in swimming also take part in another sport at the Sports Center. About how many people is that?
about 60 people

Program	Number of Participants
Basketball	128
Soccer	142
Swimming	95
Tennis	48
Weight Lifting	18

15. Each morning at 8:00 A.M. all the people signed up for weight lifting show up. They each sign up for a $\frac{1}{2}$-hour session on one of the four weight benches. At what time does the last of those people finish? **10:30 A.M.**

16. It costs the Youth Sports Center $250 to rent each 48-person bus. If they hire enough buses to take all the people signed up for basketball to a local tournament, how much do they spend on buses? **$750**

372

Practice *continued*

Choose a Computation Method

Have students compare computation methods used for Problems 8–12.

- **Problem Solving for Problems 13 and 16** Ask students to discuss their methods of solution.

---

4 Assess and Close

- **When would you express the remainder of a quotient as a whole number? a fraction? a decimal?** (Answers will vary.) Have students brainstorm different units that could be used in a division problem, and discuss how the remainders could be expressed, for example: people—whole number, money—decimal.

Assign the **LESSON QUIZ** on Transparency 14.8 to further assess student understanding.

Quick Check

Check your understanding of Lessons 5–8.

Divide. (Lesson 5)

1. $2\overline{)3}$ **1.5**
2. $5\overline{)6.4}$ **1.28**
3. $22\overline{)5.5}$ **0.25**

Change each fraction to decimal form. (Lesson 6)

4. $\frac{4}{5}$ **0.8**
5. $\frac{6}{11}$ **0.54**
6. $\frac{5}{6}$ **0.83**

Divide. Round each quotient to the nearest hundredth. (Lesson 7)

7. $0.3\overline{)1.4}$ **4.67**
8. $1.8\overline{)5}$ **2.78**
9. $2.4\overline{)9.25}$ **3.85**

Solve. (Lesson 8)

10. The Sports Center is having a soup label drive. They put rubber bands on packs of 100 labels. How many packs with rubber bands are there for the 23,285 labels they have so far? **232 packs**

Garden Math

Calculator Connection

What kind of flower do you get if you plant a crazy pickle?
A DAFFY DILL

Copy the chart at the right.

Use a calculator to find each quotient. Then use the key to decode the puzzle. Read down the last column to find the answer to the riddle.

Quotient	Letter
0.24	A
0.36	D
0.58	F
0.71	G
0.82	I
0.95	L
1.26	N
1.32	O
1.67	T
1.75	Y

Problem	Quotient	Letter
0.192 ÷ 0.8	**0.24** ▪	▪
0.9 ÷ 2.5	**0.36** ▪	▪
0.84 ÷ 3.5	**0.24** ▪	▪
0.232 ÷ 0.4	**0.58** ▪	▪
5.394 ÷ 9.3	**0.58** ▪	▪
0.665 ÷ 0.38	**1.75** ▪	▪
0.09 ÷ 0.25	**0.36** ▪	▪
0.656 ÷ 0.8	**0.82** ▪	▪
4.275 ÷ 4.5	**0.95** ▪	▪
0.931 ÷ 0.98	**0.95** ▪	▪

Chapter 14 Lesson 8   **373**

Quick Check

Quick Check

Purpose: The Quick Check allows you to assess the student's understanding of the concepts presented in Lessons 5–8.

Items	Objectives Tested	Pages	Intervention
1–3	Write one or more zeros in the dividend to help solve division problems.	362–364	Reteach Resource 14.5 *Ways to Success 14.5*
4–6	Change a fraction to a decimal using division.	366–367	Reteach Resource 14.6 *Ways to Success 14.6*
7–9	Divide one decimal by another.	368–369	Reteach Resource 14.7 *Ways to Success 14.7*
10	Decide how to write the quotient to solve a problem.	370–372	Reteach Resource 14.8 *Ways to Success 14.8*

Keeping a Journal

Have students write a few sentences explaining how the remainder of a quotient can be interpreted in one of the three ways discussed in the lesson.

Calculator Connection

Garden Math

- Have students use the paper-and-pencil method if their answers do not match the quotients given. Then guide them in using the calculator to arrive at the same quotients.

Monitoring Student Progress

 Chapter Review/Test

Purpose: This test provides an informal assessment of the Chapter 14 objectives.

Chapter Test Items 1–25

To assign a numerical grade for this Chapter Test, use 4 points for each test item.

Check Understanding

You can use the **Write About It** question to assess student understanding of a key chapter concept.

Customizing Your Instruction

For students who have not yet mastered these objectives, you can use the Reteaching Resources listed in the chart below.

 ## Assessment Options

A summary test for this chapter is also provided in the Unit Resource Folder.

Adequate Yearly Progress

Use the **End of Grade Test Prep Assessment Guide** to help familiarize your students with the format of standardized tests.

Chapter Review/Test

Write About It: Josh forgot to move the decimal place to the right in both the dividend and the divisor, so the answer is off by one decimal place. It should be 54.5.

Vocabulary
- compatible numbers
- exponent
- power of 10
- repeating decimal

VOCABULARY

1. In the expression 83×10^r, 10^r is a(n) ____. **power of 10**

2. ____ can be used to estimate a quotient. **compatible numbers**

3. When a denominator does not divide into a numerator without a remainder, the result may be a(n) ____. **repeating decimal**

CONCEPTS AND SKILLS

Model the division and write the quotient in decimal form.
(Lesson 1, pp. 352–353) **4–8. Check students' drawings.**

4. $7 \div 0.5$ **14.0** 5. $9 \div 0.9$ **10.0** 6. $9 \div 0.3$ **30.0** 7. $6 \div 0.4$ **15.0** 8. $8 \div 0.25$ **32.0**

Estimate each quotient. (Lesson 2, pp. 354–355) **9–11. Possible estimates given.**

9. $4 \div 0.19$ **20**   10. $82 \div 0.26$ **320**   11. $16 \div 0.147$ **100**

Divide. (Lessons 4–5, pp. 358–365)

12. $0.8 \div 101$ **0.00792**   13. $4.2 \div 7$ **0.6**   14. $4\overline{)6.5}$ **1.625**

15. $1,593.65 \div 104$ **15.3236**   16. $8.8 \div 5$ **1.76**   17. $8\overline{)56.36}$ **7.045**

Change each fraction to decimal form. (Lesson 6, pp. 366–367)

18. $\frac{3}{5}$ **0.6**   19. $\frac{7}{12}$ **0.583̄**   20. $\frac{2}{9}$ **0.2̄**

Divide to the greatest place or the nearest hundredth. (Lesson 7, pp. 368–369)

21. $0.4\overline{)6.4}$ **16**   22. $6.2\overline{)31.62}$ **5.1**   23. $4.1\overline{)33.62}$ **8.2**

24. **8 uniforms; 22 ÷ 2.5 = 8 R2; Since each uniform needs 2.5 yards, the 2 extra yards are kept as a remainder.**

PROBLEM SOLVING

Solve. Explain how you used each remainder. (Lesson 8, pp. 370–373)

24. Each pep squad uniform requires 2.5 yards of fabric. How many uniforms can be made from 22 yards of fabric? **See above.**

25. There are 27 people going to a soccer game. If each car can hold 5 people, how many cars will be needed?
27 ÷ 5 = 5 R2, so 6 cars will be needed.

Write About It

Show You Understand
Josh divides these two decimals incorrectly. Explain what he did wrong. Show how to find the correct quotient. **See above.**

```
       5.45
0.5)27.25
    -25
      2.2
    -20
      25
     -25
       0
```

Reteaching Support

Chapter Test Items	Summary Test Items	Chapter Objectives Tested	TE Pages	Use These Reteaching Resources
4–8	1–4	**14A** Relate division of fractions to division of decimals.	352A–353	Reteach Resource 14.1 Ways to Success CD: 14.1 Skillsheet 113
2, 9–11	5–8	**14B** Estimate decimal quotients.	354A–355	Reteach Resource 14.2 Ways to Success CD: 14.2 Skillsheet 114
1, 12–17, 21–23	9–12	**14C** Divide with decimals and whole numbers.	356A–365, 368A–369	Reteach Resource 14.3–14.5, 14.7 Ways to Success CD: 14.3–14.5, 14.7 Skillsheet 115, 116
3, 18–20	13–16	**14D** Use division to find repeating decimals.	366A–367	Reteach Resource 14.6 Ways to Success CD: 14.6 Skillsheet 117
24, 25	17–20	**14E** Decide how to write a quotient when a quotient is the solution to a problem.	370A–373	Reteach Resource 14.8 Ways to Success CD: 14.8 Skillsheet 118

CHAPTER SUMMARY TEST

Name _____ Date _____

Chapter 14 Test

Model the division. Write the quotient in decimal form.

1. $9 \div 0.3$ **30**
2. $10 \div 0.25$ **40**
3. $2 \div 0.5$ **4**
4. $14 \div 0.4$ **35**

Estimate each quotient. **5–8: Estimates will vary.**

5. $18 \div 0.61$ **About 30**
6. $30.6 \div 0.77$ **About 40**
7. $590 \div 0.29$ **About 2,000**
8. $39.8 \div 0.42$ **About 100**

Divide.

9. $6.3 \div 10^2$ **0.063**
10. $5.4 \div 3$ **1.8**
11. $0.96 \div 0.4$ **2.4**
12. $2.46 \div 0.06$ **41**

Copyright © Houghton Mifflin Company. All rights reserved.

Go on

Set A (Lesson 1, pp. 352–353)

Model the division and write the quotient in decimal form. *Check students' drawings.*

1. 6 ÷ 0.2 **30** 2. 9 ÷ 0.5 **18** 3. 5 ÷ 0.25 **20** 4. 12 ÷ 0.6 **20**

Set B (Lesson 2, pp. 354–355)

Estimate each quotient. Ex. 1–8: Possible estimates given.

1. 79 ÷ 0.77 **100** 2. 309 ÷ 0.33 **1000** 3. 26 ÷ 0.492 **50** 4. 54.7 ÷ 0.89 **60**
5. 5.63 ÷ 0.621 **10** 6. 9 ÷ 0.258 **36** 7. 16.2 ÷ 0.41 **40** 8. 22 ÷ 0.108 **200**

Set C (Lesson 3, pp. 356–357)

Multiply or divide by using patterns.

1. 6.12×10^1 **61.2** 2. 8.34×10^2 **834** 3. $2{,}745.64 \div 10^2$ **27.4564** 4. $7.25 \div 10$ **0.725**
5. $8.67 \div 10^2$ **0.0867** 6. $6.534 \div 10^3$ **0.006534** 7. 0.054×10^2 **5.4** 8. 0.19×10^3 **190**

Set D (Lesson 4, pp. 358–361)

Divide and check.

1. 6)4.8 **0.8** 2. 2)2.36 **1.18** 3. 4)21.84 **5.46** 4. 7)$61.95 **$8.85**
5. 7.2 ÷ 6 **1.2** 6. $24.75 ÷ 3 **$8.25** 7. 1.44 ÷ 6 **0.24** 8. 0.87 ÷ 3 **0.29**

Set E (Lesson 5, pp. 362–365)

Divide and check using estimation.

1. 4)4.2 **1.05** 2. 5)6.7 **1.34** 3. 10)7.74 **0.774** 4. 8)24.6 **3.075**
5. 8)4 **0.5** 6. 4)15 **3.75** 7. 63 ÷ 15 **4.2** 8. 36.8 ÷ 5 **7.36**

Set F (Lesson 6, pp. 366–367)

Change each fraction to decimal form.

1. $\frac{1}{15}$ **0.0$\overline{6}$** 2. $\frac{7}{12}$ **0.583$\overline{3}$** 3. $\frac{7}{11}$ **0.6$\overline{3}$** 4. $\frac{4}{15}$ **0.2$\overline{6}$** 5. $\frac{15}{4}$ **3.75** 6. $\frac{5}{9}$ **0.$\overline{5}$**

Set G (Lesson 7, pp. 368–369)

Divide to the greatest place or the nearest hundredth. Check that your answer is reasonable.

1. 0.5)1.5 **3** 2. 0.15)55.5 **370** 3. 0.3)3.6 **6** 4. 0.52)13 **25**
5. 0.8)5.84 **7.3** 6. 3.7)22.2 **6** 7. 0.9)5.04 **5.6** 8. 0.8)0.584 **0.73**

Chapter 14 Extra Practice **375**

CHAPTER SUMMARY TEST

Name _____ Date _____ Chapter 14 Test continued

Change each fraction to decimal form.

13. $\frac{1}{9}$ **0.$\overline{1}$** 14. $\frac{7}{12}$ **0.583$\overline{3}$**
15. $\frac{8}{11}$ **0.$\overline{72}$** 16. $\frac{2}{15}$ **0.13$\overline{3}$**

Solve.

17. Jonathan collected 63 pounds of newspapers for the recycling drive. He made as many 4 pound bundles of paper as he could. How many full bundles of newspapers did Jonathan make?
15

18. A car dealer received a shipment of 50 new cars for a sale. The cars were parked in a lot which had 8 spaces in each row. Each row was filled before the next row was started. How many rows were there?
7

19. A teacher ordered 20 books for her class. The book order totaled $310. What was the cost per book?
$15.50

20. Each row in a school auditorium had 12 seats. There were 75 fifth grade students waiting to be seated for a movie. If each row was filled before the next row was started, how many students were in the last row?
3

Additional Answers

Chapter 14

Lesson 2, pp. 354–355

19. *Estimates may vary. Possible answer:* 18 games

20. Check data and answer to word problem.

21. *Possible estimate:* You can change any decimal to a fraction. If you know how to divide by a fraction, you can use what you know to estimate the quotient for decimal division.

Lesson 4, pp. 358–360

45. *Possible answer:* The quotient of 6.56 ÷ 8 is less than 1 because you are dividing a smaller number by a larger number. The quotient of 656 ÷ 80 is greater than 1 because you are dividing a larger number by a smaller number. So, 6.56 ÷ 8 < 656 ÷ 80.

48. *Possible answer:* Dividing a decimal by a whole number is the same as dividing a whole number by a whole number in that you can ignore the decimal point to divide and different because you can place a decimal point in the quotient above the decimal point in the dividend.

Lesson 5, pp. 362–365

48. *Possible answer:* If you don't want a whole number remainder, you write zeros in the dividend so you can keep dividing. Then you keep dividing until there is no remainder.

Lesson 6, pp. 366–367

26. $\frac{16}{10} > \frac{13}{10}$ 27. $\frac{48}{21} < \frac{49}{21}$
28. $\frac{21}{4} = \frac{21}{4}$ 29. $\frac{151}{50} < \frac{150}{50}$

Lesson 8, pp. 370–372

3. 8 automobiles; to increase the number of automobiles for the 4 extra people

5. $3\frac{1}{2}$ ft; to show the customary measure as a fraction

6. 57 pizzas; to increase the number of pizzas because you can't buy part of a pizza

Divide Decimals **375**

Social Studies Connection

PURPOSE

Students use data about postage stamps to solve problems involving multiplication and division of decimals.

WEEKLY WR READER®
Social Studies Connection

Philatelic Fun

Are you a philatelist? If you collect or study postage stamps, you are. Some people collect stamps for the pure pleasure of it. Others collect stamps because some historic stamps are worth a lot of money.

The very first postage stamps were used on May 6, 1840, in England. The "1 Penny Black" and "2 Pence Blue" were so named because of their purchase price and color. Before long, most countries in the world were using postage stamps.

New stamps are being issued all the time. Recently, the U.S. Postal Service even released a series of stamps called *Stampin' the Future* that used drawings made by children between the ages of 8 and 12.

376

Using The Social Studies Connection

- Provide background on the word philatelist, which combines the Greek *phil* (love) and *ateles* (a + *telos:* free from tax). Other words with the same prefix are *philosophy* (love of wisdom) and *Philadelphia* (city of brotherly love).

- Elicit that a stamp's face value stands for an equivalent amount in coins. Point out that while coins are minted in set denominations (1¢, 5¢, 10¢, 25¢, 50¢, and $1.00), stamps are printed with face values that can change.

- Help students identify strategies for solving the multi-step problems in Exercises 1–3. Ask them to identify the operations they use.

- When discussing Exercise 4, help students evaluate the guidelines that Pilar has set out for arranging the stamps. Suggest that students model the two pages of the album so that they can try different sums of the face values.

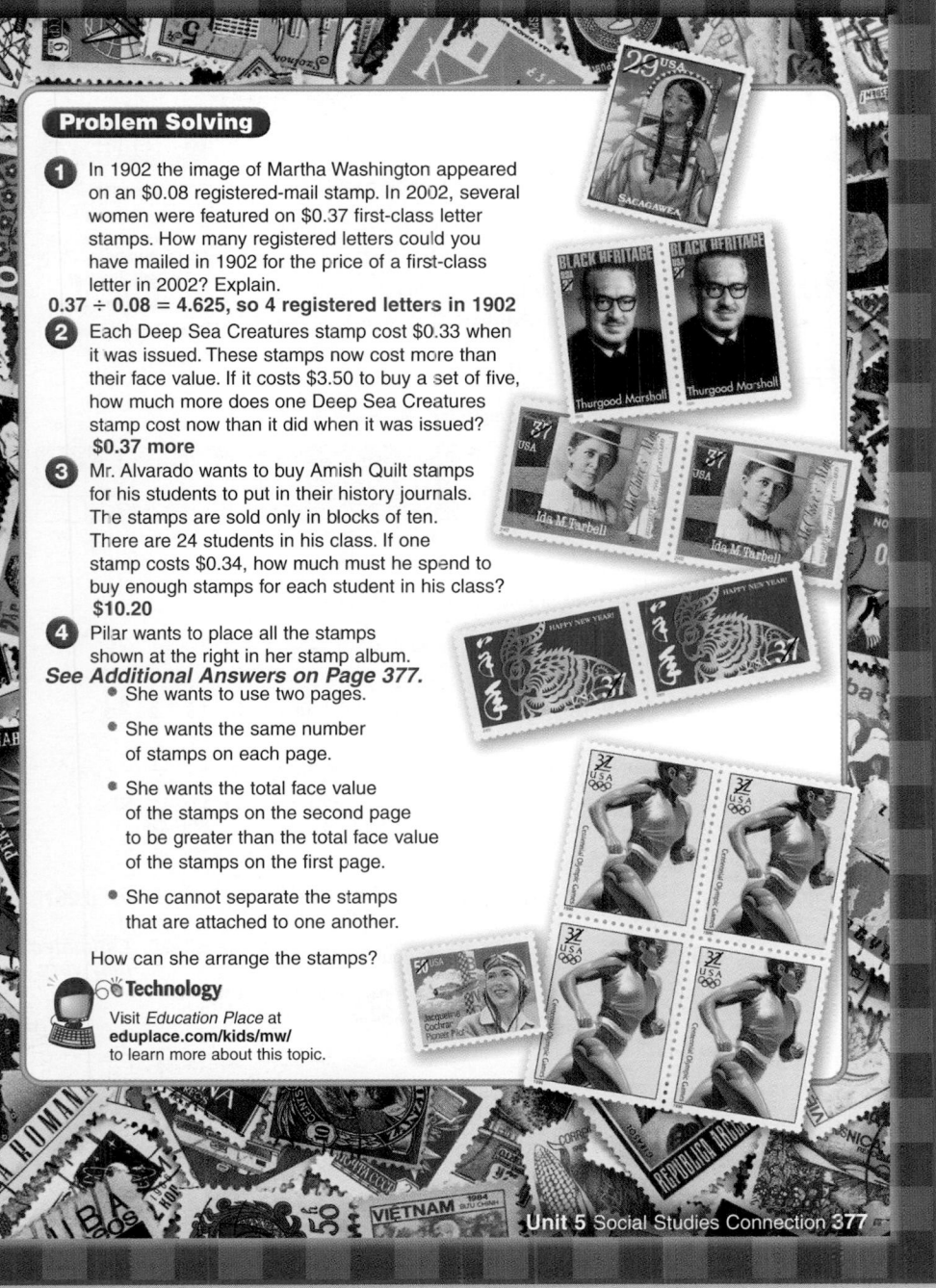

Task 2

a. *Answers will vary. Possible answer:* 3 pairs of jeans, 5 T-shirts, and 2 belts

b. *Answers will vary. Possible answer:* jeans, $49.47; T-shirts, $35.95; belts, $19.98; total, $105.40

c. 4 of each

Vocabulary Wrap-Up, p. 385

1. It is a repeating decimal: 1.22222...; the 2 goes on and on. Some students may realize this is the quotient for 11 ÷ 9.

4. *Possible answer:* Scientists record inches of rainfall in decimals because it is easier to add or compare decimals than fractions with different denominators. Finding averages is also easier with decimals.

Weekly Reader, Social Studies Connection, p. 377

4. *Possible answer:* first page – 4 USA Olympic, 2 Happy New Year; second page – 1 Sacagwea, 2 Black Heritage, 2 Ida M. Tarbell, 1 Jacqueline Cochran

---

Additional Answers

Unit 5

Unit Test, p. 379

Decision Making

Possible answer: $\frac{1}{3} \times 48 = 16$, so 16 students prefer summer; $16 \times \frac{1}{2} = 8$, so 8 students prefer winter; $16 + 8 = 24$ and $48 - 24 = 24$, so 24 students prefer spring and fall; $24 \div 2 = 12$, so 12 students like spring and 12 like fall. *Check students' graphs;* spring $= \frac{1}{4}$; summer $= \frac{1}{3}$; fall $= \frac{1}{4}$; and winter $= \frac{1}{6}$

Performance Assessment, p. 380

Task 1

b. 5 cups flour
1$\frac{1}{2}$ teaspoons baking powder
2 cups milk
7$\frac{1}{2}$ tablespoons oil
3 eggs

PURPOSE

This test provides an informal assessment of the Unit 5 objectives.

Unit Test Items 1–33

To assign a numerical grade for this Unit Test, use 3 points for each test item.

Customizing Your Instruction

For students who have not yet mastered these objectives, you can use the **Reteaching Resources** listed in the chart below. *Ways to Success* is Houghton Mifflin's Intervention program, available in CD-ROM.

 **Unit 5 Test**

 **VOCABULARY**

1. The product of a number and its ■ is 1. **reciprocal**

2. A(n) ■ is a quotient that repeats digits an unlimited number of times. **repeating decimal**

3. A(n) ■ is a number that tells how many times the base is used as a factor. **exponent**

Vocabulary
- exponent
- reciprocal
- compatible numbers
- mixed number
- repeating decimal

 **CONCEPTS AND SKILLS**

Write a multiplication sentence for each model. (Chapter 12)

4.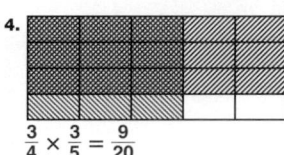

$\frac{3}{4} \times \frac{3}{5} = \frac{9}{20}$

5.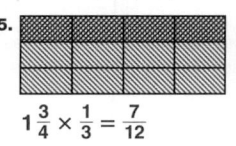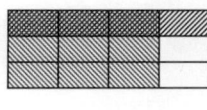

$1\frac{3}{4} \times \frac{1}{3} = \frac{7}{12}$

Multiply or divide. Write your answer in simplest form. (Chapter 12)

6. $\frac{2}{3} \times \frac{3}{9}$ $\frac{2}{9}$

7. $5\frac{1}{6} \times \frac{2}{7}$ $1\frac{10}{21}$

8. $7 \times \frac{1}{3}$ $2\frac{1}{3}$

9. $2 \div \frac{5}{6}$ $2\frac{2}{5}$

10. $2\frac{3}{4} \div \frac{5}{8}$ $4\frac{2}{5}$

11. $3\frac{1}{6} \times 1\frac{1}{3}$ $4\frac{2}{9}$

12. $\frac{3}{4} \div 2\frac{1}{2}$ $\frac{3}{10}$

13. $4\frac{1}{3} \div \frac{1}{2}$ $8\frac{2}{3}$

Estimate. Then multiply. (Chapter 13)   **14–17. Estimates may vary.**

14. 7×6.2 **43.4**

15. 1.02×0.6 **0.612**

16. 204×7.81 **1,593.24**

17. 17.24×52 **896.48**

Multiply or divide by using patterns. (Chapter 14)

18. 6.23×10^3 **6,230**

19. $8.6 \div 10^1$ **0.86**

20. 5.348×10^2 **534.8**

21. $267.9 \div 10^3$ **0.2679**

Estimate. Then find each quotient and check your answer. (Chapter 14)   **22–25. Estimates may vary.**

22. $8\overline{)20.8}$ **2.6**

23. $4\overline{)5.3}$ **1.325**

24. $426 \div 0.8$ **532.5**

25. $50.84 \div 6.2$ **8.2**

Write each as a decimal. (Chapter 14)

26. $\frac{3}{10}$ **0.3**

27. $\frac{2}{3}$ **$0.\overline{6}$**

28. $\frac{4}{11}$ **$0.\overline{36}$**

29. $\frac{1}{7}$ **$0.\overline{142857}$**

378

Reteaching Support

Unit Test Item pp. 138–139	Forms A & B	Unit Objectives Tested	TE Pages	Use These Reteaching Resources
1, 4–13	1–7	**5A** Multiply and divide with fractions and mixed numbers.	310A–318, 322A–327	Reteach Resources and *Ways to Success,* 12.1–12.3, 12.5–12.6
14–17 22–25	8–13	**5B** Estimate decimal products and quotients.	338A–339, 354A–355	Reteach Resources and *Ways to Success,* 13.3, 14.2
2, 3, 14–17, 18–21, 22–25, 26–29	14–19	**5C** Multiply and divide with decimals.	336A–337, 340A–342, 356A–364, 366A–369	Reteach Resources and *Ways to Success,* 13.2, 13.4, 14.3–14.4, 14.6–14.7
30–33	20–25	**5D** Solve problems, using skills and strategies.	314A–315, 328A–329, 336A–337	Reteach Resources and *Ways to Success,* 12.2, 12.7, 13.2

30. The Reading-For-All group raised $308 for new library books. Each book costs $5. How many new library books can they buy? **61 new books**

31. The temperature during the day on Mercury is 450°C. What is Mercury's temperature during the day in degrees Fahrenheit? Hint: $F = \frac{9}{5}C + 32$. **842°F**

32. Earth makes a complete revolution around the sun in about 365 days. Mercury revolves around the sun in 0.24 of an Earth year. How many days does it take for Mercury to revolve around the sun?
Possible answers: **87 days, 87.6 days, 87.84 days, or 88 days**

33. Lil deposited $1 in her savings account after the first week of summer, $2.50 after the second week, $4 after the third week, and $5.50 after the fourth week. If she continues this pattern, how much will Lil deposit after the tenth week? **$14.50**

Decision Making
Extended Response

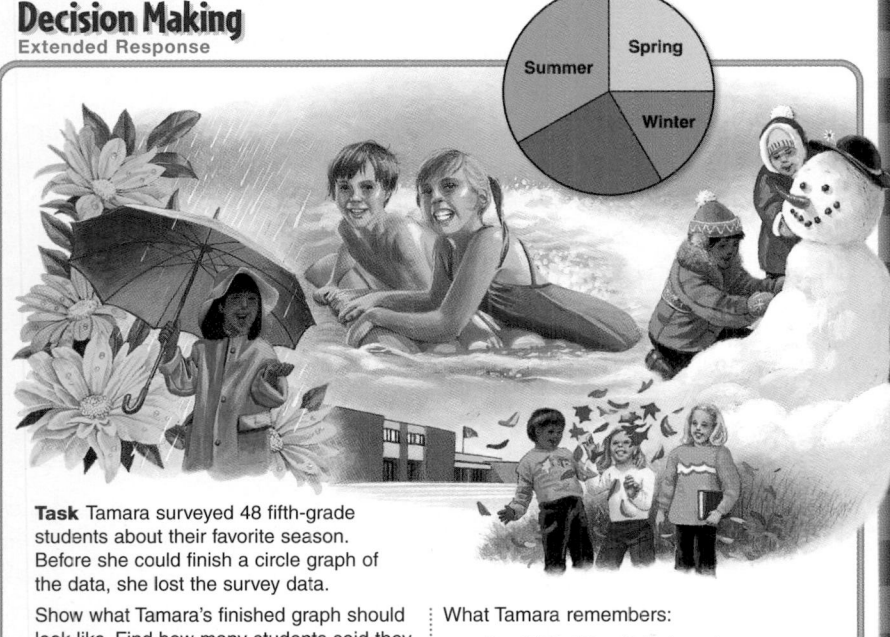

Task Tamara surveyed 48 fifth-grade students about their favorite season. Before she could finish a circle graph of the data, she lost the survey data.

Show what Tamara's finished graph should look like. Find how many students said they prefer each of the seasons. Explain how you found your answers. Show the fraction for each of the seasons on the completed circle graph of the data.
See Additional Answers on page 377.

What Tamara remembers:
- One third of the students prefer summer, and half that many prefer winter.
- Spring and fall are preferred by the same number of students.

Unit 5 Test 379

Monitoring Student Progress

✔ Assessment Options

Formal Tests for this unit are also provided in the Unit Resource Folder.

- Unit 5 Open Response Test (Form A)
- Unit 5 Multiple Choice Test (Form B)

✔ Performance Assessment

You may want to use the Performance Assessment instead of, or in addition to, the Unit Test. Performance Assessment tasks for this unit are on Student Book page 380.

✔ Adequate Yearly Progress Assessment Guide

Use the *End of Grade Test Prep Assessment Guide* to help familiarize your students with the format of standardized tests and to monitor progress.

UNIT TEST – FORM A

UNIT TEST – FORM B

Unit 5 Tests

See pages 380A–380B for answers.

Unit Test Answers: Form A

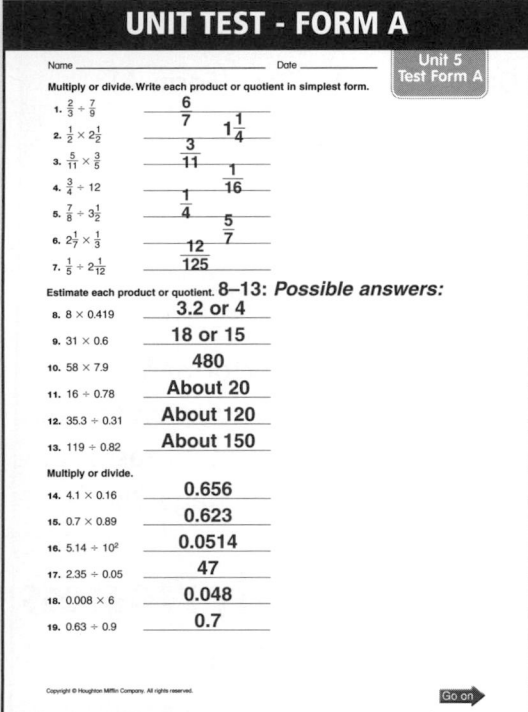

UNIT TEST - FORM A

Name _____ Date _____

Unit 5 Test Form A

Multiply or divide. Write each product or quotient in simplest form.

1. $\frac{2}{3} \div \frac{7}{9}$ — $\frac{6}{7}$

2. $\frac{1}{2} \times 2\frac{1}{2}$ — $1\frac{1}{4}$

3. $\frac{5}{11} \times \frac{3}{5}$ — $\frac{3}{11}$

4. $\frac{3}{4} \div 12$ — $\frac{1}{16}$

5. $\frac{7}{8} \div 3\frac{1}{2}$ — $\frac{1}{4}$

6. $2\frac{1}{7} \times \frac{1}{3}$ — $\frac{5}{7}$

7. $\frac{1}{5} \div 2\frac{1}{12}$ — $\frac{12}{125}$

Estimate each product or quotient. 8–13: *Possible answers:*

8. 8×0.419 — **3.2 or 4**

9. 31×0.6 — **18 or 15**

10. 58×7.9 — **480**

11. $16 \div 0.78$ — **About 20**

12. $35.3 \div 0.31$ — **About 120**

13. $119 \div 0.82$ — **About 150**

Multiply or divide.

14. 4.1×0.16 — **0.656**

15. 0.7×0.89 — **0.623**

16. 5.14×10^2 — **0.0514**

17. $2.35 \div 0.05$ — **47**

18. 0.008×6 — **0.048**

19. $0.63 \div 0.9$ — **0.7**

Go on →

UNIT TEST - FORM A

Name _____ Date _____

Unit 5 Test Form A continued

Solve.

20. A survey was taken of 90 new car owners. They voted on their favorite color for cars. Wide-Awake Blue was chosen by $\frac{1}{6}$ of the owners. How many owners chose Wide-Awake Blue?

    15

21. The distance Lila drove on a business trip was 312 miles. She stopped for dinner after she had driven $\frac{3}{4}$ of the distance. How far had she driven before she stopped for dinner?

    234

22. Steve bought an alarm clock for $23.50. The state sales tax was 0.06 of the purchase. He thought the tax would be less than $1.50. Is he correct? Explain your answer.

    Yes; $23.50 × 0.06 = $1.41

23. Amy earned $55 doing errands for her neighbor. She wanted to save 0.5 of her earnings. She figured she should put $50 in her savings. Is she correct? Explain your answer.

    No; $55 × 0.5 = $27.50

24. It cost $220 for 16 tickets to a baseball game for a scout troop. What was the cost per ticket?

    $13.75

25. Tiana had 139 paperback books to pack in boxes for the library. Each box held 7 paperback books. If Tiana filled as many boxes as she could, how many books were left over?

    6

STOP

Unit Test Answers: Form B

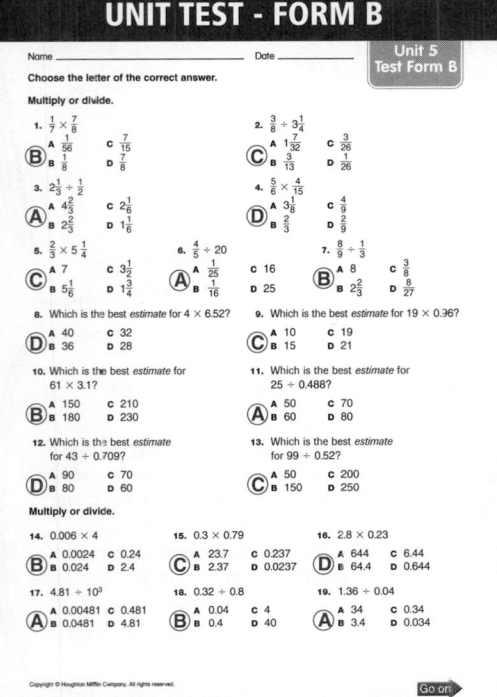

UNIT TEST - FORM B

Name _____ Date _____

Unit 5
Test Form B

Choose the letter of the correct answer.

Multiply or divide.

1. $\frac{1}{7} \times \frac{7}{8}$
   (B) A $\frac{1}{56}$ C $\frac{7}{15}$
   B $\frac{1}{8}$ D $\frac{7}{8}$

2. $\frac{3}{8} \div 3\frac{1}{4}$
   (C) A $1\frac{3}{32}$ C $\frac{3}{26}$
   B $\frac{3}{13}$ D $\frac{1}{26}$

3. $2\frac{1}{3} \div \frac{1}{2}$
   (A) A $4\frac{2}{3}$ C $2\frac{1}{6}$
   B $2\frac{2}{3}$ D $1\frac{1}{6}$

4. $\frac{5}{6} \times \frac{4}{15}$
   (D) A $\frac{4}{3}$ C $\frac{4}{9}$
   B $\frac{3}{8}$ D $\frac{2}{9}$

5. $\frac{2}{3} \times 5\frac{1}{4}$
   (C) A 7   C $3\frac{1}{2}$
   B $5\frac{7}{8}$ D $1\frac{3}{4}$

6. $\frac{4}{5} \div 20$
   (A) A $\frac{1}{25}$ C 16
   B $\frac{1}{16}$ D 25

7. $\frac{8}{9} \div \frac{1}{3}$
   (B) A 8   C $\frac{3}{8}$
   B $2\frac{2}{3}$ D $\frac{8}{27}$

8. Which is the best *estimate* for 4×6.52?
   (D) A 40   C 32
   B 36   D 28

9. Which is the best *estimate* for 19×0.96?
   (C) A 10   C 19
   B 15   D 21

10. Which is the best *estimate* for 61×3.1?
    (B) A 150   C 210
    B 180   D 230

11. Which is the best *estimate* for $25 \div 0.488$?
    (A) A 50   C 70
    B 60   D 80

12. Which is the best *estimate* for $43 \div 0.709$?
    (D) A 90   C 70
    B 80   D 60

13. Which is the best *estimate* for $99 \div 0.52$?
    (C) A 50   C 200
    B 150   D 250

Multiply or divide.

14. 0.006×4
    (B) A 0.0024   C 0.24
    B 0.024   D 2.4

15. 0.3×0.79
    (C) A 23.7   C 0.237
    B 2.37   D 0.0237

16. 2.8×0.23
    (D) A 644   C 6.44
    B 64.4   D 0.644

17. $4.81 \div 10^3$
    (A) A 0.00481   C 0.481
    B 0.0481   D 4.81

18. $0.32 \div 0.8$
    (B) A 0.04   C 4
    B 0.4   D 40

19. $1.36 \div 0.04$
    (A) A 34   C 0.34
    B 3.4   D 0.034

Go on ▶

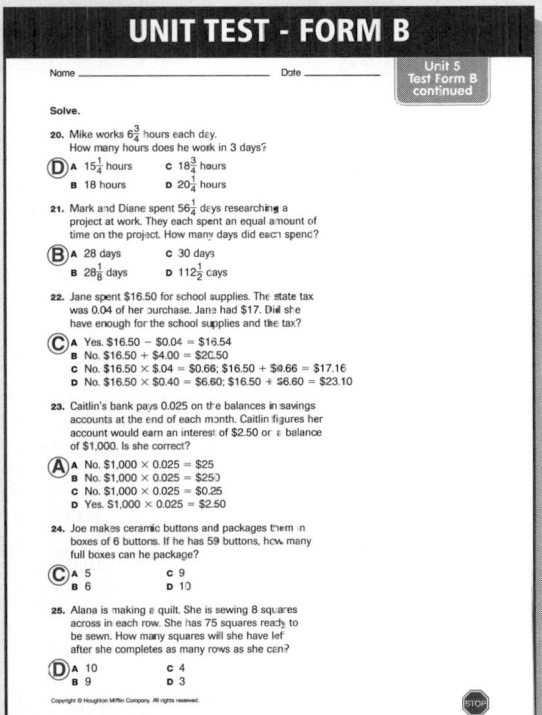

UNIT TEST - FORM B

Name _____ Date _____

Unit 5
Test Form B
continued

Solve.

20. Mike works $6\frac{3}{4}$ hours each day. How many hours does he work in 3 days?
    (D) A $15\frac{1}{4}$ hours   C $18\frac{3}{4}$ hours
    B 18 hours   D $20\frac{1}{4}$ hours

21. Mark and Diane spent $56\frac{1}{4}$ days researching a project at work. They each spent an equal amount of time on the project. How many days did each spend?
    (B) A 28 days   C 30 days
    B $28\frac{1}{8}$ days   D $112\frac{1}{2}$ days

22. Jane spent $16.50 for school supplies. The state tax was 0.04 of her purchase. Jane had $17. Did she have enough for the school supplies and the tax?
    (C) A Yes. $16.50 − $0.04 = $16.54
    B No. $16.50 + $4.00 = $20.50
    C No. $16.50 × $0.04 = $0.66; $16.50 + $0.66 = $17.16
    D No. $16.50 × $0.40 = $6.60; $16.50 + $6.60 = $23.10

23. Caitlin's bank pays 0.025 on the balances in savings accounts at the end of each month. Caitlin figures her account would earn an interest of $2.50 on a balance of $1,000. Is she correct?
    (A) A No. $1,000 × 0.025 = $25
    B No. $1,000 × 0.025 = $250
    C No. $1,000 × 0.025 = $0.25
    D Yes. $1,000 × 0.025 = $2.50

24. Joe makes ceramic buttons and packages them in boxes of 6 buttons. If he has 59 buttons, how many full boxes can he package?
    (C) A 5   C 9
    B 6   D 10

25. Alana is making a quilt. She is sewing 8 squares across in each row. She has 75 squares ready to be sewn. How many squares will she have left after she completes as many rows as she can?
    (D) A 10   C 4
    B 9   D 3

STOP

Performance Assessment

PURPOSE

In these assessments, students should be able to multiply fractions and mixed numbers by whole numbers and multiply and divide decimals.

Scoring Rubric

4 EXEMPLARY

Fully completes each task; shows an understanding of multiplying fractions and mixed numbers by whole numbers, and of multiplying and dividing decimals by whole numbers.

3 PROFICIENT

Shows an understanding of multiplying with fractions and mixed numbers and of multiplying and dividing with decimals, but needs help with 1c and 2b.

2 ACCEPTABLE

Understands multiplication with fractions and mixed numbers and multiplication and division with decimals, but makes computational errors; needs help with 1c and 2b.

1 LIMITED

Makes computational errors due to a lack of understanding of multiplication with fractions and mixed numbers and multiplication and division with decimals; is unable to complete the tasks, even with assistance.

Performance Assessment

b. *See Additional Answers on page 377.*

TASK 1

Pancakes for Twelve (Chapter 12)

You need to make 12 pancakes for a special birthday breakfast.

a. Identify the number by which to multiply the measurements in the recipe to make 12 pancakes. **Multiply by 3.**

b. Rewrite the pancake recipe so it will make 12 pancakes. Write fractions in simplest form. **c. Multiply by 6.**

c. Suppose you want to make enough pancakes so each person in your math class gets 2 pancakes. By what number would you need to multiply the measurements in the recipe?

d. How much flour will you need for the pancakes in part **c**? **10 cups flour**

Pancakes

Recipe

$1\frac{2}{3}$ cups flour

$\frac{1}{2}$ teaspoon baking powder

$\frac{2}{3}$ cup milk

$2\frac{1}{2}$ tablespoons oil

1 egg

Makes 4 pancakes

TASK 2

School Shopping Spree (Chapters 13–14)

You are shopping for school clothes.

a. Decide how to combine the items on sale to create about a week's worth of outfits. How many T-shirts, belts, and jeans will you buy? Buy at least two of each item.

b. Multiply to find the total cost of each type of item. Then find the total cost of your purchase.

c. Suppose you bought the same number of each item. If you spent a total of $134.68, how many of each item did you buy?

| T-Shirts $7.19 | Belts $9.99 | Jeans $16.49 |

See Additional Answers on page 377.

Self Check

• Did I answer the questions for each task?

• Did I check all my work?

 **Task One**

Students multiply fractions and mixed numbers by 3, and then multiply the same set of fractions and mixed numbers by a larger whole number.

 **Task Two**

Students choose a set of items having specified decimal prices, multiply a decimal by a whole number, and divide a decimal by a whole number.

Enrichment: Estimating With Mixed Numbers

The width of a parking lot is $78\frac{1}{3}$ feet, and each space is to be the same width. For compact cars, each parking space must be at least $7\frac{3}{4}$ feet wide. What is the greatest number of compact-car parking spaces that will fit in one row? How wide will each space be?

First, you need to estimate how many parking spaces will fit. Then you can divide to find how wide to make each parking space.

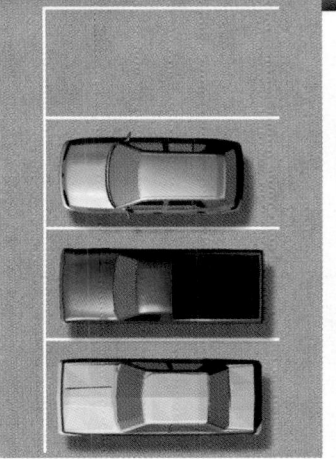

Rules for Rounding Mixed Numbers

To estimate with mixed numbers, round to the nearest whole number:

- If the fraction part of the mixed number is equal to $\frac{1}{2}$ or greater, round up.
- If the fraction part of the mixed number is less than $\frac{1}{2}$, round down.

Estimate: $78\frac{1}{3} \div 7\frac{3}{4} = ?$

Round down for fractions less than $\frac{1}{2}$. $\quad 78\frac{1}{3} \longrightarrow 78$
Round up for fractions $\frac{1}{2}$ or greater. $\quad 7\frac{3}{4} \longrightarrow 8$

$78 \div 8 = 9$ R6 or $9\frac{3}{4}$.
There will be 9 or 10 parking spaces in the lot.

Solve: Check whether 9 spaces will fit. $\quad 78\frac{1}{3} \div 9 \approx 9$; 9 feet is too wide.
Check whether 10 spaces will fit. $\quad 78\frac{1}{3} \div 10 = 7\frac{5}{6}$
$\frac{5}{6} > \frac{3}{4}$, so $7\frac{5}{6}$ feet wide works.

Solution: There will be 10 spaces, each $7\frac{5}{6}$ feet wide.

Find the greatest number of spaces that will fit in one row. Then find the width of each space.

1 The width of a compact-car parking lot is $47\frac{1}{4}$ feet. Each parking space must be at least $7\frac{3}{4}$ feet wide. Each space is to be the same width.
See above.

2 The width of a full-size car parking lot is 70 feet. Each parking space must be at least $8\frac{1}{2}$ feet wide. Each space is to be the same width.
See above.

1. There can be 6 parking spaces, each $7\frac{7}{8}$ feet wide.
2. There can be 8 parking spaces, each $8\frac{3}{4}$ feet wide.

Enrichment

▶ **Estimating With Mixed Numbers**

PURPOSE

Students use the rules for rounding to estimate quotients of whole numbers and mixed numbers that are divided by mixed numbers in a problem-solving setting.

Using the Enrichment Activity

- This lesson extends skills learned in Chapter 12 Lesson 6 (Divide Mixed Numbers) and Chapter 14 Lesson 2 (Estimate Quotients). Although students have previously rounded decimals to find compatible numbers, the concept of rounding the dividend and the divisor in order to find an estimate is the same for mixed numbers.

- Help students understand how the estimated quotient of $9\frac{3}{4}$ feet leads to the conclusion that there will be 9 or 10 parking spaces in the lot. **Why are the spaces too wide if the lot is divided into 9 spaces?** (the minimum width of a space is $7\frac{3}{4}$ feet, and the spaces formed when dividing the lot into 10 spaces are much closer to that width)

- When solving Problems 1 and 2 in *Try These*, students will use the same strategy as in the example.

▶ Practice Test

PURPOSE

This page will familiarize students with the multiple-choice and open-response formats of many standardized state tests.

Cumulative Test Prep Practice

Solve Problems 1–10.

Test-Taking Tip

Compute the answer *before* you read the answer choices. Then check whether your answer is reasonable. If you find an answer choice that matches your answer, you will feel more confident that your answer choice is correct.

Look at the example below.

It rained $\frac{3}{4}$ inch on Saturday and $1\frac{3}{4}$ inches on Sunday. How much did it rain over the weekend?

A $2\frac{1}{4}$

C $2\frac{3}{4}$

B $2\frac{1}{2}$

D 3

THINK

I must add the fractions to get the answer and show the answer in simplified form:

$\frac{3}{4} + 1\frac{3}{4} = 1\frac{6}{4} = 1 + \frac{4}{4} + \frac{2}{4}$

$= 2\frac{1}{2}$

My answer, $2\frac{1}{2}$, is answer choice **B**.

382 For more Test-Taking Tips, see pages xxii–xxv.

Multiple Choice

1. Subtract $\frac{1}{5}$ from $\frac{3}{4}$.

A $\frac{7}{20}$ B $\frac{7}{10}$ **C** $\frac{11}{20}$ D $\frac{11}{10}$

(Chapter 4, Lesson 6)

2. Mario wants to extend a shelf that is 7 feet 10 inches long by 2 feet 3 inches. What is the length of the new shelf?

F 5 feet 7 inches   **H** 10 feet 1 inch

G 9 feet 7 inches   J 10 feet 3 inches

(Chapter 3, Lesson 6)

3. In May, Roberto was $59\frac{7}{8}$ inches tall. By the end of October, he had grown $\frac{3}{4}$ inch. How tall was Roberto at the end of October?

A $59\frac{1}{8}$ inches   **C** $60\frac{5}{8}$ inches

B $59\frac{1}{4}$ inches   D $60\frac{8}{13}$ inches

(Chapter 4, Lesson 4)

4. On a camping trip, $5\frac{1}{2}$ cups of oatmeal were made for breakfast. The oatmeal is divided equally among 4 campers. How much does each camper get?

F $1\frac{3}{8}$ cups   H $1\frac{5}{6}$ cups

G $1\frac{1}{2}$ cups   J $2\frac{1}{3}$ cups

(Chapter 5, Lesson 6)

Test-Taking TIPS

Review the test-taking tips with students before they begin the test. Discuss with students some of the ways they can check their work.

- Encourage students to use the problem situation and number sense to eliminate choices that are obviously incorrect. For example, in Item 3, if Roberto was taller than $59\frac{7}{8}$ inches at the end of October, he could not be $59\frac{1}{8}$ inches or $59\frac{1}{4}$ inches tall.

- For test items having extra information, such as Item 6, tell students to underline

or circle only the information needed to solve the problem or to cross out the information that is not needed.

- Tell students that when reading a bar graph such as the one in Item 10, they can position the edge of a sheet of paper along the tops of the bars to help them make sure they are reading the correct information.

5. Every Monday for 3 weeks, a truck brought 1.5 tons of crushed stone to a construction site. How many tons of stone did the truck bring in all?

4.5 tons *(Chapter 13, Lesson 3)*

6.

Metric Units of Capacity
1,000 milliliters (mL) = 1 liter (L)
10 deciliters (dL) = 1 liter (L)

Hamid wants to pour equal amounts from a pitcher holding 2 liters of apple juice into several glasses. How many deciliters should he pour into each of 5 glasses?

4 dL *(Chapter 6, Lesson 5)*

7. The school board budget is $7,000,000. What is the largest exponent you would use to write this number in expanded form?

6 *(Chapter 1, Lesson 2)*

8. A city school district has 1,701 students in 9 elementary schools. If the same number of students go to each school, how many students are in each school?

189 students *(Chapter 4, Lesson 5)*

9. A hummingbird flaps its wings once every 0.074 second. How much time does it take a hummingbird to flap its wings 12 times?

0.888 second *(Chapter 13, Lesson 4)*

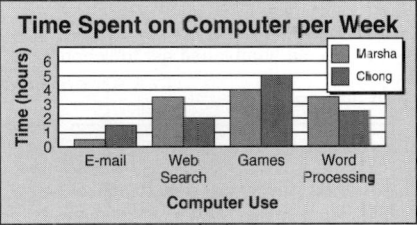

Time Spent on Computer per Week

Computer Use

10. The double bar graph shows how many hours Chong and Marsha spend on different computer activities each week.

A On which computer activity does each student spend the most time?
games for both

B Who spends more time using a word processing application?
Marsha

C What is the total time that Marsha spends using a computer each week? Chong? **11.5 hrs; 11 hrs**

D How much more time does Chong spend playing computer games than Marsha? **1 hr**

E Write two to three sentences to compare Chong and Marsha's computer use.

Possible answer: *(Chapter 7, Lesson 1)*
Chong is more interested in games and e-mail, while Marsha does more web search and word processing.

 Test Prep on the Net
Check out *Education Place* at **eduplace.com/kids/mw/** for test prep practice.

Unit 5 Cumulative Test Prep **383**

Test-Taking Vocabulary

Explain that certain phrases in test questions are clues to how a problem is to be solved. Display the following heading and phrases in one column:

<u>Phrases:</u>
how many in each   divided equally
how much in all   more time than
n number of times   total amount
equal amounts   how much more than

In the other column display:

<u>Operations:</u>
addition   multiplication
subtraction   division

Have students match phrases and processes.

National and state tests might also use this word to indicate *divided:*

● shared

Multiplication and Division of Fractions and Decimals   383

IT'S A-MAZE-ING!

PURPOSE

To provide students with an opportunity to multiply and divide decimals using a calculator.

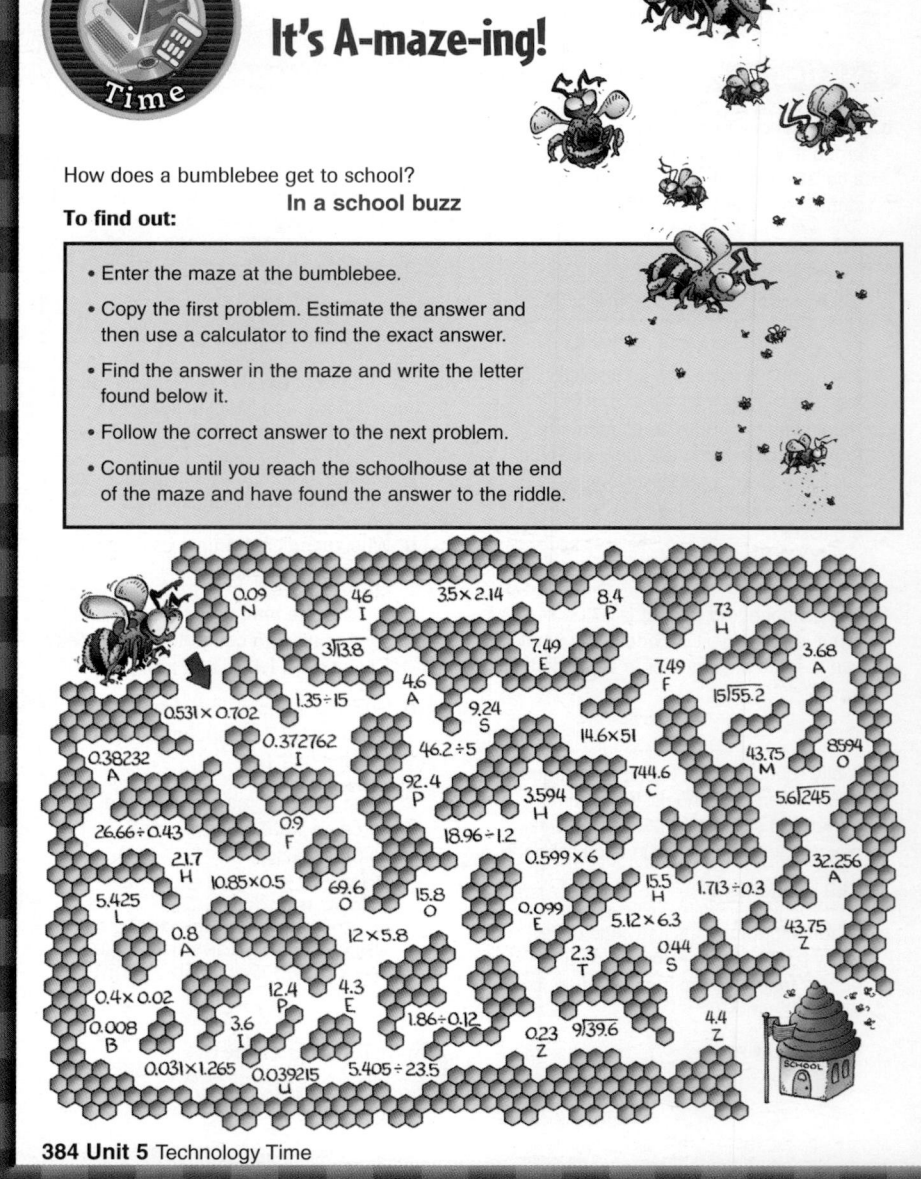

It's A-maze-ing!

How does a bumblebee get to school?
In a school buzz

To find out:

- Enter the maze at the bumblebee.
- Copy the first problem. Estimate the answer and then use a calculator to find the exact answer.
- Find the answer in the maze and write the letter found below it.
- Follow the correct answer to the next problem.
- Continue until you reach the schoolhouse at the end of the maze and have found the answer to the riddle.

Using Technology Time

- You may want to review how to estimate a product or quotient using decimals before beginning this page.

- Have students discuss the similarities and differences between using a calculator to multiply and divide whole numbers and using it to multiply and divide decimals. (The methods are the same, but a decimal point needs to be keyed when multiplying and dividing decimals.)

- Have students solve the maze independently. Then have small groups make up their own mazes for others to solve using calculators.

Vocabulary Wrap-Up for Unit 5

See page 682 for the activity for this unit.

WEEKLY WR READER
Activity Almanac

Look back at the big ideas and vocabulary in this unit.

Big Ideas

To divide a fraction by a fraction, multiply by the reciprocal of the divisor.

The product of two decimals will have the same number of decimal places as the sum of the decimal places in each factor.

e Glossary

Key Vocabulary

reciprocal
product
quotient

2. **Possible answer:** They are different names for the same number; they are equivalent forms of the same number.

Math Conversations

Use your new vocabulary to discuss these big ideas.
See Additional Answers on page 377.

1. Explain what the written form of this decimal means: $1.\overline{2}$

2. Explain how the numbers $\frac{3}{5}$, $\frac{6}{10}$, and 0.6 are related. **See above.**

3. Explain how you would locate the decimal point in this product.

    $0.02 \times 0.4 = 0008$ **See below.**

    Why are zeros used in the answer?

4. **Write About It** Meteorologists often write daily amounts of rainfall in decimal form, even when the rainfall is measured in inches. With a partner, discuss and then explain in writing some reasons why scientists might use decimals instead of fractions when measuring rainfall. *See Additional Answers on page 377.*

3. **Possible answer:** The total number of digits to the right of the decimal points in the factors is 3, so the product must have 3 digits to the right of the decimal point; the zeros are the place holders; 0.008.

To find the reciprocal of a fraction, I exchange the numerator and denominator.

Right. So the reciprocal of $\frac{1}{10}$ is $\frac{10}{1}$.

Unit 5 Vocabulary Wrap-Up **385**

Activity

Wrap Up The Unit Project

● Have students use the rough visuals and tables they made as the basis for the pages in their "Big Book of Music". Have each student write an introduction page to his or her visuals and tables explaining what she or he learned about the connection between mathematics and music.

● Have students include a section on the metronome in their big books, with drawings and a brief explanation of how one works.

Using the Vocabulary Wrap-Up

Purpose: Use this page to encourage students to use math vocabulary to talk about the important concepts they have learned in this unit.

Big Ideas and Key Vocabulary

Review and discuss with students the Big Ideas of this unit using the Key Vocabulary terms *reciprocal, product,* and *quotient.*

Math Conversations

Have students work together in small groups to discuss Exercises 1–3. Check to see whether individual students understand the key concepts and are able to use the math vocabulary correctly. Clear up any misunderstandings students may have. After students have discussed the exercises in small groups, continue the conversation as a whole class. Have volunteers from each group share what their group talked about.

Write About It Encourage students to provide specific examples of decimals that would be easier to add, compare, or find averages for than the equivalent fractions.

Multiplication and Division of Fractions and Decimals 385

UNIT 6

Geometry and Measure
Unit at a Glance

UNIT 6 GEOMETRY AND MEASURE

Assessment System

Assess Prior Knowledge

Check whether students understand the prerequisite concepts and skills.

- **REVIEWING VOCABULARY:** Unit Opener
- **CHAPTER PRETESTS:** PE pp. 389, 421, 445 (Unit Resource Folder or *Ways to Success* CD-ROM)
- **WARM-UP ACTIVITY:** Found on the third page of every TE lesson.

Ongoing Assessment

Monitor whether students are acquiring new concepts and skills.

- **PROBLEM OF THE DAY:** First page of every TE lesson
- **QUICK REVIEW:** First page of every TE lesson
- **LESSON QUIZ** First page of every TE lesson
- **COMMON ERROR:** TE lessons 15.1, 15.3–15.5, 15.9; 16.1, 16.3–16.4; 17.1, 17.3–17.4, 17.6
- **QUICK CHECK:** PE pp. 403, 417, 431, 441, 455, 467
- **DAILY REVIEW • TEST PREP:** PE pp. 391, 397, 399, 423, 433, 447, 451, 463

Test Prep and Practice

Help students prepare for state and standardized tests.

- **DAILY REVIEW • TEST PREP:** PE pp. 391, 397, 399, 423, 433, 447, 451, 463
- **DAILY TEST PREP:** TE Lessons 15.1–15.9, 16.1–16.6, and 17.1–17.7
- **PROBLEM SOLVING TEST PREP:** PE pp. 411, 427, 459
- **CUMULATIVE TEST PREP:** PE pp. 476–477
- **READING TEST QUESTIONS: UNIT OPENER:** PE p. 387
- **TEST PREP ON THE NET:** eduplace.com/kids/mw
- **TEST TAKING STRATEGIES:** eduplace.com/math/mw

Summary Assessment

Assess student mastery of new concepts and skills.

- **CHAPTER TEST**
  - ✔ PE pp. 418, 442, 468
  - ✔ Unit Resource Folder
- **UNIT TEST:**
  - ✔ PE pp. 472–473
  - ✔ Form A, Unit Resource Folder
  - ✔ Form B, Unit Resource Folder

Student Self-Assessment

Allow students to evaluate their own understanding.

- **EXPLAIN YOUR THINKING:** PE pp. 391, 397, 399, 402, 415, 423, 429, 432, 447, 451, 453, 462
- **VOCABULARY WRAP UP:** PE p. 479

Performance Assessment

Evaluate students' ability to use mathematics in real-world situations.

- **PERFORMANCE ASSESSMENT:** PE p. 474
- **WRITE ABOUT IT • TALK ABOUT IT:** in all Hands-On lessons
- **DECISION MAKING:** End of Unit Test

Technology Options

Use computer-based assessment to make testing and reporting easier.

- **WAYS TO ASSESS** (CD-ROM, LAN, or Web spiral review and test creation, administration, scoring, and report generation)
- **LEARNER PROFILE** (observations, evaluations, and reports from your handheld or desktop computer)

Reaching All Learners

Resources	On Level Students	Extra Support Students	English Learners	Inclusion/ Special Needs	Advanced Learners	Mathematically Promising
Student Editions						
Building Vocabulary	●	●	●	●	●	●
Different Ways Instruction *	●	●	●	●	●	●
Guided Practice *	●	●	●	●	○	○
MathTracks MP3 Audio CD	●	●	●	●	○	○
Teacher's Editions						
Building Vocabulary Strategies	●	●	●	●	●	○
Teacher Support	●	●	●	●	●	●
Intervention Activities	○	●	●	●	○	○
Other Resources						
Chapter Challenges	○				●	●
Combination Classroom Guide	●	●	●	●	●	●
English Learners Handbook	○	○	●	○		
Ways to Success CD-ROM	○	●	●	●		

KEY   ● **Highly Appropriate**   ○ **Appropriate**   * **Scaffolded Instruction**

Documenting Adequate Yearly Progress

National Test Correlation

UNIT 6 Objectives		ITBS	Terra Nova (CTBS)	CAT	SAT	MAT
6A	Identify and classify basic two- and three-dimensional geometric figures and their parts.	●	●	●	●	●
6B	Identify congruent figures and figures with line and rotational symmetry.	●	●	●	●	●
6C	Identify transformations as reflections, translations, or rotations.	●	●		●	
6D	Find the perimeter and area of polygons and irregular figures.	●	●	●	●	●
6E	Use pi to find the circumference of a circle.		●			
6F	Find surface area and volume of solid figures.	●	●	●		●
6G	Solve problems, using skills and strategies.	●	●	●	●	●

Activities for Reaching All Learners

Differentiated Instruction

Polishing Prerequisite Skills

Materials: paper

Students work in pairs. One student draws a geometric shape, plane or solid, which the partner cannot see. The partner's task is to ask questions that require yes or no answers, and to guess the name of the geometric shape. For each question asked, without guessing the shape, the partner is given a point. When the name of the shape is guessed, a point is taken away. The partners switch roles and begin again. After 3 rounds, the partner with the fewest points is the winner.

Repeatable Unit Game

Materials: 1 cm square graph paper

Students work in pairs. One student chooses a number between 12 and 100. Both students draw a geometric figure with that area. The student who draws the figure with the greatest perimeter scores one point. This activity is repeated until one student earns 5 points.

Home-School Activity

Materials: Boxes of various sizes

Find 4 rectangular prisms, such as cereal boxes and shoe boxes. Guess which has the greatest surface area and which has the greatest volume. Find the surface area and volume of all 4 boxes and check your guesses.

Unit Vocabulary Activity

Materials: Vocabulary Cards

The class is divided into Team A and Team B. Teacher selects a word or phrase and draws dashes on the board for each letter.

Team A draws a vocabulary card. One student from Team A writes the definition and draws a picture to illustrate the word or phrase. Team B tries to guess the vocabulary word. If correct, the team guesses a letter that might be in the word on the board. Teams trade roles. The team to guess the word or phrase on the board wins.

Remediation

Lessons with MathTracks Audio Support: 15.2, 15.6, 15.7, 15.9, 16.1, 16.3, 16.5, 17.1, 17.4, 17.6 Tracks: 2/9–2/18

Use the MathTracks MP3 Audio CD to help students who need a quick review or extra support for the lesson, to provide students who were absent with a complete lesson presentation, or to assist students with reading difficulties.

Intervention

Ways to Success CD-ROM

Use the Ways to Success CD-ROM to help children who need extra help with lessons. This software is designed to reteach the lesson objective, provide extra guided and independent practice, and if needed, reteach a key prerequisite skill.

Starting Unit 6

Building Vocabulary

Use the Building Vocabulary pages to be sure that students have adequate understanding and fluency with the unit vocabulary. This provides the key foundation for developing the unit concepts and skills.

Reviewing Vocabulary

- Give students 1 or 2 minutes to doodle freely.
- Write the vocabulary words on the board. Have students identify which of their doodles is represented in the vocabulary words.
- Have students identify which word they can't draw (*ray*).
- Give the students 1 or 2 minutes to doodle using angles, line segments, polygons, and circles.
- Alternatively, challenge the students to demonstrate all five words to see if they realize that it is impossible to draw a ray. (Recognize those who use the arrow on the end.)

Reading Words and Symbols

- Have students whose names start with B and C take the ends of a jump rope and lay it on the floor to create an angle. Have a student whose name starts with A stand at the vertex.
- Discuss how the angle can be read as BAC or CAB. Discuss why A is in the middle.
- Vary the measure of the angle from 45 to 90 to 180 degrees.
- Give each set of 3 students a jump rope. Call out the size of an angle and have students create the angle. Repeat with a variety of sizes of angles.

Building Vocabulary

Reviewing Vocabulary

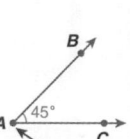

Here are some math vocabulary words that you should know.

ray	part of a line that begins at an endpoint and goes on forever in one direction
angle	a figure formed by two rays with the same endpoint
line segment	part of a line that has two endpoints
polygon	a simple closed plane figure made up of three or more line segments
circle	a closed figure in which every point is the same distance from a given point called the center

Reading Words and Symbols

The two rays that make up the angle have a common endpoint, which is called the vertex.

One way you can name angles is to name three points on the angle—a point on each ray and the vertex. The vertex must always be in the middle.

Another way you can name angles is by using only the vertex letter. In ∠*BAC*, *A* is the vertex. For ∠*BAC* (read "angle *BAC*") you can also write ∠*A* (read "angle *A*").

The measure of angles is given in degrees. The symbol for degrees is °. This angle has a measure of forty-five degrees or 45°.

Use words and symbols to answer these questions.

1. What are two other names for ∠*BAC*? Explain. **See below.**

2. What is the measure of an angle that has twice the measure of ∠*BAC*? three times the measure of ∠*BAC*? **90°; 135°**

1. *Possible answer:* ∠*CAB* or ∠*A*, the angle can be named either way, provided the vertex is in the middle.

386

Unit Project

- Explain that students are going to build a model city out of boxes, cans and other materials.
- Tell the students that for this project, they will work in groups with assigned tasks such as: planning streets or blocks, drawing streets or blocks, or planning and selecting locations for buildings. Mathematically, students will measure and label angles formed, determine building shapes, and calculate the perimeter and area of the space each building occupies. These calculations should be included in the map.
- Use the activity found on p. 479 to wrap up the Unit Project.

Reading Test Questions

Choose the correct answer for each.

3. Which figure is shown on the grid paper?

   a. square

   b. rectangle

   c. parallelogram

   (d.) all of the above

A **grid** is an arrangement of lines intersecting at right angles and dividing a plane into congruent squares.

4. As part of which group would you classify the figure?

   a. circles   c. triangles

   (b.) quadrilaterals   d. pentagons

To **classify** in geometry means to identify the type of figure.

5. How many square centimeters do you count inside the figure?

   (a.) 4   c. 12

   b. 8   d. 16

A **square centimeter** is a metric unit used for measuring the area of a figure. The symbol for square centimeter is cm². Each cm² has a measure of 1 cm × 1 cm.

Learning Vocabulary

Watch for these new words in this unit. Write their definitions in your journal.

diagonal

transformation

tessellation

circumference

π (pi)

net

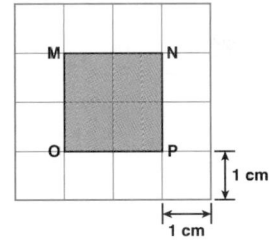 **Vocabulary**
e • Glossary
e • WordGame

Literature Connection

Read "No Place to Go" on page 646. Then work with a partner to answer the questions about the story.

 ## Reading Test Questions

- Have the students list all the potential vocabulary words in each question. Have them draw examples of each word.
- Discuss the need to identify related words, such as *square* and *parallelogram* before answering a question.
- Discuss the process of elimination, contrasting its utility in item 3 versus item 4. Remind students to use the process of elimination to narrow their choices.

Learning Vocabulary

Go over the list of new words with the class. Help students to pronounce the words correctly, and explain that they will learn about these words as they work on this unit. If students are keeping Math Journals, be sure that they enter the words and their definitions as they find them in the unit.

Home-School Connection

To foster home-school communication, *Houghton Mifflin Math* has a Family Letter for every unit. The letters include vocabulary words, worked-out examples, home activities, and literature suggestions.

Each Family Letter is in the Unit Resource Folder. Go to **eduplace.com/math/mw/** to download the letters in English, Spanish, and other languages.

Literature Connection

In the Student Book

Student Book List Selection

You may use the literature connection (Student Book page 646, Teacher Edition page T55) at any time during this unit.

See also **Math and Literature Bibliography** in the Teacher Support Handbook at the back of this Teachers Edition.

Other Literature Connections

Amazing Buildings
By Philip Wilkison
Illustrated by Paolo Donati

Shape Up!
By David A. Adler
Illustrated by Nancy Tobin

Sir Cumference and the Great Knight of Angleland
By Cindy Neuschwander
Illustrated by Wayne Geehan

See also the **Math and Literature Bibliography** in the Teacher Support Handbook at the back of this Teacher's Edition.

Geometry and Measurement   **387**

Lesson By Lesson Overview
Plane Figures and Geometric Concepts

CHAPTER 15

Lesson 1
- Students identify and label points, lines, line segments, and rays.
- Students describe different types of lines.

Lesson 2
- Students use a protractor to measure and draw angles. Students classify angles as right, acute, obtuse, or straight.

Lesson 3
- Students classify triangles by the lengths of their sides and by their angle measures.
- Students discover that the sum of the angle measures of a triangle is always 180°.

Lesson 4
- Students use tracings, rulers, and protractors to identify congruent figures and congruent parts of figures.
- Students apply what they know about congruent parts of figures to find missing measures in pairs of congruent figures.

Lesson 5
- Students identify, classify, and compare polygons.

- Students classify quadrilaterals according to their sides and angles.
- Students distinguish between figures that are and are not polygons, and between regular and irregular polygons.

Lesson 6
- Students identify and model translations, rotations, and reflections.

Lesson 7
- Students use a model in the context of solving tessellation problems.
- Students choose a strategy and use a graph to solve problems.

Lesson 8
- Students construct circles and identify parts of a circle.

Lesson 9
- Students manipulate or draw figures to determine whether they have rotational symmetry or line symmetry.

SKILLS TRACE: GEOMETRY AND MEASUREMENT

Grade 4	Grade 5	Grade 6
• name and describe characteristics of points, lines, line segments, rays, angles, and plane geometric figures (ch. 16)	• **identify basic geometric figures and their parts**	• identify relationships among angles; measure, draw, and classify angles (ch. 14)
• identify congruent figures and figures with line and rotational symmetry (ch. 17)	• **classify angles, triangles, quadrilaterals, and other polygons**	• classify and draw triangles, quadrilaterals (ch. 14), and polygons (ch. 15); draw circles (ch. 14)
• identify, perform, and predict results of transformations (ch. 17)	• **identify congruent figures and figures with line and rotational symmetry**	• calculate missing angle measures in triangles and quadrilaterals (ch. 14)
	• **identify transformations**	• identify similar and congruent figures and corresponding parts (ch. 15)

Chapter Planner

Lesson	Objective	Vocabulary	Materials	✔ NCTM Standards
15.1 Points, Lines, and Rays p. 390A	Identify and label points, lines, line segments, and rays.		paper, rulers	**Geometry:** Identify, compare, and analyze attributes of two- and three-dimensional shapes and develop vocabulary to describe the attributes.
15.2 Hands-On: Measure, Draw, and Classify Angles p. 392A	Measure, draw, and classify angles.	degree right angle acute angle obtuse angle straight angle	protractors, Protractor Transparency (Sheets 1 and 2), tracing paper, rulers, pencils, paper, blank transparency	**Geometry:** Build and draw geometric objects.
15.3 Triangles p. 396A	Classify triangles and find missing angle measures.	equilateral isosceles scalene	Angle Sum of a Triangle Transparency, blank transparency, Half-Centimeter Grid Transparency, Learning tool 14, straightedge	**Geometry:** Classify two- and three-dimensional shapes according to their properties and develop definitions of classes of shapes such as triangles and pyramids.
15.4 Congruence p. 398A	Identify congruent figures and congruent parts of figures.	congruent	Large Plane Figures, Small Plane Figures, and Triangle Transparencies; rules, protractors, blank transparency	**Geometry:** Explore congruence and similarity.
15.5 Quadrilaterals and Other Polygons p. 400A	Identify, classify, and compare polygons.	quadrilateral regular polygon irregular polygon diagonal polygon	Large Plane Figures, Small Plane Figures, and Quadrilaterals Transparencies; Learning Tool 14, rules, protractors	**Geometry:** Classify two- and three-dimensional shapes according to their properties and develop definitions of classes of shapes such as triangles and pyramids.
15.6 Hands-On: Rotations, Reflections, and Translations p. 404A	Identify and model translations, rotations, and reflections.	transformation reflection rotation translation	grid paper, rulers, Centimeter Grid Transparency, paint, paintbrushes, large paper, paper clips, Learning Tool 52	**Geometry:** Predict and describe the results of sliding, flipping, and turning two-dimensional shapes.
15.7 Problem-Solving Strategy: Make a Model p. 408A	Make models to solve tessellation problems.	tessellation	pattern blocks or tracing paper, scissors, Learning Tool 14, Problem Solving: Four Step Process Transparency	**Geometry:** Investigate, describe, and reason about the results of subdividing, combining, and transforming shapes.
15.8 Hands-On: Circles p. 412A	Draw circles and construct and identify parts of a circle	center radius diameter chord central angle	blank transparency, safe drawing compass, straight-edge, 2 yardsticks	**Geometry:** Identify, compare, and analyze attributes of two- and three-dimensional shapes and develop vocabulary to describe the attributes.
15.9 Symmetry p. 414A	Identify rotational and line symmetry.	rotational symmetry line symmetry	ruler, unlined paper, compass, scissors, clock, clockface with numerals, paper, pencils	**Geometry:** Identify and describe line and rotational symmetry in two- and three-dimensional shapes and designs.

Resources For Reaching All Learners

LESSON RESOURCES: Reteach, Practice, Enrichment, Problem Solving, Homework, English Learners, Daily Routines, Transparencies, Math Center.

ADDITIONAL RESOURCES FROM HOUGHTON MIFFLIN: Combination Classroom Planning Guide, Chapter Challenges, Every Day Counts, Math at Hand (student handbook)

Every Day Counts

The **Calendar and Measurement** activities in **Every Day Counts** support the math in this chapter.

Assessing Prior Knowledge

Before beginning the chapter, you can assess student understandings in order to assist you in differentiating instruction.

Complete Chapter Pretest in Unit Resource Folder

Use this test to assess both prerequisite skills (**Are You Ready?** — one page) and chapter content (**Check What You Know** — two pages).

Chapter 15 Prerequisite Skills Pretest

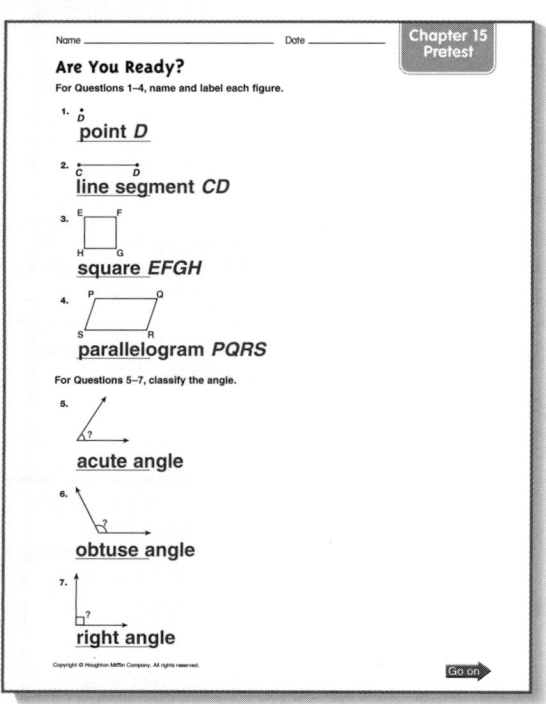

Chapter 15 New Content Pretest

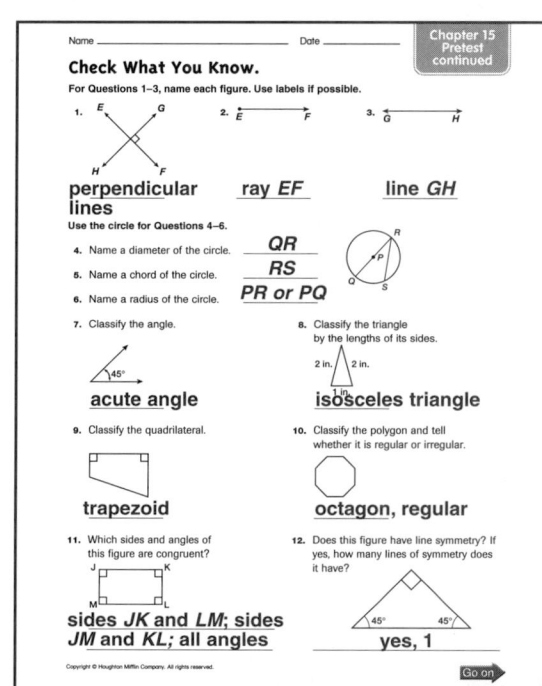

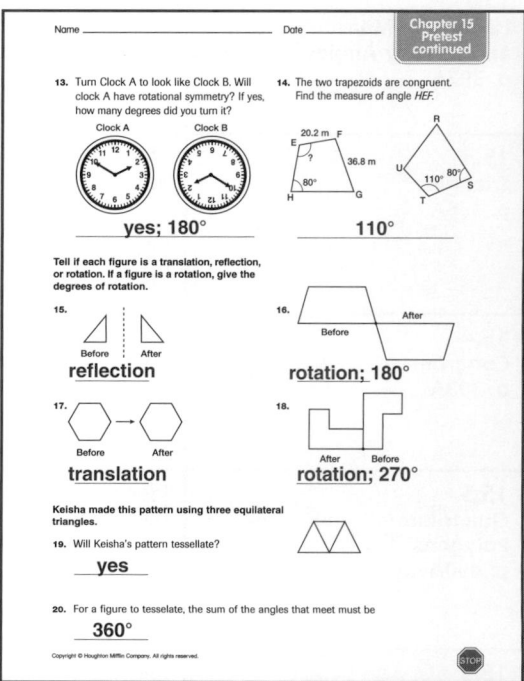

Customizing Instruction

For Students Having Difficulty

Items	Prerequisites	Ways to Success
1–2, 5–7	Name points, lines, line segments, rays, and angles	CD: 15a Skillsheet 119
3–4	Identify and classify plane geometric figures	Skillsheet 120

Ways to Success: Intervention for every concept and skill (CD-ROM or Chapter Intervention Skillsheets).

Consider using **Knowing Mathematics** with any students who are working two or more years below grade level.

For Students Having Success

Items	Objectives	Resources
1–3	**15A** Identify basic geometric figures.	Enrichment 15.1
4–10	**15B** Classify angles, triangles, quadrilaterals, and other polygons.	Enrichment 15.2, 15.3, 15.5, 15.8
11–14	**15C** Identify congruent figures and figures with line and rotational symmetry.	Enrichment 15.4, 15.9
15–18	**15D** Identify reflections, translations, or rotations.	Enrichment 15.6
19–20	**15E** Solve problems by using models.	Enrichment 15.7

Other Pretest Options

Informal Pretest in Student Book

The student book pretest assesses vocabulary and prerequisite skills needed for success in this chapter.

Ways to Success CD-ROM

The *Ways to Success* chapter pretest has automatic assignment of appropriate review lessons.

Use **Chapter Challenges** with any students who have success with all new chapter content.

Chapter Resources

Assessing Prior Knowledge

Identifying Shapes (identify plane figures)

- Display drawings of these figures: equilateral, right, scalene, and isosceles triangle; square; rectangle; pentagon. Have students describe each figure, for example, identify it by name, count the number of sides, and discuss its angles.

Activity

Ongoing Skill Activity

It's a Geometric World (identify plane figures, identify transformations)

- Have students bring in photographs of structures that illustrate the geometric figures highlighted in this chapter.
- As students progress through the chapter, ask them to display their photographs and to discuss them in light of what they learned in the lesson. For example, they can identify lines, triangles, congruent figures, and lines of symmetry.

Activity

Connecting to the Unit Project

- Have the "city planners," those who are laying out the city blocks, open spaces and parks, name and classify the shapes of the blocks. Have them locate congruent areas and paint them the same color.
- Have the "city architects," those who are working on the buildings, describe a building by naming each face.
- Encourage all to be creative as they design their city.

Teacher Support

Houghton Mifflin
Math

Professional
Resources
Handbook

Professional Resources Handbook

Research, Mathematics Content, and More Best Practices

Research-Based Teaching

Students' measurement abilities, estimation strategies, and geometric understandings are integral to their development of number sense, a critical part of students' mathematical understanding (Nickson, 2000; NCTM, 2000) Building on a history of geometry by providing opportunities for discovery and using technology and manipulatives in appropriate ways can help develop future mathematicians. *See Professional Resources Handbook, Grade 5*, Unit 6.

For more ideas relating to Unit 6, see the Teacher Support Handbook at the back of this Teacher's Edition.

Language Intervention

Visualization and geometry are considered important parts of East Asian mathematics, particularly elementary mathematics. For further explanation, see "Mathematical Language and Geometry" in the *Professional Resources Handbook Grade 5*.

 **Time Saving Technology Support**

Ways to Assess Customized Spiral Review
   and Test Generator CD-ROM
Lesson Planner CD-ROM
Ways to Success Intervention CD-ROM
Math Tracks CD-ROM
Education Place: www.eduplace.com/math/mw/
Houghton Mifflin Math eBook CD-ROM
eManipulatives
eGames

Starting Chapter 15
Plane Figures and Geometric Concepts

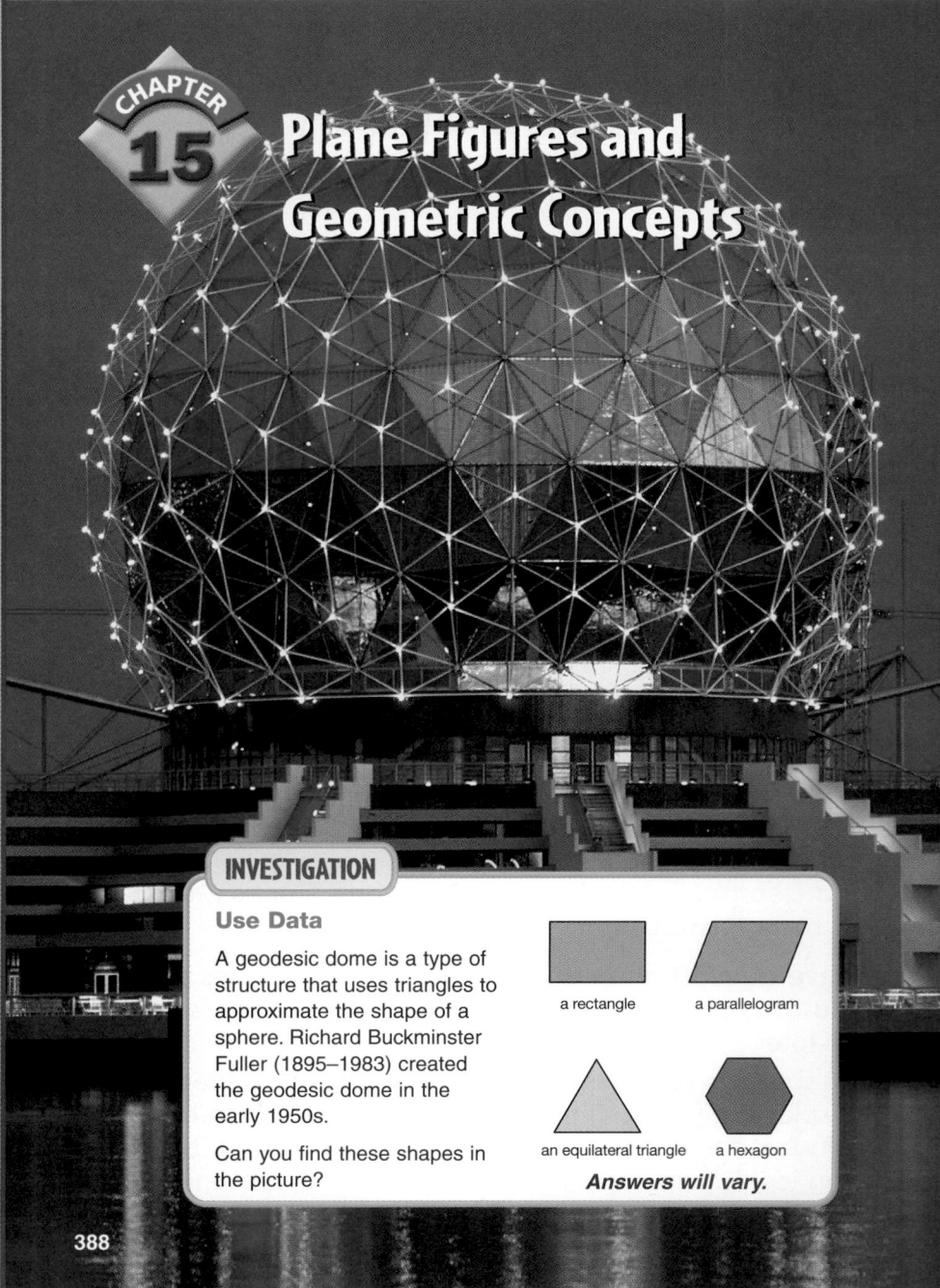

Chapter Objectives

15A Identify basic geometric figures and their parts.

15B Classify angles, triangles, quadrilaterals, and other polygons.

15C Identify congruent figures and figures with line and rotational symmetry.

15D Identify transformations as reflections, translations, or rotations.

15E Analyze and solve problems by using models.

Math Background

Geometric Concepts

The study of geometry develops spatial thinking, an awareness of the similarities and differences among real-world shapes and solids. While previously, students were allowed to use informal language, now they should begin using the formal language and standard symbolism of geometry.

By studying geometry, students learn to communicate about the shapes and forms around them. In addition, students continue to learn about number sense and measurement and to develop problem-solving skills.

Using Geometric Symbols

The symbol for a line segment is written with a bar above the letters, such as $\overline{AB}$. Writing "line segment $\overline{AB}$" would make no sense as it would mean "line segment line segment AB." The symbol AB (with no bar above the letters) refers to the length of line segment AB. $\overline{AB}$ is part of line AB, which is symbolized by $\overleftrightarrow{AB}$ Figures that are the same size and shape are congruent. Congruent parts of congruent figures are congruent. The symbol for congruence is $\cong$.

Two lines in a plane are either intersecting or parallel. To show that lines AB and CD are parallel, write $\overleftrightarrow{AB} \parallel \overleftrightarrow{CD}$ Lines that intersect at right angles are perpendicular lines. To show that lines AB and CD are perpendicular, write $\overleftrightarrow{AB} \perp \overleftrightarrow{CD}$.

INVESTIGATION

Use Data

A geodesic dome is a type of structure that uses triangles to approximate the shape of a sphere. Richard Buckminster Fuller (1895–1983) created the geodesic dome in the early 1950s.

Can you find these shapes in the picture?

a rectangle   a parallelogram

an equilateral triangle   a hexagon

Answers will vary.

388

Using the Investigation

Have students work in small groups to answer the question posed on page388.

To extend the investigation, have students do the following activity

• Find pictures of other structures that use geometric figures. On the picture of the structure or on a sketch of the structure, trace as many geometric figures as you can. Make a list of the names of the figures you find. Display your pictures and lists on a bulletin board.

For more information about projects and investigations, visit **Education Place**. **www.eduplace.com/math/mw/**

 **Chapter Pretest**

Use this page to review and remember
what you need to know for this chapter.

✔ VOCABULARY

Choose the best word to complete each sentence.

Vocabulary
circle
flip
polygon

1. A _**polygon**_ is a closed, flat figure made up of line segments.

2. A _____ is a figure made up of points that are all the same distance from the center point. **circle**

✔ CONCEPTS AND SKILLS

Is each figure a polygon? Write *yes* or *no*.

3. 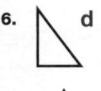 **no**

4.  **yes**

5. **no**

Match. Write the letter of the figure with the same size and shape.

6.  **d**   a.

7. **b**   b.

8. **a**   c.

9. **c**   d.

 **Write About It**

10. Is a circle a polygon? Explain your answer.

No. *Possible answer:* A polygon is a closed figure made up of line segments, which are straight. A circle is not made up of straight line segments.

 **Test Prep on the Net**
Visit *Education Place* at
eduplace.com/kids/mw/
for more review.

Chapter 15 Chapter Pretest **389**

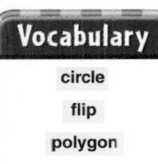 **Chapter Pretest**

Prerequisite Skills

Items	Skill
1–2	Vocabulary needed for this chapter
3–5	Identifying figures that are polygons
6–9	Matching congruent figures

Chapter Challenges

For Mathematically Promising Students

The *Chapter Challenges* resource book provides blackline masters for activities that explore, extend, and connect the mathematics in every chapter. To support this independent work, see the Teacher Notes for each activity.

Explore: Investigate Points and Lines, page 85, after Lesson 1

Extend: The Pythagorean Theorem, page 87, after Lesson 3

Connect: Analyze a Street Map, page 89, after Lesson 5

Using The Chapter Pretest

This page will help students review some of the prerequisite skills needed for this chapter. The chart above indicates which skills are covered on the pretest. If students need more help with these prerequisite skills use *Ways to Success,* Houghton Mifflin's intervention program.

 Students who need more review can visit **Education Place,** Houghton Mifflin's award-winning website.

NSF Children's Math Worlds

Using lessons from the *Children's Math Worlds* is a good way to ensure that your students will develop a deep understanding of geometry. The most effective approach is to use the *Children's Math Worlds* lessons along with the lessons in the chapter.

Plane Figures and Geometric Concepts   **389**

Lesson 15.1 — Points, Lines, and Rays

PLANNING THE LESSON

MATHEMATICS OBJECTIVE
Identify and label points, lines, line segments, and rays.

Use Lesson Planner CD-ROM for Lesson 15.1.

Daily Routines

Vocabulary
Draw one point on the chalkboard. **What do we call this?** (a point) Draw another point. Draw a straight line through those points. Draw one point on the chalkboard. **What do we call this?** (a point) Draw another point. Draw a straight line through those points with arrows at either end. **What do we call this figure?** (a line) **Why do we need to draw arrows at both ends?** (because lines are infinite in both directions) Draw another line that intersects the first line and use that visual to begin a discussion of the qualities of a plane.

Vocabulary Cards

Meeting North Carolina's Standards
Maintain Grade 4 Objective **3.02** Describe the relative position of lines using concepts of parallelism and perpendicularity.

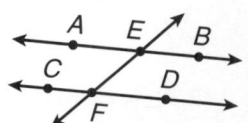

Lesson Transparency 15.1

Problem of the Day
Five points are scattered in a plane. No three points lie on the same line. How many lines can you draw through them? (10)

Quick Review
Identify each as either a "whole number," "fraction or whole number," or "a mixed number."

1. $\frac{12}{3}$ (fraction or whole number)
2. 7,345 (whole number)
3. $\frac{13}{5}$ (mixed number)
4. $\frac{6}{6}$ (fraction or whole number)

Lesson Quiz
Use the diagram to answer the questions.

1. Name a pair of parallel lines. ($\overleftrightarrow{AB}$ and $\overleftrightarrow{CD}$)
2. Name a pair of intersecting lines. ($\overleftrightarrow{AB}$ and $\overleftrightarrow{EF}$ or $\overleftrightarrow{CD}$ and $\overleftrightarrow{EF}$)
3. Name a line segment with endpoint F. ($\overline{FC}$, $\overline{FD}$, or $\overline{FE}$)

LEVELED PRACTICE

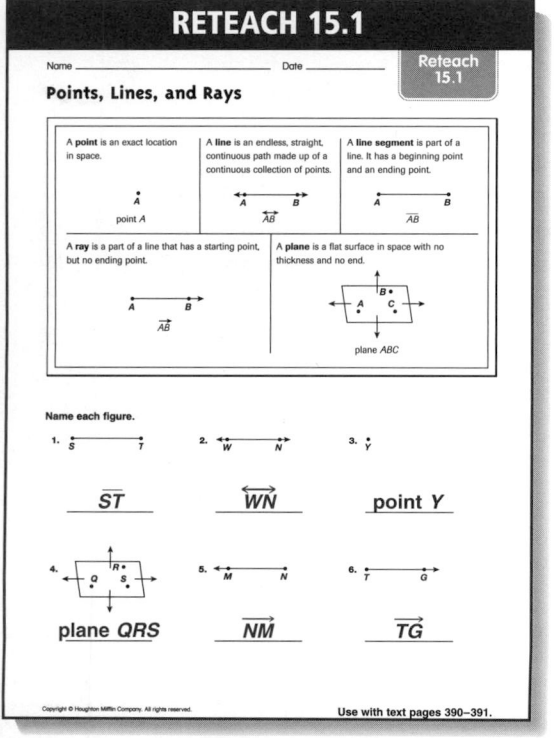

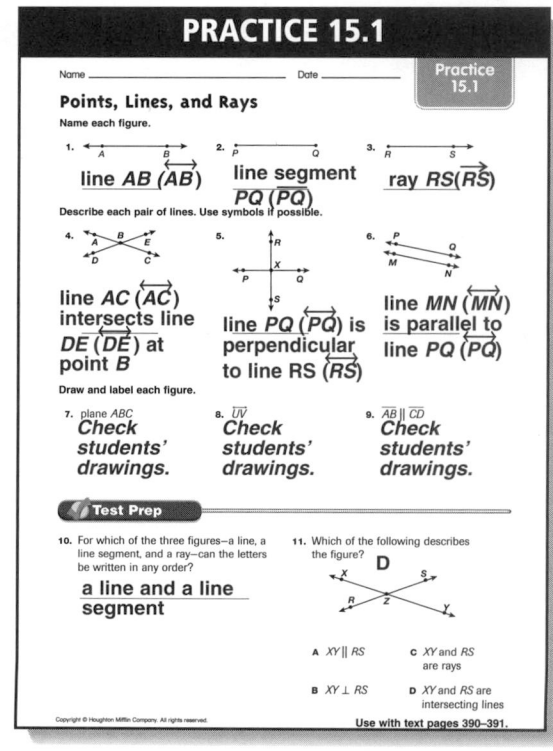

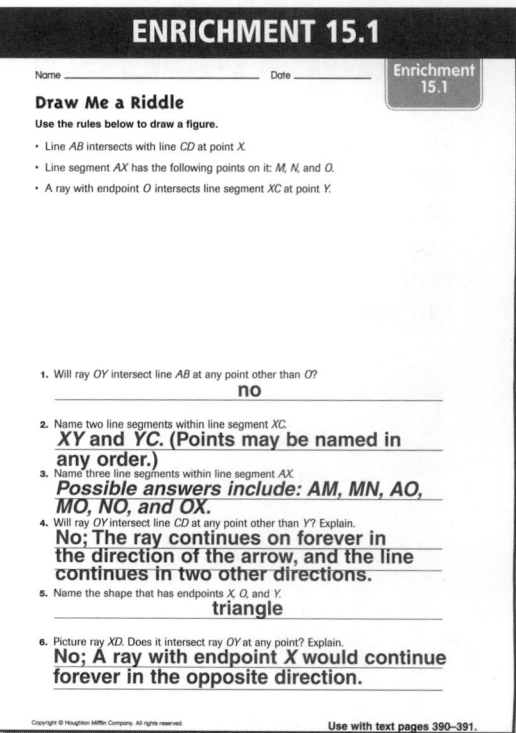

Practice Workbook Page 97

Reaching All Learners
Differentiated Instruction

English Learners

Worksheet 15.1 introduces several words formed from the base word *end* that students will encounter in Lesson 1. Students use these words, along with some verbs from the lesson, to complete sentences about points, lines, and rays.

Special Needs
VISUAL, KINESTHETIC

Materials: *pieces of string*

- Have students use the string pieces to model pairs of intersecting, parallel, and perpendicular line segments.

Early Finishers
VISUAL, KINESTHETIC

Materials: *paper, pencils*

- Place and label 4 points in a plane. No 3 can lie on a single line. How many line segments form? (6) Name them.
- Sketch intersecting, perpendicular, and parallel lines. Label the points. Use correct notation to name the figures.

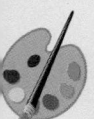

Art Connection

5-Pointed Star
Materials: coins

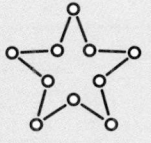

- Use coins and line ssegments to create a 5-pointed star as shown.
- **How many coins are there? How many line segments?** (10 of each)

- Predict how many coins and line segments a 6-pointed star needs. Draw one to check your predictions.

(12 of each)

- **Make a 10-pointed star. How many coins and line segments will it need?** (20 of each)

TECHNOLOGY

SPIRAL REVIEW

Using the *Ways to Assess* CD-ROM, you can create **customized** spiral review worksheets covering any lessons you choose.

Education Place

Encourage students to visit Education Place at **eduplace.com/kids/mw/** for student activities.

Lesson Planner

Use the Lesson Planner CD-ROM to see how lesson objectives for this chapter are correlated to standards.

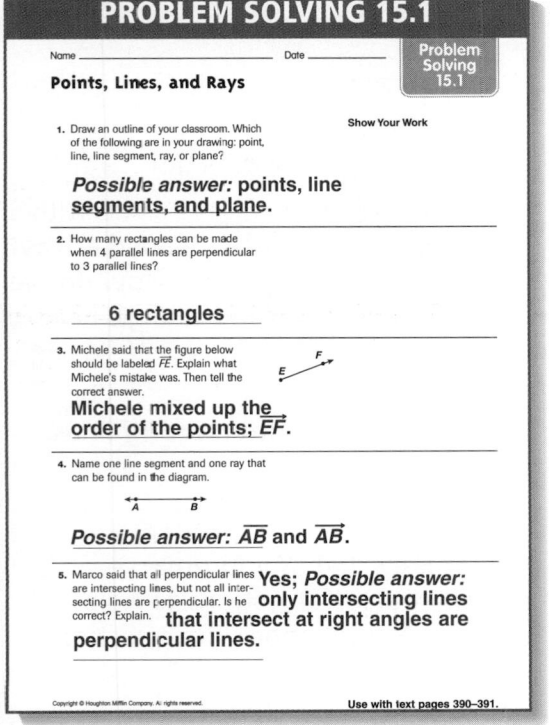

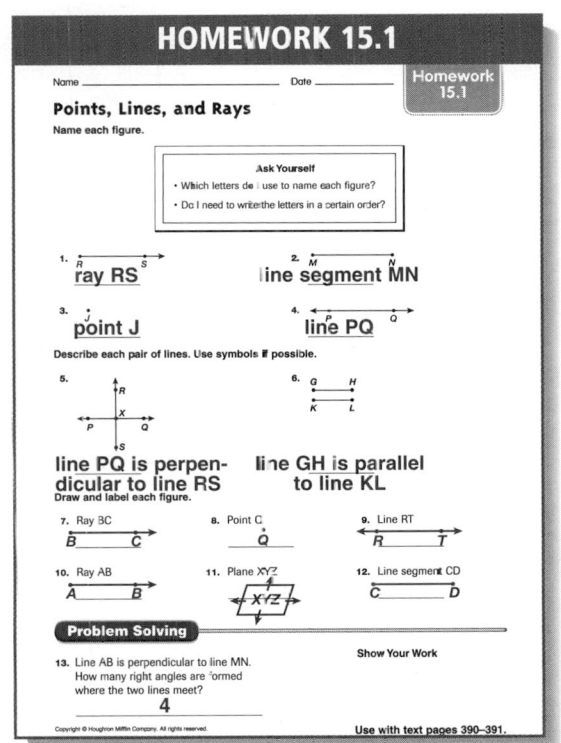

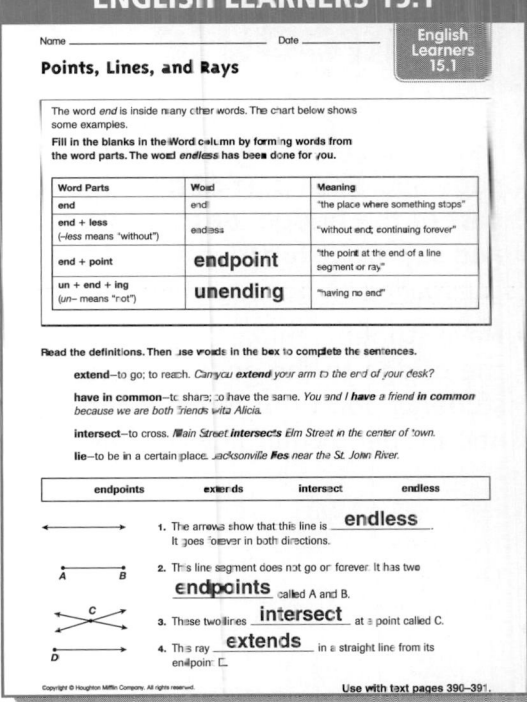

Homework Workbook Page 97

TEACHING LESSON 15.1

LESSON ORGANIZER

Objective: Identify and label points, lines, line segments, and rays.

Resources: Reteach, Practice, Enrichment, Problem Solving, Homework, English Learners, Transparencies, Math Center

Materials rulers, paper

Warm-Up Activity
Straight Lines

iiii Whole Group	⏱ 5 minutes	Auditory, Kinesthetic

- Have two students stand in front of the chalkboard with space between them. **These students represent points.**

- Have five or six other students come to the front of the classroom. **Please arrange yourselves so that you all form a straight line along the chalkboard.**

- **What does it mean to stand in a straight line?** (to stand in a straight path) **What happens if some of you step forward, and some step back?** (The line is not straight; it is broken.)

Points, Lines, and Rays

Objective Identify and label points, lines, line segments, and rays.

Learn About It

The widest cable-stayed bridge in the world spans the Charles River in Boston. In the picture you can identify many geometric features.

Leonard P. Zakim Bunker Hill Bridge

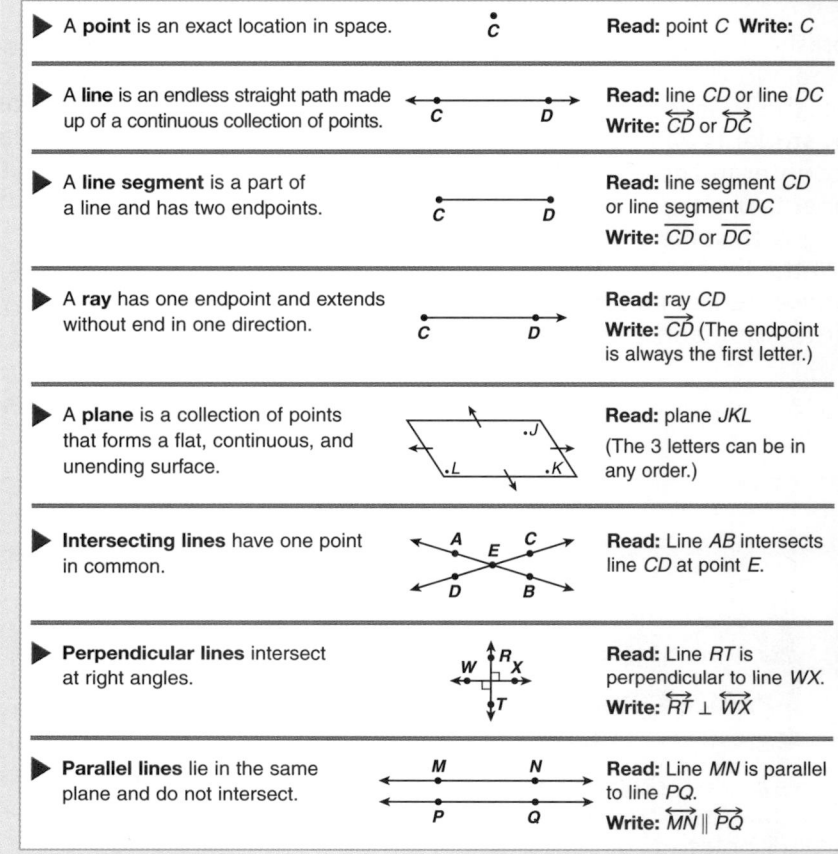

▶ A **point** is an exact location in space.	$\overset{\bullet}{C}$	**Read:** point *C* **Write:** *C*
▶ A **line** is an endless straight path made up of a continuous collection of points.	C ●————● D	**Read:** line *CD* or line *DC* **Write:** $\overleftrightarrow{CD}$ or $\overleftrightarrow{DC}$
▶ A **line segment** is a part of a line and has two endpoints.	C ●———● D	**Read:** line segment *CD* or line segment *DC* **Write:** $\overline{CD}$ or $\overline{DC}$
▶ A **ray** has one endpoint and extends without end in one direction.	C ●———●→ D	**Read:** ray *CD* **Write:** $\overrightarrow{CD}$ (The endpoint is always the first letter.)
▶ A **plane** is a collection of points that forms a flat, continuous, and unending surface.		**Read:** plane *JKL* (The 3 letters can be in any order.)
▶ **Intersecting lines** have one point in common.		**Read:** Line *AB* intersects line *CD* at point *E*.
▶ **Perpendicular lines** intersect at right angles.		**Read:** Line *RT* is perpendicular to line *WX*. **Write:** $\overleftrightarrow{RT} \perp \overleftrightarrow{WX}$
▶ **Parallel lines** lie in the same plane and do not intersect.		**Read:** Line *MN* is parallel to line *PQ*. **Write:** $\overleftrightarrow{MN} \parallel \overleftrightarrow{PQ}$

390

---

① Introduce

- Have students study the photograph of the bridge on page 390. **Each part of a bridge has a function. Name a part of the bridge, describe its relationship to the whole, and say what function you think it has.** (Possible answer: The roadbed is horizontal and supports the cars and trucks.)

- Have students make a list that relates different parts of the bridge to the geometric terms on page 390. Have students point out intersecting lines or line segments and perpendicular lines or line segments.

② Develop

Guide students through the *Learn About It* section.

- **How do we represent a line?** (the letters for two points with a double-headed arrow over them) **Why a double-headed arrow?** (to show that the line has no end in either direction) **How do we represent a ray?** (the letters for two points with a single-headed arrow over them) **What does this indicate?** (It has a beginning point, but no end in one direction.)

- **How many points in common do two intersecting lines have?** (1)

Guided Practice

Have students complete **Problems 1–4** as you observe. Remind them to use the *Ask Yourself* questions to help. Give students the opportunity to talk about the question in *Explain Your Thinking.*

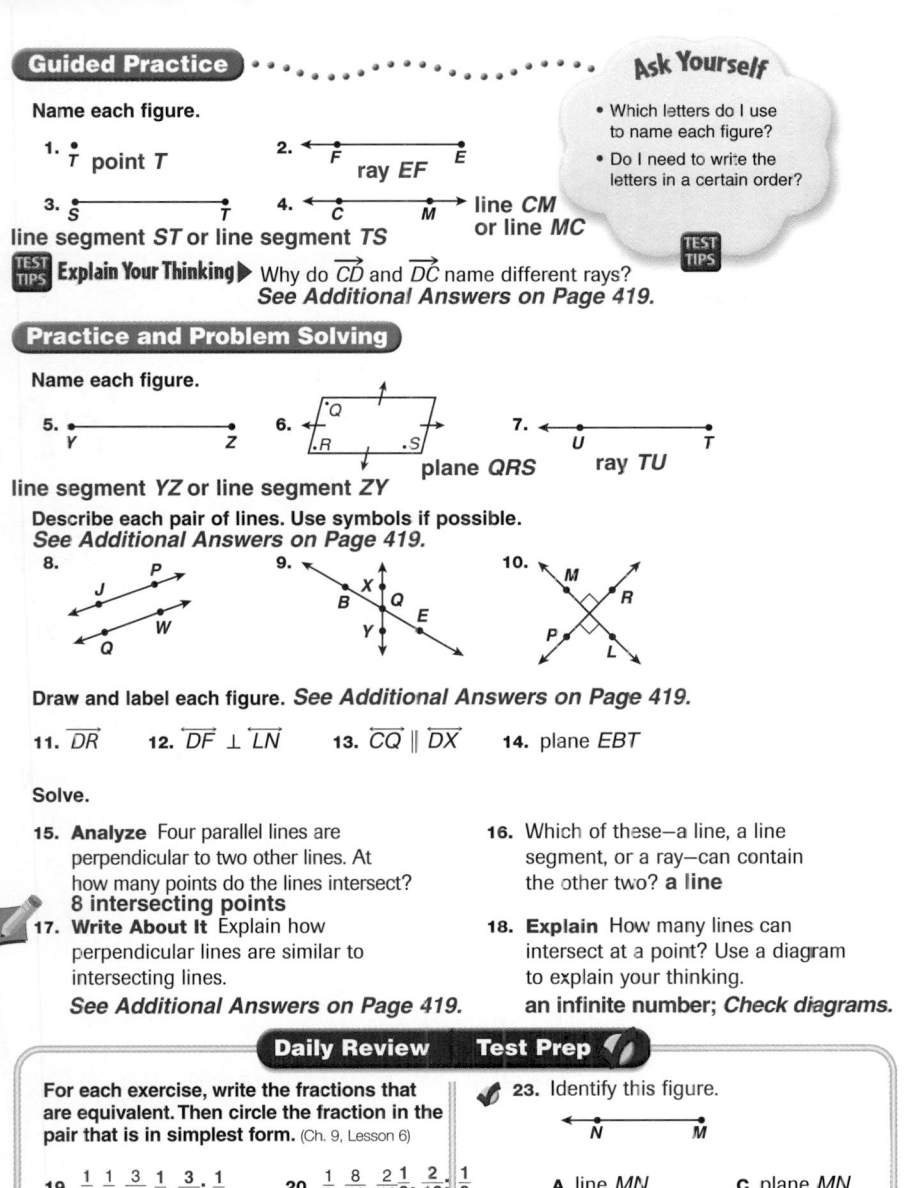

Name each figure.

1. • point T
   T

2. ray EF

3. line segment ST or line segment TS
   S   T

4. line CM or line MC
   C   M

TEST TIPS Explain Your Thinking ▸ Why do $\overrightarrow{CD}$ and $\overrightarrow{DC}$ name different rays?
See Additional Answers on Page 419.

Practice and Problem Solving

Name each figure.

5. line segment YZ or line segment ZY
   Y   Z

6. plane QRS

7. ray TU
   U   T

Describe each pair of lines. Use symbols if possible.
See Additional Answers on Page 419.

8.

9.

10.

Draw and label each figure. *See Additional Answers on Page 419.*

11. $\overrightarrow{DR}$ 12. $\overleftrightarrow{DF} \perp \overleftrightarrow{LN}$ 13. $\overleftrightarrow{CQ} \parallel \overleftrightarrow{DX}$ 14. plane EBT

Solve.

15. **Analyze** Four parallel lines are perpendicular to two other lines. At how many points do the lines intersect?
8 intersecting points

16. Which of these—a line, a line segment, or a ray—can contain the other two? **a line**

17. **Write About It** Explain how perpendicular lines are similar to intersecting lines.
See Additional Answers on Page 419.

18. **Explain** How many lines can intersect at a point? Use a diagram to explain your thinking.
an infinite number; Check diagrams.

Daily Review   Test Prep

For each exercise, write the fractions that are equivalent. Then circle the fraction in the pair that is in simplest form. (Ch. 9, Lesson 6)

19. $\frac{1}{8}, \frac{1}{4}; \frac{3}{12}, \frac{3}{4}; \frac{3}{12}, \frac{1}{4}$

20. $\frac{1}{8}, \frac{8}{16}; \frac{2}{16}, \frac{1}{8}; \frac{2}{16}, \frac{1}{8}$

21. $\frac{9}{8}, \frac{2}{6}; \frac{2}{18}, \frac{1}{2}; \frac{9}{2}, \frac{1}{2}$

22. $\frac{1}{6}, \frac{1}{3}; \frac{5}{15}, \frac{1}{3}; \frac{5}{15}, \frac{1}{3}$

23. Identify this figure.

   N   M

   A line MN   C plane MN
   B point MN   D ray MN

Extra Practice See page 419, Set A.

Test Prep Transparency
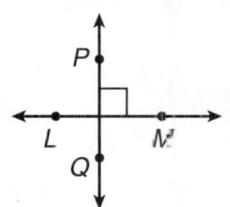
15.1

Explain in words and in symbols the relationship between $\overleftrightarrow{LM}$ and $\overleftrightarrow{PQ}$. (Line PQ and line LM are intersecting and perpendicular. $\overleftrightarrow{LM} \perp \overleftrightarrow{PQ}$)

Activity

Lesson Intervention
Points on Rulers

Or use Intervention CD-ROM Lesson 15.1

| 👥 Small Group | 🕐 5–10 minutes | Visual, Tactile |

Materials: *rulers, paper*

• Have students draw a straight line. **How do you represent point X on your line?** (Put a dot on the line. Label it X.) **Can you show the 2 rays this point determines?** (Put a point Y to the left, a point Z to the right of X on the line. Write $\overrightarrow{XZ}$ and $\overrightarrow{XZ}$.)

• **How do you draw a perpendicular line through X?** (Draw a line through X that is at a right angle to the first line.)

• Have students create other situations, writing them in symbols, such as the line containing P and Q is perpendicular to the line containing L and M. ($\overleftrightarrow{PQ} \perp \overleftrightarrow{LM}$)

---

3 Practice

Assign **Problems 5–23** as independent work.

• *Problem Solving for Problems 15–18* Have students explain their work for each problem.

Common Error

Notation errors Explain that the order of the points does not matter when writing the name of a line or line segment. However, when writing the name of a ray, the endpoint is always written first. For example, $\overleftrightarrow{AB}$ and $\overleftrightarrow{BA}$ both correctly name the same line. However, $\overrightarrow{AB}$ and $\overrightarrow{BA}$ do not name the same ray.

4 Assess and Close

• **What defines a line, a line segment, and a ray?** (A line continues in both directions in a straight path; a line segment has 2 endpoints; a ray has 1 endpoint and continues in the other direction in a straight path without end.)

• **Do parallel lines ever intersect?** (no)

• **At what angle do perpendicular lines intersect?** (right angles)

Assign the **LESSON QUIZ** on Transparency 15.1 to further assess student understanding.

Keeping a Journal

Have students explain, using illustrations and everyday language, what *points, lines* and *planes* are.

Hands-On: Measure, Draw, and Classify Angles

PLANNING THE LESSON

MATHEMATICS OBJECTIVE
Measure, draw, and classify angles.

Use Lesson Planner CD-ROM for Lesson 15.2.

Daily Routines

Vocabulary

Draw a **right angle** on the chalkboard. Tell students that it has a measure of 90°. Draw a ray that lies in the angle's interior, from the vertex of the right angle. **Would the measures of the two new angles made by this ray and the sides of the right angle be greater or less than the measure of the original angle?** (Each angle's measure is less than the measure of the right angle because each lies within the right angle.) These angles are **acute angles** because their measures are less than the measure of the **right angle**.

Vocabulary Cards

Meeting North Carolina's Standards

2.02 Identify, estimate, and measure the angles of plane figures using appropriate tools.

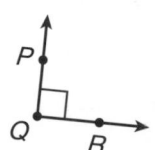

Lesson Transparency **15.2**

Problem of the Day

Draw a line with points *A, B, C,* and *D* on it in order from left to right. How many rays do these points determine? Name the rays.
(6; $\overrightarrow{BA}$, $\overrightarrow{CA}$, $\overrightarrow{DA}$, $\overrightarrow{AD}$, $\overrightarrow{BD}$, $\overrightarrow{CD}$)

Quick Review

1. 4.5×10^3 (4,500)
2. 0.8×10^5 (80,000)
3. $6,700 \div 10^4$ (0.67)
4. $900 \div 10^4$ (0.09)
5. 0.03×10^5 (3,000)
6. $1,300 \div 10^2$ (13)
7. 3.2×10^4 (32,000)
8. 7.3×10^2 (730)

Lesson Quiz

1. Classify an angle with the measure 20°. (acute)

2. Draw an angle with the measure 45°. Classify the angle. (acute)

3. Use symbols to write this angle in two ways. Classify the angle.
($\angle PQR$ or $\angle RQP$; right)

LEVELED PRACTICE

RETEACH 15.2

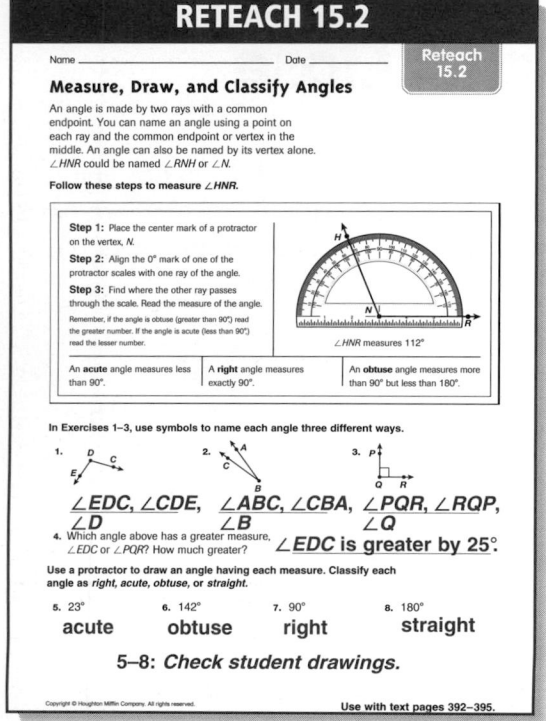

PRACTICE 15.2

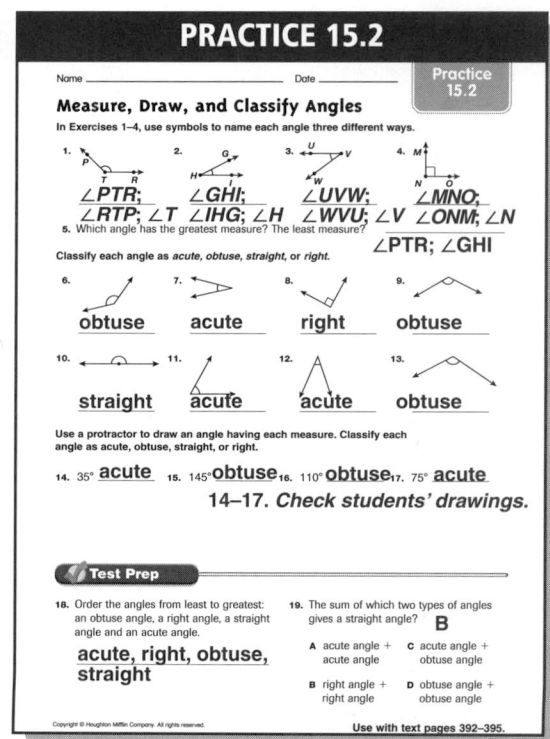

ENRICHMENT 15.2

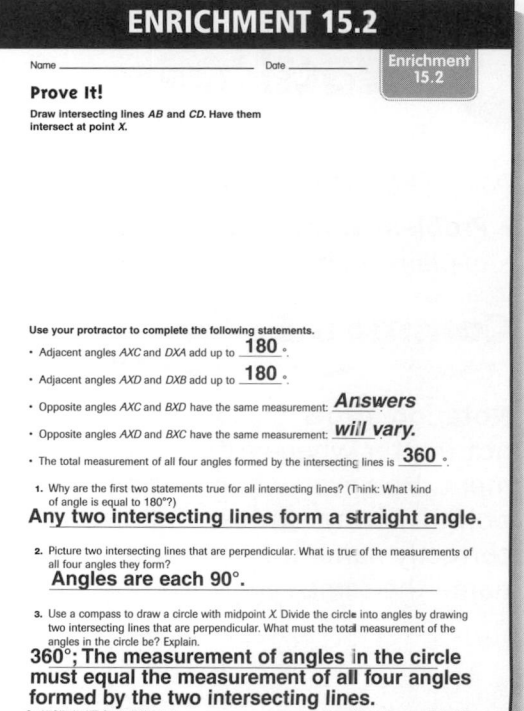

Practice Workbook Page 98

Reaching All Learners
Differentiated Instruction

English Learners

On Worksheet 15.2, students examine a labeled diagram of an angle and complete sentence frames with terms that name parts of the angle. They also explore various meanings of *mark* and *measure* that are used in the lesson.

Inclusion
KINESTHETIC, TACTILE

Materials: *paper strips, paper clips*

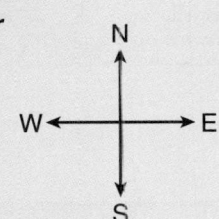

- Have students model angles as shown above.
- Have students make various angles. Ask students to classify each angle as they make it as right, acute, or obtuse.

Gifted and Talented
VISUAL, AUDITORY

- Display: *3:00, 6:00, 1:00, 2:00.* Challenge students to find the measure of the angles formed by the hands of a clock at these times. (90°, 180°, 30°, 60°)
- Have them write other times, and exchange papers with a partner. Have them figure out the angles formed by the hands of the clock for these times.

Social Studies Connection

Compass Directions
Materials: *protractor*

- **What indicates direction on a map?** (a compass rose) **Draw one.**

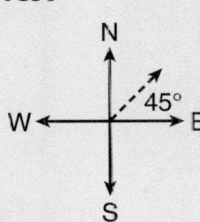

- **Classify the angle made by north and east;** (right) **and west and east.** (straight)

- **Add a 45° ray between north and east. What direction does it point?** (northeast)

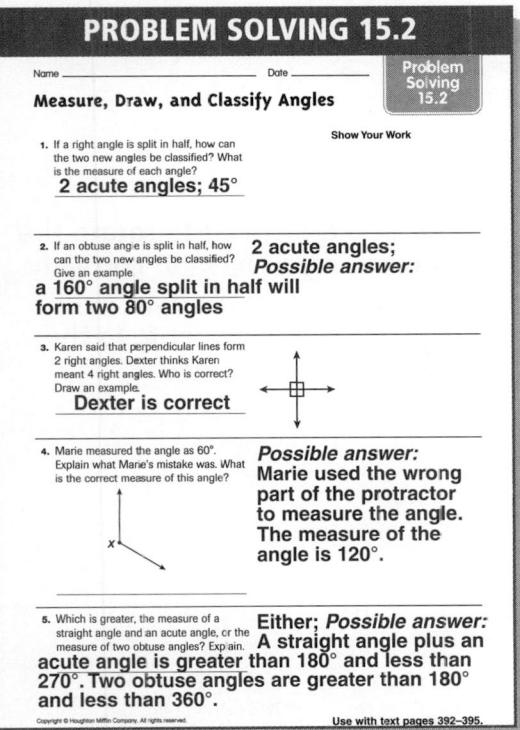

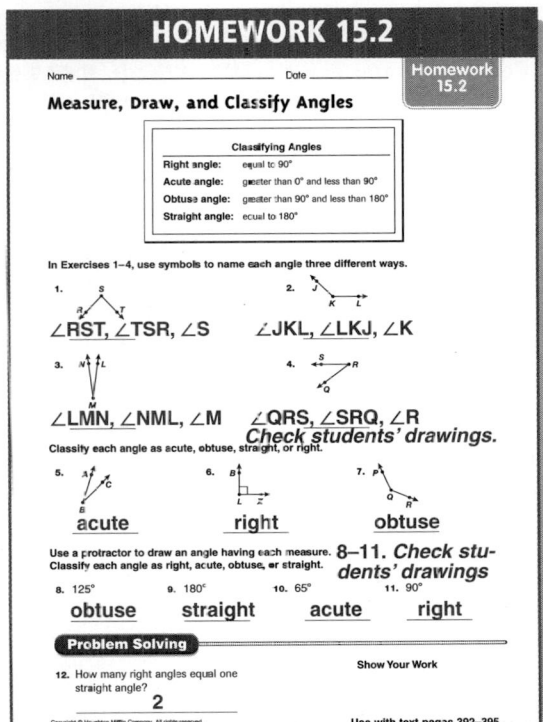

Homework Workbook Page 98

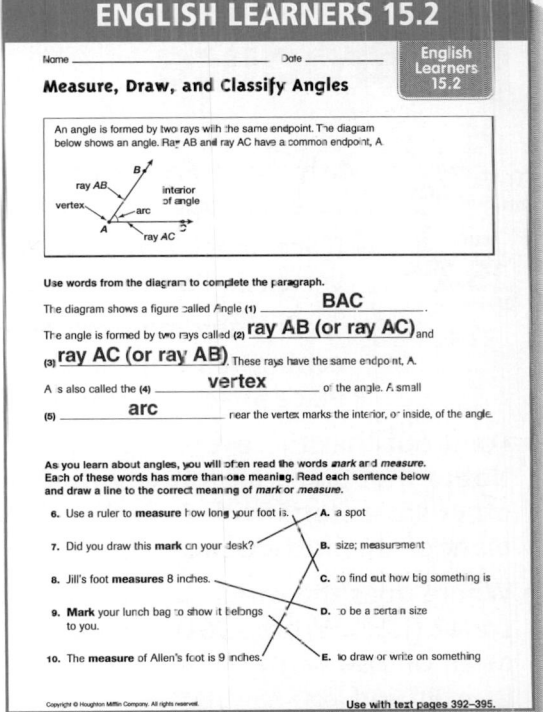

TEACHING LESSON 15.2

LESSON ORGANIZER

Objective Measure, draw, and classify angles.

Resources Reteach, Practice, Enrichment, Problem Solving, Homework, English Learners, Transparencies, Math Center

Materials Protractor Transparency (Sheets 1 and 2), protractors, rulers, tracing paper, pencils, paper, blank transparency

Activity
Warm-Up Activity
Intersecting Lines

iiii Whole Group	🕐 5 minutes	Visual, Tactile

Materials: *rulers, pencils, paper*

- Draw a pair of parallel lines. Do parallel lines intersect? (no)

- Now draw two intersecting lines. Label the point where the lines intersect as point *A*. Then label a point on each ray.

- Name the rays that are formed from where the lines intersect.

Measure, Draw, and Classify Angles

Objective Measure, draw, and classify angles.

 Glossary

Vocabulary
degrees
right angle
acute angle
obtuse angle
straight angle

Materials
protractor or Learning Tool 12

Work Together 🔵 MathTracks 2/9 Listen and Understand

Angles are formed by two rays with a common endpoint. The common endpoint of the rays is called the vertex of the angle. A small arc is used to identify the inside, or interior, of an angle.

To name an angle, you can name three points on the angle—a point on each ray and the vertex in the middle. You can also name an angle just by naming its vertex.

The symbol ∠ is used to identify an angle.

vertex M interior
X H

∠MXH, ∠HXM, ∠X

A protractor is a tool used to measure angles in **degrees** . Follow the steps below to measure ∠FDE and ∠BDC.

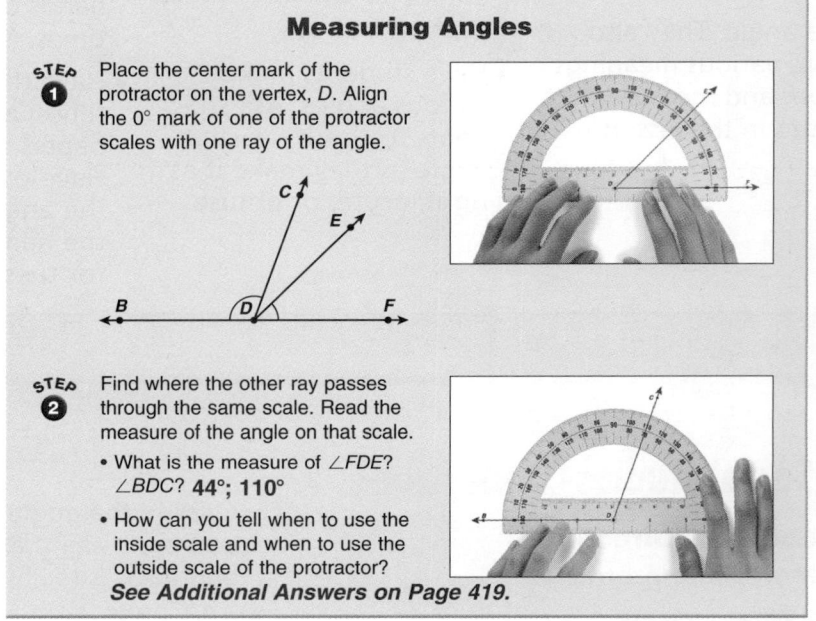

Measuring Angles

STEP 1 Place the center mark of the protractor on the vertex, *D*. Align the 0° mark of one of the protractor scales with one ray of the angle.

C
E
B D F

STEP 2 Find where the other ray passes through the same scale. Read the measure of the angle on that scale.

- What is the measure of ∠FDE? ∠BDC? **44°; 110°**

- How can you tell when to use the inside scale and when to use the outside scale of the protractor?
See Additional Answers on Page 419.

---

1 Introduce

 Teaching Transparency for **15.2**

Materials: *Protractor Transparency (Sheets 1 and 2) protractors, tracing paper*

- Place Sheet 2 (rays) on the overhead. Label the vertex *A*. **Point A is the vertex of the angle.**

- To find the measure of angle *XAY*, place the center mark of the protractor on point *A*. Place Sheet 1 (protractor) under Sheet 2 (rays).

- Point out that there are two scales on the protractor. Notice that one scale starts with 0 on the right and the other scale starts with 0 on the left. Align the 0 degree mark of the outside protractor scale with ray *AX*.

- Where does the other ray, ray *AY*, pass through the same scale? (135°) Write: ∠XAY measures 135°. Is ∠XAY an acute or an obtuse angle? (obtuse) Why? (Its measure is greater than 90° and less than 180°.)

2 Develop

Guide students through the *Work Together* section.

- **Look at Step 1 on page 392. You may need to rotate the protractor around the vertex until you have 0° correctly aligned.** Point out that one reading is more than 90° and one reading is less than 90°. Guide students to the correct choice.

You can also use a protractor to draw an angle of a given measure.

Draw an angle that measures 75°.

Drawing Angles

STEP **①** On a sheet of paper, draw and label a ray.

STEP **②** Place the center mark of the protractor on the endpoint of the ray. Align the ray with the 0° mark of one of the protractor scales. The endpoint of the ray will be the vertex of the angle.

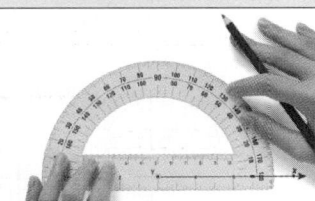

STEP **③** Using the scale on which the ray aligns with 0°, mark the point at 75°. Label the point.

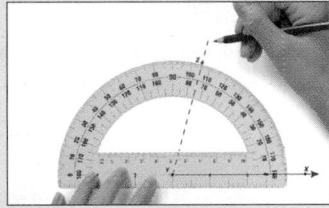

STEP **④** Draw a ray from the vertex through the point you labeled. Write the name of the angle.

• What is the measure of the angle? **75°**

• Which point is the vertex of the angle? **Answers will vary.**

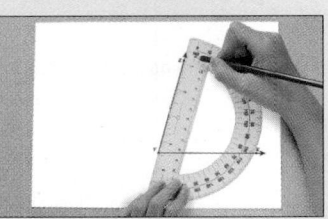

Measurement and Geometry

Angles Remind students that the hands of a clock are like two rays that form an angle at the center of a clock's face.

Have students use Learning Tool 18 (Circle/Circle Graph) to draw clock faces and find the angle measure (from 0° through 180°) between the hands at these times.

1. 3:00   **2.** 1:00   **3.** 4:00   **4.** 6:00
5. 10:00   **6.** 8:00   **7.** 11:00   **8.** 9:00
9. Have students classify each angle in Exercises 1–8 as acute, right, obtuse, or straight.

Answers

1. 90°; right   **2.** 30°; acute
3. 120°; obtuse   **4.** 180°; straight
5. 60°; acute   **6.** 120°; obtuse
7. 30°; acute   **8.** 90°; right
9. See above.

Differentiated Assignments		
At Risk	**Average**	**Advanced**
Exercises 1–5	Exercises 1–9	Exercises 1–9

• Help students work through the steps on page 393. Help students who may be making one of these mistakes: misaligning the vertex and the center point; misaligning one side and the flat of the protractor; reading the wrong scale.

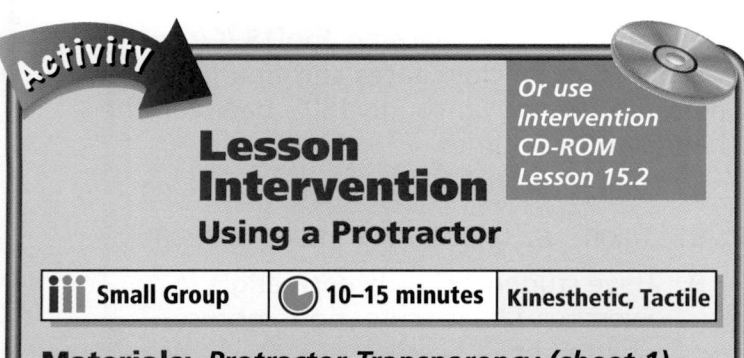

Activity

Lesson Intervention
Using a Protractor

Or use Intervention CD-ROM Lesson 15.2

| 👥 Small Group | 🕐 10–15 minutes | Kinesthetic, Tactile |

Materials: *Protractor Transparency (sheet 1), blank transparency*

• Display Protractor Transparency under blank transparency. Draw a right angle with the horizontal ray along the protractor's left side. Label the vertex *A*.

• **How do you read this angle?** Have a volunteer indicate the opening of the angle from 0° to 90° on the left side of the protractor. Draw a second right angle with the horizontal ray lying to the right.

• Draw other angles. **On which side of the protractor does each angle lie?** Point out that the outer scale is used to read angles on the left; the inner scale for angles on the right.

You can classify an angle by its measure.

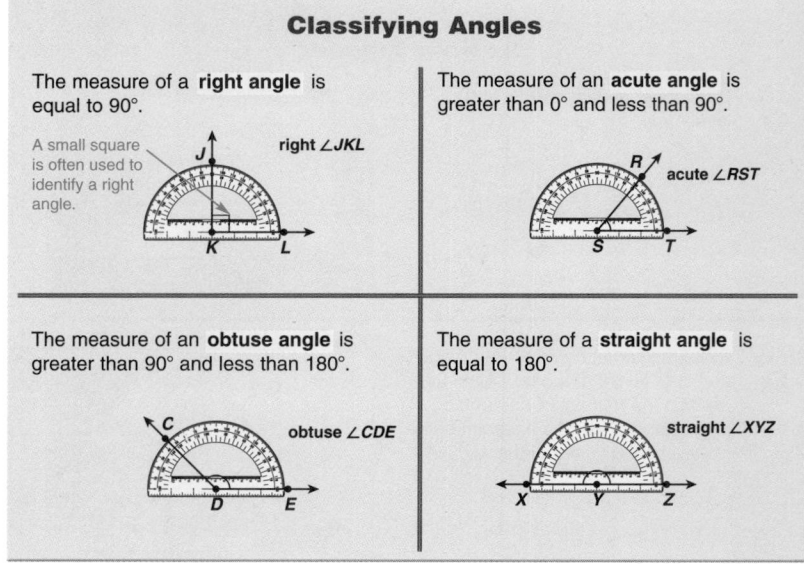

Classifying Angles

The measure of a **right angle** is equal to 90°.
A small square is often used to identify a right angle.
right ∠JKL

The measure of an **acute angle** is greater than 0° and less than 90°.
acute ∠RST

The measure of an **obtuse angle** is greater than 90° and less than 180°.
obtuse ∠CDE

The measure of a **straight angle** is equal to 180°.
straight ∠XYZ

On Your Own

In Exercises 1–4, use symbols to name each angle three different ways.

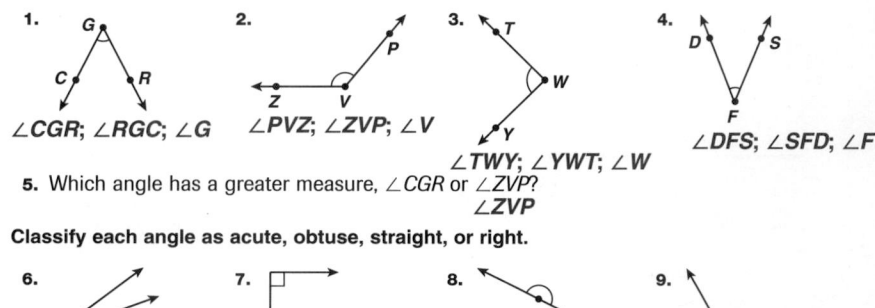

1. ∠CGR; ∠RGC; ∠G
2. ∠PVZ; ∠ZVP; ∠V
3. ∠TWY; ∠YWT; ∠W
4. ∠DFS; ∠SFD; ∠F

5. Which angle has a greater measure, ∠CGR or ∠ZVP? ∠ZVP

Classify each angle as acute, obtuse, straight, or right.

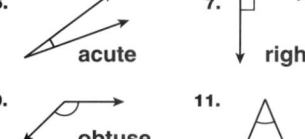
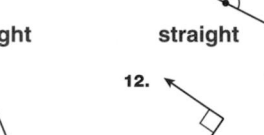
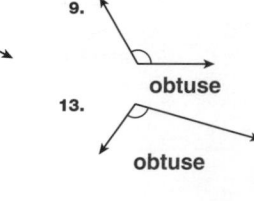

6. acute
7. right
8. straight
9. obtuse
10. obtuse
11. acute
12. right
13. obtuse

---

3 Practice

Assign **Exercises 1–21** of *On Your Own* as independent work.

4 Assess and Close

Assign **Exercises 22–23** of the *Talk About it • Write About it* section. Have volunteers explain their work.

• **Can an acute angle also be an obtuse angle? Explain.** (No; the measure of an angle cannot be less than 90° and greater than 90° at the same time.)

• **If three points are used to label an angle, which point is the vertex of the angle?** (the point in the middle)

• **When an obtuse angle is properly measured, the degree scales show 40° and 140°. Which degree measure is correct? Why?** (140°; because the measure of an obtuse angle is more than 90°)

Assign the **LESSON QUIZ** on Transparency 15.2 to further assess student understanding.

Use a protractor to draw an angle having each measure.
Classify each angle as right, acute, obtuse, or straight. *Check students' drawings.*

14. 165° **obtuse**   15. 90° **right**   16. 20° **acute**   17. 85° **acute**

18. 50° **acute**   19. 115° **obtuse**   20. 10° **acute**   21. 135° **obtuse**

Talk About It • Write About It

You have learned how to classify, draw, and measure angles.

22. **Analyze** Is the sum of the measures of two acute angles
always less than 90°? Explain why or why not.
See Additional Answers on Page 419.

23. How could you list the kinds of angles you know—right,
straight, acute, and obtuse—in order from least to greatest
measure? Explain. ***See Additional Answers on Page 419.***

Construct Perpendicular Lines
Visual Thinking — Math Reasoning

You can use a compass and a straightedge to
construct perpendicular lines. *Check students' constructions.*

Follow these steps to construct perpendicular lines.

STEP 1 Draw line *c* and point *W* as shown at the
right. Put the compass point on *W*. Draw
an arc that intersects line *c* at two points.
Label these points *X* and *Y*.

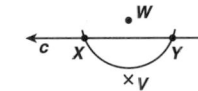

Lines can be named
using lowercase letters.

STEP 2 Place the point of the compass at *X* and draw
an arc below line *c*. From point *Y*, use the
same compass measure and draw an arc
below line *c*. Label the intersection point *V*.

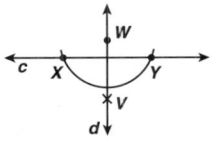

STEP 3 Draw line *WV* and label it *d*. Line *d* is
perpendicular to line *c*.

Chapter 15 Lesson 2   **395**

Visual Thinking — Math Reasoning

Construct Perpendicular Lines

Have students use a protractor to verify that right
angles are formed by the intersection of line *c* and
line *d*. Point out that if two lines meet to form 90°
angles, then the lines are perpendicular.

Keeping a Journal

Direct students to look for examples of obtuse and
acute angles in nature or in buildings as they go
home. Have them write in their journals a few sentences about what they observed.

Lesson 15.3

Triangles

PLANNING THE LESSON

MATHEMATICS OBJECTIVE
Classify triangles and find missing angle measures.

Use Lesson Planner CD-ROM for Lesson 15.3.

Daily Routines

Vocabulary

Write *equilateral, isosceles,* and *scalene* on the chalkboard. **These words name 3 kinds of triangles. Which do you think names a triangle with 3 equal sides?** (equilateral) **Why?** (It has the prefix *equi-,* or equal.) *Equi-lateral* means "equal sides." The prefix *iso* also means equal. Say "eye-SOS-uh-leez." An *isosceles* triangle has 2 equal sides. **What do you think a *scalene* triangle is?** (triangle with no equal sides)

Vocabulary Cards

Meeting North Carolina's Standards

3.01 Identify, define, describe, and accurately represent triangles, quadrilaterals, and other polygons.

Also **3.02, 3.04**

Lesson Transparency
15.3

Problem of the Day
The sum of three numbers is 180. Two of the numbers are equal. The third number is the sum of the other two numbers. What are the three numbers? (45, 45, and 90)

Quick Review
Find the value of each expression.
1. $180 - (60 + 45)$ (75)
2. $180 - 30 - 30$ (120)
3. $180 - 62$, then $- 65$ (53)
4. 180 less the sum of 70 and 40 (70)

Lesson Quiz
Classify each triangle in two ways by the measures of their sides and angles.

1.
7

7
(isosceles; right)

2.
4.5   4.5

4.5
(equilateral; acute)

3.
92°
44°   44°
(isosceles; obtuse)

LEVELED PRACTICE

RETEACH 15.3

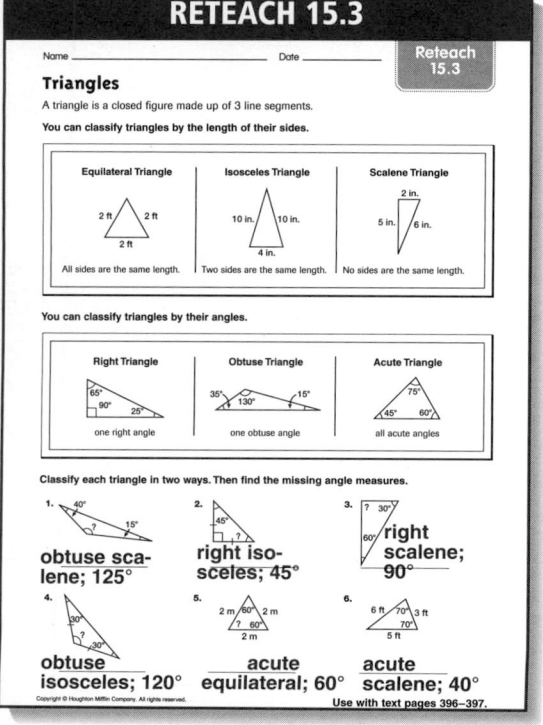

PRACTICE 15.3

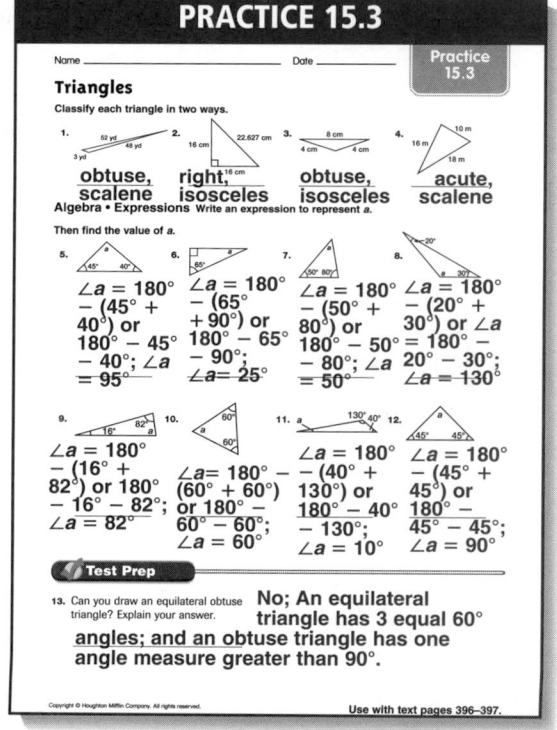

Practice Workbook Page 99

ENRICHMENT 15.3

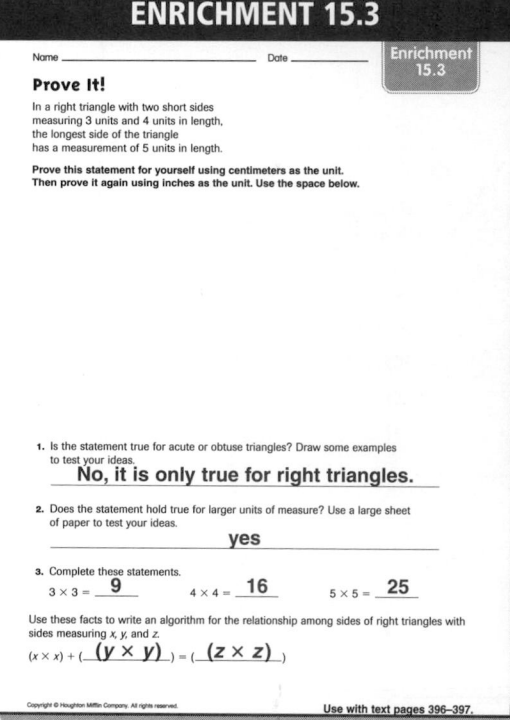

Reaching All Learners

Differentiated Instruction

English Learners

Worksheet 15.3 defines the word *classify* and allows students to practice classifying shapes in several categories. This prepares them to classify triangles in the lesson.

Inclusion
KINESTHETIC, TACTILE

Materials: *scissors, paper strips*

- Cut two of the strips in equal lengths. Cut a third strip to a length less than the sum but, greater than half the sum, of the lengths of the first two strips. Use the strips to form a triangle.

- How many equal sides does your triangle have? (2) **What kind of triangle is it?** (isosceles)

Early Finishers
VISUAL; AUDITORY

- One angle in a right triangle measures 50°. What is the measure of the third angle? (40°)

- One angle in a right triangle measures *a*°. What is the measure of the third angle? (90° − *a*°)

- What rule can you use to find the measure of an acute angle in a right triangle given the measure of the other acute angle? (Subtract the given angle measure from 90°.)

TECHNOLOGY

Spiral Review

Help students remember skills they learned earlier by creating **customized** spiral review worksheets using the *Ways to Assess* CD-ROM.

Tool Software

Use *Shape Up!* or another shapes program to explore this lesson's objectives more fully.

Lesson Planner

You can use the Lesson Planner CD-ROM to create a report of the lessons and standards you have taught.

Science Connection

Bridge Trusses
Materials: *books on bridges, research materials*

- Have students find pictures of bridges. Have them identify the kinds of triangles they see in the structures of the bridges. Have them copy the triangles and label them. Have them use the kinds of triangles they find to design their own bridges.

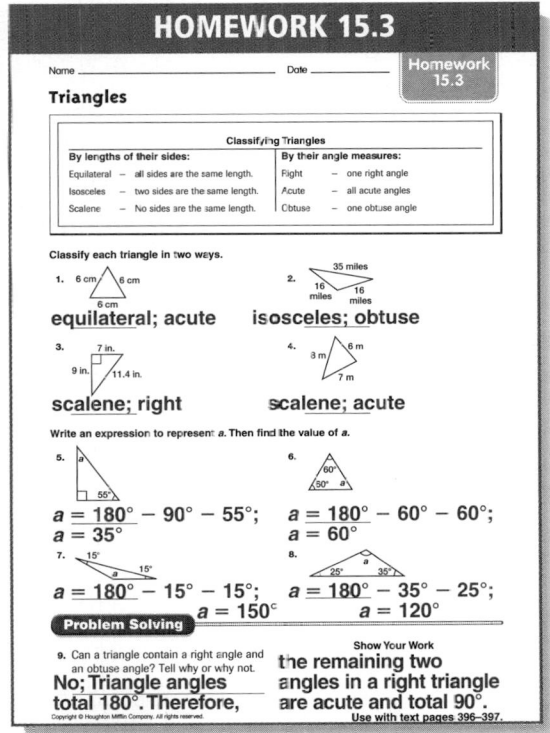

PROBLEM SOLVING 15.3

Name _____ Date _____

Problem Solving 15.3

Triangles

1. Mavis has found the measures of two angles of a triangle: 72° and 47°. Without measuring, how can she find the measure of the third angle? What is the measure of the third angle?

   Show Your Work
   Subtract the sum of 72 and 47 from 180; 61°

2. Kan measured the angles of an isosceles triangle. One angle measure is 36°. The other two angles have the same measure. What is the measure of each of the two other angles?
   72°

3. What triangles are formed when you draw a line down the middle of an equilateral triangle?
   two right triangles

4. Use the clues to find the angle measures of the following triangle:
   - The second angle is double the measure of the first angle.
   - The third angle is the sum of the other two angle measures.
   30°, 60°, and 90°

5. Can the measure of an angle in an equilateral triangle be anything other than 60°? Explain. **No; Possible answer: Since all the sides are the same length, all the angles are equal, and 180° ÷ 3 = 60°.**

Use with text pages 396–397.

HOMEWORK 15.3

Name _____ Date _____

Homework 15.3

Triangles

Classifying Triangles	
By lengths of their sides:	**By their angle measures:**
Equilateral – all sides are the same length.	Right – one right angle
Isosceles – two sides are the same length.	Acute – all acute angles
Scalene – No sides are the same length.	Obtuse – one obtuse angle

Classify each triangle in two ways.

1. 6 cm, 6 cm, 6 cm
   equilateral; acute

2. 35 miles, 16 miles, 16 miles
   isosceles; obtuse

3. 7 in., 9 in., 11.4 in.
   scalene; right

4. 3 m, 6 m, 7 m
   scalene; acute

Write an expression to represent *a*. Then find the value of *a*.

5. 55°
   $a = 180° − 90° − 55°;$
   $a = 35°$

6. 60°
   $a = 180° − 60° − 60°;$
   $a = 60°$

7. 15°, 15°
   $a = 180° − 15° − 15°;$
   $a = 150°$

8. 25°, 35°
   $a = 180° − 35° − 25°;$
   $a = 120°$

Problem Solving

9. Can a triangle contain a right angle and an obtuse angle? Tell why or why not.
   Show Your Work
   No; Triangle angles total 180°. Therefore, the remaining two angles in a right triangle are acute and total 90°.

Use with text pages 396–397.

ENGLISH LEARNERS 15.3

Name _____ Date _____

English Learners 15.3

Triangles

To *classify* means to put things in groups based on how they are alike.

Classify the shapes. Write the letters of shapes that match the description in each group below. Most shapes belong in more than one group. Group 1 has been done for you.

Group 1: Shapes formed by straight lines only	Group 2: Shapes formed by curved lines only	Group 3: Shapes formed by both straight and curved lines
D, E, F, G, H, I, J, K	**A, C, L**	**B**
Group 4: Shapes with 3 sides (lines)	Group 5: Shapes with 4 sides (lines)	Group 6: Shapes that look like letters
F, I, J	**D, E, H, K**	**G, L**

On the back of this sheet, draw ten animals, cars, foods, shapes, or other things. Then find three different groups into which you could classify the things. Describe each group in words.

Check students' work.

Use with text pages 396–397.

TEACHING LESSON 15.3

LESSON ORGANIZER

Objective Classify triangles and find missing angle measures.

Resources Reteach, Practice, Enrichment, Problem Solving, Homework, English Learners, Transparencies, Math Center

Materials Angle Sum of a Triangle Transparency, blank transparency, Half Centimeter Grid Transparency, Learning Tool 14 or grid paper, straightedge

Warm-Up Activity
Identify Angles

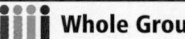

iiii Whole Group	⏱ 5 minutes	Visual, Auditory

Materials: *blank transparency*

• On the blank transparency, draw an acute angle. **What kind of angle is this?** (acute) Draw an obtuse angle. **What kind of angle is this?** (obtuse) Draw a right angle. **What kind of angle is this?** (right)

Triangles

Objective Classify triangles and find missing angle measures.

Learn About It

A triangle is made up of 3 line segments called sides. Each pair of sides has a common endpoint, or vertex, and forms an angle.

▶ You can classify triangles by the lengths of their sides.

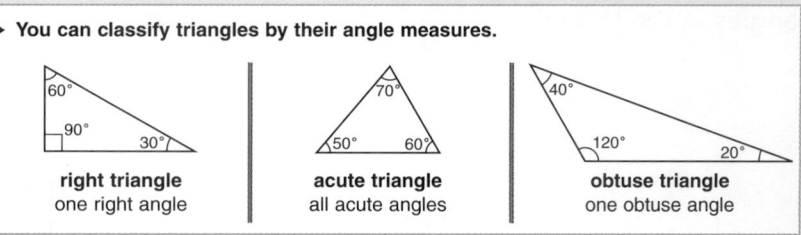

equilateral triangle
All sides are the same length.

isosceles triangle
At least two sides are the same length.

scalene triangle
No sides are the same length.

▶ You can classify triangles by their angle measures.

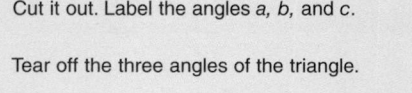
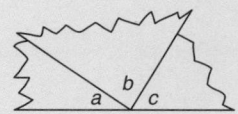

right triangle
one right angle

acute triangle
all acute angles

obtuse triangle
one obtuse angle

Try this activity with a partner to learn about angle measures in a triangle.

Materials straightedge

STEP 1 Use a straightedge to draw a triangle. Cut it out. Label the angles *a*, *b*, and *c*.

STEP 2 Tear off the three angles of the triangle.

STEP 3 Arrange the angles to make a straight angle.
• What is the measure of a straight angle?**180°**
• What is the sum of the angle measures in a triangle?**180°**
• Does this work for any triangle? Explain.
  See Additional Answers on Page 419.

396

---

① Introduce

Teaching Transparency
for
15.3

Materials: *Angle Sum of a Triangle Transparency*

• Place the Angle Sum of a Triangle Transparency on the overhead.

• **Triangles come in many different sizes and shapes, but the sum of the angle measures in any triangle is always 180 degrees. What happens if we "tear off" the three corners of triangle *ABC* and move them so that the three angles meet?** Invite a volunteer to move the angles so that they meet.

• **The angles have formed a straight angle. What is the measure of a straight angle?** (180 degrees)

• **Label the angles: *A* = 95 degrees; *B* = 50 degrees; *C* = 35 degrees. How can we check our answer?** (by adding the angle measures of triangle *ABC*) Write: 95° + 50° + 35° = 180°.

② Develop

Guide students through the *Learn About It* section.

• **What kind of triangle has sides the same length?** (equilateral) **Can an equilateral triangle also be called an isosceles triangle?** (Yes; if all three sides are the same length, then two sides are the same length.)

• **Can 60°, 70°, and 80° be measures of the angles in a triangle?** (no) **Why?** (The sum is more than 180°.) **Can 20°, 30°, and 40° be measures of the angles in a triangle?** (no) **Why?** (The sum is less than 180°.)

Have partners try the *Hands-On* activity.

Guided Practice

Have students complete **Exercises 1–2** as you observe. Remind them to use the *Ask Yourself* questions to help. Give students the opportunity to talk about the question in *Explain Your Thinking*.

Classify each triangle in two ways. Then find the missing angle measures.

1.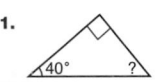
40° ?

2.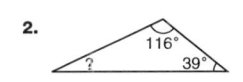
116° ? 39°

obtuse; scalene; 25°

TEST TIPS **Explain Your Thinking ▶** Is an equilateral triangle also an isosceles triangle? Explain why or why not. *See Additional Answers on Pages 419 and T86.*

Practice and Problem Solving

Classify each triangle in two ways.

3.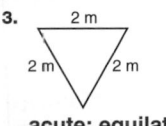
2 m
2 m   2 m

acute; equilateral

4.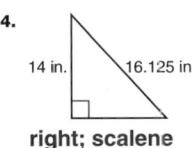
14 in.   16.125 in.

right; scalene

5.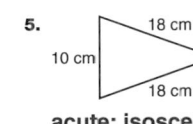
18 cm
10 cm
18 cm

acute; isosceles

6.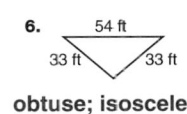
54 ft
33 ft   33 ft

obtuse; isosceles

X Algebra • **Expressions** Write an expression to represent *a*. Then find the value of *a*.

7–12. *See Additional Answers on Pages 419 and T86.*

7.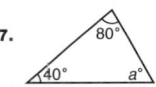
80°
40°   a°

8.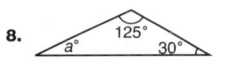
125°
a°   30°

9.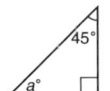
45°
a°

10.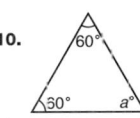
60°
30°   a°

11. **What's Wrong?** Ari says that an isosceles triangle can also be obtuse. Is Ari right or wrong? Draw triangles to help you explain.

12. **Represent** Try to draw each of the following. If a figure cannot be drawn, explain why.
   • a scalene acute triangle
   • an equilateral right triangle
   • a scalene right triangle

13. **Create and Solve** Use the sum of the angle measures in a triangle to write and solve your own triangle problem. *Check students' problems.*

Daily Review | **Test Prep**

Multiply. Write each product in simplest form. (Ch. 12, Lesson 2)

14. $\frac{2}{3} \times \frac{3}{5}\frac{2}{5}$ 15. $\frac{3}{8} \times \frac{4}{5}\frac{3}{10}$ 16. $\frac{5}{6} \times \frac{3}{10}\frac{1}{4}$

17. $\frac{4}{9} \times \frac{3}{4}\frac{1}{3}$ 18. $\frac{2}{25} \times \frac{2}{5}\frac{4}{125}$ 19. $\frac{3}{8} \times \frac{4}{11}\frac{3}{22}$

20. **Free Response** Find *p*. Explain how you found your answer.

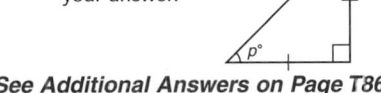
p°
p°

See Additional Answers on Page T86.

Extra Practice See page 419, Set B.

DAILY TEST PREP

Which best describes this triangle? (A)

A. right, isosceles   C. scalene, isosceles
B. right, acute   D. acute, isosceles

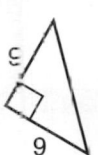
5
9

Activity

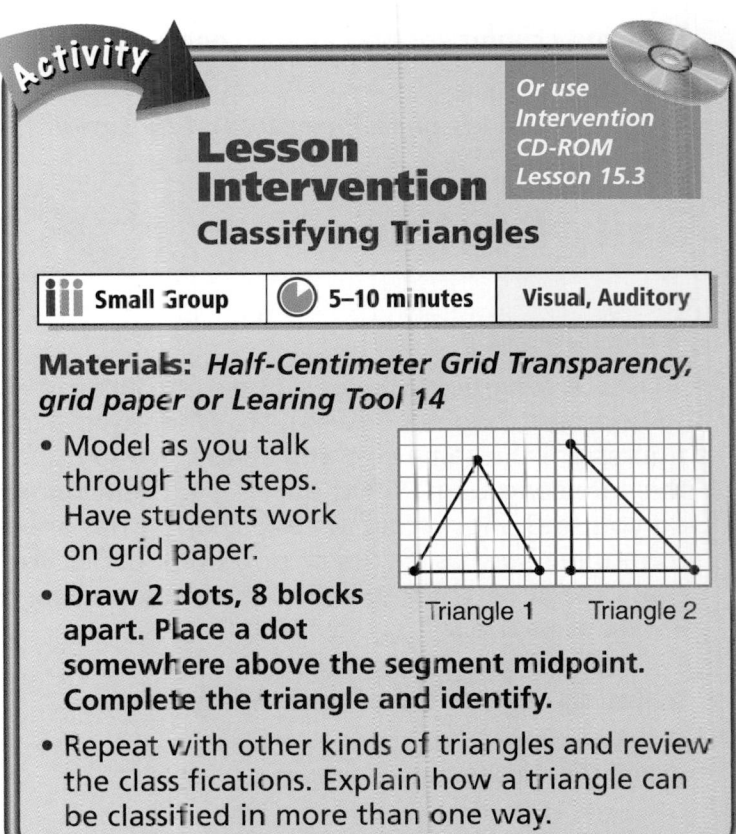

Or use Intervention CD-ROM Lesson 15.3

Lesson Intervention
Classifying Triangles

| iii Small Group | ⏱ 5–10 minutes | Visual, Auditory |

Materials: *Half-Centimeter Grid Transparency, grid paper or Learing Tool 14*

• Model as you talk through the steps. Have students work on grid paper.
• Draw 2 dots, 8 blocks apart. Place a dot somewhere above the segment midpoint. Complete the triangle and identify.
• Repeat with other kinds of triangles and review the classifications. Explain how a triangle can be classified in more than one way.

Triangle 1   Triangle 2

---

3 Practice

Assign **Problems 3–20** as independent work.

• *Algebra* • *Expressions for Exercises 7–10* Remind students that they can write two expressions for each.

Common Errors

Classification errors Explain that any triangle can be classified in more than one way. For example, an isosceles triangle can also be a right triangle.

Incorrect order of operations Suggest that students subtract one angle measure from 180° and then subtract the other angle's measure from the difference. This will give the third angle's measure. Another method is to add the two angles that are known, and subtract the sum from 180°.

4 Assess and Close

• **Can a triangle have a right angle and 2 equal sides?** (yes, a right isosceles) **Can a triangle have 2 equal sides that are also equal to the length of the 3rd side?** (yes, if it's both isosceles and equilateral) **Can a triangle have all angles equal to 70°?** (No: 3 × 70° = 210°, not 180°.)

Assign the **LESSON QUIZ** on Transparency 15.3 to further assess student understanding.

Keeping a Journal

Have students define these triangles: *acute equilateral, right scalene, acute isosceles, obtuse isosceles.* Have them consider the meaning of the words.

Lesson 15.4 Congruence

PLANNING THE LESSON

MATHEMATICS OBJECTIVE
Identify congruent figures and congruent parts of figures.

Use Lesson Planner CD-ROM for Lesson 15.4.

Daily Routines

Vocabulary

Point out *congruent* shapes in the classroom, for example, two window panes. **When two figures are the same size and shape, we say they are** *congruent*. **What other congruent figures do you see?** Show students two shapes that are *not* congruent, such as 2 sizes of notebook paper. **Are these congruent? Why not?** (Both are rectangular but not the same size.)

[Vocabulary Cards]

Meeting North Carolina's Standards

Maintain Grade 2 Objective **3.03** Identify and make symmetric and congruent figures.

Problem of the Day

Continue the pattern horizontally below to help you solve the problem.
How many triangles can you make with 31 equal line segments? (15)

Number of Line Segments	3	5	7	31
Pattern				?

Quick Review

Write each expression in symbols.
1. angle A ($\angle A$)
2. line segment LM ($\overline{LM}$)
3. ray PQ ($\overrightarrow{PQ}$)

Lesson Quiz

1. How can you tell if two squares are congruent? (See whether the sides are the same length.)
2. Are all equilateral triangles congruent? (No; they can be different sizes.)

LEVELED PRACTICE

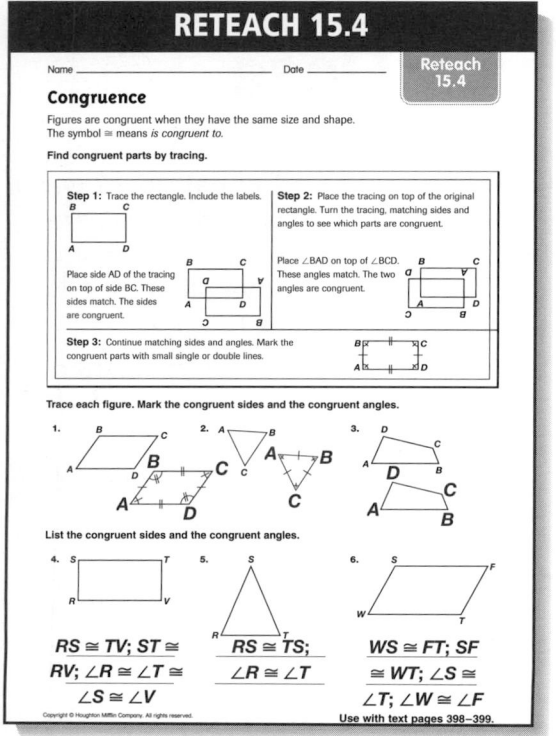

RETEACH 15.4

Congruence

Figures are congruent when they have the same size and shape. The symbol ≅ means *is congruent to*.

Find congruent parts by tracing.

Step 1: Trace the rectangle. Include the labels.
Step 2: Place the tracing on top of the original rectangle. Turn the tracing, matching sides and angles to see which parts are congruent.

Place side AD of the tracing on top of side BC. These sides match. The sides are congruent.
Place ∠BAD on top of ∠BCD. These angles match. The two angles are congruent.

Step 3: Continue matching sides and angles. Mark the congruent parts with small single or double lines.

Trace each figure. Mark the congruent sides and the congruent angles.

1. 2. 3.

List the congruent sides and the congruent angles.

4. 5. 6.

$RS \cong TV; ST \cong RV; \angle R \cong \angle T$
$\angle S \cong \angle V$

$RS \cong TS;$
$\angle R \cong \angle T$

$WS \cong FT; SF \cong WT; \angle S \cong \angle T; \angle W \cong \angle F$

Use with text pages 398–399.

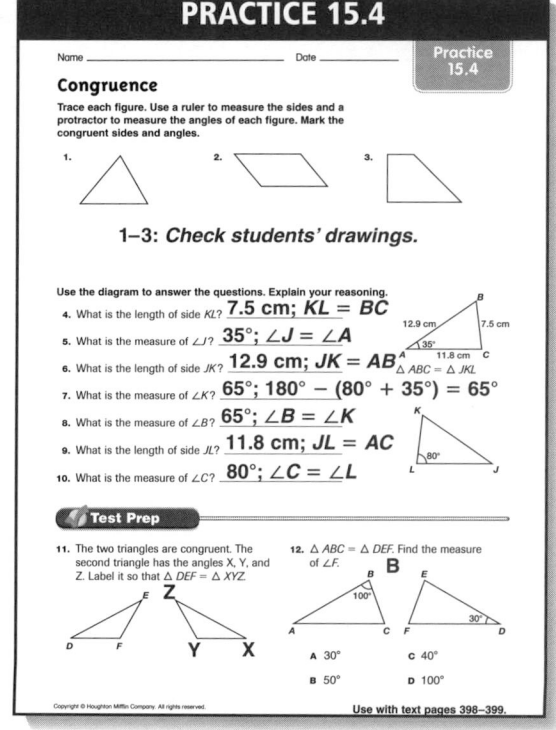

PRACTICE 15.4

Congruence

Trace each figure. Use a ruler to measure the sides and a protractor to measure the angles of each figure. Mark the congruent sides and angles.

1. 2. 3.

1–3: Check students' drawings.

Use the diagram to answer the questions. Explain your reasoning.

4. What is the length of side KL? **7.5 cm; KL = BC**
5. What is the measure of ∠J? **35°; ∠J = ∠A**
6. What is the length of side JK? **12.9 cm; JK = AB**
7. What is the measure of ∠K? **65°; 180° − (80° + 35°) = 65°**
8. What is the measure of ∠B? **65°; ∠B = ∠K**
9. What is the length of side JL? **11.8 cm; JL = AC**
10. What is the measure of ∠C? **80°; ∠C = ∠L**

Test Prep

11. The two triangles are congruent. The second triangle has the angles X, Y, and Z. Label it so that △ DEF = △ XYZ.

12. △ ABC = △ DEF. Find the measure of ∠F.
A 30°
B 50°
C 40°
D 100°

Use with text pages 398–399.

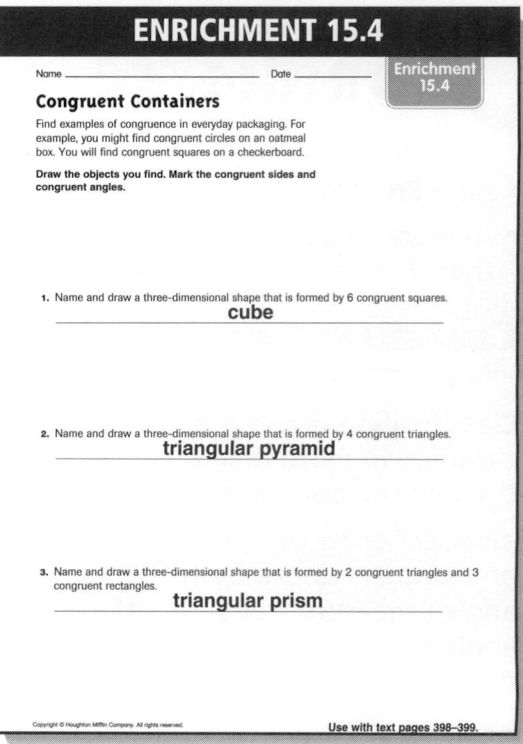

ENRICHMENT 15.4

Congruent Containers

Find examples of congruence in everyday packaging. For example, you might find congruent circles on an oatmeal box. You will find congruent squares on a checkerboard.

Draw the objects you find. Mark the congruent sides and congruent angles.

1. Name and draw a three-dimensional shape that is formed by 6 congruent squares.
cube

2. Name and draw a three-dimensional shape that is formed by 4 congruent triangles.
triangular pyramid

3. Name and draw a three-dimensional shape that is formed by 2 congruent triangles and 3 congruent rectangles.
triangular prism

Use with text pages 398–399.

Reaching All Learners

Differentiated Instruction

English Learners

Worksheet 15.4 defines *congruent*, using both pictures and words, as the term applies to lines, angles, and figures. Students apply the concept by determining whether several pairs of figures are congruent.

Special Needs
KINESTHETIC, TACTILE

Materials: *scissors*

- Cut out several congruent and incongruent triangles.
- Have students move them around on a table to find ones the same size and shape. **You may have to flip or rotate them. Two figures the same size and shape are called *congruent* figures.**

Early Finishers
VISUAL, AUDITORY

Materials: *reference books*

Are the faces of the pyramids congruent?
Challenge students to research the Egyptian pyramids. Have them find pictures or photographs or descriptions. Have them report their findings to the class. Students should find out if all sides of a pyramid are congruent.

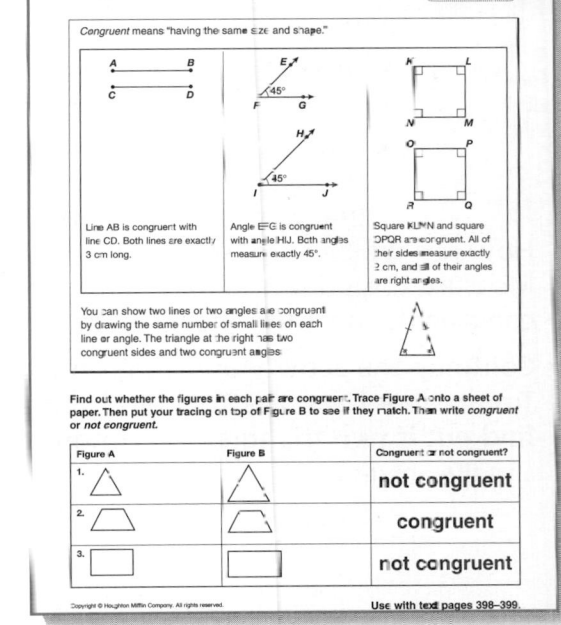

TECHNOLOGY

Spiral Review

You can prepare students for standardized tests with **customized** spiral review on key skills using the *Ways to Assess* CD–ROM.

Education Place

You can visit Education Place at **eduplace.com/math/mw/** for teacher support materials.

Science Connection

Congruent Crystals and Molecules
Materials: *reference books*

- Have students work in small groups to research congruent shapes in nature, such as in some crystals or molecules.

Have students copy the shapes and label them. Have students report their findings to the class.

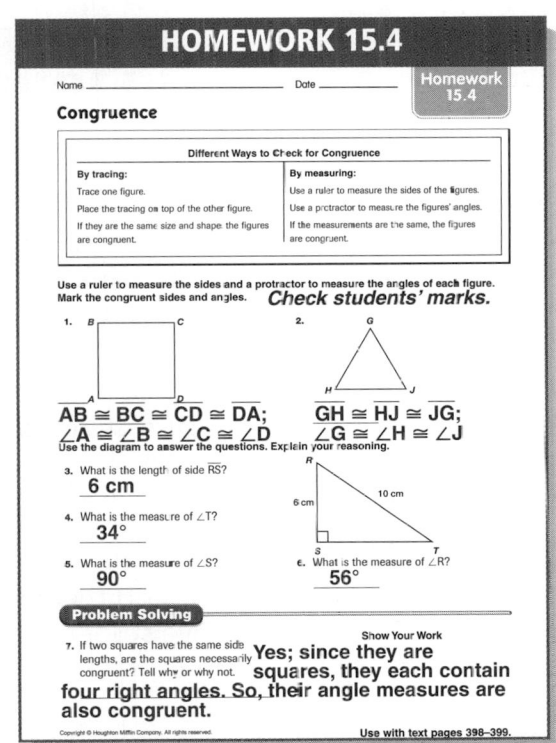

Homework Workbook Page 100

TEACHING LESSON 15.4

LESSON ORGANIZER

Objective Identify congruent figures and congruent parts of figures.

Resources Reteach, Practice, Enrichment, Problem Solving, Homework, English Learners, Transparencies, Math Center

Materials Large Plane Figures, Small Plane Figures, and Triangles Transparencies; rulers, protractors, blank transparency

Activity

Warm-Up Activity
Measuring Triangles

👥 Whole Group	⏱ 5 minutes	Visual, Tactile

Materials: *rulers, protractors, paper*

- Have each student draw a triangle on a piece of paper. Have them exchange papers with a partner. Have students work with rulers and protractors to measure the sides and angles of their partners' triangles. Have students label the triangles with the measurements.

Congruence

Objective Identify congruent figures and congruent parts of figures.

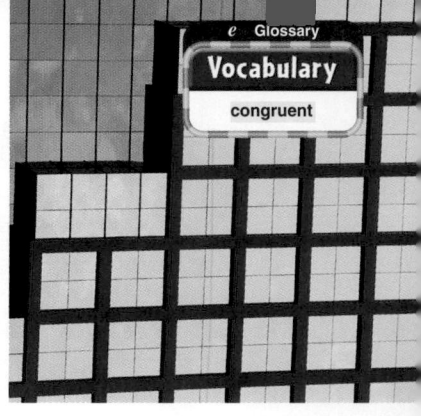

Vocabulary
congruent

Learn About It

Figures that are the same size and shape are called **congruent** figures. The symbol ≅ is used to indicate congruence.

Which figures in the photograph appear to be congruent?

Different Ways to Check for Congruence

Way ① You can use tracing.

If you trace triangle *ABC* and place the tracing on top of triangle *DEF*, you will find that the triangles are congruent.

The symbol △ is used to identify a triangle.

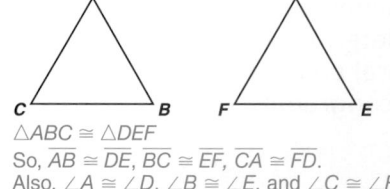

△*ABC* ≅ △*DEF*
So, $\overline{AB} \cong \overline{DE}$, $\overline{BC} \cong \overline{EF}$, $\overline{CA} \cong \overline{FD}$.
Also, ∠*A* ≅ ∠*D*, ∠*B* ≅ ∠*E*, and ∠*C* ≅ ∠*F*.

Way ② You can use a ruler and a protractor.

In an equilateral triangle, the three sides are congruent and the three angles are congruent. Small lines indicate congruent sides and congruent angles.

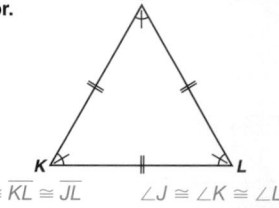

$\overline{JK} \cong \overline{KL} \cong \overline{JL}$ ∠*J* ≅ ∠*K* ≅ ∠*L*

Another Example

Squares

These squares are not congruent. They have the same shape, but they are not the same size.

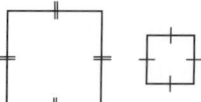

398

---

① Introduce

Teaching Transparency for 15.4

Materials: *Large Plane Figures, Small Plane Figures, Triangle Transparencies*

- Place the Large Plane Figures Transparency on the overhead. **Do you see any two figures that appear to have the same size and shape? How can we be sure?** (Measure the sides and angles.) Measure the sides of two shapes that appear to be congruent. Label the shapes with the measurements.

- Continue the activity using the Small Plane Figures Transparency and the Triangle Transparency. **How do we find out if two triangles are congruent?** (Measure the sides and the angles.)

② Develop

Guide students through the *Learn About It* section.

- **When two figures are congruent, their parts should match up. Look at △ABC and △DEF on page 398. What are two ways to find out if these two triangles are congruent?** (Place △*ABC* and △*DEF* on top of one another to see if they match up exactly; measure the sides and angles of each triangle.)

- Discuss *Another Example.* Have students explain why the two squares are *not* congruent.

Guided Practice

Have students complete **Exercises 1–2** as you observe. Remind them to use the *Ask Yourself* questions to help. Give students the opportunity to talk about the question in *Explain Your Thinking.*

Trace each figure. Mark the congruent sides and the congruent angles. *See Additional Answers on Page T86.*

Ask Yourself
• Which sides are the same length?
• Which angles have the same measure?

TEST TIPS

1.

2.

TEST TIPS Explain Your Thinking ▶ Draw three squares on a piece of paper. Can you divide each square differently into four congruent parts? Show your work. *See Additional Answers on Page T86.*

Practice and Problem Solving

Trace each figure. Use a ruler to measure the sides and a protractor to measure the angles of each figure. Mark the congruent sides and angles. 3–5. *See Additional Answers on Page T86.*

3.

4.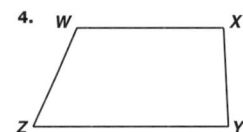

5.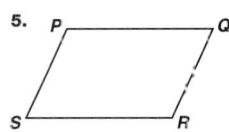

Use the diagram to answer the questions. Explain your reasoning.

6. What is the length of $\overline{DE}$?
   1 in.; $\overline{DE} \cong \overline{AB}$
7. What is the measure of ∠A?
8. What is the measure of ∠F?
   45°; ∠F ≅ ∠C
9. What is the length of $\overline{DF}$?
   1.25 in.; $\overline{DF} \cong \overline{AC}$
10. What is the measure of ∠D?

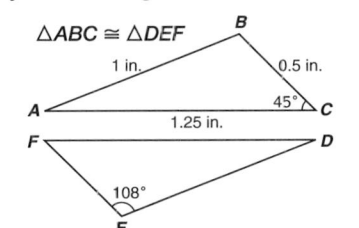
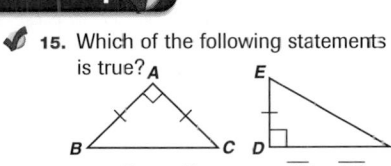

$\triangle ABC \cong \triangle DEF$

| Daily Review | Test Prep |

Find each statistic for the data below.
(Ch. 8, Lesson 2)

90, 75, 80, 80, 80

11. mean **81** 12. range **15**
13. mode **80** 14. median **80**

✏ 15. Which of the following statements is true?

A ∠B ≅ ∠D   C $\overline{EF} \cong \overline{BC}$
B $\overline{AC} \cong \overline{DF}$ (D) ∠A ≅ ∠D

Extra Practice See page 419, Set C.

DAILY TEST PREP

Suppose that △WBA and △HKM are congruent. Write the six congruence statements about angles and sides. (∠W ≅ ∠H, ∠B ≅ ∠K, and ∠A ≅ ∠M; $\overline{WB} \cong \overline{HK}$, $\overline{BA} \cong \overline{KM}$, and $\overline{WA} \cong \overline{HM}$)

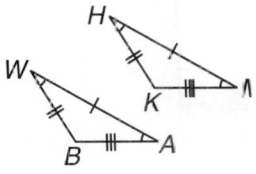

Activity

Or use Intervention CD-ROM Lesson 15.4

Lesson Intervention
Find the Right Correspondence

| 👥 Small Group | ⏱ 5 minutes | Visual, Auditory |

Materials: *blank transparency*

Display the two triangles.

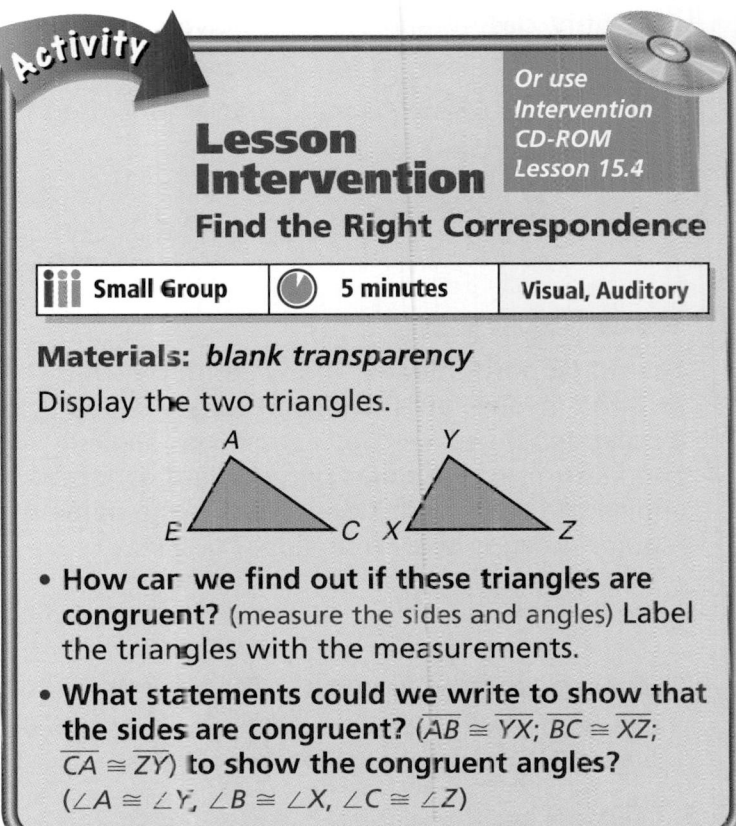

• **How can we find out if these triangles are congruent?** (measure the sides and angles) Label the triangles with the measurements.

• **What statements could we write to show that the sides are congruent?** ($\overline{AB} \cong \overline{YX}$; $\overline{BC} \cong \overline{XZ}$; $\overline{CA} \cong \overline{ZY}$) **to show the congruent angles?** (∠A ≅ ∠Y, ∠B ≅ ∠X, ∠C ≅ ∠Z)

---

3 Practice

Assign **Problems 3–15** as independent work.

• ***Problem Solving for Problems 3–5*** Have students explain their work for each problem.

Common Error

Leaving out congruence marks Students who do not mark corresponding angles with suitable markings may get confused about how pairs of figures match up. Encourage students to mark matching parts as soon as they discover them. They may want to use markers of the same color to indicate matching parts.

4 Assess and Close

• **Can you tell if two figures are congruent just by looking at them?** (you can guess, but to test your guess you need to lay one over the other or measure them.)

• **Which tool would you use to determine if two sides of a figure are congruent?** (ruler) **to determine if two angles are congruent?** (protractor)

Assign the **LESSON QUIZ** on Transparency 15.4 to further assess student understanding.

 **Keeping a Journal**

Have students write a few sentences about objects in the classroom that are congruent. Have students explain how they know these objects are congruent.

Lesson 15.5

Quadrilaterals and Other Polygons

PLANNING THE LESSON

MATHEMATICS OBJECTIVE
Identify, classify, and compare polygons.

Use Lesson Planner CD-ROM for Lesson 15.5.

Daily Routines

Vocabulary

The prefix *poly*– means "many" and the suffix *–gon* means "angles". What do you think a *polygon* is? (a plane figure with many angles)

The features of a *regular polygon* are congruent angles and congruent sides. **What is the name of a regular polygon with four sides?** (a square)

Vocabulary Cards

Meeting North Carolina's Standards

3.01 Identify, define, describe, and accurately represent triangles, quadrilaterals, and other polygons.

Also **3.04**

Problem of the Day
How many squares of all sizes are in the figure at the left? (5) in the figure at the right? (14)

Quick Review
Classify a triangle using the descriptions given for each.
1. all sides the same length (equilateral triangle)
2. has a right angle (right triangle)
3. has one obtuse angle (obtuse triangle)
4. has 40°, 70°, and 70° angles (isosceles, acute)

Lesson Quiz
1. Classify the figure at the right in three ways. (quadrilateral, parallelogram, rhombus)

2. Find the measure of the fourth angle in the figure at the right. (99°) 81°

LEVELED PRACTICE

RETEACH 15.5
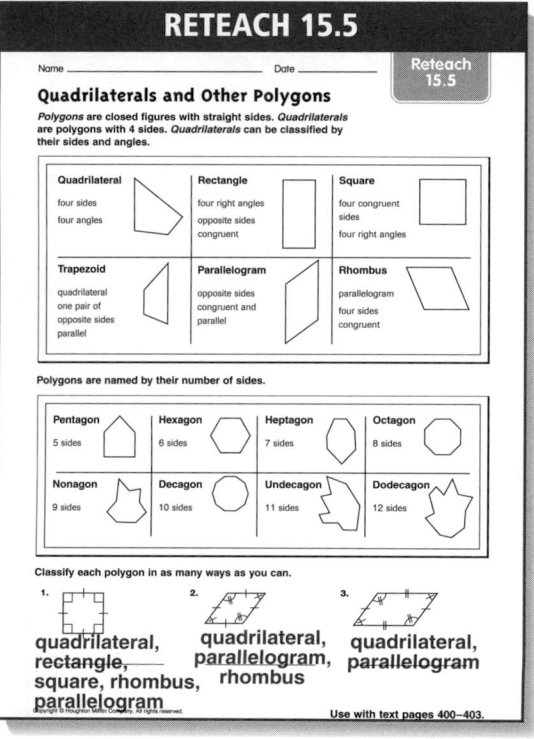

PRACTICE 15.5
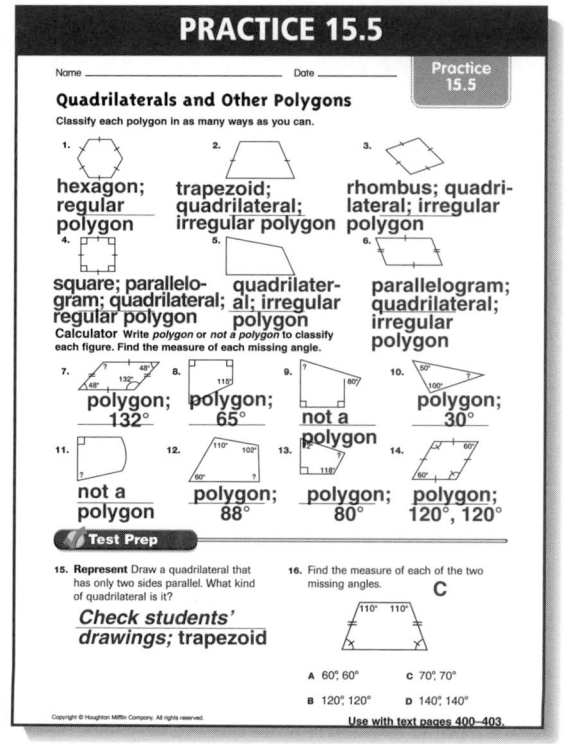

ENRICHMENT 15.5

Root Words

Work in a team of four students. Use a dictionary to explore words that begin with the roots below. Each member of the team should choose one root. List five words and their definitions. Then use each word in a sentence.

Roots
tri-   quad-   penta-   oct-

WORDS WITH ROOT

Word	Definition	Sentence

Share your findings with your group.

1. How is *quadraphonic* sound different than sound produced by the usual two-speaker stereo system?
   Possible answer: **It uses four speakers instead of two.**

2. What kind of athlete is likely to participate in a *pentathlon*?
   Possible answer: **A versatile one, since it requires skill at five sports.**

3. Give three examples of *trisyllabic* words.
   Possible answers: **beautiful, triangle, dedicate.**

Use with text pages 400–403.

Reaching All Learners
Differentiated Instruction

English Learners

Worksheet 15.5 teaches students about the prefixes used to name figures with varying numbers of sides (*tri-, quadri-, penta-,* and so on). Students apply this knowledge by identifying polygons and writing the name of each one.

Inclusion
KINESTHETIC, TACTILE

Materials: *uncooked spaghetti*

• Make a square with 4 pieces of uncooked spaghetti; adjust into a rhombus. **How is a rhombus different than a square?** (rhombus: 4 congruent sides, opposite sides parallel; square: 4 congruent sides, 4 right angles)

• Repeat with other quadrilaterals.

Gifted and Talented
VISUAL, TACTILE

Materials: *index cards*

• Have partners make a pair of cards for each quadrilateral: one card with its name, the other drawn with the figure.

• **Quiz each other, matching the right name with the right figure.**

TECHNOLOGY

Spiral Review

Create **customized** spiral review worksheets for individual students using the *Ways to Assess* CD–ROM.

Lesson Planner

You can use the Lesson Planner CD-ROM to create a report of the lessons and standards you have taught.

eBook

eMathBook allows students to review lessons and do homework without carrying their textbooks home.

Social Studies Connection

Memorial Spaces

Materials: *reference materials, grid paper*

• Have students research and find pictures of memorial sites in Washington, D.C., such as the Lincoln Memorial, the Washington Monument, or the Vietnam Memorial. Point out that the designs for these memorials and the public space around them use many geometric shapes.

• Have students design their own memorial space, labeling the geometric shapes that they use.

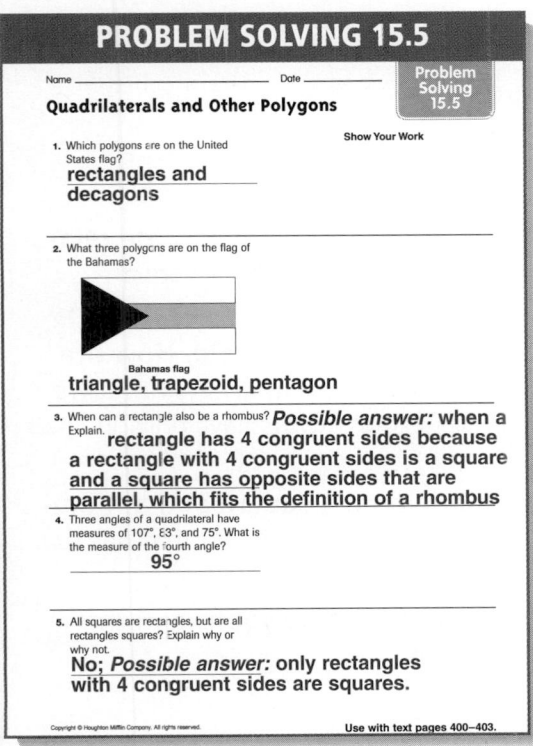

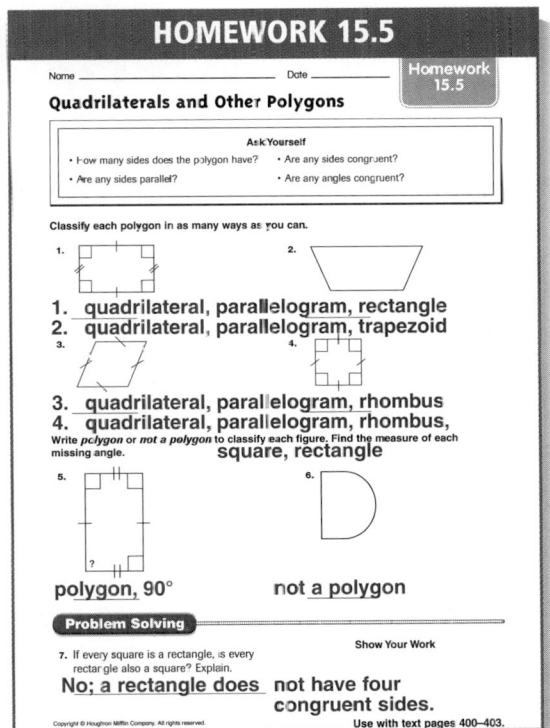

Homework Workbook Page 101

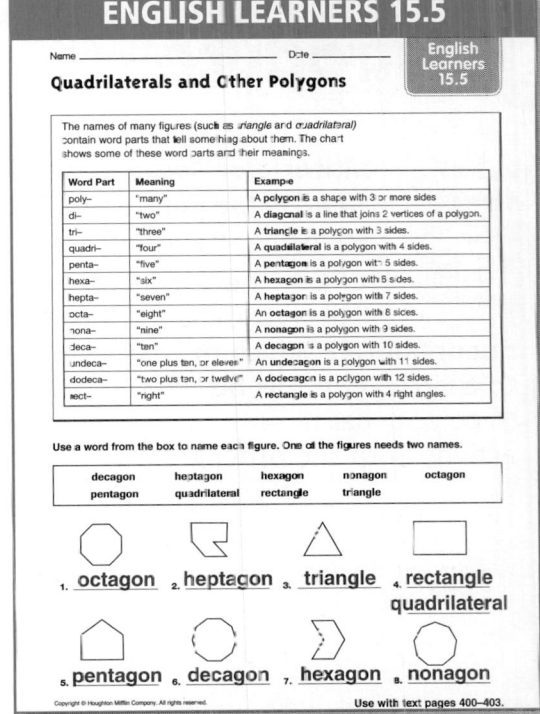

TEACHING LESSON 15.5

LESSON ORGANIZER

Objective Identify, classify, and compare polygons.

Resources Reteach, Practice, Enrichment, Problem Solving, Homework, English Learners, Transparencies, Math Center

Materials Large Plane Figures Transparency, Small Plane Figures Transparency, Quadrilateral Transparency, ruler, grid paper

Warm-Up Activity
Drawing Triangles

Whole Group	5 minutes	Auditory, Tactile

Materials: *grid paper, ruler*

- Have students draw and identify triangles according to your instructions: **There is one right angle and two sides of the triangle are 8 squares long.** (right isosceles triangle.)

- **Draw a triangle with sides that are all unequal in length.** (scalene)

Lesson 5

Quadrilaterals and Other Polygons

Objective Identify, classify, and compare polygons.

Vocabulary: quadrilateral, polygon, regular polygon, diagonal

Learn About It

A **quadrilateral** is a four-sided figure. The sum of the angle measures in any quadrilateral is 360°. In a city you will see many things that are like quadrilaterals.

There are many different kinds of quadrilaterals. You can use sides and angles to classify them.

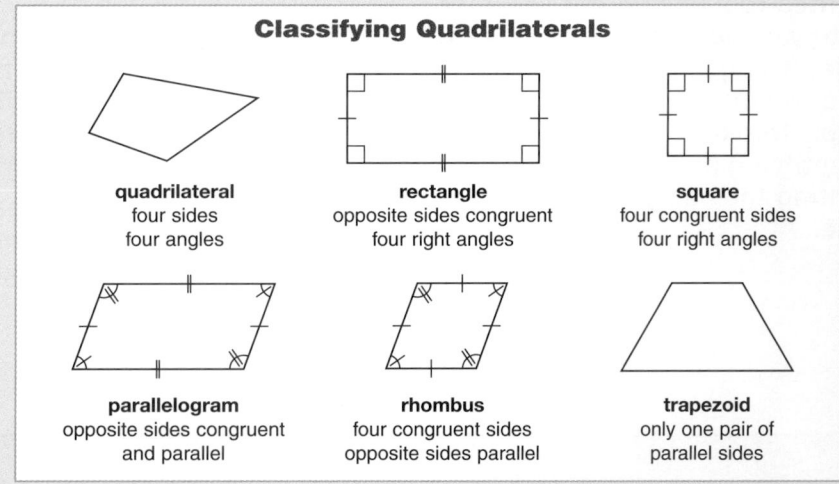

Classifying Quadrilaterals

quadrilateral
four sides
four angles

rectangle
opposite sides congruent
four right angles

square
four congruent sides
four right angles

parallelogram
opposite sides congruent
and parallel

rhombus
four congruent sides
opposite sides parallel

trapezoid
only one pair of
parallel sides

A quadrilateral is one type of **polygon**. A polygon is a closed figure that has three or more sides. Each side is a line segment, and the sides meet only at their endpoints.

Polygons

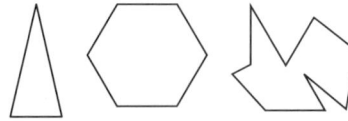

Not Polygons

400

---

1 Introduce

Teaching Transparency for 15.5

Materials: *Large Plane Figures Transparency, Small Plane Figures Transparency, Quadrilateral Transparency, ruler*

- Place the Small Planes Transparency on the overhead. **Which of these figures is a quadrilateral? Which of these figures is a polygon?** Point to a circle. **Can this be classified as a polygon? Why not?** (A polygon has three or more sides or angles.) Continue the activity with the other transparencies.

2 Develop

Guide students through the *Learn About It* section.

- **Look at the square and the rectangle. What is the relationship between rectangles and squares?** (A square is a special kind of rectangle, one that has four congruent sides.)

- **Look at the parallelogram and the trapezoid. How are they alike and different?** (Parallelograms always have two pairs of parallel sides, and trapezoids always have only one pair of parallel sides.)

- **What is the relationship between a square and a rhombus?** (A square is a special kind of rhombus, one that has four right angles.)

- Discuss the difference between the polygons and the figures that are not polygons.

▶ A **regular polygon** is a polygon with all sides congruent and all angles congruent.

Polygons			
Name	**Examples**	**Name**	**Examples**
Triangle 3 sides		**Octagon** 8 sides	
Quadrilateral 4 sides		**Nonagon** 9 sides	
Pentagon 5 sides		**Decagon** 10 sides	
Hexagon 6 sides		**Undecagon** 11 sides	
Heptagon 7 sides		**Dodecagon** 12 sides	

▶ A **diagonal** of a polygon is a segment that joins two vertices of a polygon but is not a side.

$\overline{AD}$ and $\overline{BE}$ are two diagonals of this hexagon.

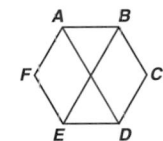

Go On

Chapter 15 Lesson 5   **401**

Quick Check Options

The following activities will help students prepare for the Quick Check or may be used as an alternative assessment.

Vocabulary Review (*individual, small group, or whole class*)

Have students review the following vocabulary words by giving an example of how each term is used in this chapter.

- degrees
- right angle
- acute angle
- obtuse angle
- straight angle
- equilateral
- diagonal
- scalene
- congruent
- quadrilateral
- polygon
- regular polygon
- isosceles

Math Conversations (*small group or whole class*)

Have students discuss what they have learned about identifying and measuring plane figures in this chapter. Encourage students to ask each other questions to clarify their understanding.

Writing Prompt (*individual or partners*)

To solidify student understanding of vocabulary and concepts, have each student complete the following sentence:

The most important thing I have learned about identifying and measuring plane figures is

_____.

• **Look at the chart on page 401.** Ask students to explain the difference between the polygons in the left column of the chart and those in the right column. Help them to read and pronounce the names for all figures.

• Point out the figure at the bottom of the page. **What points are connected by the red line?** (EB) **the blue line?** (AD) **These lines are called diagonals of a polygon because they connect two non-adjacent vertices.**

Guided Practice

Have students complete **Problems 1–3** as you observe. Remind them to use the *Ask Yourself* questions to help. Give students the opportunity to talk about the question in *Explain Your Thinking.*

DAILY TEST PREP

Which statement *cannot* be true of a trapezoid? (D)

A. It has exactly one pair of parallel sides.

B. A trapezoid may have two right angles.

C. The sum of the angle measures is 360°.

D. A trapezoid has two pairs of parallel sides.

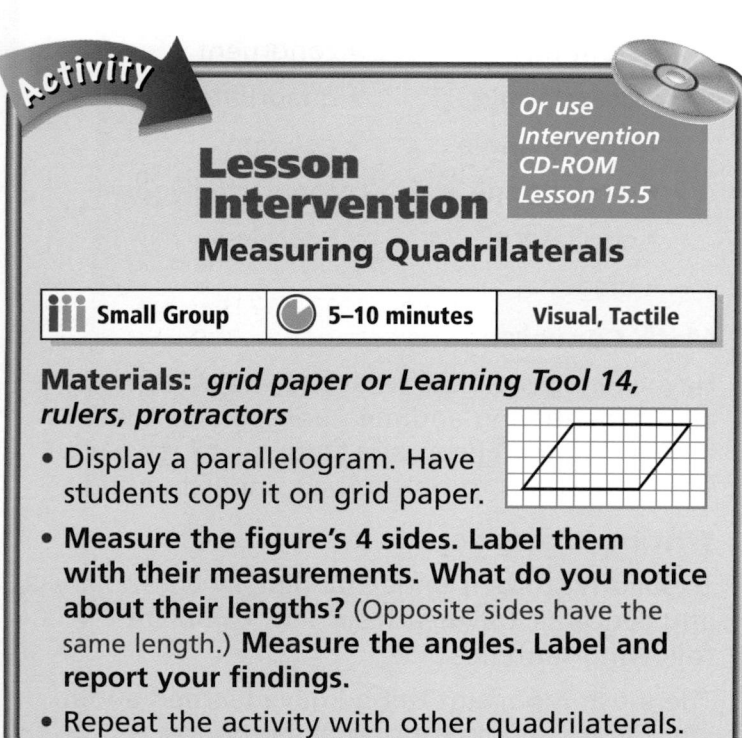

Activity

Lesson Intervention

Or use Intervention CD-ROM Lesson 15.5

Measuring Quadrilaterals

| Small Group | 5–10 minutes | Visual, Tactile |

Materials: *grid paper or Learning Tool 14, rulers, protractors*

• Display a parallelogram. Have students copy it on grid paper.

• **Measure the figure's 4 sides. Label them with their measurements. What do you notice about their lengths?** (Opposite sides have the same length.) **Measure the angles. Label and report your findings.**

• Repeat the activity with other quadrilaterals.

Guided Practice

Classify each polygon in as many ways as you can.
1–3. *See Additional Answers on Page T86.*

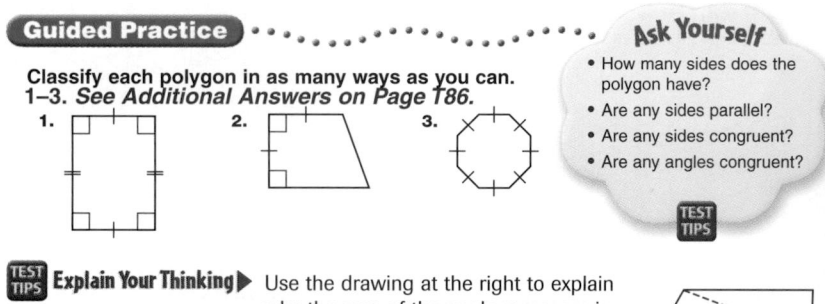

1.   2.   3.

Ask Yourself
• How many sides does the polygon have?
• Are any sides parallel?
• Are any sides congruent?
• Are any angles congruent?

TEST TIPS **Explain Your Thinking ▶** Use the drawing at the right to explain why the sum of the angle measures in a quadrilateral is 360°.

There are 2 triangles, so the sum of the angle measures is 2 × 180°, or 360°.

Practice and Problem Solving

Classify each polygon in as many ways as you can. *See Additional Answers on Page T86.*

 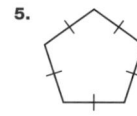 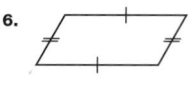 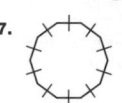

4.   5.   6.   7.

Write *polygon* or *not a polygon* to classify each figure. If possible, find the measure of each missing angle. *See Additional Answers on Page T86.*

8. 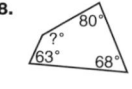   9. 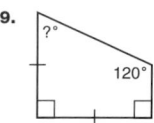   10. 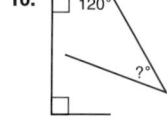   11.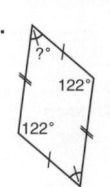

12. 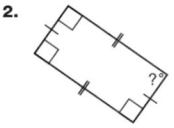   13. 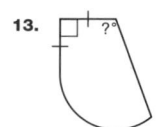   14. 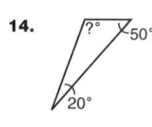   15.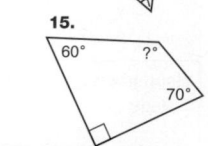

Solve.

16. **Represent** Draw a quadrilateral that is not a parallelogram and has two pairs of congruent sides.
Check students' drawings.

18. **Analyze** Is every square a rhombus? Is every rhombus a square? Explain.
See Additional Answers on Page T86.

Perpendicular: square, rhombus; Congruent: rectangle, square

17. Draw several parallelograms, including special cases—squares, rectangles, and rhombi. For each figure draw the diagonals. In which kind of parallelogram are the diagonals perpendicular? congruent?

402

Extra Practice See page 419, Set D.

---

3 Practice

Assign **Problems 4–18** as independent work.

• *Problem Solving for Problems 4–7* Have students explain their work for each problem.

Common Error

Classification errors Students might think that once they have classified a figure one way, there are no further classifications possible. Explain that often several different classifications are possible.

• Explain why a square can be classified as both a rhombus and a rectangle. (A square is a parallelogram with 4 congruent sides, as is a rhombus. A square is also a parallelogram with 4 right angles, as is a rectangle.)

4 Assess and Close

• **What is a quadrilateral?** (a four-sided figure)

• **What is the difference between a regular pentagon and a pentagon that is not regular?** (A regular pentagon has all congruent sides and all congruent angles. A pentagon that is not regular does not have all sides congruent and all angles congruent.)

Assign the **LESSON QUIZ** on Transparency 15.5 to further assess student understanding.

Quick Check

Check your understanding of Lessons 1–5.

Classify each figure in as many ways as possible. (Lessons 1–2)
See Additional Answers on Pages T86 and T87.

1.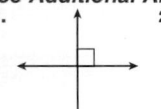
2.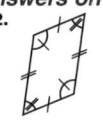
3.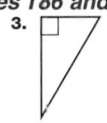
4.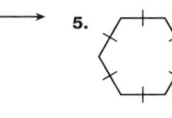
5.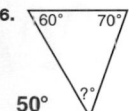

Find the missing angle measures. (Lessons 3–4)

6.
60° 70°
50°

7.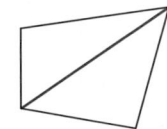
?°
90°

8.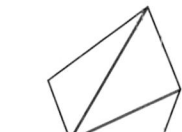
60°
?°
60° 120°

9.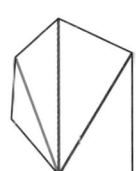
?° 160°
20°

10. Are the figures in Exercises 2 and 8 congruent?
Explain how you know. (Lesson 5) **See Additional Answers on Page T87.**

Sum It Up

These figures show how to use triangles to determine
the sum of the angle measures of a polygon.

Use a table like the one shown to
organize the information above.

1. Use the table to help you write a
   formula for finding the sum of the
   angle measures in any polygon.
   1; 2; 3; 4; $T = (s - 2) \times 180$
2. Use your formula to find the
   number of degrees in an octagon.

Number of Sides	Number of Diagonals Drawn from One Vertex	Sum of Angles	180° × ?
3	0	180°	180° × ▨
4	1	360°	180° × ▨
5	2	540°	180° × ▨
6	3	720°	180° × ▨

Chapter 15 Lesson 5 403

Quick Check

Purpose: The Quick Check allows you to
assess the students' understanding of the
concepts presented in Lessons 1–5.

Items	Objectives Tested	Pages	Intervention
1	Identify and label points, lines, line segments, and rays.	390–391	Reteach Resource 15.1 *Ways to Success* 15.1
3–4	Measure, draw, and classify angles.	392–395	Reteach Resource 15.2 *Ways to Success* 15.2
6, 9	Classify triangles and find missing angle measure.	396–397	Reteach Resource 15.3 *Ways to Success* 15.3
10	Identify congruent figures and congruent parts of figures.	398–399	Reteach Resource 15.4 *Ways to Success* 15.4
2, 5 7–8	Identify, classify, and compare polygons.	400–403	Reteach Resource 15.5 *Ways to Success* 15.5

Keeping a Journal

Have students draw different polygons, label them,
and write a definition for each in their own words.

Sum It Up

The diagrams on page 403 illustrate that polygons can
be subdivided into triangles. This observation is essential
to detecting the pattern in the table on that page. The
number of triangles in each polygon is two less than the
number of sides in the polygon.

Lesson 15.6

Hands-On: Rotations, Reflections, and Translations

PLANNING THE LESSON

MATHEMATICS OBJECTIVE
Identify and model translations, rotations, and reflections.

Use Lesson Planner CD-ROM for Lesson 15.6.

Daily Routines

Vocabulary

What happens when something is *transformed*? (It is changed.) What do you see when you look into a clear pool of water? (a *reflection*) Can you give an example of something that *rotates*? (wheels, the earth) These terms, *transformation, reflection,* and *rotation,* also describe how figures on a plane can be moved to new positions.

Vocabulary Cards

Meeting North Carolina's Standards
Maintain Grade 4 Objective **3.03** Identify, predict, and describe the results of transformations of plane figures.

Lesson Transparency 15.6

Problem of the Day
Suppose that four points lie in a plane and no three of them lie along a line. Using line segments to connect the points, how many angles do these points determine? (12)

Quick Review
Solve the following problems.
1. $\frac{1}{2} \times \frac{2}{3}$ $\left(\frac{1}{3}\right)$
2. $\frac{4}{5} \times \frac{5}{8}$ $\left(\frac{1}{2}\right)$
3. $\frac{9}{16} \times \frac{4}{27}$ $\left(\frac{1}{12}\right)$
4. $\frac{7}{21} \times \frac{4}{20}$ $\left(\frac{1}{15}\right)$
5. $\frac{7}{10} \times 100$ (70)
6. $0 \times \frac{1}{3}$ (0)

Lesson Quiz
1. Identify the transformation of the triangle. (reflection)

2. Copy the figure. Translate it 4 units right and 2 units down.

LEVELED PRACTICE

RETEACH 15.6
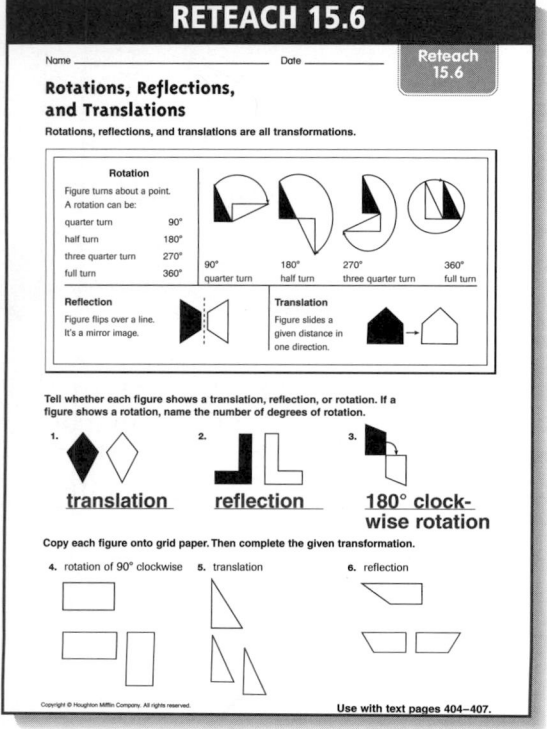

PRACTICE 15.6
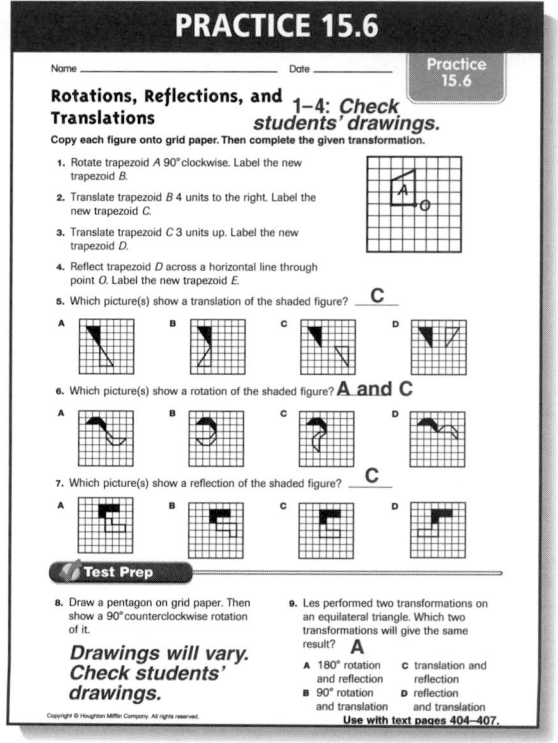

Practice Workbook Page 102

ENRICHMENT 15.6
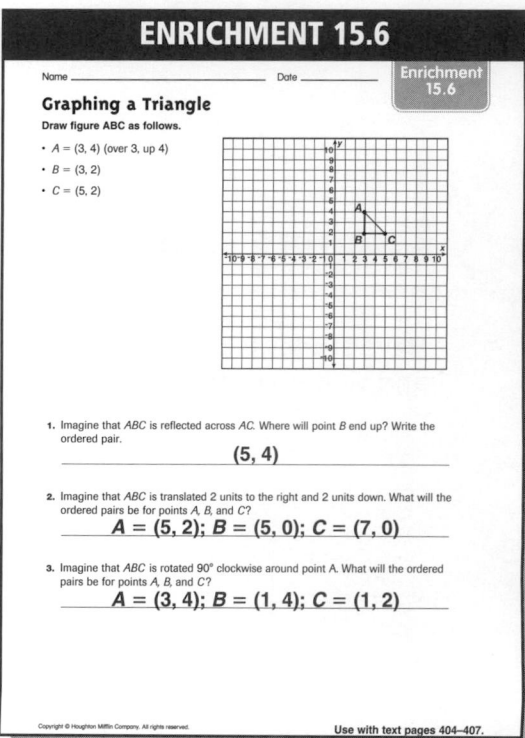

Reaching All Learners

Differentiated Instruction

English Learners

Worksheet 15.6 explores the meanings of the terms *transformation, reflection, rotation, translation, clockwise,* and *counterclockwise.* Students use the terms to complete sentences about the transformation of geometric figures.

Special Needs
AUDITORY, KINESTHETIC

- Have students model the following moves. Explain the connections to geometry.
- Turning the blindfolded person in pin-the-tail-on-the-donkey; *rotation.* Baseball player sliding into base; *translation.*
- Explain *reflection.* Ask students to find an example in movement and demonstrate.

Early Finishers
VISUAL, KINESTHETIC

Materials: *grid paper, Learning Tool 14*

- Have students draw a figure on grid paper. Underneath their figures, have them write the name of a transformation.
- Have students exchange papers with a partner and challenge one another to carry out the transformations.

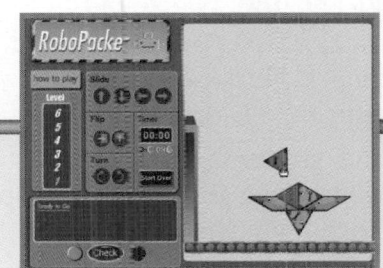

TECHNOLOGY

Spiral Review

Using the *Ways to Assess* CD–ROM, you can create **customized** spiral review worksheets covering any lessons you choose.

Manipulatives

eManipulatives are available on the *Ways to Success* CD.

Game

Students can practice their skills using the RoboPacker math game, available on the *Ways to Success* CD.

Music Connection

Marching Bands
Materials: *grid paper or Learning Tool 14*

- Have small groups form marching bands, creating a pattern of movements using reflections or translation that they then will try out. Give students these symbols to represent their movements.

↑*x* steps north →*x* steps east
↓*x* steps south ←*x* steps west

- Afterwards, have groups talk about the kinds of moves they made.

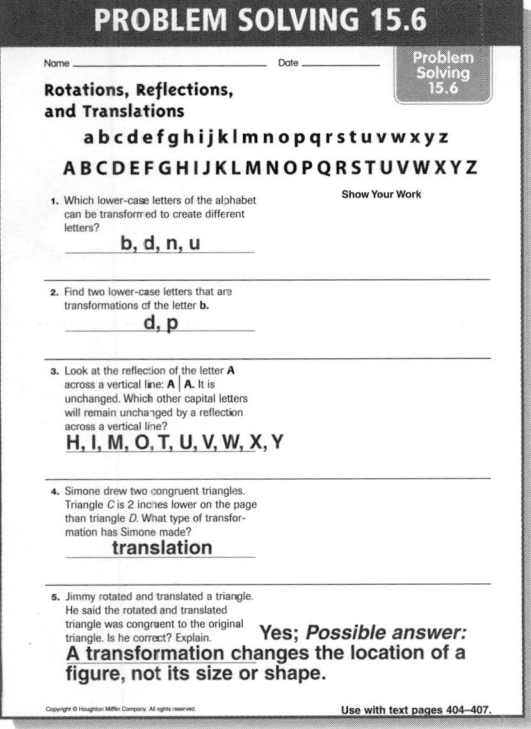

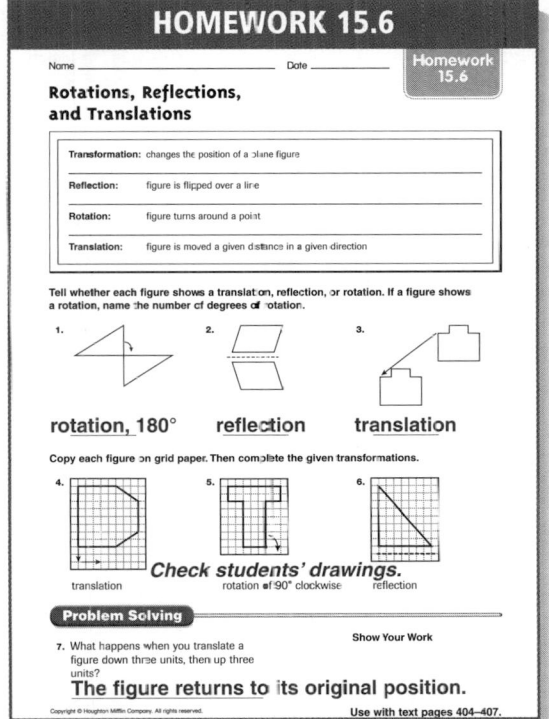

PROBLEM SOLVING 15.6

Rotations, Reflections, and Translations

abcdefghijklmnopqrstuvwxyz
ABCDEFGHIJKLMNOPQRSTUVWXYZ

1. Which lower-case letters of the alphabet can be transformed to create different letters?
   b, d, n, u

2. Find two lower-case letters that are transformations of the letter b.
   d, p

3. Look at the reflection of the letter A across a vertical line: A | A. It is unchanged. Which other capital letters will remain unchanged by a reflection across a vertical line?
   H, I, M, O, T, U, V, W, X, Y

4. Simone drew two congruent triangles. Triangle C is 2 inches lower on the page than triangle D. What type of transformation has Simone made?
   translation

5. Jimmy rotated and translated a triangle. He said the rotated and translated triangle was congruent to the original triangle. Is he correct? Explain.
   Yes; Possible answer: A transformation changes the location of a figure, not its size or shape.

HOMEWORK 15.6

Rotations, Reflections, and Translations

Transformation:	changes the position of a plane figure
Reflection:	figure is flipped over a line
Rotation:	figure turns around a point
Translation:	figure is moved a given distance in a given direction

Tell whether each figure shows a translation, reflection, or rotation. If a figure shows a rotation, name the number of degrees of rotation.

1. **rotation, 180°**   2. **reflection**   3. **translation**

Copy each figure on grid paper. Then complete the given transformations.

Check students' drawings.
4. translation   5. rotation of 90° clockwise   6. reflection

Problem Solving

7. What happens when you translate a figure down three units, then up three units?
   The figure returns to its original position.

Homework Workbook Page 102

ENGLISH LEARNERS 15.6

Rotations, Reflections, and Translations

The prefix *trans-* means "change." To *transform* something is to change its form or shape. The suffix *-tion* can change a verb to a noun. For example, the verb *transform* becomes the noun *transformation,* which means "a change in form or shape."

trans + form = transform
transform + ation = transformation

Transformation adds an between the word *transform* and the suffix *-tion.* Other verbs drop a letter when they add *-tion.*

Verb	Meaning	Noun	Meaning
reflect	"to flip over, forming a mirror image"	reflection	"the act of reflecting"
rotate	"to turn around a fixed point; to spin"	rotation	"the act of rotating"
translate	"to move from one place to another"	translation	"the act of translating"

The suffix *-wise* means "in this direction." The prefix *counter-* means "opposite."
clock + wise = clockwise ("in the same direction as a clock's hands move")
counter + clock + wise = counterclockwise ("in the opposite direction from the way a clock's hands move")

Complete each sentence by writing the correct word.

1. If you **rotate** (rotate, rotation) this square, the square will turn around a fixed point.

2. Steve performed a **reflection** (reflect, reflection) on his trapezoid, creating a backwards image of it.

3. I will **translate** (translate, translation) my polygon by moving it 4 cm to the left.

4. Carmen rotated her triangle in a **clockwise** (clockwise, counterclockwise) direction, the same direction a clock's hands move.

5. Reflection, rotation, and translation are all kinds of **transformation** (transform, transformation) because they change figures.

TEACHING LESSON 15.6

LESSON ORGANIZER

Objective Identify and model translations, rotations, and reflections.

Resources Reteach, Practice, Enrichment, Problem Solving, Homework, English Learners, Transparencies, Math Center

Materials Grid paper or Learning Tool 14, rulers, Centimeter Grid Transparency, paint, paintbrushes, large paper, paper clips, Learning Tool 52

Activity

Warm-Up Activity
Transform Triangles

⫲ Whole Group	⏱ 5 minutes	Auditory, Tactile

Materials: *grid paper or Learning Tool 14, rulers*

n blocks tall

m blocks long

- Display:
  Height: 12, 14, or 16;
  Base: 10, 11, or 13.

- Have students draw a right triangle on grid paper. Have them choose the height and width from the numbers on the board.

- Have students cut out their triangles. **See if you can find someone whose triangle matches yours. What moves of the figures did you have to make to see if your triangle matches someone else's?**

Rotations, Reflections, and Translations

Objective Identify and model translations, rotations, and reflections.

e Glossary
Vocabulary
transformation
reflection
rotation
translation

Materials
grid paper
ruler

Work Together  MathTracks 2/10 Listen and Understand

A **transformation** changes the position, but not the shape, of a plane figure. Reflections, rotations, and translations are three kinds of transformations.

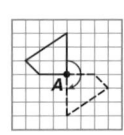

reflection
figure flips over a line

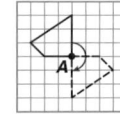

rotation
figure turns about a point

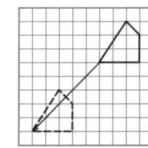

translation
figure slides a given distance in a given direction

You can describe a rotation using the 360° of a circle.

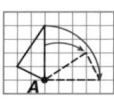

90°
a quarter turn
clockwise about point *A*

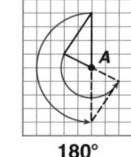

180°
a half turn
counterclockwise
about point *A*

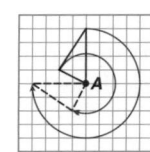

270°
a three-quarter turn
clockwise about point *A*

Work with a partner to model transformations.

STEP 1	Use a ruler to draw a right triangle on grid paper. Shade and cut out the triangle.	

STEP 2	Outline the cut-out triangle on a new sheet of grid paper. Label the triangle with *A*. Then draw and label point *O* on the grid paper as shown.	

---

1 Introduce

Materials: *Centimeter Grid Transparency, black and red erasable markers*

- On the transparency, outline a simple polygon. Put dots at the vertices. Draw a dashed line to show the line of reflection.

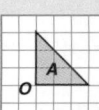

- **Where do you think point *A* will go if it is reflected across the dashed line?** (3 units to the right of the dashed line and 2 units down from the top)

- Repeat the activity for points *B* and *C*.

- **What does the resulting figure look like?** (a mirror reflection of the original)

2 Develop

Guide students through the *Work Together* section.

- Check that students follow Steps 1 and 2 correctly. Have them compare their work with the diagrams on page 404.

STEP 3 Rotate triangle A a half turn counterclockwise about point O. Outline the triangle. Label the triangle with B.

- What transformation did you perform? **rotation**
- How many degrees did you rotate the triangle? **180°**

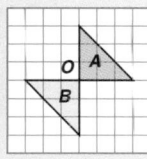

STEP 4 Now reflect triangle B across a vertical line through point O. Outline the triangle. Label the triangle with C.

- What transformation did you perform? **reflection**

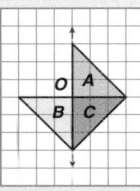

STEP 5 Rotate triangle C a half turn clockwise about point O as shown. Outline the triangle. Label the triangle with D.

- Is triangle D congruent to triangle A? **yes** Use a transformation to find out.
- Show another way to use reflections, rotations, or translations to transform triangle A into triangle D. **Reflect triangle A over the vertical line.**

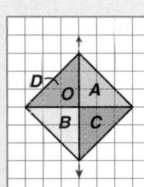

On Your Own

Tell whether each figure shows a translation, reflection, or rotation. If a figure shows a rotation, name the number of degrees of rotation.

1.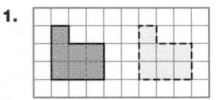
translation

2.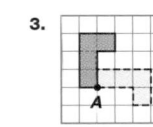
reflection

3.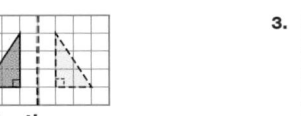
rotation; 90° clockwise or 270° counterclockwise

Copy each figure onto grid paper. Then complete the given transformation. *See Additional Answers on Page T87.*

4.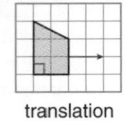
translation

5.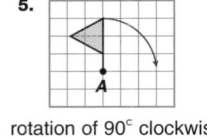
rotation of 90° clockwise

6.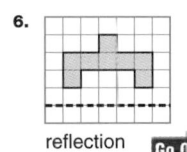
reflection

Technology Connection
Explore Symmetry with Technology

In this activity, students use Shape Up! software to test the rotational symmetry of various shapes.

Have students follow the directions below.

- Dump 2 buckets of shapes in **Pattern Block World**. Separate the shapes. Use the **Magnet** to put the same shapes directly on top of one another.
- Click the **z-Axis Rotation** button. Turn each top shape to test for rotational symmetry. Each click turns the shape 30°.

Have students answer the questions below.

1. Which shapes have rotational symmetry? How many degrees did you have to turn each of these shapes?

2. What types of shapes have rotational symmetry and what types do not? Test in other Shape Up! worlds.

---

③ Practice

Assign **Problems 1–16** of *On Your Own* as independent work.

- After completing Step 3, ask students to compare the original figure to the figure that results from the rotation. Students should see that the vertices after rotation are the same distance from O as they were before. On separate paper, have students perform the 180° clockwise rotation.

- In Step 4, point out that the figure has been transformed twice.

- In Step 5, have students examine the four triangles they see on their grid paper. **How are these triangles related?** (The transformations did not change size or shape. The triangles are congruent.)

DAILY TEST PREP

Trapezoid *KLMN* is reflected in line *c*. Which of the reflected figure's points will be closest to line *c*? (*N*)

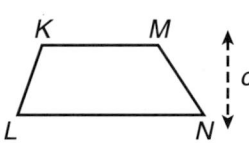

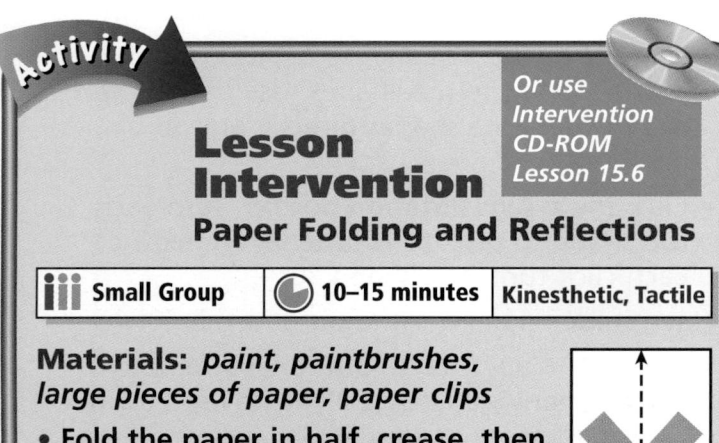

Activity

Lesson Intervention

Or use Intervention CD-ROM Lesson 15.6

Paper Folding and Reflections

| 👥 Small Group | ⏱ 10–15 minutes | Kinesthetic, Tactile |

Materials: *paint, paintbrushes, large pieces of paper, paper clips*

• **Fold the paper in half, crease, then open. Paint a quadrilateral on one side. Before the paint can dry, close at the crease, press, then open. You just printed a mirror reflection of the original.**

• **Take 2 fresh sheets of paper. Draw a figure on one, cut it out, and place it on the other sheet. Now stick the tip of an open paper clip through a vertex of the cutout, and the paper underneath.** Show students different ways to rotate the figure.

• **How are these transformations different?**

On grid paper, copy triangle *A*. Label point *O*. Draw and label the figure in each new position for Exercises 7–11. *See Additional Answers on Page T87.*

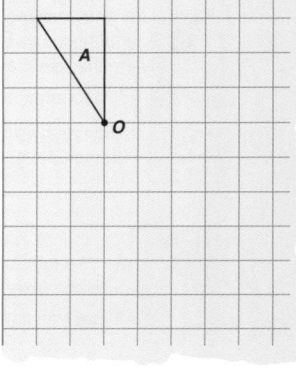

7. Translate triangle *A* 2 units to the right. Label the new triangle *B*.

8. Translate triangle *A* 5 units down. Label the new triangle *C*.

9. Rotate triangle *A* 90° counterclockwise about point *O*. Label the new triangle *D*.

10. Reflect triangle D across a vertical line through point *O*. Label the new triangle *E*.

11. What one transformation can be used to move triangle *A* to the position shown by triangle *E*?

12. Which picture shows a reflection of the shaded figure?

a. 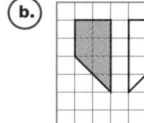 (b.) 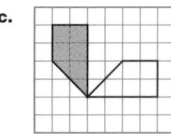 c. 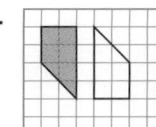 d.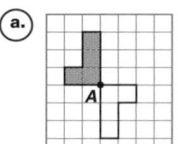

13. Which picture shows a rotation of the shaded figure?

(a.) 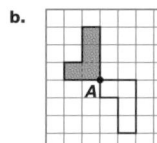 b. 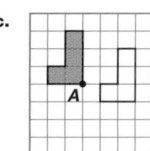 c. 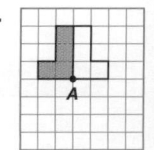 d.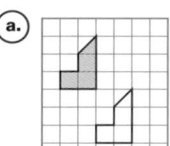

14. Which picture shows a translation of the shaded figure?

(a.) 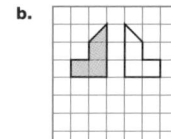 b. 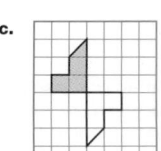 c. 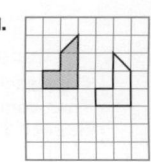 d.

Donya is not correct. *Check students' drawings.*

15. **Represent** Donya says that reflecting a right triangle across its base is the same as rotating it 180° about its right angle. Is she right? Draw a diagram to explain. ***See above.***

16. **Create and Solve** Draw a design on grid paper. Write steps to change the design using rotations, reflections, and translations. Draw the solution. ***Check designs, solutions, and drawings.***

406

Practice *continued*

• *Problem Solving for Problems 15–16* Have students explain their work for each problem.

4 Assess and Close

Assign **Exercises 17 and 18** of the *Talk About It • Write About It* section. Have volunteers explain their work.

• **Suppose you have congruent figures mirroring each other on either side of a line. What kind of transformation is that?** (reflection)

• **Suppose you have two congruent irregular polygons a given distance from each other, facing in the same direction. What kind of transformation is that?** (translation)

• **Suppose you have congruent figures having one common vertex, facing opposite directions, and flipped. What kind of transformation is that?** (rotation)

Assign the **LESSON QUIZ** on Transparency 15.6 to further assess student understanding.

You learned how to identify and model reflections, rotations, and translations. *See Additional Answers on Page T87.*

17. Explain how reflections and rotations are alike and different. Use words or a diagram.

18. Explain how rotations, reflections, and translations can help you decide if two figures are congruent.

Tangrams

2 players

What You'll Need • Learning Tool 52 or a set of tangram pieces like the ones shown.

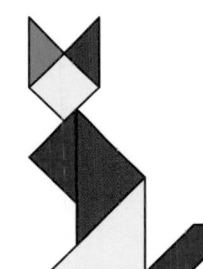

How to Play

1 If you don't have tangrams or Learning Tool 9, you can make your own pieces by tracing the ones on this page and cutting them out.

2 The first player makes a shape with the tangram pieces and traces its outline. The pieces should not overlap. At least some of them should be placed edge to edge.

3 The pieces are removed and mixed up. The second player must decide how to arrange the pieces within the outline, without any overlapping pieces.

4 Take turns repeating Steps 2 and 3.

You may want to make a sketch of your design to help you remember it if your partner can't solve the puzzle.

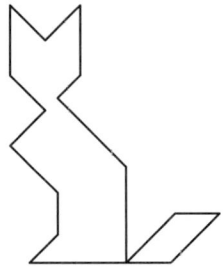

Chapter 15 Lesson 6 407

Tangrams

Materials: *Learning Tool 52 or a set of tangram pieces like the ones shown on page 407*

• Before starting the game, have students experiment with a few of the tangram pieces such as the two large isosceles right triangles.

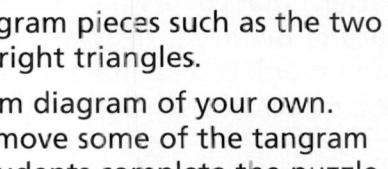

• Make a tangram diagram of your own. Trace it and remove some of the tangram pieces. Have students complete the puzzle using the rest of the pieces. After this preparation, have students play the game.

• Have students play the game, using only some of the tangram pieces. The other player will need to find out which pieces were not used.

Keeping a Journal

Have students define the terms *rotation, translation,* and *reflection* and draw a picture to illustrate each definition.

Lesson 15.7

Problem-Solving Strategy: Make a Model

PLANNING THE LESSON

MATHEMATICS OBJECTIVE
Make models to solve tessellation problems.

Use Lesson Planner CD-ROM for Lesson 15.7.

Daily Routines

Vocabulary

In geometry, a *tessellation* is a repeating pattern that covers a plane without any gaps or overlaps. *Tessellation* comes from a Latin word, tesella, for a small square stone, or a small cube of stone.

Vocabulary Cards

Meeting North Carolina's Standards

5.01 Describe, extend, and generalize numeric and geometric patterns using tables, Graphs, words, and symbols.

Lesson Transparency 15.7

Problem of the Day
How many dots would appear in the twentieth diagram in this geometric pattern? (96)

Diagram 1   Diagram 2   Diagram 3

Quick Review
Write each percent as a fraction in simplest form.
1. 60% ($\frac{3}{5}$)
2. 1% ($\frac{1}{100}$)
3. 10% ($\frac{1}{10}$)
4. 43% ($\frac{43}{100}$)
5. 11% ($\frac{11}{100}$)
6. 100% (1)

Lesson Quiz
Solve:

Will an equilateral triangle tessellate? Explain. (Yes, when translated, the congruent triangles will fit together without leaving any gaps.)

LEVELED PRACTICE

RETEACH 15.7

Name _____ Date _____

Reteach 15.7

Problem-Solving Strategy: Make a Model

Read It Look for information.
Mrs. Takacs is looking for a tessellation pattern for her kitchen. She would like to use a regular hexagon. Will a regular hexagon tessellate?

Picture It Here is a model of the information.
Use what you know about transformations to solve the problem.

Solve It Use the model to solve the problem.
A tessellation is a repeating pattern of closed figures that covers a surface with no gaps and no overlaps.

Regular hexagons tessellate.

Try This! Solve.

Show Your Work

1. Will a pattern of right triangles and squares tessellate?
   Yes; Right triangles and squares will fit together.

2. Make a set of quadrilaterals that are all the same size and same shape. Will your quadrilaterals tessellate?
   Yes; Check students' models.

Copyright © Houghton Mifflin Company. All rights reserved.   **Use with text pages 408–411.**

PRACTICE 15.7

Name _____ Date _____

Practice 15.7

Problem-Solving Strategy: Make a Model

Make a model to solve each problem.

Show Your Work

1. Copy the figure, and then draw it several times. Will this figure tessellate? Explain.
   The L-shaped figure will tesselate, because it leaves no gaps in the pattern.

2. Copy the figure, and then draw it several times. Will this figure tessellate? Explain.
   The triangle will tessellate, because it leaves no gaps in the pattern.

3. Copy the figure, and then draw it several times. Explain why this figure will not tessellate.
   The octagon will not tessellate, because it leaves gaps as the pattern is formed.

4. What is the shape of the space that is left when you try to tessellate the figures in Problem 3?
   a square

5. Give an example of a figure that will not tesselate. Explain.
   A circle will not tessellate, because it leaves gaps as the pattern is formed.

Copyright © Houghton Mifflin Company. All rights reserved.   **Use with text pages 408–411.**

ENRICHMENT 15.7

Name _____ Date _____

Enrichment 15.7

Tessellations in Art

Research the art of M. C. Escher. Find an example of tessellation in his work. Write the name of the print and describe it in your own words.

_____
_____
_____
_____
_____

1. Use tracing paper to trace the Escher print you chose. Is it a true tessellation? How can you tell?
   Possible answer: I found that the figure is a true tessellation. The same shape is used over and over again to cover a plane.

2. Trace one of the figures from the Escher print you chose. Use the traced figure as a model and cut out ten congruent figures from construction paper. Use your figures to make your own tessellation. Paste it on a separate sheet of paper.
   Tessellations will vary.

3. Design an animal or flower shape that can tessellate. Cut out multiples of your shape from construction paper. Paste them in a tessellating design on a separate sheet of paper.
   Tessellations will vary.

Copyright © Houghton Mifflin Company. All rights reserved.   **Use with text pages 408–411.**

Practice Workbook Page 103

408A   CHAPTER 15   Lesson 7

Reaching All Learners
Differentiated Instruction

English Learners

Worksheet 15.7 uses visuals and text to clarify the meanings of terms associated with tesselation. The idea that tiles may tesselate only if the sum of the angles that come together is exactly 360° is also illustrated.

Special Needs
KINESTHETIC, TACTILE

Materials: *round counters, square tiles*

- Lay several counters on a table so they touch. Does the surface show between them? (yes)
- Repeat with tiles. Does the surface show? (no) Color the tiles in a pattern. You made a *tessellation*, a repeating pattern that fully covers a plane.

Gifted and Talented
VISUAL, TACTILE

Materials: *grid paper or learning Tool 14*

- Challenge students to experiment with different quadrilaterals and polygons to create tessellations. Have them exchange papers and talk about the shapes that tessellated successfully.

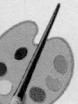

Art Connection
Geodesic Domes
Materials: *reference materials*

- page 388 shows a picture of a geodesic dome
- Have students research the work of R. Buckminster Fuller, the 20th-century thinker who designed and built the first geodesic dome. Have students find photographs or illustrations of these domes. Have them discuss Fuller's use of tessellation in architecture.

- Challenge students to design a building using tessellation. Make a display of their designs called *Tessellation in Architecture and Design.*

TECHNOLOGY

Spiral Review

To reinforce skills on lessons taught earlier, create **customized** spiral review worksheets using the *Ways to Assess* CD-ROM.

Lesson Planner

You can customize your teaching plan to meet your curriculum requirements with the Lesson Planner CD-ROM.

Education Place

Reccomend that parents visit Education Place at eduplace.com/parents/mw/ for parent support activies.

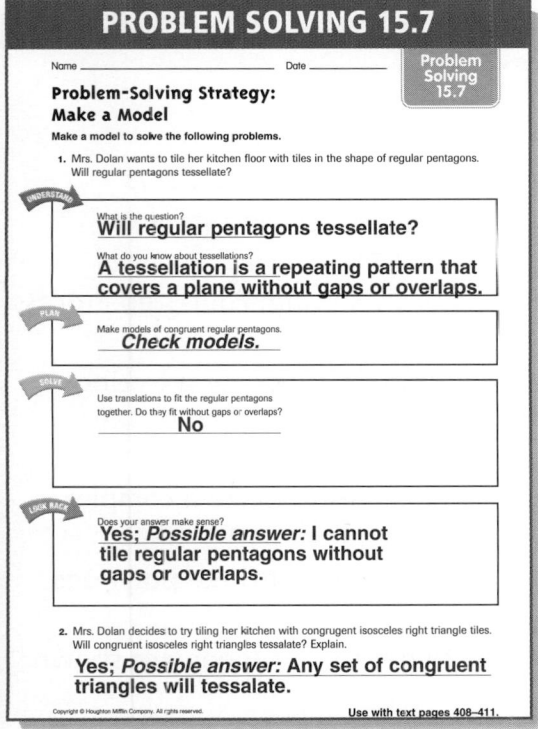

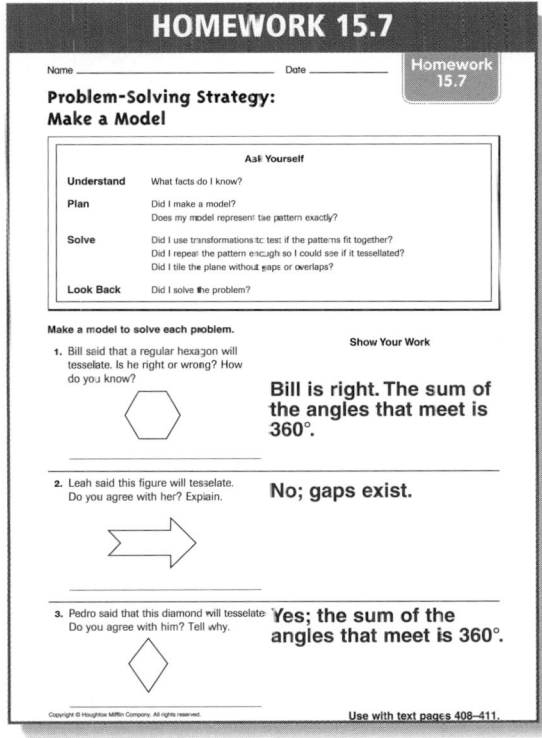

Homework Workbook Page 103

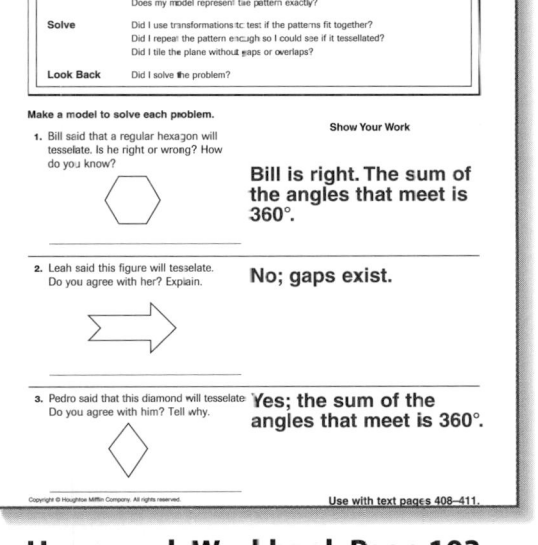

TEACHING LESSON 15.7

LESSON ORGANIZER

Objective Make models to solve tessellation problems.

Resources Reteach, Practice, Enrichment, Problem Solving, Homework, English Learners, Transparencies, Math Center

Materials Pattern blocks or tracing paper and scissors, grid paper or Learning Tool 14, Problem Solving: Four-Step Process Transparency

Activity

Warm-Up Activity
Translate, Rotate, and Draw

| 👤👤👤👤 Whole Group | 🕐 5 minutes | Auditory, Tactile |

- **What would you do to translate a square 3 inches to the right?** (Move the square so that each vertex is 3 inches to the right of where it was.)

- **How would you rotate a square 180° around its center?** (Pivot the square about the center until the upper left vertex is at the lower right.)

- **How do you draw a trapezoid?** (Draw two horizontal line segments parallel to one another but different in length and connect the two left endpoints and the two right endpoints.)

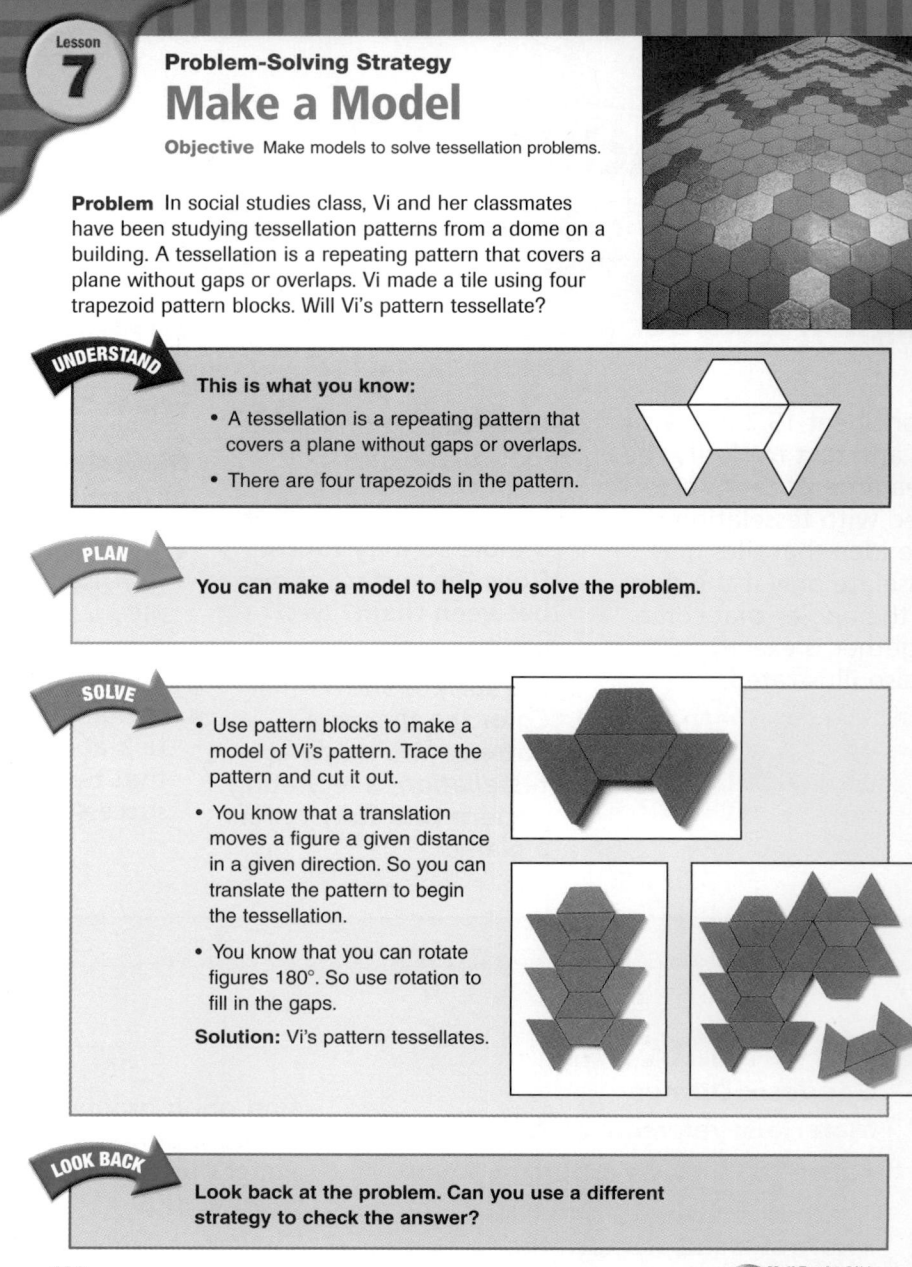

Lesson 7
Problem-Solving Strategy
Make a Model
Objective Make models to solve tessellation problems.

Problem In social studies class, Vi and her classmates have been studying tessellation patterns from a dome on a building. A tessellation is a repeating pattern that covers a plane without gaps or overlaps. Vi made a tile using four trapezoid pattern blocks. Will Vi's pattern tessellate?

UNDERSTAND

This is what you know:
- A tessellation is a repeating pattern that covers a plane without gaps or overlaps.
- There are four trapezoids in the pattern.

PLAN

You can make a model to help you solve the problem.

SOLVE

- Use pattern blocks to make a model of Vi's pattern. Trace the pattern and cut it out.
- You know that a translation moves a figure a given distance in a given direction. So you can translate the pattern to begin the tessellation.
- You know that you can rotate figures 180°. So use rotation to fill in the gaps.

Solution: Vi's pattern tessellates.

LOOK BACK

Look back at the problem. Can you use a different strategy to check the answer?

408

MathTracks 2/11
Listen and Understand

1️⃣ Introduce

Have a student read the definition of *tessellation* out loud in class.

- Focus student attention on the illustrations on page 408. **The second diagram shows a *tessellation*.**

- **What is happening in the third illustration on page 408?** (A new piece is fit into a tessellation in progress.)

2️⃣ Develop

Materials: *pattern blocks or tracing paper, scissors*

Guide students through the problem-solving steps on page 408.

You may wish to use the Problem Solving: Four-Step Process Transparency

- Model the trapezoid using pattern blocks or a tracing cut-out. Students should have multiple copies of the trapezoid.

- Put together two of the trapezoids to make a complex polygon. Have students compare their polygons.

- **What figures do you get when you put three polygons together? four?**

- Rearrange the trapezoids to get the arrangement shown on page 408.

- **Can you confirm Vi's conclusion?** (yes)

Guided Practice

Use the Ask Yourself questions to help you solve each problem.

1. Hamid cut a small square from one side of a large square and translated it to the other side of the square. Will Hamid's pattern tessellate? **yes**

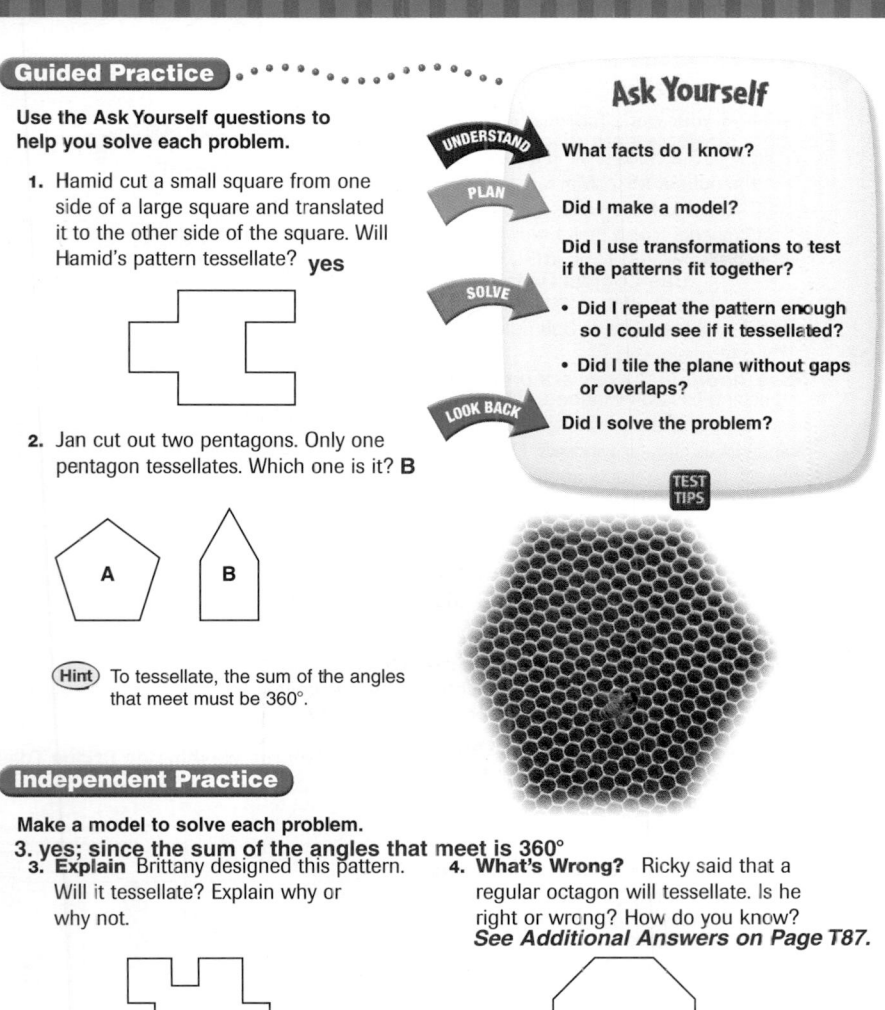

Ask Yourself

UNDERSTAND What facts do I know?

PLAN Did I make a model?

Did I use transformations to test if the patterns fit together?

SOLVE • Did I repeat the pattern enough so I could see if it tessellated?

• Did I tile the plane without gaps or overlaps?

LOOK BACK Did I solve the problem?

TEST TIPS

2. Jan cut out two pentagons. Only one pentagon tessellates. Which one is it? **B**

A   B

(Hint) To tessellate, the sum of the angles that meet must be 360°.

Independent Practice

Make a model to solve each problem.
3. yes; since the sum of the angles that meet is 360°

3. **Explain** Brittany designed this pattern. Will it tessellate? Explain why or why not.

4. **What's Wrong?** Ricky said that a regular octagon will tessellate. Is he right or wrong? How do you know? *See Additional Answers on Page T87.*

5. **Create and Solve** Start with a rectangle. Create a pattern that will tessellate. Then create a different pattern that will not tessellate. Trade patterns with a classmate. Then tell which of the two patterns will tessellate. *Check students' drawings.*

Go On

Chapter 15 Lesson 7 409

ACHIEVING
Mathematical Proficiency

Developing Geometric Sense

One way to help students develop geometric sense is to teach **informal geometry**. Rather than focusing solely on exercises or memorization of rules and algorithms, instruction should be **enjoyable at the same time that it is informative.** Instruction that does not "feel" like instruction accomplishes the most.

Students should have access to a variety of materials. It is easier to understand the concept of properties through manipulating physical objects rather than comparing static images on a page. When students have the opportunity to explore, visually and otherwise, they begin to understand the concept of space and the role of objects in it.

By developing an informal sense of geometry, students also **develop problem-solving skills that pave the way for success in other areas of math.**

---

3 Practice

Guided Practice

Have students complete **Exercises 1–2** as you observe. Remind them to use the *Ask Yourself* questions to help.

Assign **Exercises 3–5** as independent work. Have students share and discuss their work.

Problem Solving Reminders

Have students review their answers to make sure they have done the following:

• expressed the solution clearly

• used appropriate mathematical notation and terms

• supported their solution with verbal and symbolic work

• determined the reasonableness of the solution in the context of the original problem.

DAILY TEST PREP

The corner of a rectangle is cut off as shown. Will the resulting figure tessellate? How do you know? (No; tracing, making copies, and trying to put copies together so there is no overlap or gap will not work.)

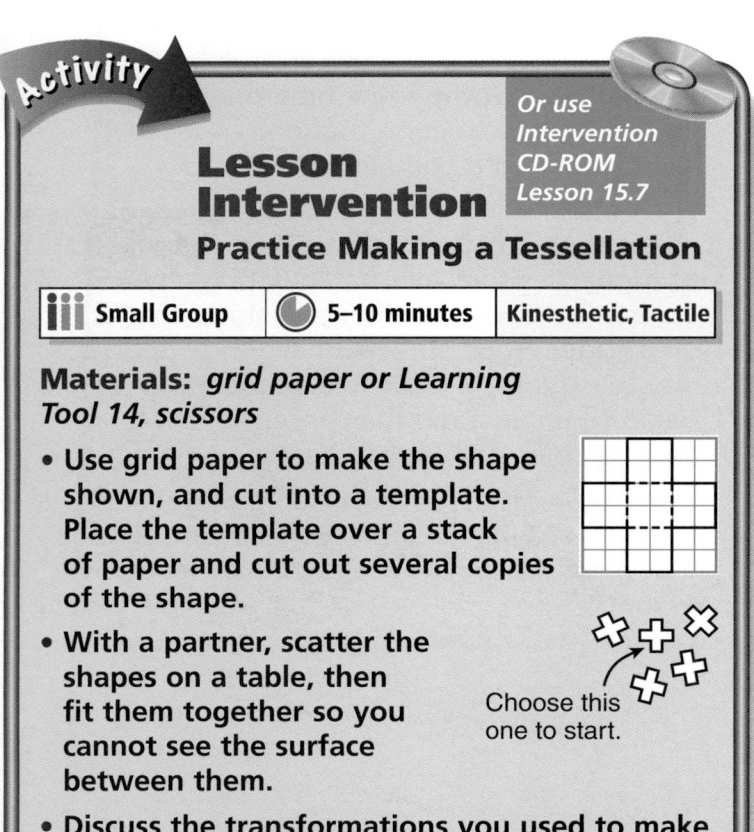

Activity

Lesson Intervention

Or use Intervention CD-ROM Lesson 15.7

Practice Making a Tessellation

| 👥 Small Group | 🕐 5–10 minutes | Kinesthetic, Tactile |

Materials: *grid paper or Learning Tool 14, scissors*

- Use grid paper to make the shape shown, and cut into a template. Place the template over a stack of paper and cut out several copies of the shape.

Choose this one to start.

- With a partner, scatter the shapes on a table, then fit them together so you cannot see the surface between them.

- Discuss the transformations you used to make the figures fit together snugly, *for instance: rotation, translation.*

Choose a Strategy ✔ TEST PREP

Solve. Show your work. Tell what strategy you used. Possible strategies are given.

6. A panel of 5 architects sit in a row. Juan is to the right of Mike. Mavis is to the left of Tara. Mike is on Yuki's right. Juan is on one end. Name their order from left to right. **Mavis, Tara, Yuki, Mike, Juan; Use Logical Reasoning**

7. **What's Wrong?** Bob says that any triangle will tessellate. Is Bob right or wrong? Explain why.
   See Additional Answers on Page T87.

8. A building has 264 windows. There are three times as many rectangular windows as circular windows. How many of each kind of window are there? **66 circular windows; 198 rectangular windows; Write an Equation**

9. Lita uses cubes to design a building. For the top four layers she uses 1, 2, 4, and 8 cubes. If she continues this way, which layer will use more than 100 cubes? **8th layer; Find a Pattern**

PROBLEM-SOLVING Strategies

Use Models
Draw a Diagram
Find a Pattern
Guess and Check
Make an Organized List
Make a Table
Solve a Simpler Problem
Use Logical Reasoning
Work Backward
Write an Equation

📊 **Data** The graph at the right shows the tolls to be paid for crossing the George Washington Bridge going into New York. Use the graph for Problems 10–13.

10. Sue drives her car into New York each Saturday afternoon. How much will she save in 4 weeks if she gets an E-Z Pass instead of paying cash? **$4**

11. Bena just got her E-Z Pass bill. She made 5 trips into the city for a cost of $21. How many peak and off-peak trips was that? **1 peak; 4 off-peak**

12. A car with an E-Z pass has 4 passengers. They travel into New York during peak hours 5 weekdays each week. If they share the cost of the tolls equally, how much do they each pay at the end of each week? **$6.25**

13. Max does not have an E-Z Pass for his 2-axle dual rear-wheel truck, but he does have one for his car. He went to New York twice in off-peak hours with each vehicle. How much more did it cost to drive the truck in? **$16**

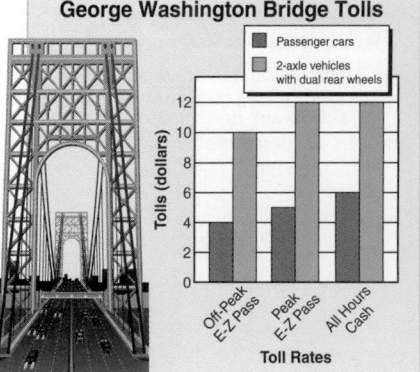

George Washington Bridge Tolls

■ Passenger cars
■ 2-axle vehicles with dual rear wheels

Tolls (dollars): 12, 10, 8, 6, 4, 2, 0

Toll Rates: Off-Peak E-Z Pass, Peak E-Z Pass, All Hours Cash

Peak hours: 6–9 A.M. and 4–7 P.M. on weekdays; 12 noon–8 P.M. on weekends

410

---

④ Assess and Close

Practice *continued*

Choose a Strategy

Assign **Exercises 6–13** as independent work.

- *Problem Solving for Problems 10–13* Have students discuss how they got the information they need from the graph. Have students explain which information was *not* relevant.

- **Explain what you know about tessellations.**

- **Can circles tessellate?** (no) **Explain.** (There are gaps between the circles.)

- **Can irregular polygons tessellate?** (yes, if they fit together)

Assign the **LESSON QUIZ** on Transparency 15.7 to further assess student understanding.

**Choose the letter of the correct answer.
If a correct answer is not here, choose NH.**

1. Use your ruler to measure the length of the segment to the nearest centimeter. How many centimeters less than a meter is this?

   •————————————————•

   A 1 centimeter   **C** 94 centimeters

   B 6 centimeters   **D** NH

   (Chapter 6, Lesson 4)

2. In a skyscraper, the first floor is 20 feet tall. All the other floors are 12.5 feet. On which floor is the ceiling 70 feet off the ground?

   F 3rd   **G** 4th   **H** 5th   **J** 6th

   (Chapter 1, Lesson 6)

3. A new building has 3 offices for rent. It has $\frac{1}{3}$ more offices than that already rented. It has twice as many offices under construction than already rented. How many offices are under construction?

   A 1 office   **C** 5 offices

   B 3 offices   **D** 8 offices

   (Chapter 5, Lesson 3)

4.

   | 1 | 2 | 3 | 4 |

   Ann's office is 2 doors down from Ed's. Jill's office is 1 door to the left of Ed's and 2 doors to the right of Jim's. Who has Office 2?

   F Ann   **H** Jill

   G Ed   **J** Jim

   (Chapter 3, Lesson 3)

5. A toll bridge charges $1.50 for a vehicle with 4 tires. It charges $0.25 more for each extra tire. Which expression shows how to find the toll for an 18-wheel truck?

   A ($1.50 + $0.25) × 18

   B ($1.50 × 18) + $0.25

   C (4 × $1.50) + ($0.25 × 18)

   D NH

   (Chapter 3, Lesson 1)

6. The greatest common factor of two numbers is 4. Their least common multiple is 120. Their sum is 52. What are the numbers?   **12, 40**

   Explain Show how to use a Venn diagram to solve the problem.
   See Additional Answers on Page T87.

   (Chapter 9, Lesson 7)

7. Angie said that all quadrilaterals tessellate. She drew these quadrilaterals to prove she is correct.

   Do all quadrilaterals tessellate?

   Represent Support your solution by making a model or drawing a picture.
   no; check drawings.

   (Chapter 15, Lesson 7)

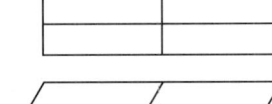
Test Prep on the Net
Check Out *Education Place* at
eduplace.com/kids/mw/
for test prep practice.

Chapter 15 Lesson 7   411

Problem-Solving Test Prep provides an opportunity for students to apply previously learned skills in the types of problem contexts typically encountered in standardized tests. *Problem-Solving Test Prep* includes practice in a variety of formats: multiple choice, free response, and open response.

Students will gain experience in writing about mathematics and using various representations to solve problems. Discuss students' solutions. Have several students explain the thinking behind their work.

 More test prep practice is available on Houghton Mifflin's Web site, **Education Place**. Go to **eduplace.com/kids/mw/**.

 # Keeping a Journal

Have students write a definition of a tessellation.
Have students illustrate their definition.

Hands-On: Circles

PLANNING THE LESSON

MATHEMATICS OBJECTIVE
Draw circles and construct and identify parts of a circle.

 Use Lesson Planner CD-ROM for Lesson 15.8.

Daily Routines

Vocabulary

Picture a bicycle wheel. What *radiates* or *comes out* from the center of the wheel to the outer circle? (spokes) Are the spokes all equal length? (yes) Are all points on the outer circle of the wheel equidistant from the center? (yes) In geometry, a *radius* connects the center of a circle to any point on the circle.

 Vocabulary Cards

Meeting North Carolina's Standards

Prepare for Grade 6 Objective **3.02** Identify the radius, diameter, chord, center, and circumference of a circle; determine the relationships among them.

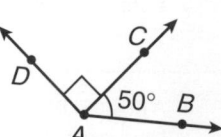
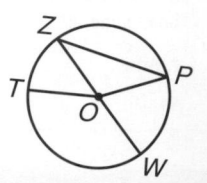
LEVELED PRACTICE

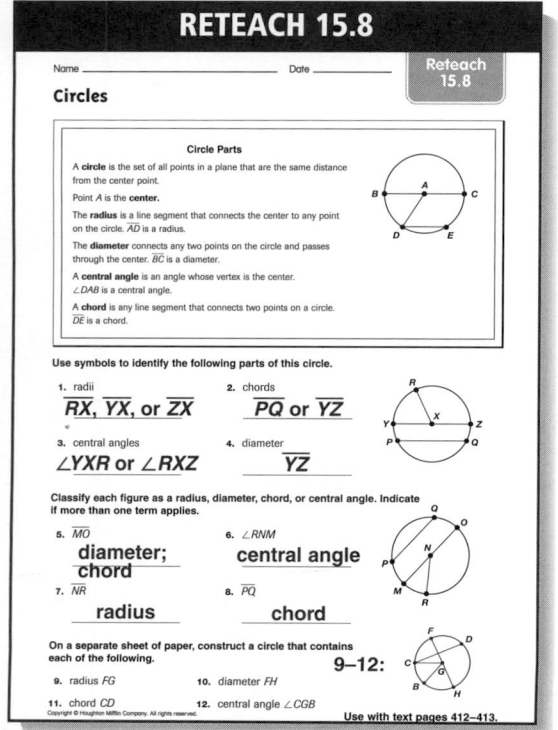

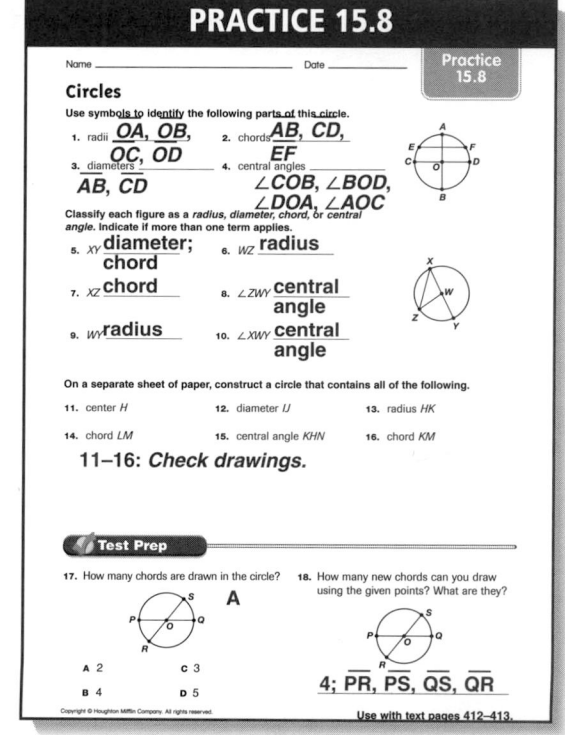

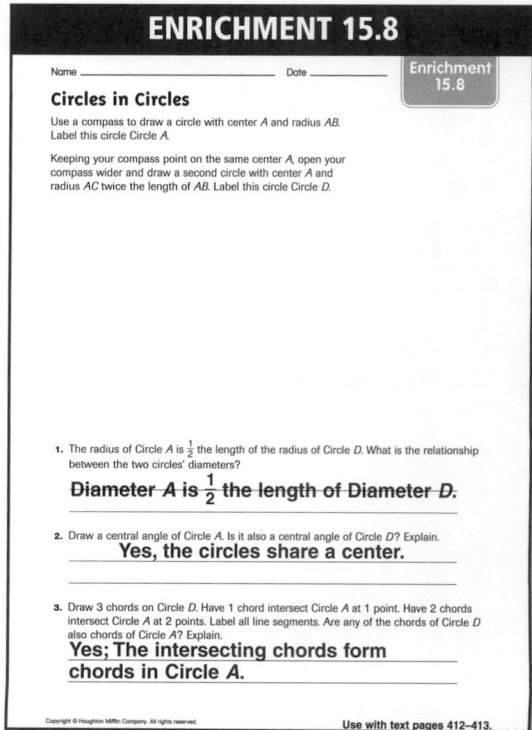

Practice Workbook Page 104

Reaching All Learners
Differentiated Instruction

English Learners

Worksheet 15.8 defines in simple language the parts of a circle and then asks students to use the terms to label a circle diagram. Students also complete sentences to make correct statements about the circle diagram.

Inclusion
KINESTHETIC, VISUAL

Materials: *safe drawing compass, ruler, paper*

- Draw a circle. Label its center point *A*, and 2 points on it *B* and *C*. Measure line segments *AB* and *AC*. Are they equal? (yes) **What is a *radius*?** (a line segment that connects the center to any point on the circle)
- **Repeat with circles of various sizes.**

Early Finishers
VISUAL, TACTILE

Materials: *reference materials*

- **Find Earth's measurements.** Have students first find its circumference (24,860 miles), then use the formula for calculating diameter. (circumference of a circle divided by pi, ≈ 3.14, = diameter)
- Have them research Eratosthenes, the ancient Greek mathematician.

TECHNOLOGY
Spiral Review

Help students remember skills they learned earlier by creating **customized** spiral review worksheets using the *Ways to Assess* CD-ROM.

Manipulatives

eManipulatives are available on the *Ways to Success* CD.

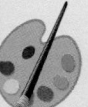 ## Art Connection

Class Logos
Materials: safe drawing compass, eraser, colored pencils, grid paper or Learning Tool 14

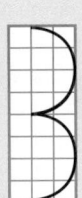

- A logo is a symbol that represents an organization, person, or group. Ask students if they can think of any well-known logos, such as the logo for the Olympic Games. Have them brainstorm ideas for a class logo.

- Have students design a class logo working with compasses and rulers. Point out to students that they can make numbers and letters of the alphabet with these two tools.

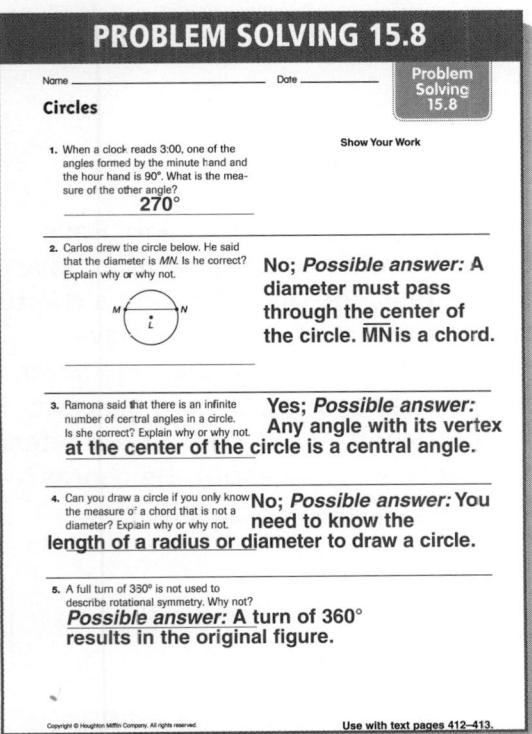

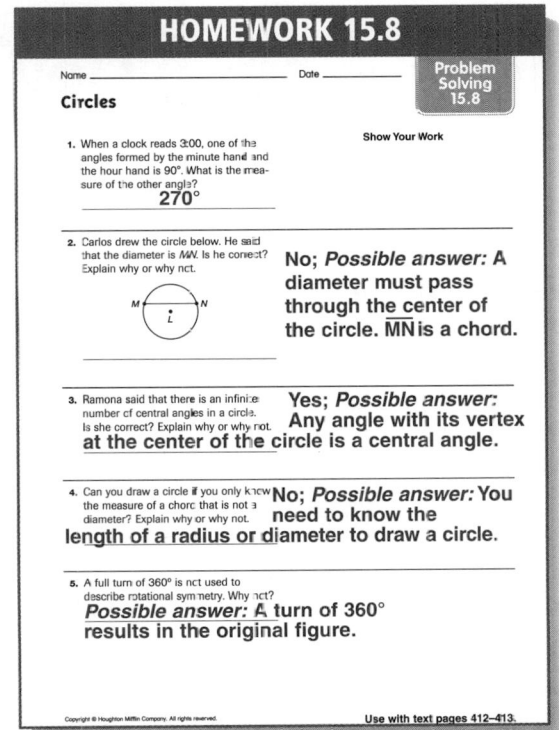

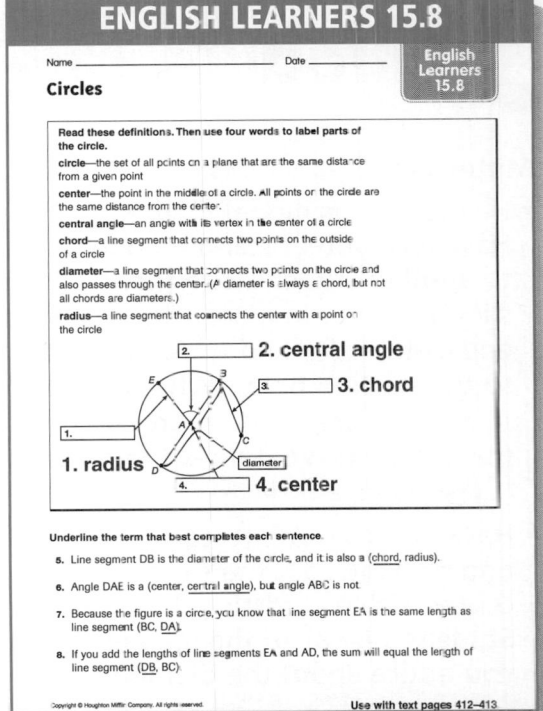

Homework Workbook Page 104

TEACHING LESSON 15.8

LESSON ORGANIZER

Objective Draw circles and construct and identify parts of a circle.

Resources Reteach, Practice, Enrichment, Problem Solving, Homework, English Learners, Transparencies, Math Center

Materials Blank transparency, safe drawing compass, 2 yardsticks, straight edge

---

Activity

Warm-Up Activity
Parts of a Square

iiii Whole Group	🕐 5 minutes	Auditory, Tactile

Materials: *blank transparency*

• On a blank transparency, draw and label a square as shown, and display it on the overhead.

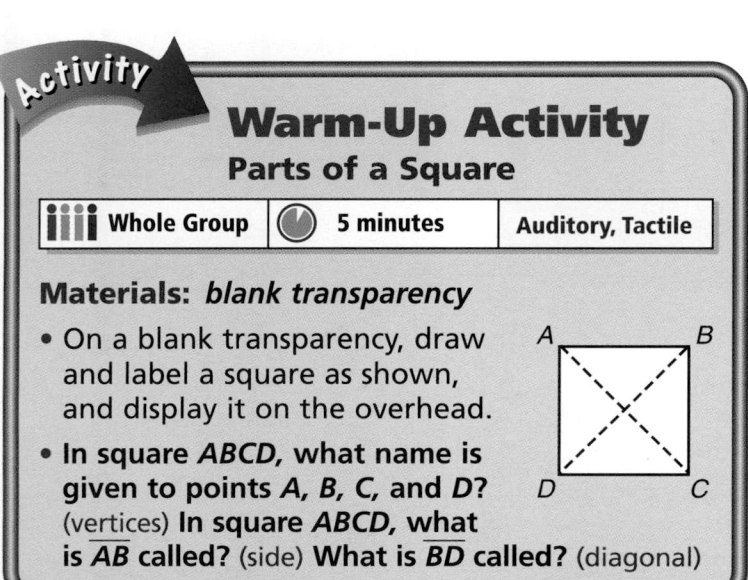

• In square *ABCD*, what name is given to points *A, B, C,* and *D*? (vertices) In square *ABCD*, what is $\overline{AB}$ called? (side) What is $\overline{BD}$ called? (diagonal)

Circles

Objective Draw circles and construct and identify parts of a circle.

e Glossary
Vocabulary
center
radius
diameter
chord
central angle

Materials
safe drawing compass
straightedge

Work Together

A circle is the set of all points in a plane that are the same distance from a given point called the **center**. A safe drawing compass and straightedge can be used to draw a circle and the parts of that circle.

Follow these steps to draw a circle with center *A* and to measure and identify parts of a circle.

STEP 1
• Draw a point and label it *A*. This is the center of the circle.
• Place the pivot point of your compass on point *A* and move the slider to any measure.
• Insert your pencil in one of the holes in the slider and draw a circle.

STEP 2
A **radius** is a segment that connects the center of a circle to any point on the circle. To draw a radius,
• Label point *B* on the circle.
• Connect *A* and *B* to draw radius $\overline{AB}$.

The plural of *radius* is *radii*. How many radii can a circle have? **an infinite number**

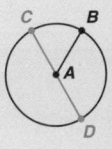

STEP 3
A **diameter** is a segment that connects two points on the circle and passes through the center of the circle. To draw a diameter,
• Draw point *C*. Connect *C* to *A* and extend the segment until it intersects the circle. Label that point *D*.
• $\overline{CD}$ is a diameter.

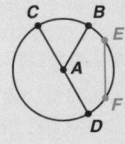

STEP 4
A **chord** is any segment that connects two points on the circle. To draw a chord,
• Draw points *E* and *F* on the circle.
• Draw chord $\overline{EF}$.

Is a diameter of a circle also a chord of that circle? **yes**

412

Activity

1 Introduce | iiii Whole Group | 🕐 5 minutes

Materials: *2 yardsticks*

• Have students model drawing a circle with this activity. Have a volunteer stand on one spot and extend a yardstick to another student. The first student holds one end of the stick and turns in place. The second student holds the other end of the stick and walks around until he or she returns to the starting point. **Who represents the center?** (student turning in place) **What represents the radius of the circle?** (the yardstick) **What does the other student represent?** (a point on the circle)

• Have a third student stand on the circle opposite the second student. Join the third student to the student at the center with a yardstick. **The line going from Student 2 to Student 3 is called the *diameter* of the circle. What do you notice about the diameter?** (It is two times the radius.)

2 Develop

Materials: *safe drawing compass*

Guide students through the *Work Together* section. Have students draw circles using the same compass setting. Have students draw and label a radius, the diameter, and a chord. Have students exchange diagrams with a partner. Have them measure and label the length of the radius, diameter, and chords on their partner's paper and compare measurements. **Are your radii equal in length?** (yes) **Are your diameters equal in length?** (yes) **What can you say about the chords?** (They vary in length. The longest one goes through the center and is a diameter.)

A **central angle** is an angle with its vertex at the center of the circle. To identify a central angle,

• Look for an angle whose vertex is the center point of the circle.

• ∠CAB is a central angle.

Name another central angle of the circle.
∠BAD, ∠DAB, ∠CAD, ∠DAC

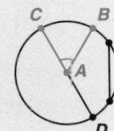

On Your Own

Use symbols to identify the following parts of this circle.

1. radii $\overline{WX}, \overline{WY}, \overline{WZ}$ 2. chords $\overline{UV}, \overline{XY}$

3. diameter $\overline{XY}$ 4. central angles
∠XWZ, ∠XWY, ∠ZWY

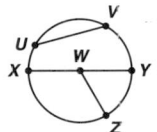

Classify each figure as a radius, diameter, chord, or central angle. Indicate if more than one term applies.

5. $\overline{MP}$
   radius
6. $\overline{MQ}$
   radius
7. ∠NMQ
   central angle
8. $\overline{QN}$
   chord
9. $\overline{NP}$
   diameter; chord
10. ∠QMP
    central angle

On a separate sheet of paper, construct a circle that contains all of the following. 11–16. *See Additional Answers on Page T87.*

11. center B   12. radius $\overline{BC}$

13. diameter $\overline{RL}$ 14. central angle RBH

15. chord $\overline{CL}$ 16. chord $\overline{RH}$

17. For the circle at the right, write a number sentence that can be used to find the missing angle measures. Then solve. $n + 60° + 90° + 90° = 360°; n = 120°$

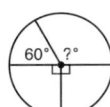

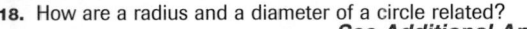

Talk About It • Write About It

18. How are a radius and a diameter of a circle related?
    See Additional Answers on Page T87.

19. **Analyze** A diameter forms two central angles of a circle. What is the sum of the measures of these central angles? **360°**

DAILY TEST PREP

In the circle with center O, which best describes ∠YOA?

A. obtuse central angle

B. chord

C. right central angle

D. acute central angle

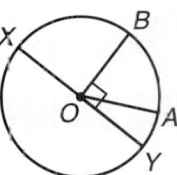

Activity

Lesson Intervention

Slicing Pies

Or use Intervention CD-ROM Lesson 15.8

| Small Group | 5–10 minutes | Visual, Tactile |

Materials: safe drawing compass

Have students use a compass to draw a circle and mark its center.

• **How would you draw a line segment through the circle to cut it in half?** (Start on the circle, go through the center, and stop when you get to the other side of the circle.) **What is that line segment called?** (the diameter)

• **Now suppose you want to cut the circle into equal quarters. How can you do that?** (Cut each half in half.)

• **How are the two diameters related?** (The diameters are perpendicular.) **What central angles do the diameters make?** (They make right angles.)

---

3 Practice

Assign **Exercises 1–17** of *On Your Own* as independent work.

4 Assess and Close

Assign Exercises 18–19 of the *Talk About It • Write About It* section. Have volunteers explain their work.

• **What is a central angle?** (any angle with a vertex at the center of the circle)

• **What does a 90° central angle look like?** (The angle cuts the circle so that one quarter of the circle is between the rays of the angle.)

Assign the **LESSON QUIZ** on Transparency 15.8 to further assess student understanding.

Keeping a Journal

Have students describe the similarities and differences between chords and diameters.

Symmetry

PLANNING THE LESSON

MATHEMATICS OBJECTIVE
Identify rotational and line symmetry.

Use Lesson Planner CD-ROM for Lesson 15.9.

Daily Routines

Vocabulary

What does the word *symmetry* mean? Ask students for examples of things that are *symmetrical* (eyeglasses, an open book). **In what ways is a square *symmetrical*?** (It has rotational symmetry and line symmetry.) **If we rotate a square 180° clockwise or counter-clockwise, will it still look the same?** (yes) Then we say the square has *rotational symmetry.* **Can we fold the square in half so that the halves are congruent?** (Yes) So, the square is said to have *line symmetry.*

Vocabulary Cards

Meeting North Carolina's Standards

3.03 Classify plane figures according to types of symmetry (line, rotational).

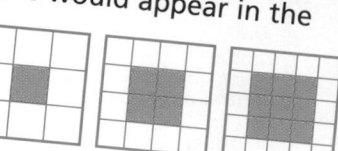

Lesson Transparency 15.9

Problem of the Day
Use the figure to answer the question. How many shaded squares would appear in the fourth and fifth diagram in the pattern? (16, 25)

Quick Review
Choose the greater number in each pair.
1. 0.35 or 0.53 (0.53) **2.** 4.8 or 4.08 (4.8)
3. 6.07 or 6.04 (6.07) **4.** 0.097 or 0.32 (0.32)

Lesson Quiz
Use the figure to answer.
1. Does it have rotational symmetry? (yes) How many degrees do you turn it in either direction to find out? (90°, 180°, 270°, 360°)
2. Does it have line symmetry? (yes) Sketch the lines of symmetry. (check sketches)

LEVELED PRACTICE

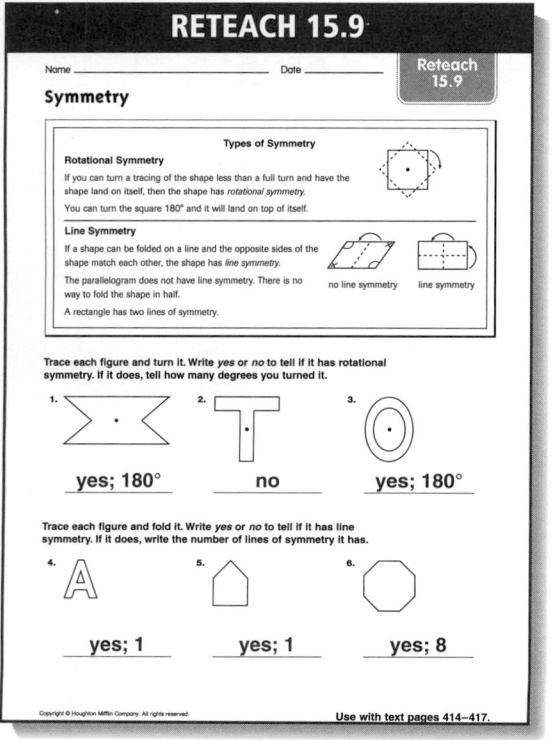

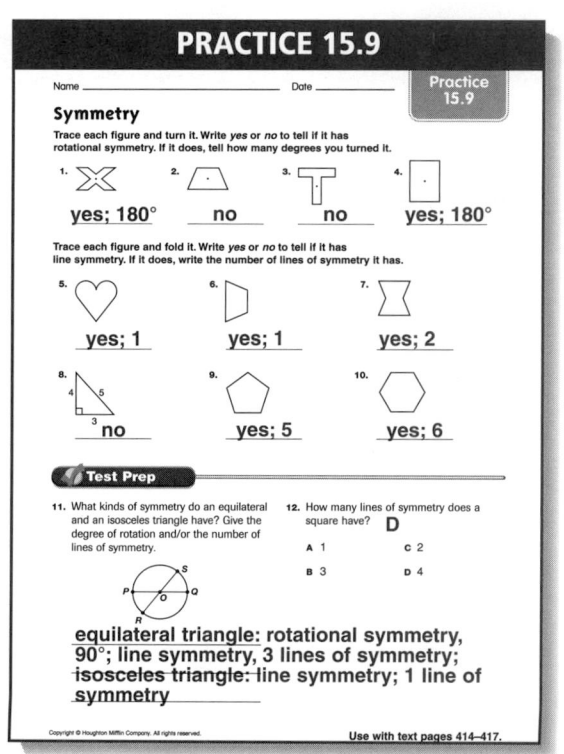

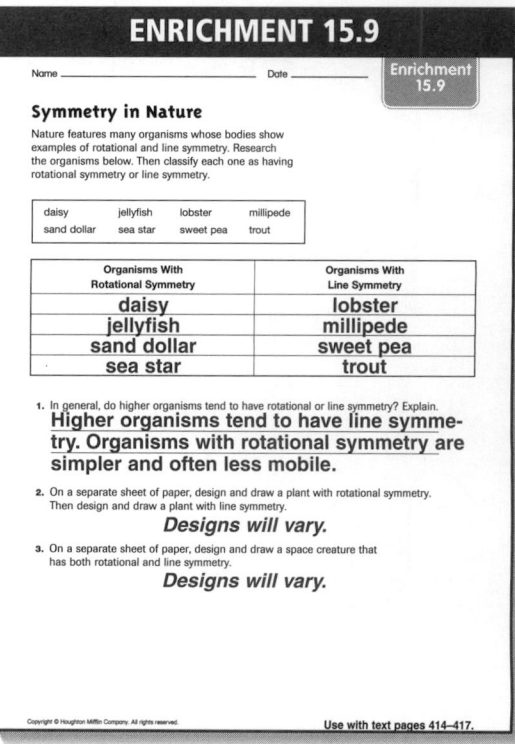

Practice Workbook Page 105

Reaching All Learners
Differentiated Instruction

English Learners

Worksheet 15.9 uses text and visuals to explain line symmetry and rotational symmetry. Students answer questions about the symmetry of several figures.

Inclusion
VISUAL, KINESTHETIC

Materials: *grid paper, colored pencils*

- Have students make two 3 × 3 block squares. On one, they shade 4 blocks so that if they rotate the square, it still always looks the same.

- **On the other, shade 4 blocks so that if you rotate the square, it does *not* look the same.**

Gifted and Talented
VISUAL, KINESTHETIC

Have students test their knowledge of rotational and line symmetry by drawing figures. One figure should have line symmetry, one have *no* rotational symmetry, and one *not* be a rectangle but have 2 lines of symmetry. (Sketches will vary.)

TECHNOLOGY

Spiral Review

You can prepare students for standardized tests with **customized** spiral review on key skills using the *Ways to Assess* CD-ROM.

Game

Students can practice their skills using the RoboPacker math game, available on the *Ways to Success* CD.

Intervention

Use the *Ways to Success* intervention software to support students who need more help in understanding the concepts and skills taught in this chapter.

Social Studies Connection

Symmetry in Flags
Materials: *reference materials*

- Have students research flags from around the world. Have them name some countries that have flags with rotational symmetry and line symmetry.

- **What are some flags that have no rotational symmetry?**

- **Are there flags that have patterns with rotational symmetry when rotated less than a half turn?**

- **Are there flags that have patterns with line.**

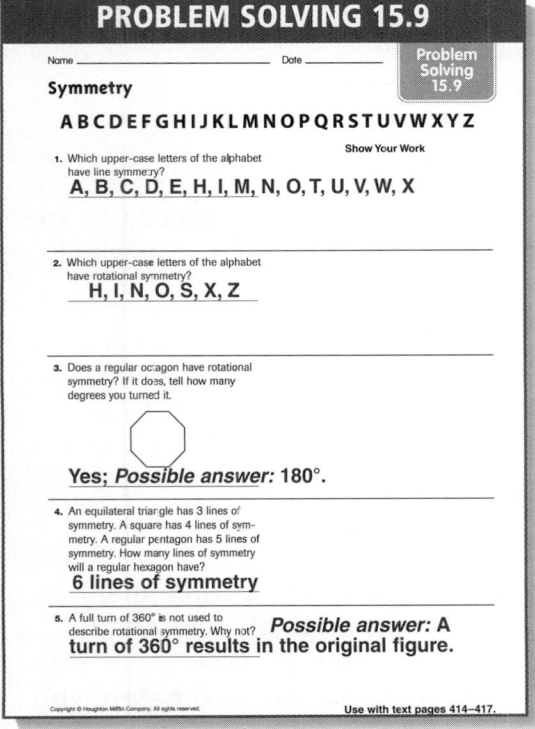

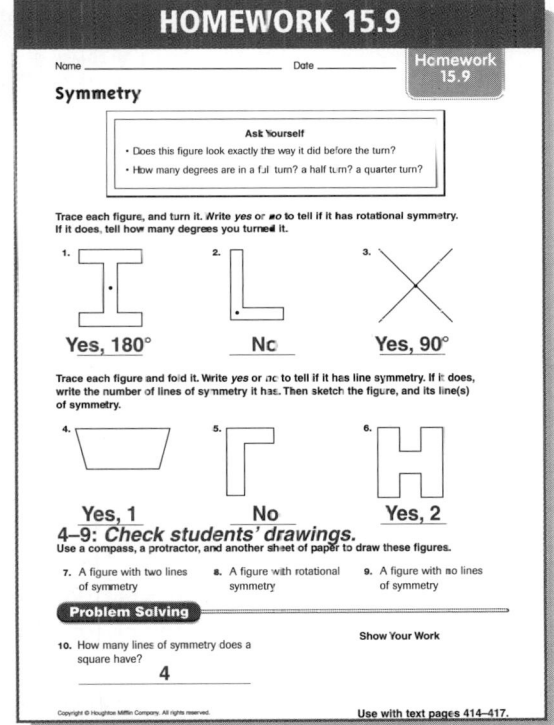

Homework Workbook Page 105

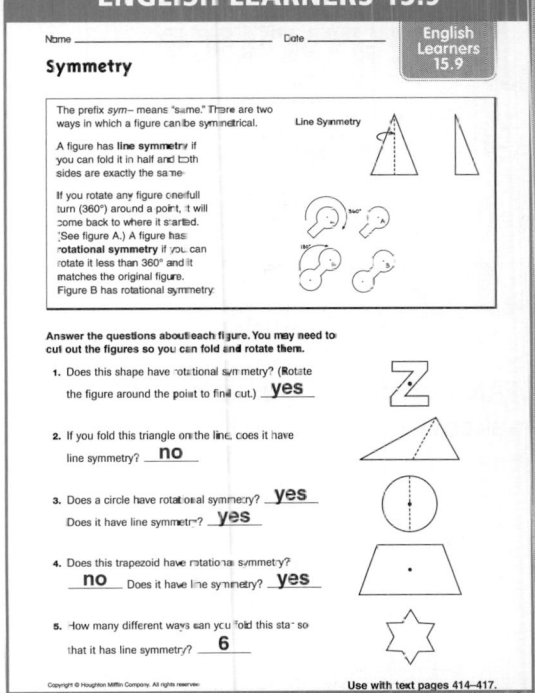

TEACHING LESSON 15.9

LESSON ORGANIZER

Objective Identify rotational and line symmetry.

Resources Reteach, Practice, Enrichment, Problem Solving, Homework, English Learners, Transparencies, Math Center

Materials Ruler, unlined paper, compass, scissors, clockface with numerals, paper, pencils

Activity

Warm-Up Activity
Clock Rotations

iiii Whole Group	⏱ 5 minutes	Tactile, Auditory

Materials: *clockface with numerals*

• Show 4:00 on the clock face. **How would you rotate the minute hand to show 4:15 or a quarter past 4?** (Rotate the minute hand 90° clockwise.) Point out that a 90° rotation is the same as a quarter turn. Show 7:00 on your clock face. **How would you rotate the minute hand to show half past 7?** (Rotate the minute hand 180° clockwise.) **This is one half of a full hour, or one half of a full turn.**

Symmetry

Objective Identify rotational and line symmetry.

e Glossary
Vocabulary
rotational symmetry
line symmetry

Learn About It 🔊 MathTracks 2/12 Listen and Understand

Suppose the blades of this windmill make a half turn (180°). How will the appearance of the windmill compare to the way it looks in this picture?

If you can turn a figure less than a full turn about a fixed point and the figure looks exactly the way it did before the turn, that figure has **rotational symmetry.**

Try this activity to explore rotational symmetry.

Materials: ruler, unlined paper, compass, scissors

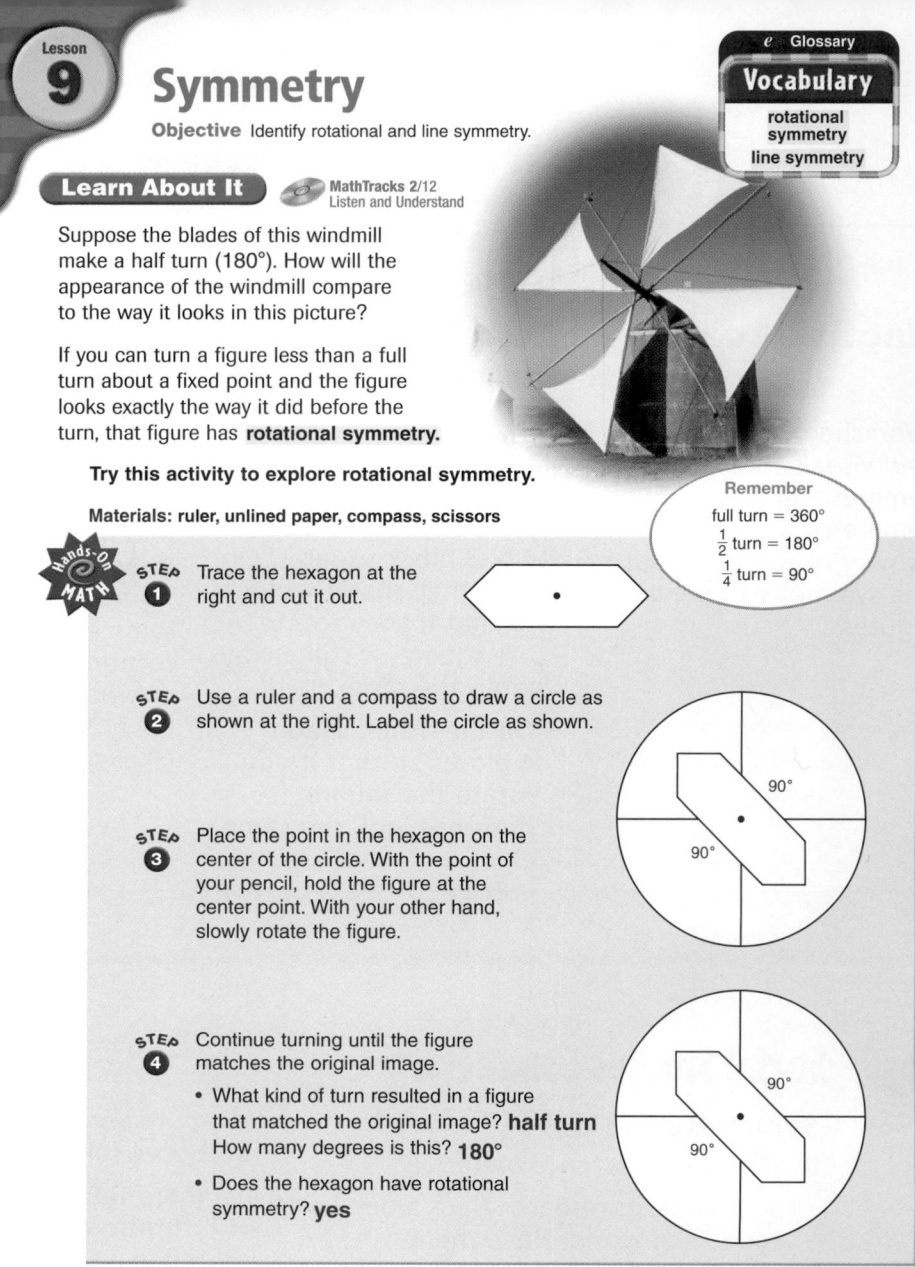

Remember
full turn = 360°
$\frac{1}{2}$ turn = 180°
$\frac{1}{4}$ turn = 90°

STEP 1 Trace the hexagon at the right and cut it out.

STEP 2 Use a ruler and a compass to draw a circle as shown at the right. Label the circle as shown.

STEP 3 Place the point in the hexagon on the center of the circle. With the point of your pencil, hold the figure at the center point. With your other hand, slowly rotate the figure.

STEP 4 Continue turning until the figure matches the original image.
• What kind of turn resulted in a figure that matched the original image? **half turn** How many degrees is this? **180°**
• Does the hexagon have rotational symmetry? **yes**

414

---

1 Introduce

At the board, sketch figures like these:

Which of these figures is symmetrical? (the star) **What makes it symmetrical?** (It has congruent halves, and it looks the same after being rotated by certain degrees.)

2 Develop

Guide students through the *Learn About It* section.

• **In Step 1, be sure to position your tracing exactly on top of the original. You should not see any of the original hexagon when you look at the tracing.**

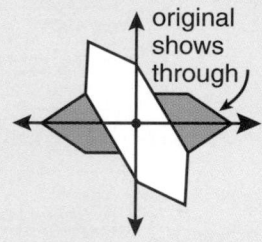
original shows through

• **In Step 3, when you start to rotate the tracing in either direction, do you see any of the original underneath?** (yes) **When does the original disappear?** (after a 180° rotation) **What happens when you pass 180° and before you reach 360°?** (The original shows through again.)

If a figure can be folded in half, and the two halves are congruent, the figure has **line symmetry**. The fold is called a line of symmetry.

Try this activity to explore line symmetry.

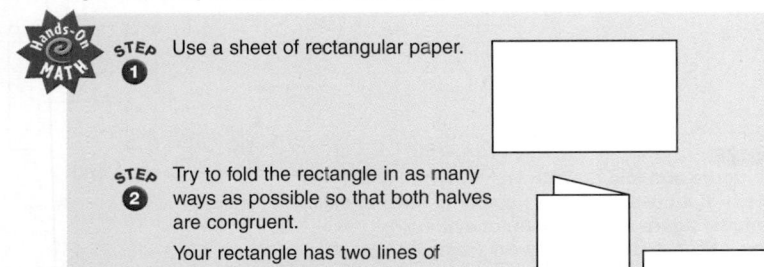

STEP **1** Use a sheet of rectangular paper.

STEP **2** Try to fold the rectangle in as many ways as possible so that both halves are congruent.

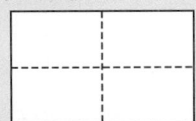

Your rectangle has two lines of symmetry. Draw dashed lines to show the lines of symmetry.

- Can a figure have more than one line of symmetry? **yes**
- Try this activity with a square. How many lines of symmetry does a square have? **4**

Guided Practice . . . .

Trace each figure and turn it. Write *yes* or *no* to tell if it has rotational symmetry. If it does, tell how many degrees you turned it.

Ask Yourself
- Does this figure look exactly the way it did before the turn?
- How many degrees are in a full turn? a half turn? a quarter turn?

TEST TIPS

1.
yes; 90°

2.  **no**

Trace each figure and fold it. Write *yes* or *no* to tell if it has line symmetry. If it does, write the number of lines of symmetry it has.

3. 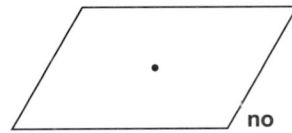 **yes; 1**

4. **yes; 5**

5. **no**

TEST TIPS **Explain Your Thinking** ▶ Can a figure have both line and rotational symmetry? Give an example to support your thinking.

Yes; a circle has both line and rotational symmetry.

Go On ▶

Chapter 15 Lesson 9 **415**

- In Step 1 on page 415, experiment with the rectangle to find if it has rotational symmetry. What do you discover? (It has rotational symmetry with 180° as the angle of rotation.)

- After the folding activity on page 415, did you find two lines of symmetry? (yes; one horizontal and one vertical line through the midpoints of opposite sides)

- Have students draw a regular hexagon and look for rotational symmetry. Help them see that the figure has 6 lines of symmetry.

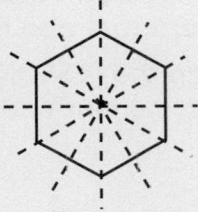

Guided Practice

Have students complete **Problems 1–5** as you observe. Remind them to use the *Ask Yourself* questions to help. Give students the opportunity to talk about the question in *Explain Your Thinking*.

DAILY TEST PREP

How many lines of symmetry does an isosceles right triangle have? (1)

Lesson Intervention

Or use
Intervention
CD-ROM
Lesson 15.9

Line or Rotational Symmetry?

| 👥 Small Group | ⏱ 10–15 minutes | Kinesthetic, Tactile |

Materials: *paper, pencils, scissors*

- Cut the letter *A* out of paper. **Can you fold the letter onto itself so that when you hold it up to the light you see only one half of the letter?** (yes) **Is there any rotation, other than 360°, that will make the letter coincide with itself?** (no)

- **Which of A, B, C, D, E, and F have line but not rotational symmetry.** (A, B, C, D, E) **Which other letters have rotational but not line symmetry?** (N, S, Z) **Does a figure with line symmetry always have rotational symmetry** (no)

Practice and Problem Solving

Trace each figure and turn it. Write *yes* or *no* to tell if it has rotational symmetry. If it does, tell how many degrees you turned it.

6. yes; 120°   7. yes; 180°   8. no   9. yes; 180°

Trace each figure and fold it. Write *yes* or *no* to tell if it has line symmetry. If it does, write the number of lines of symmetry it has. Then sketch the figure and its line(s) of symmetry.
10–17. See Additional Answers on Page T87 for art.

10. yes; 1   11. no   12. yes; 1   13. yes; 5

14. yes; 1   15. no   16. yes; 5   17. yes; 1

Use a compass and a protractor to draw these figures. *Check students' drawings.*

18. a figure that has line symmetry but not rotational symmetry

19. a figure that has rotational symmetry but not line symmetry

Use the photograph at the right for Problems 20–22.
20–22. Answers will vary.

20. **Analyze** Make a list of the geometric shapes you see.

21. **Write About It** Write a paragraph about the kinds of symmetry you see.

22. **You Decide** Windows can be squares, rectangles, circles, or semicircles. Draw the front or side of a house that has at least one line of symmetry. Decide on the shape of the house and its windows. Explain how you made it symmetrical.

416

---

③ Practice

Assign **Exercises 6–22** as independent work.

- *Problem Solving for Problems 6–9* Have students explain their work for each problem.

Common Error

Miscounting angles and lines Students may think if they find rotational symmetry with one angle, they have found all there is to find. Explain that, in the case of the hexagon on page 414, there is one angle of rotation. For a square, there are three angles of rotation.

The same applies to lines of symmetry. An isosceles triangle that is *not* an equilateral triangle has one line of symmetry. If the triangle is equilateral, there are three lines of symmetry.

④ Assess and Close

- **Can a figure have more than one line of symmetry?** (yes) Have volunteers draw on the chalkboard examples of these figures including dotted lines for the lines of symmetry. Examples should include squares and equilateral triangles.

- **Can a figure have both line and rotational symmetry?** (yes) Ask students to point at those figures on the chalkboard that also have rotational symmetry.

Assign the **LESSON QUIZ** on Transparency 15.9 to further assess student understanding.

Quick Check

Check your understanding for Lessons 6–9.

Use Figures A, B, and C for Exercises 1–8. (Lessons 6–7, 9)

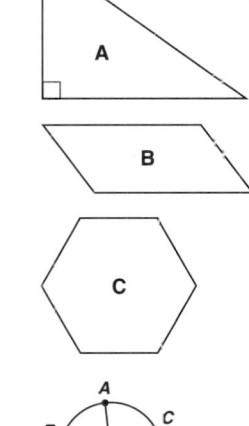

1. Trace Figure A on grid paper and then show a translation. ***Check students' drawings.***

2. Trace Figure B on grid paper and then show a reflection. ***Check students' drawings.***

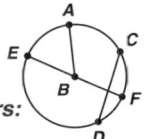

3. Which figure will tessellate? **Figures B, C**

4. Which figure has rotational symmetry? **Figures B, C**

5. Which figure has line symmetry? **Figure C**

6. How many lines of symmetry does the figure you named in Exercise 5 have? **6 lines of symmetry**

Use symbols to identify the following parts of the circle at the right. (Lesson 8)

7. radius   8. center **B**   9. diameter $\overline{EF}$ 10. chords
possible answers:
$\overline{EB}, \overline{AB}, \overline{BF}$
possible answers:
$\overline{EF}, \overline{CD}$

WEEKLY **WR** READER® eduplace.com/kids/mw/

Art Connection

Escher-esque

M. C. Escher was a famous Dutch artist who used transformations to make unusual tessellation patterns.

Use what you learned about tessellations in Lesson 7 to make an Escher-like tessellation of your own.

Check students' drawings.

Extra Practice See page 419, Set E.

Chapter 15 Lesson 9   417

Quick Check

Purpose: The Quick Check allows you to assess the students' understanding of the concepts presented in Lessons 6–9.

Items	Objectives Tested	Pages	Intervention
1–3	Identify and model translations, rotations, and reflections. Make models to solve tessellation problems.	404–407 408–411	Reteach Resource 15.6 *Ways to Success* 15.6 Reteach Resource 15.7 *Ways to Success* 15.7
4–6	Identify rotational and line symmetry.	412–413	Reteach Resource 15.8 *Ways to Success* 15.8
7–10	Identify part of a circle.	414–417	Reteach Resource 15.9 *Ways to Success* 15.9

Keeping a Journal

Have students write a paragraph about how to use spinning as a test for rotational symmetry and folding as a test for line symmetry.

Art Connection

Escher-Esque

Complicated polygons or figures with curves may be too difficult for students to work with. Encourage students to think of simpler figures such as regular polygons. Equilateral triangles or regular hexagons will work. Check that students do not overlap figures to close any gaps.

Monitoring Student Progress

 Chapter Review/Test

Purpose: This test provides an informal assessment of the Chapter 15 objectives.

Chapter Test Items 1–10

To assign a numerical grade for this Chapter Test, use 10 points for each test item.

Check Understanding

You can use the **Write About It** question to assess student understanding of a key chapter concept.

Customizing Your Instruction

For students who have not yet mastered these objectives, you can use the Reteaching Resources listed in the chart below.

 ## Assessment Options

A summary test for this chapter is also provided in the Unit Resource Folder.

Adequate Yearly Progress

Use the End of Grade Test Prep Assessment Guide to help familiarize your students with the format of standardized tests.

Chapter Review/Test

✓ **VOCABULARY**

1. Two lines that intersect at right angles are said to be ____. **perpendicular**

2. A ____ occurs when you flip a figure over a line. **reflection**

Vocabulary
diagonal
perpendicular
reflection
rotation

✓ **CONCEPTS AND SKILLS**

3. Identify this figure.   **ray QB**

4. Find the missing angle measure in △RJW. Then classify the triangle in two ways. (Lessons 2–3, pp. 292–297)
45; right triangle; isosceles triangle

5. Trace each figure. Use a ruler to measure the sides of each figure to the nearest $\frac{1}{16}$ inch. Mark congruent sides. (Lesson 4, pp. 398–399) **Check students' drawings.**

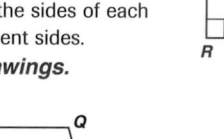

6. Classify CGKS in as many ways as possible. (Lesson 5, pp. 400–402)
quadrilateral, parallelogram

7. Tell whether CGKS has rotational and/or line symmetry. (Lesson 9, pp. 414–417)
Figure CGKS has rotational symmetry.

8. Sketch a triangle and its reflection. (Lesson 6, pp. 404–407)
Check students' drawings.

9. In the circle at the right, name each of the following: a radius, a diameter, and a chord. (Lesson 8, pp. 412–413)

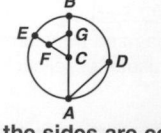

radius: BC, CB, CA, AC, EC, or CE; diameter: AB or BA; chord: AB, BA, AD, or DA

✓ **PROBLEM SOLVING**

Make a model to solve. (Lesson 7, pp. 408–411)

10. Does the figure to the right tessellate? Explain why or why not.

Possible explanation: **no; The sum of the angles that meet is not 360°.**

No; none of the sides are congruent, so there is no way to draw a line so the two parts of a triangle match.

Write About It

Show You Understand
You know that △JBW has line symmetry. Can △JBW be a scalene triangle? Explain how you know.

418   Chapter 15 Chapter Review/Test

Reteaching Support

Chapter Test Items	Summary Test Items	Chapter Objectives Tested	TE Pages	Use These Reteaching Resources
1, 3	1–5	**15A** Identify basic geometric figures and their parts.	390A–391	Reteach Resource 15.1 Ways to Success CD: 15.1 Skillsheet 121
4, 6, 9	6–9	**15B** Classify angles, triangles, quadrilaterals, and other polygons.	392A–397, 400A–403, 412A–413	Reteach Resource 15.2, 15.3, 15.5, 15.8 Ways to Success CD: 15.2, 15.3, 15.5, 15.8 Skillsheet 122, 123, 124
5, 7	10–13	**15C** Identify congruent figures and figures with line and rotational symmetry.	398A–399, 414A–417	Reteach Resource 15.4, 15.9 Ways to Success CD: 15.4, 15.9 Skillsheet 125, 126
2, 8	14–17	**15D** Identify reflections, translations, or rotations.	404A–407	Reteach Resource 15.6 Ways to Success CD: 15.6 Skillsheet 126
10	18–20	**15E** Analyze and solve problems by using models.	408A–411	Reteach Resource 15.7 Ways to Success CD: 15.7 Skillsheet 127

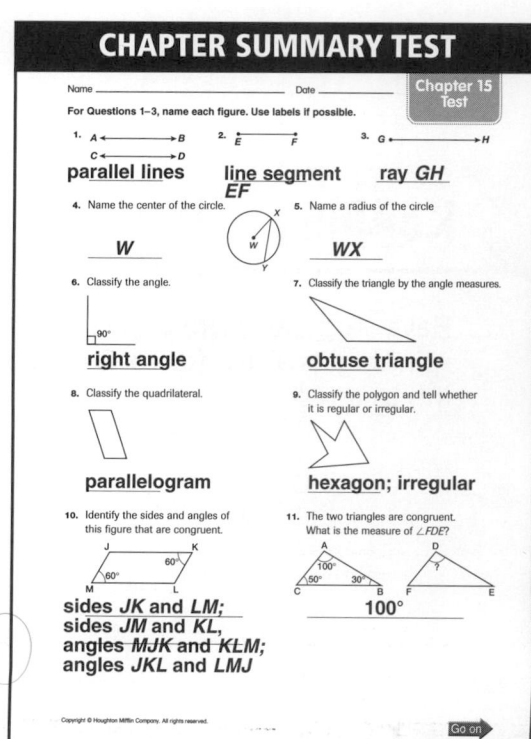

CHAPTER SUMMARY TEST

Set A (Lesson 1, pp. 390–391)

Name each figure.

1.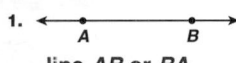
line AB or BA

2.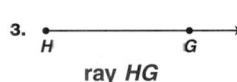
line segment SL or LS

3.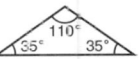
ray HG

Set B (Lesson 3, pp. 396–397)

Classify each triangle in two ways. Then find the missing angle measures.

1.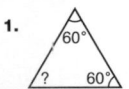
equilateral, acute, 60°

2.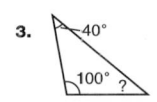
right, scalene, 30°

3.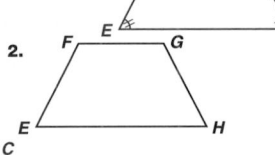
isosceles, obtuse, 40°

4.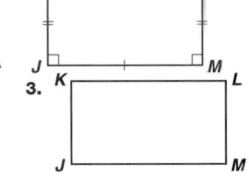
scalene, acute, 35°

Set C (Lesson 4, pp. 398–399)

Trace each figure. Mark the congruent sides and congruent angles.

1.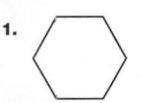

2.

3.

Set D (Lesson 5, pp. 400–403)

Classify each polygon in as many ways as possible.

1.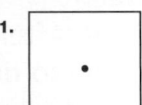
regular hexagon

2. quadrilateral, trapezoid

3. scalene right triangle

4.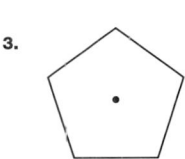
quadrilateral, parallelogram, rhombus

Set E (Lesson 9, pp. 414–417)

Tell whether each figure has rotational symmetry and/or line symmetry.

1.
rotational: yes; line: yes

2.
rotational: no; line: yes

3.
rotational: yes; line: yes

Chapter 15 Extra Practice **419**

CHAPTER SUMMARY 15 TEST

Name _____ Date _____
Chapter 15 Test continued

12. You have turned up the volume in Figure A knob to look like Figure B. Does the knob have rotational symmetry? If yes, how many degrees did you turn it?

Figure A   Figure B

yes; 270°

13. Does this figure have line symmetry? If yes, how many lines of symmetry does it have?

yes; 6

Tell if each figure is a translation, reflection, or rotation. If a figure is a rotation, give the degrees of rotation.

14. reflection

15. rotation; 90°

16. translation

17. rotation; 180°

Francisco made this pattern with trapezoids.

18. Does Francisco's pattern tessellate?

yes

19. What kind of transformation did Francisco use to create this pattern?

rotation

20. Suppose Francisco placed squares between the trapezoids in each row. Would the new pattern tessellate?

no

Copyright © Houghton Mifflin Company. All rights reserved.

Additional Answers

Chapter 15

Lesson 1, p. 391

Explain Your Thinking: On a horizontal line that has points C and D, one point must be to the left or to the right of the other. If, for example, point C is to the left of point D, then ray CD begins at point C and continues right through point D and beyond. Ray DC on the other hand, begins at point D and continues left through point C and beyond. Neither ray includes the entire line.

8. line JP is parallel to line QW ($\overrightarrow{JP} \parallel \overrightarrow{QW}$)

9. line XY intersects line BE at point Q ($\overrightarrow{XY}$ intersects $\overrightarrow{BE}$ at point Q)

10. line ML is perpendicular to line PR ($\overrightarrow{ML} \perp \overrightarrow{PR}$)

11.

12.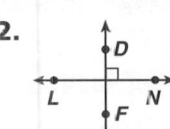

13.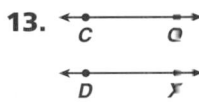

14.

17. Both lines intersect, or cross, one another. An intersecting line can cross another line at any angle. A perpendicular line can only cross another line at a 90° angle

Lesson 2, pp. 392–395

Step 2: *Possible answer:* Identify the direction in which the angle opens and then use the scale on which the numbers increase in the same direction.

22. *Possible answer:* no, because an 89° angle is an acute angle. So, even if 1° is added to it, it becomes a right angle.

23. *Possible answer:* Draw an example of each and put them in order: acute, right, obtuse, straight.

Lesson 3, pp. 396–397

Step 3: yes; *possible answer:* When rearranged, the three angles will always form a straight angle, so the sum of all the angles in any triangle is 180°.

Explain Your Thinking: Yes, an equilateral triangle is also an isosceles triangle because an equilateral triangle has three sides of the same length and the definition of an isosceles triangle states that at least two sides are the same length.

7. *a* = 180 − (80 + 40) or *a* = 180 − 80 − 40; 60

8. *a* = 180 − (125 + 30) or *a* = 180 − 125 − 30; 25

9. *a* = 180 − (90 + 45) or *a* = 180 − 90 − 45; 45

10. *a* = 180 − (60 + 60) or *a* = 180 − 60 − 60 or *a* = 180 ÷ 3; 60

11. right; *Possible answer:*

See Additional Answers on pp. T86–T87.

Plane Figures and Geometric Concepts **419**

Lesson By Lesson Overview
Perimeter, Area, and Circumference

Lesson 1

- Students review finding the perimeter of plane figures. Students develop an understanding of the concept by finding the perimeter of a rectangle on grid paper before they work with the formula.
- Students have an opportunity to analyze and explain situations involving perimeter.

Lesson 2

- Students review how to make a table to organize data and find a pattern.
- Students choose a strategy and use data from a histogram to solve problems.

Lesson 3

- Students link counting squares on grid paper with using the area formula.
- Students concretely explore the relationship of the area of a parallelogram to that of a rectangle.

Lesson 4

- Students find and use the formula for the area of a triangle.
- Students use what they know about the formula for finding the area of a parallelogram to find the area of the triangle.

Lesson 5

- Students explore estimating and finding the perimeter and area of irregular figures.
- Students use algebra to write expressions that represent the perimeters of complex figures.

Lesson 6

- Students discover the relationship between circumference and the diameter of a circle. After students discover *pi*, they learn the formula to find circumference, and also use a calculator to find circumference.

SKILLS TRACE: GEOMETRY AND MEASUREMENT

Grade 4	Grade 5	Grade 6
• find perimeter and area (ch. 18)	• **find perimeter of polygons and complex and irregular figures** • **find area of parallelograms, triangles, and irregular figures** • **use pi to find circumference**	• estimate perimeter and area; find perimeters and areas of squares (ch. 8) • find perimeters and areas of plane geometric figures (ch. 20) • find circumference and area of a circle (ch. 20)

Chapter Planner

Lesson	Objective	Vocabulary	Materials	✔ NCTM Standards
16.1 Algebra: Perimeter p. 422A	Find the perimeter of plane figures.	perimeter	Learning Tool 13 grid paper, Centimeter Grid Transparency	**Measurement:** Explore what happens to measurements of a two-dimensional shape such as its perimeter and area when the shape is changed in some way.
16.2 Problem-Solving Strategy: Find a Pattern p. 424A	Use a pattern to solve a problem.		Learning Tool 14, grid paper, chips, triangle tiles, Centimeter Grid Transparency, Problem Solving: Four-Step Process Transparency	**Problem Solving:** Solve problems that arise in mathematics and in other contexts.
16.3 Algebra: Area of a Parallelogram p. 428A	Use a formula for the areas of parallelograms.	square unit area	blank transparency, parallelogram tiles, Area of Simple Polygons = (rectangle, parallelogram), Transparency Sheets 1 and 2, Learning Tool 13, rulers, scissors	**Measurement:** Develop, understand and use formulas to find the area of rectangles and related triangles and parallelograms.
16.4 Algebra: Area of a Triangle p. 432A	Find and use the formula to find the area of a triangle.		scissors, Areas of Simple Polygons (triangle and trapezoid) Transparency, grid paper, square tiles	**Measurement:** Develop, understand and use formulas to find the area of rectangles and related triangles and parallelograms.
16.5 Hands-On: Perimeter and Area of Figures p. 434A	Find the perimeters and areas of irregular figures.		Centimeter Grid Transparency, Learning Tool 13, Learning Tool 15	**Measurement:** Develop strategies for estimating the perimeters, areas, and volumes of irregular shapes.
16.6 Algebra: Hands-On: Circumference of a Circle p. 438A	Find and use the formula to find the circumference of a circle.	circumference pi (π)	string, meter stick or centimeter ruler, circular objects of various sizes, calculator, Learning Tool 53, compass	**Measurement:** Understand that measurements are approximations and how differences in units affect precision.

Resources For Reaching All Learners

LESSON RESOURCES: Reteach, Practice, Enrichment, Problem Solving, Homework, English Learners, Daily Routines, Transparencies, Math Center.

ADDITIONAL RESOURCES FROM HOUGHTON MIFFLIN: Combination Classroom Planning Guide, Chapter Challenges, Every Day Counts, Math at Hand (student handbook).

Every Day Counts
The **Calendar and Measurement** activities in **Every Day Counts** support the math in this chapter.

Assessing Prior Knowledge

Before beginning the chapter, you can assess students understandings in order to assist you in differentiating instruction.

Complete Chapter Pretest in Unit Resource Folder

Use this test to assess both prerequisite skills (**Are You Ready?** — one page) and chapter content (**Check What You Know** — two pages).

Chapter 16 Prerequisite Skills Pretest

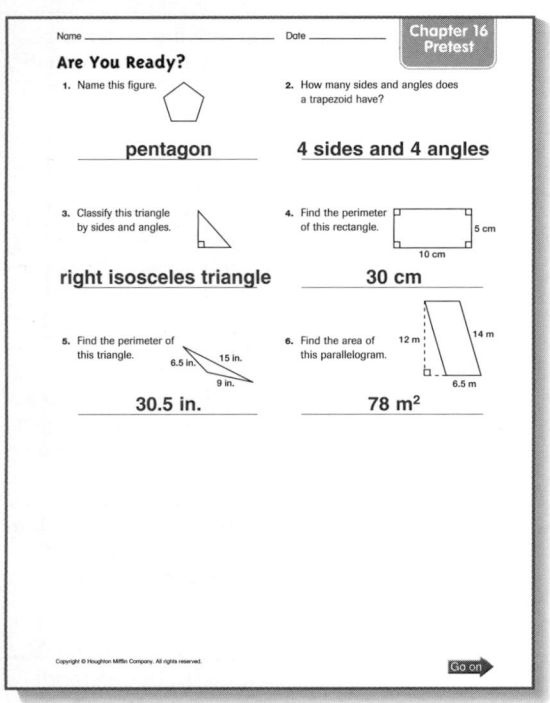

Chapter 16 New Content Pretest

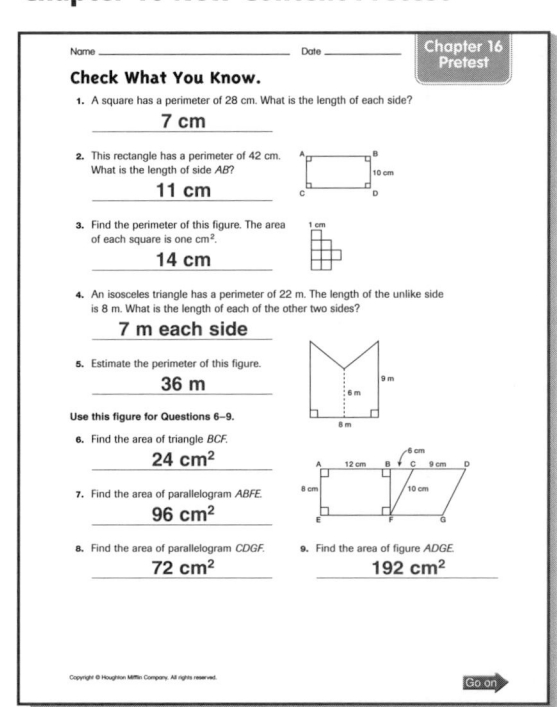

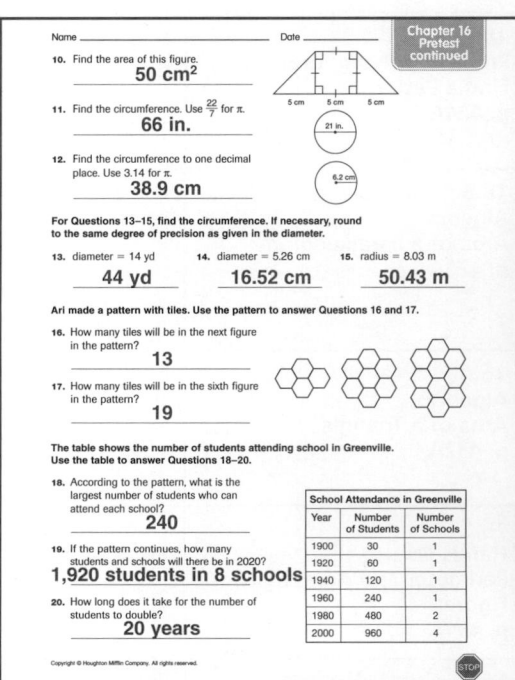

Customizing Instruction

For Students Having Difficulty

Items	Prerequisites	Ways to Success
1–3	Identify, classify, and describe plane geometric figures	CD: 16a Skillsheet: 128
4–6	Find perimeter and area	CD: 16b Skillsheet: 129

Ways to Success: Intervention for every concept and skill (CD-ROM or Chapter Intervention Skillsheets).

For Students Having Success

Items	Objectives	Resources
1–5	**16A** Find the perimeter of polygons and complex and irregular figures.	Enrichment 16.1
3,6–10	**16B** Find the area of parallelograms, triangles, and complex and irregular figures.	Enrichment 16.3, 16.4, 16.5
11–15	**16C** Use pi to find the circumference of a circle.	Enrichment 16.6
16–20	**16D** Analyze and solve problems by finding a pattern.	Enrichment 16.2

Other Pretest Options

Informal Pretest in Student Book

The student book pretest assesses vocabulary and prerequisite skills needed for success in this chapter.

Ways to Success CD-ROM

The *Ways to Success* chapter pretest has automatic assignment of appropriate review lessons.

Consider using **Knowing Mathematics** with any students who are working two or more years below grade level.

Use **Chapter Challenges** with any students who have success with all new chapter content.

Chapter Resources

Assessing Prior Knowledge

Geometric Measures (perimeter and area concepts)

- Remind students that *perimeter* is the distance around a figure and *area* is the number of square units within a region.
- Have students create two column headings– *Perimeter* and *Area*. Have them list real-world examples of when they would use each type of geometric measure.

Activity

Ongoing Skill Activity

Geometric Measures at Home (perimeter, area, and circumference)

- Display photographs of items used in the home or in home construction. Examples might include furniture, floor plans, and pipes.
- For each lesson, draw attention to a photograph and have students discuss objects in the photograph in light of the lesson's concepts.

Activity

Connecting to the Unit Project

- Have the "city planners" find the perimeter or circumference of the building zones in the plan and determine how many buildings are to be on each block. Have them discuss average building sizes with the "architects."
- Have the "city architects" find the perimeter or circumference of the bases of their buildings to be sure they will fit in the planned spaces.

Teacher Support

Houghton Mifflin
Math

Professional
Resources
Handbook

• Research-Based Teaching
• Linking With Mathematics
• Language Intervention

5

Professional Resources Handbook

Research, Mathematics Content, and Language Intervention

Research-Based Teaching

Students should have opportunities to discover and use formulas. (Tucker, Singleton, & Weaver, 2002). Conceptual understanding of formulas will follow if students are allowed to construct the origins of the equations used in measurement. See *Professional Resources Handbook,* Grade 5, Unit 6.

For more ideas relating to Unit 6, see the Teacher Support Handbook at the back of this Teacher's Edition.

Language Intervention

In East Asiar countries, children learn that just as numbers car be composed and decomposed as sets and subsets, geometric figures can be composed and decomposed as well. Many formulas for area and volume are based on the fact that geometric figures can be decomposed. For further explanation, see "Mathematical Language and Measuremert" in the *Professional Resources Handbook Grade 5.*

Time Saving Technology Support

Ways to Assess Customized Spiral Review and Test Generator CD-ROM
Lesson Planner CD-ROM
Ways to Success Intervention CD-ROM
Math Tracks CD-ROM
Education Place: **www.eduplace.com/math/mw/**
Houghton Mifflin Math eBook CD-ROM
eManipulatives
eGames/.

Starting Chapter 16
Perimeter, Area, and Circumference

Chapter Objectives

16A Find the perimeter of polygons and complex and irregular figures.

16B Find the area of parallelograms, triangles, and complex and irregular figures.

16C Use pi to find the circumference of a circle.

16D Analyze and solve problems by finding a pattern.

Math Background

Perimeter and Circumference

The perimeter of a polygon is the distance around it or the sum of the lengths of its sides. When the length and width of a rectangle are known, the perimeter and the area of the rectangle can be found. The perimeter or distance around the rectangle can be found either by finding the sum of the lengths of the sides or by using the formula $P = 2l \times 2w$. Since perimeter is a length or distance, the unit of measure is in inches, meters, yards, or kilometers, etc. The perimeter of a circle is called the circumference. The ratio of the circumference to diameter in each circle is the same. This constant ratio of circumference to diameter is denoted by the Greek letter π. So $C = \pi d$ or $C = 2\pi r$.

Area

Area is measured in square units. A square unit is a square where each side has a length of one unit. The area of an object is the number of square units it takes to cover the object without any overlap. The area of the rectangle is found by using the formula $A = l \times w$. The unit of measure for area is square inches (in.^{2}), square meters (m^2), square yards (yd^2), or square kilometers (km^2), etc.

To avoid two common misconceptions, have students use examples to show that:
- If two rectangles have the same area, they do not necessarily have the same perimeter.
- If one rectangle has perimeter twice of another rectangle, the ratio of their areas is not 1:2.

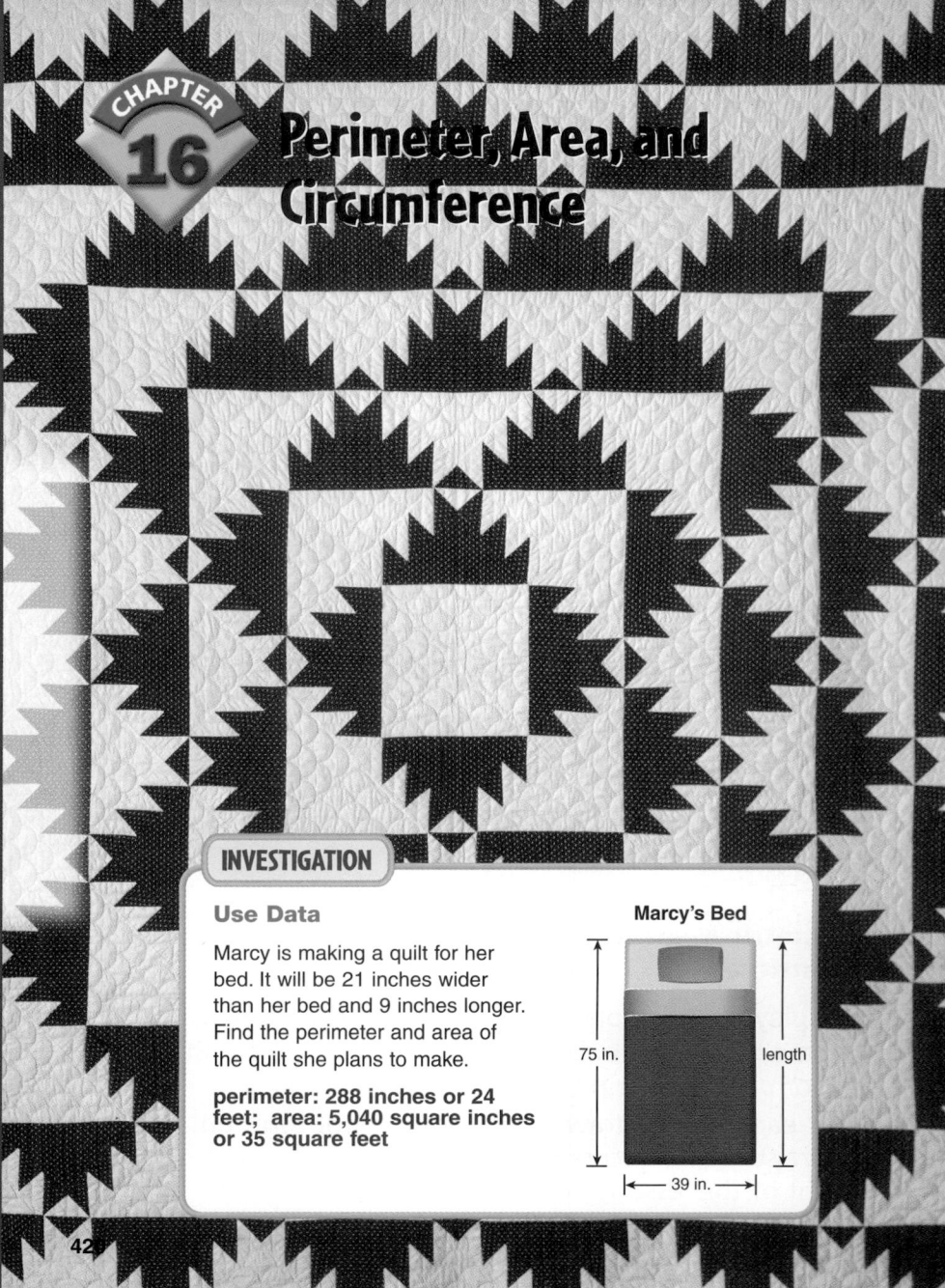

INVESTIGATION

Use Data

Marcy is making a quilt for her bed. It will be 21 inches wider than her bed and 9 inches longer. Find the perimeter and area of the quilt she plans to make.

perimeter: 288 inches or 24 feet; area: 5,040 square inches or 35 square feet

Marcy's Bed

75 in.

length

|— 39 in. —|

Using the Investigation

Have students work in small groups to solve the problem posed on page 420.

To extend the investigation, have students do the following activity.

- Make a blueprint of your classroom or of a room in your house. Label the blueprint with the dimensions of the room. Find the perimeter and area of the room.

For more information about projects and investigations, visit **Education Place**. www.eduplace.com/math/mw

 **Chapter Pretest**

Use this page to review and remember
what you need to know for this chapter.

 **VOCABULARY**

Choose the best word to complete each sentence.

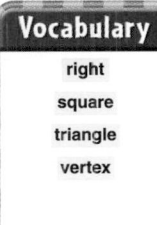

Vocabulary

right

square

triangle

vertex

1. Two sides of a polygon meet at a point called
   the ____. **vertex**

2. A polygon made up of three line segments is called
   a ____. **triangle**

3. A quadrilateral with four right angles and
   four congruent sides is a ____. **square**

 **CONCEPTS AND SKILLS**

Add.

4. $7 + 3\frac{1}{2} + 4\frac{1}{2} + 10$ **25**

5. $2.45 + 6.7 + 8.05$ **17.2**

6. $6.2 + 3.91 + 3.91 + 6.2$ **20.22**

7. $3\frac{1}{4} + 5\frac{1}{2} + 1\frac{1}{2} + 6\frac{1}{4}$ **$16\frac{1}{2}$**

Multiply.

8. $3\frac{1}{2} \times 6$ **21**

9. 3.14×25 **78.5**

Write About It

10. Copy the figures shown below. Then explain
    how to separate the figure into one rectangle
    and two triangles.

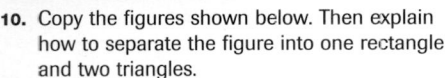

Possible answers:

 Test Prep on the Net

Visit *Education Place* at
eduplace.com/kids/mw/
for more review.

 **Chapter Pretest**

Prerequisite Skills

Items	Skill
1–3	Vocabulary needed for this chapter
4–7	Adding mixed numbers and decimals
8–9	Multiplying mixed numbers and decimals

Chapter Challenges

**For Mathematically
Promising Students**

Use the *Chapter Challenges* resource
book.

Explore: Investigate Perimeter, page
91, after Lesson 1

Extend: Estimate Area, page 93, after Lesson 3

Connect: Planetary Circumferences, page 95,
after Lesson 5

Using The Chapter Pretest

This page will help students review some of the
prerequisite skills needed for this chapter. The chart
above indicates which skills are covered on the
pretest. If students need more help with these
prerequisite skills use *Ways to Success*, Houghton
Mifflin's intervention program.

Students who need more review can visit
Education Place, Houghton Mifflin's
award-winning website.

NSF **Children's Math Worlds**

Build stronger conceptual understanding of geometry with the *Children's Math Worlds* lessons. The
most effective approach is to use the *Children's
Math Worlds* lessons along with the lessons in the
chapter.

Algebra: Perimeter

PLANNING THE LESSON

MATHEMATICS OBJECTIVE
Find the perimeter of plane figures.

Use Lesson Planner CD-ROM for Lesson 16.1.

Daily Routines

Vocabulary

In the word *perimeter,* the prefix *peri-* means "around." What are some words or phrases that have meanings similar to *perimeter*? (border, outline, distance around) **What is the *perimeter* of a picture?** (the distance around the four sides or edges)

Vocabulary Cards

Meeting North Carolina's Standards

Maintain Grade 4 Objective **2.01** Develop strategies to determine the area of rectangles and the perimeter of plane figures.

Lesson Transparency 16.1

Problem of the Day

Farmer Brown has 12 chickens and pigs. In all, the animals have 28 legs. How many chickens and how many pigs does Farmer Brown have? (10 chickens, 2 pigs)

Quick Review

1. How many feet are in 2 yards? (6 feet)
2. How many inches are in 4 feet? (48 inches)
3. How many inches are in 1.5 feet? (18 inches)
4. How many inches are in 0.25 yards? (9 inches)

Lesson Quiz
Find the perimeter.

1. square (18 ft)

4.5 ft

2. rectangle (17 cm)

$2\frac{1}{2}$ cm

6 cm

LEVELED PRACTICE

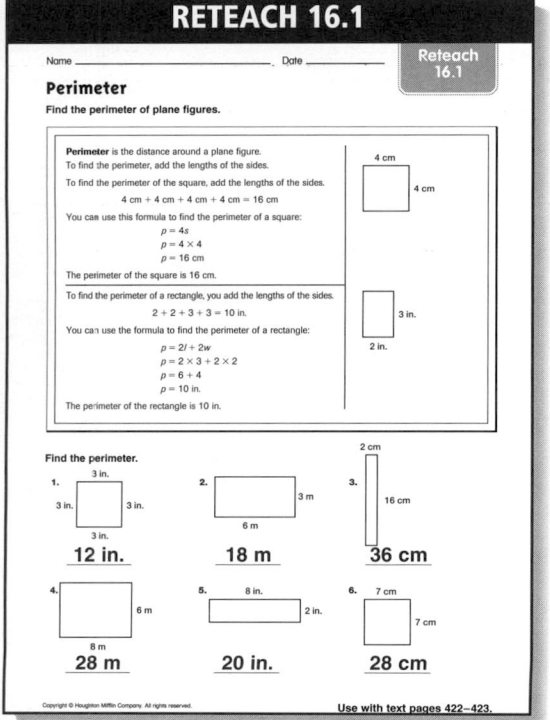

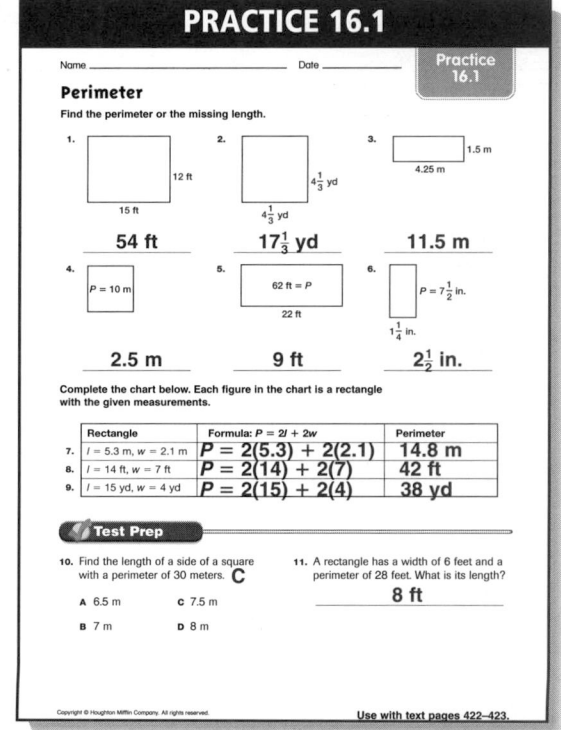

Practice Workbook Page 106

Reaching All Learners
Differentiated Instruction

English Learners

Worksheet 16.1 clarifies the difference between the length and width of rectangles and gives students an opportunity to use the perimeter formula to find missing side measurements. This practice will help them complete the activities in Lesson 1.

Special Needs
KINESTHETIC, TACTILE

Materials: *grid paper or Learning Tool 14, ruler*

- Have students draw a rectangle on grid paper.
- Have them measure and label the length of each side.
- **Add the lengths of all four sides. What is the perimeter?**

Early Finishers
VISUAL/AUDITORY

- Display the following: *A rectangle's perimeter is no more than 12 units. Its length and width are counting numbers. What could its dimension be?* (1×1, 1×2, 1×3, 1×4, 1×5, 2×2, 2×3, 2×4, 3×3) *The perimeter of a square is between 50 and 100 units. How long could the sides be?* (12.5–25 units)

TECHNOLOGY
Spiral Review

Using the *Ways to Assess* CD-ROM, you can create **customized** spiral review worksheets covering any lessons you choose.

Education Place

Encourage students to visit Education Place at **eduplace.com/kids/mw/** for more student activities.

Lesson Planner

Use the Lesson Planner CD-ROM to see how lesson objectives for this chapter are correlated to standards.

Language Arts Connection

Perimeter Poetry

Challenge students to create poems to fit around the perimeter of different plane figures.

- Have them draw a regular plane figure and measure its perimeter, then write a few sentences or a poem to fit the perimeter of their figure.
- Some students may want to write a poem in the shape of a plane figure. They can then add a verse to go around the perimeter.
- Exhibit students' "Perimeter Poetry."

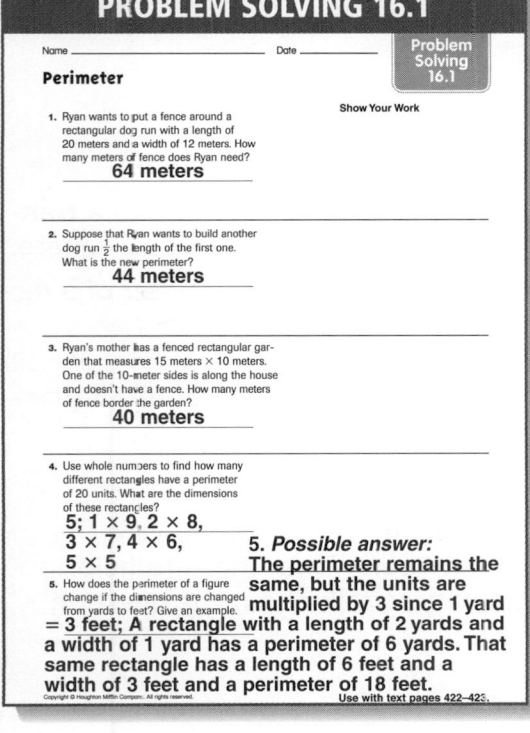

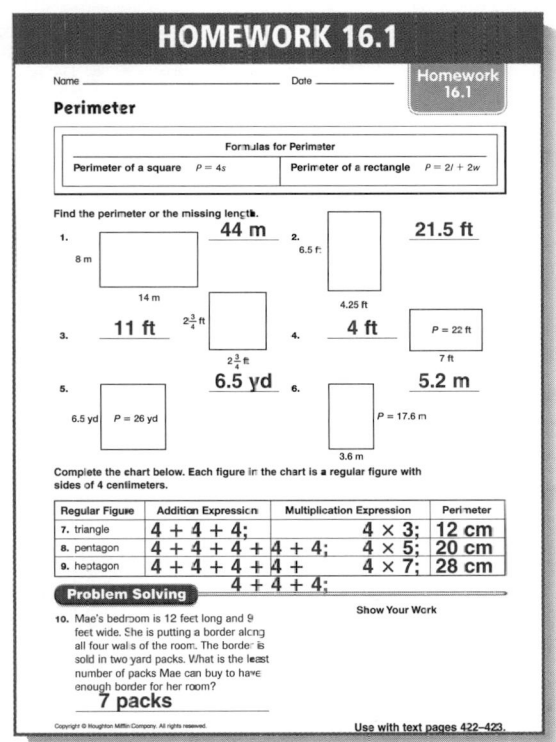

Homework Workbook Page 106

TEACHING LESSON 16.1

LESSON ORGANIZER

Objective Find the perimeter of plane figures.

Resources Reteach, Practice, Enrichment, Problem Solving, Homework, English Learners, Transparencies, Math Center

Materials Centimeter Grid Transparency, centimeter grid paper or Learning Tool 13

Activity

Warm-Up Activity
Rectangles and Squares

Whole Group	5 minutes	Visual, Tactile

- **What are some facts we know about rectangles?** (A rectangle has two sets of parallel sides; each set is equal in length; the two sets are not necessarily equal in length to each other; it has four right angles.)

- **What are some facts we know about squares?** (A square has two sets of parallel sides; all sides are equal in length; it has four right angles.)

Algebra

Perimeter

Objective Find the perimeter of plane figures.

Learn About It   MathTracks 2/13 Listen and Understand

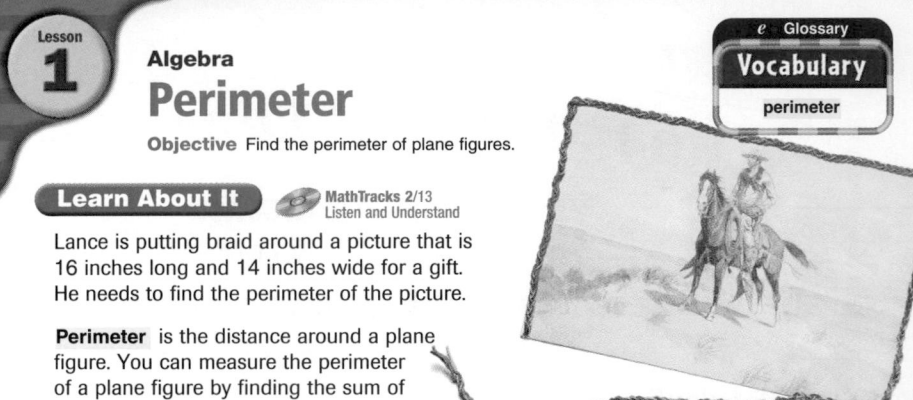

Lance is putting braid around a picture that is 16 inches long and 14 inches wide for a gift. He needs to find the perimeter of the picture.

Perimeter is the distance around a plane figure. You can measure the perimeter of a plane figure by finding the sum of the lengths of its sides.

Materials: centimeter grid paper

STEP 1 On a piece of centimeter grid paper, draw this rectangle.

STEP 2 Copy and complete the addition sentence to find the perimeter of the rectangle.

$5 + 3 + \blacksquare + \blacksquare = $ _____

$5 + 3 + 5 + 3 = 16$

You can also use a formula to find the perimeter of a rectangle. If P represents perimeter, l represents length, and w represents width, then:

$$P = l + w + l + w$$
$$= 2 \times l + 2 \times w$$
or
$$2l + 2w$$

You can use formulas to find the perimeter of any square or rectangle.

Using Formulas for Perimeter

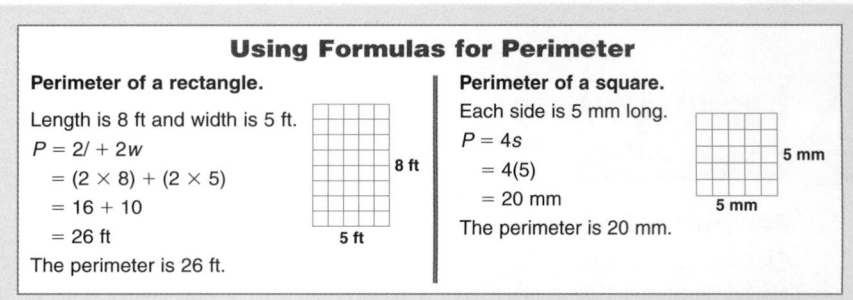

Perimeter of a rectangle.

Length is 8 ft and width is 5 ft.

$P = 2l + 2w$

$= (2 \times 8) + (2 \times 5)$

$= 16 + 10$

$= 26$ ft

The perimeter is 26 ft.

Perimeter of a square.

Each side is 5 mm long.

$P = 4s$

$= 4(5)$

$= 20$ mm

The perimeter is 20 mm.

422

---

1 Introduce

Materials: *Centimeter Grid Transparency, centimeter grid paper or Learning Tool 13*

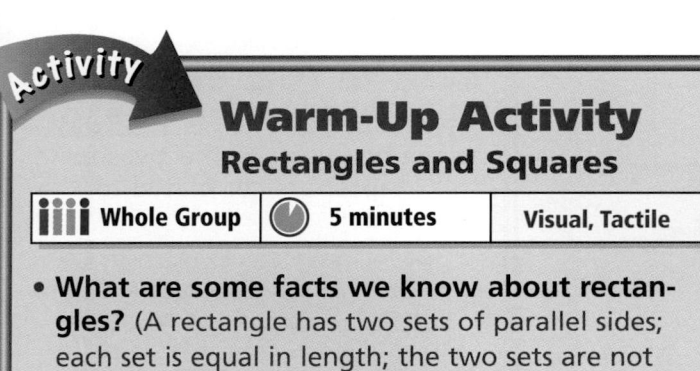

- On the transparency, draw a polygon like the one shown here. You will want to make your figure much larger. Have students copy the polygon onto their grid paper.

- **How many sides does this figure have?** (10)

- **How can you find the distance around this polygon?** (Find the lengths of the sides and add them.)

- **What is the total distance around the polygon?** (54 units)

2 Develop

Guide students through the *Learn About It* section.

- After Steps 1 and 2, use the following questions as a transition to the formula for the perimeter of a 3-by-3 square.

- **How could you use the formula for the perimeter of a rectangle to find the perimeter of the square?** Since, $l = 3$ and $w = 3$ then, $P = 2 \times 3 + 2 \times 3 = (2 + 2) \times 3 = 4 \times 3 = 12$ **What is the formula for finding the perimeter of a square with side equal to s?** ($P = 4s$)

Guided Practice

Have students complete **Exercises 1–2** as you observe. Remind them to use the *Ask Yourself* questions to help. Give students the opportunity to talk about the question in *Explain Your Thinking*.

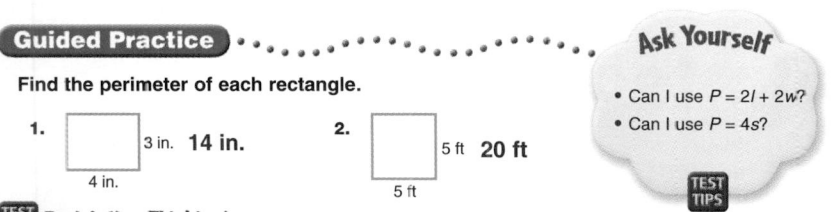
Find the perimeter of each rectangle.

Ask Yourself
- Can I use $P = 2l + 2w$?
- Can I use $P = 4s$?

1. 3 in. | 4 in. — **14 in.**

2. 5 ft | 5 ft — **20 ft**

Explain Your Thinking How much braid does Lance need for the picture shown on page 422? Explain how you know.

60 in.; The distance around the painting is $2 \times 14 + 2 \times 16$ or 60 inches.

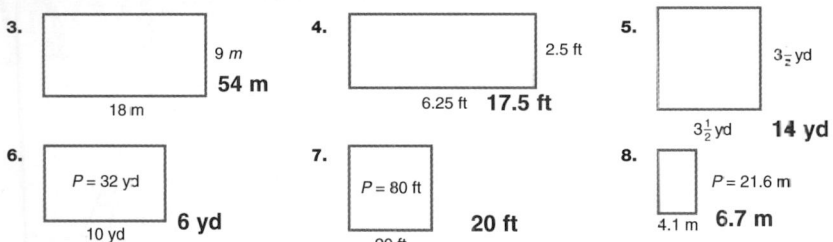
Practice and Problem Solving

Find the perimeter or the missing measurement for each rectangle.

3. 9 m | 18 m — **54 m**

4. 2.5 ft | 6.25 ft — **17.5 ft**

5. $3\frac{1}{2}$ yd | $3\frac{1}{2}$ yd — **14 yd**

6. $P = 32$ yd | 10 yd — **6 yd**

7. $P = 80$ ft | 20 ft — **20 ft**

8. $P = 21.6$ m | 4.1 m — **6.7 m**

Copy and complete the chart below. Each figure in the chart is a regular figure with sides of 3 centimeters.

	Regular Figure	Addition Expression	Multiplication Expression	Perimeter
9.	pentagon	$3 + 3 + 3 + 3 + 3$	5×3	15 cm
10.	hexagon	$3 + 3 + 3 + 3 + 3 + 3$	6×3	18 cm
11.	octagon	$3 + 3 + 3 + 3 + 3 + 3 + 3 + 3$	8×3	24 cm

Solve.

12. **Analyze** A border will be put at the top of the walls in a 12 ft by 16 ft room. What is the maximum length of border that should be bought? Why might less be needed? **12–13. See Additional Answers on Page 443.**

13. **Explain** A rectangular room has sides of 15 feet and 18 feet. You want to use the formula $P = 2l + 2w$. What values would you use for l and w? Does it matter if you switch the values? Explain.

Daily Review | Test Prep

Complete. (Ch. 6, Lessons 2–3)

6,000
14. 3 T = ▮ lb

72
15. 6 ft = ▮ in.

8
16. 2 gal = ▮ qt

48
17. 3 lb = ▮ oz

18. Find the perimeter of a rectangle with a length of 6 cm and width of 8 cm.

A 14 cm
C 28 cm
B 24 cm
D 32 cm

Extra Practice See page 443, Set A.

The width of a rectangle is 7.5 in. The length is twice that. What is the perimeter of the rectangle? (45 in.)

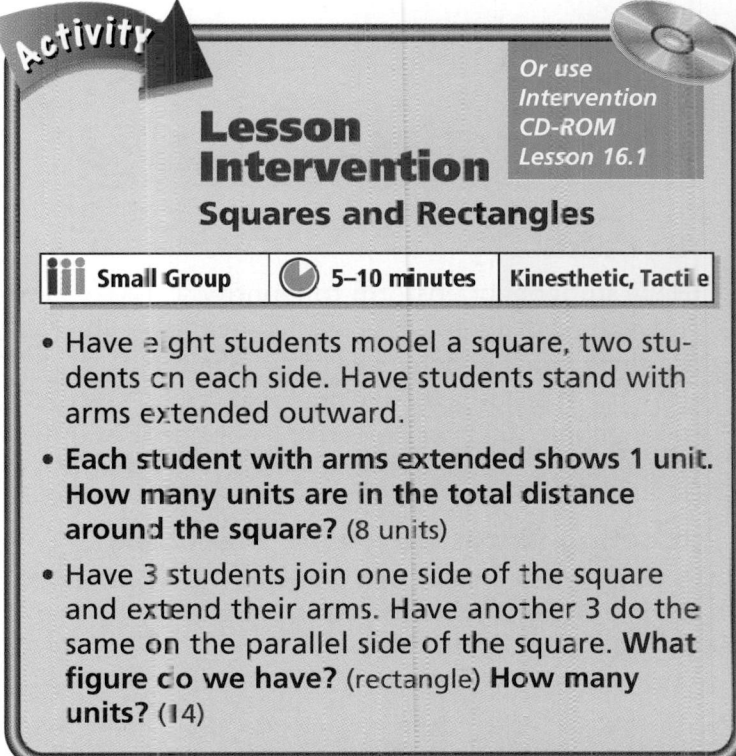

Activity

Lesson Intervention

Squares and Rectangles

Or use Intervention CD-ROM Lesson 16.1

| Small Group | 5–10 minutes | Kinesthetic, Tactile |

- Have eight students model a square, two students on each side. Have students stand with arms extended outward.
- Each student with arms extended shows 1 unit. How many units are in the total distance around the square? (8 units)
- Have 3 students join one side of the square and extend their arms. Have another 3 do the same on the parallel side of the square. **What figure do we have?** (rectangle) **How many units?** (14)

3 Practice

Assign **Exercises 3–18** as independent work.

Common Error

Choosing the wrong operation Students might automatically think that all problems involving squares and perimeter are solved by multiplication. If the length of a side is given, you use multiplication to find the perimeter. However, if the perimeter of a square is given, then you divide by 4 to get the length of a side of a square.

4 Assess and Close

- **How do you find the perimeter of a square?** (Multiply the length of any side by 4.)
- **How do you find the perimeter of a rectangle?** (Multiply the length by 2, multiply the width by 2, then add the products.)

Assign the **LESSON QUIZ** on Transparency 16.1 to further assess student understanding.

Keeping a Journal

Have students write about real-life situations that might call for finding the perimeter of a figure.

Problem-Solving Strategy: Find a Pattern

PLANNING THE LESSON

MATHEMATICS OBJECTIVE
Use a pattern to solve a problem.

 *Use Lesson Planner CD-ROM for Lesson 16.2.*

Daily Routines

Vocabulary
Have students brainstorm to identify some ways the word *pattern* is used in everyday life. (sewing or quilt pattern, play patterns in football, patterns of behavior, bird migration patterns) Discuss how people discover patterns. (People look at specific situations and see what they might have in common.)

Vocabulary Cards

Meeting North Carolina's Standards
5.01 Describe, extend, and generalize numeric and geometric patterns using tables, Graphs, words, and symbols.
Also **1.03**

Lesson Transparency 16.2

Problem of the Day
How many triangles of all sizes are in this diagram? (18)

Quick Review
Evaluate.
1. 5^2 (25)
2. 1^{10} (1)
3. 7^3 (343)
4. 10^4 (10,000)

Lesson Quiz
Use a pattern to solve each problem.
1. How many small squares will be in the tenth diagram? (100)

2. How many squares of all sizes are in this diagram? (30)

LEVELED PRACTICE

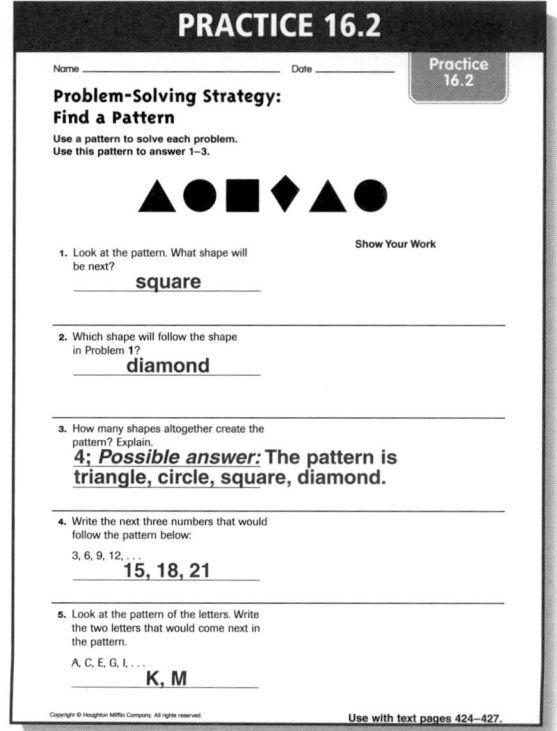

RETEACH 16.2

Name _____ Date _____

Reteach 16.2

Problem-Solving Strategy: Find a Pattern

Read It Look for information.
Billy read 2 pages on Monday, 4 pages on Tuesday, and 8 pages on Wednesday. If the pattern continues, how many pages will Billy read on Friday?

Picture It Here is a model of the information.

Solve It Use the model to solve the problem.
Make a table to organize the data.

Day	1	2	3	4	5
Pages read	2	4	8	16	32

×2 ×2 ×2 ×2

Each day Billy doubles the number of pages he reads.
On Friday, Billy will read 32 pages.

Try This! Complete the model. Solve. **Show Your Work**
1. Fred calls three people. Then each of those three people call three people. And each of those three people call three people, and so on. How many people are called after the fifth round of people calling?

243 people

Copyright © Houghton Mifflin Company. All rights reserved.   Use with text pages 424–427.

PRACTICE 16.2

Name _____ Date _____

Practice 16.2

Problem-Solving Strategy: Find a Pattern
Use a pattern to solve each problem.
Use this pattern to answer 1–3.

▲ ● ■ ◆ ▲ ●

Show Your Work

1. Look at the pattern. What shape will be next?
   square

2. Which shape will follow the shape in Problem 1?
   diamond

3. How many shapes altogether create the pattern? Explain.
   4; Possible answer: The pattern is triangle, circle, square, diamond.

4. Write the next three numbers that would follow the pattern below:
   3, 6, 9, 12, ...
   15, 18, 21

5. Look at the pattern of the letters. Write the two letters that would come next in the pattern.
   A, C, E, G, I, ...
   K, M

Copyright © Houghton Mifflin Company. All rights reserved.   Use with text pages 424–427.

ENRICHMENT 16.2

Name _____ Date _____

Enrichment 16.2

Numbers and Patterns
In this pattern, numbers are drawn with dots to make rectangles. Below are the first four numbers.

Geometric Shape	••	••• •••	•••• •••• ••••	••••• ••••• ••••• ••••• •••••

1. What are the first four numbers?
   2, 6, 12, 20

2. What are the next two numbers? Fill in the dots, if necessary.
   30, 42

3. Did you need the dots to answer Problem 2? Explain.
   Answers will vary.

4. What is the rule for this pattern of numbers that make rectangles?
   Possible answer: It has 1 more dot in each row than it has columns.

5. Pick a number between 12 and 98. Use this number as one factor of a number that makes a rectangle. Give it to a classmate to make two rectangles that use your number as a factor.
   Answers will vary.

Copyright © Houghton Mifflin Company. All rights reserved.   Use with text pages 424–427.

Practice Workbook Page 107

Reaching All Learners
Differentiated Instruction

English Learners

Worksheet 16.2 develops students' ability to recognize patterns in preparation for their completion of the problems in Lesson 2.

Inclusion
KINESTHETIC, TACTILE

Materials: *1-inch tiles*

- Have students count a 2- and 3-unit square.
- **Can you discover any pattern?** (number of units equals the square of the number of units in one side) **How many units would be in a 4-unit square?** (16)

Gifted and Talented
VISUAL, TACTILE

Materials: *grid paper or Learning Tool 14*

- Have students sketch and solve the following problem: *A 12 × 9 ft floor is patterned with alternating light and dark 1 ft² tiles. how many light and dark tiles cover the floor?* (54 light and 54 dark)

TECHNOLOGY

Spiral Review

To reinforce skills on lessons taught earlier, create **customized** spiral review worksheets using the *Ways to Assess* CD-ROM.

Tool Software

Use *Easy Sheet* or another spreadsheet to explore this lesson more fully.

eBook

An electronic version of this lesson can be found in eMath*Book*.

Houghton Mifflin
Math

e MathBook

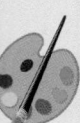

Art Connection

Op-Art
Materials: *reference materials*

- Explain to students that the term *Op-Art* (for Optical Art) was coined to describe a mathematically oriented form of abstract art that uses repetition of simple forms and colors to create visual effects.
- Have students research Op-Art in art reference books.
- Have students talk about the effects created by the patterns of some Op-Art paintings.
- Invite students to make their own Op-Art.

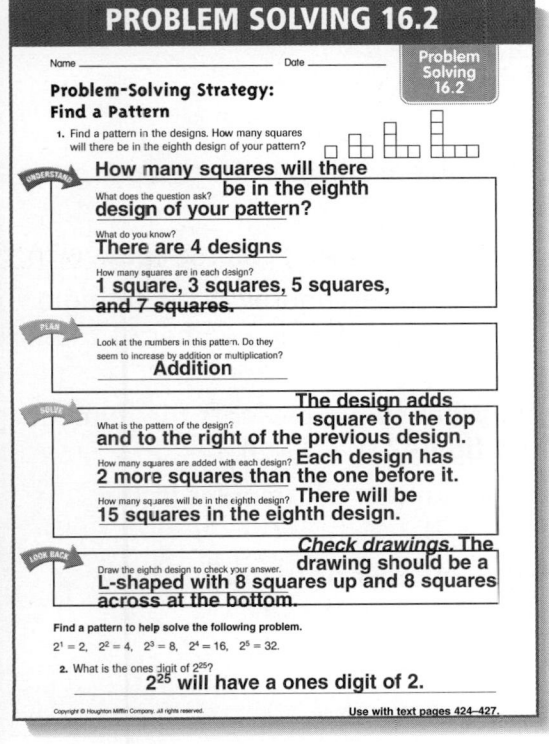

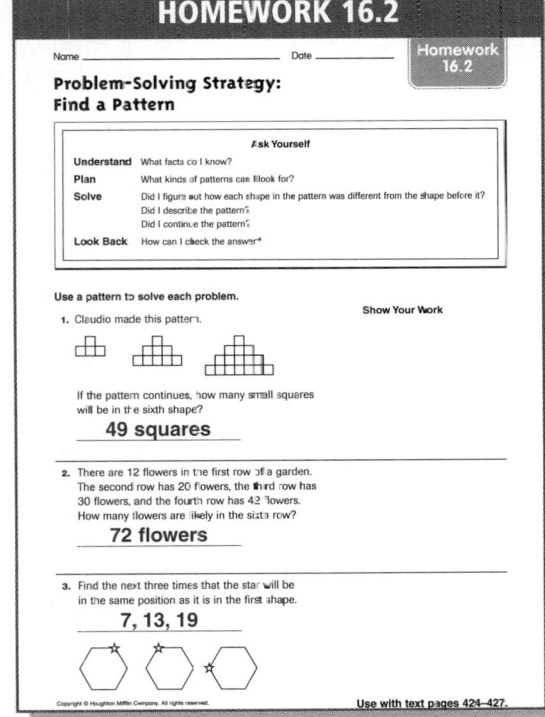

Homework Workbook Page 107

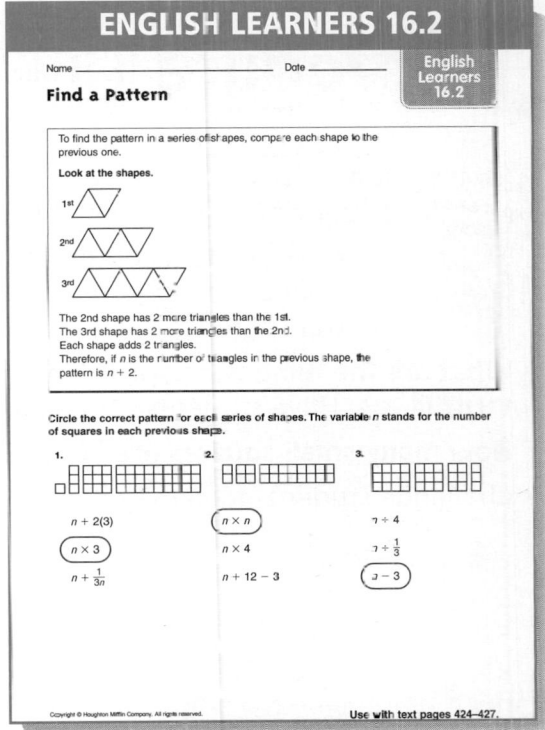

TEACHING LESSON 16.2

LESSON ORGANIZER

Objective Use a pattern to solve a problem.

Resources Reteach, Practice, Enrichment, Homework, Problem Solving, English Learners, Transparencies, Math Center

Materials Centimeter Grid Transparency, chips, triangle tiles, grid paper or Learning Tool 14, Problem Solving: Four Step Process Transparency

---

Activity

Warm-Up Activity
Make a Table

iii Small Group	⏱ 5 minutes	Visual, Tactile

Materials: *chips*

- Have each student put 4 chips into a box.

- **How might you set up a table to record the number of students and the total number of chips?** (Show 1, 2, 3, and so on as the numbers of students. In second row show 4, 4 + 4, 4 + 4 + 4, and so on as the chips accumulate.) **How would you extend the table to four students?** (In the second row under 4 students, write 4 + 4 + 4 + 4.)

Problem-Solving Strategy

Find a Pattern

Objective Use a pattern to solve a problem.

Problem Jenny uses triangular tiles to make the shapes on the right. If the pattern continues, how many tiles will be in the sixth figure in the pattern?

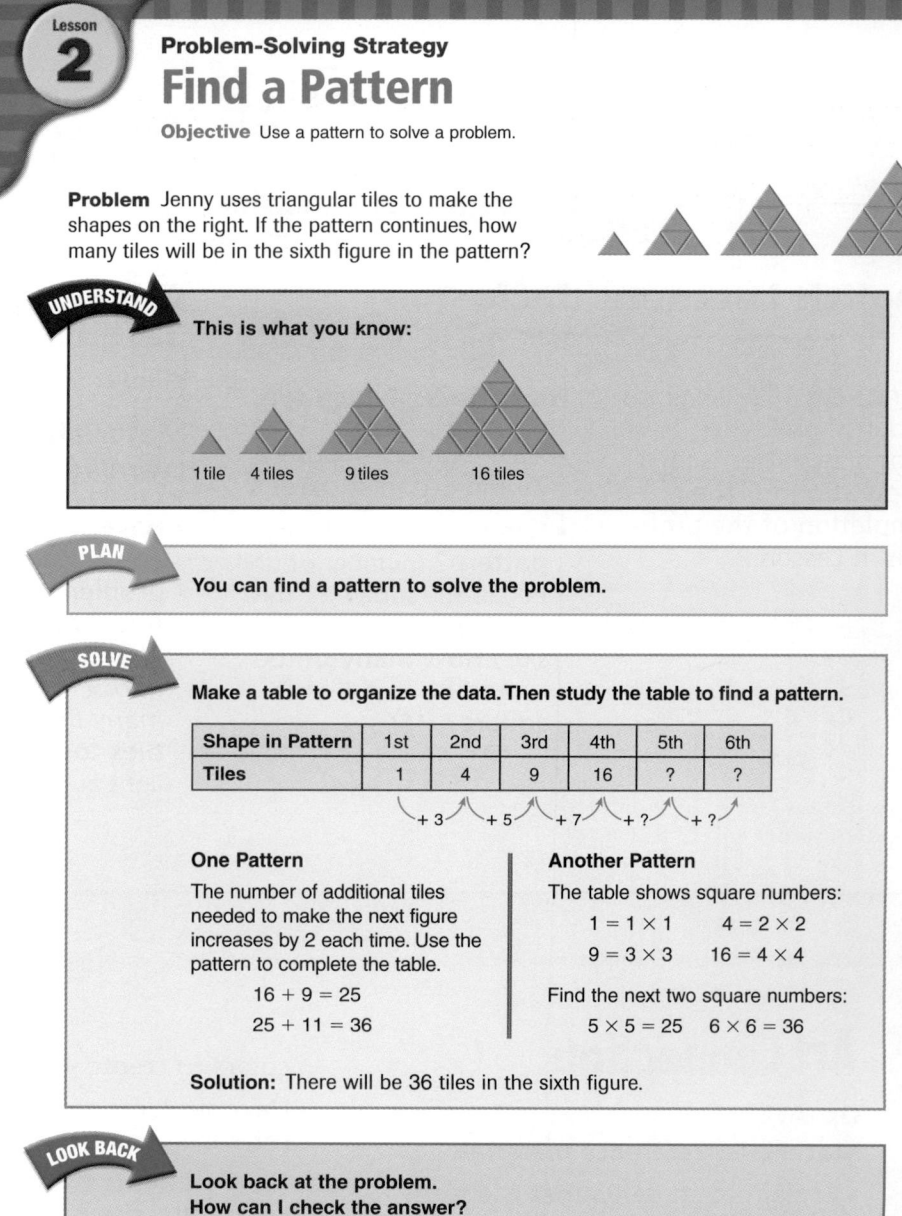

UNDERSTAND

This is what you know:

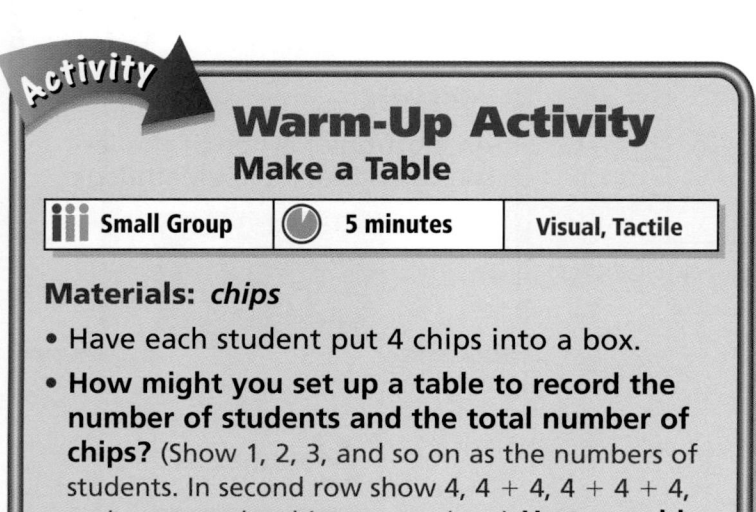

1 tile   4 tiles   9 tiles   16 tiles

PLAN

You can find a pattern to solve the problem.

SOLVE

Make a table to organize the data. Then study the table to find a pattern.

Shape in Pattern	1st	2nd	3rd	4th	5th	6th
Tiles	1	4	9	16	?	?

+ 3   + 5   + 7   + ?   + ?

One Pattern

The number of additional tiles needed to make the next figure increases by 2 each time. Use the pattern to complete the table.

$16 + 9 = 25$

$25 + 11 = 36$

Another Pattern

The table shows square numbers:

$1 = 1 \times 1$ $4 = 2 \times 2$

$9 = 3 \times 3$ $16 = 4 \times 4$

Find the next two square numbers:

$5 \times 5 = 25$ $6 \times 6 = 36$

Solution: There will be 36 tiles in the sixth figure.

LOOK BACK

Look back at the problem. How can I check the answer?

424

Activity

① Introduce   iiii Whole Group   ⏱ 5 minutes

Materials: *Centimeter Grid Transparency, grid paper or Learning Tool 14*

- Have students outline a 1 × 1, 2 × 2, and 3 × 3 square on grid paper as you do so on the transparency.

- **What are the dimensions of the next figure in the pattern?** (4 × 4) Have students outline a 4 × 4 square.

- **How many small squares are in each figure?** (1, 4, 9, 16)

- Challenge students to come up with a rule for the pattern.

② Develop

You may wish to use the Problem Solving: Four Step Process Transparency.

Guide students through problem-solving steps on page 424.

- Have students draw the first three figures in the triangle sequence and label each figure with the number of triangles in each row.

- **Look at the Solve step. What sum represents the number of triangles in the third figure?** (1 + 3 + 5)

- **What sum represents the number of triangles in the fourth figure?** (1 + 3 + 5 + 7)

- **What sum represents the number of triangles in the sixth figure?** (1 + 3 + 5 + 7 + 9 + 11)

Guided Practice

Use the Ask Yourself questions to help you solve each problem.

1. Look at the figures below. If the pattern continues, how many small squares will be in the fifth figure? **30**

2. Find the seventh figure in the pattern shown below.

(**Hint**) Think about how the shape moves.

Ask Yourself

 **UNDERSTAND** — What facts do I know?

PLAN — What kinds of patterns can I look for?

SOLVE —
• Did I figure out how each shape in the pattern was different from the shape before it?
• Did I describe the pattern?
• Did I continue the pattern?

LOOK BACK — How can I check the answer?

TEST TIPS

Independent Practice

Find a pattern to solve each problem.

3. Howard uses triangular tiles to make the figure at the right. If the finished figure has 7 rows, and the pattern continues, how many white tiles are in the figure? **21**

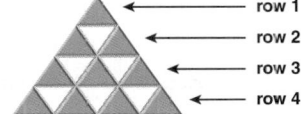
← row 1
← row 2
← row 3
← row 4

4. Look at these grids. How many squares of any size are there in a 5×5 grid? **55**

1 square

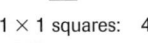

1×1 squares:	4
2×2 squares:	1
Total squares:	5

1×1 squares:	9
2×2 squares:	4
3×3 squares:	1
Total squares:	?

5. **Reasoning** Find the next three times in the pattern that the shaded triangle will be in the same position as it was in the first shape in the pattern. Explain.
5th, 9th, and 13th shapes. Every fourth shape in the pattern is in the same position as the first shape.

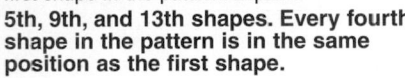
1 2 3 4

Go On

Technology Connection
Explore Patterns with Technology

Students use software to create a geometric pattern and a calculator to explore iterations of the pattern.

Have students use 2-D World in Shape Up! to design their own quilt block patterns.

Have students solve using calculators as needed.

1. How many of each different shape are in your block? (Check students' work.)

2. Imagine you are making a quilt. It has 8 rows each with 6 blocks. How many of each shape are in a row? How many of each shape are in the whole quilt? (Check students' work.)

3. How many of each shape are needed for 5 quilts?(Check students' work.)

---

③ Practice

Guided Practice

Have students complete **Exercises 1–2** as you observe. Remind them to use the *Ask Yourself* questions to help.

Assign **Exercises 3–5** as independent work. Have students share and discuss their work.

Problem-Solving Reminders

Have students review their answers to make sure they have done the following:

• expressed the solution clearly

• used appropriate mathematical notation and terms

• supported their solution with verbal and symbolic work

• determined the reasonableness of the solution in the context of the original problem.

DAILY TEST PREP

Which expression will give the seventh number in this number pattern? (B)

4, 15, 26, . . .

A. 11 × 7 − 4   C. 11 × 6

B. 11 × 6 + 4   D. 11 × 7 − 7

Activity

Lesson Intervention

Predicting Patterns

Or use Intervention CD-ROM Lesson 16.2

| i Individual | ⏱ 5–10 minutes | Visual, Tactile |

Materials: *triangle tiles*

* Display the figures. Have students build them with the tiles.

* **How many triangles in each figure?** (1, 4, 9) **Write each total under each figure. How much does each total increase?** (+3, +5)

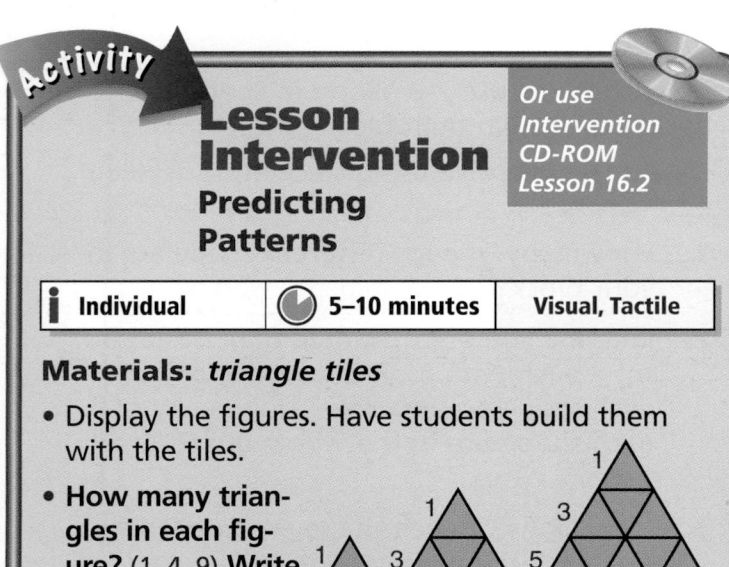

* **How many triangles are in each row of the 1st triangle?** (1) **the 2nd?** (1, 3) **the 3rd?** (1, 3, 5) **Record the numbers.**

* **How many triangles will be in each row of the next triangle in this pattern?** (1, 3, 5, 7) **Build it to check your predictions.**

Choose a Strategy

Solve. Show your work. Tell what strategy you used. *Possible strategies are given.*

6. Emma cleans her couch. She finds 8 coins worth a total of 58¢. What coins does Emma find? **1 quarter, 2 dimes, 2 nickels, 3 pennies; Guess and Check**

7. Ken cuts a 10-foot long speaker wire into two pieces. The first piece is three times as long as the second piece. How long is each piece of speaker wire? $7\frac{1}{2}$ ft, $2\frac{1}{2}$ ft; Draw a Diagram

8. Yossi used blocks to build a pattern. How many blocks will be in the next figure in the pattern? **15 blocks; Find a Pattern**

PROBLEM-SOLVING Strategies

Use Models
Draw a Diagram
Find a Pattern
Guess and Check
Make an Organized List
Make a Table
Solve a Simpler Problem
Use Logical Reasoning
Work Backward
Write an Equation

Data Use the histogram to solve Problems 9–13.

The histogram shows how old the houses on Wyoming Avenue were in the year 2000.

9. How many houses are on Wyoming Avenue? **145**

10. How many houses were built more than 30 years before 2000? **85**

11. How many houses were built less than 30 years before 2000? **60**

12. How many houses were built within 10 years before 2000? **20**

13. What years are represented by Age (years) labeled 21–30? **1970–1979**

14. **Create and Solve** Write and solve a problem involving data from the histogram. *Check students' problems and answers.*

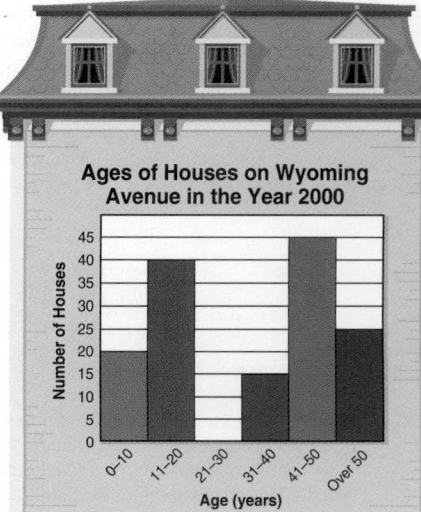

Ages of Houses on Wyoming Avenue in the Year 2000

---

④ Assess and Close

Choose a Strategy

Assign **Exercises 6–14** as independent work.

* *Problem Solving for Problems 9–14* Have students explain how they read the histogram to retrieve the data they need.

* **What steps do you take to solve a problem that requires discovering a pattern?** (Draw sketches or write a list of numbers to extend the pattern. Represent the data in a table. Look for a connection between the numbers in columns in the table. Look for a way to get from one number in a row to the next number in that row, or find the difference of the numbers in adjacent columns.)

* **When you think you know what the pattern is, what do you do?** (Check the conclusion against the data to make sure the conclusion fits it.)

Assign the **LESSON QUIZ** on Transparency 16.2 to further assess student understanding.

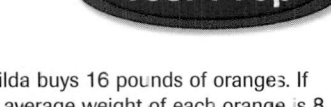

Choose the letter of the correct answer.
If a correct answer is not here, choose NH.

1. Helen is packing her collection of 250 books. Each carton can hold 75 books. How many cartons does Helen need?

   A 2   **B** 3   **(C)** 4   **D** NH

   (Chapter 14, Lesson 8)

2. What is the order of operations to solve this equation?

   $500 - (6 + 2) \times 8$

   F subtraction, addition, multiplication

   G multiplication, subtraction, addition

   H addition, subtraction, multiplication

   (J) addition, multiplication, subtraction

   (Chapter 5, Lesson 6)

3. What angle measure is missing?

   A 45°   **C** 115°

   (B) 70°   **D** NH

   (Chapter 15, Lesson 3)

4. At Sentry Avenue, 10 people leave a bus and 6 people get on. At Whitman Street, 8 people get on and 4 people leave. There are now 40 people on the bus. How many people were on the bus when it arrived at Sentry Avenue?

   F 26   **G** 32   **(H)** 40   **J** 48

   (Chapter 5, Lesson 3)

5. Awilda buys 16 pounds of oranges. If the average weight of each orange is 8 ounces, how many oranges does Awilda buy?

   A 16   **B** 24   **(C)** 32   **D** 64

   (Chapter 6, Lesson 3)

6. Two fifths of Mr. Wilson's class of 20 students are in after-school clubs. One third of Ms. Judd's class of 24 students are in after-school clubs. In which class are more students in after-school clubs?

   Represent Support your solution with a picture. **The same number of students participates from each class. Check students' drawings.** (Chapter 12 Lesson 2)

7. The table shows the population growth of Marion Falls. If the pattern continues, what will be the population in 2010?

Marion Falls Population			
Year	1980	1990	2000
Population	4500	4150	3800

   Explain How did you find the pattern? How did you use the pattern to solve the problem? **3,450. Possible answer: Found the change in population from 1980 to 1990 and from 1990 to 2000 (⁻350); since the change was the same, used the same change to find the population for 2010.** (Chapter 1, Lesson 6)

 **Test Prep on the Net**
Check out *Education Place* at **eduplace.com/kids/mw/** for test prep practice.

Chapter 16 Lesson 2   427

Problem-Solving Test Prep provides an opportunity for students to apply previously learned skills in the types of problem contexts typically encountered in standardized tests. *Problem-Solving Test Prep* includes practice in a variety of formats: multiple choice, free response, and open response.

Students will gain experience in writing about mathematics and using various representations to solve problems. Discuss students' solutions. Have several students explain the thinking behind their work.

 More test prep practice is available on Houghton Mifflin's Web site, **Education Place**. Go to **eduplace.com/kids/mw/**.

 Keeping a Journal

Have students explain how a histogram helps to solve problems.

Lesson 16.3

Algebra: Area of a Parallelogram

PLANNING THE LESSON

MATHEMATICS OBJECTIVE
Use a formula for the area of parallelograms.

Use Lesson Planner CD-ROM for Lesson 16.3.

Daily Routines

Vocabulary

You've learned that *perimeter* is the distance around the edge or boundary of a figure. What do you think we call the space inside a boundary? The space inside a boundary is called the area. What do you think the term *square unit* means? A *square unit* is a square with sides one unit long. What is different about how we measure perimeter and area? (Perimeter is measured by units of length; area by square units.)

> **Vocabulary Cards**

Meeting North Carolina's Standards

Prepare for Grade 6 Objective **2.01** Estimate and measure length, perimeter, area, angles, weight, and mass of two and three-dimensional figures using appropriate tools.

Lesson Transparency 16.3

Problem of the Day

A rectangle has an area of 96 square centimeters and a perimeter of 40 centimeters. What are its dimensions? (8 cm by 12 cm)

Quick Review

1. _____ cm = 2 m (200)
2. _____ mm = 28 cm (280)
3. _____ cm = 1.5 m (150)
4. _____ mm = 265 cm (2,650)
5. _____ m = 365 cm (3.65)
6. _____ km = 4.5 m (0.0045)

Lesson Quiz

Find the areas. Give answers in square units.

1.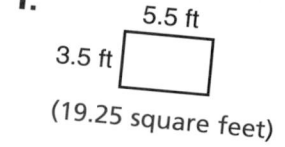
5.5 ft
3.5 ft

(19.25 square feet)

2.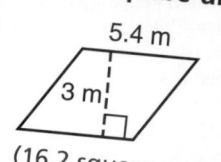
5.4 m
3 m

(16.2 square meters)

LEVELED PRACTICE

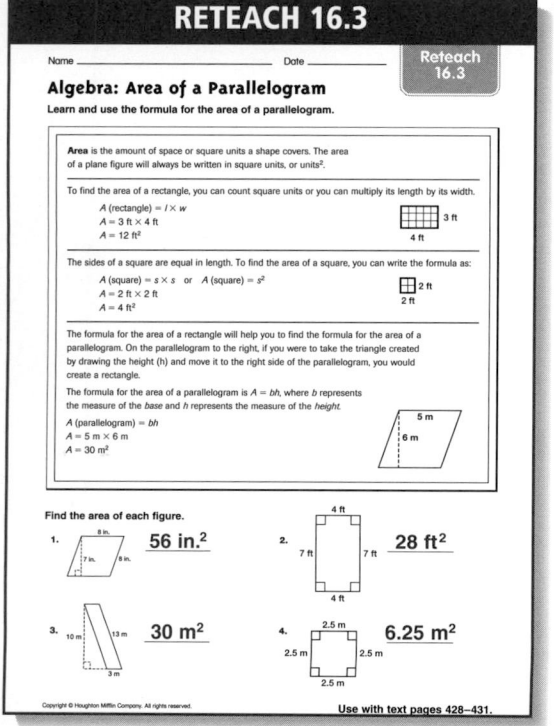

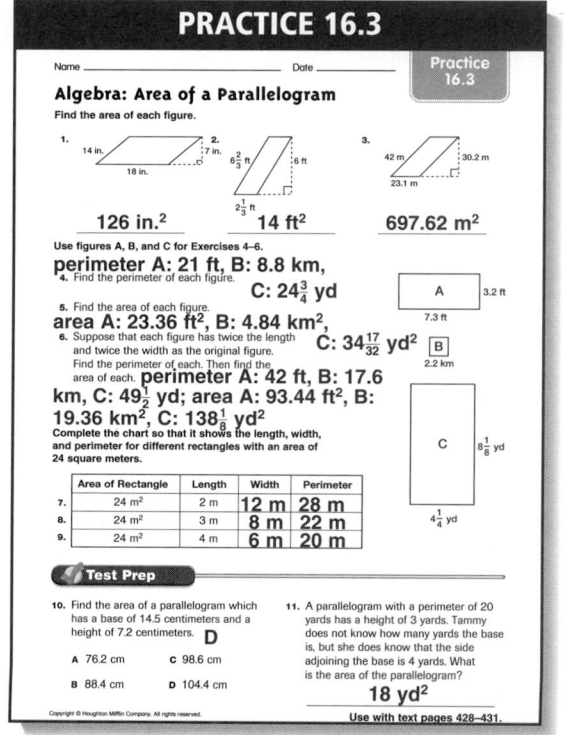

Practice Workbook Page 108

Reaching All Learners
Differentiated Instruction

English Learners

Worksheet 16.3 helps students identify the correct area formula for various types of plane figures and apply those formulas. This will prepare them to complete the activities in Lesson 3.

Special Needs
KINESTHETIC, TACTILE

Materials: *grid paper*

- Draw 3 different-sized rectangles. Count the squares and write that number below each rectangle.
- Count the squares in each rectangle's length and width. Label the rectangle.
- How do you find the total squares in a rectangle? (length × width)

Early Finishers
VISUAL, TACTILE

- On the chalkboard, copy this diagram. Have students find the area of the shaded region.
- Challenge students to write a strategy for finding such an area using basic operations. (Subtract area of square from area of rectangle.)

Art Connection

Go Fly a Kite!
Materials: *reference materials, grid paper, craft paper, tape, string or Learning Tool 14*

- Have students research designs for kites that use quadrilaterals. Have

them design and draw kites in the shape of different-sized parallelograms. Have them build their kites.

- Have students fly their kites and make observations about the dimensions of the kites that fly the best.
- Have students determine the area of their kites.

TECHNOLOGY

Spiral Review

Help students remember skills they learned earlier by creating **customized** spiral review worksheets using the *Ways to Assess* CD–ROM.

Lesson Planner

You can use the Lesson Planner CD–ROM to create a report of the lessons and standards you have taught.

eBook

eMathBook allows students to review lessons and do homework without carrying their textbooks home.

Houghton Mifflin
Math

e MathBook

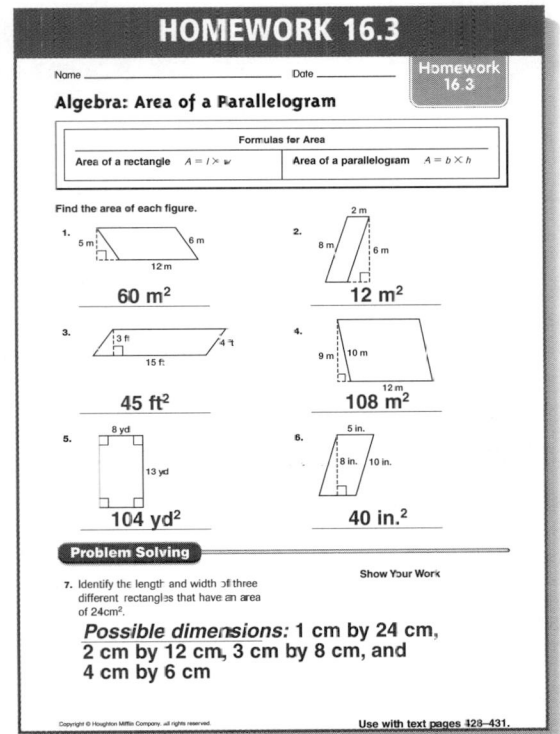

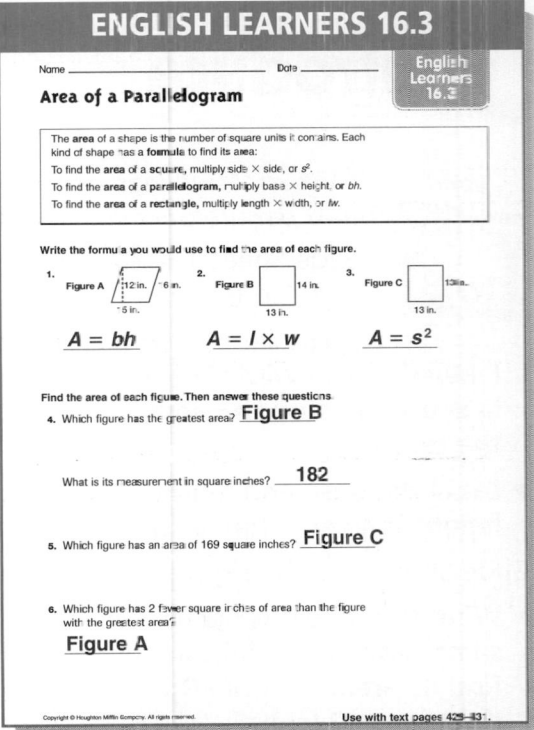

Homework Workbook Page 108

TEACHING LESSON 16.3

LESSON ORGANIZER

Objective Use a formula for the area of parallelograms.

Resources Reteach, Practice, Enrichment, Problem Solving, Homework, English Learners

Materials Blank transparency, parallelogram tiles, Areas of Simple Polygons Transparency (Rectangle, Parallelogram) Transparency Sheets 1 & 2, ruler, scissors, centimeter grid paper or Learning Tool 13

Activity

Warm-Up Activity
Perimeters and Areas of Rearranged Shapes

| 👥 Whole Group | 🕐 5 minutes | Auditory, Tactile |

Materials: *blank transparency, parallelogram tiles*

- Display these figures:

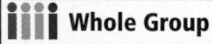

- Have students use the tiles to make these shapes.

- **How do you think the perimeters compare?** (The second perimeter is greater than the first.)

- **What can you say about the space within the two figures?** (It is the same amount.)

Lesson 3

Algebra

Area of a Parallelogram

Objective Use a formula for the area of parallelograms.

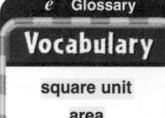

Glossary

Vocabulary
square unit
area

Learn About It  **MathTracks 2/14**
Listen and Understand

A hallway is 9 feet × 5 feet. How much carpeting do you need to cover the floor in the hallway completely? To solve the problem, you need to find the area of the hallway.

A **square unit** is a square with sides one unit long. You can measure **area** (*A*) by finding the number of square units that cover a surface with no overlap.

5 ft
9 ft

To find the area of a rectangle, you can count square units, or you can multiply its length by its width.

$$A \text{ (rectangle)} = l \times w$$
$$= 9 \times 5$$
$$= 45 \text{ square feet, or } 45 \text{ ft}^2$$

> **Remember**
> Area is expressed in square units. For example, if the length and width are measured in feet, the area will be written in square feet, or ft².

Solution: You need 45 square feet of carpeting.

Since the length and width of a square are the same, you can write the formula for area of a square as $A = s \times s$, or $A = s^2$.

$$A = s^2$$
$$A = 3^2$$
$$A = 9 \text{ square meters, or } 9 \text{ m}^2$$

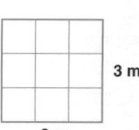
3 m
3 m

You can use what you know about the area of a rectangle to find the formula for the area of any parallelogram.

Materials: centimeter grid paper, ruler, scissors

STEP 1 On a sheet of centimeter grid paper, copy the parallelogram shown at the right. The red dotted line is perpendicular to the base, *b*, and represents the height, *h*.

STEP 2 Cut along the red dotted line. Move the right triangle to the other side of the parallelogram to form a rectangle.

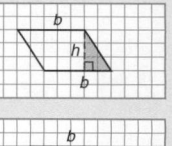

428

---

1 Introduce

Teaching Transparency

for
16.3

Materials: *Areas of Simple Polygons (rectangle and parallelogram), Transparency Sheets 1 & 2*

Slide Sheet 1 underneath Sheet 2 on the overhead to form a rectangle. Point to the rectangle.

- **The length, or base, of the rectangle is labeled *b*. The width, or height, is labeled *h*. What formula is used to find the area?** ($A = bh$) Write $A = bh$ above the rectangle.

- **Label the base and height. If the base is 8 cm and the height is 4 cm, what is its area?** (32 square cm)

Slide Sheet 2 to the right to create a parallelogram.

- **What figure is this?** (a parallelogram) **Does it have the same base and height as the rectangle?** (yes) **How can we find its area?** ($A = bh$) **Did the area change when I moved the triangle?** (no)

428   CHAPTER 16   Lesson 3

2 Develop

Guide students through the *Learn About It* section.

- **Look at Steps 1 and 2 on page 428. What transformation do you perform when you move the triangle from the right side to the left side of the parallelogram?** (translation)

- **How are the length and the width of the rectangle related to the base and height of the parallelogram?** (The lengths are equal and the width is equal to the height.)

- **How is the area of the rectangle related to that of the parallelogram?** (They are equal.)

- **What is a multiplication sentence that gives the area of the parallelogram?** (Area = base × height)

 **STEP 3** Write a multiplication sentence for the area of the rectangle. You can also use the formula for the area of a rectangle to find the formula for the area of a parallelogram. ***See Additional Answers on Page 443.***

You can use a formula to find the area of any parallelogram.

Using the Formula for Area of a Parallelogram

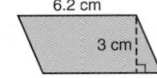

$A = bh$
$= 6.2 \times 3$
$= 18.6$

The area is 18.6 square centimeters, or 18.6 cm².

$A = bh$
$= 7 \times 5\frac{1}{2}$
$= 38\frac{1}{2}$

The area is $38\frac{1}{2}$ square inches, or $38\frac{1}{2}$ in.².

Guided Practice

Ask Yourself
- Which measure is the height?
- Which measures do I multiply?

TEST TIPS

Find the area of each figure.

1.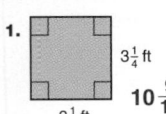
$10\frac{9}{16}$ ft²

2.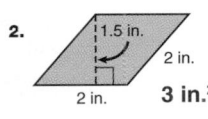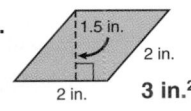
3 in.²

TEST TIPS **Explain Your Thinking ▶** Can the formula $A = bh$ be used to find the area of any rectangle? Explain. **Yes;** *Possible explanation:* **in a rectangle, adjacent sides always form right angles, so the height and the base are the same as the width and length.**

Practice and Problem Solving

Find the area of each figure.

3.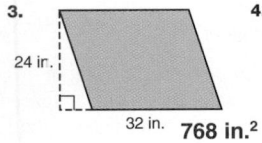
768 in.²

4.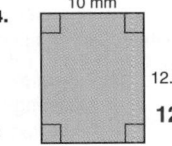

5.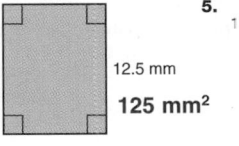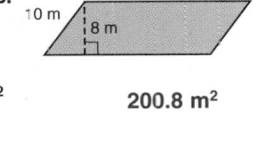
125 mm²   200.8 m²

6.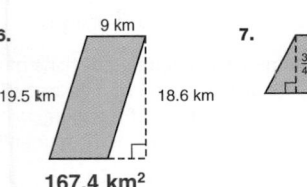
167.4 km²

7.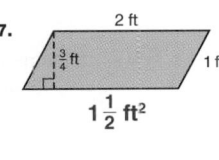
$1\frac{1}{2}$ ft²

8.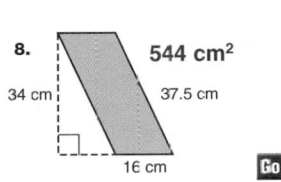
544 cm²

 **Go On**

---

③ Practice

Guided Practice

Have students complete **Exercises 1–2** as you observe. Remind them to use the *Ask Yourself* questions to help. Give students the opportunity to talk about the question in *Explain Your Thinking*.

Assign **Exercises 3–24** as independent work

DAILY TEST PREP

A rectangle has a length of 10 yd and a width of 8 yd. A parallelogram has the same base but the height is twice the width of the rectangle. What is the area of the parallelogram? (160 yd²)

Activity

Lesson Intervention

Or use Intervention CD-ROM Lesson 16.3

Finding the Area of a Rectangle

| Small Group | 5–10 minutes | Visual, Auditory |

Materials: *grid paper or Learning Tool 14*

- **On grid paper, draw a rectangle that covers 15 blocks. How many blocks across and how many down will your rectangle be?** (Possible answers: 5 blocks across, 3 blocks down; or 3 blocks across, 5 blocks down or 1 block across, 15 blocks down, 15 blocks across, 1 block down)

- **Now draw a rectangle that covers 24 blocks. What length and width does it have?** (Possible answers: 24 by 1, 1 by 24, 2 by 12, 12 by 2, 3 by 8, 8 by 3, 4 by 6, or 6 by 4)

- **A rectangle is 15 blocks across and 20 blocks down. Can you find the area without drawing a sketch?** (Yes; 15 × 20 = 300.)

- **How does a formula make it easier to find the area of a rectangle?** (You can multiply length by width without counting square units.)

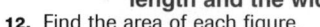

Practice and Problem Solving

Use Figures A, B, and C for Exercises 9–14.

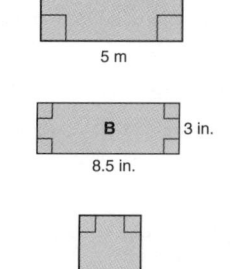
A 5 m
5 m

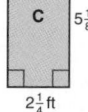
B 3 in.
8.5 in.

C $5\frac{1}{8}$ ft
$2\frac{1}{4}$ ft

9. Find the perimeter of each figure.
   A: $P = 20$ m; B: $P = 23$ in.; C: $P = 14\frac{3}{4}$ ft
10. Find the perimeter of a rectangle that has twice the length and twice the width as Figure A. Repeat for Figure B and Figure C.
    A: $P = 40$ m; B: $P = 46$ in.; C: $P = 29\frac{1}{2}$ ft
11. **Analyze** What is the relationship between the perimeter of a figure and the perimeter of a figure when the length and width are doubled. **The perimeter doubles when the length and the width double.**
12. Find the area of each figure.
    A: $A = 25$ m²; B: $A = 25.5$ in²; C: $A = 11\frac{17}{32}$ ft²
13. Find the area of a rectangle that has twice the length and twice the width as the Figure A. Repeat for Figure B and Figure C.
    A: $A = 100$ m²; B: $A = 102$ in²; C: $A = 46\frac{1}{8}$ ft²
14. **Analyze** What is the relationship between the area of a figure and the area of a figure with twice the length and width? **The area is four times greater when the length and the width double.**

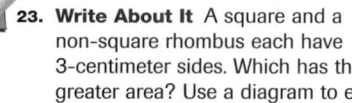

Data Copy and complete the table so that it shows the length, width, and perimeter for different rectangles with an area of 36 square inches.

	Area of Rectangle	Length	Width	Perimeter
15.	36 in.²	1 in.	36 in.	74 in.
16.	36 in.²	2 in.	18 in.	40 in.
17.	36 in.²	3 in.	12 in.	30 in.
18.	36 in.²	4 in.	9 in.	26 in.
19.	36 in.²	6 in.	6 in.	24 in.

20. **Analyze** Look at the results of Exercises 15–19. What is the relationship between the length and the width of rectangles with the same area? How does that relationship affect the perimeter?
20–21. See Additional Answers on Page 443.

21. **Represent** Joe drew a parallelogram with a height of 2 centimeters and an area of 14.7 square centimeters. Draw Joe's parallelogram. How long is its base? **7.35 cm**

22. **Reasoning** Nan used 64 feet of fencing to make a rectangular space for her dog. Find the dimensions of the space if she made the largest possible area for the dog. **16 ft × 16 ft**

23. **Write About It** A square and a non-square rhombus each have 3-centimeter sides. Which has the greater area? Use a diagram to explain. **square; as the height decreases the area decreases**

24. A garden is planted in the shape of a rhombus and fenced with 40 feet of fencing. The height of the rhombus is 3 feet. What is the area of the garden? **30 ft²**

Extra Practice See page 443, Set B.

Practice *continued*

- *Problem Solving for Problems 15–20* Remind students that they are looking for whole number factors of 36. Have students share their analysis resulting from Exercise 20.

Common Error

Misreading height If students are given the lengths of two adjacent sides of a rectangle, they are automatically given the rectangle's base and height. Remind students, however, that in a parallelogram the lengths of two adjacent sides might not be the base and height.

4 Assess and Close

Have students come to the chalkboard and draw rectangles, squares, and parallelograms. Have other students label them and write the appropriate area formulas.

- **What information do you need to find the area of a parallelogram?** (the length of the base, and the length of a segment connecting the bases that is perpendicular to the base)

- **In a rectangle, one side is 5 feet long and another side is 3 feet long. How does this information help you find the area of the rectangle?** (Multiply these numbers to get 15 square feet.)

Assign the **LESSON QUIZ** on Transparency 16.3 to further assess student understanding.

Quick Check

Check your understanding of Lessons 1–3.

Find the perimeter and area. (Lessons 1 and 3)

1.
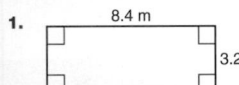
8.4 m
3.2

2.

4 ft $3\frac{1}{4}$ ft
5 ft

3.
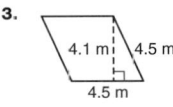
4.1 m   4.5 m
4.5 m

$P = 23.2$ m, $A = 26.88$ m² $P = 18$ ft, $A = 16\frac{1}{4}$ ft² $P = 18$ m, $A = 18.45$ m²

Solve. (Lesson 2)

4. Look at the figures below. If the pattern continues, how many small squares will be in the fifth figure? **512**

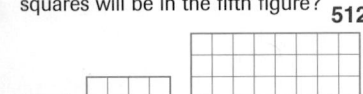

5. The first four figures in a pattern are shown below. When will the dot be in the same position as it was in the first figure in the pattern? **the 9th shape in the pattern**

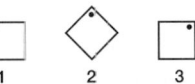
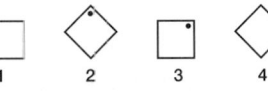
1   2   3   4

WEEKLY WR READER eduplace.com/kids/mw/

On The Farm

Social Studies **Connection**

1 square inch (in.²)   1 square foot (ft²)   1 square yard (yd³)   1 acre

1 in.
1 in.   12 in.   3 feet

12 in.   3 feet

144 square inches   9 square feet   43,560 square feet

The area of a farm is measured in acres.

1. How large is an acre in square yards? **4,840 yd²**

2. **Calculator** How many square feet are in 1 square mile? **27,878,400 ft²**

3. **Calculator** How many acres are there in 1 square mile? **640 acres**

4. **Guess and Check** A rectangular piece of land is almost a square, and is 2 acres in area. Find its dimensions in feet, rounded to the nearest ten feet. **Possible answer: 290 ft by 300 ft**

Quick Check

Purpose: The Quick Check allows you to assess the student's understanding of the concepts presented in Lessons 1–3.

Items	Objectives Tested	Pages	Intervention
1–3	Find the perimeter of plane figures.	422–423	Reteach Resource 16.1 *Ways to Success* 16.1
4–5	Use a pattern to solve a problem.	424–427	Reteach Resource 16.2 *Ways to Success* 16.2
1–3	Use a formula for the area of parallelograms.	428–431	Reteach Resource 16.3 *Ways to Success* 16.3

Keeping a Journal

Have students write a few sentences explaining how the formula for finding the area of a parallelogram is related to the formula for finding the area of a rectangle.

Social Studies Connection

On the Farm

Students will need to experiment to find a number that, when squared, has the product 43,560 square feet. A table or list along with an educated guess could be helpful.

On the board write: $200 \times 200 = 40,000$
$300 \times 300 = 90,000$

Students will need to look for a number between 200 and 300. (208)

Lesson 16.4

Algebra: Area of a Triangle

PLANNING THE LESSON

MATHEMATICS OBJECTIVE
Find and use the formula to find the area of a triangle.

Use Lesson Planner CD-ROM for Lesson 16.4.

Daily Routines

Vocabulary

How did we arrive at the *formula* for the area of a parallelogram? (By translating a triangular slice of a parallelogram, we found that a parallelogram has the same area as a rectangle with the same base and height.) **How do you think we can find the formula for the area of a triangle?** (Accept all reasonable answers. Encourage the use of transformations.)

Vocabulary Cards

Meeting North Carolina's Standards

Prepare for Grade 6 Objective **2.01** Estimate and measure length, perimeter, area, angles, weight, and mass of two and three-dimensional figures using appropriate tools.

Lesson Transparency

16.4

Problem of the Day
Start with $\frac{1}{2}$. Subtract $\frac{1}{2}$. Add $\frac{1}{2}$. Subtract $\frac{1}{2}$, and so on. What is the result if the number of terms is even? (0) if the number of terms is odd? ($\frac{1}{2}$)

Quick Review
Find the mean and mode for each.
1. 1, 8, 8, 6, 7, 7, 8 ($6\frac{3}{7}$, 8)
2. 8, 5, 4, 5, 3, 2 (4.5, 5)
3. 6, 2, 1, 0, 6, 1, 1 ($2\frac{3}{7}$, 1)
4. 5, 7, 5, 7, 5, 7, 5 ($5\frac{6}{7}$, 5)
5. 5, 8, 6, 8, 7, 5, 8 ($6\frac{5}{7}$, 8)
6. 9, 4, 3, 9, 4, 2, 9 ($5\frac{5}{7}$, 9)

Lesson Quiz
Find the area of each triangle.

1.
3.6 in.
4.5 in.
(8.1 square inches)

2.
7 m
9.8 m
(34.3 square meters)

LEVELED PRACTICE

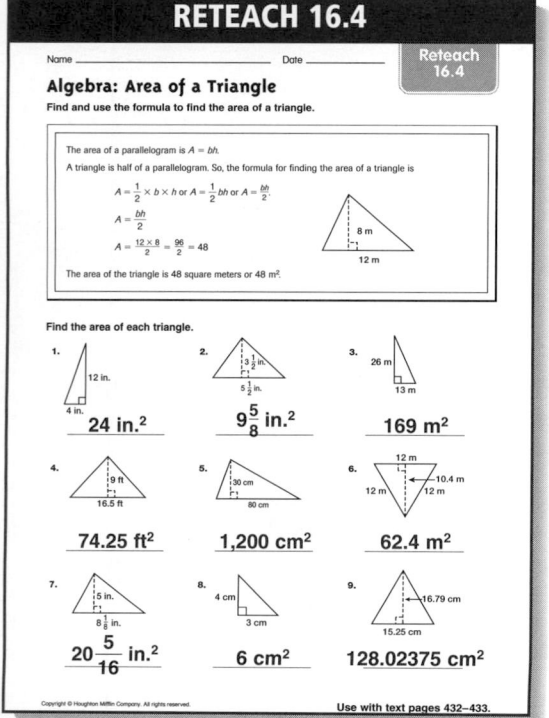

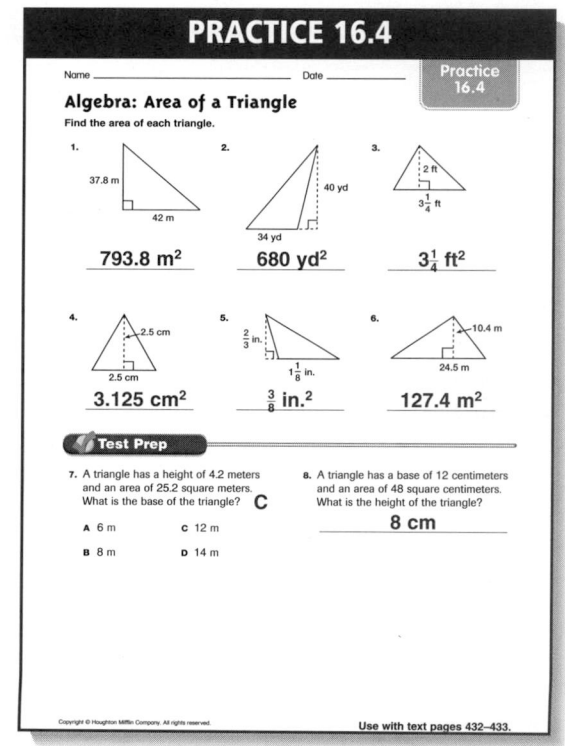

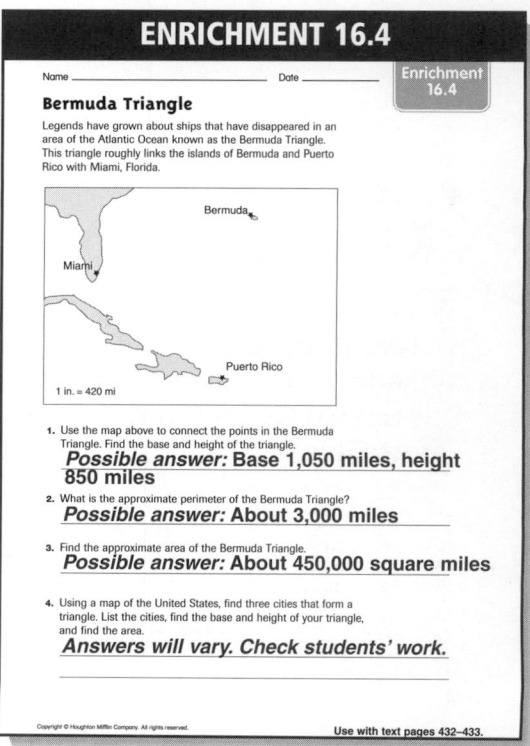

Practice Workbook Page 109

Reaching All Learners
Differentiated Instruction

English Learners

Worksheet 16.4 reinforces students' understanding of the measurement of the height of various triangles, which will help them work through the area problems in this lesson, particularly Problem 11.

Inclusion
KINESTHETIC, TACTILE

Materials: *construction paper, scissors, ruler*

- Have students cut out a large triangle. Help them measure base and height to the nearest inch.

- **What do you do now to find the area?** (Multiply the product of the two measurements and divide by 2. Write area in square inches.)

Gifted and Talented
VISUAL, AUDITORY

- **If a triangle's base and height are in inches, how do you find area in square feet?** (Divide measurements by 12, or divide product by 144)

- **If base and height are in feet, how do you find area in square yards?** (Divide measurements by 3, or divide product by 9)

TECHNOLOGY

Spiral Review

You can prepare students for standardized tests with **customized** spiral review on key skills using the *Ways to Assess* CD-ROM.

Tool Software

Use *Easy Sheet* or another spreadsheet to explore this lesson more fully.

Game

Students can practice their skills using the RoboPacker math game, available on the *Ways to Success* CD.

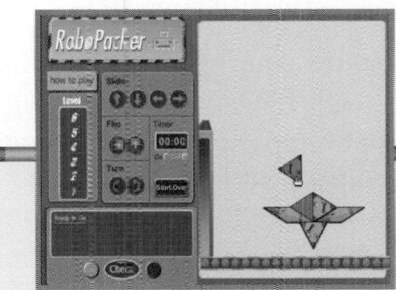

Science Connection

Surveyor's Units of Length

- Different people use different units of measurement in their work. Surveyors in the U.S. use the *rod*, which is 16.5 feet long.

- A plot of land is in the shape of a right triangle. Its base is 6 rods long, its height, 8 rods long.

- What are the base and height of this triangle in feet? How do you find out? (Multiply 6 by 16.5 feet to get 99 feet and multiply 8 by 16.5 feet to get 132 feet.)

- What is the area of the triangle in square rods and square feet? (24 square rods, or 6,534 square feet)

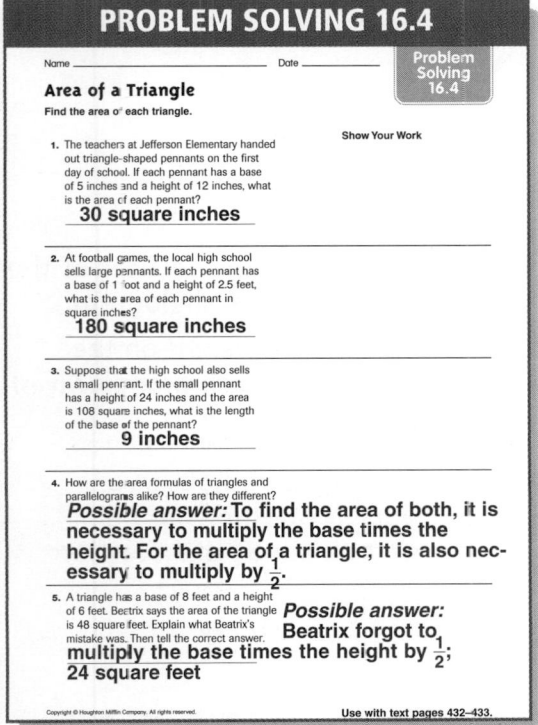

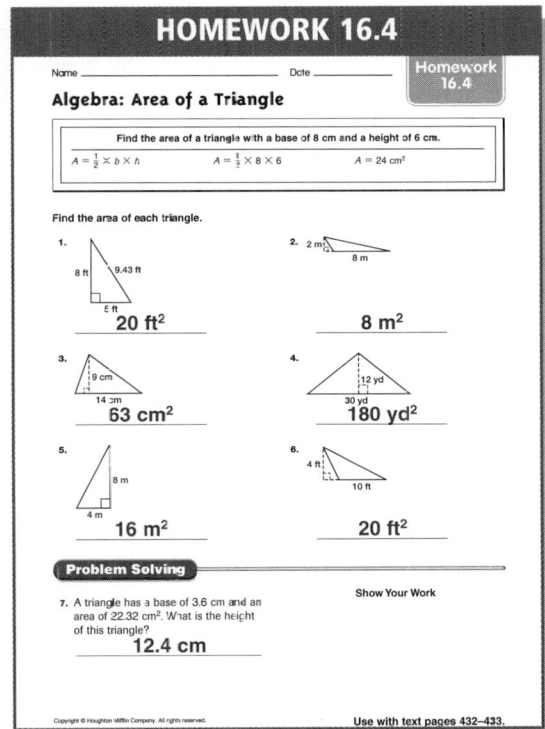

Homework Workbook Page 109

TEACHING LESSON 16.4

LESSON ORGANIZER

Objective Find and use the formula to find the area of a triangle.

Resources Reteach, Practice, Enrichment, Problem Solving, Homework, English Learners

Materials scissors, square tiles, Areas of Simple Polygons (Triangle, Trapezoid) Transparency, grid paper or Learning Tool 14

Activity

Warm-Up Activity
Area of Parallelograms

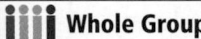 Whole Group 5 minutes | Auditory, Visual

- **How do you find the area of a rectangle?** (Multiply the length and width.)
- **How will the area be expressed if the length and width are in meters?** (square meters)
- **How do you find the area of a parallelogram?** (Multiply the base and the height.)
- **What happens when you sketch a rectangle or parallelogram and then draw one diagonal?** (You get a pair of congruent triangles.)
- **How is a formula useful in finding areas of rectangles and parallelograms?** (It tells how to find all areas using multiplication of two numbers.)

Lesson 4

Algebra
Area of a Triangle

Objective Find and use the formula to find the area of a triangle.

Learn About It

A surveyor lays out building lots along a river. Some lots are parallelograms and some are triangles. How can the surveyor find the area of a triangular lot?

Use what you know about the formula for the area of a parallelogram to write a formula for the area of the triangle.

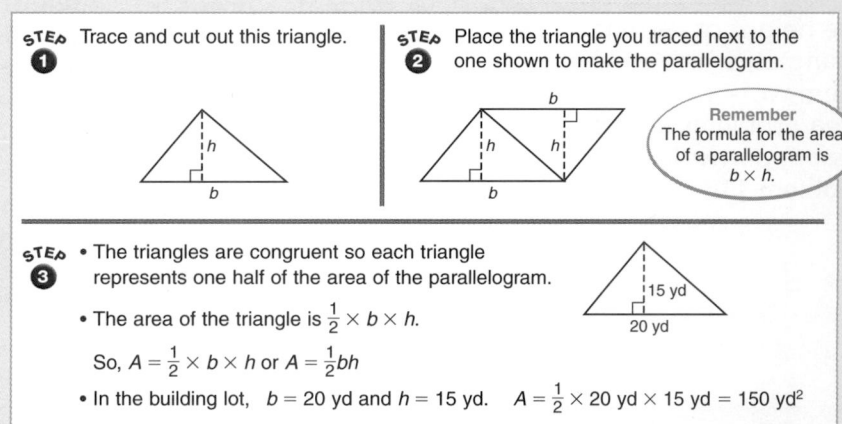

STEP 1 Trace and cut out this triangle.

STEP 2 Place the triangle you traced next to the one shown to make the parallelogram.

> **Remember**
> The formula for the area of a parallelogram is $b \times h$.

STEP 3
- The triangles are congruent so each triangle represents one half of the area of the parallelogram.
- The area of the triangle is $\frac{1}{2} \times b \times h$.

  So, $A = \frac{1}{2} \times b \times h$ or $A = \frac{1}{2}bh$

- In the building lot, $b = 20$ yd and $h = 15$ yd. $A = \frac{1}{2} \times 20$ yd $\times 15$ yd $= 150$ yd^2

Solution: The area of the building lot is 150 yd^2.

Guided Practice

Find the area of each triangle.

Ask Yourself
- What formula do I use?
- Did I use the right numbers?

1. 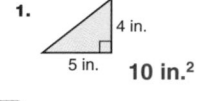 4 in.
   5 in. **10 in.²**

2. 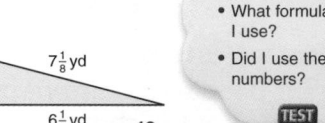 $7\frac{1}{8}$ yd
   $2\frac{1}{2}$ yd
   $6\frac{1}{4}$ yd **$7\frac{13}{16}$ yd²**

TEST TIPS Explain Your Thinking ▶ If you know the lengths of the sides of a right triangle, can you find its area? Use a diagram to explain.
See Additional Answers on Page 443.

432

---

1 Introduce

 Teaching Transparency for 16.4

Materials: *Areas of Simple Polygons (triangle and trapezoid) Transparency*

- Display the transparency so the triangles form a parallelogram. Cover the figure on the right.
- **What is the formula for finding the area of a parallelogram?** ($A = bh$) Write $A = bh$. **If $b = 8$ cm and $h = 4$ cm, what is the area of the parallelogram?** (32 cm²)

- **Into what two figures does the diagonal divide the parallelogram?** (two triangles) Rotate the top triangle so that it matches the bottom one. **Are these triangles congruent?** (yes) **Do they have the same area?** (yes) **If two congruent triangles form a parallelogram, how can we find the area of one triangle?** (Area of one triangle is equal to half the area of the parallelogram.)

2 Develop

Guide students through the *Learn About It* section.

- Have students follow **Step 1**.
- Check students' work to make sure that the vertices of the triangles match and that they form the parallelogram.
- Write $\frac{1}{2}$ *area of parallelogram* $= \frac{1}{2}$ *base* $\times$ *height* on the board. **Will this formula give the area of each triangle?** (yes)

Guided Practice

Have students complete **Exercises 1–2** as you observe. Remind them to use the *Ask Yourself* questions to help. Give students the opportunity to talk about the question in *Explain Your Thinking*.

Find the area of each triangle.

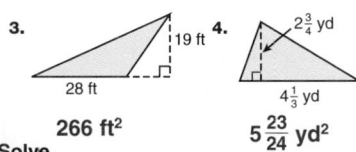

3. 28 ft, 19 ft
266 ft²

4. $2\frac{3}{4}$ yd, $4\frac{1}{3}$ yd
$5\frac{23}{24}$ **yd²**

5. 8.66 cm, 10 cm, 10 cm, 10 cm
43.3 cm²

6. 20 m, 7 m
70 m²

Solve.

7. The corners of the yellow pane of glass at the right meet at the midpoints of each side of the window. What is the area of each purple pane? What is the area of the yellow pane? (Hint: The midpoint of a side is the center point, or middle of that side.) **1.875 ft²; 7.5 ft²**

8. A triangle has a height of 6 inches and an area of 24 in.². What is the length of the base of that triangle? **8 in.**

9. A triangle has a base of 4.5 cm and an area of 27 cm². Find its height. **12 cm**

10. Represent A triangle has a height of *m* inches and a base of *p* inches. Write an expression to represent the area of that triangle. $\frac{1}{2}$ *mp*

11. What's Wrong? The notebook at the right shows how Alan found the area of a triangle. Explain what Alan did wrong.

12. You Decide You need $1\frac{1}{2}$ pounds of peanuts to make trail mix. A 6-oz jar of peanuts costs $1.99. A 10-oz can of peanuts costs $2.89. How will you buy the peanuts? Explain.

11-12. See Additional Answers on Page 443.

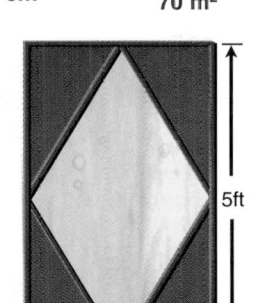
5ft, 3ft

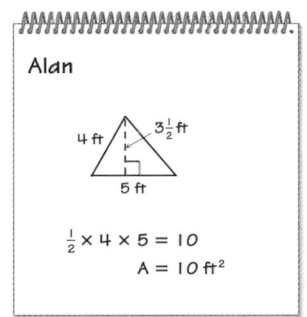
Alan
4 ft, $3\frac{1}{2}$ ft, 5 ft
$\frac{1}{2} \times 4 \times 5 = 10$
A = 10 ft²

Daily Review · Test Prep

For each figure, name the number of lines of symmetry it has. (Ch. 15, Lesson 9)

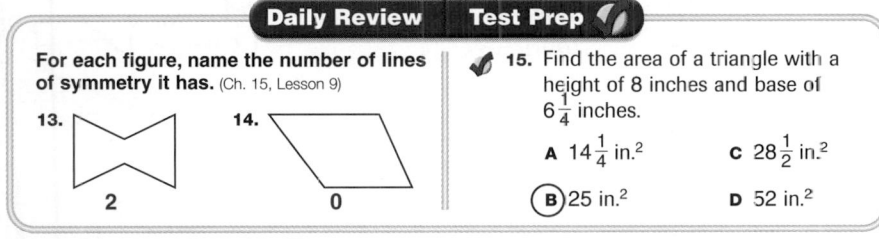

13. 2

14. 0

15. Find the area of a triangle with a height of 8 inches and base of $6\frac{1}{4}$ inches.

A $14\frac{1}{4}$ in.² **C** $28\frac{1}{2}$ in.²

B 25 in.² **D** 52 in.²

Extra Practice See page 443, Set C.

Chapter 16 Lesson 4   433

Test Prep Transparency **16.4**

DAILY TEST PREP

A square is 12 m on a side. What is the area of each triangle formed by drawing one diagonal of the square? (72 m²)

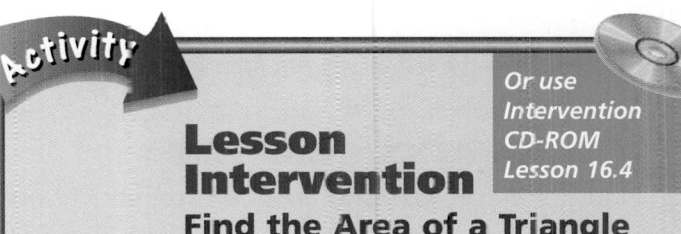

Activity

Or use Intervention CD-ROM Lesson 16.4

Lesson Intervention
Find the Area of a Triangle

| 👥 Small Group | 🕐 5–10 minutes | Visual, Tactile |

Materials: *grid paper or Learning Tool 14, square tiles*

- Have students draw a rectangle on grid paper or make from the tiles. Make the length 12 blocks and the width 8 blocks.

- **What's the area of this rectangle? Count blocks and also use the formula for area.** (96 square units)

- **Draw a diagonal from the upper left of the rectangle to the lower right vertex. What can you say about the triangles formed?** (They are congruent, have the same area, and the area is one half that of the rectangle.)

- **What is the area of each triangle?** (48 square units)

- **How do you think you would find the area of a right triangle?** (Multiply the base by the height and divide by 2.)

---

❸ Practice

Assign **Exercises 3–15** as independent work. For problem 7, have students explain the formulas used.

Common Error

Mistaking the length of a side for the height Remind students to find the height of a triangle by drawing a line perpendicular to the base to the opposite vertex. The length of two sides is *not* used to calculate the area of a triangle, unless it is a right triangle.

❹ Assess and Close

- Draw a triangle on the chalkboard.
- **What operations do you use to find the area?** ($\frac{1}{2}bh$ or $bh \div 2$)
- **How do you find the base *b* of a triangle if its area is 20 ft² and its height is 5 ft?** (Solve $20 = \frac{1}{2} \times 5 \times b$ so $b = 8$.)

Assign the **LESSON QUIZ** on Transparency 16.4 to further assess student understanding.

Keeping a Journal

Have students explain the relationship between the formulas for the area of a triangle and parallelogram.

Hands-On: Perimeter and Area of Irregular Shapes

PLANNING THE LESSON

MATHEMATICS OBJECTIVE

Find the perimeters and areas of irregular figures.

Use Lesson Planner CD-ROM for Lesson 16.5.

Daily Routines

Vocabulary

So far we have learned how to find the area of what kinds of figures? (rectangles, parallelograms, triangles) **How can we find the area of a figure that is not a parallelogram or square?** (We might separate the figure into shapes with areas that are easier to find.)

Vocabulary Cards

Meeting North Carolina's Standards

Prepare for Grade 6 Objective **2.01** Estimate and measure length, perimeter, area, angles, weight, and mass of two and three-dimensional figures using appropriate tools.

Lesson Transparency
16.5

Problem of the Day

Pat says that there is a square whose perimeter is 60 feet, and whose area is 81 ft². Is Pat right? Why or why not? (No; if the area is 81 ft², it is a square 9 feet on a side. The perimeter must be 36 feet, not 60 feet.)

Quick Review

Find the perimeter and area of each figure.
1. rectangle: length 5.5 cm, width 10 cm (perimeter: 31 cm; area 55 cm²)
2. parallelogram: base 10 feet, height 8 feet (perimeter: 36 ft; area 80 ft²)

Lesson Quiz

1. Estimate the perimeter and area. Each square represents 1 cm². (perimeter about 14 cm; area about 10 cm²)

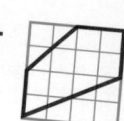

2. Find perimeter and area. (perimeter 48 units; area 63 units²)

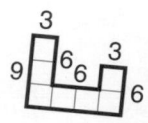

LEVELED PRACTICE

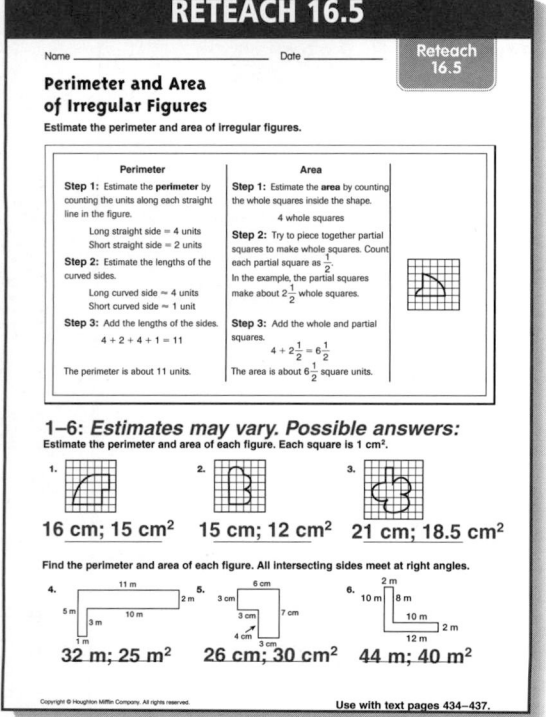

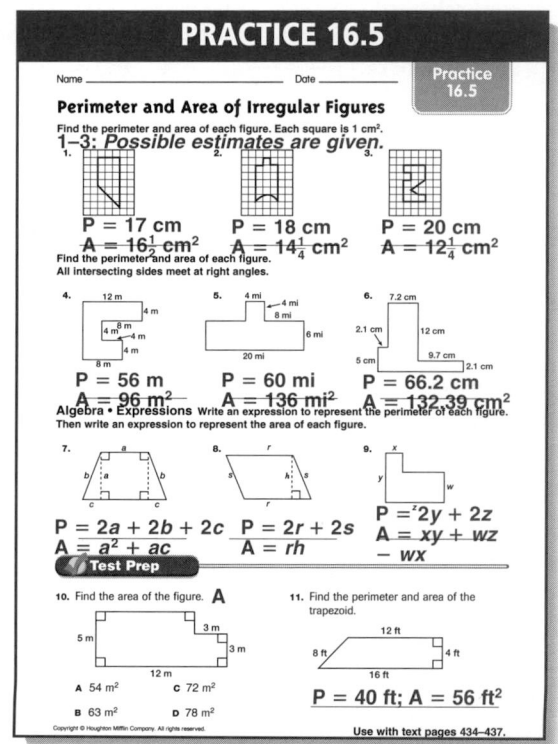

Practice Workbook Page 110

Reaching All Learners
Differentiated Instruction

English Learners

Worksheet 16.5 guides students through the process of determining the area of a complex figure and provides a verbal framework for their summary of the steps in response to Problem 17.

Special Needs
KINESTHETIC, TACTILE

Materials: *Centimeter Grid Transparency*

Draw a square like this one on the transparency.

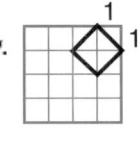

- **What is the area?** (2 square units)
- **How can you find the perimeter of the figure?** (Find the length of its sides.) **If each side is *s*, what is the perimeter?** (4*s*)

Early Finishers
VISUAL, AUDITORY

Materials: *grid paper*

Display a large square with a semicircle in it.

- **Estimate the area of the semicircle.**
- **Estimate the area of the spaces between the square and the semicircle and explain how you arrived at your estimate.** (Estimate the area of the semicircle and subtract it from the area of the square.)

TECHNOLOGY

Spiral Review

Create **customized** spiral review worksheets for individual students using the *Ways to Assess* CD-ROM.

Tool Software

Use *Easy Sheet* or another spreadsheet to explore this lesson more fully.

Lesson Planner

You can use the Lesson Planner CD-ROM to create a report of the lessons and standards you have taught.

Social Studies Connection

Baseball Fields

- Although infield dimensions of baseball fields are all the same, outfield dimensions are not. For example, center field in Yankee Stadium is 461 feet from home plate, and in Wrigley Field it is 400 feet.
- Have students research ballparks and write about their findings, including outfield dimensions.
- Have them discuss how to calculate the perimeter and area of an entire baseball field.

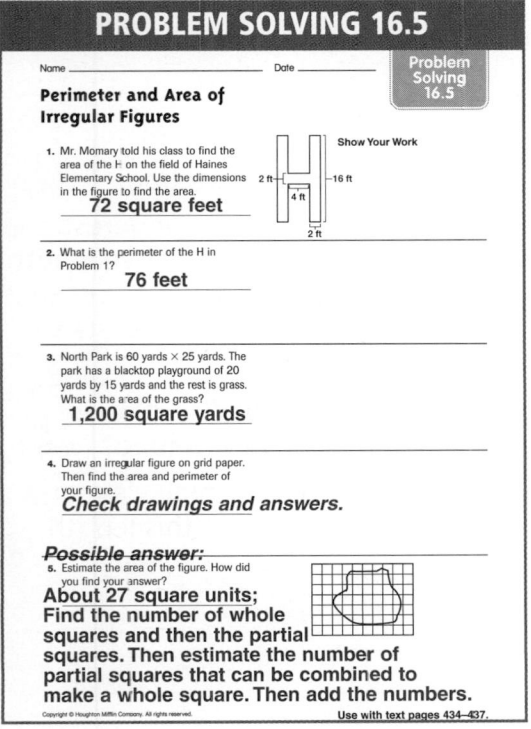

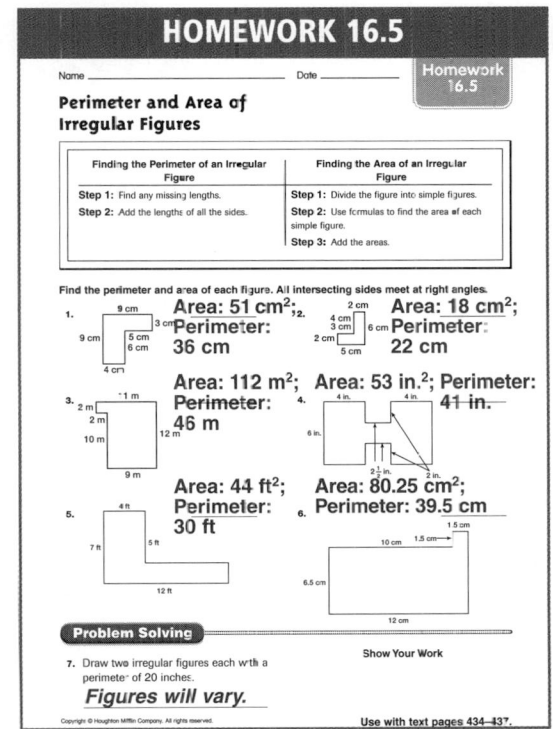

Homework Workbook Page 110

TEACHING LESSON 16.5

LESSON ORGANIZER

Objective Find the perimeters and areas of irregular figures.

Resources Reteach, Practice, Enrichment, Problem Solving, Homework, English Learners, Transparencies, Math Center

Materials Centimeter Grid Transparency, inch grid or Learning Tool 15, centimeter grid paper or Learning Tool 13 paper,

Warm-Up Activity
Find Missing Dimensions

| **i** Individual | 🕐 5 minutes | Auditory, Visual |

- Draw this figure with its labels on the board:

- **How would you find the length of DE?**
(First find the horizontal distance along the bottom: 6 + 2 = 8 units. Because BC equals 5, to find DE, subtract 5 from 8 to get 3.)

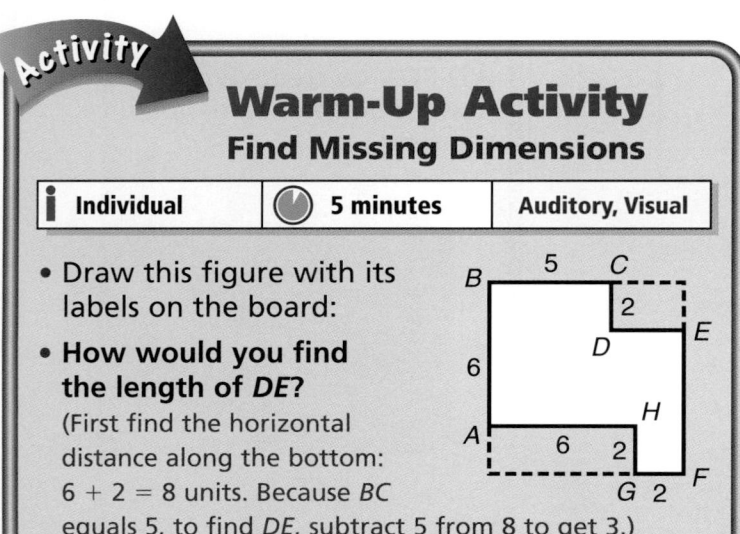

Perimeter and Area of Irregular Figures

Materials
centimeter grid paper
inch grid paper
(Learning Tool 13)
(Learning Tool 15)

Objective Find the perimeters and areas of irregular figures.

 **Work Together** 💿 **MathTracks** 2/15
Listen and Understand

Some figures are irregular and have curved sides. You can estimate the perimeter and area of these figures.

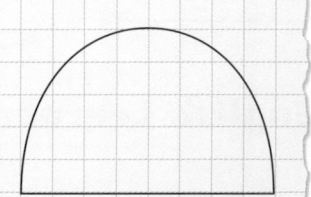

STEP 1 Estimate the perimeter of the figure above by answering these questions.
- What is the length of each straight line in the figure?
- How can you estimate the length of the curved side? About how long is the curved side?
- What is the sum of the sides?
- What is your estimate of the perimeter?

STEP 2 Estimate the area by answering these questions.
- How many whole squares are in the figure?
- How many partial squares are in the figure?
- What is your estimate of the area?

STEP 3 Now trace the same figure on a piece of grid paper that has squares of a smaller size. Estimate the perimeter and area.
- How does changing the size of the squares affect the perimeter and the area of the figure?

Steps 1–3: See Additional Answers on Page T87.

434

---

1 Introduce

Materials: Centimeter Grid Transparency

Display this figure on the transparency.

- **How many full squares are completely inside this polygon?** (36)
Count them together and shade them in lightly as you count.

- **How many half squares are inside this polygon?** (8) Count them together and shade them in with another color as you count.

- **What operation can we use to find the area of this polygon?** (addition)

2 Develop

Guide students through the *Work Together* section.

- For **Steps 1 and 2,** have students consider an underestimate of curve length and an overestimate of curve length. **For each square the curve goes through, count 0 unit to underestimate the length of the curve. Count 1 units to overestimate the length of the curve.**

- **Do you think that the length of the curved portion is between the underestimate and the overestimate?** (yes)

- Alternatively, have students lay a string or pipe cleaner along the curved portion and then measure this length with a ruler.

Some shapes are complex figures that are made of smaller polygons. You can use what you know about finding the perimeter and area of simple figures to find the perimeter and area of these shapes.

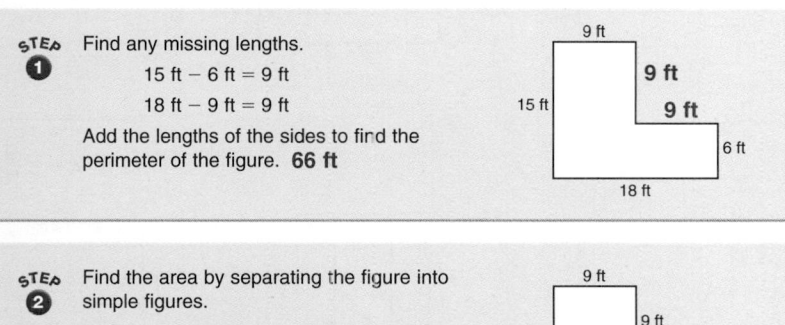

STEP 1 Find any missing lengths.

15 ft − 6 ft = 9 ft

18 ft − 9 ft = 9 ft

Add the lengths of the sides to find the perimeter of the figure. **66 ft**

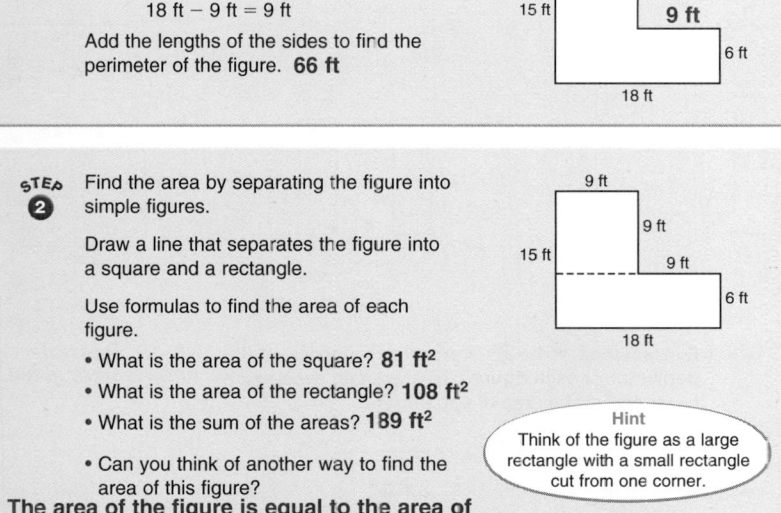

STEP 2 Find the area by separating the figure into simple figures.

Draw a line that separates the figure into a square and a rectangle.

Use formulas to find the area of each figure.

• What is the area of the square? **81 ft²**

• What is the area of the rectangle? **108 ft²**

• What is the sum of the areas? **189 ft²**

> **Hint**
> Think of the figure as a large rectangle with a small rectangle cut from one corner.

• Can you think of another way to find the area of this figure?

The area of the figure is equal to the area of 18 × 15 rectangle minus the area of a 9 × 9 square.

On Your Own   *1–6. Possible estimates given.*

Estimate the perimeter and area of each figure. Each square is 1 cm².

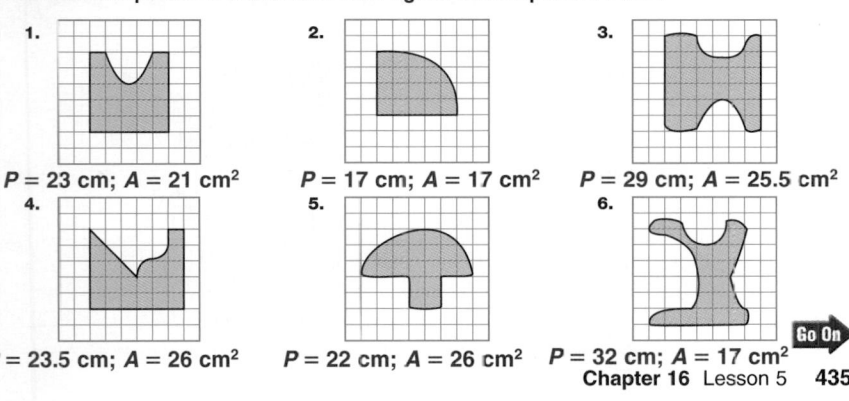

1.

$P = 23$ cm; $A = 21$ cm²

2.

$P = 17$ cm; $A = 17$ cm²

3.

$P = 29$ cm; $A = 25.5$ cm²

4.

$P = 23.5$ cm; $A = 26$ cm²

5.

$P = 22$ cm; $A = 26$ cm²

6.

$P = 32$ cm; $A = 17$ cm²

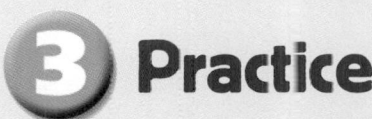

---

3 Practice

• Have students look at the figure at the top of page 435. **Look at Step 1. Do you have all the information you need to find the perimeter?** (No; two lengths are unknown.)

• **How can you find the unknown lengths** (Subtract the smaller known vertical length from the greater known vertical length. Do the some with horizontal lengths)

• **How do you know that addition is needed to find perimeter?** (Perimeter is the sum of the lengths of the sides.)

• **Look at Step 2. What two figures are created by the dotted line?** (a square and a rectangle)

• **How could you find the area of this figure?** (Find the area of the rectangle, the area of the square, and add these together.)

Assign **Exercises 1–15** of *On Your Own* as independent work.

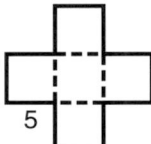
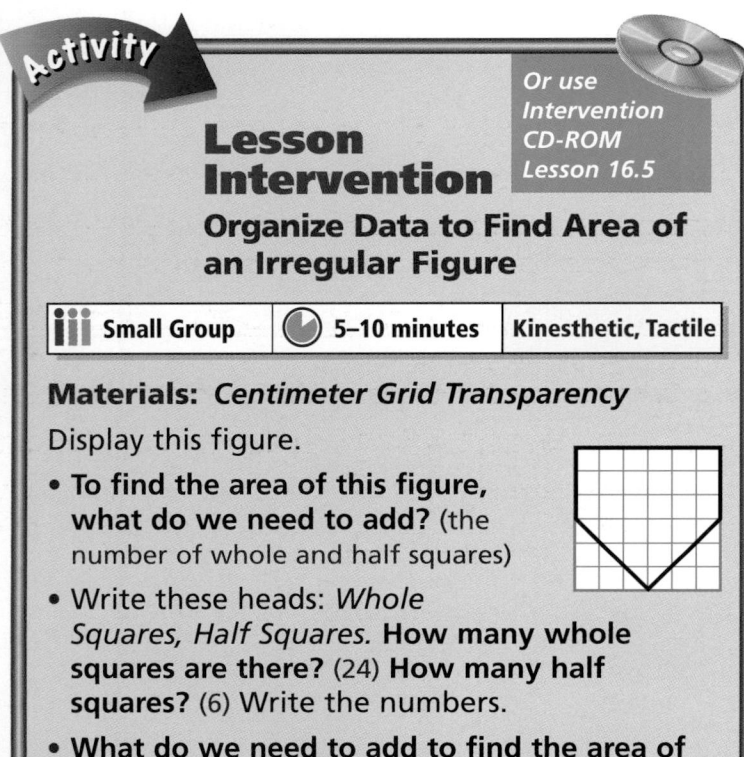

Activity

Or use Intervention CD-ROM Lesson 16.5

Lesson Intervention

Organize Data to Find Area of an Irregular Figure

| 👥 Small Group | ⏱ 5–10 minutes | Kinesthetic, Tactile |

Materials: *Centimeter Grid Transparency*

Display this figure.

• **To find the area of this figure, what do we need to add?** (the number of whole and half squares)

• Write these heads: *Whole Squares, Half Squares.* **How many whole squares are there?** (24) **How many half squares?** (6) Write the numbers.

• **What do we need to add to find the area of the figure?** (24 + 3) **What is the area?** (27 cm²)

Find the perimeter and area of each figure. All intersecting sides meet at right angles.

7.
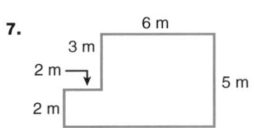

8.
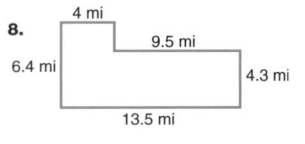

9.
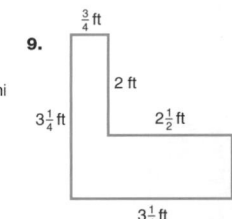

$P = 13$ ft; $A = 5\frac{9}{16}$ ft²

10.
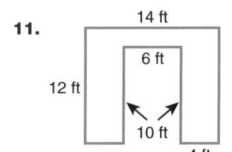

11.
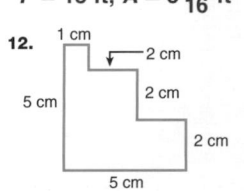

12.
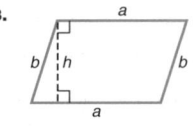 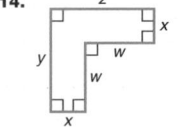 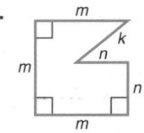

✕ **Algebra** • **Expressions** Write an expression to represent the perimeter of each figure. Then write an expression to represent the area of each figure.

13–15. *Possible answers are given.*

13.
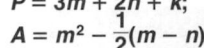

$P = 2a + 2b$; $A = ah$

14.

$P = 2w + 2x + y + z$; $A = wx + xy$

15.

$P = 3m + 2n + k$; $A = m^2 - \frac{1}{2}(m - n)n$

Talk About It • Write About It

You learned how to estimate and find the area and perimeter of irregular and complex figures.

16. Explain how to estimate the perimeter and area of Shape A.

17. Explain how to find the area of Shape B.

See Additional Answers on Page T87.

A
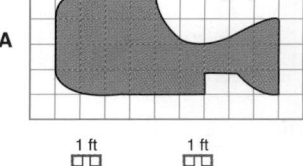

B
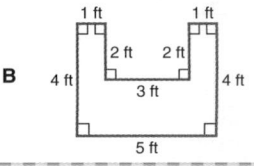

436

---

4 Assess and Close

Practice *continued*

• *Algebra • Expressions for Exercises 13–15* Students are asked to write mathematical expressions but they are not asked to evaluate them. Look to see that students apply formulas correctly to write the expressions.

• Assign **Exercises 16–17** of the *Talk About It • Write About It* section. Have volunteers explain their work.

• **What are some ways to estimate the perimeter of an irregular figure?** (Add all dimensions that are multiples of one unit. Use fractions such as one-half or one-quarter to estimate lengths that are not multiples of the unit. Add whole numbers and fractions or mixed numbers.)

Assign the **LESSON QUIZ** on Transparency 16.5 to further assess student understanding.

Historical Blueprints

Thomas Jefferson was an author of the Declaration of Independence and was the third President of the United States (1801–1809). Jefferson was also one of the leading architects of his time.

Besides designing the Virginia Capitol and the University of Virginia, Jefferson designed his home, called Monticello. The diagram at the right shows floor plans for the tea room and the dining room in Monticello.

Study the floor plan.

- Estimate the area of the tea room. You may wish to trace the diagram on a piece of grid paper to help you.
- About how much smaller is the tea room than the dining room?
- About how much of the tea room's area does the large table in the center cover?
- Would the rug from the dining room fit in the tea room? Explain.

See Additional Answers on Page T87.

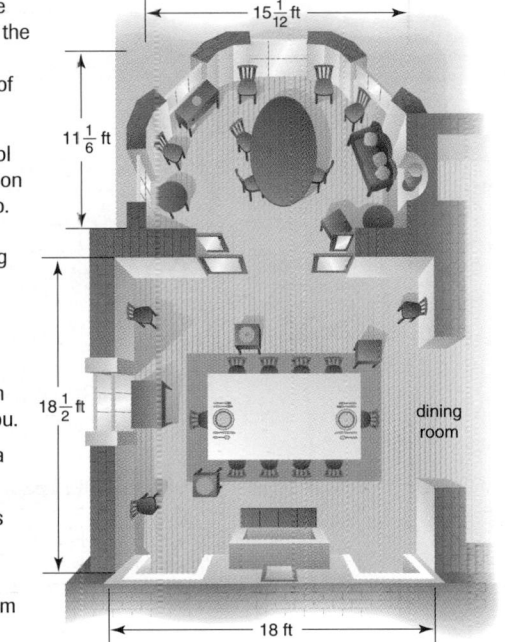

Tetrominoes

A tetromino is a design made of 4 squares. Each square has at least one side in common with another.

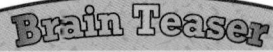

Two tetrominoes are shown. How many different tetrominoes can you make?

Square Deal

The area of one square is 16 times the area of another square. How are the side lengths of the two squares related? How are the perimeters of the two squares related?

A side of the larger square is 4 times the side of the smaller square. The perimeter of the larger square is 4 times the perimeter of the smaller square.

 **Technology**

Visit *Education Place* at **eduplace.com/kids/mw/** to try more brain teasers.

Historical Blueprints

Discuss with students how the skills they learned earlier help them with the questions. For example, subtraction is used in the second question and comparing numbers helps in the fourth question.

Tetrominoes

Have students organize their work in a list of shapes so that they do not duplicate any and do not miss any. Tell them that if two shapes match, they are the same.

Brain Teaser

Have students suppose that one square has an area of 1 unit^2 and the second square has area 16 units^2. Have them make a model of the two squares to find their relationship.

 # Keeping a Journal

Have students write a few sentences about ways to figure out the perimeter and area of irregular figures.

Hands-On: Algebra: Circumference of a Circle

PLANNING THE LESSON

MATHEMATICS OBJECTIVE
Find and use the formula to find the circumference of a circle.

Use Lesson Planner CD-ROM for Lesson 16.6.

Daily Routines

Vocabulary

Have students look up these words in the dictionary: *circumnavigate, circumscribe, circumference, circumvent.* **What do the words have in common?** (the prefix *circum-*) **What do the meanings have in common?** (They all mean "to go around something.") **What is the *circumference* of a circle?** (the distance around the circle) **How does *circumference* relate to *perimeter*?** (They both describe distance around a figure.)

Vocabulary Cards

Meeting North Carolina's Standards

Prepare for Grade 6 Objective **2.02** Solve problems involving perimeter/ circumference and area of plane figures.

Lesson Transparency

16.6

Problem of the Day
The radius of circle A is the diameter of circle B. The radius of circle B is the diameter of circle C. The diameter of circle A is 12 meters. What is the radius of circle C? (1.5 m)

Quick Review
1. $\frac{22}{7} \times 7$ (22)
2. 3.14×8 (25.12)
3. $\frac{22}{7} \times \frac{3}{11}$ $(\frac{6}{7})$
4. $\frac{22}{7} \times 2\frac{1}{2}$ $(7\frac{6}{7})$
5. $\frac{22}{7} \times 10$ $(31\frac{3}{7})$
6. 3.14×10 (31.4)

Lesson Quiz
Find the circumference of each circle. Round your answer to the nearest whole unit.

1. 14 in. (88 in.)
2. 21 ft (66 ft)
3. diameter 15 cm (47 cm)
4. radius 18 yd (113 yd)

LEVELED PRACTICE

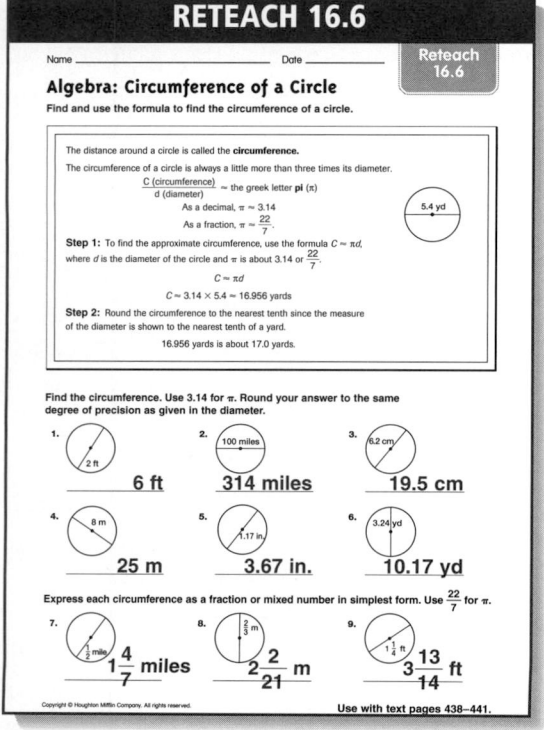

RETEACH 16.6

Name _____ Date _____

Reteach 16.6

Algebra: Circumference of a Circle
Find and use the formula to find the circumference of a circle.

The distance around a circle is called the **circumference**.

The circumference of a circle is always a little more than three times its diameter.

$\frac{C \text{ (circumference)}}{d \text{ (diameter)}} \approx$ the greek letter **pi** (π)

As a decimal, $\pi \approx 3.14$
As a fraction, $\pi \approx \frac{22}{7}$

5.4 yd

Step 1: To find the approximate circumference, use the formula $C \approx \pi d$, where d is the diameter of the circle and π is about 3.14 or $\frac{22}{7}$.

$C \approx \pi d$
$C \approx 3.14 \times 5.4 \approx 16.956$ yards

Step 2: Round the circumference to the nearest tenth since the measure of the diameter is shown to the nearest tenth of a yard.

16.956 yards is about 17.0 yards.

Find the circumference. Use 3.14 for π. Round your answer to the same degree of precision as given in the diameter.

1. 2 ft — 6 ft
2. 100 miles — 314 miles
3. 6.2 cm — 19.5 cm
4. 8 m — 25 m
5. 1.17 in. — 3.67 in.
6. 3.24 yd — 10.17 yd

Express each circumference as a fraction or mixed number in simplest form. Use $\frac{22}{7}$ for π.

7. $\frac{1}{2}$ miles — $1\frac{4}{7}$ miles
8. $\frac{2}{3}$ m — $2\frac{2}{21}$ m
9. $1\frac{1}{8}$ ft — $3\frac{13}{14}$ ft

Copyright © Houghton Mifflin Company. All rights reserved.

Use with text pages 438–441.

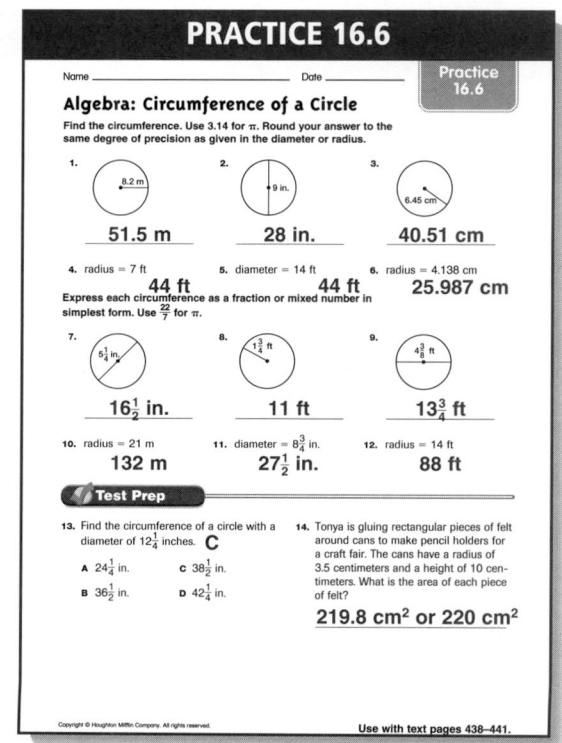

PRACTICE 16.6

Name _____ Date _____

Practice 16.6

Algebra: Circumference of a Circle
Find the circumference. Use 3.14 for π. Round your answer to the same degree of precision as given in the diameter or radius.

1. 8.2 m — 51.5 m
2. 9 in. — 28 in.
3. 6.45 cm — 40.51 cm
4. radius = 7 ft — 44 ft
5. diameter = 14 ft — 44 ft
6. radius = 4.138 cm — 25.987 cm

Express each circumference as a fraction or mixed number in simplest form. Use $\frac{22}{7}$ for π.

7. $5\frac{1}{4}$ in. — $16\frac{1}{2}$ in.
8. $1\frac{3}{4}$ ft — 11 ft
9. $4\frac{3}{8}$ ft — $13\frac{3}{4}$ ft
10. radius = 21 m — 132 m
11. diameter = $8\frac{3}{4}$ in. — $27\frac{1}{2}$ in.
12. radius = 14 ft — 88 ft

Test Prep

13. Find the circumference of a circle with a diameter of $12\frac{1}{4}$ inches. **C**

A $24\frac{1}{2}$ in.   C $38\frac{1}{2}$ in.
B $36\frac{1}{2}$ in.   D $42\frac{1}{4}$ in.

14. Tonya is gluing rectangular pieces of felt around cans to make pencil holders for a craft fair. The cans have a radius of 3.5 centimeters and a height of 10 centimeters. What is the area of each piece of felt?

219.8 cm² or 220 cm²

Copyright © Houghton Mifflin Company. All rights reserved.

Use with text pages 438–441.

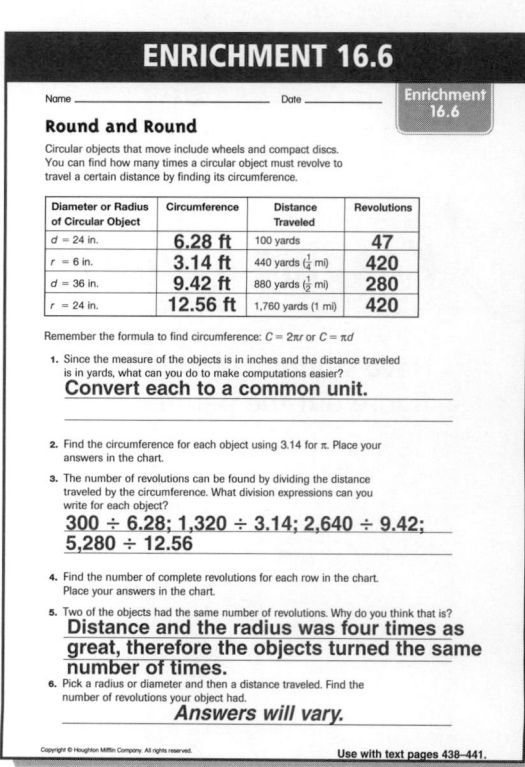

ENRICHMENT 16.6

Name _____ Date _____

Enrichment 16.6

Round and Round

Circular objects that move include wheels and compact discs. You can find how many times a circular object must revolve to travel a certain distance by finding its circumference.

Diameter or Radius of Circular Object	Circumference	Distance Traveled	Revolutions
$d = 24$ in.	6.28 ft	100 yards	47
$r = 6$ in.	3.14 ft	440 yards ($\frac{1}{4}$ mi)	420
$d = 36$ in.	9.42 ft	880 yards ($\frac{1}{2}$ mi)	280
$r = 24$ in.	12.56 ft	1,760 yards (1 mi)	420

Remember the formula to find circumference: $C = 2\pi r$ or $C = \pi d$

1. Since the measure of the objects is in inches and the distance traveled is in yards, what can you do to make computations easier?
Convert each to a common unit.

2. Find the circumference for each object using 3.14 for π. Place your answers in the chart.

3. The number of revolutions can be found by dividing the distance traveled by the circumference. What division expressions can you write for each object?
300 ÷ 6.28; 1,320 ÷ 3.14; 2,640 ÷ 9.42; 5,280 ÷ 12.56

4. Find the number of complete revolutions for each row in the chart. Place your answers in the chart.

5. Two of the objects had the same number of revolutions. Why do you think that is?
Distance and the radius was four times as great, therefore the objects turned the same number of times.

6. Pick a radius or diameter and then a distance traveled. Find the number of revolutions your object had.
Answers will vary.

Copyright © Houghton Mifflin Company. All rights reserved.

Use with text pages 438–441.

Practice Workbook Page 111

Reaching All Learners
Differentiated Instruction

English Learners

Worksheet 16.6 helps students recognize the parts of a circle, which prepares them to use the formulas introduced in Lesson 6.

Inclusion
KINESTHETIC, TACTILE

Materials: *circles cut from cardboard, rulers*

- Distribute the circles. **Mark a starting place on the circle and on a flat surface.**
- **Roll the circle in a straight line until you return to the starting place. Mark the surface where you stop. Measure the line. This is the circumference of the circle.**

Gifted and Talented
VISUAL, TACTILE

- Have students design a class logo with a circle snugly inside a square. The square is 21 inches on a side.
- **What is the diameter and circumference of the circle?** (21 inches, 66 inches)

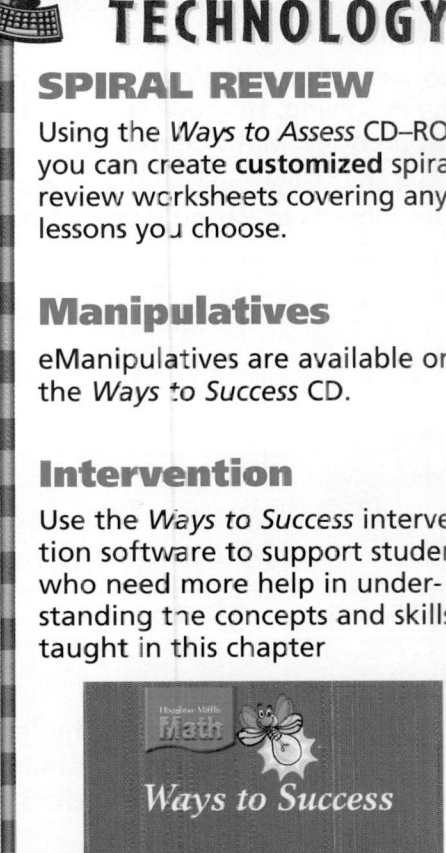

Science Connection

Orbits Around the Sun
Materials: *compass, almanac*

- Ask students to name the nine planets. Explain that, although the planets' orbits are not circular, they can use circles to draw a very simple diagram of the Solar System.

- Have students use their compasses to draw and label nine concentric circles to represent the orbits of the planets around the Sun.
- Have students research the planetary distances and orbits. Then discuss how their diagrams differ from an accurate Solar System model.

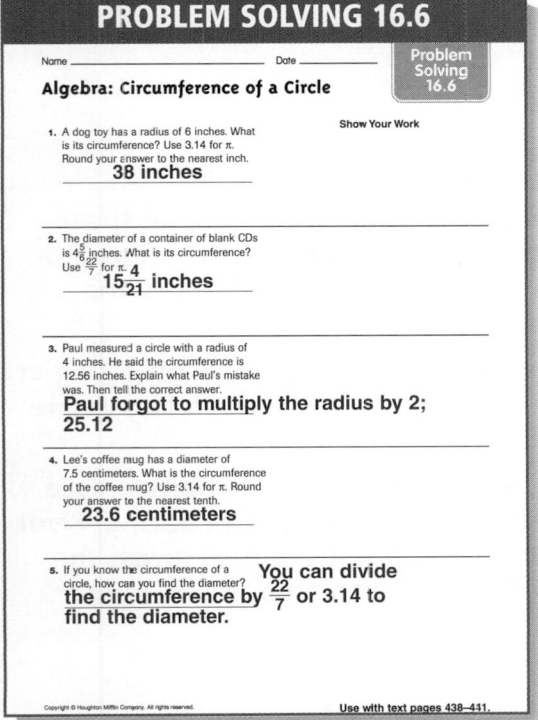

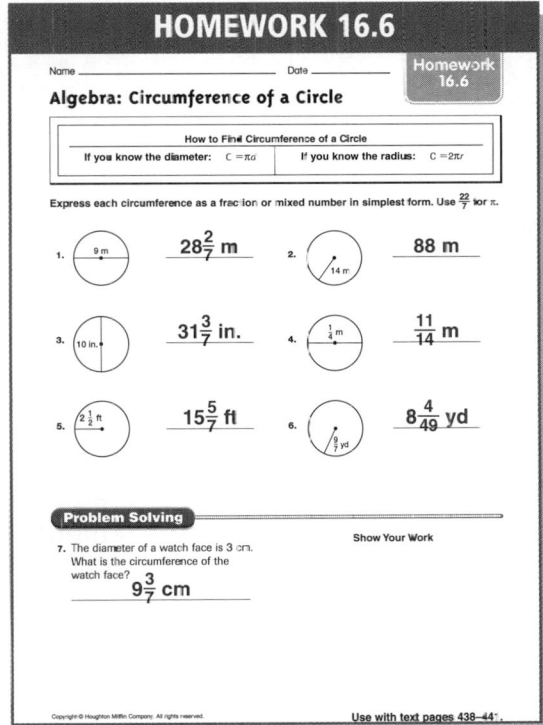

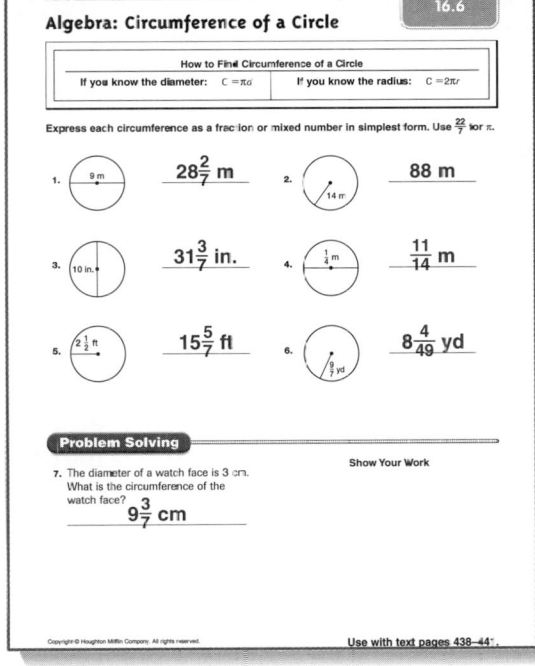

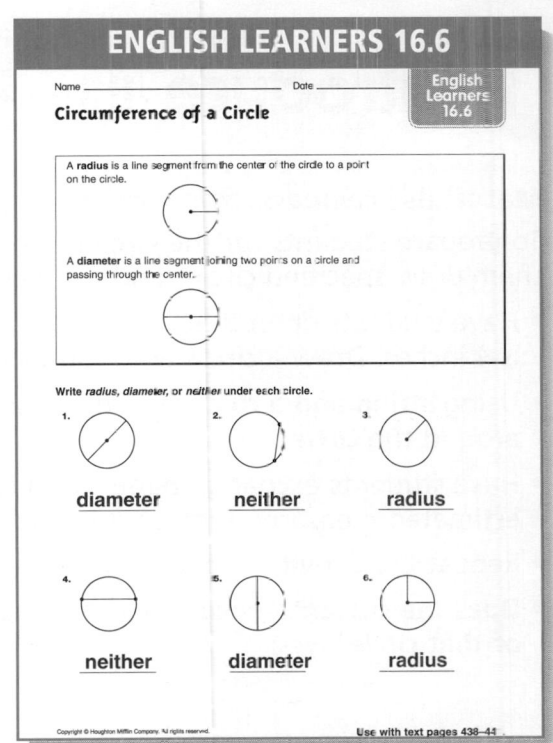

Homework Workbook Page 111

TEACHING LESSON 16.6

LESSON ORGANIZER

Objective Find and use the formula to find the circumference of a circle.

Resources Reteach, Practice, Enrichment, Problem Solving, Homework, English Learners, Transparencies, Math Center

Materials String, meter stick or centimeter ruler, circular objects of various sizes, calculator, compass

---

Activity

Warm-Up Activity
Review Measuring Length

| 👥 Whole Group | ⏱ 5 minutes | Auditory, Tactile |

Materials: *ruler*

- Use your ruler to measure the length of a pen or pencil. Give your measurement to the nearest inch, the nearest half-inch, and the nearest quarter-inch.

- **How would you estimate the perimeter of a square formed by four of the pens you measured?** (Multiply the estimated length of the pen by 4.)

Algebra
Circumference of a Circle

Objective Find and use the formula to find the circumference of a circle.

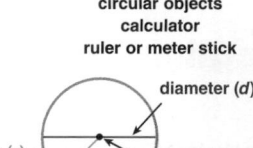

e Glossary

Vocabulary
circumference
pi (π)

Work Together

The diagram shows the parts of a circle. The distance around a circle is called the **circumference** *(C)* The circumference of a circle is related to the diameter of the circle.

Work with a partner to determine the relationship of the circumference and the diameter of a circle.

Materials
Learning Tool 53
string
circular objects
calculator
ruler or meter stick

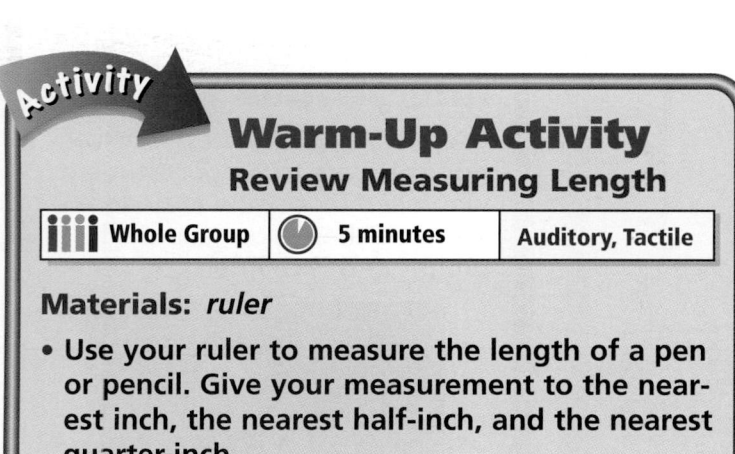

diameter (*d*)
radius (*r*)
center
circumference (*C*)

STEP 1 Choose 3 circular objects. List the objects on the recording sheet.

Circumference and Diameter			
Object	Circumference (*C*)	Diameter (*d*)	*C* ÷ *d*
Can			

STEP 2 Wrap a piece of string around the circumference of the circular object and mark where the ends meet. Use a meter stick or ruler to find the length of this part of the string. Record this measurement.

STEP 3 Measure the diameter of the circular object. Record this measurement.

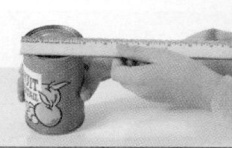

STEP 4 Use a calculator to complete the last column of the recording sheet. Round each quotient (*C* ÷ *d*) to the nearest hundredth.

- What patterns do you see?
- How is the circumference of a circle related to its diameter? **circumference of a circle is about 3 times the diameter**

438

---

1 Introduce | 👥 Whole Group | ⏱ 5 minutes | ## 2 Develop

Materials: *compass, string, ruler*

To prepare students for the circumference activity, have them draw specified circles and estimate circumference.

- Have students open their compasses so that the setting is 4 inches. **Draw a circle with radius 4 inches.**

- **Using string and a ruler, find the estimated distance around the circle.**

- Have students exchange papers and check one another's estimated measurements of circumference.

- Repeat the activity with a compass setting of 3 inches.

- **Does the circumference of a circle depend on the radius of that circle?** (yes)

Guide students through the *Work Together* section.

- In Step 2, it is important that students do not let the string be too loose or pull the string too tight. Have students tape one end of the string to the object so the starting point of the string is fixed.

- **Lay the ruler on your desk. Place one end of the string at the 0 mark on the ruler. What is the ruler reading where the string is marked?**

- For Step 3, have students trace around the object. **Place the 0 mark on the ruler at one point on the tracing. Pivot the ruler until you find the longest segment across the tracing. This will give you the diameter.**

In the activity, you found that the circumference of a circle is always a little more than three times its diameter. The quotient for $C \div d$ is represented by the Greek letter π. The name for that letter is **pi**.

As a decimal, $\pi \approx 3.14$
As a fraction, $\pi \approx \frac{22}{7}$

$\approx$ means "is approximately equal to"

If you know the diameter of a circle, you can use π to find the circumference.

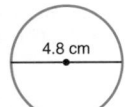
4.8 cm

$C = \pi d$
$\approx 3.14 \times 4.8$
≈ 15.072

Rounded to the nearest tenth of a centimeter, the circumference is about 15.1 centimeters.

The diameter of a circle is twice as long as the radius, $d = 2r$. If you know the radius of a circle, you can use π to find the circumference.

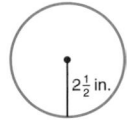
$2\frac{1}{2}$ in.

$C = 2\pi r$
$\approx 2 \times \frac{22}{7} \times 2\frac{1}{2}$
$\approx 15\frac{5}{7}$

The circumference of the circle is about $15\frac{5}{7}$ inches.

You can check your answer by using the value of π rounded to a whole number, 3.
$C \approx 2 \times 3 \times 2\frac{1}{2}$
≈ 15

Sometimes you should round your answers when working with measurements.

 You can use the π key to find the circumference of the circle at the right.

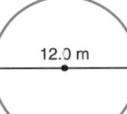
12.0 m

The result will be:

37.699112

An answer of 37.699112 meters indicates that the answer is accurate to six decimal places. A more sensible answer would be 37.7 meters. The diameter of the circle is given in tenths, so the answer should also be given in tenths.

When working with measurements, round the answer to the same degree of precision as the least precise of the measurements in the problem.

The circumference of the circle is 37.7 m.

Go On

• For Step 4, be sure students understand to enter circumference first and then diameter into the calculator.

• **When you read the display and want to round the number to the nearest hundredth, which decimal place do you look at?** (thousandths)

• **Examine the examples on page 439. How are they different?** (In one example, diameter is given. In the other example, radius is given.)

• **Estimation can be helpful in finding the circumference. Estimate 3.14 × 4.8.** ($3 \times 5 = 15$) **Estimate $2 \times \frac{22}{7} \times 2\frac{1}{2}$.** ($2 \times 3 \times 3 = 18$)

DAILY TEST PREP

Debbie and Minola want to make a flower bed that is exactly one half of a circle whose radius is 14 feet. About how much fencing will they need for the curved portion of the bed? (about 44 feet)

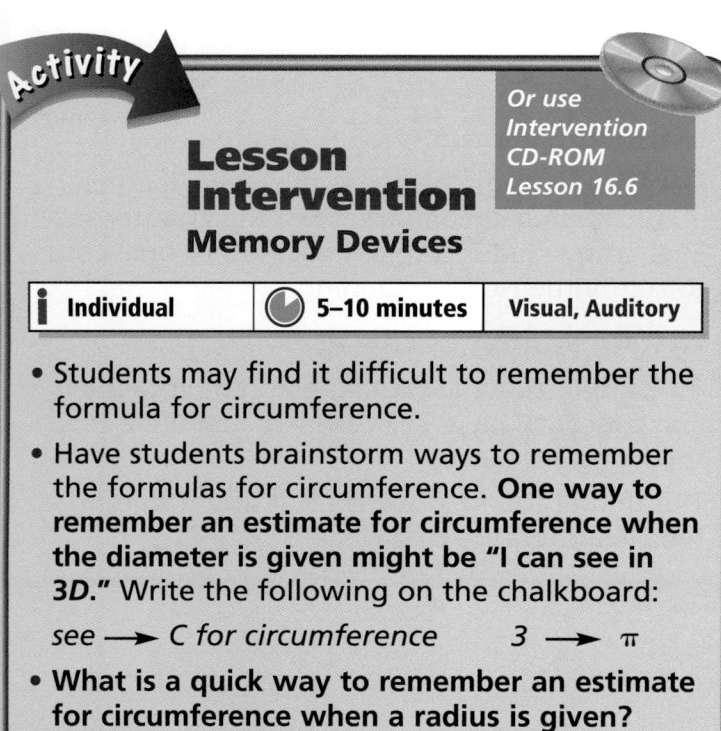

Activity

Lesson Intervention

Or use Intervention CD-ROM Lesson 16.6

Memory Devices

| ℹ Individual | ⏲ 5–10 minutes | Visual, Auditory |

- Students may find it difficult to remember the formula for circumference.

- Have students brainstorm ways to remember the formulas for circumference. **One way to remember an estimate for circumference when the diameter is given might be "I can see in 3D."** Write the following on the chalkboard:

    see ⟶ *C* for circumference   3 ⟶ π

- **What is a quick way to remember an estimate for circumference when a radius is given?**

On Your Own

Find the circumference. Use 3.14 for π. Round your answer to the same degree of precision as given in the diameter.

1.
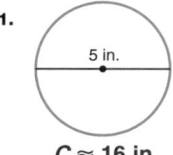
5 in.

$C \approx 16$ in.

2.
3.6 cm

$C \approx 22.6$ cm

3.
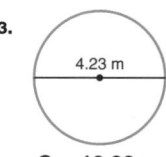
4.23 m

$C \approx 13.28$ m

4. diameter = 10 yd
$C \approx 31$ yd

5. radius = 10 m
$C \approx 63$ m

6. diameter = 24.362 m
$C \approx 76.497$ m

Express each circumference as a fraction or mixed number in simplest form. Use $\frac{22}{7}$ for π.

7.
$5\frac{5}{6}$ in.

$C \approx 36\frac{2}{3}$ in.

8.
$3\frac{1}{2}$ in.

$C \approx 11$ in.

9.
$7\frac{7}{12}$ ft

$C \approx 23\frac{5}{6}$ ft

10. diameter = 7 ft
$C \approx 22$ ft

11. radius = 7 in.
$C \approx 44$ in.

12. diameter = $22\frac{3}{4}$ ft
$C \approx 71\frac{1}{2}$ ft

Data Use the table for Problems 13 and 14.

13. Calculate the length of the label around each can. Use 3.14 for π. tomatoes, 31 cm; fruit cocktail, 23.6 cm; soup, 7.9 in.; peas, 267 mm

14. If the height of the label of the tomato can is 11 cm, what is the approximate area of the label?
$A \approx 341$ cm²

15. Suppose the cans of fruit cocktail and peas are both 10 cm tall. Find the difference between the areas of the labels. about 31 cm²

Can	Diameter
tomatoes	10 cm
fruit cocktail	7.5 cm
soup	2.5 in.
peas	85 mm

Talk About It • Write About It

You learned how to use a formula to find the circumference of a circle, and how to round your answer.

16. Explain how you can find the circumference of the circle at the right. **Double the radius to find the diameter. Multiply the diameter by π.**

6.8 in.

17. To which digit should you round your answer? Explain.
Since the diameter of 13.6 m is given to the nearest tenth of an inch, round the product π*d* (42.704) to the nearest tenth.

---

③ Practice

Assign **Exercises 1–15** of *On Your Own* as independent work.

- *Problem Solving for Problems 13–14* In Problem 14, point out that students need to use information from the table and from the problem itself. Have students share the thinking they used to arrive at their answer.

④ Assess and Close

Assign **Exercises 16–17** of the *Talk About It • Write About It* section. Have volunteers explain their work.

- **What formula would you use to find the circumference of a circle when you are given the radius?** ($C = 2\pi r$) **The diameter?** ($C = \pi d$)

Assign the **LESSON QUIZ** on Transparency 16.6 to further assess student understanding.

Quick Check

Check your understanding of Lessons 4–6. (Lessons 4, 5)

A.

1. Find the perimeter of Figure A. **P = $21\frac{1}{4}$ in.**

2. Find the area of Figure A. **A = $12\frac{1}{4}$ in.²**

B.

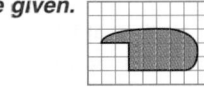

3. Find the perimeter of Figure B. **P = 17 m**

4. Find the area of Figure B. **13 m²**

In Exercises 5 and 6, each square represents 1 cm². (Lesson 5)
5–6. *Estimates may vary. Possible estimates are given.*

5. Estimate the perimeter of Figure C.

   P = 17 cm

6. Estimate the area of Figure C.

   A = 14.5 cm²

Find the circumference of each circle. Use 3.14 or $\frac{22}{7}$. (Lesson 6)

7. diameter = 3.2 cm
   10.0 cm
8. radius = $1\frac{3}{4}$ in.
   11 in.
9. diameter = $\frac{7}{8}$ ft
   $2\frac{3}{4}$ ft
10. radius = 10.5 m
    65.9 m

Cut-Ups

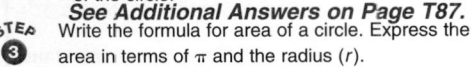

Measurement Sense / Math Reasoning

Materials: paper plate, scissors

Use this activity to find the formula for the area of a circle.

STEP 1 Fold a paper plate into eighths. Unfold the plate. Shade $\frac{1}{2}$ of the circle red. Cut along the folds.

STEP 2 Rearrange the pieces to form a shape somewhat like a parallelogram, as shown at right.

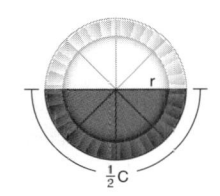

$\frac{1}{2}$C

- What part of the circle could be used as the height of the "parallelogram?"
- How is the circumference of the circle related to the base of the parallelogram?
- How would you find the approximate area of the parallelogram? Express your answer using parts of the circle.
  See Additional Answers on Page T87.

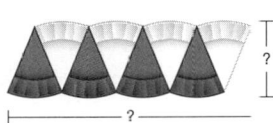

STEP 3 Write the formula for area of a circle. Express the area in terms of π and the radius (r).

Find each area to the nearest whole number.

a. radius = 4 cm   **b.** diameter = 6 m

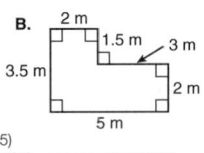

Quick Check

Purpose: The Quick Check allows you to assess the student's understanding of the concepts presented in Lessons 4–6.

Items	Objectives Tested	Pages	Intervention
1–2	Find and use the formula to find the area of a triangle.	432–433	Reteach Resource 16.4 *Ways to Success* 16.4
3–6	Find the perimeters and areas of irregular figures.	434–437	Reteach Resource 16.5 *Ways to Success* 16.5
7–10	Find and use the formula to find the circumference of a circle.	438–440	Reteach Resource 16.6 *Ways to Success* 16.6

Keeping a Journal

Have students outline a step-by-step plan for solving circumference problems. Suggest that they include: what information is needed, what formula to use, how to choose a computation method, and how to express their answers using the correct labels.

Measurement Sense / Math Reasoning

Cut-Ups

Explain to students that if a circle is divided into a very large number of congruent slices and rearranged, the formula for the area of a parallelogram can be used to approximate the circle's area. The more slices, the better the approximation of area.

Monitoring Student Progress

Chapter Review/Test

Purpose: This test provides an informal assessment of the Chapter 16 objectives.

Chapter Test Items 1–10

To assign a numerical grade for this Chapter Test, use 10 points for each test item.

Check Understanding

You can use the **Write About It** question to assess student understanding of a key chapter concept.

Customizing Your Instruction

For students who have not yet mastered these objectives, you can use the Reteaching Resources listed in the chart below.

 ## Assessment Options

A summary test for this chapter is also provided in the Unit Resource Folder.

 ## Adequate Yearly Progress

Use the End of Grade Test Prep Assessment Guide to help familiarize your students with the format of standardized tests.

Chapter Review/Test

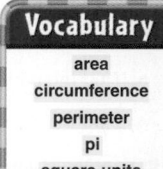

VOCABULARY

Vocabulary
area
circumference
perimeter
pi
square units

1. The distance around a circle is called the ___. **circumference**

2. The quotient of $C \div d$ is called ___. **pi**

3. ___ is the number of square units needed to cover a region. **area**

CONCEPTS AND SKILLS

Find the perimeter and area of each figure. (Lessons 1, 3, 4; pp. 422–423, 428–433)

4. **93 yd; $480\frac{1}{2}$ yd²**

$15\frac{1}{2}$ yd — rectangle — 31 yd

5. 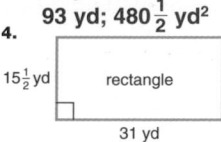 6 m parallelogram 8 m — 16 m
48 m; 96 m²

6. 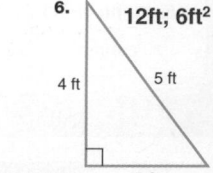 12ft; 6ft²
4 ft, 5 ft, 3 ft

Estimate the area of each figure. Then find the area and perimeter of the figures. (Lesson 5, 434–437) **7–8. Estimates may vary.**

7. 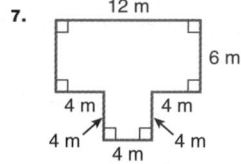 12 m, 6 m, 4 m, 4 m, 4 m, 4 m
area: 88 m²; perimeter: 44 m

8. 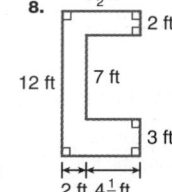 $6\frac{1}{2}$ ft, 2 ft, 7 ft, 12 ft, 3 ft, 2 ft, $4\frac{1}{2}$ ft
area: $46\frac{1}{2}$ ft²; perimeter: 46 ft

Write About It: *Possible answer:* Both perimeter and circumference are measurements of the distance around figures. Circumference, however, refers only to the distance around a circle and is an approximation.

9. Find the circumference of the circle at right to the nearest tenth. Use 3.14 for π. (Lesson 6, pp. 438–441)
172.7 in.

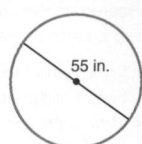 55 in.

PROBLEM SOLVING

Find a pattern to solve. (Lesson 2, pp. 424–427)

10. If the pattern continues, draw the ninth figure.

Check students' drawings of a 9-by-9 square.

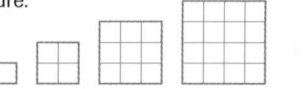 **Write About It**

Show You Understand
How are perimeter and circumference alike? How are they different?
See above.

Reteaching Support

Chapter Test Items	Summary Test Items	Chapter Objectives Tested	TE Pages	Use These Reteaching Resources
4–8	1–5	**16A** Find the perimeter of polygons and complex and irregular figures.	422A–423	Reteach Resource 16.1 *Ways to Success* CD: 16.1 Skillsheet 130
3–8	6–10	**16B** Find the area of parallelograms, triangles, and complex and irregular figures.	428A–437	Reteach Resource 16.3–16.5 *Ways to Success* CD: 16.3–16.5 Skillsheet 131, 132, 133
1, 2, 9	11–15	**16C** Use pi to find the circumference of a circle.	438A–440	Reteach Resource 16.6 *Ways to Success* CD: 16.6 Skillsheet 134
10	16–20	**16D** Analyze and solve problems by finding a pattern.	424A–426	Reteach Resource 16.2 *Ways to Success* CD: 16.2 Skillsheet 135

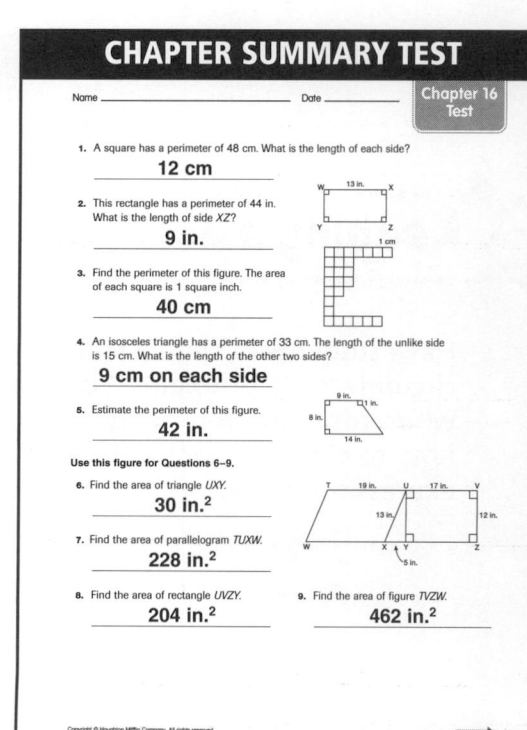

CHAPTER SUMMARY TEST

Name ___ Date ___ Chapter 16 Test

1. A square has a perimeter of 48 cm. What is the length of each side?
12 cm

2. This rectangle has a perimeter of 44 in. What is the length of side XZ?
9 in.

3. Find the perimeter of this figure. The area of each square is 1 square inch.
40 cm

4. An isosceles triangle has a perimeter of 33 cm. The length of the unlike side is 15 cm. What is the length of the other two sides?
9 cm on each side

5. Estimate the perimeter of this figure.
42 in.

Use this figure for Questions 6–9.

6. Find the area of triangle UXY.
30 in.²

7. Find the area of parallelogram TUXW.
228 in.²

8. Find the area of rectangle UVZY.
204 in.²

9. Find the area of figure TVZW.
462 in.²

Set A (Lesson 1, pp. 422–423)

Find the perimeter or missing length for each rectangle.

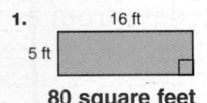
1. 4 ft / 9 ft **26 ft**

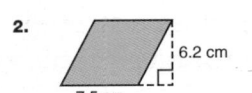
2. 11 yd / 11 yd **44 yd**

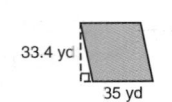
3. 2 in. / 14 in. **32 in.**

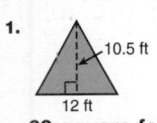
4. 10 m / 22 m **64 m**

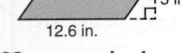
5. 16 mm **8 mm**
P = 48 mm

6. 6 ft **15 ft**
P = 42 ft

Set B (Lesson 3, pp. 428–431)

Find the area of each figure.

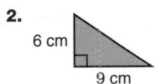
1. 16 ft / 5 ft
80 square feet

2. 6.2 cm / 7.5 cm
46.5 square centimeter

3. 33.4 yd / 35 yd
1,169 square yard

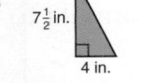
4. 5 in. / 12.6 in.
63 square inches

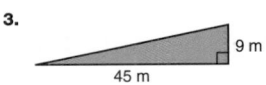
5. 19 m / 42.7 m
811.3 square meter

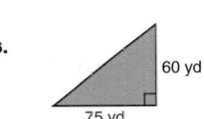
6. 12.5 mm
156.25 square millimeters

Set C (Lesson 4, pp. 432–433)

Find the area of each triangle.

1. 10.5 ft / 12 ft
63 square feet

2. 6 cm / 9 cm
27 square centimeters

3. 9 m / 45 m
202.5 square meter

4. $7\frac{1}{2}$ in. / 4 in.
15 square inches

5. 6 ft / 15 ft
45 square feet

6. 60 yd / 75 yd
2,250 square yards

CHAPTER SUMMARY TEST

Name _____ Date _____

Chapter 16 Test continued

10. Find the area of this figure.
54 in.²

11. Find the circumference. Use $\frac{22}{7}$ for π.
88 cm

12. Find the circumference to one decimal place. Use 3.14 for π.
27.3 cm

For Questions 13–15, find the circumference. If necessary, round to the same degree of precision as given in the diameter.

13. diameter = 42 yd
132 yd

14. diameter = 8.56 cm
26.88 cm

15. radius = 9.13 m
57.34 m

Gila made a pattern with pattern blocks. Use it to answer Questions 16 and 17.

16. How many tiles will be in the next figure in the pattern?
25

17. How many tiles will be in the fifth figure in the pattern?
36

The table shows the number of fifth-grade students who caught colds for every month in a winter. Use it to answer Questions 18–20.

18. If the pattern continues, how many fifth graders will catch colds in February?
16

19. If the pattern continues, how many fifth graders will go to the doctor in February?
8

20. According to the pattern, if 10 fifth graders catch colds, how many will visit the doctor?
5

Month	Number of Colds	Number of Visits to the Doctor
Nov.	2	1
Dec.	4	2
Jan.	8	4

Additional Answers

Chapter 16

Lesson 1, pp. 422-423

12. 56 ft; the room must have a doorway or other opening, and this opening will not require wallpaper.

13. No; the words length and width can refer to either of the dimensions of a rectangle.

Lesson 3, pp. 428–431

Step 3: The length of the rectangle equals the base of the parallelogram; the width of the rectangle equals the height of the parallelogram. The area of the parallelogram equals the area of the rectangle. 4 units × 3 units = 12 square units. $A = b \times h$, because any parallelogram with a base b and height h has the same area as rectangle with a length equal to b and a width equal to h.

20. The length and width are factors of the area. As the measures of the length and width get closer the perimeter decreases.

21. Check students' drawings; 7.35 cm

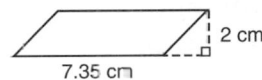
2 cm
7.35 cm

Lesson 4, pp. 432–433

Explain Your Thinking: Yes; in a right triangle, the sides that intersect to make a right angle are the base and height.
h / b

11. When Alan multiplied to find the area, he chose the wrong measurement for the height of the triangle.

12. *Possible response:* Two 10-oz cans and one 6-oz jar; (2 × 2.89 + 1.99 = \$7.77, 4 × 1.99 = \$7.96, so buying two 10-oz cans and one 6-oz jar is cheaper than buying four 6-oz jars.

13.

14.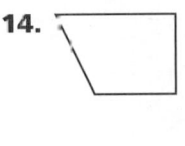

Lesson 5, pp. 434–437

Step 1: Check students' drawings and answers. Grid drawing does not need to match grid drawing in book. Answers should reflect the following point:
• The estimate for curved sides should be less than the sum of two straight sides covering the same vertical and horizontal distance.

Step 2: Check students' answers. Grid drawing does not need to match grid drawing in book. Answers should reflect the following point:
• Students should distinguish between whole squares and partial squares.

See Additional Answers on p. T87.

Perimeter, Area, and Circumference **443**

Lesson By Lesson Overview
Solid Figures, Surface Area, and Volume

Lesson 1

- Students identify various solid figures based on attributes such as faces, bases, vertices, and edges.
- Students draw a figure based on a given description and then name the figure.

Lesson 2

- Students examine solid figures made from cubes. They identify different two-dimensional views of the figure.
- Students use spatial reasoning to visualize aspects of a solid from different viewpoints and to build three-dimensional figures.

Lesson 3

- Students identify the net of a solid figure.
- Students examine a net and predict what shape it will make before assembling it.

Lesson 4

- Students find the surface area of solid figures.
- Students use a net to identify the faces of a rectangular prism. The steps for finding the surface area of the rectangular prism and a triangular prism are also shown.

Lesson 5

- Students solve a simpler problem to solve a given problem.
- Students choose a strategy and use data from a bar graph to solve problems.

Lesson 6

- Students find the volume of a cube, a rectangular prism, and a triangular prism.
- Students first build a rectangular prism with cubes to help them understand what volume actually represents and to lay the groundwork for the volume formula.

Lesson 7

- Students identify when to use a formula to solve a problem and how to determine what formula to use.

SKILLS TRACE: GEOMETRY AND MEASUREMENT

Grade 4	Grade 5	Grade 6
• identify, classify, and describe solid geometric figures (ch. 18)	• identify, classify, and find two-dimensional views of solid figures	• identify, describe, and classify solid figures (ch. 21)
• determine volume of solid figures (ch. 18)	• find surface area and volume of solid figures	• find surface area and volume (ch. 21)
		• estimate volume (ch. 21)

Chapter Planner

Lesson	Objective	Vocabulary	Materials	✓ NCTM Standards
17.1 Solid Figures p. 446A	Identify solid figures.	solid figure base edge vertex prism pyramid	Centimeter Grid Transparency, Solid Figures Transparency, models of solid figures	**Geometry:** Identify, compare, and analyze attributes of two- and three-dimensional shapes and develop vocabulary to describe the attributes.
17.2 Hands-On: Two-Dimensional Views of Solid Figures p. 448A	Identify different two-dimensional views of a solid figure.		Solid Figures Transparency, cubes, grid paper or Learning Tool 14 , triangular dot paper or Learning Tool 17, 13 textbooks, copies of diagram	**Geometry:** Identify and build a three-dimensional object from two-dimensional representations of that object.
17.3 Nets p. 450A	Identify the nets of solid figures.	net	grid paper or Learning Tool 15, scissors, tape, Solid Figures Transparency, Nets I Transparency, blank Transparency, Learning Tools 45–51	**Geometry:** Identify and build a three-dimensional object from two-dimensional representations of that object.
17.4 Surface Area p. 452A	Use nets to find the surface area of solid figures.	surface area	grid paper or Learning Tool 14, cut-out Net A from the Nets I Transparency, cut-out rectangular prism from the Solid Figures Transparency, blank transparency, rulers, textbooks	**Measurement:** Understand such attributes as length, area, weight, volume, and size of angle and select the appropriate type of unit for measuring each attribute.
17.5 Problem-Solving Strategy: Solve a Simpler Problem p. 456A	Solve problems by first solving simpler problems.		Problem Solving: Four Step Process Transparency	**Problem Solving:** Apply and adapt a variety of appropriate strategies to solve problems.
17.6 Algebra: Volume p. 460A	Use a formula to find the volume of a cube, a rectangular prism, and a triangular prism.	volume cubic unit	cubes, Volume of Cubes Transparency, cutouts, blank transparency, scissors	**Measurement:** Understand such attributes as length, area, weight, volume, and size of angle and select the appropriate type of unit for measuring each attribute.
17.7 Algebra: Problem-Solving Application: Use Formulas p. 464A	Use a formula to solve a problem.		cubes, blank transparency, Problem Solving: Four Step Process Transparency	**Algebra:** Model problem situations with objects and use representations such as graphs, tables, and equations to draw conclusions.

Resources For Reaching All Learners

LESSON RESOURCES: Reteach, Practice, Enrichment, Problem Solving, Homework, English Learners, Daily Routines, Transparencies, Math Center.

ADDITIONAL RESOURCES FROM HOUGHTON MIFFLIN: Combination Classroom Planning Guide, Chapter Challenges, Every Day Counts, Math at Hand (student handbook)

Every Day Counts

The **Calendar and Measurement** activities in **Every Day Counts** support the math in this chapter.

Assessing Prior Knowledge

Before beginning the chapter, you can assess student understandings in order to assist you in differentiating instruction.

Complete Chapter Pretest in Unit Resource Folder

Use this test to assess both prerequisite skills (**Are You Ready?** — one page) and chapter content (**Check What You Know** — two pages).

Chapter 17 Prerequisite Skills Pretest

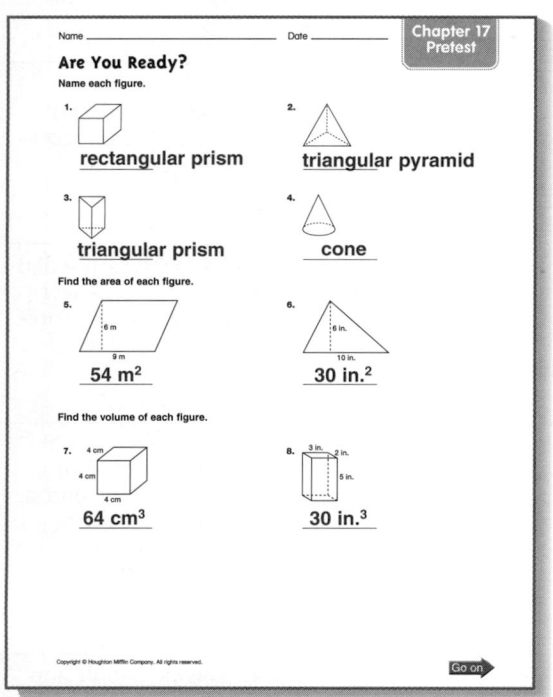

Chapter 17 New Content Pretest

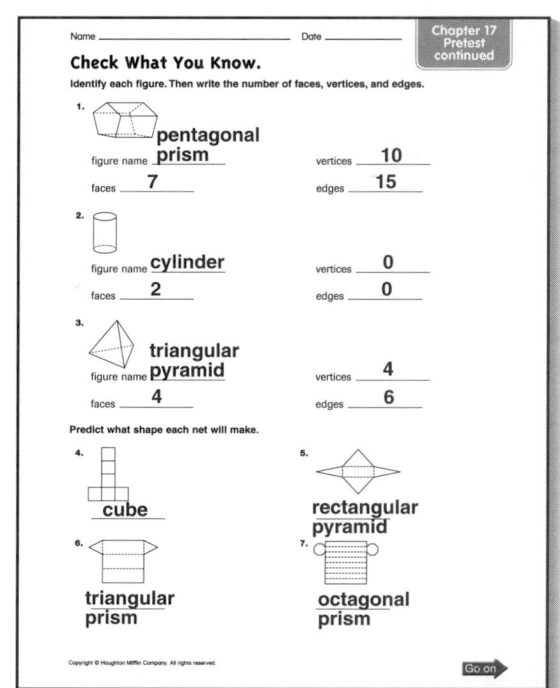

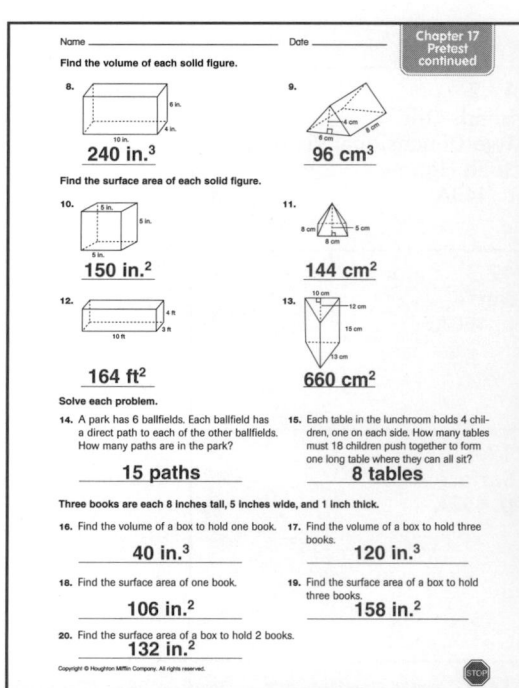

Customizing Instruction

For Students Having Difficulty

Items	Prerequisites	Ways to Success
1–4	Identify and classify solid geometric figures	CD: 17a Skillsheet: 136
5–6	Find area	CD: 17b Skillsheet: 137
7–8	Determine the volume of solid figures	CD: 17b Skillsheet: 138

Ways to Success: Intervention for every concept and skill (CD-ROM or Chapter Intervention Skillsheets).

Consider using **Knowing Mathematics** with any students who are working two or more years below grade level.

For Students Having Success

Items	New Content	Resources
1–7	**17A** Identify, classify, and find two-dimensional views of solid figures.	Enrichment 17.1, 17.2, 17.3
8–13	**17B** Find surface area and volume of solid figures.	Enrichment 17.4, 17.6
14–20	**17C** Analyze and solve problems by solving a simpler problem and by using formulas.	Enrichment 17.5, 17.7

Use **Chapter Challenges** with any students who have success with all new chapter content.

Other Pretest Options

Informal Pretest in Student Book

The student book pretest assesses vocabulary and prerequisite skills needed for success in this chapter.

Ways to Success CD-ROM

The *Ways to Success* chapter pretest has automatic assignment of appropriate review lessons.

Chapter Resources

Assessing Prior Knowledge

Surface Area and Volume (surface area, net, and volume of solids)

- Display geometric solids as well as real-world objects that have faces that are polygons.
- Have students name the different polygons they see in the faces of the three-dimensional objects.

Ongoing Skill Activity

Get Your Hands on a Solid (two-dimensional views and nets of solids, surface area, and volume)

- After Lesson 1, have students identify objects in the classroom that most closely resemble each solid figure.
- For each lesson that follows, have students use the objects as hands-on models. For example, they can sketch various 2-dimensional views of the objects after Lesson 2, draw nets after Lesson 3, use and measure wrapping paper to find surface area after Lesson 4, and measure the objects to calculate their volumes after Lesson 6.

Connecting to the Unit Project

- Have "city planners" find the area covered by 1 or several city blocks, and of the open spaces such as ball fields and parks.
- Have "city architects" draw nets of pyramids and triangular prisms on card stock and use them to make buildings. Have students determine the surface area of all buildings before covering them with construction paper, foil, or paint.

Professional Resources Handbook

Research, Mathematics Content, and Language Intervention

Research-Based Teaching

Students need a conceptual understanding of area and perimeter. They can then explore area and volume in three dimensions. An activity recommended in *Principles and Standards* (2000) is to have students "identify and build a three-dimensional object from two-dimensional representation of that object" and vice versa. See Professional *Resources Handbook, Grade 5,* Unit 6.

For more ideas relating to Unit 6, see the Teacher Support Handbook at the back of this Teacher's Edition.

Language Intervention

In East Asian countries, children learn that just as numbers can be composed and decomposed as sets and subsets, solid figures can be composed and decomposed as well. For further explanation, see "Mathematical Language and Measurement" in the *Professional Resources Handbook Grade 5.*

 **Time Saving Technology Support**

Ways to Assess Customized Spiral Review and Test Generator CD-ROM
Lesson Planner CD-ROM
Ways to Success Intervention CD-ROM
Math Tracks CD-ROM
Education Place: www.eduplace.com/math/mw/
Houghton Mifflin Math eBook CD-ROM
eManipulatives
eGames

Starting Chapter 17
Solid Figures, Surface Area, and Volume

Chapter Objectives

17A Identify, classify, and find two-dimensional views of solid figures.

17B Find surface area and volume of solid figures.

17C Analyze and solve problems by solving a simpler problem and by using formulas.

Math Background

Solid Figures

At this grade level, only right solid figures are considered. This means that prisms have rectangular faces, that the curved surface of a cylinder is perpendicular to the bases, and that the line from the vertex of a pyramid or a cone to the base is perpendicular to the base. Solid figures are also called space figures or three-dimensional figures.

Surface Area

The surface area of a solid figure is the sum of the areas of all surfaces of the figure. A net is a two-dimensional pattern that can be cut and folded to make a solid figure. Drawing a net often simplifies finding the surface area of a solid figure.

Volume

The volume of a prism is the area of the base times the height. If the height is 1, then each unit square in the base will give rise to 1 unit cube in the prism. In general, each unit cube in the base corresponds to a rectangular prism with base area 1 and height h. Taking the sum of the volumes explains the formula volume formula $V = B \times h$ where B is the area of the base and h is the height. Since the area of the base of a rectangular prism is equal to the length times the width, the formula for the volume of a rectangular prism can also be written as $V = l \times w \times h$.

INVESTIGATION

Use Data

Container ships carry thousands of boxes, all the same sizes. At the right is a drawing of a twenty-foot container that holds 1 TEU. The abbreviation TEU means Twenty-feet Equivalent Units. How many cubic feet are in 1 TEU?

$8\frac{1}{2}$ feet

20 feet

8 feet

1,360 cubic feet

Using the Investigation

Have students work in small groups to answer the question posed on page 444.

To extend the investigation, provide students with the following problem.

- Suppose that the container shown on page 444 were filled with smaller containers that were all the same size. What could be the dimensions of the smaller containers, if they fill the larger one with no space left over? How many of the smaller containers would there be? (Possible answer: 32 containers that are 2 feet wide by 5 feet long by $4\frac{1}{4}$ feet high.)

For more information about projects and investigations, visit **Education Place**.
www.eduplace.com/math/mw/

 **Chapter Pretest**

Use this page to review and remember
what you need to know for this chapter.

VOCABULARY

Choose the best word to complete each sentence.

Vocabulary

area

polygon

rectangle

volume

1. A ____ is a simple closed plane figure made up of three
   or more line segments. **polygon**

2. The ____ of a solid figure is the number of cubic units
   that make up a solid figure. **volume**

3. The number of square units in a region is called the ____
   of the region. **area**

CONCEPTS AND SKILLS

Identify each figure.

4. 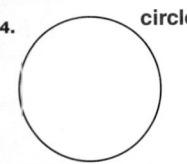 **circle**

5. **regular pentagon**

6. **quadrilateral, trapezoid**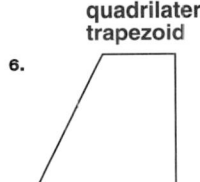

Find the perimeter and area of each figure.

7.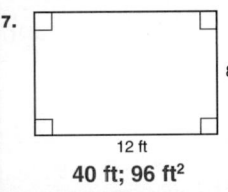

8 ft

12 ft

40 ft; 96 ft²

8.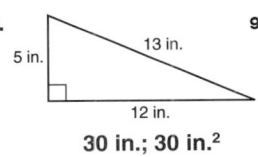

5 in. 13 in.

12 in.

30 in.; 30 in.²

9.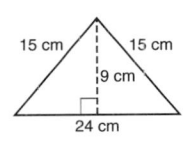

15 cm 15 cm

9 cm

24 cm

54 cm; 108 cm²

 Write About It

10. Suppose you know the area of a
    parallelogram. Can you find the area of
    a triangle that has the same base and
    height as the parallelogram? Explain.

    **Yes. Possible answer: Divide the
    area of the parallelogram by 2.**

Test Prep on the Net

Visit *Education Place* at
eduplace.com/kids/mw/
for more review.

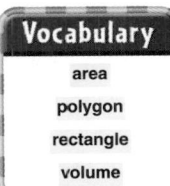 **Chapter Pretest**

Prerequisite Skills

Items	Skill
1–3	Vocabulary needed for this chapter
4–6	Identifying plane figures
7–9	Finding area and perimeter

Chapter Challenges

**For Mathematically
Promising Students**

The *Chapter Challenges* resource book
provides blackline masters for activities that explore, extend, and connect
the mathematics in every chapter. To
support this independent work, see
the Teacher Notes for each activity.

Explore: Triangular Pyramids, page 97, after
Lesson 1

Extend: Nets, page 99, after Lesson 3

Connect: Area and Volume, page 101, after
Lesson 5

Using The Chapter Pretest

This page will help students review some of the
prerequisite skills needed for this chapter. The chart
above indicates which skills are covered on the
pretest. If students need more help with these
prerequisite skills use **Ways to Success,** Houghton
Mifflin's intervention program.

 Students who need more review can visit
Education Place, Houghton Mifflin's
award-winning website.

 **NSF** **Children's Math Worlds**

Using lessons from the *Children's Math Worlds* is a
good way to ensure that your students will develop
a deep understanding of geometry. The most effective approach is to use *Children's Math Worlds*
lessons along with the lessons in the chapter.

Lesson 17.1 Solid Figures

PLANNING THE LESSON

MATHEMATICS OBJECTIVE
Identify solid figures.

Use Lesson Planner CD-ROM for Lesson 17.1.

Daily Routines

Vocabulary

What is the difference between a triangle and a *pyramid*? (triangle is 2-dimensional, pyramid is 3-dimensional) **between a circle and a *cylinder*? between a circle and a *cone*? A pyramid, a cylinder, and a cone are examples of what we call *solid figures*.**

Vocabulary Cards

Meeting North Carolina's Standards

Maintain Grade 3 Objective **3.01** Use appropriate vocabulary to compare, describe, and classify two- and three-dimensional figures.

Lesson Transparency **17.1**

Problem of the Day
When folded, the figure shown makes a cube. If 3 is on the front face, which number is on the bottom? (5)

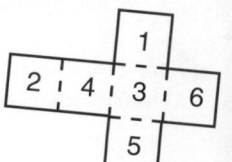

Quick Review
Find the perimeter or area.

1. area of a rectangle: length 8.5 ft and width 2.5 ft (21.25 ft²)

2. area of a triangle with base 5.2 yd and height 10 yd (26 yd²)

Lesson Quiz
Name each solid figure. Then write the number of faces, edges, and vertices.

1. 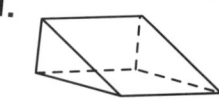 (triangular prism, 5 faces, 9 edges, 6 vertices)

2. 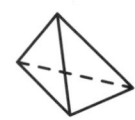 (triangular pyramid, 4 faces, 6 edges, 4 vertices)

LEVELED PRACTICE

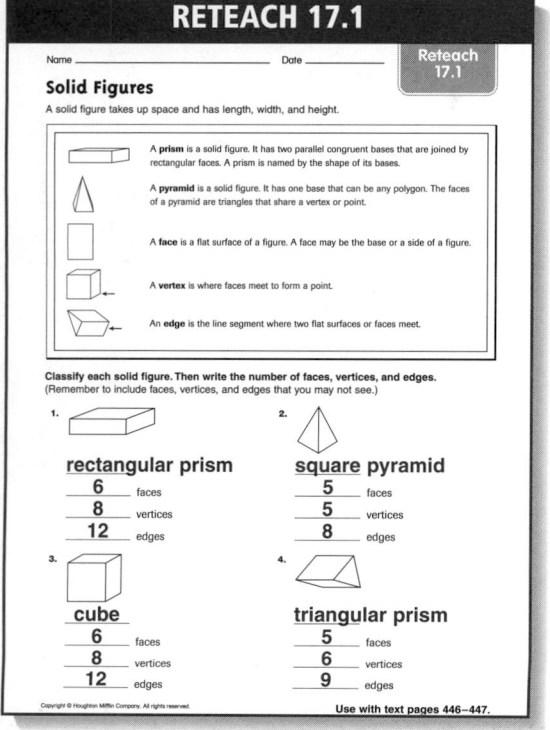

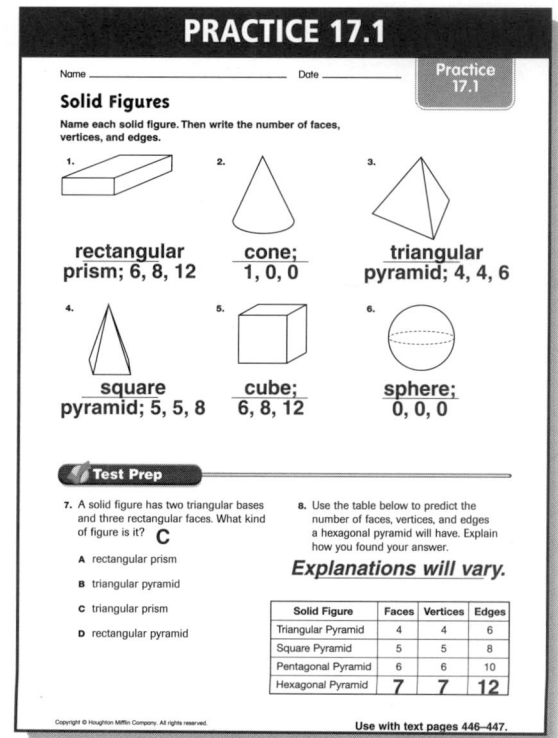

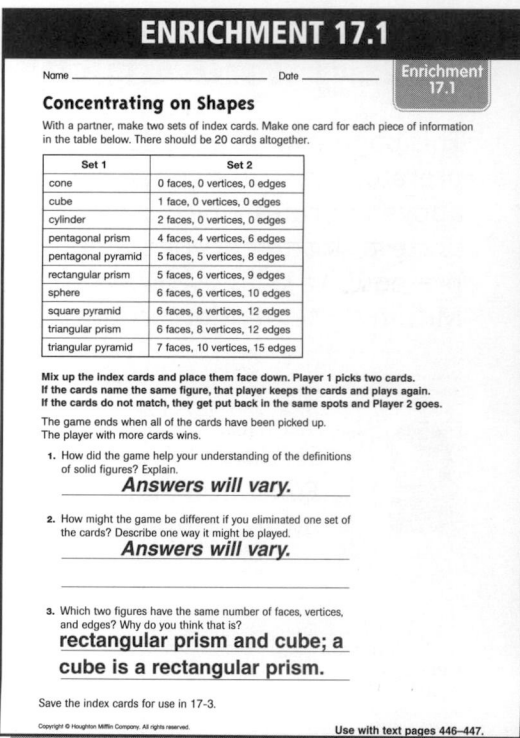

Practice Workbook Page 112

Reaching All Learners
Differentiated Instruction

English Learners

Worksheet 17.1 reviews how plural nouns are formed, including irregular plurals like *vertices*. Students write plural forms to complete sentences about the parts of solid figures, which serves as an introduction to the content of Lesson 1.

Special Needs
KINESTHETIC, TACTILE

Materials: *models of solid figures*

- Display the models. **Which of these models do you think is a rectangular prism? Why?** (one side is a rectangle)
- Continue by asking students to identify a sphere, a pyramid, and other models.
- **What solid figures can you think of that are found in daily life?**

Early Finishers
VISUAL, TACTILE

- **What are the dimensions of two different rectangular prisms you could make using 24 cubes assuming no dimension is 1 unit?** ($2 \times 2 \times 6$, $2 \times 3 \times 4$)
- **How many rectangular prisms can you make using 30 cubes assuming no dimension is 1 unit?** (just one: $2 \times 3 \times 5$)

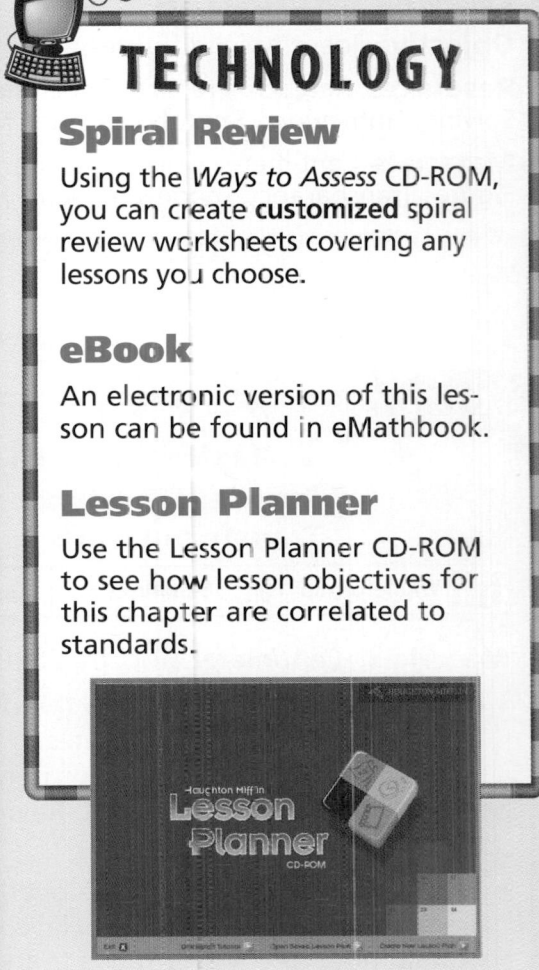

TECHNOLOGY

Spiral Review

Using the *Ways to Assess* CD-ROM, you can create **customized** spiral review worksheets covering any lessons you choose.

eBook

An electronic version of this lesson can be found in eMathbook.

Lesson Planner

Use the Lesson Planner CD-ROM to see how lesson objectives for this chapter are correlated to standards.

Social Studies Connection

Modern Architecture
Materials: *reference materials*

- Have students find pictures of modern buildings such as the Sydney Opera House (Australia); the new dome of the Reichstag (Berlin); the Pompidou Center, and the Pyramide de Louvre (Paris).

- Have students copy pictures of the buildings, and label each: building name, architect, location, building use, and the solid shapes that can be identified in the building's structure. Have students create an exhibit with their pictures.

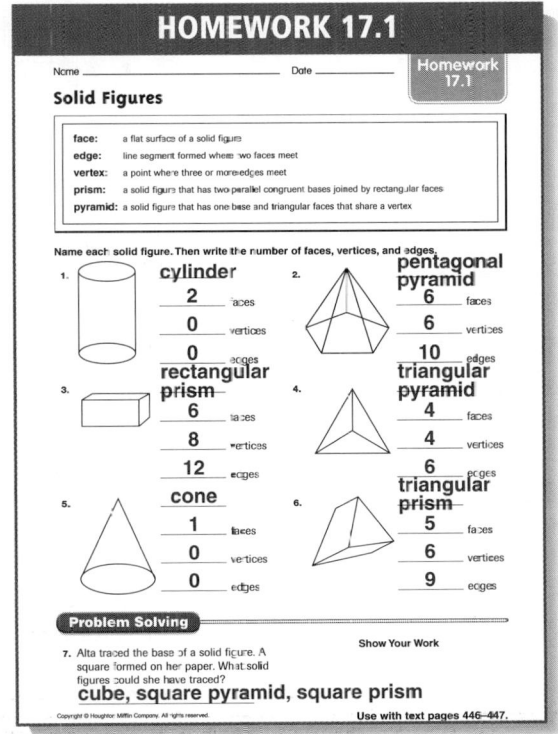

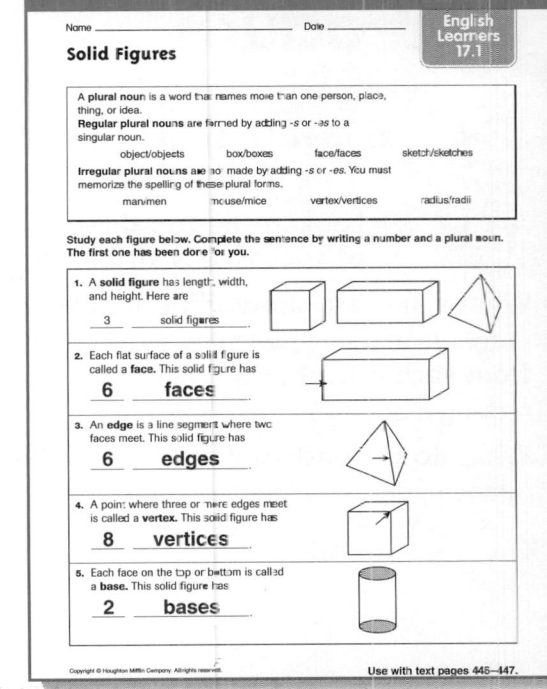

Homework Workbook Page 112

TEACHING LESSON 17.1

LESSON ORGANIZER

Objective Identify solid figures.

Resources Reteach, Practice, Enrichment, Problem Solving, Homework, English Learners, Math Center

Materials Centimeter Grid Transparency, Solid Figures Transparency, models of solid figures

Warm-Up Activity
Parallel Lines and Transformations

 Whole Group | 5 minutes | Auditory, Tactile

Materials: *Centimeter Grid Transparency*

- Invite a volunteer to come to the overhead and draw a pair of parallel lines. Have another volunteer draw a second set of parallel lines at right angles to the first set. Review a definition of right angles.

- Have a volunteer come to the overhead and draw an equilateral triangle. Have volunteers explain how to transform the triangle in three different ways through movement (rotation, reflection, and translation).

Lesson 1

Solid Figures

Objective Identify solid figures.

Learn About It  MathTracks 2/16
Listen and Understand

Most of the objects that you see every day are solid figures. Boxes, cups, cans, and other containers are all examples of solid figures.

▶ A **solid figure** has length, width, height, and takes up space.

Each flat surface is a **face**. Each face is a polygon.

The line segment formed where two faces meet is an **edge**.

The point where three or more edges meet is a **vertex**.

The faces on the top and bottom are called **bases**.

▶ A **prism** is a solid figure that has two parallel congruent bases joined by rectangular faces. Each prism is named by the shape of its base. The pasta box to the right is a rectangular prism since its bases are rectangles.

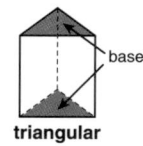
triangular prism

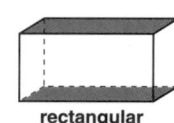
rectangular prism

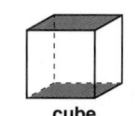
cube
(all faces are congruent)

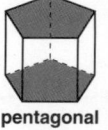
pentagonal prism

bases

▶ A **pyramid** has one base that can be any polygon. All of the other faces are triangles that share a vertex.

Some solid figures have curved surfaces.

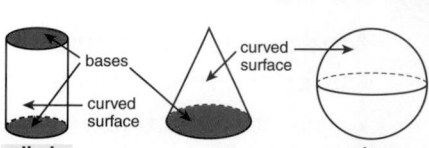

triangular pyramid | **square pyramid** | **pentagonal pyramid** | **cylinder** | **cone** | **sphere**

base | bases | curved surface | curved surface

446

---

1 Introduce

Teaching Transparency for **17.1**

Materials: *Solid Figures Transparency*

- Place the transparency on the overhead.
- **Look at the top three solids. How many faces of each one is visible to the eye?** (3)

- **What solids are shown in the bottom row on the sheet?** (a sphere and two pyramids) **How are the pyramids different from each other?** (one on right has triangle as base; other has rectangle as base)

- **What do the dashed lines in the solid figures indicate?** (hidden portions of the figures)

2 Develop

Guide students through the *Learn About It* section.

- **What features define a cone?** (a circular base, sloping sides that come to a point)

- **What features define a pyramid?** (polygon base, triangular faces; triangles share a vertex)

- **What features define a prism?** (two parallel congruent bases joined by rectangular faces)

Guided Practice

Have students complete **Exercises 1–3** as you observe. Remind them to use the *Ask Yourself* questions to help. Give students the opportunity to talk about the question in *Explain Your Thinking*.

Classify each solid figure. Then write the number of faces, vertices, and edges.

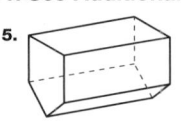
1. rectangular prism; 6 faces, 8 vertices, 12 edges

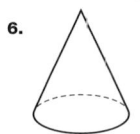
2. cylinder; 2 faces, 0 vertices, 0 edges

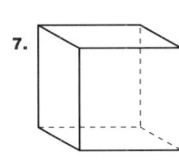
3. square pyramid; 5 faces, 5 vertices, 8 edges

Explain Your Thinking ▶ What is the difference between a rectangular pyramid and a rectangular prism?
A rectangular prism has 2 rectangular bases and 4 other rectangular faces. A rectangular pyramid has 1 rectangular base and 4 faces that are triangles.

Practice and Problem Solving

Name each solid figure. Then write the number of faces, vertices, and edges. *4–11. See Additional Answers on Page 469.*

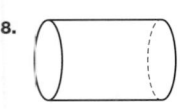
4.

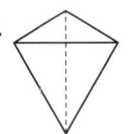
5.

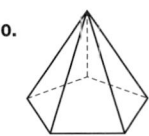
6.

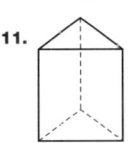
7.

8.

9.

10.

11.

Solve.

12. Model Use 24 cubes to build a rectangular prism. Then sketch it on a sheet of graph paper. ***Check students' drawings.***

13. Represent Sketch a figure with one square base and four triangular faces. Then name the figure. ***Check students' drawings; square pyramid***

14. Write About It What solid figure can you make if you combine two congruent cubes? Explain.

15. Reasoning A pyramid has six faces, including the base. What type of pyramid must it be? Explain.

14–15. See Additional Answers on Page 469.

Daily Review	Test Prep ✓
Estimate. Then add or subtract. (Ch. 11, Lessons 2–3) *Possible estimates given.* 16. 4.73 + 6.8 **10; 11.53** 17. 23.81 − 5.64 **18; 18.17** 18. 0.69 + 0.45 **1; 1.14** 19. 0.9 − 0.44 **0.5; 0.46**	✓ 20. Which solid figure has exactly one circular base? Ⓐ cone C pyramid B cylinder D sphere

---

Test Prep Transparency
17.1

A solid has a regular pentagon as its base and five congruent triangles as its other faces. What is it? (pentagonal pyramid)

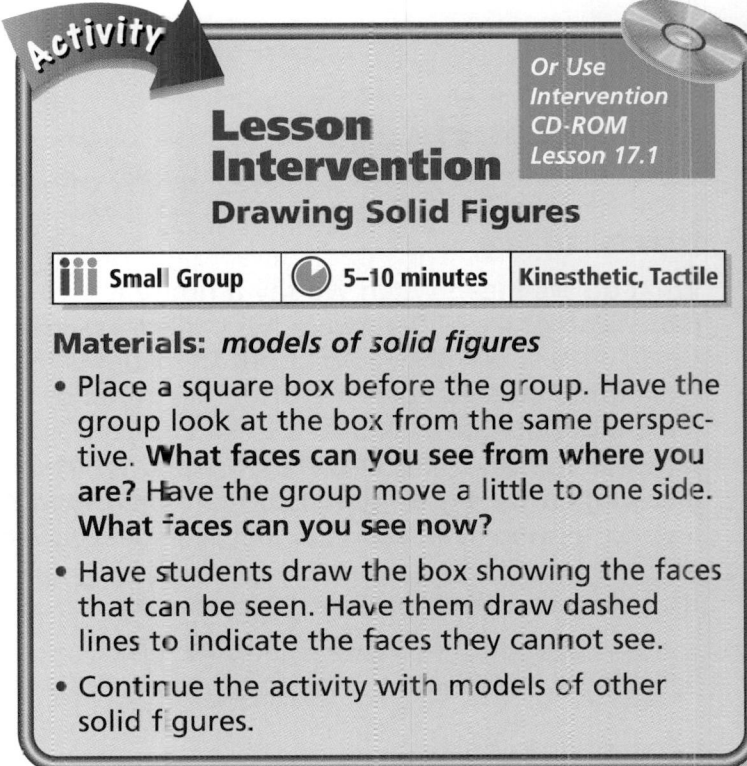

Activity

Lesson Intervention

Or Use Intervention CD-ROM Lesson 17.1

Drawing Solid Figures

👥 Small Group	🕐 5–10 minutes	Kinesthetic, Tactile

Materials: *models of solid figures*

• Place a square box before the group. Have the group look at the box from the same perspective. **What faces can you see from where you are?** Have the group move a little to one side. **What faces can you see now?**

• Have students draw the box showing the faces that can be seen. Have them draw dashed lines to indicate the faces they cannot see.

• Continue the activity with models of other solid figures.

---

③ Practice

Assign **Exercises 4–20** as independent work.

• *Exercises 12–15* Have students share their drawings and explanations.

Common Error

Invisible edges Some students may not be able to visualize a solid figure because only part of it is visible. Have students draw the solid figures with dashed lines to show the edges that are not visible. Have them bring in models of solids such as boxes, cans, and other containers.

④ Assess and Close

Have volunteers draw and label solid figures.

• **What gives a prism its name?** (the shape of its base)

• **How is a pyramid different from a cone?** (pyramid has polygon as base and triangular faces; cone has circle as base)

• **When we draw solid figures, how do we indicate parts that the eye cannot see?** (with dashed lines)

Assign the **LESSON QUIZ** on Transparency 17.1 to further assess student understanding.

Keeping a Journal

Have students list all of the solid figures, then name and sketch everyday objects that correspond to each.

Lesson 17.2

Hands-On: Two-Dimensional Views of Solid Figures

PLANNING THE LESSON

MATHEMATICS OBJECTIVE
Identify different two-dimensional views of a solid figure.

Use Lesson Planner CD-ROM for Lesson 17.2.

Daily Routines

Vocabulary

What do we mean when we say a figure is *two-dimensional*? (Possible answers: It is flat like a piece of paper; It lies in one plane.) Point out to students that 2-dimensional rectangles are often described by their dimensions, length × width, for example, a 3 × 5 index card or an $8\frac{1}{2}$ × 11 piece of paper. **What do we mean when we say a figure is *three-dimensional*?** (Possible answer: It has depth, as well as length and width.)

Vocabulary Cards

Meeting North Carolina's Standards
Prepare for Grade 7 Objective 3.01 Using three-dimensional figures.

Lesson Transparency
17.2

Problem of the Day
How can you draw 3 congruent triangles using 6 line segments?

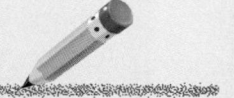

Quick Review
Compare. Write <, >, or = for each ●.

1. $\frac{6}{8}$ ● $\frac{24}{32}$ (=)　　**2.** $\frac{5}{7}$ ● $\frac{4}{7}$ (>)

3. $\frac{6}{7}$ ● $\frac{7}{6}$ (<)　　**4.** $\frac{16}{40}$ ● $\frac{2}{5}$ (=)

Lesson Quiz
1. Draw two-dimensional front, side, and top views for this three-dimensional figure.

front　　top　　right

2. Given these views, draw the figure on triangular dot paper.

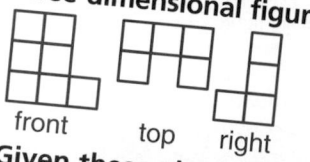

front　　top　　right

LEVELED PRACTICE

RETEACH 17.2
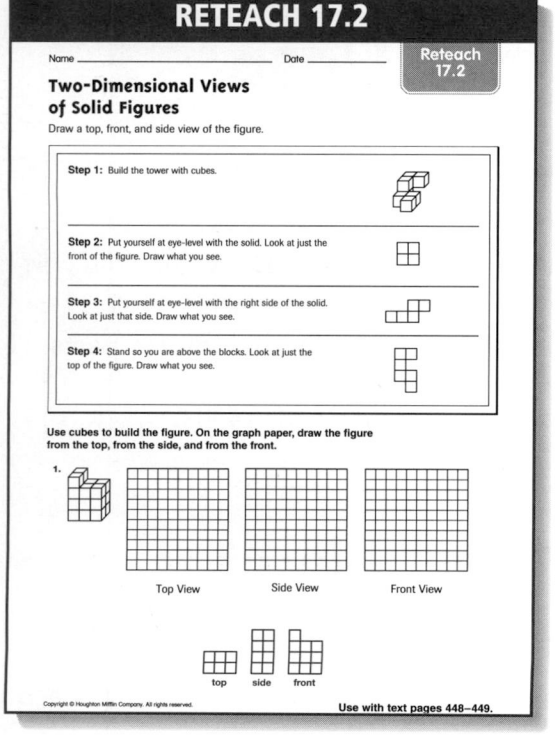

PRACTICE 17.2
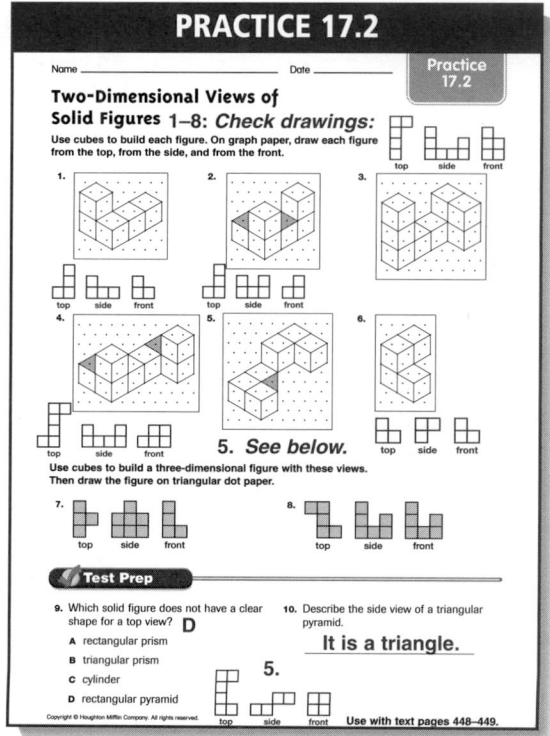

ENRICHMENT 17.2
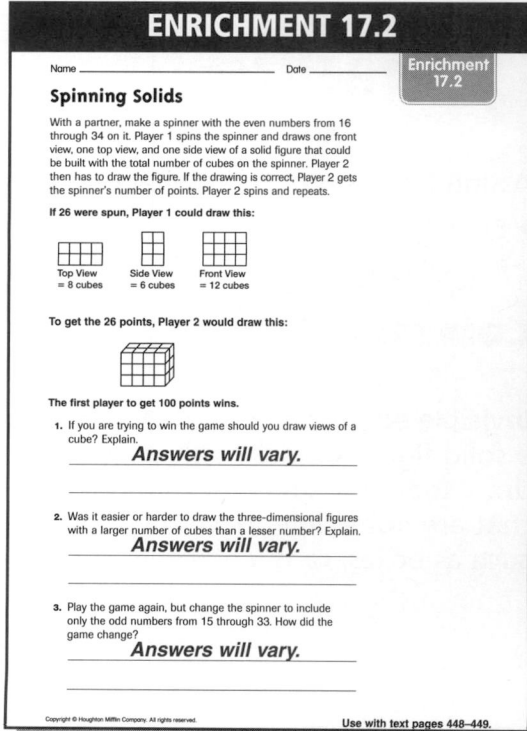

Reaching All Learners
Differentiated Instruction

English Learners

Worksheet 17.2 familiarizes students with the definitions of *dimension, two-dimensional,* and *three-dimensional.* Illustrations of each concept are provided.

Inclusion
KINESTHETIC, VISUAL

Materials: *cubes*

- Display:

- Have students use cubes to model the drawing.

- **How many cubes tall is the tallest part of the figure?** (3) **Where does the 2-cube stack go? Where do the other cubes go?**

Gifted and Talented
VISUAL, TACTILE

Materials: *cubes, grid paper*

Have students work alone or with partners. Have them build a cube construction and then draw it from different angles (above, from the side, from the front).

TECHNOLOGY

Spiral Review

To reinforce skills on lessons taught earlier, create **customized** spiral review worksheets using the *Ways to Assess* CD-ROM.

Tool Software

Use Sunburst's *Shape Up!* or another shapes program to explore this lesson's objectives more fully.

Manipulatives

eManipulatives are available on the *Ways to Success* CD.

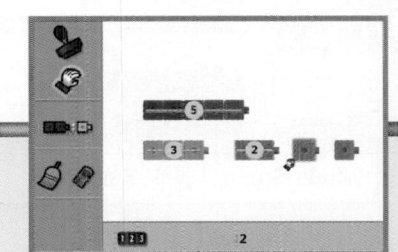

Art Connection

Floor Plan
Materials: *grid paper or Learning Tool 14*

- Show students an example of a floor plan. You may find examples on the Internet or in reference books. Explain that floor plans are representations of the layout of a space. Point out how doors and other features are represented.

- Challenge students to draw a floor plan of the classroom or of a room in their home. Have them label items in the floor plan and title the floor plan.

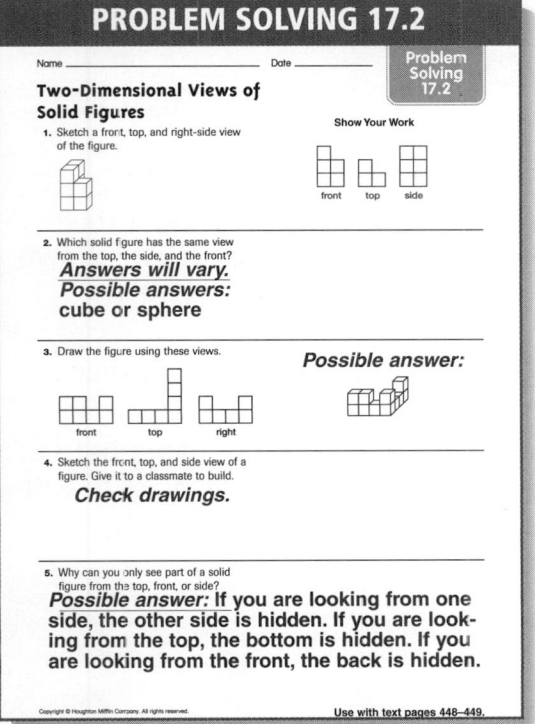

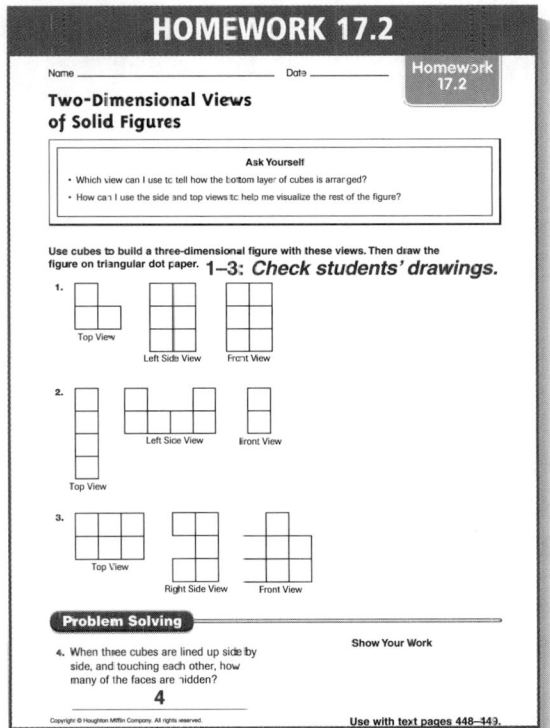

Homework Workbook Page 113

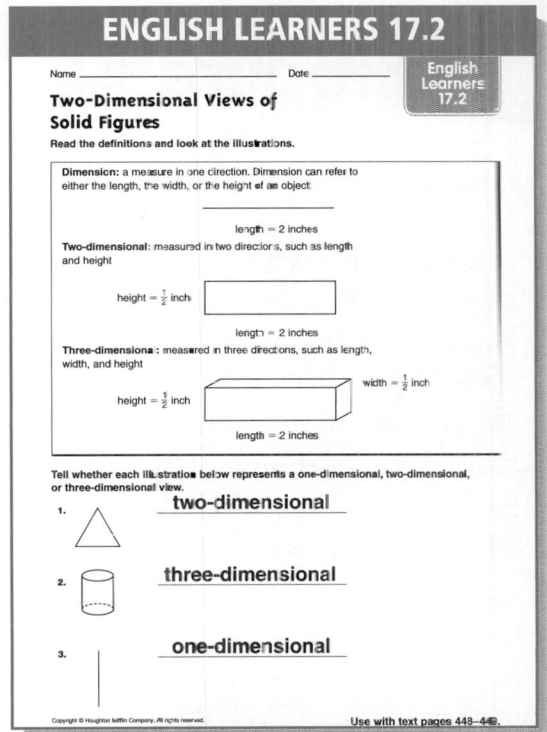

TEACHING LESSON 17.2

LESSON ORGANIZER

Objective Identify different two-dimensional views of a solid figure.

Resources Reteach, Practice, Enrichment, Problem-Solving, Homework, English Learners, Transparencies, Math Center

Materials Solid Figures Transparency, cubes, grid paper or Learning Tool 14, triangular dot paper or Learning Tool 17, 13 textbooks, copies of diagram

Activity

Warm-Up Activity
Identify Solid Figures

 Whole Group	5 minutes	Auditory, Tactile

Materials: *Solid Figures Transparency*

Display the Solid Figures Transparency on the overhead. Invite volunteers to identify the figures. Review the characteristics of each figure.

 **Lesson 2 Hands-On**

Two-Dimensional Views of Solid Figures

Objective Identify different two-dimensional views of a solid figure.

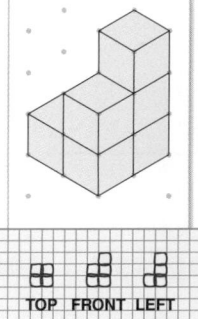

Work Together

To make a two-dimensional drawing of the solid figure, you can use triangular dot paper and grid paper as shown at the right. You can also use two-dimensional drawings to show what solid figures look like from different views.

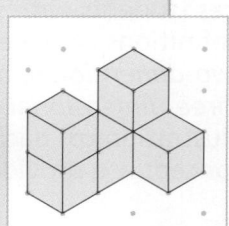
TOP   FRONT   LEFT

Materials: cubes, grid paper (Learning Tool 14)

Try this activity to identify different two-dimensional views of the figure shown below.

STEP 1 Use cubes to build the figure.

STEP 2 Draw these views on grid paper:
• the top view
• the view from the right side
• the front view

See Additional Answers on Page 469.

You can use two-dimensional views to build and draw a three-dimensional figure.

Materials: cubes, triangular dot paper (Learning Tool 17)

Try this activity to create a solid figure that looks like this:

top   right side   front

STEP 1 Look at the top view. What can you say about the bottom of the figure? Use cubes to build the bottom layer of the figure.

STEP 2 Use the side and front views to visualize the middle layer and then the top layer of the figure. Build each layer.

STEP 3 Draw the figure on triangular dot paper. Could you draw another figure? Explain.

See Additional Answers on Page 469.

You can draw another figure because a different figure could have the same views.

448

---

① Introduce | Whole Group | 5 minutes |

Materials: *13 textbooks*

• **Build a stack of six textbooks. In front of them, place a stack of four textbooks. To the right of the original stack, place a stack of three textbooks.**

• Have students walk around the construction of books, looking at it from different angles.

• **Do you see all thirteen books from all angles?** (no)

• **Does the collection look the same from all angles?** (no)

• **To represent the construction on paper, or two-dimensionally, we need to show different views of it.**

② Develop

Guide students through the *Work Together* section.

• For the first activity, have students check to see if their cube construction accurately represents the figure shown. Then have them check to see if the views accurately represent the construction.

• For the second activity, have students verify that their object corresponds to the given views.

• Students may not have seen triangular dot paper before. Prior to taking Step 3 of the second activity, practice with students drawing cubes on triangular dot paper.

Use cubes to build each figure. On graph paper, draw each figure from the top, from the side, and from the front.   *See Additional Answers on Page 469.*

1.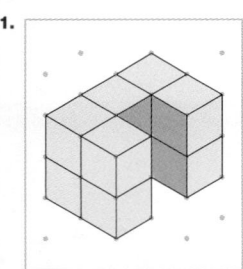

2.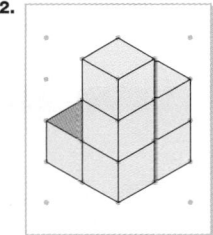

3.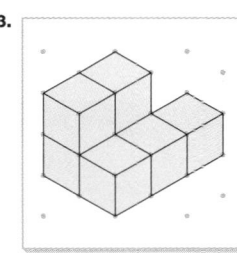

Use cubes to build a three-dimensional figure with these views. Then draw the figure on triangular dot paper.   4–5. *Check students' drawings.*

4.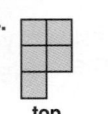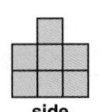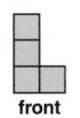

top   side   front

5.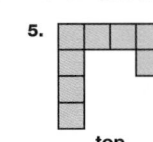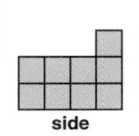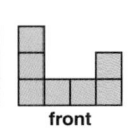

top   side   front

6. **Reasoning** Could the three views shown below be views of a rectangular prism? Explain.
See Additional Answers on Page 469.

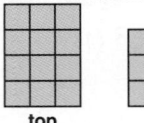 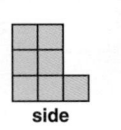 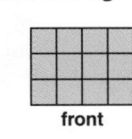

top   side   front

8. *Possible answer:* Every cube in the top view must be either in the bottom layer or supported by a cube in the bottom layer.

7. Name a solid figure that is a triangle from the top view and has congruent rectangles from the side views.   **triangular prism**

8. Sketch the top, side, and front views of each solid figure.
Check students' drawings.
   a. cube   b. cylinder
   c. cone   d. sphere

Talk About It • Write About It

Use what you have learned about modeling and drawing solid figures to answer these questions.

9. Why does the top view tell you how the bottom layer of cubes must be arranged? *See above.*

10. A figure has a top view and side view that are identical. What type solid figure might this be? Explain how you know.   *Possible answer: a cube*

Test Prep Transparency

17.2

How many cubes are represented in this diagram? (B)

A. 8   C. 21
B. 12   D. 22

Activity

Or Use Intervention CD-ROM Lesson 17.2

Lesson Intervention
Organize Information in Tables

| Individual | 5–10 minutes | Kinesthetic, Visual |

Materials: *copies of diagram*

• Make a copy of this diagram and give it to students.

• Let's create a table to show how many cubes are in each level of cubes in this diagram.

• Copy this table on the chalkboard:

• Have students build a model with cubes based on the information in the table.

Level of stack	# of Cubes
Bottom	(8)
Middle	(4)
Top	(1)

---

3 Practice

Assign **Exercises 1–8** of *On Your Own* as independent work.

• *Exercises 1–5* Some students may misrepresent or confuse front, side, or top views. Encourage students to shade the faces of a figure in different colors to indicate the front, back, sides, top and bottom, to prevent confusion.

4 Assess and Close

Assign **Exercises 9–10** of the *Talk About It • Write About It* section. Have volunteers explain their work.

Assign the **LESSON QUIZ** on Transparency 17.2 to further assess student understanding.

Keeping a Journal

Have students write a few sentences about why it is important to be able to represent three dimensional constructions in two-dimensional form, and to be able to build three-dimensional models from two-dimensional drawings.

Lesson 17.3 Nets

PLANNING THE LESSON

MATHEMATICS OBJECTIVE
Identify the nets of solid figures.

Use Lesson Planner CD-ROM for Lesson 17.3.

Daily Routines

Vocabulary

Have you ever seen a cardboard box before it is put together? What does it look like?
(It is a flat piece of cardboard with lines that indicate where the cardboard should be folded.) **What do you do to put the box together?** (Fold the sides in a certain pattern.) **In math, a *net* is a flat pattern that can be folded to make a solid figure.**

Vocabulary Cards

Meeting North Carolina's Standards
Prepare for Grade 7 Objective **3.01** Using three-dimensional figures.

Lesson Transparency 17.3

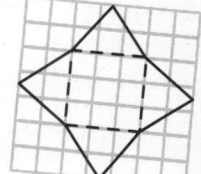

Problem of the Day
What is the greatest number of regions you can make by using three chords in a circle? (7)

Quick Review
Estimate.
1. $3\frac{1}{5} + 3\frac{1}{4}$ (6)
2. $3\frac{7}{8} + 3\frac{1}{8}$ (7)
3. $3\frac{7}{8} + 3\frac{6}{7}$ (8)
4. $3\frac{1}{4} - 3\frac{1}{5}$ (0)
5. $3\frac{7}{8} - 3\frac{1}{9}$ (1)
6. $3\frac{7}{8} - 3$ (1)

Lesson Quiz
1. Predict what shape this net will make.
(square pyramid)

2. Make two different nets for a rectangular prism. (Diagrams may vary. Possible answer:)

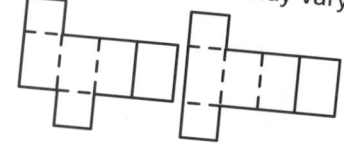

LEVELED PRACTICE

RETEACH 17.3
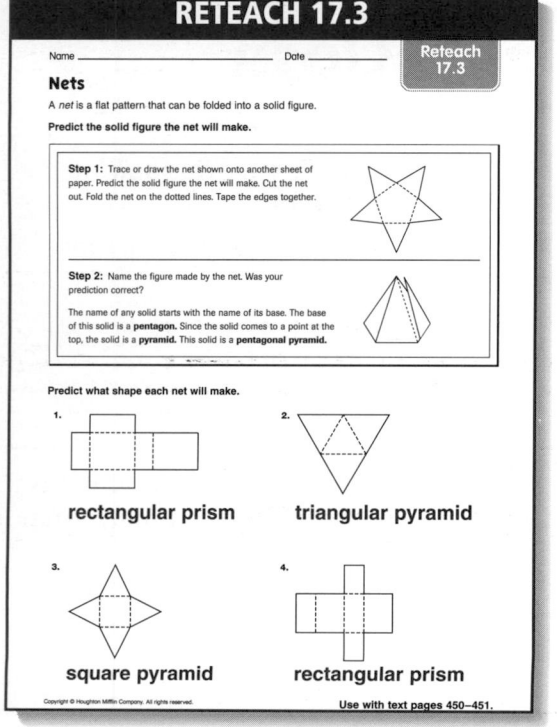

PRACTICE 17.3
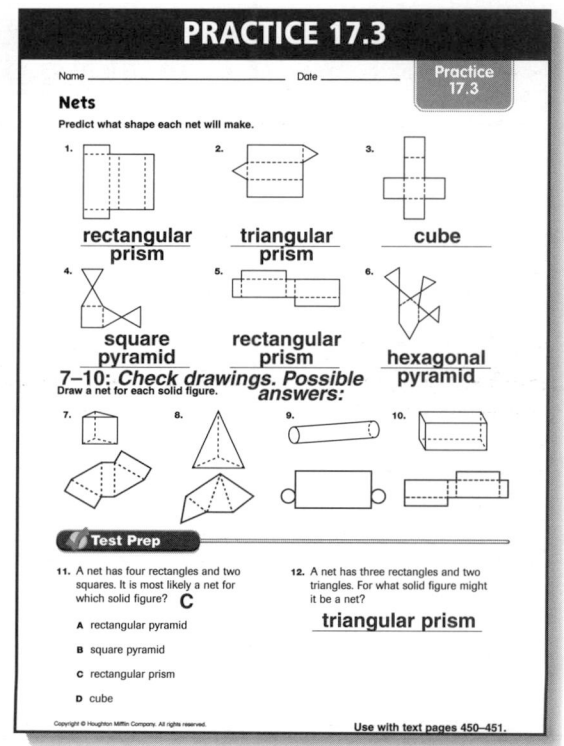

ENRICHMENT 17.3
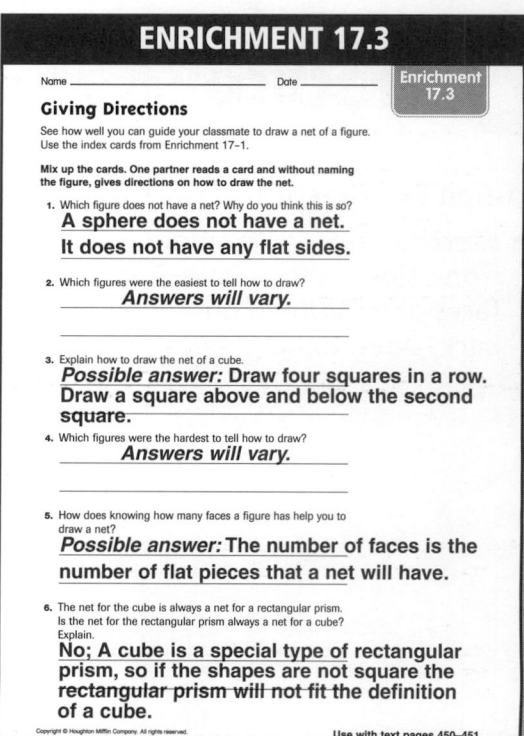

Practice Workbook Page 114

Reaching All Learners
Differentiated Instruction

English Learners

Worksheet 17.3 illustrates several definitions of the word *net*, including the mathematical one. Students are asked to identify the solid figures that could be made from several nets.

Special Needs
VISUAL, AUDITORY

Materials: *grid paper or Learning Tool 14, scissors, tape*

- Give students copies of this diagram:

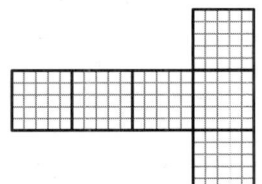

- Have students copy the diagram on grid paper and cut it out. Challenge them to make a cube out of this net.

Early Finishers
VISUAL, TACTILE

- Give students copies of this diagram:

- Challenge students to draw a net that, when put together, would make a solid figure like the one shown in the diagram.
- Challenge students to make nets for other solid figures.

Social Studies Connection

Monument to a Mathematician
Materials: *reference materials, large sheets of paper, scissors, tape*

- Have students research the life and work of Euclid, an ancient Greek mathematician, best known for his book, *The Elements.*

- Have students make a large net for a rectangular prism with a square base. Have them construct the solid figure and use it as a square base for a monument. Have students make a monument to Euclid and erect it on the base.

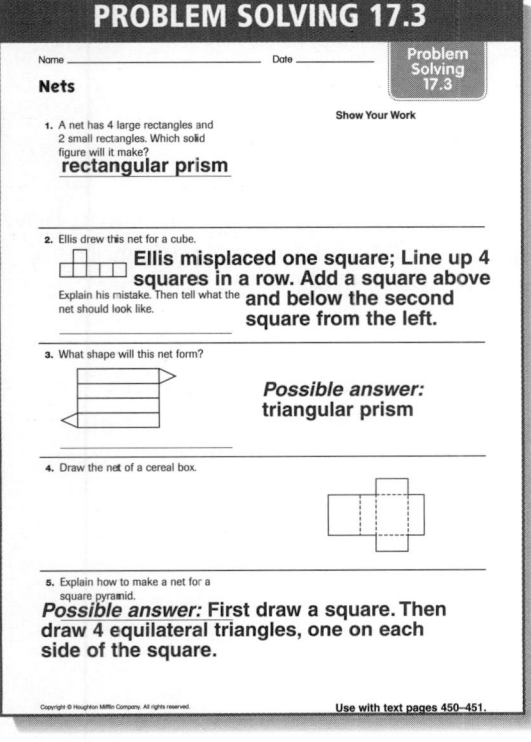

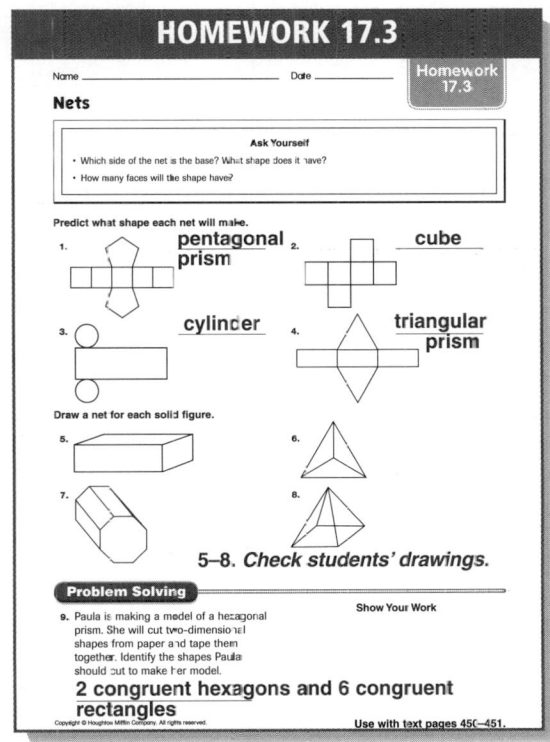

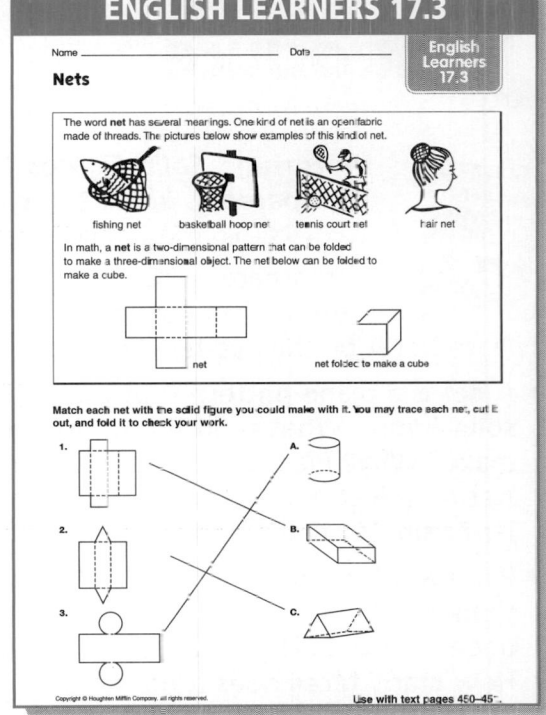

Homework Workbook Page 114

TEACHING LESSON 17.3

LESSON ORGANIZER

Objective Identify the nets of solid figures.

Resources Reteach, Practice, Enrichment, Problem Solving, Homework, English Learners, Transparencies, Math Center

Materials Solid Figures Transparency, Nets I Transparency, blank transparency, inch grid paper, scissors, tape, Learning Tools 45–51

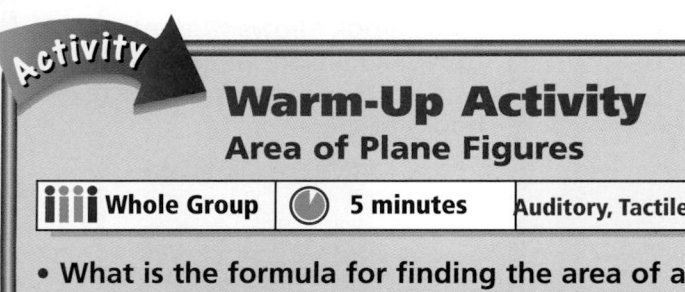

Warm-Up Activity
Area of Plane Figures

iiii Whole Group	⏱ 5 minutes	Auditory, Tactile

- **What is the formula for finding the area of a square?** ($s^2 = A$) **What is the formula for the area of a rectangle?** ($l \times w = A$) Review the formula for the area of other plane figures (triangle, parallelogram, trapezoid, circle).

Nets

Objective Identify the nets of solid figures.

Learn About It

Cardboard boxes and other containers are made from nets. A **net** is a flat pattern that can be folded into a solid figure.

A solid figure can have more than one net. For example, both nets below can be folded to make a triangular prism.

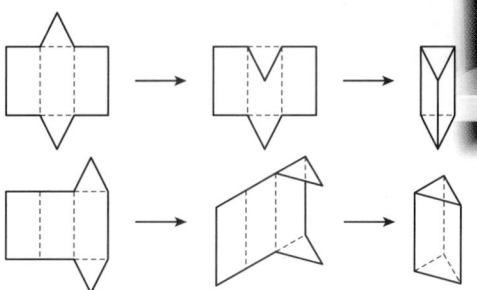

When making a net, you may need to add "flaps" in order to secure the net. However, the "flaps" are not part of a geometric net.

Try this activity to make nets.
Materials: inch grid paper (**Learning Tool 15**), scissors, tape

STEP 1 On a sheet of grid paper, draw the net shown at the right. Then cut it out.
- Predict what solid figure the net will make. **rectangular prism**

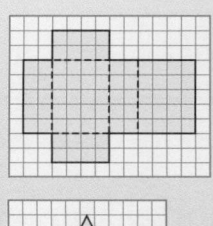

STEP 2 Fold the net on the dotted lines. Tape the edges together.
- Was your prediction correct? **Answers will vary.**

STEP 3 Repeat Step 1 and Step 2 using the net at the right. **square pyramid**

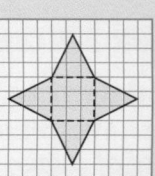

450

---

① Introduce

Teaching Transparency for **17.3**

Materials: *Solid Figures Transparency, Nets I Transparency, blank transparency*
- Cut out Net A and Net B from the Nets I Transparency. Cut out the cube and rectangular prism from the Solid Figures Transparency. Place Net A on the overhead on top of a blank transparency.

- **A net is a plane pattern that can be folded to make a solid figure. What solid figure do you think Net A will make? Why?** Place the cut-out rectangular prism below Net A. **In Net A we can see all of the faces of a rectangular prism. How many faces does it have?** (6)

- Place Net B on the overhead. **What solid figure do you think Net B will make? Why?** Place the cut-out cube under Net B. **In Net B we see all the faces of a cube. How many faces does it have?** (6)

② Develop

Guide students through the *Learn About It* section.

- In Steps 1 and 2, ask how many faces the net has and how these shapes are arranged relative to one another. Then have students make their predictions.

Guided Practice

Have students complete **Exercises 1–3** as you observe. Remind them to use the *Ask Yourself* questions to help. Give students the opportunity to talk about the question in *Explain Your Thinking*.

Ask Yourself

• Which side of the net is the base? What shape does it have?

• How many faces will the shape have?

Predict what shape each net will make.

1. cube
2. triangular pyramid
3. rectangular prism

Explain Your Thinking ▶ How did you make your prediction for Exercise 2?
Possible answer: Identified the number of bases (1) the shape of the base (triangle) and the shape of the other faces (triangles).

Practice and Problem Solving

Predict what shape each net will make.

4. square pyramid
5. rectangular prism
6. cylinder
7. hexagonal prism

Draw a net for each solid figure. *Check student's drawings.*

8. 9. 10. 11.

Solve.

12. **Predict** Which of the nets to the right will not form a cube? Explain your answer. *See below.*

13. **Represent** Draw another net that will form a cube. *Check students' drawings.*

14. **Calculator** A rectangular room is 15 feet by 17 feet. How much will it cost to cover the floor with carpet that costs $8.99 per square foot? **$2,292.45**

A B
C D

12. **D.** *Possible answer:* two of the faces will overlap and one side of the figure will be open.

Daily Review   Test Prep

Find the area. (Ch. 16, Lessons 3–4)

15. 8 in. / 6 in. / 8 in. **24 in.²**

16. 9 cm / 11 cm / 15 cm **135 cm²**

17. **Free Response** Describe the solid that could be made from this net. Explain your thinking.
triangular pyramid

Extra Practice See page 469, Set B.

Chapter 17 Lesson 3 **451**

Test Prep Transparency 17.3

DAILY TEST PREP

Which represents a square pyramid? (B)

A. a net with six squares

3. a net with one square and four triangles

C. a net with four squares and one triangle

D. a net with five triangles

Activity

Or Use Intervention CD-ROM Lesson 17.3

Lesson Intervention
Faces of a Solid Figure

👥 Small Group   🕐 10 minutes   Visual, Auditory

• Have students copy this figure including the dashed lines.

• **What shape is the sloping plane?** (rectangle) **What shape is the base?** (rectangle) **What shape is the face in the back which is filled in with dotted lines?** (rectangle) **What shape is the face closest to us, on the left?** (right triangle) **Is there another face congruent to this one?** (yes, opposite it) **So this solid figure consists of two right triangles and three rectangles.**

• Have students build a model of this solid figure. Point out that the three rectangular faces are not congruent.

---

3 Practice

Assign **Exercises 4–17** as independent work.

Common Error

Only one net? Some students may think that there is only one net possible for a given solid figure. Have students make four rectangles, 3 inches by 5 inches, and two squares, 3 inches by 3 inches. Have students arrange the shapes to make a net for a rectangular prism; then have students rearrange the shapes to make a different net for the same solid.

4 Assess and Close

• **Suppose you want to represent a cereal box as a net. What should you do?** (Count the faces (6). Identify and measure the faces—2 large congruent rectangles, 2 long congruent rectangles, 2 small congruent rectangles. Measure and cut out the shapes. Arrange the shapes so that, when folded, they will make a cereal box.)

Assign the **LESSON QUIZ** on Transparency 17.3 to further assess student understanding.

Keeping a Journal

Have students explain why someone might need to represent a solid figure.

Surface Area

PLANNING THE LESSON

MATHEMATICS OBJECTIVE
Use nets to find the surface area of solid figures.

Use Lesson Planner CD-ROM for Lesson 17.4.

Daily Routines

Vocabulary
The surface of a solid is the layer you can touch from outside the solid. What do you think is meant by *surface area*? (The surface area is finding the amount of surface the solid has.)

Vocabulary Cards

Meeting North Carolina's Standards
Prepare for Grade 6 Objective **2.01** Estimate and measure length, perimeter, area, angles, weight, and mass of two and three-dimensional figures using appropriate tools.

Lesson Transparency **17.4**

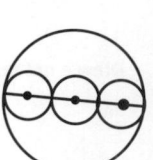

Problem of the Day
Each of the small circles in the diagram below has a circumference of 4π. What is the circumference of the large circle? (12π)

Quick Review
Solve.
1. $2(3 + 7)$ (20)
2. $5(7 - 4) + 8(2 - 1)$ (23)
3. $(5 + 4)(4 + 5)$ (81)
4. $2(6 + 5 + 7)$ (36)
5. $5(8 + 2) + 3(8 - 2)$ (68)

Lesson Quiz
1. Find the surface area of this rectangular prism. (52.5 mm²)

   4.0 mm
   2.5 mm
   2.5 mm

2. What is the surface area of a cube if the length of one edge is 10 in.? (600 in.²)

LEVELED PRACTICE

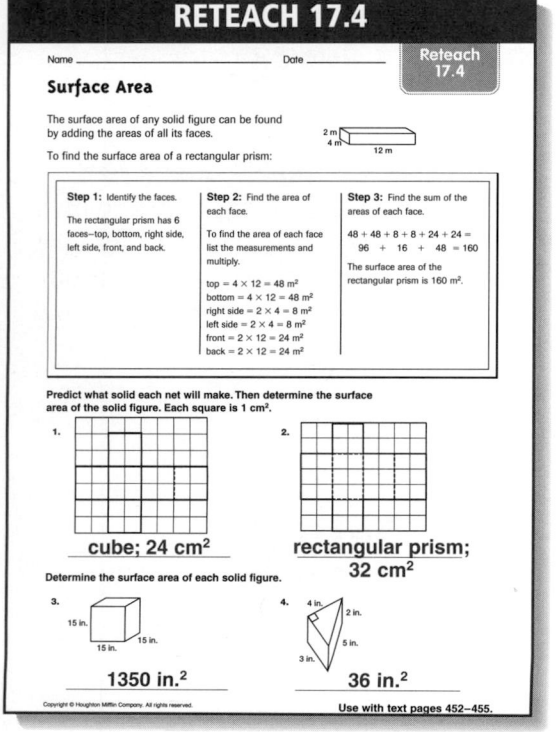

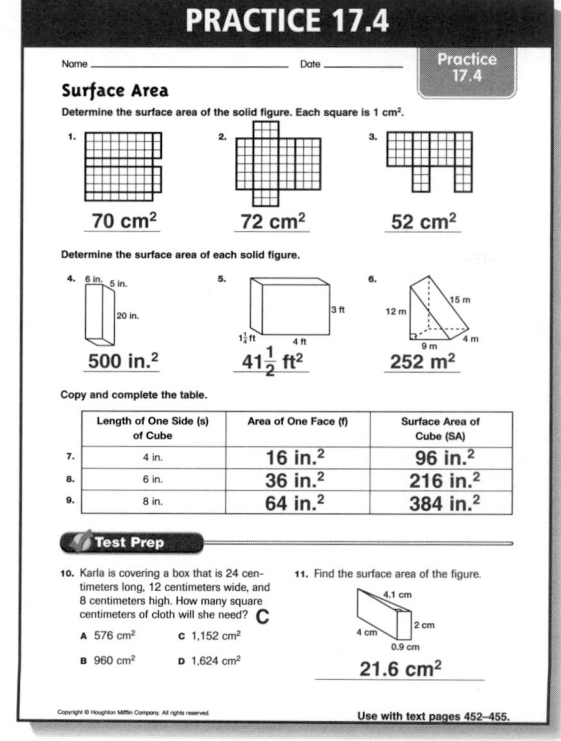

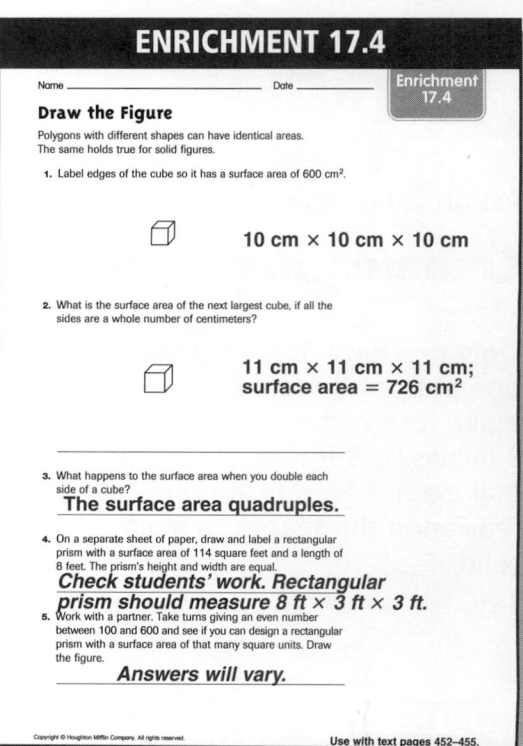

Practice Workbook Page 115

Reaching All Learners
Differentiated Instruction

English Learners

Worksheet 17.4 teaches the meaning of *surface*, using both text and illustrations, to prepare students for the lesson on surface area.

Inclusion
KINESTHETIC, TACTILE

- Display:

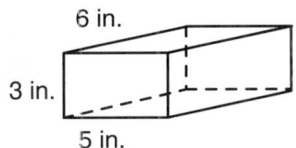

6 in.
3 in.
5 in.

- The surface area is the sum of the areas of all the faces. Help students see the 3 sets of congruent rectangles, and find their dimensions.
- What is the surface area? (126 square inches)

Gifted and Talented
VISUAL, TACTILE

Give students this problem:

- A rectangular prism has square bases 6 ft on a side. The surface area of the prism is 312 ft^2. What is the height of the prism? (10 ft)

TECHNOLOGY

Spiral Review

You can prepare students for standardized tests with **customized** spiral review on key skills using the *Ways to Assess* CD-ROM.

Education Place

You can visit Education Place at eduplace.com/math/mw/ for teacher support materials.

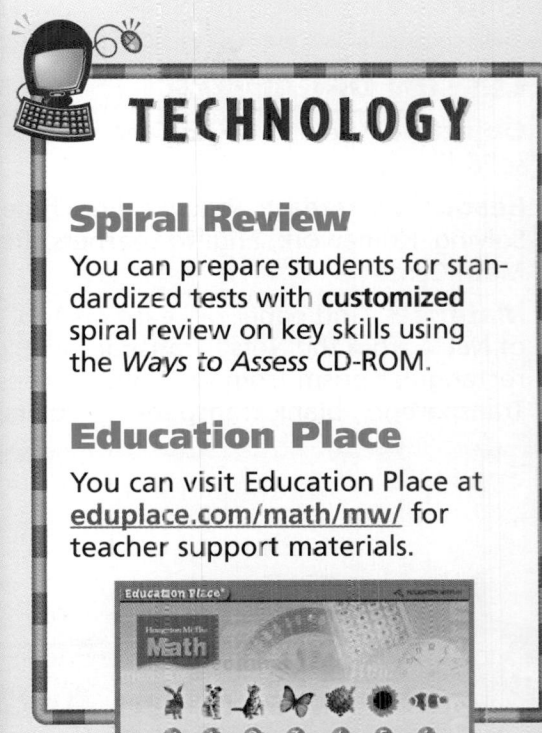

Art Connection

Wrap a Landmark
Materials: *reference materials, or almanac*

- Have students research the work of Christo, the artist who has wrapped entire buildings in fabric. Have students find out how much fabric it took to wrap some of his projects, such as the Reichstag in Berlin.
- Have students choose a landmark building in your state and find its surface area. **How much fabric would you need to wrap it up?**

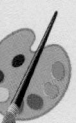

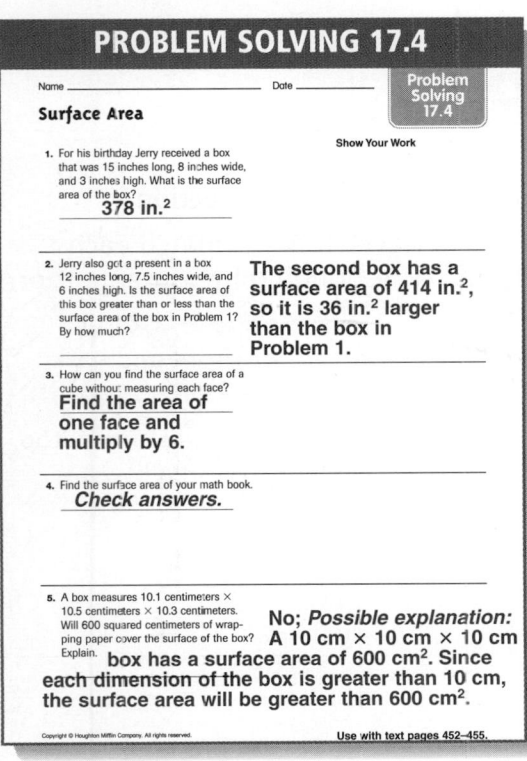

PROBLEM SOLVING 17.4

Name _____ Date _____

Problem Solving 17.4

Surface Area

Show Your Work

1. For his birthday Jerry received a box that was 15 inches long, 8 inches wide, and 3 inches high. What is the surface area of the box?
   378 in.²

2. Jerry also got a present in a box 12 inches long, 7.5 inches wide, and 6 inches high. Is the surface area of this box greater than or less than the surface area of the box in Problem 1? By how much?
   The second box has a surface area of 414 in.², so it is 36 in.² larger than the box in Problem 1.

3. How can you find the surface area of a cube without measuring each face?
   Find the area of one face and multiply by 6.

4. Find the surface area of your math book.
   Check answers.

5. A box measures 10.1 centimeters × 10.5 centimeters × 10.3 centimeters. Will 600 squared centimeters of wrapping paper cover the surface of the box? Explain.
   No; Possible explanation: A 10 cm × 10 cm × 10 cm box has a surface area of 600 cm². Since each dimension of the box is greater than 10 cm, the surface area will be greater than 600 cm².

Copyright © Houghton Mifflin Company. All rights reserved.
Use with text pages 452–455.

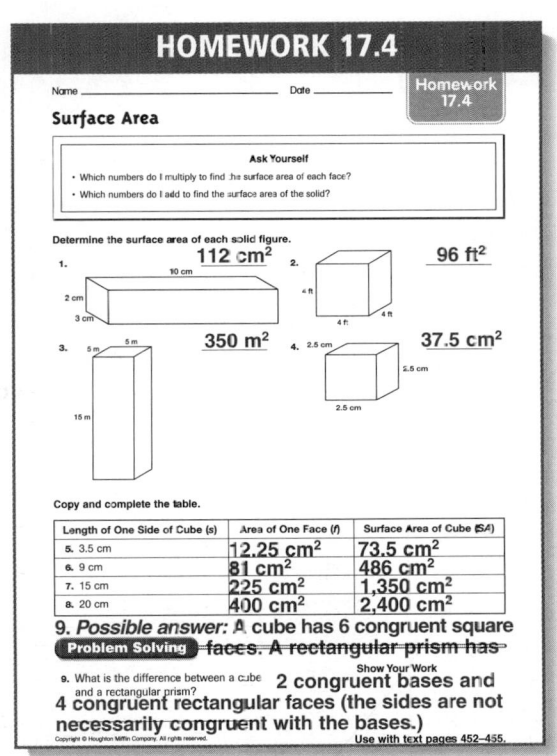

HOMEWORK 17.4

Name _____ Date _____

Homework 17.4

Surface Area

Ask Yourself
- Which numbers do I multiply to find the surface area of each face?
- Which numbers do I add to find the surface area of the solid?

Determine the surface area of each solid figure.

1. 10 cm, 2 cm, 3 cm **112 cm²**
2. 4 ft, 4 ft, 4 ft **96 ft²**
3. 5 m, 5 m, 15 m **350 m²**
4. 2.5 cm, 2.5 cm, 2.5 cm **37.5 cm²**

Copy and complete the table.

Length of One Side of Cube (s)	Area of One Face (f)	Surface Area of Cube (SA)
5. 3.5 cm	12.25 cm²	73.5 cm²
6. 9 cm	81 cm²	486 cm²
7. 15 cm	225 cm²	1,350 cm²
8. 20 cm	400 cm²	2,400 cm²

9. *Possible answer:* A cube has 6 congruent square faces. A rectangular prism has

Problem Solving

Show Your Work

9. What is the difference between a cube and a rectangular prism? 2 congruent bases and 4 congruent rectangular faces (the sides are not necessarily congruent with the bases.)

Copyright © Houghton Mifflin Company. All rights reserved.
Use with text pages 452–455.

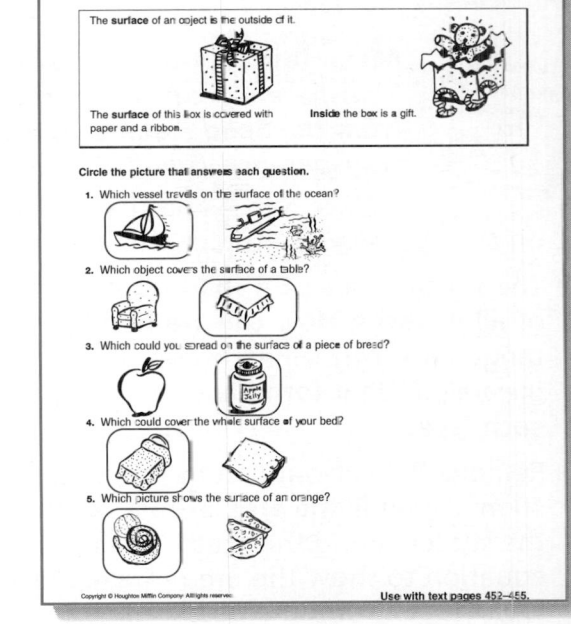

ENGLISH LEARNERS 17.4

Name _____ Date _____

English Learners 17.4

Surface Area

The **surface** of an object is the outside of it.

The **surface** of this box is covered with paper and a ribbon.   **Inside** the box is a gift.

Circle the picture that answers each question.

1. Which vessel travels on the surface of the ocean?

2. Which object covers the surface of a table?

3. Which could you spread on the surface of a piece of bread?

4. Which could cover the whole surface of your bed?

5. Which picture shows the surface of an orange?

Copyright © Houghton Mifflin Company. All rights reserved.
Use with text pages 452–455.

Homework Workbook Page 115

TEACHING LESSON 17.4

LESSON ORGANIZER

Objective Use nets to find the surface area of solid figures.

Resources Reteach, Practice, Enrichment, Problem Solving, Homework, English Learners, Transparencies, Math Center

Materials Grid paper or Learning Tool 14, cut-out of Net A from the Nets I Transparency, cut-out of rectangular prism from the Solid Figures Transparency, blank transparency, rulers, text books

Activity

Warm-Up Activity
Making A Net

| iiii Whole Group | ⏱ 5–10 minutes | Auditory, Tactile |

Materials: *grid paper or Learning Tool 14*

- Suppose the front face of a rectangular prism has a length of 10 units, and a width of 6 units. The height of the solid is 8 units.
- On grid paper, draw and label the rectangular prism starting with these measurements.
- Have students make a net for this solid figure.

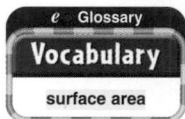
e Glossary

Surface Area

Objective Use nets to find the surface area of solid figures.

Learn About It  MathTracks 2/17
Listen and Understand

A department store stocks wrapping paper that can be folded to wrap shirt boxes. What is the least amount of wrapping paper you need to cover this shirt box?

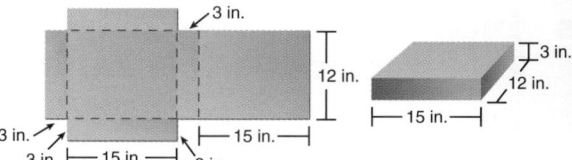

To solve the problem, find the surface area of the box. The **surface area** of a solid figure is the sum of the areas of all its faces and is measured in square units.

You can use a table to list the area of each face.

Face	Length	Width	Area
top	15 in.	12 in.	180 in.^{2}
bottom	15 in.	12 in.	180 in.^{2}
front	3 in.	12 in.	36 in.^{2}
back	3 in.	12 in.	36 in.^{2}
left side	3 in.	15 in.	45 in.^{2}
right side	3 in.	15 in.	45 in.^{2}
		sum:	522 in.^{2}

Solution: You need at least 522 in.^{2} of wrapping paper to cover the shirt box.

Think However, you will probably need more paper, because the paper will have to overlap.

Since rectangular prisms have opposite faces that are congruent, you can compute the areas of opposite faces to find surface area.

Determine the surface area of the solid figure.

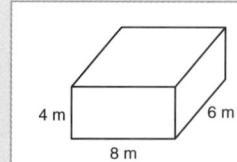

Area of Faces:
top and bottom: $2 \times (8 \times 6) = 96$
front and back: $2 \times (8 \times 4) = 64$
right and left sides: $2 \times (6 \times 4) = 48$
The sum of the areas is: $96 + 64 + 48 = 208$

Solution: The surface area is 208 m^2.

452

---

1 Introduce

Teaching Transparency
for
17.4

Materials: *cut-out of Net A from the Nets I Transparency, cut-out of rectangular prism from the Solid Figures Transparency, blank transparency, ruler*

• Place Net A and the cut-out rectangular prism on the overhead on top of the blank transparency.

• **The surface area of a solid figure is the sum of the areas of all its faces. How can we find the surface area of a rectangular prism?** (Find the area of each face. Find the sum of the areas.) **What formula can we use to find the area of each face?** ($A = l \times w$)

• Remove the cut-out rectangular prism. Write: $A = 2 \times 5 = 10 \ m^2$. **What is the area of face A?** (10 square meters) Have the students find the area of each of the faces. Write an equation to show the area of each face. Have students find the sum of the areas.

2 Develop

Guide students through the *Learn About It* section.

• **Look carefully at the table.** Have students match each entry in the table with its corresponding measurement on the figure and on the net.

• **Which faces have the same dimensions?** (front and back, top and bottom, left and right)

• **Can you make the table simpler to use?** (Yes; list front, top, and right only and multiply each calculation of area by 2.)

Another Example

Surface Area of a Triangular Prism

Think
The top and the bottom are congruent triangles. The front, left side, and right side are rectangles that are not congruent.

Area of Faces:

top and bottom: $2 \times (\frac{1}{2} \times 3 \times 4) = 12$

front: $3 \times 2 = 6$

left side: $2 \times 4 = 8$

right side: $2 \times 5 = 10$

The sum of the area is: $12 + 6 + 8 + 10 = 36$

Solution: The surface area is 36 cm².

Guided Practice

Predict what solid each net will make. Then determine the surface area of the solid figure. Each square is 1 cm².

Ask Yourself
- Which numbers do I multiply to find the surface area of each face?
- Which numbers do I add to find the surface area of the solid?

TEST TIPS

1.

rectangular prism
80 cm²

2.

cube
96 cm²

Determine the surface area of each solid figure.

3.
$\frac{1}{2}$ ft, $2\frac{1}{2}$ ft, $\frac{3}{4}$ ft
7 ft²

4.
1.2 dm, 1.2 dm, 1.2 dm
8.64 dm²

5.
10 cm, 8 cm, 15 cm, 12 cm
576 cm²

TEST TIPS **Explain Your Thinking** ▶ Explain how you found the surface area in Exercise 5.
Possible answer: Find the sum of the areas of the 2 triangles and 3 rectangles; $2 \times (\frac{1}{2} \times 8 \times 12) + 2 \times (15 \times 10) + (12 \times 15)$

Go On ▶

Chapter 17 Lesson 4 **453**

Quick Check Options

- Have students draw the triangular prism at the top of page 453. Have them outline the triangular face at the top.
- **In the triangular face at the top, which measurements are the base and the height?** (3 and 4)
- After finding the area of the top and bottom faces, have students outline one of the rectangular faces and find its dimensions.
- Have students outline the other two rectangular faces and label their diagram with these dimensions.
- Discuss with students the value of making a sketch and writing measurements on it as a computational aid.

Guided Practice

Have students complete **Exercises 1–5** as you observe. Remind them to use the *Ask Yourself* questions to help. Give students the opportunity to talk about the question in *Explain Your Thinking*.

DAILY TEST PREP

The area of one face of a cube is 40 cm². What is the surface area of the cube? (240 cm²)

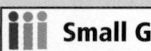

Activity

Or Use
Intervention
CD-ROM
Lesson 17.4

Lesson Intervention

Measure to Find Surface Area

| Small Group | 10 minutes | Kinesthetic, Tactile |

Materials: *textbooks, rulers*

• Have students take actual measurements to find surface area.

• **Think of your textbook as a rectangular prism. Using a ruler, estimate the dimensions of the front cover, or face, of your textbook. Give whole-number estimates.**

• **What is the area of the cover? If you know the area of the front face, you also know the area of what other face?** (the back)

• Have students measure the dimensions of the other four faces of the book, and calculate the areas of each face.

• **Once you have found and listed the areas, what do you do to find the surface area? Why?** (Add the areas because surface area means total area of the faces.)

Practice and Problem Solving

Determine the surface area of each solid figure.

6.
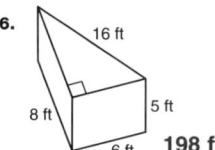
16 ft
8 ft   5 ft
6 ft   **198 ft²**

7.
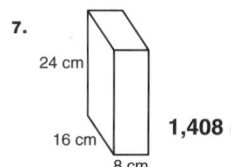
24 cm
16 cm
8 cm   **1,408 cm²**

8.
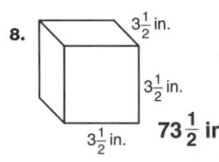
$3\frac{1}{2}$ in.
$3\frac{1}{2}$ in.
$3\frac{1}{2}$ in.   **$73\frac{1}{2}$ in.²**

Copy and complete the table.

	Length of One Side (s) of cube	Area of One Face (f)	Surface Area of Cube (SA)	
9.	3 cm			9 cm², 54 cm²
10.	4 cm			16 cm², 96 cm²
11.	15 cm			225 cm², 1350 cm²
12.	6 cm			36 cm², 216 cm²
13.	7 cm			49 cm², 294 cm²
14.	8 cm			64 cm², 384 cm²

Solve.

15. **Analyze** Study your results from Exercises 9–14. Write a formula that uses the length of a side (s) to find the surface area of a cube (SA). $SA = 6s^2$

16. What is the minimum amount of wrapping paper needed to wrap a box that has a length of 6 inches, a height of 4 inches, and a width of 5 inches? **148 in.²**

17. The Graysons are sending 140 holiday cards. The cards come in boxes of 25. How many boxes of cards do the Graysons need? **6 boxes**

18. **Predict** A box that is 10 inches long, 3 inches deep, and 4 inches high holds 6 pounds of snack mix. What size box will hold 12 pounds?
See Additional Answers on Page T87.

19. A fish tank is $2\frac{2}{3}$ feet long, $1\frac{1}{3}$ feet wide, and $1\frac{1}{2}$ feet high. The tank is open on top. How many square feet of glass were used to make the tank? $15\frac{5}{9}$ ft²

20. Find the volume of the tank in Exercise 19. Suppose it is $\frac{3}{4}$ full of water. What is the volume of the water in that tank? $5\frac{1}{3}$ ft³; 4 ft²

21. **Write About It** How does the surface area of a box change if you double each dimension of the box? Give examples to support your conclusion.

22. **Explain** A box is 10 cm long, 12 cm wide, and 14 cm high. Does doubling the height double the surface area of the figure? Explain.

---

3 Practice

Assign **Exercises 6–22** as independent work.

• *Problem Solving for Problems 16–18.* Have students share their solutions.

Common Error

Choosing the wrong dimensions Some students may choose the wrong dimensions as factors. Suggest that students take a minute to write dimensions on the top, the front, and the right faces, then make a table of factors to find the areas. Students might get this far and then forget to multiply by 2. Remind them that there are six, not three, faces in a rectangular prism.

4 Assess and Close

• Have students draw and label a rectangular prism according to the following dimensions: 10 in. across the front, 18 in. front to back, and 15 in. tall.

• **What is the equation for the area of the front face?** (10 in. × 15 in.) **the opposite face?** (same)

• **What is the equation for the area of the right and left faces?** (18 in. × 15 in.) **What is the equation for the area of the top and bottom faces?** (10 in. × 18 in.)

• **How do you find the surface area of the rectangular solid?** (Find the sum of the areas of the faces; 1,200 in.²)

Assign the **LESSON QUIZ** on Transparency 17.4 to further assess student understanding.

Quick Check

Check your understanding of Lessons 1–4.

Name each solid figure. Then write the number
of faces, vertices, and edges. (Lesson 1)

sphere; 0 faces, 0 vertices, 0 edges

1.

2. 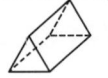 triangular prism; 5 faces,
6 vertices, 9 edges

Predict what solid figure the net will make.
Then determine the surface area.
Each square is 1 cm². (Lessons 3–4)

3.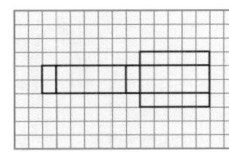

rectangular prism; 34 cm²

Use cubes to build each figure. Then draw the top
view, the side view, and the front view of each figure. (Lesson 2)

4.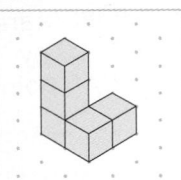

5.

4–5. *See Additional
Answers on Page T87.*

Wrap It Up

Visual Thinking

Math Reasoning

Find the approximate length and width of a
single rectangular sheet of wrapping paper
that will completely wrap each gift below.
Explain how you found your answers.

Remember
when you wrap a gift, some of the
paper usually overlaps. Note the
overlap allowed for each.

1.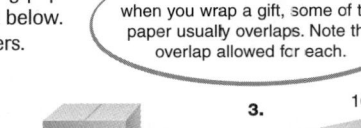
25 cm
25 cm
25 cm

2. 4 in.
5 in. 3 in.

3. 16 in.
7 in.
5 in. 7 in.
16 in.
5 in.

1–3. *See Additional Answers on Page T88.*

Quick Check

Purpose: The Quick Check allows you to
assess the students' understanding of the
concepts presented in Lessons 1–4.

Items	Objectives Tested	Pages	Intervention
1–2	Identify solid figures.	446–447	Reteach Resource 17.1 *Ways to Success 17.1*
4–5	Identify different two-dimensional views of a solid figure.	448–449	Reteach Resource 17.2 *Ways to Success 17.2* Reteach Resource 17.3 *Ways to Success 17.3*
3	Identify the nets of solid figures. Use nets to find the surface area of solid figures.	450–454	Reteach Resource 17.4 *Ways to Success 17.4*

Keeping a Journal

Have students write a few sentences explaining how
to find the surface area of a solid figure.

Visual Thinking

Math Reasoning

Wrap It Up

Encourage students to work backwards, that is, imagine
unfolding a rectangular prism to make a net. Once students find measurements for the net, they can begin to
see what size rectangular sheet they will need to enclose
the net.

Lesson 17.5

Problem-Solving Strategy: Solve a Simpler Problem

PLANNING THE LESSON

MATHEMATICS OBJECTIVE
Solve problems by first solving simpler problems.

Use Lesson Planner CD-ROM for Lesson 17.5.

Daily Routines

Vocabulary
What is the *perimeter* of a two-dimensional figure? (the distance around the outside) **If the dimensions of the figure are in inches, in what unit should the perimeter be expressed?** (inches) **What is the *surface area* of a three-dimensional figure?** (the area of the outside of the figure) **If the dimensions of the figure are in inches, what unit should the surface area be expressed in?** (square inches)

Vocabulary Cards

Meeting North Carolina's Standards
1.03 Develop flexibility in solving problems by selecting strategies and using mental computation, estimation, calculators or computers, and paper and pencil.
Also **5.01**

Lesson Transparency 17.5

Problem of the Day
Given that no 3 points lie on a single line, how many different line segments are determined by 3 points on a plane? (3) by 4 points? (6) by 5 points? (10) by 6 points? (15)

Quick Review
Estimate to determine if each answer is reasonable.
1. $85 \times 2,329 = 19,000$ (no)
2. $48 \times 659 = 19,000$ (no)
3. $59 \times 1,746 = 103,000$ (yes)
4. $94 \times 422 = 42,000$ (yes)

Lesson Quiz
A $4 \times 5 \times 6$ rectangular prism is made of red, blue, and white blocks. The number of red blocks equals the number of blue blocks. The number of white blocks is twice the number of blue blocks. How many blocks are white? (60)

LEVELED PRACTICE

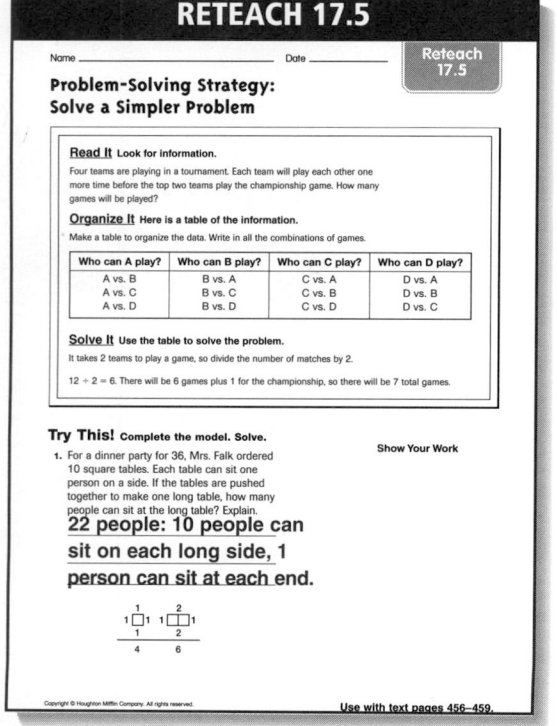

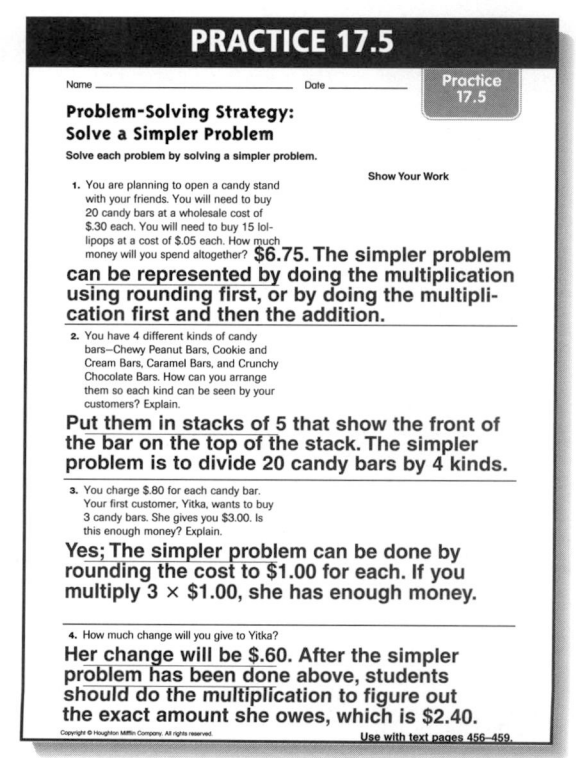

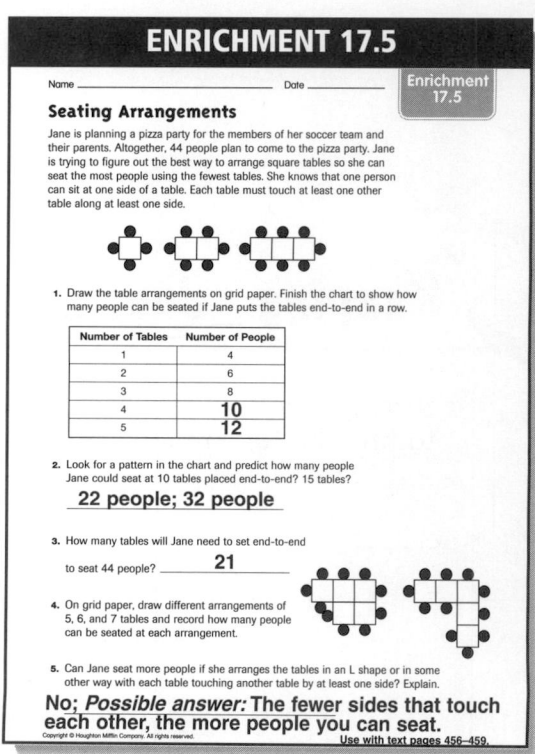

Practice Workbook Page 116

Reaching All Learners
Differentiated Instruction

English Learners

Worksheet 17.5 familiarizes English learners with the concepts of homophones and homographs in the English language. Students are then asked to identify homophones and homographs in the text of Lesson 5.

Special Needs
KINESTHETIC, TACTILE

- One person can sit at each side of a square table. How many tables can you push together to make one long table to seat 40 people? (19)
- Have students draw square tables pushed together to fit 4, 6, 8, 10, and 12. **What is the pattern?** ((people − 2 on ends) ÷ 2 = tables)

Early Finishers
VISUAL, TACTILE

- Copy the table on page 456. Highlight *one* dimension of each cube in the 1st column, and the base in the 3rd column. What is the pattern? (The base is 2 less than dimension one.)
- Predict the number of small unpainted cubes in a 10 × 10 × 10 figure. ($(10 − 2)^3$, 8^3, or 512)

TECHNOLOGY

Spiral Review

Create customized spiral review worksheets for individual students using the *Ways to Assess* CD-ROM.

Software

Use *Shape Up!* or another shapes program to explore this lesson's objectives more fully.

Lesson Planner

You can customize your teaching plan to meet your curriculum requirements with the Lesson Planner CD-ROM.

Art Connection

Sculptures with Cubes
Materials: *1-inch cubes, 1-inch grid paper, markers, paste*

- Have students read about Pablo Picasso and the cubist movement (*Picasso for Kids* by Margaret Hyde 1996).

- Have students draw a face on grid paper with 1-inch squares. Encourage them to use broad strokes and to fill the entire page.
- Then have students cut their drawing along the grid lines and paste the sections on the front faces of the one-inch cubes to make an abstract sculpture.

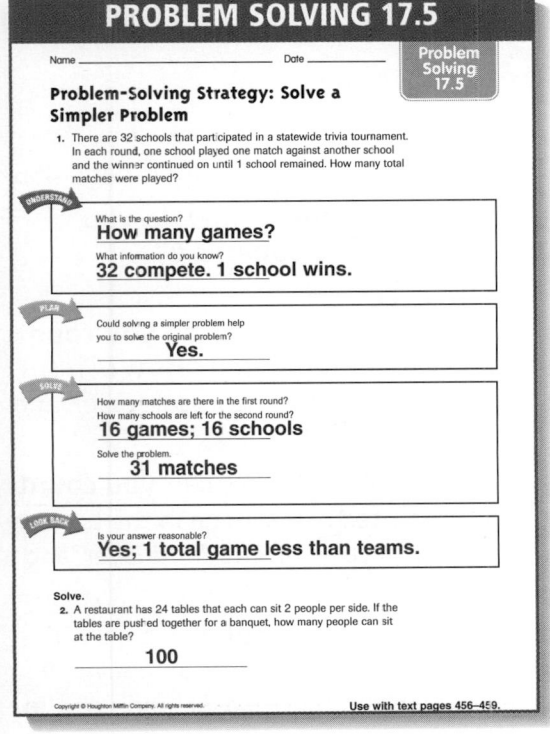

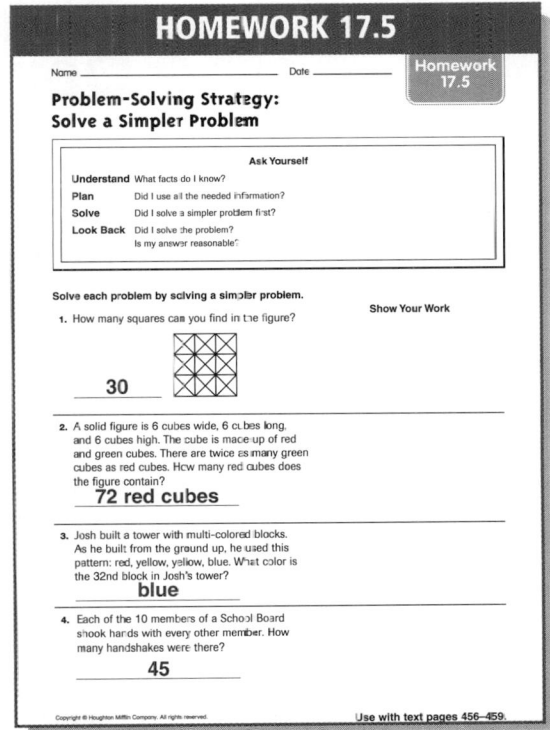

Homework Workbook Page 116

TEACHING LESSON 17.5

LESSON ORGANIZER

Objective Solve problems by first solving simpler problems.

Resources Reteach, Practice, Enrichment, Problem-Solving, Homework, English Learners, Transparencies, Math Center

Materials Problem Solving: Four Step Process Transparency

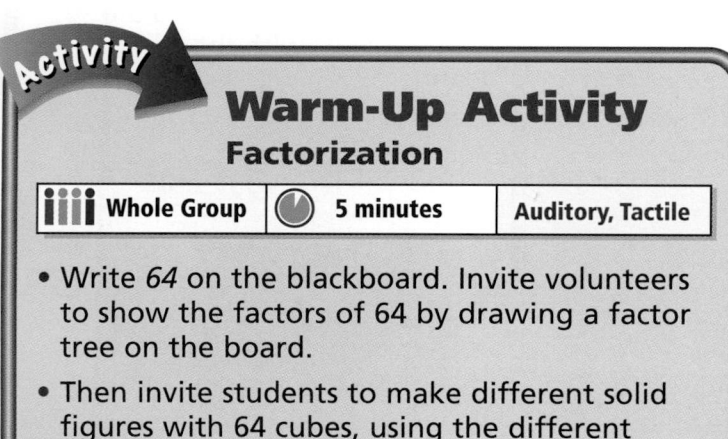

Warm-Up Activity
Factorization

👤 Whole Group	⏱ 5 minutes	Auditory, Tactile

- Write *64* on the blackboard. Invite volunteers to show the factors of 64 by drawing a factor tree on the board.

- Then invite students to make different solid figures with 64 cubes, using the different factors as dimensions.

Problem-Solving Strategy
Solve a Simpler Problem
Objective Solve problems by first solving simpler problems.

Problem José makes a solid figure that is 6 cubes long, 6 cubes high, and 6 cubes wide. José paints the outside of the figure orange. Suppose José takes the figure apart. How many of the cubes will have no orange paint on them?

UNDERSTAND

This is what you know:
- The large cube is made of 6 × 6 × 6 small cubes.
- The outside faces of the small cubes are painted orange.

PLAN

You can solve a simpler problem.

SOLVE

Use models to represent the problem for smaller solid figures.

- Build a large cube that is 2 cubes long, 2 cubes wide, and 2 cubes high.
- Put a sticker or small piece of tape on the outside of each small cube.
- Take the large cube apart. Count the number of cubes with no stickers. Record that number in a table.
- Repeat the steps above.
- Look for a pattern in your results. Use the pattern to find the answer.

Solution: The pattern shows that there will be 4^3, or 64 cubes with no orange paint.

Dimensions of Large Cube	Cubes With No Orange Paint	Pattern
2 × 2 × 2	0	0^3
3 × 3 × 3	1	1^3
4 × 4 × 4	8	2^3
5 × 5 × 5	27	3^3
6 × 6 × 6	?	?

Visualize the cubes without paint as a solid figure within the larger cube. What are the dimensions of the figure without paint?

LOOK BACK

Look back at the problem. Does the solution answer the question? Is the answer reasonable? yes, yes

---

① Introduce

- Discuss some ways students could approach solving the problem on page 456.

- **Could you solve this problem by building the 6 × 6 × 6 cube solid? How?** (Yes; build the cube, paint it, then take it apart and count.) **What are some problems you would have with this method?** (Possible answer: requires 216 cubes)

- **Why do you think smaller cubes and patterns would help solve the problem?** (Fewer cubes and tape are easier to work with. Once a pattern is found, it can be used to solve problems involving more cubes.)

② Develop

Guide students through the problem-solving steps on page 456.

- **Now you have built the 2 × 2 × 2 cube. How do you know that the number of unpainted cubes is 0?** (There are no cubes "inside" the full cube.)

- **While you are building the 3 × 3 × 3 cube, can you count the number of cubes that will be unpainted? How?** (Yes; 1 cube is put above the bottom layer, within the middle layer, and below the top layer.)

- **While you are building the 4 × 4 × 4 cube, can you count how many cubes will be unpainted?** (Yes; none in the bottom layer, 4 cubes in the second layer, 4 cubes in the third layer, and none in the top layer. $2 \times 4 = 2^3$)

- **What is your prediction for a 5 × 5 × 5 cube?** (There will be no cubes in the bottom layer, 9 cubes in the second layer, 9 cubes in the third layer, 9 cubes in the fourth layer, and none in the top layer; $3 \times 9 = 3^3$.)

Guided Practice

Use the Ask Yourself questions to help you solve each problem.

1. Suppose 7 friends meet for dinner. Each friend shakes hands with every other friend. How many handshakes will there be? **21**

   (Hint) Draw pictures of simpler problems with fewer handshakes.

2 friends	3 friends	4 friends
1 handshake	3 handshakes	6 handshakes

2. Pilar makes a figure 6 cubes long, 6 cubes high, and 6 cubes wide. She paints the outside of the figure red. How many of the cubes have 2 or more red faces? **56**

Ask Yourself

UNDERSTAND What facts do I know?

PLAN Did I use all the needed information?

SOLVE Did I solve a simpler problem first?
- Did I find the pattern?
- Did I continue the pattern to find the number of handshakes for 7 friends?

LOOK BACK Did I solve the problem?

TEST TIPS

4. 76 sides. *Possible answer:* The columns on either end of the wall have 10 sides painted each, while each of the other columns has 7 sides painted.

Independent Practice

Solve each problem by solving a simpler problem.

3. A warehouse has 10 security guards. A team of 2 guards must be present at any given time. How many different teams of 2 guards are possible? **45**

4. **Explain** Mark builds a brick wall that is 10 bricks long and 3 bricks high. He paints the front, back, top, and sides of the wall. How many of the sides of individual bricks are painted? Explain the pattern you used to find the answer. ***See above.***

5. Janelle's Restaurant has 12 square tables. Each table can seat one person on each side. If the tables are pushed together to make one long table, how many people can sit at the long table? **26**

6. An industrial park has 8 storage centers. Each storage center has a direct road to each of the other storage centers. How many roads are in the industrial park? **28**

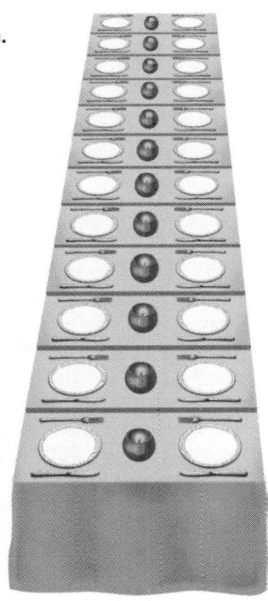

 Go On

Chapter 17 Lesson 5 **457**

ACHIEVING
Mathematical Proficiency

The Importance of Vocabulary

While materials and ideas for teaching language arts vocabulary abound, fewer resources exist for teaching mathematics vocabulary. This is despite the fact that **many students struggle with math precisely because they do not understand key math terms.**

Teachers can approach mathematics vocabulary in a variety of ways. When introducing new vocabulary, it is helpful to show the word used in context, for example, in a simplified version of the problem that is the focus of the lesson. This also serves to introduce the students to the mathematical concept.

Students who understand math vocabulary are better equipped to understand math concepts. A solid foundation in mathematical terminology will translate to success at all levels of mathematics.

---

3 Practice

Guided Practice

Have students complete **Problems 1–2** as you observe. Remind them to use the *Ask Yourself* questions to help.

Assign **Problems 3–14** as independent work. Have students share and discuss their work.

Problem-Solving Reminders

Have students review their answers to make sure they have done the following:
- expressed the solution clearly
- used appropriate mathematical notation and terms
- supported their solution with verbal and symbolic work
- determined the reasonableness of the solution in the context of the original problem.

DAILY TEST PREP

If today is Tuesday, which day of the week is 200 days from now? (D)

A. Monday   C. Thursday

B. Tuesday   D. Saturday

Activity

Lesson Intervention

Or Use Intervention CD-ROM Lesson 17.5

Solve a Simpler Problem

| 👥👥👥 Small Group | 🕐 10–15 minutes | Visual, Auditory |

- **Ten people stand around a circle and shake hands, how many handshakes are there? What simpler problems might you first solve?** (Start with 2 people, then add 1 at a time. Make a table and look for a pattern.)

- Have students make organized lists to fill in a table for 2–5, then tell what pattern they found in order to solve the problem for 10.

Number of People	Number of Handshakes
2	(1)
3	(3)
4	(6)
5	(10)
10	(45)

Choose a Strategy

Solve each problem. Tell what strategy you used. *Possible strategies are given.*

7. Find the seventh figure in the pattern shown below.
   See Additional Answers on Page T88.

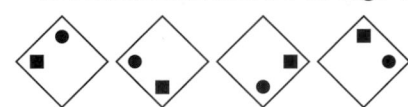

8. The LCM of two numbers is 60. The GCF of the same two numbers is 4. The sum of the numbers is 32. What are the numbers? **12, 20; Guess and Check**

9. A solid figure is made up of blue cubes and white cubes. It is 4 cubes wide, 4 cubes long, and 4 cubes high. There are 3 times as many blue cubes as white cubes. How many blue cubes are there? **48 blue cubes; Draw a Diagram**

10. A supply store sells 10 boxes of glasses. Then it receives 24 boxes of glasses. The store now has 40 boxes of glasses. How many boxes of glasses did the store have before it sold the 10 boxes? **26 boxes; Work Backward**

PROBLEM-SOLVING Strategies

Use Models
Draw a Diagram
Find a Pattern
Guess and Check
Make an Organized List
Make a Table
Solve a Simpler Problem
Use Logical Reasoning
Work Backward
Write an Equation

📊 **Data** Use the graph to solve Problems 11–14.

The graph shows the sales and expenses for a toy company for the first five years in business.

11. When sales are greater than expenses, the company earns a profit. What was the first year in which the toy company earned a profit? In which year did the company earn its greatest profit? **2003; 2004**

12. In business, the "break-even point" occurs when expenses are equal to sales. Between which two years did the break-even point occur? **2002–2003**

13. When expenses are greater than sales, the company has a loss. During which years was there a loss? In which year did the company have its greatest loss? **2000, 2001, 2002; 2001**

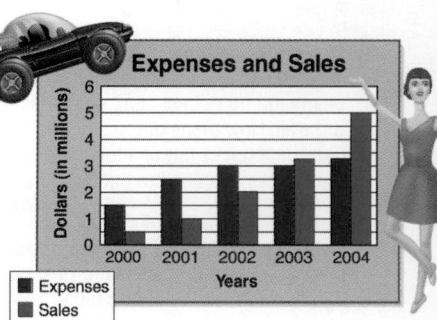

Expenses and Sales

■ Expenses ■ Sales

14. **Predict** Do you think the company will have a profit or loss in 2005? About how great do you think that profit or loss will be? Explain your answer.
    See Additional Answers on Page T88.

458

Practice continued

Choose a Strategy

- *Problem Solving for Problems 11–14* Have students examine the heights of the bars. If the profit bar is taller than the expense bar, then there is a profit. Have students discuss how they arrived at their conclusions by examining heights of bars.

---

4 Assess and Close

- **How does the table on page 456 help solve the problem?** (The table organizes the information gained from simpler problems. Then the table helps make the pattern more evident.)

- **Once you have solved a complicated problem by solving simpler ones, how can that help you solve other problems like the one given?** (Once you know the pattern, you can extend it until you can solve the new problem. Use a rule based on the pattern with numbers from the new problem.)

Assign the **LESSON QUIZ** on Transparency 17.5 to further assess student understanding.

Choose the letter of the correct answer.
If a correct answer is not here, choose NH.

1. Nick buys 5 packs of baseball cards. When he adds these cards to the 64 cards he already has, he has a total of 124 cards. Which equation could you use to find the number of cards in each pack?

A $64 + n = 124$ **C** $124 - 64 = n$

B $124 = 5n$ **(D) NH**

(Chapter 4, Lesson 7)

2. The area of the triangle is 30 square centimeters. What is the measure of side A?

F 3 cm   **(H) 8 cm**

G 7.5 cm   **J** 15 cm

(Chapter 16, Lesson 4)

3. This month, Gary has read twice as many books as Erin. Li has read three times as many books as Gary. Li has read 18 books. How many books has Erin read?

(A) 3   **C** 6

B 4   **D** 9

(Chapter 5, Lesson 3)

4. Measurement Gracie feeds her dog an average of 8 ounces of dog food per day. About how many pounds of dog food does Gracie feed her dog per month?

(F) 15 lb   **H** 60 lb

G 20 lb   **J** NH

(Chapter 6, Lesson 3)

5. Measurement The diagram shows how Kerri painted the door to her room. How many square feet were painted gray?

A 10 ft²

(B) 11 ft²

C 21 ft²

D 31 ft²

(Chapter 15, Lesson 3)

6. Melanie uses 6-inch blocks to build a tower that is 24 inches high. Jack uses 8-inch blocks to build a tower of the same height. Who uses more blocks? How many more?

Melanie; 1 more

Represent Support your solution with a picture. **Check students' drawings.**

(Chapter 11, Lesson 7)

7. In the first six games of a seven-game tournament, a basketball player has these point totals: 18, 24, 22, 12, 15, and 24. The player's score in the seventh game does not change her median score. What does the player score in the seventh game?

Explain How did you find your answer?

(Chapter 8, Lesson 2)

7. 20 points; *Possible answer:* found the median for 6 games and used that score for the 7th game.

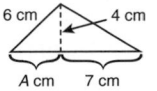 **Test Prep on the Net**
Check out *Education Place* at **eduplace.com/kids/mw/** for test prep practice.

Chapter 17 Lesson 5   **459**

 ## Keeping a Journal

Have students write a brief paragraph explaining how solving problems with smaller numbers can help them solve a problem with larger numbers.

Lesson 17.6 Volume

PLANNING THE LESSON

MATHEMATICS OBJECTIVE
Use a formula to find the volume of a cube, a rectangular prism, and a triangular prism.

Use Lesson Planner CD-ROM for Lesson 17.6.

Daily Routines

Vocabulary

When you find the surface area of a solid figure, what are you measuring? (Possible answer: the sum of the areas of the faces) **How do you think we measure the amount of space *within* a solid figure?** (Accept all reasonable answers.) **The word *volume* describes the amount of space a solid figure occupies.**

Vocabulary Cards

Meeting North Carolina's Standards

Prepare for Grade 6 Objective **2.01** Estimate and measure length, perimeter, area, angles, weight, and mass of two and three-dimensional figures using appropriate tools.

Lesson Transparency 17.6

Problem of the Day
Toby has a rectangular garden with an area of 200 ft². What will be the area of the garden if the length is doubled and the width is doubled? (800 ft²)

Quick Review
Write *prime* or *composite* for each number.
1. 12 (composite)
2. 63 (composite)
3. 17 (prime)
4. 39 (composite)
5. 26 (composite)
6. 59 (prime)
7. 6 (composite)
8. 29 (prime)

Lesson Quiz
Determine the volume of each solid figure.

1.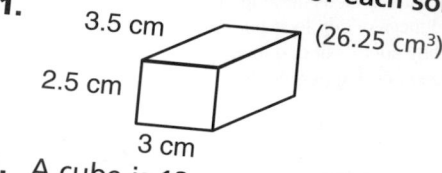
3.5 cm   (26.25 cm³)
2.5 cm
3 cm

2. A cube is 12 m on one edge. What is its volume? (1,728 m³)

LEVELED PRACTICE

RETEACH 17.6

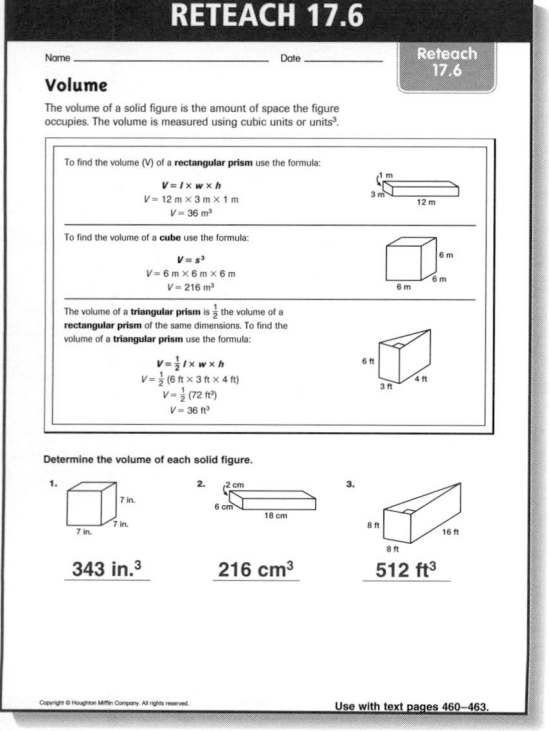

Name _____ Date _____   Reteach 17.6

Volume

The volume of a solid figure is the amount of space the figure occupies. The volume is measured using cubic units or units³.

To find the volume (V) of a **rectangular prism** use the formula:
$V = l \times w \times h$
$V = 12\ m \times 3\ m \times 1\ m$
$V = 36\ m^3$

To find the volume of a **cube** use the formula:
$V = s^3$
$V = 6\ m \times 6\ m \times 6\ m$
$V = 216\ m^3$

The volume of a **triangular prism** is $\frac{1}{2}$ the volume of a **rectangular prism** of the same dimensions. To find the volume of a **triangular prism** use the formula:
$V = \frac{1}{2} l \times w \times h$
$V = \frac{1}{2} (6\ ft \times 3\ ft \times 4\ ft)$
$V = \frac{1}{2} (72\ ft^3)$
$V = 36\ ft^3$

Determine the volume of each solid figure.
1. 7 in. 7 in. 7 in.
2. 2 cm 6 cm 18 cm
3. 8 ft 8 ft 16 ft

343 in.³   216 cm³   512 ft³

Use with text pages 460–463.

PRACTICE 17.6

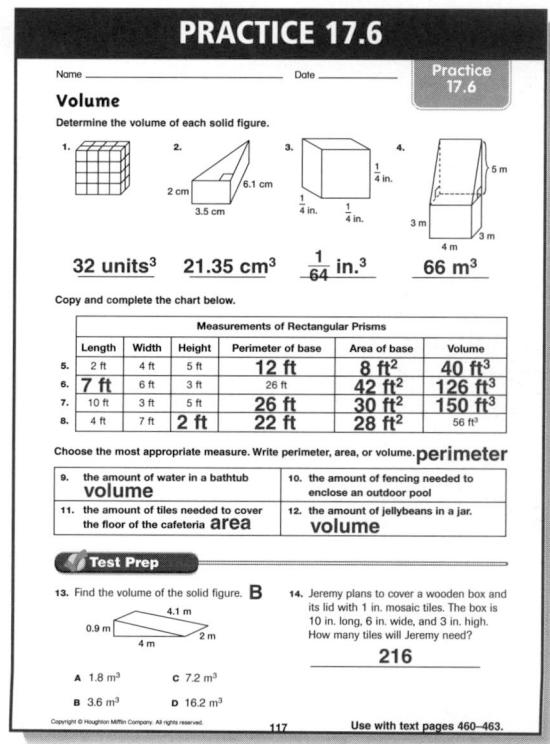

Name _____ Date _____   Practice 17.6

Volume

Determine the volume of each solid figure.
1.
2. 2 cm 6.1 cm 3.5 cm
3. ¼ in. ¼ in. ¼ in.
4. 5 m 3 m 4 m 3 m

32 units³   21.35 cm³ $\frac{1}{64}$ in.³   66 m³

Copy and complete the chart below.

	Length	Width	Height	Perimeter of base	Area of base	Volume
				Measurements of Rectangular Prisms		
5.	2 ft	4 ft	5 ft	**12 ft**	8 ft²	40 ft³
6.	**7 ft**	6 ft	3 ft	26 ft	**42 ft²**	**126 ft³**
7.	10 ft	3 ft	5 ft	**26 ft**	30 ft²	**150 ft³**
8.	4 ft	7 ft	**2 ft**	22 ft	28 ft²	56 ft³

Choose the most appropriate measure. Write *perimeter*, *area*, or *volume*.
9. the amount of water in a bathtub **volume**
10. the amount of fencing needed to enclose an outdoor pool **perimeter**
11. the amount of tiles needed to cover the floor of the cafeteria **area**
12. the amount of jellybeans in a jar. **volume**

Test Prep
13. Find the volume of the solid figure. **B**
4.1 m 0.9 m 4 m 2 m
A 1.8 m³   C 7.2 m³
B 3.6 m³   D 16.2 m³

14. Jeremy plans to cover a wooden box and its lid with 1 in. mosaic tiles. The box is 10 in. long, 6 in. wide, and 3 in. high. How many tiles will Jeremy need?
216

117 Use with text pages 460–463.

ENRICHMENT 17.6

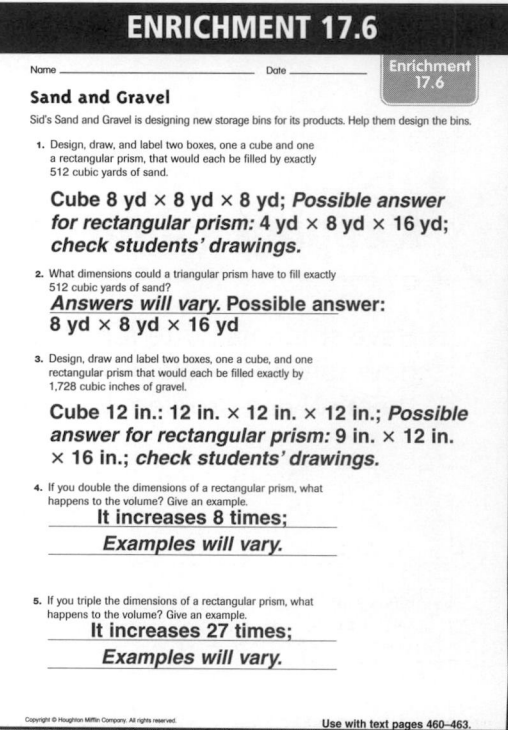

Name _____ Date _____   Enrichment 17.6

Sand and Gravel

Sid's Sand and Gravel is designing new storage bins for its products. Help them design the bins.

1. Design, draw, and label two boxes, one a cube and one a rectangular prism, that would each be filled by exactly 512 cubic yards of sand.

Cube 8 yd × 8 yd × 8 yd; *Possible answer for rectangular prism:* 4 yd × 8 yd × 16 yd; check students' drawings.

2. What dimensions could a triangular prism have to fill exactly 512 cubic yards of sand?
Answers will vary. Possible answer: 8 yd × 8 yd × 16 yd

3. Design, draw and label two boxes, one a cube, and one rectangular prism that would each be filled exactly by 1,728 cubic inches of gravel.

Cube 12 in.: 12 in. × 12 in. × 12 in.; *Possible answer for rectangular prism:* 9 in. × 12 in. × 16 in.; check students' drawings.

4. If you double the dimensions of a rectangular prism, what happens to the volume? Give an example.
It increases 8 times; Examples will vary.

5. If you triple the dimensions of a rectangular prism, what happens to the volume? Give an example.
It increases 27 times; Examples will vary.

Use with text pages 460–463.

Reaching All Learners
Differentiated Instruction

English Learners

Use Worksheet 17.6 to clarify for English learners some potentially unfamiliar terms used in the Practice and Problem Solving section on pages 462–463.

Inclusion
KINESTHETIC, TACTILE

Materials: *cubes*

- **Arrange 27 cubes so that you have a cube. Use them all. No stack can be taller than any other.**
- **How are the cubes in the base arranged?** (They form a 3 × 3 set of cubes.) **How many layers do you have?** (3)
- **How can you find the volume of a cube?** (Cube the length of any edge.)

Gifted and Talented
VISUAL, AUDITORY

Materials: *cubes*

- Have students solve this problem: *Is it possible to build a cube using only unit cubes and that has a volume of 40 cubic units? Explain.* (No. You can make a cube with a volume of 27 cubic units or 64 cubic units. There is no cube that has a volume of 40 cubic units.)

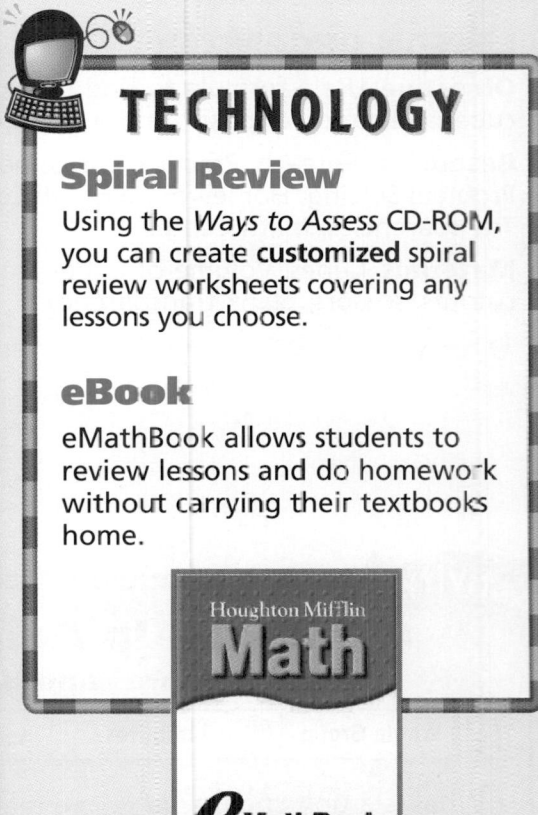

Science Connection

How Heavy is the Water?

- Water weighs about 62 pounds per cubic foot. There are 2,000 pounds in 1 ton.

- A swimming pool has a length of 100 ft, width 40 ft, and average depth 6 ft. Make a drawing of the pool.

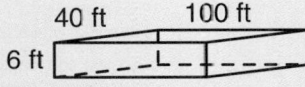

40 ft 100 ft
6 ft

- **What is the volume of water in the pool when filled?** (24,000 ft³) **What is the weight in tons?** (744 tons)

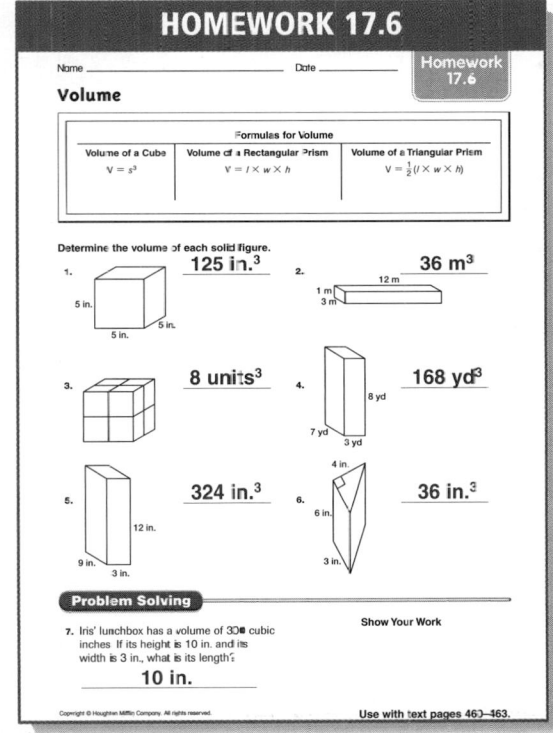

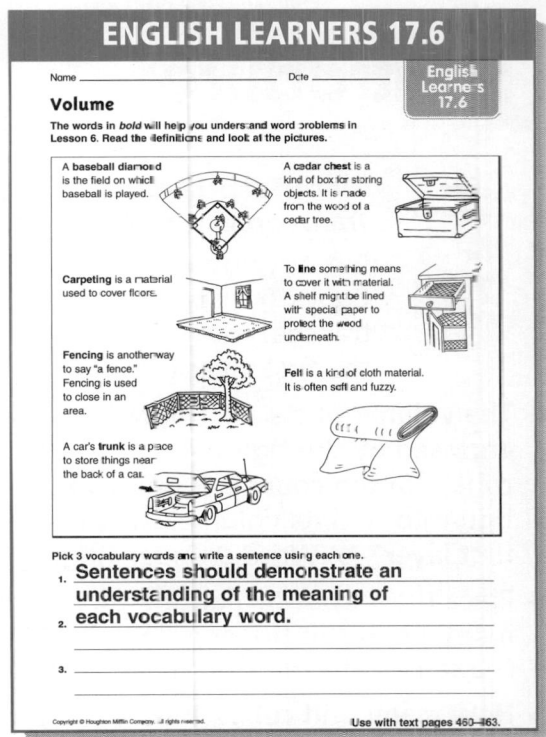

Homework Workbook Page 117

TEACHING LESSON 17.6

LESSON ORGANIZER

Objective Use a formula to find the volume of a cube, a rectangular prism, and a triangular prism.

Resources Reteach, Practice, Enrichment, Problem Solving, Homework, English Learners, Transparencies, Math Center

Materials Cubes, Volume of Cubes Transparency, cutouts, scissors, blank transparency

Warm-Up Activity
Unit Squares and Unit Cubes

 Whole Group	5 minutes	Auditory, Tactile

- **What is a unit square?** (a square that is 1 unit long) **How do you find area using unit squares?** (You count how many unit squares are on the whole figure.)

- **What is a unit cube?** (a cube that is 1 unit long)

- A unit cube is a basic unit used to measure space inside a solid figure.

Algebra
Volume

Objective Use a formula to find the volume of a cube, a rectangular prism, and a triangular prism.

Learn About It MathTracks 2/18
Listen and Understand

Cedric's collection of CDs is growing. Each case is a rectangular prism, and when he stacks the cases, they form an even larger prism. Soon the "prism" of CDs will be too large for Cedric's shelf!

The **volume** of a solid figure is the amount of space the figure occupies. Volume is measured using **cubic units**. A cube measuring 1 unit on each edge has a volume of 1 cubic unit.

1 unit →
1 unit
1 unit

Try this activity to find the volume of a solid figure.
Materials: cubes

STEP 1 Create a rectangular prism that is 2 cubes long, 3 cubes wide, and 1 cube high. Count the number of cubes. Record the data on the recording sheet.
2 units, 3 units, 1 unit, 6 cubic units

STEP 2 Add a second layer of cubes on top of the figure. Record the data.
2 units, 3 units, 2 units, 12 cubic units

STEP 3 Add a third layer of cubes on top of the figure. Record the data.
2 units, 3 units, 3 units, 18 cubic units

STEP 4 Write a multiplication sentence that shows how to find the volume of each of the following:
 a. one layer of cubes
 b. two layers of cubes
 c. three layers of cubes

What multiplication equation could you use to find the volume (V) of any rectangular prism with length l, width w, and height h? Explain.

In a cube, the length, width, and height are equal and are represented by the variable s. What equation could you use to find the volume of any cube?
$2 \times 3 \times 1 = 6; 2 \times 3 \times 2 = 12; 2 \times 3 \times 3 = 18; V = l \times w \times h; V = s^3$

460

---

1 Introduce

Teaching Transparency for 17.6

Materials: *cutouts of Volume of Cubes Transparency, scissors, blank transparency*

Cut out figures A, C, and D from the Volume of Cubes Transparency and place them on a blank transparency on the overhead. Place figure D as the first layer of figure C.

- **The volume of a solid figure is a measure of the space enclosed by the figure.** Point to figure A. **This is a unit cube. We can count the unit cubes that make up a solid figure to find its volume. How many unit cubes are in the first layer?** (9) Write *9* under figure C.

- Place the cutout of figure E on top of figure D. **How many figures in the next layer?** (9) Write: *9 + 9 = 18*. Do the same with the cutout of figure F. Write: *18 + 9 = 27*.

- **How many unit cubes make up figure C?** (27) **What is the volume of figure C?** (27 cubic units)

460   CHAPTER 17   Lesson 6

---

2 Develop

Guide students through the *Learn About It* section.

- **To find volume, look at base area and height.**

- After completing Step 4 of the activity, ask students how $l \times w \times h$ is related to base area and height. (The base area is $l \times w$. So if B is the area of the base, then $V = B \times h$.)

You can use a formula to find the volume of any prism.

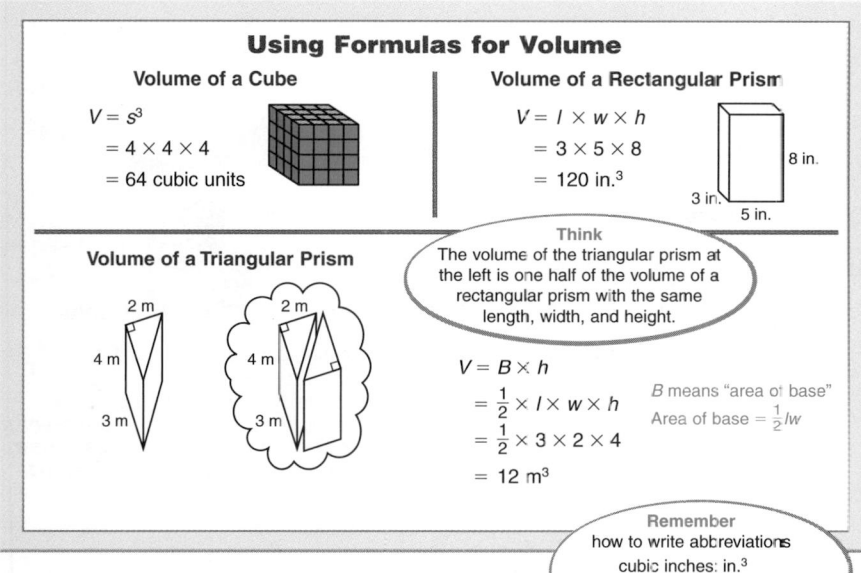

Using Formulas for Volume

Volume of a Cube

$V = s^3$
$= 4 \times 4 \times 4$
$= 64$ cubic units

Volume of a Rectangular Prism

$V = l \times w \times h$
$= 3 \times 5 \times 8$
$= 120$ in.^{3}

8 in.
3 in.
5 in.

Volume of a Triangular Prism

2 m
4 m
3 m

2 m
4 m
3 m

Think
The volume of the triangular prism at the left is one half of the volume of a rectangular prism with the same length, width, and height.

$V = B \times h$
$= \frac{1}{2} \times l \times w \times h$ *B* means "area of base"
                          Area of base $= \frac{1}{2} lw$
$= \frac{1}{2} \times 3 \times 2 \times 4$
$= 12$ m^3

Remember
how to write abbreviations
cubic inches: in.^{3}
cubic centimeters: cm^3
cubic meters: m^3

Some solid figures are complex figures that are made of smaller prisms. You can use what you know about finding the volume of prisms to find the volume for these figures.

Determine the volume of the solid figure.

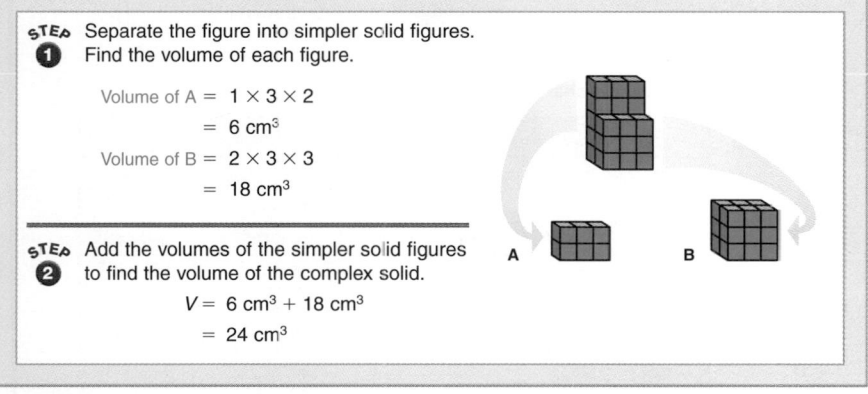

STEP 1 Separate the figure into simpler solid figures. Find the volume of each figure.

Volume of A = $1 \times 3 \times 2$
$= 6$ cm^3
Volume of B = $2 \times 3 \times 3$
$= 18$ cm^3

STEP 2 Add the volumes of the simpler solid figures to find the volume of the complex solid.

A   B

$V = 6$ cm^3 + 18 cm^3
$= 24$ cm^3

Solution: The volume of the solid figure is 24 cm^3.

 Go On

ACHIEVING

Mathematical Proficiency

What Is Good Assessment?

Assessment can take many forms. Some types of assessment are formal, such as tests, homework, and reports. Others are less structured, such as projects, notebooks, and journals. Whatever form it takes, the goal of assessment should be to **help students develop mathematical proficiency.**

Having students ask questions during a lesson is an informal assessment that allows teachers to find out what and how students are thinking. Having students work out a sample problem on the board or overhead projector is another means of accomplishing this. Teachers who assess students' understanding as they instruct can adjust their instruction accordingly.

When information gathered through assessments **is used to shape the course of instruction, teaching becomes clearer, more focused, and more effective.**

• Suppose that all the edges of a rectangular prism are equal in length. What solid do you have and what is the volume formula for that solid? [cube; $V = s^3$]

• Suppose you slice through a rectangular solid along a diagonal of a base, what solid do you get and how does the volume formula change? (triangular prism; $V = \frac{1}{2} B \times h$)

• At the bottom of page 461, students have an opportunity to solve a multi-step problem.

• **Why do you think that addition is used to solve the problem?** (One solid is attached to another. So, total volume equals the sum of the two volumes.)

• Pose this additional problem. **A cube 5-cm on a side is cut from a cube 10-cm on a side. How would you find the volume of the portion remaining?** (Subtract the volume of the small cube 125 cm^3 from that of larger one, 1,000 cm^3.)

TechnologyConnection
Explore Volume With a Computer

In this activity, students use software to gain a conceptual understanding of volume.

Have students follow the directions in 3-D World in Shape Up! to create solids with different volumes.

- Click the **Paging Arrows** twice. Stamp a cube onto the workspace. Using the **Hand Rotate** button, click and turn the cube so 3 sides are showing.

- Click **Duplicate**. Click the cube 7 times. Arrange the cubes into a solid with a volume of 8 units³.

Have students make solids with the volumes given. For greater volumes, tell them to reduce the size of the first cube before copying it.

1. 12 units³   **2.** 27 units³

3. 30 units³   **4.** Make 3 solids each with a volume of 40 units³.

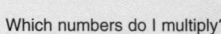

Ask Yourself
- Which numbers do I multiply?
- Which unit symbol do I use?
- Is the answer in cubic units?

Determine the volume of each solid figure.

1. 60 units³

2. 5 in. 5 in. 5 in. 5 in. **125 in.³**

3. 5 cm, 2 cm, 12 cm **120 cm³**

4. 8 yd, 5 yd, 6 yd **120 yd³**

5.  **20 units³**

Explain Your Thinking ▶ How can you use multiplication and addition to find the volume of the figure in Exercise 5?
Possible answer: Split the figure into two smaller rectangular prisms. Multiply $l \times w \times h$ to find the volume of each smaller rectangular prism. Add the two volumes to find the volume of the larger figure.

Practice and Problem Solving

Determine the volume of each solid figure.

6. 27 units³

7. 20 cm, 10 cm, 10 cm **2,000 cm³**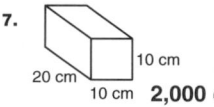

8. 4 in., 6 in., 3 in. **36 in.³**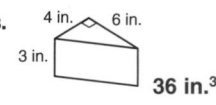

9. 3.5 m, 3.5 m, 3.5 m **42.875 m³**

10. 24 units³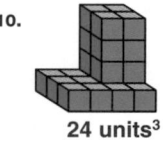

11. 6 ft, 4 ft, 3 ft, 3 ft, 6 ft **72 ft³**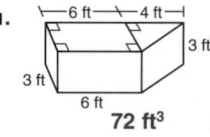

Copy and complete the chart below.

	length	width	height	perimeter of base	area of base	volume
12.	3 cm	5 cm	2 cm	16 cm	15 cm²	30 cm³
13.	4 cm	5 cm	2 cm	18 cm	20 cm²	40 cm³
14.	5 cm	5 cm	4 cm	20 cm	25 cm²	100 cm³
15.	8 cm	3 cm	3 cm	22 cm	24 cm²	72 cm³
16.	3 cm	6 cm	10 cm	18 cm	18 cm²	180 cm³
17.	7 cm	8 cm	4 cm	30 cm	56 cm²	224 cm³

---

3 Practice

Guided Practice

Have students complete **Exercises 1–5** as you observe. Remind them to use the *Ask Yourself* questions to help. Give students the opportunity to talk about the question in *Explain Your Thinking*.

Assign **Exercises 6–38** as independent work.

- *Problem Solving for Problems 24–29* For Problem 27, have students show how they counted the number of sweater bags that fit, and how they dealt with remainders.

Common Error

Incorrect units Some students may not understand that perimeter, area, and volume are measured with different units. Point out that a sum of feet is a number of feet. The product of measurements in feet is a number of square feet. The product of three measurements in feet is a number of cubic feet.

Choose the most appropriate measure.
Write *perimeter,* *area,* **or** *volume.*

18. the distance around a baseball diamond
perimeter

19. the amount of sand needed to fill a box
volume

20. the amount of carpeting to cover a floor
area

21. the amount of space in a car's trunk
volume

22. the amount of fencing to enclose a
rectangular garden
perimeter

23. the amount of wall space one gallon of
paint will cover
area

 **Data**   Use the picture to solve Problems 24–28.

Cynthia builds the cedar chest shown on
the right. The bottom and each side is 1
inch thick.

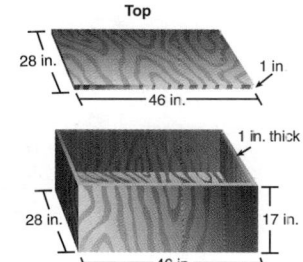
Top
28 in.   1 in
46 in.

1 in. thick
28 in.   17 in.
46 in.

24. She lines the bottom of the inside with
felt. How much felt does she need?
Explain how you found your answer.
See Additional Answers on Page 469.

25. Cynthia puts a strip of copper around
the top of the chest. How much copper
does she need? **148 in.**

26. **Analyze** What is the volume of the
cedar chest? Explain how you decided
what dimensions should be used to find
the volume. [*Hint:* The volume is not
21,896 in.³.] **18,304 in.³**

27. Cynthia packs the chest with sweater
bags that are 12 inches wide, 13 inches
long, and 2 inches high. How many
sweater bags can Cynthia fit in the
chest? **48 sweater bags**

28. **What If?** Suppose that Cynthia
increases the height of the chest by 2
inches. How would that increased height
change the volume of the chest? How
many more sweater bags would Cynthia
be able to put in the chest?

29. **You Decide** Think of something you
might need to store, such as books or
clothing. Design a container for storing
that item. Include the dimensions and an
explanation of why that container would
be suited for storing that item.
See Additional Answers on Page T88.

The volume would increase by 2,288 in.³;
6 more sweater bags

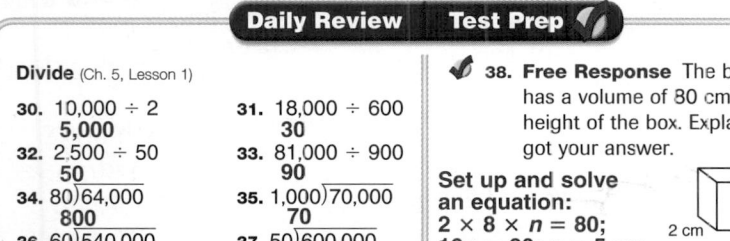

Daily Review	**Test Prep**
Divide (Ch. 5, Lesson 1)	

30. 10,000 ÷ 2
5,000

31. 18,000 ÷ 600
30

32. 2,500 ÷ 50
50

33. 81,000 ÷ 900
90

34. 80)‾64,000
800

35. 1,000)‾70,000
70

36. 60)‾540,000
9,000

37. 50)‾600,000
12,000

38. Free Response The box below
has a volume of 80 cm³. Find the
height of the box. Explain how you
got your answer.

Set up and solve
an equation:
$2 \times 8 \times n = 80$;
$16n = 80$; $n = 5$ **cm.**

2 cm   8 cm   ?

Extra Practice See page 469, Set D.

Chapter 17   Lesson 6   **463**

What is the volume of a box whose dimensions
are one half the dimensions of a box with
length 10 units, width 6 units, and height 4
units? (30 units³)

Activity

**Lesson
Intervention**

*Or Use
Intervention
CD-ROM
Lesson 17.6*

Volume of a Rectangular Solid

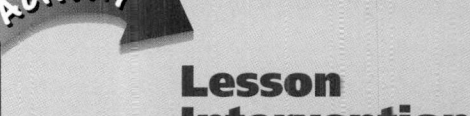

Small Group	**5–10 minutes**	**Visual, Tactile**

- A rectangular solid has length 6.7 in., width
8.5 in., and height 10 in. What is its volume to
the nearest whole number?

- Have students write the formula and then
substitute the numbers given.
  $$l \times w \times h = V$$
  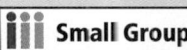 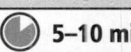
  $$6.7 \times 8.5 \times 10$$

- **You multiply numbers two at a time. Multiply
6.7 by 8.5. What do you get?** (56.95)

- Now multiply 56.95 by 10. (569.5)

- How do you round the answer? (Since the 5 to
the right of the decimal point is 5 or more, round
up. The answer is 570 in.³)

4 Assess and Close

- **For which solids have you learned volume formulas?**
(cube, rectangular prism, triangular prism)

- **A metal box has length 18 in., width 20 in., and height
10 in. What is it and how would you find its volume?**
(rectangular prism; multiply the three dimensions)

- **Suppose that you know the area of the base of a
triangular prism. What else do you need to know to
find its volume?** (You need to know the height of the prism.)

Assign the **LESSON QUIZ** on Transparency 17.6 to further
assess student understanding.

 **Keeping a Journal**

Have students make up a volume problem that
involves a rectangular prism and a volume problem
that involves a cube. Have students write solutions
to their problems and explain the answers in the
contexts of those problems.

Problem-Solving Application: Use Formulas

Lesson 17.7

PLANNING THE LESSON

MATHEMATICS OBJECTIVE
Use a formula to solve a problem.

Use Lesson Planner CD-ROM for Lesson 17.7.

Daily Routines

Vocabulary

Write the terms *formula, function,* and *rule* on the chalkboard. **What are some of the formulas we have learned?** (Possible answers: circumference of a circle, area of a rectangle, and so on) Ask students to define the terms on the chalkboard in their own words, giving examples of when each is used. **How are these terms similar in meaning?** (Possible answer: they are equations that use variables and that name a pattern.)

Vocabulary Cards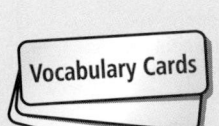

Meeting North Carolina's Standards

1.03 Develop flexibility in solving problems by selecting strategies and using mental computation, estimation, calculators or computers, and paper and pencil.

Lesson Transparency 17.7

Problem of the Day
What is the cost of the design below if ▲ = $0.05, ● = $1.10, and ★ = $0.25?
▲●★▲★▲★▲★▲★●▲ ($3.75)

Quick Review
1. $(6 \times 10^3) + (4 \times 10^2)$ (6,400)
2. $(5 \times 10^4) + (3 \times 10^3)$ (53,000)
3. $(4 \times 10^4) + (9 \times 10^2)$ (40,900)
4. $(7 \times 10^5) + (8 \times 10^1)$ (700,080)

Lesson Quiz
1. A planter 18 in. long, 6 in. wide, and 6 in. tall has wooden sides and a metal bottom. What is the area of the outside of the wooden portion? (288 in.²)
2. A packing carton is 24 in. on each edge. Is it possible to fill it completely with no overflow with cubical boxes 6 in. on an edge? Explain. (yes; 4 layers of boxes, each layer 4 boxes by 4 boxes)

LEVELED PRACTICE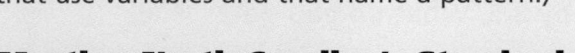

RETEACH 17.7

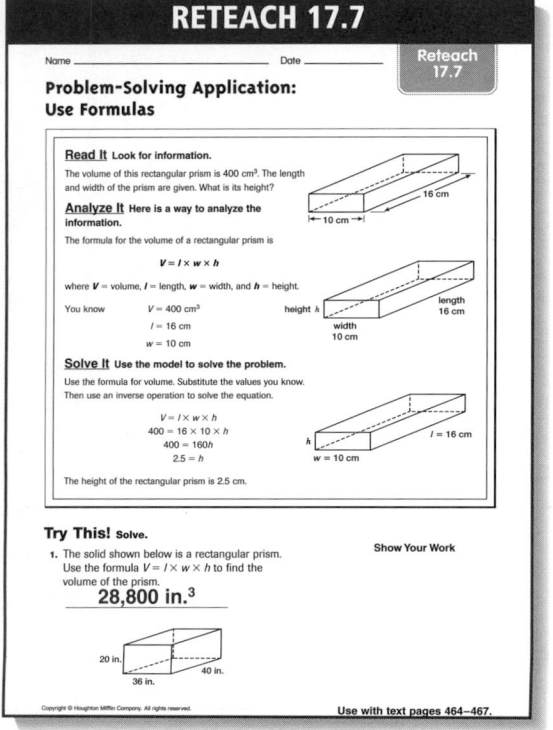

PRACTICE 17.7

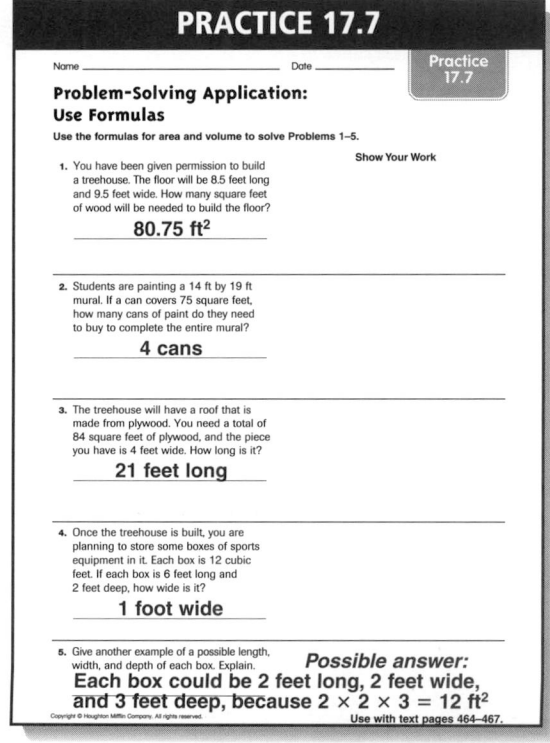

ENRICHMENT 17.7

Splashy Swim Club

The Splashy Swim Club wants to open a new pool in May. The pool is rectangular and has dimensions of 40 feet long, 25 feet wide, and 8 feet deep. To open the pool, the club needs to erect a fence, purchase a pool cover, paint the pool, and then refill the pool with water.

1. The club wants to leave 10 feet on each side of the pool for a deck, before the fence goes up. How much fencing does the club need to buy?
   210 feet

2. Each piece of 8-foot fence costs $45. How much is the fence going to cost?
   $1,215.00

3. The pool cover the club wants to buy costs $0.25 per square foot. How much will the pool cover cost?
   $250

4. At the beginning of the season, the swim club will need to paint the inside of the pool. If the floor and all the walls are painted, how much surface area does the club need to paint?
   2,040 ft²

5. Each gallon of paint covers about 300 square feet. If each gallon costs $12, how much is the paint going to cost?
   7 gallons; $84

6. How much water does the pool hold?
   8,000 ft³

7. How much will it cost to open the pool?
   $1,549

Copyright © Houghton Mifflin Company. All rights reserved.   Use with text pages 464–467.

Practice Workbook Page 118

Reaching All Learners
Differentiated Instruction

English Learners

Worksheet 17.7 familiarizes students with ways the word *deep* is used in some of the math problems that they will encounter in the lesson.

Special Needs
KINESTHETIC, TACTILE

- **Make a 3 × 4 × 2 figure with unit cubes. How many cubes did you use?** (24) **Find the volume using the formula, $V = l \times w \times h$.** (24 cubic units.)

- **Use the formula to find the volume of a 2 × 2 × 6 figure.** (24 cubic units) **Model the figure to check your answer.**

Gifted and Talented
VISUAL, TACTILE

- Refer students to the problem on page 464.

- If the total volume is 3,240 ft³ and each box is 27 ft³, how many boxes are there? ($\frac{3,240 \text{ ft}^3}{27 \text{ ft}^3} = 120$)

- **How does the number of boxes help you?** (If the collection is 6 high and 4 deep, then it is 5 wide because 120 ÷ (6 × 4) = 5; 3 × 5 ft = 15 ft.)

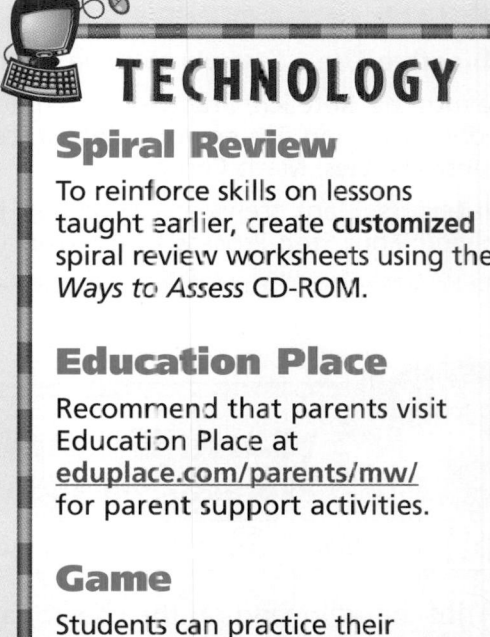

TECHNOLOGY
Spiral Review

To reinforce skills on lessons taught earlier, create **customized** spiral review worksheets using the *Ways to Assess* CD-ROM.

Education Place

Recommend that parents visit Education Place at **eduplace.com/parents/mw/** for parent support activities.

Game

Students can practice their skills using Robo Packer math game, available on the *Ways to Success* CD

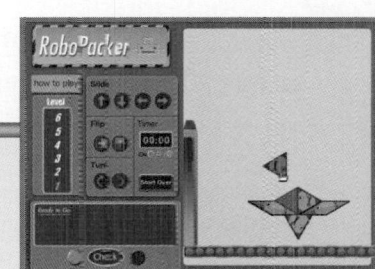

Science Connection

Density

- **What do you mean when you say an object is *dense*?** Accept all reasonable responses.

- **Suppose you had two rectangular solids with the same volume: one a brick and the other a block of styrofoam. Which is more dense?** (the brick)

- *Density* is the ratio of mass to volume. So you need to know both the mass and the volume of an object to find its density.

- Write the following formula on the chalkboard: *density = mass ÷ volume*

- Provide students with the masses and dimensions of different objects. Have them use the formula to find the density of each object.

PROBLEM SOLVING 17.7

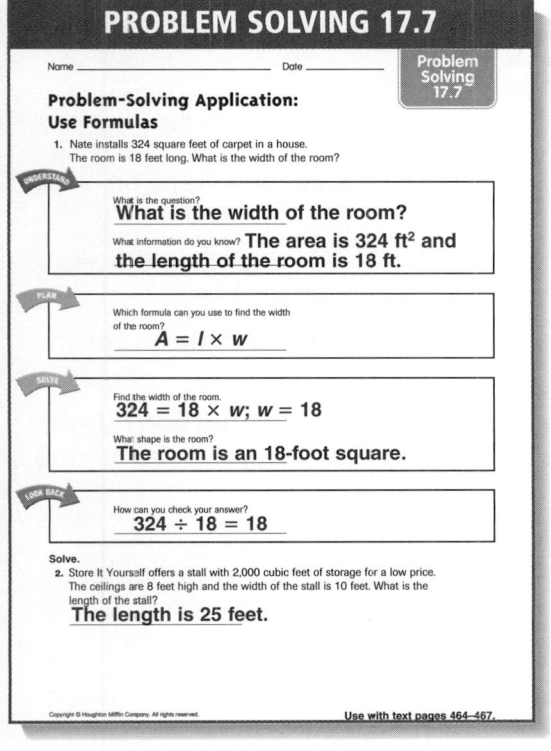

Homework Workbook Page 118

HOMEWORK 17.7

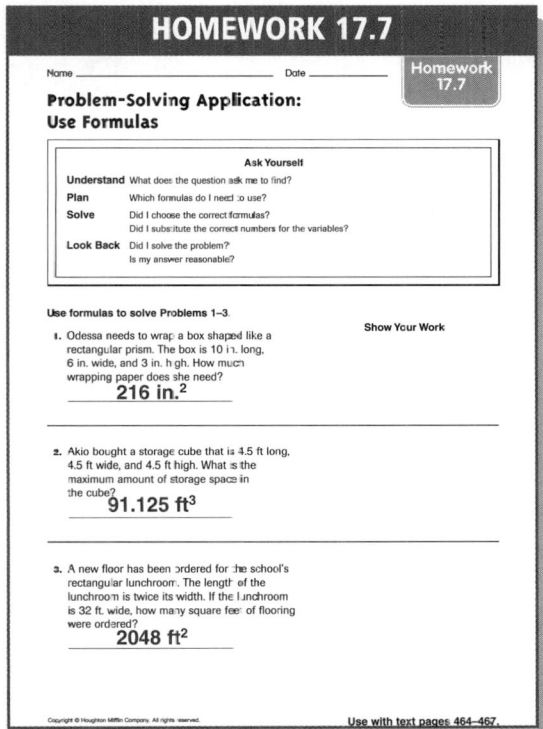

ENGLISH LEARNERS 17.7

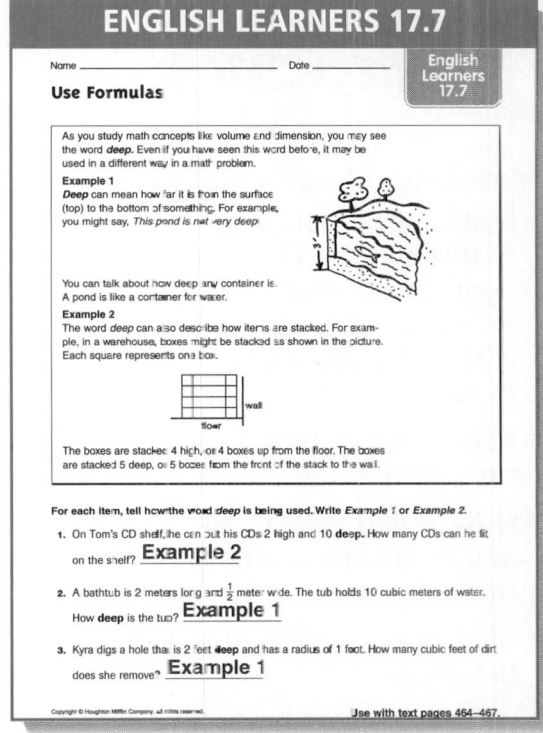

TEACHING LESSON 17.7

LESSON ORGANIZER

Objective Use a formula to solve a problem.

Resources Reteach, Practice, Enrichment, Problem Solving, Homework, English Learners, Transparencies, Math Center

Materials Blank transparency, cubes, Problem Solving: Four Step Process Transparency

Warm-Up Activity
Express Area and Volume

👤👤👤👤 Whole Group	⏱ 5 minutes	Auditory, Visual

Write the following on the chalkboard. Have volunteers take turns drawing lines to match the terms in column 1 and column 2.

	ft²
	three-dimensional
area	two-dimensional
	ft³
	$l \times w$
volume	$l \times w \times h$
	cubic unit
	square unit

Lesson 7
Problem-Solving Application
Use Formulas
Objective Use a formula to solve a problem.

You can use formulas to solve problems.

Problem The manager of a warehouse wants to know how much space he will need to stack a shipment of boxes. Each edge of each box is 3 feet long. The total shipment will take up 3,240 cubic feet of space. If the boxes are stacked 6 high and 4 deep, how many feet wide will the stack of boxes be?

UNDERSTAND

What is the question?
• How many feet wide will the stack of boxes be?

What do you know?
• Each edge of each box is 3 feet long.
• The entire shipment is 3,240 cubic feet.
• The boxes can be stacked 6 high and 4 deep.

PLAN

Find the height of 6 boxes and the length of 4 boxes. Then divide the volume by the product of the height and length.

Volume of a rectangular prism = length × width × height = $l \times w \times h$

SOLVE

• Find the height of 6 boxes.
  $h = 3$ ft × 6 = 18 ft
• Find the length of 4 boxes.
  $l = 3$ ft × 4 = 12 ft

• Multiply $l \times h$.
  18 × 12 = 216
• Then divide.
  3,240 ÷ 216 = 15

Solution: The stack of boxes will be 15 ft wide.

LOOK BACK

Look back at the problem.
Does the solution make sense?

464

---

① Introduce

Materials: *blank transparency*

• Make a transparency that shows the highlights of the problem on page 464 along with a diagram like this one.

**1 box is a cube
3 feet on an edge**

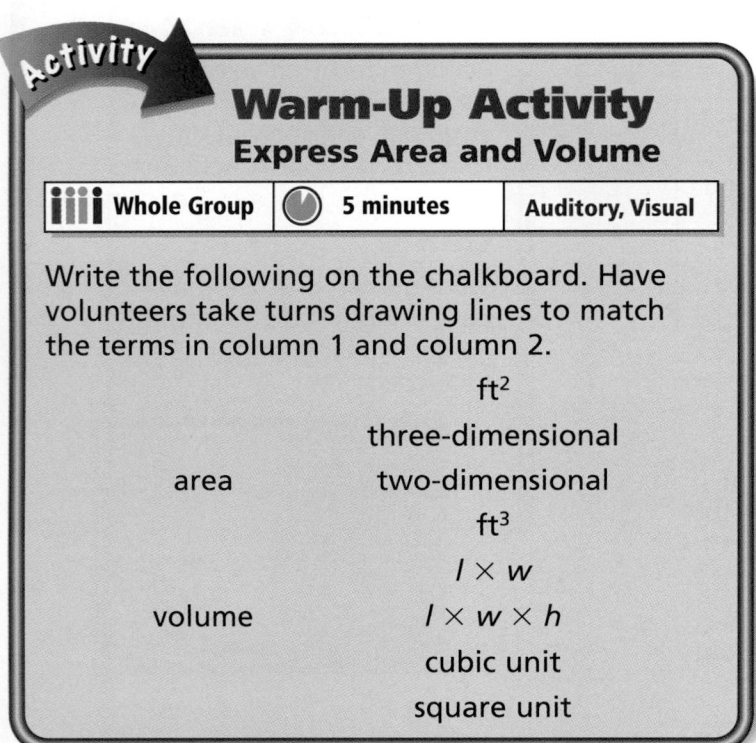

4 boxes

6 boxes

? boxes

• **Copy this diagram onto your paper.**

• **How would you change this diagram so that the height and depth are in feet rather than numbers of boxes?** (Multiply 6 and 4 by 3 as each box is 3 ft on an edge.)

• **Modify your diagram to show the known dimensions in feet.** (18 ft high and 12 ft front to back)

② Develop

Guide students through the problem-solving steps on page 464.

You may wish to use the Problem Solving: Four Step Process Transparency.

• **Refer to your diagram as we work through the steps in the solution.**

• **How does $\frac{3,240}{18 \times 12}$ give the answer to the question?** (Divide volume by the product of height times depth, and you get the third dimension.)

• After completing the solution to the problem, ask students to generalize. **If the volume of a rectangular prism is V and it has height h and width w, what equation gives length l?** ($l = V \div (h \times w)$)

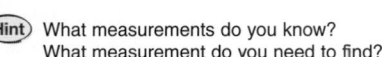

Use the formulas for area and volume to solve Problems 1 and 2.

1. Warren builds a flower planter that is 4 feet long, 3 feet wide, and 2 feet high. He paints the outside of the planter, but not the bottom. What area did Warren paint? **28 ft²**

2. A tank is 5 meters long and 3 meters wide. The tank holds 30 cubic meters of water. How deep is the tank? **2 m**

(Hint) What measurements do you know? What measurement do you need to find?

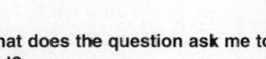

Ask Yourself

UNDERSTAND → What does the question ask me to find?

PLAN → Which formulas do I need to use?

SOLVE →
- Did I choose the correct formulas?
- Did I substitute the correct numbers for the variables?

LOOK BACK → Is the answer reasonable?

TEST TIPS

Independent Practice

Use the formulas for perimeter, area, and volume to solve Problems 3–7.

3. A manufacturer packages soccer balls in 10-inch cubes. How many boxes of soccer balls can fit in a cardboard container that is 30 in. by 40 in. by 20 in.? **24**

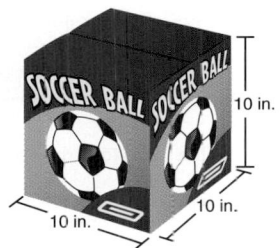

4. What is the minimum amount of cardboard that is needed to make one soccer-ball box as shown at the right? **600 in.²**

5. Kevin covers the rectangular floor of his room with 240 square feet of carpet. The length of the room is 20 feet. What is the width of the room? What is the perimeter of the room? **12 ft; 64 ft**

6. **Calculator** A restaurant buys the freezer shown at the right. What is the volume of the freezer in cubic inches? **51,840 in.³**

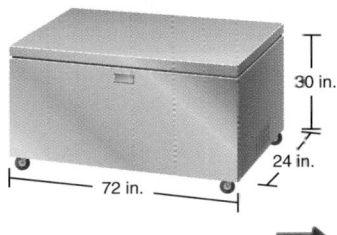

7. **Reasoning** There are 1,728 cubic inches in one cubic foot. What is a reasonable estimate for the volume of the freezer in cubic feet? Explain how you made your estimate.
about 30 ft³; 51,840 ÷ 1,728 ≈ 30

Go On

Chapter 17 Lesson 7 **465**

---

3 Practice

Guided Practice

Have students complete **Exercises 1–2** as you observe. Remind them to use the *Ask Yourself* questions to help.

Assign **Exercises 3–15** as independent work. Have students share and discuss their work.

Problem-Solving Reminders

Have students review their answers to make sure they have done the following

- expressed the solution clearly
- used appropriate mathematical notation and terms
- supported their solution with verbal and symbolic work
- determined the reasonableness of the solution in the context of the original problem.

DAILY TEST PREP

A large cube consists of 27 identical small cubes. Each small cube is a unit cube. What are the dimensions of the large cube? (3 units on an edge)

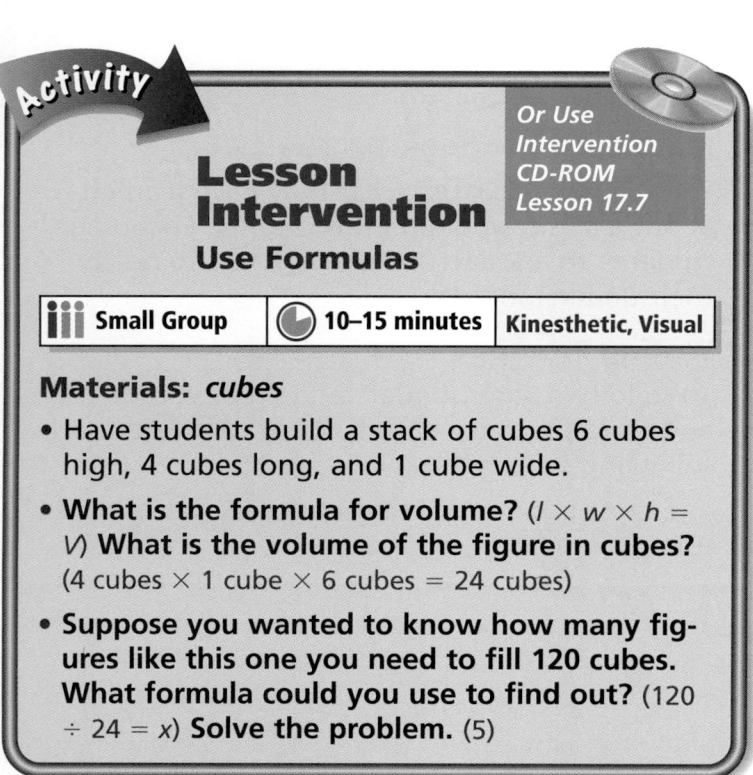

Activity

Or Use Intervention CD-ROM Lesson 17.7

Lesson Intervention

Use Formulas

| 👤👤👤 Small Group | 🕐 10–15 minutes | Kinesthetic, Visual |

Materials: *cubes*

• Have students build a stack of cubes 6 cubes high, 4 cubes long, and 1 cube wide.

• **What is the formula for volume?** ($l \times w \times h = V$) **What is the volume of the figure in cubes?** (4 cubes $\times$ 1 cube $\times$ 6 cubes = 24 cubes)

• **Suppose you wanted to know how many figures like this one you need to fill 120 cubes. What formula could you use to find out?** (120 $\div$ 24 = x) **Solve the problem.** (5)

Choose a Strategy

Solve. Show your work. Tell what strategy you used. *Possible strategies are given.*

8. Three containers have a combined volume of 144 cubic feet. The larger container has two times the volume of each of the other two containers. What is the volume of each container? **See below.**

9. At the end of its first month, a health club had 240 members. The manager's goal is to sign up at least 25 new members per month. If the manager meets her goal, how many members will there be at the end of the first year? **515 members; Find a Pattern**

10. Sarah, Michael, Fred, and Tawana are waiting in line. Neither Sarah nor Michael is first. Tawana is behind Sarah. Fred is ahead of Michael. The two girls are not next to each other. In what order are the four friends? **Fred, Sarah, Michael, Tawana; Use Logical Reasoning**

PROBLEM-SOLVING Strategies

Use Models
Draw a Diagram
Find a Pattern
Guess and Check
Make an Organized List
Make a Table
Solve a Simpler Problem
Use Logical Reasoning
Work Backward
Write an Equation

8. **The large container has a volume of 72 ft³, and each of the other containers has a volume of 36 ft³; Draw a Diagram**

Choose a Computation Method

Mental Math • Estimation • Paper and Pencil • Calculator

📊 **Data** Use the table for Problems 11–15.

11. The backpack with the least volume is recommended for kindergartners and first-graders. Which backpack is this? What is the volume of this backpack? **Alpha; 432 in.³**

12. **What If?** Suppose the company makes a wheeled version of the Alpha Backpack that is 2 inches wider than the version without wheels. What will be the change in volume? **216 in.³**

13. **What's Wrong?** Martin says that the volume of the Gym Bag is 1,200 square inches. What mistake did Martin make? What is the correct answer? **Martin found the surface area; 2,000 in.³**

14. Donna has a Mars Backpack. The backpack is about half full. About how many cubic inches of it are filled? *Estimates will vary. Possible answer: about 1,700 in.³*

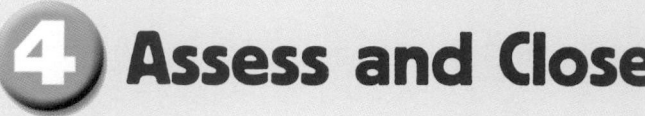

U-Tote Products

Name	Wheels?	Dimensions (in.) $h \times l \times w$
Saturn Backpack	Yes	20 x 16 x 14
Mars Backpack	Yes	18 x 15 x 12 $\frac{1}{2}$
Alpha Backpack	No	12 x 9 x 4
Gym Bag	No	10 x 20 x 10

15. **Create and Solve** Use the data from the table to create and solve your own problem. **Check students' work.**

---

4 Assess and Close

Practice *continued*

Choose a Strategy

• *Problem Solving for Problems 8–10* Have students describe the strategies they used to solve each problem.

Choose a Computation Method

• *Problem Solving for Problems 11–15* Have students explain their decision-making process in Exercise 11. Have students describe which computation method they used to arrive at their answers and conclusions.

• Ask students to list the formulas they have learned.

• **What formula do you need for finding the volume of a cube? rectangular prism? triangular prism?** ($V = s^3$, $V = l \times w \times h$, $V = B \times h$)

• **In what kind of units do you express the product of a volume equation?** (cube units)

• **How would you use a formula to find the width of a rectangular prism given the volume, length, and height?** (use inverse operations to isolate the variable w, $w = \frac{V}{l \times h}$)

Assign the **LESSON QUIZ** on Transparency 17.7 to further assess student understanding.

Quick Check

Check your understanding of Lessons 5–7.

Determine the volume of each solid figure. (Lesson 6)

1.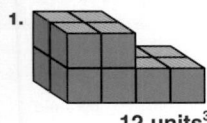
12 units³

2.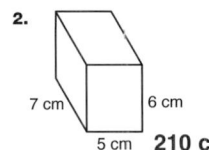
7 cm   6 cm
5 cm   **210 cm³**

3.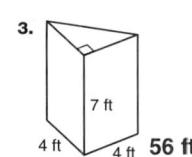
7 ft
4 ft   4 ft   **56 ft³**

Solve. (Lessons 5 and 7)

4. Eleven friends play in a chess match. After the match, each player shakes hands with every other player. How many handshakes will there be? **55**

5. A small rectangular playground is 2,250 square feet. The width of the playground is 45 feet. What is the length of the playground? **50 ft**

Science Connection

Fish for an Aquarium

To choose fish for an aquarium, you need to know the size of the aquarium and the size of the fish.

1. Find the volume of the aquarium at the right. **16,500 in.³**

2. The volume of 1 gallon of water is about 231 cubic inches. About how many gallons will the aquarium hold? **71 gal**

3. Many aquarium owners follow this rule: 1 inch of fish per gallon of tank space. According to this rule, about how many 2-inch fish can fit in the aquarium? **35**

4. **You Decide** Suppose you stock your aquarium with the fish shown in the table. How many of each type of fish will you put in your tank?
Possible answer: **Neon Tetra 47; Tiger Barb 25; Marble Angelfish 11; Goldfish 14**

Fish	Length (in inches)
Neon Tetra	1.5
Tiger Barb	2.75
Marble Angelfish	6
Goldfish	5

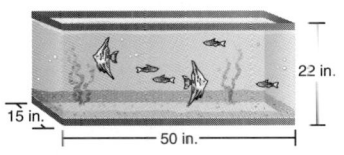
22 in.
15 in.
50 in.

Chapter 17 Lesson 7 **467**

Items	Objectives Tested	Pages	Intervention
4	Solve problems by first solving simpler problems.	456–459	Reteach Resource 17.5 *Ways to Success 17.5*
1–3	Use a formula to find the volume of a cube, a rectangular prism, and a triangular prism.	460–463	Reteach Resource 17.6 *Ways to Success 17.6*
5	Use a formula to solve a problem.	464–467	Reteach Resource 17.7 *Ways to Success 17.7*

Keeping a Journal

Have students make a list of the solid figures they have learned about in chapter 17, sketch the figures, and write the formulas for finding the volume and surface area for each.

Science Connection

Fish for an Aquarium

- **Why is it important to know that 1 gallon of water is equal to 231 cubic inches?** (You need to convert cubic inches to gallons because the dimensions of the tank are given in inches.)

- **What is the volume of the tank in cubic inches? in gallons?** (16,500 in.³; 71 gallons)

- **How many of the smallest fish can you fit in the tank?** (47) **How many of the largest fish can you fit in the tank?** (11) **How can these numbers help you with Exercise 4?** (It gives a range of number of fish that can reasonably fit in the tank.)

 Chapter Review/Test

Purpose: This test provides an informal assessment of the Chapter 17 objectives.

Chapter Test Items 1–10

To assign a numerical grade for this Chapter Test, use 10 points for each test item.

Check Understanding

You can use the **Write About It** question to assess student understanding of a key chapter concept.

Customizing Your Instruction

For students who have not yet mastered these objectives, you can use the Reteaching Resources listed in the chart below.

 ## Assessment Options

A summary test for this chapter is also provided in the Unit Resource Folder.

Adequate Yearly Progress

Use the End of Grade Test Prep Assessment Guide to help familiarize your students with the format of standardized tests.

 **Chapter Review/Test**

 **VOCABULARY**

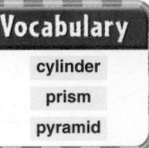
Vocabulary
cylinder
prism
pyramid

1. A ____ is a solid figure that has two parallel congruent bases and rectangles and parallelograms for faces. **prism**

2. A solid figure whose base can be a polygon and whose faces are triangles is called a ____. **pyramid**

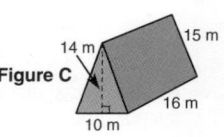 **CONCEPTS AND SKILLS**

Use Figures A, B, and C for Exercises 3–8.

Figure A — 7 in., 9 in., 9 in.
Figure B — 8 ft, 11 ft, 7 ft
Figure C — 14 m, 15 m, 16 m, 10 m

3. Name each solid figure. (Lesson 1, pp. 446–447)
square pyramid; rectangular prism; triangular prism

4. Determine the number of faces, vertices, and edges for each figure. (Lesson 1, pp. 446–447)
5 faces, 5 vertices, 8 edges; 6 faces, 8 vertices, 12 edges; 5 faces, 6 vertices, 9 edges

5. Draw a net for Figure A. (Lessons 2–3, pp. 448–451)

6. Draw a net for Figure C. (Lessons 2–3, pp. 448–451)

7. Determine the surface area for each figure. (Lesson 4, pp. 452–455) **207 in.^{2}; 442 ft^2; 780 m^2**

8. Find the volume for Figures B and C. (Lesson 6, pp. 460–463) **616 ft^3; 1,120 m^3**

 **PROBLEM SOLVING**

Solve. (Lessons 5, 7, pp. 456–458, 464–466)

9. Elyse plans to cover the triangular prism below with gold foil. How much gold foil will she need?
344 in.^{2}

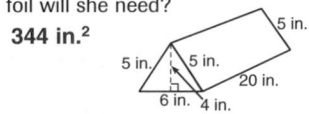 5 in., 5 in., 5 in., 20 in., 6 in., 4 in.

10. A box shaped like a rectangular prism is 24 cm wide and 8 cm high. Its volume is 1,920 cm^3. How long is the box? **10 cm**

Write About It

Show You Understand

If you know the number of sides of the base of a pyramid, can you determine the number of its faces and vertices with or without counting? Explain.

Write About It: Without counting. *Possible answer:* In any pyramid, the number of both faces and vertices is 1 more than the number of sides of its base.

468 Chapter 17 Chapter Review/Test

Reteaching Support

Chapter Test Items	Summary Test Items	Chapter Objectives Tested	TE Pages	Use These Reteaching Resources
1–6	1–7	**17A** Identify, classify, and find two-dimensional views of solid figures.	446A–451	Reteach Resource 17.1–17.3 Ways to Success CD: 17.1–17.3 Skillsheet 139, 140
7, 8	8–13	**17B** Find surface area and volume of solid figures.	452A–455, 460A–463	Reteach Resource 17.4, 17.6 Ways to Success CD: 17.4, 17.6 Skillsheet 141, 142
9, 10	14–20	**17C** Analyze and solve problems by solving a simpler problem and by using formulas.	456A–459, 464A–467	Reteach Resource 17.5, 17.7 Ways to Success CD: 17.5, 17.7 Skillsheet 143

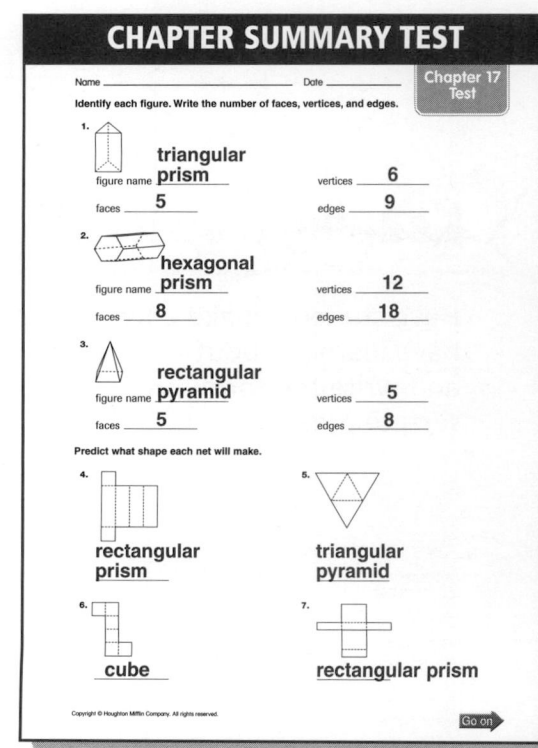

CHAPTER SUMMARY TEST

1. triangular prism; 5 faces, 6 vertices, 9 edges
2. rectangular prism; 6 faces, 8 vertices, 12 edges
3. cone; 1 face, 1 vertex, 0 edges
4. rectangular pyramid; 5 faces, 5 vertices, 8 edges

Set A (Lesson 1, pp. 446–447)

Name each solid figure. Then write the number of faces, vertices, and edges.

1.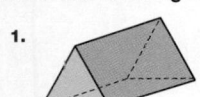
2.
3.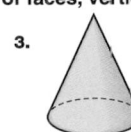
4.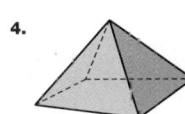

Set B (Lesson 3, pp. 450–451)

Draw a net for each solid figure.

1.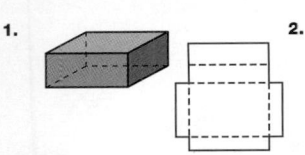
2.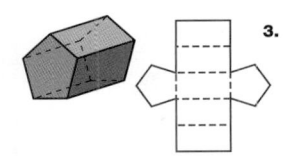
3.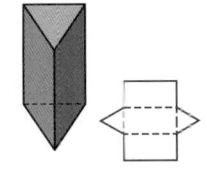

Set C (Lesson 4, pp. 452–455)

Determine the surface area of each solid figure.

1.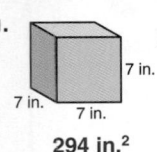
7 in.
7 in.   7 in.
294 in.²

2.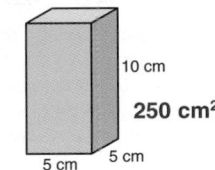
10 cm
5 cm   5 cm
250 cm²

3.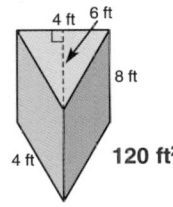
4 ft   6 ft
8 ft
4 ft
120 ft²

Set D (Lesson 6, pp. 460–463)

Determine the volume of each solid figure.

1.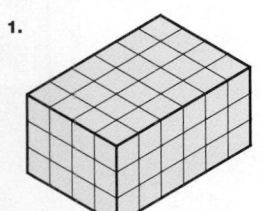
72 cubic units

2.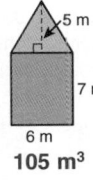
5 m
7 m
6 m
105 m³

3.
12 cm
6 cm   15 cm
1,080 cm³

Name _____ Date _____   Chapter 17 Test continued

Find the volume of each solid figure.

8.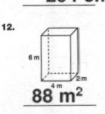
9 mm
9 mm   9 mm
729 mm³

9.
12 cm   10 cm
10 cm   10 cm
900 cm³

Find the surface area of each solid figure.

10.
7 cm
7 cm   7 cm
294 cm²

11.
8 in.   8 in.
8 in.
132 in.²

12.
6 m
2 m   2 m
88 m²

13.
8 in.   10 in.
8 in.   9 in.
264 in.²

Solve each problem.

14. A camp has 8 cabins. Each cabin has a direct path to each of the other cabins. How many paths are in the camp?
28

15. Joline makes a figure that is 5 cubes long, 5 cubes high, and 5 cubes wide. She paints the outside of the figure yellow. How many cubes have *no* yellow faces?
27

Four games are each 5 inches high, 4 inches long, and 3 inches wide.

16. Find the volume of a box to hold one game.
60 in.³

17. Find the volume of a box to hold three games stacked on top of each other.
180 in.³

18. Find the surface area of one game.
94 in.²

19. Find the surface area of a box to hold three games stacked on top of each other.
202 in.²

20. Find the surface area of a box to hold 2 games stacked on top of each other.
148 in.²

Chapter 17

Lesson 1, pp. 446–447

4. sphere; 0 faces, 0 vertices, 0 edges

5. pentagonal prism; 7 faces, 10 vertices, 15 edges

6. cone; 1 face, 0 vertices, 0 edges

7. cube; 6 faces, 8 vertices, 12 edges

8. cylinder; 2 faces, 0 vertices, 0 edges

9. triangular pyramid; 4 faces, 4 vertices, 6 edges

10. pentagonal pyramid; 6 faces, 6 vertices, 10 edges

11. triangular prism; 5 faces, 6 vertices, 9 edges

14. rectangular prism; combining two cubes creates a figure that has two square faces and four rectangular faces that are not squares

15. pentagonal pyramid *Possible answer:* if a pyramid has six faces, one is the base and five are triangles, which means that the base has five sides, and is a pentagon.

Lesson 2, pp. 448–449

Step 2: Possible drawing:

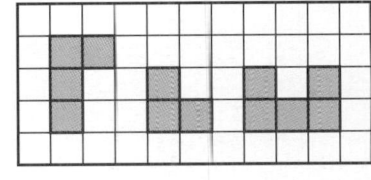

Top   Right   Front

Step 3: Possible drawing:

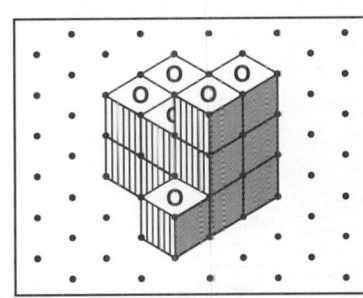

1–3. Possible drawings:

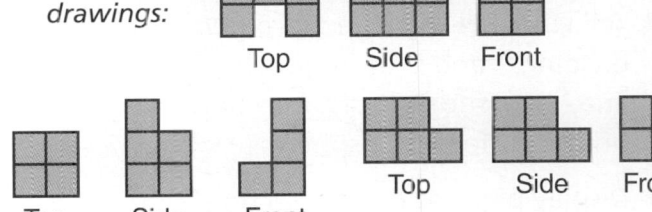

Top   Side   Front

Top   Side   Front

Top   Side   Front

6. No; the side view does not show a rectangle, and each face of a rectangular prism must be a rectangle.

Lesson 4, pp. 452–455

18. Accept any answer that shows doubling of one of the dimensions, such as 10 in. long by 6 in. deep by 4 in. high.

21. *Possible answer:* Original SA = $2lw + 2hl + 2wh$ when each dimension is doubled SA = $8lw + 8hl + 8wh$ hence, the area of each face is four times as great as it was. Therefore, doubling each dimension of the box multiplies the surface area of the box by 4.

Solid Figures, Surface Area, and Volume   **469**

PURPOSE

Students relate geometric concepts and measures to the design of a Buckminster Fuller geodesic dome.

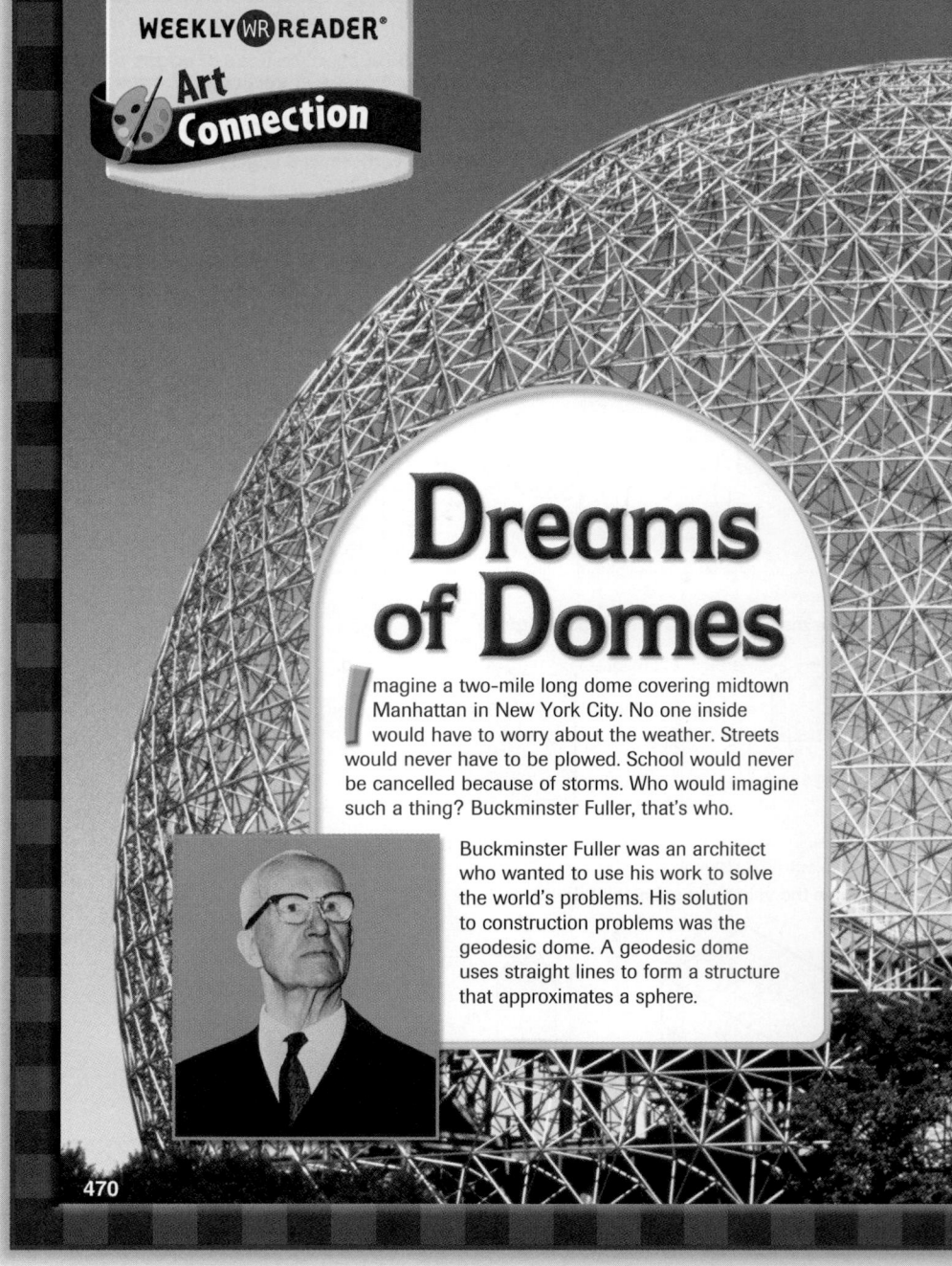

Dreams of Domes

Imagine a two-mile long dome covering midtown Manhattan in New York City. No one inside would have to worry about the weather. Streets would never have to be plowed. School would never be cancelled because of storms. Who would imagine such a thing? Buckminster Fuller, that's who.

Buckminster Fuller was an architect who wanted to use his work to solve the world's problems. His solution to construction problems was the geodesic dome. A geodesic dome uses straight lines to form a structure that approximates a sphere.

470

Using The Art Connection

- Tell students that the word *geodesic* means "earth dividing," and that in general usage, a geodesic line is the shortest distance between two points on the surface of a sphere.

- Display pictures of architectural domes such as the Pantheon and Monticello. Elicit that the geodesic dome is different because it is really a portion of a sphere.

- For Exercise 2, make sure students understand that the height of an outer dome triangle is the length of a segment drawn from any vertex and intersecting the opposite side at a 90° angle.

- For Exercises 3–4, note that the surface of the dome is not really curved. It is actually a collection of flat surfaces like a polyhedron's. Because the dome is so large, however, the diameter given in the chart is a reasonable measure for finding the circumference.

1. equilateral; each side of each triangle is 8 ft; equilateral triangles have three congruent sides.

Use the data in the chart to solve Problems 1–6. Use π = 3.14.

1 Classify the kind of triangle Fuller used to make the outer part of the dome. Explain how you decided. **see above**

U.S. Pavilion	
Height	206 ft
Diameter of outer dome	250 ft
Side length of outer dome triangle	8 ft
Side length of inner dome hexagon	5 ft

2 If the height of an outer dome triangle of the U.S. pavilion is about 7 feet, estimate the area of a hexagon made from six of these triangles. **168 ft²**

4. 766.16 ft; *Possible answer:*
To find the diameter of the inner dome I would subtract 6 feet from the diameter of 250 feet, because the inner dome is a distance of 3 feet from the outer dome from either side. Then I would multiply the diameter 244 by 3.14.

Since a geodesic dome approximates a sphere, you can use the formula for the circumference of a circle to find the circumference of the dome.

3 What is the circumference of the outer dome of the U.S. Pavilion? **785 ft**

4 The outer dome of the U.S. Pavilion is made of triangles, and the inner dome is made of hexagons. If the surface of the inner dome is 3 feet inside the outer dome, what is the circumference of the inner dome? Explain your thinking. **see above**

5 What about the triangles and hexagons that Fuller used make them excellent choices for building the geodesic dome? **5. *Possible answer:* Both equilateral triangles and regular hexagons tessellate. The triangle is also a very sturdy shape for constructing a building.**

6 The U.S. Pavilion is not a complete sphere. Draw a top and front view of the dome. How are the views different?

Top   Front

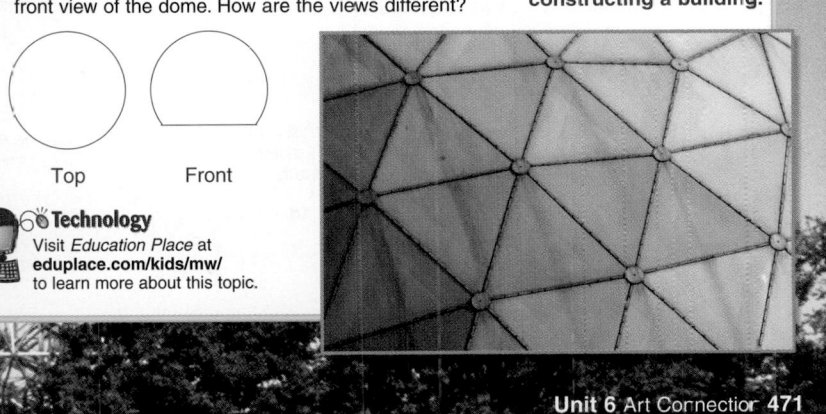

Technology
Visit *Education Place* at **eduplace.com/kids/mw/** to learn more about this topic.

Unit 6 Art Connection 471

Try These!

1.

 ; 13 shaded triangles

2. *Possible answer:* There is no limit to the number of stages. You can keep dividing the triangles in half, even though it would become physically difficult to do.

3.

Vocabulary Wrap-Up, p. 479

1. *Possible answer:* Intersecting lines cross each other at one point exactly; perpendicular lines intersect to form four 90° angles; parallel lines lie in the same plane and never intersect.

3. *Possible answer:* The perimeter of a polygon is the sum of the lengths of the sides; perimeter may be measured with a ruler. The circumference of a circle is the perimeter, or distance around, a circle; circumference cannot be measured with a ruler. To find the circumference of a circle, you multiply the diameter of the circle by π.

Additional Answers

Unit 6

Decision Making, p. 473

Check drawings.

perimeter: 78 ft; area: 205 ft²

Students should explain how they found the perimeter and area and how they decided to distribute images of the activities on the wall.

Unit 6 Test

PURPOSE

This test provides an informal assessment of the Unit 6 objectives.

Unit Test Items 1–25

To assign a numerical grade for this Unit Test, use 4 points for each test item.

Customizing Your Instruction

For students who have not yet mastered these objectives, you can use the **Reteaching Resources** listed in the chart below. *Ways to Success* is Houghton Mifflin's Intervention program, available in CD-ROM and blackline master formats.

Unit 6 Test

✔ VOCABULARY

Match each definition with the correct vocabulary word.

Vocabulary
pi
net
radius
diameter
circumference
obtuse angle

1. The distance around a circle is called its ■. **circumference**

2. A(n) ■ is a flat pattern that can be folded to represent a solid figure. **net**

3. A segment that connects the center of a circle to any point on the circle is called a(n) ■. **radius**

4. A(n) ■ has a measure greater than that of a right angle and less than 180º. **obtuse angle**

✔ CONCEPTS AND SKILLS

Classify each polygon in as many ways as you can. (Chapter 15)

5. **quadrilateral, trapezoid**
6. **pentagon, regular polygon**
7. **equilateral triangle, isosceles triangle, acute triangle**
8. **scalene triangle, obtuse triangle**

Identify each transformation. (Chapter 15)

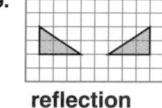 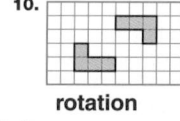 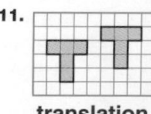

9. **reflection**
10. **rotation**
11. **translation**

Find the perimeter and area of each figure. (Chapter 16)

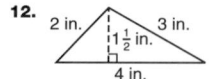

12. 2 in. 1½ in. 3 in. 4 in.
perimeter: 9 in.; area: 3 in.²

13. 8 cm
perimeter: 32 cm; area: 64 cm²

14. 4.2 yd 3.1 yd 6.4 yd
perimeter: 21.2 yd; area: 19.84 yd²

15. 3 km 3 km 5 km 1 km 2 km 4 km
perimeter: 18 km; area: 17 km²

Name the figure. Then find the information for each. (Chapter 17)

16. 2-dimensional view of base: ■
cone; ◯

17. 6 ft
surface area: ■
cube; 216 ft²

18. 1 cm 2.5 cm 3 cm
volume: ■
rectangular prism; 7.5 cm³

19. number of faces: ■
triangular pyramid; 4

472

Reteaching Support

Unit Test Item pp. 472–473	Forms A & B		Unit Objectives Tested	TE Pages	Use These Reteaching Resources
3–8	1–4	6A	Identify and classify basic two- and three-dimensional geometric figures and their parts.	390A–397, 400A–403, 412A–413	Reteach Resources and *Ways to Success,* 15.2–15.3, 15.5, 15.8
21	5–7	6B	Identify congruent figures and figures with line and rotational symmetry.	398A–399	Reteach Resources and *Ways to Success,* 15.4
9–11	8–10	6C	Identify transformations as reflections, translations, or rotations.	404A–407	Reteach Resources and *Ways to Success,* 15.6
12–15	11–14	6D	Find the perimeter and area of polygons and irregular figures.	422A–423, 428A–437	Reteach Resources and *Ways to Success,* 16.1, 16.3–16.5
1	15–16	6E	Use pi to find the circumference of a circle.	438A–441	Reteach Resources and *Ways to Success,* 16.6
2, 16–19	17–20	6F	Find surface area and volume of solid figures.	446A–447, 450A–454, 460A–463	Reteach Resources and *Ways to Success,* 17.1, 17.3, 17.4, 17.6
20–25	17–20	6G	Solve problems, using skills and strategies.	400A–403, 408A–411, 428A–431, 438A–441, 460A–463	Reteach Resources and *Ways to Success,* 15.5, 15.7, 16.3, 16.6, 17.6

21. *Possible answer:* no; even though the triangles used to draw the interior pentagon are congruent to one another, they are not congruent to the triangles used to draw the points because they are smaller.

✓ **PROBLEM SOLVING**

20. Gaby is designing a tessellation using a right triangle that measures 3 inches by 4 inches by 5 inches. To fill in an area that is 8 inches by 9 inches, how many triangles must she use? **12 triangles**

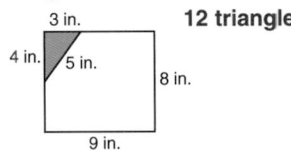

21. Represent Jennifer is tracing pattern blocks to draw a five-pointed star like the one below. Will she be able to use the same triangle pattern block to draw the entire star? Explain. *See above.*

22. Reasoning Sandra is measuring the angles in a parallelogram. One of the angles has a measure of 60°. What are the measures of the other three angles? **60°, 120°, and 120°**

23. Measurement Hamid builds a sandbox that is 4 feet long, 2 feet wide, and 1.5 feet high. How many cubic feet of sand does he need to fill it completely? **12 ft³**

24. Measurement Robert draws a rectangle that is 8 inches long and 5 inches wide. If he decides to double the dimensions, what will the area of the new rectangle be? **160 in.²**

25. Algebra Franklin is digging a circular flower bed. He wants to place flexible edging around the entire bed. If the radius is 5 feet, how many feet of edging will he need? (Use $\pi = 3.14$.) **about 31.4 ft**

Decision Making
Extended Response

The students in Mrs. Pierce's art class are painting a mural on the wall near the cafeteria. The mural will show various school activities. Copy the diagram of the wall at the right to plan your mural. You may use grid paper or dot paper to help you. Find the wall's perimeter and area. Decide how much of the area you will use for each image of an activity. Explain your thinking.

Information You Need
- You can't paint on the doors.
- Activities to show include: after-school sports, chorus, school clean-up day, science fair, art fair, local history day.

See Additional Answers on page 471.

Unit 6 Test **473**

 ### Assessment Options

Formal Tests for this unit are also provided in the Unit Resource Folder.
- Unit 6 Open Response Test (Form A)
- Unit 6 Multiple Choice Test (Form B)

 ### Performance Assessment

You may want to use the Performance Assessment instead of, or in addition to, the Unit Test. Performance Assessment tasks for this unit are on Student Book page 474.

 ### Adequate Yearly Progress Assessment Guide

Use the *End of Grade Test Prep Assessment Guide* to help familiarize your students with the format of standardized tests and to monitor progress.

Unit 6 Tests

See pages 474A–474B for answers.

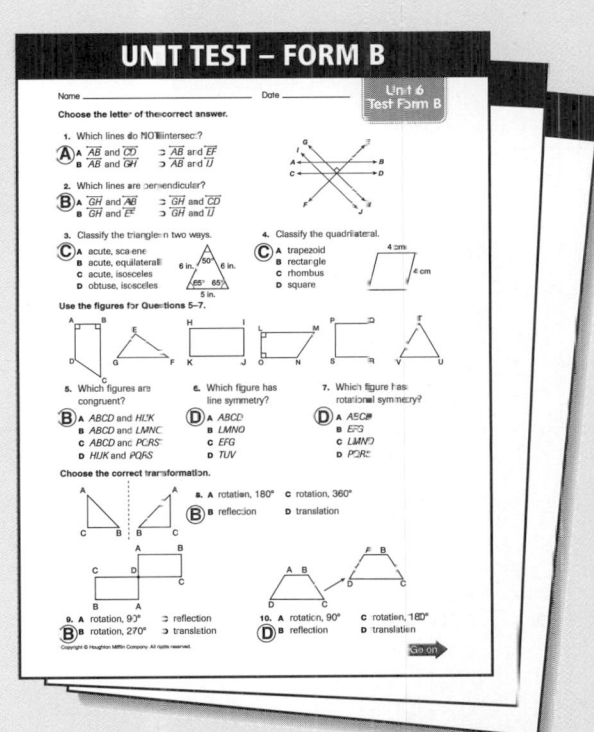

Geometry and Measurement   **473**

Unit Test Answers: Form A

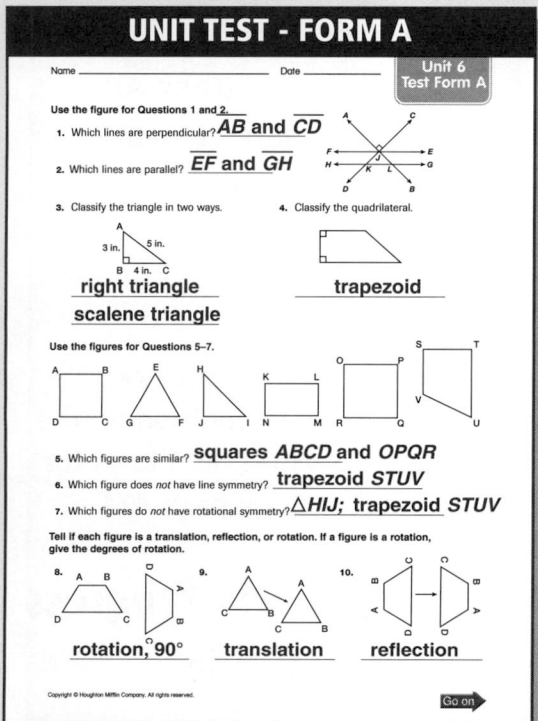

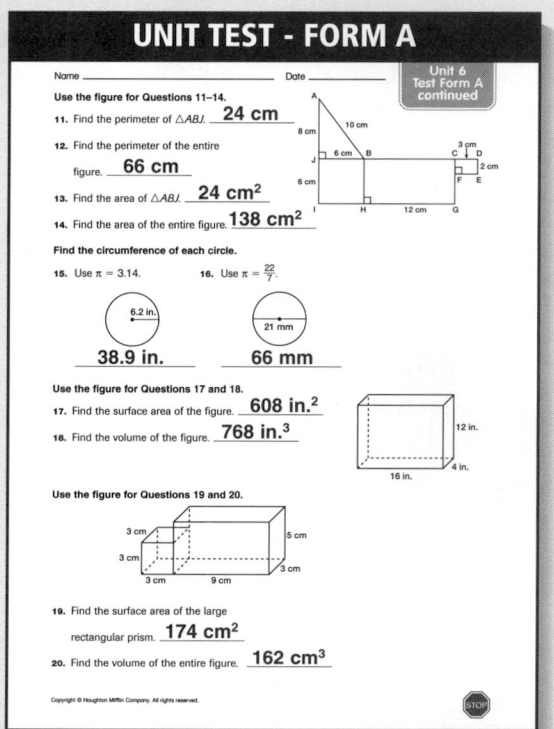

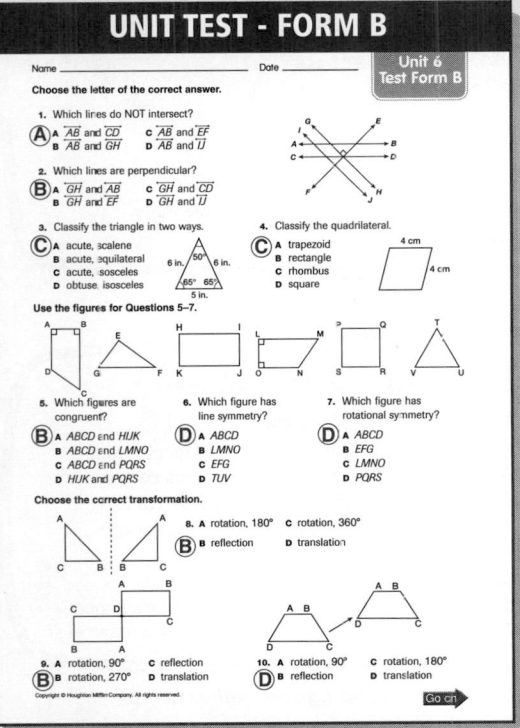

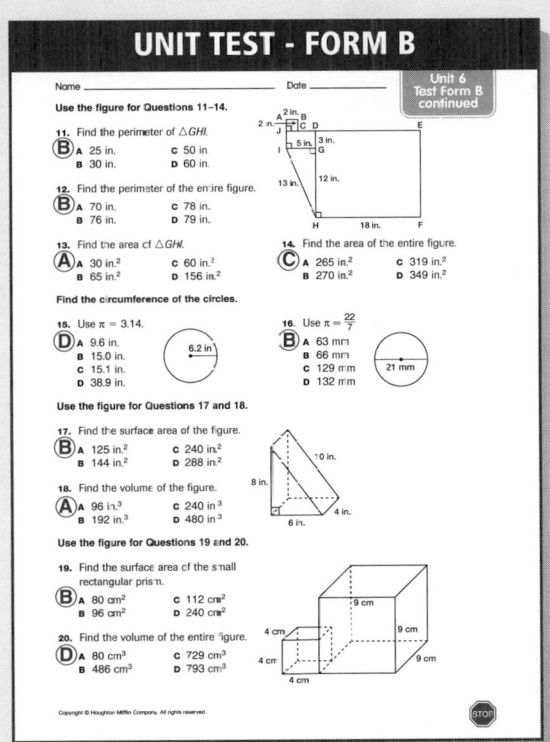

Performance Assessment

PURPOSE

In these assessments, students should be able to draw segments (congruent and perpendicular) and reflections, measure and compare objects, and create a net.

Scoring Rubric

4 EXEMPLARY

Fully completes each task, showing an understanding of congruence, right angles, reflections, how to draw polygons that reflect measurements, and how to create an accurate net.

3 PROFICIENT

Fully completes each task, showing an understanding of congruence, right angles, and how to draw polygons based on measurements, but needs help drawing a reflection and arranging polygons into an accurate net.

2 ACCEPTABLE

Shows an understanding of congruence, right angles, and how to draw polygons based on measurements, but needs help drawing a reflection, forms an inaccurate net, and cannot tell which solid(s) the classroom resembles.

1 LIMITED

Displays a lack of understanding of congruence, right angles, and reflections by drawing a non-square quadrilateral, and shows limited measuring and visualization skills by drawing inaccurate polygons for the net.

Performance Assessment

1a. The length of the line segment should be appropriate to the size of the paper.
1b. The line segments should form a 90° angle.

TASK 1

Cover all the Bases (Chapters 15, 16)

You want to make a diagram of a baseball diamond.

See above.
a. Use grid paper. Choose the length of the line segment you will draw to represent the baseline between home plate and first base.

b. Draw a line segment of the same length to represent the baseline between first base and second base. What is the measure of the angle whose vertex is first base?

c. To complete the diamond, draw a reflection of the angle formed by the two line segments. Label the bases and mark the location of the pitcher's mound with a circle. ***Check drawings.***

d. Give the perimeter and area of your baseball diamond. Show how you found your answers. ***Perimeter and area will vary.***

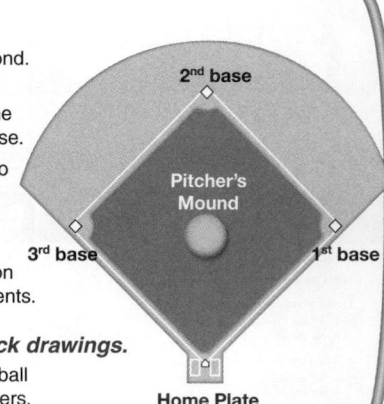

TASK 2

A Net of Your Classroom (Chapter 17)

You want to make a net of your classroom.

a. Measure and record your classroom's length, width, and height. How do these measurements compare to one another? ***Measurements will vary.***

b. Draw polygons to represent the floor, the ceiling, and each wall. ***Check drawings.***

c. Decide how to arrange the parts of your net so that they fold up into the shape of your classroom. What solid figure does your classroom most resemble?

Check nets. Solid figures will vary.

Self Check
• Did I answer the questions for each task?
• Did I check all my work?

474 Unit 6 Performance Assessment

Task One

Students follow directions for drawing congruent and perpendicular segments, and draw a reflection of the angle formed by the segments.

Task Two

Students measure the length, width, and height of their classroom and use the measurements to draw polygons and form a net.

Enrichment: Fractals

INFINITE SIMILARITY

Have you ever noticed that each small piece of broccoli is similar to the shape of the whole head? This type of pattern occurs often in nature and is called **self-similarity**. In mathematics, self-similar patterns are called **fractals**.

You can make a self-similar pattern using an equilateral triangle. This pattern was invented by the mathematician Waclaw Sierpinski. It is called the Sierpinski Triangle.

STEP 1 Draw a large equilateral triangle.
Remember: Each angle of an equilateral triangle measures 60°.

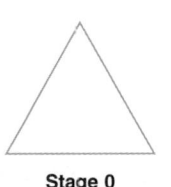

Stage 0

STEP 2 Find the midpoint of each side, and connect them to form 4 similar triangles. "Remove" the middle triangle by shading it.

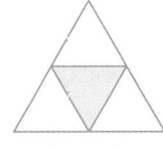

Stage 1

STEP 3 Connect the midpoints to make more similar triangles. Shade the middle triangle in each to continue the pattern.

Stage 2

Try These!

Use the Sierpinski Triangle above for Problems 1–2.

1. Draw Stage 3 of the Sierpinski Triangle. How many shaded triangles are in your drawing?

2. If you continue the Sierpinski Triangle from Problem 1, how many stages are possible? Explain how you decided.

3. At the right is Stage 1 of a fractal pattern that divides each side of the triangle into thirds. Draw Stage 2.
   See Additional Answers on page 471.

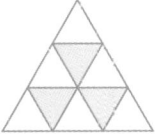

PURPOSE

The page defines self-similar figures and enables students to generate and analyze repeating geometric patterns in fractals (Sierpinski's Triangle). Students explore infinite iteration.

Using the Enrichment Activity

- Similar figures are taught in the following unit, so you may need to provide students with a brief review of the concept. This page draws upon skills students have learned in Chapter 15 Lesson 3 (Triangles) and Chapter 16 Lesson 2 (Problem-Solving Strategy: Find a Pattern).

- Display photographs of other objects in nature that display self-similarity, such as a fern frond. Ask students to identify other examples of self-similarity in natural objects. Examples might include other cruciferous vegetables such as cauliflower, the capillaries in a maple leaf resembling the entire tree, umbelliferous herbs such as dill or parsley, a river delta, and so on.

- Have students define *midpoint* and describe ways to locate the midpoint of each segment.

- **How is the pattern of equilateral triangles the same as the self-similarity in the broccoli? How is it different?** (The triangles in each succeeding stage are small versions of the original triangle, and the florets of broccoli are small versions of the whole head; the triangles in succeeding stages are inside the original triangle, whereas the broccoli florets branch out from the main stems.)

Cumulative Test Prep

▶ Practice Test

PURPOSE

This page will familiarize students with the multiple-choice and open-response formats of many standardized state tests.

Cumulative Test Prep Practice

Solve Problems 1–10.

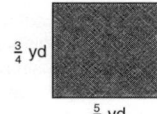

Test-Taking Tip

If one of the answer choices is *none of the above*, compute to see if your solution is one of the other choices.

Look at the example below.

$\frac{3}{4}$ yd

$\frac{5}{6}$ yd

If a cloth measures $\frac{5}{6}$ yard by $\frac{3}{4}$ yard, how many square yards of fabric do you have?

A $\frac{3}{8}$ square yard   C $1\frac{1}{8}$ square yards

B $\frac{5}{8}$ square yard   D none of the above

THINK

First solve the problem.

$\frac{5}{6} \times \frac{3}{4} = \frac{5}{\overset{}{\underset{2}{6}}} \times \frac{\overset{1}{3}}{4} = \frac{5}{8}$

After you compute, look to see if your solution is one of the choices. Choice B matches the solution, so the answer is **B**. Choice D, *none of the above*, cannot be the answer.

476   For more Test-Taking Tips, see pages xxii–xxv.

Multiple Choice

1. About 60,000 people live in Albertville. How would you express this estimate using expanded form with exponents?

A 6×10^3 C 6×10^5

B 6×10^4 D none of the above

(Chapter 1, Lesson 2)

2. Millie takes 2,000 milligrams of Vitamin C each day. How many grams of Vitamin C does she take?

F 1 gram   H 5 grams

G 2 grams   J none of the above

(Chapter 6, Lesson 5)

3. One fourth of the students in Mr. Roger's class were absent on Wednesday. If there are 24 students in the class, how many were present on Wednesday?

A 16   C 22

B 20   D none of the above

(Chapter 12, Lesson 3)

4. Name the figure.

F ray   H segment

G line   J none of the above

(Chapter 15, Lesson 1)

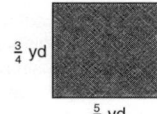

Test-Taking TIPS

Review the test-taking tips with students before they begin the test. Discuss with students some of the ways they can check their work.

- With questions that are based on a graph, such as Item 6, tell students to read the labels and key and try to understand the graph before beginning work.

- Tell students that if a question seems confusing, they should try to relax and then reread it.

- Suggest that if time permits, students should check computational items that they found to be difficult by using the answer they chose to work backward.

9A. *Possible answer:* $\overline{RQ}$ is a chord. It is also a diameter of circle P. The radii are PS, RP, and PQ. The central angles are $\angle RPS$, $\angle SPQ$, $\angle RPQ$.

10B. *Possible answer:* Yes, because centimeters are a smaller unit of measure. If the diameter is 800 centimeters, the circumference is 2,512 cm.

Free Response

5. A stadium can seat 52,320 people. If there are 24 seating sections of equal capacity, how many people does each section seat?

2,180 people   (Chapter 5, Lesson 5)

6. Katrina made this stem-and-leaf plot to show scores for a card game. What is the mean of the scores?

Card Game Scores

Stem	Leaf
0	7 8
1	2 4 9
2	0 1 6 6

Key: 2|0 means 20.

17 people   (Chapter 8, Lesson 3)

7. Ms. Johnson ordered 5 jumbo pizzas for a class party. If each pizza cost $14.59, how much did she pay for the pizzas?

$72.95   (Chapter 13, Lesson 3)

8. This net is for a prism. What is the volume of the prism in cubic centimeters?

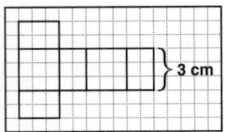

3 cm

18 cm³   (Chapter 17, Lesson 1)

Extended Response

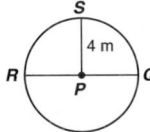

S

4 m

R   P   Q

9. In the circle above, $\overline{RQ}$ passes through the center, P.

A You have a friend visiting from a foreign country. Use the proper vocabulary to talk about the line segments in circle P. Assume your friend knows about circles, but does not know the English words to name each line segment.   **See above.**

B If $\overline{SP}$ is perpendicular to $\overline{RQ}$, what are each of the measures of $\angle RPS$ and $\angle SPQ$?   **Each measures 90°.**

(Chapter 15, Lesson 8)

10. You can use a formula to find the circumference of circle P.

A Use the formula $C = \pi d$ to find the circumference of circle P. Round your answer to the nearest whole number. (Use $\pi = 3.14$)   **25 m**

B The radius of the circle is given in meters. If the radius had been given in centimeters, would your computation of the circle's circumference be more exact? Explain.   **See above.**

(Chapter 16, Lesson 6)

 Test Prep on the Net
Check out *Education Place* at
eduplace.com/kids/mw/
for test prep practice.

Unit 6 Cumulative Test Prep **477**

Test-Taking Vocabulary

Explain to students that *context clues* can help them figure out the meanings of words. Display the following and have students tell which clue in each sentence helped them understand the meaning of the underlined word.

- A pentagon is a five-sided <u>figure</u>.

- The sign stated not to fill the tub to its <u>capacity</u>.

- You will cut the correct size if you <u>measure</u> first.

- When you multiply length by width, you are using the <u>formula</u> for finding area.

- If using a calculator, <u>estimate</u> to check the answer.

- Find the <u>volume</u> by multiplying height by length by width.

National and state tests might also use these words to indicate *none of the above*:

- not here

IS IT RIGHT?

PURPOSE

To provide students with an opportunity to use a calculator and the Pythagorean Theorem to prove if a triangle is a right triangle.

Is it Right?

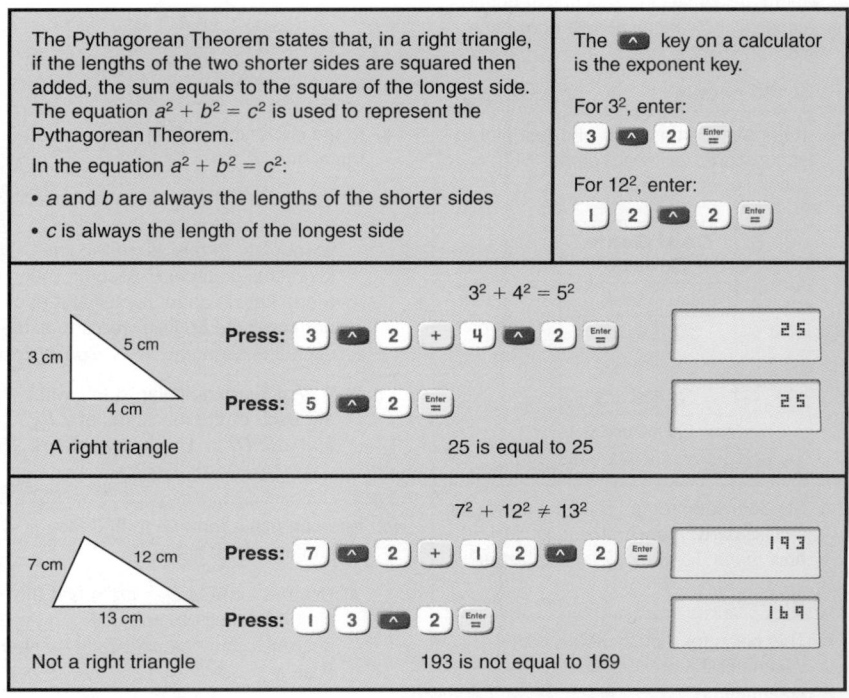

The Pythagorean Theorem states that, in a right triangle, if the lengths of the two shorter sides are squared then added, the sum equals to the square of the longest side. The equation $a^2 + b^2 = c^2$ is used to represent the Pythagorean Theorem.

In the equation $a^2 + b^2 = c^2$:
- a and b are always the lengths of the shorter sides
- c is always the length of the longest side

The ⌃ key on a calculator is the exponent key.

For 3^2, enter:
[3] [^] [2] [Enter =]

For 12^2, enter:
[1] [2] [^] [2] [Enter =]

$$3^2 + 4^2 = 5^2$$

3 cm, 5 cm, 4 cm

Press: [3] [^] [2] [+] [4] [^] [2] [Enter =] → 25

Press: [5] [^] [2] [Enter =] → 25

A right triangle   25 is equal to 25

$$7^2 + 12^2 \neq 13^2$$

7 cm, 12 cm, 13 cm

Press: [7] [^] [2] [+] [1] [2] [^] [2] [Enter =] → 193

Press: [1] [3] [^] [2] [Enter =] → 169

Not a right triangle   193 is not equal to 169

Use your calculator to determine if the lengths of sides given below will form right triangles.

1. 28, 45, and 53 **yes**
2. 16, 18, and 28 **no**
3. 20, 21, and 29 **yes**
4. 20, 25, and 36 **no**
5. 23, 264, and 265 **yes**
6. 15, 112, and 113 **yes**
7. 8, 12, and 120 **no**
8. 16, 63, and 65 **yes**
9. 62, 67, and 114 **no**

478 Unit 6 Technology Time

Using Technology Time

- You may want to discuss with students how an exponent is shown on a calculator display. Show students that the symbol ^ is used to show an exponent. **Why is the ^ symbol necessary on a calculator?** (It shows where the base ends and the exponent begins.)

- **How can using a calculator help you quickly determine whether or not a triangle is right?** (The Pythagorean Theorem can be quickly calculated.)

- Have students work individually to complete the page. Review the results as a class before sharing the answer to the puzzle.

Vocabulary Wrap-Up for Unit 6

WEEKLY WR READER
Activity Almanac
See page 683 for the activity for this unit.

Look back at the big ideas and vocabulary in this unit.

Big Ideas

A geometric figure may have line symmetry or rotational symmetry, or both.

You can use formulas to find the area of a polygon, the circumference of a circle, and the volume of a solid figure.

e Glossary

Key Vocabulary

symmetry
area
circumference
volume

2. *Possible answer:* If a figure can be folded along a line so two congruent figures are created, that figure has line symmetry.

Math Conversations

Use your new vocabulary to discuss these big ideas.

1. Explain how these pairs of lines are similar and different: intersecting lines, perpendicular lines, and parallel lines. **See Additional Answers on page 471.**

2. Explain how congruent figures are used to determine whether or not a figure has symmetry. **See above.**

3. Explain how you find the perimeter of a regular polygon. Then explain how circumference is related to perimeter and tell how to find the circumference of a circle. **See Additional Answers on page 471.**

4. **Write About It** Look around to find examples of geometric figures in buildings, bridges, furniture, and other objects. Describe how some of these figures serve a particular purpose. **Answers will vary.**

How can I find the volume of a box?

Use the formula length × width × height.

Unit 6 Vocabulary Wrap-Up **479**

Activity

Wrap Up The Unit Project

● Have students work in small groups to write summaries. They are to include what they learned as they worked through the project. Have students share their writings and then display these with the model.

● Invite other classes to view the city. Ask volunteers from among your students to describe the city and how they determined the location of streets, buildings, and open spaces. Have them relate what they learned by completing this project.

Using the Vocabulary Wrap-Up

Purpose: Use this page to encourage students to use math vocabulary to talk about the important concepts they have learned in this unit.

Big Ideas and Key Vocabulary

Review and discuss with students the Big Ideas of this unit using the Key Vocabulary terms *symmetry, area, circumference,* and *volume.*

Math Conversations

Have students work together in small groups to discuss Exercises 1–3. Check to see whether individual students understand the key concepts and are able to use the math vocabulary correctly. Clear up any misunderstandings students may have. After students have discussed the exercises in small groups, continue the conversation as a whole class. Have volunteers from each group share what their group talked about.

Write About It Have volunteers share the figures they find with the class. Discuss similarities and differences in the purpose for each type of figure.

Ratio, Proportion, Percent, and Probability

Unit at a Glance

Assessment System

Assess Prior Knowledge

Check whether students understand the prerequisite concepts and skills.

- **REVIEWING VOCABULARY:** Unit Opener
- **CHAPTER PRETESTS:** PE pp. 83, 505, 527 (Unit Resource Folder or *Ways to Success* CD-ROM)
- **WARM-UP ACTIVITY:** Found on the third page of every TE Lesson.

Ongoing Assessment

Monitor whether students are acquiring new concepts and skills.

- **PROBLEM OF THE DAY:** First page of every TE lesson
- **QUICK REVIEW:** First page of every TE lesson
- **LESSON QUIZ:** First page of every TE lesson
- **COMMON ERROR:** TE Lessons 18.1–18.5; 19.2–19.5; 20.1–20.3, 20.6
- **QUICK CHECK:** PE pp. 7491, 501, 513, 523, 535, 549
- **DAILY REVIEW • TEST PREP:** PE pp. 485, 487, 495, 498, 509, 515, 518, 529, 531, 545

Test Prep and Practice

Help students prepare for state and standardized tests.

- **DAILY REVIEW • TEST PREP:** PE pp. 485, 487, 495, 498, 509, 515, 518, 529, 531, 545
- **DAILY TEST PREP:** TE Lessons 18.1–18.6, 19.1–19.6 and 20.1-20.7
- **PROBLEM SOLVING TEST PREP:** PE p. 539
- **CUMULATIVE TEST PREP:** PE pp. 558–559
- **READING TEST QUESTIONS: UNIT OPENER:** PE p. 481
- **TEST PREP ON THE NET:** eduplace.com/kids/mw
- **TEST TAKING STRATEGIES:** eduplace.com/math/mw

Summary Assessment

Assess student mastery of new concepts and skills.

- **CHAPTER TEST:**
  - ✔ PE pp. 502, 524, 550
  - ✔ Unit Resource Folder
- **UNIT TEST:**
  - ✔ PE pp. 554–555
  - ✔ Form A, Unit Resource Folder
  - ✔ Form B, Unit Resource Folder

Student Self-Assessment

TEST TIPS

Allow students to evaluate their own understanding.

- **EXPLAIN YOUR THINKING:** PE pp. 484, 487, 489, 493, 497, 509, 511, 515, 517, 528, 531, 533, 544
- **VOCABULARY WRAP UP:** PE p. 561

Performance Assessment

Evaluate students' ability to use mathematics in real-world situations.

- **PERFORMANCE ASSESSMENT:** PE p. 556
- **WRITE ABOUT IT • TALK ABOUT IT:** in all Hands-On lessons
- **DECISION MAKING:** End of Unit Test

Technology Options

Use computer-based assessment to make testing and reporting easier.

- **WAYS TO ASSESS** (CD-ROM, LAN, or Web spiral review and test creation, administration, scoring, and report generation)
- **LEARNER PROFILE** (observations, evaluations, and reports from your handheld or desktop computer)

Reaching All Learners

Resources	On Level Students	Extra Support Students	English Learners	Inclusion/ Special Needs	Advanced Learners	Mathematically Promising
Student Editions						
Building Vocabulary	●	●	●	●	●	●
Different Ways Instruction ✶	●	●	●	●	●	●
Guided Practice ✶	●	●	●	●	○	○
MathTracks MP3 Audio CD	●	●	●	●	○	○
Teacher's Editions						
Building Vocabulary Strategies	●	●	●	●	●	○
Teacher Support	●	●	●	●	●	●
Intervention Activities	○	●	●	●	○	○
Other Resources						
Chapter Challenges	○				●	●
Combination Classroom Guide	●	●	●	●	●	●
English Learners Handbook	○	○	●	○		
Ways to Success CD ROM	○	●	●	●		

KEY   ● **Highly Appropriate**   ○ **Appropriate**   ✶ **Scaffolded Instruction**

Documenting Adequate Yearly Progress

National Test Correlation

UNIT 7 Objectives		ITBS	Terra Nova (CTBS)	CAT	SAT	MAT
7A	Read, write, and use ratios, equivalent ratios, and rates.		●	●	●	●
7B	Identify proportions and use them to solve problems, including similar figures and scale drawings.	●	●		●	
7C	Use ratios to write percents; relate and compare percents, decimals, fractions, and mixed numbers.	●	●	●		
7D	Find a percent of a number.	●	●	●	●	●
7E	Determine combinations.			●	●	●
7F	Find the theoretical or experimental probability of single and compound events.	●	●	●	●	●
7G	Solve problems, using skills and strategies.	●	●	●	●	●

Activities for Reaching all Learners

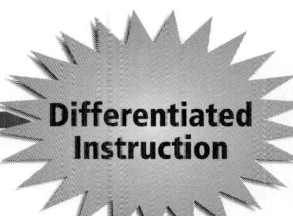

Polishing Prerequisite Skills

Materials: 2 number cubes, 10 index cards with different 2-digit numbers

Place cards facedown between two students. The first student rolls 2 number cubes and uses the digits rolled to make a fraction $(6, 4 = \frac{4}{6})$. The greater number is the denominator. Each student draws a card and then multiplies his order fraction by the number shown on the card. The student with the higher product wins. Students play 5 times.

Repeatable Unit Game

Materials: 12 sets of 3 "equivalent" cards: 1st card has a fraction, 2nd card has its equivalent percent, 3rd card has its equivalent decimal

Mix and distribute 3 cards to each team of two students in the class. The goal of the game is to make equivalent cards. Teams take turns asking other teams for the equivalent card(s) in order to complete a set of 3. Play ends when everyone has a matched set.

Home-School Activity

Materials: a map of a state or country

Students locate 3 cities on the map and label them A, B, and C. Students draw a line to connect cities A and B, B and C, C and A. Students then use the map's scale to determine the number of actual miles between the pairs of cities.

Unit Vocabulary Activity

Materials: 32 blank index cards

Select 16 vocabulary words from the unit. Write a vocabulary word on one card and its definition on another. Mix cards and place facedown in 4 rows of 8. The first player turns over two cards and tries to match a word with its definition. If there is no match, the student replaces the cards and the next player turns over two cards to make a match. Cards that are matched are left face up. Students take turns until all cards are matched.

Remediation

Lessons with MathTracks Audio Support:
18.1, 18.2, 18.4, 19.3, 19.5, 20.2, 20.3, 20.4, 20.6 (Tracks: 2/19–2/20, 2/22–2/27

Use the MathTracks MP3 Audio CD to help children who need a quick review or extra support for the lesson, to provide children who were absent with a complete lesson presentation, or to assist children with reading difficulties.

Intervention

Ways to Success CD-ROM

Use the Ways to Success CD-ROM to help children who need extra help with lessons. This software is designed to reteach the lesson objective, provide extra guided and independent practice, and if needed, reteach a key prerequisite skill.

Starting Unit 7

Building Vocabulary

Use the Building Vocabulary pages to be sure that students have adequate understanding and fluency with the unit vocabulary. This provides the key foundation for developing the unit concepts and skills.

Reviewing Vocabulary

- For *fraction* and *unit fraction* have students write everything they ate in the past 24 hours. Ask how many of them ate only portions of certain foods. Have them express the portions that they ate as *fractions* and as *unit fractions.*
- Have the students convert the unit fractions to decimals.
- Have students convert the fractions of the foods they ate to *circle graphs.*

Reading Words and Symbols

- Have 1 girl and nine boys stand up. State: 1 out of the 10 students is a girl. Have a girl replace one of the boys. State: 2 out of the 10 students are girls. Continue until all 10 students are girls, having the students state the new situations.
- Read the crayon problem in the book. Have 3 girls and 7 boys stand up. Restate the situations as in the book. (Of the 10 students, there are 3 girls.)
- Have the students create new situations using a variety of features (hair color, clothing color, etc.).

---

1. $\frac{1}{10}$; 0.1; one out of the ten crayons is green.
2. $\frac{3}{10}$; 0.3; three out of the ten crayons are red.

Building Vocabulary

4. One out of the ten crayons is green.

Reviewing Vocabulary
5. Four out of the ten crayons are red or orange.

Here are some math vocabulary words that you should know.

fraction	a number that describes part of a whole or part of a group
unit fraction	a fraction in which the numerator is 1, such as $\frac{1}{3}$
decimal	a number with one or more digits to the right of a decimal point
circle graph	a circular graph that shows data as part of a whole

Reading Words and Symbols

A fraction or a decimal can represent parts of a whole or part of a group. Statements about parts of a whole or part of a group can be written with words, a combination of words and symbols, or only symbols.

All these statements represent the same situation:

- Three out of the ten crayons are yellow.
- Of the ten crayons, there are three yellow crayons.
- The part of the group that is yellow is three tenths.
- $\frac{3}{10}$ of the crayons are yellow.
- 0.3 of the crayons are yellow.

1–5. *Answers will vary. Possible answers are given.* Use the picture of the crayons. Write a statement for each situation. Use words, words and symbols, or just symbols. 1–2. *See above.*

1. The part of the crayons that is green
2. The part of the crayons that is red

Use the picture of the crayons. For each fraction or decimal, write a word statement. 4–5. *See above.*

3. 0.2   4. $\frac{1}{10}$ 5. 0.4

3. Two out of the ten crayons are blue.

480

Unit Project

- Tell students that for this Unit Project they are going to track at least two weatherperons' predictions about temperature and conditions—rain, snow, cloudy, partly cloudy, or sun on a daily basis. They will do this for a period of 20 days.
- The students are to find out how accurate these people's forecasts are by observing the weather, the percentage of times they are correct, and the probability that their forecasts will be correct.
- Have students develop recording sheets to use as their tracking devices
- Use activity found on p. 561 to wrap-up the Unit Project.

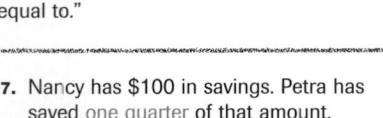

Reading Test Questions

Choose the correct answer for each.

6. Write a fraction to tell how much of the pizza has been eaten. Then write an equivalent fraction.

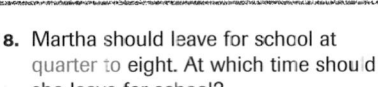

a. $\frac{2}{6}, \frac{1}{4}$ **c.** $\frac{2}{8}, \frac{1}{5}$

b. $\frac{2}{6}, \frac{1}{3}$ **(d.)** $\frac{2}{8}, \frac{1}{4}$

Equivalent means "the same value" or "equal to."

7. Nancy has $100 in savings. Petra has saved one quarter of that amount. How much does Petra have in savings?

a. $4   **c.** $40

(b.) $25   **d.** $2,500

One quarter in this problem means $\frac{1}{4}$. So to find one quarter of an amount, you multiply by $\frac{1}{4}$ or divide by 4. Find $\frac{1}{4} \times 100$.

8. Martha should leave for school at quarter to eight. At which time should she leave for school?

a. 8:45   **c.** 8:15

b. 8:25   **(d.)** 7:45

Quarter to in this problem refers to $\frac{1}{4}$ hour before eight. Since 1 hour = 60 minutes, find one fourth of 60. $\frac{1}{4} \times 60 = 15$.

Learning Vocabulary

Watch for these new words in this unit. Write their definitions in your journal.

- ratio
- rate
- proportion
- similar figures
- percent
- probability

Vocabulary
e • Glossary
e • WordGame

Literature Connection

Read "Numbers" on page 647. Then work with a partner to answer the questions about this story.

Reading Test Questions

- Before reading the test questions, have students brainstorm all the ways they might use the word *quarter*.
- Elaborate on their answers, such as a quarter ($0.25) is $\frac{1}{4}$ of a dollar, 25 cents out of 100 cents, and so forth.
- Discuss how the word *quarter* can equal $\frac{1}{4}$th and be used in different ways. Review the questions. Then have the students create additional problems that use $\frac{1}{4}$ or 1 quarter.

Learning Vocabulary

Go over the list of new words with the class. Help students to pronounce the words correctly and explain that they will learn about these words as they work on this unit. If students are keeping Math Journals, be sure that they enter the words and their definitions as they find them in the unit.

Home-School Connection

To foster home-school communication, *Houghton Mifflin Math* has a Family Letter for every unit. The letters include vocabulary words, worked-out examples, home activities, and literature suggestions.

Each Family Letter is in the Unit Resource Folder. Go to **eduplace.com/math/mw/** to download the letters in English, Spanish, and other languages.

In the Student Book

Literature Connection

Student Book List Selection

You may use the literature connection (Student Book page 647, Teachers Edition page T55) at any time during this unit.

Other Literature Connections

Anno's Math Games
By Mitsumasa Anno

Real-World Math for Hands-On Fun!
By Cindy A. Littlefield
Illustrated by Michael Kline

The Adventures of Penrose the Mathematical Cat
By Theoni Pappas

See also the **Math and Literature Bibliography** in the Teacher Support Handbook at the back of this Teacher's Edition.

Lesson By Lesson Overview
Ratio and Proportion

Lesson 1

- Students learn how to read and write a ratio in word, ratio, and fraction form.
- Students use data from a table to solve ratio problems.

Lesson 2

- Students use multiplication or division to find an equivalent ratio. Students apply this skill to finding a missing term in a ratio.
- Students learn how to read and simplify ratios.

Lesson 3

- Students compare two quantities with different units. The concepts of *rate* and *unit rate* are introduced.
- Students are shown how to find time when speed and distance are known and how to find rates involving money.

Lesson 4

- Students learn what a proportion is and how to use cross products to determine whether two ratios form a proportion.
- Students use multiplication, division and cross products to find a missing term in a proportion.

Lesson 5

- Students learn to use equivalent ratios to interpret scale drawings.
- Students are shown that finding a missing term for a scale drawing is like finding a missing term in a proportion.
- Students apply the skill of using equivalent ratios to determine if two figures are similar.

Lesson 6

- Students review deciding when an exact answer is needed and when an estimate is sufficient.

SKILLS TRACE: RATIO AND PROPORTION		
Grade 4	**Grade 5**	**Grade 6**
	• read, write, and use ratios, equivalent ratios, and rates	• represent, read, write, and use ratios and rates (ch. 16)
	• identify proportions and use them to solve problems	• write, solve, and use proportions (ch. 16)
	• use proportions to interpret similar figures and scale drawings	

Chapter Planner

Lesson	Objective	Vocabulary	Materials	✓ NCTM Standards
18.1 **Ratios** p. 484A	Read, write, and simplify ratios.	terms ratio	12 red cubes, 6 blue cubes, centimeter grid paper, red and yellow pencils, half-centimeter grid paper, paper clips, scissors, two-color counters, overhead counters, blank transparency	**Number and Operations:** Understand numbers, ways of representing numbers, relationships among numbers, and number systems.
18.2 **Equivalent Ratios** p. 486A	Use multiplication and division to find equivalent ratios.	equivalent ratio simplest form	for each student 6 red and 12 yellow counters, sheet of paper folded into fourths	**Number and Operations:** Recognize and generate equivalent forms of commonly used fractions, decimals, and percents.
18.3 **Rates** p. 488A	Compare two quantities with different units.	rate unit rate per speed	Number Line 2 from the Number Line Transparency	**Algebra:** Identify and describe situations with constant or varying rates of change and compare them.
18.4 **Algebra: Proportions** p. 492A	Learn what a proportion is, how to form cross products, and whether two ratios form a proportion.	proportion cross product	yard stick, masking tape, Learning Tool 55, 4 sets of Learning Tool 6	**Number and Operations:** Recognize and generate equivalent forms of commonly used fractions, decimals, and percents.
18.5 **Similar Figures and Scale Drawings** p. 496A	Use equivalent ratios to interpret scale drawings.	scale drawing scale similar figures	Centimeter Grid Transparency, centimeter ruler,	**Geometry:** Explore congruence and similarity.
18.6 **Problem-Solving Decision: Estimate or Exact Answer** p. 500A	Decide when to estimate or calculate an exact answer.			**Number and Operations:** Select appropriate methods and tools for computing with whole numbers from among mental computation, estimation, calculators, and paper and pencil according to the context and nature of the computation and use the selected method or tools.

Resources For Reaching All Learners

LESSON RESOURCES: Reteach, Practice, Enrichment, Problem Solving, Homework, English Learners, Daily Routines, Transparencies, Math Center.

ADDITIONAL RESOURCES FROM HOUGHTON MIFFLIN: Combination Classroom Planning Guide, Chapter Challenges, Every Day Counts, Math at Hand (student handbook)

Every Day Counts

The **Daily Decimal** activities in **Every Day Counts** support the math in this chapter.

Assessing Prior Knowledge

Before beginning the chapter, you can assess student understandings in order to assist you in differentiating instruction.

Complete Chapter Pretest in Unit Resource Folder

Use this test to assess both prerequisite skills (**Are You Ready?** — one page) and chapter content (**Check What You Know** — two pages).

Chapter 18 Prerequisite Skills Pretest

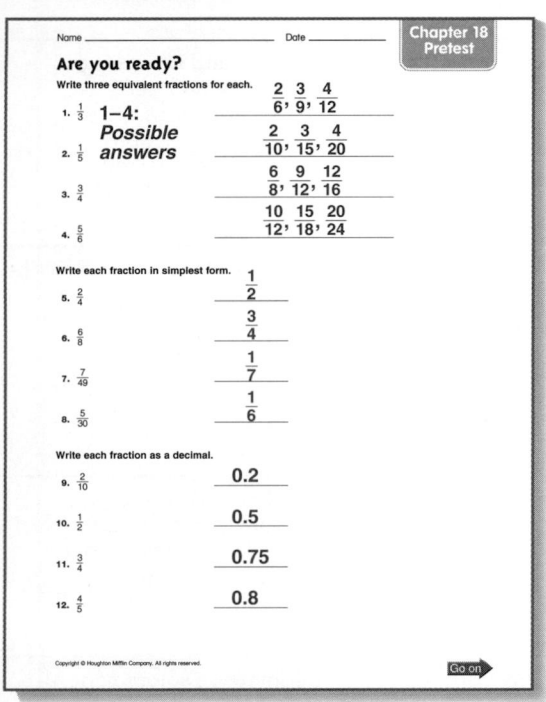

Chapter 18 New Content Pretest

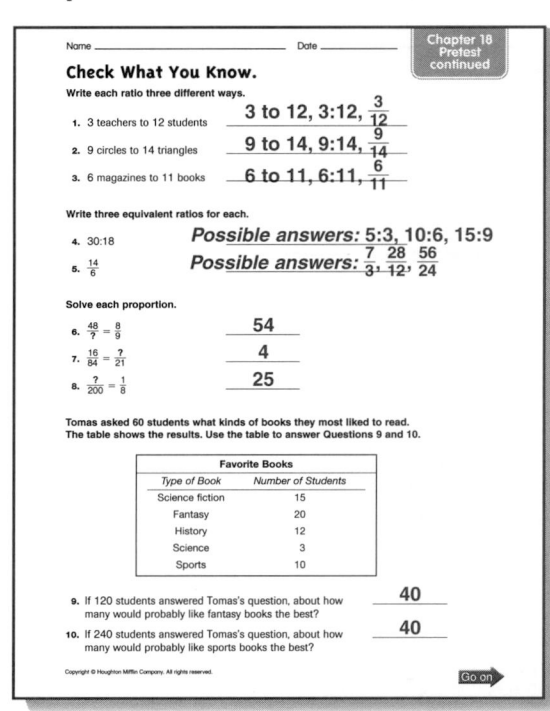

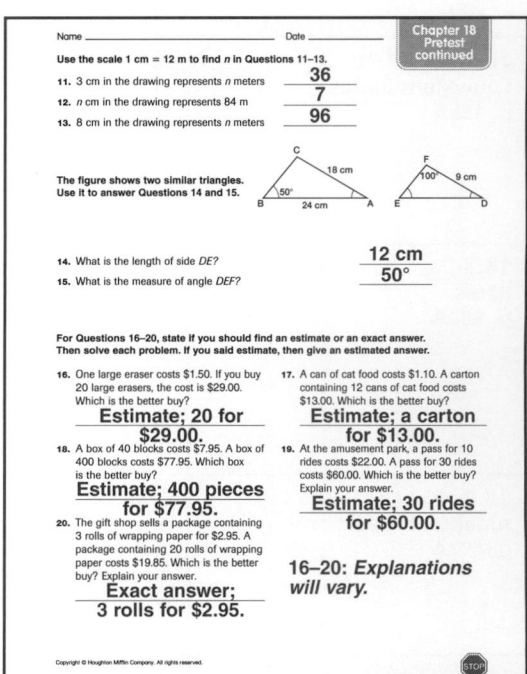

Customizing Instruction

For Students Having Difficulty

Items	Prerequisites	Ways to Success
1–8	Find equivalent fractions	CD: 18a Skillsheet: 144
9–12	Write fractions as decimals	CD: 18b Skillsheet: 145

Ways to Success: Intervention for every concept and skill (CD-ROM or Chapter Intervention Skillsheets).

Consider using **Knowing Mathematics** with any students who are working two or more years below grade level.

For Students Having Success

Items	Objectives	Resources
1–5,	**18A** Read, write, and use ratios, equivalent ratios, and rates.	Enrichment 18.1, 18.2
6–10	**18B** Identify proportions and use them to solve problems.	Enrichment 18.4
11–15	**18C** Use proportions to interpret similar figures and scale drawings.	Enrichment 18.5
16–20	**18D** Decide if the solution to a problem should be an estimate of an exact amount.	Enrichment 18.6

Other Pretest Options

Informal Pretest in Student Book

The student book pretest assesses vocabulary and prerequisite skills needed for success in this chapter.

Ways to Success CD-ROM

The *Ways to Success* chapter pretest has automatic assignment of appropriate review lessons.

Use **Chapter Challenges** with any students who have success with all new chapter content.

Chapter Resources

Assessing Prior Knowledge

Ratio and Proportion (ratios)

- Have students draw pictures to model situations you describe, for example, "Three-fifths are squares."
- If the fraction you name can be simplified, have students draw pictures to model both the original and the simplified fraction.

Ongoing Skill Activity

Ratio Grab Bag (ratios, rates, proportions, and similar figures)

- Have students model the concepts in this chapter by using counters in two different colors.
- After each lesson, have a volunteer pull out a handful of counters from a bag. Have the students use the total of each color to write ratios, find equivalent ratios of the two colors (or set up proportions), and represent rates symbolically.
- For Lesson 5, have students arrange tiles in proportional arrays to model similar rectangles and scale.

Connecting to the Unit Project

- Ask students to write the number of times over the past week the weatherperson they are tracking has been entirely accurate. Have them express their findings as ratios and compare their results.
- Have students who have watched the same weatherperson compare ratios to discover if they are equivalent.
- Have students report results weekly.

Teacher Support

Math
Professional Resources Handbook

Professional Resources Handbook

Research, Mathematics Content, and Language Intervention

Research-Based Teaching

A study by Lo and Watanabe (1997) found that, to fully understand ratio and proportion, students must first understand both multiplication and division, and be familiar with a variety of situations involving the two. Also they must be able to integrate this knowledge with fraction concepts. The study found that "limited understanding of multiplication, division, and fraction and decimal concepts" was the root of difficulties in developing ratio and proportion concepts. See *Professional Resources Handbook, Grade 5*, Unit 7.

For more ideas relating to Unit 7, see the Teacher Support Handbook at the back of this Teacher's Edition.

Language Intervention

When new vocabulary words (for example, *ratio, rate, proportion*) are introduced in a lesson, have students write their own definitions. Have students share their definitions with the class. Help students improve their definitions.

 **Time Saving Technology Support**

Ways to Assess Customized Spiral Review and Test Generator CD-ROM
Lesson Planner CD-ROM
Ways to Success Intervention CD-ROM
Math Tracks CD-ROM
Education Place: **www.eduplace.com/math/mw/**
Houghton Mifflin Math eBook CD-ROM
eManipulatives
eGames

Starting Chapter 18
Ratio and Proportion

Chapter Objectives

18A Read, write, and use ratios, equivalent ratios, and rates.

18B Identify proportions and use them to solve problems.

18C Use proportions to interpret similar figures and scale drawings.

18D Decide if the solution to a problem should be an estimate or an exact amount.

Math Background

Ratios and Rates

A ratio compares two numbers or two quantities. The two numbers being compared are called terms. A ratio can involve a comparison of a part to another part, a part to the whole, or of two wholes. Ratios can be written in three different ways: *a* to *b*, *a:b*, and $\frac{a}{b}$, all if which are read "the ratio of *a* to *b*."

A rate is a special ratio that compares two quantities that have different units of measure. If the second term in a rate is 1, the ratio is called a unit rate. Unit rates are often described as so much per a unit of time or per item. Students frequently deal with rates in their lives, such as being in a car traveling 30 miles per hour, making a long distance telephone call that costs 20¢ per minute, skating at a private ice rink that costs $10 for 2 hours.

Scale Drawings

Scale drawings make use of ratios between the real object and a drawing of that object. The scale of the drawing is that ratio between the two. In some scale drawings, the scale involves the same unit of measure, such as 2 cm:10 cm. In other scale drawings, the scale involves different units of measure, such as 1 in.:200 mi. Blueprints and maps are two common scale drawings that students may be familiar with.

INVESTIGATION

Use Data

Ray plays with and collects marbles. He has 64 marbles in a cloth sack and another 80 marbles in a box. What is the ratio of the marbles in the cloth sack to the total number of marbles Ray has collected?

$\frac{64}{144}$ or $\frac{4}{9}$

482

Using the Investigation

Have students work in small groups to answer the question posed on page 482.

To extend the investigation, have students do the following activity.

- Work together with the members of your group to make a collection of items. Sort the items in your collection in as many ways as you can, for example, by color, by shape, by material. Write as many ratios as you can to describe your group's collection. Be sure to label each ratio.

For more information about projects and investigations, visit **Education Place**.
www.eduplace.com/math/mw/

✔ Chapter Pretest

Use this page to review and remember what you need to know for this chapter.

✔ VOCABULARY

Choose the best word to complete each sentence.

Vocabulary
common denominator
equivalent fractions
estimate
simplest form

1. When the numerator and denominator have 1 as their only common factor, the fraction is in ____. **simplest form**

2. ____ are two or more fractions that have the same value. **equivalent fractions**

3. The fractions $\frac{2}{4}$ and $\frac{3}{4}$ have a(n) ____. **common denominator**

✔ CONCEPTS AND SKILLS

Write three equivalent fractions for each. *Exercises 4–7. Possible answers given.*

4. $\frac{3}{4}, \frac{12}{16}, \frac{18}{24}$

5. $\frac{2}{3}, \frac{4}{6}, \frac{16}{24}$

6. $\frac{3}{5}, \frac{12}{20}, \frac{18}{30}$

7. $\frac{2}{3}, \frac{20}{30}, \frac{30}{45}$

20. Yes. *Possible answer:* The fraction $\frac{60}{100}$ can be written in simplest form as $\frac{3}{5}$.

Write each fraction in simplest form.

8. $\frac{8}{10}$ $\frac{4}{5}$

9. $\frac{32}{36}$ $\frac{8}{9}$

10. $\frac{75}{100}$ $\frac{3}{4}$

11. $\frac{56}{84}$ $\frac{2}{3}$

Complete.

12. $\frac{1}{2} = \frac{\blacksquare}{10}$ 5

13. $\frac{2}{3} = \frac{\blacksquare}{24}$ 16

14. $\frac{8}{48} = \frac{1}{\blacksquare}$ 6

15. $\frac{20}{55} = \frac{\blacksquare}{1\blacksquare}$ 4

16. $\frac{\blacksquare}{8} = \frac{24}{32}$ 6

17. $\frac{3}{\blacksquare} = \frac{18}{24}$ 4

18. $\frac{7}{100} = \frac{\blacksquare}{900}$ 63

19. $\frac{\blacksquare}{5} = \frac{48}{60}$ 4

 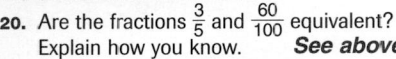 **Write About It**

20. Are the fractions $\frac{3}{5}$ and $\frac{60}{100}$ equivalent? Explain how you know. **See above.**

 **Test Prep on the Net**
Visit *Education Place* at **eduplace.com/kids/mw/** for more review.

✔ Chapter Pretest

Prerequisite Skills

Items	Skill
1–3	Vocabulary needed for this chapter
4–7	Writing equivalent fractions from models
8–11	Writing fractions in simplest form
12–19	Finding equivalent fractions
20	Understanding equivalent fractions

Chapter Challenges

For Mathematically Promising Students

Use *Chapter Challenges* resource book.

Explore: Ratios in the Garden, page 103, after Lesson 1

Extend: Rates, page 105, after Lesson 3

Connect: Estimating Distances on a Map, page 107, after Lesson 5

Using The Chapter Pretest

This page will help students review some of the prerequisite skills needed for this chapter. The chart above indicates which skills are covered on the pretest. If students need more help with these prerequisite skills use **Ways to Success,** Houghton Mifflin's intervention program.

 Students who need more review can visit **Education Place,** Houghton Mifflin's award-winning website.

NSF Children's Math Worlds

Using *Children's Math Worlds* helps develop student communication skills because of the daily work with Math Talk, a teaching practice that can be used with all lessons. The emphasis on building a helping community will also enhance student participation in all classroom discussion.

Ratios

PLANNING THE LESSON

MATHEMATICS OBJECTIVE
Read, write, and simplify ratios.

Use Lesson Planner CD-ROM for Lesson 18.1.

Daily Routines

Vocabulary

How many steering wheels does a passenger car have? (1) Write 1 on the chalkboard. **How many tires does a passenger car have?** (4) Write 4. One steering wheel to 4 tires can be written 1 to 4; 1:4: $\frac{1}{4}$. These are different forms of the same *ratio*.

In the ratio $\frac{1}{4}$, what is the first term of the *ratio*? (1) **What is the second term of the *ratio*?** (4)

Vocabulary Cards

Meeting North Carolina's Standards
Prepare for Grade 6 Objective **5.04** Use graphs, tables, and symbols to model and solve problems involving rates of change and ratios.

Problem of the Day
Find the next three numbers in the sequence.
(Hint: Simplify each number.)
$\frac{2}{16}, \frac{4}{16}, \frac{3}{8}, \frac{1}{2},$ _____ $(\frac{5}{8}, \frac{3}{4}, \frac{7}{8})$

Quick Review
Write in simplest form.
1. $\frac{2}{6}$ $(\frac{1}{3})$ 2. $\frac{4}{8}$ $(\frac{1}{2})$ 3. $\frac{3}{12}$ $(\frac{1}{4})$
4. $\frac{3}{6}$ $(\frac{1}{2})$ 5. $\frac{4}{12}$ $(\frac{1}{3})$ 6. $\frac{4}{10}$ $(\frac{2}{5})$
7. $\frac{2}{8}$ $(\frac{1}{4})$ 8. $\frac{8}{10}$ $(\frac{4}{5})$ 9. $\frac{3}{6}$ $(\frac{1}{2})$

Lesson Quiz
Write each ratio three different ways.
1. 2 buttons to 1 cuff ____ (2 to 1; 2 : 1; $\frac{2}{1}$)
2. 2 pints green to 3 pints blue ____ (2 to 3; 2 : 3; $\frac{2}{3}$)
3. 3 onions to 5 potatoes ____ (3 to 5; 3 : 5; $\frac{3}{5}$)

LEVELED PRACTICE

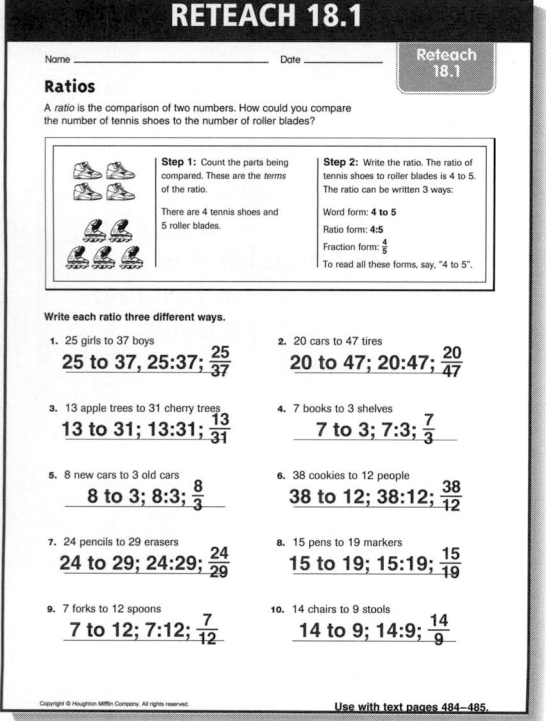

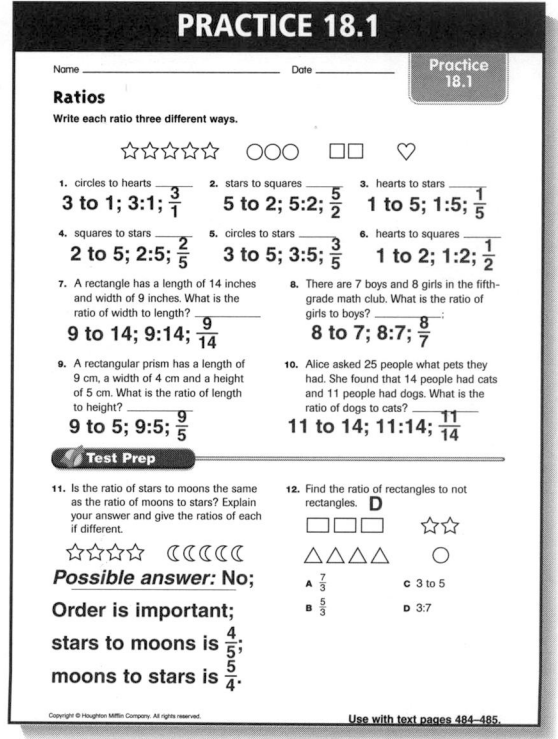

ENRICHMENT 18.1

Ratios in the Room

Ratios are all around us. At home, at school, and everywhere in between, you can find two objects that can be compared. Start with the ratios in your classroom.

1. What different terms can you use to compare the number of people in your classroom? Find the ratios.
Answers will vary.

2. At the chalkboard, what terms can you use to compare the number of pieces of chalk and erasers? Find the ratios. **chalk to erasers, eraser to chalk, chalk to total number of chalk and erasers, erasers to total number of chalk and erasers, total number of chalk and erasers to chalk, total number of chalk and erasers to erasers; *Ratios will vary.***

3. Are there posters on the walls of your classroom? What terms can you use to compare the posters and the number of walls? Find the ratios. **posters to walls, walls to posters; *Ratios will vary.***

4. Is there something in your classroom that has a ratio with two equal terms? If so, what is it?
Answers will vary.

5. Give a classmate a pair of terms of something inside your classroom. Have the classmate write the ratio in as many ways as possible.
Answers will vary.

6. If you were planning a party, how could knowing about ratios help you?
***Possible answer:* Ratios help you know how many materials to get and how much a party could cost.**

Use with text pages 484–485.

Practice Workbook Page 119

Reaching All Learners
Differentiated Instruction

English Learners

Worksheet 18.1 illustrates the concept of ratios with pictures and text. Students then complete sentences to describe the ratios shown in several illustrations.

Special Needs
TACTILE, VISUAL

Materials: *12 red cubes, 6 blue cubes*

- Have students make one group of 4 red and 2 blue cubes. **How many red cubes?** (4) **How many blue?** (2) Display: *4 : 2.* There is a ratio of four red to two blue cubes in the group, or a ratio of 4 to 2.

- The ratio can also be written in fraction form: $\frac{4}{2}$. The first number, 4, is the numerator. The second number, 2, is the denominator. Repeat the process.

Early Finishers
TACTILE, VISUAL

Materials: *centimeter grid paper or Learning Tool 13, red and yellow pencils*

- Outline a 5 × 5 box and a 10 × 10 box.

- Shade a pattern with the colored pencils in the 5 × 5 box. Enlarge that pattern in the 10 × 10 box.

- Write ratios that compare the red in each box to one another and the yellow squares in each box to one another.

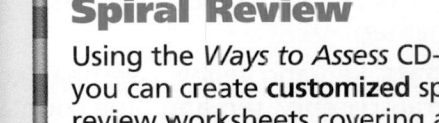

TECHNOLOGY

Spiral Review

Using the *Ways to Assess* CD-ROM, you can create **customized** spiral review worksheets covering any lessons you choose.

Education Place

Encourage students to visit Education Place at **eduplace.com/kids/mw/** for more student activities.

Lesson Planner

Use the Lesson Planner CD-ROM to see how lesson objectives for this chapter are correlated to standards.

Science Connection

Chemistry
Materials: *reference materials*

- Have students use reference materials to research the ingredients for making glass. Tell them that the most common type is called soda-lime glass.

- Have them use ratios to compare the ingredients.

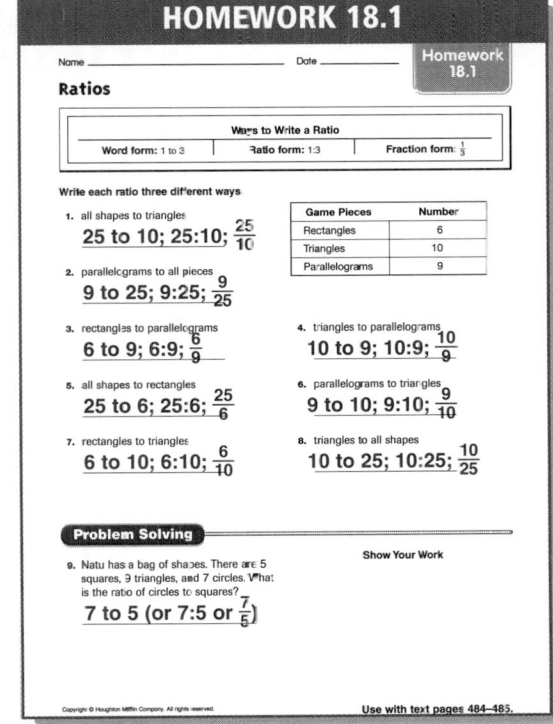

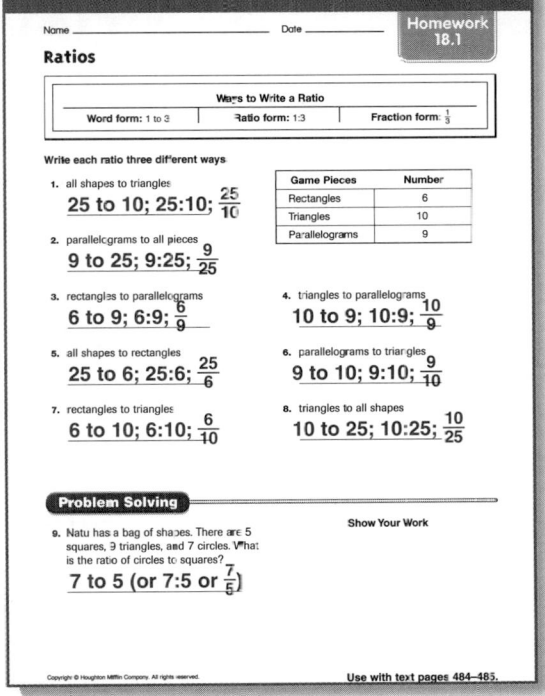

Homework Workbook Page 119

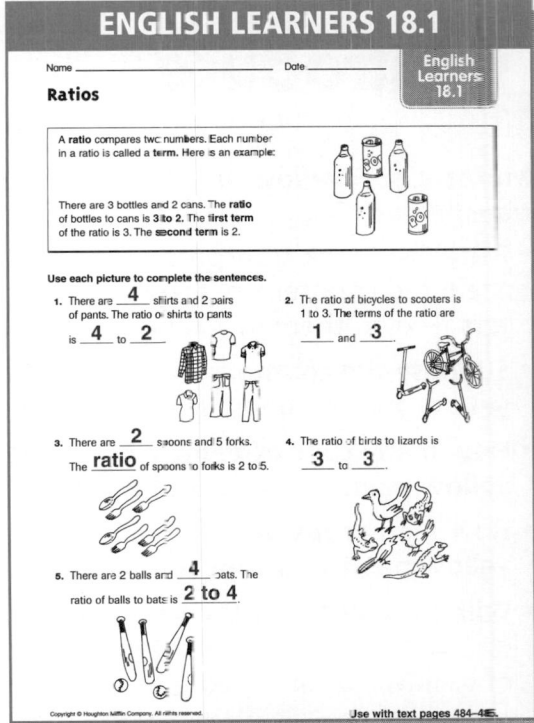

TEACHING LESSON 18.1

Activity

Warm-Up Activity
Understanding Relationships

iii Small Group	⏱ 5 minutes	Kinesthetic, Tactile

- **Suppose we were making a pizza. How would it taste if we spread two cups of cheese and one cup of tomato sauce on it?** (very cheesy) **How would it taste if we spread two cups of tomato sauce and one cup of cheese?** (very "tomato-y")

- **Are these two recipes the same?** (no) **How many cups of topping does each recipe make?** (3 cups)

- **Both recipes have the same ingredients, and make the same amount. What makes them different?** (The relationship between the amounts of ingredients changes.)

Ratios

Objective Read, write, and simplify ratios.

Learn About It MathTracks 2/19 Listen and Understand

Olga finds 7 wooden tangram pieces in a box. Two shapes are quadrilaterals and 5 are triangles. One way to compare the number of quadrilaterals with the number of triangles is to write a ratio.

The **terms** of a ratio are the numbers you are comparing. You can write a **ratio** in fraction form, with the first term above the bar and the second term below the bar.

What is the ratio of quadrilaterals to triangles?

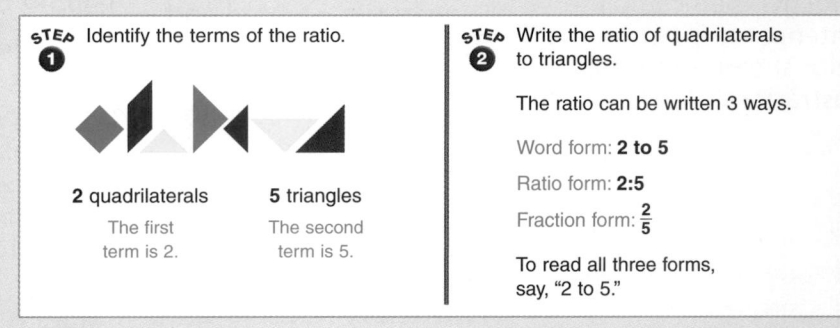

STEP 1 Identify the terms of the ratio.

2 quadrilaterals The first term is 2. **5 triangles** The second term is 5.

STEP 2 Write the ratio of quadrilaterals to triangles.

The ratio can be written 3 ways.

Word form: **2 to 5**

Ratio form: **2:5**

Fraction form: $\frac{2}{5}$

To read all three forms, say, "2 to 5."

Solution: The ratio of quadrilaterals to triangles is 2 to 5, 2:5, or $\frac{2}{5}$.

Guided Practice

Write each ratio three different ways.

1. 5 cars to 6 trucks — 5 to 6; 5:6; $\frac{5}{6}$
2. 16 cats to 3 dogs — 16 to 3; 16:3; $\frac{16}{3}$
3. 2 balls to 3 bats — 2 to 3; 2:3; $\frac{2}{3}$
4. 4 caps to 5 coats — 4 to 5; 4:5; $\frac{4}{5}$
5. 7 squares to 2 triangles — 7 to 2; 7:2; $\frac{7}{2}$
6. 9 paints to 4 brushes — 9 to 4; 9:4; $\frac{9}{4}$

Ask Yourself
- Did I write the terms in the correct order?
- Did I write each ratio three different ways?

TEST TIPS The order of the numbers must match the order of the items that are being compared.

TEST TIPS Explain Your Thinking ▶ In Exercise 6, if you write the ratio of brushes to paints, why write 4:9 instead of 9:4?

---

1 Introduce

Materials: *9 yellow and 6 red overhead counters, blank transparency*

- Place the blank transparency on the overhead and place the 6 red counters in 3 rows of 2 and the 9 yellow counters next to them in 3 rows of 3 on it.

- **Suppose the counters were cups of paint. When you mix yellow and red paint what color do you get?** (orange)

- **How many cups of paint will you get if you mix 9 cups yellow paint to 6 cups red paint?** (15 cups of paint)

- **How many cups of paint will you get if you mix 6 cups yellow paint to 9 cups red paint?** (15 cups of paint)

- **Will this paint look the same as the first batch of paint?** (No, since the ratio of yellow to red changed, this second batch of paint will be more red than the first batch in color.)

2 Develop

Guide students through the *Learn About It* section.

- **Look at Step 1. Why is order important when writing the ratio 2 : 5?** (If the ratio were ordered 5 : 2, the comparison would be triangles to quadrilaterals, which is a different comparison.)

- **Look at Step 2.** Write each form of the ratio *2 : 5* on the board and read out loud "two to five." Next write the following ratios on the board: *4 : 5; $\frac{10}{3}$; 100 to 1.* Point to each ratio and ask the class to read each ratio out loud. (four to five; ten to three; one hundred to one)

Guided Practice

Have students complete **Exercises 1–6** as you observe. Remind them to use the *Ask Yourself* questions to help. Give students the opportunity to talk about the question in *Explain Your Thinking.*

Use the triangles, squares, and circles below to write each ratio three different ways.

7. squares to triangles **2 to 7; 2:7; $\frac{2}{7}$**

8. circles to squares **5 to 2; 5:2; $\frac{5}{2}$**

9. circles to triangles **5 to 7; 5:7; $\frac{5}{7}$**

10. squares to circles **2 to 5; 2:5; $\frac{2}{5}$**

11. triangles to squares **7 to 2; 7:2; $\frac{7}{2}$**

12. triangles to circles **7 to 5; 7:5; $\frac{7}{5}$**

13. circles to all figures **5 to 14; 5:14; $\frac{5}{14}$**

14. triangles to squares and circles **7 to 7; 7:7; $\frac{7}{7}$**

Data Use the table and the completed tangram to answer Problems 15–19.

15. Olivia emptied a box of wooden tangram pieces onto the desk. She counted the number of each shape and organized her findings in a table. What is the ratio of triangles to squares? **15:3 or 5:1**

Tangram Pieces	Number of Each Shape
triangles	15
squares	3
parallelograms	3

16. **Analyze** A tangram is made from 5 triangles, 1 square, and 1 parallelogram. If all the pieces are the right size, how many complete tangrams can be made from the shapes Olivia has? **3**

17. Write the ratio of the number of yellow pieces to the number of blue pieces. **2:1**

18. Write the ratio of the number of blue pieces to the number of yellow pieces. **1:2**

19. **Write About It** Explain why the answers to Problems 17 and 18 are not the same. *See Additional Answers on Page 503.*

24. **3:4.** *Possible answer:* counted the number of triangles and the number of shapes that were not triangles and wrote a ratio of numbers in that order.

Daily Review   Test Prep

Possible answers given
Write two equivalent fractions. Use multiplication and division. (Ch. 9, Lesson 6)

20. $\frac{4}{6}$ **$\frac{2}{3}$, $\frac{8}{12}$**

21. $\frac{5}{20}$ **$\frac{1}{4}$, $\frac{10}{40}$**

22. $\frac{7}{14}$ **$\frac{1}{2}$, $\frac{14}{28}$**

23. $\frac{8}{20}$ **$\frac{2}{5}$, $\frac{16}{40}$**

24. **Free Response** Write the ratio of triangles to figures that are not triangles. Explain. *See above.*

Extra Practice See page 503, Set A.

Chapter 18 Lesson 1   **485**

There are 4 soccer balls for every 5 players on the team. Which expression shows the ratio of players to soccer balls? (D)

A. 4 : 5   B. $\frac{5}{9}$ C. 4 to 5   D. 5 : 4

Activity

Lesson Intervention

Or use Intervention CD-ROM Lesson 18.1

Understanding the Difference Between Ratios and Fractions

Small Group	5 minutes	Visual, Auditory

Materials: *red and blue counters*

- Have students create a grouping of 10 red and 2 blue counters. **What is the ratio of red to blue counters?** (ten to two) **How can we write that in fractional form?** ($\frac{10}{2}$) **Can the fraction be written in a simpler form?** (yes, $\frac{5}{1}$) **If we were working with fractions, could we change $\frac{5}{1}$ into a whole number?** (yes, $\frac{5}{1} = 5$) **Why can't we do that with a ratio?** (Possible answer: because we don't have five of anything. We have a ratio of five things to one thing.)

- Have students create other groupings and say and write the ratios that describe the relationship of red and blue counters. Have them explain how their ratios are different from fractions.

---

③ Practice

Assign **Problems 7–24** as independent work.

Problem Solving for Problems 15–19 Be sure students understand they are to use the information in the table for Problem 15, and the artwork for Problems 16 and 17.

For Problem 15, students may wonder if they should write their answer $\frac{15}{3}$, in the simplified form $\frac{5}{1}$. Tell students both answers are appropriate.

Common Error

Ordering terms incorrectly To help students order terms correctly, have them write the first numbers with the words they represent. For example, have them write 1 catcher to 9 baseball players instead of just 1 to 9.

④ Assess and Close

Write $\frac{3}{14}$ on the chalkboard.

- **What number is the first term?** (3) **the second term?** (14) **What are the other ways to write this ratio?** (3 : 14 and 3 to 14) **How do you say this ratio?** (three to fourteen)

- Have them write ratios in three forms for the following: doors to the classroom, number of girls to boys in the class, number of girls to all students.

Assign the **LESSON QUIZ** on Transparency 18.1 to further assess student understanding.

Keeping a Journal

Have students describe an outcome that depends on a ratio, such as a recipe.

Equivalent Ratios

PLANNING THE LESSON

MATHEMATICS OBJECTIVE
Use multiplication and division to find equivalent ratios.

Use Lesson Planner CD-ROM for Lesson 18.2.

Daily Routines

Vocabulary
Write $\frac{2}{5}$ and $\frac{4}{12}$ on the chalkboard. Circle the ratio $\frac{2}{5}$. Hold up the vocabulary card *simplest form*. **Is there any number besides 1 that will go into 2 and into 5 evenly?** (No) **The ratio $\frac{2}{5}$ is in** *simplest form* **because 1 is the only number that divides each term.** Show that both terms of $\frac{4}{12}$ can be divided by 4 to write the ratio $\frac{1}{3}$ in *simplest form*.

Vocabulary Cards

Meeting North Carolina's Standards
Prepare for Grade 6 Objective **5.04** Use graphs, tables, and symbols to model and solve problems involving rates of change and ratios.

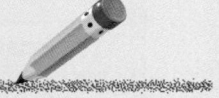

Lesson Transparency 18.2

Problem of the Day
Kyle had a piece of rope that was $7\frac{1}{2}$ inches long. He has $1\frac{1}{3}$ inches of rope left after cutting off two equal lengths. How many inches long is each of the equal length pieces of rope? ($3\frac{1}{12}$ inches)

Quick Review
Find the greatest common factor (GCF) for each pair of numbers.
1. 12 and 20 (4)
2. 30 and 40 (10)
3. 12 and 25 (1)
4. 16 and 40 (8)
5. 28 and 42 (14)
6. 24 and 42 (6)

Lesson Quiz
Write each ratio as a fraction in simplest form.
1. 9 : 72 ($\frac{1}{8}$)
2. 20 : 30 ($\frac{2}{3}$)
3. $\frac{18}{20}$ ($\frac{9}{10}$)
4. $\frac{25}{60}$ ($\frac{5}{12}$)
5. 12 to 27 ($\frac{4}{9}$)
6. 13 to 39 ($\frac{1}{3}$)

LEVELED PRACTICE

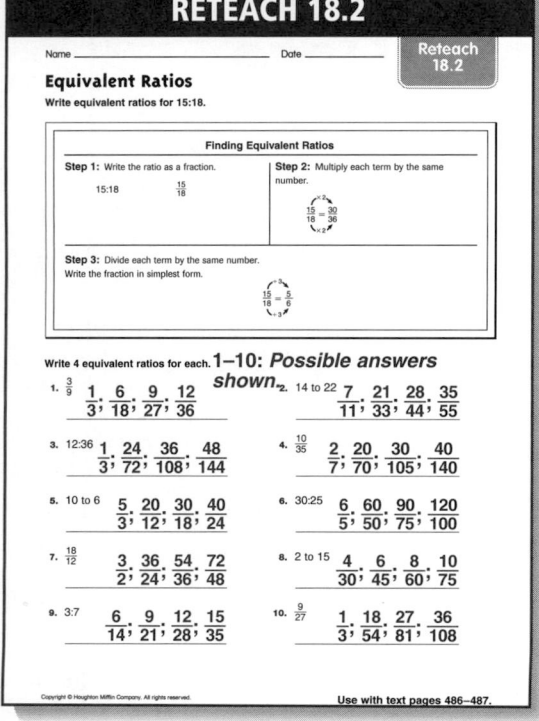

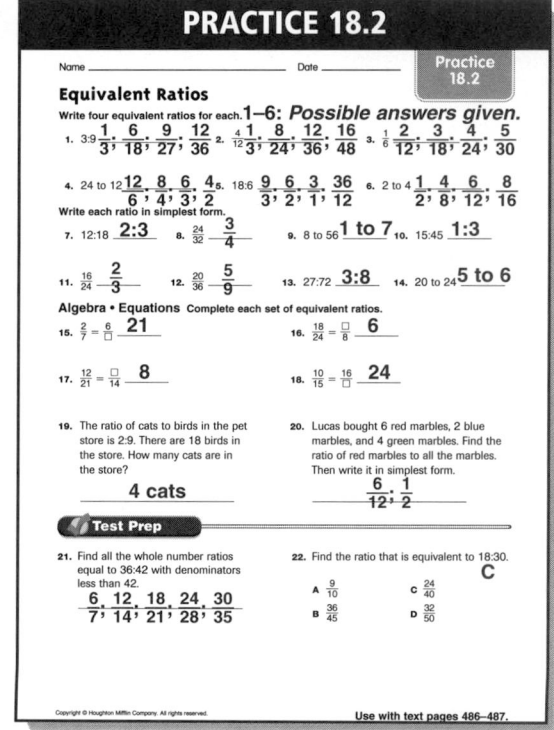

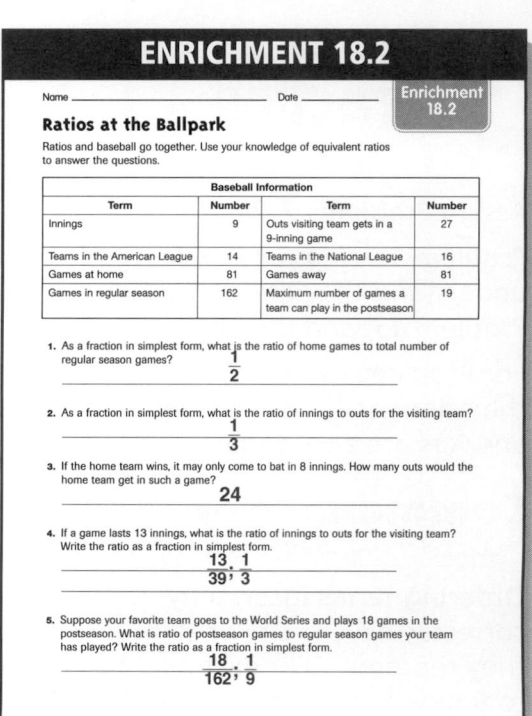

Practice Workbook Page 120

Reaching All Learners

Differentiated Instruction

English Learners

Worksheet 18.2 uses pictures and a chart to illustrate the concept of equivalent ratios. Students are given a definition of *simplest form* and then identify the simplest forms of several ratios.

Inclusion
VISUAL, TACTILE

Materials: *fraction circle*

- Display a fraction circle and have students count the units of fourths. (4) Have them point to 2 units. **The ratio of these units to all the units in the circle is two to four.** Display: $\frac{2}{4}$.

- Place 2 fourths units together and ask what these show. ($\frac{1}{2}$)

- Write: $\frac{2}{4} = \frac{1}{2}$. **We call equal ratios *equivalent ratios*.**

Gifted and Talented
AUDITORY, KINESTHETIC

- **Does every ratio have an equivalent ratio?** Challenge students to answer this question. Have them demonstrate by finding equivalent ratios for $\frac{5}{12}$ or for $\frac{3}{15}$. Have them explain why any ratio can have an equivalent ratio. (because you can always multiply the first term and the second term by the same number)

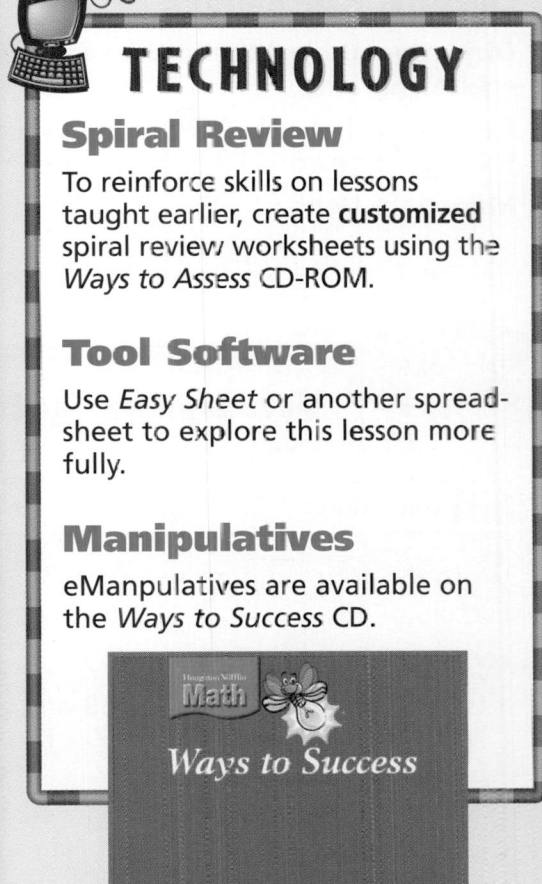

TECHNOLOGY

Spiral Review

To reinforce skills on lessons taught earlier, create **customized** spiral review worksheets using the *Ways to Assess* CD-ROM.

Tool Software

Use *Easy Sheet* or another spreadsheet to explore this lesson more fully.

Manipulatives

eManipulatives are available on the *Ways to Success* CD.

Social Studies Connection

American Flags

Materials: *centimeter grid paper Learning Tool 13; red, white, and blue pencils*

- On one sheet of grid paper, have students draw a 10 cm × 16 cm rectangle. Tell them to color an American flag. Have them shade only full squares.

- On the other sheet, have them make a flag that is 20 cm × 32 cm.

- Then have them write the following ratios: *red squares in little flag to all squares in little flag; red squares in big flag to all squares in big flag.*

- Have them explain if the two ratios are equivalent. (If students drew their two flags carefully, the ratios should be equivalent.)

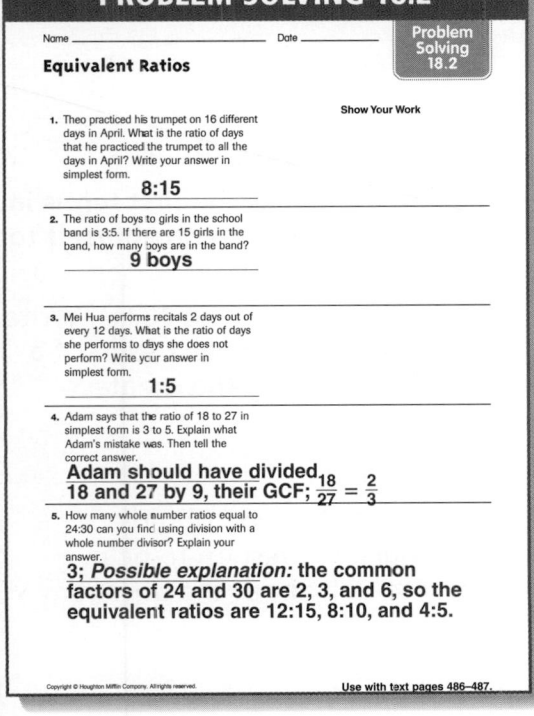

PROBLEM SOLVING 18.2

Name _____ Date _____

Problem Solving 18.2

Equivalent Ratios

Show Your Work

1. Theo practiced his trumpet on 16 different days in April. What is the ratio of days that he practiced the trumpet to all the days in April? Write your answer in simplest form.

   8:15

2. The ratio of boys to girls in the school band is 3:5. If there are 15 girls in the band, how many boys are in the band?

   9 boys

3. Mei Hua performs recitals 2 days out of every 12 days. What is the ratio of days she performs to days she does not perform? Write your answer in simplest form.

   1:5

4. Adam says that the ratio of 18 to 27 in simplest form is 3 to 5. Explain what Adam's mistake was. Then tell the correct answer.

   Adam should have divided 18 and 27 by 9, their GCF; $\frac{18}{27} = \frac{2}{3}$

5. How many whole number ratios equal to 24:30 can you find using division with a whole number divisor? Explain your answer.

   3; *Possible explanation:* the common factors of 24 and 30 are 2, 3, and 6, so the equivalent ratios are 12:15, 8:10, and 4:5.

Copyright © Houghton Mifflin Company. All rights reserved.

Use with text pages 486–487.

HOMEWORK 18.2

Name _____ Date _____

Homework 18.2

Equivalent Ratios

Different Ways to Find Equivalent Ratios	
Way 1: Multiply each term by the same number.	**Way 2:** Divide each term by the same number.
$\frac{6}{9} = \frac{6 \times 2}{9 \times 2} = \frac{12}{18}$	$\frac{6}{9} = \frac{6 \div 3}{9 \div 3} = \frac{2}{3}$

Write four equivalent ratios for each.   *Possible answers given.*

1. $\frac{2}{5}$ $\frac{4}{10}$; $\frac{6}{15}$; $\frac{8}{20}$; $\frac{10}{25}$

2. 3:7 6:14; 9:21; 12:28;15:35

3. 2 to 9 4 to 18; 6 to 27; 8 to 36; 10 to 45

14. $\frac{1}{6}$ $\frac{2}{12}$, $\frac{3}{18}$; $\frac{4}{24}$, $\frac{5}{30}$

5. 2:4 1:2; 4:8; 5:10; 6:12

6. 4 to 7 8 to 14; 12 to 21; 16 to 28; 20 to 35

7. $\frac{5}{5}$ $\frac{12}{10}$, $\frac{18}{15}$; $\frac{24}{20}$, $\frac{30}{25}$

8. 5 to 8 10 to 16; 15 to 24; 20 to 32; 25 to 40

Write each ratio in simplest form.

9. 18:24 **2:3**

10. 35 to 14 **5 to 2**

11. 20:15 **4:3**

12. 24 to 72 **1 to 3**

13. 42:14 **3:1**

14. 50 to 75 **2 to 3**

15. 30:45 **2:3**

16. 28 to 35 **4 to 5**

Complete each set of equivalent ratios.

17. $\frac{8}{3} = \frac{\square}{64}$ **64**

18. $\frac{6}{21} = \frac{\square}{2}$ **2**

19. $\frac{13}{52} = \frac{1}{\square}$ **4**

Problem Solving

20. Three copies of a book cost $20. Write an equivalent ratio to show the cost of 9 copies.

   Show Your Work

   9 to $60

Copyright © Houghton Mifflin Company. All rights reserved.

Use with text pages 486–487.

ENGLISH LEARNERS 18.2

Name _____ Date _____

English Learners 18.2

Equivalent Ratios

Pedro is a painter. He mixes colors of paints to make new colors. Today he will mix blue paint and yellow paint to make green paint. He must use one part of blue for every two parts of yellow. A "part" can be any amount—one drop or one gallon—but it must stay the same as he mixes his paint.

Pedro's green paint = 1 part blue to 2 parts yellow. The ratio is 1 to 2. This may also be written as 1:2 or $\frac{1}{2}$.

Equivalent ratios are ratios that mean the same thing. The chart below shows equivalent ratios for Pedro's green paint. Fill in the blank sections of the chart with ratios or pictures.

Equivalent Ratios for Pedro's Green Paint		
Parts of Blue Paint	Parts of Yellow Paint	Ratio
PAINT	PAINT PAINT	1:2
PAINT PAINT	PAINT PAINT PAINT PAINT	**2:4**
PAINT PAINT PAINT	**six cans of paint**	3:6
PAINT PAINT PAINT PAINT	**eight cans of paint**	4:8

The **simplest form** of a ratio is the one with the smallest numbers. In the chart above, 1:2 is the simplest form.

For each set of equivalent ratios, circle the simplest form.

1. 2:6 **(1:3)** 4:12

2. 3:12 6:24 **(1:4)**

3. 4:10 **(2:5)** 6:15

Copyright © Houghton Mifflin Company. All rights reserved.

Use with text pages 486–487.

Homework Workbook Page 120

TEACHING LESSON 18.2

LESSON ORGANIZER

Objective Use multiplication and division to find equivalent ratios.

Resources Reteach, Practice, Enrichment, Problem Solving, Homework, English Learners

Materials None

Activity

Warm-Up Activity
Greatest Common Factor

👥 Whole Group	⏱ 5 minutes	Kinesthetic, Visual

Write the following on the chalkboard:

Factors of 18: <u>1</u>, __, __, __, __, __, __, __

Factors of 24: <u>1</u>, __, __, __, __, __, __, __

- **Let's find all the factors of 18 and 24. Is 1 a factor of 18?** (yes, 1 × 18) Fill in the following on the chalkboard:

  Factors of 18: <u>1</u>, __, __, __, __, __, __, <u>18</u>

- **Is 2 a factor of 18?** (yes, 2 × 9) Fill in the following on the chalkboard:

  Factors of 18: <u>1</u>, <u>2</u>, __, __, __, __, <u>9</u>, <u>18</u>

- Continue filling in all the factors of 18. Repeat for the factors of 24. Circle the common factors. Draw a box around the greatest common factor.

Equivalent Ratios

Objective Use multiplication and division to find equivalent ratios.

Vocabulary
equivalent ratio
simplest form

Learn About It
MathTracks 2/20
Listen and Understand

Melinda wants to paint her little sister's dollhouse. She has chosen a color that requires 4 parts of red for every 12 parts of yellow. The ratio of red to yellow is $\frac{4}{12}$.

If Melinda uses 8 parts of red, how many parts of yellow will she need? If Melinda uses 2 parts of red, how many parts of yellow will she need?

You can find an **equivalent ratio** for $\frac{4}{12}$ that has 8 as its first term. Then you can find an equivalent ratio for $\frac{4}{12}$ that has 2 as its first term.

Different Ways to Find Equivalent Ratios

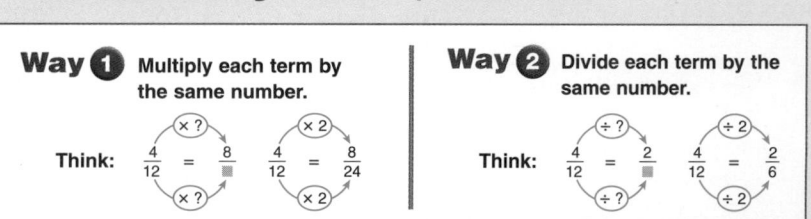

Way 1 Multiply each term by the same number.

Think: $\frac{4}{12} = \frac{8}{\blacksquare}$ $\frac{4}{12} = \frac{8}{24}$

Way 2 Divide each term by the same number.

Think: $\frac{4}{12} = \frac{2}{\blacksquare}$ $\frac{4}{12} = \frac{2}{6}$

Solution: If Melinda uses 8 units of red, she will need 24 units of yellow. If Melinda uses 2 units of red, she will need 6 units of yellow.

▶ A ratio is in **simplest form** when 1 is the only number that divides each term with no remainder. To write a ratio in simplest form, divide each term by its greatest common factor (GCF).

Write $\frac{12}{16}$ in simplest form.

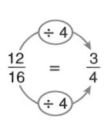

$\frac{12}{16} = \frac{3}{4}$

> Think
> $12 = 2 \times 2 \times 3$
> $16 = 2 \times 2 \times 2 \times 2$
> 2 × 2, or 4, is the GCF.

The simplest form of $\frac{12}{16}$ is $\frac{3}{4}$.

486

---

1 Introduce

- Write *10 : 15, 2 : 3,* and *6 : 9* on the chalkboard. **How would you read these ratios aloud?** (10 to 15; 2 to 3; 6 to 9)

- **Which numbers are the first terms in each ratio?** (10; 2; 6) **Which are the second terms?** (15; 3; 9)

- Have students write each ratio as a fraction. ($\frac{10}{15}$; $\frac{2}{3}$; $\frac{6}{9}$) **What do you notice about these fractions?** (They are equivalent.) **Which is in simplest form?** ($\frac{2}{3}$) **Which ratio is in simplest form?** (2 : 3)

Explain that when the ratio 10 : 15 is written as 2 : 3, it is in its simplest form.

2 Develop

Guide students through the *Learn About It* section.

- **Look at Way 1. When you see 4 and 8 as the first terms in the two equivalent ratios, what can you say to yourself to find the number to multiply by?** (4 times what number is 8?)

- **What is the greatest common factor of 12 and 16?** (4) Write on the board: $\frac{12}{16} \div \frac{4}{4} = \frac{3}{4}$. **To write the simplest form of a ratio such as 12 : 16, divide each term by the greatest common factor of both terms.**

Guided Practice

Have students complete **Exercises 1–4** as you observe. Remind them to use the *Ask Yourself* question to help. Give students the opportunity to talk about the question in *Explain Your Thinking.*

Complete the equivalent ratio: $\frac{4}{6} = \frac{\blacksquare}{9}$.

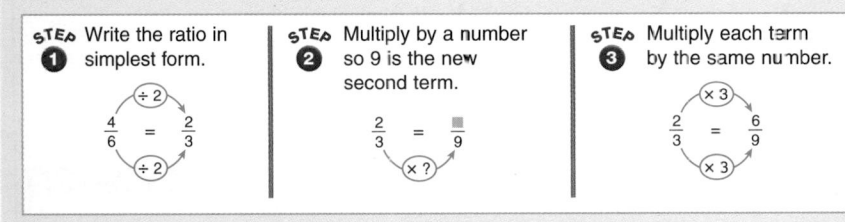

STEP 1 Write the ratio in simplest form.	STEP 2 Multiply by a number so 9 is the new second term.	STEP 3 Multiply each term by the same number.
$\frac{4}{6} = \frac{2}{3}$ (÷2)	$\frac{2}{3} = \frac{\blacksquare}{9}$ (×?)	$\frac{2}{3} = \frac{6}{9}$ (×3)

Solution: $\frac{4}{6} = \frac{6}{9}$.

Guided Practice

Write four equivalent ratios for each.

Ask Yourself
• Did I multiply or divide both terms by the same number?

TEST TIPS

1. $\frac{4}{8}$
   $\frac{1}{2}, \frac{2}{4}, \frac{8}{16}, \frac{12}{24}$

2. 8 to 12
   $\frac{2}{3}, \frac{4}{6}, \frac{6}{9}, \frac{10}{15}$

3. 6:15
   $\frac{2}{5}, \frac{4}{10}, \frac{8}{20}, \frac{10}{25}$

4. $\frac{20}{25}$
   $\frac{4}{5}, \frac{8}{10}, \frac{12}{15}, \frac{16}{20}$

TEST TIPS **Explain Your Thinking** ▶ How would you write 6:15 in simplest form? How did you get your answer?
2:5; I found the GCF of the two terms which is 3 and divided it into each term.

Practice and Problem Solving

Write four equivalent ratios for each.

5. $\frac{1}{3}$
   $\frac{2}{6}, \frac{3}{9}, \frac{4}{12}, \frac{5}{15}$

6. 5 to 6
   $\frac{10}{12}, \frac{15}{18}, \frac{20}{24}, \frac{25}{30}$

7. 1:5
   $\frac{2}{10}, \frac{3}{15}, \frac{4}{20}, \frac{5}{25}$

8. 10 to 4

9. 10:16
   $\frac{5}{8}, \frac{15}{24}, \frac{20}{32}, \frac{30}{48}$

10. $\frac{6}{3}$
   $\frac{2}{1}, \frac{4}{2}, \frac{8}{4}, \frac{10}{5}$

Write each ratio in simplest form.

11. $\frac{10}{40}$ $\frac{1}{4}$

12. 6:18 $\frac{1}{3}$

13. 24 to 42 $\frac{4}{7}$

14. 12:60 $\frac{1}{5}$

15. $\frac{16}{36}$ $\frac{4}{9}$

16. 28:32 $\frac{7}{8}$

X Algebra • Equations Complete each set of equivalent ratios.

17. $\frac{1}{4} = \frac{\blacksquare}{12}$ 3

18. $\frac{8}{24} = \frac{\blacksquare}{6}$ 2

19. $\frac{15}{25} = \frac{9}{\blacksquare}$ 15

20. $\frac{6}{9} = \frac{\blacksquare}{12}$ 8

Daily Review	Test Prep
Multiply. (Ch. 13, Lessons 4–5)	✓ 27. Complete the equivalent ratio:
21. 0.09×0.8 **0.072**	$\frac{20}{24} = \frac{\blacksquare}{6}$.
22. 3.2×0.6 **1.92**	
23. 0.21×0.9 **0.189**	A 4
24. 8.34×4.7 **39.198**	C 80
25. 0.002×0.6 **0.0012**	Ⓑ 5
26. 0.03×0.03 **0.0009**	D 120

Extra Practice See page 503, Set B.

Chapter 18 Lesson 2   487

DAILY TEST PREP

Test Prep Transparency 18.2

List 5 ratios equivalent to $\frac{12}{30}$. (Possible answers: $\frac{2}{5}, \frac{4}{10}, \frac{48}{120}, \frac{8}{20}, \frac{20}{50}$; also $\frac{6}{15}$)

Activity

Lesson Intervention

Visualizing Equivalent Ratios

Or use Intervention CD-ROM Lesson 18.2

iiii Whole Group	🕐 5–10 minutes	Tactile, Visual

Materials: *for each student: 6 red and 12 yellow counters, paper folded into fourths*

• Write the following on the chalkboard: *1 yellow : 2 red*. Tell students to model this ratio with counters on the left side of their paper.

• Next, write on the chalkboard: *2 yellow : 4 red*. Have them model this ratio with counters on the right side of their paper. **We multiply both terms of the first ratio by 2 to make the equivalent ratio $\frac{2}{4}$.**

• Repeat this activity beginning with 3 red : 6 yellow. Ask students to show the equivalent ratio 1 red : 2 yellow. **By what number can we divide both terms 3 and 6 to make the equivalent ratio $\frac{1}{2}$?** (3) Have students clear the right side ratio. **Show another ratio equivalent to $\frac{3}{6}$.** ($\frac{6}{12}$)

---

③ Practice

Assign **Exercises 5–27** as independent work.

• *Problem Solving for Problems 5–10* To extend Problems 5–10, ask students how many equivalent ratios can be found using multiplication. (an infinite number)

Common Error

Incorrectly multiplying or dividing to find equivalent ratios
Remind students that to find an equivalent ratio, you multiply or divide the ratio by 1, or $\frac{n}{n}$. Have students draw models of each ratio to check their answers.

④ Assess and Close

• Write $\frac{3}{9} = \frac{15}{45}$ on the chalkboard. **How can you check to see if the ratio $\frac{3}{9}$ is equivalent to $\frac{15}{45}$?** (Look at the first term of each: 3 and 15. Ask: *3 times what is 15?* Since 3 times 5 is 15, use 5 to check the second term. *9 times 5 is 45* and so $\frac{3}{9}$ is equivalent to $\frac{15}{45}$.)

• **How do you know if $\frac{3}{9}$ is in simplest form?** (Look at each term. If the only factor that divides each is 1, the ratio is in simplest form. Since 3 and 9 are divisible by 3, $\frac{3}{9}$ is *not* in simplest form.)

Assign the **LESSON QUIZ** on Transparency 18.2 to further assess student understanding.

 **Keeping a Journal**

Have students write a rule for finding equivalent ratios.

PLANNING THE LESSON

MATHEMATICS OBJECTIVE
Compare two quantities with different units.

Use Lesson Planner CD-ROM for Lesson 18.3.

Daily Routines

Vocabulary

Write on the chalkboard: $\frac{7,000 \text{ m}}{7 \text{ km}} \cdot \frac{1,000 \text{ m}}{1 \text{ km}}$
Explain that the rate 1,000 m per km is a
unit rate because the second term is 1.

Vocabulary Cards

Meeting North Carolina's Standards

5.03 Identify, describe, and analyze situations with
constant or varying rates of change.

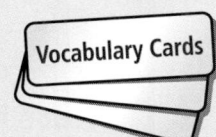

Lesson
Transparency

18.3

Problem of the Day
Write two fractions whose numerators are 1
and whose sum is $\frac{1}{2}$. (Possible answer: $\frac{1}{3}, \frac{1}{6}; \frac{1}{4}, \frac{1}{4}$)

Quick Review

Find the value of *x*.

1. $\frac{2}{5} = \frac{x}{40}$ (16)

2. $\frac{1}{6} = \frac{5}{x}$ (30)

3. $\frac{x}{20} = \frac{12}{40}$ (6)

4. $\frac{3}{x} = \frac{18}{30}$ (5)

5. $\frac{24}{8} = \frac{x}{1}$ (3)

6. $\frac{9}{10} = \frac{45}{x}$ (50)

7. $\frac{25}{5} = \frac{x}{1}$ (5)

8. $\frac{5}{8} = \frac{50}{x}$ (80)

9. $\frac{7}{x} = \frac{42}{48}$ (8)

Lesson Quiz

Find the unit rate.

1. 60 cars : 5 min = ▮ cars : 1 min (12)

2. 750 mi : 2 h = ▮ mi : 1 h (375)

3. \$8.32 : 16 oz = \$ ▮ : 1 oz (0.52)

LEVELED PRACTICE

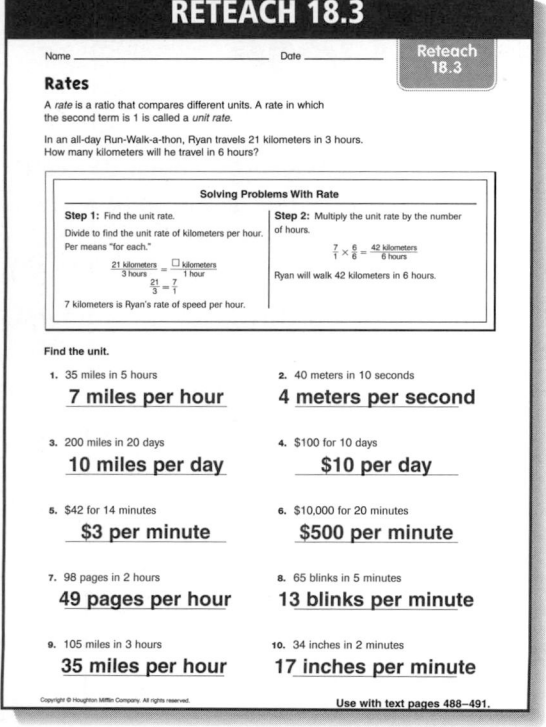

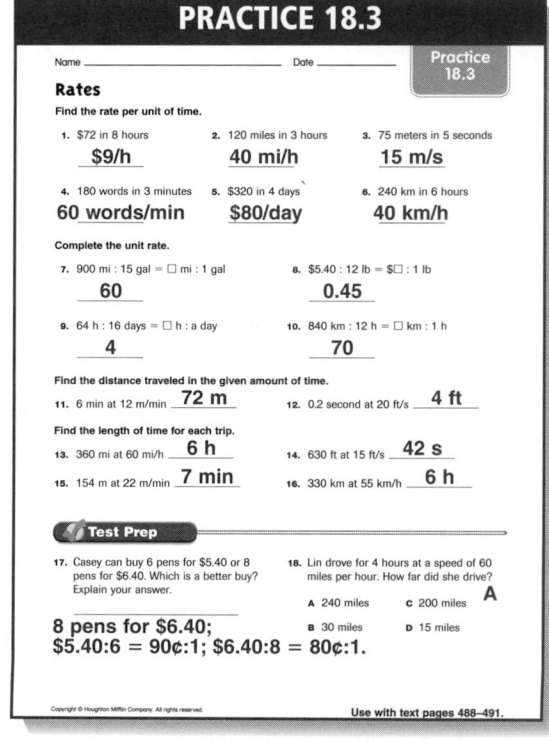

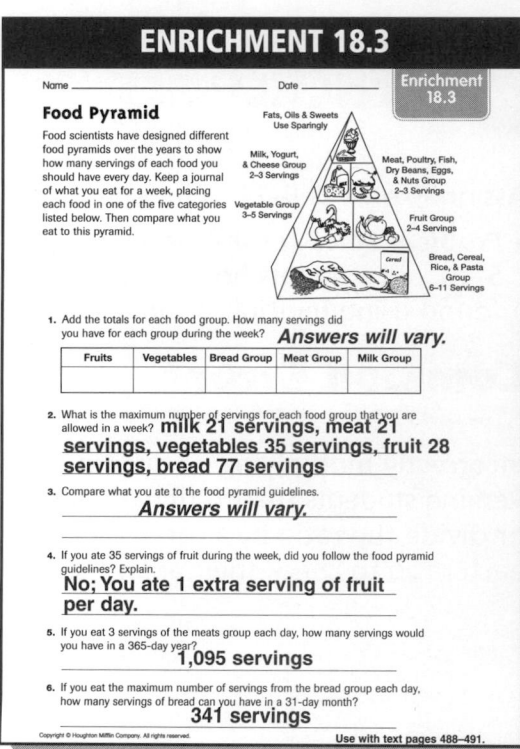

Practice Workbook Page 121

Reaching All Learners
Differentiated Instruction

English Learners

Worksheet 18.3 introduces students to the concept of rate (a kind of ratio) and to the language used in word problems to describe rates.

Special Needs
VISUAL, AUDITORY

- **Suppose a turtle crawls at a rate of one inch per minute.** On the chalkboard write: 1 in./min. **We call this a** *unit rate.* **It indicates how far the turtle goes in one minute. When used with rates,** *unit* **means "one of something."**

- **How far would the turtle go in five minutes?** (5 in.) Write: 5 in./5 min. **Suppose it goes 2 inches in one minute. Write:** *unit rate:* 2 in./min.

Early Finishers
VISUAL, TACTILE

Materials: *newspaper grocery advertisements*

- Have them fold a sheet of paper in thirds lengthwise. Ask them to label and complete the columns in the following way:

  Col. 1 (Item): Apples
  Col. 2 (Unit Price):
  Col. 3 (Price for multiple units):

- Have students complete the chart for 20 items.

Social Studies Connection

Hiking the Appalachian Trail
Materials: *simple East Coast map showing the Appalachian Trail*

- Explain where the Appalachian Trail is and its historical importance. Write on the chalkboard: *The trail is 2,160 miles. The average hiker walks 2 miles/hour. Many hikers cover 8–10 miles a day.*

- Help students calculate the hours it would take to hike the entire trail at that rate of speed walking 5 hours/day; 7 hours/day. Have partners use the map to show starting and ending points and rate of travel. Have them figure out how long it would take them to reach 2 or 3 locations along the way.

TECHNOLOGY

Spiral Review

Help students remember skills they learned earlier by creating **customized** spiral review worksheets using the *Ways to Assess* CD-ROM.

Lesson Planner

You can use the Lesson Planner CD-ROM to create a report of the lessons and standards you have taught.

eBook

eMathBook allows students to review lessons and do homework without carrying their textbooks home.

Houghton Mifflin
Math

e**MathBook**

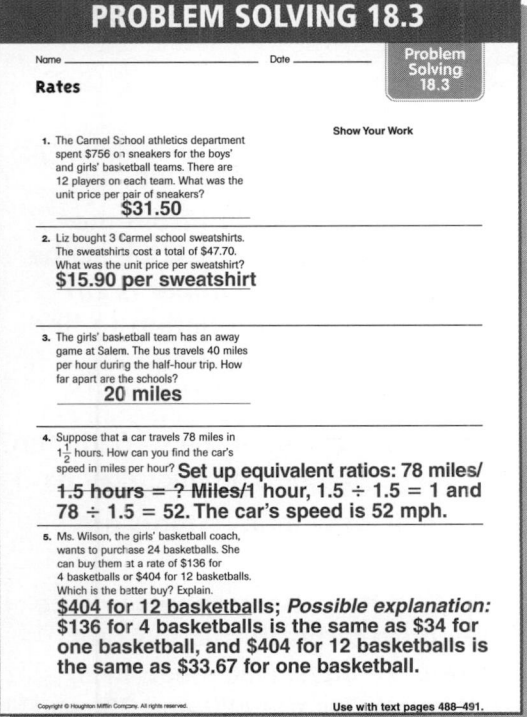

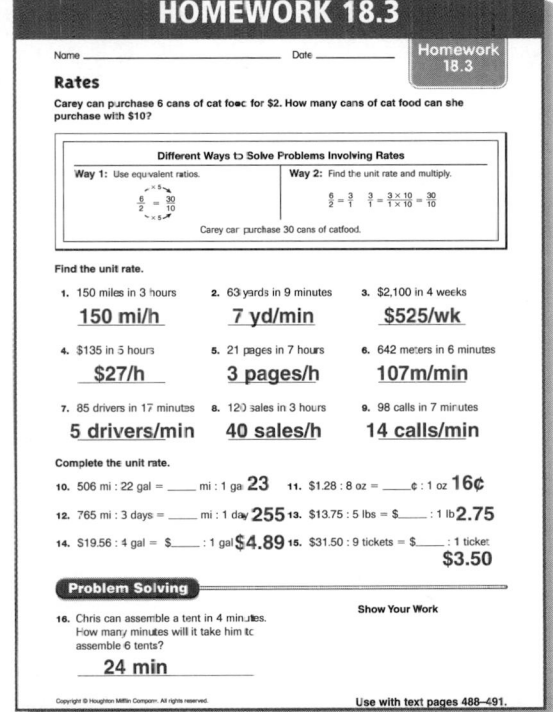

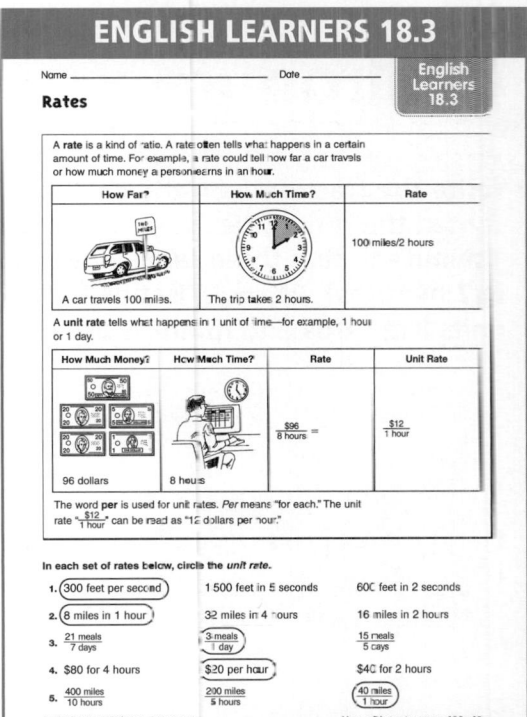

TEACHING LESSON 18.3

LESSON ORGANIZER

Objective Compare two quantities with different units.

Resources Reteach, Practice, Enrichment, Problem Solving, Homework, English Learners, Transparencies, Math Center

Materials Number Line 2 from the Number Line Transparency

Activity

Warm-Up Activity
Simplest Forms of Fractions

| 👥 Whole Group | ⏱ 5 minutes | Visual, Auditory |

- Write the following on the chalkboard:
  $\frac{12}{18}, \frac{49}{70}, \frac{7}{21}, \frac{32}{64}, \frac{14}{30}, \frac{9}{45}$

- **How do you know if a fraction is in simplest form?** (The only common factor of the numerator and the denominator is 1.)

- **What is the simplest form of each of the fractions on the chalkboard?** ($\frac{2}{3}, \frac{7}{10}, \frac{1}{3}, \frac{1}{2}, \frac{7}{15}, \frac{1}{5}$) As students suggest the answers, write them on the chalkboard.

Rates

Objective Compare two quantities with different units.

Glossary
Vocabulary
rate
unit rate
per
speed

Learn About It

A **rate** is a ratio that compares numbers expressed in different units. A rate in which the second term is 1 is called a **unit rate**.

A toy factory produces 120 robots in 5 days. At this rate, how many robots will it produce in 20 days?

Different Ways to Solve Problems With Rates

Way ❶ Use equivalent ratios.

 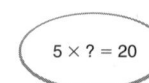 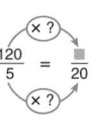 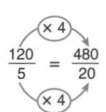

$\frac{120 \text{ robots}}{5 \text{ days}} = \frac{\blacksquare \text{ robots}}{20 \text{ days}}$ $5 \times ? = 20$ $\frac{120}{5} = \frac{\blacksquare}{20}$ $\frac{120}{5} = \frac{480}{20}$

Way ❷ Find the unit rate and multiply.

STEP ❶ Divide to find the unit rate in robots per day. **Per** means "for each."

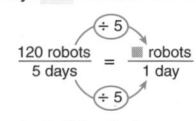

$\frac{120 \text{ robots}}{5 \text{ days}} = \frac{\blacksquare \text{ robots}}{1 \text{ day}}$

The rate is 24 robots per day.

STEP ❷ Multiply by the number of days.

$\frac{24 \text{ robots}}{1 \text{ day}} = \frac{480 \text{ robots}}{20 \text{ days}}$

Solution: The factory will produce 480 robots in 20 days.

Other Examples

A. Speed as a Unit Rate

A car travels 220 miles in 4 hours. Find the unit rate in miles per hour.

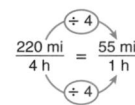

$\frac{220 \text{ mi}}{4 \text{ h}} = \frac{55 \text{ mi}}{1 \text{ h}}$

A rate that shows distance per unit of time is called **speed**. A slash, /, is often used for the word *per*.

The rate is 55 miles per hour, or 55 mi/h.

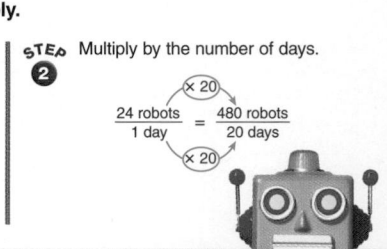

488

---

❶ Introduce

- Write the fraction $\frac{1}{3}$ on the chalkboard. **Suppose $\frac{1}{3}$ represented the ratio *time in minutes to cards signed*. If it takes 1 minute to sign three cards, how many cards can be signed in 7 minutes?** (21 cards) Ratios that compare two different units like cards and minutes are called *rates.*

❷ Develop

Guide students through the *Learn About It* section.

- **Look at Way 1. Notice how the information from the problem is written as two equivalent ratios. Look at the two terms, 5 and 20. Say, *5 times what number is 20?* 5 times 4 is 20. How do you use this information to find the missing number?** (Multiply the first term by the same number: 120 times 4 equals 480.)

- **Look at Way 2. Why is 1 the second term of the second ratio?** (It shows the unit rate, or number of robots produced per day.)

- **If 24 robots are made in 1 day, how many robots are made in 2 days?** (48)

- **Look at Way 2, Step 2. To find how many robots will be made in 20 days, multiply both terms in the unit rate $\frac{24 \text{ robots}}{1 \text{ day}}$ by 20. Write the rate $\frac{480}{20}$ days.** (480 robots in 20 days) **How is the line that separates the 480 and 20 read?** (When talking about rate, the line is read as *per* or *in*.)

B. Use Speed to Find Time

How long will it take to travel 450 km at a rate of 90 km/h?

$$\frac{90 \text{ km}}{1 \text{ h}} = \frac{450 \text{ km}}{? \text{ h}}$$

It will take 5 hours.

C. Rates With Money

A worker receives $75 for 6 hours of work. What is the rate of pay per hour?

$$\frac{\$75}{6 \text{ h}} = \frac{\$?}{1 \text{ h}}$$

The rate is $12.50 per hour.

Guided Practice

Find the unit rate.

Ask Yourself
• Did I write the units?
• Is my answer reasonable?

TEST TIPS

1. 30 toys in 10 days
   3 toys/d
2. $20 in 4 hours
   $5/h
3. 60 meters in 5 seconds
   12 m/s
4. $1,000 in 5 days
   $200/d
5. 100 miles in 4 hours
   25 mi/h
6. 50 km in 5 hours
   10 km/h

TEST TIPS **Explain Your Thinking ▶** How can you use division to find any unit rate?
Divide the first term by the second term.

Practice and Problem Solving

Find the unit rate.

7. 80 miles in 16 min
   5 mi/min
8. 72 ft in 9 seconds
   8 ft/s
9. 108 meters in 18 min
   6 m/min
10. 160 pages in 8 days
    20 pages/d
11. $100 in 5 hours
    $20/h
12. $56 in 7 hours
    $8/h

Complete the unit rate.

13. 400 mi:16 gal = $\overset{\textbf{25}}{\blacksquare}$ mi:1 gal

14. 84¢:12 copies = $\overset{\textbf{7}}{\blacksquare}$ ¢:1 copy

15. $6:2 oz = $$\overset{\textbf{3}}{\blacksquare}$:1 oz

16. 437 mi:23 gal = $\overset{\textbf{19}}{\blacksquare}$ mi:1 gal

17. 1,394 people:34 square miles = $\overset{\textbf{41}}{\blacksquare}$ people:1 square mile

18. 288 photos:12 rolls of film = $\overset{\textbf{24}}{\blacksquare}$ photos:1 roll of film

Find the distance traveled in the given amount of time.

19. 5 hours at 50 mi/h
    250 mi
20. 3 min at 9 m/min
    27 m
21. 12 seconds at 16 ft/s
    192 ft
22. 0.5 hour at 30 mi/h
    15 mi
23. 7 days at 25 mi/day
    175 mi
24. 2.5 hours at 40 km/h
    100 km

Go On ▶

 **Quick Check Options**

The following activities will help students prepare for the Quick Check or may be used as an alternative assessment.

Vocabulary Review *(individual, small group, or whole class)*

Have students review the following vocabulary words by giving an example of how each term is used in this chapter.

- terms
- ratio
- equivalent ratio
- simplest form
- rate
- unit rate
- per
- speed

Math Conversations *(small group or whole class)*

Have students discuss what they have learned about ratios and rates in this chapter. Encourage students to ask each other questions to clarify their understanding.

Writing Prompt *(individual or partners)*

To solidify student understanding of vocabulary and concepts, have each student complete the following sentence:

The most useful thing I have learned about ratios and rates is _____.

---

3 Practice

Guided Practice

Have students complete **Exercises 1–6** as you observe. Remind them to use the *Ask Yourself* questions to help. Give students the opportunity to talk about the question in *Explain Your Thinking*.

Assign **Exercises 7–41** as independent work.

Encourage students to develop the habit of writing rates vertically. The relationship between the following rate and its corresponding unit rate emerge when the phrase *80 mi in 16 min* is written this way: $\frac{80 \text{ mi}}{16 \text{ min}} = \frac{\blacksquare}{1 \text{ min}}$

DAILY TEST PREP

Mark eats 1,800 grams of protein in 30 days. He eats equal protein amounts each day. How many protein grams does he eat per day? (D)

A. 54,000 g/day   C. 900 g/15 days

B. 600 g/day   D. 60 g/day

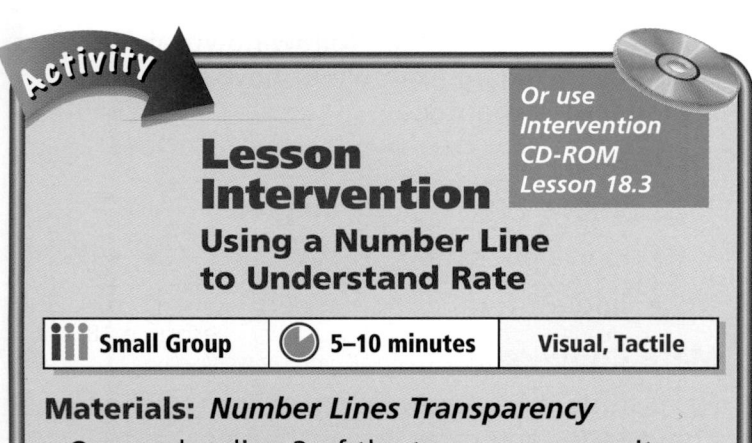

Activity

Or use Intervention CD-ROM Lesson 18.3

Lesson Intervention

Using a Number Line to Understand Rate

| 👥 Small Group | 🕐 5–10 minutes | Visual, Tactile |

Materials: *Number Lines Transparency*

- On number line 2 of the transparency write "Meters" at the upper far left. Then label from left to right, 0, 10, 20, 30, 40, 50, 60. Below far left, write "Seconds." Label the space between tick marks with looping right-facing arrows. Label each arrow: 1, 2, 3, 4, 5, 6.

- Use the number line to explain unit rate. **Boat A travels 60 meters in 6 seconds. The boat travels at a constant rate. It travels 10 meters in 1 second, 20 meters in 2 seconds, 30 meters in 3 seconds, and 60 meters in 6 seconds. The unit rate is 10 meters/second.**

Find the length of time for each trip.

25. 200 mi at 50 mi/h
    4 h
26. 75 km at 25 km/h
    3 h
27. 1,500 ft at 30 ft/s
    50 s
28. 225 mi at 45 mi/h
    5 h
29. 252 ft at 12 ft/sec
    21 s
30. 175 m at 35 m/min
    5 min

✗ Algebra • Variables

Use the rate of 140 toy robots produced in 5 days to complete each rate.

31. $\frac{224}{n}$ robots in 8 days
32. $\frac{56}{n}$ robots in 2 days
33. $\frac{14}{n}$ robots in 0.5 days
34. 420 robots in $\frac{15}{n}$ days
35. 350 robots in $\frac{12.5}{n}$ days
36. 490 robots in $\frac{17.5}{n}$ days

📖 **Data** Use the advertisement for Problems 37–40.

37. To the nearest cent, what is the unit price of an action figure? **$4.19 per figure**

38. Which has a greater price per game, the Action Games package or the Software 5-Game package? What is the difference between the two unit prices? **Software; $0.45**

39. Which package of building blocks has a greater price per block, the 75-block pack or the 125-block bucket? To the nearest cent, what is the difference between the two unit prices? **75-block pack; 2¢**

40. **You Decide** Suppose you play a game in which you need at least 50 Can-Do Canned Zoo animals. How would you buy the animals? To the nearest cent, what is the unit rate per animal? **See below.**

41. **What's Wrong?** Hal's car travels 450 miles on 15 gallons of gas. Hal calculated that he would need 63,000 gallons for a 2,100-mile trip. What did Hal do wrong? **See Additional Answers on Page 503.**

40. *Check students' work. Possible answer:* 1 barrel of 30 animals, 2 barrels of 12 animals; 92¢ per animal

ACTION GAMES
4-Game package
$98

ACTION FIGURES
Pack of 4
$16.75

BUILDING BLOCKS
75-Block pack
$15.89
125-Block bucket
$23.50

SOFTWARE
5-Game package
$124.75

CAN-DO CANNED ZOO
Barrel of 12 animals
$11.50
Barrel of 30 animals
$26.75

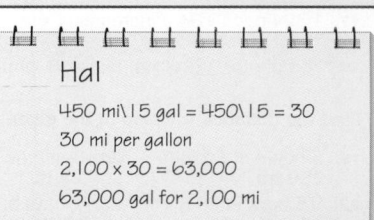

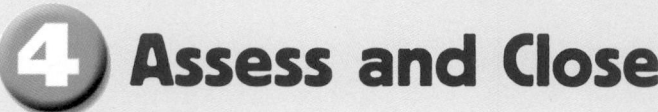

Hal
450 mi\15 gal = 450\15 = 30
30 mi per gallon
2,100 × 30 = 63,000
63,000 gal for 2,100 mi

Extra Practice See page 503, Set C.

---

4 Assess and Close

Practice *continued*

Problem Solving for Problems 37–41 Explain to students that a *unit price* is the unit rate or the price for one item. For example, toothbrushes selling as 2 for $3.00 have a unit price of $1.50 per toothbrush.

Common Error

Writing equivalent ratios Watch for students who set up ratios incorrectly. Remind students if the first ratio represents $\frac{hours}{game}$, the second ratio must also be $\frac{hours}{game}$.

Write on the chalkboard: *A car travels 280 miles in 4 hours. Moving at a constant rate, how far will it travel in 6 hours?*

- **What are you being asked?** (miles traveled in 6 hours) **How do you write "It takes 4 hours to travel 280 miles," as a rate?** ($\frac{280\ miles}{4\ hours}$) **How do you find the unit rate of travel?** (Divide the miles, 280, by the hours, 4, to find 70 miles/hour.)

- **What two equivalent ratios show how far the car travels in 6 hours?** ($\frac{4\ hours}{280\ miles} = \frac{6\ hours}{\blacksquare\ miles}$) **How far does the car travel?** (420 miles)

Assign the **LESSON QUIZ** on Transparency 18.3 to further assess student understanding.

Quick Check

Check your understanding for Lessons 1–3.

Write each ratio three different ways. (Lesson 1)

1. circles to rectangles **5 to 3; 5:3; $\frac{5}{3}$**

2. rectangles to circles **3 to 5; 3:5; $\frac{3}{5}$**

3. pentagons to circles **1 to 5; 1:5; $\frac{1}{5}$**

4. pentagons to other shapes **1 to 8; 1:8; $\frac{1}{8}$**

Write four equivalent ratios for each. (Lesson 2) *Possible answers given.*

5. $\frac{2}{7}$ $\frac{4}{14}$; $\frac{6}{21}$; $\frac{8}{28}$; $\frac{10}{35}$

6. 8 to 10 **$\frac{4}{5}$, $\frac{12}{15}$, $\frac{16}{20}$, $\frac{20}{25}$**

7. 6:2 **$\frac{3}{1}$, $\frac{9}{3}$, $\frac{12}{4}$, $\frac{15}{5}$**

8. 12 to 9 **$\frac{4}{3}$; $\frac{8}{6}$; $\frac{16}{12}$; $\frac{24}{18}$**

Complete the unit rate. (Lesson 3)

9. 252 mi:9 gal = ■ mi:1 gal **28**

10. $3.48:6 cans = $■:1 can **0.58**

Math Challenge

Heart Smart   *Check tables.*

Complete the following activity in order to determine your heart rate for a minute, an hour, a day, and a week.

The easiest place to find your pulse is on the side of your neck.

STEP 1 Make the following table.

Time	10 seconds	1 minute	1 hour	1 day	1 week
Number of ♥ beats at rest					
Number of ♥ beats after exercise					

STEP 2 Take your pulse for 10 seconds. Based on your 10-second heart rate, fill in the first row of your table.

STEP 3 *Let's exercise!!* Do as many jumping jacks as you can in 1 minute.

STEP 4 Take your pulse for 10 seconds. Based on your 10-second heart rate after exercising, fill in the second row of your table.

Quick Check

Quick Check

Purpose: The Quick Check allows you to assess the students' understanding of the concepts presented in Lessons 1–3.

Items	Objectives Tested	Pages	Intervention
1–4	Read, write, and simplify ratios.	484–485	Reteach Resource 18.1 *Ways to Success* 18.1
5–8	Use multiplication and division to find equivalent ratios.	486–487	Reteach Resource 18.2 *Ways to Success* 18.2
9–10	Compare two quantities with different units.	488–491	Reteach Resource 18.3 *Ways to Success* 18.3

Keeping a Journal

Have students write a rule for finding unit rates.

Math Challenge

Heart Smart

Share these facts about heart rate and the human circulatory system with students before they complete the activity.

- Pulse is the volume of blood pumped per beat of the heart. The human circulatory system continually pumps about 5 quarts of blood through the body. The heart rate is often used to measure health.

- Every quart of blood contains about 2 cups of a liquid called plasma. The rest is red blood cells. One drop of blood contains about 4,600,000 red blood cells per cubic millimeter. The average life span of a red blood cell is 120 days.

- The larger the animal, the slower the rate—a whale: 8 beats/minute; a mouse: 650 beats/minute.

Lesson 18.4

Proportions

PLANNING THE LESSON

MATHEMATICS OBJECTIVE

Learn what a proportion is, how to form cross products, and whether two ratios form a proportion.

Use Lesson Planner CD-ROM for Lesson 18.4.

Daily Routines

Vocabulary

Tell students that 36 slices of bread will make 12 club sandwiches. **How would you write this *ratio*?** ($\frac{36}{12}$) **Based on this, how many slices of bread would yo need to make 8 club sandwiches?** (24 slices) **How would you write this *ratio*?** ($\frac{24}{8}$) So, that means that $\frac{36}{12} = \frac{24}{8}$. A *proportion* is a statement that two ratios are equal.

Vocabulary Cards

Meeting North Carolina's Standards

Prepare for Grade 6 Objective **5.04** Use graphs, tables, and symbols to model and solve problems involving rates of change and ratios.

Lesson
Transparency
18.4

Problem of the Day

Emilio is comparing prices of pencils. One package of 8 pencils costs $0.56. Another package of 6 pencils costs $0.48. Which package is the better buy? (the package of 8 pencils)

Quick Review

Complete.

1. 5 ft = ___ in. (60)
2. 4 lb = ___ oz (64)
3. 30 cm = ___ dm (3)
4. 5 kg = ___ g (5,000)
5. ___ ft = 9 yd (27)

Lesson Quiz

Solve each proportion.

1. $\frac{2}{9} = \frac{18}{n}$ (81)
2. $\frac{64}{100} = \frac{a}{25}$ (16)
3. $\frac{1}{5} = \frac{k}{30}$ (6)

LEVELED PRACTICE

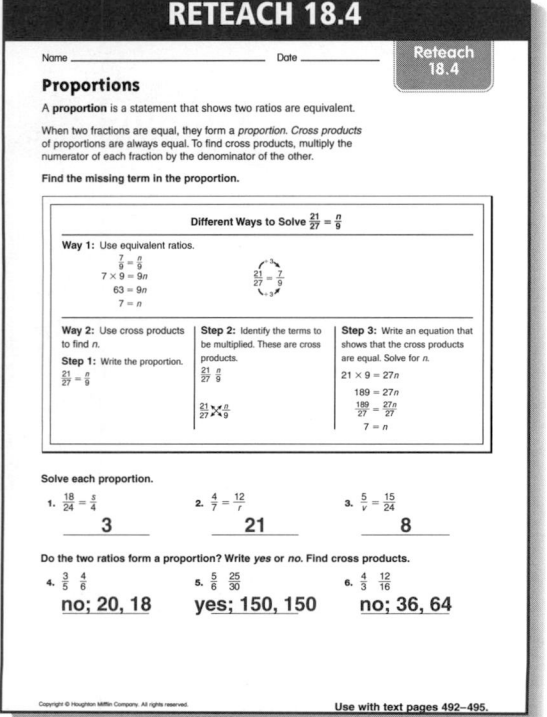

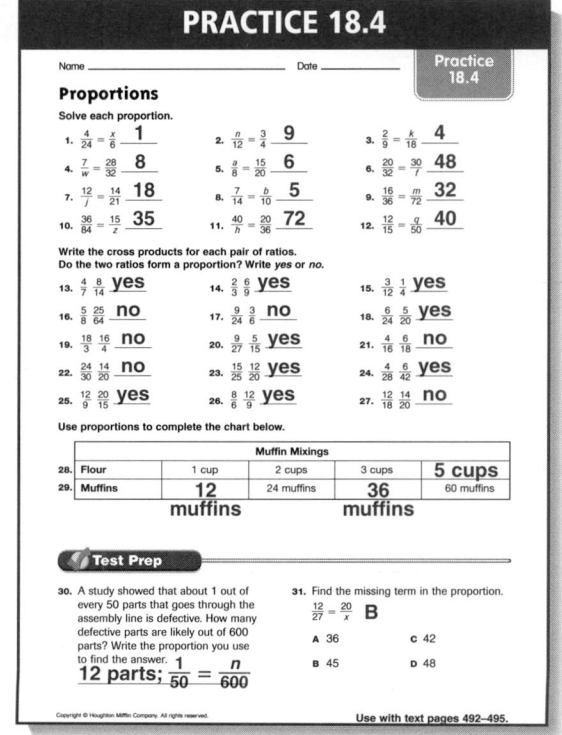

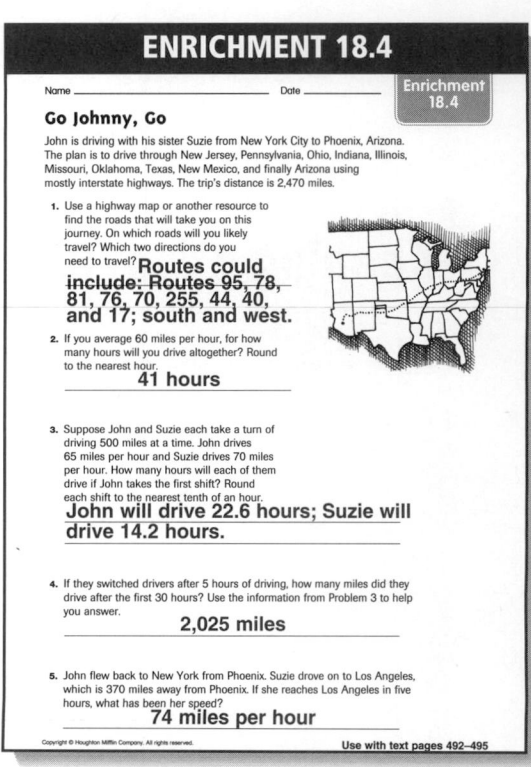

Practice Workbook Page 122

Reaching All Learners

Differentiated Instruction

English Learners

Worksheet 18.4 reviews words and symbols used to express ratios, defines *proportion,* and gives students practice interpreting word problems that involve proportions.

Inclusion
VISUAL, AUDITORY

- Display $\frac{3}{4}$ and $\frac{6}{8}$. **Are these fractions equivalent?** (yes)
- Then display $\frac{3}{4} \times \frac{6}{8}$. Trace over the cross-arrows as you explain finding cross products.
- Display $\frac{2}{3} \times \frac{8}{12}$. Have students come to the chalkboard and trace with their fingers to show you how they arrive at the cross product. Explain that finding cross products is a shortcut for finding equivalent fractions.

Gifted and Talented
VISUAL, TACTILE

Materials: *pattern blocks*

Have students use pattern blocks to make a square quilt pattern.

- Have them write a ratio that describes their pattern.
- Then have them write a word problem about their pattern that a proportion can solve.
- Ask students to exchange problems and solve.

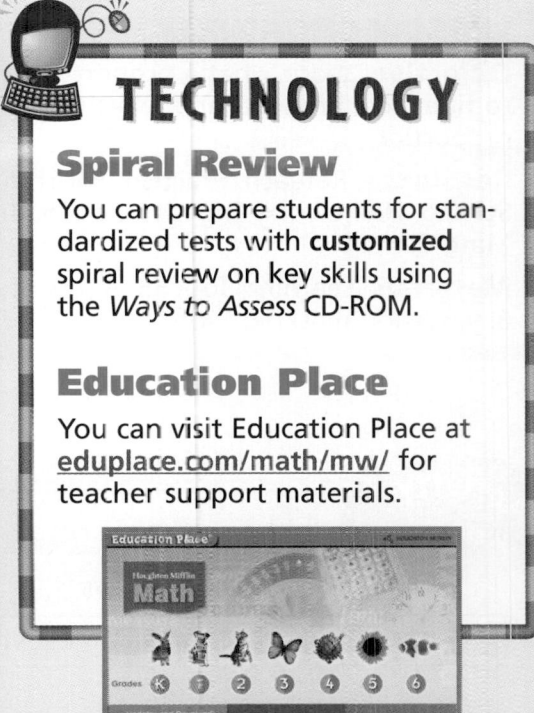

TECHNOLOGY

Spiral Review

You can prepare students for standardized tests with **customized** spiral review on key skills using the *Ways to Assess* CD-ROM.

Education Place

You can visit Education Place at eduplace.com/math/mw/ for teacher support materials.

Art Connection

Proportional Figures

Materials: *centimeter grid paper Learning Tool 13, color pencils*

- Challenge students to see how many proportional rectangles they can draw on a page. Have them shade each

one in a different color. Have them think up a title for their artwork.

- Have students write a ratio for the length and width of each rectangle. Have them check the cross products of the ratios to see if their rectangles are truly proportional to one another.

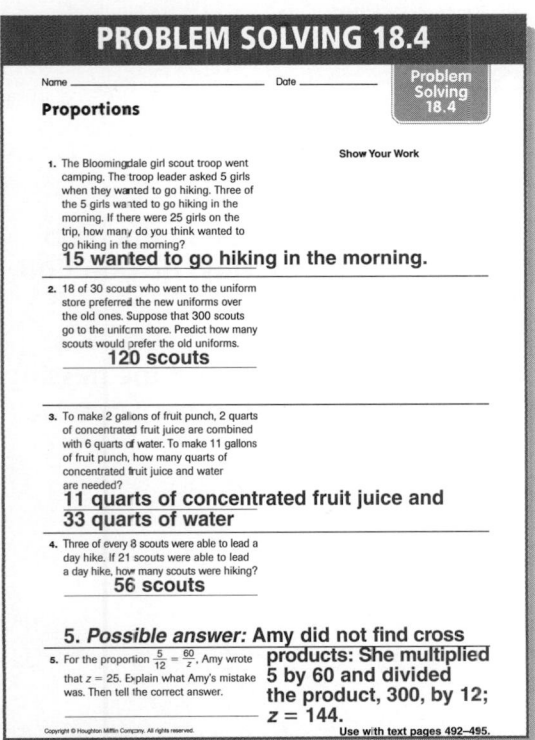

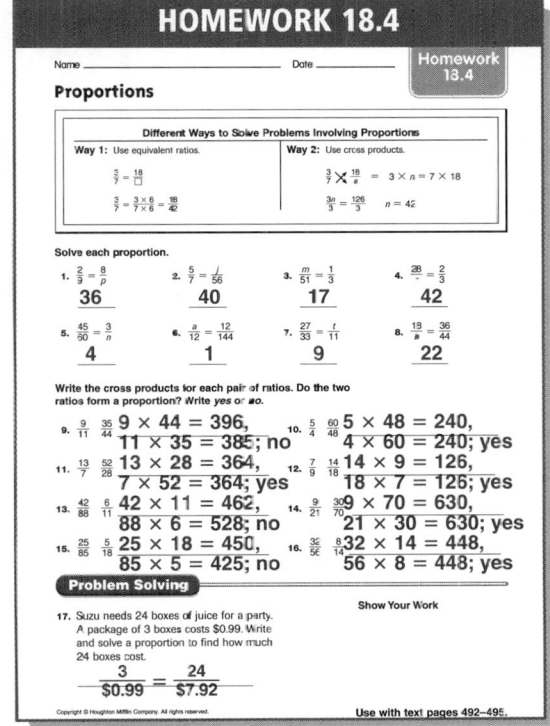

Homework Workbook Page 122

TEACHING LESSON 18.4

LESSON ORGANIZER

Objective Learn what a proportion is and how to find cross products and whether ratios form a proportion.

Resources Reteach, Practice, Enrichment, Problem Solving, Homework, English Learners, Transparencies, Math Center

Materials Learning Tool 55, 4 sets of Learnig Tool 6, yardstick, masking tape

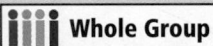

Warm-Up Activity
Finding Ratios

🏃 Whole Group	⏱ 5 minutes	Visual, Auditory

Write the information from the problem on the chalkboard as you read it.

- *A necklace is made up of 12 beads and is strung with 1 white bead between every 3 gray beads.*

- Have a student come to the chalkboard and draw the necklace. **What is the ratio of white beads to all beads?** (3 : 12)

- **Suppose the necklace is 48 beads long. How many white beads are needed?** Have students extend the drawing. (12 white beads)

Algebra
Proportions

Objective Learn what a proportion is and how to find cross products.

Learn About It 🎧 MathTracks 2/21
Listen and Understand

Martin and Tina are playing a word game. In Martin's group of tiles, the ratio of vowel tiles to his total tiles is 5 to 9. This is the same as the ratio of vowel tiles to the total tiles in the game. The game has a total of 81 tiles. How many vowel tiles does the game have?

To solve the problem, you can write a proportion. A **proportion** is a statement that two ratios are equivalent.

Martin's vowel tiles → $\dfrac{5}{9} = \dfrac{n}{81}$ ← vowel tiles in the game
Martin's total tiles → ← total tiles in the game

Solve for n. $\dfrac{5}{9} = \dfrac{n}{81}$

Different Ways to Solve $\dfrac{5}{9} = \dfrac{n}{81}$

Way ❶ Use equivalent ratios.

$\dfrac{5}{9} = \dfrac{\blacksquare}{81}$ $9 \times ? = 81$

Way ❷ Use cross products.

STEP ❶ Write the proportion.

$\dfrac{5}{9} = \dfrac{n}{81}$

STEP ❷ Identify the terms to be multiplied. These are the **cross products**.

 $\rightarrow 9 \times n$
$\rightarrow 5 \times 81$

STEP ❸ Write an equation that shows cross products are equal. Solve for n.

$5 \times 81 = 9 \times n$
$\dfrac{405}{9} = \dfrac{9 \times n}{9}$
$45 = n$

Solution: The game has 45 vowel tiles.

492

---

① Introduce

- **In mathematics, the *cross product* is the product you get when you multiply *across* a proportion.** On the chalkboard, write: $\dfrac{2}{5}$ and $\dfrac{8}{20}$. Draw the cross marks between the ratios and put arrows to show the direction you are multiplying. **20 times 2 equals 40. Write 40 over the 2. 8 times 5 equals 40. Write 40 over the 8. If the cross products of two ratios are equal, it means that the ratios are equivalent. When two ratios are equivalent, we say they form a** *proportion.*

② Develop

Guide students through the *Learn About It* section.

- **Look at Way 1. Notice how the information in the problem is written as two equivalent ratios. How do you find the missing term in the second ratio?** (Look at the two terms that are there: 9 and 81. Say, "9 times what number is 81?") **How do you use this information to find the missing number?** (Multiply both terms by the same number. Since you multiply 9 by 9 to get 81, multiply 5 by 9 to get 45.)

Dina says that you can use $\frac{18}{48}$ and $\frac{3}{8}$ to form a proportion. Is she correct? You can use cross multiplication to find out if two ratios form a proportion.

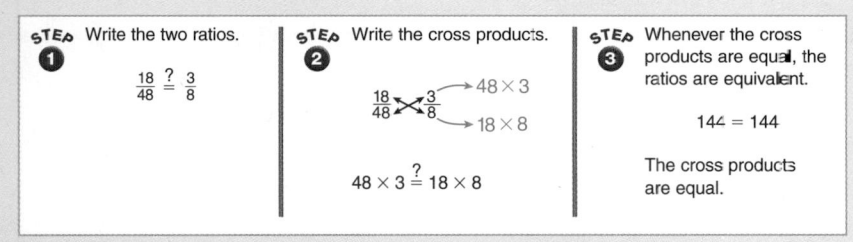
Is $\frac{18}{48} = \frac{3}{8}$ a proportion?

Do $\frac{18}{48}$ and $\frac{3}{8}$ form a proportion?

STEP 1 Write the two ratios.	**STEP 2** Write the cross products.	**STEP 3** Whenever the cross products are equal, the ratios are equivalent.
$\frac{18}{48} \overset{?}{=} \frac{3}{8}$	$\frac{18}{48} \times \frac{3}{8}$ $\begin{array}{l} 48 \times 3 \\ 18 \times 8 \end{array}$ $48 \times 3 \overset{?}{=} 18 \times 8$	$144 = 144$ The cross products are equal.

Solution: Since the cross products are equal, the ratios are equivalent, and therefore, form a proportion.

Another Example

Find Another Term

$\frac{15}{18} = \frac{10}{t}$ Cross multiply. $\frac{15}{18} \times \frac{10}{t}$ $\begin{array}{l} 18 \times 10 \\ 15 \times t \end{array}$

Cross products are equal. $15 \times t = 180$

Solve for t. $\frac{15 \times t}{15} = \frac{180}{15}$ $t = 12$

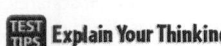

Solve each proportion.

1. $\frac{18}{24} = \frac{a}{8}$ $a = 6$ 2. $\frac{t}{20} = \frac{9}{15}$ $t = 12$ 3. $\frac{6}{30} = \frac{2}{b}$ $b = 10$

Ask Yourself
- Did I write the cross products correctly?
- Are the cross products equal?

Write the cross products for each pair of ratios. Do the two ratios form a proportion? Write *yes* or *no*.

4. $\frac{3}{8}, \frac{12}{40}$ 5. $\frac{12}{8}, \frac{3}{2}$ 6. $\frac{5}{6}, \frac{10}{18}$
no, $8 \times 12 \neq 3 \times 40$ yes, $8 \times 3 = 12 \times 2$ no, $5 \times 18 \neq 6 \times 10$

Explain Your Thinking ▶ How can you tell if the ratios $\frac{6}{9}$ and $\frac{8}{12}$ form a proportion?

Possible answer: Write the cross products 6×12 and 9×8 and determine whether they are equal.

Go On

Chapter 18 Lesson 4 **493**

- **Look at Way 2, Step 1. If the first term in one ratio relates to vowel tiles, which term in the equivalent ratio also has to relate to vowel tiles?** (the first)

- **Look at Way 2, Step 2. What do you do when you multiply cross products?** (Multiply diagonally: 5×81 and $9 \times n$.)

- The cross products are equal and can be written as the equation $5 \times 81 = 9 \times n$. **What is the first thing you must do to solve for n?** (multiply) Now you have $405 = 9n$. **What is the next thing you must do to solve for n?** (Divide each side by 9.)

Guided Practice

Have students complete **Exercises 1–6** as you observe. Remind them to use the *Ask Yourself* questions to help. Give students the opportunity to talk about the question in *Explain Your Thinking.*

DAILY TEST PREP

An Olympic level sprinter can run the 100-meter dash in 10 seconds. The same sprinter can run the 400-meter event in 44 seconds. Are the two speeds proportional? (The ratios are not equivalent. $\frac{100 \text{ m}}{10 \text{ s}} \neq \frac{400 \text{ m}}{44 \text{ s}}$)

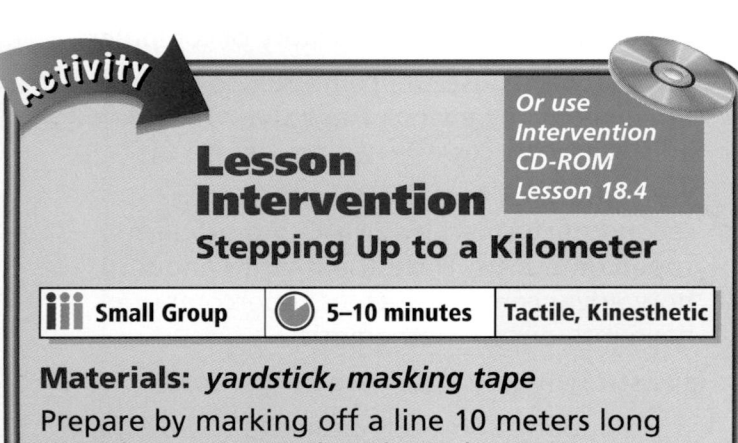

Activity

Lesson Intervention

Or use Intervention CD-ROM Lesson 18.4

Stepping Up to a Kilometer

| 👤👤👤 Small Group | ⏱ 5–10 minutes | Tactile, Kinesthetic |

Materials: *yardstick, masking tape*

Prepare by marking off a line 10 meters long (3.28 feet = 1 meter) with masking tape.

- On the chalkboard, write: *1,000 meters = 1 kilometer.*

- Have students record how many paces it takes to walk 10 meters. Tell students that a pace is counted every time the right foot touches the ground. Have them write a ratio that compares number of paces to 10 meters.

- Have them find the number of paces needed to walk 100 meters and 1,000 meters. Help them set up ratios and find cross products.

Practice and Problem Solving

Solve each proportion.

7. $\frac{5}{15} = \frac{h}{3}$ $h = 1$
8. $\frac{4}{9} = \frac{12}{n}$ $n = 27$
9. $\frac{k}{16} = \frac{4}{8}$ $k = 8$
10. $\frac{12}{j} = \frac{6}{2}$ $j = 4$

11. $\frac{32}{24} = \frac{8}{f}$ $f = 6$
12. $\frac{w}{7} = \frac{8}{8}$ $w = 7$
13. $\frac{14}{20} = \frac{a}{30}$ $a = 21$
14. $\frac{16}{y} = \frac{14}{35}$ $y = 40$

15. $\frac{9}{20} = \frac{m}{100}$ $m = 45$
16. $\frac{36}{48} = \frac{21}{v}$ $v = 28$
17. $\frac{q}{12} = \frac{14}{24}$ $q = 7$
18. $\frac{s}{90} = \frac{16}{60}$ $s = 24$

Write the cross products for each pair of ratios. Do the two ratios form a proportion? Write *yes* or *no*.

19. $\frac{3}{5}, \frac{9}{15}$
$3 \times 15 = 5 \times 9$; yes
20. $\frac{6}{18}, \frac{1}{3}$
$6 \times 3 = 18 \times 1$; yes
21. $\frac{3}{8}, \frac{9}{32}$
$3 \times 32 \neq 8 \times 9$; no
22. $\frac{15}{20}, \frac{3}{5}$
$15 \times 5 \neq 20 \times 3$; no

23. $\frac{8}{24}, \frac{3}{9}$
$8 \times 9 = 24 \times 3$; yes
24. $\frac{10}{12}, \frac{24}{30}$
$12 \times 24 \neq 10 \times 30$; no
25. $\frac{3}{12}, \frac{9}{36}$
$12 \times 9 = 3 \times 36$; yes
26. $\frac{12}{3}, \frac{2}{2}$
$12 \times 2 \neq 3 \times 6$; no

27. $\frac{32}{40}, \frac{6}{10}$
$32 \times 10 \neq 40 \times 6$; no
28. $\frac{15}{27}, \frac{25}{45}$
$15 \times 45 = 27 \times 25$; yes
29. $\frac{42}{28}, \frac{12}{8}$
$42 \times 8 = 28 \times 12$; yes
30. $\frac{4}{7}, \frac{16}{21}$
$4 \times 21 \neq 7 \times 16$; no

31. $\frac{20}{5}, \frac{16}{4}$
$20 \times 4 = 5 \times 16$; yes
32. $\frac{40}{48}, \frac{12}{16}$
$40 \times 16 \neq 48 \times 12$; no
33. $\frac{9}{6}, \frac{15}{10}$
$9 \times 10 = 6 \times 15$; yes
34. $\frac{10}{8}, \frac{25}{16}$
$10 \times 16 \neq 8 \times 25$; no

📊 **Data** Use the table for Problems 35–37.

At the right are the results of a survey of two fifth grade classes. Six students did not respond to the survey.

35. **Predict** Suppose 350 students are in your school. Based on the survey, about how many of those students would you expect to choose Gem Star 5? **63**

36. Suppose there are 500 students in a school. Predict how many more students would choose Good Knight than Final Race. **40**

37. **Create and Solve** Write and solve a problem in which the data from the survey and proportions are used. *Check students' problems.*

38. **Estimate** A survey of 239 voters shows that 148 people plan to vote for McAllen for Mayor. About 10,000 people are expected to vote. About how many do you think will vote for McAllen? *Estimates will vary. Possible estimate:* **about 6,000**

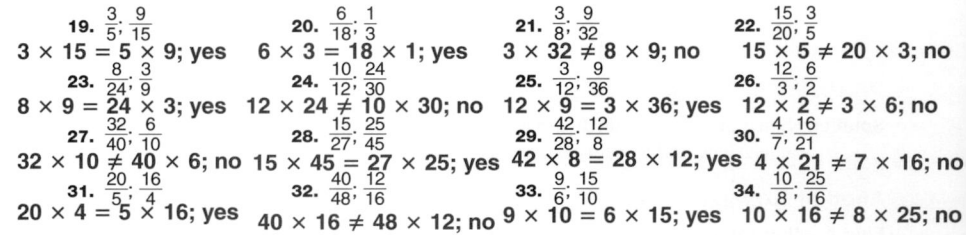

Favorite Computer Game	
Name of Game	**Chosen by**
City Builder	15 of 50 students
Gem Star 5	9 of 50 students
Good Knight	12 of 50 students
Final Race	8 of 50 students

Check students' drawings. **Drawings should show 12 green squares and 15 red squares.**

39. **Represent** Nick draws 4 green squares and 5 red squares. Draw a group of 27 squares in which the ratio of green squares to red squares is equivalent to the ratio shown in Nick's drawing.

494

Extra Practice See page 503, Set D.

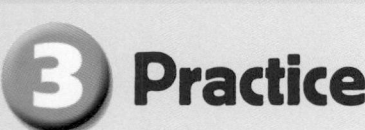

Practice

Assign **Problems 7–44** as independent work.

Problem Solving for Problems 7–18 Encourage students to solve for the variable as shown in either Way 1 or Way 2 of the lesson.

Problem Solving for Problems 35–37 For the purposes of this lesson, ask students to assume that the sampling method noted is representative of the entire student body.

Common Error

Solving proportions Watch for students who fail to completely solve for the variable. Some students will multiply cross products but forget to divide.

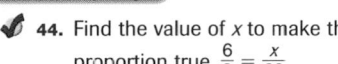

Possible estimates.
Exact answers are given.
Estimate. Then add or subtract. (Ch. 10,
Lessons 1, 4, and 8)

8;

40. $12\frac{7}{8} - 5\frac{1}{8}$ **$7\frac{3}{4}$**

18;

41. $9\frac{1}{2} + 8\frac{3}{10}$ **$17\frac{4}{5}$**

42. $20\frac{1}{10} - 7\frac{4}{5}$ **13;**
$12\frac{3}{10}$

43. $6\frac{3}{4} + 9\frac{7}{8}$ **17;**
$16\frac{5}{8}$

 **44.** Find the value of x to make the
proportion true. $\frac{6}{8} = \frac{x}{32}$

A $x = 18$ **C** $x = 22$

B $x = 20$ **(D)** $x = 24$

Practice GAME

Proportion Pushups

Practice making proportions by playing this game with a partner or several
friends. Two to six can play. Try to be the first person to score 10 points.

2 Players

What You'll Need • 2 proportion cards (Learning Tool 55)
• 4 sets of number cards, numbered 1–9 (Learning Tool 6)

Here's What to Do

1 Shuffle the number cards. Deal 4 cards
facedown to each player. Place the
next two cards faceup on the
Proportion Card (Learning Tool 55).

2 Each player, in turn, tries to use 2
cards to make a proportion.

• If a correct proportion is made,
that player scores 2 points.
• If an incorrect proportion is made,
the other players score 1 point.
• If no proportion is made, the
player scores 0 points.

Reshuffle all cards and repeat Steps 1 and 2.
The first player to score 10 points wins.

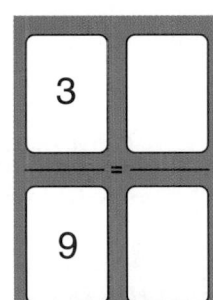

 **Practice GAME**

Proportion Pushups

Materials: *2 proportion cards (Learning
Tool 55; 4 sets of number cards,
numbered 1–9*

How to Play:

• Have students read and follow the directions. Help them make a scoring sheet
divided into 4 columns with headings:
student name, 2 points, 1 point, 0 points.

• Extend the game by having students make
4 sets of number cards 10–20 and add these
to the mix of cards.

---

4 Assess and Close

Write the following ratios on the chalkboard: $\frac{9}{40}$ and $\frac{3}{12}$.
**What is the first step in deciding if these two ratios form a
proportion?** (Use cross products.)

• **What are the cross products?** ($9 \times 12 = 108$ and $3 \times 40 = 120$)

• **How can you tell if these two ratios form a proportion?**
(If the cross products are equivalent, they form a proportion.)

• **Do $\frac{9}{40}$ and $\frac{3}{12}$ form a proportion?** (No)

Assign the **LESSON QUIZ** on Transparency 18.4 to further
assess student understanding.

 **Keeping a Journal**

Have students explain how solving problems with
proportions can help solve problems involving room
floor plans or house plans.

Similar Figures and Scale Drawings

PLANNING THE LESSON

MATHEMATICS OBJECTIVE
Use equivalent ratios to interpret scale drawings.

Use Lesson Planner CD-ROM for Lesson 18.5.

Daily Routines

Vocabulary

What does "to draw something to scale" mean? What are some examples of *scale drawings?* (maps, architectural drawings) What do we use to compare the size of an object to its size in a drawing? (a ratio) A *scale* is a ratio that compares the measurements in a drawing to the measurements of the actual object.

Vocabulary Cards

Meeting North Carolina's Standards

Prepare for Grade 7 Objective **3.02** Identify, define, and describe similar and congruent polygons with respect to angle measures, length of sides, and proportionality of sides.

Lesson Transparency

18.5

Problem of the Day
Luther spent $3.25 on soft drinks. He spent three times this amount on snacks. He spent double the cost of drinks and snacks on a gift for his father. Did Luther spend less or more than $40.00 on his father's party? (less than)

Quick Review
Write an expression describing each situation.
1. 20 divided by y $\left(\frac{20}{y}\right)$
2. The product of 5 and 3 (5×3)
3. 15 more than k $(k + 15)$
4. 4 times 3 times j $(4 \times 3 \times j)$
5. 12 less than 36 $(36 - 12)$

Lesson Quiz
Use the scale 1 in. : 3 ft to find r.
1. 4 in. in the drawing represents r ft. (12)
2. 12 in. in the drawing represents r ft. (36)
3. r in. in the drawing represents 90 ft. (30)
4. r in. in the drawing represents 150 ft. (50)

LEVELED PRACTICE

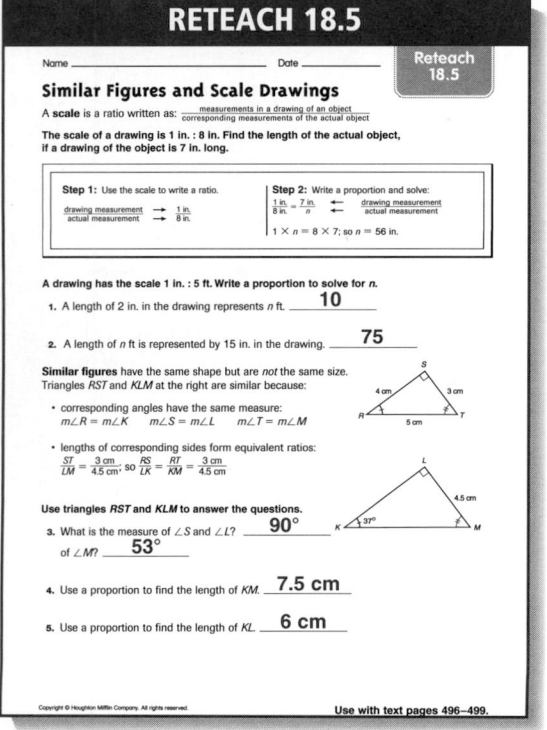

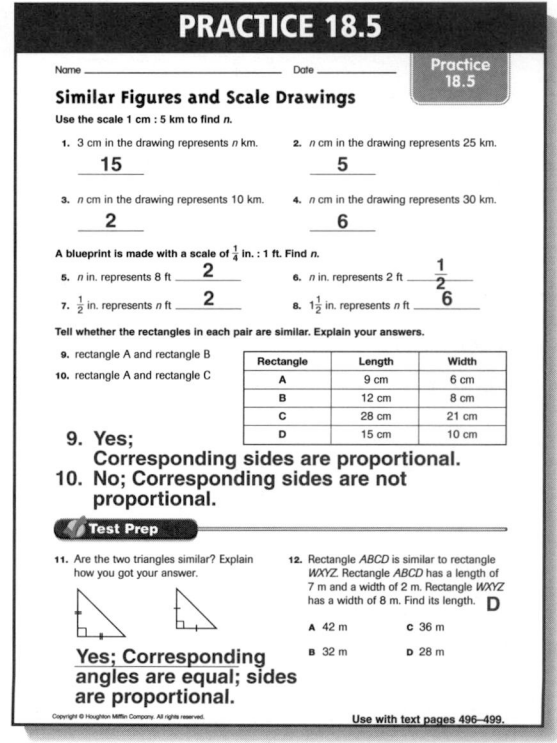

Practice Workbook Page 123

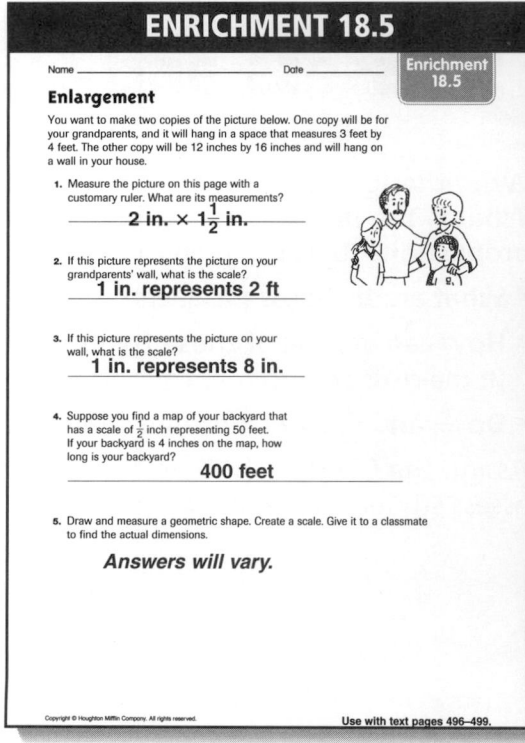

Reaching All Learners

Differentiated Instruction

English Learners

Worksheet 18.5 uses pictures and text to introduce the concepts of similar figures and scale drawings.

Special Needs
VISUAL, AUDITORY

Materials: *Centimeter Grid Transparency*

- On a blank transparency, draw a 2 cm × 4 cm rectangle and a 4 cm × 8 cm rectangle. Label corresponding sides and angles.
- Overlay the centimeter grid to measure each side length and show each angle measure of 90°. Discuss how to prove that the rectangles are proportional to each other, or *similar figures*.

Early Finishers
VISUAL, TACTILE

Materials: *centimeter ruler, protractor*

- Display: *Draw three polygons each on a separate paper: Pentagon: Angles = 108°; Octagon: Angles = 135°; Dodecagon: Angles = 150°. Make each side 4 centimeters long. Inside each figure draw a similar figure with side lengths 2 centimeters long.*
- Discuss how to determine if figures are similar.

TECHNOLOGY

Spiral Review

Create **customized** spiral review worksheets for individual students using the *Ways to Assess* CD-ROM.

Tool Software

Use *Shape Up!* or another shapes program to explore this lesson's objectives more fully.

Game

Students can practice their skills using the Robo Packer math game, available on the *Ways to Success* CD.

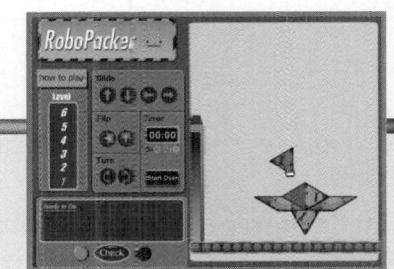

Social Studies Connection

Historical Celtic Knots
Materials: *rulers, inch and $\frac{1}{2}$ inch grid paper or Learning Tools 15 and 14, colored pencils*

- Have students research the meaning of *Celtic* as it is used today and share findings.

- Copy the Celtic knot and grid onto a transparency and display.
- Students make 3 copies: 1 actual size; 1 twice as large; 1 half-sized. They then explain how they made the drawings.

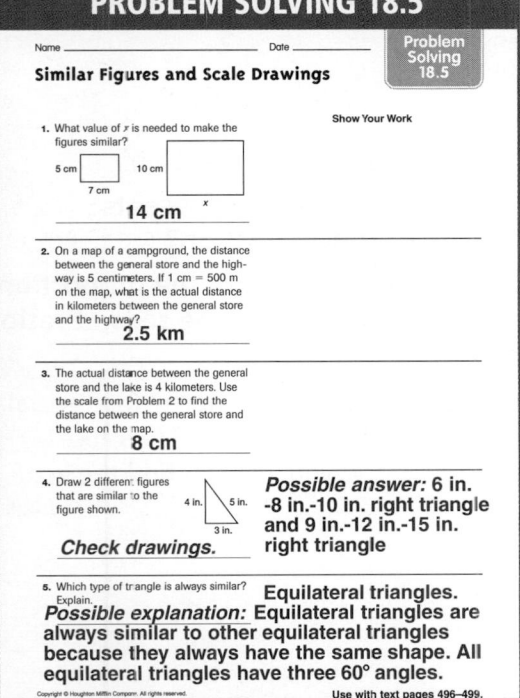

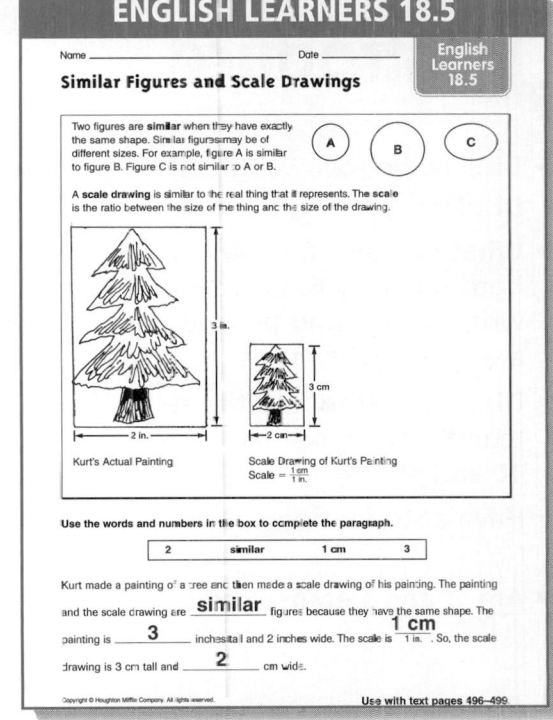

Homework Workbook Page 123

TEACHING LESSON 18.5

LESSON ORGANIZER

Objective Use equivalent ratios to interpret scale drawings.

Resources Reteach, Practice, Enrichment, Problem Solving, Homework, English Learners, Transparencies, Math Center

Materials Customary ruler, centimeter ruler, Centimeter Grid Transparency

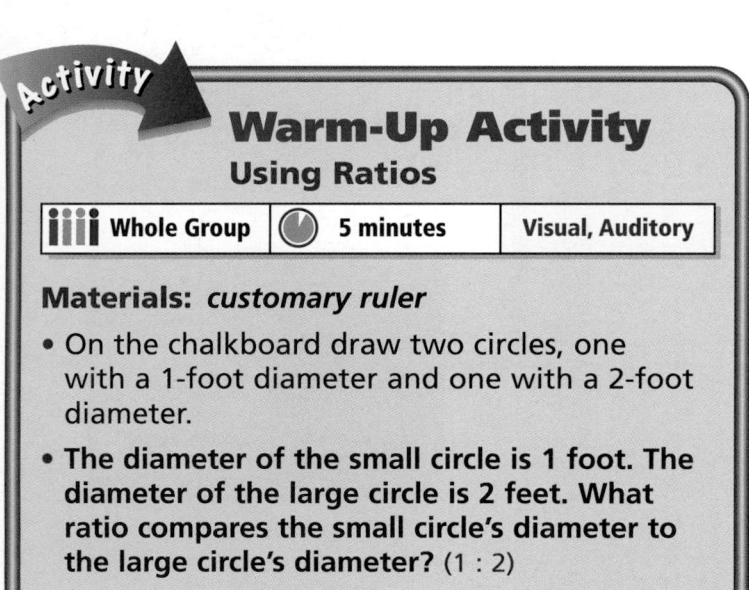

Activity

Warm-Up Activity
Using Ratios

👤👤👤👤 Whole Group	⏲ 5 minutes	Visual, Auditory

Materials: *customary ruler*

• On the chalkboard draw two circles, one with a 1-foot diameter and one with a 2-foot diameter.

• **The diameter of the small circle is 1 foot. The diameter of the large circle is 2 feet. What ratio compares the small circle's diameter to the large circle's diameter?** (1 : 2)

---

e Glossary

Vocabulary
scale drawing
scale
similar figures

Similar Figures and Scale Drawings

Objective Use equivalent ratios to interpret scale drawings.

Learn About It

A **scale** is a ratio of the measurements in a drawing of an object to the corresponding measurements of the actual object. When a drawing is created using a scale, it is called a **scale drawing.**

You can create a scale drawing by enlarging or reducing all of the actual measurements by the same factor.

Make a scale drawing of a football field using the scale 1 cm:10 yd.

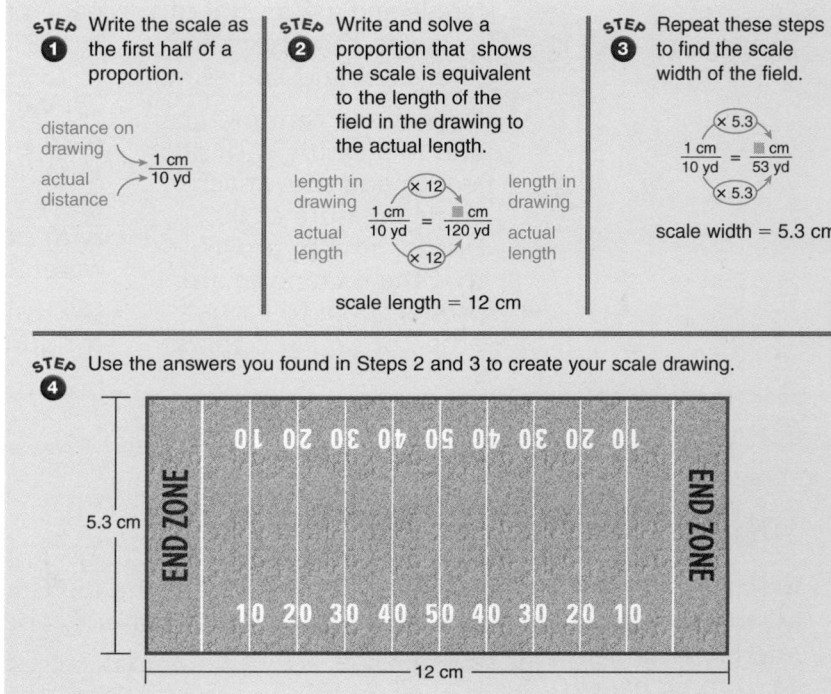

STEP 1 Write the scale as the first half of a proportion.

distance on drawing → 1 cm
actual distance → 10 yd

STEP 2 Write and solve a proportion that shows the scale is equivalent to the length of the field in the drawing to the actual length.

length in drawing → $\frac{1 \text{ cm}}{10 \text{ yd}}$ (×12) = $\frac{\blacksquare \text{ cm}}{120 \text{ yd}}$ ← length in drawing
actual length (×12) actual length

scale length = 12 cm

STEP 3 Repeat these steps to find the scale width of the field.

(× 5.3)
$\frac{1 \text{ cm}}{10 \text{ yd}} = \frac{\blacksquare \text{ cm}}{53 \text{ yd}}$
(× 5.3)

scale width = 5.3 cm

STEP 4 Use the answers you found in Steps 2 and 3 to create your scale drawing.

496

---

1 Introduce

• Display the following: $\frac{3}{4}$. **The ratio 3 to 4 is in fraction form.** Display $\frac{3 \times \square}{4 \times \square} = \frac{\square}{24}$.

• **What number can you multiply by 4 to get 24?** (6) Multiply both terms by 6. Write 6 in both boxes. Have a student write the missing product. **The ratio 3 to 4 and 18 to 24 are equivalent ratios.**

• Display $\frac{10}{15}$. **How can the ratio $\frac{10}{15}$ be simplified?** (Divide both terms by a common factor.) **What is a common factor of 10 and 15?** (5)

• Have a student demonstrate how to simplify the ratios. ($\frac{10 \div 5}{15 \div 5} = \frac{2}{3}$)

• **Are $\frac{10}{15}$ and $\frac{2}{3}$ equivalent ratios?** (yes)

2 Develop

Guide students through the *Learn About It* section.

• **Look at Step 1. Each cm in this drawing represents 10 yards. How do we write that as a fraction?** ($\frac{1 \text{ cm}}{10 \text{ yards}}$)

• **Look at Step 2. What does the first ratio in the proportion tell us?** (the scale) **What does *120 yards* in the second ratio represent?** (length of the real-life object)

• **Look at Step 3. What are you looking for here?** (the actual width of the field) **Why do we multiply by *5.3*?** (because 5.3 is the scale width of the field and you want to find the actual width)

Scale drawings and the actual figures they represent are similar figures. **Similar figures** have the same shape, but they do not have to be the same size.

If figures are similar, the lengths of their corresponding sides are proportional and the measures of their corresponding angles are equal.

The symbol ~ is read as "is similar to."

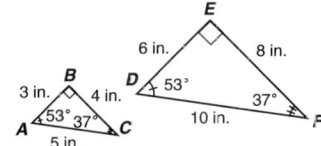

Determine whether or not the given triangles are similar.

STEP 1	STEP 2	STEP 3
Make sure all corresponding angles have equal measures. $\angle A \cong \angle D$ $\angle B \cong \angle E$ $\angle C \cong \angle F$	Write a proportion to represent the relationship between the pairs of corresponding sides. $\frac{3}{6} = \frac{4}{8} = \frac{5}{10}$	Write each ratio in simplest form. If they are equivalent, the figures are similar. $\frac{3}{6} = \frac{4}{8} = \frac{5}{10}$ $\frac{1}{2} = \frac{1}{2} = \frac{1}{2}$

Solution: $\triangle ABC \sim \triangle DEF$

Guided Practice

Ask Yourself
- Did I write a proportion?
- Did I use the correct units in my answers?

Use the scale 1 in.:5 ft to find n.

1. 4 in. in the drawing represents n ft. **20**

(Hint) in drawing → $\frac{1 \text{ in.}}{5 \text{ ft}} = \frac{4 \text{ in.}}{n \text{ ft}}$ ← in drawing / actual

2. 6 in. in the drawing represents n ft. **30**   3. n in. in the drawing represents 45 ft. **9**

Use the figures to the right to answer each question.

In the triangles, $\angle J \cong \angle P$ and $\angle K \cong \angle Q$. The measure of $\angle J$ is 53°.

4. What is the measure of $\angle P$? **53°**

5. What is the measure of $\angle K$? **37°**

6. What is the measure of $\angle Q$? **37°**

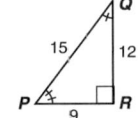

7. Write a proportion to represent the relationship between the pairs of corresponding sides. Are the ratios equivalent? Explain how you know. **7–8. See Additional Answers on page 503.**

8. Are the two triangles similar? How do you know?

Explain Your Thinking ► Can you determine if two figures are similar just by looking at them? Explain why or why not.

Go On

See Additional Answers on page 503.

Chapter 18 Lesson 5   497

Reaching All Learners

A drawing made using a scale is called a scale drawing. In a scale drawing every measure is enlarged or reduced by the same factor.

1. Have students trace their hands on centimeter grid paper (Learning Tool 13). Have them make a scale drawing of it using 1 cm for every 3 cm of the hand.

2. Is the drawing in Exercise 1 an enlargement or a reduction?

3. Make a scale drawing of your hand using a scale of 3 cm for every 1 cm of the hand? Is the drawing an enlargement or a reduction?

4. What scale would you use to make a scale drawing of your hand that is double its size?

Answers

1. Check students' drawings.

2. Reduction

3. Check students' drawings; enlargement.

4. 2 cm for every 1 cm.

Differentiated Assignments		
At Risk	**Average**	**Advanced**
Exercises 1, 2	Exercises 1–3	Exercises 1–4

• **Look at Step 1.** Ask students to point to the right angle in $\triangle ABC$ and the right angle in $\triangle DEF$. **How do you know that $\angle A$ and $\angle D$ are corresponding angles?** (Because both are located along the shortest side of each triangle adjacent to the right angle, and each has the same measure.)

• **Look at Step 2. Are the sides of the triangle equal in measure?** (no) Point to the shortest side of each triangle. **What are the measures of the shortest side of the triangles?** (3 units and 6 units) **This is the ratio $\frac{3}{6}$.**

• **Look at Step 3. Why write each side length comparison ratio in simplest form?** (to see if each figure's side lengths are proportional)

Guided Practice

Have students complete **Problems 1–8** as you observe. Remind them to use the *Ask Yourself* questions to help. Give students the opportunity to talk about the question in *Explain Your Thinking.*

CHAPTER 18 Lesson 5   497

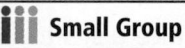
DAILY TEST PREP

The schoolyard map is made with the scale $\frac{1}{2}$ inch: 5 yards. How many yards long is the playground if it measures 7 inches on the map? (C)

A. 35 yards   C. 70 yards

B. 17.5 yards   D. $35\frac{1}{2}$ yards

Activity

Lesson Intervention

Or use Intervention CD-ROM Lesson 18.5

Seeing Scale Come to Life

| iii Small Group | ⏱ 5–10 minutes | Tactile, Kinesthetic |

Materials: *Centimeter Grid Transparency*

- On the transparency, draw a 4 cm × 16 cm rectangle. **This is a scale drawing of an object.** Write $\frac{1\,cm}{3\,ft} = \frac{4\,cm}{n\,ft}$. **Can we find the dimensions of the object with this information?** (yes)

- **Which ratio is the scale? What does this scale mean?** ($\frac{1\,cm}{3\,ft}$; Every centimeter on the scale drawing equals 3 feet.)

- **How do we find the width of the rectangle?** (solve for *n*) Have a student solve for *n*. (*n* = 12 feet)

- Write $\frac{1\,cm}{3\,ft} = \frac{16\,cm}{n\,ft}$. **How do we find the length of the rectangle?** (solve for *n*) Have a student solve for *n*. (*n* = 48 ft)

Practice and Problem Solving

Use the scale 1 cm:4 m to find *n*.

9. 2 cm in the drawing represents *n* m. **8**

10. 7 cm in the drawing represents *n* m. **28**

11. *n* cm in the drawing represents 100 m. **25**

12. *n* cm in the drawing represents 60 m. **15**

13. 6 cm in the drawing represents *n* m. **24**

14. *n* cm in the drawing represents 80 m. **20**

A blueprint is made with a scale of $\frac{1}{8}$ in.:1 ft. Find *n*.

15. *n* in. represents 5 ft. **$\frac{5}{8}$**

16. $\frac{1}{4}$ in. represents *n* ft. **2**

17. $\frac{3}{4}$ in. represents *n* ft. **6**

18. *n* in. represents 12 ft. **$1\frac{1}{2}$**

19. *n* in. represents 1.5 ft. **$\frac{3}{16}$**

20. $\frac{5}{16}$ in. represents *n* ft. **$2\frac{1}{2}$**

Tell whether the rectangles in each pair are similar. Explain your answers.
21–23. See Additional Answers on Page 503.

21. rectangle ABCD and rectangle EFGH

22. rectangle EFGH and rectangle WXYZ

23. rectangle STUV and rectangle ABCD

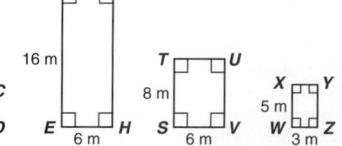

Solve.

24. An architect is making a scale drawing of a room that is 12 ft by 18 ft. He is using a scale of 1 in.:2 ft. What are the measurements of the drawing? **6 in. × 9 in.**

25. An architect's drawing of a room has a scale of 1 in.:2 ft. What are the measurements of the actual room if it is 30 in. by 16 in. in the drawing? **60 ft × 32 ft**

26. Name something that would require a scale enlargement in order for the human eye to see what the actual object looks like.

27. The official measurements of an NBA basketball court are 94 ft by 50 ft. Make a scale drawing of an NBA basketball court using the scale 1cm:10 ft.

26–27. See Additional Answers on page 503.

Daily Review	**Test Prep** 🖊
Write each quotient in simplest form. (Ch.12, Lessons 5-6)	✔ 34. **Free Response** Are these two triangles similar? Explain.
28. $6 \div 1\frac{1}{5}$ **5** 29. $1\frac{1}{3} \div 3$ **$\frac{4}{9}$**	
30. $\frac{5}{8} \div 1\frac{1}{4}$ **$\frac{1}{2}$** 31. $2\frac{3}{4} \div 3$ **$\frac{11}{12}$**	
32. $\frac{5}{6} \div 3\frac{2}{3}$ **$\frac{5}{22}$** 33. $2\frac{1}{4} \div 1\frac{3}{4}$ **$1\frac{2}{7}$**	**No, they don't have the same shape**

498

Extra Practice See page 503, Set E.

---

③ Practice

Assign **Problems 9–34** as independent work.

Problem Solving for Problems 15–20 For Problem 15, remind students that when they divide a fraction, they need to rewrite the expression, for example: $\frac{1}{4} \div \frac{1}{8} \longrightarrow \frac{1}{4} \times \frac{8}{1}$.

Problem Solving for Problems 21–27 Remind students that by definition rectangles contain four 90° angles. Since every figure has right angles, only the side lengths need to be compared in order to determine if the figures are similar.

Common Error

Transposing units Suggest students write the scale as a ratio with units and then write the corresponding quantities. They can highlight the units for each equivalent ratio to make sure they correspond. For example: $\frac{in.}{ft} = \frac{in.}{ft}$.

④ Assess and Close

- **What are the steps for making a scale drawing?** (Decide on a scale. Find the measures of the real-life object (the length and width of the room). Write a proportion of the scale and the real-life width of the object to find the width of the drawing. Repeat for length. Make the drawing.)

Assign the **LESSON QUIZ** on Transparency 18.5 to further assess student understanding.

Social Studies Connection

Map Skills

A standard orienteering course consists of a start, a series of control sites marked on the map, and a finish. The person who visits all of the control sites in the fastest time wins.

At the right, there is an example of an orienteering map. The standard scale on an orienteering map is 1 cm:15,000 cm, which is the same as 1 cm:150 m.

The map's scale is used to compare the distance on the map with the actual distance.

On the map, the distance between the start of the course and the first control site is 2 cm. What is the actual distance? Use the scale 1 cm:150 m.

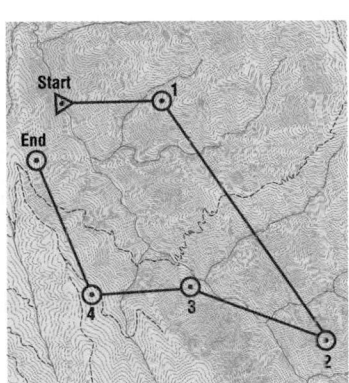

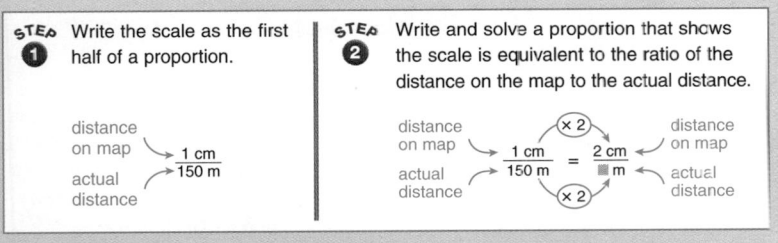

STEP 1 Write the scale as the first half of a proportion.

distance on map → 1 cm
actual distance → 150 m

STEP 2 Write and solve a proportion that shows the scale is equivalent to the ratio of the distance on the map to the actual distance.

distance on map → $\frac{1 \text{ cm}}{150 \text{ m}} = \frac{2 \text{ cm}}{\blacksquare \text{ m}}$ ← distance on map
actual distance → ← actual distance

Solution: The actual distance between the start of the course and the first control site is 300 meters.

Use the map above and a centimeter ruler to answer each question.

1. What is the distance between control site 2 and control site 3? **450 m**

2. What is the distance along the course from control site 3 to the end of the course? **750 m**

3. How much longer is it from site 4 to the end of the course than it is from the beginning of the course to site 1? **150 m**

4. **Create and Solve** Create your own problem based on the map above. Ask a partner to solve your problem. *Check students' problems*

Chapter 18 Lesson 5   499

Social Studies Connection

Map Skills

Orienteering Share the following information with students: *The sport of orienteering offers an intellectual challenge in addition to physical exercise. A key to success is to keep one's eyes open and to problem solve while in motion. One must keep track of the distance traveled through pace counting. It is also important that one is able to decipher map features such as hills and stone walls, and to match these features with the actual surroundings.*

Keeping a Journal

Have students measure their bedrooms and place a scale drawing of that room in their journal. Have them explain how they determined the scale they used for the drawing.

Problem-Solving Decision: Estimate or Exact Answer?

PLANNING THE LESSON

MATHEMATICS OBJECTIVE
Decide when to estimate or calculate an exact answer.

Use Lesson Planner CD-ROM for Lesson 18.6.

Daily Routines

Vocabulary

What does it mean to *estimate*? (Find an approximate calculation.) **What are some times when you estimate? Why?** (Accept a variety of answers.) **What are some times when you need to make an *exact* calculation? Why?** (Possible answer: how much money you have; without the right amount, you can't make the purchase.)

Vocabulary Cards

Meeting North Carolina's Standards

1.03 Develop flexibility in solving problems by selecting strategies and using mental computation, estimation, calculators or computers, and paper and pencil.

Lesson Transparency 18.6

Problem of the Day
The ratio of girls to boys in a choir is 5 to 2. If there are 10 boys in the choir, how many students are there in the choir? (35 students)

Quick Review
Write each ratio in simplest form.

1. 12 to 20 (3 to 5) **2.** $\frac{50}{60}$ $\left(\frac{5}{6}\right)$

3. 24 : 4 (6 : 1) **4.** 4 to 16 (1 to 4)

5. 50 : 50 (1 : 1) **6.** 90 to 30 (3 to 1)

7. $\frac{20}{5}$ $\left(\frac{4}{1}\right)$ **8.** $\frac{21}{7}$ (3 : 1)

Lesson Quiz
Tell whether you should estimate or find an exact answer.

For Friday's banana split party, which is the better buy? Green Grocer's $1.56 for 4 pounds, or Big Buy's $3.19 for 8 pounds? (4 pounds for $1.56; Exact answer. Estimates of $160 ÷ 4 = 40 or $0.40/lb and 320 ÷ 8 = 40 or $0.40/lb are too close.)

LEVELED PRACTICE

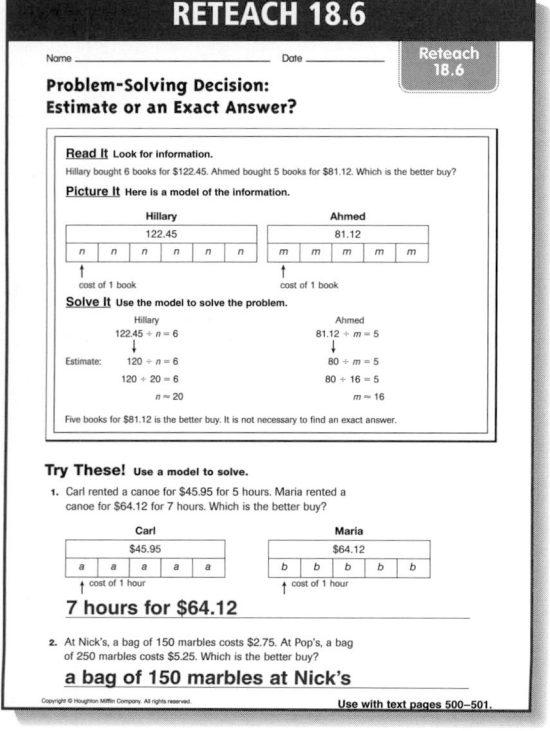

RETEACH 18.6

Name _____ Date _____ Reteach 18.6

Problem-Solving Decision: Estimate or an Exact Answer?

Read It Look for information.
Hillary bought 6 books for $122.45. Ahmed bought 5 books for $81.12. Which is the better buy?

Picture It Here is a model of the information.

Hillary	Ahmed
122.45	81.12

Solve It Use the model to solve the problem.

Hillary: 122.45 ÷ n = 6
Ahmed: 81.12 ÷ m = 5
Estimate: 120 ÷ n = 6 → 80 ÷ m = 5
120 ÷ 20 = 6 → 80 ÷ 16 = 5
n ≈ 20 → m ≈ 16

Five books for $81.12 is the better buy. It is not necessary to find an exact answer.

Try These! Use a model to solve.

1. Carl rented a canoe for $45.95 for 5 hours. Maria rented a canoe for $64.12 for 7 hours. Which is the better buy?

7 hours for $64.12

2. At Nick's, a bag of 150 marbles costs $2.75. At Pop's, a bag of 250 marbles costs $5.25. Which is the better buy?
a bag of 150 marbles at Nick's

Use with text pages 500–501.

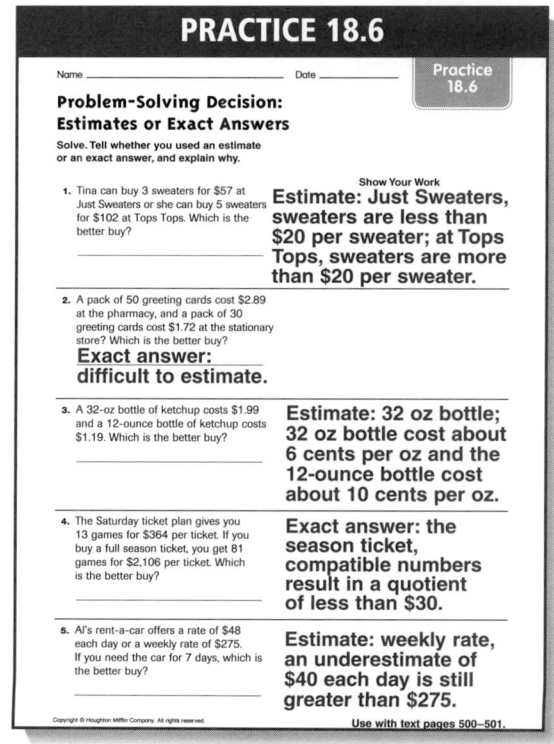

PRACTICE 18.6

Name _____ Date _____ Practice 18.6

Problem-Solving Decision: Estimates or Exact Answers

Solve. Tell whether you used an estimate or an exact answer, and explain why.

Show Your Work

1. Tina can buy 3 sweaters for $57 at Just Sweaters or she can buy 5 sweaters for $102 at Tops Tops. Which is the better buy?
Estimate: Just Sweaters, sweaters are less than $20 per sweater; at Tops Tops, sweaters are more than $20 per sweater.

2. A pack of 50 greeting cards cost $2.89 at the pharmacy, and a pack of 30 greeting cards cost $1.72 at the stationary store? Which is the better buy?
Exact answer: difficult to estimate.

3. A 32-oz bottle of ketchup costs $1.99 and a 12-ounce bottle of ketchup costs $1.19. Which is the better buy?
Estimate: 32 oz bottle; 32 oz bottle cost about 6 cents per oz and the 12-ounce bottle cost about 10 cents per oz.

4. The Saturday ticket plan gives you 13 games for $364 per ticket. If you buy a full season ticket, you get 81 games for $2,106 per ticket. Which is the better buy?
Exact answer: the season ticket, compatible numbers result in a quotient of less than $30.

5. Al's rent-a-car offers a rate of $48 each day or a weekly rate of $275. If you need the car for 7 days, which is the better buy?
Estimate: weekly rate, an underestimate of $40 each day is still greater than $275.

Use with text pages 500–501.

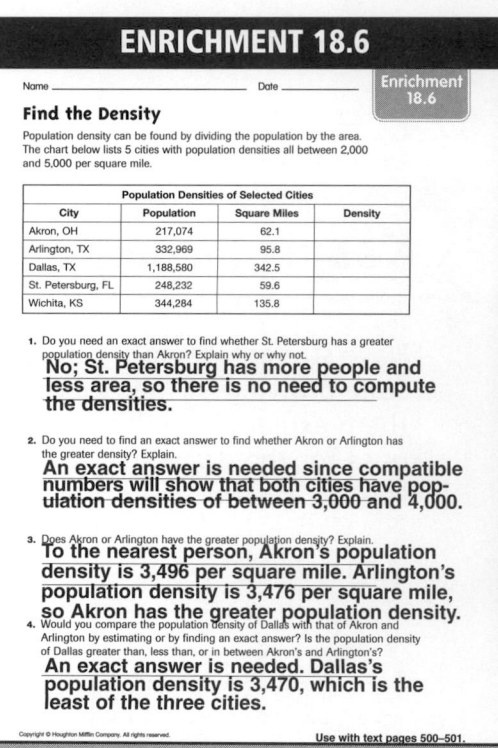

ENRICHMENT 18.6

Name _____ Date _____ Enrichment 18.6

Find the Density

Population density can be found by dividing the population by the area. The chart below lists 5 cities with population densities all between 2,000 and 5,000 per square mile.

City	Population	Square Miles	Density
Akron, OH	217,074	62.1	
Arlington, TX	332,969	95.8	
Dallas, TX	1,188,580	342.5	
St. Petersburg, FL	248,232	59.6	
Wichita, KS	344,284	135.8	

1. Do you need an exact answer to find whether St. Petersburg has a greater population density than Akron? Explain why or why not.
No; St. Petersburg has more people and less area, so there is no need to compute the densities.

2. Do you need to find an exact answer to find whether Akron or Arlington has the greater density? Explain.
An exact answer is needed since compatible numbers will show that both cities have population densities of between 3,000 and 4,000.

3. Does Akron or Arlington have the greater population density? Explain.
To the nearest person, Akron's population density is 3,496 per square mile. Arlington's population density is 3,476 per square mile, so Akron has the greater population density.

4. Would you compare the population density of Dallas with that of Akron and Arlington by estimating or by finding an exact answer? Is the population density of Dallas greater than, less than, or in between Akron's and Arlington's?
An exact answer is needed. Dallas's population density is 3,470, which is the least of the three cities.

Use with text pages 500–501.

Practice Workbook Page 124

Reaching All Learners
Differentiated Instruction

English Learners

Worksheet 18.6 defines content vocabulary used in Lesson 6 and asks students to complete sentences using these words.

Inclusion
TACTILE, VISUAL

- Display the following: *Which is the better buy? 5 items for $2.90 or 6 items for $3.24?*
- **To estimate the cost per unit of the first offer, round $2.90 to the nearest dollar. What is $3.00 divided by 5?** (60) **To estimate the cost per unit of the second offer, round $3.24 to $3.25 and divide by 6.** (54) **Can we estimate which offer is better?** (yes)

Gifted and Talented
VISUAL, AUDITORY

- Have students make up and solve 3 division problems using money. The divisors should be in cents; the dividends in dollars and cents.
- Then have students round the dividends and solve the problems. Have them tell if the quotients are greater than, less than, or equal to the actual quotients.

TECHNOLOGY

Spiral Review

Using the *Ways to Assess* CD-ROM, you can create **customized** spiral review worksheets covering any lessons you choose.

Intervention

Use the *Ways to Success* intervention software to support students who need more help in understanding the concepts and skills taught in this chapter.

Ways to Success

Literature Connection

Land of the Lilliputians

- Children's versions of Jonathan Swift's *Gulliver's Travels* are available. Read the section about the Lilliputians to the class.

- Have students estimate how tall the Lilliputians would be if they lived in a different world. Have them also estimate the difference in height between Gulliver and the Lilliputians.

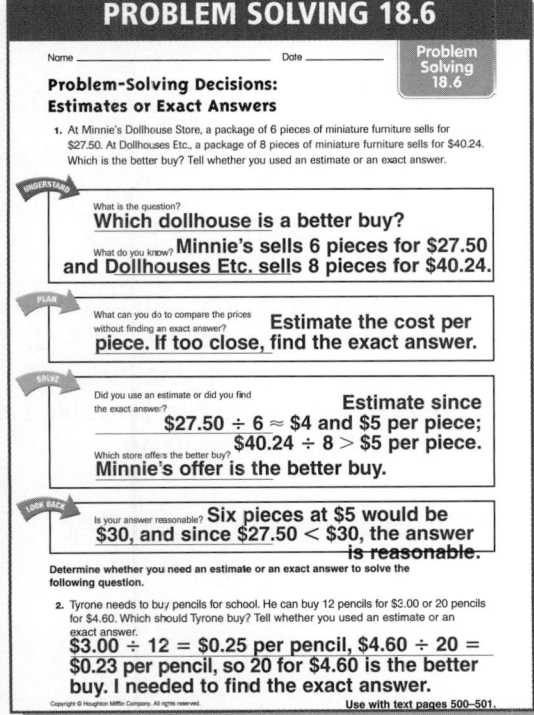

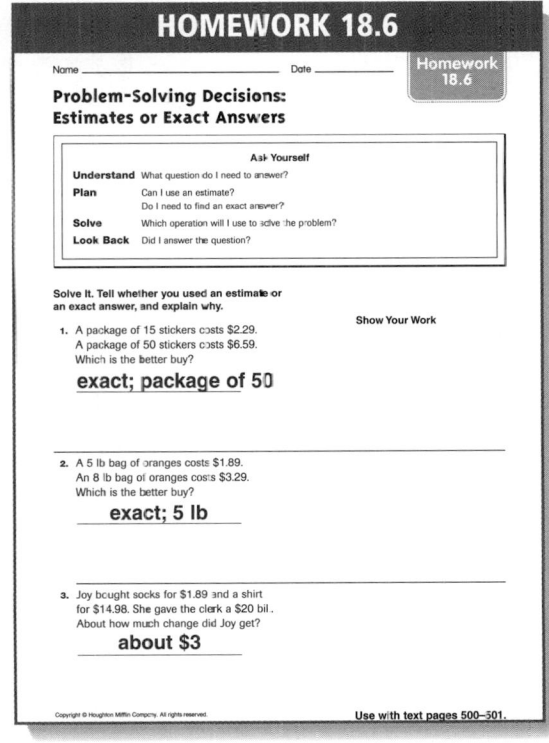

Homework Workbook Page 124

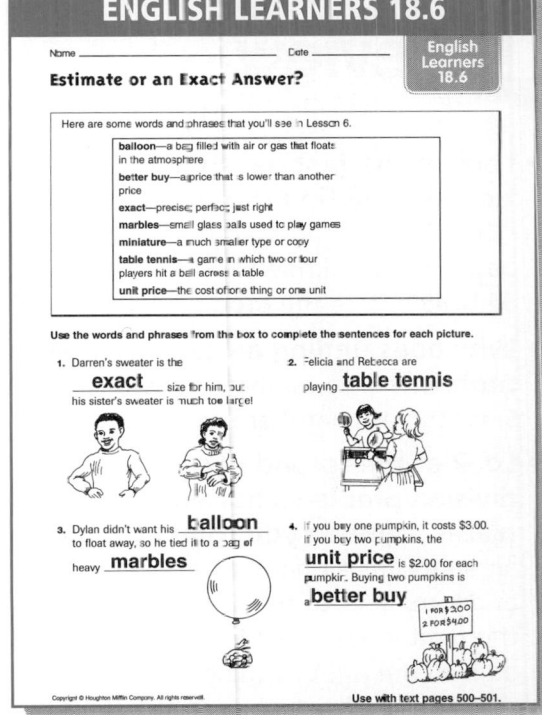

TEACHING LESSON 18.6

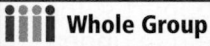

Warm-Up Activity
Estimating

𝗂𝗂𝗂𝗂 Whole Group	⏱ 5 minutes	Visual, Auditory

- Write the following on the chalkboard:

Mammal	Weight	Daily Food Requirement (in grams)
Grizzly Bear	450 kg	10,400 g
Arctic Wolf	80 kg	2,300 g
Bobcat	9 kg	420 g

- **About how many bobcats equal the weight of an arctic wolf?** (about 9) **Suppose a bobcat ate the same type of food as a grizzly bear. About how many bobcats could you feed with the amount of food a grizzly bear eats?** (about 20)

- Have students use the data to write questions.

Lesson 6

Problem-Solving Decision
Estimate or Exact Answer?

Objective Decide when to estimate or calculate an exact answer.

When you solve a problem, you can sometimes use an estimate. An estimate is often easier. At other times, you need an exact answer. An exact answer gives you more precise information.

Problem Look at the ads for table tennis balls shown at the right. Which is the better buy?

Ask Yourself
TEST TIPS

Can I use an estimate?	**Do I need to find the exact answer?**
If I use compatible numbers to estimate the unit prices: $$\frac{\$4.49}{5} \approx \frac{\$4.50}{5} = \$0.90$$ $$\frac{\$7.09}{8} \approx \frac{\$7.20}{8} = \$0.90$$ $$\$0.90 = \$0.90$$	$$\frac{\$4.49}{5} = \$0.898 \approx \$0.90$$ $$\frac{\$7.09}{8} = \$0.886 \approx \$0.89$$ $$\$0.89 < \$0.90$$
The estimated unit prices are equal.	The exact unit prices are slightly different.

Solution: The exact answer shows that $7.09 for 8 table tennis balls is a better buy than $4.49 for 5 table tennis balls. The estimate did not show a difference. Therefore, I would need an exact answer.

Try These

Solve. Tell whether you used an estimate or an exact answer, and explain why. 1–4. *See Additional Answers on page 503.*

1. At Ted's Toys, a bag of 20 marbles costs $3.99. At Toy Club, a bag of 30 marbles costs $7.49. Which is the better buy?

2. A package of 6 miniature flags costs $11.95. A package of 10 miniature flags costs $19.79. Which is the better buy?

3. The Balloon Stop sells 200 balloons for $99. The Fun Factory sells 500 balloons for $299. Which is the better buy?

4. A barrel of 50 Tough Tiles costs $15.99. A barrel of 75 Tough Tiles costs $22.49. Which is the better buy?

500

---

① Review

- **Look at the first question of the Ask Yourself section. How do you find the compatible numbers for $4.49 ÷ 5?** (Think of the money amount as the number 449. Then think of basic facts you know: 5 × 80 = 400 and 5 × 90 = 450. Use 5 × 90 = 450, since the product 450 is very close to 449.)

- **Why does finding an estimated answer not solve this problem?** (The estimated answers are both equal to $0.90. Since the estimates are so close, an exact answer is needed.)

- **Look at the second part of the *Ask Yourself* section. The division problems have answers with three decimal places. How do you round for money answers?** (Money amounts are rounded to the hundredths place. To do this, look at the number to the right of the hundredths place. Round up if this digit is 5 or greater. Then drop the remaining digits. If the digit to the right of the hundredths place is less than 5, keep the hundredths place as is, and drop the remaining digits.)

② Practice

Assign **Problems 1–4** as independent work.

- Watch for students who only find exact calculated answers or who just make random guesses.

- Students who have not memorized basic fact families such as 4 ÷ 2 = 2 and related expressions such as 40 ÷ 20 = 2, 400 ÷ 20 = 20, and 4.00 ÷ 20 = 0.20 may be challenged in this lesson. Help them see how 3.99 ÷ 20 can be solved with the compatible expressions 400 ÷ 20 = 20 or 4.00 ÷ 20 = 0.20.

Assign the **LESSON QUIZ** on Transparency 18.6 to further assess student understanding.

Quick Check

Check your understanding for Lessons 4–6.

Solve each proportion. (Lesson 4)

1. $\frac{4}{7} = \frac{y}{21}$ $y = 12$
2. $\frac{15}{18} = \frac{5}{t}$ $t = 6$
3. $\frac{w}{16} = \frac{5}{20}$ $w = 4$
4. $\frac{12}{j} = \frac{30}{5}$ $j = 2$
5. $\frac{8}{12} = \frac{12}{p}$ $p = 18$
6. $\frac{g}{8} = \frac{21}{24}$ $g = 7$

Use the scale 1 in.:8 ft to find _n_. (Lesson 5)

7. *n* in. in the drawing represents 240 ft.
30 in.

8. *n* in. in the drawing represents 112 ft.
14 in.

Solve. Tell whether you used an estimate or an exact answer, and explain why. (Lesson 6)
See Additional Answers on page 503.

9. A 6-oz tube of toothpaste costs $2.98. A 10-oz tube of toothpaste costs $3.99. Which one is the better buy? *See above.*

10. At Mel's Office Supplies, a package of 6 pens costs $4.09. At Office King, a package of 8 pens costs $5.55. Which is the better buy?

9. 10-oz tube; estimate; an estimate shows the 10-oz tube has a unit price of about 40¢ per ounce ($4 ÷ 10) and that the 6-oz tube has a unit price of about 50¢ ($3 ÷ 6).

 **WEEKLY WR READER** eduplace.com/kids/mw/

 **Real World Connection**

Model Railroads

Model railroad designs have many of the features of an actual railroad system. They include such items as trains, stations, signals, and bridges.

Model railroad cars are exact scale replicas of real trains. Many model trains use the HO scale, which is 1 in.:87 in. Another popular scale is the *N* scale, which is 1 in.:160 in.

1. The length of a model boxcar done in HO scale is 6.07 in. What is the actual length of the boxcar in inches? **528.09 in.**

2. The length of a model engine done in *N* scale is 4.8 in. What is the actual length of the engine in inches? **768 in.**

Chapter 18 Lesson 6   **501**

Quick Check

Purpose: The Quick Check allows you to assess the student's understanding of the concepts presented in Lessons 4–6.

Items	Objectives Tested	Pages	Intervention
1–6	Learn what a proportion is and how to find cross products.	492–495	Reteach Resource 18.4 *Way to Success* 18.4
7–8	Use equivalent ratios to interpret scale drawings.	496–498	Reteach Resource 18.5 *Way to Success* 18.5
9–10	Decide when to estimate or calculate an exact answer.	500	Reteach Resource 18.6 *Way to Success* 18.6

 **Test Prep Transparency 18.6**

DAILY TEST PREP

A package of 6 cakes of soap is on sale for $5.49. A single cake of soap costs $0.90. Which is the better buy? Should you estimate or find an exact answer? (Exact answer; the better buy is 6 single cakes at $0.90.)

 ### Keeping a Journal

Have students write two situations when estimating answers can be used.

Real World Connection

Model Railroads

You may like to share with students the origins of American train model collecting. In 1933 and 1934, model railroads were shown at *The Century of Progress* exposition in Chicago, Illinois. The popularity of these model railroads led manufacturers to begin the production of model railroad trains and kits, including miniature towns and scenery such as trees, mountains, and rivers.

 Chapter Review/Test

Purpose: This test provides an informal assessment of the Chapter 18 objectives.

Chapter Test Items 1–20

To assign a numerical grade for this Chapter Test, use 5 points for each test item.

Check Understanding

You can use the **Write About It** question to assess student understanding of a key chapter concept.

Customizing Your Instruction

For students who have not yet mastered these objectives, you can use the Reteaching Resources listed in the chart below.

 Assessment Options

A summary test for this chapter is also provided in the Unit Resource Folder.

Adequate Yearly Progress

Use the End of Grade Test Prep Assessment Guide to help familiarize your students with the format of standardized tests.

Chapter Review/Test

7. $\frac{4}{6}; \frac{6}{9}; \frac{8}{12}; \frac{10}{15}$ 9. $\frac{4}{3}; \frac{24}{18}; \frac{36}{27}; \frac{48}{36}$

VOCABULARY 8. $\frac{2}{14}; \frac{3}{21}; \frac{4}{28}; \frac{5}{35}$ 10. $\frac{5}{3}; \frac{20}{12}; \frac{30}{18}; \frac{40}{24}$

Vocabulary
proportion
rate
ratio
scale
similar

1. Two figures that have the same shape but are not the same size are ____. **similar**

2. A ratio that compares different units is called a ____. **rate**

3. A ____ is a ratio of the measurements in a scale drawing of an object to the corresponding measurements of the actual object. **scale**

4. A statement that two ratios are equivalent is a ____. **proportion**

CONCEPTS AND SKILLS

Write each ratio three different ways. (Lesson 1, pp. 484–485)

5. 7 drums to 14 drumsticks   6. 11 forks to 8 knives
7 to 14; 7:14; $\frac{7}{14}$ **11 to 8; 11:8; $\frac{11}{8}$**

Write 4 equivalent ratios for each. (Lesson 2, pp. 486–487) *See above. Possible answers given.*

7. $\frac{2}{3}$ 8. 1 to 7   9. 12:9   10. $\frac{10}{6}$

Find the rate per unit of time. (Lesson 3, pp. 488–491)

11. $240 in 6 days   12. 455 km in 7 h   13. 360 beats in 5 min
$40 per day   **65 km/h**   **72 beats per min**

Do the two ratios form a proportion? Write *yes* or *no*. (Lesson 4, pp. 492–495)

14. $\frac{3}{4}$ $\frac{39}{52}$ **yes**   15. $\frac{5}{6}$ $\frac{4}{5}$ **no**   16. $\frac{77}{132}$ $\frac{7}{12}$ **yes**

Use the scale $\frac{1}{2}$ in.:5 mi to find *n*. (Lesson 5, pp. 496–499)

17. *n* in. represents 20 mi   18. 3 in. represents *n* mi   19. *n* in. represents 45 mi
n = 2   *n* = 30 $n = 4\frac{1}{2}$

PROBLEM SOLVING

Solve. Tell whether you used an estimate or an exact answer, and explain why. (Lesson 6, pp. 500–501)

20. A box of 30 diskettes costs $15.99. A box of 50 diskettes costs $26.00. Which is the better buy?
50 diskettes for $26. Exact answer. *Possible explanation:* **Using compatible numbers to divide, the quotients were identical.**

Write About It

Show You Understand
Alan says that the ratios $\frac{3}{5}$ and $\frac{4}{6}$ form a proportion. Is he correct? Explain your thinking.

No. *Possible answer:* **Using cross products, 5 × 4 = 20 and 3 × 6 = 18. 20 ≠ 18.**

502   Chapter 18 Chapter Review/Test

Reteaching Support

Chapter Test Items	Summary Test Items	Chapter Objectives Tested	TE Pages	Use These Reteaching Resources
2, 5–13	1–5	**18A** Read, write, and use ratios, equivalent ratios, and rates.	484A–491	Reteach Resource 18.1–18.3 Ways to Success CD: 18.1–18.3 Skillsheet 146, 147, 148
4, 14–16	6–10	**18B** Identify proportions and use them to solve problems.	492A–495	Reteach Resource 18.4 Ways to Success CD: 18.4 Skillsheet 149
1, 3, 17–19	11–15	**18C** Use proportions to interpret similar figures and scale drawings.	496A–499	Reteach Resource 18.5 Ways to Success CD: 18.5 Skillsheet 150
20	16–20	**18D** Decide if the solution to a problem should be an estimate or an exact amount.	500A	Reteach Resource 18.6 Ways to Success CD: 18.6 Skillsheet 151

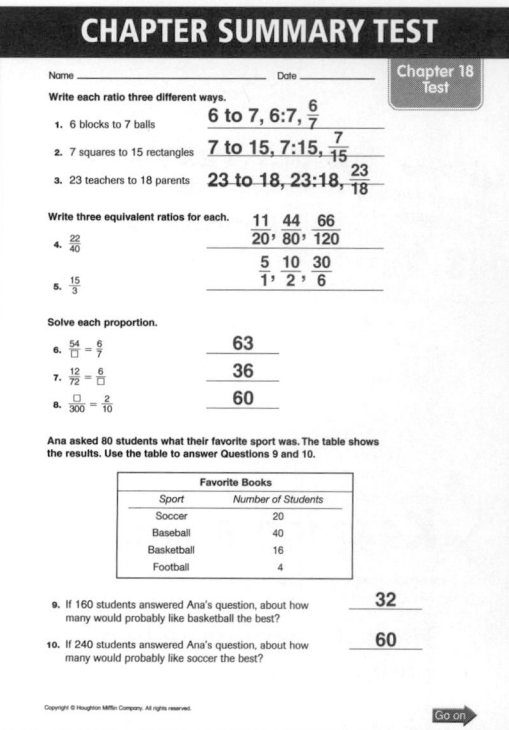

CHAPTER SUMMARY TEST

7. $\frac{2}{6}, \frac{3}{9}, \frac{4}{12}, \frac{5}{15}$
$\frac{4}{10}, \frac{6}{15}, \frac{8}{20}, \frac{10}{25}$
8. $\frac{4}{10}, \frac{6}{15}, \frac{8}{20}, \frac{10}{25}$
9. $\frac{6}{14}, \frac{9}{21}, \frac{12}{28}, \frac{15}{35}$

10. $\frac{2}{4}, \frac{3}{6}, \frac{4}{8}, \frac{5}{10}$
11. $\frac{2}{8}, \frac{3}{12}, \frac{4}{16}, \frac{5}{20}$
12. $\frac{10}{12}, \frac{15}{18}, \frac{20}{24}, \frac{25}{30}$

Set A (Lesson 1, pp. 484–485)

Write each ratio three different ways.

1. 5 cups to 8 saucers 5 to 8; $\frac{5}{8}$; 5:8

2. 3 windows to 2 doors 3 to 2; $\frac{3}{2}$; 3:2

3. 6 girls to 7 boys 6 to 7; $\frac{6}{7}$; 6:7

4. 9 red to 4 blue 9 to 4; $\frac{9}{4}$; 9:4

5. 1 car to 5 buses 1 to 5; $\frac{1}{5}$; 1:5

6. 13 horses to 6 sheep 13 to 6; $\frac{13}{6}$; 13:6

Set B (Lesson 2, pp. 486–487)

Write each ratio in simplest form.

1. 6 to 10 $\frac{3}{5}$ 2. 9:24 $\frac{3}{8}$ 3. $\frac{25}{100}$ $\frac{1}{4}$ 4. 14:56 $\frac{1}{4}$ 5. $\frac{8}{12}$ $\frac{2}{3}$ 6. 30:72 $\frac{5}{12}$

Write four equivalent ratios for each. Ex. 7–12. See above. Possible answers given.

7. $\frac{1}{3}$ 8. $\frac{2}{5}$ 9. $\frac{3}{7}$ 10. $\frac{1}{2}$ 11. $\frac{1}{4}$ 12. $\frac{5}{6}$

Set C (Lesson 3, pp. 488–491)

Find the rate per unit of time.

1. 96 meters in 12 seconds 8 m/sec

2. 360 words in 3 min 120 words/min

3. $420 in 35 hours $12/h

Complete the unit rate.

4. $4:5 lb = $■:1 lb $0.80

5. 275 mi:11 gal = ■ mi:1 gal 25 mi

Set D (Lesson 4, pp. 492–495)

Solve each proportion.

1. $\frac{6}{30} = \frac{u}{5}$ $u = 1$ 2. $\frac{5}{75} = \frac{1}{v}$ $v = 15$ 3. $\frac{24}{w} = \frac{8}{2}$ $w = 6$ 4. $\frac{x}{100} = \frac{4}{25}$ $x = 16$

Do the ratios form a proportion? Write yes or no.

5. $\frac{2}{3}$ $\frac{9}{12}$ no 6. $\frac{5}{8}$ $\frac{30}{48}$ yes 7. $\frac{32}{80}$ $\frac{2}{5}$ yes 8. $\frac{10}{4}$ $\frac{15}{5}$ no

Set E (Lesson 5, pp. 496–499)

Use the scale $\frac{1}{4}$ in.:1 ft to find n.

1. n in. represents 8 ft $n = 2$ 2. 3 in. represents n ft $n = 12$

Use the figure at the right to answer each question.

3. What is the measure of $\angle G$? 30°

4. Are the triangles similar? How do you know?
Yes; the measures of the angles are equal and the ratios of all corresponding sides are equivalent to $\frac{1}{2}$.

Chapter 18 Extra Practice 503

CHAPTER SUMMARY TEST

Name _____ Date _____

Chapter 18 Test continued

Use the scale 1 in. = 15 ft to find n in Questions 11–13.

11. 3 in. represents n feet 45
12. n in. represents 75 ft 5
13. 7 in. represents n feet 105

The figure shows two similar trapezoids. Use it to answer Questions 14 and 15.

14. What is the length of side HG? 6 cm
15. What is the measure of angle HEF? 110°

For Questions 16–20, state if you should find an estimate or an exact answer. Then solve the problem. If you said estimate, then give an estimated answer.

16. A store sells a pack of 10 baseball cards for $4.95 or five 10-packs for $49.95. Which is the better buy?
Estimate; 10 cards for $4.95.

17. A 10-oz bottle of juice costs $1.49. A 30-oz bottle costs $4.25. Which is the better buy?
Estimate; 30-oz. bottle for $4.25.

18. A package of 25 stickers costs $2.10. A package of 75 stickers costs $6.50. Which is the better buy?
Estimate; 25 for $2.10.

19. A store charges $79.95 for 5 soccer balls. If you buy 12 soccer balls, the store charges $189.95. Which is the better buy? Explain your answer.
Exact answer; 12 for $189.95.

20. It costs $1.50 to make 15 photocopies. It costs $9.50 to make 100 photocopies. Which is the better buy? Explain your answer.
Estimate; 100 for $9.50.

16–20: Explanations will vary.

Chapter 18

Lesson 1, p. 485

19. The order of the terms must match the order of the items being compared.

Lesson 3, pp. 488–491

41. Hal multiplied by 30 when he should have divided 2,100 mi by 30 mi/gal. Hal would need 70 gal. of gas.

Lesson 5, pp. 497–498

7. $\frac{5}{15} = \frac{3}{9} = \frac{4}{-2}$; The ratios are equivalent because they all are equal to $\frac{1}{3}$.

8. Yes; the corresponding angles are congruent and the lengths of their corresponding sides are proportional.

Explain Your Thinking: *Possible answer:* You may be able to determine that they are not similar, but to be sure that they are similar you must check the measure of the angles and confirm that corresponding sides are proportional.

21. no; the lengths of their corresponding sides are not proportional

22. no; the lengths of their corresponding sides are not proportional

23. yes; the lengths of their corresponding sides are proportional

26. *Possible answer:* a cell, an atom, or a small insect

27. *Check students' drawings.* Measurements should be 8.4 cm × 3 cm

Lesson 6, pp. 500–501

1. a bag of 20 marbles from Ted's Toys; estimate; an estimate shows that marbles cost about 20¢ each ($4.00 ÷ 20) at Ted's Toys and about 25¢ each ($7.50 ÷ 30) at Toy Club.

2. a package of 10 flags; exact answer; an estimate gives the same unit price for each package of flags ($12 ÷ 2 = $2.00; $20 ÷ 10 = $2.00), while an exact answer shows that the package of 10 flags has a unit price that is about 1¢ less per flag.

3. 200 balloons from The Balloon Stop; estimate; an estimate shows that balloons cost about 50¢ each ($100 ÷ 200) at The Balloon Stop and about 60¢ each ($300 ÷ 500) at The Fun Factory.

4. a barrel of 75 Tough Tiles; exact answer; an estimate gives the same unit price for each barrel of tiles ($15 ÷ 50 = $0.30; $24 ÷ 80 = $0.30), while an exact answer shows that barrel of 75 Tough Tiles has a unit price that is about 2¢ less per tile.

10. package of 6 pens; exact answer; an estimate gives the same unit price for each package of pens ($4.20 ÷ 6 = $0.70; $5.60 ÷ 8 = $0.70), while an exact answer shows that the package of 6 pens has a unit price that is about 1¢ less per pen.

Lesson By Lesson Overview
Percent

Lesson 1

- Students connect percents to ratios by writing a ratio and a percent for a shaded portion of a grid.
- Students write ratios as percents and vice versa.

Lesson 2

- Students build on their knowledge of percents by relating percents to fractions and decimals.
- Students practice writing a number given in one form in the other two forms.
- Students solve for n in equations that involve proportions and percents.

Lesson 3

- Students compare fractions, decimals, and percents.
- Students shade grids to show and compare numbers in the three forms.

Lesson 4

- Students find 10% of a number and multiples of 10% of a number.
- Students are shown three ways to find 10% of a number. They apply these methods to finding multiples of 10% of a number.

Lesson 5

- Students practice three different ways of finding a percent of a number
- Students apply what they have learned in this lesson to completing function tables that involve percents of numbers.

Lesson 6

- Students use circle graphs to solve problems.
- Students to choose a strategy and a computation method.

SKILLS TRACE: PERCENT

Grade 4	Grade 5	Grade 6
	• use ratios to write percents	• represent, read, and write percents; relate percents to decimals (ch. 4)
	• relate and compare percents, decimals, fractions, and mixed numbers	• relate, compare, and order ratios, decimals, and percents (ch. 17)
	• find a percent of a number	• estimate with percents (ch. 17)
		• find and compute with percents (ch. 18)

Chapter Planner

Lesson	Objective	Vocabulary	Materials	✓ NCTM Standards
19.1 **Hands-On:** **Understand Percent** p. 506A	Understand percents as ratios.	percent	grid paper, rulers, colored pencils, Centimeter Grid Transparency, red erasable marker, 2 sheets of paper, centimeter grid paper, scissors, Learning Tool 13	**Numbers and Operations:** Recognize and generate equivalent forms of commonly used fractions, decimals, and percents.
19.2 **Relate Fractions, Decimals, and Percents** p. 508A	Relate fractions, decimals, and percents.		grid paper, rulers, colored pencils, Centimeter Grid transparency, Number line 1 of the Number Line Transparency, calculators	**Numbers and Operations:** Recognize and generate equivalent forms of commonly used fractions, decimals, and percents.
19.3 **Compare Fractions, Decimals, and Percents** p. 510A	Use fractions, decimals, and percents to compare numbers.	ratio	grid paper, rulers, colored pencils, Decimal Place-Value Chart transparency, blank transparency, copies made from Number Line transparency	**Numbers and Operations:** Recognize and generate equivalent forms of commonly used fractions, decimals, and percents.
19.4 **Find 10% of a Number** p. 514A	Use mental math to find 10% and multiples of 10% of a number.		blank transparency	**Numbers and Operations:** Recognize and generate equivalent forms of commonly used fractions, decimals, and percents.
19.5 **Algebra: Percent of a Number** p. 516A	Use different ways to find a percent of a number.		rulers, blank transparency, scissors	**Numbers and Operations:** Recognize and generate equivalent forms of commonly used fractions, decimals, and percents.
19.6 **Problem-Solving Application: Use Circle Graphs** p. 520A	Interpret data to make circle graphs to solve problems.		blank transparencies, Mixed Numbers Transparency, scissors, Problem Solving: Four Step Process Transparency	**Data Analysis and Probability:** Represent data using tables and graphs such as line plots, bar graphs, and line graphs.

Resources For Reaching All Learners

LESSON RESOURCES: Reteach, Practice, Enrichment, Problem Solving, Homework, English Learners, Daily Routines, Transparencies, Math Center.

ADDITIONAL RESOURCES FROM HOUGHTON MIFFLIN: Combination Classroom Planning Guide, Chapter Challenges, Every Day Counts, Math at Hand (student handbook)

Every Day Counts

The **Counting Tape** activities in **Every Day Counts** support the math in this chapter.

Assessing Prior Knowledge

Before beginning the chapter, you can assess students' understanding in order to assist you in differentiating instruction.

Complete Chapter Pretest in Unit Resource Folder

Use this test to assess both prerequisite skills (**Are You Ready?** — one page) and chapter content (**Check What You Know** — two pages).

Chapter 19 Prerequisite Skills Pretest

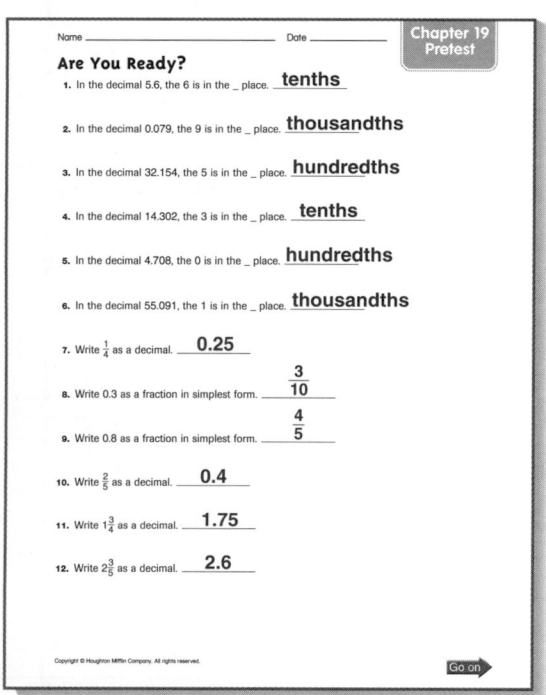

Chapter 19 New Content Pretest

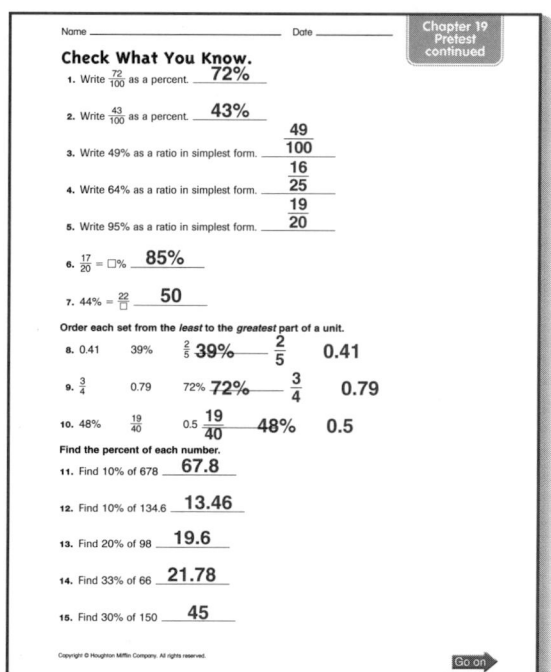

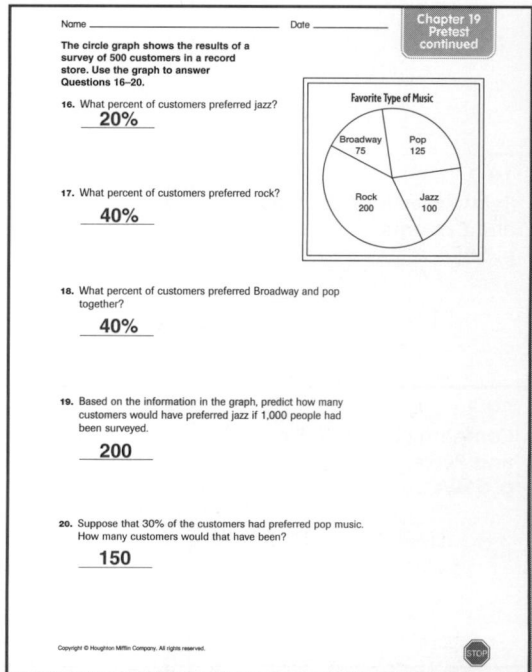

Customizing Instruction

For Students Having Difficulty

Items	Prerequisites	Ways to Success
1–6	Place value of decimals through thousandths	CD: 19a Skillsheet: 152
7–12	Write fractions and mixed numbers as decimals and vice-versa	CD: 19b Skillsheet: 153

Ways to Success: Intervention for every concept and skill (CD-ROM or Chapter Intervention Skillsheet).

Consider using **Knowing Mathematics** with any students who are working two or more years below grade level.

For Students Having Success

Items	Objectives	Resources
1–7	**19A** Use ratios to write percents and percents to write ratios.	Enrichment 19.1, 19.2
8–10	**19B** Relate and compare percents, decimals, fractions, and mixed numbers.	Enrichment 19.3
11–15	**19C** Find a percent of a number	Enrichment 19.4, 19.5
16–20	**19D** Analyze and solve problems using circle graphs.	Enrichment 19.6

Other Pretest Options

Informal Pretest in Student Book

The student book pretest assesses vocabulary and prerequisite skills needed for success in this chapter.

Ways to Success CD-ROM

The *Ways to Success* chapter pretest has automatic assignment of appropriate review lessons.

Use **Chapter Challenges** with any students who have success with all new chapter content.

Chapter Resources

 Activity

Assessing Prior Knowledge

Reviewing Fractions (equivalent fractions)

- Distribute 10 × 10 grid paper to students. Have them shade squares to represent fractions with denominators of 100.
- Have students read their fractions and write as many equivalent fractions as possible.

 Activity

Ongoing Skill Activity

All That You Can Survey (relate percents to fractions and decimals, find percent of a number, percents on circle graphs)

- Have students write a list of survey questions, some asking for a yes or no response, others asking for a preference from among specified items. Have them pose their survey questions to 10 people.
- After Lesson 2, have students use each number type to write the ratio of a certain response to the whole.
- After Lesson 5, have students find common percents (10%, 25%, 50%) of the class and compare them to actual numbers of survey responses.
- After Lesson 6, have students display survey results on circle graphs.

 Activity

Connecting to the Unit Project

- Have students use the data from their tracking sheets to express each outcome predicted by their weatherperson (for example, rain) first as a ratio or fraction of the total, then as a decimal, and then as a percent.
- Have students who are following the same weatherperson compare their work and discuss results. Have them use their data to write two problems involving percent for others to solve.

Teacher Support

Professional Resources Handbook

Research, Mathematics Content, and Language Intervention

Research-Based Teaching

Carter (2002) et al, discusses curricular methods in Singapore where teachers use problem-solving techniques with all primary school students. Pictorial representations of both the known and unknown quantities in a problem are illustrated in a diagram. See *Professional Resources Handbook, Grade 5*, Unit 7.

For more ideas relating to Unit 7, see the Teacher Support Handbook at the back of this Teacher's Edition.

Language Intervention

Be sure students understand the difference between finding "the percent" and finding "the percent of a number." For example, the question *What percent of 50 is 6?* requires students to find a percent. The question *What is 10% of 50?* requires students to find the percent of a number. In the first case, the answer will be a number which includes a percent sign. In the second case, the answer will not have a percent sign.

Time Saving Technology Support

Ways to Assess Customized Spiral Review and Test Generator CD-ROM
Lesson Planner CD-ROM
Ways to Success Intervention CD-ROM
Math Tracks CD-ROM
Education Place: **www.eduplace.com/math/mw/**
Houghton Mifflin Math eBook CD-ROM
eManipulatives
eGames

Starting Chapter 19
Percent

Chapter Objectives

19A Use ratios to write percents.

19B Relate and compare percents, decimals, fractions, and mixed numbers.

19C Find a percent of a number.

19D Analyze and solve problems using circle graphs.

Math Background

Percent

Percent is a ratio of a number to 100 and means "per hundred." It is another way of writing fractions and decimals.

It is important to tie in the relationship between percents, decimals, and fractions. Comparison of fractions, decimals, and percents can be made in several ways including locating each on a number line, rewriting each as a fraction with a common denominator or rewriting each as a decimal or as a percent.

To find a percent of a number, first change the percent to either a fraction or a decimal and then multiply the given number by that fraction or decimal. The percent of a number can also be found by writing the percent as a fraction and then finding an equivalent fraction with the given number as the second term.

To find what percent one number is of another number, write the two numbers as a fraction, with the whole as the denominator. Then find an equivalent ratio with a denominator of 100 and write that ratio as a percent.

In later grades students will learn to use the percent equation, which is usually set up as "whole × percent = part."

CHAPTER 19 Percent

INVESTIGATION

Use Data

Eva's family made the budget shown by the circle graph. The family income is $3,000 per month. How much does Eva's family spend on food each month? How much do they save each month? **$600; $150**

Wishnok Family Budget

- Other 15%
- Housing 25%
- Transportation 10%
- Savings 5%
- Insurance and Taxes 25%
- Food 20%

504

Using the Investigation

Have students work in small groups to answer the questions posed on page 504.

To extend the investigation, have students do the following activity.

- Have your group plan a class party with a budget of $50. Work together to decide how you would spend the money. Consider how much you would spend on food, decorations, paper products, etc. Make a circle graph to show what fraction of the money you would spend in each category.

For more information about projects and investigations, visit **Education Place**. www.eduplace.com/math/mw/

✓ Chapter Pretest

Use this page to review and remember what you need to know for this chapter.

✓ VOCABULARY

Choose the best word to complete each sentence.

Vocabulary
- decimal point
- denominator
- hundredths
- numerator
- tenths

1. In the decimal 3.45, the 5 is in the ____ place. **hundredths**

2. The ____ of a fraction tells the number of equal parts in the whole. **denominator**

3. In writing money amounts, the dollars and cents are separated by a ____ . **decimal point**

✓ CONCEPTS AND SKILLS

Write a decimal and a fraction to represent the shaded part of each model.

4.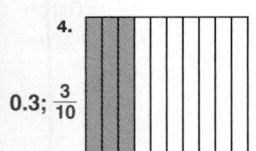
$0.3; \frac{3}{10}$

5.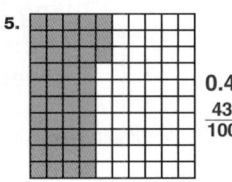
$0.43; \frac{43}{100}$

6.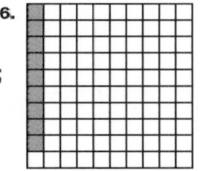
$0.09; \frac{9}{100}$

Write each decimal as a fraction in simplest form.

7. 0.4 $\frac{2}{5}$ 8. 0.75 $\frac{3}{4}$ 9. 0.35 $\frac{7}{20}$ 10. 0.66 $\frac{33}{50}$

Find each product.

11. 0.5 × 21 **10.5**   12. 0.26 × 300 **78**   13. 0.34 × 192 **65.28**

14. 0.62 × 475 **294.5**   15. $\frac{3}{4}$ × 80 **60**   16. $\frac{1}{2}$ × 644 **322**

17. $\frac{4}{5}$ of 135 **108**   18. $\frac{3}{8}$ of 96 **36**   19. $\frac{1}{5}$ of 200 **40**

▶ **Write About It**

20. Would you prefer to multiply 0.25 × 84 or $\frac{1}{4}$ × 84? Explain.

Possible answer: **I would use $\frac{1}{4}$. I can see that 4 divides into 84 evenly, so I can do the computation more quickly in my head.**

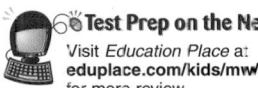 **Test Prep on the Net**
Visit *Education Place* at:
eduplace.com/kids/mw
for more review.

✓ Chapter Pretest

Prerequisite Skills

Items	Skill
1–3	Vocabulary needed for this chapter
4–6	Writing fractions and decimals from models
7–10	Writing decimals as fractions in simplest form
11–19	Multiplying whole numbers by fractions and decimals
20	Using number sense and mental math

Chapter Challenges

For Mathematically Promising Students

Use *Chapter Challenges* resource book.

Explore: Determining Percents, page 109, after Lesson 1

Extend: Use Percents, page 111, after Lesson 3

Connect: People Percentages, page 113, after Lesson 5

Using The Chapter Pretest

This page will help students review some of the prerequisite skills needed for this chapter. The chart above indicates which skills are covered on the pretest. If students need more help with these prerequisite skills use **Ways to Success,** Houghton Mifflin's intervention program.

Students who need more review can visit **Education Place,** Houghton Mifflin's award-winning website.

NSF Children's Math Worlds

Children's Math Worlds focuses on the use of models to represent mathematical situations. Thus, using a *Children's Math Worlds* lesson helps students develop a general facility with drawing models to support their thinking that will transfer to all their mathematical work.

Hands-On: Understand Percent

PLANNING THE LESSON

MATHEMATICS OBJECTIVE
Understand percents as ratios.

Use Lesson Planner CD-ROM for Lesson 19.1.

Daily Routines

Vocabulary

How many *cents* are in one dollar? (100)
Write *per* + *cent* on the chalkboard. Remind
students that *per* means "for every." Tell
students that the word *cent* is from the Latin word
centum, meaning "100." **What is the meaning of *per-cent*?** (for every hundred) Ask students to think of other
words that contain the root *cent* to help them con-
nect the meaning with 100. (Possible answers: century,
centimeter)

Meeting North Carolina's Standards

Prepare for Grade 6 Objective **1.02** Develop meaning
for percents.

Lesson Transparency

19.1

Problem of the Day
On a scale drawing of a soccer field, the
scale is 1 cm = 10 m. What are the actual
dimensions of the soccer field if the length
of the scale drawing is 12 cm long and the
width is three-fourths of the length?
(120 m long, 90 m wide)

Quick Review
Use mental math to compute.
1. 10×10 (100)
2. 25×4 (100)
3. $75 + 25$ (100)
4. 2×50 (100)
5. $100 \div 5$ (20)
6. $100 \div 25$ (4)
7. $69 + 31$ (100)
8. $199 - 98$ (101)

Lesson Quiz
Write each ratio as a percent.
1. $\frac{45}{100}$ (45%)
2. $\frac{92}{100}$ (92%)
3. $\frac{15}{100}$ (15%)
4. $\frac{30}{100}$ (30%)
5. 2 out of 100 (2%)
6. 54 out of 100 (54%)
7. 100 out of 100 (100%)

LEVELED PRACTICE

RETEACH 19.1
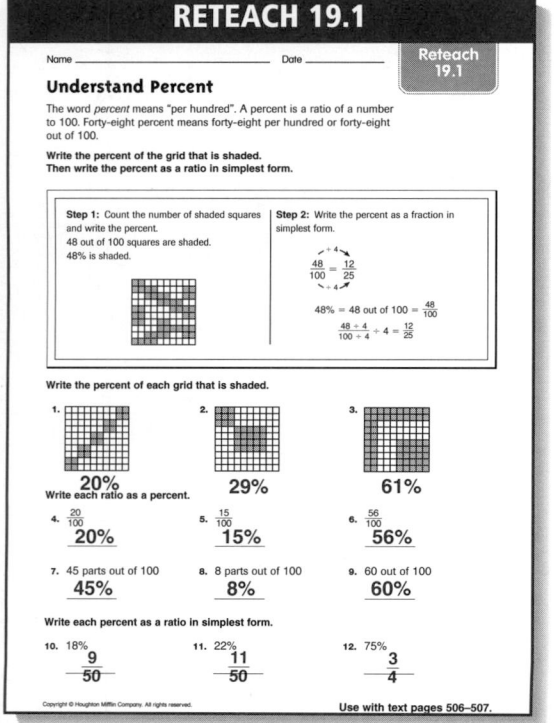

PRACTICE 19.1
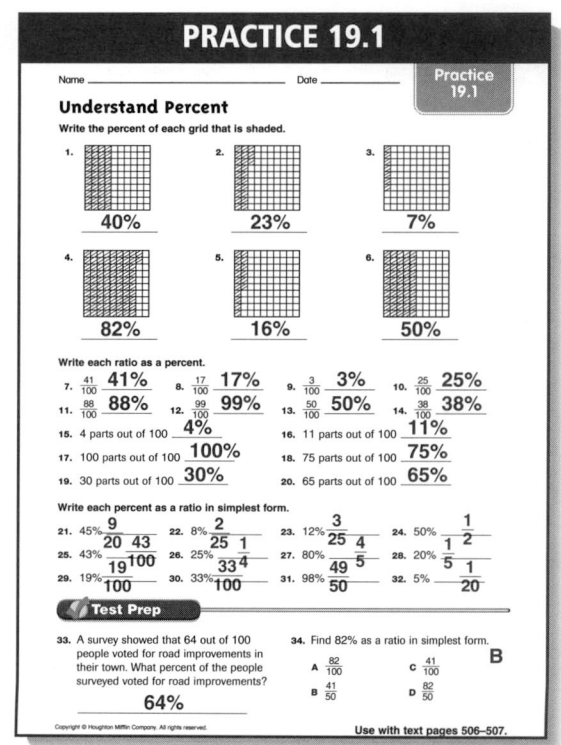

ENRICHMENT 19.1
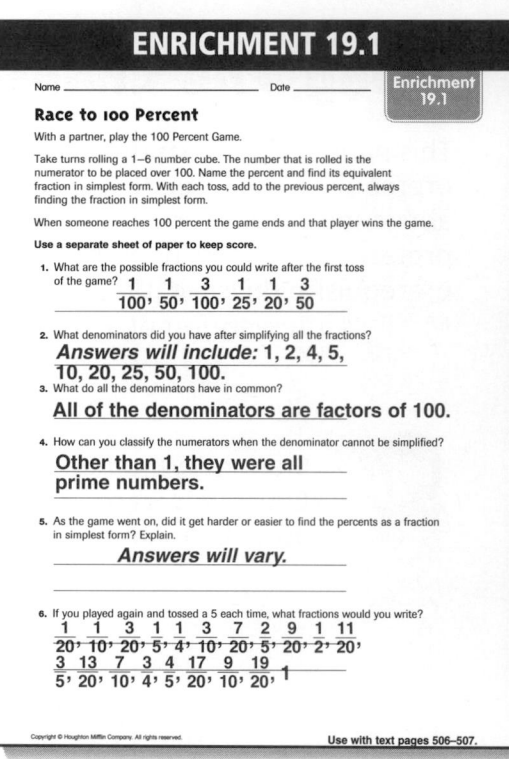

Practice Workbook Page 125

Reaching All Learners
Differentiated Instruction

English Learners

Worksheet 19.1 helps students articulate their thoughts in response to Problem 37 through a series of sentence frames.

Inclusion
VISUAL, SPATIAL

Materials: *grid paper, blue pencils*

Prepare paper in advance by outlining four 10 × 10 unit squares.

- Display *10%*. Have students shade 10 squares. Have them write *10 squares out of 100 are blue: 10%*.
- Repeat for 25%, 50%, and 75%.

Early Finishers
VISUAL, SPATIAL

Materials: *grid paper, red and blue pencils*

- On a new square, have students draw a 2-color design. Have them find the percents of each color.
- Have them make a square that is 36% red, 64% blue.

Technology
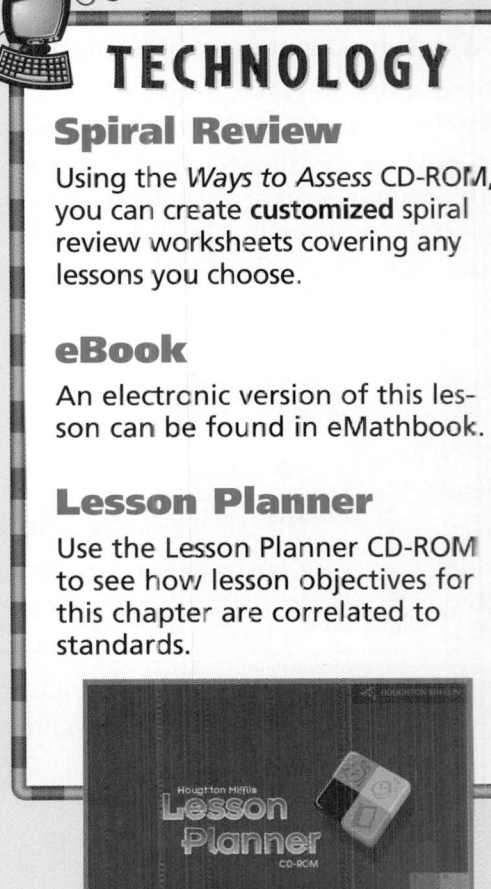

Spiral Review

Using the *Ways to Assess* CD-ROM, you can create **customized** spiral review worksheets covering any lessons you choose.

eBook

An electronic version of this lesson can be found in eMathbook.

Lesson Planner

Use the Lesson Planner CD-ROM to see how lesson objectives for this chapter are correlated to standards.

Science Connection
What's in a Dollar?
Materials: *grid paper, ruler, colored pencils, coins*

- Display the metal composition of 3 U.S. coins:
  Penny: 2.5% copper, 97.5% zinc
  Nickel: 25% nickel, 75% copper
  Dime: 8.3% nickel, 91.7% copper

- Have students make a 10 × 10 grid for each coin. Have them make a color key for each metal. Have them shade the grids to show the metal content of each coin.

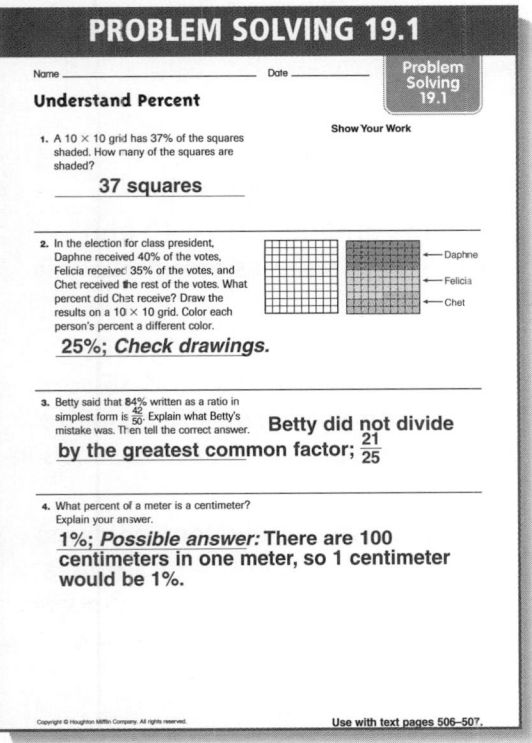

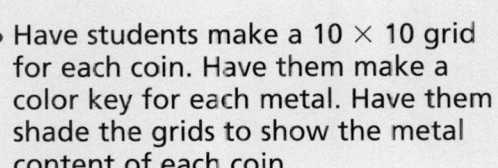

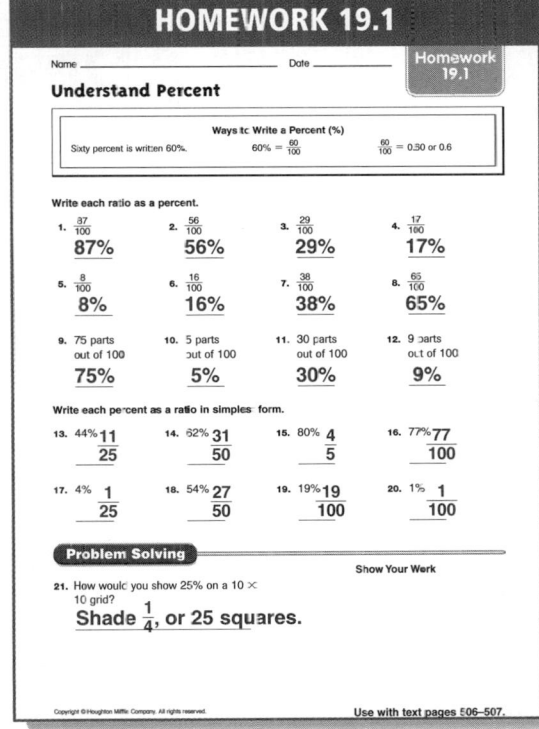

Homework Workbook Page 125

TEACHING LESSON 19.1

LESSON ORGANIZER

Objective Understand percents as ratios.

Resources Reteach, Practice, Enrichment, Problem Solving, Homework, English Learners

Materials Centimeter Grid Transparency, red erasable marker, 2 sheets of paper, grid paper, rulers, colored pencils Learning Tool 13, scissors

Warm-Up Activity
Converting to Decimals

| 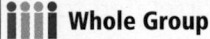 Whole Group | 5 minutes | Visual, Auditory |

- Display: *Tenths, Hundredths, Thousandths.* Write *0.3* under *Tenths.* **What decimal is represented?** (three tenths) Have a volunteer write the fraction that is represented. ($\frac{3}{10}$)

- **Three tenths is equal to how many hundredths?** (30) **What must I add to 0.3 to write thirty hundredths?** (0) Write *0.30* under *Hundredths.* Write $\frac{30}{100}$ under *0.30.*

- Note that the decimals and fractions name the same amount. Repeat with 0.7 and 0.9.

Understand Percent

Objective Understand percents as ratios.

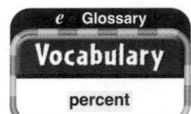
e Glossary
Vocabulary
percent

Materials
grid paper
ruler
colored pencils

Work Together

Work with a partner to write percents.

A **percent** is a ratio that compares a number to 100. The word *percent* means "per hundred." So *fifty percent* means "fifty per hundred," or "fifty out of 100." Percents can also be written in fraction or decimal form.

The symbol for percent is %.

Fifty percent is written 50%.

$50\% = 50{:}100 = \frac{50}{100} = 0.50 \text{ or } 0.5$

STEP 1 On a sheet of grid paper, use a ruler to outline an area that measures 10 units by 10 units.
- How many square units are in the figure? **100**

STEP 2 Shade 40 square units blue, 25 square units yellow, and 15 square units green.
- What is the ratio of blue squares to the total number of squares? **40:100 or 2:5**
- What is the ratio of yellow squares to the total number of squares? **25:100 or 1:4**
- What is the ratio of shaded squares to the total number of squares? **80:100 or 4:5**

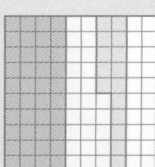

STEP 3 Use the percent symbol to write each percent. What percent of the figure is
- blue?   **40%**
- yellow?   **25%**
- green?   **15%**
- shaded?   **80%**
- unshaded? **20%**

1 Introduce

Materials: *Centimeter Grid Transparency, red erasable marker, 2 sheets of paper*
- Outline a 10 × 10 square on the Centimeter Grid Transparency. Cover up the remaining grid with two sheets of paper. Shade 39 squares red.

- **How many squares are in this grid?** (100) **How many of the squares are shaded red?** (39) Invite a volunteer to go to the chalkboard and write a ratio in fraction form comparing the number of shaded squares to the total number of squares. ($\frac{39}{100}$) Label the first term *number of squares shaded red* and the second term *total number of squares.*

- **When the second term of a ratio is 100, we can write the ratio as a percent.** To write $\frac{39}{100}$ as a percent, write the first term with a percent sign. Write $\frac{39}{100} = 39\%$ on the chalkboard.

2 Develop

Guide students through the *Work Together* section.

- **Look at Step 1.** Have students outline a 10 × 10 unit square on grid paper. **How many squares are inside this 10 × 10 square?** (100)

- **Look at Step 2.** Ask students to shade 40 contiguous squares blue, 25 contiguous squares yellow, and 15 contiguous squares green. **How can you write the ratios so that you remember what they represent?** (Include labels in the ratio. For example, $\frac{40 \text{ blue squares}}{100 \text{ total squares}}$)

- **Look at Step 3.** Have students write equivalent percents for each ratio. **How do you find the number of squares shaded?** (Count the number of blue, yellow, and green squares; add 40 + 25 + 15 for a total of 80 squares shaded, or 80%.)

Write the percent of each grid that is shaded.

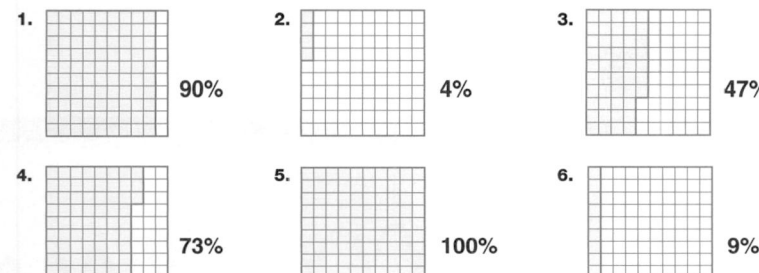

1. 90% 2. 4% 3. 47%

4. 73% 5. 100% 6. 9%

Write each ratio as a percent.

7. $\frac{55}{100}$ **55%** 8. $\frac{2}{100}$ **2%** 9. $\frac{31}{100}$ **31%** 10. $\frac{79}{100}$ **79%** 11. $\frac{90}{100}$ **90%**

12. 48:100 **48%** 13. 16:100 **16%** 14. 91:100 **91%** 15. 63:100 **63%** 16. 8:100 **8%**

17. 35 parts out of 100 **35%** 18. 6 parts out of 100 **6%** 19. 15 parts out of 100 **15%**

20. 1 part out of 100 **1%** 21. 0 parts out of 100 **0%** 22. 50 parts out of 100 **50%**

Write each percent as a ratio in simplest form.

23. 10% $\frac{1}{10}$ 24. 28% $\frac{7}{25}$ 25. 81% $\frac{81}{100}$ 26. 12% $\frac{3}{25}$

27. 39% $\frac{39}{100}$ 28. 53% $\frac{53}{100}$ 29. 62% $\frac{31}{50}$ 30. 98% $\frac{49}{50}$

31. 70% $\frac{7}{10}$ 32. 23% $\frac{23}{100}$ 33. 40% $\frac{2}{5}$ 34. 75% $\frac{3}{4}$

35. 65% $\frac{13}{20}$ 36. 17% $\frac{17}{100}$ 37. 99% $\frac{99}{100}$ 38. 100% $\frac{1}{1}$ or 1

Talk About It • Write About It

You learned about percents as ratios and how to write percents.

39. How would you show 10% on a 10 × 10 grid? How would you show 100%? **shade in 10 squares; shade in all 100 squares**

40. Use models to show how 9% and 90% are different. Which model shows the decimal 0.9? Which model shows the decimal 0.09? **the model that shows 90%; the model that shows 9%**

DAILY TEST PREP

Which ratio represents 50%? (A)

A. $\frac{1}{2}$ C. 0.05

B. $\frac{5}{100}$ D. 50

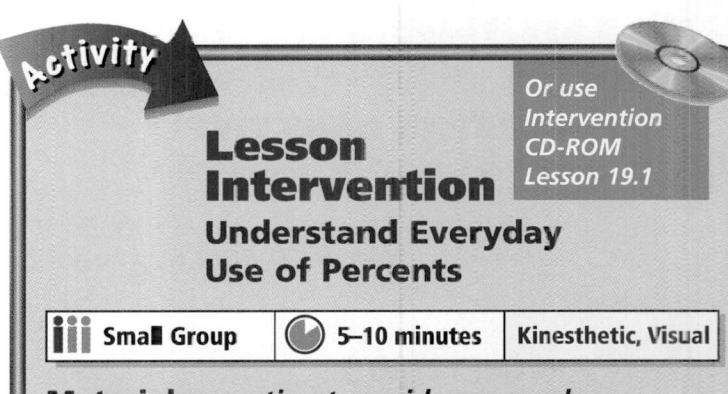

Activity

Lesson Intervention

Or use Intervention CD-ROM Lesson 19.1

Understand Everyday Use of Percents

| Small Group | 5–10 minutes | Kinesthetic, Visual |

Materials: *centimeter grid paper, rulers, colored pencils, scissors*

• **Make and cut out six 10 × 10 squares. Show** students how to make the following flashcards: **0%, 10%, 25%, 50%, 75%, 100%. Label the back of each card with the percent and matching fraction.**

• **Here are some examples of how one of these cards could be used to answer a real-life percent question: If you drank half of your juice, how much of the glass is empty?** (50%) **If your cereal bowl has just a little milk and a few bites of soggy cereal left in it, about how much cereal is in the bowl?** (10%) **If all of your answers on a test are correct, your score will be what percent?** (100%)

---

3 Practice

Assign **Exercises 1–38** as independent work.

• *Exercises 23–38* Remind students to check that each ratio is in lowest terms. For example, many students will write 40% as $\frac{40}{100}$ and may then reduce the ratio to $\frac{4}{10}$. The ratio in simplest form is $\frac{2}{5}$.

• *Exercises 29–30* Help students see that they can reduce the ratios to $\frac{31}{50}$ and $\frac{49}{50}$.

4 Assess and Close

• **What is a percent?** (a ratio that compares a number to 100)

• Assign Exercises 39–40 of the *Talk about It • Write About It* section. Discuss Problem 40. The model for 9% will have 9 shaded parts out of 100 total parts. The model for 90% will have 90 shaded parts out of 100 total parts. Write *0.9* and *0.90* on the chalkboard. **How do you read this number?** (nine tenths) Then point to *0.90* and ask, **How do you read this number?** (ninety hundredths) Write $\frac{9}{10} = \frac{90}{100}$.

Assign the **LESSON QUIZ** on Transparency 19.1 to further assess student understanding.

Keeping a Journal

Have students describe how coins can help them understand percents.

Relate Fractions, Decimals, and Percents

PLANNING THE LESSON

MATHEMATICS OBJECTIVE
Relate fractions, decimals, and percents.

Use Lesson Planner CD-ROM for Lesson 19.2.

Daily Routines

Vocabulary

Ask students what *percent* means. (*Percent* is the *ratio* of a number to 100.) **How would you write 45% as a *ratio*?** ($\frac{45}{100}$) **How would you write an equivalent fraction in simplest terms for $\frac{45}{100}$?** ($\frac{9}{20}$) **How would you write 45% as a *decimal*?** (0.45)

Vocabulary Cards

Meeting North Carolina's Standards
Prepare for Grade 6 Objective **1.02** Develop meaning for percents.

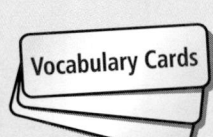

Lesson Transparency **19.2**

Problem of the Day
A pitcher of water is half full. Kareem adds 3 cups of water to make it $\frac{3}{4}$ full. How many cups of water can the pitcher hold? (12 cups)

Quick Review
Write a ratio for each.
1. dollars to cents (1:100)
2. miles to feet (1:5,280)
3. centimeters to millimeters (1:10)
4. inches to feet (12:1)
5. grams to kilograms (1,000:1)
6. ounces to pounds (16:1)

Lesson Quiz
Solve each equation for *n*.
1. $\frac{30}{90} = \frac{1}{n}$ (3)
2. $\frac{80}{100} = \frac{16}{n}$ (20)
3. $70\% = \frac{35}{n}$ (50)
4. $n\% = \frac{13}{50}$ (26)
5. $12\% = \frac{n}{25}$ (3)
6. $0.42 = n\%$ (42)

LEVELED PRACTICE

RETEACH 19.2
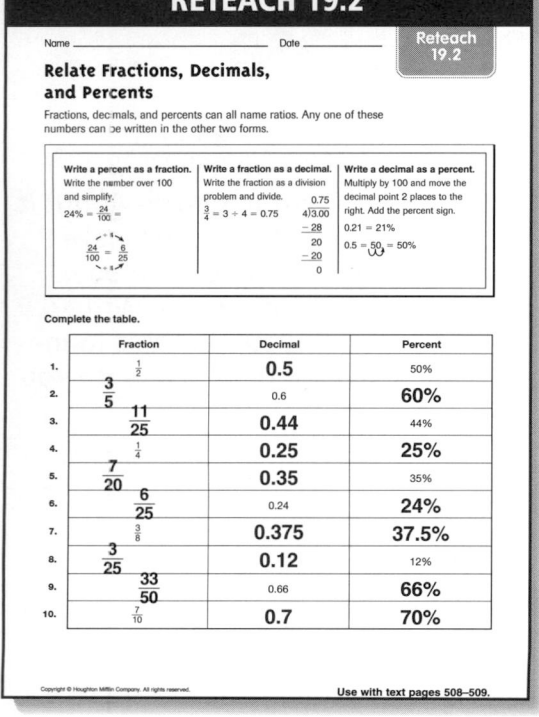

PRACTICE 19.2
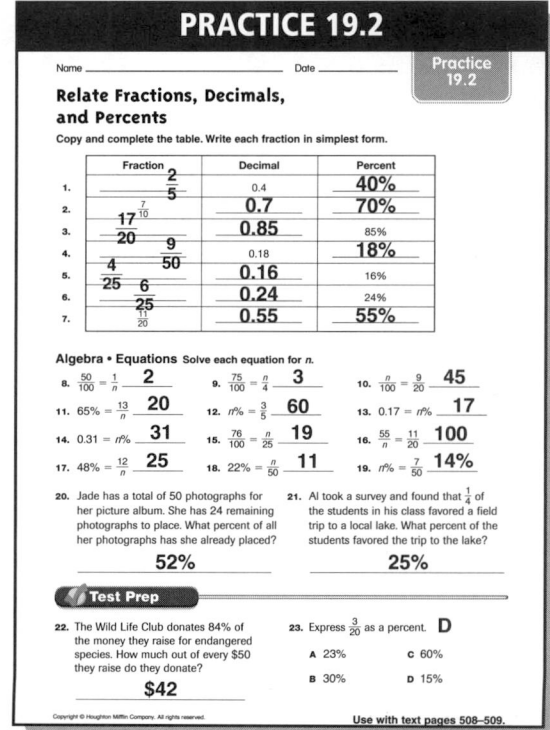

ENRICHMENT 19.2
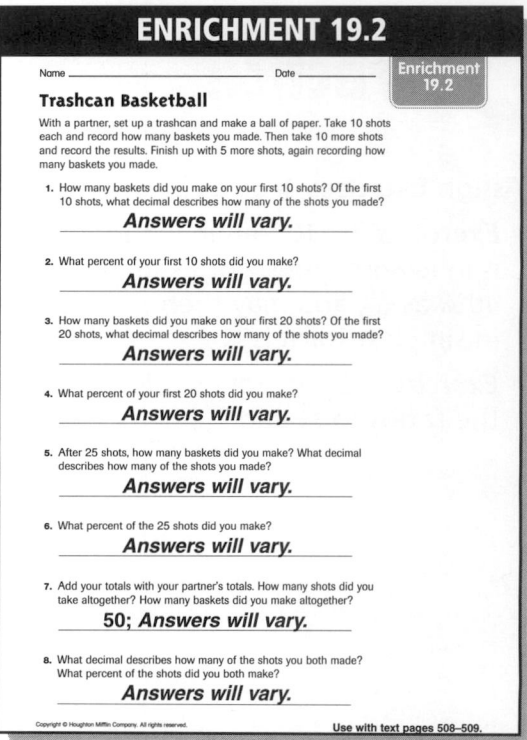

Practice Workbook Page 126

Reaching All Learners

Differentiated Instruction

English Learners

Use Worksheet 19.2 to help students understand how to express ratios as percents and percents as decimals in preparation for completing the tables and other activities in Lesson 2.

Special Needs
VISUAL, AUDITORY

Prepare and distribute a table as shown below:

Fraction →	Decimal →	Percent
$\frac{2}{5}$		
$\frac{10}{50}$		
$\frac{3}{4}$		

Have students fill in the chart.

Early Finishers
VISUAL, AUDITORY

- In 1943, the U.S. mint made 684,628,670 steel pennies. Of those, 217,660,000 were marked with a "D," and 191,550,000 were marked with an "S." About what percent were "D" pennies? "S" pennies? Neither?
(D = 32%; S = 28%; Neither = 40%)

TECHNOLOGY

Spiral Review

To reinforce skills on lessons taught earlier, create **customized** spiral review worksheets using the *Ways to Assess* CD-ROM.

Software

Use *Easy Sheet* or another spreadsheet to explore this lesson more fully.

Education Place

Encourage students to visit Education Place at **eduplace.com/kids/mw/** for more student activities.

Science Connection

Percent of Fat in Food
Materials: *food labels showing grams of fat*

- Show students how to find the number of calories from fat in a hotdog. Write, *Hotdog: 175 calories, 15.8 grams of fat.*

- Tell students that 1 gram of fat corresponds to 9 calories. **Round the** grams of fat and multiply by 9 to find the number of calories from fat. Write, *16 × 9 = 144.* **Write the ratio of fat calories to total calories.** ($\frac{144}{175}$) **Divide to find an equivalent decimal.** (0.82286) **Multiply the decimal by 100 and round to find the percent of calories from fat.** (82%)

- Repeat with other food labels.

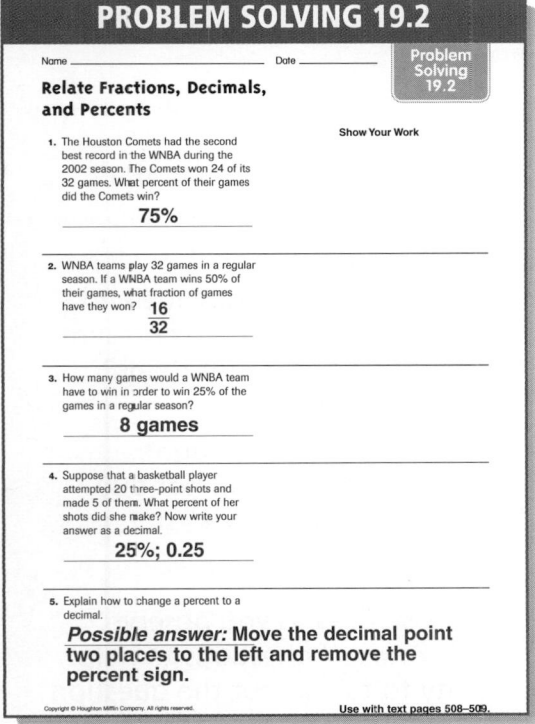

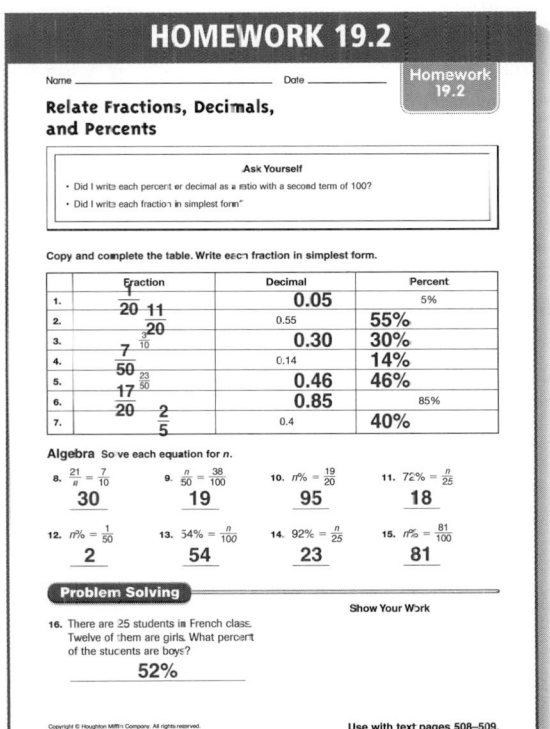

Homework Workbook Page 126

TEACHING LESSON 19.2

Warm-Up Activity
Find Equivalent Ratios With 100 as the Second Term

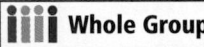 Whole Group | 5 minutes | Visual, Auditory

- Take notes on each step as I find an equivalent ratio using proportions.

- **What ratio is equivalent to $\frac{3}{5}$, yet has 100 in the second term?** Display:

Write a proportion.	$\frac{3}{5} = \frac{n}{100}$
Find cross products.	$300 = 5n$
Simplify.	$\frac{300}{5} = \frac{5n}{5}$
	$n = 60$

- **How do we write the equivalent ratio?** (Substitute the value of n to write $\frac{60}{100}$.)

- Have volunteers repeat the activity finding equivalent ratios with 100 in the second term. Use the ratios $\frac{2}{8}$, $\frac{1}{10}$, and $\frac{5}{4}$. ($\frac{25}{100}$, $\frac{10}{100}$, $\frac{125}{100}$)

Relate Fractions, Decimals, and Percents

Objective Relate fractions, decimals, and percents.

Learn About It

On Saturday, 50% of the people who visited a department store bought only one item and one out of four people bought more than one item. The rest of the people did not buy anything. What decimal represents the percent of people who bought nothing?

You can write percents in fraction form or in decimal form.

Try this activity to relate fractions, decimals, and percents.

Materials grid paper, ruler, colored pencils

STEP 1 Fifty percent of the people bought only one item. Outline a 10 × 10 grid on grid paper. Shade 50% of the grid red.
- How many square units do you need to shade? **50**
- What decimal can you write for 50%? **0.50, or 0.5**
- What fraction of the grid is shaded? $\frac{50}{100}$, or $\frac{1}{2}$

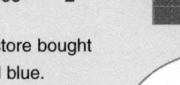

STEP 2 One out of four people who visited the store bought more than one item. Shade $\frac{1}{4}$ of the grid blue.
- How many square units did you shade blue? **25**
- What percent of the grid is shaded blue? **25%**
- What decimal can you write for that percent? **0.25**

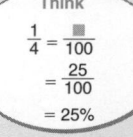
Think
$\frac{1}{4} = \frac{\blacksquare}{100}$
$= \frac{25}{100}$
$= 25\%$

STEP 3 The part of the grid that is unshaded represents the percent of the people who bought nothing on Saturday.
- What percent of the grid is unshaded? **25%**
- What decimal can you write for that percent? **0.25**

Solution: 25% of the people bought nothing at the store on Saturday. The decimal form of this percent is 0.25.

---

1 Introduce

Teaching Transparency for 19.2

Materials: _Centimeter Grid Transparency, blue erasable marker, 2 sheets of paper_

- Outline a 10 × 10 square on the transparency. Cover up the remaining grid with two sheets of paper. Shade 3 squares blue.

- **How many squares are in this grid?** (100) **How many are shaded blue?** (3) Invite a volunteer to the chalkboard to write a ratio in fraction form that compares the number of shaded squares to the total number of squares. ($\frac{3}{100}$) **Can we write this ratio as a decimal?** (0.03) Write $\frac{3}{100} = 0.03$ on the chalkboard.

- **When the second term of a ratio is 100, we can write the ratio as a percent.** To write $\frac{3}{100}$ as a percent, write the first term with a percent sign: $\frac{3}{100} = 0.03 = 3\%$.

2 Develop

Guide students through the _Learn About It_ section.

- **What do we need to find out?** (the decimal that represents the percent of people who did not buy anything)

- **Look at Steps 1 and 2.** Have students shade blue and red squares. **What equation can we write to represent the total percent of the people who bought items?** (50% + 25% = 75%)

- **Look at Step 3. Since 75% of the people bought something, what percent of the people did not buy something?** (25%) **What decimal equals 25%?** (0.25)

Guided Practice

Have students complete **Exercises 1–3** as you observe. Remind them to use the _Ask Yourself_ questions to help. Give students the opportunity to talk about the question in _Explain Your Thinking._

Copy and complete the table. Write each fraction in simplest form.

Ask Yourself
- Did I write each percent or decimal as a ratio with a second term of 100?
- Did I write each fraction in simplest form?

	Fraction Form	Decimal Form	Percent	
1.	$\frac{1}{10}$	■	10%	0.1
2.	■	0.2	■	$\frac{1}{5}$; 20%
3.	■	■	65%	$\frac{13}{20}$; 0.65

TEST TIPS *Possible answer:* $\frac{5}{100}$ written as a decimal is 0.05 and 5% written as a decimal is also 0.05 so $\frac{5}{100}$ and 5% represent the same ratio.

 **TEST TIPS Explain Your Thinking** ▶ Explain why $\frac{5}{100}$ and 5% represent the same ratio.

Practice and Problem Solving

Copy and complete the table. Write each fraction in simplest form.

	Fraction Form	Decimal Form	Percent	
4.	■	■	50%	$\frac{1}{2}$; 0.5
5.	■	0.6	■	$\frac{3}{5}$; 60%
6.	$\frac{3}{4}$	■	■	0.75; 75%

	Fraction Form	Decimal Form	Percent	
7.	■	■	80%	$\frac{4}{5}$; 0.8
8.	■	0.9	■	$\frac{9}{10}$; 90%
9.	■	0.4	■	$\frac{2}{5}$; 40%

✗ Algebra • **Equations** Solve each equation for *n*.

10. $\frac{25}{100} = \frac{1}{n}$ **4**   11. $\frac{36}{n} = \frac{9}{25}$ **100**   12. $12\% = \frac{n}{25}$ **3**   13. $18\% = \frac{36}{n}$ **200**

14. $n\% = \frac{7}{20}$ **35**   15. $n\% = \frac{23}{50}$ **46**   16. $0.94 = n\%$ **94**   17. $0.72 = n\%$ **72**

22. **19;** *Possible answer:* $95\% = \frac{95}{100}$, so divide 95 by 5 to find how many shots out of 20 the goalie blocked.

Solve.

18. Three fifths of the items in a grocery store are marked down from their original prices. What percent of the items in the store are marked down? **60%**

19. There are 25 students practicing soccer. Nine of them are girls. What percent of the students are girls? What percent of the students are boys? **36%; 64%**

Daily Review	Test Prep

Estimate. Then add or subtract.
(Ch. 11, Lessons 2-4)

20. $5.691 + 0.78$ 21. $0.932 - 0.64$
   7; 6.471   **0; 0.292**

 22. **Free Response** A goalie blocked 95% of the shots during a soccer game. How many shots out of 20 did the goalie block? Explain.
See above.

Extra Practice See page 525, Set A.

Test Prep Transparency
19.2

How do you write $\frac{20}{100}$ as a percent? (D)

A. $\frac{1}{5}$ B. $\frac{5}{100}$ C. 0.02   D. 20%

Activity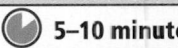

Or use Intervention CD-ROM Lesson 19.2

Lesson Intervention
Writing Equivalent Fractions, Decimals, and Percents

👥 Small Group	🕐 5–10 minutes	Kinesthetic, Visual

Materials: *Number Lines transparency and copies for students, calculators (optional)*

- Give out copies of number line 1. Write 0%, 50%, and 100% above the line and 0.00, 0.50, and 1.00 below. Beneath these numbers write $\frac{0}{100}$, $\frac{50}{100}$, and $\frac{100}{100}$.

- Write $\frac{20}{100}$. Have students divide to find the equivalent decimal. (0.20) Next have them multiply the decimal by 100 to find the equivalent percent. (20%) Write 20% above the line; below it write 0.20 and $\frac{20}{100}$. Repeat with $\frac{70}{100}$ and $\frac{35}{100}$.

 **Practice**

Assign **Exercises 4–22** as independent work.

- **Algebra • Equations for Exercises 10–17** If necessary, remind students that each of these equations can be solved by writing a proportion with equivalent ratios. Suggest they rewrite equations such as $12\% = \frac{n}{25}$ as $\frac{12}{100} = \frac{n}{25}$ and solve for *n*.

Common Error

Forgetting the simplest form Sometimes students do not write equivalent fractions in simplest form. Help them by reminding them to check their solutions.

 **Assess and Close**

- **How do you write the ratio $\frac{4}{5}$ as an equivalent ratio with a second term of 100?** (Write $\frac{4}{5} = \frac{n}{100}$ and solve for *n*; $\frac{80}{100}$.) **How do you write it as a decimal?** (Divide 80 by 100 to find the decimal, .80)

- **How do you say 0.80?** (eighty hundredths) **How do you write it as a fraction?** ($\frac{80}{100}$) **What is $\frac{80}{100}$ in simplest form?** ($\frac{4}{5}$)

Assign the **LESSON QUIZ** on Transparency 19.2 to further assess student understanding.

📝 Keeping a Journal

Have students explain how to find each equivalent form of $\frac{45}{100}$.

Compare Fractions, Decimals, and Percents

Lesson 19.3

PLANNING THE LESSON

MATHEMATICS OBJECTIVE
Use fractions, decimals, and percents to compare numbers.

Use Lesson Planner CD-ROM for Lesson 19.3.

Daily Routines

Vocabulary

Write the following on the chalkboard: *Shall I compare thee to a summer's day?* **How can Shakespeare compare someone to a summer day?** (Allow a variety of responses. He is saying that some aspect of the person is like the warmth of a summer day.) Explain that the word *compare* means to describe the likeness or unlikeness between two objects or ideas.

Vocabulary Cards

Meeting North Carolina's Standards
Prepare for Grade 6 Objective **1.02** Develop meaning for percents.

Lesson Transparency 19.3

Problem of the Day
At 7:00 A.M., the bag of puffed cereal is 50% full. At 10:00 A.M., five cups of cereal are eaten and now the bag is $\frac{1}{4}$ full. How many cups of cereal does the bag hold? (20)

Quick Review
Write each in word form.
1. 27.04 (twenty-seven and four hundredths)
2. $\frac{32}{100}$ (thirty-two hundredths)
3. $3\frac{2}{10}$ (three and two tenths)
4. 207.4 (two hundred seven and four tenths)

Lesson Quiz
Order each set from least to greatest.
1. $\frac{12}{25}$, 0.6, 25% (25%, $\frac{12}{25}$, 0.6)
2. $\frac{5}{10}$, $\frac{18}{20}$, 45% (45%, $\frac{5}{10}$, $\frac{18}{20}$)
3. 19%, $\frac{20}{100}$, $\frac{13}{50}$ (19%, $\frac{20}{100}$, $\frac{13}{50}$)
4. $\frac{75}{100}$, $\frac{2}{3}$, 64% (64%, $\frac{2}{3}$, $\frac{75}{100}$)

LEVELED PRACTICE

RETEACH 19.3
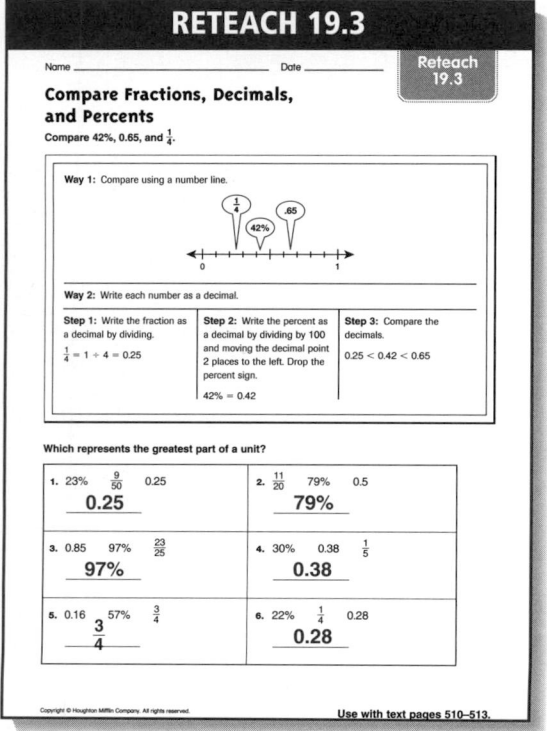

PRACTICE 19.3
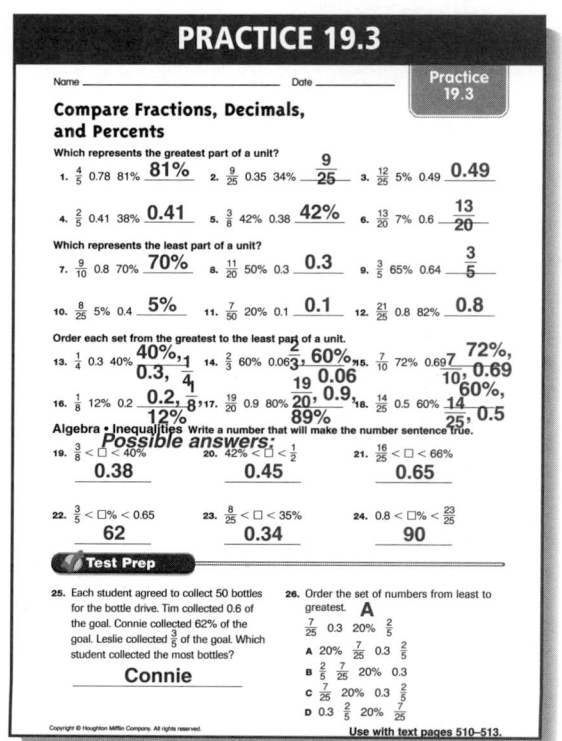

ENRICHMENT 19.3
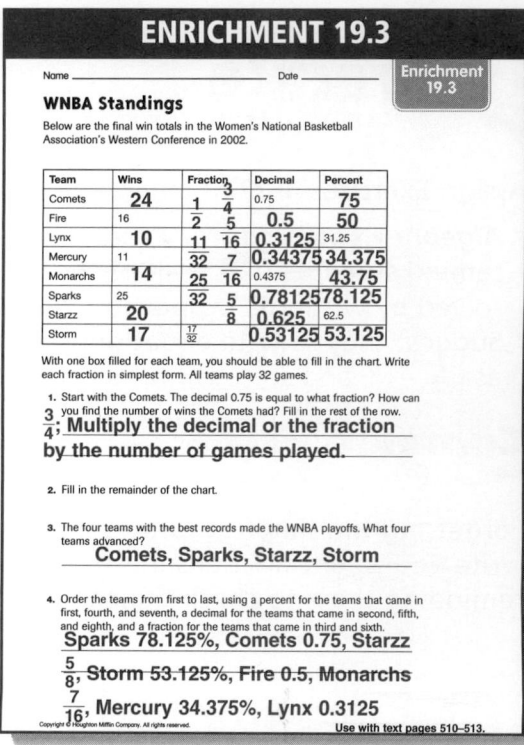

Practice Workbook Page 127

Reaching All Learners
Differentiated Instruction

English Learners

Worksheet 19.3 explains the use of the quantitative adjectives *great* and *little* and their related word forms to help students understand and complete the activities in Lesson 3.

Inclusion
VISUAL, SPATIAL

Materials: *chalk*

- Display 2 grids: 10×1 and 10×10. Display $\frac{7}{10}$ 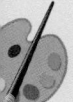 $\frac{69}{100}$. Shade grids to match fractions.

- Show students how to divide the 10×1 grid into a 10×10 grid. Have them count the shaded squares. Compare the grids. Then write the greater-than symbol inside the oval. Have students repeat with other fractions.

Gifted and Talented
VISUAL, SPATIAL

- Display these sequences:
  1. $\frac{1}{2}, \frac{2}{3}, \frac{3}{4}, \frac{4}{5}, \frac{5}{6}, \ldots$
  2. 0.15, 0.30, 0.45, . . .
  3. $\frac{1}{4}$, 0.5, $\frac{3}{4}$, 1.0, $\frac{5}{4}$, . . .

  Have students find the next three terms in each set.

- Have students model the exercise to write their own sequences.

Art Connection

Color Solutions
Materials: *red and blue food coloring, 9 clear plastic cups*

- Fill cups with equal amounts of water. Arrange in a row. Moving left to right, put 8 drops of red in the first cup, 7 in the second, and so on down to 0 drops in the 9th. Then go right to left with the blue.

- **What can we label the left-most cup? right-most? middle?** (100% red; 100% blue; purple: 50% red, 50% blue)

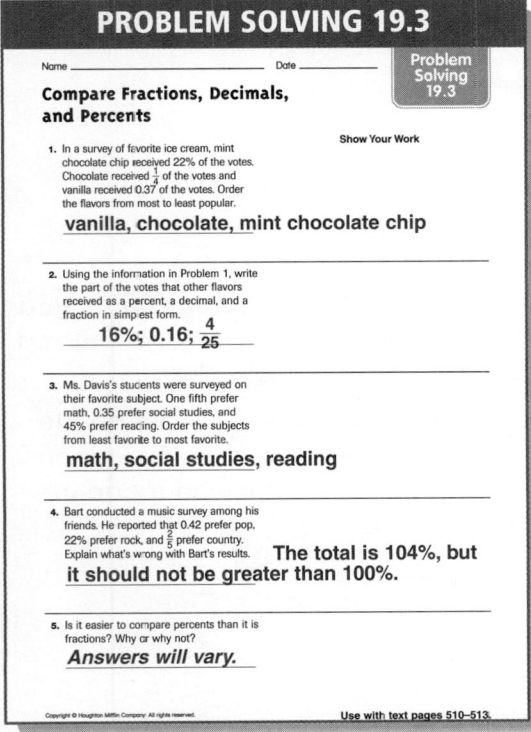

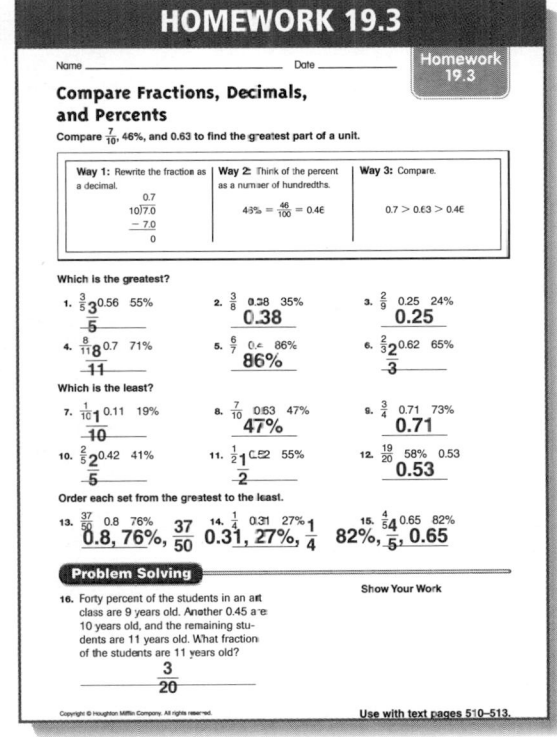

Homework Workbook Page 127

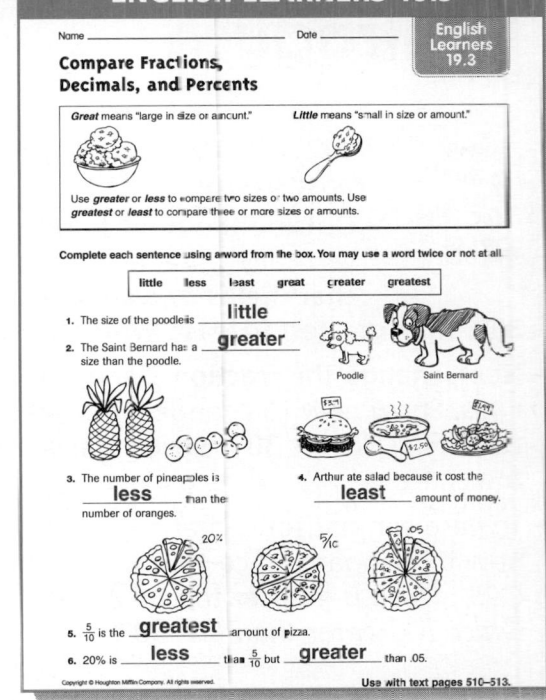

TEACHING LESSON 19.3

Activity

Warm-Up Activity
Using Decimals to Compare Fractions

|  Whole Group | ⏱ 5 minutes | Visual, Auditory |

Materials: *Decimal Place-Value Chart Transparency, blank transparency*

- Write: $\frac{3}{4}$ ⬤ $\frac{4}{5}$. **To write any fraction as a decimal, divide the numerator by the denominator. On the blank transparency, demonstrate** *3 ÷ 4* **and** *4 ÷ 5.* $(\frac{3}{4} = \frac{0.75}{4)3.00} \quad \frac{4}{5} = \frac{0.8}{5)4.00})$

- Write each quotient, *0.75* and *0.8*, on the Decimal Place-Value Chart Transparency.

- **0.8 equals 0.80. Write a zero at the end to help compare them.** Write a zero in the chart so *0.8* becomes *0.80.* Write: *Since 0.75 < 0.80, then* $\frac{3}{4} < \frac{4}{5}$.

 Lesson 3

Compare Fractions, Decimals, and Percents

Objective Use fractions, decimals, and percents to compare numbers.

Learn About It  MathTracks 2/22 Listen and Understand

On the first of the month, The Beach Shop received a shipment of shorts in 3 colors—red, blue, and green. There were equal numbers of each color.

By the end of the month, $\frac{2}{5}$ of the red shorts, 78% of the blue shorts, and 0.55 of the green shorts had been sold. Which color of shorts was the most popular that month?

Try this activity to represent and compare $\frac{2}{5}$, **78%, and 0.55.**

Materials grid paper, ruler, colored pencils

 STEP 1 Outline a 10 × 10 grid on grid paper. Shade 2 of every 5 squares red.
- How did you find $\frac{2}{5}$ of the grid? **See at right.**
- What decimal does the grid show? **0.4**

Possible answer: Color 2 out of every 5 squares red or divide the grid into five equal parts and shade two of them.

STEP 2 Outline another 10 × 10 grid and shade 78% blue.
- How did you know how to show 78%? **78% means 78 out of 100**
- What decimal does the grid show? **0.78**

STEP 3 Outline a third 10 × 10 grid and shade 0.55 green.
- How did you know how to show 0.55? **0.55 means 55 out of 100 or fifty-five hundredths**

STEP 4 Compare the three grids.
- Which color had the greatest number of squares shaded? **blue** Which percent is greatest? **78% is greatest.**

Solution: Blue shorts were the most popular that month.

Introduce

Teaching Transparency for **19.3**

Materials: *Decimal Place-Value Chart Transparency*

- Outside the right-hand side of the chart, write vertically $\frac{1}{4}$, *0.2*, and *30%.* **A decimal place-value chart helps to compare and order** $\frac{1}{4}$, **0.2 and 30% from greatest to least.** Write the decimal *0.2* in the chart.

- **Next, change the fraction** $\frac{1}{4}$ **and the percent 30% to decimals.** Show how to change $\frac{1}{4}$ to a decimal. Write *0.25* in the chart. **How is 30% written as a decimal?** Write *0.30* in the chart.

- To ease comparisons, change *0.2* to *0.20.* Demonstrate how to compare place values. Display: *0.30 is greater than 0.25, which is greater than 0.20; 30% is greater than* $\frac{1}{4}$, *which is greater than 0.2.* 30% $> \frac{1}{4} > 0.2$

Develop

Guide students through the *Learn About It* section.

- **What do you need to find out?** (which color shorts were most popular in a certain month)

When you compare fractions, decimals, and percents you can write each as either a decimal or percent. This allows you to see the relationship of one to the other.

- **Look at Step 1.** Write on the board: $\frac{2}{5} = \frac{n}{100}$. **How do we find the equivalent ratio?** (Solve by using cross-products and then solving for *n*.) **So 40 out of 100 squares on a grid are shaded red. What percent is this?** (40%)

Compare $\frac{4}{5}$, 27%, and 0.7.

Different Ways to Compare $\frac{4}{5}$, 27%, and 0.7

Way ❶ You can use a number line.

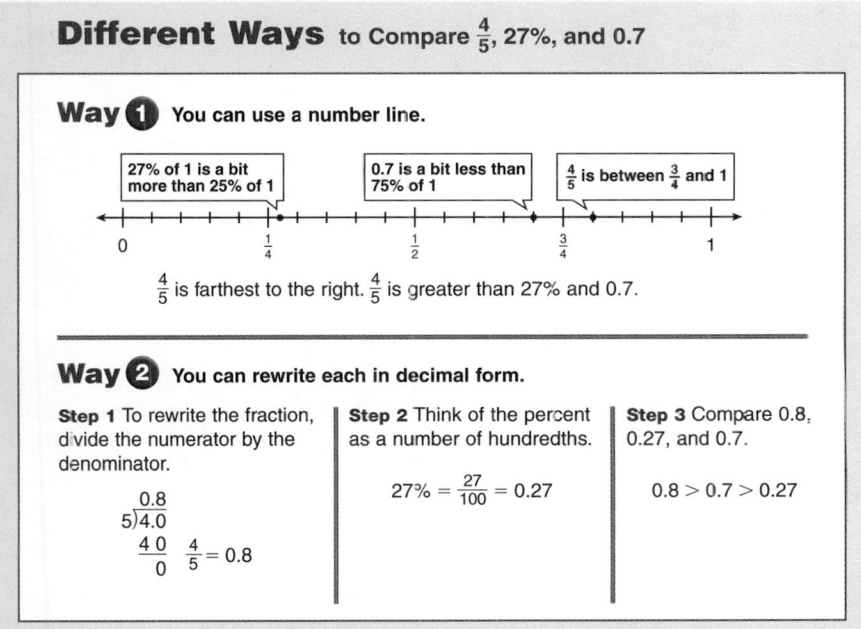

27% of 1 is a bit more than 25% of 1

0.7 is a bit less than 75% of 1

$\frac{4}{5}$ is between $\frac{3}{4}$ and 1

$\frac{4}{5}$ is farthest to the right. $\frac{4}{5}$ is greater than 27% and 0.7.

Way ❷ You can rewrite each in decimal form.

Step 1 To rewrite the fraction, divide the numerator by the denominator.

$$5)\overline{4.0}$$ with 0.8, $\frac{4\;0}{0}$ $\frac{4}{5} = 0.8$

Step 2 Think of the percent as a number of hundredths.

$$27\% = \frac{27}{100} = 0.27$$

Step 3 Compare 0.8, 0.27, and 0.7.

$$0.8 > 0.7 > 0.27$$

Solution: $\frac{4}{5}$ is greater than either 27% or 0.7.

Another Example

Order $\frac{9}{25}$, 38%, and 0.313 from the greatest to the least.

$9 \div 25 = 0.36$, so $\frac{9}{25} = 0.36$. 38% can be written in decimal form as 0.38.

$0.38 > 0.36 > 0.313$, so $38\% > \frac{9}{25} > 0.313$.

Guided Practice

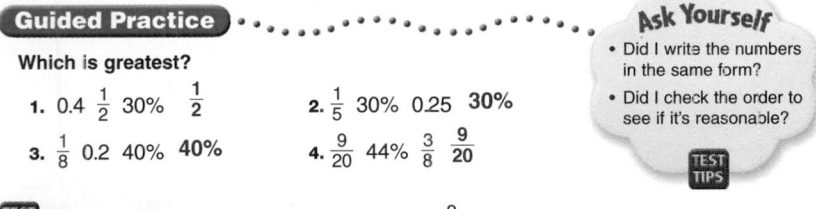

Which is greatest?

1. 0.4 $\frac{1}{2}$ 30% $\frac{1}{2}$

2. $\frac{1}{5}$ 30% 0.25 **30%**

3. $\frac{1}{8}$ 0.2 40% **40%**

4. $\frac{9}{20}$ 44% $\frac{3}{8}$ $\frac{9}{20}$

Ask Yourself
- Did I write the numbers in the same form?
- Did I check the order to see if it's reasonable?

TEST TIPS **Explain Your Thinking ▶** How could you write $\frac{9}{20}$ in decimal form by first writing it as a percent in ratio form?

Write $\frac{9}{20}$ as $\frac{45}{100}$, $\frac{45}{100} = 0.45$.

Go On ▶

Quick Check Options

The following activities will help students prepare for the Quick Check or may be used as an alternative assessment.

Vocabulary Review *(individual, small group, or whole class)*

Have students review the following vocabulary words by giving an example of how each term is used in this chapter.

- proportion

Math Conversations *(small group or whole class)*

Have students discuss what they have learned about comparing, fractions, decimals and percents in this chapter. Encourage students to ask each other questions to clarify their understanding.

Writing Prompt *(individual or partners)*

To solidify student understanding of vocabulary and concepts, have each student complete the following sentence:

The thing I found most difficult about comparing. fractions, decimals, and percents is _____.

- **Look at Step 2.** In a 100-square grid, how many squares equal 78%? (Since 78% means 78 out of 100, 78 squares.) **So 78 squares out of 100 squares are shaded blue.**

- **Look at Step 3. How can 0.55 be written as a fraction with a denominator of 100?** ($\frac{55}{100}$) So, 55 out of 100 squares are shaded green.

- **Look at Step 4. What percent does each shaded grid represent?** (40% of the red shorts were sold, 78% of the blue shorts were sold, and 55% of the green shorts were sold.) **The blue shorts were the most popular, since 78 out of 100 or 78% were sold.**

Look at Different Ways. Point out to students that on page 510, students wrote each value as a percent to compare. In the *Different Ways* section, students wrote each value as a decimal.

Guided Practice

Have students complete **Exercises 1–4** as you observe. Remind them to use the *Ask Yourself* questions to help. Give students the opportunity to talk about the question in *Explain Your Thinking*.

DAILY TEST PREP

What fraction in simplest form with the denominator 4 makes this inequality true? ($\frac{3}{4}$)

65% < ■ < 0.80

Or use Intervention CD-ROM Lesson 19.3

Lesson Intervention

Comparing Fractions, Decimals, and Percents With a Number Line

| iii Small Group | 🕐 5–10 minutes | Kinesthetic, Visual |

Materials: *Number Lines Transparency and copies of it for students, rulers*

- Write on the transparency: *Compare from least to greatest: 39%, $\frac{7}{20}$, and $\frac{1}{4}$.*

- Label Number Line 2 evenly from 0% to 100%. Label Number Line 1 evenly $\frac{0}{20}$, $\frac{1}{20}$, $\frac{2}{20}$ and so on to $\frac{20}{20}$. Have students label their number lines along with you.

- Draw a vertical line through both number lines to show that $\frac{5}{20}$ (or $\frac{1}{4}$) equals 25%. Place a point for $\frac{1}{4}$. Repeat the activity for $\frac{7}{20}$ and 39% and then compare all three points.

Practice and Problem Solving

Which is greatest?

5. $\frac{3}{5}$ 59% 0.62 **0.62**   6. $\frac{3}{8}$ 9% 0.8 **0.8**   7. $\frac{11}{25}$ 0.4 43% $\frac{11}{25}$

8. $\frac{5}{8}$ 0.56 59% $\frac{5}{8}$ 9. $\frac{17}{25}$ 70% 0.69 **70%**   10. $\frac{1}{10}$ 8% 0.09 $\frac{1}{10}$

Which is least?

11. $\frac{4}{5}$ 0.2 60% **0.2**   12. $\frac{3}{5}$ 0.4 80% **0.4**   13. $\frac{4}{5}$ 0.9 85% $\frac{4}{5}$

14. $\frac{1}{5}$ 0.1 25% **0.1**   15. $\frac{3}{20}$ 4% 0.06 **4%**   16. $\frac{7}{10}$ 0.6 30% **30%**

Order each set from greatest to least.

17. $\frac{3}{10}$ 0.25 $\frac{3}{10}$ 20% **0.25, 20%**   18. $\frac{9}{10}$ 0.75 $\frac{9}{10}$ 80% **80%, 0.75**   19. $\frac{7}{20}$ 0.3 40% **40%, $\frac{7}{20}$, 0.3**

20. $\frac{12}{25}$ 0.3 50% **50%, $\frac{12}{25}$, 0.3**   21. $\frac{13}{20}$ 0.7 67% **0.7, 67%, $\frac{13}{20}$**   22. $\frac{3}{50}$ 0.6 $\frac{3}{50}$ 3% **0.6, $\frac{3}{50}$, 3%**

23. $\frac{19}{20}$ 0.99 98% $\frac{19}{20}$ **0.99, 98%, $\frac{19}{20}$**   24. $\frac{1}{3}$ 0.25 30% **$\frac{1}{3}$, 30%, 0.25**   25. $\frac{3}{8}$ 0.43 52% **52%, 0.43, $\frac{3}{8}$**

X Algebra • Inequalities Write a number that will make the number sentence true. *Possible answers are given.*

26. $\frac{2}{5}$ < ■ < 45% **0.41**   27. 62% < ■ < $\frac{2}{3}$ **0.63**   28. $\frac{12}{25}$ < ■ < 50% **0.49**

29. 0.82 < ■% < $\frac{17}{20}$ **83**   30. $\frac{5}{8}$ < ■ < 63% **0.626**   31. 0.03 < ■% < $\frac{1}{16}$ **5**

Solve.   33. He wrote 4% as 0.4, but 4% is actually written 0.04 as a decimal.

32. **Analyze** In Ben's Books, 0.3 of the shelves have adult fiction, 25% have adult nonfiction, and $\frac{9}{20}$ of the shelves have children's books. Which kinds of books take up the most shelves in the bookstore? **children's books**

33. **What's Wrong?** Sam ordered the numbers $\frac{7}{20}$, 4%, and 0.34 from least to greatest. What did Sam do wrong?

34. Orange juice and lemonade were sold during a concert intermission. Three fifths of the sales were orange juice and 40% were lemonade. Which drink was less popular? **lemonade**

Sam

$\frac{7}{20}$ 4%   0.34
↓   ↓
0.35 0.4

$20\overline{)70}$
 60
───
 100
 100
───
  0

0.34 < 0.35 < 0.4
So, 0.34 < $\frac{7}{20}$ < 4%

Extra Practice See page 525, Set B.

---

3 Practice

Assign **Exercises 5–34** as independent work.

- *Exercises 5–25* Students can write numbers as percents, decimals, or fractions with the same denominator. For example, $\frac{17}{25}$, 70%, and 0.69 can be written as 0.68, 0.70, and 0.69; as 68%, 70%, and 69%; or as $\frac{68}{100}$, $\frac{70}{100}$, and $\frac{69}{100}$.

- *Algebra • Inequalities for Exercises 26–31* Help students understand that several values will make the sentence true.

- *Problem Solving for Problems 32–34* Have students share their solutions.

Common Error

Misinterpreting percents Students may sometimes write single digit percents such as 9% as the decimal 0.9. Remind them that 9% equals $\frac{9}{100}$ or 0.09.

4 Assess and Close

- **What do you need to do in order to compare the values of a decimal, a percent, and a fraction?** (Write them in an equivalent form.)

- **How do I write a fraction as a decimal?** (Divide the numerator by the denominator.)

- **If you write $\frac{1}{4}$, 0.23, and 22% as equivalent decimals you have 0.25, 0.23, and 0.22. How do you compare these three decimals?** (Compare from the greatest place-value to the least place-value (left to right).)

Assign the **LESSON QUIZ** on Transparency 19.3 to further assess student understanding.

Quick Check

Check your understanding of Lessons 1–3.

Write each ratio as a percent. (Lesson 1)

1. $\frac{27}{100}$ **27%**   2. 6:100 **6 %**   3. 41 out of 100 **41%**

Write a decimal, a percent, and a fraction in simplest form for each ratio. (Lesson 2)

4. $\frac{12}{50}$ **0.24; 24%; $\frac{6}{25}$** 5. $\frac{29}{100}$ **0.29; 29%; $\frac{29}{100}$** 6. $\frac{40}{100}$ **0.4; 40%; $\frac{2}{5}$** 7. $\frac{112}{200}$ **0.56; 56%; $\frac{14}{25}$**

Order each set from the greatest to the least. (Lesson 3)

8. $\frac{13}{40}$ 0.3 25%   9. 0.65 $\frac{21}{25}$ 70%   10. 5% 0.1 $\frac{1}{8}$
  $\frac{13}{40}$, 0.3, 25%   **$\frac{21}{25}$, 70%, 0.65**   **$\frac{1}{8}$, 0.1, 5%**

Quick Check

Purpose: The Quick Check allows you to assess the students' understanding of the concepts presented in Lessons 1–3.

Items	Objectives Tested	Pages	Intervention
1–3	Understand percents as ratios.	506–507	Reteach Resource 19.1 *Ways to Success* 19.1
4–7	Relate fractions, decimals, and percents.	508–509	Reteach Resource 19.2 *Ways to Success* 19.2
8–10	Use fractions, decimals, and percents to compare numbers	510–513	Reteach Resource 19.3 *Ways to Success* 19.3

WEEKLY WR READER® eduplace.com/kids/mw/

Real World Connection

L👀KING AROUND

You have learned about percent.

Look around your school, your home, and your shopping mall. Make a display of all the places where you see percents! ***Displays will vary.***

Chapter 19 Lesson 3 513

Keeping a Journal

Ask students to write a paragraph about how the old saying "You can't compare apples to oranges," applies to the experience of comparing fractions, decimals, and percents.

Real World Connection

Looking Around

- Review the examples of percents shown. **The Nutrition Facts label provides the percent of the Recommended Daily Allowance (RDA) for each nutrient. The bank advertisement shows the interest rate at which the bank will lend money. The quiz shows the percent of questions that were answered correctly. The store advertisement shows the percent reduction in price.**

- Suggest that students try to find examples of percents in as many different contexts as possible. Provide clues such as weather predictions and demographic statistics.

Find 10% of a Number

PLANNING THE LESSON

MATHEMATICS OBJECTIVE

Use mental math to find 10% and multiples of 10% of a number.

 Use Lesson Planner CD-ROM for Lesson 19.4.

Daily Routines

Vocabulary

Review the meaning of *multiple.* In arithmitic, a *multiple* is a number which is the product of a given integer and another integer. What are the first ten multiples of 2? (2, 4, 6, 8, 10, 12, 14, 16, 18, 20) What are the first ten multiples of 10? (10, 20, 30, 40, 50, 60, 70, 80, 90, 100)

Vocabulary Cards

Meeting North Carolina's Standards

Prepare for Grade 7 Objective **1.02** Develop fluency in addition, subtraction, multiplication, and division of rational numbers.

Lesson
Transparency
19.4

Problem of the Day

I am a fraction with the digits 1, 2, and 4. I am less than $\frac{1}{4}$. Which fractions could I be? ($\frac{1}{24}$, $\frac{1}{42}$, $\frac{2}{14}$, $\frac{2}{41}$, $\frac{4}{21}$)

Quick Review

Add mentally.

1. $\frac{8}{10} + \frac{4}{10}$ ($\frac{12}{10}$ or $1\frac{1}{5}$)
2. $11.2 + 2.3$ (13.5)
3. $\frac{1}{5} + \frac{3}{5}$ ($\frac{4}{5}$)
4. $2.6 + 8.2$ (10.8)
5. $\frac{1}{2} + \frac{3}{4}$ ($\frac{5}{4}$ or $1\frac{1}{4}$)

Lesson Quiz

Find 10% of each number.

1. 60 (6)
2. 39 (3.9)
3. 213 (21.3)
4. 45.7 (4.57)
5. 5 (0.5)
6. 8,348 (834.8)

LEVELED PRACTICE

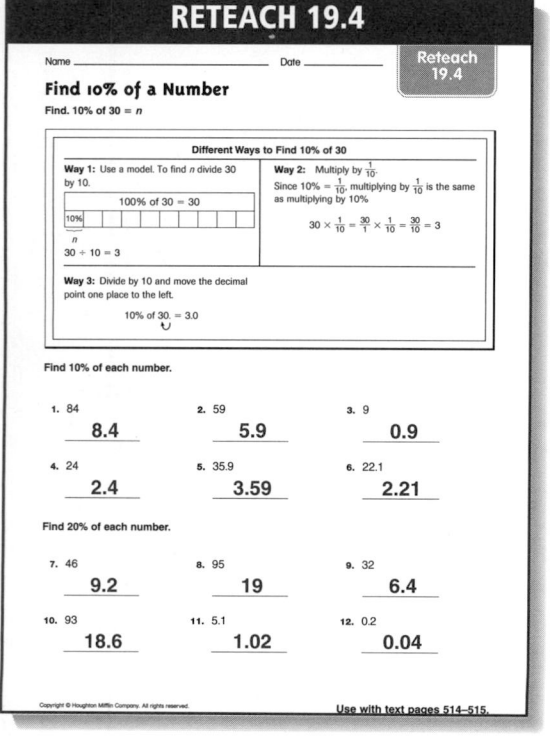

RETEACH 19.4

Name _____ Date _____

Reteach 19.4

Find 10% of a Number

Find. 10% of 30 = n

Different Ways to Find 10% of 30

Way 1: Use a model. To find *n* divide 30 by 10.

100% of 30 = 30

10%

n

30 ÷ 10 = 3

Way 2: Multiply by $\frac{1}{10}$

Since 10% = $\frac{1}{10}$, multiplying by $\frac{1}{10}$ is the same as multiplying by 10%

$30 \times \frac{1}{10} = \frac{30}{1} \times \frac{1}{10} = \frac{30}{10} = 3$

Way 3: Divide by 10 and move the decimal point one place to the left.

10% of 30 = 3.0

Find 10% of each number.

1. 84   **8.4**
2. 59   **5.9**
3. 9   **0.9**
4. 24   **2.4**
5. 35.9   **3.59**
6. 22.1   **2.21**

Find 20% of each number.

7. 46   **9.2**
8. 95   **19**
9. 32   **6.4**
10. 93   **18.6**
11. 5.1   **1.02**
12. 0.2   **0.04**

Use with text pages 514–515.

PRACTICE 19.4

Name _____ Date _____

Practice 19.4

Find 10% of a Number

Find 10% of each number.

1. 56 **5.6**
2. 8 **0.8**
3. 11 **1.1**
4. 2 **0.2**
5. 32 **3.2**
6. 345 **34.5**
7. 5,004 **500.4**
8. 63.2 **6.32**
9. 0.7 **0.07**
10. 1.2 **0.12**

Find 20% of each number.

11. 50 **10**
12. 136 **27.2**
13. 28 **5.6**
14. 1,890 **378**
15. 4.5 **0.9**
16. 0.5 **0.1**
17. 7.08 **1.416**
18. 432 **86.4**
19. 0.18 **0.036**

Estimate each percent of a number. *Possible answers:*

20. 19% of 82   **16**
21. 8% of 49   **5**
22. 13% of 704   **70**
23. 22% of 215   **40**

Find the number.

24. 10% of a number is 89 **890**   10% = 89
25. 10% of a number is 7 **70**   10% = 7
26. 20% of a number is 41 **205**   20% = 41

Test Prep

27. Jan says that 10% of 80 is greater than 20% of 40 because 80 is much greater than 40. Is she correct? Explain your answer.

No; 10% of 80 is 8 and 20% of 40 is 8.

28. 20% of a number is 45. What is the number?

A 90   **D**   C 180
B 200   D 225

Use with text pages 514–515.

ENRICHMENT 19.4

Name _____ Date _____

Enrichment 19.4

Service Matters

Waiters and waitresses generally receive tips of 15 percent or 20 percent.

Sometimes they get more, sometimes less.

Play the game below with a partner. Roll a number cube to see how many spaces to move. After you've each had a turn, the customer's bill increases by $2. For your first tosses, the bill is $10. For your second, it is $12, and so on. If you land on **Start**, you must pay $5 to the restaurant.

Add your tips. The first player to get $100 wins the game.

Start	10%	15%	No Tip	20%	15%	20%	10%	15%	20%
No Tip									$1 Tip
10%									10%
15%									15%
25%	20%	$2 Tip	15%	20%	15%	No Tip	5%	20%	Day Off

1. What happened to the tips as you played the game?
   The tips got larger as the bills got larger.

2. What method did you use to multiply by 15%?
   Answers will vary.

3. What method did you use to multiply by 20%?
   Answers will vary.

4. What is the smallest bill needed to get a $10 tip? Hint: it's a 25% tip.
   $40

Use with text pages 514–515.

Practice Workbook Page 128

Reaching All Learners

Differentiated Instruction

English Learners

Worksheet 19.4 presents the steps involved in estimating percents of numbers and helps students apply these steps in preparation for undertaking Problems 33–36.

Inclusion
VISUAL, SPATIAL

- To help students write 10% of a number, have them copy and analyze this table. **The arrow moves the decimal point one space to the left, which gives 10% of the number.**

Number with a Decimal Point	Decimal Point 1 Space to Left	10% of Number
100.	100.	10.0
340.	340.	34.0
42.5	42.5	4.25

Early Finishers
LOGICAL, SPATIAL

Materials: *meter stick*

- Have students make a table that shows:

0% of a meter = ■ cm (0)
10% of a meter = ■ cm (10)

- Challenge them to continue the table so it includes 20% through 100%. Then have them find several things that have lengths equal to about 50% of a meter. Repeat for objects with a length equal to about 20% of a meter.

Social Studies Connection

Materials: *grid paper, colored pencils, reference materials*

- Have students research various national flags and copy the flag of any nation.

- Have them estimate what percent of the flag is represented by each color.

- Ask groups to create a rectangular "school" flag in the style of a national flag. Have them describe their flag using percents for each color.

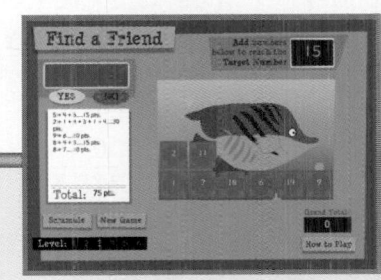

TECHNOLOGY

Spiral Review

You can prepare students for standardized tests with **customized** spiral review on key skills using the *Ways to Assess* CD-ROM.

Education Place

You can visit Education Place at eduplace.com/math/mw/ for teacher support materials.

Game

Students can practice their skills using the Find a Friend math game, available on the *Ways to Success* CD.

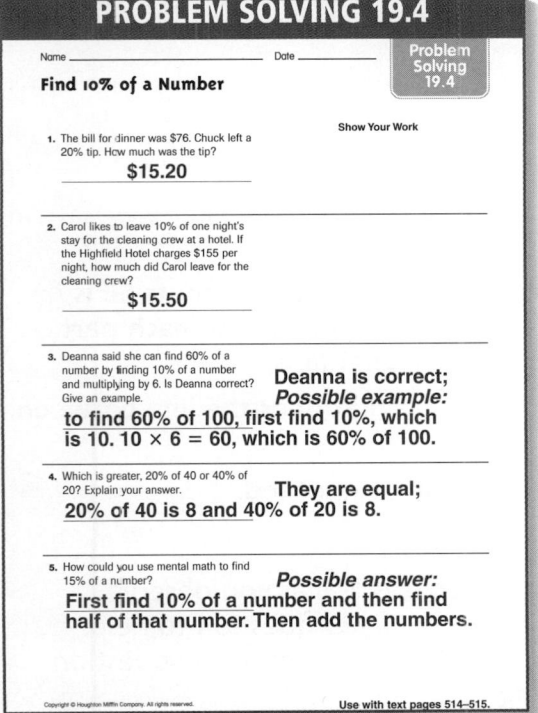

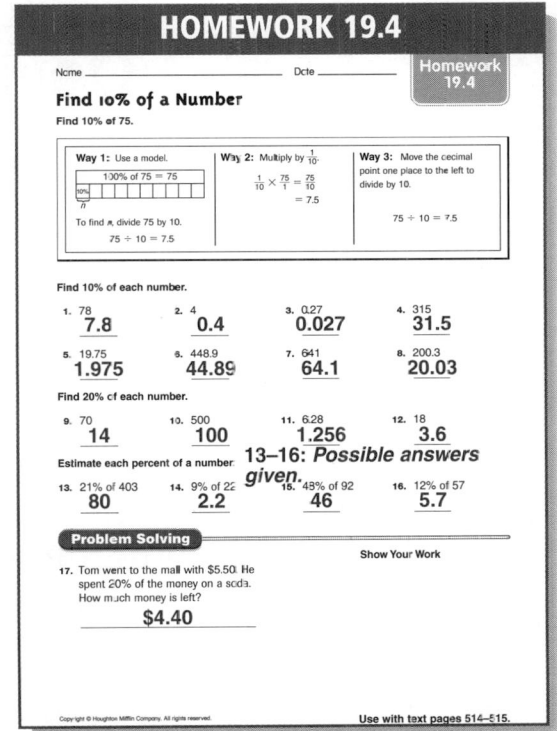

Homework Workbook Page 128

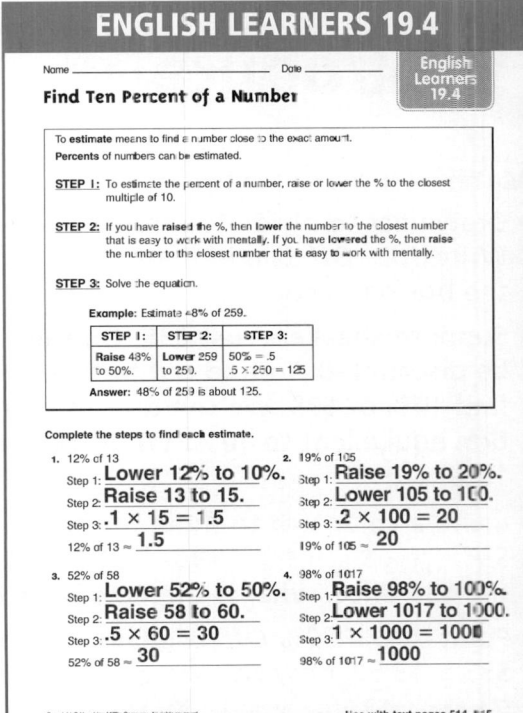

TEACHING LESSON 19.4

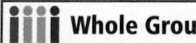 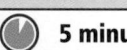

Warm-Up Activity
Dividing by 10

🏃 Whole Group	🕐 5 minutes	Visual, Tactile

- Write on the chalkboard:

  $78.5 \div 10$ is the same as $10\overline{)78.5}$

- **How many times does 10 divide into 7?** (It doesn't.) Since 10 is greater than 7, it does not divide into 7. **How many times does 10 divide into 78?** ($10 \times 7 = 70$, so write 7 in the tens place above the 8 in the dividend.)

$$
\begin{array}{r}
07. \\
10\overline{)78.5} \\
-70 \\
\hline
8.5
\end{array}
$$

- Continue the division process. Emphasize how to place the decimal point in the quotient.

Lesson 4 — Find 10% of a Number

Objective Use mental math to find 10% and multiples of 10% of a number.

Learn About It

A skateboard regularly sells for $60. The skateboard is on sale for 10% off the regular price. How much money would you save if you bought the skateboard on sale?

10% of 60 = n

Different Ways to Find 10% of 60

Way ❶ You can use a model.

To find n, divide $60 by 10.

$60 \div 10 = \$6$

100% of $60 = $60

Way ❷ You can multiply by $\frac{1}{10}$.

Finding 10% of a number is the same as finding $\frac{1}{10}$ of that number.

$10\% \times 60 = \frac{1}{10} \times 60$

$\frac{1}{10} \times \frac{60}{1} = \frac{60}{10} = 6$

Way ❸ You can divide by 10 by moving the decimal point to the left.

An easy way to find 10% of any number is to move the decimal point one place to the left to divide the number by 10.

$60 \div 10 = 6.0$

Solution: You would save $6.

Other Examples

A. Find 20% of a Number

Find 20% of 42.

20% of 42 = 42 ÷ 5

= 8.4

100% of 42 = 42

20% of 42

B. Estimate a Percent of a Number

Estimate 11% of 47.

11% of 47 is about 10% of 50

$10\% \times 50 = \frac{1}{10} \times 50 = 5$

11% of 47 ≈ 5

514

---

1 Introduce

Materials: *blank transparency*

- Draw lines to divide the transparency into two sections. Write *10% Off Sale* in the top section and *20% Off Sale* in the bottom section.

- Suppose sneakers cost $35. On sale, 10% of the cost will be discounted. To find out how much will be discounted, find 10% of $35. We can do this by multiplying by a fraction equivalent to 10%. What fraction is equivalent to 10%? ($\frac{1}{10}$)

- Invite a volunteer to show the steps used to multiply $\frac{1}{10} \times$ $35. ($\frac{1}{10} \times \$\frac{35}{1} = \$\frac{35}{10} = \$3\frac{5}{10} = \$3.50$) If $3.50 is taken from the $35 price, what is the new price of the shoes? ($31.50)

- Point to the *20% Off Sale*. Since we know 10% off of $35 is $3.50, how can we quickly find 20% off of $35? (Multiply $3.50 × 2 = $7.00) What is the cost of the shoes during a 20% off sale? ($28.00)

2 Develop

Guide students through the *Learn About It* section.

- **What do we need to find out?** (how much money we save in the sale)

- **Look at Way 1. When the model that represents 60 is divided into 10 equal parts, how much does each part represent in number and percent?** (6, or 10%)

- **Look at Way 2: $\frac{1}{10} \times 60 = \frac{60}{10}$. What does the line between 60 and 10 mean?** (Divide.)

- **Look at Way 3. This is a shortcut method.**

Guided Practice

Have students complete **Exercises 1–8** as you observe. Remind them to use the *Ask Yourself* question to help. Give students the opportunity to talk about the question in *Explain Your Thinking*.

Guided Practice

Find 10% of each number.

1. 75 **7.5**   2. 19 **1.9**   3. 3.8 **0.38**   4. 0.4 **0.04**

Find 20% of each number.

5. 40 **8**   6. 120 **24**   7. 26 **5.2**   8. 8.2 **1.64**

Ask Yourself
- Did I move the decimal point one place to the left to find 10%?

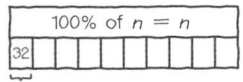

Explain Your Thinking ▶ What decimal would you multiply by to find 10% of a number? Explain.
0.1; you multiply by $\frac{1}{10}$ to find 10% of a number, and $\frac{1}{10}$ = 0.1.

Practice and Problem Solving

Find 10% of each number.

9. 42 **4.2**   10. 25 **2.5**   11. 9 **0.9**   12. 3 **0.3**   13. 1 **0.1**

14. 783 **78.3**   15. 4,012 **401.2**   16. 7.8 **0.78**   17. 100.5 **10.05**   18. 4.41 **0.441**

Find 20% of each number.

19. 20 **4**   20. 46 **9.2**   21. 1,020 **204**   22. 8.4 **1.68**   23. 0.6 **0.12**

Estimate each percent of a number. *Estimates will vary. Possible answers are given.*

24. 12% of 73 **7**   25. 48% of 69 **35**   26. 18% of 503 **100**   27. 9% of 397 **40**

Find the number.

28. 10% of a number is 32. **320**

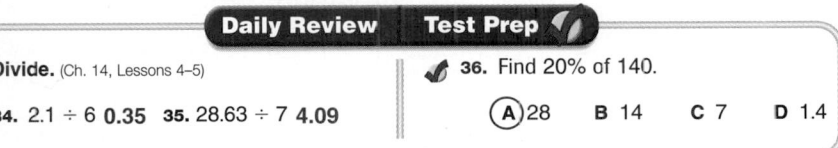

10% of n = 32

29. 20% of a number is 27. **135**

100% of n = n

20% of n = 27

32. 13% of 152 is about 10% of 150, which is 15; 50 is too great an estimate.
33. Find $\frac{1}{2}$ of a number; 100% of a number is the number itself.

Solve.

30. Mel's bill comes to $31. He leaves 20% of the bill as a tip. How much is the tip? **$6.20**

31. The sum of two numbers is 17. Their product is 60. Find the two numbers. **5 and 12**

32. **What's Wrong?** Monique says that 13% of 152 is about 50. Is her estimate reasonable? Tell how you know. *See above.*

33. **Explain** How can you find 50% of a number? How can you find 100% of a number? *See above.*

Daily Review   Test Prep ✔

Divide. (Ch. 14, Lessons 4–5)

34. 2.1 ÷ 6 **0.35**   35. 28.63 ÷ 7 **4.09**

✔ 36. Find 20% of 140.
(A) 28   B 14   C 7   D 1.4

Extra Practice See page 525, Set C.

Chapter 19 Lesson 4   **515**

DAILY TEST PREP

If 20% of a number is 28, what is the number? (D)

A. 14   B. 280   C. 28   D. 140

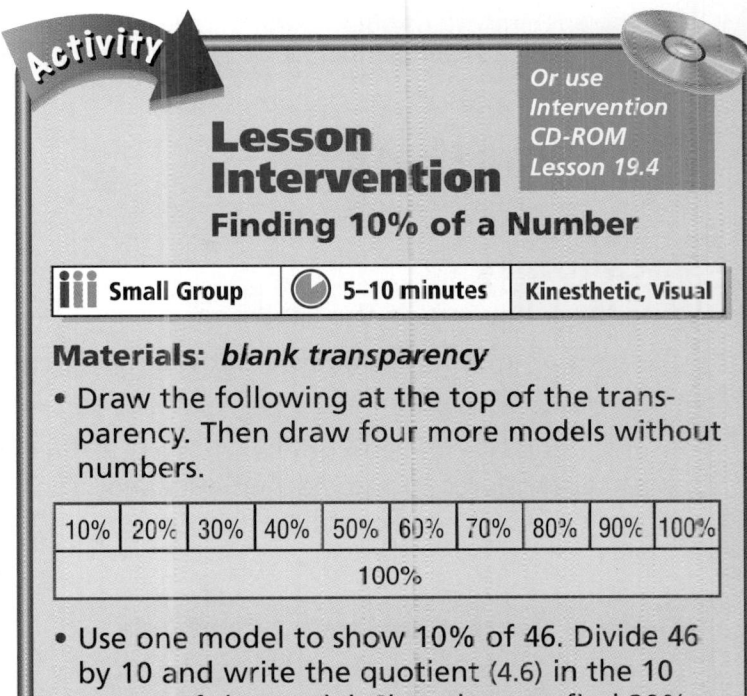

Activity

Or use Intervention CD-ROM Lesson 19.4

Lesson Intervention
Finding 10% of a Number

| ⅲ Small Group | 🕐 5–10 minutes | Kinesthetic, Visual |

Materials: *blank transparency*

- Draw the following at the top of the transparency. Then draw four more models without numbers.

10%	20%	30%	40%	50%	60%	70%	80%	90%	100%
100%									

- Use one model to show 10% of 46. Divide 46 by 10 and write the quotient (4.6) in the 10 spaces of the model. Show how to find 20% of 46. Repeat with 3 more models.

---

③ Practice

Assign **Exercises 9–36** as independent work.

- *Exercises 9–18* Encourage students to use either of the first two methods shown for finding 10%.
- *Exercises 24–27* Suggest students round both the percent and the number to the nearest multiple of 10.
- *Problem-Solving for Problems 30–33* Suggest students find the value for 100%.

Common Error

Leaving out the zeros When students use the "move the decimal one place to the left" pattern for writing 10% of a number, make sure they understand that they need to keep the zero, as in "10% of 0.6 is 0.06."

④ Assess and Close

- **Is 42 × $\frac{1}{10}$ the same as 42 ÷ 10?** Explain. (Yes; multiplying by $\frac{1}{10}$ is the same as dividing by 10.)
- **How do you mentally find 20% of 340?** (Find 10% of 340, which is 34. Double it to find 20%: 68.)

Assign the **LESSON QUIZ** on Transparency 19.4 to further assess student understanding.

Keeping a Journal

Have students write problems and solutions that show how to find percent of a number (such as the number of correct answers on a test).

Percent of a Number

PLANNING THE LESSON

MATHEMATICS OBJECTIVE
Use different ways to find a percent of a number.

Use Lesson Planner CD-ROM for Lesson 19.5.

Daily Routines
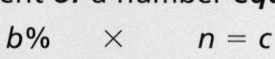

Vocabulary
Write the following on the chalkboard:

Vocabulary Cards

A percent *of* a number *equals* what number?

$$b\% \quad \times \quad n = c$$

Use colored chalk to show how each part of the verbal sentence translates to the mathematical equation. The sentence $b\% \times n = c$ is equivalent to *b* percent of *n* equals *c*.

Meeting North Carolina's Standards
Prepare for Grade 7 Objective **1.02** Develop fluency in addition, subtraction, multiplication, and division of rational numbers.

Lesson Transparency
19.5

Problem of the Day
On a social studies test, Jordan answered 75% of the questions correctly. Lucas answered $\frac{1}{5}$ of the questions incorrectly. Katy answered $\frac{7}{10}$ of the questions correctly. Who answered the most questions correctly? (Lucas)

Quick Review
Compute mentally.
1. 645×100 (64,500)
2. 216×100 (21,600)
3. $3,400 \div 10$ (340)
4. $53,200 \div 100$ (532)
5. $(250 \div 10) \times 10$ (250)

Lesson Quiz
Solve. Use any method.
1. 25% of 424 (106) 2. 8% of 40 (3.2)
3. 70% of 200 (140) 4. 45% of 10 (4.5)
5. 49% of 600 (294)

LEVELED PRACTICE

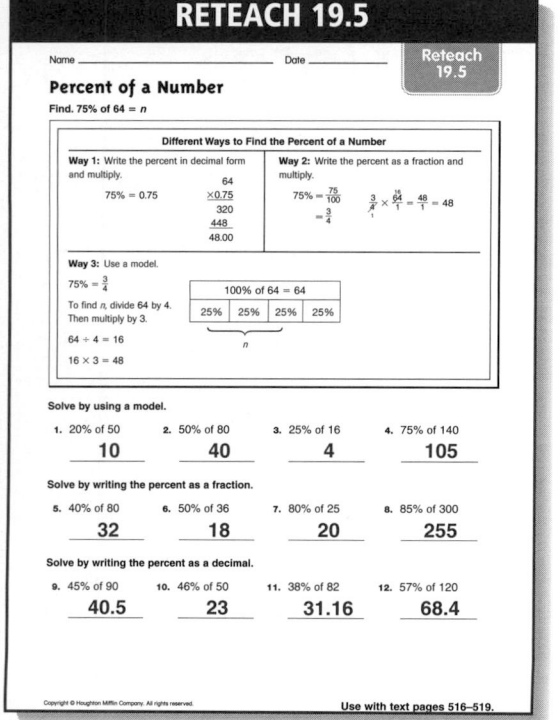

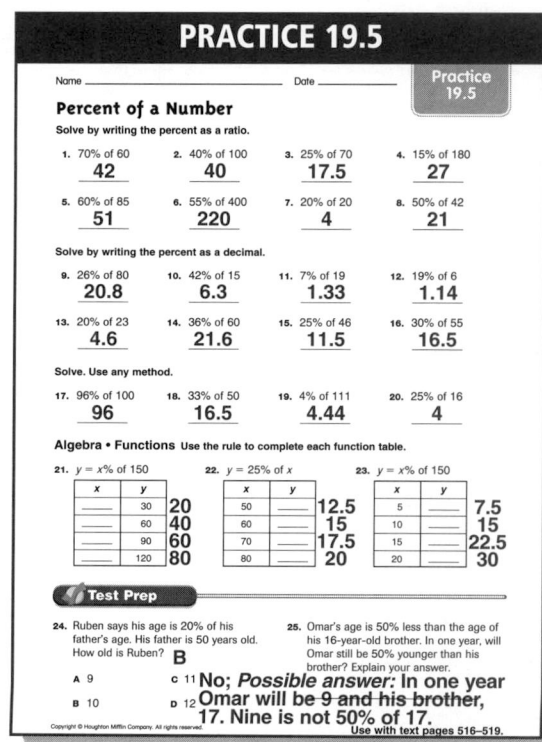

Practice Workbook Page 129

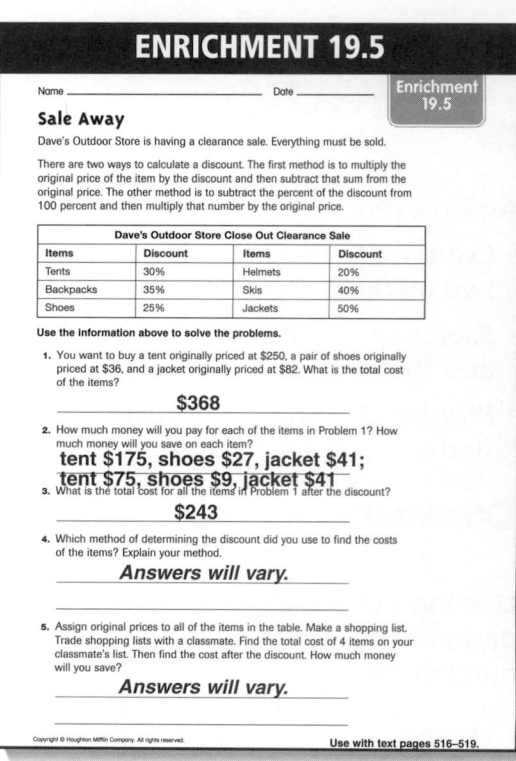

Reaching All Learners
Differentiated Instruction

English Learners

English-language learners may be unfamiliar with the principle of discounts. Use Worksheet 19.5 to help students understand the concept of a discount and figure out discounts that are given in percents. This instruction will give students the background and strategies for addressing Problems 34–36.

Special Needs
VISUAL, KINESTHETIC

Materials: *spinner*

- Label a spinner with various percents and display their decimal equivalents. Then display this equation: ▪ $\times 100 = ?$
- Have students take turns spinning a percent and then putting their percent into the equation. Help them solve the equation.

Gifted and Talented
VISUAL, SPATIAL

Materials: *grid paper, highlighters, calculator*

- Ask students for the definition of *prime number*, then have them make a chart listing whole numbers from 1 to 100, highlighting the prime numbers.
- Have them find the percent of whole numbers from 1 to 100 that are prime. (25%)

TECHNOLOGY

Spiral Review

Create **customized** spiral review worksheets for individual students using the *Ways to Assess* CD-ROM.

Software

Use *Easy Sheet* or another spreadsheet to explore this lesson more fully.

Lesson Planner

You can customize your teaching plan or to meet your curriculum requirements with the Lesson Planner CD-ROM.

Art Connection

Visual Patterns
Materials: *grid paper, rulers, colored pencils*

- Artists use patterns in many projects, such as floor tiles, wall decorations, and perspective drawings. Geometric patterns often have interesting number patterns also. Have students draw the following squares on grid paper: 2×2, 3×3, 4×4,. . .through 10×10.
- Have students shade a checkerboard pattern in each square. Discuss the percentage of shaded squares in each checkerboard and any patterns that students see.

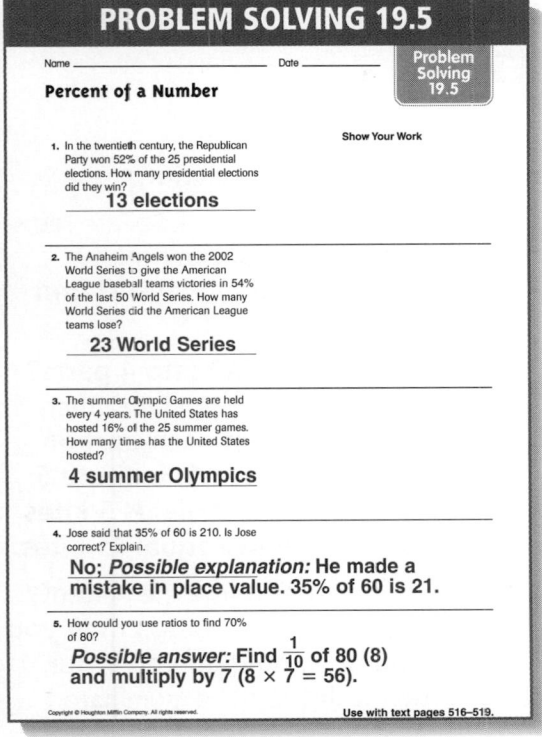

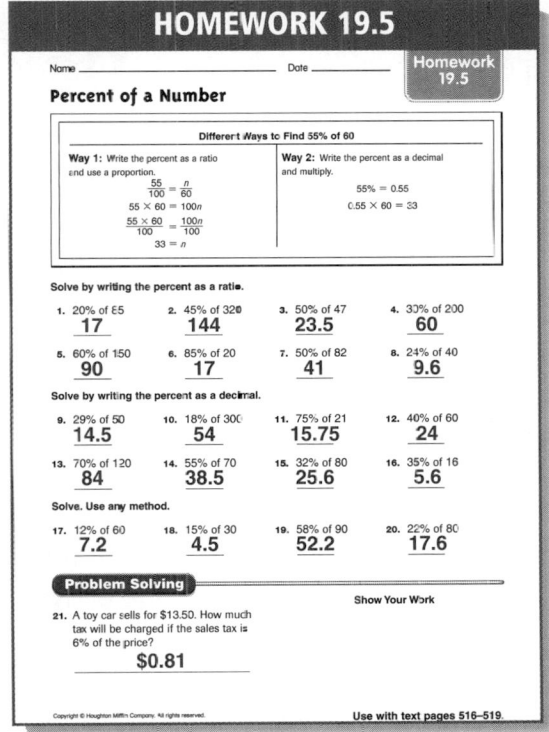

Homework Workbook Page 129

TEACHING LESSON 19.5

LESSON ORGANIZER

Objective Use different ways to find a percent of a number.

Resources Reteach, Practice, Enrichment, Problem Solving, Homework, English Learners

Materials Blank transparency, scissors, rulers

 **Activity**

Warm-Up Activity
Estimating Products

Whole Group	⏱ 5 minutes	Visual, Auditory

Materials: *blank transparency*

Write on the transparency:

$$138 \times 0.48$$

- **What is 138 rounded to the tens place?** (140) **What is 0.48 rounded to the tenths place?** (0.50) Write another expression:

$$140 \times 0.50$$

- **What fraction does 0.50 represent?** ($\frac{1}{2}$) **What is half of 140?** (70) **The exact answer should be close to 70.** Demonstrate how to multiply to find the exact answer. (66.24)

Lesson 5

Algebra
Percent of a Number

Objective Use different ways to find a percent of a number.

Learn About It 💿 **MathTracks 2/23** Listen and Understand

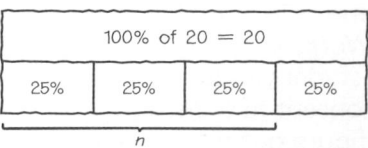

On display in a store window are 20 kites. If 75 percent of the kites are red, how many kites are red?

75% of 20 = n

Different Ways to Find 75% of 20

Way ① You can use a model.

To find *n*, divide 20 by 4. Then multiply by 3.

$$20 \div 4 = 5 \qquad 5 \times 3 = 15$$

100% of 20 = 20			
25%	25%	25%	25%

n

Way ② You can write the percent as a fraction and multiply.

STEP 1 Write the percent as a ratio.

$$75\% = \frac{75}{100}$$
$$= \frac{3}{4}$$

STEP 2 Multiply.

$$\frac{3}{4} \times \frac{20}{1} = \frac{60}{4}$$
$$= 15$$

Way ③ You can write the percent in decimal form and multiply.

STEP 1 Write the percent in decimal form.

$$75\% = 75 \text{ hundredths}$$
$$= 0.75$$

STEP 2 Multiply.

$$\begin{array}{r} 20 \\ \times\ 0.75 \\ \hline 1\ 00 \\ 14\ 00 \\ \hline 15.00 \end{array}$$

← 2 decimal places in the factors

← 2 decimal places in the product

Solution: There are 15 red kites.

516

 **Activity**

1 Introduce | Whole Group | ⏱ 5–10 minutes

Materials: *blank transparency*

- Draw lines to divide the transparency into two sections. In the top section, write: *28% of 50 students choose grapes. How many students choose grapes?*

- Invite a volunteer to read the problem. **You can find 28% of 50 several different ways. One way is to write the percent as a decimal and multiply.** Invite another volunteer to write 28% as a decimal. (0.28) In the second section, write:

$$\begin{array}{r} 50 \\ \times\ 0.28 \end{array}$$

- Invite a volunteer to show the steps used to multiply 50 × 0.28. (14) **So 14 students out of 50 choose grapes.**

2 Develop

Guide students through the *Learn About It* section.

- **What do you need to find out?** (If 75% of the kites are red, how many are red?) **If there were 100 kites, how many would be red?** (75) **This lesson shows three ways to find 75% of 20.**

- **Look at Way 1. Why divide the model of 20 into 4 parts?** (75% is the same as $\frac{75}{100}$ or $\frac{3}{4}$. If $\frac{3}{4}$ represents the red kites, then divide 20 into 4 parts.) **How many kites does each part of the model represent?** (5) Display the model. Substitute 5 for 25%. 20 kites divided into 4 equal parts yields 5 kites in each part, and 3 of those parts together equal 15 kites.

- **Look at Way 2. What are the two steps?** (Write the percent as a fraction; then multiply by the total number of kites.) **When you multiply fractions by a whole number, how do you write the whole number?** (as a fraction with 1 as the denominator)

Guided Practice

Solve by using a model.

1. 50% of 80 **40**   2. 75% of 28 **21**

Solve by writing the percent as a fraction.

3. 70% of 90 **63**   4. 5% of 80 **4**

Solve by writing the percent as a decimal.

5. 16% of 40 **6.4**   6. 80% of 150 **120**

TEST TIPS Explain Your Thinking ▶ Which method would you use to find 28% of 66? Why?

Possible answer: Change 28% to a decimal and multiply. The fraction $\frac{28}{100}$ simplifies to $\frac{7}{25}$, which gives you large numbers to multiply.

Practice and Problem Solving

Solve by writing the percent as a fraction.

7. 90% of 30 **27**   8. 35% of 300 **105**   9. 20% of 45 **9**   10. 40% of 25 **10**

11. 75% of 80 **60**   12. 15% of 40 **6**   13. 50% of 36 **18**   14. 30% of 1,000 **300**

Solve by writing the percent as a decimal.

15. 25% of 44 **11**   16. 33% of 30 **9.9**   17. 16% of 15 **2.4**   18. 90% of 50 **45**

19. 7% of 20 **1.4**   20. 60% of 12 **7.2**   21. 37% of 20 **7.4**   22. 14% of 300 **42**

Solve. Use any method.

23. 25% of 232 **58**   24. 20% of 20 **4**   25. 1% of 100 **1**   26. 65% of 40 **26**

27. 7% of 30 **2.1**   28. 19% of 200 **38**   29. 75% of 4 **3**   30. 49% of 300 **147**

✗ Algebra • Functions Use the rule to complete each function table.

31. $y = x\%$ of 200

x	y
5	■
10	■
15	■
20	■

10
20
30
40

32. $y = 25\%$ of x

x	y
10	■
20	■
30	■
40	■

2.5
5
7.5
10

33. $y = x\%$ of 200

x	y
■	50
■	100
■	150
■	200

25
50
75
100

Go On

Number Sense

What's My Score? Copy on the chalkboard.

Test	Questions	Missed
Science	50	8
Social Studies	20	3
Reading	5	1
Math	50	2

1. Have students write ratios to show the number of questions missed to the number of questions correct for each test.

2. Have students calculate each score.

3. Order the scores from least to greatest.

Answers

1. Science: 8 : 42 or 4 : 21; Social Studies: 4 : 17; Reading: 1 : 4; Math: 2 : 48 or 1 : 24

2. Science: 84%; Social Studies: 85%; Reading: 80%; Math: 96%

3. The order of the scores should be reading, science, social studies, math.

Differentiated Assignments		
At Risk	**Average**	**Advanced**
Exercises 1, 2	Exercises 1–2	Exercises 1–3

---

③ Practice

- **Look at Way 3. What are the two steps?** (Write the percent as a decimal; then multiply by the total number of kites.) **How do you write percent as a decimal?** (Move the decimal two places to the left.)

Guided Practice

Have students complete **Exercises 1–6** as you observe. Remind them to use the *Ask Yourself* questions to help. Give students the opportunity to discuss each of the following methods when answering the question in *Explain Your Thinking:* percent as an equivalent decimal and percent as a ratio in fraction form.

Assign **Exercises 7–41** as independent work.

- *Exercises 7–30* When students are required to use two solution methods, ask them to show all their work.

- *Algebra • Functions for Exercises 31–33* For Exercises 31–32, have students show how to substitute a value for x to find the value of y. For Exercise 33, draw a model on the chalkboard to help students visualize the problem. You may wish to rephrase the equation $50 = x\%$ of 200 by saying "50 is what percent of 200?"

DAILY TEST PREP

A bike that usually sells for $240 is on sale for 25% off. What is the sale price? (D)

A. $215   B. $170   C. $200   D. $180

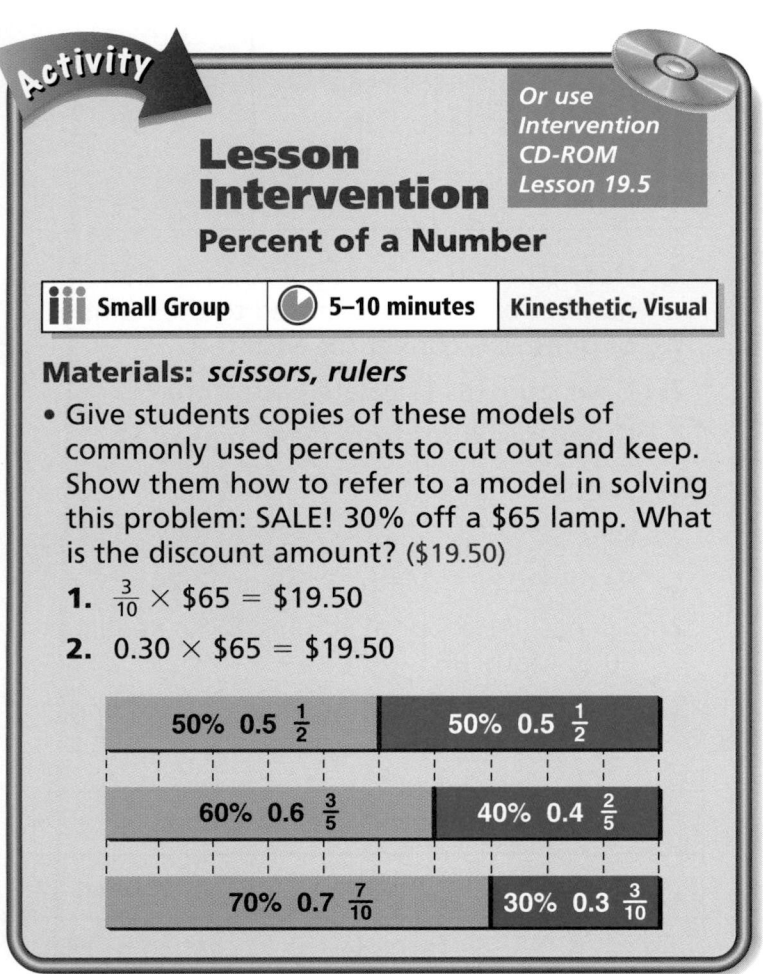

Activity

Or use Intervention CD-ROM Lesson 19.5

Lesson Intervention
Percent of a Number

| iii Small Group | 5–10 minutes | Kinesthetic, Visual |

Materials: *scissors, rulers*

• Give students copies of these models of commonly used percents to cut out and keep. Show them how to refer to a model in solving this problem: SALE! 30% off a $65 lamp. What is the discount amount? ($19.50)

1. $\frac{3}{10} \times \$65 = \$19.50$

2. $0.30 \times \$65 = \$19.50$

50% 0.5 $\frac{1}{2}$	50% 0.5 $\frac{1}{2}$
60% 0.6 $\frac{3}{5}$	40% 0.4 $\frac{2}{5}$
70% 0.7 $\frac{7}{10}$	30% 0.3 $\frac{3}{10}$

Mental Math • Estimation • Paper and Pencil • Calculator

Data Use the table for Problems 34–36.

34. A *discount* is the amount of money deducted from the price of an item. Use a calculator to find the price of a box kite after the discount indicated in the table has been subtracted. **$14.00**

35. **Analyze** Elena has saved $15. Does she have enough money to buy a dragon kite after the discount? Explain how you know.
See Additional Answers on Page 525.

36. **You Decide** You are in charge of buying kites for the kite club. You have $100 to spend, and want to buy a few different kinds of kites. Which kites will you buy? What is the total cost?
See Additional Answers on Page 525.

37. **Estimate** At the Flying Kite Festival, 7,958 children's tickets were sold. The total number of tickets sold was about 20,608. About what percent were children's tickets? **about 40%**

38. **Create and Solve** A newspaper reported that the attendance at this year's kite festival was 20% less than the year before. This year's attendance was 12,000. Use this information to write your own problem. Then solve the problem.
Check students' problems and answers.

Kite	Price	Discount
Parafoil	$50.00	10%
Dragon	$25.00	20%
Box	$20.00	30%
Delta	$40.00	50%

41. No. Helena needs at least $27.30 to buy the disc player.

Daily Review   **Test Prep**

Find the area and perimeter.
(Ch. 16, Lessons 1 and 3)

39.

5 in.

2.5 in.

$P = 15$ in.;
$A = 12.5$ in.²

40.

$\frac{1}{2}$ yd $\frac{1}{2}$ yd

$\frac{3}{8}$ yd

$\frac{1}{2}$ yd

$1\frac{1}{2}$ yd; $\frac{3}{32}$ yd²

41. **Free Response** Helena has $25. She wants to buy a disc player that has a regular price of $39. The player is on sale with a 30% discount. Does Helena have enough money? Explain how you found your answer.

518

Extra Practice See page 525, Set D.

Practice *continued*

Choose a Computation Method

• *Problem Solving for Problems 34–38* Have students discuss how to solve the problem using either one of two steps.

Common Error

Forgetting to move the decimal point Some students may be getting products that are too large when finding percents of a number. Remind students that when they are asked to find less than 100% of a number, the answer will be less than the original number. Have them count the number of places they need to move the decimal.

4 Assess and Close

• **What are the steps for finding 30% of 80 using a model?** (Make a model divided into ten parts. Divide 80 by 10 to find that each part equals 8. Then multiply 8 by 3. So, 24 is 30% of 80.)

• **How do you find 30% of 80 using a fraction?** (Write $\frac{30}{100}$ and then simplify to $\frac{3}{10}$. Multiply $\frac{3}{10}$ by $\frac{80}{1}$. The product is $\frac{240}{10}$, which simplifies to 24.)

• **What are the steps for finding 30% of 80 using decimal form?** (Write 30% as 0.30. Then multiply 0.30 × 80. The product is 24.)

Assign the **LESSON QUIZ** on Transparency 19.5 to further assess student understanding.

Ratios and Percents

You buy a sweatshirt that is on sale. How much will you save? When you estimate or calculate a percent of a number, it helps to think of ratios and their related percents. Here are some relationships you should know.

Ratio	$\frac{1}{20}$	$\frac{1}{10}$	$\frac{1}{8}$	$\frac{1}{6}$	$\frac{1}{5}$	$\frac{1}{4}$	$\frac{1}{3}$	$\frac{1}{2}$
Percent	5%	10%	12.5%	$16\frac{2}{3}$%	20%	25%	$33\frac{1}{3}$%	50%

Estimate 35% of 48.

If you only need an estimate, you can find a ratio that converts to a percent close to 35%.

Estimate

$33\frac{1}{3}$% = $\frac{1}{3}$, so 35% of 48 is about $\frac{1}{3}$ of 48.

$48 \div 3 = 16$

So 35% of 48 must be slightly more than 16.

You will save about $16.

Find 35% of 48.

If you need an exact calculation, you can find ratios whose corresponding percents have a sum or difference of 35%.

Think: Add 25% of 48 and 10% of 48 to get 35% of 48.

$25\% + 10\% = 35\%$

25% of 48 = $\frac{1}{4}$ of 48 = $48 \div 4 = 12$

10% of 48 = $\frac{1}{10}$ of 48 = $48 \div 10 = 4.8$

So, 35% of 48 = $12 + 4.8 = 16.8$.

You will save $16.80

Possible answer: Using ratios and related percents allows you to break up less common percents, such as 45%, into percents or ratios that are easier to use, such as 20% and 25%, or $\frac{1}{5}$ and $\frac{1}{4}$.

1. Why are ratios and their related percents helpful if you want to find the percent of a number using mental math?

$\frac{1}{5} \times 60 = 12$; 20% of 90 + 25% of 90 = $\frac{1}{5} \times 90 + \frac{1}{4} \times 90$ $= 18 + 22.5 = 40.5$

2. How could you use ratios to find 20% of 60? to find 45% of 90?

Chapter 19 Lesson 5   **519**

Ratios and Percents

A lifetime skill is the ability to estimate a percent while shopping. A close estimate of a percent discount can help someone decide whether to make a purchase

As students calculate percent of a number over and over again, they may begin to memorize equivalent decimal and ratio values. For example, $33\frac{1}{3}$% equals $\frac{1}{3}$ and 0.3333 . . . or $0.\overline{3}$.

Keeping a Journal

Have students explain two ways to solve a problem using percents.

Problem-Solving Application: Use Circle Graphs

PLANNING THE LESSON

MATHEMATICS OBJECTIVE
Interpret data to make circle graphs to solve problems.

Use Lesson Planner CD-ROM for Lesson 19.6.

Daily Routines

Vocabulary

How many degrees in a circle? (360°)
What part of one rotation around the center cle is represented by 1 degree? ($\frac{1}{360}$)
Draw a circle and sketch 90°, 45°, and 10°.

Vocabulary Cards

Meeting North Carolina's Standards

1.03 Develop flexibility in solving problems by selecting strategies and using mental computation, estimation, calculators or computers, and paper and pencil.

Lesson Transparency
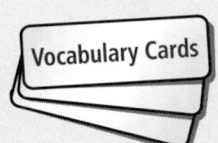
19.6

Problem of the Day

Al made 11 out of 25 free throws, Jeff made 13 of 20, and Yoshi made 12 of 18. What percent of the total shots did each make? (Al = 44%, Jeff = 65%, Yoshi = $66\frac{2}{3}$%)

Quick Review

Substitute and compare to $\frac{1}{2}$. Write < or >.

1. $\frac{7}{16}$ (<)
2. 58% (>)
3. 0.13 (<)
4. 60% (>)
5. 18% (<)
6. 0.400 (<)

Lesson Quiz

Make a circle graph to display the data in the table as percents.

Graduation Celebration Costs	
Catering	$60 (33%)
Gifts	$30 (17%)
Flowers	$45 (25%)
Transportation	$45 (25%)

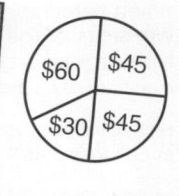

LEVELED PRACTICE

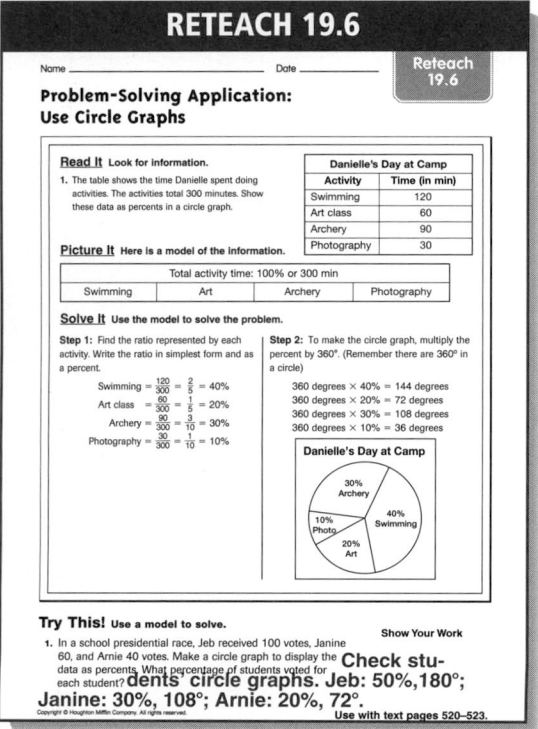

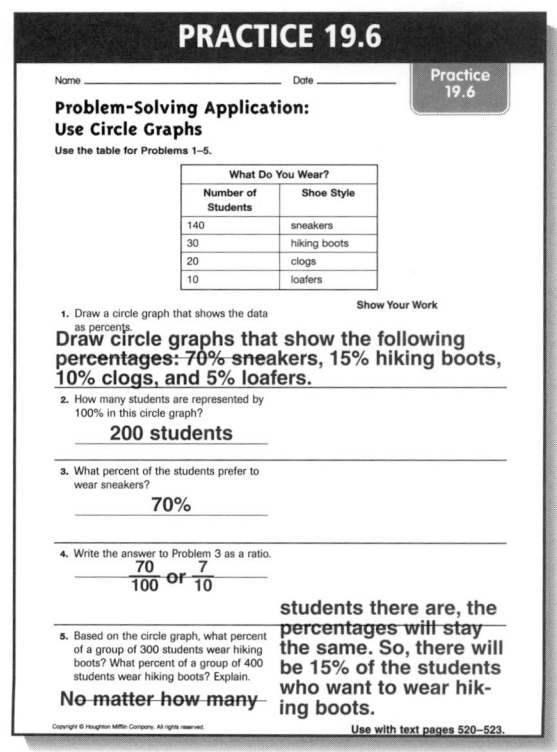

Practice Workbook Page 130

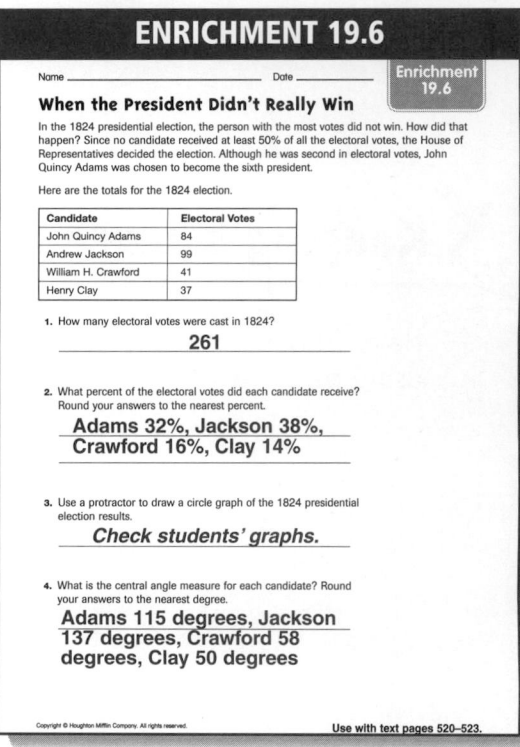

Reaching All Learners

Differentiated Instruction

English Learners

Worksheet 19.6 relates the size of the sectors in a circle graph to the percents they represent in order to help students understand how a circle graph may be used to compare data visually. This worksheet prepares students to complete the problems in Lesson 6.

Inclusion
VISUAL, KINESTHETIC

Materials: *Protractor transparency*

- Mark the following degrees: 90°, 180°, 270°, 360°. **Into how many sections is the circle divided?** (4)
- Repeat with 60°, 120°, 180°, 240°, 300°, 360°. Help students see the relationship between degrees and how a circle is divided.

Early Finishers
VISUAL, SPATIAL

Materials: *calculator, protractor, compass*

Display:

$$\text{part} \rightarrow \frac{1}{6} = \frac{n°}{360°} \leftarrow \text{part}$$
$$\text{whole} \rightarrow \qquad \qquad \leftarrow \text{whole}$$

- Help students solve for $n°$. (60°)
- Have them find degrees in these circle sections: $\frac{1}{2}$, $\frac{1}{3}$, $\frac{1}{4}$, $\frac{1}{6}$, and $\frac{1}{10}$.

TECHNOLOGY

Spiral Review

Using the *Ways to Assess* CD-ROM, you can create **customized** spiral review worksheets covering any lessons you choose.

Intervention

Use the *Ways to Success* intervention software to support students who need more help in understanding the concepts and skills taught in this chapter.

Ways to Success

Science Connection

Basic Elements

Materials: *grid paper, rulers, blue colored pencils*

The table shows the most important elements found in Earth's crust. Make a circle graph of the information in the table. You will need to determine how many degrees of the circle represent each percent. (Check graphs.)

Elements	Found in Earth's Crust (by mass)
Oxygen	47%
Aluminum	8%
Silicon	28%
Iron, Calcium, Sodium, Potassium, Others	17%

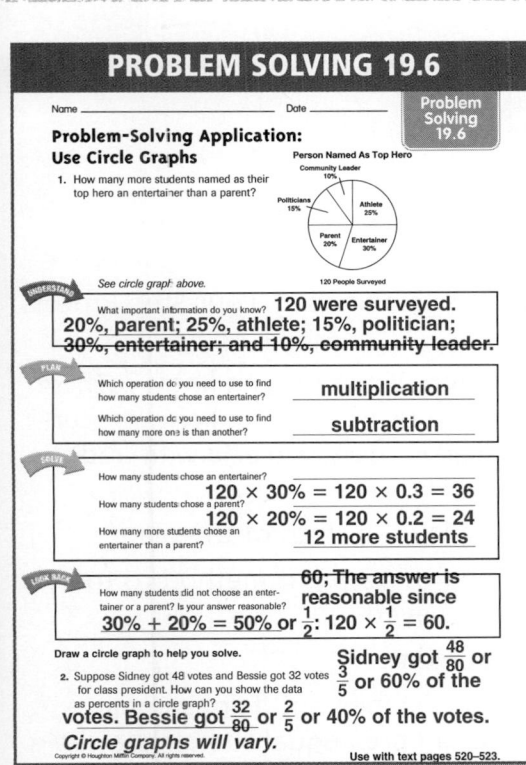

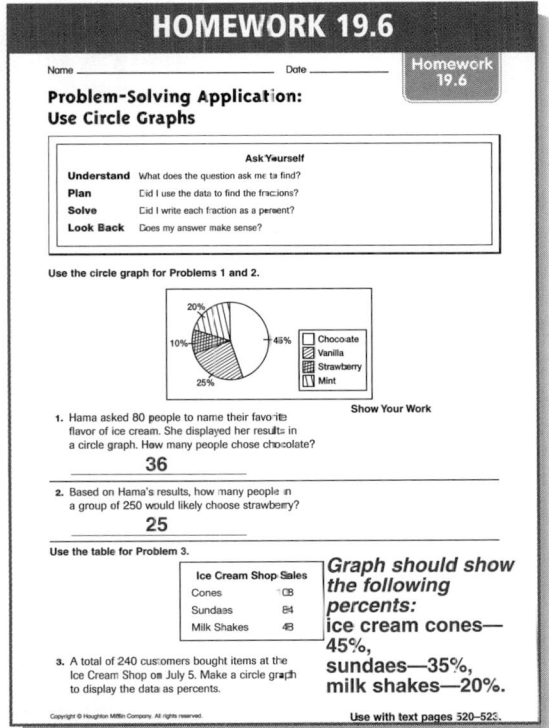

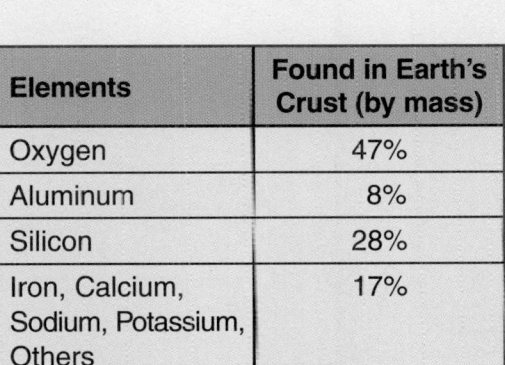

Homework Workbook Page 130

TEACHING LESSON 19.6

LESSON ORGANIZER

Objective Interpret data to make circle graphs to solve problems.

Resources Reteach, Practice, Enrichment, Problem Solving, Homework, English Learners

Materials Blank transparency, Problem-Solving: Four-Step Process Transparency, Mixed Numbers Transparency, scissors

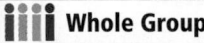

Warm-Up Activity
Proportions

 Whole Group	⏱ 5 minutes	Visual, Auditory

Materials: *blank transparency*

Display: *Jean earns $3 for every 8 hats she sells. How much does she earn when she sells 20 hats?*

$$\text{part} \rightarrow \frac{3}{8} = \frac{x}{20} \leftarrow \text{part} \\ \text{whole} \rightarrow \quad\quad\quad \leftarrow \text{whole}$$

Demonstrate on the transparency:

$$3 \times 20 = 8x$$
$$60 = 8x$$
$$\frac{60}{8} = \frac{8x}{8}$$
$$7.5 = x$$

Jean will make $7.50 when she sells 20 hats.

Lesson 6

Problem-Solving Application
Use Circle Graphs

Objective Interpret data to make circle graphs to solve problems.

Making a circle graph is a good way to display data expressed as percents.

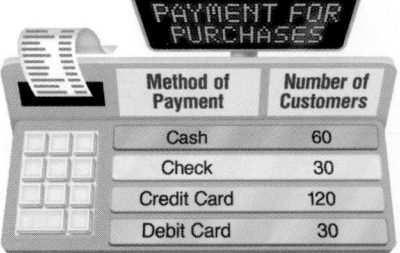

PAYMENT FOR PURCHASES

Method of Payment	Number of Customers
Cash	60
Check	30
Credit Card	120
Debit Card	30

Problem The table at the right shows the results of a survey of 240 customers at a department store. How can you show the data from the table as percents in a circle graph?

 **UNDERSTAND**

What is the question?
How can you show the data from the table as percents in a circle graph?

What do you know?
- 60 customers used cash.
- 120 customers used credit cards.
- 240 customers were in the survey.
- 30 customers used checks.
- 30 customers used debit cards.

 PLAN

Find the ratio of the data represented by each method of payment to total sales. Write each ratio as a percent. Then divide a circle so that it shows the percent.

 SOLVE

- Find the ratio for each method.
- Write the ratio in simplest form and as a percent.

$$\text{Cash} = \frac{60}{240} = \frac{1}{4} = 25\%$$

$$\text{Check} = \frac{30}{240} = \frac{1}{8} = 12.5\%$$

$$\text{Credit card} = \frac{120}{240} = \frac{1}{2} = 50\%$$

$$\text{Debit card} = \frac{30}{240} = \frac{1}{8} = 12.5\%$$

- Use the ratios to make a circle graph.
- Label each section.

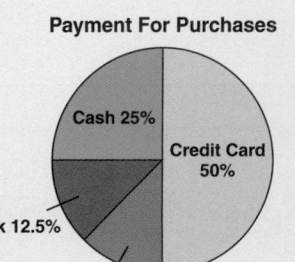

Payment For Purchases

Cash 25%
Credit Card 50%
Check 12.5%
Debit Card 12.5%

 **LOOK BACK**

Look back at the data. Does the graph seem reasonable?

520

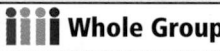

① Introduce   iiii Whole Group   ⏱ 5 minutes

Materials: *blank transparency*

- Draw lines to divide the transparency into two sections. In the top section, write: *35% of 40 students chose volleyball. How many chose volleyball?*

- Invite a volunteer to read the problem. **You can find 35% of 40 by writing the percent as a ratio in fraction form.** Invite another volunteer to write 35% as a ratio with 100 in the second term. ($\frac{35}{100}$) In the second section, write:

$$\text{part} \rightarrow \frac{35}{100} = \frac{x}{40} \leftarrow \text{part} \\ \text{whole} \rightarrow \quad\quad\quad\quad \leftarrow \text{whole}$$

Invite a volunteer to show the steps used to solve the proportion. (14) **So 14 students out of 40 chose volleyball.**

② Develop

Guide students through the problem-solving steps on page 520.

You may wish to use the Problem-Solving: Four-Step Process Transparency

- **Look at the Understand step. What do you know?** (There are four payment methods; a total of 240 customers were surveyed; 60 paid in cash, 30 paid in check, 120 paid with credit card, 30 paid with debit card.)

- **Look at the Plan step.** Display the steps of the plan:

  1. Write a ratio that compares payment method to total number of customers surveyed.

  2. Write each ratio as a percent.

  3. Divide a circle to match each percent. For example, $\frac{120}{240}$ or $\frac{1}{2}$ or 50% requires an area equal to half the circle.

  4. Label the sections of the graph with percent labels.

Guided Practice

Use the circle graph on page 520 to solve each problem.

1. Predict the number of customers out of 1,000 that would use a method other than cash. $\frac{3}{4}$ or 75%; 750

   (Hint) What part of the circle represents other payment methods?
   See Additional Answers on Page 525.

2. Suppose 120 more customers are surveyed. Of these customers, 60 use credit cards, 30 use checks, and 30 use debit cards. If that data is added to the existing data, how will the circle graph change?

Independent Practice

Use the circle graph for Problems 3 and 4.

3. The circle graph at the right shows how Ted budgets his money. If his total budget is $3,000, how much money does Ted spend on his rent? **$900**

4. **You Decide** Ted wants to increase his savings to $600 per month. Suggest a way that Ted can change his spending to increase his savings.
   See Additional Answers on Page 525.

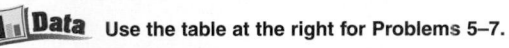 **Data** Use the table at the right for Problems 5–7.

5. The table at the right shows the results of a survey of 560 people who bought sneakers at 4 kinds of stores. Make a circle graph to display the data as percents.
   See Additional Answers on Page 525.

6. Use the circle graph that you made in Problem 5. What percent of the people bought their sneakers in a store other than a sneaker store? **87.5%**

7. **Predict** Based on the survey results, how many people out of 1,600 would you expect to buy sneakers from a sneaker store? **About 200**

Ask Yourself

UNDERSTAND — What does the question ask me to find?

PLAN — Did I use the data to find the ratio?

SOLVE — Did I write each ratio as a percent?

LOOK BACK — Does my answer make sense?

TEST TIPS

Ted's Budget

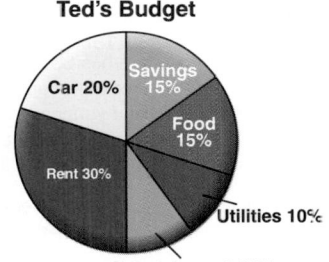

Car 20% | Savings 15% | Food 15% | Rent 30% | Utilities 10% | Entertainment 10%

Buying Sneakers

Type of Store	Number of People
Sporting Goods	140
Department or Discount	280
Sneaker	70
Other	70

 Go On

Chapter 19 Lesson 6 **521**

 **Quick Check Options**

The following activities will help students prepare for the Quick Check or may be used as an alternative assessment.

Vocabulary Review (individual, small group, or whole class)

Have students review the following vocabulary words by giving an example of how each term is used in this chapter.

• percent

Math Conversations (small group or whole class)

Have students discuss what they have learned about using circle graphs in this chapter. Encourage students to ask each other questions to clarify their understanding.

Writing Prompt (individual or partners)

To solidify student understanding of vocabulary and concepts, have each student complete the following sentence:

The most useful thing I have learned about using circle graphs is _____.

---

③ Practice

• **Look at the Solve step. How do you write $\frac{60}{240}$ in simplest form?** (Divide both terms by the GCF, 60. $\frac{60}{240} \div \frac{60}{60} = \frac{1}{4}$.) **How do you write the ratio $\frac{1}{4}$ as a percent?** (Divide 1 by 4. Or write an equivalent proportion: $\frac{1}{4} = \frac{n}{100}$.)

• **Draw a circle. Think of it as the face of a clock. Mark 12, 3, 6, and 9 o'clock. To write the percents in the circle graph, begin with the largest percent. The area from 12 to 6 o'clock is 50% or half of the graph.** Label it *50%* and *Credit Card;* label 9 to 12 o'clock *25%* and *Cash.*

• **We've labeled 75% of the circle. What percent is left?** (25%) **What is half of 25%?** (12.5%) Divide the last quarter of the circle in half and label.

Guided Practice

Have students complete **Problems 1–2** as you observe. Remind them to use the *Ask Yourself* questions.

Assign **Problems 3–7** as independent work. Have students share and discuss their work.

Problem-Solving Reminders

Have students review their answers to make sure they have done the following:

• expressed the solution clearly

• used appropriate mathematical notation and terms

• supported their solution with verbal and symbolic work

• determined the reasonableness of the solution in the context of the original problem.

DAILY TEST PREP

The school tennis team is made up of 12 seniors, 8 juniors, and 4 sophomores. Make a circle graph that represents the team. (circle graph with: $\frac{1}{2}$ as as seniors, $\frac{1}{3}$ as juniors, and $\frac{1}{6}$ as sophomores)

Activity

Or use Intervention CD-ROM Lesson 19.6

Lesson Intervention

Circle Graph Models

👥 Small Group	⏱ 5 minutes	Kinesthetic, Visual

Materials: *Mixed Numbers Transparency, blank transparency, scissors*

- On a blank transparency, trace a circle from the Mixed Numbers Transparency. Write: *12 apples, 12 bananas. 12 peaches, 12 apricots.* **What ratio compares the numbers of apples to all the fruit?** ($\frac{12}{48}$) **Simplify** ($\frac{1}{4}$) Label one quarter: *Apples, $\frac{1}{4}$, 25%*. Label the other quarters in this way for the other fruits.

- Cut one circle from the Mixed Numbers Transparency into 4 equal parts. Use the parts to find answers to questions such as these: **How many fruits are round?** (36) **What percent is this?** (75%)

Choose a Strategy ✓

Possible strategies given.
Solve. Show your work. Tell what strategy you used.

PROBLEM-SOLVING
Strategies
- Use Models
- Draw a Diagram
- Find a Pattern
- Guess and Check
- Make an Organized List
- Make a Table
- Solve a Simpler Problem
- Use Logical Reasoning
- Work Backward
- Write an Equation

8. **Measurement** A rectangle has a perimeter of 26 cm and an area of 36 cm². What are the dimensions of the rectangle?
   9 cm × 4 cm (Guess and Check)

9. The Drama Club spends $600 on sets and props, $500 on costumes, $250 on tickets and programs, and $200 on a cast party. After spending this money, the club is left with $325. How much did the club start with?
   $1,875 (Work Backward)

10. The monthly rent on an apartment was $1,000 in 2000, $1,050 in 2001, and $1,103 in 2002. What was the rent increase each year? What percent is each increase? Predict the rent in 2003, to the nearest dollar.
    $50, $53; 5%; $1,158 (Find a Pattern)

11. **Represent** A store has 36 employees. Twenty-five percent of the employees are managers. How many managers does the store have? Draw a picture that supports your solution. **See at right.**

    9 managers. *Check students' drawings. They should show a total of 36 units and a group of $\frac{1}{4}$, or 9, of those units.* **(Draw a Picture)**

Choose a Computation Method ✓

Mental Math • Estimation • Paper and Pencil • Calculator

Data Use the diagram for Problems 12–14.

The diagram shows the floor plan of a home supplies store. The labels show the different departments within the store.

12. **Measurement** How many square feet of space does the store have? **38,400 ft²**

13. Find the percent of each department's space in the store. Round your answers to the nearest tenth of a percent. **See above.**

14. The store has total sales of $10,000,000. The ratio of the Kitchen Wares Department's sales to total sales is equal to the ratio of its floor area to the total floor area. Find the Kitchen Wares Department's sales. **$2,500,000**

13. Appliances, 50%; Bath, 8.3%; Bedroom, 16.7%; Kitchen, 25%

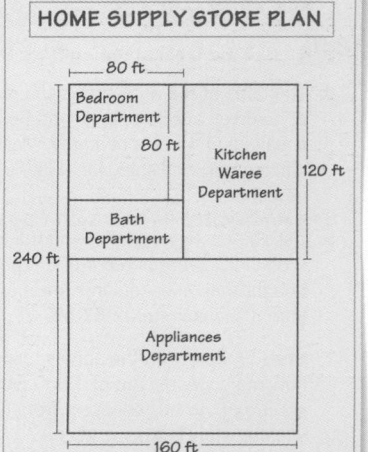

HOME SUPPLY STORE PLAN

Practice *continued*

Choose a Strategy

Assign **Problems 8–11** as independent work.

- *Problem Solving for Problems 8–11* Have students describe the strategies they used to solve each problem.

Choose a Computation Method

- *Problem Solving for Problems 12–14* Have students share which computation method they chose to use.

4 Assess and Close

Have students discuss making and interpreting data in circle graphs. Refer to the circle graph on page 520 and review how to compare fractions, ratios, decimals and percents.

- **Add the sectors using ratios for the circle graph. What is the sum?** ($\frac{240}{240}$ or 1)

- **Add the sectors using decimals within the circle graph. What is the sum?** (1.000 or 1)

- **Add the sectors using percentages within the circle graph. What is the sum?** (100% or 1)

- **Add the sectors using degrees within the circle graph. What is the sum?** (360° or 1 whole circle)

- **What might you conclude from these computations?** (All computations add up to 1 complete circle.)

Assign the **LESSON QUIZ** on Transparency 19.6 to further assess student understanding.

Quick Check

Check your understanding of Lessons 4–6.

Find each percent. (Lessons 4 and 5)

1. 10% of 98 **9.8** 2. 10% of 0.94 **0.094** 3. 20% of 200 **40** 4. 20% of 413 **82.6**

5. 25% of 120 **30** 6. 47% of 20 **9.4** 7. 58% of 300 **174** 8. 45% of 40 **18**

Solve. (Lesson 6)

9. At Sandy's Subs, 120 customers bought sandwiches—90 Sandy's Specials, 15 roast beef sandwiches, and 15 subs. Create a circle graph to display these data as percents.

Check students' graphs. They should show the following sections: Sandy's Special, $\frac{3}{4}$; Roast Beef, $\frac{1}{8}$; Submarine, $\frac{1}{8}$.

10. Use the circle graph that you made in Problem 9. What percent of lunch customers bought sandwiches that were not Sandy's Specials? **25%**

Line 'Em Up

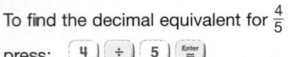

Calculator Connection

You can use a calculator to convert ratios and percents to decimal form.

To find the decimal equivalent for $\frac{4}{5}$

press: 4 ÷ 5 Enter=

To find the decimal equivalent for 75%

press: 7 5 ÷ 1 0 0 Enter=

Use a calculator to rewrite each set in order from least to greatest.
Then match each one to a word to solve the riddle below.

1. $\frac{3}{20}$ 0.2 18%

 $\underline{\frac{3}{20}}$ $\underline{18\%}$ $\underline{0.2}$

2. $\frac{5}{7}$ 0.688 74%

 $\underline{0.688}$ $\underline{\frac{5}{7}}$ $\underline{74\%}$

3. $\frac{7}{16}$ 45% 0.4499

 $\underline{\frac{7}{16}}$ $\underline{0.4499}$ $\underline{45\%}$

Riddle: Why didn't the fraction slurp his soup?

Key:	$\frac{3}{20}$	$\frac{7}{16}$	$\frac{5}{7}$	0.2	0.4499	0.688	18%	45%	74%
	He	he	would	afraid	was	someone	was	improper	think

He was afraid someone would think he was improper.

Keeping a Journal

Have students explain when it is appropriate to use a circle graph to represent data.

Calculator Connection

Line 'Em Up

- Review the examples. Have students recall how they found repeating decimals in Chapter 14 Lesson 6. Explain that in this case dividing the numerator by the denominator results in a quotient that is a terminating decimal. For the second example, have students recall that all percents are ratios expressed as a number compared to 100. **Because 75% is the same number as $\frac{75}{100}$, you can once again divide the numerator by the denominator.**

- For the Riddle, make sure students understand that converting each of the numbers to a decimal will allow them to order the corresponding words into a sentence.

Monitoring Student Progress

Purpose: This test provides an informal assessment of the Chapter 19 objectives.

Chapter Test Items 1–20

To assign a numerical grade for this Chapter Test, use 5 points for each test item.

Check Understanding

You can use the **Write About It** question to assess student understanding of a key chapter concept.

Customizing Your Instruction

For students who have not yet mastered these objectives, you can use the Reteaching Resources listed in the chart below.

 ## Assessment Options

A summary test for this chapter is also provided in the Unit Resource Folder.

 ## Adequate Yearly Progress

Use the End of Grade Test Prep Assessment Guide to help familiarize your students with the format of standardized tests.

Chapter Review/Test

VOCABULARY

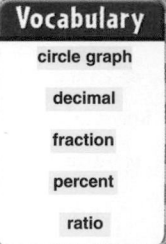

Vocabulary
- circle graph
- decimal
- fraction
- percent
- ratio

1. A ____ is a ratio of a number to 100. **percent**

2. You can show how parts of a whole are related in a ____. **circle graph**

3. A ____ is a number that shows tenths, hundredths, thousandths, and so on. **decimal**

CONCEPTS AND SKILLS

Copy and complete each table. Write each fraction in simplest form. (Lessons 1–2, pp. 506–509)

	Fraction	Decimal	Percent
4.	$\frac{1}{2}$	■	■	0.5, 50%
5.	■	0.08	■	$\frac{2}{25}$, 8%

	Fraction	Decimal	Percent
6.	$\frac{1}{5}$	■	■	0.20, 20%
7.	■	■	15%	$\frac{3}{20}$, 0.15

Order each set from the greatest to the least part of a unit. (Lesson 3, pp. 510–513)

8. $\frac{17}{40}$ 35% 0.4   **$\frac{17}{40}$, 0.4, 35%**

9. $\frac{7}{20}$ 68% 0.37   **68%, 0.37, $\frac{7}{20}$**

10. $\frac{8}{10}$ 75% 0.95   **0.95, $\frac{8}{10}$, 75%**

Find 10% of each number. Then find 20% of each number. (Lesson 4, pp. 514–515)

11. 95 **9.5, 19**   12. 3,780 **378, 756**   13. 54.7 **5.47, 10.94**   14. 0.14 **0.014, 0.028**

Solve. Use any method. (Lesson 5, pp. 516–519)

15. 25% of 96 **24**   16. 70% of 120 **84**   17. 60% of 60 **36**   18. 30% of 40 **12**

PROBLEM SOLVING

Use the circle graph to solve.
(Lesson 6, pp. 520–523)

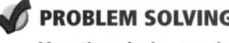

500 Students' Activities

- 13% Biking
- 35% Baseball
- 40% Soccer
- 10% Football
- 2% Swimming

19. How many students play soccer and baseball? **375 students**

20. What fraction of the students surveyed play football? **$\frac{1}{10}$**

Write About It

Show You Understand

Sue says that $\frac{15}{20}$ is equal to 60%. Is this reasonable? Explain.

Possible answer: No. $\frac{15}{20}$ = 75%. Sue might have mistakenly thought that 100 ÷ 20 = 4 and then multiplied 15 by 4.

524 **Chapter 19** Chapter Review/Test

Reteaching Support

Chapter Test Items	Summary Test Items	Chapter Objectives Tested	TE Pages	Use These Reteaching Resources
1, 3–7	1–7	**19A** Use ratios to write percents.	506A–507	Reteach Resource 19.1, 19.2 Ways to Success CD: 19.1, 19.2 Skillsheet 154
8–10	8–10	**19B** Relate and compare percents, decimals, fractions, and mixed numbers.	508A–513	Reteach Resource 19.3 Ways to Success CD: 19.3 Skillsheet 155
11–18	11–15	**19C** Find a percent of a number.	514A–519	Reteach Resource 19.4, 19.5 Ways to Success CD: 19.4, 19.5 Skillsheet 156
2, 19, 20	16–20	**19D** Analyze and solve problems using circle graphs.	520A–523	Reteach Resource 19.6 Ways to Success CD: 19.6 Skillsheet 157

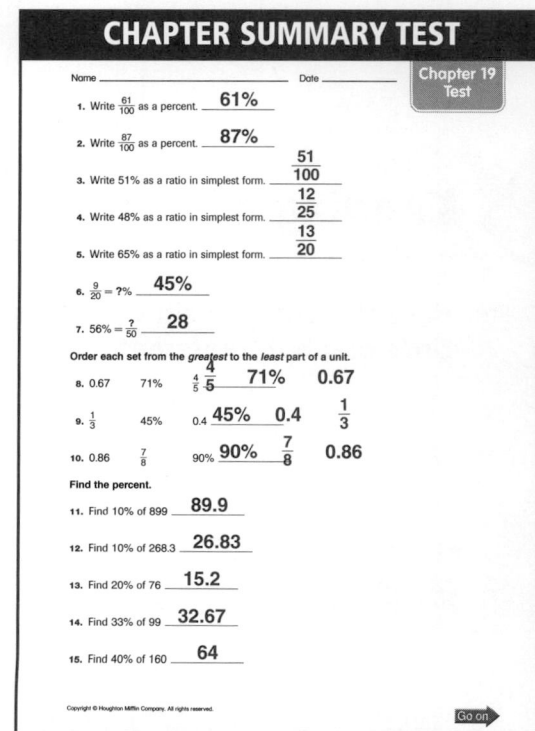

CHAPTER SUMMARY TEST

Name _____ Date _____ Chapter 19 Test

1. Write $\frac{61}{100}$ as a percent. **61%**

2. Write $\frac{87}{100}$ as a percent. **87%**

3. Write 51% as a ratio in simplest form. **$\frac{51}{100}$**

4. Write 48% as a ratio in simplest form. **$\frac{12}{25}$**

5. Write 65% as a ratio in simplest form. **$\frac{13}{20}$**

6. $\frac{9}{20}$ = ?% **45%**

7. 56% = $\frac{?}{50}$ **28**

Order each set from the *greatest* to the *least* part of a unit.

8. 0.67 71% $\frac{4}{5}$ **$\frac{4}{5}$ 71% 0.67**

9. $\frac{1}{3}$ 45% 0.4 **45% 0.4 $\frac{1}{3}$**

10. 0.86 $\frac{7}{8}$ 90% **90% $\frac{7}{8}$ 0.86**

Find the percent.

11. Find 10% of 899 **89.9**

12. Find 10% of 268.3 **26.83**

13. Find 20% of 76 **15.2**

14. Find 33% of 99 **32.67**

15. Find 40% of 160 **64**

Go on

Set A (Lesson 2, pp. 508–509)

Copy and complete each table. Write each fraction in simplest form.

	Fraction	Decimal	Percent			Fraction	Decimal	Percent	
1.	$\frac{3}{10}$	0.3	■	**30%**	2.	$\frac{21}{100}$	■	■	**0.21; 21%**
3.	$\frac{7}{10}$	■	■	**0.7; 70%**	4.	■	■	40%	**$\frac{2}{5}$; 0.4**
5.	■	0.09	■	**$\frac{9}{100}$; 9%**	6.	■	■	84%	**$\frac{21}{25}$; 0.84**
7.	■	0.45	■	**$\frac{9}{20}$; 45%**	8.	$\frac{3}{5}$	■	■	**0.60; 60%**

Set B (Lesson 3, pp. 510–513)

Order each set from the greatest to the least part of a unit.

6. $\frac{7}{8}$, 86%, $\frac{37}{50}$ 9. $\frac{8}{10}$, 0.6, 59%

1. $\frac{7}{10}$ 0.5 80% **80%, $\frac{7}{10}$, 0.5**

2. $\frac{2}{5}$ 0.35 27% **$\frac{2}{5}$, 0.35, 27%**

3. $\frac{13}{20}$ 0.92 30% **0.92, $\frac{13}{20}$, 30%**

4. $\frac{5}{8}$ 50% 0.61 **$\frac{5}{8}$, 0.61, 50%**

5. $\frac{12}{25}$ 78% 0.4 **78%, $\frac{12}{25}$, 0.4**

6. $\frac{7}{8}$ $\frac{37}{50}$ 86%

7. 0.47 $\frac{3}{8}$ 39% **0.47, 39%, $\frac{3}{8}$**

8. 28% 0.27 $\frac{7}{20}$ **$\frac{7}{20}$, 28%, 0.27**

9. 0.6 59% $\frac{8}{10}$

Set C (Lesson 4, pp. 514–515)

Find 10% of each number. Then find 20% of each number.

1. 72 **7.2; 14.4**

2. 2,410 **241; 482**

3. 5 **0.5; 1**

4. 700 **70; 140**

5. 12,305 **1,230.5; 2,461**

6. 39.5 **3.95; 7.9**

7. 8.31 **0.831; 1.662**

8. 2 **0.2; 0.4**

9. 514.74 **51.474; 102.948**

10. 6.3502 **0.63502; 1.27004**

Set D (Lesson 5, pp. 516–519)

Solve by writing the percent as a fraction.

1. 30% of 70 **21**   2. 75% of 96 **72**   3. 60% of 85 **51**   4. 50% of 64 **32**

5. 25% of 40 **10**   6. 20% of 10 **2**   7. 45% of 200 **90**   8. 55% of 800 **440**

Solve by writing the percent as a decimal.

9. 25% of 88 **22**   10. 37% of 90 **33.3**   11. 15% of 70 **10.5**   12. 85% of 200 **170**

13. 40% of 20 **8**   14. 75% of 400 **300**   15. 8% of 64 **5.12**   16. 1% of 6 **0.06**

Chapter 19 Extra Practice   **525**

CHAPTER SUMMARY TEST

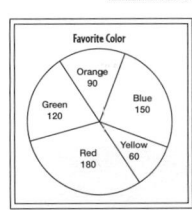

Name _____ Date _____

Chapter 19 Test continued

The circle graph shows the results of a survey of 600 customers in a clothing store. Use the graph to answer Questions 16–20.

Favorite Color
Orange 90
Green 120
Blue 150
Red 180
Yellow 60

16. What percent of customers preferred yellow?
10%

17. What percent of customers preferred blue?
25%

18. What percent of customers preferred orange and green together?
35%

19. Based on the information in the graph, predict how many customers would have preferred green if 1,200 people had been surveyed.
240

20. Suppose that 50% of the customers had preferred red. How many customers would that have been?
300

STOP

Additional Answers

Chapter 19

Lesson 5, pp. 516–519

35. No; 20% of $25 is $5, $25 − $5 = $20. Elena does not have enough money.

36. *Possible answer:* 1 Parafoil, 1 Dragon, and 1 Delta; $85.00

Lesson 6, pp. 520–523

2. The circle graph will have the following parts: Check, $\frac{1}{6}$; Cash, $\frac{1}{6}$; Credit card, $\frac{1}{2}$; Debit card, $\frac{1}{6}$.

4. *Check students' responses. Possible answer:* Cut $150 from Entertainment and use it for Savings.

5. *Check students' graphs. They should show the following sections:* Sporting goods, $\frac{1}{4}$; Department or discount, $\frac{1}{2}$; Sneaker, $\frac{1}{8}$; Other, $\frac{1}{8}$.

Lesson By Lesson Overview
Probability

Lesson 1

- Students find all the possible combinations of given items using an organized list, tree diagram, or multiplication.
- Students use data from a menu to solve problems.

Lesson 2

- Students describe the probability of an event.
- Students identify outcomes that are more likely, less likely, certain, and impossible.

Lesson 3

- Students use fractions in simplest form to find theoretical probability.

Lesson 4

- Students make an organized list to solve problems.
- Students choose a strategy and use data from a pictograph to solve problems.

Lesson 5

- Students determine experimental probability.
- Students conduct an experiment, record the outcomes, and then compare their experimental probability with the theoretical probability.

Lesson 6

- Students find the probability of compound events using either a tree diagram or an organized list.

Lesson 7

- Students use data to make predictions.
- Students choose a strategy and a computation method to solve problems.

SKILLS TRACE: PROBABILITY

Grade 4	Grade 5	Grade 6
• describe the probability of an event and determine the number of possible outcomes in an experiment (ch. 23)	• **determine combinations**	• represent probabilities using ratios, percents, and decimals; determine sample space (ch. 19)
• use probability to make predictions (ch. 23)	• **find the theoretical probability of single and compound events**	• find probabilities of dependent and independent events (ch. 19)
• use tables, graphs, and tree diagrams to represent outcomes (ch. 23)		• find combinations and permutations (ch. 19)

Chapter Planner

Lesson	Objective	Vocabulary	Materials	✔ NCTM Standards
20.1 Make Choices p. 528A	Use organized lists, tree diagrams, and multiplication to find all the possible combinations of given items.	organized list tree diagram	Quadrilaterals Transparency and copies, snap cubes, colored pencils or crayons	**Representation:** Create and use representations to organize, record, and communicate mathematical ideas.
20.2 Probability Concepts p. 530A	Describe the probability of an event.	event probability impossible event certain event	Circle Spinner Transparency, number cubes, color erasable markers, number cubes, Number Lines Transparency	**Data Analysis and Probability:** Describe events as likely or unlikely and discuss the degree of likelihood using such words as certain, equally likely, and impossible.
20.3 Theoretical Probability p. 532A	Use fractions to find theoretical probability.	outcome theoretical probability equally likely	Large Plane Figures Transparency	**Data Analysis and Probability:** Understand and apply basic concepts of probability. Predict the probability of outcomes of simple experiments.
20.4 Problem-Solving Strategy: Make an Organized List p. 536A	Solve a problem by making an organized list.		pennies (4 per student), blank transparency, poster board, scissors, Problem-Solving: Four Step Process Transparency	**Problem Solving:** Apply and adapt a variety of appropriate strategies to solve problems.
20.5 Hands-On: Experimental Probability p. 540A	Determine the experimental probability for a given set of data.	experimental probability	number cube (labeled 1-6), Learning Tool 56, red, blue, and yellow connecting cubes, blank transparency, Circle Spinner Transparency, spinner	**Data Analysis and Probability:** Predict the probability of outcomes of simple experiments.
20.6 Compound Events p. 544A	Find the probability of compound events.	compound event	coin, Circle Spinner Transparency, red and blue erasable markers	**Data Analysis and Probability:** Understand and apply basic concepts of probability.
20.7 Problem-Solving Application: Make Predictions p. 546A	Use data to make predictions.		index cards (2 sets labeled 1-10), Problem-Solving: Four Step Process Transparency	**Data Analysis and Probability:** Propose and justify conclusions and predictions that are based on data and design studies to further investigate the conclusions or predictions.

Resources For Reaching All Learners

LESSON RESOURCES: Reteach, Practice, Enrichment, Problem Solving, Homework, English Learners, Daily Routines, Transparencies, Math Center.

ADDITIONAL RESOURCES FROM HOUGHTON MIFFLIN: Combination Classroom Planning Guide, Chapter Challenges, Every Day Counts, Math at Hand (student handbook)

Every Day Counts

The **Graph** activities in **Every Day Counts** support the math in this chapter.

Assessing Prior Knowledge

Before beginning the chapter, you can assess student understandings in order to assist you in differentiating instruction.

Complete Chapter Pretest in Unit Resource Folder

Use this test to assess both prerequisite skills (**Are You Ready?** — one page) and chapter content (**Check What You Know** — two pages).

Chapter 20 Prerequisite Skills Pretest

Chapter 20 New Content Pretest

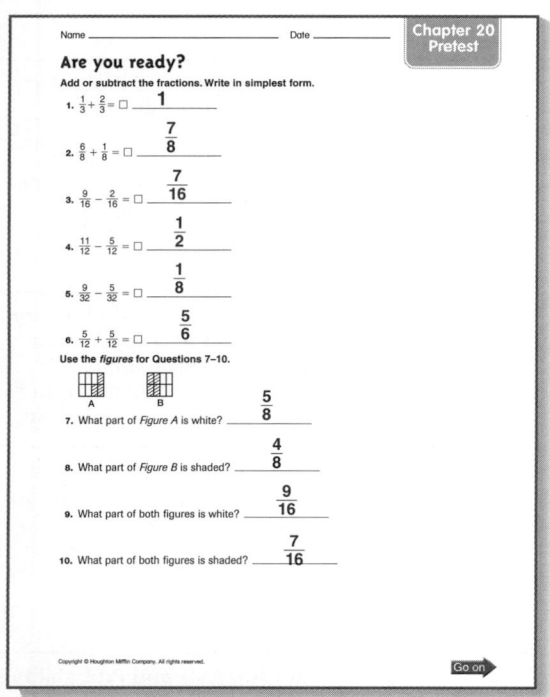

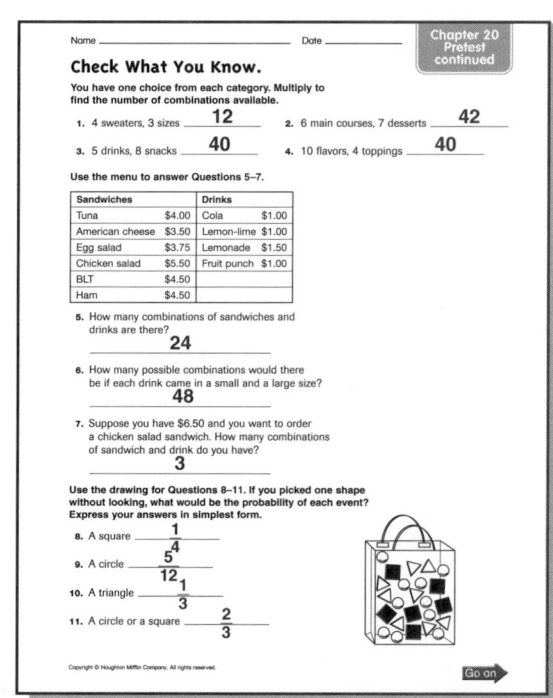

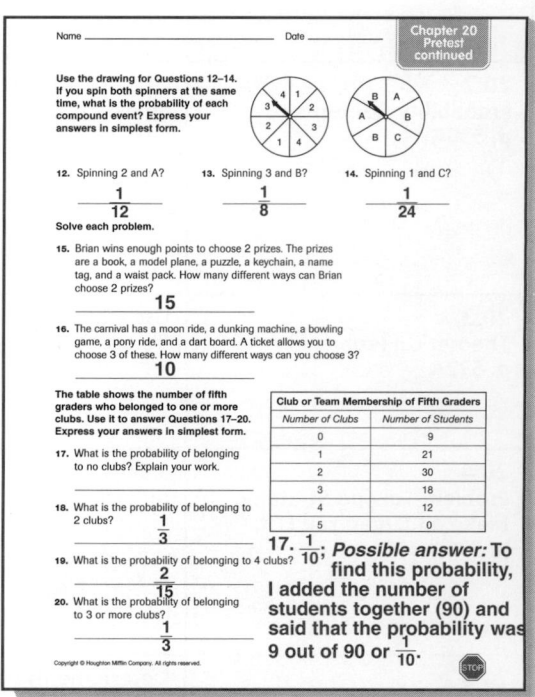

Customizing Instruction

For Students Having Difficulty

Items	Prerequisites	Ways to Success
1–6	Add and subtract fractions and mixed numbers with like denominators	CD: 20a Skillsheet: 158
7–10	Describe the probability of an event and determine the number of possible outcomes in an experiment	CD: 20b Skillsheet: 159

Ways to Success: Intervention for every concept and skill (CD-ROM or Chapter Intervention Skillsheets).

Consider using **Knowing Mathematics** with any students who are working two or more years below grade level.

For Students Having Success

Items	Objectives	Resources
1–7	**20A** Determine combinations.	Enrichment 20.1
8–14	**20B** Find the theoretical probability of single and compound events.	Enrichment 20.2, 20.3, 20.5, 20.6
15–20	**20C** Analyze and solve problems by making an organized list and by using data to make predictions.	Enrichment 20.4, 20.7

Use **Chapter Challenges** with any students who have success with all new chapter content.

Other Pretest Options

Informal Pretest in Student Book

The student book pretest assesses vocabulary and prerequisite skills needed for success in this chapter.

Ways to Success CD-ROM

The *Ways to Success* chapter pretest has automatic assignment of appropriate review lessons.

Chapter Resources

Assessing Prior Knowledge

Spin It (probability concepts)

- Display an 8–section spinner with sections in these colors: 1 red, 2 blue, 3 yellow, 2 green.
- Pose questions such as: **How many sections are there? How many are blue? Out of the 8 chances, what are the chances of landing on blue? on purple?**

Ongoing Skill Activity

Student ID Events (theoretical and experimental probability, compound events)

- Have students write their name, age, and gender on index cards. Tally and display a list of the number of each: names with 4 or fewer letters, names with 5 or more letters, ages (e.g., 9, 10, or 11), boys, and girls.
- Place the cards in a bag. Depending upon the lesson, have students write the theoretical probability of an event (for example, picking the card of a boy) and calculate compound events, such as picking the card of a girl aged 10. Then, have them draw cards from a bag to model experimental probability.

Connecting to the Unit Project

- Have students list possible outcomes for weather conditions in terms of forms of precipitation (e.g., snow, rain, sleet, hail), degree of sunshine (e.g., sunny, partly sunny, cloudy) and humidity (high, low).
- Have students tell which are more likely than others given your geographic location and the time of year.

Professional Resources Handbook
Research, Mathematics Content, and Language Intervention

Research-Based Teaching

Stree (1995) found that tying in the concepts of ratio and proportion with those of chance and probability serves to strengthen both concepts in the minds of students. This thought ties in nicely with the curricular decision to teach probability along with ratio. See *Professional Resources Handbook, Grade 5*, Unit 7.

For more ideas relating to Unit 7, see the Teacher Support Handbook at the back of this Teacher's Edition.

Language Intervention

When new vocabulary words (for example, *outcome, equally likely, compound events*) are introduced in a lesson, have students write their own definitions. Have students share their definitions with the class and have other students help you critique the quality of the definitions and help make improvements.

Time Saving Technology Support

Ways to Assess Customized Spiral Review and Test Generator CD-ROM
Lesson Planner CD-ROM
Ways to Success Intervention CD-ROM
Math Tracks CD-ROM
Education Place: **www.eduplace.com/math/mw/**
Houghton Mifflin Math eBook CD-ROM
eManipulatives
eGames

Starting Chapter 20
Probability

Chapter Objectives

20A Determine combinations.

20B Find the theoretical probability of single and compound events.

20C Analyze and solve problems by making an organized list and by using data to make predictions.

Math Background

Probability

When two or more events are being considered, the likelihood that a specific event will occur is the *probability* of that event. Before determining the probability of an event, students must be able to find the total number of possible outcomes. The total number of possible outcomes can be found by making an organized list, a tree diagram, or by using multiplication.

If there are m possible choices or outcomes for one experiment or problem and n possible choices or outcomes for a second experiment or problem, then the total number of possible choices or outcomes is $m \times n$. For example, if you have 3 sizes of shirts and 2 choices for color, for each of the 3 sizes there are two possible colors, so there are 6 possible outcomes because $3 \times 2 = 6$.

The result of an *experiment* is called an *outcome*. If the experiment is tossing a number cube, then there are six possible outcomes, one for each face of the cube. An event is any collection of outcomes. An event for tossing a number cube could be that the number tossed is even, that the number is 1 or 2, or that the number is 3. The *probability of an event* is the percent of the time that the event is expected to happen if the experiment is repeated a large number of times. The probability is always a number between 0 and 1. When an experiment only has a finite number of outcomes, a probability of 0 means an event is impossible while a probability of 1 means an event is certain.

INVESTIGATION

Use Data

Table Tennis Tournament

These athletes have come from all over the world to compete for a medal in table tennis. The table shows the games currently being played. If each of these 8 athletes plays each other athlete once, how many games will be played? **28 games**

(Round 2)
Player versus Player
H ←→ C
D ←→ A
F ←→ E
B ←→ G

526

Using The Investigation

Have students work in small groups to answer the question posed on page 526.

To extend the investigation, provide students with the following problem.

• In *elimination* tournaments, only the winners of each game move on to the next round and after all the rounds are played, there is one winner. How many rounds would need to be played if the athletes described on page 526 played an elimination tournament? How many games would need to be played? (3 rounds: In the first round, each player plays one other player and 4 go on. In the second round, 4 players each play and 2 go on. In the third round, 2 players play each other and there is one winner. 7 games)

For more information about projects and investigations, visit **Education Place**.
www.eduplace.com/math/mw/

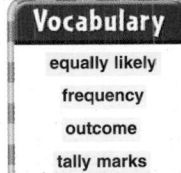

Chapter Pretest

Use this page to review and remember
what you need to know for this chapter.

VOCABULARY

Choose the best word to complete each sentence.

Vocabulary
equally likely
frequency
outcome
tally marks

tally marks
1. Groups of five ____ help you keep a running
count of how often an object appears or
something occurs.

outcome
2. A(n) ____ is a possible result of a probability experiment.

3. In a table, the number that tells how often something
happens is called the ____. **frequency**

CONCEPTS AND SKILLS

Write the fraction for the shaded part in simplest form.

4. 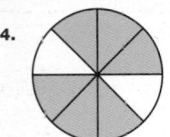 $\frac{3}{4}$

5.  $\frac{5}{6}$

Write each ratio in simplest form.

6. 2 to 6 $\frac{1}{3}$

7. $\frac{4}{10}$ $\frac{2}{5}$

8. 30:72 $\frac{5}{12}$

9. $\frac{8}{48}$ $\frac{1}{6}$

Write About It

10. How do you write a fraction in
simplest form?
10. *Possible answer:* You can write a fraction in
simplest form by dividing the numerator and the
denominator by their greatest common factor.

 **Test Prep on the Net**
Visit *Education Place* at
eduplace.com/kids/mw/
for more review.

 # Chapter Pretest

Prerequisite Skills

Items	Skill
1–3	Vocabulary needed for this chapter
4–5	Writing fractions in simplest form from models
6–9	Writing ratios in simplest form

Chapter Challenges

For Mathematically Promising Students

The *Chapter Challenges* resource book
provides blackline masters for activities that explore, extend, and connect
the mathematics in every chapter. To
support this independent work, see
the Teacher Notes for each activity.

Explore: Determining Percents, page 109, after
Lesson 1

Extend: Use Percents, page 111, after Lesson 3

Connect: People Percentages, page 113, after
Lesson 5

Using The Chapter Pretest

This page will help students review some of the
prerequisite skills needed for this chapter. The chart
above indicates which skills are covered on the
pretest. If students need more help with these
prerequisite skills use *Ways to Success,* Houghton
Mifflin's intervention program.

 Students who need more review can visit
Education Place, Houghton Mifflin's
award-winning website.

NSF Children's Math Worlds

Using *Children's Math Worlds* helps develop
student communication skills because of the daily
work with Math Talk, a teaching practice that can
be used with all lessons. The emphasis on building
a helping community will also enhance student
participation in all classroom discussion.

Make Choices

PLANNING THE LESSON

MATHEMATICS OBJECTIVE
Use organized lists, tree diagrams, and multiplication to find all the possible combinations of given items.

Use Lesson Planner CD-ROM for Lesson 20.1.

Daily Routines

Vocabulary
In order to represent the possible outcomes of an event, we can use a **tree diagram.** Show students a tree deagram which represents all of the possible combinations of 2 shirts and 5 pair of shorts.

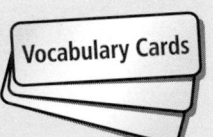
Vocabulary Cards

Meeting North Carolina's Standards
Prepare for Grade 6 Objective **4.01** Develop fluency with counting strategies to determine the sample space for an event. Include lists, tree diagrams, frequency distribution tables, permutations, combinations, and the Fundamental Counting Principle.

Lesson
Transparency

20.1

Problem of the Day
Greg rolled two number cubes, each numbered 1 to 6. How many possible sums could he roll? (11 different sums: 2 through 12)

Quick Review
Write each product.
1. 2×5 (10)
2. 7×2 (14)
3. 6×4 (24)
4. 9×3 (27)
5. 3×3 (9)
6. 4×3 (12)
7. 8×6 (48)
8. 8×8 (64)

Lesson Quiz
You have one choice from each category. Multiply to find the number of choices possible.
1. 6 bikes, 4 sizes (24)
2. 3 doors, 7 door handles (21)
3. 4 types of yogurt, 3 types of fruit (12)

LEVELED PRACTICE

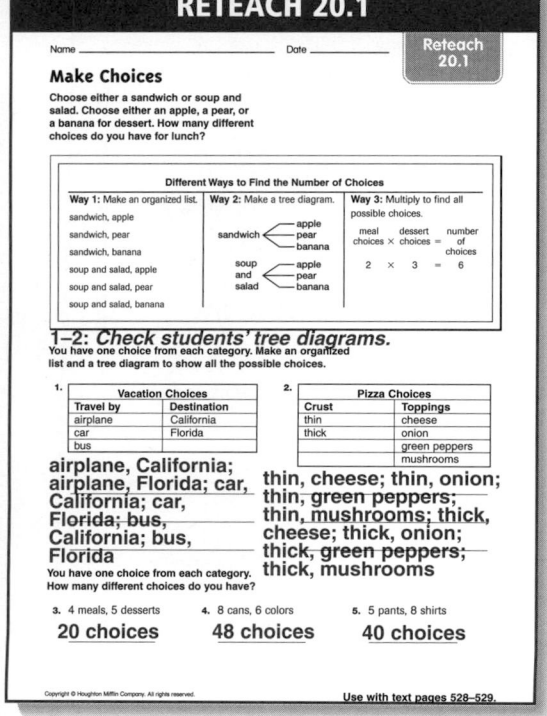

RETEACH 20.1

Name _____ Date _____   Reteach 20.1

Make Choices

Choose either a sandwich or soup and salad. Choose either an apple, a pear, or a banana for dessert. How many different choices do you have for lunch?

Different Ways to Find the Number of Choices

Way 1: Make an organized list.	Way 2: Make a tree diagram.	Way 3: Multiply to find all possible choices.
sandwich, apple		
sandwich, pear		
sandwich, banana		
soup and salad, apple		
soup and salad, pear		
soup and salad, banana		

meal × dessert = number
choices × choices = of choices
2 × 3 = 6

1–2: Check students' tree diagrams.
You have one choice from each category. Make an organized list and a tree diagram to show all the possible choices.

1.
Vacation Choices	
Travel by	Destination
airplane	California
car	Florida
bus	

airplane, California;
airplane, Florida; car,
California; car,
Florida; bus,
California; bus,
Florida

2.
Pizza Choices	
Crust	Toppings
thin	cheese
thick	onion
	green peppers
	mushrooms

thin, cheese; thin, onion;
thin, green peppers;
thin, mushrooms; thick,
cheese; thick, onion;
thick, green peppers;
thick, mushrooms

You have one choice from each category. How many different choices do you have?

3. 4 meals, 5 desserts
20 choices
4. 8 cans, 6 colors
48 choices
5. 5 pants, 8 shirts
40 choices

Copyright © Houghton Mifflin Company. All rights reserved.   **Use with text pages 528–529.**

PRACTICE 20.1

Name _____ Date _____   Practice 20.1

Make Choices

In each chart, you have one choice from each column. Make an organized list and a tree diagram to show all the possible choices for each chart.

1.
Sports Events	
Sport	Level
Hockey	College
Basketball	Pro
Football	

6 choices

2.
Drinks	
Size	Flavor
Small	Cola
Medium	Orange
Large	Grape
Extra Large	Fruit Punch

16 choices

3.
Books	
Type	Level
Paperback	History
Hardcover	Mystery
	Fantasy
	Romance
	Sci-Fi

10 choices

1–3: Organized lists and tree diagrams will vary. Number of possible choices is given. Check tree diagrams.
You have one choice from each category. Multiply to find the number of choices possible.

4. 3 cars, 8 colors
24 choices
5. 4 movies, 4 snacks
16 choices
6. 6 topics, 3 projects
18 choices

7. 10 entrees, 7 desserts
70 choices
8. 4 rings, 5 stones
20 choices
9. 6 dog, 9 collars
54 choices

Test Prep

10. Cherie wants to order soup and a sandwich. The soups are vegetable, black bean, and chicken. The sandwiches are tuna fish, chicken, egg salad, and tofu burger. How many choices does she have? **C**

A 4   C 12
B 8   D 16

11. Angela is writing a story. Each character will be a boy, a girl, or a talking animal. Each character will have or will not have special powers. How many choices does she have for characters?
6 choices

Copyright © Houghton Mifflin Company. All rights reserved.   **Use with text pages 528–529.**

ENRICHMENT 20.1

Name _____ Date _____   Enrichment 20.1

Class Election

In the first four U.S. presidential elections, the candidate who finished second became the vice president. This method was changed in 1804, but suppose the election for class president was run the same way.

The candidates for class president are Holly, Ernesto, Mya, Paul, Christie, and Alf.

1. On a separate sheet of paper, make a tree diagram to find all the possible combinations of class president and class vice president.
Tree diagrams should show the following combinations: H-E, H-M, H-P, H-C, H-A, E-H, E-M, E-P, E-C, E-A, M-H, M-E, M-P, M-C, M-A, P-H, P-E, P-M, P-C, P-A, C-H, C-E, C-M, C-P, C-A, A-H, A-E, A-M, A-P, A-C

2. Why was the total number of combinations different than the result of multiplying 6 × 6?
Since one student is elected president, there are only five candidates for vice president. That means 6 × 5, not 6 × 6.

3. How many possibilities are there that the class president and vice president are both girls? What are those possibilities?
6; H-M, H-C, M-H, M-C, C-H, C-M

4. Suppose Paul drops out of the race at the last minute. How many combinations of presidents and vice presidents are there now?
20

5. If Paul drops out, how many possibilities are there of having boys as both president and vice president? What are those possibilities?
2; E-A, A-E

Copyright © Houghton Mifflin Company. All rights reserved.   **Use with text pages 528–529.**

Practice Workbook Page 131

Reaching All Learners

Differentiated Instruction

English Learners

English-language learners may be unfamiliar with using the word *choice* to describe the act of choosing and the item that is chosen. Worksheet 20.1 introduces this and other key language used in the lesson. It also teaches students problem-solving methods for identifying the number of combinations of given items.

Special Needs
VISUAL, KINESTHETIC

Materials: *blue, red, green, and black pencils*

- Display this list: *1 white shirt, 1 black shirt, 3 pants in blue, red, green.*
- **How many different ways can you dress combining the shirts and pants in the list?** Have students draw and color their own diagrams to find the combinations.

Gifted and Talented
VISUAL, KINESTHETIC

- Have students use these ingredients to make as many different pizzas as possible:

Crust	Topping
thick	mushroom
thin	sausage
	onion
	pineapple

- Have them list all the possible combinations.

TECHNOLOGY

Spiral Review

Using the *Ways to Assess* CD-ROM, you can create **customized** spiral review worksheets covering any lessons you choose.

Education Place

Encourage students to visit Education Place at **eduplace.com/kids/mw/** for more student activities.

Lesson Planner

Use the Lesson Planner CD-ROM to see how lesson objectives for this chapter are correlated to standards.

Language Arts
Connection

Letter Combinations

- Write on the chalkboard:

All possible combinations for the letters C, A, and T are:

CAT	CTA
TAC	TCA
ACT	ATC

Circle *CAT* and *ACT*.

- Help students find other three-letter words that can be rearranged.
- Repeat this activity with four-letter words. Display and discuss answers.

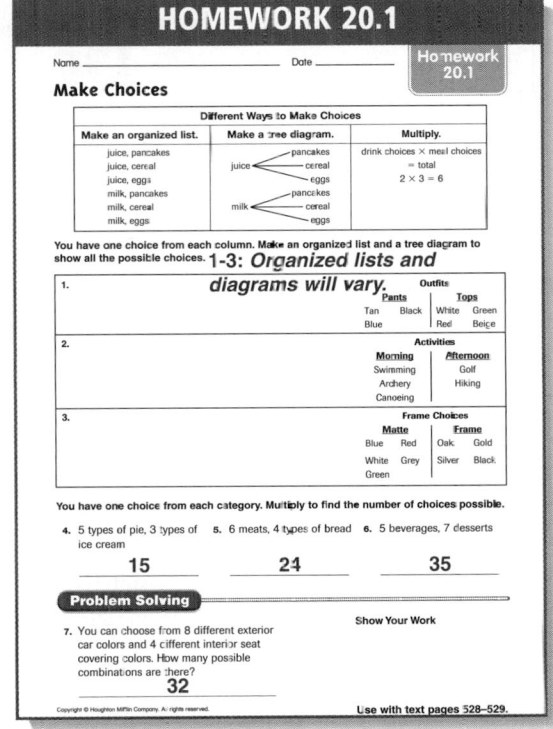

PROBLEM SOLVING 20.1

Name _____ Date _____

Problem Solving 20.1

Make Choices

Show Your Work

1. Hunan Express offers 3 types of soup and 8 main courses. How many choices are there if you want to order a soup and a main course?

24 choices

2. Suppose that Hunan Express also offers 5 drinks. How many choices are there if you want to order a soup, a main course, and a drink?

120 choices

3. Antarctic Ice Cream makes blend-ins, a combination of ice cream and candy. If there are 9 ice cream flavors and 7 candies, how many choices are there if you pick an ice cream flavor and a candy?

63 choices

4. Enzo's Pizzeria offers a lunch special. For $3.95 a customer can order a slice of pizza with a choice of one of 8 toppings and one of 4 desserts. How many possible choices are there for the lunch special?

32 choices

5. Enzo's Pizzeria changed the lunch special so that a customer can row order a slice of pizza with a choice of 8 toppings or a plain calzone and one of 4 desserts. To find the new number of possible choices, should you add 1 to your solution to Problem 3? Explain.

No; Possible answer: To find the number of new choices, multiply: 9 × 4 = 36.

Copyright © Houghton Mifflin Company. All rights reserved.

Use with text pages 528–529.

HOMEWORK 20.1

Name _____ Date _____

Homework 20.1

Make Choices

Different Ways to Make Choices		
Make an organized list.	**Make a tree diagram.**	**Multiply.**
juice, pancakes / juice, cereal / juice, eggs / milk, pancakes / milk, cereal / milk, eggs	juice → pancakes, cereal, eggs / milk → pancakes, cereal, eggs	drink choices × meal choices = total 2 × 3 = 6

You have one choice from each column. Make an organized list and a tree diagram to show all the possible choices. **1-3: Organized lists and diagrams will vary.**

1.

Outfits		
Pants		**Tops**
Tan	Black	White Green
Blue	Red	Red Beige

2.

Activities	
Morning	**Afternoon**
Swimming	Golf
Archery	Hiking
Canoeing	

3.

Frame Choices		
Matte		**Frame**
Blue	Red	Oak Gold
White	Grey	Silver Black
Green		

You have one choice from each category. Multiply to find the number of choices possible.

4. 5 types of pie, 3 types of ice cream

15

5. 6 meats, 4 types of bread

24

6. 5 beverages, 7 desserts

35

Problem Solving

Show Your Work

7. You can choose from 8 different exterior car colors and 4 different interior seat covering colors. How many possible combinations are there?

32

Copyright © Houghton Mifflin Company. All rights reserved.

Use with text pages 528–529.

ENGLISH LEARNERS 20.1

Name _____ Date _____

English Learners 20.1

Make Choices
1–2: Possible responses given.

To **make a choice** is to choose or pick an item. The item that you choose is also called your **choice**.

A **category** is a group of similar things. Often you must make a choice among items in a category. In each category below, list three possible choices. An example has been done for you.

	small	medium	large
size	red	green	blue
1. color			
2. flavor	vanilla	chocolate	strawberry

Imagine that a store sells ice cream in two sizes (small and large) and two flavors (vanilla and chocolate). How many total choices do you have? Here are three ways to find the number of choices.

Organized List: List the possible combinations in a logical way. Then count the items in your list.	**Tree Diagram:** Draw lines or "branches" from each item in one category to the items in another category. Then count the branches.	**Multiplication:** Multiply the number of items in one category by the number of items in another category.
small, vanilla 1 / small, chocolate 2 / large, vanilla 3 / large, chocolate 4	small → 1 vanilla, 2 chocolate / large → 3 vanilla, 4 chocolate	2 sizes × 2 flavors = 4 choices

Answer these questions. Use the back of this sheet for your list, tree diagram, and multiplication.

3. Soda comes in three flavors (orange, lemon-lime, and cola) and three sizes (small, medium, and large). Make an organized list to find the number of possible choices.

9 choices

4. You may order a slice of cheese, vegetable, or pepperoni pizza with either red or white sauce. Make a tree diagram to find the number of possible choices.

6 choices

5. A shirt is sold in five colors and two patterns. Multiply to find the number of choices.

10 choices

Copyright © Houghton Mifflin Company. All rights reserved.

Use with text pages 528–529.

Homework Workbook Page 131

TEACHING LESSON 20.1

Activity

Warm-Up Activity
Recall Multiplication Facts

iiii Whole Group	🕐 5–10 minutes	Verbal, Tactile

- Split the class into halves. Have a student from each half stand at the board. Read aloud a multiplication fact, such as 5×8.

- Have students write the expression and its answer as quickly as possible. When they are finished they are to turn around, face the class, and say, "Five times eight is forty." Continue so that everyone gets a few opportunities at the board.

Lesson 1

Make Choices

Objective Use organized lists, tree diagrams, and multiplication to find all the possible combinations of given items.

Learn About It

At the school fair frozen yogurt is sold in two flavors—vanilla and peach. You can choose one of three toppings for your yogurt—fruit, nuts, or sprinkles. How many different ways can you choose one flavor and one topping?

Different Ways to Find the Number of Choices

Way 1 You can make an **organized list**.

peach, fruit
peach, nuts
peach, sprinkles
vanilla, fruit
vanilla, nuts
vanilla, sprinkles

Way 2 You can make a **tree diagram**.

Yogurt   Toppings

Desserts
- peach — fruit, nuts, sprinkles
- vanilla — fruit, nuts, sprinkles

Way 3 You can multiply to find the number of possible choices. Look at the tree diagram.

$$\text{flavor choices} \times \text{topping choices} = \text{number of choices}$$

$$2 \times 3 = 6$$

Solution: You can choose one flavor and one topping in 6 different ways.

Guided Practice

You have one choice from each category. Make an organized list to show all the possible choices. *Ex. 1–3. Check students' lists.*

1. 3 flavors, 4 toppings
   12 choices
2. 4 styles, 5 colors
   20 choices
3. 7 colors, 3 designs
   21 choices

Ask Yourself
- How do I organize the list so I don't miss any choices?

TEST TIPS

TEST TIPS **Explain Your Thinking** ▶ How can you be sure that an organized list of choices is complete?
Possible answer: You can multiply to find what the number of choices should be.
528

Activity

1 Introduce | iiii Whole Group | 🕐 5–10 minutes

Teaching Transparency for 20.1

Materials: *Quadrilaterals Transparency and copies, colored pencils or crayons*

- **Suppose I want to make a design with a trapezoid and a rectangle. What are all the possible combinations if the choices for trapezoids are yellow and purple, and the choices for rectangles are red, green, and yellow?**

- Demonstrate the combinations on the transparency. Ask volunteers to color each design on the transparency as you create it. Have other students draw and complete the patterns on their copies.

- **How many designs are possible?** (6)

2 Develop

Guide students through the *Learn About It* section.

- **Look at Way 1. What makes this list organized?** (The pattern of listing.)

- **Look at Way 2. How is this method of finding the number of choices similar to the first method?** (It also lists choices in an organized way.)

- **Look at Way 3. This summarizes the choices and shows how to find the number of possible choices.**

Guided Practice

Have students complete **Exercises 1–3** as you observe. Remind them to use the *Ask Yourself* question to help. Give students the opportunity to talk about the question in *Explain Your Thinking*.

You have one choice from each column. Make an organized list and a tree diagram to show all the possible choices.

Ex. 4–6. Check students' lists and tree diagrams.

4.

T-Shirts	
Style	Color
V-neck	blue
crew neck	yellow
sleeveless	black
	red

12 choices

5.

School Ring	
Metal	Stone
silver	turquoise
gold	amber
	agate
	lapis

8 choices

6.

Games	
3:00 Game	3:45 Game
Ring Toss	Frisbee Golf
Darts	Sack Race
Spelling	Brain Teasers
Horseshoes	Extreme Math

16 choices

You have one choice from each category. Multiply to find the number of choices possible.

7. 5 styles, 3 sizes
15 choices

8. 4 colors, 12 designs
48 choices

9. 8 flavors, 4 toppings
32 choices

10. 7 cars, 4 colors
28 choices

11. 8 dinners, 7 desserts
56 choices

12. 3 drinks, 1 flavor
3 choices

Data Use the menu to solve Problems 13–15.

School Fair Menu

Hot Sandwiches $5.25
• Grilled Chicken • Hamburger
• Roast Beef • Grilled Tuna
• Roast Turkey

Salads $3.25
• Caesar
• Oriental

Drinks
Small 75¢
Medium $1.00
Large $1.50
• Lemonade
• Orange Juice
• Apple Juice
• Sparkling Water

13. How many choices are there if you want to order a hot sandwich and a large drink?
20 choices

14. How many choices are there if you want to order a salad and a small drink?
8 choices

15. **Reasoning** How could you find the number of choices for a hot sandwich, a salad, and a small drink?
See Additional Answers on Page 551.

16. Write About It Does the order in which the choices are listed on a tree diagram affect the number of possible choices? Explain your thinking.
No. *Possible answer:* Multiplying in any order gives the same product.

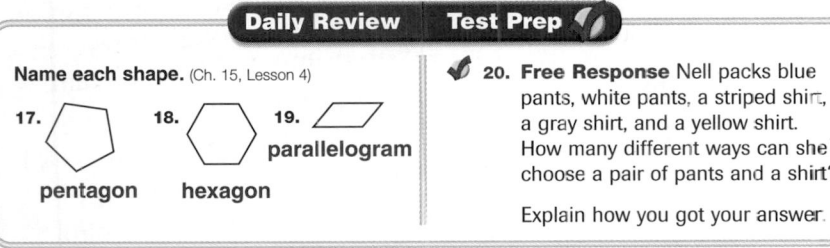

Daily Review | **Test Prep**

Name each shape. (Ch. 15, Lesson 4)

17. pentagon
18. hexagon
19. parallelogram

20. Free Response Nell packs blue pants, white pants, a striped shirt, a gray shirt, and a yellow shirt. How many different ways can she choose a pair of pants and a shirt? Explain how you got your answer.

See Additional Answers on Page 551.

DAILY TEST PREP

How many possible combinations are there when making a salad with either spinach or lettuce and three different dressings? (D)

A. 0 B. 5 C. 3 D. 6

Activity

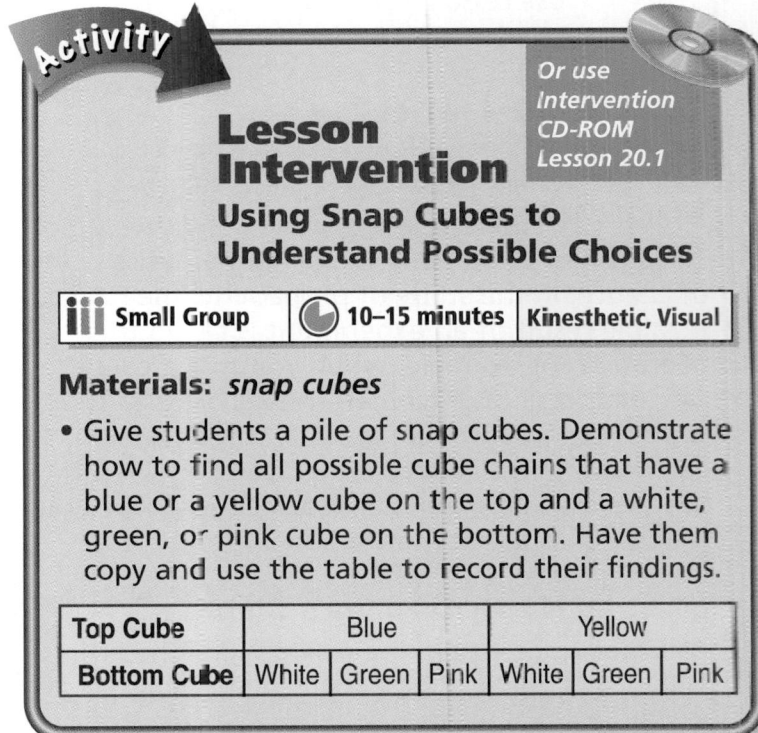

Lesson Intervention
Using Snap Cubes to Understand Possible Choices

Or use Intervention CD-ROM Lesson 20.1

| Small Group | 10–15 minutes | Kinesthetic, Visual |

Materials: *snap cubes*

• Give students a pile of snap cubes. Demonstrate how to find all possible cube chains that have a blue or a yellow cube on the top and a white, green, or pink cube on the bottom. Have them copy and use the table to record their findings.

Top Cube	Blue			Yellow		
Bottom Cube	White	Green	Pink	White	Green	Pink

3 Practice

Assign **Exercises 4–20** as independent work.

• *Problem Solving for Problems 4–6* Remind students to list every possible combination.

• *Problem Solving for Problems 13–15* Help students with Problem 15 by making a tree diagram that shows 3 different types of food combinations.

Common Error

Making an incomplete list Students may sometimes make an organized list that is missing one or more elements. Show them how to organize items so they can easily check to see what they might be missing.

4 Assess and Close

• Display the following:
1 Crust — graham cracker
3 Fillings — banana, pumpkin, cheesecake
3 Toppings — whipped cream, ice cream, strawberries

• Have students make an organized list of all the pies made from one crust, one filling, and one topping.

• **How many total choices of pies are there?** (9)

Assign the **LESSON QUIZ** on Transparency 20.1 to further assess student understanding.

 **Keeping a Journal**

Have students describe all the eyeglass combinations possible using 2 frames and 4 lens shades. Have students sketch the choices.

Lesson 20.2

Probability Concepts

PLANNING THE LESSON

MATHEMATICS OBJECTIVE
Describe the probability of an event.

Use Lesson Planner CD-ROM for Lesson 20.2.

Daily Routines

Vocabulary

Explain that **probability** is the mathematics of chance. In the study of probability, the possible result of an experiment is called the **outcome.** For example, when you toss a coin there are two possible outcomes—heads or tails. The *event* is a collection of outcomes. Ask students to think of examples where chance is involved (Possible answers: a board game where you spin a spinner or choose a card)

Vocabulary Cards

Meeting North Carolina's Standards

Maintain Grade 4 Objective **4.04** Design experiments and list all possible outcomes and probabilities for an event.

Lesson Transparency

20.2

Problem of the Day
Jerry bought a red ball, a yellow ball, and a green ball. The red ball was most expensive. The mean price of the balls was $3. The range of prices was $4. The yellow ball cost $1. What were the prices of the green ball and the red ball? (Green ball: $3; Red ball: $5)

Quick Review
Write <, >, or = in each ⬤.
1. 0.4 ⬤ 0.1 (>)   2. 0.5 ⬤ 0.45 (>)
3. 0.8 ⬤ 0.82 (<)   4. 0.01 ⬤ 0.10 (<)

Lesson Quiz
You spin once on the spinners below. Tell which event is more likely. If necessary, describe an event as impossible or certain.
1. If the spinner is split in half, $\frac{1}{2}$ red and $\frac{1}{2}$ blue (Spinning red or blue is equally likely.)
2. If the sections of the spinner have an even number written in them (Spinning an even number is certain.)

LEVELED PRACTICE

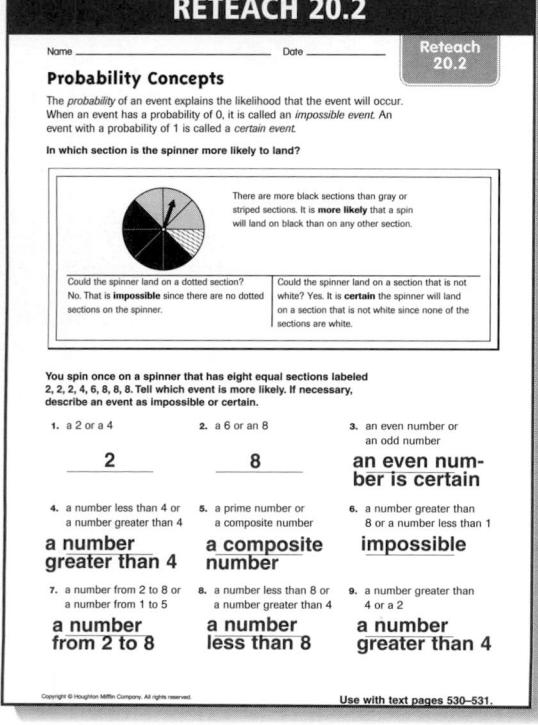

RETEACH 20.2

Name _____ Date _____

Reteach 20.2

Probability Concepts

The *probability* of an event explains the likelihood that the event will occur. When an event has a probability of 0, it is called an *impossible event.* An event with a probability of 1 is called a *certain event.*

In which section is the spinner more likely to land?

There are more black sections than gray or striped sections. It is **more likely** that a spin will land on black than on any other section.

Could the spinner land on a dotted section?	Could the spinner land on a section that is not white?
No. That is **impossible** since there are no dotted sections on the spinner.	Yes. It is **certain** the spinner will land on a section that is not white since none of the sections are white.

You spin once on a spinner that has eight equal sections labeled 2, 2, 2, 4, 6, 8, 8, 8. Tell which event is more likely. If necessary, describe an event as impossible or certain.

1. a 2 or a 4	2. a 6 or an 8	3. an even number or an odd number
2	8	an even number is certain

4. a number less than 4 or a number greater than 4	5. a prime number or a composite number	6. a number greater than 8 or a number less than 1
a number greater than 4	a composite number	impossible

7. a number from 2 to 8 or a number from 1 to 5	8. a number less than 8 or a number greater than 4	9. a number greater than 4 or a 2
a number from 2 to 8	a number less than 8	a number greater than 4

Copyright © Houghton Mifflin Company. All rights reserved.

Use with text pages 530–531.

PRACTICE 20.2

Name _____ Date _____

Practice 20.2

Probability Concepts

You turn the cards to the right face down and shuffle. Then you turn one card face up. Tell which event is more likely. If necessary, describe an event as impossible or certain.

1. circle or trapezoid __trapezoid__
2. triangle or pentagon __pentagon__
3. parallelogram or trapezoid __trapezoid; parallelogram is impossible__
4. triangle or circle __triangle__
5. square or any other shape __Any other shape is certain.__
6. circle or octagon __circle; octagon is impossible__

You spin once on the spinner at the right. Tell which event is *less* likely. If necessary, describe an event as impossible or certain.

7. C or D __C__	8. A or B __A__
9. A or E __E is impossible.__	10. C or B __C__
11. C or K __K is impossible.__	12. C or A __C__
13. B or F __F is impossible.__	14. B or D __D__

Test Prep

15. A number cube has numbers 1 to 6. What is the probability of tossing a 7? **A**

A 0   C $\frac{1}{4}$

B $\frac{1}{6}$ D 1

16. Ben and Cassie each have a bag of snap cubes. Ben's bag has 3 blue, 3 red, 4 purple, 2 yellow, and 2 green cubes. Cassie's bag has 4 blue, 3 red, 3 purple, 2 yellow, and 2 green cubes. They take turns drawing cubes out of their bags until one of them draws a purple cube. Whoever draws a purple cube first wins the game. Is the game fair? Explain.

No; Ben has more purple cubes than Cassie, and so he is more likely to draw a purple.

Copyright © Houghton Mifflin Company. All rights reserved.

Use with text pages 530–531.

ENRICHMENT 20.2

Name _____ Date _____

Enrichment 20.2

Make It Fair

For a game to be fair, both teams must have an equal chance of winning. You are going to design fair games, using a number cube, a spinner, and a coin. For each game use two of the items.

1. What are the rules and the object of your game? Play your game with a classmate.
   Answers will vary.

2. How is your game fair?
   Answers will vary.

3. Design a second game using a spinner and the item that you did not use in the first game. What are the rules and the object of this game? Play your game with a classmate.
   Answers will vary.

4. How is your game fair?
   Answers will vary.

Copyright © Houghton Mifflin Company. All rights reserved.

Use with text pages 530–531.

Practice Workbook Page 132

Reaching All Learners
Differentiated Instruction

English Learners

Worksheet 20.2 teaches concept vocabulary about probability and familiarizes students with the types of problems they will solve in Lesson 2.

Inclusion
VISUAL, TACTILE

Materials: *Circle Spinner Transparency, blue and red markers*

Color half of the spinner red, half blue. Have a volunteer demonstrate that it is *impossible* for the spinner to land on green, that it is *certain* to land on blue or red, and that it is *equally likely* to land on red or blue.

Early Finishers
VISUAL, TACTILE

Materials: *protractors, rulers, index cards*

- Make a spinner that is more likely to land on 1 than 5, that cannot spin a number greater than 7, and that is certain to land on an odd number.
- Help students define terms for a second spinner. **Exchange terms and make the spinner.**

TECHNOLOGY

Spiral Review

To reinforce skills on lessons taught earlier, create **customized** spiral review worksheets using the *Ways to Assess* CD-ROM.

Tool Software

Use *Easy Sheet* or another spreadsheet to explore this lesson more fully.

Education Place

You can visit Education Place at eduplace.com/math/mw/ for teachers support materials.

Language Arts Connection

Idioms
Materials: *dictionary, thesaurus*

Display:

on the off chance—in the slight hope or possibility

once in a blue moon—a rarely occurring event

Have students research the word *idiom*. Then have them brainstorm, research, and record idioms related to chance and probability. Have them write sentences using their idioms in context.

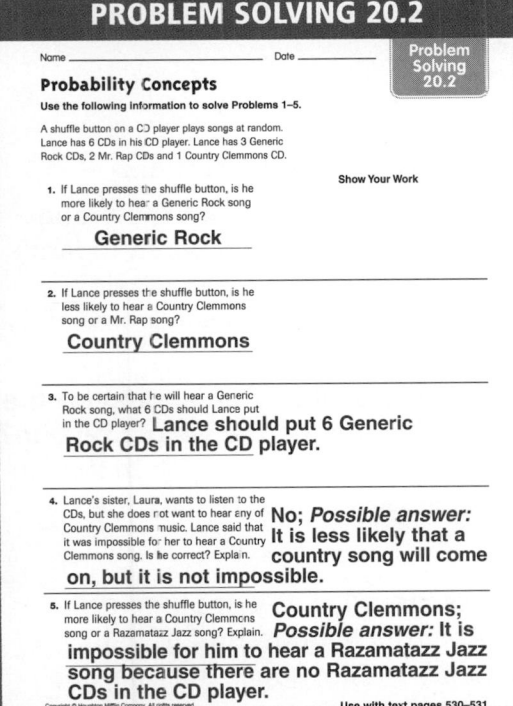

PROBLEM SOLVING 20.2

Name _____ Date _____   Problem Solving 20.2

Probability Concepts

Use the following information to solve Problems 1–5.

A shuffle button on a CD player plays songs at random. Lance has 6 CDs in his CD player. Lance has 3 Generic Rock CDs, 2 Mr. Rap CDs and 1 Country Clemmons CD.

Show Your Work

1. If Lance presses the shuffle button, is he more likely to hear a Generic Rock song or a Country Clemmons song? Explain.
   Generic Rock

2. If Lance presses the shuffle button, is he less likely to hear a Country Clemmons song or a Mr. Rap song?
   Country Clemmons

3. To be certain that he will hear a Generic Rock song, what 6 CDs should Lance put in the CD player? **Lance should put 6 Generic Rock CDs in the CD player.**

4. Lance's sister, Laura, wants to listen to the CDs, but she does not want to hear any of Country Clemmons music. Lance said that it was impossible for her to hear a Country Clemmons song. Is he correct? Explain. **No; Possible answer: It is less likely that a country song will come on, but it is not impossible.**

5. If Lance presses the shuffle button, is he more likely to hear a Country Clemmons song or a Razamatazz Jazz song? Explain. **Country Clemmons; Possible answer: It is impossible for him to hear a Razamatazz Jazz song because there are no Razamatazz Jazz CDs in the CD player.**

Use with text pages 530–531.

HOMEWORK 20.2

Name _____ Date _____   Homework 20.2

Probability Concepts

The probability of an event describes the likelihood the event will occur.

Impossible ———————— Certain
0 Probability   1 Probability

As the probability of an event gets closer to 0, the event becomes less likely. As the probability of an event gets closer to 1, the event becomes more likely.

You spin once on the spinner at the right. Tell which event is less likely. If necessary, describe an event as impossible or certain.

1. red or purple
   red

2. orange or brown
   impossible

3. yellow or purple
   purple

4. green or any other color
   green

5. purple or blue
   blue

6. green or orange
   orange—impossible

7. silver or gold
   impossible

8. yellow or blue
   blue

Problem Solving

9. If Mack tosses a coin two times, what outcomes are possible?
   tails/tails, tails/heads, heads/tails, head/heads

Show Your Work

Use with text pages 530–531.

ENGLISH LEARNERS 20.2

Name _____ Date _____   English Learners 20.2

Probability Concepts

To describe the **probability** of an event is to tell how likely it is that the event will happen. An **impossible event**, or an event that could not happen, has a probability of 0. A **certain event**, or an event that must happen, has a probability of 1.

Look at the game spinner. Answer each question about what will happen when a player spins the spinner.

1. What is the probability that the arrow will land on either a square, a triangle, a circle, or a star?
   1

2. What is the probability that the arrow will land on a trapezoid?
   0

3. Is it more likely or less likely that the arrow will land on a square than on a circle?
   less likely

4. Is the arrow more likely to land on a star than on a square or a triangle? Why?
   The spinner is more likely to land on a star because there are more stars than squares or triangles.

5. You and a friend play a game. If the arrow lands on a triangle, you win. If the arrow lands on a circle, your friend wins. Is the game fair? Why?
   Yes; The game is fair because the number of triangles equals the number of circles.

Use with text pages 530–531.

Homework Workbook Page 132

TEACHING LESSON 20.2

LESSON ORGANIZER

Objective Describe the probability of an event.

Resources Reteach, Practice, Enrichment, Problem Solving, Homework, English Learners, Transparencies, Math Center

Materials Number cubes, Circle Spinner Transparency, colored erasable markers, Number Lines Transparency

Warm-Up Activity
Using a Frequency Table

 Whole Group | 5 minutes | Visual, Tactile

Materials: *number cubes*

- **How many faces are on a cube?** (6 faces) **What are the numbers on the face of a traditional number cube?** (1, 2, 3, 4, 5, and 6)

- **Many games use a cube to generate numbers randomly. Any one of the 6 numbers on the cube may appear as a result of the roll.**

- Have students make a frequency table to record how often each number on a cube is rolled. Ask students to roll a number cube 100 times. When students are finished, make one large table on the board that combines the collected data. Discuss the patterns that emerge.

Lesson 2

Probability Concepts

Objective Describe the probability of an event.

Learn About It  MathTracks 2/24
Listen and Understand

Vocabulary
- probability
- event
- impossible event
- certain event

Look at this game spinner. It has four congruent sectors.

- If the spinner lands on green, Player *A* wins.
- If the spinner lands on purple, Player *B* wins.
- If the spinner lands on yellow, no one wins.

Is this a fair game?

When a player spins the spinner, there are three possible results, or outcomes. The spinner can land on a green, yellow, or purple sector. Why is the spinner more likely to land on purple than on green or yellow?

Solution: There are more purple sectors than green sectors. The game is not fair, because Player *B* has a greater chance of winning than Player *A*.

▶ The **probability** of an **event** describes the likelihood that the event will occur. When an event has a probability of 0, it is called an **impossible event**. An event that has a probability of 1 is a **certain event**. The sum of all the experimental probabilities of an event must equal 1.

less likely — more likely

impossible		certain
The probability of spinning red is 0.	0 ←---------------------→ 1	The probability of landing on a colored section is 1.

Look at the diagram above. As the probability of an event gets closer to 1, it becomes more likely. As it gets closer to 0, the event becomes less likely.

If Event *A* is more likely than Event *B*, Event *A* has a greater probability than Event *B*. If Event *A* is less likely than Event *B*, Event *A* has a lesser probability than Event *B*. In the spinner at the top of the page, having the spinner land on purple is more likely than it landing on yellow.

530

Introduce

Teaching Transparency
for
20.2

Materials: *Circle Spinner Transparency, colored erasable markers*

- Divide the spinner into four equal parts. Shade 1 part yellow, 1 part green, and 2 parts purple.

- **Is it possible to predict where the spinner will land when I spin it?** (No, only that it will land.)

- Spin the spinner ten times. Have a volunteer record the result of each spin. (Spins will vary, but there should be a majority of spins landing on purple.)

Develop

Guide students through the *Learn About It* section.

- **Look at the spinner. What can you say about the probability of landing on the green sections compared to landing on the purple sections?** (The spinner is more likely to land on the purple sections. Purple covers a larger area of the circle.)

- **What can you say about the probability of landing on the green section compared to landing on the yellow section?** (The spinner is equally likely to land on green as it is to land on yellow. Both sections cover the same portion of the circle.)

Guided Practice

Have students complete **Exercises 1–4** as you observe. Remind them to use the *Ask Yourself* question to help. Give students the opportunity to talk about the question in *Explain Your Thinking*.

Ask Yourself
• How many sectors of the spinner are labeled with each number?

You spin once on a spinner that has six congruent sectors labeled 2, 3, 4, 5, and 5. Tell which event is more likely. If possible, describe an event that is impossible or certain.

TEST TIPS

1. a 2 or a 6
   a 2; 6 is impossible

2. a 3 or a 5 **a 5**

3. a composite number or a prime number
   a prime number

4. a number greater than 5 or a number less than 5
   a number less than 5; a number greater than 5 is impossible

TEST TIPS **Explain Your Thinking** ▶ Why is the second event in Exercise 2 more likely?
Possible answer: Two of the 6 sectors are labeled 5 and only one is labeled 3.

Practice and Problem Solving

You spin once on the spinner at the right. Tell which event is less likely. If possible, describe an event as impossible or certain.

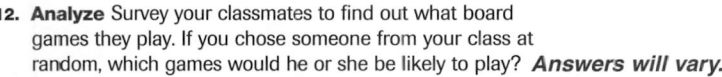

5. yellow or green
   green

6. orange or green
   orange; orange is impossible

7. green or blue
   green

8. red or blue
   blue

9. purple or any other color on the spinner
   purple; purple is impossible; any other color on the spinner is certain

Use the spinner at the right for Problems 10 and 11.

10. **Explain** Shari and Sam play a game. If the spinner lands on red or blue, Shari wins. If the spinner lands on green, Sam wins. Is the game fair? Explain. *See Additional Answers on Page 551.*

11. **Create and Solve** Use the spinner to create a fair game and an unfair game that are different from the game in Problem 10. Explain why each game is fair or unfair. *See Additional Answers on Page 551.*

12. **Analyze** Survey your classmates to find out what board games they play. If you chose someone from your class at random, which games would he or she be likely to play? *Answers will vary.*

Ex. 13–20. See Additional Answers on Page 551.

Daily Review	**Test Prep**
Write 4 equivalent ratios for each. (Ch. 18, Lesson 2)	21. A spinner has congruent sectors labeled 1, 3, 5, 7, 9, and 11. What is the probability of spinning an odd number?
13. 1 to 4 14. 10 to 12	A 0 C $\frac{1}{2}$
15. 2:3 16. 20 to 25	
17. 3:8 18. 6:10	B $\frac{1}{6}$ (D) 1
19. 5 to 1 20. 14:6	

Extra Practice See page 551, Set B.

Chapter 20 Lesson 2 **531**

Test Prep Transparency
20.2

DAILY TEST PREP

Draw a spinner in which it is certain to spin an even number, but impossible to spin a number divisible by 4. (Spinners may vary in the number of sections and the numbers listed within each section. All numbers should be even numbers. No numbers should be divisible by 4.)

Activity

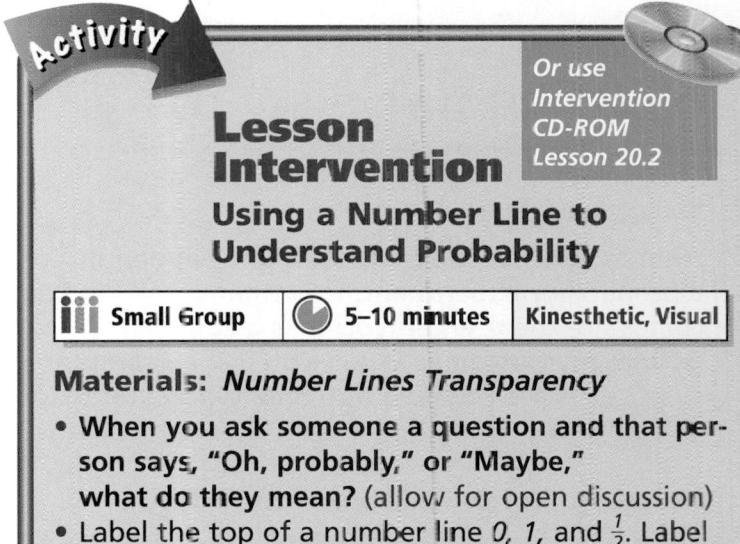

Or use Intervention CD-ROM Lesson 20.2

Lesson Intervention
Using a Number Line to Understand Probability

👥 Small Group	🕐 5–10 minutes	Kinesthetic, Visual

Materials: *Number Lines Transparency*

• When you ask someone a question and that person says, "Oh, probably," or "Maybe," what do they mean? (allow for open discussion)

• Label the top of a number line *0, 1,* and $\frac{1}{2}$. Label the bottom *impossible, certain,* and *equally likely.*

• Have students brainstorm for situations that are impossible, certain, and equally likely. Record their situations at the bottom of the number line.

---

③ Practice

Assign **Exercises 5–21** as independent work.

• *Problem Solving for Problems 10–12* Have students think about what makes a probability problem fair or unfair.

Common Error

Losing track of colored sections Since the equal-sized color sections of the spinner are not adjacent to one another, students may lose track of the number of each color section. For easier comparison, suggest students write down the total number of color sections.

④ Assess and Close

• Draw this spinner.

• **How is the spinner divided?** (8 sections) **Which color is it most likely to land on?** (yellow) **Is it more likely to land on red or blue?** (blue) **Why?** (2 blue sections, 1 red) **Which colors is it equally likely to land on?** (red, green, purple) **Why?** (all have 1 section)

Assign the **LESSON QUIZ** on Transparency 20.2 to further assess student understanding.

✏️ Keeping a Journal

Have students describe events with probabilities of 0, $\frac{1}{2}$, and 1. Have them explain whether or not an event can have a probability of $1\frac{1}{2}$.

CHAPTER 20 **Lesson 2** **531**

Theoretical Probability

PLANNING THE LESSON

MATHEMATICS OBJECTIVE
Use fractions to find theoretical probability.

Use Lesson Planner CD-ROM for Lesson 20.3.

Daily Routines

Vocabulary

An *outcome* describes what might happen in a probability experiment. How many outcomes are there when you toss a coin? (2) How many outcomes when you roll a 1–6 number cube? (6) Is 4 a possible outcome when you toss a coin? (no)

Vocabulary Cards

Meeting North Carolina's Standards

Prepare for Grade 6 Objective **4.04** Determine and compare experimental and theoretical probabilities for simple and compound events.

Lesson Transparency **20.3**

Problem of the Day

The perimeter of the rectangular swimming pool is 50 meters. One of the sides is 10 meters long. What area would a pool cover be if it exactly covered the water's surface? (150 square meters)

Quick Review

Simplify.

1. $\frac{4}{8}$ $\left(\frac{1}{2}\right)$

2. $\frac{10}{30}$ $\left(\frac{1}{3}\right)$

3. $\frac{4}{10}$ $\left(\frac{2}{5}\right)$

4. $\frac{14}{28}$ $\left(\frac{1}{2}\right)$

5. $\frac{3}{21}$ $\left(\frac{1}{7}\right)$

6. $\frac{4}{20}$ $\left(\frac{1}{5}\right)$

Lesson Quiz

Suppose you toss a number cube that has sides labeled *1, 1, 2, 3, 4,* and *5.* Find the probability of each event.

1. The number 6 $\left(\frac{0}{6}\text{ or }0\right)$

2. The number 1 $\left(\frac{1}{3}\right)$

3. A number greater than 2 $\left(\frac{1}{2}\right)$

4. A number divisible by 5 $\left(\frac{1}{6}\right)$

LEVELED PRACTICE

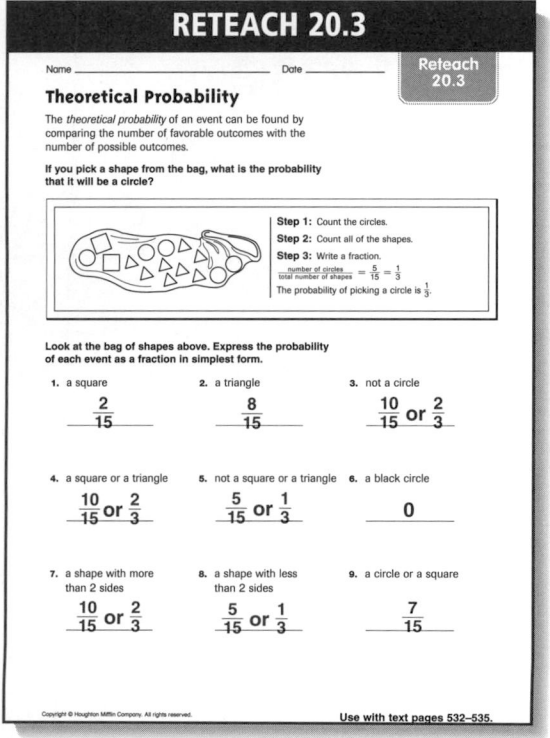

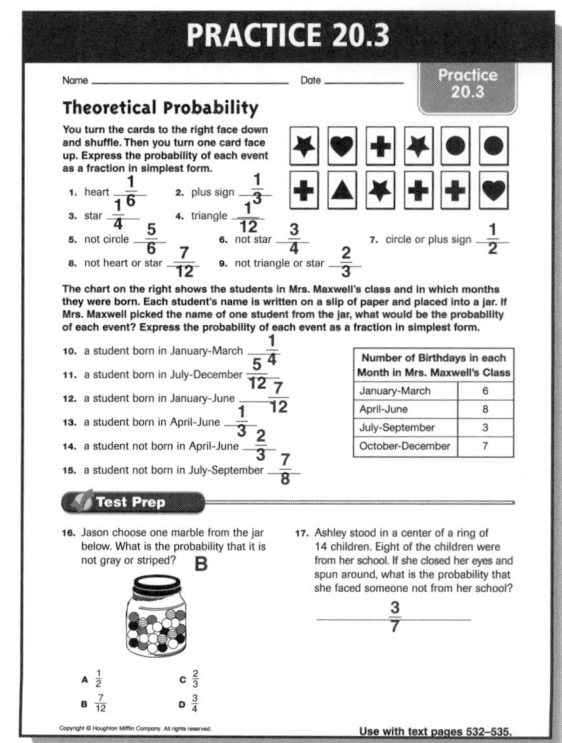

ENRICHMENT 20.3

Enrichment 20.3

Name _____ Date _____

Designing Probability

With a partner design situations that have varying probabilities. On separate index cards write the following fractions:

$0, \frac{1}{2}, \frac{1}{3}, \frac{1}{4}, \frac{1}{5}, \frac{1}{6}, \frac{1}{8}, \frac{1}{10}, \frac{3}{4}, \frac{2}{3}, \frac{2}{5}, \frac{3}{5}, \frac{5}{6}, \frac{7}{8}, \frac{7}{10}, \frac{9}{10}, 1$

Mix up the cards. In turns, pick a card and design a situation that has a probability that matches the card. If you are correct, you keep the card. If you are incorrect, your partner gets the card. Play continues until all the cards are gone. The player with more cards wins.

1. What situations did you use for the probabilities?
   Answers will vary.

2. For which cards would a number cube not work? Why is this?
   $\frac{1}{3}, \frac{5}{8}, \frac{7}{8}, \frac{1}{8}, \frac{3}{10}, \frac{7}{10}, \frac{9}{10}$; **A number cube only has 6 possibilities.**

3. What is the probability if you picked the 0 or 1 cards?
   Examples will vary. Zero is impossible. One is a certainty.

4. If you included fractions with twelfths, how could you develop a situation for those probabilities?
   Possible answer: Make a spinner with 12 equal sections.

5. The probability of an event happening or not happening always equals 1. Which cards when added together equal 1?
   $0 + 1; \frac{1}{10} + \frac{9}{10}, \frac{1}{8} + \frac{7}{8}, \frac{1}{6} + \frac{5}{6}, \frac{1}{4} + \frac{3}{4}, \frac{3}{10} + \frac{7}{10};$
   $\frac{3}{5} + \frac{2}{5}, \frac{1}{3} + \frac{2}{3}, \frac{1}{5} + \frac{4}{5}, \frac{2}{5} + \frac{3}{5}$

Use with text pages 532–535.

Practice Workbook Page 133

Reaching All Learners

Differentiated Instruction

English Learners

Worksheet 20.3 teaches key concepts used in Lesson 3. It also provides students with a step-by-step method for determining theoretical probability.

Special Needs
VISUAL, TACTILE

Materials: *coins*

- Give each student a coin.
- Display $\frac{1 \text{ heads}}{2 \text{ outcomes}}$ or $\frac{1}{2}$. Since there is one heads side of the coin, the probability of tossing heads is written $\frac{1 \text{ heads}}{2 \text{ outcomes}}$ or $\frac{1}{2}$. What is the probability of tossing tails? ($\frac{1 \text{ tails}}{2 \text{ outcomes}}$ or $\frac{1}{2}$) Both events are equally likely.

Early Finishers
VISUAL, SPATIAL

Suppose you put 3 pennies, 1 nickel, 2 dimes, and 4 quarters in a bag, and then pulled one coin out without looking. What is the probability of picking a penny? a nickel? a dime? a quarter? ($\frac{3}{10}$, $\frac{1}{10}$, $\frac{2}{10}$, $\frac{4}{10}$)

Science Connection

Life's Expression

Display the table:

- The Punnett Square has been used for decades to demonstrate how traits are inherited. This table shows the off-

Punnett Square

	T	t
t	Tt	tt
t	Tt	tt

spring of two pea plants. One parent has both the dominant "tall" gene and the recessive "short" gene (Tt), the other has only the recessive "short" gene (tt). The square shows that $\frac{2}{4}$, or $\frac{1}{2}$, of the offspring will be tall, and $\frac{1}{2}$ will be short.

- Find the probability of tall offspring when both parents are Tt. (P(Tall) = $\frac{3}{4}$)

TECHNOLOGY

Spiral Review

Help students remember skills they learned earlier by creating **customized** spiral review worksheets using the *Ways to Assess CD-ROM*.

Lesson Planner

You can use the Lesson Planner CD-ROM to create a report of the lessons and standards you have taught.

eBook

eMathBook allows students to review lessons and do homework without carrying their textbooks home.

eMathBook

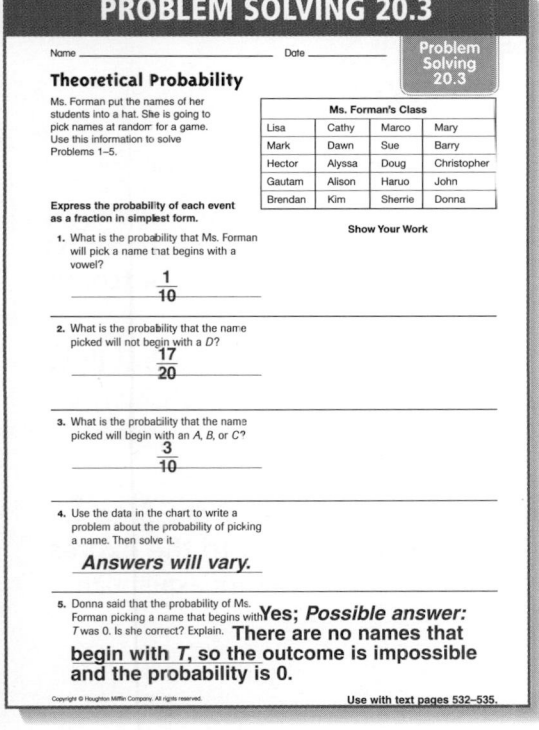

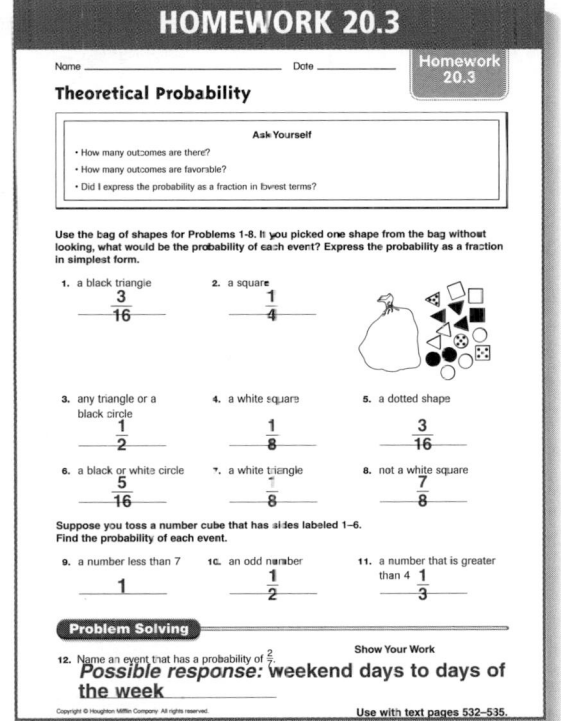

Homework Workbook Page 133

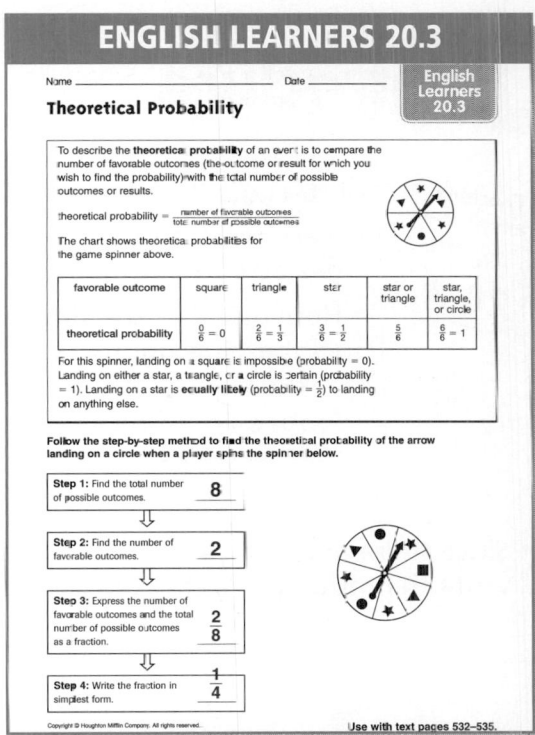

TEACHING LESSON 20.3

LESSON ORGANIZER

Objective Use fractions to find theoretical probability.

Resources Reteach, Practice, Enrichment, Problem Solving, Homework, English Learners

Materials Large Plane Figures Transparency

Warm-Up Activity
Writing Equivalent Ratios

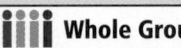 Whole Group	5 minutes	Visual, Tactile

- Display the following chart on the chalkboard. Have students fill it in by writing ratios equivalent to the first ratio. If students have a hard time getting started, review how to write and solve a proportion.

12 cups pudding : 8 cups whip cream

12	15	18	24	9	60	72
8	10	12	16	6	40	48

- After students complete the chart, ask them to write each ratio in simplest form. (all the ratios simplify to 3 : 2)

Theoretical Probability

Objective Use fractions to find theoretical probability.

Vocabulary
- outcome
- theoretical probability
- equally likely

Learn About It MathTracks 2/25 Listen and Understand

If the wheel stops on a red sector, Tamara wins a prize. What is the probability that the wheel will stop on red?

Since the wheel has 16 sectors of equal size, there are 16 possible **outcomes**.

To solve the problem, you want to find out how likely it is that the wheel will stop on a red sector. Stopping on red is called a favorable outcome.

The **theoretical probability** of an event can be found by comparing the number of favorable outcomes with the number of possible outcomes.

Find the theoretical probability that the wheel will stop on red.

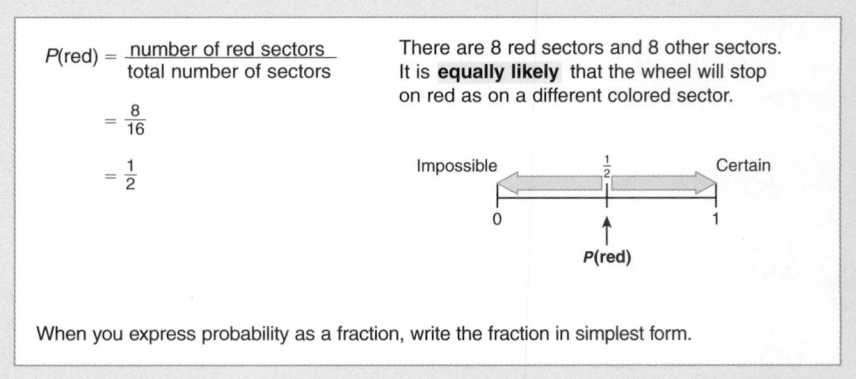

$P(\text{red}) = \dfrac{\text{number of red sectors}}{\text{total number of sectors}}$

$= \dfrac{8}{16}$

$= \dfrac{1}{2}$

There are 8 red sectors and 8 other sectors. It is **equally likely** that the wheel will stop on red as on a different colored sector.

When you express probability as a fraction, write the fraction in simplest form.

Solution: The theoretical probability that the wheel will stop on red is $\frac{1}{2}$.

532

---

1 Introduce

Teaching Transparency for 20.3

Materials: *Large Plane Figures Transparency*

- Place the transparency on the overhead projector. **How many figures are there?** (20)
- **How many of the figures are blue?** (5) Circle all the blue figures. Write on the board:

Probability of blue → $P(\text{blue}) = \dfrac{\text{number of blue figures}}{\text{total number of figures}}$

$P(\text{blue}) = \dfrac{5}{20}$

- Since there are 20 figures in all and 5 blue figures we can write the ratio $\frac{5}{20}$. **What is the simplest form of $\frac{5}{20}$?** ($\frac{1}{4}$)

2 Develop

Guide students through the *Learn About It* section.

- **When you toss a coin there are two possible outcomes, heads or tails. When you spin the wheel it may land on any one of 16 sections. Yellow is one possible outcome. What are the others?** (red, green, blue)

- **Look at the box that shows how to write a probability. What does the notation $P(\text{red})$ mean?** (the probability of spinning red) **What does $\frac{8}{16}$ mean?** (8 red sections out of 16 total sections)

- **The probability of spinning red simplifies from $\frac{8}{16}$ to $\frac{1}{2}$. How do you think this probability relates to the expression "he has a $\frac{50}{50}$ chance of winning"?** (Both explain an equally likely probability.)

Look at the wheel on page 532. Express the theoretical probability of each event as a fraction in simplest form.

Ask Yourself
• How many outcomes are there?
• How many outcomes are favorable?

1. yellow $\frac{1}{16}$ 2. green $\frac{1}{4}$ 3. blue $\frac{3}{16}$

4. not yellow $\frac{15}{16}$ 5. orange 0 or $\frac{0}{16}$ 6. blue or yellow $\frac{1}{4}$

Explain Your Thinking ▶ In Exercise 6, how did you find the theoretical probability?

Possible answer: Found the number of blue sectors and the number of yellow sectors, added those numbers, and compared the sum with the total number of sectors.

Practice and Problem Solving

Use the spinner for Problems 7–14. Express the theoretical probability of each event as a fraction in simplest form.

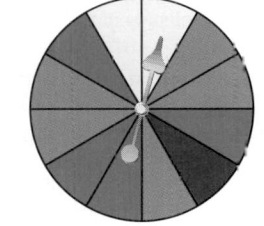

7. yellow $\frac{1}{6}$ 8. red $\frac{1}{12}$

9. green $\frac{5}{12}$ 10. blue $\frac{1}{3}$

11. blue or yellow $\frac{1}{2}$ 12. not red $\frac{11}{12}$

13. not yellow $\frac{5}{6}$ 14. not green or blue $\frac{1}{4}$

Use the bag of marbles for Problems 15–26. You pick one marble from the bag without looking. Find the theoretical probability of each event. Express the probability as a fraction in simplest form.

15. a black marble $\frac{4}{15}$ 16. a marble that is not black $\frac{11}{15}$

17. a yellow marble $\frac{1}{5}$ 18. a marble that is not yellow $\frac{4}{5}$

19. a green marble $\frac{1}{15}$ 20. a marble that is not green $\frac{14}{15}$

21. a purple marble $\frac{1}{3}$ 22. a marble that is not purple $\frac{2}{3}$

23. a red or black marble $\frac{2}{5}$ 24. a white marble 0

25. a marble that is not green or red or black $\frac{8}{15}$ 26. a marble that is green or yellow $\frac{4}{15}$

Suppose you toss a number cube that has sides labeled 1–6. Find the theoretical probability of each event.

27. a 6 $\frac{1}{6}$ 28. an even number $\frac{1}{2}$

29. a number that is not 2 or 4 $\frac{2}{3}$ 30. a number greater than 1 and less than 6 $\frac{2}{3}$

 Go On

The following activities will help students prepare for the Quick Check or may be used as an alternative assessment.

Vocabulary Review *(individual, small group, or whole class)*

Have students review the following vocabulary words by giving an example of how each term is used in this chapter.

- organized list
- tree diagram
- probability
- event
- impossible event
- certain event
- outcome
- theoretical probability
- equally likely

Math Conversations *(small group or whole class)*

Have students discuss what they have learned about probability in this chapter. Encourage students to ask each other questions to clarify their understanding.

Writing Prompt *(individual or partners)*

To solidify student understanding of vocabulary and concepts, have each student complete the following sentence:

The thing I found easiest about probability is
_____.

---

③ Practice

- **How many sections are green?** (4) **What is the probability of spinning green?** ($\frac{4}{16}$ or $\frac{1}{4}$) **If you were playing this game and could pick any two colors for the wheel to land on, which two colors will give you greatest chance of winning?** (red and green) **What is the probability of spinning either red or green?** ($\frac{12}{16}$ or $\frac{3}{4}$)

- **Where on the probability number line does $\frac{3}{4}$ fall?** (close to 1) **If you want to win a game do you want your probability for winning to be closer to 0 or 1?** (1)

Guided Practice

Have students complete **Exercises 1–6** as you observe. Remind them to use the *Ask Yourself* questions to help. Give students the opportunity to talk about the question in *Explain Your Thinking*.

Assign **Exercises 7–41** as independent work.

- **Problem Solving for Problems 7–14** Show students how to organize the information in a table by recording the number of sections for each color.

- **Problem Solving for Problems 15–26 and 36–41** Encourage students to organize the information in a table.

DAILY TEST PREP

How many outcomes are possible when you toss a cube labeled 2, 3, 4, 4, 5, and 6? (A)

A. 5   B. $\frac{1}{3}$ C. $\frac{2}{6}$ D. 24

Activity

Or use Intervention CD-ROM Lesson 20.3

Lesson Intervention

Using Plane Figures to Understand Probability

| 👥 Small Group | 🕐 5–10 minutes | Kinesthetic, Visual |

Materials: *Large Plane Figures Transparency*

- On the chalkboard, write the following:

  number of circles = __(2)__

  number of figures = __(20)__

- **Suppose all these plane figures were blocks in a box. Then suppose we picked one out without looking. Is it likely that we will pick a circle?** (No, there are not many circles.)

- **This is how we write the probability of picking a circle as a ratio. How many figures are there?** (20) Write 20 as the second term. **How many of the figures are circles?** (2) Write 2 as the first term. **What is $\frac{2}{20}$ in simplest form?** ($\frac{1}{10}$) Repeat for other figures and colors.

Use the bag of cubes for Problems 31–35.
Ex. 31–35. Possible answers given.
The bag of cubes is used for a game in which you pick one cube without looking. Tell how you would add or remove cubes in order to create the given situation.

31. The probability of picking a red cube is $\frac{1}{3}$.
    Add 1 red cube and remove 1 yellow.

32. The chances of picking any color cube are equally likely.
    See below.

33. The chance of picking a black cube is 1 out of 10.
    Add 5 cubes of any color except black.

34. The probability of picking a blue cube is $\frac{1}{6}$.
    Add 3 cubes of any color except blue.

35. The chance of picking a purple cube is 1 out of 4.
    Add 5 purple cubes.

32. **Add 1 red cube, 2 blue cubes, 3 black cubes, and 4 yellow cubes.**

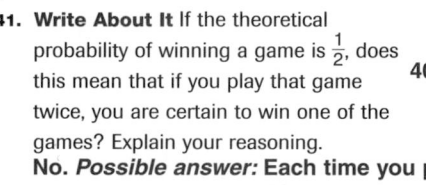

📊**Data**   **Use the pictograph for Problems 36–40.**

Toy ducks are picked without looking and replaced in the pond after each pick.

36. How many ducks are in the pond if each duck symbol represents 1 duck? **20 ducks**

37. What is the probability of picking a yellow duck with a number 5 on the bottom? $\frac{1}{20}$

38. **Analyze** Which two numbers are the most likely to be picked? **1 and 3**

39. The probability of picking a duck with one of two numbers is $\frac{9}{20}$. What could those two numbers be? **3 and 4; 1 and 5**

40. **Reasoning** Suppose each duck symbol represented 3 ducks instead of 1 duck. Would the probability of picking each number change? Explain. *See at right.*

Duck Pond Game

Number of Ducks (vertical axis)

Number on Bottom: 1   2   3   4   5

41. **Write About It** If the theoretical probability of winning a game is $\frac{1}{2}$, does this mean that if you play that game twice, you are certain to win one of the games? Explain your reasoning.
No. *Possible answer:* Each time you play the game your probability of winning is $\frac{1}{2}$.

40. **No; the ratio of each number to the total number of ducks would stay the same.**

Extra Practice See page 551, Set C.

Practice *continued*

Common Error

Failing to use the proper form Some students fail to write probabilities in the proper form. Encourage students to record all the possible outcomes before they begin answering questions.

---

4 Assess and Close

- **What is an outcome?** (It is what can happen in a probability experiment.) Sketch a number cube on the board. **What are the possible outcomes for a traditional number cube?** (1, 2, 3, 4, 5, and 6)

- **How do you write a probability for picking a blue marble from a bag filled with different colored marbles?** (Find the total number of possible outcomes—the total number of marbles. Find the number of favorable outcomes—the number of blue marbles. Write a ratio comparing favorable outcomes to possible outcomes in simplest form.)

Assign the **LESSON QUIZ** on Transparency 20.3 to further assess student understanding.

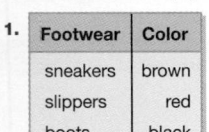

Quick Check

Check your understanding of Lessons 1–3.

Ex. 1–2. Check students' lists and tree diagrams.

Make an organized list and a tree diagram to show all the possible choices. Then multiply to find the number of possible choices. (Lesson 1)

1. 12 choices

Footwear	Color
sneakers	brown
slippers	red
boots	black
	white

2. 8 choices

Snack	Size
peanuts	small
cashews	large
walnuts	
almonds	

Use the spinner for Problems 3–6. Tell which event is more likely. If possible, describe an event as impossible or certain. (Lesson 2)

3. yellow or blue
both events have
same possibility

4. red or green
red

5. blue or green
green

6. red or orange
red; orange is
impossible

Suppose you toss a number cube that has sides labeled 2, 2, 2, 4, 8, and 10. Find the theoretical probability of each event. (Lesson 3)

7. a 4 $\frac{1}{6}$

8. an even number 1

9. a number that is not a 2 $2\frac{1}{2}$

Quick Check

Purpose: The Quick Check allows you to assess the student's understanding of the concepts presented in Lessons 1–3.

Items	Objectives Tested	Pages	Intervention
1–2	Use organized lists, tree diagrams, and multiplication to find all the possible combinations of given items.	528–529	Reteach Resource 20.1 *Ways to Success* 20.1
3–6	Describe the probability of an event.	530–531	Reteach Resource 20.2 *Ways to Success* 20.2
7–9	Use fractions to find theoretical probability.	532–535	Reteach Resource 20.3 *Ways to Success* 20.3

Logical Thinking
Math Reasoning

NOT a Chance

Look at the spinner. The probability of spinning blue is $\frac{5}{12}$. What is the probability of NOT spinning blue? To find the probability of NOT spinning blue, you can subtract $\frac{5}{12}$ from 1.

$$1 - \frac{5}{12} = \frac{12}{12} - \frac{5}{12} = \frac{7}{12}$$

Solution: The probability of NOT spinning blue is $\frac{7}{12}$.

Use the spinner above. Subtract to find each probability.

1. not spinning green $1 - \frac{1}{12} = \frac{11}{12}$

2. not spinning red $1 - \frac{1}{6} = \frac{5}{6}$

3. not spinning purple $1 - \frac{1}{3} = \frac{2}{3}$

4. Explain Use what you know about probability to explain why this method works. ***See Additional Answers on Page 551.***

Chapter 20 Lesson 3 **535**

Keeping a Journal

Ask students to make a spinner that is $\frac{2}{8}$ blue, $\frac{1}{8}$ green, $\frac{1}{8}$ white, and $\frac{4}{8}$ yellow. Then ask them to write a paragraph that explains the theoretical probability of landing on blue, green, white, yellow, or red.

Logical Thinking

Math Reasoning

NOT a Chance

For the spinner used in this activity, have students organize the information by counting the number of sections in each color on the spinner, and recording in a table like this. Then they can more easily write the opposite or "not" probabilities.

Color	P	G	B	R
Probability of	$\frac{4}{12}$	$\frac{1}{12}$	$\frac{5}{12}$	$\frac{2}{12}$
	↓	↓	↓	↓
Not Probability of	$\frac{8}{12}$	$\frac{11}{12}$	$\frac{7}{12}$	$\frac{10}{12}$

Problem-Solving Strategy: Make an Organized List

PLANNING THE LESSON

MATHEMATICS OBJECTIVE
Solve a problem by making an organized list.

Use Lesson Planner CD-ROM for Lesson 20.4.

Daily Routines

Vocabulary

Explain that the word *organize* means "to put together into an orderly, functional, structured whole." **When you solve a problem with a lot of possible answers, why is displaying the data in an organized list helpful?** (An organized list allows you to see patterns, find all possible answers, and eliminate duplicate answers.)

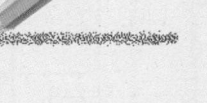
Vocabulary Cards

Meeting North Carolina's Standards

Prepare for Grade 6 Objective **4.01** Develop fluency with counting strategies to determine the sample space for an event. Include lists, tree diagrams, frequency distribution tables, permutations, combinations, and the Fundamental Counting Principle.

Lesson Transparency 20.4

Problem of the Day
The theoretical probability of choosing a blue marble from a bag of marbles is $\frac{1}{3}$. There are 18 marbles in the bag. How many marbles are blue? (6)

Quick Review
Add and then simplify.

1. $\frac{3}{8} + \frac{4}{8}$ $\left(\frac{7}{8}\right)$
2. $\frac{2}{6} + \frac{3}{6}$ $\left(\frac{5}{6}\right)$
3. $\frac{4}{9} + \frac{4}{9}$ $\left(\frac{8}{9}\right)$
4. $\frac{1}{8} + \frac{5}{8}$ $\left(\frac{3}{4}\right)$
5. $\frac{2}{7} + \frac{3}{7}$ $\left(\frac{5}{7}\right)$
6. $\frac{2}{10} + \frac{7}{10}$ $\left(\frac{9}{10}\right)$

Lesson Quiz
Make an organized list to solve the problem.

Two of the following nominees will be elected for the school leadership council: Karen, Sandy, Troy, Ravi, and Erin. How many possible combinations with two students are there? (10)

LEVELED PRACTICE

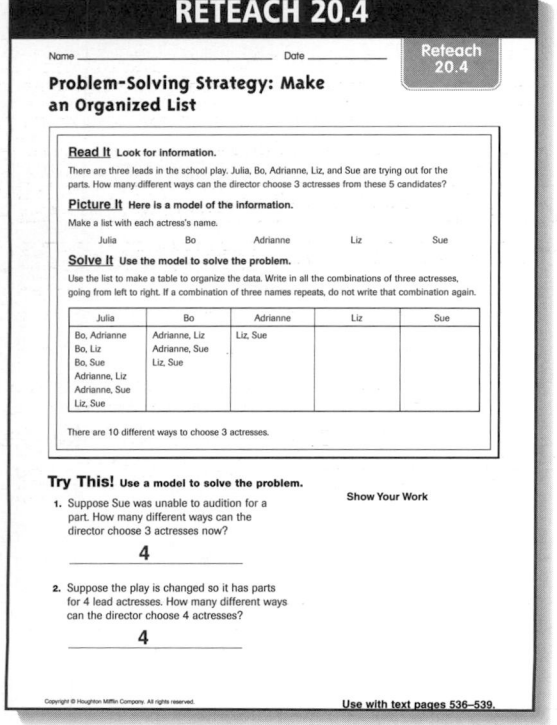

RETEACH 20.4

Name _____ Date _____
Reteach 20.4

Problem-Solving Strategy: Make an Organized List

Read It Look for information.
There are three leads in the school play. Julia, Bo, Adrianne, Liz, and Sue are trying out for the parts. How many different ways can the director choose 3 actresses from these 5 candidates?

Picture It Here is a model of the information.
Make a list with each actress's name.

| Julia | Bo | Adrianne | Liz | Sue |

Solve It Use the model to solve the problem.
Use the list to make a table to organize the data. Write in all the combinations of three actresses, going from left to right. If a combination of three names repeats, do not write that combination again.

Julia	Bo	Adrianne		
Bo, Adrianne	Adrianne, Liz	Liz, Sue		
Bo, Liz	Adrianne, Sue			
Bo, Sue	Liz, Sue			
Adrianne, Liz				
Adrianne, Sue				
Liz, Sue				

There are 10 different ways to choose 3 actresses.

Try This! Use a model to solve the problem.

Show Your Work

1. Suppose Sue was unable to audition for a part. How many different ways can the director choose 3 actresses now?
   4

2. Suppose the play is changed so it has parts for 4 lead actresses. How many different ways can the director choose 4 actresses?
   4

Copyright © Houghton Mifflin Company. All rights reserved.
Use with text pages 536–539.

PRACTICE 20.4

Name _____ Date _____
Practice 20.4

Problem-Solving Strategy: Make an Organized List
Make an organized list to solve each problem.

Show Your Work

1. You and 3 of your friends—Gary, Janet, and Simone—are going to the movies. How many different ways can the four of you stand in line for the tickets?
   24

2. When you get into the theater, Gary and Janet go to buy popcorn and drinks for everyone. How many different ways could the snacks be carried to your seats?
   4

3. You find out that there are two empty seats in the front row and two seats in the last row. In how many combinations can you and your friends sit? (It does not matter who sits on the left or the right.)
   6

4. The four of you go to a restaurant where each of you can order one hamburger or one cheeseburger. How many different combinations of people and food choices are there?
   8

5. As you leave the theater, you are wearing a red jacket, Gary is wearing a blue jacket, Janet is wearing a green jacket, and Simone is wearing a yellow jacket. If you traded jackets, how many different combinations of people and jackets could you make?
   24

Copyright © Houghton Mifflin Company. All rights reserved.
Use with text pages 536–539.

ENRICHMENT 20.4

Name _____ Date _____
Enrichment 20.4

Hoop It Up
The Hooper Elementary School three-on-three basketball tournament is being held this weekend. Six friends have to split themselves into two teams, but they cannot decide how to do this. Help them.

The friends are Suzanne, Tamika, Lucie, Jen, Pam, and Nicole.

1. How many different ways can the girls form two teams of three? How many different teams can be formed?
   10 different ways; 20

2. What are the combinations? Write your answers in the table below.

Team A	Team B
J-L-N	P-S-T
J-L-P	N-S-T
J-L-S	N-P-T
J-L-T	N-P-S
J-N-P	L-S-T
J-N-S	L-P-T
J-N-T	L-P-S
J-P-S	L-N-T
J-P-T	L-N-S
J-S-T	L-N-P

3. How many possible teams can each of the girls be on?
   10

4. The girls put each of the team possibilities on an index card. If they can only have one team of three, what is the probability that Pam will be on that team?
   $\frac{1}{2}$

Copyright © Houghton Mifflin Company. All rights reserved.
Use with text pages 536–539.

Practice Workbook Page 134

Reaching All Learners
Differentiated Instruction

English Learners
English-language learners may be unfamiliar with several terms related to games and amusement. Use Worksheet 20.4 to introduce the content vocabulary and give students the opportunity to use it in context. This will help prepare them for understanding the explanation on page 536 as well as provide them with the necessary background to complete Problems 3–13 on pages 537–538.

Inclusion
VISUAL, KINESTHETIC

Materials: *Table II Transparency*

- Al, Barb, and Cleo are in line at the movies. How many different ways can they line up?
- **Make an organized list to find out.** Write *A, B,* and *C* in the table. Demonstrate the different orders (ABC, ACB, BAC, BCA, CAB, CBA)

Gifted and Talented
VISUAL, SPATIAL

Materials: *calculator*

Challenge students to solve this problem by making an organized list (and eliminating): *What is the largest two-digit number that is divisible by 3 whose digits differ by 2? Hint: Start by listing then eliminating. 99, 98, 97, 96, 95, 94, . . .* (75)

TECHNOLOGY

Spiral Review
You can prepare students for standardized tests with **customized** spiral review on key skills using the *Ways to Assess* CD-ROM.

Education Place
You can visit Education Place at eduplace.com/math/mw/ for teacher support materials.

Literature Connection

Problem Solving and Logical Reasoning
Materials: *The book* Anno's Hat Tricks *by Akihiro Nozaki*

- Explain that by making lists and looking for patterns we can break a complicated problem into smaller parts. This helps us to see solutions to otherwise confusing problems.
- *Anno's Hat Tricks* builds a step-by-step foundation in logical reasoning while exploring probability. Read the book aloud with students. Ask students to assume they are the Shadowchild in the story.

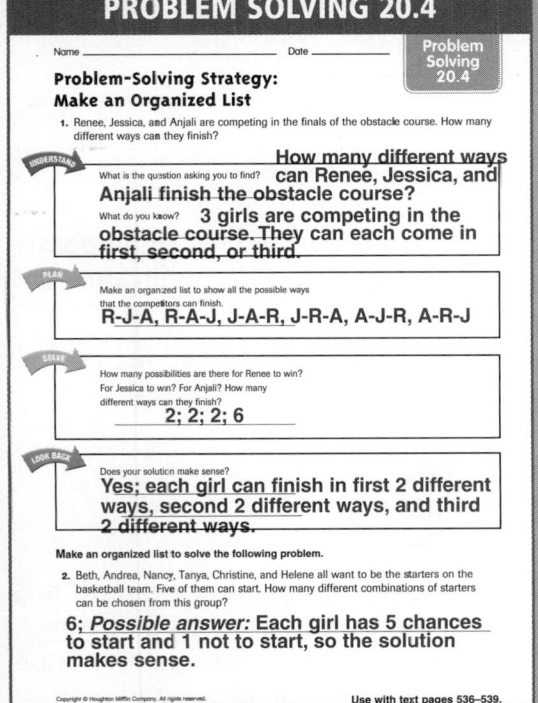

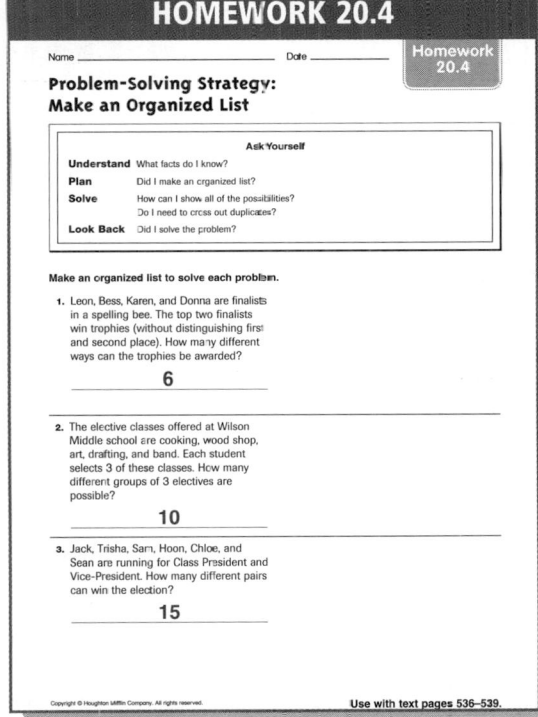

Homework Workbook Page 134

TEACHING LESSON 20.4

LESSON ORGANIZER

Objective Solve a problem by making an organized list.

Resources Reteach, Practice, Enrichment, Problem Solving, Homework, English Learners

Materials Blank transparency, pennies, poster board, scissors, Problem Solving: Four Step Process Transparency

Warm-Up Activity
Making Tables to Solve Problems

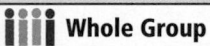 Whole Group 5 minutes | Visual, Auditory

Materials: *blank transparency*

- **Mark wants to buy a $100 scooter. He has $35. He can save $14 more per week. How many weeks will it take him to save for the scooter?** (5)

- Have students make a table to solve. Explain that the problem can also be solved with arithmetic, but a table can make it easier to see whole numbers. ($100 − $35 = $65 and $65 ÷ 14 = 4.64 weeks)

 **Lesson 4**

Problem-Solving Strategy
Make an Organized List
Objective: Solve a problem by making an organized list.

There is room for one more team of 2 players in the three-legged race. Sal, Ed, Juan, and Mia are willing to be on the team. How many different ways can you choose a team of 2 players from these 4 children?

 **UNDERSTAND**

This is what you know:
Sal, Ed, Juan, and Mia are willing to be on the team.
Each team has 2 players.

 **PLAN**

You can make an organized list to show all of the possible ways to select the team.

 SOLVE

Make an organized list. Use letters to stand for each player's name.
- List all teams of 2 that include Sal (S).
- List all teams of 2 that include Ed (E).
- List all teams of 2 that include Juan (J).
- List all teams of 2 that include Mia (M).

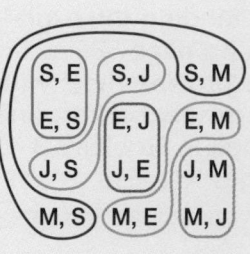

S, E   S, J   S, M
E, S   E, J   E, M
J, S   J, E   J, M
M, S   M, E   M, J

- Ring teams with the same 2 players. Then count the rings. The order of the players does not matter. The team of Sal and Ed is the same as the team of Ed and Sal.

Solution: There are 6 different ways to choose a team of 2 players.

 **LOOK BACK**

Look back at the problem.
Does the solution make sense?

536   MathTracks 2/26
Listen and Understand

1 Introduce   Whole Group   ⏱ 5–10 minutes

Materials: *pennies (4 per student), blank transparency*

Draw the following table on the overhead transparency. Leave the second column blank. Have students act out each possible outcome.

Experiment	Possible Outcomes	
Toss a Coin	You can get either heads or tails (H or T)	2
Toss 2 Coins	HT, HH, TH, TT	4
Toss 3 Coins	HHH, HTT, HTH, TTT, THH, THT, HHT, TTH	8

- **If you toss a penny how many ways can it land?** (2) **What are the possible outcomes?** (heads or tails) Write in the second column. **We'll use *H* to represent heads and *T* to represent tails.** Repeat for tossing 2, 3 and 4 coins.

- Discuss with students how making the organized list helps understand the possible outcomes.

2 Develop

Guide students through the problem-solving steps on page 536.

- **Look at the Plan step. Make an organized list of all possible 2-person team combinations. Eliminate duplicate teams.**

- **Look at the Solve step. What will an organized list of teams look like?** Write the list on the board as students name the teams:

SE   EJ   JM   ~~MS~~
SJ   EM   ~~JS~~   ~~ME~~
SM   ~~ES~~   ~~JE~~   ~~MJ~~

Point to student textbook page. **Let's find and cross off any possible duplicate teams. Is there another team that contains both E and S?** (Yes; ES is in the second column.) Continue crossing out duplicate teams. Move in an organized manner, down column 1 and then down the other columns.

Use the Ask Yourself questions to help
you solve each problem.

1. Billy wins enough points to choose
3 prizes. The available prizes are a
puzzle, a goldfish, a pack of cards,
a toy monkey, and a model car. How
many different ways can Billy choose
3 different prizes? **60**

2. Benjamin, Erin, Chun, Julia, Amanda,
and Elizabeth are in a race. First place
receives a gold medal and second
place receives a silver medal. How
many different ways can the medals be
given out? **30**

 (Hint) Since the order of the racers matters, there are
no duplicates in a list of possible first and second
place winners.

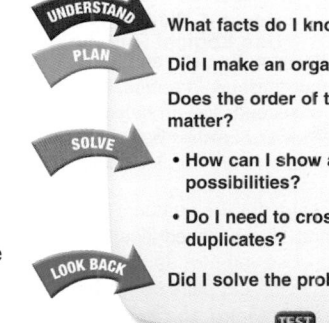

Ask Yourself

UNDERSTAND What facts do I know?

PLAN Did I make an organized list?

Does the order of the possibilities
matter?

SOLVE • How can I show all of the
possibilities?

• Do I need to cross out
duplicates?

LOOK BACK Did I solve the problem?

TEST TIPS

Independent Practice

Make an organized list to solve each problem.
Ex. 3–6. Check organized lists.

3. A team of 4 players is needed for tug of
war. How many different teams of 4 players
can be chosen from a group of 5 children? **5**

4. The 4 finalists in a history quiz game are
Jessica, Brian, Evan, and Grace. The top 2
finalists win first prize and second prize. In
how many different ways can these prizes
be given out to the 4 finalists? **12**

5. The school fair has a hall of mirrors, a
carousel, a horse ride, and a maze. You buy
a ticket that allows you to do 3 of these
activities. In how many different ways can
you go to 3 of these activities? **24**

6. Shawn, Scott, Rip, Trish, and Yoshi are
finalists in a drawing for a trip to Water
World. Two winners will be picked at
random. How many different pairs could
go to Water World? **10**

 Go On

ACHIEVING
Mathematical Proficiency

Helping Students Become Learners

In the traditional mathematics classroom, a
teacher introduces a new idea and students
practice it. Research suggests that this
approach may not be the most effective. The
new mathematics classroom needs to reflect a
change in the roles of teacher and students.

When teachers take on the role of guide
rather than lecturer, students have more
opportunity to actively participate in their
own learning process. Students **learn to make
connections between representations, arrive
at alternative solution methods, and justify
and explain their thinking.**

Students who experience taking a more
active role in their own education are likely
to transfer this self-knowledge across curriculums throughout their entire school careers.

• **Look Back. What pattern do you see as we have crossed
out duplicate teams?** (When order does not matter, $\frac{1}{2}$ the
teams are duplicates. The pattern of duplicate teams divides
the rectangular list diagonally.)

Guided Practice

Have students complete **Problems 1–2** as you observe.
Remind them to use the *Ask Yourself* questions.

③ Practice

Assign **Problems 3–6** as independent work. Have students
share and discuss their work.

Problem-Solving Reminders

Have students review their answers to make sure they have
done the following:

• expressed the solution clearly

• used appropriate mathematical notation and terms

• supported their solution with verbal and symbolic work

• determined the reasonableness of the solution in the context of the original problem.

DAILY TEST PREP

How many two-person teams can you make with the following individuals—Kayla, Sean, Marco, and Raul? (C)

A. 2   B. 12   C. 6   D. 4

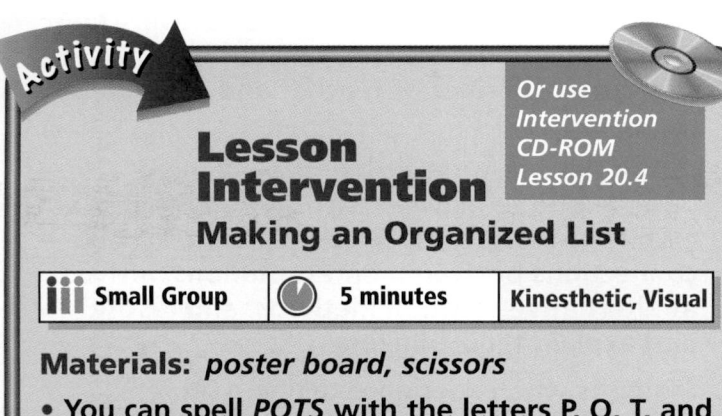

Activity

Lesson Intervention

Or use Intervention CD-ROM Lesson 20.4

Making an Organized List

| iii Small Group | ⏱ 5 minutes | Kinesthetic, Visual |

Materials: *poster board, scissors*

- You can spell *POTS* with the letters P, O, T, and S. What other words can you spell with those letters?

- You can try guessing the words, but an organized list allows you to systematically find all the possible letter arrangements.

- Have the students make an organized list. Have them start with the letters *P* and *O*. Help them move the last two letters around to show all possible arrangements with *PO* first. Continue in this manner. **There are 24 arrangements but only 6 spell a word.** (pots, post, opts, tops, stop, spot)

Choose a Strategy ✓

Possible strategies are given.

Solve. Show your work. Tell what strategy you used.   Howard, Wendy, Barbara, Marvin; Use Logical Reasoning

7. Wendy, Barbara, Howard, and Marvin are the top four finishers in a race. Barbara is not first or second. Marvin finishes after Barbara. Howard finishes before Wendy. Who is in each of the top four places?

8. Number cards for the numbers 3, 4, 5, 6, 7, 8, 9, and 10 are placed facedown on a table. Suppose you turn up two cards. How many different pairs of numbers are possible? **28; Make an Organized List**

9. Mr. Willard has 8 bills in his wallet. The bills are $10, $5, and $1. If Mr. Willard has $29, what bills does he have in his wallet? **1 $10-bill, 3 $5-bills, 4 $1-bills; Guess and Check**

Data Use the graph to solve Problems 10–13.

The graph shows the number of game tickets that each of four students sold.

10. How many more tickets did Daisy sell than Evan? **70 more tickets**

11. **Estimate** A game ticket sells for $2.95. About how many dollars worth of game tickets did Myra sell? **Possible estimate: about $210**

12. **Calculator** How many game tickets did the four students sell in all? How many dollars worth of tickets is this? **340; $1,003**

13. Last year, George's ticket sales were 20% greater than his total shown in the graph. How many tickets did George sell last year? **120**

14. **Explain** Sierra, Gavin, Kayla, John, and Catherine can tutor some third-grade students in math. Only 2 tutors are needed. How many different pairs of tutors can there be? Explain how you found your answer. **10; made a list**

PROBLEM-SOLVING Strategies

Use Models
Draw a Diagram
Find a Pattern
Guess and Check
Make an Organized List
Make a Table
Solve a Simpler Problem
Use Logical Reasoning
Work Backward
Write an Equation

Game Tickets Sold		
	Number of Tickets	
George	▭ ▭ ▭ ▭ ▭ ▭	
Myra	▭ ▭ ▭ ◻	
Evan	▭ ▭ ▭	
Daisy	▭ ▭ ▭ ▭ ◻	
	▭ = 20 Tickets	

538

Practice *continued*

Choose a Strategy

Assign **Problems 7–14** as independent work.

- *Problem Solving for Problems 7–9* Have students describe the strategies they used to solve each problem.

- *Problem Solving for Problems 10–14* Have students share which computation method they choose to use.

4 Assess and Close

Have students discuss making an organized list to solve problems.

- **Why is an organized list helpful?** (It systematically orders possible answers. It keeps you from skipping possible answers. It allows you to look for patterns and duplicate answers. It allows you to break the problem into two tasks—1) listing and 2) looking for arrangements that solve the problem.)

- **When order is not important, why do you delete half the choices?** (Because color combinations such as blue + green and green + blue are the same thing.)

Assign the **LESSON QUIZ** on Transparency 20.4 to further assess student understanding.

Choose the letter of the correct answer. If a correct answer is not here, choose NH.

1. What is the next picture in this pattern?

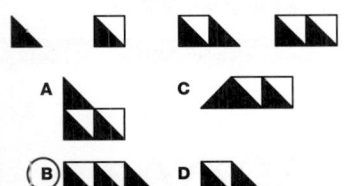

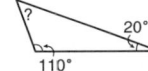

A

C

(B)

D

(Chapter 16, Lesson 2)

2. Howard is 4 feet 11 inches tall. Howard's father is 17 inches taller than Howard. How tall is Howard's father?

F 5 feet 6 inches

G 6 feet

(H) 6 feet 4 inches

J 6 feet 6 inches

(Chapter 6, Lesson 6)

3. Daniel has bowling scores of 192, 180, 212, 214, and 177. What score does Daniel need in his sixth game to have a mean score of 200?

A 195   (C) 225

B 202   D 250

(Chapter 8, Lesson 2)

4. In a survey of 200 students at Warren High School, 88 say they favor year-round schools. Warren High School has a total of 950 students. Based on the survey, how many students are likely to favor year-round schools?

(F) 418   H 880

G 440   J 936

(Chapter 18, Lesson 4)

5. What is the missing angle measure?

A 60°   C 160°

B 70°   (D) NH

(Chapter 15, Lesson 3)

6. A restaurant has 3 tables. Each table can seat 1 person on each end and 3 people along each of the other sides. The ends of the tables are pushed together to make one long table. How many people can sit at the long table?

Represent Support your solution with a picture.
20; *Check students' pictures.*

(Chapter 10, Lesson 7)

7. Measurement A rug that measures 2 yards by 3 yards costs $540. Another rug that measures 5 feet by 8 feet costs $360. Which rug has a higher price per square foot of area?

Explain How did you find your answer?

(Chapter 16, Lesson 3)

7. the 2 yards by 3 yards rug. *Possible answer:* Convert the measurements of the first rug to feet, find the area in square feet of each rug, divide the price by the number of square feet, and compare.

 **Test Prep on the Net**
Check out *Education Place* at **eduplace.com/kids/mw/** for test prep practice.

Chapter 20 Lesson 4   539

Problem-Solving Test Prep provides an opportunity for students to apply previously learned skills in the types of problem contexts typically encountered in standardized tests. *Problem-Solving Test Prep* includes practice in a variety of formats: multiple choice, free response, and open response.

Students will gain experience in writing about mathematics and using various representations to solve problems. Discuss students' solutions. Have several students explain the thinking behind their work.

More test prep practice is available on Houghton Mifflin's Web site, Education Place. Go to **eduplace.com/kids/mw/**.

 **Keeping a Journal**

Ask students to imagine that their club is making bows with two ribbons. Ask them to make an organized list that shows two color combinations from a group of 5 colors. Have them describe how they will determine how many combinations are possible.

Hands-On: Experimental Probability

PLANNING THE LESSON

MATHEMATICS OBJECTIVE

Determine the experimental probability for a given set of data.

Use Lesson Planner CD-ROM for Lesson 20.5.

Daily Routines

Vocabulary

Explain that there are two types of probability: *theoretical* and *experimental.* **In Lesson 20.3,** you calculated that the *theoretical probability* of a coin toss landing on heads is $\frac{1}{2}$. With *experimental probability,* the results may vary from experiment to experiment. For example, if you toss a coin 20 times, it may land on heads 12 times. The *experimental probability* is $\frac{3}{5}$ for that experiment.

Vocabulary Cards

Meeting North Carolina's Standards

Prepare for Grade 6 Objective **4.01** Develop fluency with counting strategies to determine the sample space for an event. Include lists, tree diagrams, frequency distribution tables, permutations, combinations, and the Fundamental Counting Principle.

Lesson Transparency 20.5

Problem of the Day

The range of a set of three numbers is 9. The median is 12. One of the numbers is 6. What is the other number? (15)

Quick Review

Write each difference.

1. $18 - 7$ (11)
2. $28 - 19$ (9)
3. $41 - 27$ (14)
4. $34 - 16$ (18)
5. $25 - 17$ (8)
6. $38 - 31$ (7)
7. $57 - 32$ (25)
8. $93 - 48$ (45)

Lesson Quiz

Record the probability as a fraction in simplest form.

1. Suppose you toss a number cube that is labeled 1–6 a total of 60 times. What is the theoretical probability of tossing a 6? ($\frac{1}{6}$)

2. If a number cube labeled 1–6 is tossed 60 times and 15 times it lands on 6, what is the experimental probability of tossing a 6? ($\frac{1}{4}$)

LEVELED PRACTICE

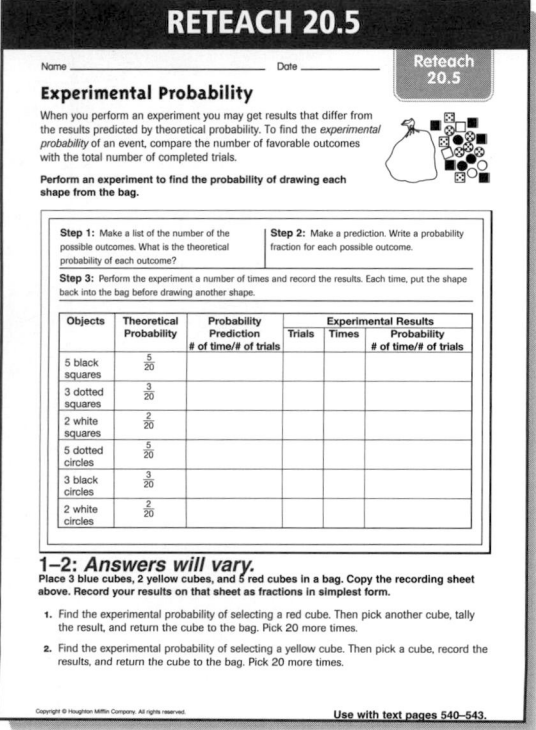

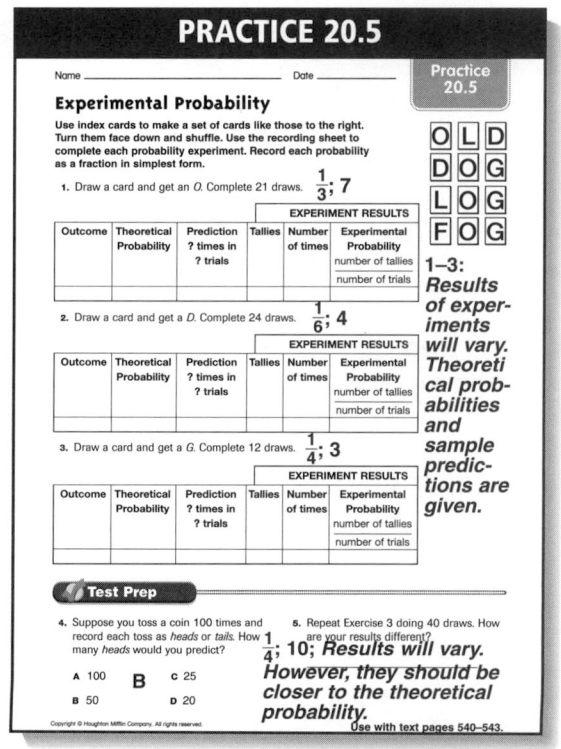

ENRICHMENT 20.5

Name _____ Date _____ Enrichment 20.5

Play With Spinners

Make a spinner like the one shown.

1. What is the probability of spinning an A? B? C?
   A $\frac{1}{2}$; B $\frac{1}{3}$; C $\frac{1}{6}$

2. If you spin the spinner 30 times, how many times should you get an A? B? C?
   A 15; B 10; C 5

3. Spin the spinner 30 times and record the results of each spin.
   Did the results match your prediction?
   Answers will vary.

Spin	Frequency
A	
B	
C	

4. How does the experimental probability compare to the theoretical probability the more times you spin the spinner?
   Possible answer: When the spinner is spun many times the more likely it is that the experimental probability will match the theoretical probability.

5. Spin the spinner 30 more times and record the results of each spin.
   How did your second 30 spins compare with the first 30 spins? Add the results of the two sets. How does the experimental probability compare to the theoretical probability?
   Answers will vary.

Spin	Frequency
A	
B	
C	

Use with text pages 540–543.

Practice Workbook Page 135

Reaching All Learners
Differentiated Instruction

English Learners

Worksheet 20.5 introduces students to experimental probability and explains the difference between experimental probability and theoretical probability. It also provides students with a formula to determine experimental probability.

Inclusion
VISUAL, TACTILE

Materials: *Cubes (2 black, 8 red), paper bag*

- **There are 10 cubes in the bag.** Have a student pick one, then replace. Display a table and record the color; continue for 25 picks.
- **What is a more likely pick: black or red?** (red) Guess how many of each color are in the bag. Show the bag.

Early Finishers
VISUAL, VERBAL

Materials: *10 pennies, shoebox*

- Give groups of students a bag and 10 pennies. Have them shake and empty the bag. Have them record the number of heads and tails. Repeat 10 times.
- Have them predict the outcome of the 11th trial.

TECHNOLOGY

Spiral Review

Create **customized** spiral review worksheets for individual students using the *Ways to Assess* CD-ROM.

Lesson Planner

You can customize your teaching plan or to meet your curriculum requirements with the Lesson Planner CD-ROM.

Education Place

Encourage students to visit Education Place at **eduplace.com/kids/mw/** for more student activities.

Science Connection

The Probability of Blood Types
Materials: *encyclopedia*

- Blood donors and recipients must be typed and matched very carefully before transfusions are given. To avoid blood rejection, hospitals sort blood by type—A, B, AB, and O.

- People with type AB can receive any blood type. People with type O can receive type O only. People with type A can receive A or O, and people with type B can receive B or O.

- Research how hospitals estimate the quantity of blood types they need to have.

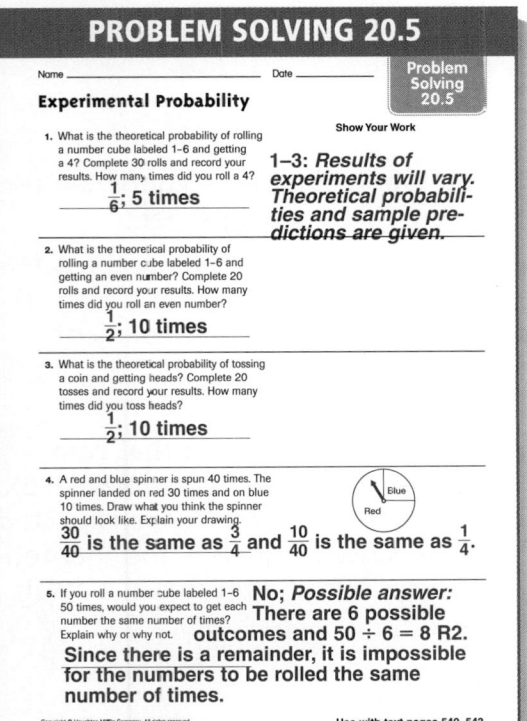

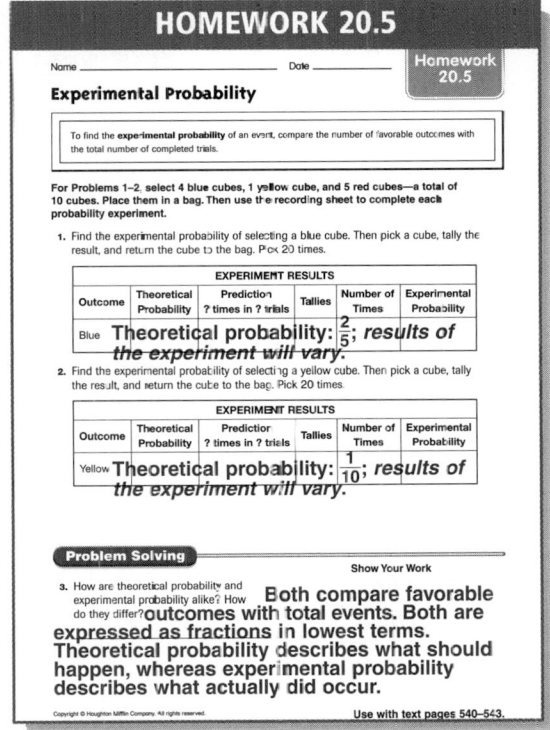

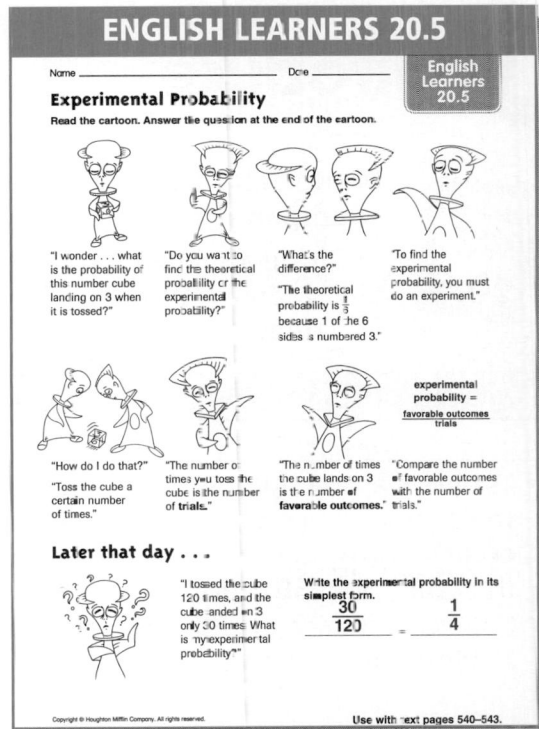

Homework Workbook Page 135

TEACHING LESSON 20.5

LESSON ORGANIZER

Objective Determine the experimental probability for a given set of data.

Resources Reteach, Practice, Enrichment, Problem Solving, Homework, English Learners

Materials Number cube (labeled 1–6), Learning Tool 56, red, blue, and yellow connecting cubes, Circle Spinner Transparency, blank transparency, spinner

Warm-Up Activity
Calculate Theoretical Probability

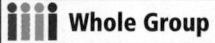 Whole Group | 5 minutes | Visual, Tactile

Display: *Suppose you put 3 pennies, 1 nickel, 2 dimes, and 4 quarters in a bag, then pulled one coin out without looking.*

- **What is the probability of picking a penny? a nickel? a dime? a quarter?** ($\frac{3}{10}, \frac{1}{10}, \frac{1}{5}, \frac{2}{5}$)

- Sketch a line divided into ten equal sections. Show the probability of picking each coin. **What is the probability of picking a penny or a dime?** ($\frac{1}{2}$) **of picking a coin that is not a nickel?** ($\frac{9}{10}$)

Experimental Probability

Objective Determine the experimental probability for a given set of data.

Materials
number cube
Learning Tool 56
red, blue, and yellow connecting cubes

Work Together

When you perform an experiment, you may get results that differ from the results predicted by theoretical probability.

To find the **experimental probability** of an event, compare the number of favorable outcomes with the total number of completed trials or experiments.

Work with a partner to find experimental probability of tossing each number on a number cube.

STEP 1 On the recording sheet, list all the possible outcomes for tossing a number cube once. Then write the theoretical probability for each outcome.
- How many possible outcomes are there?
- How can you find the theoretical probability of each outcome?

Event	Theoretical Probability	Prediction ? times in ? trials
1	$\frac{1}{6}$	$\frac{1}{6} = \frac{x}{30}$
2		
3		

STEP 2 Use theoretical probability to predict the number of times each outcome should occur in an experiment with 30 trials. Write your predictions on the recording sheet.
- How did you make your predictions?

540

---

1 Introduce

Materials: *blank transparency, Circle Spinner Transparency*

- Divide a spinner into thirds. Label the sections *1, 2,* and *3.* Draw the following on the transparency:

Outcome	Theoretical Probability	Prediction ? times in ? trials

- **I select 3 as my number for a board game. I win a point if the spinner lands on three. What outcome do I want to occur?** (spin 3) Continue showing students how to fill in the table. Spin 30 times. Ask students to record the spins. (Answers will vary, but if the spinner is fair, it will be close to 10 times out of 30 trials.)

2 Develop

Guide students through the *Work Together* section. Review each part of the *Learning Tool 56* recording sheet.

- **Look at Step 1. Since a number cube has the numbers 1–6 on it, there are 6 possible outcomes.** Explain that it is equally likely to land on 1, 2, 3, 4, 5, or 6. So, the probability of landing on 1 is $\frac{1}{6}$, the probability of landing on 2 is $\frac{1}{6}$, and so on.

- **Look at Step 2. The probability of $\frac{1}{6}$ is a ratio that compares a favorable outcome to all possible outcomes (1–6).** Explain that equivalent ratios help to predict the expected outcome. $\frac{1}{6} = \frac{x}{30}$. Solve for *x.* Since *x* equals 5, the theoretical probability is $\frac{5}{30}$, or 5 tosses out of 30 tosses will result in tossing, for example, a 1.

STEP 3 Perform the experiment. Toss the number cube 30 times. Record each outcome. Then find the total number of times each outcome occurred.

• Find the experimental probability of each outcome and record it in the last column on the sheet.

• How close are the experimental probabilities to the theoretical probabilities?

...RIMENT RESULTS

Event	Number of Favorable Outcomes	Experimental Probability
1	7	$\frac{7}{30}$
2	5	$\frac{5}{30} = \frac{1}{6}$
3	4	$\frac{4}{30} = \frac{2}{15}$
4	5	$\frac{5}{30} = \frac{1}{6}$
5	4	$\frac{4}{30} = \frac{2}{15}$
6	5	$\frac{5}{30} = \frac{1}{6}$

 STEP 4 Repeat the experiment. Toss the cube another 30 times. Combine your results with the results of the original experiment.

• How did including the additional 30 trials affect the results of the entire experiment?

On Your Own *Ex. 1–5. Results of experiments will vary. Theoretical probabilities and product predictions are given.*

Use the recording sheet to complete each probability experiment. Record each probability as a fraction in simplest form.

1. Toss a number cube and get an even number. $\frac{1}{2}$; 10 Complete 20 tosses.

Event	Theoretical Probability	Prediction ? times in ? trials	EXPERIMENT RESULTS		
			Tally of Favorable Outcomes	Number of Favorable Outcomes	Experimental Probability
Even (2, 4, 6)	$\frac{3}{6} = \frac{1}{2}$	$\frac{1}{2} = \frac{X}{20}$			

 Go On

Chapter 20 Lesson 5 **541**

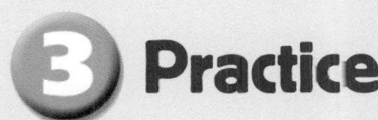 ## ③ Practice

• **Look at Step 3.** Ask students to review the artwork on page 541 that shows *Experiment Results.* Explain that this example shows them how to record the results of their own experiment. **The experimental probabilities may or may not be close to the theoretical probabilities.**

• **Look at Step 4.** Ask students to toss the cube in a consistent manner. **Mathematicians have observed that the greater the number of trials, the closer the experimental probability is to the theoretical probability.**

Assign *Exercises 1–5* of *On Your Own* as independent work.

• *Exercises 1–5* Have students complete Exercises 1–2 as you observe. Some students may need help writing the theoretical probabilities for each exercise.

DAILY TEST PREP

In a board game, you have a number cube labeled 1–6. You move forward when you roll an even number. How likely are you to move forward? (It is equally likely that I will move forward as not move forward.)

Activity

Lesson Intervention

Or use
*Intervention
CD-ROM
Lesson 20.5*

Experimental Probability

| Small Group | 5–10 minutes | Kinesthetic, Visual |

Materials: *spinner*

- Divide the spinner into 8 equal sections. Shade 2 sections blue and 6 sections green.

$$\frac{\text{number of blue sections}}{\text{total number of sections}} = \frac{}{} = \frac{}{}$$

- **How many blue sections?** (2) **How many total sections?** (8) Display the *theoretical probability* $\frac{2}{8}$. **What is $\frac{2}{8}$ in simplest form?** ($\frac{1}{4}$)

- **Display $\frac{1}{4} = \frac{x}{40}$. What is the value of x?** (10) **If we spin 40 times, we can predict that we will spin blue 10 times.** Demonstrate. Record results.

For Problems 2–5, select 2 blue cubes, 5 yellow cubes, and 3 red cubes—a total of 10 cubes. Place them in a bag. Then use the recording sheet to complete each probability experiment.

2–5. Theoretical probability given; experimental probability will vary.

2. Find the theoretical probability of selecting a blue cube. Then pick a cube, tally the result, and return the cube to the bag. Repeat 20 times. Then find the experimental probability. $\frac{1}{5}$

3. Find the theoretical probability of selecting a yellow cube. Then pick a cube, tally the result, and return the cube to the bag. Repeat 20 times. Then find the experimental probability. $\frac{1}{2}$

4. Find the theoretical probability of selecting a red cube. Then pick a cube, tally the result, and return the cube to the bag. Repeat 20 times. Then find the experimental probability. $\frac{3}{10}$

5. Do the experiment in Problem 4 of selecting a red cube, but repeat 50 times. Then find the experimental probability. $\frac{3}{10}$

Event	Theoretical Probability	Prediction ? times in ? trials	EXPERIMENT RESULTS		
			Tally of Favorable Outcomes	Number of Favorable Outcomes	Experimental Probability
Blue	$\frac{2}{10} = \frac{1}{5}$	$\frac{1}{5} = \frac{x}{20}$			
Yellow					$\frac{?}{20}$
Red					

Talk About It • Write About It

You learned the difference between experimental probability and theoretical probability.

6. Suppose you spin this spinner 20 times and find the experimental probability of spinning red is $\frac{1}{5}$. Is this close to what you would have predicted? Explain.

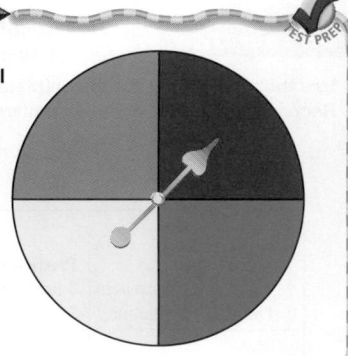

7. Use your results from Problems 4 and 5. Does the experimental probability get closer to or farther from the theoretical probability as the number of trials increases?

6–7. See Additional Answers on Page 551.

542

---

4 Assess and Close

- Assign **Exercises 6–7** of the *Talk About It • Write About It* section. Have volunteers explain their work

- **What is a probability experiment?** (It is when you look for a specific event, make predictions, and run trials.)

- **Will the experimental probability match the theoretical probability?** (No, but it should be close.)

- **The theoretical probability of tossing heads on a coin is $\frac{1}{2}$. The results of ten tosses is $\frac{3}{10}$, of 100 tosses is $\frac{49}{100}$, the results of 1,000 tosses is $\frac{499}{1,000}$. What is happening?** (The greater the number of experimental trials, the closer the experimental probability gets to the theoretical probability.)

Assign the **LESSON QUIZ** on Transparency 20.5 to further assess student understanding.

The 50 States

Suppose you choose one of the 50 states at random.

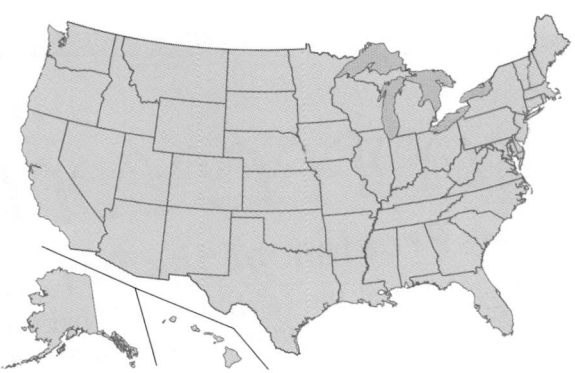

1. What is the probability of choosing a state name that begins with the letter F? the letter N? $\frac{1}{50}$, $\frac{4}{25}$

2. Is there a greater chance of choosing a state east of the Mississippi River or west of it? Explain. **east of it; there are 26 states east of the Mississippi**

3. Write 5 probability problems about the 50 states. Solve your problems and then give them to a partner to solve.
Check students' problems and solutions.

Common Sense

Describe each event as *likely, unlikely, impossible,* or *certain.*

- It will snow tomorrow.
- You will read a book today.
- Your school will grow legs and walk.
- The sun will set tonight.
- You will finish reading this sentence.
Check that students' answers are reasonable.

Brain Teaser

The cards shown are numbered 1 to 4. One card has been set aside. What is the probability that the next card is a 2?

Ask Yourself
What is the probability if 3 cards are set aside?

Technology
Visit *Education Place* at **eduplace.com/kids/mw/** to try more brain teasers.

The probability that the next card is a 2 is $\frac{1}{4}$.

Chapter 20 Lesson 5   543

Take A Break

The 50 States

If students have not memorized the names of each state, you may need an almanac. Review the location of the source and the termination of the Mississippi River.

 ## Keeping a Journal

Have students describe how understanding and experimenting with probability might be useful in a real-world situation, such as shopping or traveling.

Lesson 20.6 — Compound Events

PLANNING THE LESSON

MATHEMATICS OBJECTIVE
Find the probability of compound events.

Use Lesson Planner CD-ROM for Lesson 20.6.

Daily Routines

Vocabulary

Write the following examples of compound words on the chalkboard: *news* + *stand* = *newsstand*; *thumb* + *nail* = *thumbnail*; *sand* + *paper* = *sandpaper*. The word *compound* comes from the Old French and means "to put together." **Just as a compound word is composed of two or more words, in probability a *compound event* is composed of two or more events.**

Vocabulary Cards

Meeting North Carolina's Standards

Prepare for Grade 6 Objective **4.03** Conduct experiments involving simple and compound events.

Problem of the Day
Look at the cards shown. What is the probability of drawing a card where the letter is the first letter of a month of a year? ($\frac{2}{5}$)

 A B C D E

Quick Review
Find the product, then simplify.
1. $\frac{3}{4} \times \frac{1}{3}$ ($\frac{1}{4}$)
2. $\frac{4}{5} \times \frac{2}{10}$ ($\frac{4}{25}$)
3. $\frac{4}{6} \times \frac{1}{2}$ ($\frac{1}{3}$)
4. $\frac{2}{3} \times \frac{5}{6}$ ($\frac{5}{9}$)
5. $\frac{3}{9} \times \frac{5}{6}$ ($\frac{5}{18}$)
6. $\frac{4}{8} \times \frac{1}{3}$ ($\frac{1}{6}$)

Lesson Quiz
Find the probability of compound events.

You have a spinner that is equally divided into four sections: red, green, blue, and yellow. You have a number cube labeled 1–6. What is the probability of spinning a *green* and tossing a 5? ($\frac{1}{24}$)

LEVELED PRACTICE

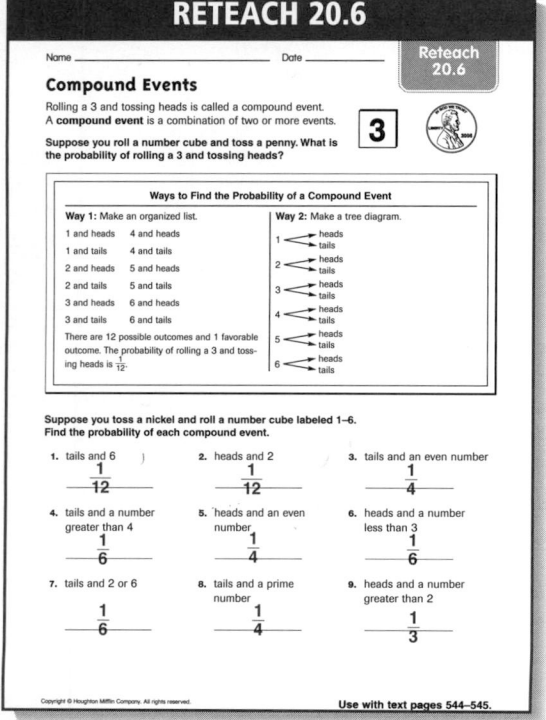

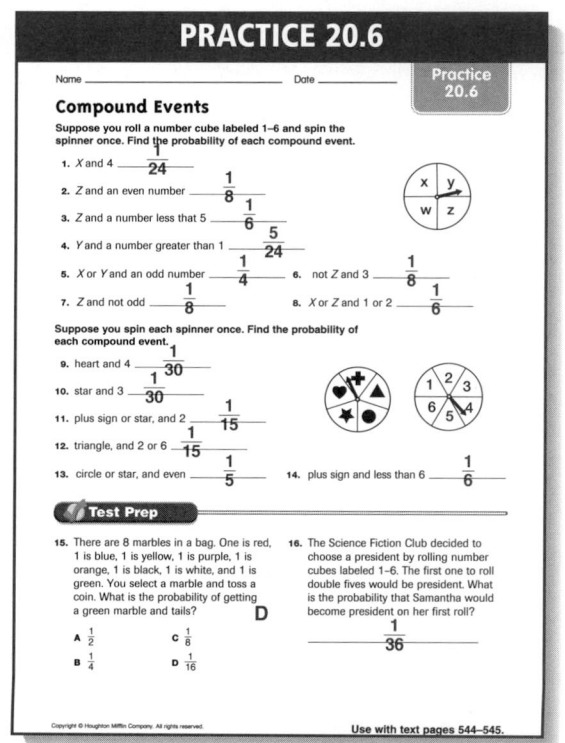

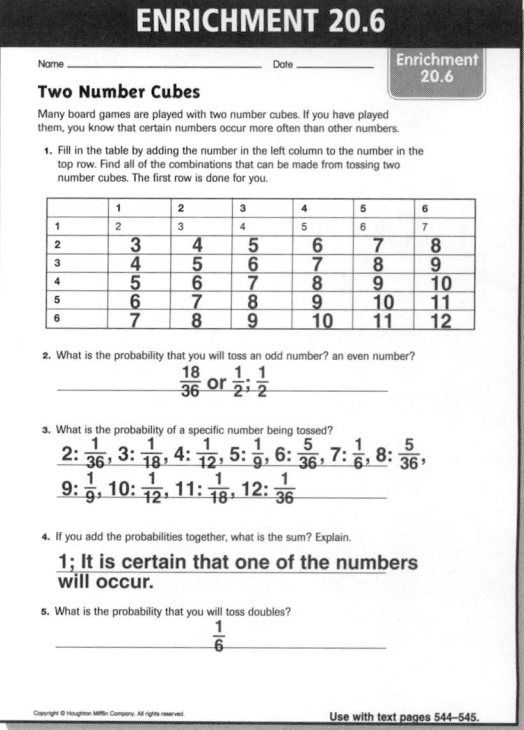

Practice Workbook Page 136

Reaching All Learners

Differentiated Instruction

English Learners

Worksheet 20.6 teaches the methods of determining the probability of a compound event and familiarizes students with the types of problems they will solve in Lesson 6.

Special Needs
VISUAL, KINESTHETIC

Materials: *coin, number cube*

- Prepare a compound events chart on blank transparency. Show all the possible outcomes. Make copies for the class.

- Have students take turns tossing the coin and cube. Help them locate their outcomes on the chart.

Gifted and Talented
VISUAL, KINESTHETIC

- Plan a menu that has 3 appetizers, 4 main dishes, and 3 desserts.

- Make a tree diagram of all combinations.

- Pick one item at random from each category. What is the probability of someone selecting the same items? ($\frac{1}{36}$)

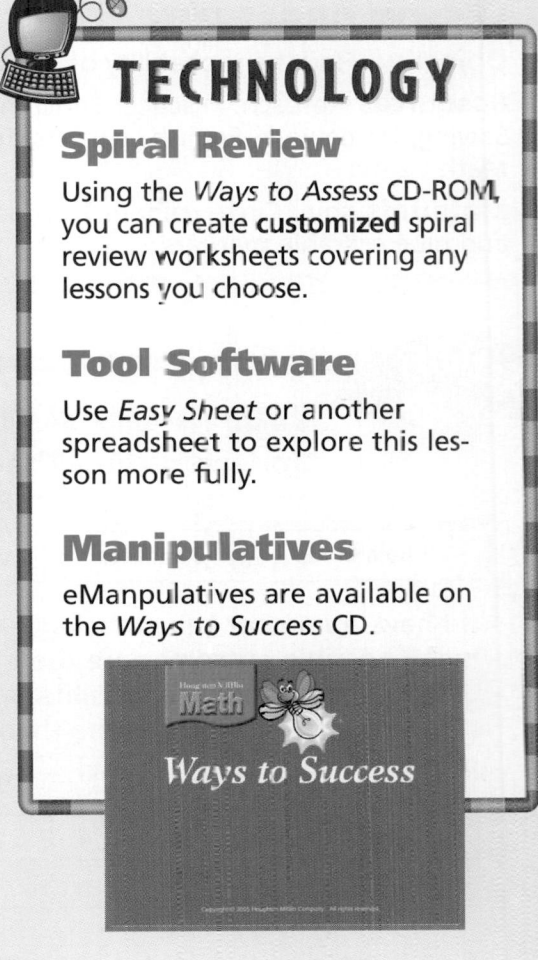

TECHNOLOGY

Spiral Review

Using the *Ways to Assess* CD-ROM, you can create **customized** spiral review worksheets covering any lessons you choose.

Tool Software

Use *Easy Sheet* or another spreadsheet to explore this lesson more fully.

Manipulatives

eManipulatives are available on the *Ways to Success* CD.

Science Connection

Crossing Peas

- Tell students that Gregor Mendel was an Austrian monk who lived in the 1800s. Mendel crossed pea plants and studied how different traits were inherited.

- Suppose you were to cross two types of pea plants. Also suppose the offspring are equally likely to have the following traits: round or wrinkled seeds, yellow or green seeds, purple or white flowers.

- What is the probability that an individual offspring will have wrinkled green seeds and purple flowers? **Explain.** ($\frac{1}{8}$; the probability of wrinkled is $\frac{1}{2}$, the probability of green is $\frac{1}{2}$, and the probability of purple flowers is $\frac{1}{2}$; $\frac{1}{2} \times \frac{1}{2} \times \frac{1}{2} = \frac{1}{8}$.)

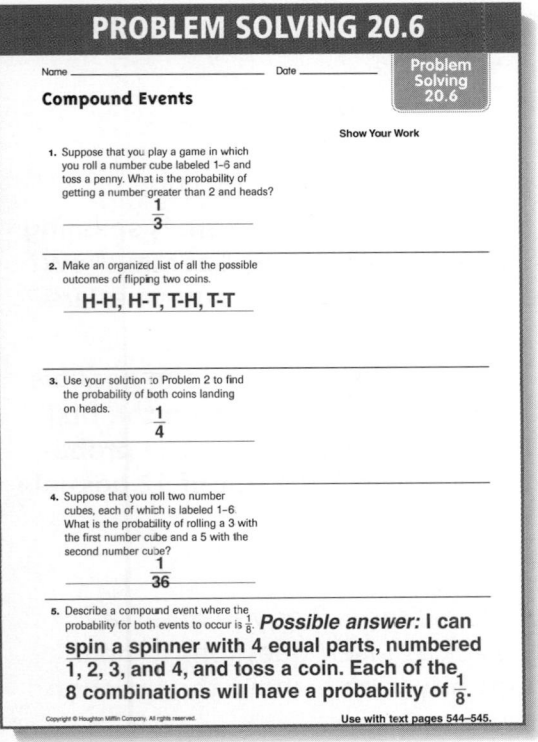

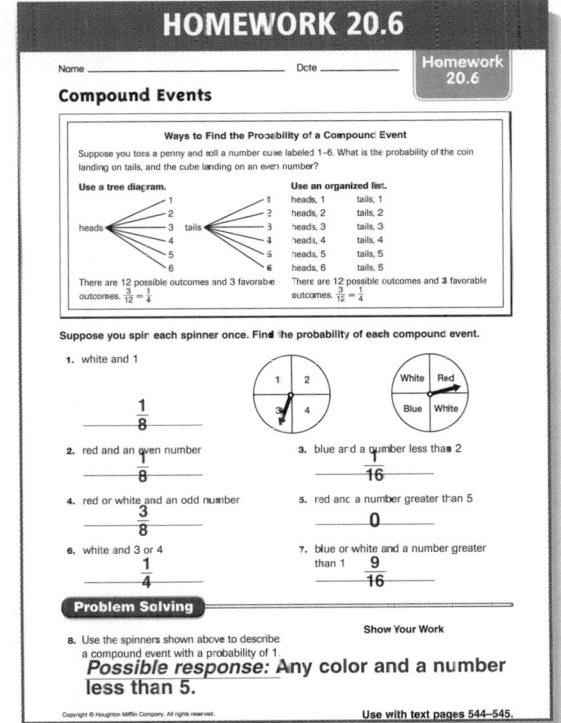

Homework Workbook Page 136

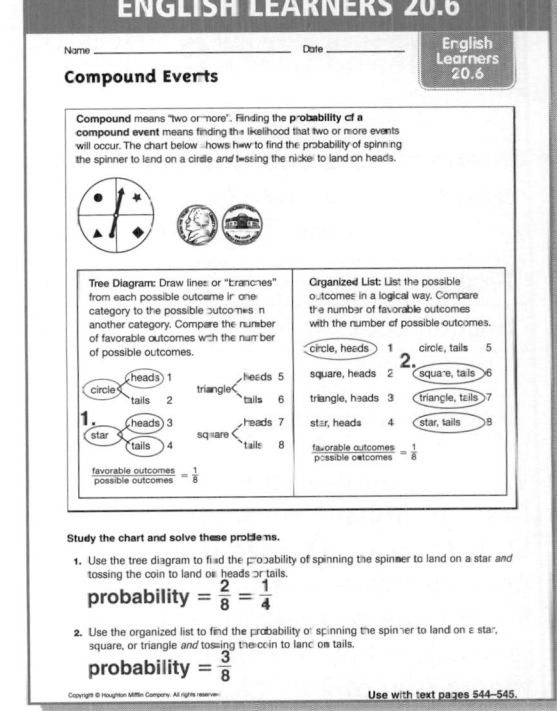

TEACHING LESSON 20.6

Warm-Up Activity
Understanding Theoretical and Experimental Probability

 Whole Group	⏱ 5 minutes	Visual, Tactile

- **If I have a number cube labeled 1–6, how many possible outcomes are there?** (6 possible outcomes) **What are the possible outcomes?** (1, 2, 3, 4, 5, and 6) **What is the theoretical probability of tossing a 5?** ($\frac{1}{6}$)

- Write on the board:

Number	1	2	3	4	5	6
Frequency	I	II		II		I

Suppose I tossed a number cube 6 times and tallied the results. Why doesn't the table have a tally for 3 and 5? (Because experimental probability does not always match theoretical probability.)

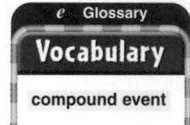

Compound Events

Objective Find the probability of compound events.

 **Learn About It** 💿 MathTracks 2/27
Listen and Understand

Lara and Will play a game using two spinners. If Lara spins both spinners once, what is the probability of spinning 3 and red?

Spinning 3 and red is called a compound event. A **compound event** is a combination of two or more events.

Here are some different ways to find the probability of a compound event.

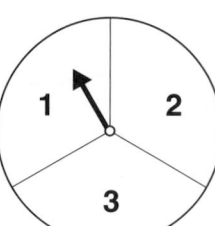 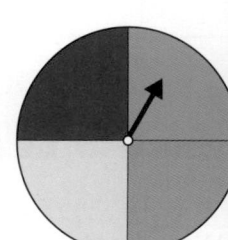

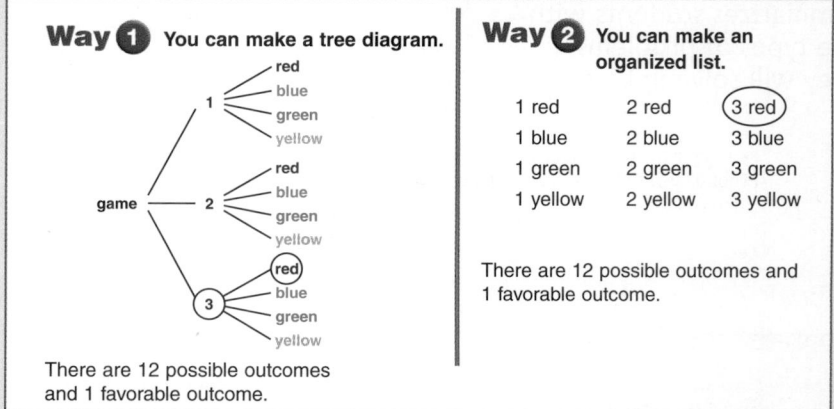

Different Ways to Find the Probability of a Compound Event

Way ❶ You can make a tree diagram.

There are 12 possible outcomes and 1 favorable outcome.

Way ❷ You can make an organized list.

1 red	2 red	3 red
1 blue	2 blue	3 blue
1 green	2 green	3 green
1 yellow	2 yellow	3 yellow

There are 12 possible outcomes and 1 favorable outcome.

Solution: The probability of spinning red and 3 can be expressed as $\frac{1}{12}$.

 **Guided Practice**

Ask Yourself
- Did I find all of the possible outcomes?
- What is the favorable outcome?

Suppose you toss a nickel and roll a number cube labeled 1–6. Find the probability of each compound event.

1. heads and 3 $\frac{1}{12}$ **2.** tails and an odd number $\frac{1}{4}$

TEST TIPS ▶ **Explain Your Thinking** ▶ In Exercise 2, how did you find the probability? **See Additional Answers on Page 551.**

544

---

① Introduce
Whole Group	⏱ 15 minutes

- **When you toss two number cubes, what is the least number you can toss?** (1 + 1 = 2) **What is the greatest?** (6 + 6 = 12) Draw the table on the board:

First cube	1	1	1	1	1	1
Second cube	1	2	3	4	5	6
	↓	↓	↓	↓	↓	↓
Possible Outcomes	(1, 1)	(1, 2)	(1, 3)	(1, 4)	(1, 5)	(1, 6)

- **What are all the possible outcomes if the first cube is 2? Draw a similar tree diagram to find out.** ((2, 1), (2, 2), (2, 3), (2, 4), (2, 5), (2,6)) Have students draw four more tree diagrams in which the first cube is 3, 4, 5, and 6. **Draw a 6 × 6 table and record all the possible outcomes.** Discuss why a possible outcome with a sum of 7 is more likely then a sum of 2 or 12.

② Develop

Guide students through the *Learn About It* section.

- **Look at Way 1. A *favorable outcome* for Lara is spinning red then spinning 3. What does the tree diagram show?** (all possible outcomes) **How many possible outcomes are there?** (12)

- **Look at Way 2. The organized list shows all the *possible outcomes*. Is it possible for Lara to spin red on the first spinner and a 4 on the second spinner?** (no) The probability Lara will spin red and then 3 is 1 out of 12 possible outcomes or $\frac{1}{12}$.

Guided Practice

Have students complete **Exercises 1–2** as you observe. Remind them to use the *Ask Yourself* questions to help. Give students the opportunity to talk about the question in *Explain Your Thinking.*

Suppose you spin each spinner once. Find the probability of each compound event.

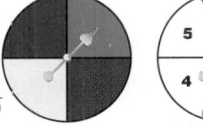

3. purple and 5 $\frac{1}{20}$

4. yellow and 3 $\frac{1}{20}$

5. red and even $\frac{1}{10}$

6. yellow and odd $\frac{3}{20}$

7. blue or purple, and 4 $\frac{1}{10}$

8. purple, and 2 or 3 $\frac{1}{10}$

9. red or purple, and even $\frac{1}{5}$

10. yellow or red, and odd $\frac{3}{10}$

Use a penny and the spinners to solve Problems 11–15.

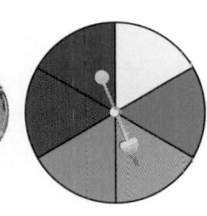

11. Use a tree diagram to show all the possible outcomes of the compound event of tossing a penny and spinning the color spinner. Then find the probability of tossing tails and spinning green. **See students' diagrams.** $\frac{1}{12}$

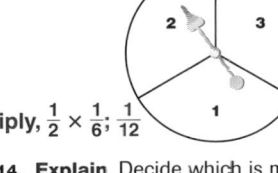

12. Find the probability of tossing heads with the penny. Then find the probability of spinning the color red on the color spinner. How can you use the first two probabilities to find the probability of tossing heads and spinning red? $\frac{1}{2}$; $\frac{1}{6}$; multiply, $\frac{1}{2} \times \frac{1}{6}$, $\frac{1}{12}$

13. Make an organized list to show all the possible outcomes of spinning the number and color spinners. What is the probability of spinning 2 and purple? **See students' lists.** $\frac{1}{18}$

14. **Explain** Decide which is more likely: to spin red and toss heads or to spin purple and 2? Explain how you made your decision. **spin red and toss heads; explanations will vary**

15. **Write Your Own** Write and solve a probability problem of your own involving the penny, the number spinner, and/or the color spinner. **See students' problems.**

16. **Analyze** Suppose you toss the penny and spin both spinners above. What is the probability of getting heads, the number 2, and red? $\frac{1}{36}$

Daily Review	Test Prep
Find the product. (Ch. 13, Lessons 3–5)	22. **Free Response** You toss a coin and roll a number cube labeled 1–6. Find the probability of getting heads and an even number. **See Additional Answers on Page 551.** Explain how you got your answer.
16. 0.7 × 0.4 **0.28**	
17. 5 × 1.49 **7.45**	
18. 0.68 × 0.3 **0.204**	
19. 0.9 × 0.2 **0.18**	
20. 1.63 × 2.5 **4.075**	
21. 4.29 × 1.3 **5.577**	

Extra Practice See page 551, Set D.

Chapter 20 Lesson 6   **545**

Test Prep Transparency
20.6

DAILY TEST PREP

Keegan has a 2-part spinner labeled A and B. She also has a number cube labeled 1–6. How many possible outcomes are there for spinning the spinner and then tossing the cube? (A)

A. 12   B. 6   C. $\frac{1}{8}$ D. 8

Activity

Or use Intervention CD-ROM Lesson 20.6

Lesson Intervention
Understanding Compound Events

iii Small Group	⏱ 5–10 minutes	Kinesthetic, Visual

Materials: *coin, Circle Spinner Transparency, red and blue erasable markers*

- Shade half of the spinner blue, half red.
- **What is the probability of tossing heads?** ($\frac{1}{2}$) **of spinning red?** ($\frac{1}{2}$) **Let's find the probability of tossing heads and then spinning red.** Display the four possible outcomes

  Tails, Blue   Tails, Red
  Heads, Blue   Heads, Red

- **There are 4 possible outcomes. Since one of the four outcomes is heads and red, the probability is $\frac{1}{4}$.**

---

3 Practice

Assign **Exercises 3–22** as independent work.

- ***Problem Solving for Problems 3–10*** Before students begin answering the problems, have them make a table of all possible outcomes. In Exercise 4 when students are looking for the probability of spinning yellow and 3, point out that since there are 2 out of 20 possible outcomes for this event, the probability is $\frac{2}{20}$ or $\frac{1}{10}$.

Common Error

Failing to organize information Sometimes students do not organize information by writing it in the form of a list or a chart. Remind them that organizing information will greatly increase accurate responses to problems.

4 Assess and Close

- **Probability describes the likelihood of an event.** Display the words *impossible, unlikely, equally likely, likely,* and *certain.*
- Offer the example of tossing a coin and spinning a 3-color spinner. Ask volunteers to name compound events and have other students determine their likelihood.

Assign the **LESSON QUIZ** on Transparency 20.6 to further assess student understanding.

Keeping a Journal

Have students describe how making a list of all possible outcomes helps them to organize information.

Problem-Solving Application: Make Predictions

PLANNING THE LESSON

MATHEMATICS OBJECTIVE
Use data to make predictions.

Use Lesson Planner CD-ROM for Lesson 20.7.

Daily Routines

Vocabulary

Review the meaning of the word *predict*. Write the following phrases on the board: *Predict the outcome of an election; Forecast the weather; He foretold the game's final score.* The verbs *predict, forecast,* and *foretold* all mean to tell about something in advance of its occurrence through having particular knowledge.

> Vocabulary Cards

Meeting North Carolina's Standards

Prepare for Grade 6 Objective **4.02** Use a sample space to determine the probability of an event.

Lesson Transparency 20.7

Problem of the Day

There are 180 students at the spring fair. The ratio of girls to boys is 5 to 4. How many boys are at the spring fair? (80 boys)

Quick Review

A number cube labeled 2, 2, 3, 3, 4, and 6 is rolled once. Describe each event as *equally likely, likely, unlikely, certain,* or *impossible.*

1. rolling a 2 or a 3 (equally likely)
2. rolling a 7 (impossible)
3. rolling a 2 or a 4 (likely)
4. rolling a one-digit number (certain)

Lesson Quiz

Use the table to solve the problem.

At the state fair, 160 people redeemed their entry tickets and 40 people won cowboy hats. If 20,000 people redeemed their tickets, how many could expect to win a cowboy hat? (5,000)

LEVELED PRACTICE

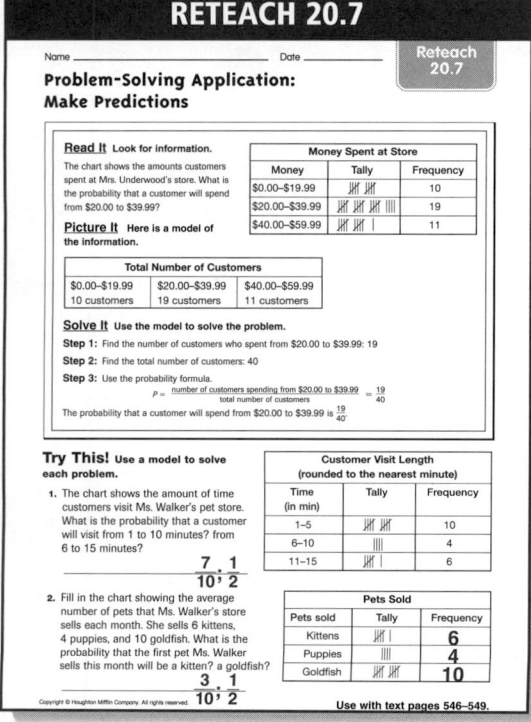

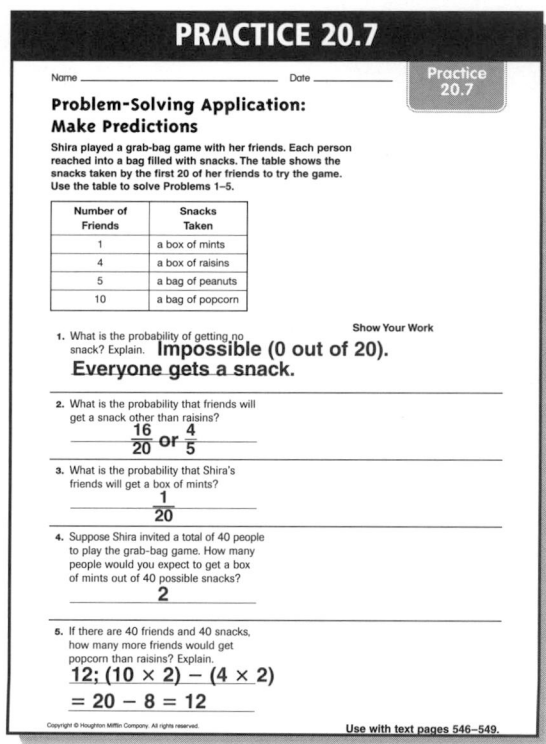

Practice Workbook Page 137

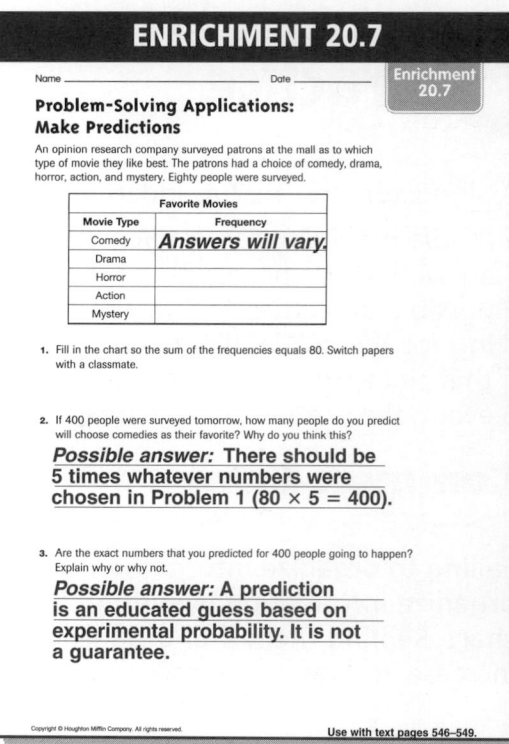

Reaching All Learners

Differentiated Instruction

English Learners

Worksheet 20.7 provides students with a step-by-step method for using data and probability to make predictions.

Inclusion

VISUAL, KINESTHETIC

Materials: *connecting cubes*

- Place cubes in a bag (1 pink, 3 blue, 6 yellow). **You win this game by picking a pink cube.** Show the cubes to the students. **What is the probability of picking a pink cube?** ($\frac{1}{10}$)
- **Is it likely that you will win this game?** (no)

Early Finishers

VISUAL, TACTILE

Materials: *stickers, cube*

- **Use stickers to label the cube *A, B, B, C, D, D.* Find the theoretical probability of rolling each letter.** (A, $\frac{1}{6}$; B, $\frac{1}{3}$; C, $\frac{1}{6}$; D, $\frac{1}{3}$) **Make 60 tosses and record your results.**
- **Predict the results for 12,000 tosses. Support your prediction.**

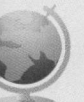

Social Studies Connection

Groundwater: Preserving Quality

Materials: biology reference books, state water agency booklets

- **Why do some people drink bottled water instead of tap water? Where does tap water originate?** (ground water) Explain that many states monitor ground water quality.

- Have students research water quality programs in their state. What standards do they use? Do they differ from other states' programs?
- Lead a discussion about how probability, sampling, and water quality relate to one another.

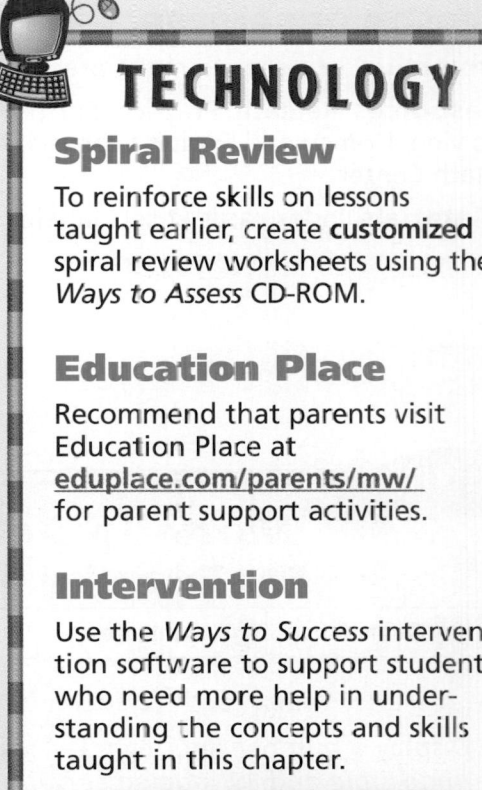

TECHNOLOGY

Spiral Review

To reinforce skills on lessons taught earlier, create **customized** spiral review worksheets using the *Ways to Assess* CD-ROM.

Education Place

Recommend that parents visit Education Place at **eduplace.com/parents/mw/** for parent support activities.

Intervention

Use the *Ways to Success* intervention software to support students who need more help in understanding the concepts and skills taught in this chapter.

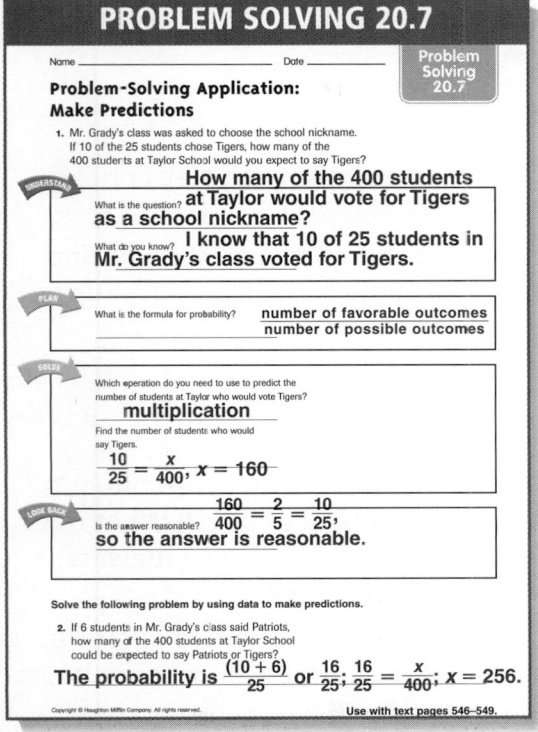
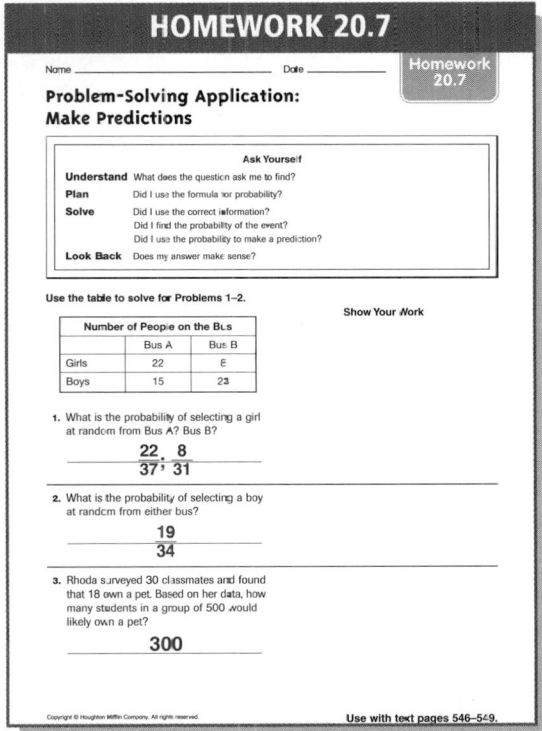
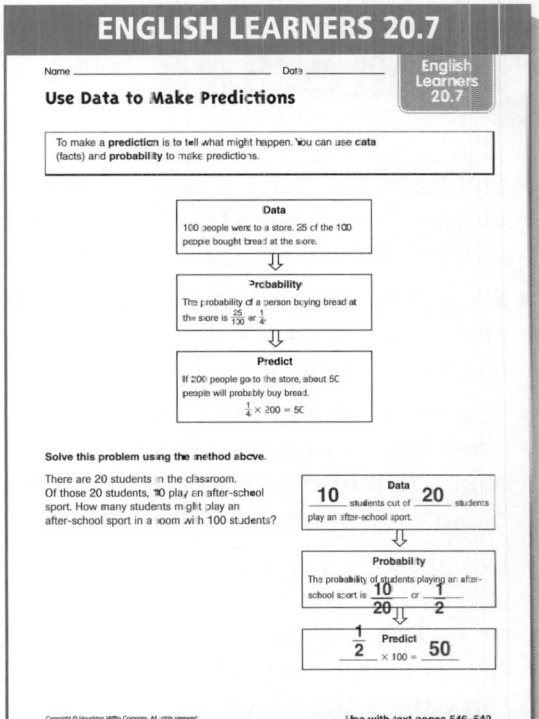
Homework Workbook Page 137

TEACHING LESSON 20.7

LESSON ORGANIZER

Objective Use data to make predictions.

Resources Reteach, Practice, Enrichment, Problem Solving, Homework, English Learners, Transparencies, Math Center

Materials Index cards (2 sets labeled 1–10)

Warm-Up Activity
Find Theoretical Probability

iiiii Whole Group	🕐 5 minutes	Visual, Auditory

Materials: *index cards (2 sets labeled 1–10)*

- Display a number line from 0–1 with 0 labeled *impossible* and 12 labeled *certain*.

- Display: *1, 1, 2, 2, 3, 3, 4, 4, 5, 5, 6, 6, 7, 7, 8, 8, 9, 9, 10, 10.* **This stack of cards is made from 2 sets of cards labeled 1–10. There are 20 cards.**

- **What is the probability of picking a 1-digit number?** ($\frac{18}{20}$ or $\frac{9}{10}$) Have a student label the approximate location of $\frac{9}{10}$ on the number line. Repeat this process with different numbers.

Problem-Solving Application
Make Predictions

Objective Use data to make predictions.

Sometimes you can use data to make predictions about outcomes.

Problem At the Tuscan Middle School Fair some students conducted a homework survey. The table shows the results.

What is the probability that a student chosen at random does 15 or more hours of homework per week?

Homework Survey Results		
Hours of Home Work per Week	Tally of Students	Frequency
0 – 4.9	|||	3
5 – 9.9	~~||||~~ |||	8
10 – 14.9	~~||||~~ ~~||||~~ ~~||||~~ ~~||||~~ ||	22
15 – 19.9	~~||||~~ |	6
20 – 24.9	|	1

 **UNDERSTAND**

What is the question?
- What is the probability that a student chosen at random does 15 or more hours of homework per week?

What do you know?
- A total of 40 students were surveyed.
- 6 students did between 15 and 19.9 hours of homework.
- 1 student did between 20 and 24.9 hours of homework.

 **PLAN**

Use the formula for probability. $P = \dfrac{\text{number of favorable outcomes}}{\text{number of possible outcomes}}$

 **SOLVE**

- Use the number of students who were surveyed as the number of possible outcomes.
- Use the number of students who did 15 or more hours of homework per week as the number of favorable outcomes.

$P = \dfrac{6 + 1}{40} = \dfrac{7}{40}$

Solution: The probability that a randomly chosen student does 15 or more hours of homework per week is $\frac{7}{40}$.

LOOK BACK

Look back at the problem.
Is the answer reasonable?

546

---

1 Introduce

- **Suppose I say "pick a card at random." What does the word *random* mean?** (Picking a card at random means every card has the same probability of being chosen.)

- A *random sample* is a sample of a population for which each member of the population has an equally likely chance of being selected.

- **You can take a *random sample* to check the quality of products. In a lunch-box factory one lunch box out of every 10 might be checked for defects. If the factory makes 500 a day, how many are in the sample?** (50)

- Explain that if 2 out of 50 lunch boxes are defective then you can say the probability for a defective lunch box is $\frac{2}{50}$ or $\frac{1}{25}$. **This probability can be applied to the entire population or entire number of lunch boxes produced. The factory can expect that $\frac{1}{25}$ of the 500 lunch boxes or 20 lunch boxes are defective.**

2 Develop

Guide students through the problem-solving steps on page 546.

- **Look at the Understand step. What do we want to find out through the survey?** (the probability of a student doing 15 or more hours of homework per week)

- **Where are the results recorded?** (the table)

- **What does *favorable outcomes* mean?** (It means the outcomes we are looking for; we are looking for how many students studied 15 or more hours/week.) **How many favorable outcomes occurred in this survey?** (7 students or 7) **What does *number of possible outcomes* mean?** (Since 40 students were interviewed, it means 40 students or 40.)

- **Look at the Plan step. The probability formula allows us to compare how many students studied 15 or more hours out of the 40 students interviewed.**

Use the table on page 546 to solve each problem.

1. What is the probability of a student doing less than 10 hours of homework per week? $\frac{11}{40}$

2. Tuscan Middle School has 600 students. How many students would you expect to do between 5 and 15 hours of homework per week? **450**

(Hint) What part of the students surveyed did between 5 and 15 hours of homework per week?

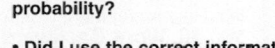

Ask Yourself

UNDERSTAND — What does the question ask me to find?

PLAN — Did I use the formula for probability?

SOLVE —
• Did I use the correct information from the table?
• Did I find the probability of the event?
• Did I use the probability to make a prediction?

LOOK BACK — Does my answer make sense?

TEST TIPS

Independent Practice

Use the table to solve Problems 3–7.

Each ticket to the Tuscan Middle School Fair gives you a chance to win a prize. The table shows the prizes won by the first 50 people who came to the fair.

3. What is the probability of winning no prize? $\frac{19}{25}$

4. Suppose 400 people come to the fair. How many people would you expect to win a prize? **96**

5. Suppose 500 people come to the fair. About how many more people would you expect to win flashlights than school caps? **20**

6. **What's Wrong?** Marina found the probability of winning a school cap. What did Marina do wrong?

7. Of 800 tickets, 8 have a code that shows that the owner wins a pizza party. Is the number of winners in the first 50 tickets less than, greater than, or the same as you would expect? Explain your answer.
See Additional Answers on Page T88.

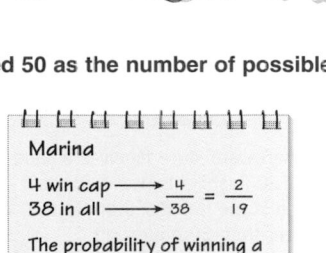

Prizes Won at Middle School Fair

Prize Won	Number of Ticket Holders
No prize	38
Flashlight	6
School cap	4
Pizza party	2

Marina should have used 50 as the number of possible outcomes, not 38.

Marina

4 win cap ⟶ 4
38 in all ⟶ 38 = $\frac{2}{19}$

The probability of winning a cap is $\frac{2}{19}$.

 Go On

Chapter 20 Lesson 7 **547**

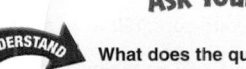 **Quick Check Options**

The following activities will help students prepare for the Quick Check or may be used as an alternative assessment.

Vocabulary Review (individual, small group, or whole class)

Have students review the following vocabulary words by giving an example of how each term is used in this chapter.

• compound event

Math Conversations (small group or whole class)

Have students discuss what they have learned about probability of compound events in this chapter. Encourage students to ask each other questions to clarify their understanding.

Writing Prompt (individual or partners)

To solidify student understanding of vocabulary and concepts, have each student complete the following sentence:

The most important thing I have learned about finding the probability of compound events is

_____.

• **Look at the Solve step. What does the solution $\frac{7}{40}$ mean?** (It means 7 students out of 40 students surveyed studied 15 or more hours per week.) **Since 7 out of 40 students did 15 or more hours of homework/week, how many did less than 15 hours of homework/week?** (33 out of 40)

• **Look at the Look Back step. Think of a number line labeled from 0 to 1. An impossible event equals 0, a certain event equals 1. Where on the number line does $\frac{7}{40}$ lie?** (near 0) **Are students at Tuscan Middle School likely to study 15 or more hours/week?** (no)

Guided Practice

Have students complete **Problems 1–2** as you observe. Remind them to use the *Ask Yourself* questions.

③ Practice

Assign **Problems 3–7** as independent work. Have students share and discuss their work.

Problem-Solving Reminders

Have students review their answers to make sure they have done the following:

• expressed the solution clearly
• used appropriate mathematical notation and terms
• supported their solution with verbal and symbolic work
• determined the reasonableness of the solution in the context of the original problem.

DAILY TEST PREP

In a random sample, 3 out of 5 12-year olds preferred playing soccer to any other sport. How many of the 100,000 12-year olds in the state would you expect to prefer to play soccer? (B)

A. $7\frac{1}{5}$ B. 60,000   C. 16,667   D. $\frac{2}{5}$

Activity

Lesson Intervention
Using Data to Make Predictions

Or use Intervention CD-ROM Lesson 20.7

| Small Group | 5 minutes | Kinesthetic, Visual |

- *The cook at Math Camp asked a random sampling of campers, "Which breakfast do you like best? Display:*

Favorite Breakfasts	
Meal	**Number of Campers**
Oatmeal	18
Pancakes	12

- **What does the table tell us?** ($\frac{18}{30}$ or $\frac{3}{5}$ campers prefer oatmeal; $\frac{12}{30}$ or $\frac{2}{5}$ campers prefer pancakes)

- **There are 600 kids at Math Camp. Let's predict how many will like oatmeal.** *Display $\frac{3}{5} \times \frac{600}{1}$.* Help students simplify the expression. (360 kids)

Choose a Strategy

Solve. Show your work. Tell what strategy you used.

8. Norma spends $7 on playing games, $5.95 on a sandwich, $2.50 on drinks, and $19.95 on a sweatshirt. She has $25 left. How much money did she start with? **$60.40; Work Backward**

9. Two numbers have a sum of 54 and a quotient of 5. What are the numbers? **45 and 9; Guess and Check**

10. Sabrina, Paul, Nina, Fred, and Tyrone are the last players left in the Math Challenge contest. The last two players will win first prize and second prize. How many different ways can the prizes be given out? **20; Draw a Diagram**

PROBLEM-SOLVING Strategies

Use Models
Draw a Diagram
Find a Pattern
Guess and Check
Make an Organized List
Make a Table
Solve a Simpler Problem
Use Logical Reasoning
Work Backward
Write an Equation

Choose a Computation Method

Mental Math • Estimation • Paper and Pencil • Calculator

Data Use the histogram to solve Problems 11–14. Then explain which method you chose.

A hardware store donated flashlights with new batteries to the Tuscan Middle School Fair. The flashlights were given out as prizes. The histogram shows the results of the number of hours that the flashlight batteries last.

11. About what percent of flashlight batteries last between 30 and 34 hours? **about 50%**

12. **Explain** Is it reasonable to expect one of these flashlights to last 35 hours or more? Use probability to explain your answer. **See below.**

13. A hardware store receives a case of 120 flashlights with batteries. Predict the number that will last fewer than 30 hours. **32**

14. **Create and Solve** Use the data from the histogram to create and solve your own problem. **Check students' problems and answers.**

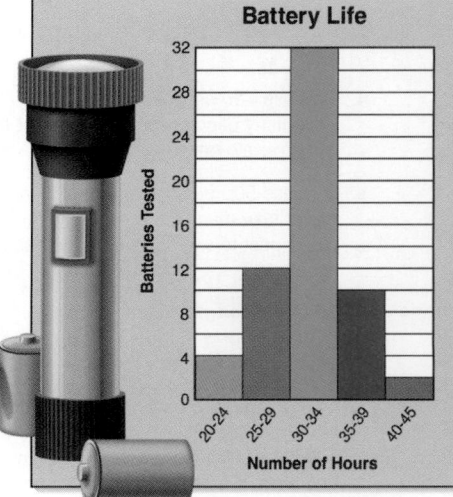

12. No; the probability of a flashlight lasting 35 hours or more is only $\frac{1}{5}$.

Practice *continued*

Choose a Strategy

Assign **Problems 8–10** as independent work.

- *Problem Solving for Problems 8–10* Have students describe the strategies they used to solve each problem.

Choose a Computation Method

- *Problems 11–14* Have students share which computation method they choose.

---

4 Assess and Close

Have students discuss how to predict using data.

- **How does using data from a sample help predict the outcomes for an entire population?** (If the sample is random, it allows you to question a few individuals and then apply the data to a much larger population.)

Assign the **LESSON QUIZ** on Transparency 20.4 to further assess student understanding.

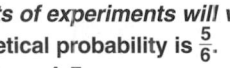

Quick Check

Check your understanding of Lessons 4–7.

1. *Results of experiments will vary.*
   Theoretical probability is $\frac{5}{6}$.

Use the recording sheet to complete the probability experiment. Record each probability as a fraction in simplest form. (Lesson 5)

Event	Theoretical Probability	Prediction ? times in ? trials
n > 1		

1. Toss a number cube and get a number greater than 1. Complete 30 tosses. **See above.**

Suppose you spin each spinner once. Find the theoretical probability of each compound event. (Lesson 6)

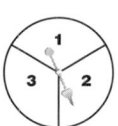 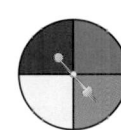

2. red and 1 $\frac{1}{12}$ 3. blue and odd $\frac{1}{6}$

Solve each problem. (Lessons 4 and 7)

4. There are 2 seats left on an airplane. There are 5 people who want to fly on the airplane. In how many different ways can these 2 seats be filled? **10**

5. A spinner has five congruent sectors labeled 1, 2, 3, 2, and 4. Suppose you spin the spinner 100 times. How many times would you expect to spin 2? **40**

WEEKLY WR READER eduplace.com/kids/mw/

Reading Connection

Likely Letters

The letter E is the most frequently occurring letter in the English language. When you read, you probably will see the letter E more often than any other letter.

Count 100 letters in a newspaper, magazine, or a favorite book. Record how many times each of the letters in the list occurs.

• Use your data to predict how many times out of 500 letters you will see each letter in the list. Then test your predictions.

• Repeat this activity for other letters of the alphabet.
Answers will vary.

Chapter 20 Lesson 7 **549**

Quick Check

Purpose: The Quick Check allows you to assess the students' understanding of the concepts presented in Lessons 4–7.

Items	Objectives Tested	Pages	Intervention
4–5	Solve a problem by making an organized list.	536–539	Reteach Resource 20.4 *Ways to Success 20.4*
1	Determine the experimental probability for a given set of data.	540–543	Reteach Resource 20.5 *Ways to Success 20.5*
2-3	Find the probability of compound events.	544–545	Reteach Resource 20.6 *Ways to Success 20.6*
4–5	Use data to make predictions.	546–549	Reteach Resource 20.7 *Ways to Success 20.7*

Keeping a Journal

Have students explain why your prediction may not be exact if you take a random sample and then apply the data to a larger population.

Reading Connection

Likely Letters

As students contemplate the frequency of the most commonly used letters in English you may wish to suggest the following tips:

• Have them highlight each letter, then count each one.

• Or, you may wish to have them find how many letters are in an area of the newspaper. With a ruler, have them outline a 1-in. square of newsprint. Have them count the number of Es.

• Then check the frequency of Es in a 2-in. square (4 times) and a 3-in. square (9 times).

Chapter Review/Test

Purpose: This test provides an informal assessment of the Chapter 20 objectives.

Chapter Test Items 1–20

To assign a numerical grade for this Chapter Test, use 5 points for each test item.

Check Understanding

You can use the **Write About It** question to assess student understanding of a key chapter concept.

Customizing Your Instruction

For students who have not yet mastered these objectives, you can use the Reteaching Resources listed in the chart below.

 ## Assessment Options

A summary test for this chapter is also provided in the Unit Resource Folder.

Adequate Yearly Progress

Use the End of Grade Test Prep Assessment Guide to help familiarize your students with the format of standardized tests.

Chapter Review/Test

✔ VOCABULARY

1. The chance that an event will occur is called the ____ of the event. **probability**

2. Rolling a 9 on a 1–6 number cube is a(n) ____. **impossible event**

3. If there are 12 different letters on each equal section of a spinner, each letter is a(n) ____. **outcome**

> **Vocabulary**
> certain event
> impossible event
> outcome
> probability

✔ CONCEPTS AND SKILLS

You have one choice from each category.
Multiply to find the number of choices possible. (Lesson 1, pp. 528–529)

4. 3 sizes, 5 flavors **15**   5. 6 colors, 5 styles **30**   6. 4 salads, 9 soups **36**

Use the bag of balls to tell which event is more likely.
Then find the probability of that event. (Lessons 2–3, pp. 530–535)

7. 0 or 5 **5; $\frac{1}{6}$**   8. 3 or 4 **4; $\frac{1}{4}$**   9. 1 or 3 **1; $\frac{1}{3}$**

10. 1 or 5 **1; $\frac{1}{3}$**   11. 2 or 3 **2; $\frac{1}{6}$**   12. not 4 or not 5 **not 5; $\frac{5}{6}$**

Suppose you toss a 1–6 number cube and spin the spinner once.
Find the probability of each compound event. (Lessons 5–6, pp. 540–545)

13. 1 and white **$\frac{2}{36}$,**   14. 6 and blue **$\frac{1}{36}$**   15. 4 or 5 and white **$\frac{4}{36}$,**
or **$\frac{1}{18}$**   or **$\frac{1}{9}$**

16. 5 and red   17. odd and red   18. even and white
$\frac{3}{36}$, or $\frac{1}{12}$ **$\frac{9}{36}$, or $\frac{1}{4}$**   **$\frac{6}{36}$, or $\frac{1}{6}$**

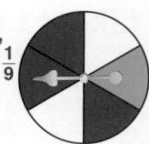

✔ PROBLEM SOLVING

Solve. (Lessons 4, 7, pp. 536–537, 547–549)

19. Shannon wants to enter 3 pies in the 4-H fair. The pie categories are apple, squash, pecan, lemon meringue, and banana cream. How many different sets of 3 pies can she bake? **10 different sets**

20. A wheel is divided into 20 equal sections. Each section is labeled differently. Suppose you spin 100 times. How many times would you expect to land on any one of the sections? **5 times**

> **Write About It**
>
> **Show You Understand**
> What is the difference between theoretical probability and experimental probability?
>
> Describe a situation for each to show this difference.

See Additional Answers on Page T88.

Reteaching Support

Chapter Test Items	Summary Test Items	Chapter Objectives Tested	TE Pages	Use These Reteaching Resources
4–6	1–7	**20A** Determine combinations.	528A–529	Reteach Resource 20.1 Ways to Success CD: 20.1 Skillsheet 160
1–3, 7–18	8–14, 17–20	**20B** Find the theoretical probability of single and compound events.	530A–535, 540A–545	Reteach Resource 20.2, 20.3, 20.5, 20.6 Ways to Success CD: 20.2, 20.3, 20.5, 20.6 Skillsheet 161, 162, 163, 164
19, 20	15–16	**20C** Analyze and solve problems by making an organized list and by using data to make predictions.	536A–539, 546A–549	Reteach Resource 20.4, 20.7 Ways to Success CD: 20.4, 20.7 Skillsheet 165

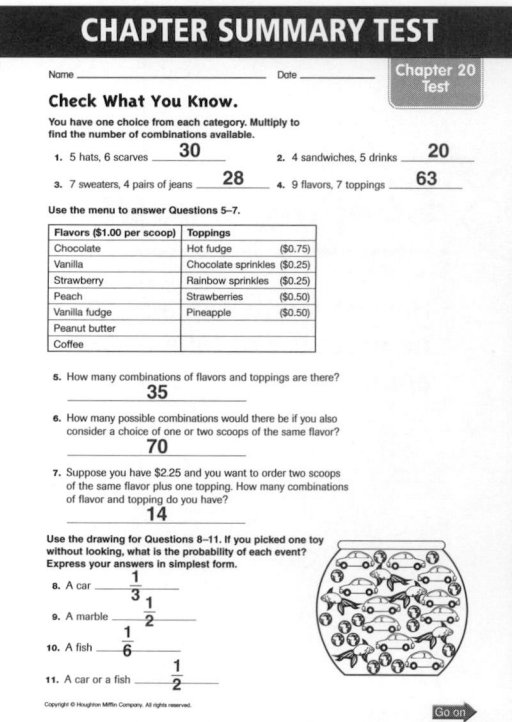

CHAPTER SUMMARY TEST

Name _____ Date _____   Chapter 20 Test

Check What You Know.

You have one choice from each category. Multiply to find the number of combinations available.

1. 5 hats, 6 scarves **30**   2. 4 sandwiches, 5 drinks **20**
3. 7 sweaters, 4 pairs of jeans **28**   4. 9 flavors, 7 toppings **63**

Use the menu to answer Questions 5–7.

Flavors ($1.00 per scoop)	Toppings
Chocolate	Hot fudge ($0.75)
Vanilla	Chocolate sprinkles ($0.25)
Strawberry	Rainbow sprinkles ($0.25)
Peach	Strawberries ($0.50)
Vanilla fudge	Pineapple ($0.50)
Peanut butter	
Coffee	

5. How many combinations of flavors and toppings are there? **35**

6. How many possible combinations would there be if you also consider a choice of one or two scoops of the same flavor? **70**

7. Suppose you have $2.25 and you want to order two scoops of the same flavor plus one topping. How many combinations of flavor and topping do you have? **14**

Use the drawing for Questions 8–11. If you picked one toy without looking, what is the probability of each event? Express your answers in simplest form.

8. A car **$\frac{1}{3}$**
9. A marble **$\frac{1}{2}$**
10. A fish **$\frac{1}{6}$**
11. A car or a fish **$\frac{1}{2}$**

Go on ▶

Set A (Lesson 1, pp. 528–529)

You have one choice from each column. Make an organized list and a tree diagram to show all the possible choices. **Ex. 1–3. Check students'**
lists and tree diagrams.

1. **Sweaters**

Style	Color
crew neck	red
V-neck	blue
	black
	yellow

8

2. **Pizzas**

Size	Topping
small	green peppers
medium	mushrooms
large	onions

9

3. **Book Reports**

Type	Subject
fiction	people
non-fiction	animals
	places

6

Set B (Lesson 2, pp. 530–531)

You spin once on the spinner at the right. Tell which event is more likely. If possible, describe an event as impossible or certain.

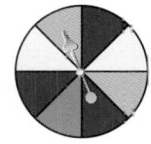

1. red or blue
red
2. green or yellow
yellow
3. blue or green
blue
4. green or red
red
5. black or red
red, black is impossible
6. yellow or red
red

Set C (Lesson 3, pp. 532–535)

Use the spinner at the right. Express the probability of each event as a fraction in simplest form.

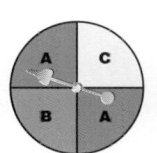

1. A $\frac{1}{4}$
2. C $\frac{1}{6}$
3. D $\frac{1}{6}$
4. B $\frac{1}{3}$
5. A or B $\frac{7}{12}$
6. A or C $\frac{5}{12}$
7. D or E $\frac{1}{4}$
8. not F 1
9. not E $\frac{11}{12}$
10. not A or C $\frac{7}{12}$
11. not D or E $\frac{3}{4}$
12. not A or E $\frac{2}{3}$

Set D (Lesson 6, pp. 544–545)

Suppose you spin each spinner once. Find the probability of each compound event.

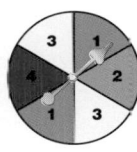

1. A and 3 $\frac{4}{24}$, or $\frac{1}{6}$
2. C and odd $\frac{4}{24}$, or $\frac{1}{6}$
3. B and 1 $\frac{2}{24}$, or $\frac{1}{12}$
4. A and even $\frac{4}{24}$, or $\frac{1}{6}$
5. C or B, and 3 $\frac{4}{24}$, or $\frac{1}{6}$
6. A or C, and 4 $\frac{3}{24}$, or $\frac{1}{8}$
7. not B, and 3 $\frac{6}{24}$, or $\frac{1}{4}$
8. B or C, and not 4 $\frac{10}{24}$, or $\frac{5}{12}$

Chapter 20 Extra Practice **551**

CHAPTER SUMMARY TEST

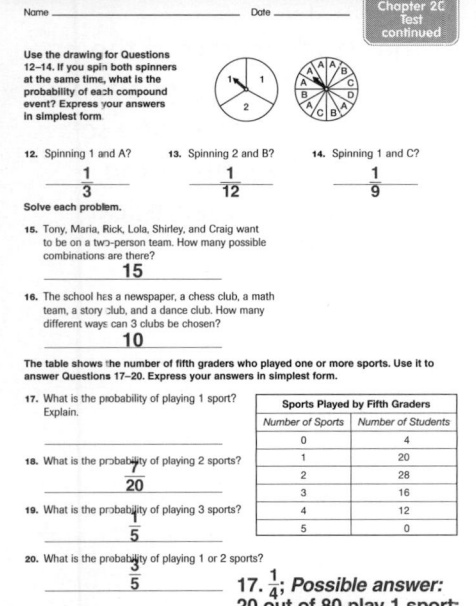

Additional Answers

Chapter 20

Lesson 1, pp. 528–529

15. *Possible answer:* You could make an organized list, or a tree diagram, or multiply, $5 \times 2 \times 4$.

20. *Possible answer:* Made an organized list; made a tree diagram; multiplied 2 and 3; 6 different ways

Lesson 2, pp. 530–531

10. Yes; *Possible answer:* Since the number of red and blue sectors is equal to the number of green sectors, each player has the same chance of winning.

11. Check students' games and explanations. A good answer should include the following points:
   • If the game is fair, players are equally likely to win.
   • If the game is unfair, one player is more likely to win than another.

Daily Review/Test Prep, p. 531

13–20. *Possible answers given:*

13. $\frac{2}{8}, \frac{3}{12}, \frac{4}{16}, \frac{5}{20}$
14. $\frac{5}{6}, \frac{15}{18}, \frac{20}{24}, \frac{25}{30}$
15. $\frac{4}{6}, \frac{6}{9}, \frac{8}{12}, \frac{10}{15}$
16. $\frac{4}{5}, \frac{8}{10}, \frac{12}{15}, \frac{16}{20}$
17. $\frac{6}{16}, \frac{9}{24}, \frac{12}{32}, \frac{15}{40}$
18. $\frac{3}{5}, \frac{9}{15}, \frac{12}{20}, \frac{15}{25}$
19. $\frac{10}{2}, \frac{20}{4}, \frac{25}{5}, \frac{30}{6}$
20. $\frac{7}{3}, \frac{21}{9}, \frac{28}{12}, \frac{35}{15}$

Lesson 3, pp. 532–535

Math Reasoning

4. The probability of spinning any color on the spinner is **1**. If you subtract the probability of spinning one color from 1, you get the probability of spinning any other color.

Lesson 5, pp. 540–543

6. *Answers will vary. Possible answer:* The theoretical probability of spinning red is $\frac{1}{4}$. Since the experimental probability of $\frac{1}{5}$ is close to the theoretical probability of $\frac{1}{4}$, the results are close to what you might expect.

7. Check students' work. Experimental probability should get closer to theoretical probability as the number of trials increases.

Lesson 6, pp. 544–545

Explain Your Thinking: *Possible answer:* Made a tree diagram or organized list, counted the favorable outcomes (tails and 1, 3, or 5), then compared the number of favorable outcomes with the number if possible outcomes.

22. $\frac{1}{4}$; made a tree diagram or an organized list, counted the favorable outcomes, and compared the number of favorable outcomes with the number of possible outcomes.

See Additional Answers on p. T88.

Probability 551

Science Connection

PURPOSE

Students compare theoretical and experimental probabilities in the context of genetics.

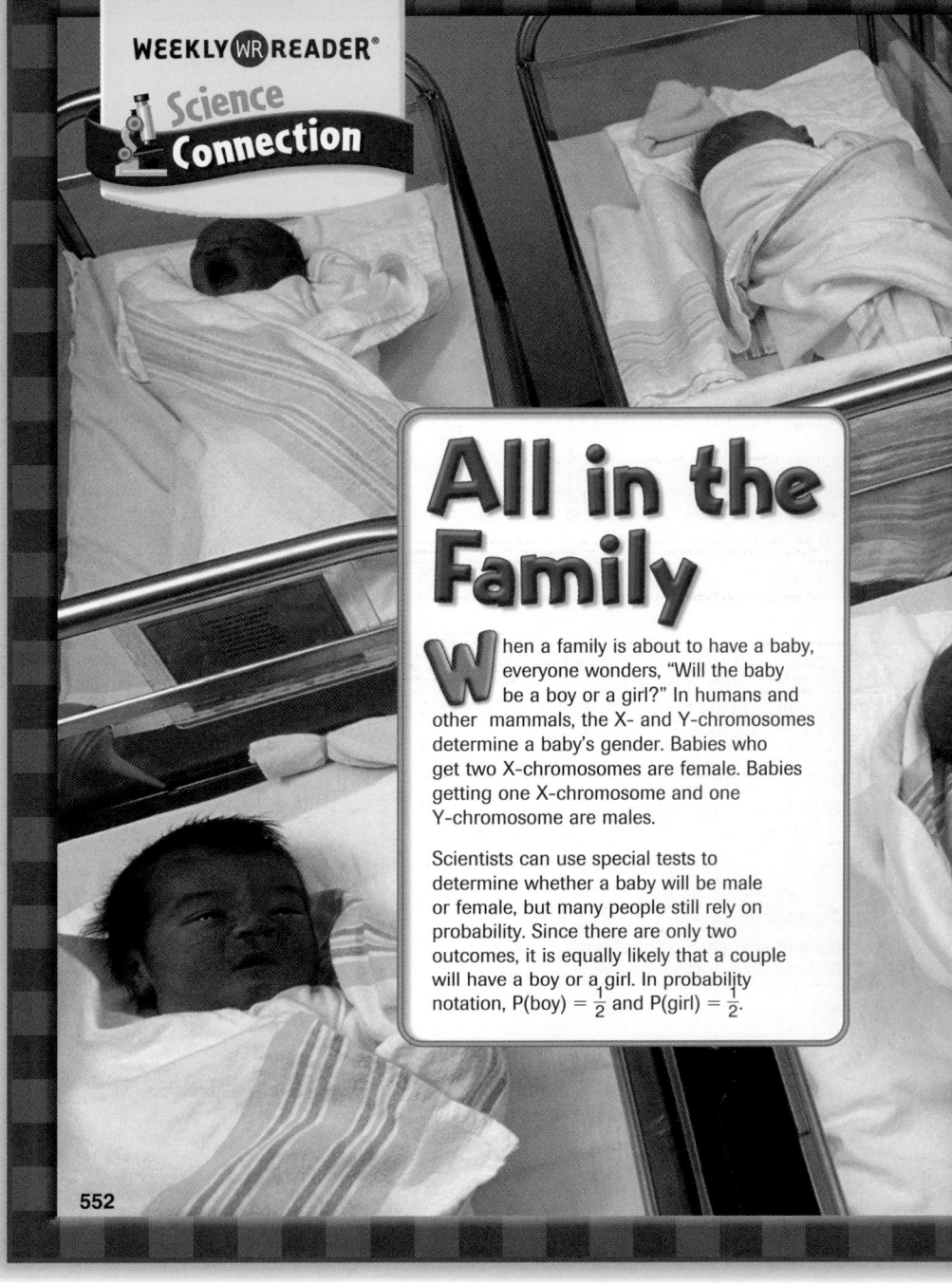

WEEKLY WR READER®
Science Connection

All in the Family

When a family is about to have a baby, everyone wonders, "Will the baby be a boy or a girl?" In humans and other mammals, the X- and Y-chromosomes determine a baby's gender. Babies who get two X-chromosomes are female. Babies getting one X-chromosome and one Y-chromosome are males.

Scientists can use special tests to determine whether a baby will be male or female, but many people still rely on probability. Since there are only two outcomes, it is equally likely that a couple will have a boy or a girl. In probability notation, $P(\text{boy}) = \frac{1}{2}$ and $P(\text{girl}) = \frac{1}{2}$.

552

Using The Science Connection

- For Exercise 1, have students make tree diagrams to show all the combinations for 2 genders in 4 successive births. Have students identify the unique birth order for each of the 6 combinations. (BBGG, BGBG, BGGB, GBBG, GBGB, GGBB)

- As students perform the experimental trials in Exercise 2, ask them if the experimental results will include all sixteen outcomes. (probably not) Remind them that the chance of reproducing the experimental probability increases with the number of trials.

- For Exercise 4, suggest that students record the survey results for families with 1 child in one table, families with 2 children in another table, and so on. Then they can make a tree diagram of the possible outcomes and compare the theoretical probability to their survey results.

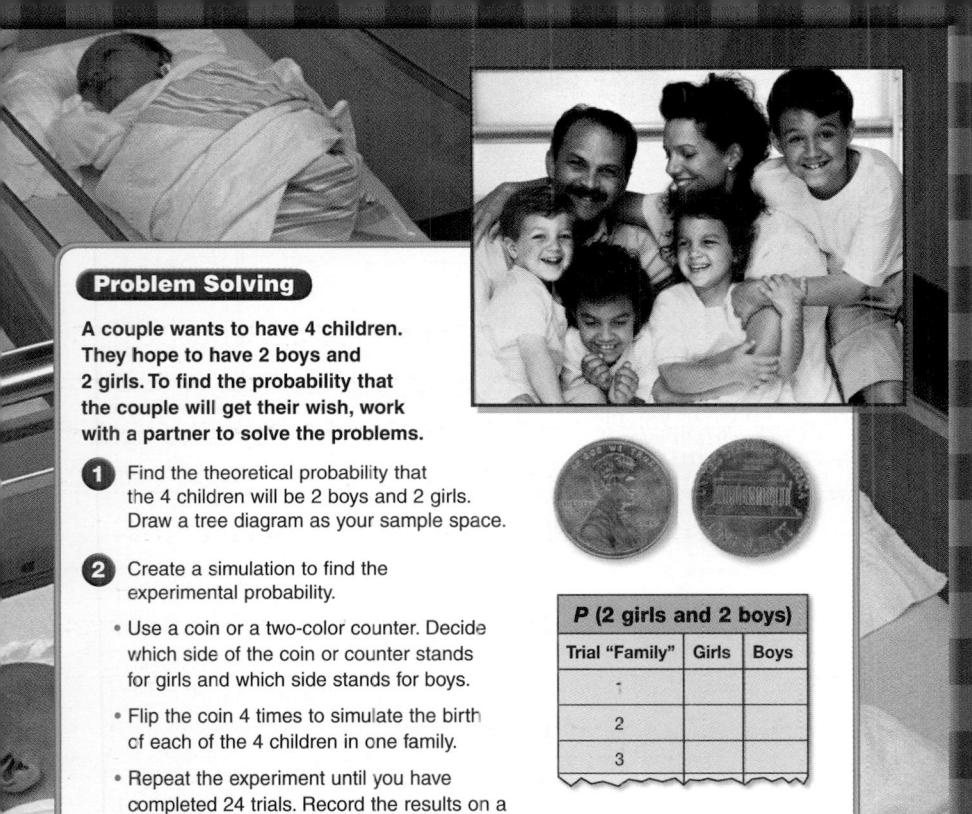

Problem Solving

A couple wants to have 4 children. They hope to have 2 boys and 2 girls. To find the probability that the couple will get their wish, work with a partner to solve the problems.

1 Find the theoretical probability that the 4 children will be 2 boys and 2 girls. Draw a tree diagram as your sample space.

2 Create a simulation to find the experimental probability.

- Use a coin or a two-color counter. Decide which side of the coin or counter stands for girls and which side stands for boys.

- Flip the coin 4 times to simulate the birth of each of the 4 children in one family.

- Repeat the experiment until you have completed 24 trials. Record the results on a recording sheet to show the number of girls and the number of boys in each "family."

- Use your results to find the experimental probability P(2 girls and 2 boys).

3 Compare the results of your experiment with the theoretical probability. Describe any differences.

4 Conduct a survey with a large number of students in your school. Ask for the number of boys and girls in each family, and record each as a trial in a probability experiment. Compare the survey results with results from your coin-tossing experiment.

P (2 girls and 2 boys)

Trial "Family"	Girls	Boys
1		
2		
3		

Technology

Visit *Education Place* at eduplace.com/kids/mw/ to learn more about this topic.

Additional Answers

Unit 7

Unit Test, p. 555

32. *Check graphs.*

Favorite Lunch

Sandwiches 25%
Pizza 50%
Salad 25%

Decision Making

1. Soccer, Baseball, Volleyball, Basketball, Football

2. *Possible answer:* I wrote each of the known values as a fraction. Then I found the missing value for soccer by subtracting the sum of the known values from 1. Then I ordered the values from greatest to least.

Performance Assessment, p. 556

Task 2

a. spinning 2 and spinning 3

b. spinning 1

c. *Possible answer:* spinning 1 or 4

d. *Possible answer:* Spinning a number greater than 4, $P(>4)$, has a probability of 0 because it is an impossible outcome on this spinner. Spinning a number less than 5, $P(<5)$, has a probability of 1 because it is a certain outcome on this spinner.

e. *Possible answer:* tossing a 1 and coin landing heads

Enrichment, p. 557

3. Bean Bag Toss Game; *Answers will vary. Possible answer:* I wrote the question, "4 is what percent of 20?"; then I set up the equation $4 = \frac{n}{100} \times \frac{20}{1}$; and I solved for n: $4 = \frac{n}{5}$; $n = 20$.

4. Ring Toss Game, Balloon-Dart Game, Bean Bag Toss Game, Face Painting, Fishing Pond Game

5. 1 student; *Answers will vary. Possible answer:* I added the existing percents and subtracted the sum from 100%. Then I found 5% of 20.

6. *Answers will vary. Check problems.*

Weekly Reader, Science Connection, p. 553

1. $\frac{3}{8}$;

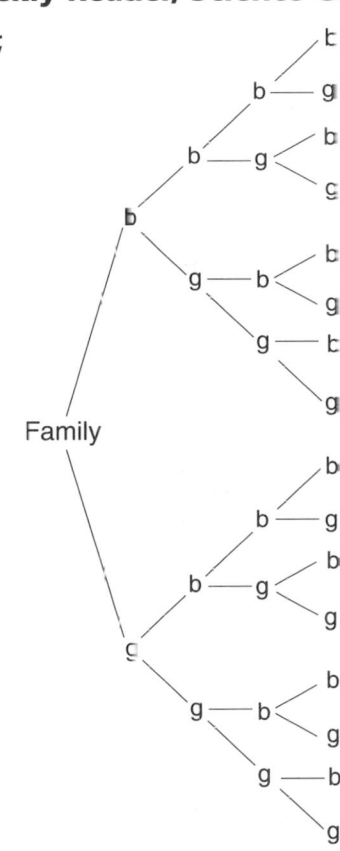

PURPOSE

This test provides an informal assessment of the Unit 7 objectives.

Unit Test Items 1–33

To assign a numerical grade for this Unit Test, use 3 points for each test item.

Customizing Your Instruction

For students who have not yet mastered these objectives, you can use the **Reteaching Resources** listed in the chart below. *Ways to Success* is Houghton Mifflin's Intervention program, available in CD-ROM and blackline master formats.

 **Unit 7 Test**

VOCABULARY

Write *true* or *false* for each. Rewrite each false statement to make it true.

1. A rate is a ratio that compares different units. **true**

2. A probability shows that two ratios are equal.
false; A proportion shows that two ratios are equal.

3. Similar figures have the same shape. **true**

4. An event that has a probability of 0 is a certain event.
false; An event that has a probability of 1 is a certain event.

Vocabulary
ratio
rate
percent
proportion
probability
certain event
similar figures
impossible event

CONCEPTS AND SKILLS

Write each ratio three different ways. (Chapter 18)

5. 2 trucks to 5 cars   **2 to 5; 2:5; $\frac{2}{5}$**

6. 9 rectangles to 5 triangles   **9 to 5; 9:5; $\frac{9}{5}$**

Find the unit rate. (Chapter 18)

7. 90 miles in 15 minutes   **6 mi/min**

8. $105 in 7 hours   **$15/h**

Find the missing term in each proportion. (Chapter 18)

9. $\frac{n}{5} = \frac{6}{30}$ **n = 1**

10. $\frac{4}{6} = \frac{6}{n}$ **n = 9**

11. $\frac{10}{8} = \frac{n}{12}$ **n = 15**

A blueprint has a scale of $\frac{1}{4}$ inch:1 foot. Find *n*. (Chapter 18)

12. *n* inches represent 7 feet   **$1\frac{3}{4}$ inches**

13. $\frac{1}{2}$ inch represents *n* feet   **2 feet**

Copy and complete the table. Write each fraction in simplest form. (Chapter 19)

	Fraction	Decimal	Percent	
14.	■	■	30%	$\frac{3}{10}$; 0.3
15.	■	0.8	■	$\frac{4}{5}$; 80%
16.	$\frac{9}{20}$	■	■	0.45; 45%

Order each set from the greatest to the least part of a unit. (Chapter 19)

17. $\frac{1}{3}$, 0.25, 13%   **$\frac{1}{3}$, 0.25, 13%**

18. $\frac{5}{8}$, 0.65, 63%   **0.65, 63%, $\frac{5}{8}$**

Estimate each percent of a number. (Chapter 19)   **19–20. *Estimates may vary.***

19. 11% of 59   **6**

20. 48% of 81   **40**

Solve by writing each percent as a fraction or as a decimal. (Chapter 19)

21. 15% of 80   **12**

22. 75% of 64   **48**

23. 2% of 300   **6**

554

Reteaching Support

Unit Test Item pp. 554–555	Forms A & B		Unit Objectives Tested	TE Pages	Use These Reteaching Resources
1, 5–8	1–4	7A	Read, write, and use ratios, equivalent ratios, and rates.	484A–485, 488A–491	Reteach Resources and *Ways to Success*, 18.1, 18.3
2–3, 9–13	5–7	7B	Identify proportions and use them to solve problems, including similar figures and scale drawings.	492A–499	Reteach Resources and *Ways to Success*, 18.4–18.5
14–18	8–11	7C	Use ratios to write percents; relate and compare percents, decimals, fractions, and mixed numbers.	508A–513	Reteach Resources and *Ways to Success*, 19.2–19.3
19–23	12–15	7D	Find a percent of a number.	514A–519	Reteach Resources and *Ways to Success*, 19.4–19.5
24–25	16–18	7E	Determine combinations.	528A–529	Reteach Resources and *Ways to Success*, 20.1
4, 26–29	19–22	7F	Find the theoretical or experimental probability of single and compound events.	530A–535, 544A–547	Reteach Resources and *Ways to Success*, 20.2–20.3, 20.6
30–33	23–25	7G	Solve problems, using skills and strategies.	492A–495, 520A–523, 528A–529, 532A–539	Reteach Resources and *Ways to Success*, 18.4, 19.6, 20.1, 20.3–20.4

You have one choice from each category. Find the total number of possible combinations. (Chapter 20)

24. 3 styles, 4 colors **12** 25. 7 flavors, 3 toppings **21**

Use the spinner. Express the probability of each event in simplest form. (Chapter 20)

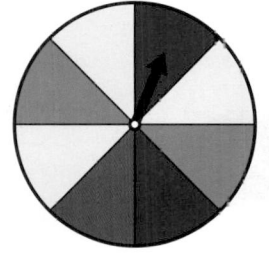

26. red $\frac{1}{4}$ 27. not yellow or green $\frac{3}{8}$

Suppose you flip a penny and roll a 1–6 number cube. Find the probability of each compound event. (Chapter 20)

28. heads and 5 $\frac{1}{12}$ 29. tails and an even number $\frac{1}{4}$

 **PROBLEM SOLVING**

30. At Produce Patch market, a bag of 20 large green apples sells for $5.99. At Fruit Fresh market a bag of 30 large green apples sells for $7.59. Which is the better buy? **30 for $7.59**

31. Tad wants to buy 3 T-shirts in different colors. The available colors are blue, red, yellow, brown, and black. How many different ways can he choose 3 different colors of T-shirts? **10**

32. The school cafeteria surveyed 160 students about favorite lunches. There were 40 votes for salad, 80 votes for pizza, and 40 votes for sandwiches. Create a circle graph to display these data as percents.

33. Use the data from Problem 32. Suppose you interviewed a student from the school in which the favorite lunch survey was conducted. What is the probability that the student prefers sandwiches for lunch? $\frac{1}{4}$

Decision Making
Extended Response

See Additional Answers on page 553.

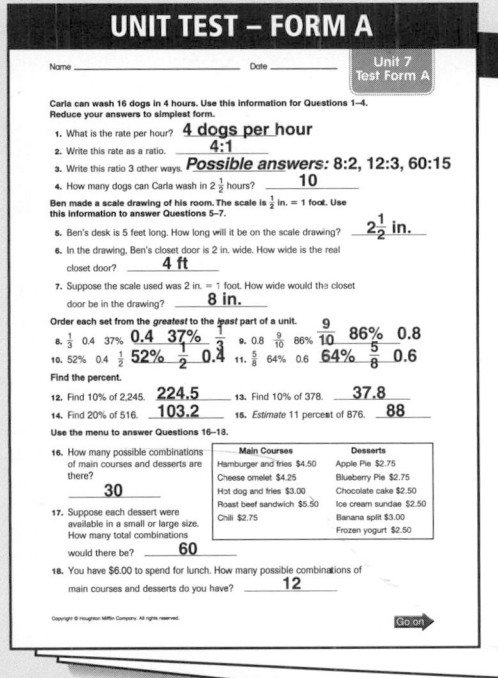

Which sport is most important in our school sports program? Please check only one choice.

☐ Baseball   ☐ Basketball   ☐ Volleyball   ☐ Soccer   ☐ Football

Task Students used the survey form above to collect data. They plan to present the results to the school athletic committee.

Use the information at the right. Arrange the sports in order from first to last choice. Explain your thinking.

Information You Need
- $\frac{1}{5}$ chose baseball.
- The probability that a student voted for basketball was $\frac{1}{8}$.
- 0.12 chose football.
- 18% chose volleyball.
- The remaining students chose soccer.

See Additional Answers on page 553.   **Unit 7 Test 555**

 Assessment Options

Formal Tests for this unit are also provided in the Unit Resource Folder.

- **Unit 7 Open Response Test (Form A)**
- **Unit 7 Multiple Choice Test (Form B)**

 Performance Assessment

You may want to use the Performance Assessment instead of, or in addition to, the Unit Test. Performance Assessment tasks for this unit are on Student Book page 556.

Adequate Yearly Progress Assessment Guide

Use the *End of Grade Test Prep Assessment Guide* to help familiarize your students with the format of standardized tests and to monitor progress.

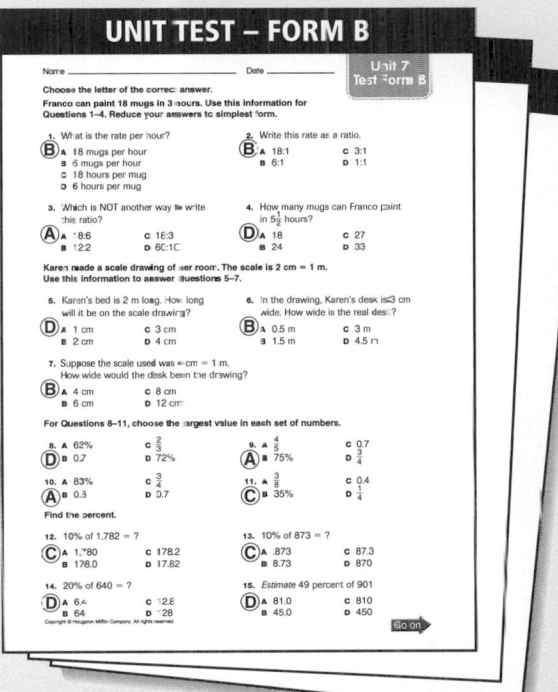

Unit 7 Tests

See pages 556A–556B for answers.

Ratio, Proportion, Percent, and Probability 555

Unit Test Answers: Form A

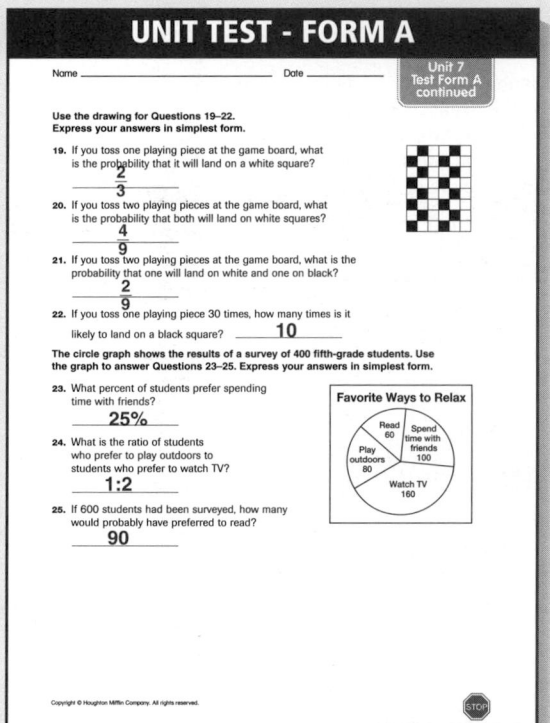

UNIT TEST - FORM A

Name _____ Date _____

**Unit 7
Test Form A**

Carla can wash 16 dogs in 4 hours. Use this information for Questions 1–4. Reduce your answers to simplest form.

1. What is the rate per hour? **4 dogs per hour**

2. Write this rate as a ratio. **4:1**

3. Write this ratio 3 other ways. **Possible answers: 8:2, 12:3, 60:15**

4. How many dogs can Carla wash in $2\frac{1}{2}$ hours? **10**

Ben made a scale drawing of his room. The scale is $\frac{1}{2}$ in. = 1 foot. Use this information to answer Questions 5–7.

5. Ben's desk is 5 feet long. How long will it be on the scale drawing? **$2\frac{1}{2}$ in.**

6. In the drawing, Ben's closet door is 2 in. wide. How wide is the real closet door? **4 ft**

7. Suppose the scale used was 2 in. = 1 foot. How wide would the closet door be in the drawing? **8 in.**

Order each set from the *greatest* to the *least* part of a unit.

8. $\frac{1}{3}$ 0.4   37%   **0.4   37% $\frac{1}{3}$**

9. 0.8 $\frac{9}{10}$ 86%   **$\frac{9}{10}$ 86%   0.8**

10. 52%   0.4 $\frac{1}{2}$ **52% $\frac{1}{2}$ 0.4**

11. $\frac{5}{8}$ 64%   0.6   **64% $\frac{5}{8}$ 0.6**

Find the percent.

12. Find 10% of 2,245. **224.5**

13. Find 10% of 378. **37.8**

14. Find 20% of 516. **103.2**

15. *Estimate* 11 percent of 876. **88**

Use the menu to answer Questions 16–18.

16. How many possible combinations of main courses and desserts are there? **30**

Main Courses	Desserts
Hamburger and fries $4.50	Apple Pie $2.75
Cheese omelet $4.25	Blueberry Pie $2.75
Hot dog and fries $3.00	Chocolate cake $2.50
Roast beef sandwich $5.50	Ice cream sundae $2.50
Chili $2.75	Banana split $3.00
	Frozen yogurt $2.50

17. Suppose each dessert were available in a small or large size. How many total combinations would there be? **60**

18. You have $6.00 to spend for lunch. How many possible combinations of main courses and desserts do you have? **12**

Go on

UNIT TEST - FORM A

Name _____ Date _____

**Unit 7
Test Form A
continued**

Use the drawing for Questions 19–22. Express your answers in simplest form.

19. If you toss one playing piece at the game board, what is the probability that it will land on a white square? **$\frac{2}{3}$**

20. If you toss two playing pieces at the game board, what is the probability that both will land on white squares? **$\frac{4}{9}$**

21. If you toss two playing pieces at the game board, what is the probability that one will land on white and one on black? **$\frac{2}{9}$**

22. If you toss one playing piece 30 times, how many times is it likely to land on a black square? **10**

The circle graph shows the results of a survey of 400 fifth-grade students. Use the graph to answer Questions 23–25. Express your answers in simplest form.

23. What percent of students prefer spending time with friends? **25%**

24. What is the ratio of students who prefer to play outdoors to students who prefer to watch TV? **1:2**

25. If 600 students had been surveyed, how many would probably have preferred to read? **90**

Favorite Ways to Relax

- Read 60
- Spend time with friends 100
- Play outdoors 80
- Watch TV 160

STOP

Unit Test Answers: Form B

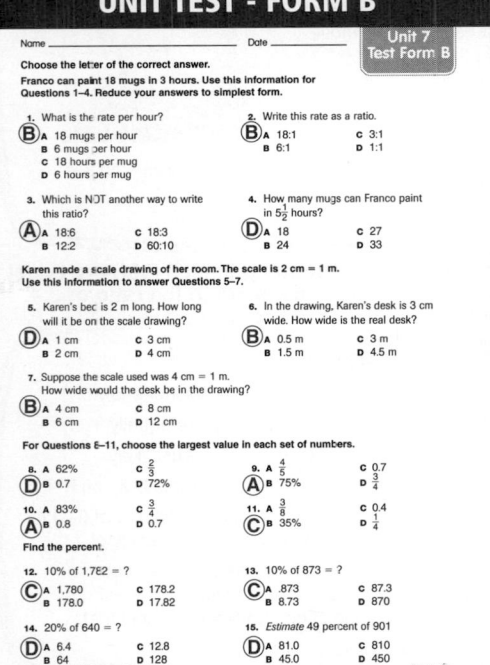

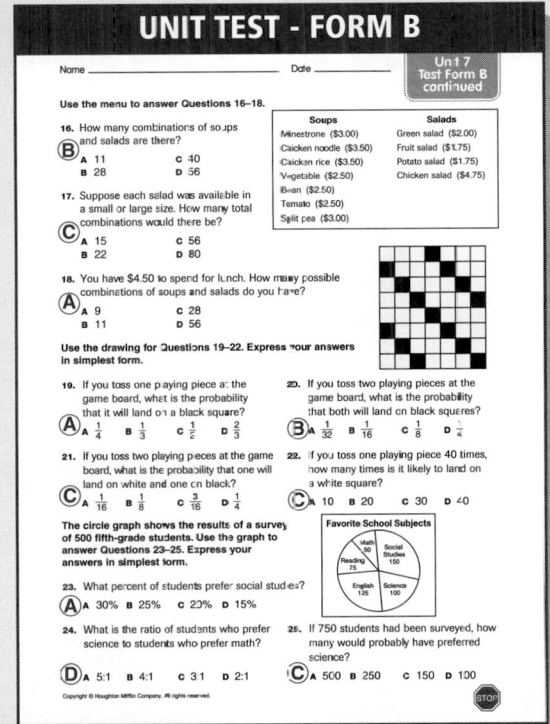

PURPOSE

In these assessments, students should be able to interpret scale drawings, find percents, determine similar figures, and use probability within specified parameters.

Scoring Rubric

4 EXEMPLARY

Fully completes each task, shows an understanding of interpreting scale drawings, of finding a percent, of similarity, of how to name events and probabilities based on specified parameters.

3 PROFICIENT

Shows an understanding of interpreting scale drawings, of finding a percent, and of likelihood of outcomes, but needs help in explaining similarity and in finding a compound event for a probability.

2 ACCEPTABLE

Shows an understanding of interpreting scale drawings, of finding a percent, and of likelihood of outcomes, but does not explain similarity and gives an incorrect compound event for a given probability.

I LIMITED

Shows a lack of understanding by giving incorrect or reversed scale and actual values, by giving an incorrect explanation for similarity, or by giving inaccurate events for given probabilities.

Performance Assessment

TASK 1

A Plant Plan (Chapters 18–19)   b. $\frac{3}{4}$ in. × $\frac{3}{4}$ in.

You are using the plan at the right to design a garden. Use an inch ruler to measure the scale drawing and help you complete this task.   **100 ft × 60 ft**

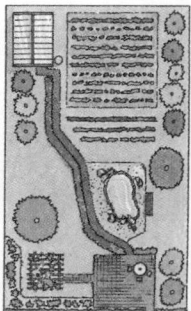

a. What are the actual dimensions of the garden?

b. You need to include a square planting area whose actual sides measure 30 feet. What will be the dimensions of the square in the drawing? *See above.*

c. Suppose you have to design a new garden whose dimensions are 75% of the length and 75% of the width of the garden pictured on the right. What will be the actual dimensions of the new garden? **75 ft × 45 ft**

d. Will the polygon defining the shape of the new garden (in part c) and that of the original garden be similar? Explain.

Scale: $\frac{1}{4}$ inch = 10 feet

d. **Yes; all the corresponding angles (90°) are equal and corresponding sides are in the ratio of 3:4.**

TASK 2

Game Playing (Chapter 20)

You are playing a game with the spinner shown.

a. Name two outcomes that are equally likely.

b. Name the outcome that is least likely.

c. Name an event that has a probability of $\frac{1}{2}$.

d. Name an event that has a probability of 0. Then name an event that has a probability of 1.

e. Another game also has a number cube labeled 1–6. Name a compound event of tossing the cube and flipping a coin that has a probability of $\frac{1}{12}$.

See Additional Answers on page 553.

Self Check
• Did I answer the questions for each task?
• Did I check all my work?

556 Unit 7 Performance Assessment

Task One

Students use a scale drawing to find scale measures and actual measures, find percents of measurements, and explain why figures are similar.

Task Two

Students use a spinner and a number cube to determine the likelihood of various outcomes, and find possible events for given probabilities.

Enrichment: Circle Graphs and Percents

Vote for Fun!

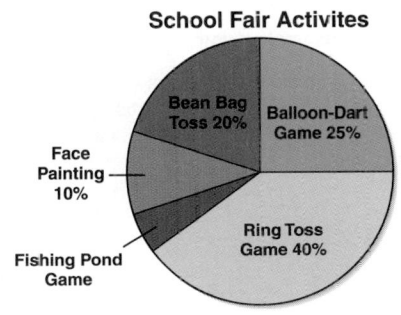

The 20 students in a fifth-grade class wanted to decide on the kind of booth they would have at the school fair. The sections of the circle graph show the percent of the class that voted for each kind of booth.

The graph shows that 25% of the students voted for the Balloon-Dart Game. The figure 25% means $\frac{25}{100}$. You can write 25% as a fraction or as a decimal.

$$25\% = \frac{25}{100} = \frac{1}{4}$$

$$25\% = 0.25$$

School Fair Activites

- Bean Bag Toss 20%
- Balloon-Dart Game 25%
- Face Painting 10%
- Ring Toss Game 40%
- Fishing Pond Game

Try These!

Use the circle graph to solve the problems.

1. Write a fraction for the part of the class that voted for the Ring-Toss Game. How many students does that represent? $\frac{2}{5}$; **8 students**

2. Write a decimal for the part of the class that voted for the Face Painting booth. How many students does that represent? **0.1; 2 students**

3. Which activity received 4 votes? Explain how you found your answer.

4. Arrange all the games in order from greatest to least number of votes.

5. **Represent** Find the number of students who voted for the Fishing Pond Game. Explain how you found your answer.

6. **Write Your Own** Create and solve a problem using the data in the graph. The problem should involve working with percents.

3–6. **See Additional Answers on page 553.**

Unit 7 Enrichment **557**

PURPOSE

This page asks students to use their knowledge of percents to analyze a circle graph and to use the data to solve problems.

Using the Enrichment Activity

- This lesson follows up on the skills that students learned in the lessons in Chapter 19. While they found the percents to be represented on the circle graph in Lesson 6 (Problem-Solving Application: Use Circle Graphs) by first writing ratios, here they are asked to derive the ratios from the percents shown on the graph. Students will also draw indirectly on their knowledge of proportion.

- Ask students to reiterate how to write a ratio given any percent. **What number is always used as the second term? Why?** (100; because *percent* means *compared to 100*)

- For Exercises 1–3 of *Try These*, have students explain which operations they used to find their answers. For example, in Exercise 1, students use division to find equivalent ratios ($40\% = \frac{40}{100} = \frac{2}{5}$) and multiplication to find the number of students. ($20 \times \frac{2}{5} = 8$)

- Have students explain the steps they used to solve the multi-step problem in Exercise 5.

Cumulative Test Prep

▶ Practice Test

PURPOSE

This page will familiarize students with the multiple-choice and open-response formats of many standardized state tests.

 Cumulative Test Prep Practice

Solve Problems 1–10.

Test-Taking Tip

When a test question involves an equation with variables, you can check your answer by substituting answer choices for the variable in the given equation.

Look at the example below.

Last week, Ivan worked 21 hours and Jeff worked 34 hours. In this equation, *h* represents the difference in the number of hours they worked.

$$34 - h = 21$$

What is the value of *h*?

A 3   C 17

Ⓑ 13   D 23

THINK

Substitute each value in the left side of the equation:

A 34 − 3
B 34 − 13
C 34 − 17
D 34 − 23

Then simplify, and compare the result with 21. The difference between 34 and 13 is 21, so the answer is **B**.

558   For more Test-Taking Tips, see pages xxii–xxv.

Multiple Choice

1. Kendra earned $40 and Lenny earned $19. In this equation, *n* represents the number of dollars more than Lenny that Kendra earned.

$$19 + n = 40$$

What is the value of *n*?

A 11   Ⓑ 21   C 31   D 59

(Chapter 2, Lesson 5)

2. Twenty-four ride tickets were shared equally by some students. Each student received 4 tickets. In this equation, *s* represents the number of students.

$$24 \div s = 4$$

What is the value of *s*?

F 2   Ⓖ 6   H 20   J 28

(Chapter 4, Lesson 7)

3. Mona drove 120 miles at a speed of 40 miles per hour. In this equation, *t* represents the number of hours she drove.

$$120 = 40 \times t$$

What is the value of *t*?

Ⓐ 3   B 30   C 80   D 160

(Chapter 4, Lesson 7)

4. Nina completed 12 more laps than Otis. Otis completed 9 laps. In this equation, *n* represents the number of laps Nina completed.

$$n - 12 = 9$$

What is the value of *n*?

F 3   Ⓖ 21   H 31   J 41

(Chapter 2, Lesson 5)

Test-Taking TIPS

Review the test-taking tips with students before they begin the test. Discuss with students some of the ways they can check their work.

● Remind students to draw pictures to help them visualize and solve problems such as that in Item 7. Encourage students to reread the question after making their drawing to ensure the drawing reflects the information given.

● Encourage students to read questions carefully and to think about what is being asked. For example, In Item 8, they could underline "number of square inches" to focus them on finding the surface area, not volume, of the box.

5. Tracey collected these data on the number of calories consumed by classmates at lunch.

   640, 570, 710, 640, 720, 690, 700

   What is the median of her data?

   690   (Chapter 8, Lesson 2)

6. Stuart has a piece of wood that is 135 inches long. How many blocks, each 1.5 inches long, can he cut from the wood?

   90   (Chapter 14, Lesson 7)

7. Paolo wants to fence in a square patch of basil plants. The patch measures 500 centimeters on a side. How many meters of fencing will he need?

   20   (Chapter 16, Lesson 1)

8. Rosa wants to cover this gift box with wrapping paper. What is the least number of square inches of wrapping paper she'll need?

   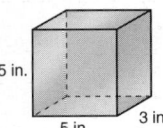
   5 in.
   5 in.   3 in.

   110   (Chapter 17, Lesson 4)

9. The original price of a DVD was $50. Hugo bought the DVD on sale and paid 75% of the original price. How much did Hugo pay for the DVD?

   $37.50   (Chapter 19, Lesson 5)

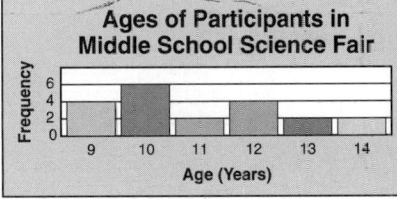

Ages of Participants in Middle School Science Fair

Frequency

Age (Years)

10. Use the bar graph above to answer the following questions.

   A How many students were at least 11 years old?   **10**

   B How many students were under 12 years old?   **12**

   C What is the mode of the data?   **10**

   D What is the median of the data? Explain how you found the answer.

   E Find the mean of the data to the nearest whole number. Explain how you found the answer.

   (Chapter 7, Lesson 2 and Chapter 8, Lesson 2)

D **10.5;** *Possible answer:* **There are a total of 20 data items so the median is the average of the tenth and eleventh items. The average of 10 and 11 is 10.5.**

E **11;** *Answers will vary.* **Find the total of the ages (9 × 4 + 10 × 6 + 11 × 2 + 12 × 4 + 13 × 2 + 14 × 2 = 220) and divide by 20; 220 ÷ 20 = 11.**

Test Prep on the Net
Check out *Education Place* at
eduplace.com/kids/mw/
for test prep practice.

Unit 7 Cumulative Test Prep **559**

Test-Taking Vocabulary

- Explain that students can benefit from reviewing words that appear often in test questions. Have them make flash cards with a word on one side and a definition and an example on the other for the following: *represents, equation, square inches, variable, percent, mode, median,* and *mean.*

- Encourage them to add new or unfamiliar words to the set each time they encounter such a word.

National and state tests might also use these words to indicate *value of:*

- equal to

IT TAKES TIME!

PURPOSE

To provide students with an opportunity to make a circle graph on a computer by inputting data into a spreadsheet.

It Takes Time!

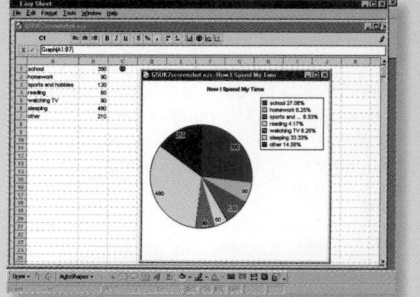

How do you spend your time each day? Estimate the number of minutes you spend in one day on each of the following categories: school, homework, sports and hobbies, reading, watching TV, sleeping, and other. Make sure you have a total of 24 hours.

You can make a circle graph of your data using Easy Sheet.

- Enter the categories in column A.
- Enter the number of minutes you spend on each category in column B.
- Click on cell A1 and drag to cell B7 to highlight all the cells with data.
- Click [●].
- Double click anywhere on the graph.
- Click on the tab marked **Labels**. Enter a title. Click the box next to **Label Data**. Click **OK**.

Use the graph you created to answer Problems 1–5.   *Answers will vary. Check student's work.*

1. On which activity do you spend the most amount of time? the least amount of time?

2. What percentage of your day is spent on things other than school and homework?

3. Suppose you added eating as another category. How would it affect your graph?

4. Look at the legend. Round each percent to the nearest whole number and then write as a ratio in simplest form.

5. Write the ratio of the number of minutes spent on each activity to 1,440, the number of minutes in a day. Use a calculator to simplify each ratio. Do these ratios match the ones from Problem 4?

Using Technology Time

- You may want to help students verify that they have a total of 24 hours of activities, written in minutes, before they input their data into Easy Sheet.

- **Why do you click and drag from cell A1 through cell B7 to create a circle graph?** (The data in those cells are used to make the circle graph.)

- **Why is a circle graph made with a computer more accurate than one made by hand?** (The computer can accurately represent the divisions of the circle graph to the nearest minute, but a circle graph made by hand would most likely not be as accurate and would be more prone to error.)

- Have students answer the questions about the circle graphs.

Vocabulary Wrap-Up for **Unit 7**

WEEKLY WR READER
Activity Almanac
See page 684 for the activity for this unit.

Look back at the big ideas and vocabulary in this unit.

Big Ideas

You can use equivalent fractions or cross products to find the missing term in a proportion.

The theoretical probability of an event is the ratio of the number of favorable outcomes to the total number of outcomes.

e • Glossary
Key Vocabulary

proportion
ratio
probability

1. An event has a probability of 1 when it is certain to happen.

Math Conversations

2. Change 25% to a fraction and multiply by 60, or change 25% to a decimal and multiply by 60. The answer is 15.

Use your new vocabulary to discuss these big ideas.

1. Explain what it means when an event has a probability of 1. **See above.**

2. Explain how to find 25% of 60 in two different ways. **See above.**

3. Explain how to find the missing term in this proportion. $\frac{10}{n} = \frac{15}{9}$. **See below.**

4. Explain how to find the probability of this compound event: tails when tossing a coin and rolling a number less than 5 on a 1–6 number cube. **See below.**

5. **Write About It** Look for examples of percents in newspapers, magazines, and on television. Make a list of the kinds of articles that use percents. Tell why percents are used in these articles. **Answers will vary.**

3. Either use equivalent fractions or cross multiply. $n = 6$

4. Make a tree diagram and write the ratio of the favorable outcomes to total possible outcomes; $\frac{4}{12}$ or $\frac{1}{3}$.

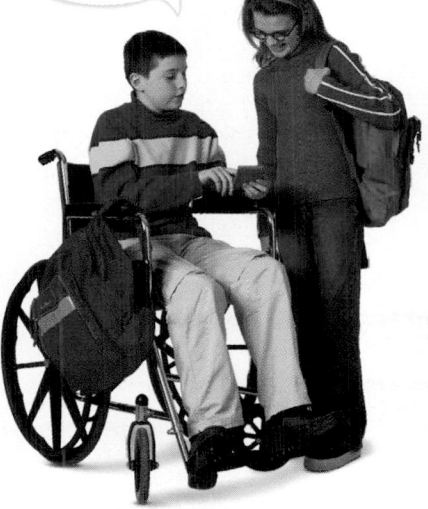

8 percent of the class likes brussel sprouts.

You can also write that as $\frac{8}{100}$ or 0.08

Unit 7 Vocabulary Wrap-Up **561**

Wrap Up The Unit Project

- Have students who are tracking the same weather persons compare data and report the results of their work to the class in terms of ratios and percents.

- After combining results, ask students to discuss how closely the results compare with theoretical probability.

- Ask if they think their results might be different in another month or season. Have them explain their thinking.

Using the Vocabulary Wrap-Up

Purpose: Use this page to encourage students to use math vocabulary to talk about the important concepts they have learned in this unit.

Big Ideas and Key Vocabulary

Review and discuss with students the Big Ideas of this unit using the Key Vocabulary terms *proportion*, *ratio*, and *probability*.

Math Conversations

Have students work together in small groups to discuss Exercises 1–4. Check to see whether individual students understand the key concepts and are able to use the math vocabulary correctly. Clear up any misunderstandings students may have. After students have discussed the exercises in small groups, continue the conversation as a whole class. Have volunteers from each group share what their group talked about.

Write About It Encourage students to look in the financial sections of newspapers and magazines for examples of percents. Make a list of the sections where students found the most examples.

Ratio, Proportion, Percent, and Probability   **561**

UNIT 8

UNIT 8 ALGEBRA, INTEGERS, AND COORDINATE GRAPHING

562A

Assessment System

Assess Prior Knowledge

Check whether students understand the prerequisite concepts and skills.

- **REVIEWING VOCABULARY:** Unit Opener
- **CHAPTER PRETESTS:** PE pp. 565, 585, 609 (Unit Resource Folder or *Ways to Success* CD-ROM/Kit)
- **WARM-UP ACTIVITY:** Found on the third page of TE lesson.

Ongoing Assessment

Monitor whether students are acquiring new concepts and skills.

- **PROBLEM OF THE DAY:** First page of every TE lesson
- **QUICK REVIEW:** First page of every TE lesson
- **LESSON QUIZ:** First page of every TE lesson
- **COMMON ERROR:** TE Lessons 21.2, 21.4, 21.5; 22.1–22.2, 22.5; 23.2–23.3, 23.5
- **QUICK CHECK** PE pp. 581, 595, 605, 625
- **DAILY REVIEW • TEST PREP:** PE pp. 570, 577, 587, 589, 600, 613, 615, 618

 Test Prep and Practice

Help students prepare for state and standardized tests.

- **DAILY REVIEW • TEST PREP:** PE pp. 570, 577, 587, 589, 600, 613, 615, 618
- **DAILY TEST PREP:** TE Lessons 21.1–21.5, 22.1–22.6, and 23.1–23.5
- **PROBLEM SOLVING TEST PREP:** PE p. 575
- **CUMULATIVE TEST PREP:** PE pp. 634–635
- **READING TEST QUESTIONS: UNIT OPENER:** PE p. 563
- **TEST PREP ON THE NET:** eduplace.com/kids/mw
- **TEST TAKING STRATEGIES:** eduplace.com/math/mw

Summary Assessment

Assess student mastery of new concepts and skills.

- **CHAPTER TEST**
  - ✔ PE pp. 582, 606, 626
  - ✔ Unit Resource Folder
- **UNIT TEST:**
  - ✔ PE pp. 630–631
  - ✔ Form A, Unit Resource Folder
  - ✔ Form B, Unit Resource Folder

Student Self-Assessment

Allow students to evaluate their own understanding.

- **EXPLAIN YOUR THINKING:** PE pp. 569, 577, 579, 586, 588, 599, 611, 615, 617, 624
- **VOCABULARY WRAP UP:** PE p. 637

Performance Assessment

Evaluate students' ability to use mathematics in real-world situations.

- **PERFORMANCE ASSESSMENT:** PE p. 632
- **WRITE ABOUT IT • TALK ABOUT IT:** in all Hands-On lessons
- **DECISION MAKING:** End of Unit Test

 Technology Options

Use computer-based assessment to make testing and reporting easier.

- **WAYS TO ASSESS** (CD-ROM, LAN, or Web spiral review and test creation, administration, scoring, and report generation)
- **LEARNER PROFILE** (observations, evaluations, and reports from your handheld or desktop computer)

Reaching All Learners

Resources	On Level Students	Extra Support Students	English Learners	Inclusion/ Special Needs	Advanced Learners	Mathematically Promising
Student Editions						
Building Vocabulary	●	●	●	●	●	●
Different Ways Instruction ✱	●	●	●	●	●	●
Guided Practice ✱	●	●	●	●	○	○
MathTracks MP3 Audio CD 💿	●	●	●	●	○	○
Teacher's Editions						
Building Vocabulary Strategies	●	●	●	●	●	○
Teacher Support	●	●	●	●	●	●
Intervention Activities	○	●	●	●	○	○
Other Resources						
Chapter Challenges	○				●	●
Combination Classroom Guide	●	●	●	●	●	●
English Learners Handbook	○	○	●	○		
Ways to Success CD-ROM 💿	○	●	●	●		

KEY   ● **Highly Appropriate**   ○ **Appropriate**   ✱ **Scaffolded Instruction**

Documenting Adequate Yearly Progress

National Test Correlation

UNIT 8 Objectives		ITBS	Terra Nova (CTBS)	CAT	SAT	MAT
8A	Write and solve equations.		●	●	●	●
8B	Use functions and function tables to solve equations.	●	●	●	●	●
8C	Compare and order integers, and find the absolute value of integers.	●				
8D	Add and subtract integers.			●		
8E	Graph ordered pairs in the four quadrants of the coordinate plane.	●	●		●	●
8F	Complete functions tables using integers and graph a line in the coordinate plane.		●		●	●
8G	Identify and describe transformations on the coordinate plane.		●		●	
8H	Solve problems, using skills and strategies.	●	●	●	●	●

Activities for Reaching All Learners

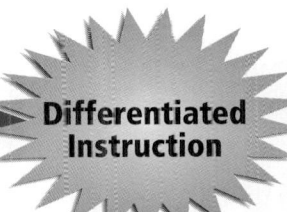

Differentiated Instruction

Polishing Prerequisite Skills

Materials: number line from ⁻15 to 15, 2 number cubes (each a different color), 2 different color counters

Students work in pairs. One color cube represents a negative number. The other color cube represents a positive number. Each student starts on 0. One student rolls both cubes and moves his or her counter to the right (positive number) from 0, and then (negative number) to the left. Second student repeats the process. Game ends when one student lands on ⁻15 or 15.

Repeatable Unit Game

Materials: 1 number cube (1–6) another number cube (1–4)

Each student rolls both number cubes and use the base and the number from the 1–4 cube as the exponent. (For example, 5 on 1–6 cube, and 3 on 1–4 cube would be 5^3.) The student then computes the answer, $5 \times 5 \times 5 = 125$. Students keep a running total for 5 rounds. The highest total wins.

Home School Activity

Materials: copies of a coordinate plane drawn on a piece of graph paper

Students play in pairs. On a coordinate plane that goes from ⁻15 to 15 on both x and y axes, each player secretly draws a line. Players take turns naming coordinate pairs to identify the location of the line on their partner's graph. Game ends when one partner locates 6 points on his or her partner's line.

Unit Vocabulary Activity

Materials: graph paper

Teacher lists vocabulary words on the board. Students work in pairs to make up a crossword puzzle using the vocabulary words. The definitions are the crossword clues.

Remediation

Lessons with MathTracks Audio Support: 21.2, 21.3, 21.4, 21.5, 22.1, 22.5, 23.1, 23.2 (Tracks 2/28–2/35)

Use the MathTracks MP3 Audio CD to help children who need a quick review or extra support for the lesson, to provide children who were absent with a complete lesson presentation, or to assist children with reading difficulties.

Intervention

Ways to Success CD-ROM

Use the Intervention CD-ROM to help children who need extra help with lessons. This software is designed to reteach the lesson objective, provide extra guided and independent practice, and if needed, reteach a key prerequisite skill.

Starting Unit 8

Building Vocabulary

Use the Building Vocabulary pages to be sure that students have adequate understanding and fluency with the unit vocabulary. This provides the key foundation for developing the unit concepts and skills.

Reviewing Vocabulary

- Have students work in small groups to select a vocabulary word(s) they would like to dramatize. Allow students to use objects if necessary. Have the class guess the word(s) being dramatized.
- Have the students brainstorm problems that demonstrate the vocabulary word(s).

Reading Words and Symbols

- Review the examples. Have students create new problems based on a school routine, such as choosing food from the lunch menu.
- Bring in newspapers. Have students use ads, the classified section, or the sports section to create statements of mathematical relationships that use numerals, symbols, words, and a picture. Students should create the problem so that they are solving for the picture. (The picture represents *n*.)

Building Vocabulary

Reviewing Vocabulary

Here are some math vocabulary words that you should know.

function	a rule that pairs each input value *x* with exactly one output value *y*
function table	a table that shows the *x* and corresponding *y* values for a function rule
equation	a mathematical sentence with an equals sign
negative number	a number that is less than zero
inverse operations	a pair of operations that have opposite effects, such as addition and subtraction or multiplication and division
ordered pair	a pair of numbers in which one number is considered to be first and the other number second

Reading Words and Symbols

You can use words, a combination of words and symbols, or symbols to describe relationships between numbers.

Words: Carola, who is fifteen, is three times as old as Donald.

Words and symbols: Carola's age = 3 × Donald's age

Symbols: $15 = 3 \times d$ (with *d* representing Donald's age)

See Additional Answers on page 629.
Use words and symbols or only symbols to describe each situation.

1. Eddie saved seventeen dollars, which is four dollars more than Frieda saved.

2. Ginny completed twelve laps, which is five fewer laps than Hal completed.

3. Thirty-six apples were divided into equal shares. There were four apples in each share.

SPEED LIMIT 55

NEW TOWN 15 MILES

562

Unit Project

- Tell students that code writing dates back to ancient times. Explain that during World War II, the U. S. used the complex Navaho language as the code for sending highly secret messages. Tell them neither Germany nor Japan was able to crack or decode it.
- Group students in pairs. Tell them that they are to develop four different codes based on integers and one based on points on a coordinate plane. They are to write at least one message for each code.
- Help students get started by developing a simple alphabet/numerical code with them. Have them use this code to write a message.
- Use activity found p. 637 to wrap-up the Unit Project.

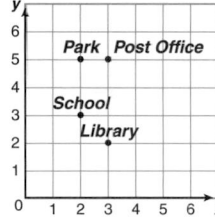
Choose the correct answer for each.

4. Which ordered pair shows the location of the library?

   a. (2, 3)

   b. (3, 2)

   c. (2, 5)

   d. (3, 5)

Location means "position" or "place."

5. Which number is the solution of this equation?

$$m - 34 = 19$$

   a. 15   **c.** 45

   b. 43   **d.** 53

To find the solution of an equation means to find "a number that can be substituted for the variable to make the equation true."

6. Al, Ben, Cara, and Donna scored ⁻4, 3, 2, and ⁻3 points respectively. Who scored the fewest points?

   a. Al   **c.** Cara

   b. Ben   **d.** Donna

Respectively means the scores are in the same order as the names. So, Al scored ⁻4, Ben scored 3, Cara scored 2, and Donna scored ⁻3.

Learning Vocabulary

Watch for these new words in this unit. Write their definitions in your journal.

   integer

   coordinates

   origin

   translation

   reflection

   rotation

Vocabulary
e • Glossary
e • WordGame

Literature Connection

Read "Treasure Hunt" on pages 648–649. Then work with a partner to answer the questions about the story.

Reading Test Questions

- For item 4, have students create a grid that shows the location of items in or on their desks.
- For item 5, have the students rewrite the equation into an addition problem to solve for *m*. Have students create problems to use in a math challenge with a partner.
- For item 6, reorder the scores so that they are ordered from least to greatest. Then list the names in the same order as their scores.

Learning Vocabulary

Go over the list of new words with the class. Help students to pronounce the words correctly and explain that they will learn about these words as they work on this unit. If students are keeping Math Journals, be sure that they enter the words and their definitions as they find them in the unit.

Home-School Connection

To foster home-school communication, *Houghton Mifflin Math* has a Family Letter for every unit. The letters include vocabulary words, worked-out examples, home activities, and literature suggestions.

Each Family Letter is in the Unit Resource Folder. Go to **eduplace.com/math/mw/** to download the letters in English, Spanish, and other languages.

In the Student Book

Literature Connection
Student Book List Selection

You may use the literature connection (Student Book page 648–649, Teachers Edition page T56) at any time during this unit.

Other Literature Connections

Family Math/Plotting Points and Position
By Jean Kerr Stanmark, Virginia Thompson, and Ruth Cossey

Math for Smarty Pants (a Brown Paper School book)
By Marilyn Burns
Illustrated by Martha Weston

Fractals, Googols and Other Mathematical Tales

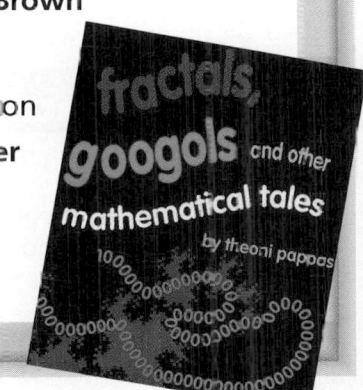

See also the **Math and Literature Bibliography** in the Teacher Support Handbook at the back of this Teacher's Edition.

Lesson By Lesson Overview
Equations and Functions

Lesson 1

- Students use variable cards and counters to demonstrate what happens when the same operation is performed on both sides of an equation.

Lesson 2

- Students practice solving addition and subtraction equations as well as multiplication and division equations by using inverse operations.
- Students use words to describe equations and practice writing and solving equations to solve problems.

Lesson 3

- Students practice writing equations to solve problems.
- Students choose a strategy and use data from a table to solve problems.

Lesson 4

- Students learn different ways to present functions and to use a given relationship involving only one operation to make and complete function tables.

Lesson 5

- Students use functions and equations that involve more than one operation to describe and extend patterns.
- Students complete function tables.

SKILLS TRACE: ALGEBRA, EXPRESSIONS, EQUATIONS, AND FUNCTIONS

Grade 4	Grade 5	Grade 6
• write expressions and equations, evaluate expressions and functions, and solve equations (ch. 5)	• **write and solve equations using equality properties** • **use functions and function tables to solve equations**	• write expressions and equations (ch. 12) • add, subtract, multiply, and divide to solve equations (ch. 12)

Chapter Planner

Lesson	Objective	Vocabulary	Materials	✔ NCTM Standards
21.1 Hands-on: Algebra: Model Equations p. 566A	Determine what happens when you perform the same operation on both sides of an equation.	equation	variable cards; equals sign cards, counters, colored cards labeled "x", plus sign cards	**Algebra:** Represent the idea of a variable as an unknown quantity using a letter or a symbol.
21.2 Algebra: Write and Solve Equations p. 568A	Write and solve equations.	inverse operation	variable card; plus, minus, and equals sign card; counters, Balance Transparency	**Algebra:** Express mathematical relationships using equations; use mathematical models to represent and understand quantitative relationships.
21.3 Problem-Solving Strategy: Write an Equation p. 572A	Write an equation to solve a problem.		Problem Solving: Four Step Process Transparency	**Algebra:** Express mathematical relationships using equations.
21.4 Algebra: Variables and Functions p. 576A	Use a function table to solve equations.	function function table	Table I Transparency	**Algebra:** Represent and analyze patterns and functions, using words, tables, and graphs.
21.5 Algebra: Patterns and Functions p. 578A	Use function tables and equations to describe and extend patterns.		Table I Transparency	**Algebra:** Use mathematical models to represent and understand quantitative relationships.

Resources For Reaching All Learners

LESSON RESOURCES: Reteach, Practice, Enrichment, Problem Solving, Homework, English Learners, Daily Routines, Transparencies, Math Center.

ADDITIONAL RESOURCES FROM HOUGHTON MIFFLIN: Combination Classroom Planning Guide, Chapter Challenges, Every Day Counts, Math at Hand (student handbook)

Every Day Counts

The **Ending the Year** activities in **Every Day Counts** support the math in this chapter.

Assessing Prior Knowledge

Before beginning the chapter, you can assess student understandings in order to assist you in differentiating instruction.

Complete Chapter Pretest in Unit Resource Folder

Use this test to assess both prerequisite skills (**Are You Ready?** — one page) and chapter content (**Check What You Know** — two pages).

Chapter 21 Prerequisite Skills Pretest

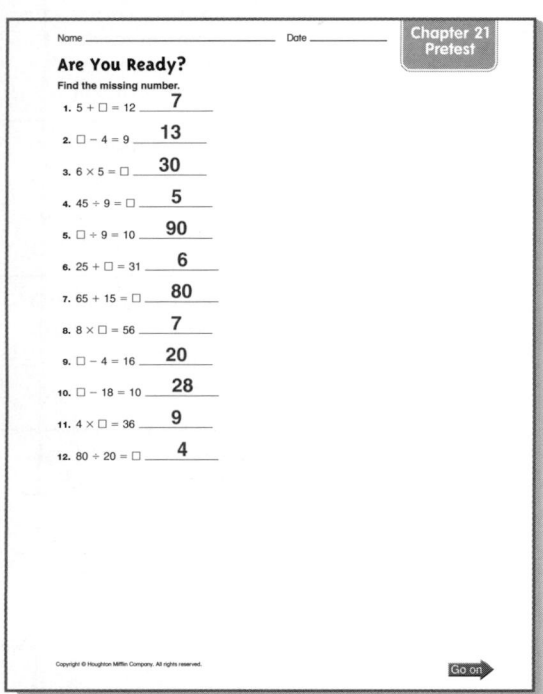

Chapter 21 New Content Pretest

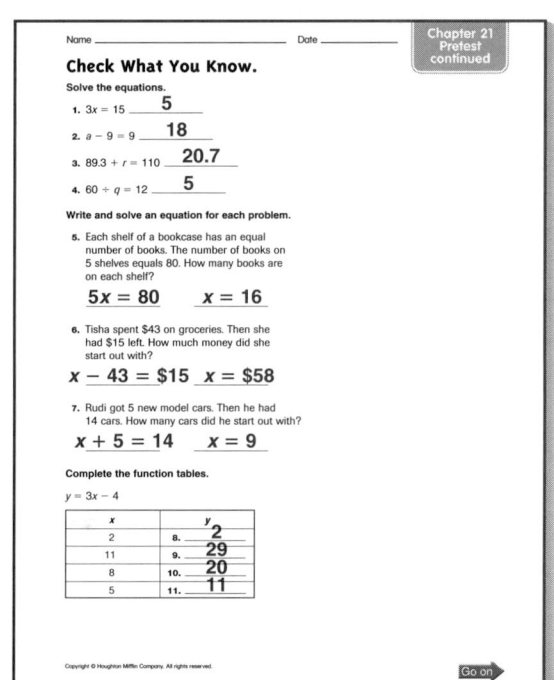

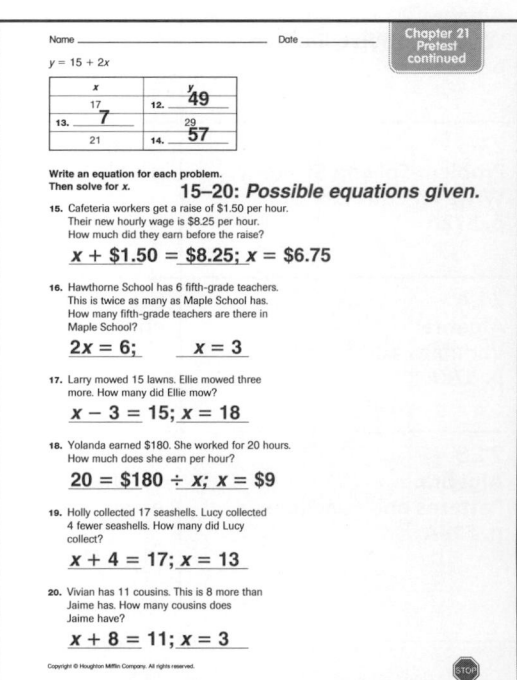

Customizing Instruction

For Students Having Difficulty

Items	Prerequisites	Ways to Success
1–2, 6–7, 9–10	Solve addition and subtraction equations	Skillsheet: 166
3–5, 8, 11–12	Solve multiplication and division equations	Skillsheet: 167

Ways to Success: Intervention for every concept and skill (CD-ROM or Chapter Intervention Skillsheets).

Consider using **Knowing Mathematics** with any students who are working two or more years below grade level.

For Students Having Success

Items	Objectives	Resources
1–7, 15–20	**21A** Write and solve equations using equality properties.	Enrichment 21.1, 21.2
8–14	**21B** Use functions and function tables to solve equations.	Enrichment 21.4, 21.5
5–7, 15–20	**21C** Analyze and solve problems by writing an equation.	Enrichment 21.3

Other Pretest Options

Informal Pretest in Student Book

The student book pretest assesses vocabulary and prerequisite skills needed for success in this chapter.

Ways to Success CD-ROM

The *Ways to Success* chapter pretest has automatic assignment of appropriate review lessons.

Use **Chapter Challenges** with any students wh
success with all new chapter content.

Chapter Resources

Assessing Prior Knowledge

It Varies (equations)

- On the chalkboard, write:
  $x = 10$, so $5x = y$
  Have students solve the equation.
- Then have them substitute four other values for x and solve for each value.

Ongoing Skill Activity

A Date With an Equation (write and solve equations, functions)

- Pose this problem: If you tell me the sum of any four dates that form a square on a calendar (e.g., 3, 4, 10, and 11), how can I find the individual dates by using variables to write equations?
- After Lesson 2, display $d + (d + 1) + (d + 7) + (d + 8) = s$. Tell students that d = the first date and s = the sum. Use properties to simplify: $4d + 16 = s$.
- After Lesson 5, use the Distributive Property to show that the function $4d + 16 = s$ is the same as $4(d + 4) = s$, and $d + 4 = \frac{s}{4}$. Have students try each.

Connecting to the Unit Project

- Have student pairs write riddles where the answers can be deciphered, letter by letter, by using a code based on solutions to equations. Have them share the riddles and codes with the class.
- Display the riddles and solutions on the bulletin board.

Teacher Support

Professional Resources Handbook

Research, Mathematics Content, and Language Intervention

Research-Based Teaching

Nickson (2000) reviewed research related to algebra in the school curriculum and found that many students find themselves confused in the transition from arithmetic to algebra. In primary school children are taught basic concepts such as the notion of equivalence. Students often fail to recognize that the equals sign does not necessarily indicate that a numerical answer is required, and need to be reminded of the requirement of balance of an equation. See *Professional Resources Handbook, Grade 5,* Unit 8.

For more ideas relating to Unit 8, see the Teacher Support Handbook at the back of this Teacher's Edition.

Language Intervention

When students are working together on hands-on activities, encourage them to verbalize what they are doing and why. This will help them build their own understanding and math vocabulary.

 **Time Saving Technology Support**

Ways to Assess Customized Spiral Review and Test Generator CD-ROM
Lesson Planner CD-ROM
Ways to Success Intervention CD-ROM
Math Tracks CD-ROM
Education Place: **www.eduplace.com/math/mw/**
Houghton Mifflin Math eBook CD-ROM
eManipulatives
eGames

Starting Chapter 21
Equations and Functions

Chapter Objectives

21A Write and solve equations using equality properties.

21B Use functions and function tables to solve equations.

21C Analyze and solve problems by writing an equation.

Math Background

Equations

When learning about equations and functions, it is important for students to understand the meaning of variables. For instance, in algebra $4m$ means "4 times the value of m" and in arithmetic 45 means "four tens and five ones." A common misconception among students is after solving for m and finding out that $m = 3$ for instance, interpreting $4m$ as 43.

It is necessary to learn to use inverse operations to solve simple equations before learning to solve more difficult equations. To develop student understanding of solving equations it is good to model a balance scale that has part of the equation in each pan. Additionally, to avoid students doing "guess and check" method, you may want to use larger numbers and avoid nice whole number answers.

Functions

One type of equation is a function. A function is a rule that associates one and only one value of one variable with each value of another variable. The function $y = 2x$ expresses y in terms of x. For each value of x there is one and only one value of y. We say that an equation determines y as a function of x, if for each x, the equation can be solved to give exactly one value of y. The introductory work with function in this chapter simply has students substituting values in a function to make a function table.

INVESTIGATION

Use Data

Artists often use scale drawings and grids to plan large pieces of art. Each square contains a simple part of the total form. Part of one of the stained-glass pieces in the picture has been copied onto a grid. To enlarge this, use 1 in. × 1 in. graph paper to reproduce this part of the picture, square by square.

Check students' drawings.

564

Using the Investigation

Have students work in small groups to answer the question posed on page 564.

To extend the investigation, have students do the following activity.

- Look through magazines or comic strips to find a picture that you would like to enlarge. Use a method similar to the one described on page 564 to enlarge the picture.

For more information about projects and investigations, visit **Education Place**. **www.eduplace.com/math/mw/**

Chapter Pretest

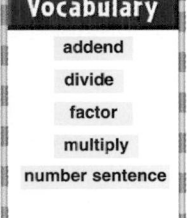

Use this page to review and remember what you need to know for this chapter.

✓ VOCABULARY

Choose the best word to complete each sentence.

Vocabulary
addend
divide
factor
multiply
number sentence

1. In the expression $4 + x = 5$, the 4 is a(n) ____. **addend**

2. The equation $36 \div 9 = 4$ asks that you ____ 36 by 9. **divide**

3. To check division, you ____ the quotient and the divisor. **multiply**

✓ CONCEPTS AND SKILLS

Find the missing addend.

4. $5 + \blacksquare = 13$ **8**   5. $\blacksquare + 11 = 31$ **20**   6. $22 + \blacksquare = 61$ **39**   7. $\blacksquare + 49 = 74$ **25**

Find the missing factor.

8. $7 \times \blacksquare = 42$ **6**   9. $\blacksquare \times 9 = 99$ **11**   10. $\blacksquare \times 8 = 56$ **7**   11. $\blacksquare \times 15 = 60$ **4**

Match. Write the letter of the correct missing number.

12. $42 - \blacksquare = 33$ **b**   a. 8

13. $\blacksquare \div 9 = 7$ **d**   b. 9

14. $\blacksquare - 16 = 40$ **c**   c. 56

15. $96 \div \blacksquare = 12$ **a**   d. 63

Write the next two numbers in each pattern.

16. 2, 9, 16, 23, 30, … **37, 44**   17. 2, 10, 18, 26, 34, … **42, 50**

18. 5, 20, 35, 50, 65, … **80, 95**   19. 79, 67, 55, 43, 31, … **19, 7**

 **Write About It**

20. Describe this pattern in words. Then name the next two numbers.

79, 85, 75, 81, 71
First add 6, then subtract 10; 77, 67

 **Test Prep on the Net**
Visit *Education Place* at **eduplace.com/kids/mw/** for more review.

Chapter 21 Chapter Pretest **565**

✓ Chapter Pretest

Prerequisite Skills	
Items	**Skill**
1–3	Vocabulary needed for this chapter
4–7	Finding missing addends
8–11	Finding missing factors
12–15	Finding missing numbers in subtraction and division
16–19	Extending patterns

Chapter Challenges

For Mathematically Promising Students

Use *Chapter Challenges* resource book.

Explore: Combinations, page 115, after Lesson 1

Extend: Probability at Play, page 117, after Lesson 3

Connect: The Weather, page 119, after Lesson 5

Using The Chapter Pretest

This page will help students review some of the prerequisite skills needed for this chapter. The chart above indicates which skills are covered on the pretest. If students need more help with these prerequisite skills use *Ways to Success,* Houghton Mifflin's intervention program.

Students who need more review can visit **Education Place,** Houghton Mifflin's award-winning website.

⚙ Children's Math Worlds

Using *Children's Math Worlds* helps develop student communication skills because of the daily work with Math Talk, a teaching practice that can be used with all lessons. The emphasis on building a helping community will also enhance student participation in all classroom discussion.

Equations and Functions   **565**

Lesson 21.1

Algebra: Model Equations

PLANNING THE LESSON

MATHEMATICS OBJECTIVE

Determine what happens when you perform the same operation on both sides of an equation.

Use Lesson Planner CD-ROM for Lesson 21.1.

Daily Routines

Vocabulary

Write the equation *n + 2 = 5* on the chalkboard. **What two expressions are equal to each other?** (*n + 2; 5*) **What symbol shows that they are equal?** (the equals sign, =) *n + 2 = 5* is an *equation,* a mathematical sentence that shows that two expressions are equal. Have students give other examples of equations.

Vocabulary Cards

Meeting North Carolina's Standards

5.02 Use algebraic expressions, patterns, and one-step equations and inequalities to solve problems.

Lesson Transparency

21.1

Problem of the Day

Out of 40 marbles, if 10 are red and the rest are white, what is the probability of choosing a red marble? Express the probability as a fraction. $(\frac{1}{4})$ If only 5 marbles were red and the rest were white, what would the probability be of picking a red marble? Express the probability as a fraction. $(\frac{1}{8})$

Quick Review

Name the product or quotient.
1. 14×5 (70)
2. 8×90 (720)
3. $100 \div 20$ (5)
4. $121 \div 11$ (11)

Lesson Quiz

Name the value of *x* in each of the following pairs of equations.
1. $x + 4 = 8, x + 6 = 10$ ($x = 4$)
2. $x + 2 = 6, x + 1 = 5$ ($x = 4$)
3. $3x = 12, 5x = 20$ ($x = 4$)

LEVELED PRACTICE

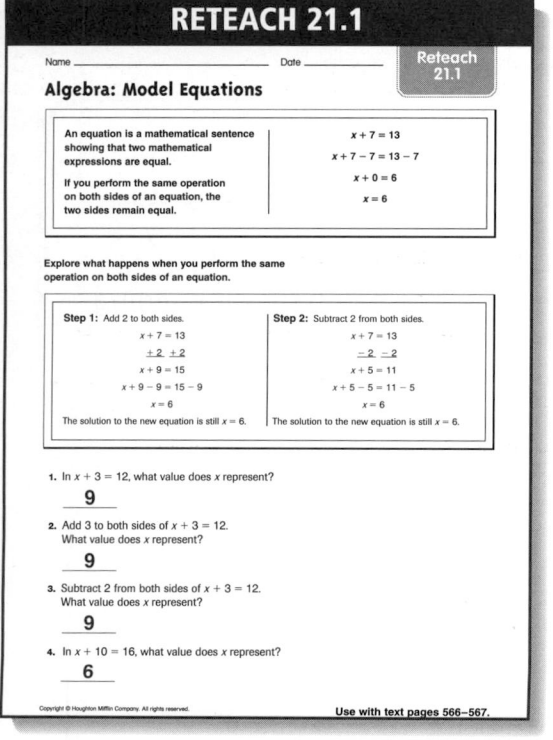

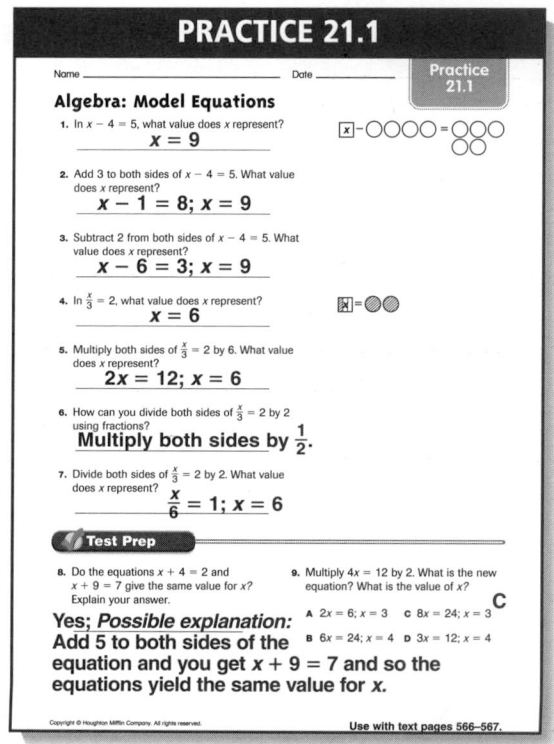

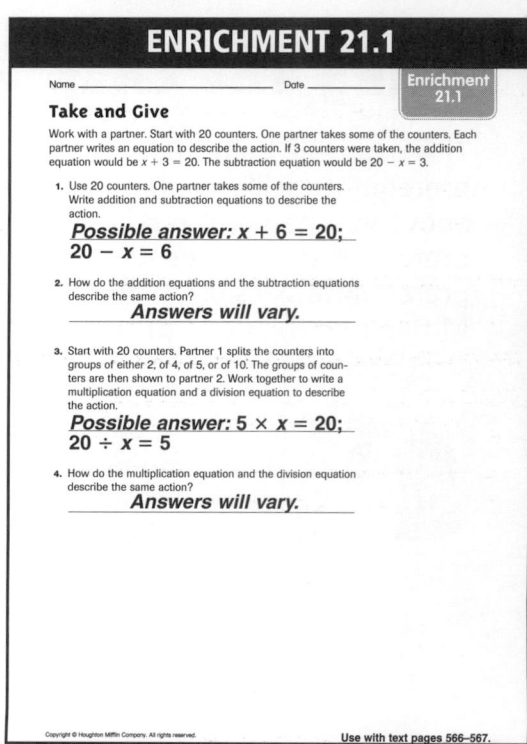

Practice Workbook Page 138

566A   CHAPTER 21   Lesson 1

Reaching All Learners

Differentiated Instruction

English Learners

Worksheet 21.1 reviews key vocabulary and concepts used in the lesson. Students then balance and solve equations to tell what numbers variables represent.

Special Needs
VISUAL, TACTILE

Materials: *variable cards, equals sign cards, counters*

- Give each student 8 counters and 1 of each card. Display $x + 2 = 5$.
- Now model the equation. What does the variable card represent? (x)
- Do the same for the equation $x + 3 = 4$.

Early Finishers
VISUAL, TACTILE

Materials: *counters, equals sign and variable cards*

Pair up. Each make an equation by picking cards, such as $x + 2 = 5$, and model it with counters. Trade models. Find and solve each other's equations. (For $x + 2 = 5$: take 2 from the left and right of the equals sign to make $x = 3$.)

TECHNOLOGY

Spiral Review

Using the *Ways to Assess* CD-ROM, you can create **customized** spiral review worksheets covering any lessons you choose.

Manipulatives

eManipulatives are available on the *Ways to Success* CD.

Lesson Planner

Use the Lesson Planner CD-ROM to see how lesson objectives for this chapter are correlated to standards.

Science Connection

Balances

A mathematical equation shows that two expressions are equal. In science a *fulcrum*, or pivot point, could be likened to an equals sign. Talk with students about a seesaw. Have them describe one and tell what has to happen for a seesaw to balance. (The forces on either side of the fulcrum need to be the same; the lengths of the board on each side of the fulcrum also need to be equal.) Discuss with students how a seesaw is similar to an equation. Continue with a discussion of a pan balance.

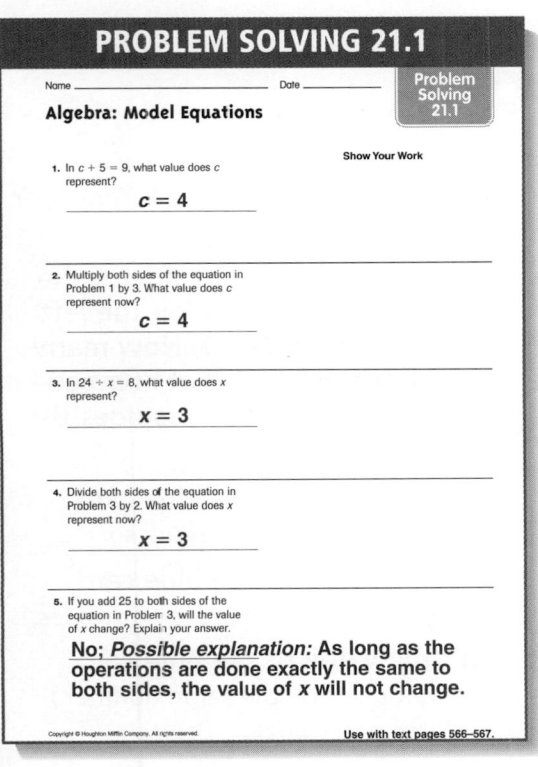

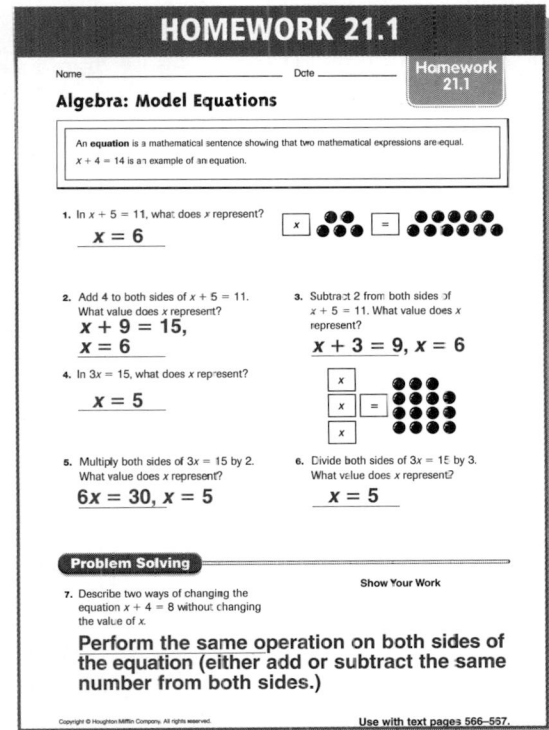

Homework Workbook Page 138

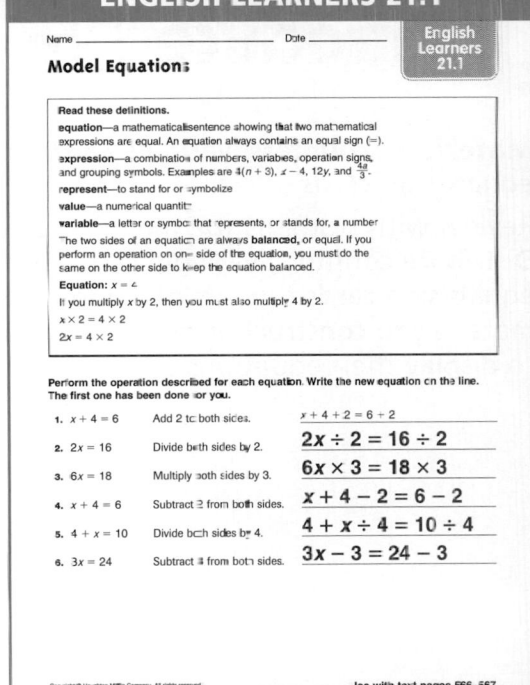

TEACHING LESSON 21.1

LESSON ORGANIZER

Objective Determine what happens when you perform the same operation on both sides of an equation.

Resources Reteach, Practice, Enrichment, Problem Solving, Homework, English Learners

Materials Counters, variable cards, plus sign cards, equals sign cards

Warm-Up Activity
Corresponding Sentences

|  Whole Group | 5 minutes | Visual, Auditory |

- Display these addition sentences. **What are the related sentences?**

  1. $6 + 4 = 10$ $(10 - 4 = 6; 10 - 6 = 4)$

  2. $7 + 8 = 15$ $(15 - 8 = 7, 15 - 7 = 8)$

- Display these multiplication sentences. **What are the corresponding division sentences?**

  3. $5 \times 4 = 20$ $(20 \div 5 = 4, 20 \div 4 = 5)$

  4. $7 \times 5 = 35$ $(35 \div 7 = 5, 35 \div 5 = 7)$

  5. $5 \times 7 = 35$ $(35 \div 5 = 7, 35 \div 7 = 5)$

 **Lesson 1 Hands-On**

Algebra
Model Equations

Objective Determine what happens when you perform the same operation on both sides of an equation.

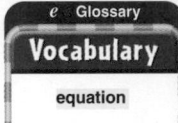
Materials
counters
variable cards
plus sign cards
equal sign cards

 **Work Together**

An **equation** is a mathematical sentence showing that two mathematical expressions are equal. You can use counters to model equations.

The blue variable card represents the number of hidden counters. How many counters are hidden?

$$x + 3 = 7$$

What number plus 3 equals 7? Since $4 + 3 = 7$, then $x = 4$. There are 4 hidden counters.

Work with a partner to see what happens when you perform the same operation on both sides of an equation.

STEP 1 Use the variable card, counters, and an equal sign card to model the equation $x + 3 = 7$.

- Add 2 counters to each side of the equal sign. What equation does your model represent now?

- How many counters does the blue card represent? Did adding 2 counters to each side change the value of x? **4; no**

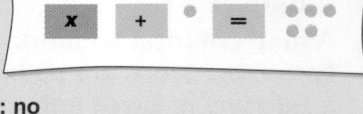
$$x + 5 = 9$$

STEP 2 Model the equation $x + 3 = 7$ again.

- Subtract 2 counters from each side of the equal sign. What equation does your model represent now? $x + 1 = 5$

- How many counters does the blue card represent? Did taking away 2 counters from each side change the value of x? **4; no**

566

---

1 Introduce

|  Whole Group | 5 minutes |

Materials: *counters, variable cards, plus sign cards, equals sign cards*

Review with students the meaning of the word *equation*. Distribute counters, variable cards, plus sign cards, and equals sign cards to pairs of students. Have them use these materials to construct an equation. Call on various students to display their equations on the chalkboard.

2 Develop

Guide students through the first part of the *Work Together* section.

- **How many counters do you see on the right side of the equation?** (7) **How many counters should be on the left side, if the left side equals the right side?** (7) **How many counters do you see on the left side?** (3) **What number plus 3 equals 7?** (4) **How many hidden counters does the blue card represent?** (4)

- Review Step 1. **Why hasn't the value of the blue card changed?** (The same number was added to both sides.)

- Review Step 2. **Why hasn't the value of the blue card changed?** (The same number was subtracted from both sides.)

- Review Step 3. **Why hasn't the value of the blue card changed?** (Both sides were multiplied by the same number.)

STEP 3 Model the equation $x = 2$ with 1 variable card and 2 counters.

- Use variable cards and counters to show multiplying both sides of the equation by 5. What equation does your model represent now? **$5x = 10$**
- How many counters does the blue card represent? Did multiplying each side by 5 change the value of x? **2; no**

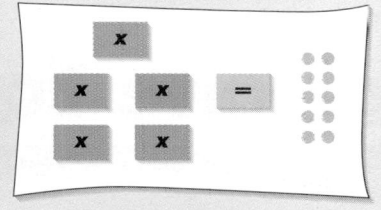

On Your Own

1. In $x + 3 = 5$, what value does x represent? **$x = 2$**

2. Add 2 to both sides of $x + 3 = 5$. What value does x represent? **$x = 2$**

3. Subtract 1 from both sides of $x + 3 = 5$. What value does x represent? **$x = 2$**

4. In $4x = 12$, what value does x represent? **$x = 3$**

5. Multiply both sides of $4x = 12$ by 2. What value does x represent? **$x = 3$**

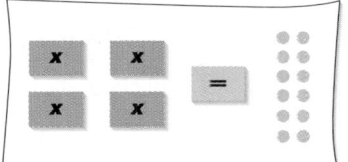

6. Divide both sides of $4x = 12$ by 2. What value does x represent? **$x = 3$**

Talk About It • Write About It

You learned that the two sides of an equation are always balanced.

7. What happens to the value of the variable when you add or subtract the same number from both sides of the equation? **It stays the same.**

8. What happens to the value of the variable when you multiply or divide both sides of the equation by the same counting number? **It stays the same.**

Test Prep Transparency **21.1**

DAILY TEST PREP

Write a pair of equations to show that adding the same number to both sides of an equation does not change the value of the variable. (Possible answer: $x - 6 = 8$ and $x + 9 = 11$; 3 has been added to both sides; the value of x in both equations is 2.)

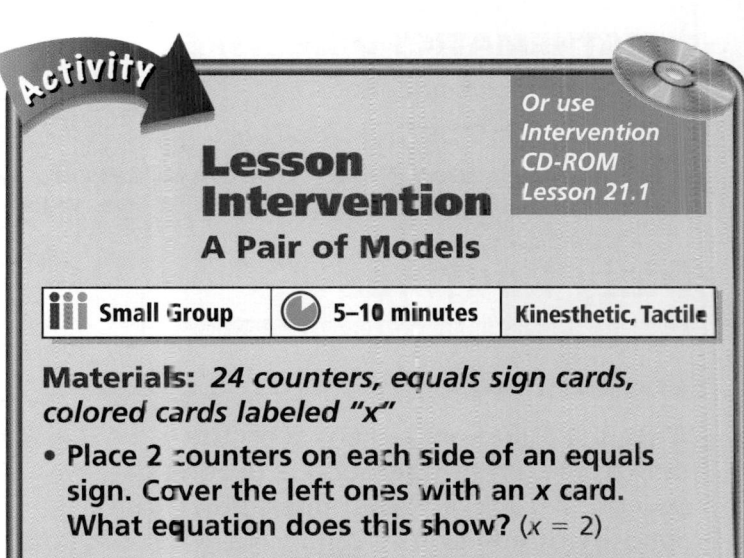

Activity

Lesson Intervention

A Pair of Models

Or use Intervention CD-ROM Lesson 21.1

| 👥 Small Group | 🕐 5–10 minutes | Kinesthetic, Tactile |

Materials: *24 counters, equals sign cards, colored cards labeled "x"*

- Place 2 counters on each side of an equals sign. Cover the left ones with an x card. What equation does this show? ($x = 2$)

- How can we model $3x = 6$ using counters and x cards? (3 groups of 2 counters on the left, 6 counters on the right, each group on the left covered with an x card.)

- What about $x = 2$? (2 counters on each side of equals sign, counters on the left covered with x card.) $2x = 4$? (2 pairs of 2 counters on the left of equals sign, 4 counters on the right, each group on the left covered with an x card.)

---

3 Practice

Assign **Exercises 1–6** of *On Your Own* as independent work.

4 Assess and Close

Assign **Exercises 7 and 8** of the *Talk About It • Write About It* section. Have volunteers explain their work.

Keeping a Journal

Have students write definitions for the words *equation* and *equilateral*. Have them write a few sentences telling how these terms are related.

Algebra: Write and Solve Equations

PLANNING THE LESSON

MATHEMATICS OBJECTIVE
Write and solve equations.

Use Lesson Planner CD-ROM for Lesson 21.2.

Daily Routines

Vocabulary

Write the equation $n + 5 = 8$ on the chalkboard. **What operation is used in the equation?** (addition) **What operation is the opposite of addition?** (subtraction) **What can you do to get n alone on the left side of the equation?** (Subtract 5 from both sides.) **When you subtract 5 from each side you are performing an** *inverse operation.*

Vocabulary Cards

Meeting North Carolina's Standards
5.02 Use algebraic expressions, patterns, and one-step equations and inequalities to solve problems.

Lesson Transparency 21.2

Problem of the Day
Miko earns a weekly salary of $256. She spends $64 of it on food. What percent of her salary is used for food? (25%)

Quick Check
Find the product or quotient.
1. $\frac{1}{3} \times \frac{3}{4}$ $(\frac{1}{4})$
2. $\frac{2}{5} \times \frac{5}{18}$ $(\frac{1}{9})$
3. $\frac{5}{8} \times \frac{4}{15}$ $(\frac{1}{6})$
4. $\frac{18}{21} \div \frac{6}{7}$ (1)

Lesson Quiz
Tell the inverse operation you would use to solve the equation. Then solve.
1. $x + 12 = 78$ (subtract 12 from both sides; $x = 66$)
2. $y - 11 = 13$ (add 11 to both sides; $y = 24$)
3. $16m = 48$ (divide both sides by 16; $m = 3$)
4. $84 = 7a$ (divide both sides by 7; $a = 12$)

LEVELED PRACTICE

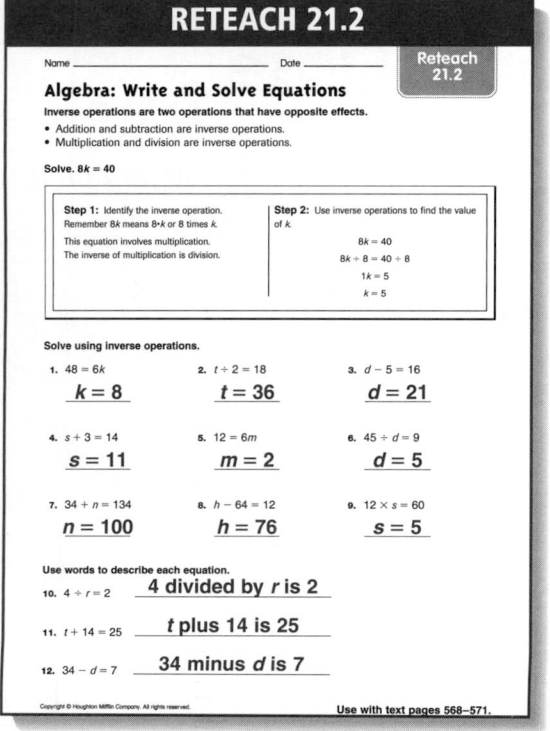

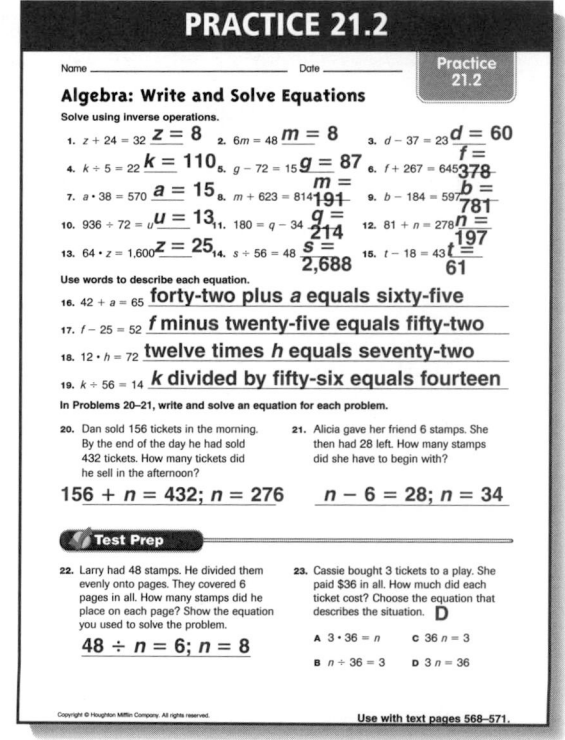

ENRICHMENT 21.2

Four in a Row

With a partner, use the game board below to try to get 4 in a row.

$42 + x = 7$	$21 - x = 17$	$10x = 10$	$8 \div x = 8$	$x - 2 = 4$
$11x = 55$	$x + 7 = 10$	$12 \div x = 3$	$7 - x = 5$	$4 + x = 9$
$8 - x = 5$	$4x = 16$	$x - 1 = 0$	$3 + x = 5$	$24 \div x = 12$
$x + 12 = 13$	$x \div 5 = 1$	$9 + x = 15$	$6x = 12$	$9x = 54$
$13 - x = 8$	$7x = 42$	$x^2 = 9$	$9 \div x = 3$	$7 + x = 11$

One player uses counters of one color and the other player uses counters of another color. Taking turns, a player rolls a number cube and finds an equation with that number that is equal to x. If no number remains with that solution, the player loses a turn. The first player to cover 4 equations across, down, or diagonally is the winner.

1. Which equations were easiest for you to solve? Which were hardest?
   Answers will vary.

2. What strategy did you use to try to win the game?
   Answers will vary.

3. If you were to play again using a spinner instead of a number cube, how could the equations change?
   Possible answer: A spinner with more than 6 sections would allow the value of x to be greater than 6.

Use with text pages 568–571.

Practice Workbook Page 139

Reaching All Learners

Differentiated Instruction

English Learners

On Worksheet 21.2, students learn mathematical language by matching verbal phrases to mathematical equations. Students then write their own phrases to describe equations.

Inclusion
VISUAL, TACTILE

Materials: *variable card, equals sign card, 13 counters*

- Model $x + 4 = 9$ with a variable card and 13 counters. **To get x by itself, how many counters do we subtract from the left?** (4) **How do we balance the equation?** (take 4 from the right)

- **What is the solution?** ($x = 5$)

Gifted and Talented
VISUAL, AUDITORY

- Write a word problem expressed by $x - 12 = 40$ or $3x = 24$. (Possible answer: I spent $12 and have $40 left. How much did I start with?)

- Exchange problems. Make equations for one another's problem and solve.

TECHNOLOGY

Spiral Review

To reinforce skills on lessons taught earlier, create **customized** spiral review worksheets using the *Ways to Assess* CD-ROM.

Software

Use *Easy Sheet* or another spreadsheet to explore this lesson more fully.

Education Place

Encourage students to visit Education Place at **eduplace.com/kids/mw/** for more student activities.

Science Connection

Planet Diameters

- Earth's diameter at the equator is 26 miles greater than its diameter between the poles, which is 7,900 miles. Write and solve an equation to find the diameter of Earth at the equator. ($d = 26 + 7,900$; 7,926 miles)

- Give students this problem: The diameter of Mars at its equator is 4,222 miles. The diameter of Mercury at its equator is 1,191 miles less than the diameter of Mars. Choose a variable and write and solve an equation to find Mercury's diameter. ($d + 1,191 = 4,222$; 3,032 miles)

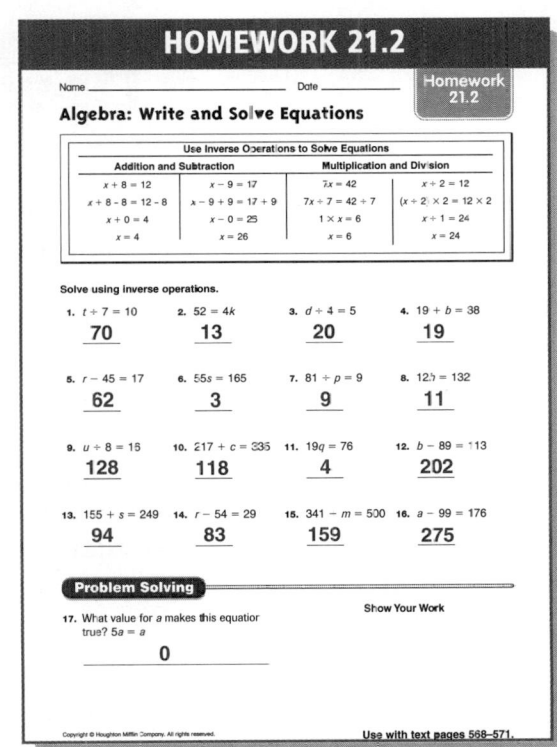

Homework Workbook Page 139

TEACHING LESSON 21.2

LESSON ORGANIZER

Objective Write and solve equations.

Resources Reteach, Practice, Enrichment, Problem Solving, Homework, English Learners

Materials Variable cards; plus, minus, and equal sign cards; counters, Balance Transparency

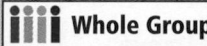

Warm-Up Activity
Model Equations

𝄃𝄃𝄃𝄃 Whole Group	⏱ 5 minutes	Kinesthetic, Visual

Materials: *variable cards; +, −, = cards; counters*

Model the following equations. Should you add or subtract counters on both sides to get the variable alone on the left side? How many? How many counters are remaining on the right side of each equation?

1. $x + 5 = 6$ (subtract; 5 counters; $x = 1$)

2. $x − 4 = 8$ (add, 4 counters; $x = 12$)

3. $x + 1 = 4$ (subtract, 1 counter; $x = 3$)

4. $x − 3 = 1$ (add, 3 counters; $x = 4$)

5. $x − 4 = 3$ (add, 4 counters, 7)

Algebra
Write and Solve Equations

Objective Write and solve equations.

Learn About It
MathTracks 2/28
Listen and Understand

Wayne and his friends are answering telephones at a 24-hour telethon to raise money for local youth programs. There are 18 hours left in the telethon. How many hours has the telethon been on?

Write and solve an equation to solve the problem.

Let n represent the number of hours the telethon has been on.

Equation: $n + 18 = 24$ ← total number of hours in telethon

hours telethon has been on   number of hours left

▶ You can use inverse operations to solve equations. **Inverse operations** are two operations that have opposite effects.

Addition and subtraction are inverse operations.

Inverse Operations
addition ←→ subtraction
multiplication ←→ division

Solve Addition and Subtraction Equations

Solve: $n + 18 = 24$

$n + 18 = 24$

$n + 18 − 18 = 24 − 18$

$n + 0 = 6$

$n = 6$

Think
18 is added to n. Addition and subtraction are inverse operations. So subtract 18 from both sides.

Solve: $x − 8 = 27$

$x − 8 = 27$

$x − 8 + 8 = 27 + 8$

$x + 0 = 35$

$x = 35$

Think
8 is subtracted from x. Addition and subtraction are inverse operations. So add 8 to both sides.

568

---

1 Introduce

Teaching Transparency
21.2

Materials: *Balance Transparency, variable card, counters*

On the left pan of the Balance Transparency, place a variable card and 3 counters. On the right pan, place 6 counters. The two pans should be balanced.

- **How can I get the variable alone on the left pan?** (Take away the 3 counters.) Take away the 3 counters, leaving the variable card alone. Tip the balance so that the right pan is lower (heavier) than the left because it has 6 counters on it.

- Point out that the scale is no longer balanced. **Three counters have been taken away from the left pan. What do I need to do to keep both sides balanced?** (Take 3 counters away from the right pan.) Do this, making sure that the two pans are again even. **What is the value of the variable?** (3)

2 Develop

Guide students through the *Learn About It* section.

- **What information is given in the problem?** (telethon lasts 24 hours; 18 hours left) **What question does the problem ask?** (How many hours has the telethon been going?)

- Discuss *inverse operations.* **Which operations are inverse operations?** (addition and subtraction, multiplication and division)

- Discuss the first example, $n + 18 = 24$, an addition equation. **Subtraction will undo the addition.** Make sure students understand each step of the solution.

- Go over the second example, $x − 8 = 27$. **This equation involves subtraction, so addition can be used to undo the subtraction.** Go over each step.

Multiplication and division are inverse operations.

Multiplication and Division Equations

Solve: $4m = 36$

$$4m = 36$$
$$4m \div 4 = 36 \div 4$$
$$1 \cdot m = 9$$
$$m = 9$$

Think
m is multiplied by 4. Multiplication and division are inverses. So divide by 4 on both sides.

Remember
$4m$ means $4 \cdot m$, or four times m. The multiplication sign, $\times$, is not used to avoid confusion with the variable x.

Solve: $t \div 6 = 12$

$$t \div 6 = 12$$
$$(t \div 6) \cdot 6 = 12 \cdot 6$$
$$t \div 1 = 72$$
$$t = 72$$

Think
t is divided by 6. Multiplication and division are inverse operations. So multiply by 6 on both sides.

Guided Practice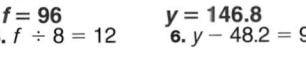

Solve using inverse operations.

1. $7d = 28$ $d = 4$
2. $c \div 9 = 3$ $c = 27$
3. $h + 26.5 = 51.3$ $d = 24.8$

4. $j - 14 = 13$ $j = 27$
5. $f \div 8 = 12$ $f = 96$
6. $y - 48.2 = 98.6$ $y = 146.8$

Ask Yourself
• Which operation can I use to undo the operation in the equation?

TEST TIPS

Use words to describe each equation.

7. $15 + x = 20$ 15 plus x equals 20
8. $3c = 16$ 3 times c equals 16
9. $y \div 6 = 8$ y divided by 6 equals 8

TEST TIPS **Explain Your Thinking** 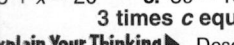 Describe how you can write and solve an equation that shows increasing the number of hours worked by 7 hours equals 32 hours in all. $h + 7 = 32$; $h = 25$

Practice and Problem Solving

Solve using inverse operations.

10. $6k = 42$ $k = 7$
11. $c + 108 = 242$ $c = 134$
12. $g \div 6 = 90$ $g = 540$

13. $n + 484 = 911$ $n = 427$
14. $h \div 14 = 84$ $h = 1176$
15. $n \cdot 29 = 319$ $n = 11$

16. $a - 174 = 308$ $a = 482$
17. $333 = 9f$ $f = 37$
18. $u \div 12 = 70$ $u = 840$

19. $92 \cdot k = 2{,}208$ $k = 24$
20. $r \div 8 = 18$ $r = 144$
21. $49 + w = 102$ $w = 53$

 Go On

Reaching All Learners

Algebra

Plant Growth Copy this table on the board, omitting the answers. Explain that it shows the height of two plants during a five-week period.

Week	1	2	3	4	5
Plant A	4 in.	5 in.	*(6 in.)*	*(7 in.)*	8 in.
Plant B	6 in.	8 in.	10 in.	*(12 in.)*	*(14 in.)*

1. Check the table.
2. Have students make a double bar graph of the data, and write a summary of the data.
3. Have students describe the growth rate of each plant, using a equation, with variables.

Answers

1. See table for answers.
2. Check students' graphs. Students should describe a pattern with Plant *B*'s height always greater than Plant *A*'s height.
3. *Variables may vary.* For $h =$ height in inches and $w =$ week: Plant A: $h = w + 3$; Plant B: $h = 2w + 4$.

Differentiated Assignments		
At Risk	**Average**	**Advanced**
Exercises 1	Exercises 1, 2	Exercises 1–3

• Look at the equation $4m = 36$. **Here, the equation involves multiplication. It is solved by dividing.** Go over each step with students.

• Go over the last example, $t \div 6 = 12$. If students have difficulty understanding the third step in the solution, point out that $t \div 6$ can be written as the fraction $\frac{t}{6}$. Write the solution on the chalkboard.

Guided Practice

Have students complete **Exercises 1–9** as you observe. Remind them to use the *Ask Yourself* question to help. Give students the opportunity to talk about the question in *Explain Your Thinking*.

DAILY TEST PREP

Marcus spent $36 on four gifts. He spent an equal amount of money on each gift. How much did he spend for each gift? Write and solve an equation to answer the question.

($4a = 36$; $a = 9$; he spent $9 per gift.)

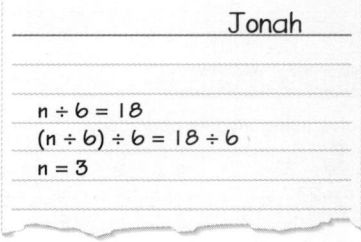

Activity

Or use Intervention CD-ROM Lesson 21.2

Lesson Intervention

Solving Problems with Equations

👥 Small Group	🕐 5–10 minutes	Kinesthetic, Tactile

- Display: *Jill has 15 dimes, 5 times as many as Ed has. How many dimes does Ed have?*

- **What facts are given in the problem?** (Jill has 15 dimes, 5 times as many as Ed has.) **What do we want to find?** (how many dimes Ed has) **Jill has 5 times as many dimes as Ed. How can we use d to show this?** (5 times d, or $5d$) **Jill has 15 dimes, 5 times what Ed has. What equation shows this?** ($5d = 15$)

- **To solve the equation, you must isolate the variable on one side. How do you isolate d on the left?** (divide $5d$ by 5) **You also need to divide 15 by 5. What equation results?** ($d = 3$) **How many dimes does Ed have?** (3)

Use words to describe each equation. *Possible answers are given.*

22. $m + 14 = 20$
m plus 14 equals 20

23. $p \div 3 = 12$
p divided by 3 equals 12

24. $w - 6 = 18$
w minus 6 equals 18

25. $31 + b = 72$
31 plus b equals 72

26. $5 \cdot x = 50$
5 times x equals 50

27. $24 - r = 17$
24 minus r equals 17

In Problems 28–31, write and solve an equation for each problem. *Sample equations are given.*

28. Matt raised $18 on Saturday morning. He raised more money Saturday afternoon. In all, he raised $43 on Saturday. How much did he raise Saturday afternoon?
$18 + n = 43$; $n = 25$; $25

29. Marcus had 28 ride tickets. Each ride took the same number of tickets. Marcus rode 7 rides and used all his tickets. How many tickets did it take for each ride? $28 \div n = 7$; $n = 4$; 4 tickets

30. Margarita had some money. She spent $28 on jewelry. Then she had $29. How much did she have before buying jewelry? $n - 28 = 29$; $n = $57

31. Each floor of a hotel has an equal number of rooms. The total number of rooms on 12 floors is 240 rooms. How many rooms are on each floor?
$12n = 240$; $n = 20$; 20 rooms

32. What's Wrong? Jonah solved the equation $n \div 6 = 18$. What did Jonah do wrong? What is the value of n?
See below.

33. Create and Solve Write a problem that could be described by the equation $5r = 125$. Then solve the problem.
See below.

34. Janice, Ellen, Roberto, Heather, and Christopher are finalists in a contest. The contest has prizes for first and second place. How many different ways can the prizes be awarded? **32.**
20 ways

Jonah

$n \div 6 = 18$
$(n \div 6) \div 6 = 18 \div 6$
$n = 3$

32. Jonah divided each side by 6 instead of using the inverse operation (multiplication).
33. Check students' problems and solutions.

Daily Review — **Test Prep**

Divide. (Ch. 12, Lessons 5–6)

35. $\frac{15}{32} \div \frac{3}{4}$ $\frac{5}{8}$

36. $2\frac{2}{3} \div \frac{5}{6}$ $3\frac{1}{5}$

37. $7 \div \frac{4}{5}$ $8\frac{3}{4}$

38. $4\frac{1}{2} \div 2\frac{3}{4}$ $1\frac{7}{11}$

39. $3\frac{5}{8} \div 4$ $\frac{29}{32}$

40. $\frac{6}{7} \div 3$ $\frac{2}{7}$

41. $12 \div \frac{3}{4}$ 16

42. $\frac{3}{4} \div 12$ $\frac{1}{16}$

43. $12 \div 1\frac{1}{3}$ 9

44. $1\frac{1}{3} \div 12$ $\frac{1}{9}$

✏️ **45.** In a crew of 32 workers, each member works the same number of hours. They work a total of 1,600 hours in a week. Choose the equation for this situation.

Ⓐ $32h = 1,600$

B $1,600h = 32$

C $32 \div h = 1,600$

D $h \div 1,600 = 32$

Extra Practice See page 583, Set A.

---

3 Practice

Assign **Exercises 10–45** as independent work.

- *Exercises 10–27* Have students explain their answers.

- *Problems 28–34* For Problems 32 and 33, have volunteers share and discuss their work with the class.

Common Error

Applying the inverse operation to only one side When students use the inverse operation to solve an equation, they often forget to "balance the equation" by applying the inverse operation to both sides of the equation. Remind them that whatever they do to one side of the equation they must do to the other side.

4 Assess and Close

- **How would you use the inverse operation to solve an addition equation?** (apply subtraction to both sides of the equation)

- **How would you use the inverse operation to solve a multiplication equation?** (apply division to both sides of the equation)

Assign the **LESSON QUIZ** on Transparency 21.2 to further assess student understanding.

Square Numbers and Exponents

You can use your calculator to work with square numbers and exponents. The product of a number multiplied by itself is a **square number**. For example, 9 is a square number because it is the product of 3×3.

To show that a number has been squared, write the number and then the exponent 2.

$3^2 \leftarrow$ exponent

base

The exponent tells you how many times the base is a factor in the product. So, $3^2 = 3 \times 3$.

To find the square of 3, press

Sometimes you need to multiply a number by itself more than once. This means you are raising it to a power greater than 2.

To show $5 \times 5 \times 5$, write 5^3. The exponent 3 tells you that the base, 5, is a factor 3 times. So, $5 \times 5 \times 5 = 5^3$.

To find 5^3 on your calculator, press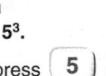

---

1. **a.** Multiply to square the numbers 1 through 8.
   b. Write an equation in the form of $a^2 = a \times a$ to represent each square number. **See below.**
   c. Complete the table at the right. Describe the patterns you notice. **See Additional Answers on Page 583.**

1	1
2	4
3	9
4	■ 16
5	■ 25
6	■ 36
7	49
8	■ 64

Use the ▲ key to simplify the expressions below.

2. $4^3 + 5^2 - 2^2$ **85**   3. $5^3 - 3 \times 2^4$ **77**   4. $6^2 \div 3^2 + 5^3$ **129**

5. $30 \times (40 - 3^2)$ **930**   6. $a^2 + 9$, if $a = 5$ **34**   7. $b^3 - b^2 \times 2$, if $b = 3$ **9**

1b. $1^2 = 1 \times 1$; $2^2 = 2 \times 2$; $3^2 = 3 \times 3$; $4^2 = 4 \times 4$;
$5^2 = 5 \times 5$; $6^2 = 6 \times 6$; $7^2 = 7 \times 7$; $8^2 = 8 \times 8$

Chapter 21 Lesson 2 571

Square Numbers and Exponents

- Tell students the expression 3^2 is read "3 squared." Explain that numbers such as 9 and 16 are called *perfect squares.* Point out that when a number is a factor three times, the product is called a *cube,* and 5^3 is read "5 cubed."

- Be sure students follow the order of operations in Exercises 2–7.

- Explain that the square root of a square number $(\sqrt{n^2})$ is the number *n.* The term *square root* refers to the number that is multiplied by itself to give the square number.

Keeping a Journal

Have students write a few sentences explaining how to use inverse operations to find the value of a variable.

Problem-Solving Strategy: Write an Equation

PLANNING THE LESSON

MATHEMATICS OBJECTIVE
Write an equation to solve a problem.

Use Lesson Planner CD-ROM for Lesson 21.3.

Daily Routines

Vocabulary

Discuss the meaning and use of *variables* in equations. **What does the variable in an equation stand for?** (an unknown amount) **What is the reason for solving an equation?** (to determine the value of the variable) **How do you solve an equation?** (Use inverse operations to get the variable alone on one side of the equation.)

Vocabulary Cards

Meeting North Carolina's Standards

5.02 Use algebraic expressions, patterns, and one-step equations and inequalities to solve problems.

Also **1.03**

Lesson Transparency
21.3

Problem of the Day
At Jackson Elementary School there are 431 boys. There are 59 more girls than boys at the school. How many students are there in all? (921 students)

Quick Review

Find the sum or difference.
1. $157 + 123$ (280)
2. $486 + 298$ (784)
3. $3,647 - 1,674$ (1,973)
4. $5,343 - 1,761$ (3,582)

Lesson Quiz

Write an equation to solve each problem.
1. Belle paid her brother Bo $112 for working in her gift shop for 16 hours. What was Bo's hourly wage? ($112 = 16x$; $x = \$7$ per hour)
2. Inez earns $78 more per week than Paco. Paco's weekly salary is $665. What is Inez's weekly salary? ($665 + \$78 = x$; $x = \$743$)

LEVELED PRACTICE

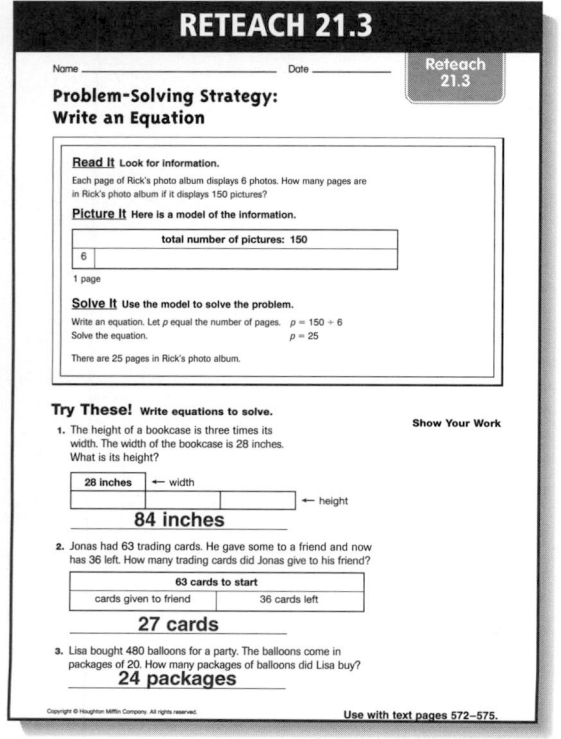

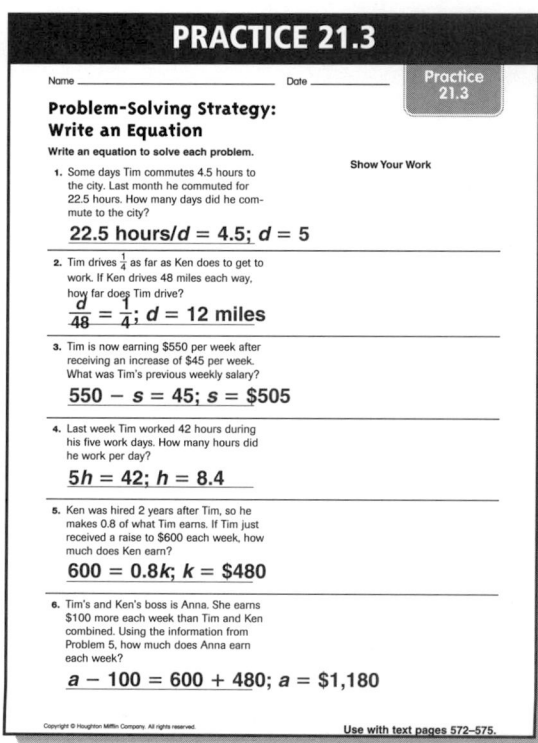

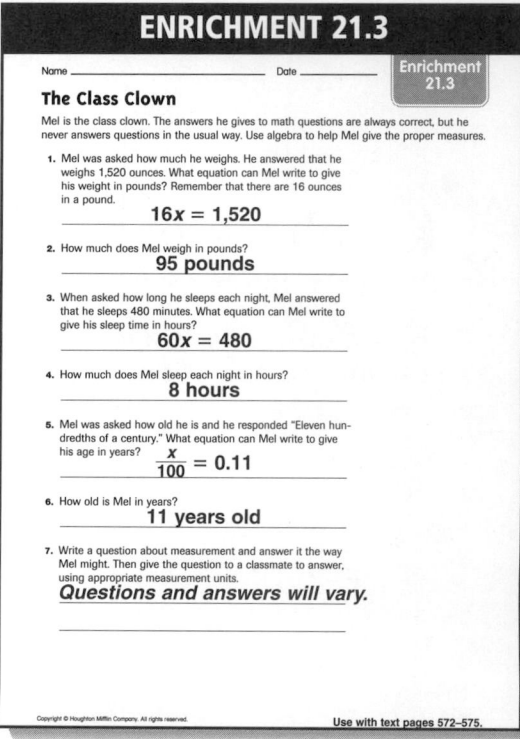

Practice Workbook Page 140

Reaching All Learners
Differentiated Instruction

English Learners

English-language learners may be unfamiliar with terms related to restaurants. Use Worksheet 21.3 to introduce content vocabulary and give students the opportunity to use it in context. This exercise helps support students as they complete the *Independent Practice* section of the lesson.

Special Needs
VISUAL, TACTILE

Materials: *play money*

- Have pairs role-play this problem: *Al lent Mel $7. Mel has $13. How much did Mel have before?*

- **What addition equation expresses the problem?** ($x + 7 = 13$) **What equation can you write to solve using the inverse operation, subtraction?** ($13 - 7 = x$; Mel had $6)

Early Finishers
VISUAL, AUDITORY

- **Write an original problem that can be solved with an equation.**

- Have partners exchange problems and create equations to solve them.

- **Discuss the equations you created.**

TECHNOLOGY
Spiral Review

Help students remember skills they learned earlier by creating **customized** spiral review worksheets using the *Ways to Assess CD-ROM*.

Lesson Planner

You can use the Lesson Planner CD-ROM to create a report of the lessons and standards you have taught.

eBook

eMathBook allows students to review lessons and do homework without carrying their textbooks home.

Houghton Mifflin **Math**

e MathBook

Social Studies Connection
Population Change
- Display this table. Have students write word problems about population changes in these cities, then have them exchange problems and solve.

City	Population (1998)	Population (1990)	Difference
Dallas, TX	1,075,894	? (1,007,168)	68,726
San Francisco, CA	? (1,220,666)	1,110,623	110,043
Chicago, IL	2,802,079	2,783,726	? (18,353)

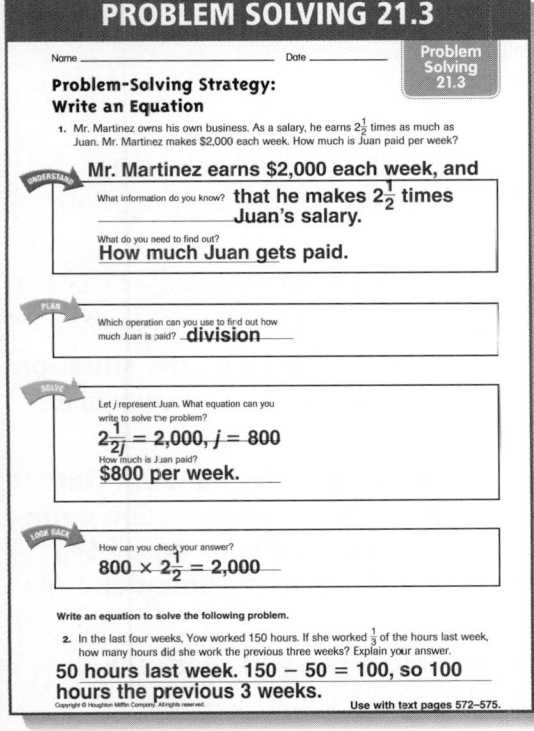

PROBLEM SOLVING 21.3

Name _____ Date _____

Problem Solving 21.3

Problem-Solving Strategy: Write an Equation

1. Mr. Martinez owns his own business. As a salary, he earns $2\frac{1}{2}$ times as much as Juan. Mr. Martinez makes $2,000 each week. How much is Juan paid per week?

UNDERSTAND

Mr. Martinez earns $2,000 each week, and

What information do you know? **that he makes $2\frac{1}{2}$ times Juan's salary.**

What do you need to find out? **How much Juan gets paid.**

PLAN

Which operation can you use to find out how much Juan is paid? **division**

SOLVE

Let *j* represent Juan. What equation can you write to solve the problem?
$2\frac{1}{2}j = 2,000$, $j = 800$
How much is Juan paid?
$800 per week.

LOOK BACK

How can you check your answer?
800 × $2\frac{1}{2}$ = 2,000

Write an equation to solve the following problem.

2. In the last four weeks, Yow worked 150 hours. If she worked $\frac{1}{3}$ of the hours last week, how many hours did she work the previous three weeks? Explain your answer.
50 hours last week. 150 − 50 = 100, so 100 hours the previous 3 weeks.

Copyright © Houghton Mifflin Company. All rights reserved.   Use with text pages 572–575.

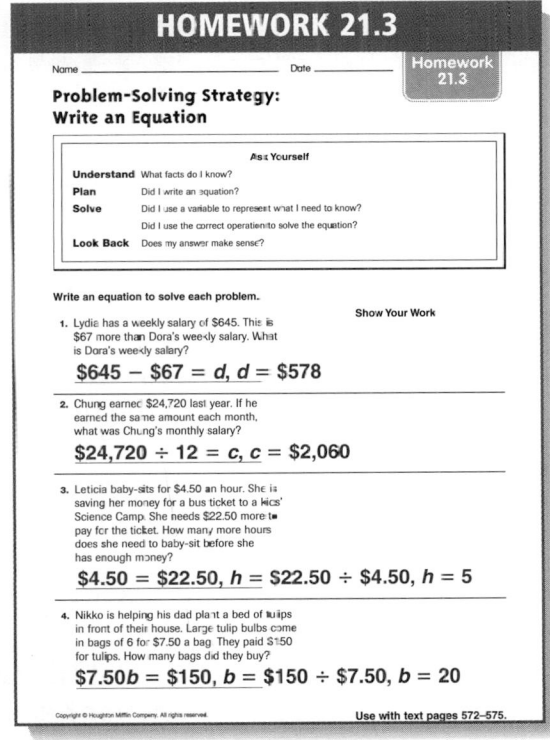

HOMEWORK 21.3

Name _____ Date _____

Homework 21.3

Problem-Solving Strategy: Write an Equation

Ask Yourself

Understand	What facts do I know?
Plan	Did I write an equation?
Solve	Did I use a variable to represent what I need to know?
	Did I use the correct operation to solve the equation?
Look Back	Does my answer make sense?

Write an equation to solve each problem.   **Show Your Work**

1. Lydia has a weekly salary of $645. This is $67 more than Dora's weekly salary. What is Dora's weekly salary?
   $645 − $67 = d, d = $578

2. Chung earned $24,720 last year. If he earned the same amount each month, what was Chung's monthly salary?
   $24,720 ÷ 12 = c, c = $2,060

3. Leticia baby-sits for $4.50 an hour. She is saving her money for a bus ticket to a kids' Science Camp. She needs $22.50 more to pay for the ticket. How many more hours does she need to baby-sit before she has enough money?
   $4.50 = $22.50, h = $22.50 ÷ $4.50, h = 5

4. Nikko is helping his dad plant a bed of tulips in front of their house. Large tulip bulbs come in bags of 6 for $7.50 a bag. They paid $150 for tulips. How many bags did they buy?
   $7.50b = $150, b = $150 ÷ $7.50, b = 20

Copyright © Houghton Mifflin Company. All rights reserved.   Use with text pages 572–575.

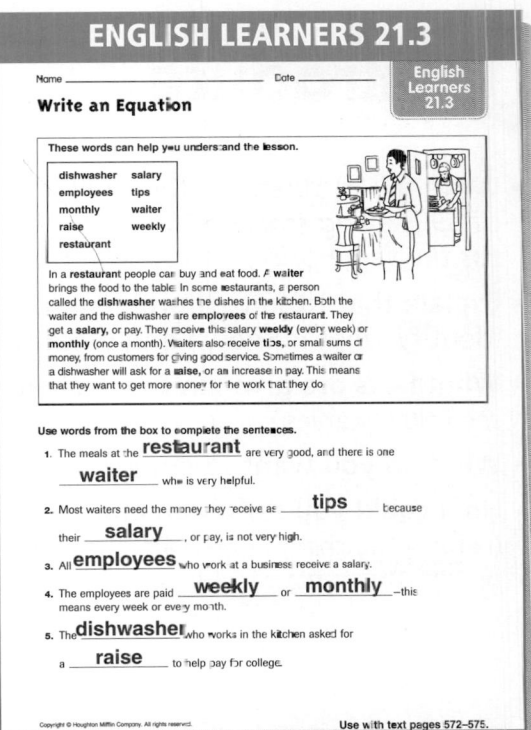

ENGLISH LEARNERS 21.3

Name _____ Date _____

English Learners 21.3

Write an Equation

These words can help you understand the lesson.

dishwasher	salary
employees	tips
monthly	waiter
raise	weekly
restaurant	

In a **restaurant** people can buy and eat food. A **waiter** brings the food to the table. In some restaurants, a person called the **dishwasher** washes the dishes in the kitchen. Both the waiter and the dishwasher are **employees** of the restaurant. They get a **salary**, or pay. They receive this salary **weekly** (every week) or **monthly** (once a month). Waiters also receive **tips**, or small sums of money, from customers for giving good service. Sometimes a waiter or a dishwasher will ask for a **raise**, or an increase in pay. This means that they want to get more money for the work that they do.

Use words from the box to complete the sentences.

1. The meals at the **restaurant** are very good, and there is one **waiter** who is very helpful.

2. Most waiters need the money they receive as **tips** because their **salary**, or pay, is not very high.

3. All **employees** who work at a business receive a salary.

4. The employees are paid **weekly** or **monthly** —this means every week or every month.

5. The **dishwasher** who works in the kitchen asked for a **raise** to help pay for college.

Copyright © Houghton Mifflin Company. All rights reserved.   Use with text pages 572–575.

TEACHING LESSON 21.3

LESSON ORGANIZER

Objective Write an equation to solve a problem.

Resources Reteach, Practice, Enrichment, Problem Solving, Homework, English Learners, Transparencies, Math Center

Materials Problem Solving: Four Step Process Transparency

Warm-Up Activity
Multiply or Divide?

Whole Group	⏱ 5 minutes	Visual, Auditory

For each of the following equations, ask: **Should you multiply or divide on both sides to get the variable alone on the left side? By what number?** Ask students to perform the operation on both sides of the equation. **What is the value of the variable?**

1. $5x = 30$ (divide by 5; $x = 6$)

2. $3x = 24$ (divide by 3, $x = 8$)

3. $\frac{x}{4} = 5$ (multiply by 4; $x = 20$)

4. $\frac{x}{6} = 2$ (multiply by 6; $x = 12$)

Problem-Solving Strategy
Write an Equation

Objective Write an equation to solve a problem.

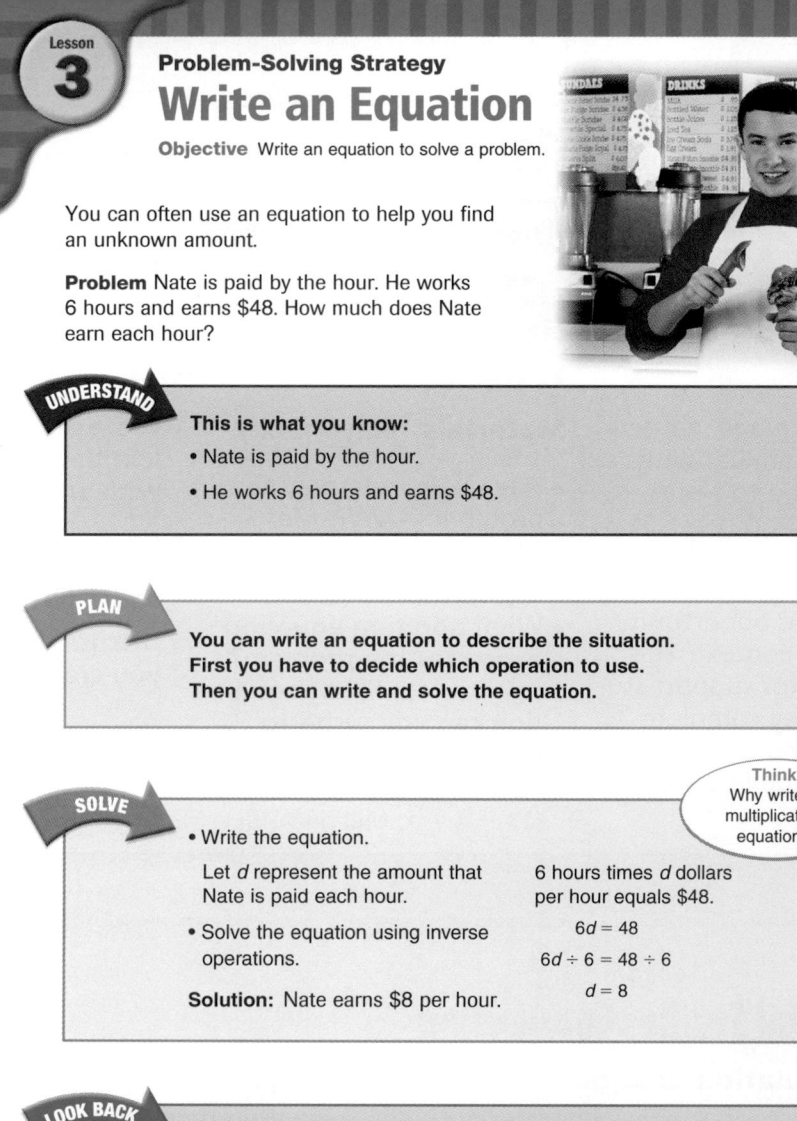

You can often use an equation to help you find an unknown amount.

Problem Nate is paid by the hour. He works 6 hours and earns $48. How much does Nate earn each hour?

UNDERSTAND

This is what you know:
- Nate is paid by the hour.
- He works 6 hours and earns $48.

PLAN

You can write an equation to describe the situation. First you have to decide which operation to use. Then you can write and solve the equation.

SOLVE

- Write the equation.
  Let d represent the amount that Nate is paid each hour.

  6 hours times d dollars per hour equals $48.

  $6d = 48$

- Solve the equation using inverse operations.

  $6d \div 6 = 48 \div 6$

  $d = 8$

  Solution: Nate earns $8 per hour.

> **Think** Why write a multiplication equation?

LOOK BACK

Look back at the problem. How can you check your answer?

572

MathTracks 2/29
Listen and Understand

---

1 Introduce

- Write this problem on the chalkboard: *Lu earned a total of $90 selling scarves. She sold 6 scarves. If each scarf sells for the same price, what is the cost of each scarf?*

- Explain that to solve a problem, the first thing to do is to identify what is known and what is not known.

- **What facts are given in the problem?** (Lu earned $90 in all; she sold 6 scarves.)

- **What do you want to know?** (the cost of each scarf)

- **How could you set up an equation to model the problem?** (Let x = the cost of one scarf; then $6x$ = the cost of 6 scarves, or $90. The equation will be $6x = \$90$.)

2 Develop

Guide students through the problem-solving steps on page 572. You may wish to use the Problem Solving: Four Step Transparency.

- **Look at the Understand step. What do you know?** (Nate is paid by the hour. He makes $48 in 6 hours.)

- **Look at the Plan step. How can you describe the situation in the problem?** (Write an equation; decide on the operation to use in writing it; solve the equation.)

- **Look at the Solve step. Let d stand for the amount Nate earns each hour. Why do you write a multiplication equation?** (You know that 6 times d (dollars per hour) equals $48.) **What inverse operation is used to solve the equation?** (division)

- **Look at the Look Back step. How can you check the solution?** (Multiply 6 by 8.)

Guided Practice

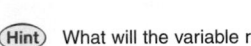

Use the Ask Yourself questions to help you solve each problem.

1. Last week, Terri worked 9.5 hours. This was 3.5 hours less than the number of hours that Brad worked. How many hours did Brad work? **13 hours**

2. A company has 160 employees. This is 4 times the number of employees that it had ten years ago. How many employees did the company have ten years ago? **40 employees**

(Hint) What will the variable represent?

Ask Yourself

UNDERSTAND What facts do I know?

PLAN Did I write an equation?

SOLVE
• Did I use a variable to represent what I need to know?
• Did I use the correct operation to solve the equation?

LOOK BACK Does my answer make sense?

TEST TIPS

Independent Practice

Write an equation to solve each problem.

3. Benita gets a raise of $315 per month. Her new monthly salary is $3,425. What was Benita's monthly salary before she got a raise? **$3,110**

4. In one restaurant, the waiter gives the dishwasher $\frac{1}{4}$ of his tips. On Friday night, the waiter receives $88 in tips. How much does the waiter give to the dishwasher? **$22**

5. You Decide Find how much each job listed to the right pays per hour. Decide which job you would prefer. Give reasons for your decision. *See below.*

6. Tom has a weekly salary of $750. This is $95 less than Carol's weekly salary. What is Carol's weekly salary? **$845**

7. One department has 4 employees. Each employee works the same number of hours per week. The employees in that department worked a total of 150 hours in one week. How many hours did each employee work? **37.5 hours**

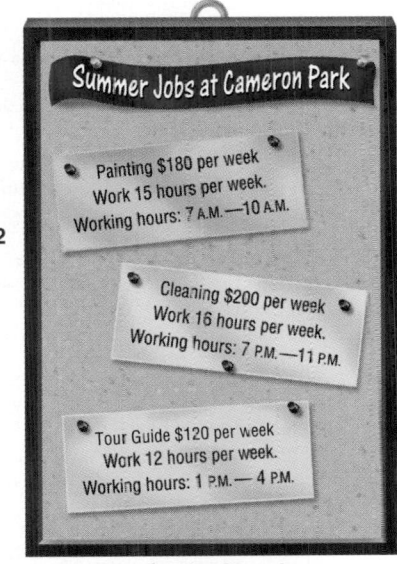

Summer Jobs at Cameron Park

Painting $180 per week
Work 15 hours per week.
Working hours: 7 A.M.—10 A.M.

Cleaning $200 per week
Work 16 hours per week.
Working hours: 7 P.M.—11 P.M.

Tour Guide $120 per week
Work 12 hours per week.
Working hours: 1 P.M.— 4 P.M.

5. **Painting $12/h; Cleaning $12.50/h; Tour Guide $10/h;** *Choices will vary.*

Go On

Chapter 21 Lesson 3   **573**

ACHIEVING Mathematical Proficiency

Understanding Algebraic Thinking

Algebra is an important stepping stone for the study of mathematics. It is the **generalization of arithmetic** and the key to the study of higher mathematics. However, it can also be an obstacle for many students. Today's students must begin to develop concepts of algebraic thinking in the years before they start their first formal course in algebra.

When students learn how to write equations to represent problem situations, they learn to **use a letter to represent an unknown quantity** in the equation. They begin to understand the power of representation when they learn that they can use any letter, not just *x*, to do this.

As students become familiar with using a variable to represent an unknown quantity, **they build their understanding of the importance of representation** in mathematics.

3 Practice

Guided Practice

Have students complete **Exercises 1 and 2** as you observe. Remind them to use the *Ask Yourself* questions to help.

Assign **Problems 3–7** as independent work. Have students share and discuss their work.

Problem-Solving Reminders

Have students review their answers to make sure they have done the following:

• expressed the solution properly
• used appropriate mathematical notation and terms
• supported their solutions with verbal and symbolic work
• determined the reasonableness of the solution in the context of the original problem.

DAILY TEST PREP

Ravi has three times as many stamps as Marcia does. Together, they have 256 stamps. Which equation could you use to find how many stamps Marcia has? (A)

A. $3x + x = 256$ C. $x \div 4 = 256$

B. $4 + 3x = 256$ D. $3x - 4 = 256$

Activity

Or use Intervention CD-ROM Lesson 21.3

Lesson Intervention
Algebraic Expressions

Small Group	5–10 minutes	Visual, Kinesthetic

- Explain that when students solve problems by writing an equation, they need to translate verbal expressions into algebraic expressions.

- Give students this series of phrases. Ask them to write an algebraic expression using the variable n to represent the unknown number. Ask volunteers to share their work.

5 more than a number ($n + 5$)

5 minus a number ($5 - n$)

5 less than a number ($n - 5$)

Five times a number ($5n$)

2 more than three times a number ($3n + 2$)

Choose a Strategy ✓ *Possible strategy given.*

Solve. Show your work. Tell what strategy you used.

8. In a blizzard, a technician monitors the snowfall each hour. The total snowfall is 2.8 cm after 2 hours, 4.2 after 3 hours, and 5.6 cm after 4 hours. If the pattern continues, what will be the total snowfall after 5 hours? **7 cm (Find a Pattern or Make a Table)**

9. Fran makes a set of 49 prints. If all 49 prints sell for a total of $9,800, how much does Fran charge for one print? **$200 (Write an Equation)**

10. A jewelry store has 7 clerks. Two clerks must be working at the store at any time that it is open. How many different combinations of 2 clerks are possible? **21 (Make a Table)**

11. Julianna earned $344 last week working at a local print shop. She earned $8 per hour. How many hours did Julianna work last week at the print shop? **43 hr (Write an Equation)**

PROBLEM-SOLVING Strategies

Use Models
Draw a Diagram
Find a Pattern
Guess and Check
Make an Organized List
Make a Table
Solve a Simpler Problem
Use Logical Reasoning
Work Backward
Write an Equation

Data Use the table to solve Problems 12–15.

The Dog Bone Inn offers the services to dog owners shown in the table.

12. Mari's dog, Jiffy, weighs 32 lbs. How much will it be to board and feed Jiffy for two days at the Dog Bone Inn? **$51**

13. Ms. Owens has two small dogs, one large dog, and two giant dogs to groom at the Doggie Spa. What is the total amount she will charge the owners of the dogs? **$185.00**

14. **Calculator** Which will cost less: day care for a large dog for 5 days with a field trip to the beach or boarding a medium dog for 6 days with 3 field trips to the lake, and a grooming at the Doggie Spa? How much less? **See below.**

15. **Create and Solve** Use the data from the table to create and solve a problem. **Check students' problems.**

DOG BONE INN

Daily Charges

	Small	Medium	Large	Giant
Day Care	$11	$14	$17	$30
Boarding	$16	$22	$27	$50
Doggie Spa	$15	$20	$35	$60
Feeding	$1.75	$3.50	$3.50	$3.50

Field Trips To:	Tail-wagging Bakery	$15
	Lake	$25
	Beach	$100

Small dogs: Up to 25 pounds   **Large dogs:** 61 to 110 pounds
Medium dogs: 26 to 60 pounds   **Giant dogs:** Over 110 pounds

574

14. daycare for a large dog; $227 - 185 = 42 less.

Practice *continued*

Choose a Strategy

Assign **Problems 8–15** as independent work.

- *Problem-Solving for Problems 8–15* Have students describe the strategies they used to solve each problem. Have students explain their solutions for Problem 14. For Problem 15, have students solve one another's problems.

---

4 Assess and Close

Have students discuss the four steps for writing an equation to solve a problem.

- **What should you do in the Understand step?** (Determine the facts given in the problem and what you are to find.)

- **What should you do in the Plan step?** (Decide what information you need to find and which operation to use.)

- **What should you do in the Solve step?** (Choose a variable to represent what you want to know; write the equation; use inverse operations to solve it.)

- **What should you do in the Look Back step?** (Check your answer.)

Assign the **LESSON QUIZ** on Transparency 21.3 to further assess student understanding.

Problem-Solving Test Prep

Choose the letter of the correct answer.
If a correct answer is not here, choose NH.

1. Yuri makes a scale model of his house. The scale model is shown below. What is the actual height of Yuri's house?

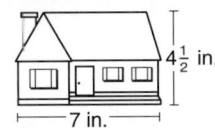

$4\frac{1}{2}$ in.

7 in.

Scale: 1 in. = 6 ft

A 24 ft   **B** 27 ft   **C** 30 ft   **D** 42 ft

(Chapter 18, Lesson 5)

2. A telephone pole that is 45 feet high falls into the street. A worker cuts the pole into logs. What is the greatest number of 18-inch logs that can be made from the telephone pole?

F 25   **G** 29   **H** 30   **J** 45

(Chapter 6, Lesson 2)

3. A sound system is on sale for 10% off list price. Including a sales tax of $9, Jeremy pays $189 for the sound system. Which equation could you use to find the list price (P)?

A $0.9 \times P = \$189$

B $(0.9 \times P) - \$9 = \$189$

C $(0.9 \times P) + \$9 = \$189$

D $(0.1 \times P) - (\$9) = \$189$

(Chapter 19, Lesson 5)

4. Which set of numbers is equivalent?

F $\frac{1}{3}$, 0.3, 3%   **G** $\frac{1}{5}$, 0.25, 25%

H $\frac{3}{10}$, 0.03, 3%   **J** $\frac{3}{5}$, 0.6, 60%

(Chapter 19, Lesson 3)

5. The area of the parallelogram is 72 square centimeters. What is the measure of side A?

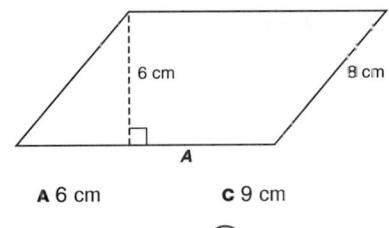

6 cm

8 cm

A

A 6 cm   **C** 9 cm

B 8 cm   **D** 12 cm

(Chapter 16, Lesson 3)

6. A park has 6 entrance gates. A direct path connects each gate to every other gate. How many paths are there in all?

Represent Support your solution with a picture. **15; check drawings.**

(Chapter 17, Lesson 5)

7. Bill has twice as many stickers as Amy. Together they have 24 stickers. Let *a* represent the number of stickers that Amy has. Write an equation that you can use to find how many stickers Amy has.

Explain How does your equation represent the situation?

$2a + a = 24$, or $3a = 24$.
Possible answer: Since *a*
(Chapter 21, Lesson 3)
represents the number of stickers Amy has, 2a represents the number of stickers Bill has, and 2a + a, or 3a, represents the total number of stickers, which is 24.

 Test Prep on the Net

Check out *Education Place* at **eduplace.com/kids/mw/** for test prep practice.

Chapter 21 Lesson 3   575

Problem-Solving Test Prep

Problem-Solving Test Prep provides an opportunity for students to apply previously learned skills in the types of problem contexts typically encountered in standardized tests. *Problem-Solving Test Prep* includes practice in a variety of formats: multiple choice, free response, and open response.

Students will gain experience in writing about mathematics and using various representations to solve problems. Discuss students' solutions. Have several students explain the thinking behind their work.

 More test prep practice is available on Houghton Mifflin's Web site, **Education Place**. Go to **eduplace.com/kids/mw/**.

Keeping a Journal

Have students write a few sentences explaining why equations are useful in solving problems where there is an unknown number. Have students write a word problem that can be solved by writing an equation, then write the equation.

Algebra: Variables and Functions

PLANNING THE LESSON

MATHEMATICS OBJECTIVE
Use a function table to solve equations.

Use Lesson Planner CD-ROM for Lesson 21.4.

Daily Routines

Vocabulary

Suppose we have a problem to solve and we know that $y = x + 1$. What do we know about y? (It will *always* be equal to one more than x.) We could say the equation, $y = x + 1$, is a *rule* in that particular problem. The mathematical term for an equation that relates two variables so that for each value for x there is exactly one related value for y is a *function*. What do you think a *function table* shows? (The given values of one variable and the corresponding values of another variable after applying the function, or rule.)

Vocabulary Cards

Meeting North Carolina's Standards

5.01 Describe, extend, and generalize numeric and geometric patterns using tables, graphs, words, and symbols.

Also **5.03**

Lesson Transparency 21.4

Problem of the Day

Conrad made 30 sandwiches. He made half as many sandwiches with turkey as with ham. The rest were peanut butter sandwiches. If he made 5 turkey sandwiches, how many ham sandwiches and peanut butter sandwiches did he make? (10 ham and 15 peanut butter sandwiches)

Quick Review
Find the value of y when $x = 8$.
1. $15 + x = y$ (23)
2. $65 - x = y$ (57)
3. $x + 28 = y$ (36)
4. $y = 47 + x$ (55)
5. $78 - x = y$ (70)

Lesson Quiz
Copy and complete each function table.

1. $y = x - 1$

x	1	2	3	4
y	(0)	(1)	(2)	(3)

2. $y = 3x$

x	1	2	3	4
y	(3)	(6)	(9)	(12)

LEVELED PRACTICE

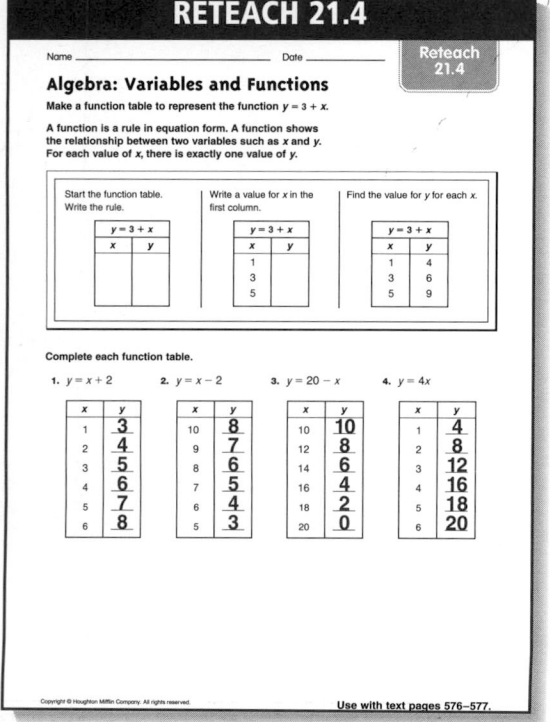

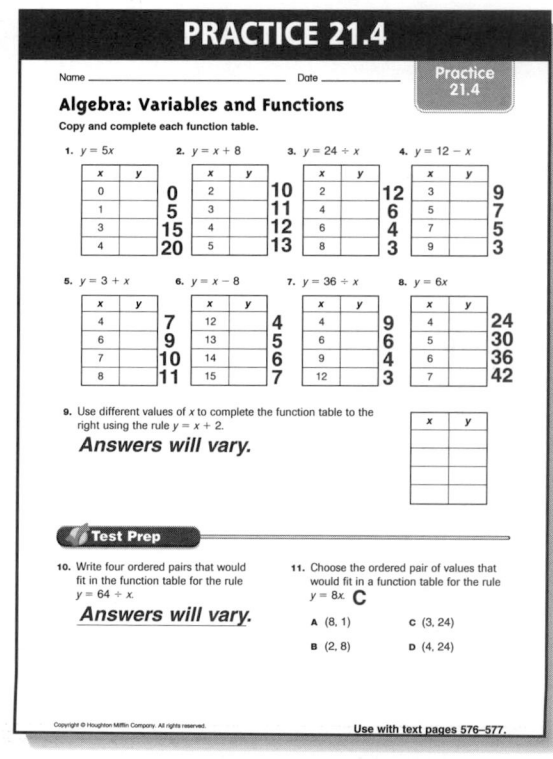

ENRICHMENT 21.4

Name _____ Date _____ Enrichment 21.4

Functioning Across America

With a partner make Road Cards labeled Backroads, State Highway, and Interstate, 5 of each, for a total of 15 cards. Take turns picking a card and tossing a number cube. The number you toss will be the number of hours you are on the road of the card you choose. Enter this number on your trip table. Find the distance you traveled and the total distance you traveled. The player who travels farther in 6 turns wins.

Backroads: 40 mi/h; State Highway: 55 mi/h; Interstate: 65 mi/h

My Trip Table: _____

Kind of Road	Time in hours (t)	Distance in miles (d)	Total Distance

1. Write the rule for distance for each kind of road.
   $d = 40t$; $d = 55t$; $d = 65t$

2. If you drove a total of 26 hours on backroads, how far did you drive?
   1,040 miles

3. In the game, how many miles did you travel on each road?
   Answers will vary.

4. On which road did you travel the greatest distance? Why do you think that was? *Answers will vary. Possible answer:* **The interstate, because you could go the fastest.**

5. Explain how you could change the number of Road Cards to increase the total distance.
   Possible answer: **Make more Interstate Cards.**

Use with text pages 576–577.

Practice Workbook Page 141

Reaching All Learners
Differentiated Instruction

English Learners

Worksheet 21.4 reviews terms important to understanding the text. Students receive support in examining shapes and demonstrating that they understand a pattern. Each student also creates a function table and writes an equation.

Inclusion
VISUAL, AUDITORY

Materials: *Table I Transparency*

- **This is a *function.*** Write $y = x + 3$. **Compare *x* and *y*.** (*y* is 3 more than *x*)
- On the transparency, write *x* in the top left cell, *y* in the top right, and *1, 2, 3, 4* in the column under *x*. **How do you find the value of *y* given each value of *x*?** (Add 3 to each value of *x*.)

Early Finishers
VISUAL, AUDITORY

- Have students create a function rule similar to one of those in the lesson.
- Ask them to share the rule with two other classmates who then create and complete a table of values of *x* and *y* that fit the rule. Explain that the values of *x* need not be 1, 2, 3, 4, but could be 2, 4, 6, 8, and so on, as long as they are sequential and fit the rule.

TECHNOLOGY

Spiral Review

You can prepare students for standardized tests with **customized** spiral review on key skills using the *Ways to Assess* CD-ROM.

Tool Software

Use *Easy Sheet* or another spreadsheet to explore this lesson more fully.

Education Place

You can visit Education Place at eduplace.com/math/mw/ for teacher support materials.

Social Studies Connection

Map Reading Skills
Materials: *copies of different maps with different scales of miles*

- Give partners copies of two different maps with two different scales of miles. Have students develop a function table for each map based on the scale of miles per inch.
- Give students an example. **If one inch equals 50 miles, we can write the function *y = 50x* with *x* representing inches and *y* representing miles.**

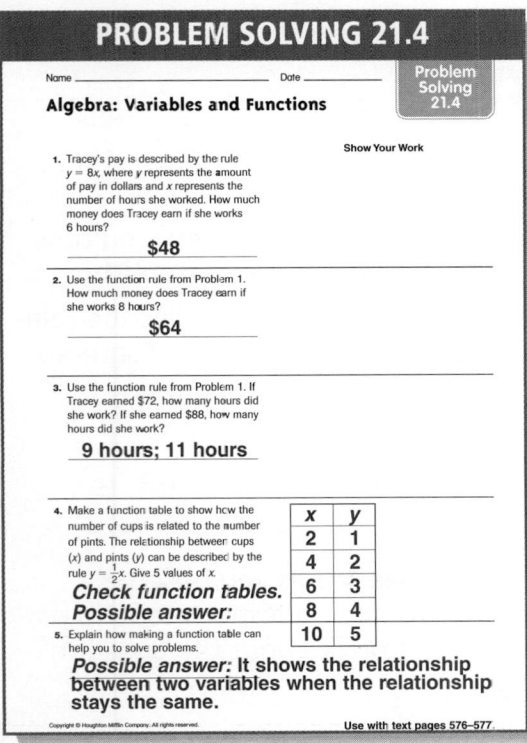

PROBLEM SOLVING 21.4

Name _____ Date _____ | Problem Solving 21.4

Algebra: Variables and Functions

Show Your Work

1. Tracey's pay is described by the rule $y = 8x$, where *y* represents the amount of pay in dollars and *x* represents the number of hours she worked. How much money does Tracey earn if she works 6 hours?

    $48

2. Use the function rule from Problem 1. How much money does Tracey earn if she works 8 hours?

    $64

3. Use the function rule from Problem 1. If Tracey earned $72, how many hours did she work? If she earned $88, how many hours did she work?

    9 hours; 11 hours

4. Make a function table to show how the number of cups is related to the number of pints. The relationship between cups (*x*) and pints (*y*) can be described by the rule $y = \frac{1}{2}x$. Give 5 values of *x*.
   Check function tables.
   Possible answer:

x	y
2	1
4	2
6	3
8	4
10	5

5. Explain how making a function table can help you to solve problems.

    Possible answer: It shows the relationship between two variables when the relationship stays the same.

Copyright © Houghton Mifflin Company. All rights reserved. | Use with text pages 576–577.

HOMEWORK 21.4

Name _____ Date _____ | Homework 21.4

Algebra: Variable and Functions
Use a function table to find values for the function, $y = 5 + x$.

- Replace *x* in the function rule with values for *x* from the first column of the function table. Then solve the rule for *y*.
- Remember: In a function table, there is **exactly one entry** in the second column (*y*) for every entry in the first column (*x*).
- For the function rule, $y = 5 + x$:
  If $x = 1$, then $y = 5 + 1 = 6$.
  If $x = 2$, then $y = 5 + 2 = 7$.
  If $x = 3$, then $y = 5 + 3 = 8$.
  If $x = 4$, then $y = 5 + 4 = 9$.

Function Table
$y = 5 + x$

x	y
1	6
2	7
3	8
4	9

enter *x* values → solve for *y* values

Copy and complete each function table.

1. $y = 14 - x$

x	y
0	14,
1	13,
2	12,
3	11

2. $y = 7x$

x	y
0	0,
1	7,
2	14,
3	21

3. $y = 36 \div x$

x	y
1	36,
2	18,
3	12,
4	9

Problem Solving

4. There are 8 servings in one bag of popcorn. Make a function table to show how many servings are in 2, 3, 4, and 5 bags of popcorn.

Show Your Work

Bags of Popcorn	Servings
1	8
2	16
3	24
4	32
5	40

Copyright © Houghton Mifflin Company. All rights reserved. | Use with text pages 576–577.

ENGLISH LEARNERS 21.4

Name _____ Date _____ | English Learners 21.4

Variables and Functions

These words will help you understand the lesson.
pattern—a model or example that is repeated, or that happens again and again
relate—to link in a logical way to make a connection between
relationship—a connection
rule—a standard method or procedure
table—columns and rows that contain data

How many triangles do you see in each shape? Can you find a pattern in the number of triangles in each shape? Draw the missing triangles in Shape 6 to continue the pattern.

Shape 1   Shape 2   Shape 3

Shape 4   Shape 5   Shape 6

Complete the function table. Write the shape number in the first column. Write the number of triangles in the second column.

Shape Number (x)	Number of Triangles (y)
1	5
2	6
3	7
4	8
5	9
6	10

Write an equation that describes the relationship between *x* (Shape Number) and *y* (Number of Triangles).
$y = x + 4$

Copyright © Houghton Mifflin Company. All rights reserved. | Use with text pages 576–577.

Homework Workbook Page 141

TEACHING LESSON 21.4

LESSON ORGANIZER

Objective Use a function table to solve equations.

Resources Reteach, Practice, Enrichment, Problem Solving, Homework, English Learners, Transparencies, Math Center

Materials Table I Transparency

Warm-Up Activity
Solving for *x*

Whole Group	5 minutes	Visual, Auditory

Have students solve each equation for *x*.

1. $17 = 5 + x$ (12)
2. $16 = 4x$ (4)
3. $2x + 5 = 29$ (12)
4. $5x - 3 = 27$ (6)
5. $6x - 2 = 58$ (10)

Lesson 4

Variables and Functions

Objective Use a function table to solve equations.

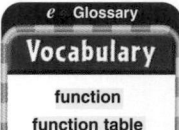

Vocabulary
function
function table

Learn About It  MathTracks 2/30 Listen and Understand

A **function** is a rule that relates pairs of variables, such as *x* and *y*. For each value of *x*, there is exactly one related value of *y*. A function is often written as an equation.

Look at the pattern. How many squares will there be in Shape 10?

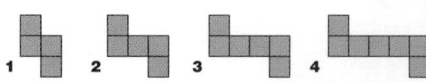

STEP 1 Organize the information in a table. Write the shape number in the first column. Write the number of squares in the second column.

The table of values is called a **function table** because there is exactly one entry in the second column for each shape number.

Shape Number	Number of Squares
1	4
2	5
3	6
4	7

STEP 2 Write the equation that describes the relationship between *x* and *y*.

The number of squares is always equal to 3 more than the shape number.

$$y = x + 3$$

number of squares ↑ ↑ shape number

STEP 3 To find the number of squares in Shape 10, substitute 10 for *x* and simplify.

$$y = x + 3$$
$$y = 10 + 3$$
$$y = 13$$

Solution: There will be 13 squares in Shape 10.

Another Example

Find the Value

The rule $y = 9x$ describes a function. What is the value of *y* when $x = 4$?

$y = 9x$ Substitute 4 for *x* in the equation.

$$y = 9(4)$$
$$y = 36$$

576

---

1 Introduce

Teaching Transparency 21.4

Materials: *Table I Transparency*

• Review the definition of *function*. (a rule in the form of an equation in which for every value of *x*, there is exactly one value of *y*)

• Then put the Table I Transparency on the overhead and write this function rule above the table: $y = x + 4$. Label the top left cell of the table *x*. Label the top right cell *y*.

• Write values *1, 2, 3, 4, 5* in the *x* column. Leave the *y* column blank. Tell students they are going use the rule to fill in the *y* values.

• Ask a volunteer how to use the rule to find the *y* value for $x = 1$. (Substitute 1 for *x* in the rule; $y = 1 + 4 = 5$.)

• Follow the same procedure for the other values of *x* in the table.

2 Develop

Guide students through the *Learn About It* section.

• Review Step 1. Make sure that students understand how the numbers in the columns relate to the pattern shown.

• Review Step 2. Point out that the equation gives the relationship between shape number and number of squares.

• Review Step 3. Make sure students understand the substitution.

• Work through *Another Example* with students.

Guided Practice

Have students complete **Exercises 1–3** as you observe. Remind them to use the *Ask Yourself* questions to help. Give students the opportunity to talk about the question in *Explain Your Thinking.*

Ask Yourself
- What value did I use for x?
- How did I get the value of y?
- Did a pattern help me find the missing values?

TEST TIPS

Copy and complete each function table.

1. $y = 5 + x$

x	y
4	■ 9
3	■ 8
2	■ 7

2. $y = x - 5$

x	y
10	■ 5
7	■ 2
6	■ 1

3. $y = 7x$

x	y
12	■ 84
■	14 · 2
8	■ 56

TEST TIPS **Explain Your Thinking** ▶ What are some other pairs of values that would fit in the function table in Exercise 2? **Possible answers: 12, 7; 20, 15; 15, 10**

Practice and Problem Solving

Copy and complete each function table.

4. $y = 12 \div x$

x	y
1	■ 12
2	■ 6
3	■ 4

5. $y = 4 - x$

x	y
0	■ 4
3	■ 1
4	■ 0

6. $y = 1 + x$

x	y
0	■ 1
6	■ 7
9	■ 10

7. $y = 9x$

x	y
0	■ 0
■	9 · 1
2	■ 18

Use the figures for Problems 8–10.

Figure 1

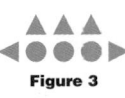
Figure 2

Figure 3

8. Make a function table to show how the number of circles in each figure is related to the figure number.

9. Make a function table to show how the number of triangles in each figure is related to the figure number.

10. **Analyze** Write an expression for the number of circles and for the number of triangles in the nth figure. Use the expressions to find how many circles and triangles are in the nth figure.

8.

figure	circles
1	1
2	2
3	3

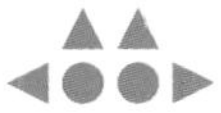

9.

figure	triangles
1	3
2	4
3	5

10. Circles, n; triangles, $n + 2$; circles and triangles, $n + n + 2$ or $2n + 2$ or $2(n + 1)$

Daily Review | **Test Prep**

Find the missing term.
(Ch. 18, Lesson 4)

11. $\frac{6}{9} = \frac{g}{3}$ $g = 2$

12. $\frac{8}{10} = \frac{20}{a}$ $a = 25$

13. $\frac{3}{z} = \frac{9}{21}$ $z = 7$

14. Free Response Ron's earnings (y) for a number of hours (x) are given by the rule $y = 10x$. Make a function table for five values of x. **Check students' tables.**

Extra Practice See page 583, Set B.

Chapter 21 Lesson 4   **577**

Test Prep Transparency

21.4

DAILY TEST PREP

For the function rule $y = 6x$, which of the following is the correct value of y if the value of x is 9? **(B)**

A. 48   B. 54   C. 15   D. 63

Activity

Or use Intervention CD-ROM Lesson 21.4

Lesson Intervention

Function Tables and Rules

| 👥 Small Group | ⏱ 5–10 minutes | Visual, Auditory |

Materials: *Table I Transparency*

- Display and number: *1-triangle, 2-quadrilateral, 3-pentagon, 4-hexagon, 5-heptagon, 6-octagon.*
- Label the transparency's left column *Figure Number*; insert figure numbers in order. Label the right column *Number of Sides*. **What numbers go in the right column?**
- **Describe the relationship between the figure's number and the number of its sides.** (Figure's number is 2 more than number of its sides.) **Write a function rule with x as figure number; y as number of sides.** ($y = x + 2$)

---

③ Practice

Assign **Exercises 4–14** as independent work.

- **Problem Solving for Problems 8–10** For Problem 10, have students discuss their answers.

Common Error

Substituting from the wrong row When students substitute an x-value into the rule to calculate the corresponding y-value, they should make sure to read straight across the row to avoid picking up an incorrect x-value.

④ Assess and Close

- **Explain what a function rule is.** (An equation relating two variables; for each value of one variable, there is exactly one value for the other.)
- **How can you calculate the m-values in a function table if the rule is $m = 5 - n$?** (Substitute values of n in the rule and use the rule to find the value of m for each n-value.)

Assign the **LESSON QUIZ** on Transparency 21.4 to further assess student understanding.

Keeping a Journal

Have students write about a real-life situation involving two variables. Have them write a function rule for the situation, and construct a function table.

Algebra: Patterns and Functions

PLANNING THE LESSON

MATHEMATICS OBJECTIVE

Use function tables and equations to describe and extend patterns.

Use Lesson Planner CD-ROM for Lesson 21.5.

Daily Routines

Vocabulary

Review the term *operation*. Ask students what the four basic operations are. (addition, subtraction, multiplication, and division) Point out that the equations so far in this chapter have been those that involve one operation. This lesson focuses on functions and function tables that involve more than one operation.

Vocabulary Cards

Meeting North Carolina's Standards

5.01 Describe, extend, and generalize numeric and geometric patterns using tables, graphs, words, and symbols.

Also **5.03**

Lesson Transparency 21.5

Problem of the Day

Ning used $40 to buy 3 CDs. He received $2.50 in change. What was the cost of each CD if each cost the same amount? ($12.50)

Quick Review

Give the inverse operation, then solve.

1. $x + 18 = 30$ (subtract 18 from both sides; $x = 12$)

2. $y - 5 = 32$ (add 5 to both sides; $y = 37$)

3. $14m = 70$ (divide both sides by 14; $m = 5$)

4. $128 = 16a$ (divide both sides by 16; $a = 8$)

Lesson Quiz

Bela began a new job and has $10 per week taken out of her salary to put in an IRA account. The company put $100 into her account as an encouragement to save.

1. Write a function rule that shows the relationship between number of weeks and total amount saved. ($y = 100 + 10x$)

LEVELED PRACTICE

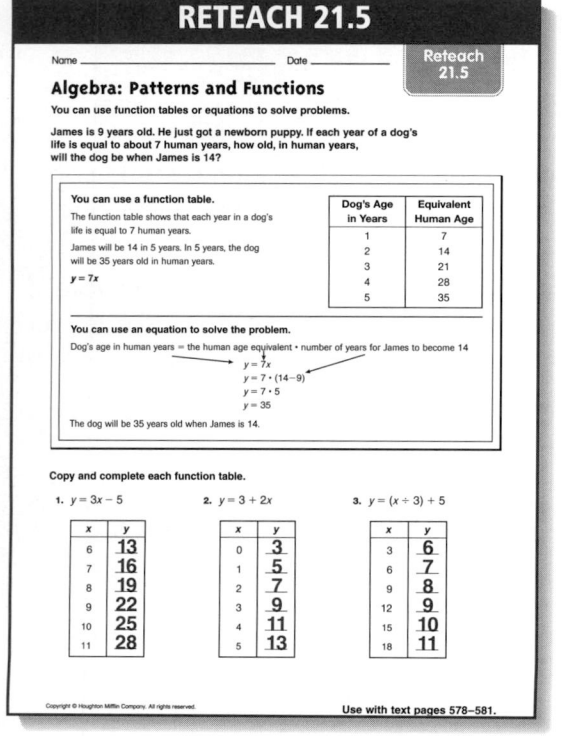

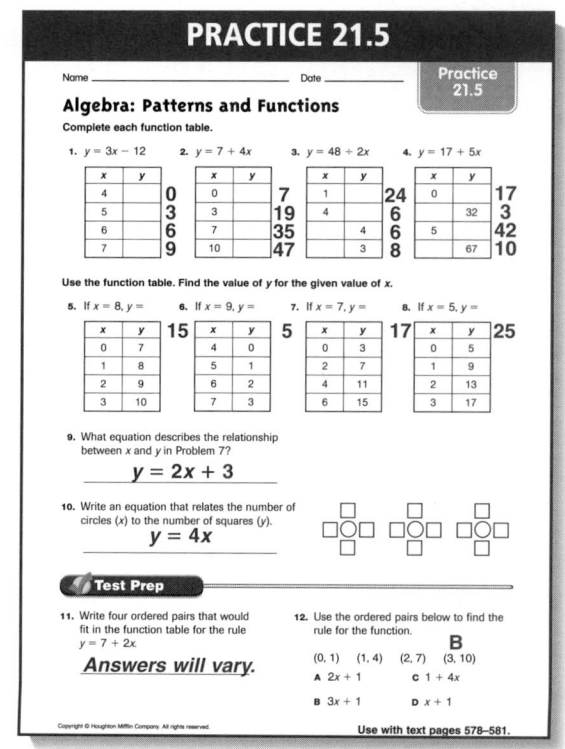

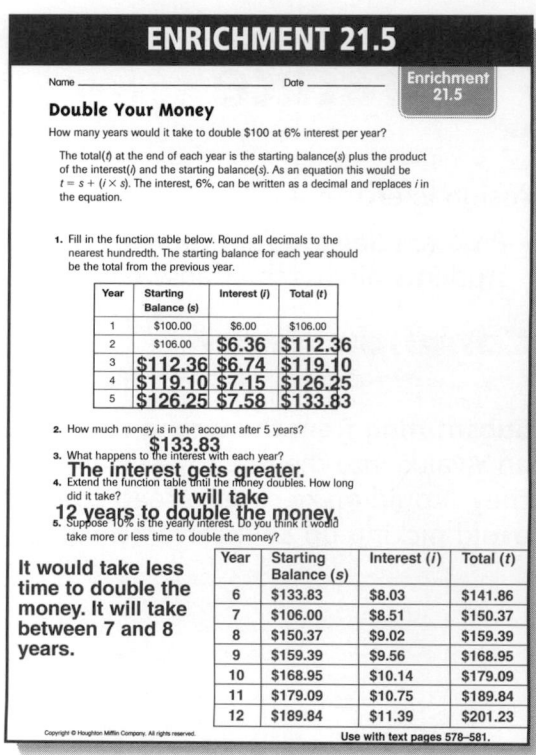

Practice Workbook Page 142

Reaching All Learners

Differentiated Instruction

English Learners

Worksheet 21.5 helps students answer the Explain Your Thinking section of Lesson 5. The step-by-step instructions also provide students with a model for writing equations that describe relationships between variables.

Special Needs
VISUAL, TACTILE

Materials: *counters*

- **You saved $5. Saving $3 more per week, how much will you save in 4 weeks?**
- **Model your $5 savings. Now show your next 2 "deposits." How many counters do you have?** $(5 + 3(2) = 11)$
- **Write $y = 5 + 3x$; $y =$ savings after x weeks. What do you save in 4 weeks?** $(5 + 3 (4) = 17)$

Gifted and Talented
VISUAL, AUDITORY

- Have students write a problem of their own that can be represented by a function rule and a function table.
- Have them share their problems with two other classmates. Each student should write a function rule and construct a function table in order to solve each problem.

TECHNOLOGY

Spiral Review

Create **customized** spiral review worksheets for individual students using the *Ways to Assess* CD-ROM.

Intervention

Use the *Ways to Success* intervention software to support students who need more help in understanding the concepts and skills taught in this chapter.

Lesson Planner

You can customize your teaching plan to meet your curriculum requirements with the Lesson Planner CD-ROM.

Language Arts Connection

It's a Matter of Function

- Review with students that in mathematics, a *function* is a rule that relates two variables.

- Have students list real-world situations where one entity is a function of another, for example, "climate is a function of location." Encourage students to share their lists and to discuss how the two "variables" are related.

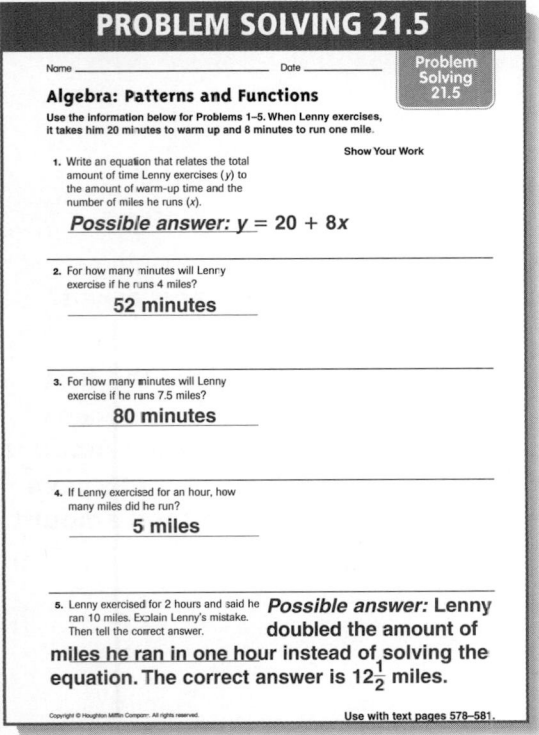

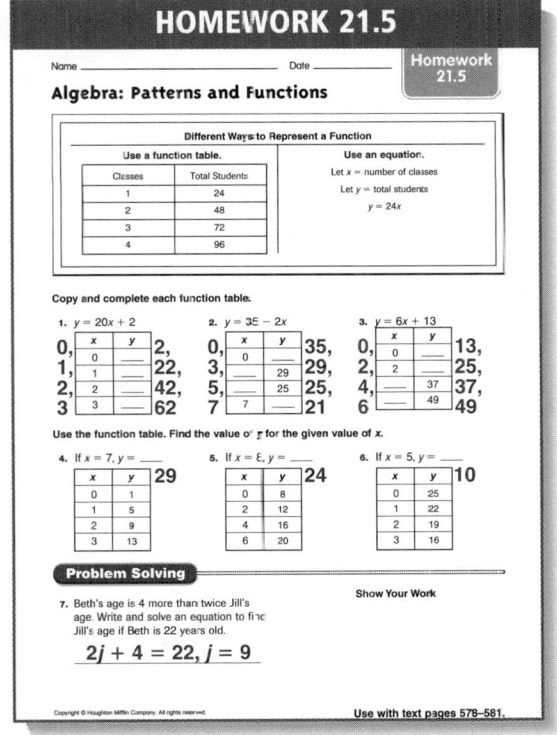

Homework Workbook Page 142

TEACHING LESSON 21.5

LESSON ORGANIZER

Objective Use function tables and equations to describe and extend patterns.

Resources Reteach, Practice, Enrichment, Problem Solving, Homework, English Learners, Transparencies, Math Center

Materials Table I Transparency

Warm-Up Activity
Solving for *y*

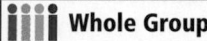 Whole Group | 5 minutes | Visual, Auditory

Have students solve each equation to find the value of *y* if *x* = 4.

1. $y = x + 3$ (7)

2. $y = 4x$ (16)

3. $y = 6x$ (24)

4. $y = x + 35$ (39)

5. $y = 2x + 1$ (9)

Algebra
Patterns and Functions

Objective Use function tables and equations to describe and extend patterns.

Learn About It  MathTracks 2/31
Listen and Understand

Some functions involve more than one operation.

Theo opened a savings account at the local bank with a deposit of $250. Theo intends to deposit $5 each week. How much will Theo have in his savings account after 7 weeks?

Different Ways to Represent Functions

Way ❶ You can use a function table.

The function table for the first $250 shows that each week after the first deposit adds $5 to the bank account.

Use that pattern to extend the function table so that it shows the amount for 7 weeks.

Number of weeks(x)	Amount in Savings(y)
0	$250
1	$255
2	$260
3	$265
4	$270
5	$275
6	$280
7	$285

Way ❷ You can use an equation that represents the values in the function table.

STEP 1 Write an equation that represents the relationship between *x* and *y*.

The function table shows that the initial deposit is $250 and each week adds $5 to the account.

amount deposited each week
↓
$y = 250 + 5x$ ←number of weeks
↑   ↑
total amount   beginning deposit

STEP 2 To find the amount, substitute the number of weeks after the initial deposit for *x* and simplify.

Think
7 weeks in all.
x = 7

$y = 250 + 5(7)$
$y = 250 + 35$
$y = 285$

Solution: Theo will have $285 in his bank account in 7 weeks.

578

---

❶ Introduce

 Teaching Transparency **21.5**

Materials: *Table I Transparency*

- Give students this problem: *Earl opens a savings account with a deposit of $50. He deposits $10 from his salary each week into the account. If he never withdraws any money, how much will he have in the account in 5 weeks?*

- Place the Table I Transparency on the overhead. Ask students to help you fill it out. Label the left column *Number of Weeks (x)*. Label the right column *Amount Saved (y)*.

- Begin with 0 weeks in the first row. **How much is in the account at the beginning of the first week?** ($50) **How much will be there at the end of the first week?** ($60) Continue with each row up to week 5.

- Ask students to find the answer to the problem in the table. ($100)

❷ Develop

Guide students through the *Learn About It* portion of the lesson.

- **What information is given in the problem?** (opening deposit of $250, and weekly deposits of $5) **What is asked?** (how much will be in the account in 7 weeks)

- **Look at Way 1. Notice the headings. Why does the first row at the function table have 0 weeks?** (It shows Theo's original deposit.) **What is the pattern shown in the *Amount* column?** (The amount for each week after the first is $5 more than it was for the previous week.) **What is the total amount after 7 weeks?** ($285)

Copy and complete each function table.

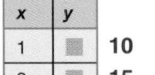

Ask Yourself
• What pattern does the function table show?

1. $y = 2x - 3$

x	y
3	■	3
4	■	5
5	■	7

2. $y = 5 + 5x$

x	y
1	■	10
2	■	15
3	■	20

3. $y = (x \div 2) - 4$

x	y
26	■	9
24	■	8
22	■	7

Use the function table. Find the value of y for the given value of x.

4. If $x = 6$, $y = $ ■.   **5.** If $x = 8$, $y = $ ■.   **6.** If $x = 10$, $y = $ ■.   **7.** If $x = 25$, $y = $ ■.

22

x	y
0	4
1	7
2	10
3	13

$y = 3x + 4$

45

x	y
0	5
1	10
2	15
3	20

$y = 5x + 5$

47

x	y
0	7
1	11
2	15
3	19

$y = 4x + 7$

74

x	y
3	8
5	14
7	20
9	26

$y = 3x - 1$

Explain Your Thinking ▶ What equation describes the relationship between x and y in Exercise 6? $y = 7 + 4x$

Practice and Problem Solving

Copy and complete each function table.

8. $y = 10x + 2$

x	y
0	■	2
1	■	12
2	■	22

9. $y = 65 + 2x$

x	y
0	■	65
3	■	71
6	■	77

10. $y = 20 - 4x$

x	y
0	■	20
2	■	12
■	8	3

11. $y = 9 + 4x$

x	y
0	■	9
■	13	1
■	25	4

Use the function table. Find the value of y for the given value of x. Then write the equation.

12. If $x = 5$, $y = $ ■.   **13.** If $x = 9$, $y = $ ■.   **14.** If $x = 8$, $y = $ ■.   **15.** If $x = 6$, $y = $ ■.

31

x	y
0	1
1	7
2	13
3	19

$y = 6x + 1$

18

x	y
0	9
3	12
5	14
7	16

$y = x + 9$

48

x	y
0	8
2	18
4	28
6	38

$y = 5x + 8$

34

x	y
0	10
1	14
2	18
3	22

$y = 4x + 10$

Go On

Chapter 21 Lesson 5   579

Quick Check Options

---

3 Practice

- **Look at Step 1 in Way 2. How does the equation represent the situation?** (The total, y, equals the deposit, $250, plus $5 multiplied by the number of weeks, x.)

- **Look at Step 2 in Way 2. How do you find the total amount?** (substitute number of weeks for x in the equation) **What is the total?** ($285)

Guided Practice

Have students complete **Exercises 1–7** as you observe. Remind them to use the *Ask Yourself* question to help. Give students the opportunity to talk about the question in *Explain Your Thinking*.

Assign **Exercises 8–24** as independent work.
- *Exercises 8–15* Have students explain their answers.

DAILY TEST PREP

For the equation $y = 17 + 5x$, what is the value of y when $x = 12$? (B)

A. 29   C. 67

B. 77   D. 34

Activity

Lesson Intervention

Or use Intervention CD-ROM Lesson 21.5

Make a Function Table

👤👤👤 Small Group	⏱ 5–10 minutes	Visual, Auditory

- Display: *Zia opens a savings account with $25. She deposits $5 a week. How much does she have in 5 weeks?*

- **What facts does the problem give?** (Zia opens an account with $25, saving $5 a week.) **What does the problem ask?** ($ she has in 5 weeks)

- **Draw a function table. How many columns does it need?** (2) **Label them** *Weeks (x)* **and** *Amount Saved (y).* **How many rows do we need?** (6: 1 for 0 weeks and 5 more) **Fill out the 1st and 2nd rows. How much does Zia have after 1 week?** ($30) **Complete the table. How much does she have after 5 weeks?** ($50)

 Data Problems 16–20. Julio's grandfather designed the gardens shown in the diagram below. For every tree there are 7 flower plants.

16. **Analyze** Look at the trees and flowers of the gardens. What patterns do you see?

17. **Reasoning** Write an equation that relates the number of trees of a garden (x) to the number of flowers of the garden (y).
    y = 7x

18. **Represent** Draw diagrams to show three more gardens in which the relationship between the number of trees and the number of flowers is the same as in the gardens shown at the right.
    Check students' diagrams.

19. Create a function table that shows the values for the number of trees (x) and the number of flowers (y) for the gardens shown at the right. Then extend the function table to show the next five gardens in the pattern.

x	y
1	7
2	14
3	21
4	28
5	35
6	42
7	49
8	56

20. Suppose Julio's grandfather creates another garden that fits this pattern. The number of flowers is 84. What is the number of trees?
    12 trees

19.

Garden 1

Garden 2

Garden 3

Key
🌸 — tree
✳ — flower

Aftershock Studios Rental Rates

Number of Hours (x)	Total Costs (y)
1	$250
2	$300
3	$350
4	$400

Use the function table to solve Problems 21–23.

21. Cindy records a CD at Aftershock Studios. She rents a studio for 8 hours. How much does Cindy pay? **$600**

22. **Write About It** Write an equation that represents the function in the function table. Explain why the equation represents the function.
    See Additional Answers on Page 583.

23. **You Decide** Echo Studios charges a flat fee of $100 plus a charge of $75 per hour. Describe a situation in which you would record at Echo Studios, and one in which you would record at Aftershock Recording. Explain your examples.
    See Additional Answers on Page 583.

24. Two numbers have a greatest common factor of 3 and a least common multiple of 45. What are the numbers?
    9, 15; 3, 45

Extra Practice See page 583, Set C.

Practice *continued*

- *Problem Solving for Problems 16–24* Have students explain their answers. For Problems 18 and 19, have students compare their answers.

Common Error

Evaluating part of the expression When students find the value of y in equations like those in this lesson, they may substitute a value for y but forget to evaluate the rest of the expression.

④ Assess and Close

- **Explain why there must be a zero row in function tables for equations such as $y = 15 + 2x$.** (The zero row accounts for the numerical value before evaluating the expression for $x = 1, 2$, and so forth.)

- **Explain why an equation is a good way to evaluate a function rule.** (You can substitute the value of x and evaluate quickly.)

Assign the **LESSON QUIZ** on Transparency 21.5 to further assess student understanding.

Quick Check

Check your understanding of Lessons 1–5.

Solve. (Lessons 1 and 2)

1. $5t = 80$ $t = 16$
2. $j - 7 = 46$ $j = 53$
3. $a \div 4 = 32$ $a = 128$
4. $v + 84 = 152$ $v = 68$

Copy and complete each function table. (Lessons 4 and 5)

5. $y = x \div 2$

x	y
2	▪ 1
4	▪ 2
6	▪ 3

6. $y = 5 - x$

x	y
0	▪ 5
1	▪ 4
2	▪ 3

7. $y = 2x + 15$

x	y
3	▪ 21
5	▪ 25
7	▪ 29

8. $y = 3x + 2$

x	y
1	▪ 5
5	▪ 17
7	▪ 23

Write an equation to solve each problem. (Lesson 3)

9. Greg works 35 hours and earns $525. How much does Greg earn each hour? $35x = 525$; $15

Science Connection

Nutrition Facts

Nutritionists study the way a body uses the nutrients that are in food. Three of the main kinds of nutrients are:

- **Carbohydrates** come from starch and sugar in food.
- **Fats** are contained in eggs, fish, meat, nuts, butter, and shortening.
- **Proteins** come from cheese, eggs, meat, fish, milk, beans, grains, nuts, and vegetables.

You might see the information about nutrients at the right on a yogurt container.

Amount per serving	
Total Fat	2 g
Total Carbohydrate	40 g
Protein	9 g

Use the label and an equation to solve.

1. How many times more carbohydrates are there than fats? **20**
2. **Estimate** About how many times more proteins are there than fats?
3. How many times more carbohydrates are there than proteins? **4.$\overline{4}$**

Estimates will vary. Possible answers: 4 or 5

Chapter 21 Lesson 5 581

Quick Check

Purpose: The Quick Check allows you to assess the student's understanding of the concepts presented in Lessons 1–5.

Items	Objectives Tested	Pages	Intervention
1–4	Determine what happens when you perform the same operation on both sides of an equation.	566–567	Reteach Resource 21.1 *Way to Success 21.1*
1–4	Write and solve equations.	568–571	Reteach Resource 21.2 *Way to Success 21.2*
9	Write an equation to solve a problem.	572–575	Reteach Resource 21.3 *Way to Success 21.3*
5–8	Use a function table to solve equations.	576–577	Reteach Resource 21.4 *Way to Success 21.4*
5–8	Use function tables and equations to describe and extend patterns.	578–581	Reteach Resource 21.5 *Way to Success 21.5*

Keeping a Journal

Have students write a problem based on a real-life situation and use it to explain how to write an equation from a function table.

Science Connection

Nutrition Facts

- Point out that mathematical skills are important in investigating and comparing the nutritional value of food products.
- Point out that to answer Exercises 1 and 2, students must divide the carbohydrate and protein content by fat content or estimate the contents before dividing.

 **Chapter Review/Test**

Purpose: This test provides an informal assessment of the Chapter 21 objectives.

Chapter Test Items 1–10

To assign a numerical grade for this Chapter Test, use 10 points for each test item.

Check Understanding

You can use the **Write About It** question to assess student understanding of a key chapter concept.

Customizing Your Instruction

For students who have not yet mastered these objectives, you can use the Reteaching Resources listed in the chart below.

 # Assessment Options

A summary test for this chapter is also provided in the Unit Resource Folder.

 ## Adequate Yearly Progress

Use the End of Grade Test Prep Assessment Guide to help familiarize your students with the format of standardized tests.

 **Chapter Review/Test**

 **VOCABULARY**

Vocabulary
equation
function
inverse operations
variable

1. A letter that stands for a number in an algebraic expression is called a(n) **variable**

2. **inverse operations** ___ are two operations that have opposite effects.

 **CONCEPTS AND SKILLS**

Solve using inverse operations. (Lessons 1–2, pp. 566–571)

3. $w - 95 = 890$
   $w = 985$

4. $231 = x + 67$
   $x = 164$

5. $9y = 135$

Copy and complete each function table. (Lesson 4, pp. 576–577)

6. $y = 9 - x$

x	y	
4	▣	5
5	▣	4
6	▣	3

7. $y = 8 + x$

x	y	
10	▣	18
12	▣	20
14	▣	22

8. $y = 36 \div x$

x	y	
3	▣	12
6	▣	6
9	▣	4

Use the function table. Find the value of **y** for the given value of **x**. (Lesson 5, pp. 578–579)

9. If $x = 9$, $y = $ ▣. **19**

x	y
3	7
4	9
5	11

Check equation and function table. Possible answer: A function table shows the values of the equation as well as describes and extends the pattern.

 **PROBLEM SOLVING**

Solve. (Lesson 3, pp. 572–573)

10. Last week, each of 5 students spent the same amount of time on homework. They spent a total of 68 hours on homework. How many hours did each student spend on homework?
   $5x = 68$; $x = 13.6$; 13.6 hours

Write About It

Show You Understand

Write an equation and then make a function table for the equation. Explain how a function table works.

582 **Chapter 21** Chapter Review/Test

Reteaching Support

Chapter Test Items	Summary Test Items	Chapter Objectives Tested	TE Pages	Use These Reteaching Resources
1–5	1–7	**21A** Write and solve equations using equality properties.	566A–571	Reteach Resource 21.1, 21.2 Ways to Success CD: 21.1, 21.2 Skillsheet 168
6–9	8–14	**21B** Use functions and function tables to solve equations.	576A–581	Reteach Resource 21.4, 21.5 Ways to Success CD: 21.4, 21.5 Skillsheet 169, 170
10	15–20	**21C** Analyze and solve problems by writing an equation.	572A–575	Reteach Resource 21.3 Ways to Success CD: 21.3 Skillsheet ... 171

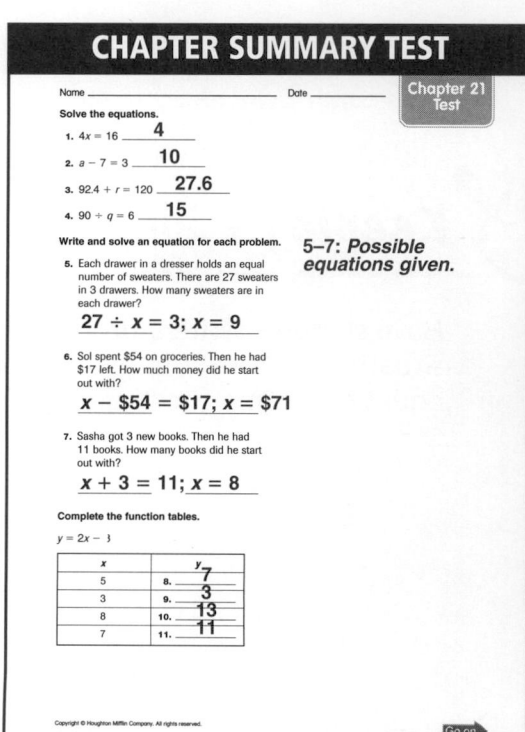

CHAPTER SUMMARY TEST

Name _____ Date _____ | Chapter 21 Test

Solve the equations.

1. $4x = 16$ __**4**__

2. $a - 7 = 3$ __**10**__

3. $92.4 + r = 120$ __**27.6**__

4. $90 \div q = 6$ __**15**__

Write and solve an equation for each problem.

5–7: Possible equations given.

5. Each drawer in a dresser holds an equal number of sweaters. There are 27 sweaters in 3 drawers. How many sweaters are in each drawer?
   $27 \div x = 3$; $x = 9$

6. Sol spent $54 on groceries. Then he had $17 left. How much money did he start out with?
   $x - \$54 = \$17$; $x = \$71$

7. Sasha got 3 new books. Then he had 11 books. How many books did he start out with?
   $x + 3 = 11$; $x = 8$

Complete the function tables.

$y = 2x - 3$

x	y
5	8. **7**
3	9. **3**
8	10. **13**
7	11. **11**

Copyright © Houghton Mifflin Company. All rights reserved.

Go on

Set A (Lesson 2, pp. 568–571)

Solve using inverse operations.

1. $15 + d = 27$
2. $e - 118 = 110$
   $e = 228$
3. $6f = 48$
   $f = 8$
4. $12 = g \div 9$
   $g = 108$
5. $h + 76 = 201$
   $h = 125$
6. $12 \cdot j = 132$
   $j = 11$
7. $145 = k - 423$
8. $m \div 8 = 23$
   $m = 184$
9. $15n = 1,275$
   $n = 85$
10. $p + 167 = 903$
    $p = 736$
11. $q \div 13 = 9$
    $q = 117$
12. $r - 619 = 586$
    $r = 1,205$

Set B (Lesson 4, pp. 576–578)

Copy and complete each function table.

1. $y = 2 + x$

x	y	
6	▓	8
8	▓	10
10	▓	12
12	▓	14

2. $y = 8 - x$

x	y	
0	▓	8
1	▓	7
2	▓	6
3	▓	5

3. $y = 5x$

x	y	
2	▓	10
4	▓	20
6	▓	30
8	▓	40

4. $y = 24 \div x$

x	y	
1	▓	24
2	▓	12
3	▓	8
4	▓	6

Set C (Lesson 5, pp. 579–581)

Copy and complete each function table.

1. $y = 3x + 4$

x	y	
0	▓	4
2	▓	10
4	▓	16
6	▓	22

2. $y = 7x - 5$

x	y	
2	▓	9
3	▓	16
4	▓	23
5	▓	30

3. $y = (x \div 2) + 6$

x	y	
4	▓	8
6	▓	9
8	▓	10
10	▓	11

4. $y = 10x - 8$

x	y	
3	▓	22
6	▓	52
▓	82	9
▓	112	12

Use the function table. Find the value of y for the given value of x.

5. If $x = 6$, $y = n$.
   $n = 12$

x	y
1	7
2	8
3	9
4	10

6. If $x = 8$, $y = n$.
   $n = 26$

x	y
0	2
1	5
2	8
3	11

7. If $x = 10$, $y = n$.
   $n = 110$

x	y
0	10
2	30
4	50
6	70

8. If $x = 12$, $y = n$.
   $n = 144$

x	y
2	4
4	16
6	36
8	64

Chapter 21 Extra Practice   **583**

Chapter 21

Lesson 2, pp. 568–571

Calculator Connection

1c. Possible answer: Add $1 + 3$ to get 4, $4 + 5$ to get 9, $9 + 7$ to get 16; add consecutive odd numbers to the numbers in the 2nd column.

Lesson 5, pp. 578–581

22. Possible answer: $y = 200 + 50x$, where x represents the number of hours; $y = 250 + 50x$, where x represents the number of hours after the first hour.

23. A good answer will reflect these points:
- For a situation in which the number of hours is less than 4, you would record at Echo Studios because the cost is less.
- For a situation in which the number of hours is greater than 4, you would record at Aftershock Studios because the cost is less.

CHAPTER SUMMARY TEST

Name _____   Date _____   Chapter 21 Test continued

$y = 26 - 2x$

x	
4	12. __18__
0	
8	14. __10__

13. __0__

26. __10__

Write and solve an equation for each problem.

15–20: Possible equations given.

15. Department store workers get a raise of $1.75 per hour. Their new hourly wage is $9.25 per hour. How much did they earn before the raise?

   $x + \$1.75 = \$9.25$; $x = \$7.50$

16. Robin School has 64 fifth-graders. This is half as many as Bluebird School has. How many fifth-graders are there in Bluebird School?

   $x = 64 \times 2$; $x = 128$

17. Howard shoveled 7 driveways. Meredith shoveled 6 more. How many did Meredith shovel?

   $x = 7 + 6$; $x = 13$

18. Vic earned $210. He worked for 30 hours. How much does he earn per hour?

   $\$210 \div x = 30$; $x = \$7$

19. Kim collected 35 leaves. Zora collected 12 more leaves. How many leaves did Zora collect?

   $x - 12 = 35$; $x = 47$

20. Thelma has 9 pairs of jeans. This is 2 more pairs than Janet has. How many pairs of jeans does Janet have?

   $x + 2 = 9$; $x = 7$

Equations and Functions   583

Lesson By Lesson Overview
Integers

Lesson 1

- Students learn about integers.
- Negative integers are introduced by extending the number line to the left of zero and by presenting them as the opposites of positive whole numbers.

Lesson 2

- Students use a number line to compare and order integers.

Lesson 3

- Students model adding integers using two-color counters.
- Students use counters to compare two addition expressions that involve integers and solve word problems.

Lesson 4

- Students model subtraction of integers using two-color counters.

Lesson 5

- Students use a number line to add and subtract integers.
- Students use rules to decide whether the sum of two integers will be positive or negative.
- Students add and subtract integers to solve equations.

Lesson 6

- Students solve problems that involve adding or subtracting integers. Students choose a strategy or a computation method to solve problems.

SKILLS TRACE: INTEGERS		
Grade 4	**Grade 5**	**Grade 6**
• write integers (ch. 24)	• locate integers on a number line and find absolute value of integers	• represent, write, compare, and order integers (ch. 11)
	• compare and order integers	• add, subtract, multiply, and divide integers (ch. 11)
	• add and subtract integers	

Chapter Planner

Lesson	Objective	Vocabulary	Materials	✔ NCTM Standards
22.1 **Integers and Absolute Value** p. 586A	Identify integers and find the absolute value of an integer	positive numbers negative numbers opposite integers absolute value	Number Line Transparency, blank transparency, student copies of Number Line Transparency	**Numbers and Operations:** Understand numbers, ways of representing numbers, relations among numbers, and number systems.
22.2 **Compare and Order Integers** p. 588A	Use a number line to compare integers.		Number line Transparency, student copies of Number Line Transparency	**Numbers and Operations:** Understand numbers, ways of representing numbers, relations among numbers, and number systems.
22.3 **Hands-On: Model Addition of Integers** p. 592A	Use counters to model addition of integers.		red and yellow counters	**Numbers and Operations:** Understand numbers, ways of representing numbers, relations among numbers, and number systems.
22.4 **Hands-On: Model Subtraction of Integers** p. 596A	Use counters to model subtraction of integers.		red and yellow counters	**Numbers and Operations:** Understand numbers, ways of representing numbers, relations among numbers, and number systems; Understand meanings of operations and how they relate to one another.
22.5 **Add and Subtract Integers** p. 598A	Use a number line to add and subtract integers.	integers opposite	Number Lines Transparency	**Numbers and Operations:** Understand numbers, ways of representing numbers, relations among numbers, and number systems; Understand meanings of operations and how they relate to one another.
22.6 **Problem-Solving Application: Use Integers** p. 602A	Solve problems that include integers.		Problem Solving: Four Step Process Transparency	**Numbers and Operations:** Explore numbers less than 0 by extending the number line and through familiar applications.

Resources For Reaching All Learners

LESSON RESOURCES: Reteach, Practice, Enrichment, Problem Solving, Homework, English Learners, Daily Routines, Transparencies, Math Center.

ADDITIONAL RESOURCES FROM HOUGHTON MIFFLIN: Combination Classroom Planning Guide, Chapter Challenges, Every Day Counts, Math at Hand (student handbook)

Every Day Counts

The **Measurement** activities in **Every Day Counts** support the math in this chapter.

Assessing Prior Knowledge

Before beginning the chapter, you can assess student understandings in order to assist you in differentiating instruction.

Complete Chapter Pretest in Unit Resource Folder

Use this test to assess both prerequisite skills (**Are You Ready?** — one page) and chapter content (**Check What You Know** — two pages).

Chapter 22 Prerequisite Skills Pretest

Chapter 22 New Content Pretest

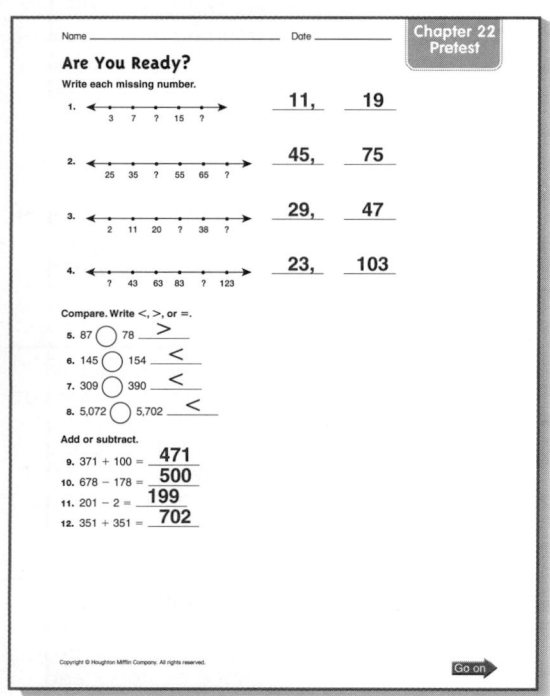

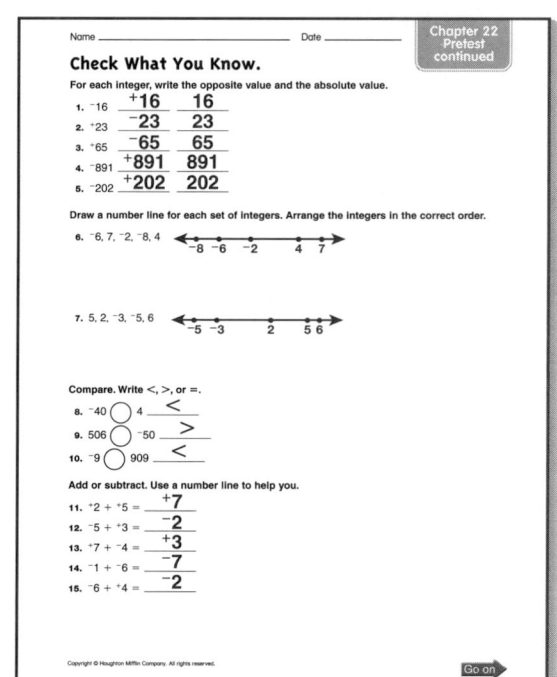

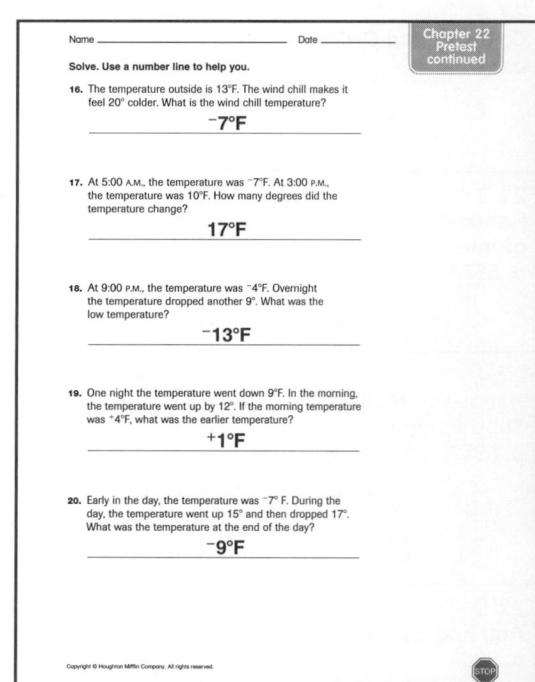

Customizing Instruction

For Students Having Difficulty

Items	Prerequisites	Ways to Success
1–4	Locate numbers on a number line	Skillsheet: 172
5–8	Compare whole numbers	Skillsheet: 173
9–12	Add and subtract whole numbers	Skillsheet: 174

Ways to Success: Intervention for every concept and skill (CD-ROM or Chapter Intervention Skillsheets).

For Students Having Success

Items	Objectives	Resources
1–5	**22A** Locate integers on a number line and find the absolute value of integers	Enrichment 22.1
6–10	**22B** Compare and order integers.	Enrichment 22.2
11–18	**22C** Add and subtract integers.	Enrichment 22.3, 22.4, 22.5
16–20	**22D** Analyze and solve problems using integers.	Enrichment 22.6

Use **Chapter Challenges** with any students who have success with all new chapter content.

Other Pretest Options

Informal Pretest in Student Book

The student book pretest assesses vocabulary and prerequisite skills needed for success in this chapter.

Ways to Success CD-ROM

The *Ways to Success* chapter pretest has automatic assignment of appropriate review lessons.

Consider using **Knowing Mathematics** with any students who are working two or more years below grade level.

Chapter Resources

Assessing Prior Knowledge

- Have students draw a number line from 0 to 100. Ask them to mark off and label intervals of 10.
- Then have them locate and label these numbers on the number line: 32, 75, 9, 58, 86, 23, 60.

 Activity

Ongoing Skill Activity

Human Integers (absolute value, add and subtract integers)

- Write "+" , "−" , or "0" on several name tags and have students represent zero and integers.
- At the beginning of the chapter have equal numbers of "positive" and "negative" students on either side of a "zero" student form a number line to model absolute value.
- Have students model addition by returning "zero pairs" of students to their seats. Then, have them model subtraction by asking "zero pairs" of students to join the "equation."

 Activity

Connecting to the Unit Project

- Have student pairs write two riddles where the answers can be deciphered, letter by letter, using a code based on adding, subtracting, comparing, and/or ordering integers. Have students exchange riddles and solve.
- Have pairs report on the progress they are making in developing codes and writing messages. As pairs complete a code, you might have them present it to the class for decoding.

Teacher Support

Professional Resources Handbook

Research, Mathematics Content, and Language Intervention

Research-Based Teaching

NCTM recognizes and supports the need for restructuring algebra so that it becomes part of the mathematics curriculum for all Grade K–12 students. Students must know and be able to successfully use algebra in order to continue learning mathematics. See *Professional Resources Handbook, Grade 5,* Unit 8.

For more ideas relating to Unit 8, see the Teacher Support Handbook at the back of this Teacher's Edition.

Language Intervention

Be sure students understand the meaning of the word integers. Integers include zero, all positive whole numbers, and their opposites. 5 1/2 and −5 1/2 are *not* integers. Also be sure students are reading numbers correctly. Numbers greater than zero are positive numbers; so, +4 is read as "positive four," not "plus four." Numbers less than zero are negative numbers; so, −4 is read as "negative four," not "minus four."

 **Time Saving Technology Support**

Ways to Assess Customized Spiral Review
   and Test Generator CD-ROM
Lesson Planner CD-ROM
Ways to Success Intervention CD-ROM
Math Tracks CD-ROM
Education Place: **www.eduplace.com/math/mw/**
Houghton Mifflin Math eBook CD-ROM
eManipulatives
eGames

Starting Chapter 22
Integers

Chapter Objectives

22A Locate integers on a number line and find the absolute value of integers.

22B Compare and order integers.

22C Add and subtract integers.

22D Analyze and solve problems using integers.

Math Background

Integers

The set of integers consists of the counting numbers 1, 2, 3..., their opposites ⁻1, ⁻2, ⁻3..., and the number 0. Students might have a hard time grasping the idea of negative integers, hence it is important to explain the need of negative integers to record such quantities as the temperature below zero, the amount below sea level, or an amount lost or owed.

Integers can be represented on a number line that extends both to the left and to the right of zero. The positive integers are represented to the right of 0 and the negative integers are represented to the left. Numbers such as ⁻3 and ⁺3 are opposite numbers.

This number line is very helpful when comparing integers. On a number line, the number farthest to the left is the least and the number farthest to the right is the greatest. Students need to develop the idea that the greater the absolute value of a negative integer, the smaller the number. For example: ⁻332 < ⁻2 and ⁻332 < ⁻299.

A raised minus sign is used for negative integers and a raised plus sign is used for positive numbers. Whether students are required to write the raised plus sign is left to the discretion of the teacher.

INVESTIGATION

Use Data

The lowest elevation in the United States is in the Badwater Basin in Death Valley National Park. Elevation is based upon sea level, so ⁻282 feet means 282 feet below sea level. Look at the diagram below. What is the difference in elevation between Telescope Peak and Badwater Basin?   **11,331 feet**

Telescope Peak — 11,049 ft

Death Valley

Sea Level ⁻282 ft

Badwater Basin

584

Using The Investigation

Have students work in small groups to answer the question posed on page 584.

To extend the investigation, have students do the following activity.

- Research the elevations of different places in the world. Pick two places with elevations above sea level and two places that are below sea level. Order these elevations from greatest to least. What is the difference between the greatest elevation and the least? Write a short paragraph describing each place.

For more information about projects and investigations, visit **Education Place**. www.eduplace.com/math/mw/

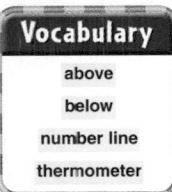 # Chapter Pretest

Use this page to review and remember
what you need to know for this chapter.

VOCABULARY

Choose the best word to complete each sentence.

Vocabulary
above
below
number line
thermometer

1. Use a ____ to measure temperature. **thermometer**

2. On a ____, numbers are assigned to equally
spaced points. **number line**

3. The temperature ⁻5°C is read as "five degrees **below**
zero Celsius."

CONCEPTS AND SKILLS

Compare. Write >, <, or = for each .

4. 357 **<** 375   5. 89 **<** 98   6. 0.7 **=** 0.70   7. 2 **>** 0.2

Add or subtract.

8. 156 + 10 **166**   9. 459 − 250 **209**   10. 348 − 121 **469**   11. 627 − 227 **400**

Write each missing number.

12. 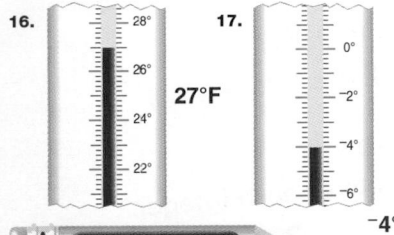 **80, 95**
75 ▪ 85 90 ▪ 100 105

13. **125, 150, 225**
75 100 ▪ ▪ 175 200 ▪

14. **55, 63**
47 51 ▪ 59 67 71

15. **325, 700, 950**
200 ▪ 450 575 ▪ 825 ▪

Write each temperature in °F.

16. **27°F**
17. **⁻4°F**
18. **⁻9°F**
19. **1°F**

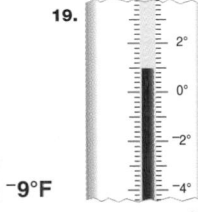

Write About It   *See Additional Answers on page 607.*

20. Suppose the temperature at 8:00 A.M. is
6°F and at 8:00 P.M. is ⁻2°F. How many
degrees did the temperature drop? Use
pictures or words to explain your answer.

 **Test Prep on the Net**
Visit *Education Place* at
eduplace.com/kids/mw/
for more review.

 Chapter Pretest

Prerequisite Skills

Items	Skill
1–3	Vocabulary needed for this chapter
4–7	Comparing whole numbers and decimals
8–11	Add and subtract whole numbers
12–15	Finding missing numbers in sequences
16–19	Reading and writing temperatures
20	Understanding temperature

Chapter Challenges

For Mathematically Promising Students

Use *Chapter Challenges* resource book.

Explore: Integers and the Motion of a
Spring, page 127, after Lesson 1

Extend: Integer Cubes, page 129,
after Lesson 3

Connect: Integer Puzzles, page 131, after
Lesson 5

Using The Chapter Pretest

This page will help students review some of the
prerequisite skills needed for this chapter. The chart
above indicates which skills are covered on the
pretest. If students need more help with these
prerequisite skills use **Ways to Success,** Houghton
Mifflin's intervention program.

 Students who need more review can visit
Education Place, Houghton Mifflin's
award-winning website.

NSF Children's Math Worlds

Children's Math Worlds focuses on the use of
models to represent mathematical situations.
Thus, using a *Children's Math Worlds lesson* helps
students develop a general facility with drawing
models to support their thinking that will transfer
to all their mathematical work.

Integers and Absolute Value

PLANNING THE LESSON

MATHEMATICS OBJECTIVE
Identify integers and find the absolute value of an integer.

Use Lesson Planner CD-ROM for Lesson 22.1.

 **Daily Routines**

Vocabulary
Ask students what they think the term *negative numbers* means. (Responses will vary.) Give examples of temperatures above and below 0° Celsius. Then display a number line. Mark the numbers *1, 2, 3,* and so on, to the right of *0* on the line. Then extend the number line to the left of *0*. Mark ⁻1, ⁻2, ⁻3, and so on. Explain that these are *negative numbers*.

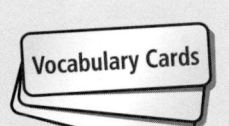
Vocabulary Cards

Meeting North Carolina's Standards
Prepare for Grade 6 Objective **1.01** Develop number sense for negative rational numbers.

Lesson Transparency **22.1**

Problem of the Day
The Handy Hardware Store is open Monday through Saturday from 9:30 A.M. to 6:00 P.M. How many hours is it open per week? (51 h)

Quick Review
Round the number 483,709,681 to the place indicated.
1. ten thousands (483,710,000)
2. hundred thousands (483,700,000)
3. millions (484,000,000)
4. ten millions (480,000,000)
5. hundred millions (500,000,000)

Lesson Quiz
Write the opposite of each integer.
1. ⁺8 (⁻8)
2. ⁻5 (⁺5)
3. ⁺27 (⁻27)
4. ⁻14 (⁺14)
5. ⁺32 (⁻32)

LEVELED PRACTICE

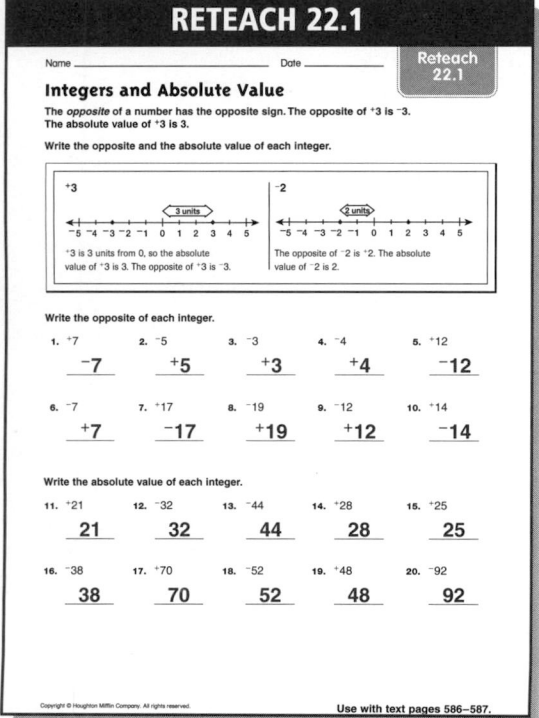

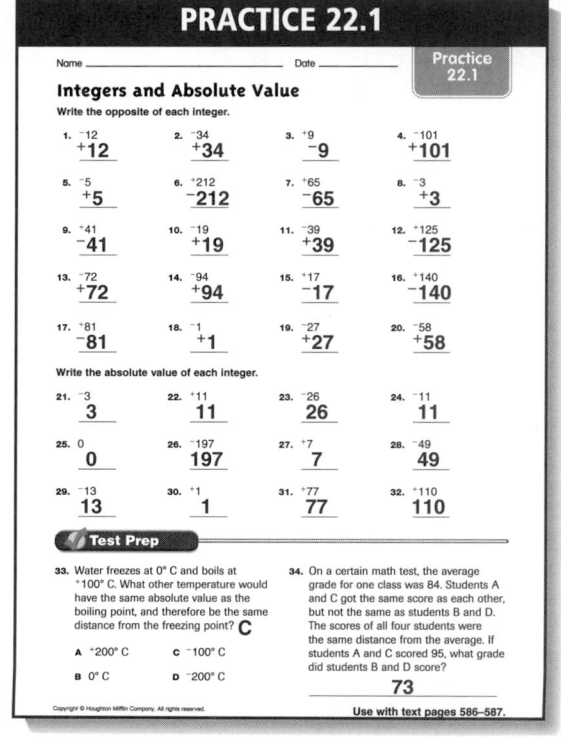

Practice Workbook Page 143

Reaching All Learners
Differentiated Instruction

English Learners

Worksheet 22.1 teaches key vocabulary used in Lesson 1. It also helps students understand the bar graph on page 587 and provides practice in preparation for completing Problems 37–40.

Special Needs
VISUAL, AUDITORY

- Display a number line marked from ⁻5 to ⁺5. Draw an arrow from 0 to ⁺4. **How many units is it from 0 to ⁺4?** (4) **How many units from 0 to ⁻4?** (4)
- Explain that ⁺4 and ⁻4 are both 4 units from 0. Help students understand opposites and absolute value.

Gifted and Talented
VISUAL, AUDITORY

- Challenge students to write five positive and five negative integers. Invite them to exchange papers with a classmate. Have them write the opposite of each integer and then identify the absolute value of each pair of numbers.

Literature Connection

Math Talk
- Have students read *Math Talk: Mathematical Ideas in Poems for Two Voices* by Theoni Pappas (Wide World Publishing-Tetra, 1991).

- Suggest that different pairs of students might wish to prepare and read one of the dialogues for the class.

TECHNOLOGY

Spiral Review

Using the *Ways to Assess* CD-ROM, you can create **customized** spiral review worksheets covering any lessons you choose.

Education Place

Encourage students to visit Education Place at **eduplace.com/kids/mw/** for more student activities.

Lesson Planner

Use the Lesson Planner CD-ROM to see how lesson objectives for this chapter are correlated to standards.

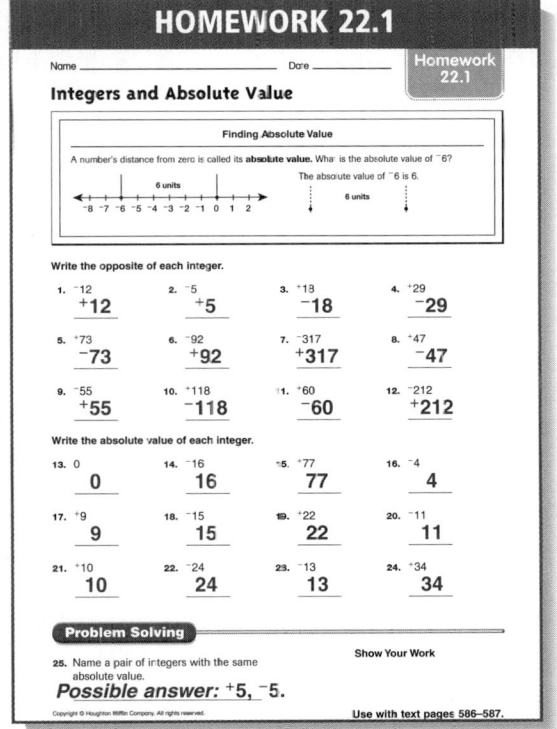

PROBLEM SOLVING 22.1

Problem Solving 22.1

Name _____ Date _____

Integers and Absolute Value

Show Your Work

1. The lowest temperature ever recorded in Alaska was 80 degrees Fahrenheit below zero. Write that temperature as an integer.
$$-80°F$$

2. The lowest temperature ever recorded in Hawaii was 12 degrees Fahrenheit. What is the opposite of that temperature written as an integer?
$$-12°F$$

3. A quarterback is sacked for a loss of 8 yards. Write that distance as an integer. What is its opposite?
$$-8 \text{ yards}; 8 \text{ yards}$$

4. Professional golfers try to score under par. Draw a number line to show a golfer with a score of ⁺4 and another with a score of ⁺3.
⁻5 ⁻4 ⁻3 ⁻2 ⁻1 0 1 2 3 4 5

5. Is ⁺2 greater than all the negative integers? Explain.
Yes; *Possible explanation:* ⁺2 is to the right of 0 on a number line, and all the negative integers are to the left of 0. The farther a number is to the right of 0, the greater the number.

Copyright © Houghton Mifflin Company. All rights reserved. **Use with text pages 586–587.**

HOMEWORK 22.1

Homework 22.1

Name _____ Date _____

Integers and Absolute Value

Finding Absolute Value

A number's distance from zero is called its **absolute value**. What is the absolute value of ⁻6?

6 units
⁻8 ⁻7 ⁻6 ⁻5 ⁻4 ⁻3 ⁻2 ⁻1 0 1 2

The absolute value of ⁻6 is 6.
6 units

Write the opposite of each integer.

1. ⁻12 → ⁺12
2. ⁻5 → ⁺5
3. ⁺18 → ⁻18
4. ⁺29 → ⁻29

5. ⁺73 → ⁻73
6. ⁻92 → ⁺92
7. ⁻317 → ⁺317
8. ⁺47 → ⁻47

9. ⁻55 → ⁺55
10. ⁺118 → ⁻118
11. ⁺60 → ⁻60
12. ⁻212 → ⁺212

Write the absolute value of each integer.

13. 0 → 0
14. ⁻16 → 16
15. ⁺77 → 77
16. ⁻4 → 4

17. ⁺9 → 9
18. ⁻15 → 15
19. ⁺22 → 22
20. ⁻11 → 11

21. ⁺10 → 10
22. ⁻24 → 24
23. ⁻13 → 13
24. ⁺34 → 34

Problem Solving

Show Your Work

25. Name a pair of integers with the same absolute value.
Possible answer: ⁺5, ⁻5.

Copyright © Houghton Mifflin Company. All rights reserved. **Use with text pages 586–587.**

ENGLISH LEARNERS 22.1

English Learners 22.1

Name _____ Date _____

Integers and Absolute Value

An opposite is an item in a pair that is the reverse of the other item in the pair. Write the opposite of each item below. An example has been done for you.

Example: short tall

1. large **small**
2. up **down**
3. open **closed**
4. happy **sad**

Numbers also have opposites. The number line below shows **integers**. Integers include the number zero, positive counting numbers, and their opposites. **Positive numbers** are greater than 0. **Negative numbers** are less than 0. The opposite of a positive number is a negative number that is the same distance from 0 on the number line.

⁻5 ⁻4 ⁻3 ⁻2 ⁻1 0 1 2 3 4 5

Write the opposite of each integer. An example has been done for you.

Example: ⁺2 → ⁻2

5. ⁺3 → **⁻3**
6. ⁻5 → **⁺5**
7. ⁺15 → **⁻15**

The graph below shows the low temperatures of four cities. The mean low temperature is the average low temperature of each city. The extreme low temperature is the lowest temperature of each city. Use the graph to answer Questions 8–10.

Low Temperatures of Selected Cities
■ Mean low temperature
□ Extreme low temperature

8. What four cities are shown on the graph?
Houston, Mobile, Los Angeles, Seattle

9. Which city had a mean low temperature of 4°C?
Houston

10. Which city's mean low temperature was the opposite of ⁻10°C?
Los Angeles

Copyright © Houghton Mifflin Company. All rights reserved. **Use with text pages 586–587.**

Homework Workbook Page 143

TEACHING LESSON 22.1

LESSON ORGANIZER

Objective Identify integers and find the absolute value of an integer.

Resources Reteach, Practice, Enrichment, Problem Solving, Homework, English Learners, Transparencies, Math Center

Materials Number Lines Transparency, blank transparency, student copies of Number Lines Transparency

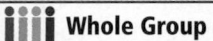

Warm-Up Activity
Add and Subtract 2-Digit Numbers

iiii Whole Group	⏲ 5 minutes	Visual, Auditory

Write the following exercises on the chalkboard for students to solve:

1. 17 + 49 (66)
2. 86 − 17 (69)
3. 99 + 99 (198)
4. 83 + 117 (200)
5. 312 − 119 (193)

Integers and Absolute Value

Objective Identify integers and find the absolute value of an integer.

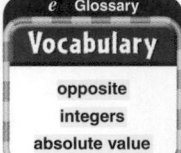

Learn About It  MathTracks 2/32 Listen and Understand

The number zero and the numbers greater than zero, called the *positive numbers*, can be shown on a number line. You can extend the number line from zero to show numbers less than zero, called the *negative numbers*.

‾10 ‾9 ‾8 ‾7 ‾6 ‾5 ‾4 ‾3 ‾2 ‾1 0 +1 +2 +3 +4 +5 +6 +7 +8 +9 +10

Negative 7, or ‾7, is the **opposite** of positive 7, or +7. The set of **integers** includes zero, the counting numbers, and their opposites.

To write the opposite of an integer, change its sign.

The opposite of +8 is ‾8.　　　The opposite of ‾15 is +15.

Opposite numbers are the same distance from zero on the number line. A number's distance from zero is called its **absolute value.** The absolute value of ‾3 and +3 is 3 because both are 3 units from zero.

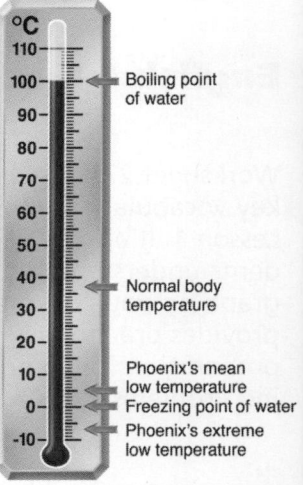

°C
110 —
100 — ← Boiling point of water
90 —
80 —
70 —
60 —
50 —
40 — ← Normal body temperature
30 —
20 —
10 — ← Phoenix's mean low temperature
0 — ← Freezing point of water
‾10 — ← Phoenix's extreme low temperature

Finding Absolute Value

What is the absolute value of +5?

| 5 units |

‾1　0　+1　+2　+3　+4　+5　+6

What is the absolute value of ‾4?

| 4 units |

‾7　‾6　‾5　‾4　‾3　‾2　‾1　0　+1

Solution: The absolute value of +5 is 5. The absolute value of ‾4 is 4.

Guided Practice

No. *Possible answer:* The absolute value has no sign. It is the distance of the integer from zero, regardless of the integer's sign. If the integer is positive, the opposite will be negative, and vice versa.

Write the opposite of each integer.

1. ‾9 +9　　2. +6 ‾6　　3. ‾4 +4　　4. ‾45 +45　　5. +134 ‾134　　6. +87 ‾87

Write the absolute value of each integer.

7. +3 3　　8. ‾1 1　　9. ‾8 8　　10. 0 0　　11. +11 11　　12. ‾23 23

TEST TIPS Explain Your Thinking ▶ Is the absolute value of an integer the same as the opposite of that integer? Explain. **See above.**

586

1 Introduce

iiii Whole Group	⏲ 5 minutes

Teaching Transparency **22.1**

Materials: *Number Lines Transparency, blanks transparency, student copies of Number Lines Transparency*

• Place the blank transparency on the overhead with the Number Lines Transparency over it. Label Number Line 1 from ‾10 to +10 with 0 in the middle. **The sign of the integer tells in which direction to move from 0 on the number line. The digit tells you how many units the number is from 0.**

• Ask a volunteer to find ‾6 in the number line and find its distance from 0. Draw an arrow from *0 to ‾6.*

• Do the same for +6. **Numbers with the same digit, such as +6 and ‾6, are the same distance from 0. That is, they have the same *absolute value*. They are called *opposites* because they are in opposite directions from 0 on the number line.**

• Ask volunteers to identify other pairs of opposites.

2 Develop

Guide students through the *Learn About It* section.

• **What is the absolute value of +5?** (5) **What is the absolute value of ‾4?** (4)

• **Notice that +4 and ‾4 have the same absolute value. They are *opposites* because they have the same absolute value with opposite signs.**

• **What numbers are included in the set of integers?** (0, the counting numbers, and their opposites)

Guided Practice

Have students complete **Exercises 1–12** as you observe. Give students the opportunity to talk about the question in *Explain Your Thinking*.

586　CHAPTER 22　Lesson 1

Write the opposite of each integer.

13. ⁻17 **⁺17**   14. ⁻30 **⁺30**   15. ⁺6 **⁻6**   16. ⁻12 **⁺12**   17. ⁺28 **⁻28**   18. ⁺106 **⁻106**

19. ⁺82 **⁻82**   20. ⁺184 **⁻184** 21. ⁺19 **⁻19**   22. ⁻44 **⁺44**   23. ⁺102 **⁻102** 24. ⁻59 **⁺59**

Write the absolute value of each integer.

25. ⁺7 **7**   26. ⁻6 **6**   27. ⁺1 **1**   28. ⁻7 **7**   29. ⁻16 **16**   30. ⁻9 **9**

31. ⁻10 **10**   32. ⁺15 **15**   33. ⁺6 **6**   34. ⁻3 **3**   35. ⁺8 **8**   36. ⁺10 **10**

Data Use the graph to solve Problems 37–40.

37. Which city had an extreme low temperature of ⁻16°C? **Mobile, AL**

38. **Mental Math** Which two temperatures shown on the graph are opposites? **⁻2°C and 2°C**

39. **Estimate** Which city does not have about a 20°C difference between its mean and extreme low temperatures? **Los Angeles, CA**

40. Charleston, South Carolina, has an extreme low temperature of ⁻14°C. Which city from the graph has that same extreme low temperature? **Houston, TX**

41. **Represent** Mobile, Alabama, is about 8 feet above sea level. New Orleans, Louisiana, is about 5 feet below sea level. Draw a graph to show the elevations of these two cities. **Check graphs.**

42. **Explain** Zero is not positive or negative. What is the opposite of 0? **The opposite of 0 is 0.**

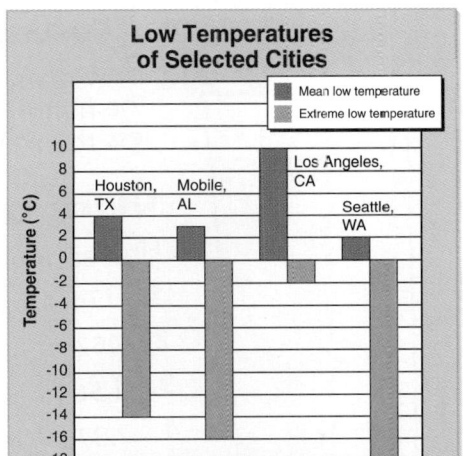

Low Temperatures of Selected Cities

■ Mean low temperature
■ Extreme low temperature

Daily Review	Test Prep

Solve each equation. (Ch. 21, Lesson 2)

43. 55 = 11y **y = 5**   44. n ÷ 6 = 5 **n = 30**

45. x ÷ 8 = 2 **x = 16**   46. 6c = 18 **c = 3**

47. c ÷ 9 = 45 **c = 405** 48. 3x = 33 **x = 11**

49. The lowest point in the United States is in Death Valley, California. Its elevation is ⁻282 feet. What is the absolute value of this elevation?

A ⁻2   B ⁻282   C 2   (D) 282

Extra Practice See page 607, Set A.

Test Prep Transparency
22.1

DAILY TEST PREP

Which of the following is the absolute value of ⁻37? (B)

A. ⁻37   C. ⁺17

B. 37   D. none of these

Activity

Lesson Intervention

Or use Intervention CD-ROM Lesson 22.1

Identifying Opposites on a Number Line

👥 Small Group	⏱ 5–10 minutes	Visual, Auditory

- Draw a vertical number line from ⁻10 to ⁺10 on the chalkboard. Ask a volunteer to find ⁺7 on the line. **How many units is ⁺7 from 0?** (7) Then ask another volunteer to find ⁻7. **How many units is ⁻7 from 0?** (7)

- **The distance of a number from 0 on the number line is its absolute value. What is the absolute value of ⁻7?** (7) **What is the absolute value of ⁺7?** (7)

- Follow the same procedure for other integers on the number line.

3 Practice

Assign **Exercises 13–49** as independent work.

- *Problem Solving for Problems 37–42* For Problem 41, have volunteers share and discuss their graphs with the class.

Common Error

Forgetting to write the sign of an integer At this stage in their work with integers, students should always indicate a counting number by writing a positive sign before it and indicate a negative number by writing a negative sign before it.

4 Assess and Close

- **How do you find an integer's absolute value?** (count the number of units from the integer to 0)

- **What is the opposite of an integer?** (an integer with the same absolute value on the opposite end of a number line)

Assign the **LESSON QUIZ** on Transparency 22.1 to further assess student understanding.

Keeping a Journal

Have students research the elevations of cities above or below sea level. Have them express these elevations as integers.

Lesson 22.2

Compare and Order Integers

PLANNING THE LESSON

MATHEMATICS OBJECTIVE
Use a number line to compare integers.

Use Lesson Planner CD-ROM for Lesson 22.2.

Daily Routines

Vocabulary

Review the terms *integers* and *absolute value.* What numbers make up the set of integers? (zero, the counting numbers, and their opposites) What is the absolute value of an integer? (its distance from 0 on the number line)

Vocabulary Cards

Meeting North Carolina's Standards
Prepare for Grade 6 Objective **1.03** Compare and order rational numbers.

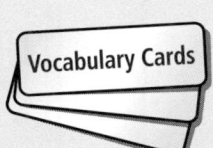

Lesson Transparency **22.2**

Problem of the Day
How many different numbers with digits to the hundredths place are greater than 2 and less than 3? (99)

Quick Check
Find each difference.
1. 174 − 43 (131)
2. 462 − 341 (121)
3. 1,503 − 402 (1,101)
4. 2,375 − 1,254 (1,121)
5. 1,434 − 131 (1,303)

Lesson Quiz
Write the integers in order from least to greatest. Draw a number line if you wish.
1. 0, ⁻3, ⁻1, ⁺4 (⁻3, ⁻1, 0, ⁺4)
2. ⁺3, ⁻3, ⁺5, ⁻5 (⁻5, ⁻3, ⁺3, ⁺5)
3. ⁻6, ⁻8, ⁻10, ⁻5 (⁻10, ⁻8, ⁻6, ⁻5)
4. ⁺6, ⁻7, ⁻4, ⁺5 (⁻7, ⁻4, ⁺5, ⁺6)
5. ⁺8, ⁻11, ⁺1, ⁻9 (⁻11, ⁻9, ⁺1, ⁺8)

LEVELED PRACTICE

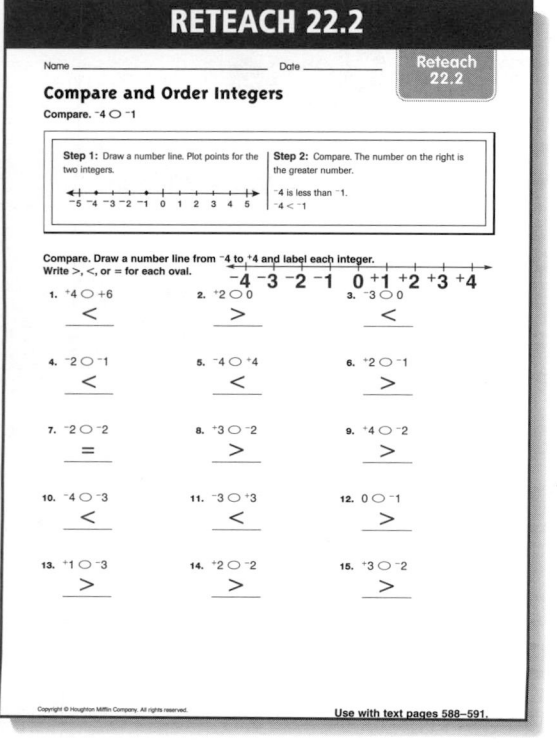

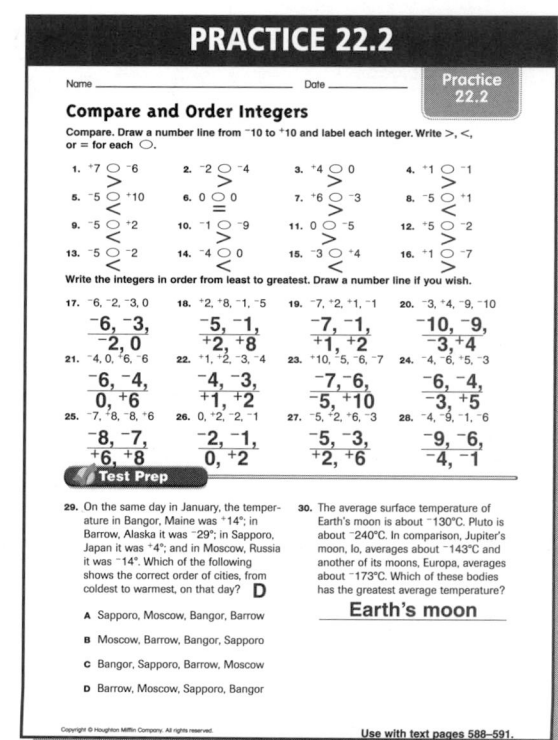

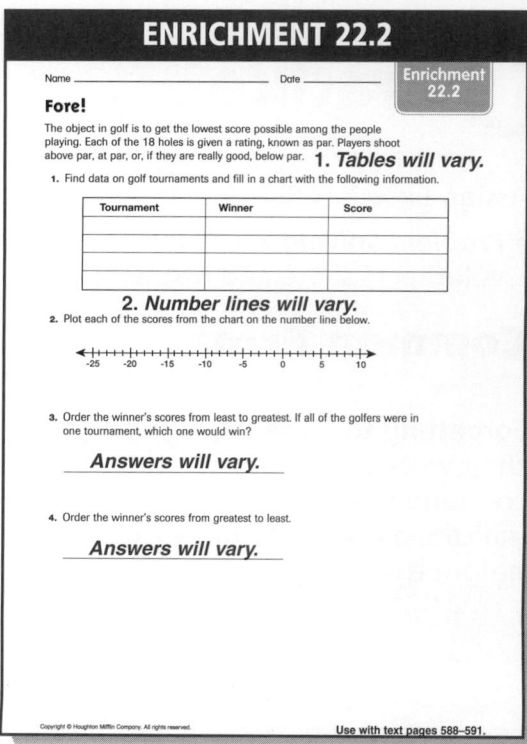

Practice Workbook Page 144

Reaching All Learners
Differentiated Instruction

English Learners

Worksheet 22.2 teaches students common comparative and superlative modifiers to help them understand the concept of comparing integers. It also introduces the terms *order* and *range*, which students must understand to complete Problems 39–50 on pages 589–590.

Inclusion
VISUAL, TACTILE

- Display a number line marked from $^-5$ to $^+5$. Have students help you to locate 3 negative and 3 positive numbers.
- **Which integers are to left of 0? Which are to the right of 0?**
- Help students see that the least integer is the leftmost number and that the greatest integer is the rightmost.

Early Finishers
VISUAL, AUDITORY

- Challenge students to write 5 inequalities, for example, $^-8 < ^-3$ or $^+3 > ^-1$.
- Then have them exchange papers with a classmate and investigate them together. Have students compare and discuss their inequality expressions.

TECHNOLOGY

Spiral Review

To reinforce skills on lessons taught earlier, create **customized** spiral review worksheets using the *Ways to Assess* CD-ROM.

Software

Use *Easy Sheet* or another spreadsheet to explore this lesson more fully.

Education Place

Encourage students to visit Education Place at **eduplace.com/kids/mw/** for more student activities.

Science Connection

Record Low Temperatures Through 1999
- Have students research the following states to find their lowest recorded temperatures last century (in degrees Farenheit): Alaska, Florida, Hawaii, Iowa, Maine, Ohio, Texas, Utah.
- Have students order temperatures from least to greatest.

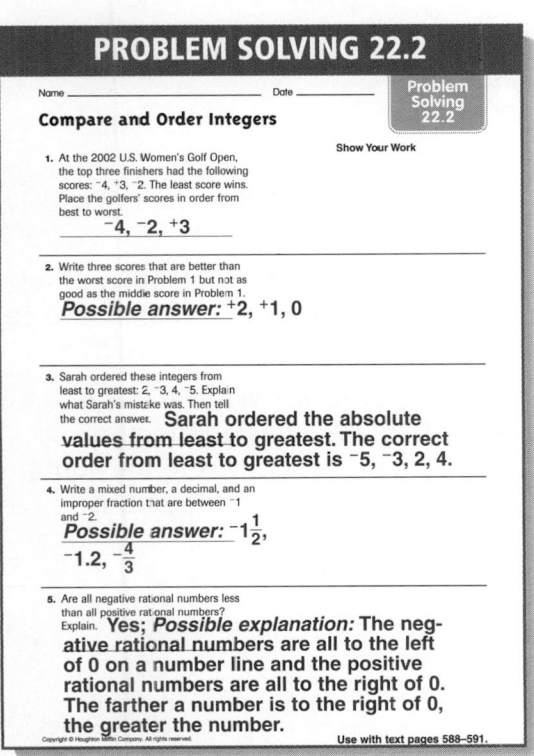

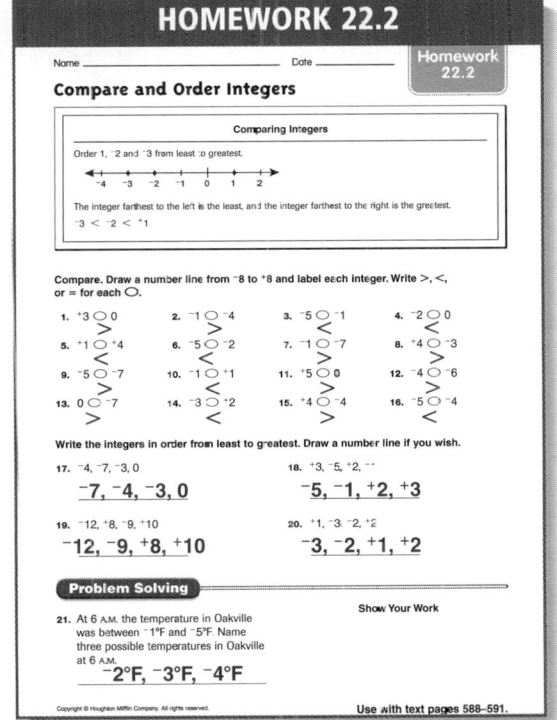

Homework Workbook Page 144

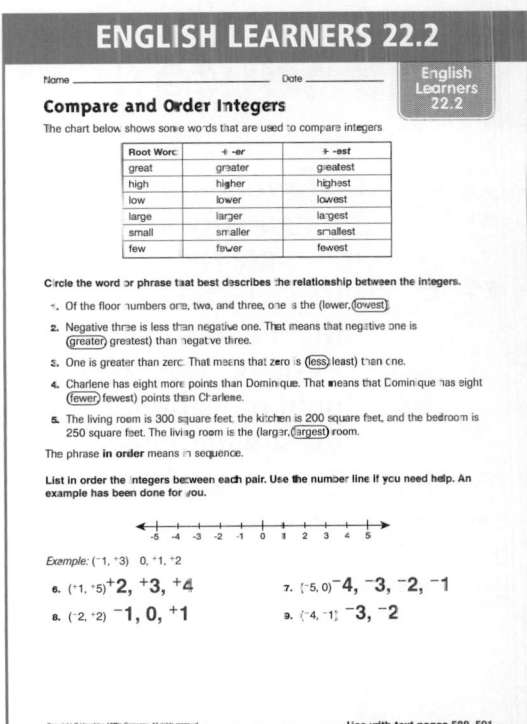

TEACHING LESSON 22.2

Warm-Up Activity
Opposite and Absolute Values

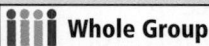 Whole Group	5 minutes	Visual, Auditory

Write the following exercises on the chalkboard. Have students give the opposite and the absolute value of each integer.

1. ⁻5 (5, 5)
2. 45 (⁻45, 45)
3. ⁻7 (7, 7)
4. ⁻12 (12, 12)
5. 9 (⁻9, 9)
6. 18 (⁻18, 18)
7. ⁻8 (8, 8)
8. 27 (⁻27, 27)
9. 32 (⁻32, 32)
10. ⁻19 (19, 19)

Lesson 2

Compare and Order Integers

Objective Use a number line to compare integers.

Learn About It

People in northern climates expect snow in the winter. Snow crystals have different shapes depending on the temperature at which they are formed.

At 0°C, water begins to freeze, and ice crystals shaped like thin plates begin to form. At ⁻4°C, the crystals look like needles. At ⁺1°C, the ice crystals begin to melt. Order the temperatures from lowest to highest.

You can use a number line to compare and order integers, just as you compare and order other numbers.

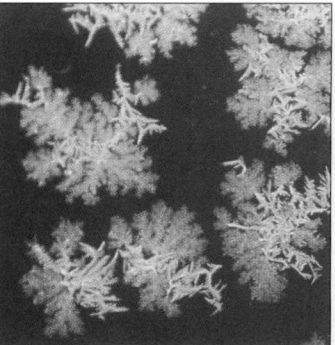

Compare 0, ⁻4, and ⁺1.

> Locate each integer on the number line.
>
> Compare. The integer farthest to the left is the least, and the integer farthest to the right is the greatest.
>
>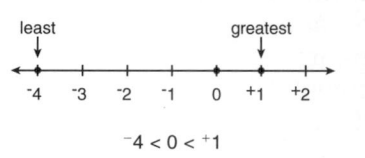
>
> $$^-4 < 0 < {}^+1$$

Solution: The temperatures in order from lowest to highest are ⁻4°C, 0°C, and ⁺1°C.

Guided Practice

Compare. Draw a number line from ⁻4 to ⁺4 and label each integer. Write >, <, or = for each .

1. ⁺1  < ⁺2
2. ⁺1 ● > ⁻1
3. ⁻3 ● < 0
4. ⁻3 ● < ⁻1
5. ⁻3 ● < ⁺2
6. ⁻3 ● > ⁻4

Ask Yourself
- Did I check on the number line that the integer to the left is less than the integer to the right?

TEST TIPS

TEST TIPS Explain Your Thinking ▶ If you are comparing two negative integers, how can you tell which one is greater?

Possible answer: **The integer whose value is greater is closer to zero on the number line.**

588

---

① Introduce

Teaching Transparency for 22.2

Materials: *Number Line 1 on Number Lines Transparency, student copies of Number Lines Transparency*

- Begin by labeling marks from ⁻9 to ⁺9 on Number Line 1. **Which is the greater integer, ⁺9 or ⁺8?** (⁺9) Point out theat ⁺9 is to the right of ⁺8 on the number line, and therefore the greater integer.

- Then point to the integers to the left of zero on the number line. **Which integer is less, ⁻9 or ⁻8?** (⁻8) Point out that ⁻8 is to the right of ⁻9 on the number line, so ⁻8 is the greater integer

② Develop

Guide students through the *Learn About It* section of the lesson.

- You may wish to use Number Line 2 on the Number Lines Transparency, or draw a number line on the chalkboard to illustrate the temperatures discussed.

- **Which temperature is lowest, or least? Why?** (⁻4°C; of the three, it is the farthest to the left.) **Which is greatest, or highest? Why?** (⁺1°C; of the three, it is farthest to the right.) **What is the order of these three temperatures from lowest to highest?** (⁻4, 0, ⁺1)

Compare. Draw a number line from ⁻5 to ⁺5 and
label each integer. Write >, <, or = for each ●.

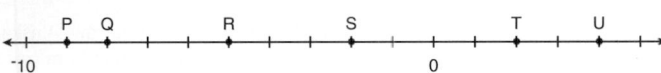

7. ⁺2 **>** ⁻1   8. ⁻5 **<** ⁻2   9. ⁺5 **>** ⁻3   10. ⁺1 **>** 0

11. ⁻5 **<** ⁺3   12. ⁻5 **<** ⁺5   13. ⁻1 **<** ⁺1   14. 0 **<** ⁺2

15. ⁻4 **<** ⁻2   16. 0 **>** ⁻1   17. ⁻3 **>** ⁻4   18. ⁻2 **<** ⁺1

Use your number line from Exercises 7–18. *Possible answers are given.*
Write an integer to make the statement true.

19. ■ < ⁻1   20. ■ > 0   21. ⁻2 > ■   22. ⁻5 < ■
  ⁻5, ⁻4, ⁻3, ⁻2   ⁺1, ⁺2, ...⁺5   ⁻3, ⁻4, ⁻5   ⁻4, ⁻3, ⁻2, ...⁻5

23. ⁻1 > ■   24. ■ < ⁻3   25. ⁻4 > ■   26. ■ < ⁺2
  ⁻2, ⁻3, ⁻4, ⁻5   ⁻5, ⁻4   ⁻5   ⁻5, ⁻4, ⁻3, ...⁻1

Write the integer that belongs at each point.

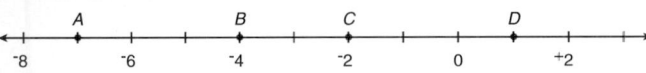

27. point P ⁻9   28. point Q ⁻8   29. point R ⁻5

30. point S ⁻2   31. point T ⁺2   32. point U ⁺4

Use the number line below. Write *true* or *false* to
describe each statement.

33. D > C **true**   34. C < B **false**   35. D < A **false**

36. A > B **false**   37. C > A **true**   38. B > D **false**

Write the integers in order from least to greatest.
Draw a number line if you wish.

39. 0, ⁻4, ⁻2, ⁺3   40. ⁺2, ⁻2, ⁺4, ⁻5   41. ⁻7, ⁻10, ⁻6, ⁻4
  ⁻4, ⁻2, 0, ⁺3   ⁻5, ⁻2, ⁺2, ⁺4   ⁻10, ⁻7, ⁻6, ⁻4

42. ⁻9, 0, ⁻10, ⁻5   43. ⁻3, ⁻8, ⁻7, ⁻2   44. ⁺5, ⁻2, ⁻6, ⁺6
  ⁻10, ⁻9, ⁻5, 0   ⁻8, ⁻7, ⁻3, ⁻2   ⁻6, ⁻2, ⁺5, ⁺6

Go On

---

③ Practice

• Discuss the use of the "is less than" and "is greater than"
to write comparison statements. Write ⁻4 < 0 on the board.
Ask a volunteer to read it. (Negative 4 is less than 0.) Then
write 0 < ⁺1 and ask a volunteer to read it. (0 is less than
positive 1.)

• Ask a volunteer to read the comparison statement in
the box. (Negative 4 is less than 0, and is less than positive 1.)

Guided Practice

Have students complete **Exercises 1–6** as you observe.
Remind them to use the *Ask Yourself* question to help.
Give students the opportunity to talk about the question
in *Explain Your Thinking*.

Assign **Exercises 7–61** as independent work.

• **Exercises 7–44** Have students explain or discuss their
answers.

DAILY TEST PREP

Which of the following shows the order of these integers from least to greatest? $^+8$, $^-4$, $^+5$, $^-1$, $^-9$ (D)

A. $^+8$, $^-4$, $^+5$, $^-1$, $^-9$ C. $^-1$, $^-4$, $^+5$, $^+8$, $^-9$

B. $^-1$, $^-4$, $^-9$, $^+5$, $^+8$ D. $^-9$, $^-4$, $^-1$, $^+5$, $^+8$

Activity

 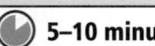

Lesson Intervention

Ordering Temperatures

Or use Intervention CD-ROM Lesson 22.2

Small Group	5–10 minutes	Kinesthetic, Tactile

- Draw both a horizontal and a vertical number line. Label the marks on the lines from $^-5°C$ to $^+5°C$. Plot the points $^-4$, 0, and $^+1$ on each scale. Point out that the lowest temperature on the vertical scale ($^-4$) represents the same temperature as the point farthest to the left ($^-4$) on the horizontal scale.

- Point out that the highest temperature point ($^+1$) on the vertical scale represents the same temperature as the point farthest to the right on the horizontal scale.

- Ask students to put the temperatures in order from lowest to highest. ($^-4°C$, $0°C$, $^+1°C$)

Solve. Draw number lines if you wish.

45. Ice crystals that look like hollow columns first form at $^-6°C$. Ice crystals called sector plates look like flowers. Sector plates begin to form at $^-10°C$. Which kind of ice crystal forms at the lower temperature? **sector plates**

46. **Reasoning** Hollow column ice crystals first form between $^-6°C$ and $^-10°C$. They also form at temperatures lower than $^-22°C$. Name three temperatures lower than $^-22°C$ at which hollow column crystals form. *Possible answer:* **$^-23°$, $^-24°$, $^-25°$**

47. Ice crystals called dendrites look like tree branches. This kind of ice crystal forms between $^-12°C$ and $^-16°C$. Write the integers that are in this temperature range. **$^-13$, $^-14$, $^-15$**

49. **Create and Solve** Use the data given in Problems 45–47 to create your own problem. Solve your problem. Give your problem to a classmate to solve. *Check students' problem and solution.*

51. **What's Wrong?** Debra drew and labeled the number line at the right. Why is it incorrect? How should she have labeled the number line? *See Additional Answers on Page 607.*

52. **Write About It** How can drawing a number line help you compare and order integers? *See Additional Answers on Page 607.*

48. **Represent** Use the information in Problems 45–47 to draw and label a number line showing the temperatures at which different kinds of ice crystals begin to form. *Check number lines.*

50. **Explain** In January in Barrow, Alaska, normal temperatures range from $^-22°C$ to $^-28°C$. Which is the higher temperature? **$^-22°C$**

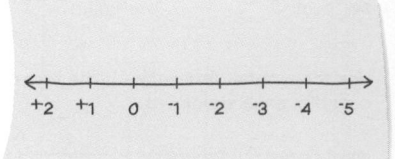

Daily Review	Test Prep

Find the percent of the number. Use mental math if you can. (Ch. 19, Lessons 4–5)

53. 10% of 50 **5**

54. 5% of $10 **$0.50**

55. 50% of 60 **30**

56. 20% of 200 **40**

57. 15% of 20 **3**

58. 35% of $60 **$21**

59. 24% of 90 **21.6**

60. 18% of 7 **1.26**

61. **Free Response** At $^-15°C$, water molecules form snowflakes. From $^-6°C$ to $^-4°C$, water molecules make hollow columns. Is the water temperature lower when they form snowflakes or when they form hollow columns? Explain. *See Additional Answers on Page 607.*

Extra Practice See page 607, Set B.

Practice *continued*

- *Problem Solving for Problems 45–52* For Problems 46 and 48, have volunteers share and discuss their work with the class. For Problem 50, have volunteers share their number lines with the class.

Common Error

Ordering negative integers by the value of the digit When students order a set of negative integers, they often forget that the value of the digit is the distance from 0 but a negative integer with the greatest absolute value will be farthest to the left of 0 and so will be less than others in the set.

---

4 Assess and Close

- **How can you determine which of two negative integers is less?** (Plot them on a number line. The integer that is farther to the left is the lesser of the two.)

- **What statement could you write to show the order of $^-2$, $^+2$, and $^-3$?** ($^-3 < ^-2 < ^+2$)

Assign the **LESSON QUIZ** on Transparency 22.2 to further assess student understanding.

Compare and Order Rational Numbers

Rational numbers are numbers that can be expressed in the form $\frac{a}{b}$, where a and b are integers, and b is not zero. Integers, fractions, improper fractions, mixed numbers, and repeating or terminating decimals are all rational numbers.

A number line can be used to order rational numbers just as it is used to order and compare integers and other numbers.

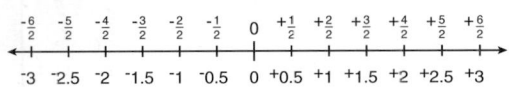

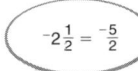
$^-2\frac{1}{2} = \frac{^-5}{2}$

Order $^-1.5$, $^+\frac{1}{2}$, and $^-2\frac{1}{2}$ from least to greatest.

STEP 1 Locate each number on a number line.

STEP 2 Compare the numbers. Use > and <.

• Since $\frac{^-5}{2}$ is farthest to the left, $\frac{^-5}{2}$ is the least number.

• Since $^+\frac{1}{2}$ is farthest to the right, $^+\frac{1}{2}$ is the greatest number.

$$\frac{^-5}{2} < {^-1.5} < \frac{^-1}{2}$$

STEP 3 Write the numbers in order from least to greatest.

$$^-2\frac{1}{2}, {^-1.5}, {^+\frac{1}{2}}$$

Order the rational numbers from least to greatest.

1. $\frac{^-3}{2}$, $^+0.5$, $^-1$
   $\frac{^-3}{2}$, $^-1$, $^+0.5$

2. $^+\frac{4}{2}$, $\frac{^-4}{2}$, 0 $\frac{^-4}{2}$, 0, $^+\frac{4}{2}$

3. $\frac{^-2}{2}$, $^+1\frac{1}{2}$, $\frac{^-1}{2}$ $\frac{^-2}{2}$, $\frac{^-1}{2}$, $^+1\frac{1}{2}$

4. $^+\frac{1}{2}$, $\frac{^-6}{2}$, $^-2.5$
   $\frac{^-6}{2}$, $^-2.5$, $^+\frac{1}{2}$

5. $^+1.5$, $^-3$, $^-0.5$
   $^-3$, $^-0.5$, $^+1.5$

6. $\frac{^-4}{2}$, $^-1$, $^-1\frac{1}{2}$ $\frac{^-4}{2}$, $^-1\frac{1}{2}$, $^-1$

Number Sense

Math Reasoning

Compare and Order Rational Numbers

• Go over the definition of rational numbers. Be sure students understand that integers may be written as fractions: $^+8 = \frac{^+3}{1}$ and $^-5 = {^-(\frac{5}{1})}$.

• **Look at Step 1.** Ask volunteers to locate and order $^-1 5$, $^+\frac{1}{2}$, and $^-2\frac{1}{2}$ on a number line.

• **Look at Step 2.** Ask volunteers to compare the numbers and write inequalities.

Keeping a Journal

Have students gather data about local temperatures, and make number lines showing the average high and low temperatures for January and July. Have them write a few sentences analyzing the information.

Hands-On: Model Addition of Integers

PLANNING THE LESSON

MATHEMATICS OBJECTIVE
Use counters to model addition of integers.

Use Lesson Planner CD-ROM for Lesson 22.3.

Daily Routines

Vocabulary

Review the numbers included in the *set of integers.* Remind students that the integers include the whole numbers—zero and the positive integers (or counting numbers)—and the negative integers (the opposites of the positive integers).

Vocabulary Cards

Meeting North Carolina's Standards

Prepare for Grade 7 Objective **1.02** Develop fluency in addition, subtraction, multiplication, and division of rational numbers.

Lesson
Transparency
22.3

Problem of the Day
The sum of the digits of a three-digit number is 20. The ones digit is twice the hundreds digit. What is the number? (488)

Quick Review
Add 101 to each number.
1. 368 (469)
2. 469 (570)
3. 592 (693)
4. 638 (739)
5. 319 (420)
6. 4,789 (4,890)
7. 2,805 (2,906)
8. 1,638 (1,739)
9. 3,909 (4,010)
10. 5,790 (5,891)

Lesson Quiz
Use two-color counters to find each sum.
1. $^+4 + {}^-2$ ($^+2$)
2. $^+6 + {}^-1$ ($^+5$)
3. $^+3 + {}^-7$ ($^-4$)
4. $^-6 + {}^+8$ ($^+2$)
5. $^-6 + {}^+6$ (0)

LEVELED PRACTICE

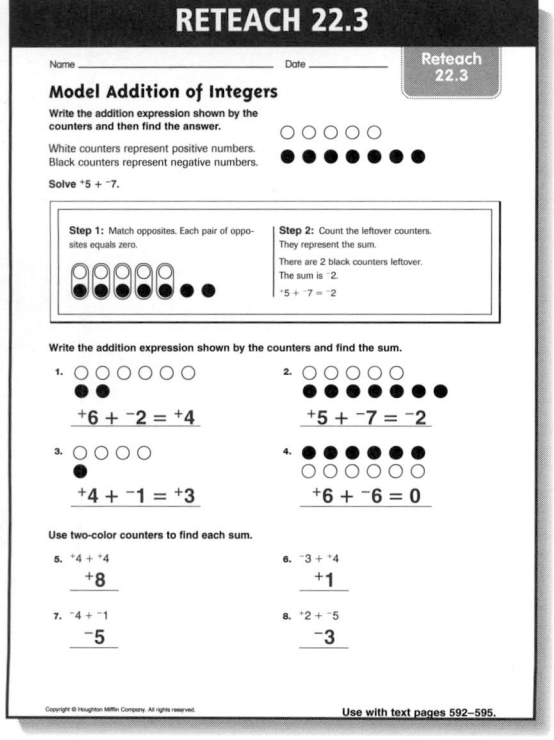

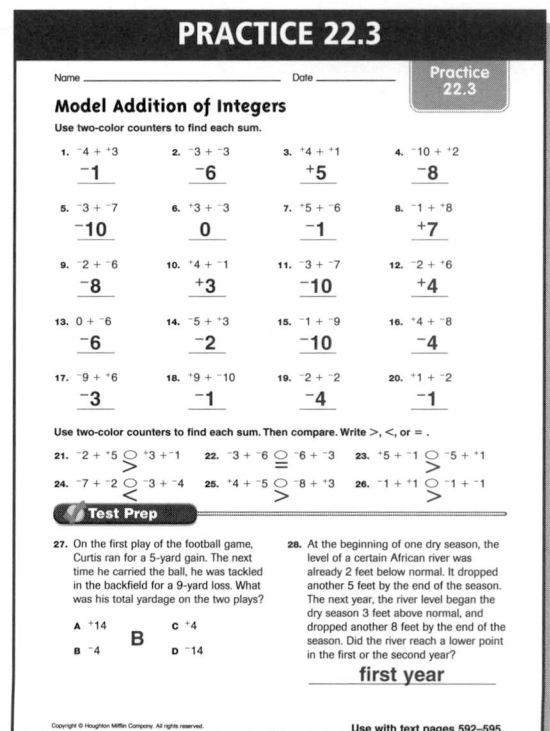

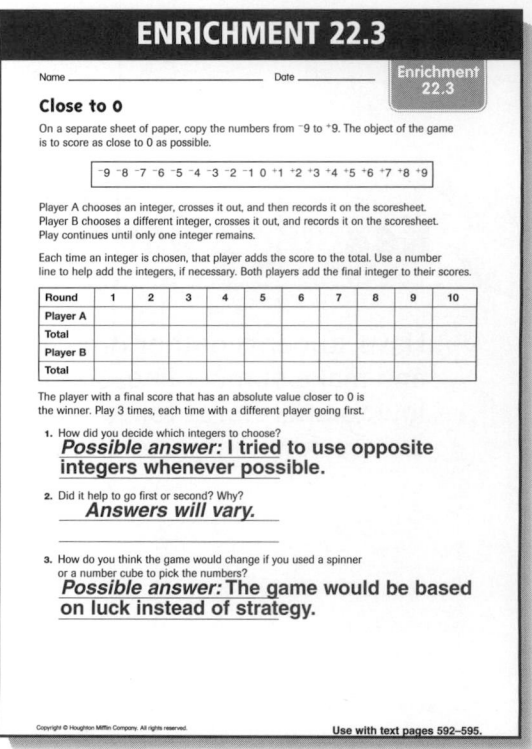

Practice Workbook Page 145

Reaching All Learners
Differentiated Instruction

English Learners

Use Worksheet 22.3 to help students identify adjectives and verbs that indicate whether an integer is positive or negative. This will help them solve the word problems on page 594.

Special Needs
VISUAL, TACTILE

Materials: *paper, pencils*

- Have students make score cards with their names on the top, and two columns labeled + and −. Play a game such as I Spy. Each time students guess correctly, have them write ⁺1 in the + column. Each time they guess incorrectly, have them enter ⁻1 in the − column. Have students figure out their scores at the end.

Early Finishers
VISUAL, TACTILE

Materials: *yellow and red counters*

- Challenge students to use yellow and red counters to model two addition problems with integers.
- Then invite students to show one another their arrangements and give the sums for the problems modeled by others.

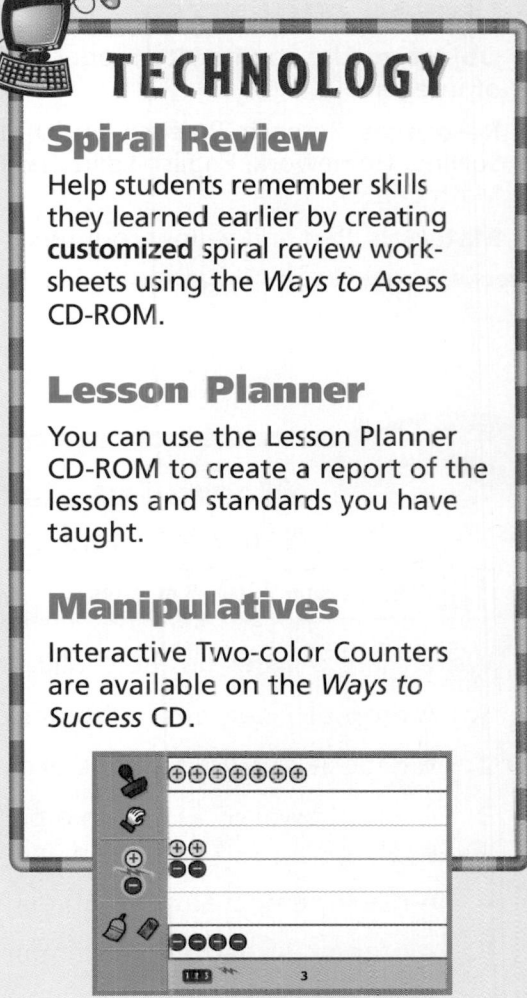

TECHNOLOGY

Spiral Review
Help students remember skills they learned earlier by creating **customized** spiral review worksheets using the *Ways to Assess* CD-ROM.

Lesson Planner
You can use the Lesson Planner CD-ROM to create a report of the lessons and standards you have taught.

Manipulatives
Interactive Two-color Counters are available on the *Ways to Success* CD.

Social Studies Connection

Credit and Debit
- Have students devise a board game called Credit and Debit. Explain that a credit card gives you money to spend (which you have to pay back). A debit card subtracts (−) money from your account.

- Have students create a game board (stores at the mall, for example). Have them write the rules for their game. They can use counters or play money, or make "credit" and "debit" cards. Have them keep track of their credits and debits. The one with the most credit at the end wins!

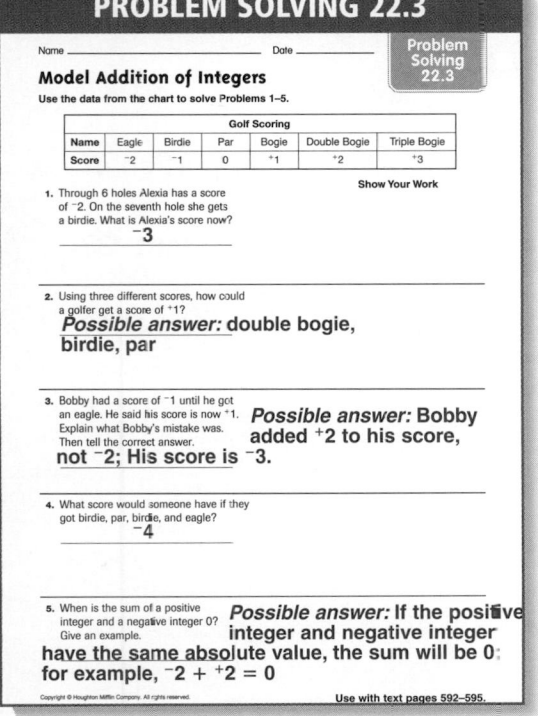

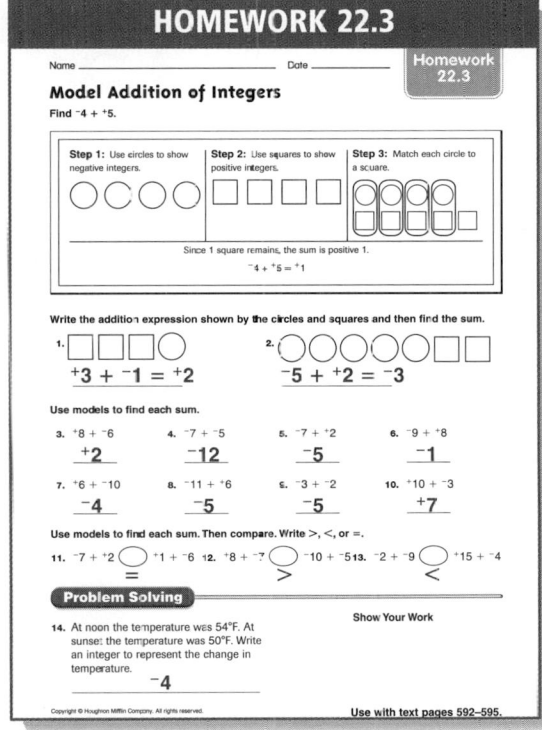

Homework Workbook Page 145

TEACHING LESSON 22.3

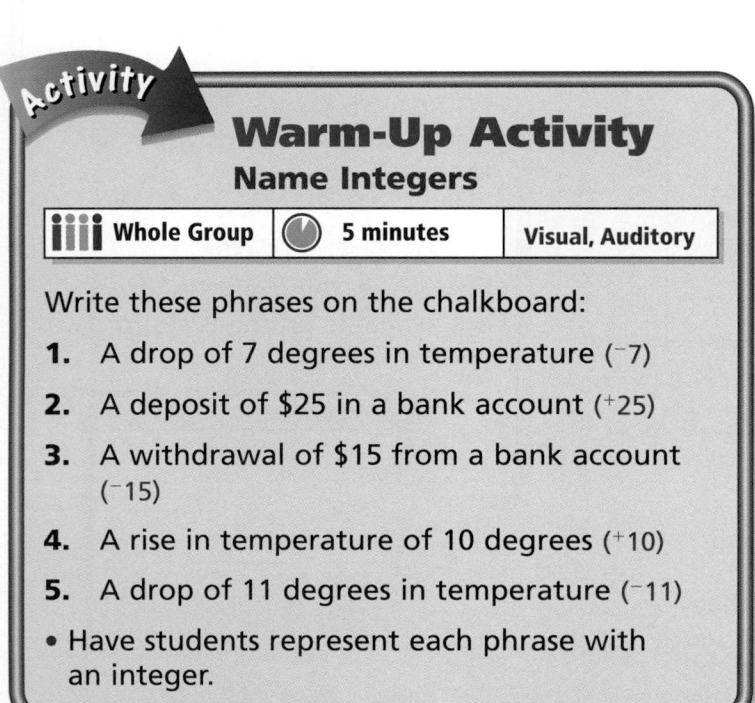

Warm-Up Activity
Name Integers

Whole Group	**5 minutes**	**Visual, Auditory**

Write these phrases on the chalkboard:

1. A drop of 7 degrees in temperature (⁻7)

2. A deposit of $25 in a bank account (⁺25)

3. A withdrawal of $15 from a bank account (⁻15)

4. A rise in temperature of 10 degrees (⁺10)

5. A drop of 11 degrees in temperature (⁻11)

• Have students represent each phrase with an integer.

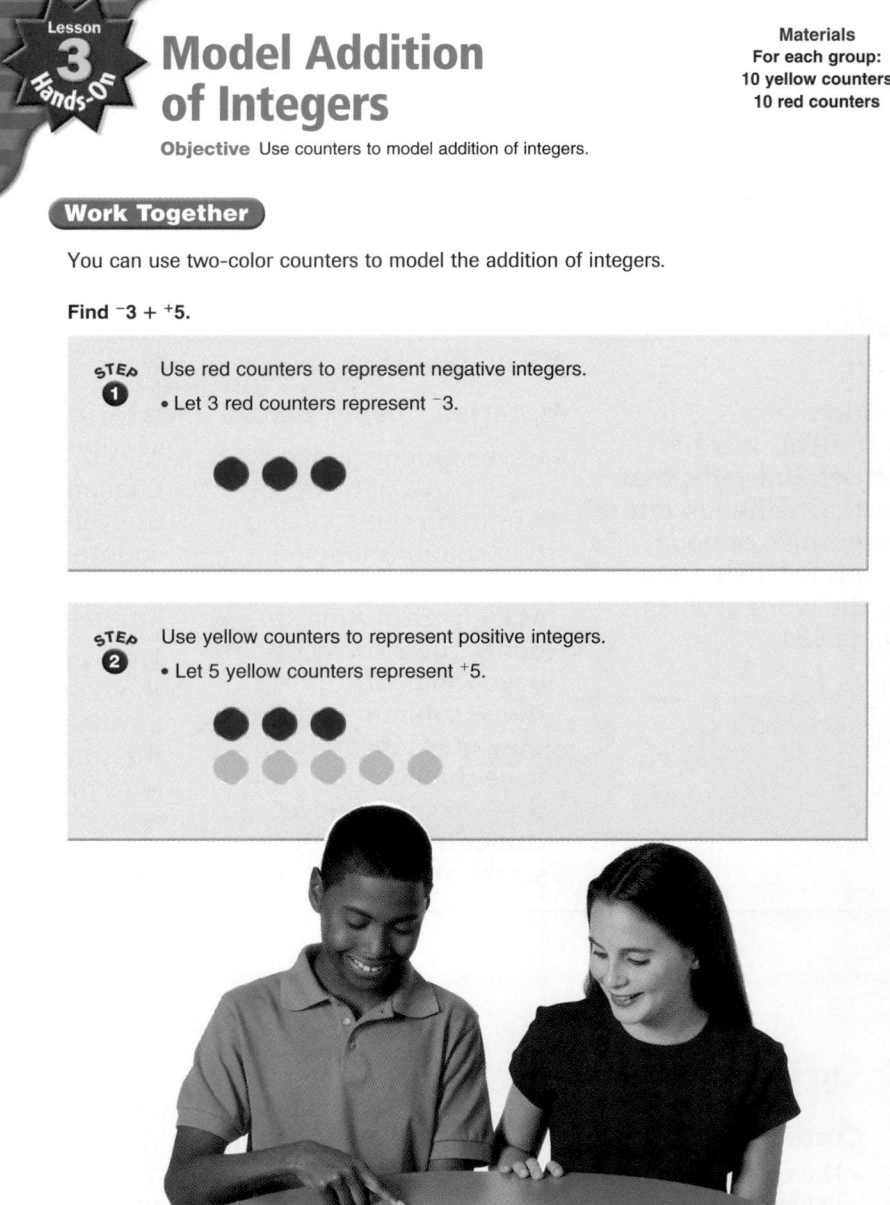

Model Addition of Integers

Objective Use counters to model addition of integers.

Work Together

You can use two-color counters to model the addition of integers.

Find ⁻3 + ⁺5.

STEP 1 Use red counters to represent negative integers.
• Let 3 red counters represent ⁻3.

STEP 2 Use yellow counters to represent positive integers.
• Let 5 yellow counters represent ⁺5.

592

---

1 Introduce

Materials: red and yellow counters

• Explain that each red counter represents ⁻1. Each yellow counter represents ⁺1.

• Write this problem on the chalkboard: *Find ⁺4 + ⁻2.* **How many yellow counters do we need to represent ⁺4?** (4) Draw 4 yellow counters. **How many red counters do we need to represent ⁻2?** (2) Draw 2 red counters.

• Explain that one red counter plus one yellow counter equals 0 since ⁺1 + ⁻1 = 0. **How many red counters can be matched with yellow counters?** (2 pairs) **How many counters are left?** (2 yellow counters) **What number does that model?** (⁺2) **What is ⁺4 + ⁻2?** (⁺2)

2 Develop

Guide students through the *Work Together* portion of the lesson.

• **Look at Step 1. What model is used to represent ⁻3?** (three red counters)

• **Look at Step 2. What model is used to represent ⁺5?** (five yellow counters)

STEP 3 Match each red counter to a yellow counter.

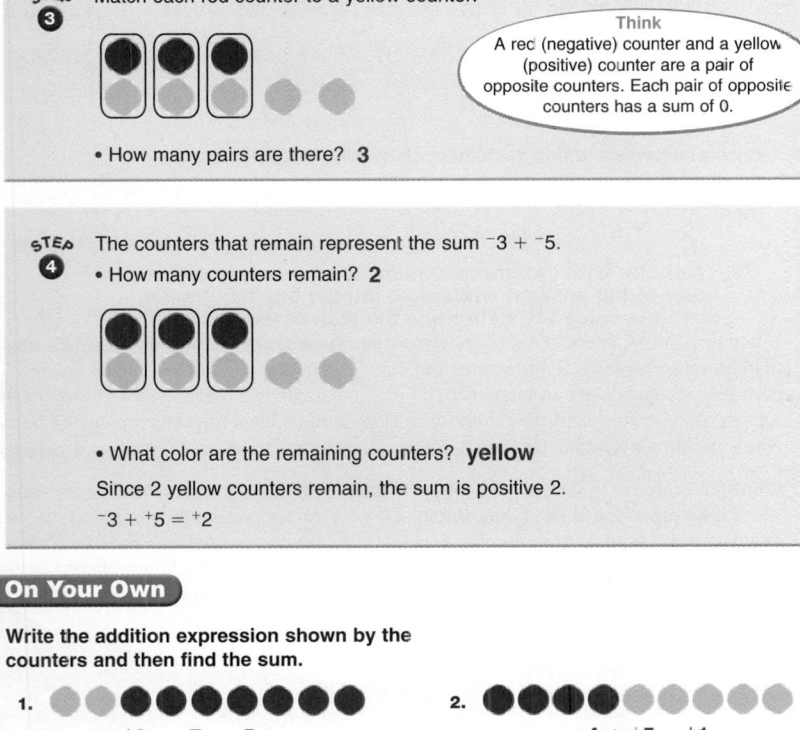

Think
A red (negative) counter and a yellow (positive) counter are a pair of opposite counters. Each pair of opposite counters has a sum of 0.

- How many pairs are there? **3**

STEP 4 The counters that remain represent the sum $^-3 + ^-5$.
- How many counters remain? **2**

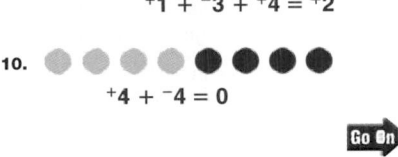

- What color are the remaining counters? **yellow**

Since 2 yellow counters remain, the sum is positive 2.

$^-3 + ^+5 = ^+2$

On Your Own

Write the addition expression shown by the counters and then find the sum.

1. $^+2 + ^-7 = ^-5$

2. $^-4 + ^+5 = ^+1$

3. $^-3 + ^+3 = 0$

4. $^+1 + ^-4 = ^-3$

5. $^+3 + ^-2 = ^+1$

6. $^-4 + ^+2 = ^-2$

7. $^-2 + ^+2 + ^-2 = ^-2$

8. $^+1 + ^-3 + ^+4 = ^+2$

9. $^-6 + ^+1 = ^-5$

10. $^+4 + ^-4 = 0$

Go On

Chapter 22 Lesson 3 593

Quick Check Options

The following activities will help students prepare for the Quick Check or may be used as an alternative assessment.

Vocabulary Review (individual, small group, or whole class)

Have students review the following vocabulary words by giving an example of how each term is used in this chapter.

- negative numbers
- opposite
- integers
- absolute value

Math Conversations (small group or whole class)

Have students discuss what they have learned about integers in this chapter. Encourage students to ask each other questions to clarify their understanding.

Writing Prompt (individual or partners)

To solidify student understanding of vocabulary and concepts, have each student complete the following sentence:
The most useful thing I have learned about integers is _____.

---

③ Practice

- **Look at Step 3.** Draw students' attention to the *Think* balloon. Explain that the sum of each pair of opposites is zero, because $^+1 + ^-1 = 0$. **How many pairs of red and yellow counters are there?** (3) **What addition sentence do these counters represent?** ($^+3 + ^-3$) **What is that sum?** (0)

- **Look at Step 4.** After we take away the 3 pairs of red and yellow counters, how many yellow counters are left over? (2) **What is** $^-3 + ^+5$**?** ($^+2$)

- Assign **Exercises 1–32** of *On Your Own* as independent work. Make sure that students write the correct integer for each group of counters.

DAILY TEST PREP

Which of the following is the sum of $^-8 + ^+5$? (B)

A. $^+3$ B. $^-3$ C. $^+13$ D. $^-13$

Activity

Lesson Intervention

Matching Counters

Or use Intervention CD-ROM Lesson 22.3

| 👥 Small Group | 🕐 5–10 minutes | Visual, Auditory |

Materials: *red and yellow counters*

- Have each student lay out 1 red counter. **What integer does that represent?** ($^+1$) Have them place a yellow counter under the red one. **What does that represent?** ($^-1$) **What addition sentence does 1 red and 1 yellow represent?** ($^+1 + ^-1$)

- Have students lay out 3 red and 2 yellow counters. **What do the counters represent?** ($^+3$, $^-2$) **How many red counters can be matched with yellow?** (2) **How many are left unmatched?** (1 red) **What is the value of this counter?** ($^+1$) **What does the sum of +3 + -2 equal?** ($^+1$)

Use two-color counters to find each sum.

11. $^+7 + ^+3$ **$^+10$** 12. $^-6 + ^-2$ **$^-8$** 13. $^-9 + ^-1$ **$^-10$** 14. $^-4 + ^-9$ **$^-13$**

15. $^-7 + ^+4$ **$^-3$** 16. $^-2 + ^+5$ **$^+3$** 17. $^+3 + ^-8$ **$^-5$** 18. $^-5 + ^+10$ **$^+5$**

19. $^-5 + ^+3$ **$^-2$** 20. $^+7 + ^-6$ **$^+1$** 21. $^+8 + ^-8$ **0** 22. $^-4 + ^+5$ **$^+1$**

Use two-color counters to find each sum. Then compare. Write >, <, or =.

23. $^-5 + ^+5$ **>** ⬤ $^-4 + ^+2$ 24. $^-6 + ^+5$ **=** ⬤ $^+3 + ^-4$ 25. $^+9 + ^-3$ **>** ⬤ $^-2 + ^+4$

26. $^-6 + ^-1$ **<** ⬤ $^+3 + ^-4$ 27. $^-5 + ^-5$ **<** ⬤ $^-8 + ^+2$ 28. $^-4 + ^+6$ **>** ⬤ $^+4 + ^-6$

Solve.

35. The color with the greatest number of counters will be the color of the answer; whichever integer has the greater absolute value will determine the sign of the answer.

29. A farmer plants 8 fewer acres of corn than normal. He plants 3 more acres of soybeans instead. Write an integer to represent the change in the number of acres the farmer typically plants. **$^-5$ acres**

30. **Represent** In May, the level of a town's water supply drops 6 inches below normal. In June, it rises 2 inches. At the end of June, how much above or below normal is the water level? **$^-4$ inches**

31. **What If?** Suppose in Problem 30 the water level drops 2 inches in July. What integer would represent the number of inches above or below normal the water level is at the end of July? **$^-6$ inches**

32. For 6 months, rainfall in an area was 5 inches below normal. During the next 6 months, rainfall was another 3 inches below normal. How many inches below normal is the rainfall in that year? **$^-8$ inches**

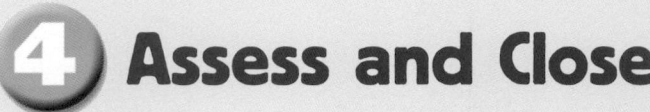
Talk About It • Write About It

You learned how to use counters to model addition of integers. *Possible answers given.*

33. If you were to combine two sets of yellow counters, what color counter would represent the answer? What does that tell you about the sum of two positive integers? **yellow; the sum is always positive.**

34. If you were to combine two sets of red counters, what color counter represents the answer? What does that tell you about the sum of two negative integers? **red; the sum is always negative.**

35. When you combine a set of yellow counters and a set of red counters, how can you tell what color counters will represent the answer? What does that tell you about the sum of a positive and a negative integer? **See above.**

594

Practice *continued*

- *Problem-Solving for Problems 29–32* Have students share their answers.

---

④ Assess and Close

Assign **Exercises 33–35** of the *Talk About It • Write About It* section. Have volunteers explain their work.

Assign the **LESSON QUIZ** on Transparency 22.3 to further assess student understanding.

Quick Check

Check your understanding for Lessons 1–3.

Write the absolute value of each integer. (Lesson 1)

1. ⁻5 **5**   2. ⁺4 **4**   3. ⁻6 **6**

Compare. Write >, <, or = for each ●. (Lesson 2)

4. ⁻3 ● ⁺3   5. 0 ● ⁻1   6. ⁻4 ● ⁺5
   <   **>**   **<**

Use red and yellow counters to add. (Lesson 3)

7. ⁺4 + ⁻6 **⁻2**   8. ⁻8 + ⁻1 **⁻9**   9. ⁻5 + ⁺8 **⁺3**

Solve. (Lesson 3)

10. The water level in a well fell 3 inches from last year to the beginning of this year. Now the water level is up 5 inches from the beginning of the year. Write an integer to represent the water level now as compared to the beginning of last year. **⁺2**

Target Practice

Choose one beanbag from each basket so the sum of the three numbers is equal to the number on the target.

Use counters to help you.

Possible answers given.
1. Basket A, ⁺2; Basket B, ⁻4; Basket C, ⁺2
2. Basket A, ⁻3; Basket B, ⁺3; Basket C, ⁺2
3. Basket A, ⁻1; Basket B, ⁺3; Basket C, ⁻3

Chapter 22 Lesson 3   595

Quick Check

Purpose: The Quick Check allows you to assess the student's understanding of the concepts presented in Lessons 1–3.

Items	Objectives Tested	Pages	Intervention
1–3	Identify integers and find the absolute value of an integer.	586–587	Reteach Resource 22.1 *Ways to Success* 22.1
4–6	Use a number line to compare integers.	588–591	Reteach Resource 22.2 *Ways to Success* 22.2
7–10	Use counters to model addition of integers.	592–595	Reteach Resource 22.3 *Ways to Success* 22.3

Keeping a Journal

Have students explain what a matching pair of counters is and why getting rid of all the matching pairs always leaves the number of counters that represents the sum of two integers.

Math Challenge

Target Practice

- Make sure students understand that they need to try different combinations of integers from each basket in order to find three that add to the sum given in each of items 1–3. For example, for item 1, from A, ⁻1, B, ⁺3, and ⁻C, 2 will sum to 0.

- You might wish to extend the challenge by giving other sums that can be found.

Hands-On: Model Subtraction of Integers

PLANNING THE LESSON

MATHEMATICS OBJECTIVE
Use counters to model subtraction of integers.

Use Lesson Planner CD-ROM for Lesson 22.4.

Daily Routines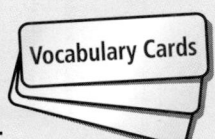

Vocabulary
Remind students that each yellow counter represents the *positive integer* $+1$ and each red counter represents the *negative integer* -1.

Vocabulary Cards

Meeting North Carolina's Standards
Prepare for Grade 7 Objective **1.02** Develop fluency in addition, subtraction, multiplication, and division of rational numbers.

Lesson Transparency **22.4**

Problem of the Day
Megan walked home from school in 20 minutes, took 5 minutes to change clothes, did homework for 35 minutes, and practiced the piano for 45 minutes. If she finished practicing at 5:30 P.M., at what time did she leave school? (3:45 P.M.)

Quick Review
Find each sum or product.
1. $300 + 5,000 + 80$ (5,380)
2. $300 \times 5,000 \times 0$ (0)
3. $800 \times 10 \times 100$ (800,000)
4. $400 + 30 + 3,000$ (3,430)
5. $4,000 + 30,000 + 10$ (34,010)

Lesson Quiz
Use two-color counters to find each difference.
1. $+2 - -4$ (-2)
2. $+6 - +2$ ($+4$)
3. $-7 - -7$ (0)
4. $+7 - -9$ ($+16$)
5. $+9 - +9$ (0)
6. $-11 - -3$ (-8)

LEVELED PRACTICE

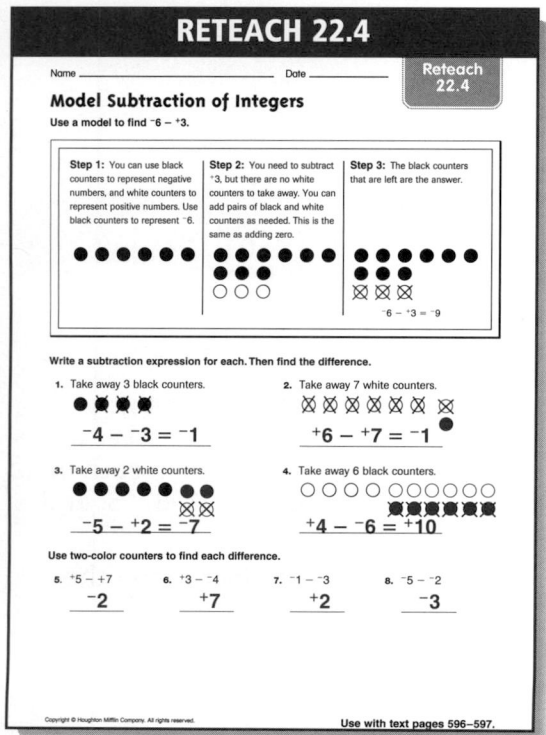

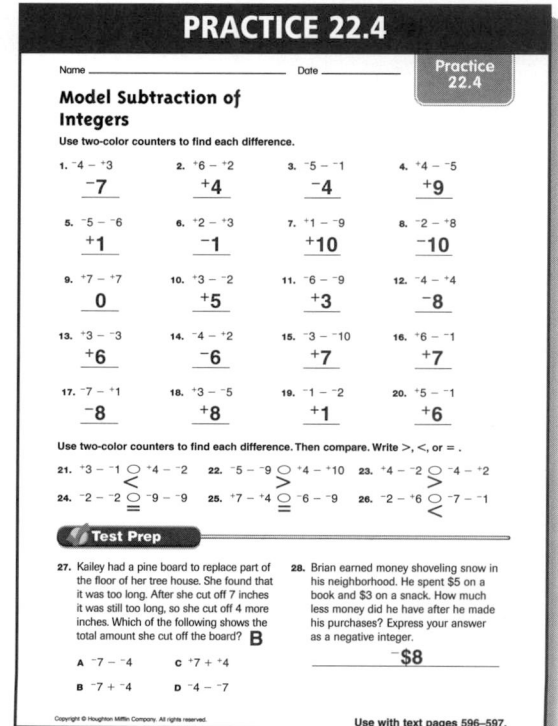

Practice Workbook Page 146

Reaching All Learners
Differentiated Instruction

English Learners

Worksheet 22.4 introduces students to several meanings of the word *take*, including its use in word problems involving subtraction ("take away"). Students then solve some subtraction problems using two-color counters.

Inclusion
VISUAL, TACTILE

Materials: *red counters*

- Display ⁻3 − ⁻2.
- Help students model ⁻3 by using 3 red counters. **What does each counter represent?** (⁻1)
- **The problem says to subtract ⁻2 from ⁻3. What can you do to subtract ⁻2?** (Take away 2 red counters.) **How many counters are left?** (1) **What color are they?** (red) **What is ⁻3 − ⁻2?** (⁻1)

Gifted and Talented
VISUAL, TACTILE

- Challenge students to use two-colored counters to model and solve these subtraction problems.
  1. ⁻2 − ⁻4 − ⁻3 (⁺5)
  2. ⁻5 − ⁻9 − ⁺7 (⁻3)
  3. ⁺4 − ⁻8 − ⁺5 (⁺7)
  4. ⁻3 − ⁻6 − ⁻3 (⁺6)
  5. ⁻4 − ⁻7 + ⁻5 (⁻2)
- Challenge students to create two subtraction problems. Invite them to exchange, model, and solve their problems.

Literature Connection

Managing Money
- Suggest that students read *Neale S. Godfrey's Ultimate Kids' Money Book*, by Neale S. Godfrey (Simon & Schuster, 1998), which discusses money management, such as making change, opening a checking account at a bank, and investing in the stock market.

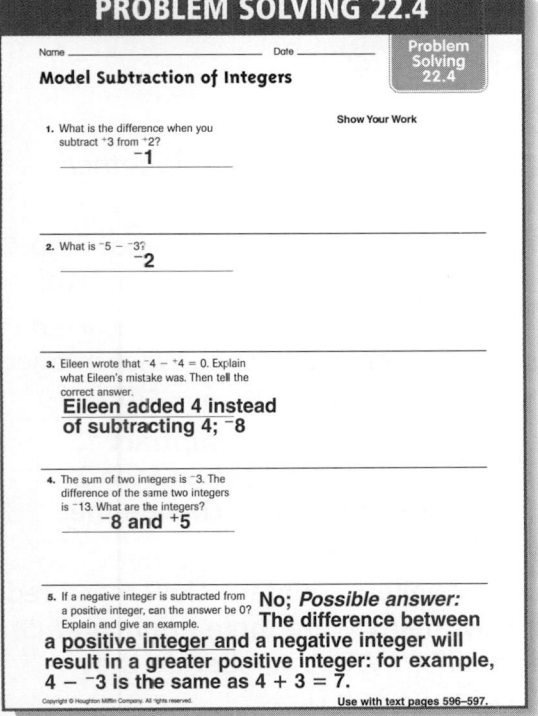

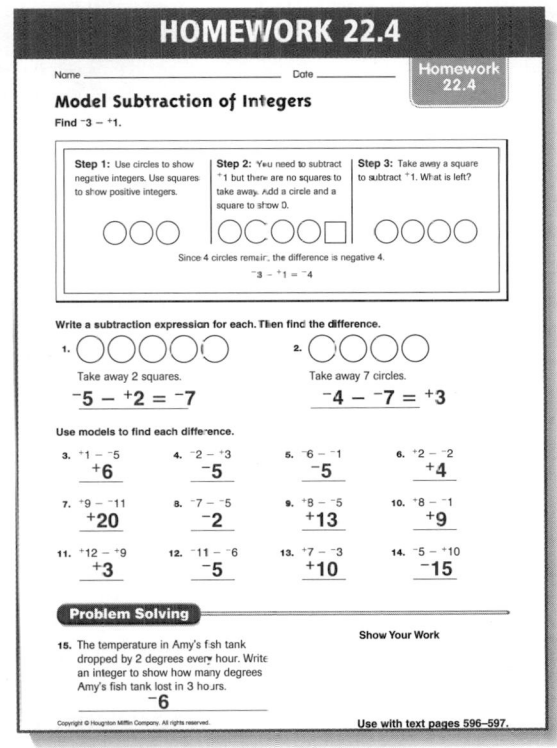

Homework Workbook Page 146

TEACHING LESSON 22.4

LESSON ORGANIZER

Objective Use counters to model subtraction of integers.

Resources Reteach, Practice, Enrichment, Problem Solving, Homework, English Learners, Transparencies, Math Center

Materials Red and yellow counters

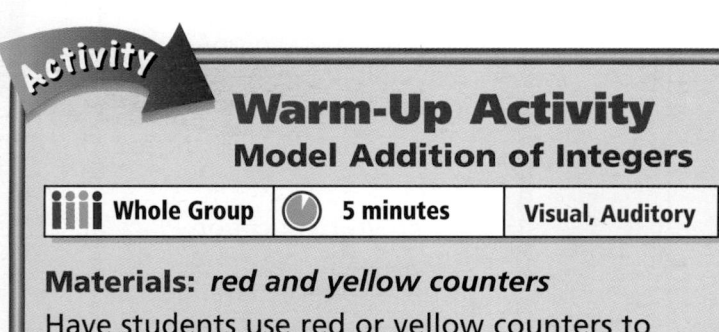

Warm-Up Activity
Model Addition of Integers

| iiii Whole Group | ⏱ 5 minutes | Visual, Auditory |

Materials: *red and yellow counters*

Have students use red or yellow counters to model each addition expression and then give the sum of the integers. Write the following exercises on the chalkboard:

1. $^+3 + ^-2$ ($^+1$)

2. $^-6 + ^-2$ ($^-8$)

3. $^+4 + ^-5$ ($^-1$)

4. $^+1 + ^-1$ (0)

5. $^+5 + ^-6$ ($^-1$)

Model Subtraction of Integers

Materials
For each group:
10 yellow counters
10 red counters

Objective Use counters to model subtraction of integers.

Work Together

You can use two-color counters to model the subtraction of integers.

Find $^-6 - ^-4$.

| **STEP 1** Use red counters to represent $^-6$.
 • What does each counter represent? $^-1$
 • How many counters will you use? 6
  | **STEP 2** Take away counters to subtract $^-4$.
 • How many red counters will you take away? 4
 • What is $^-6 - ^-4$? How do you know? $^-2$
  |

Sometimes you may not have enough counters to subtract.

Find $^-5 - ^+2$.

STEP 1 Use red counters to represent $^-5$.
• How many counters will you place down? 5

You need to subtract $^+2$ but there are no yellow counters to take away.

STEP 2 Add pairs of red and yellow counters. Each pair represents 0. Adding zero does not change the answer.
• How many pairs do you need to add in order to be able to remove 2 yellow counters? 2

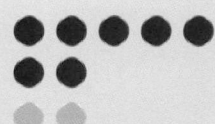

STEP 3 Take away counters to subtract $^+2$.
• How many counters will you take away? 2 What color will they be? **yellow**

The counters that remain represent the answer.
• How many counters are left? 7
• What color are they? **red**
• What is $^-5 - ^+2$? $^-7$

---

1 Introduce

Materials: *red and yellow counters*

• Have students follow as you model the following sentence: $^-3 - ^-2$. **How can I model $^-3$?** (Lay down 3 red counters.) **How can I subtract $^-2$ from $^-3$?** (Take 2 of the 3 red counters away.) **How many red counters are left?** (1) **What is the value of 1 red counter?** ($^-1$) **What is $^-3 - ^-2$?** ($^-1$)

• Model $^-3 - ^+2$. Model $^-3$ with 3 red counters. **I need to subtract 2 yellow counters. Before I can subtract, I need to add 2 matching pairs of red and yellow counters to the model. Have I added any value to the subtraction sentence? Why?** (No, because each pair equals 0.) **Now how can I subtract $^+2$?** (Take the 2 yellow counters away.) **How many counters are left?** (5) **What color are they?** (red) **What number do they represent?** ($^-5$) **What is $^-3 - ^+2$?** ($^-5$)

2 Develop

Guide students through the steps of the *Work Together* section.

• For $^-6 - ^-4$, have a volunteer read each question of Step 1 and answer it. Be sure students understand each answer.

• **Look at Step 2. How do you subtract $^-4$?** (Take away 4 red counters.) **How many red counters are left?** (2) **What integer do these counters represent?** ($^-2$) **What is $^-6 - ^-4$?** ($^-2$)

• For $^-5 - ^+2$, say, **Look at Step 1. You can't subtract $^+2$ because there are no yellow counters. Look at Step 2. Does adding 2 matching pairs of counters change the value?** (no) **Why?** (Each pair equals 0.)

• **Now you can take away 2 yellow counters. How many red counters are left?** (2) **How many were there originally?** (5) **How many are there in all?** (7) **What number do they represent?** ($^-7$) **What is $^-5 - ^+2$?** ($^-7$)

On Your Own

Write a subtraction expression for each.
Then find the difference.

1. ● ● ● ● ● ●

Take away 4 reds. ⁻6 − ⁻4 = ⁻2

2. ● ● ● ● ●

Take away 3 yellows. ⁺5 − ⁺3 = ⁺2

3. ● ● ● ●

Take away 5 reds. ⁻4 − ⁻5 = ⁺1

4. ● ● ● ●

Take away 6 yellows. ⁺4 − ⁺6 = ⁻2

5. ● ● ●

Take away 2 yellows. ⁻3 − ⁺2 = ⁻5

6. ● ● ● ● ● ●

Take away 3 reds. ⁺6 − ⁻3 = ⁺9

7. ● ● ● ● ●

Take away 5 reds. ⁻5 − ⁻5 = 0

8. ● ● ●

Take away 3 yellows. ⁺3 − ⁺3 = 0

9. ●

Take away 3 yellows. ⁻1 − ⁺3 = ⁻4

10. ● ●

Take away 5 reds. ⁺2 − ⁻5 = ⁺7

Use two-color counters to find each difference.

11. ⁺3 − ⁻6 ⁺9
12. ⁺2 − ⁻8 ⁺10
13. ⁻2 − ⁻6 ⁺4
14. ⁻8 − ⁻3 ⁻5

15. ⁻8 − ⁻8 0
16. ⁺8 − ⁺4 ⁺4
17. ⁺8 − ⁺8 0
18. ⁻8 − ⁺8 ⁻16

19. ⁻4 − ⁻4 0
20. ⁻3 − ⁻7 ⁺4
21. ⁺5 − ⁻4 ⁺9
22. ⁺2 − ⁺7 ⁻5

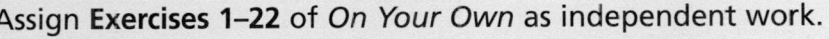
Talk About It • Write About It

Use counter models to answer these questions.

23. Find ⁻3 − ⁺4 and ⁻3 + ⁻4. Did you get the same result
adding the opposite of an integer instead of subtracting? **⁻7 in both cases; yes**

24. How can you tell if one integer is greater than another
integer? *Possible answer:* **by its position on a number line; the
farther right on the number line, the greater the number.**

25. If a greater integer is being subtracted from a lesser integer,
is the answer positive or is it negative? **negative**

26. If a lesser integer is being subtracted from a greater integer,
is the answer positive or is it negative? **positive**

Chapter 22 Lesson 4 **597**

Test Prep Transparency

22.4

DAILY TEST PREP

Which of these is the difference ⁻6 − ⁻3? (D)

A. ⁻9   B. ⁺9   C. ⁺3   D. ⁻3

Activity

Lesson Intervention

Or use Intervention CD-ROM Lesson 22.4

Matching Pairs Are Important

| Individual | 5–10 minutes | Kinesthetic, Tactile |

Materials: *yellow and red counters*

- Display ⁺2 − ⁻3. Give each student 2 yellow counters. **The yellow counters represent ⁺2. How can we represent ⁻3?** (red counters) **But we don't have any red counters. How can we get 3 red counters?** (add 3 pairs of yellow and red counters) **Give students 3 pairs of yellow and red counters.**

- **What does each new pair equal?** (0, because ⁺1 + ⁻1 = 0) **Stress that no extra value has been added to the equation. Now, how do we subtract ⁻3 from ⁺2?** (subtract 3 red counters) **What is left?** (5 yellow counters) **What is their value?** (⁺5) **What is ⁺2 − ⁻3?** (⁺5)

3 Practice

Assign **Exercises 1–22** of *On Your Own* as independent work.

4 Assess and Close

Assign **Exercises 23–26** of the *Talk About It • Write About It* section. Have volunteers share and discuss their work.

Assign the **LESSON QUIZ** on Transparency 22.4 to further assess student understanding.

Keeping a Journal

Have students describe the steps they would take to model these two number sentences:
⁺3 − ⁻5 = 8
3 + 5 = 8

Add and Subtract Integers

PLANNING THE LESSON

MATHEMATICS OBJECTIVE
Use a number line to add and subtract integers.

Use Lesson Planner CD-ROM for Lesson 22.5.

Daily Routines

Vocabulary

Discuss how using a **number line** allows you to easily add and subtract integers. Ask students to explain the relationship between subtraction and addition. (They are opposites.) Explain that another word for opposite is *additive inverse,* and that subtraction and addition are inverse operations that can be shown on a number line.

Vocabulary Cards

Meeting North Carolina's Standards

Prepare for Grade 7 Objective **1.02** Develop fluency in addition, subtraction, multiplication, and division of rational numbers.

Lesson Transparency **22.5**

Problem of the Day
Every fifth customer at Biff's Bargain Barn wins a prize. How many prizes are awarded if there are 188 customers? (37)

Quick Review
Find the sum or difference.
1. $^+12 + ^-18$ ($^-6$)
2. $^+7 - ^-3$ ($^+10$)
3. $^-7 + ^-2$ ($^-9$)
4. $^-5 - ^-8$ ($^+3$)

Lesson Quiz
Decide whether the answer will be positive or negative. Then use a number line to add or subtract.

1. At noon one February day, the temperature was $^+18$°F. From 6:00 A.M. to noon, the temperature rose by 22°F. What was the temperature at 6:00 A.M.? ($^-4$°F)

2. In the first two rounds of a game, Ali's scores were $^-3$ and $^-4$. Mala's scores were $^-4$ and $^-4$. Who had the greater total score? Why? (Ali; $^-3 + ^-4 > ^-4 + ^-4$)

LEVELED PRACTICE

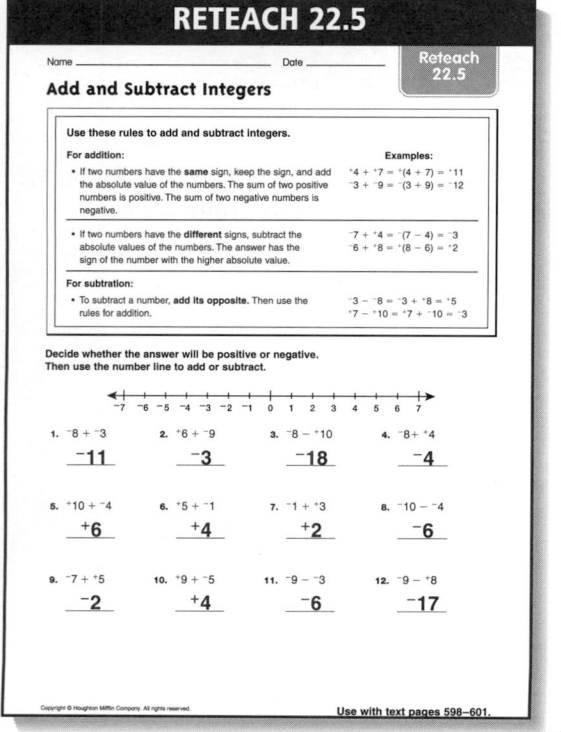

RETEACH 22.5

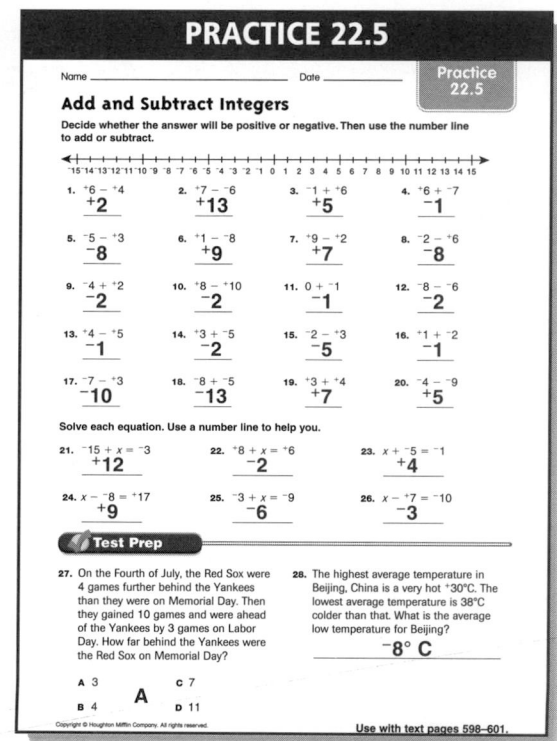

PRACTICE 22.5

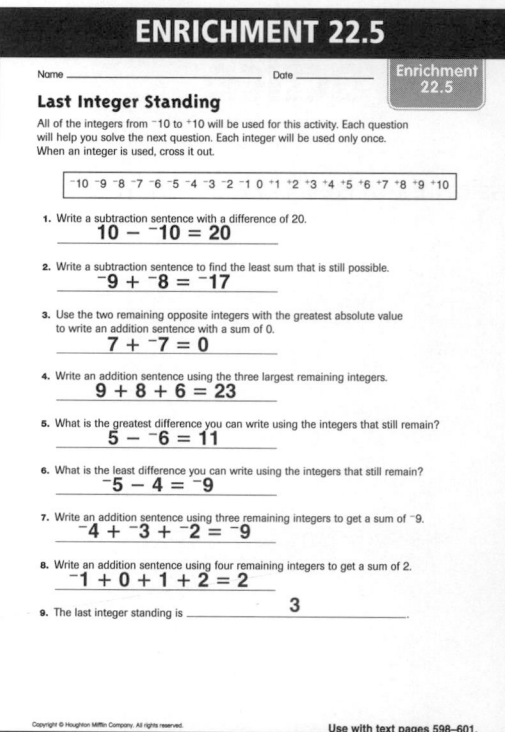

ENRICHMENT 22.5

Practice Workbook Page 147

Reaching All Learners

Differentiated Instruction

English Learners

Worksheet 22.5 provides step-by-step support for solving Problem 36 on page 600. Students are encouraged to use a number line as a graphic aid.

Special Needs
VISUAL, AUDITORY

- Display: $^-4 + ^+2$. Label a number line from $^-5$ to $^+5$. **Where is $^-4$?** (4 units left of 0) **In which direction do we move when adding positive integers?** (right)
- Draw an arrow from $^-4$ two units to the right. **What is $^-4 + ^+2$?** ($^-2$)
- Continue with other problems.

Early Learners
VISUAL, AUDITORY

- Challenge students to create original addition and subtraction problems using positive and negative integers. Have students exchange problems with a classmate and use a number line to solve each other's problems.

Science Connection

High and Low

Give students this table. Have them find the temperature difference in each city. (Anchorage, 83°; Bismarck, 126°; Buffalo, 88°; Chicago, 102° Minneapolis, 111°)

High and Low Temperatures in 2000 (°F)		
City	High	Low
Anchorage, AK	73	$^-10$
Bismarck, ND	104	$^-22$
Buffalo, NY	88	$^-0$
Chicago, IL	93	$^-9$
Minneapolis, MN	94	$^-17$

TECHNOLOGY

Spiral Review

Create **customized** spiral review worksheets for individual students using the *Ways to Assess* CD-ROM.

Lesson Planner

You can customize your teaching plan to meet your curriculum requirements with the Lesson Planner CD-ROM.

Game

Students can practice their skills using the Find a Friend math game, available on the *Ways to Success* CD.

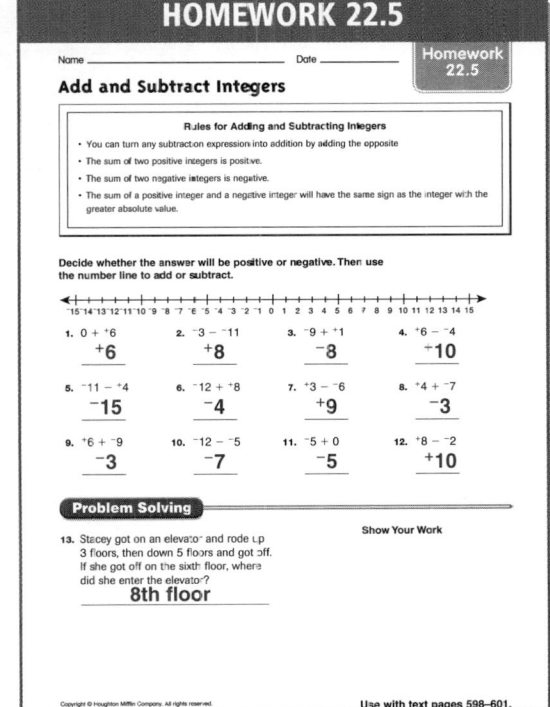

PROBLEM SOLVING 22.5

Name _____ Date _____

Problem Solving 22.5

Add and Subtract Integers

Show Your Work

1. In 2001, the lowest temperature in Anchorage, Alaska, was $^-15$°F. The lowest temperature in Fairbanks, Alaska, was $^-41$°F. How many degrees colder was the lowest temperature in Fairbanks?

   26°F

2. The lowest temperature in Chicago, Illinois, was $^-27$°F. The lowest temperature in Portland, Maine, was 12° colder. What was the lowest temperature in Portland?

   $^-39$°F

3. The lowest temperature ever recorded in Florida was $^-2$°F. If you subtract 38, you will find the lowest temperature ever recorded in Arizona. What is that temperature?

   $^-40$°F

4. The lowest temperature in Bismarck, North Dakota, was $^-44$°F. If you subtract $^-153$°, you will find Bismarck's highest temperature. What is that temperature?

   109°F

5. Can you subtract two positive numbers and get a negative number? Explain and give an example. **Yes; Possible explanation: When the number being subtracted is greater than the number it is being subtracted from, the difference will be negative: for example, 4 − 5 = $^-1$.**

Copyright © Houghton Mifflin Company. All rights reserved.

Use with text pages 598–601.

HOMEWORK 22.5

Name _____ Date _____

Homework 22.5

Add and Subtract Integers

Rules for Adding and Subtracting Integers
• You can turn any subtraction expression into addition by adding the opposite
• The sum of two positive integers is positive.
• The sum of two negative integers is negative.
• The sum of a positive integer and a negative integer will have the same sign as the integer with the greater absolute value.

Decide whether the answer will be positive or negative. Then use the number line to add or subtract.

$-15\ -14\ -13\ -12\ -11\ -10\ -9\ -8\ -7\ -6\ -5\ -4\ -3\ -2\ -1\ 0\ 1\ 2\ 3\ 4\ 5\ 6\ 7\ 8\ 9\ 10\ 11\ 12\ 13\ 14\ 15$

1. $0 + ^+6$	2. $^-3 - ^-11$	3. $^-9 + ^-1$	4. $^-6 - ^-4$
$^+6$	$^+8$	$^-8$	$^+10$

5. $^-11 - ^-4$	6. $^-12 + ^+8$	7. $^+3 - ^-6$	8. $^+4 + ^-7$
$^-15$	$^-4$	$^+9$	$^-3$

9. $^+6 + ^-9$	10. $^-12 - ^-5$	11. $^-5 + 0$	12. $^+8 - ^-2$
$^-3$	$^-7$	$^-5$	$^+10$

Problem Solving

13. Stacey got on an elevator and rode up 3 floors, then down 5 floors and got off. If she got off on the sixth floor, where did she enter the elevator?

   8th floor

Show Your Work

Copyright © Houghton Mifflin Company. All rights reserved.

Use with text pages 598–601.

Homework Workbook Page 147

ENGLISH LEARNERS 22.5

Name _____ Date _____

English Learners 22.5

Add and Subtract Integers

Read this problem and then follow the steps to solve it.

Problem: On a warm day, 5 inches of snow melted. That night a storm brought 10 inches of snow. If there is now 20 inches of snow, how much snow was there in the beginning?

STEP 1: Make sure you understand key terms.

- **warm**—having moderate heat
- **melt**—change from solid to liquid by heat
- **storm**—weather with heavy wind, rain, or snow
- **snow**—ice crystals that fall to the earth
- **beginning**—a start

STEP 2: Identify what the problem asks. Write the question you must answer:

How much snow was there in the beginning?

STEP 3: Make a number line for the problem. Start with the line below.

STEP 4: On the number line, start at 0. Make arrows to show the change in the amount of snow. Include the amount that melted and the amount that fell. Write this change as a positive or negative integer:

integer = $^+5$

STEP 5: Write an equation. Show the relationship between the amount of snow now (20 inches) and the change in the amount of snow (your integer from Step 4). Solve the equation.

$20 - ^+5$ = amount of snow at beginning
15 = amount of snow at beginning

Copyright © Houghton Mifflin Company. All rights reserved.

Use with text pages 598–601.

TEACHING LESSON 22.5

LESSON ORGANIZER

Objective Use a number line to add and subtract integers.

Resources Reteach, Practice, Enrichment, Problem Solving, Homework, English Learners, Transparencies, Math Center

Materials Number Lines Transparency

Warm-Up Activity
Add Integers

Whole Group	5 minutes	Visual, Auditory

Have students find the sum or difference. Tell them to use counters if necessary.

1. $^+5 + {}^-4$ ($^+1$)
2. $^+4 + {}^-5$ ($^-1$)
3. $^+6 + {}^-2$ ($^+4$)
4. $^+5 + {}^-2$ ($^+3$)
5. $^+2 + {}^-7$ ($^-5$)

Add and Subtract Integers

e Glossary **Vocabulary**
integers
opposite

Objective Use a number line to add and subtract integers.

Learn About It — MathTracks 2/33 Listen and Understand

Two winters with above-average temperatures caused a decrease in snow cover on a mountain. The snow cover was down 6 inches from normal in one year and down another 3 inches the next year. By how much did the snow cover change during those two years?

You can use a number line to add **integers**.

Find $^-6 + {}^-3$.

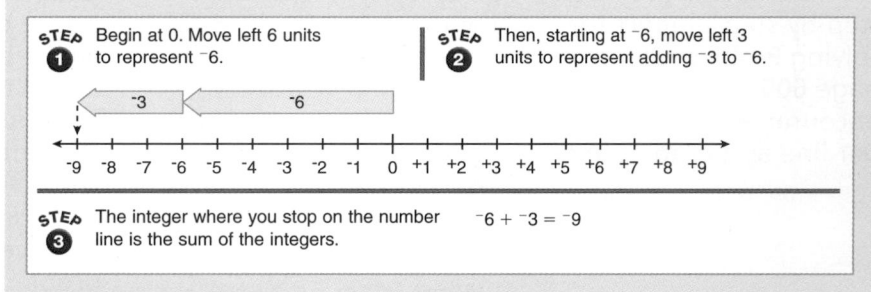

STEP 1 Begin at 0. Move left 6 units to represent $^-6$.

STEP 2 Then, starting at $^-6$, move left 3 units to represent adding $^-3$ to $^-6$.

STEP 3 The integer where you stop on the number line is the sum of the integers. $^-6 + {}^-3 = {}^-9$

Solution: The snow cover changed $^-9$ inches.

You can also use a number line to subtract integers.

Find $^-7 - {}^-5$.

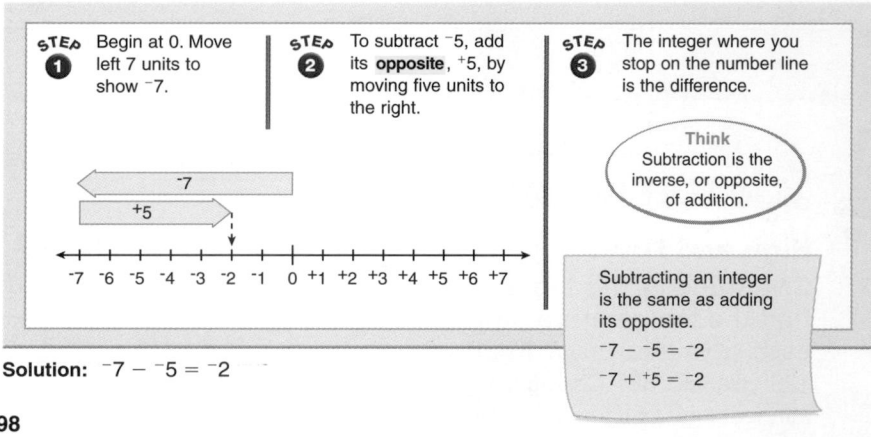

STEP 1 Begin at 0. Move left 7 units to show $^-7$.

STEP 2 To subtract $^-5$, add its **opposite**, $^+5$, by moving five units to the right.

STEP 3 The integer where you stop on the number line is the difference.

Think
Subtraction is the inverse, or opposite, of addition.

Subtracting an integer is the same as adding its opposite.
$^-7 - {}^-5 = {}^-2$
$^-7 + {}^+5 = {}^-2$

Solution: $^-7 - {}^-5 = {}^-2$

598

---

1 Introduce

Teaching Transparency for 22.5

Materials: *Number Lines Transparency*

- At the top of the transparency write: $^+2 + {}^+3$. **To locate $^+2$ on the number line, begin at 0 and move right 2 units. How can we add $^+3$ to $^+2$?** (Move right 3 units from $^+2$) **Where does that put us?** (at $^+5$) **What is $^+2 + {}^+3$?** ($^+5$)

- Write: $^-2 + {}^-4$. **What is the first thing to do?** (Move 2 units left from 0 to locate $^-2$.) **In which direction should we move from $^-2$ to add $^-4$?** (left, since $^-4$ is negative) **How many units do we move?** (4) **Where does that put us on the line?** (at $^-6$) **What is $^-2 + {}^-4$?** ($^-6$)

- **When we add a *positive* integer, in which direction do we move?** (right) **When we add a *negative* integer, in which direction do we move?** (left)

2 Develop

Guide students through the *Learn About It* section of the lesson.

- Example 1 involves adding negative integers. **Look at Step 1. In which direction from 0 do we move to find $^-6$?** (left) **Look at Step 2. Remember that when adding a negative number, we move to the left.**

- Example 2 involves subtracting negative integers. **Look at Step 2. In which direction do we move when subtracting a negative integer?** (right) **Look at Step 3. Have a volunteer read aloud the circled statement.**

Before adding or subtracting, you can use these rules to decide whether the sum of two integers will be positive or negative.

The sum of two positive integers is positive.	$^+3 - ^-5 = ^+8$ $^+3 + ^+5 = ^+8$
The sum of two negative numbers is negative.	$^-3 - ^+5 = ^-8$ $^-3 + ^-5 = ^-8$
The sum of a positive integer and a negative integer will have the same sign as the integer with the greater absolute value.	$^+3 - ^+5 = ^-2$ $^+3 + ^-5 = ^-2$ $^-3 - ^-5 = ^+2$ $^-3 + ^+5 = ^+2$

Remember
You can change any subtraction expression to addition by adding the opposite.

Other Examples

A. Sum of a Positive and a Negative Integer

Find $^-5 + ^+2$.

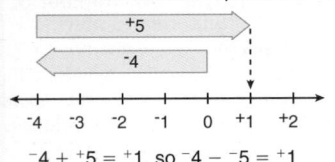

$^-5 + ^+2 = ^-3$

B. Sum of Two Negative Integers

Find $^-3 + ^-1$.

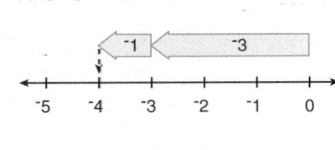

$^-3 + ^-1 = ^-4$

C. Difference of Two Negative Integers

Find $^-4 - ^-5$.
Write a related addition expression: $^-4 + ^+5$.

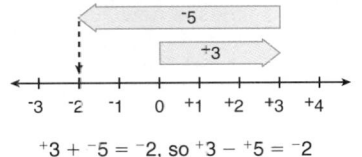

$^-4 + ^+5 = ^+1$, so $^-4 - ^-5 = ^+1$

D. Difference of Two Positive Integers

Find $^+3 - ^+5$.
Write a related addition expression: $^+3 + ^-5$.

$^+3 + ^-5 = ^-2$, so $^+3 - ^+5 = ^-2$

Guided Practice

Decide whether the answer will be positive or negative. Then use a number line to add or subtract.

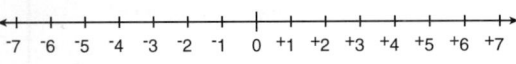

1. $^+1 + ^+3$ $^+4$
2. $^-4 + ^+2$ $^-2$
3. $^-2 + ^-5$ $^-7$
4. $^-2 - ^-5$ $^+3$
5. $^+3 - ^-4$ $^+7$
6. $^-7 - ^-5$ $^-2$

Ask Yourself
- Do I move left or right from 0 for the first integer?
- Can I add the opposite?
- What is the sign of the integer with the greater absolute value?

TEST TIPS Explain Your Thinking ▶ Why is subtracting an integer the same as adding its opposite?

See Additional Answers on page 607.

Go On

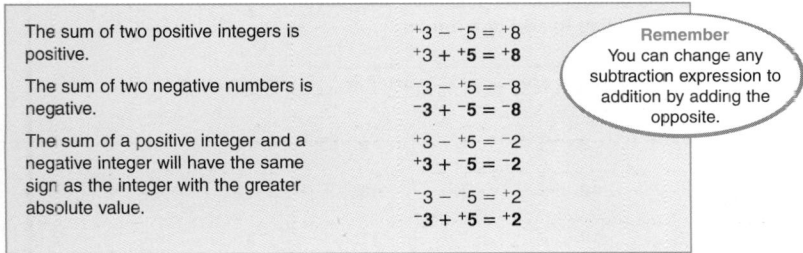

Reaching All Learners

Number Sense

Use Counters to Subtract Give students two-color counters. Remind students that the yellow side of the counter represents $^+1$ and that the red side represents $^-1$.

Have students use two-color counters and take-away subtraction to find each difference.

1. $^-5 - ^-2$
2. $^-6 - ^-5$
3. $^+3 - ^+7$
4. $^+2 - ^+6$
5. $^-1 - ^-4$
6. $^-3 - ^-8$
7. $^+6 - ^-3$
8. $^-3 - ^+4$

9. Have students write a corresponding addition sentence for each exercises in the form $^-5 + \underline{} = ^-3$ (for $^-5 - ^-2 = ^-3$).

Answers

1–8. Check students' representations.

1. $^-3$
2. $^-1$
3. $^-4$
4. $^-4$
5. $^+3$
6. $^+5$
7. $^+9$
8. $^-7$

9. $^-5 + ^+2 = ^-3$; $^-6 + ^+5 = ^-1$; $^+3 + ^-7 = ^-4$; $^+2 + ^-6 = ^-4$; $^-1 + ^+4 = ^+3$; $^-3 + ^+8 = ^+5$; $^+6 + ^+3 = ^+9$; $^-3 + ^-4 = ^-7$

Differentiated Assignments		
At Risk	**Average**	**Advanced**
Exercises 1-4	Exercises 1–8	Exercises 1–9

- Go over the rules and examples at the top of page 599. Point out that the examples are paired: for each rule, a subtraction sentence is rewritten as an addition sentence. Also point out that when adding two integers with different signs, subtract the lesser absolute value from the greater absolute value. The sign of the result is the same sign as the integer with the greater absolute value.

- Go over each of the *Other Examples*. For *A*, ask, **Which number has the greater absolute value?** ($^-5$)

- For *C*, have students read both the subtraction and the related addition sentence. **Which integer has the greater absolute value?** ($^+5$)

- Follow the same procedure for D.

Guided Practice

Have students complete **Exercises 1–6** as you observe. Remind them to use the *Ask Yourself* questions to help. Give students the opportunity to talk about the question in *Explain Your Thinking*.

DAILY TEST PREP

Which of the following expressions would you use to find the difference: $^-4 - {}^-3$? (C)

A. $^-4 + {}^-3$ C. $^-4 + {}^+3$

B. $^-4 - {}^+3$ D. $^-4 - {}^+3$

Activity

Lesson Intervention

Or use Intervention CD-ROM Lesson 22.5

Subtracting Integers on a Number Line

| 👥 Small Group | 🕐 5–10 minutes | Visual, Auditory |

Materials: *Number Lines Transparency*

• Display $^-4 - {}^-2$. Have students draw number lines and label them from $^-5$ to $^+5$.

• **Where is $^-4$?** (4 units left of 0) **Which way do we move to subtract $^-2$?** (right) **How many units do we move?** (2) **Where do you land on the number line?** ($^-2$)

• Have students repeat the process with $^-4 + {}^+2$. **What do you notice about your answer?** (It is the same, because subtracting a negative integer is the same as adding a positive one.)

Practice and Problem Solving

Decide whether the answer will be positive or negative.
Then use the number line to add or subtract.

$\overset{\longleftarrow}{\underset{^-10\ ^-9\ ^-8\ ^-7\ ^-6\ ^-5\ ^-4\ ^-3\ ^-2\ ^-1\ \ 0\ ^+1\ ^+2\ ^+3\ ^+4\ ^+5\ ^+6\ ^+7\ ^+8\ ^+9\ ^+10}{\longrightarrow}}$

7. $^+9 + {}^-2$ **$^+7$**   **8.** $^+5 + {}^+1$ **$^+6$**   **9.** $^-3 + {}^+4$ **$^+1$**   **10.** $^+6 + {}^-10$ **$^-4$**

11. $^-1 + 3$ **$^+2$**   **12.** $^+6 - {}^+6$ **0**   **13.** $^-7 + {}^+9$ **$^+2$**   **14.** $^+2 - {}^-5$ **$^+7$**

15. $^-7 - {}^-2$ **$^-5$**   **16.** $^-10 - 6$ **$^-4$**   **17.** $^-1 - 0$ **$^-1$**   **18.** $^-9 - {}^-9$ **0**

⭐**Algebra** • **Equations** Solve each equation. Use a number line to help you.

19. $^-4 - {}^-4 = \blacksquare$
$^-4 + {}^+4 = \blacksquare$ **0; 0**

20. $^+8 - {}^+3 = \blacksquare$
$^+8 + {}^-3 = \blacksquare$ **$^+5$; $^+5$**

21. $^+7 - {}^-2 = \blacksquare$
$^+7 + {}^+2 = \blacksquare$ **$^+9$; $^+9$**

22. $^+10 - {}^-3 = \blacksquare$
$^+10 + {}^+3 = \blacksquare$ **$^+13$; $^+13$**

23. $^-9 - {}^+4 = \blacksquare$
$^-9 + {}^-4 = \blacksquare$ **$^-13$; $^-13$**

24. $^-12 - {}^-5 = \blacksquare$
$^-12 + {}^+5 = \blacksquare$ **$^-7$; $^-7$**

25. $^-11 + x = {}^-13$ **$x = {}^-2$**

26. $x + {}^+4 = {}^-8$ **$x = {}^-12$**

27. $^+8 + x = {}^+14$ **$x = {}^+6$**

28. $x + {}^-2 = {}^-4$ **$x = {}^-2$**

29. $x + {}^-2 = {}^+4$ **$x = {}^+6$**

30. $x - {}^-2 = {}^-4$ **$x = {}^-6$**

Solve. **31. 15 inches.** *Possible answer:* Five inches melted and 10 inches fell, so $x + {}^-5 + {}^+10 = {}^+20$, $x + {}^+5 = {}^+20$, $x = {}^+15$: the total number of inches is now 20, so there must have been 15 inches to start.

✏️ **31. Write About It** On a warm day, 5 inches of snow melted. That night a storm brought 10 inches of snow. If there is now 20 inches of snow, how much snow was there in the beginning? Explain.

32. Without the natural greenhouse effect, Earth's temperature would be a frigid $^-18°C$. Instead, the global temperature is 33° higher than $^-18°C$. What is Earth's temperature? **$^+15°C$**

| **Daily Review** | **Test Prep** |

Use the GCF to write each ratio in simplest form. (Ch. 18, Lesson 2)

33. $\frac{16}{48}$ **$\frac{1}{3}$**

34. 20:30 **2:3**

35. 15 to 5 **3 to 1**

36. $\frac{19}{26}$ **$\frac{19}{26}$**

37. 7:31 **7:31**

38. $\frac{81}{9}$ **$\frac{9}{1}$**

39. 60:6 **10:1**

40. 3:300 **1:100**

✔ **41.** You earn $6 and spend $5. Then you earn $4 more and spend $5. Which of these does NOT tell you how much you have?

A $(^+6 - {}^+5) + (^+4 - {}^+5)$

Ⓑ $(^+6 - {}^-5) + (^+4 - {}^-5)$

C $(^+6 + {}^-5) + (^+4 + {}^-5)$

D $(^+6 + {}^+4) - (^+5 + {}^+5)$

600

Extra Practice See page 607, Set C.

---

③ Practice

Assign **Exercises 7–41** as independent work. Have students explain their answers for Exercises 7–18.

• *Algebra • Equations* **for Problems 19–30** Have students discuss and explain their answers.

• *Problem Solving* **for Problems 31–32** Have students share their answers and discuss their work.

Common Error

~~~~~~~~~~~~~~~~~~~~~~~~~~~~~~~~~~~~~~

Rewriting an expression incorrectly When students rewrite a subtraction expression as an addition expression, they may change the sign of the operation but forget to change the sign of the second integer. Remind them to change both signs.

④ Assess and Close

• **What do we do to rewrite a subtraction expression with integers as an addition expression with integers?** (Change the sign of the operation and add the opposite of the second integer.)

• **Give one or two examples.** (Examples may vary.)

• **What is an example of how addition and subtraction with integers can be shown in an easy way?** (Use a number line.)

Assign the **LESSON QUIZ** on Transparency 22.5 to further assess student understanding.

Back Track

Start with $^+1$. Add as you move to each number. Find a path that leads to each sum. Can you find different solutions?

path to 0: start: $^+1$, $^+3$ $^+1$, $^-10$, $^+2$, $^+3$

path to $^+4$: $^+1$, $^-1$, $^+4$

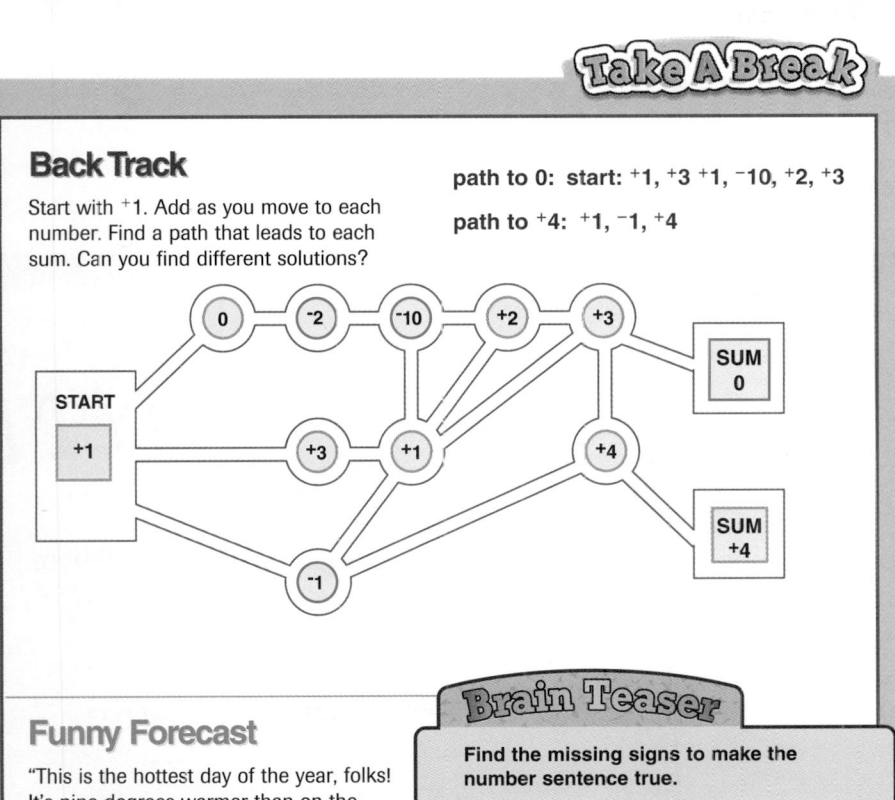

Funny Forecast

"This is the hottest day of the year, folks! It's nine degrees warmer than on the same day last year, which was fifteen degrees warmer than yesterday. Get out your swimsuits and sunscreen! This isn't going to last long. Rain is moving in tomorrow, bringing the temperature down about five degrees to 85°F." **66°F**

What was the temperature yesterday?

Write your own funny forecast for a partner to solve.

Brain Teaser

Find the missing signs to make the number sentence true.

$$\blacksquare 1 - \blacksquare 2 + \blacksquare 3 < {}^-4$$
$$^-1 - {}^+2 + {}^-3 < {}^-4$$

Ask Yourself
How can I find all the possible choices?

**Technology**
Visit *Education Place* at **eduplace.com/kids/mw/** to try more brain teasers.

Chapter 22 Lesson 5 **601**

Back Track
- Suggest that students record the integer they add or subtract for each move. For example, to get from $^+1$ to $^-1$, add $^-2$.

Funny Forecast
- Students have to work backward from 85° to find 90°, today's temperature. Then go on to find the temperature on the same day last year.

Brain Teaser
- Students might list all possible combinations: If the first integer is $+$, there are 4 possibilities for the other two: $+\ +$, $+\ -$, $-\ +$, $-\ -$. If the first integer is $-$, there are 4 possibilities for the other two: $+\ +$, $+\ -$, $-\ +$, $-\ -$.

Keeping a Journal

Have students write a few sentences explaining how to subtract a negative integer from a positive integer and from a negative integer.

Problem-Solving Application: Use Integers

PLANNING THE LESSON

MATHEMATICS OBJECTIVE
Solve problems that include integers.

Use Lesson Planner CD-ROM for Lesson 22.6.

Daily Routines

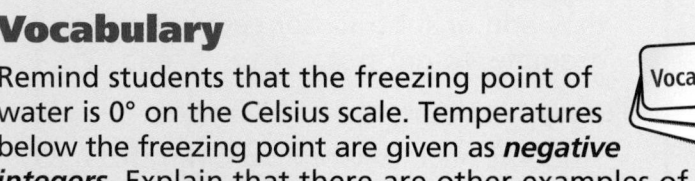

Vocabulary

Remind students that the freezing point of water is 0° on the Celsius scale. Temperatures below the freezing point are given as *negative integers.* Explain that there are other examples of how we use positive and negative integers: The distance above or below sea level of any location on earth is its *elevation.* The elevation at sea level is given as 0. Elevations below sea level are given as negative integers.

Vocabulary Cards

Meeting North Carolina's Standards

Prepare for Grade 7 Objective **1.02** Develop fluency in addition, subtraction, multiplication, and division of rational numbers.

Lesson Transparency 22.6

Problem of the Day

In the equation $60 \div 6 \times 2 + 3 = n$, where should parentheses be placed so that $n = 4$? (Possible answer: $60 \div (6 \times 2 + 3) = 4$)

Quick Review
Write the missing number.
1. 8 m = ___ cm (800)
2. 2,000 mL = ___ L (2)
3. 250 mm = ___ cm (25)
4. 30 m = ___ dm (300)

Lesson Quiz
Solve. Use a number line to help you.
1. At 6:00 A.M., the temperature was ⁻3°F. By 3:00 P.M. the temperature was ⁺10°F. What was the change in temperature during those 9 hours? (⁺13°F)
2. At 7:00 A.M., the temperature was ⁻10°F. By noon, it had risen 15°. By 8:00 P.M. the temperature had dropped 8°. What was the temperature at 8:00 P.M.? (⁻3°F)

LEVELED PRACTICE

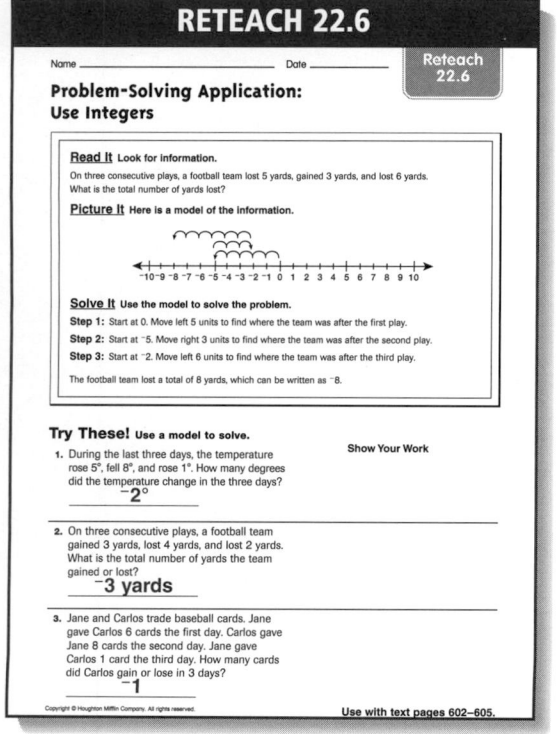

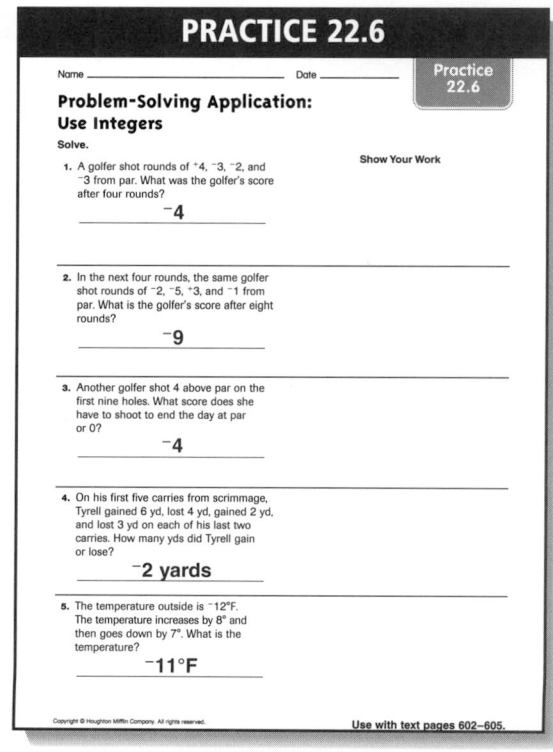

ENRICHMENT 22.6

Name _____ Date _____

Enrichment 22.6

Hot and Cold in the U.S.A.

Many areas in the United States have record high and low temperatures that are more than 100 degrees apart. **1–5: Possible answers.**

1. Use an almanac or other resource to find the record high and low temperatures in degrees Fahrenheit for the five states shown in the table.

State	Record High Temperature	Record Low Temperature
Alaska	100	⁻80
Florida	109	⁻2
Michigan	112	⁻51
North Dakota	121	⁻60
Wyoming	114	⁻66

2. Make a number line to display the data in your chart. **Number lines may vary. Make sure students' number lines display the data.**

3. Using the data, which state has the greatest temperature difference between its record high and record low temperature? What is it?

North Dakota; 181 degrees

4. Order the remaining temperature differences from greatest to least.

Alaska and Wyoming, 180 degrees; Michigan, 163 degrees; Florida, 111 degrees

5. Of all 50 states, which one do you think has the least difference between its record high and low temperatures? Use the same resource you used to fill in the chart to find out. **Hawaii has a high of 100 degrees and a low of 12 degrees for a difference of 88 degrees.**

Copyright © Houghton Mifflin Company. All rights reserved. **Use with text pages 602–605.**

Practice Workbook Page 148

Reaching All Learners

Differentiated Instruction

English Learners

Worksheet 22.6 teaches content vocabulary relating to cold weather. This vocabulary building will prepare students to understand the word problems in Lesson 6.

Inclusion
VISUAL, TACTILE

- Display a number line.
- **At 7:00 A.M., it was ⁻4°F. At noon it was ⁺8°F.** Have students count units between ⁻4 and ⁺8. **How much warmer did it get?** (12°)
- **Display ⁺8 − ⁻4. Can we write it as an addition expression?** (⁺8 + ⁺4) **What is ⁺8 + ⁺4?** (12)

Gifted and Talented
VISUAL, AUDITORY

- Write these numbers on the chalkboard: ⁻1, ⁻4, ⁻9, ⁻4, 0, ⁺5, ⁺8, ⁺15.
- Challenge students to select some of these numbers to write two temperature problems of their own. Ask them to exchange their problems with a classmate and then solve each other's problems.

TECHNOLOGY

Spiral Review

Using the *Ways to Assess* CD-ROM, you can create **customized** spiral review worksheets covering any lessons you choose.

Intervention

Use the *Ways to Success* intervention software to support students who need more help in understanding the concepts and skills taught in this chapter.

Ways to Success

Science Connection

Check Out the Wind Chill

- Have students suppose that they have been asked to illustrate a brochure about protecting oneself against the effects of wind chill.

- Have them use the *Data* table given on page 604 as the basis for one or two illustrations. Tell them they should write captions or a short paragraph to go with each illustration.

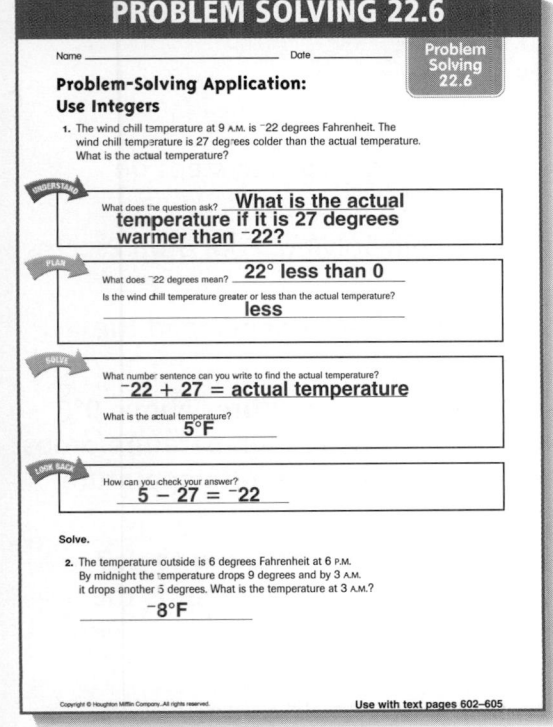

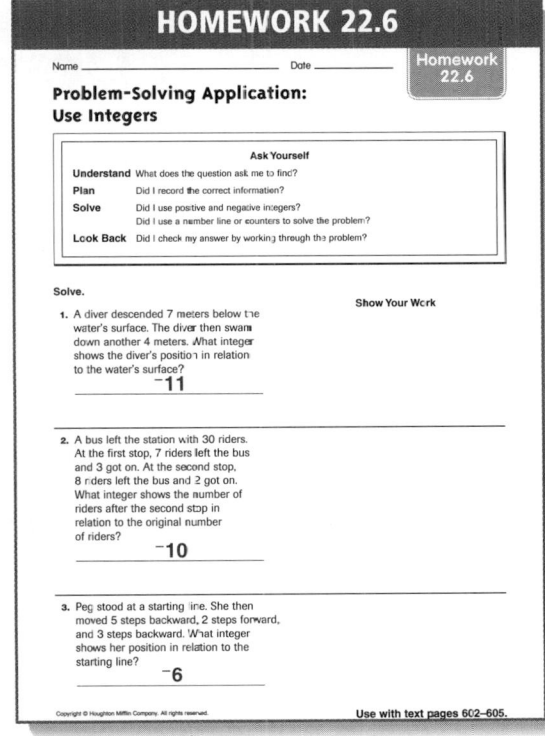

Homework Workbook Page 148

TEACHING LESSON 22.6

Activity

Warm-Up Activity
Subtract Integers

👤👤👤👤 Whole Group	⏱ 5 minutes	Visual, Auditory

Rewrite each subtraction expression as an addition expression, and find the sum.

1. $^-2 - ^-4$ ($^-2 + ^+4; ^+2$)

2. $^-3 - ^+5$ ($^-3 + ^-5; ^-8$)

3. $^-6 - ^-4$ ($^-6 + ^+4; ^-2$)

4. $^+6 - ^-4$ ($^+6 + ^+4; ^+10$)

Problem-Solving Application
Use Integers

Objective Solve problems that include integers.

You can use integers to solve problems.

Problem When Alma stepped outside, the wind was blowing at 5 miles per hour, which made the actual temperature of 10°F feel 9° colder. Ten minutes later, the wind was blowing at 20 miles per hour, which made Alma feel 10° colder than when she first stepped out. What is the wind chill temperature now?

*The wind cools your skin and you feel colder than the actual temperature. This is called **wind chill**.*

 **UNDERSTAND**

What is the question?
What is the wind chill temperature that Alma feels now?

What do you know?
- The actual temperature is 10°F.
- At first, the wind chill was 9° less than the actual temperature.
- Now the wind chill is 10° less than when Alma first went outside.

PLAN

Record actual temperatures above 0°F as positive integers. Record temperature drops as negative integers. Then find the total change in temperature.

SOLVE

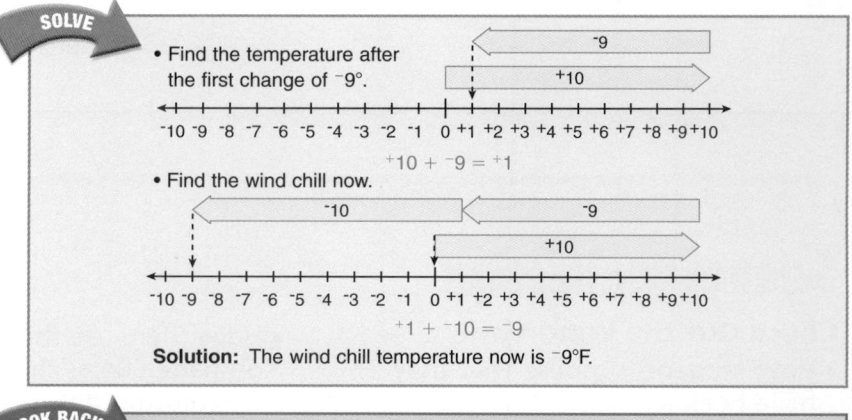

- Find the temperature after the first change of $^-9°$.

$$^+10 + ^-9 = ^+1$$

- Find the wind chill now.

$$^+1 + ^-10 = ^-9$$

Solution: The wind chill temperature now is $^-9°F$.

LOOK BACK

Look back at the problem. How can you check your answer?

---

1 Introduce

- Tell students that translating verbal descriptions into expressions with integers is important in solving problems. Have students write expressions with integers for the following problems, then solve.

  1. Monday's temperature was 4°F. On Tuesday, the temperature dropped 3° from what it was on Monday. What was Tuesday's temperature? ($4 - ^+3$ or $4 + ^-3 = ^+1°F$)

  2. On Wednesday, it was 5° warmer than it was on Tuesday. What was Wednesday's temperature? ($^+1 + ^+5 = ^+6°F$)

2 Develop

Guide students through the problem-solving steps on page 602.

You may wish to use the Problem Solving: Four Step Process Transparency.

- **Look at the Understand step.** Have students read the questions and responses.

- **Look at the Plan step. How are temperatures above 0°F expressed?** (as positive integers) **How are temperature drops recorded?** (as negative integers) **How would temperature rises be recorded?** (as positive integers)

- **Look at the Solve step. What is the first thing to do?** (Find the temperature after the first change.) **What is the second thing to do?** (Find the wind chill temperature with a 20-mph wind.)

- **Look at the Look Back step. How could you check the solution?** (Work backward from $^-9$ by adding.)

Guided Practice

Use the Ask Yourself questions to help you solve each problem.

1. Use an integer to describe the rise and fall of temperatures, in degrees Fahrenheit, represented by the set of integers ($^-$3, $^+$4, 0). **$^+$1°F**

2. One day the temperature went up 8° and then down 12°. If the final temperature is $^-$31°F, what was the temperature at first? **$^-$27°F**

(Hint) How do you record temperatures that go up and those that go down?

Ask Yourself

UNDERSTAND — What does the question ask me to find?

PLAN — Did I record the correct information?

SOLVE
• Did I use positive and negative integers?
• Did I use a number line or counters to solve?

LOOK BACK — Did I check my answer by working through the problem?

TEST TIPS

Independent Practice

Solve. Use a number line to help you.

3. At halftime, the temperature was 17° lower than at the start of the game. By the end, the temperature was 6° higher than at halftime. The temperature at the end was $^-$16°F. Find the temperature at the start of the game. **$^-$5°F**

4. At a certain temperature, unprotected skin will get frostbitten in 30 minutes. If the temperature drops 26° to $^-$48°F, that will cause frostbite in 5 minutes. At what temperature will unprotected skin get frostbitten in 30 minutes? **$^-$22°F**

5. At 6:00 A.M., the temperature was $^-$5°F. By noon of the same day, the temperature was 6°F. How many degrees did the temperature change in 6 hours? **11°F**

6. At the beginning of the day, the temperature was $^+$2°F. During the day, the temperature rose 4° and then dropped 10°. What was the temperature at the end of the day? **$^-$4°F**

7. **What's Wrong?** Roberta left the note below for her father. What did Roberta do wrong? What should she have written? **See above.**

7. She added the temperatures instead of subtracting; $^-$3 $-$ $^-$12 = 9; that's 9° colder than now.

> Dad,
> Temperature now: $^-$3°
> Going down to $^-$12° tonight.
> That's 15° colder than now.
> Roberta

Go On

Quick Check Options

The following activities will help students prepare for the Quick Check or may be used as an alternative assessment.

Vocabulary Review *(individual, small group, or whole class)*

Have students review the following vocabulary words by giving an example of how each term is used in this chapter.

• positive integers
• negative integers

Math Conversations *(small group or whole class)*

Have students discuss what they have learned about using integers in this chapter. Encourage students to ask each other questions to clarify their understanding.

Writing Prompt *(individual or partners)*

To solidify student understanding of vocabulary and concepts, have each student complete the following sentence:
The thing I found most difficult about using integers is _____.

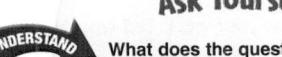

❸ Practice

Guided Practice

Have students complete **Problems 1 and 2** as you observe. Remind them to use the *Ask Yourself* questions to help.

Assign **Problems 3–7** as independent work. Have students share and discuss their work.

Problem-Solving Reminders

Have students review their answers to make sure they have done the following:

• expressed the solution properly
• used appropriate mathematical notation and terms
• supported their solutions with verbal and symbolic work
• determined the reasonableness of the solution in the context of the original problem.

DAILY TEST PREP

What will the next integer in this pattern be?

$^-25, ^-19, ^-13, ^-7, ^-1, \underline{\quad}$ (A)

A. $^+5$　　　B. $^+4$　　　C. $^-5$　　　D. $^-4$

Activity

Lesson Intervention

Or use Intervention CD-ROM Lesson 22.6

Adding Yardage

| 👥 Small Group | 🕐 5–10 minutes | Visual, Kinesthetic |

- Write this problem on the chalkboard: *On three consecutive plays, a football team gained 3 yards, lost 6 yards, and gained 7 yards. What was the total number of yards gained or lost?*

- **How many yards did they gain on the first play?** (3) **How can you express that as an integer?** ($^+3$)

- **How many yards did they then lose on the next play?** (6) **Will you express that as $^+6$ or $^-6$?** ($^-6$) **What addition expression can you write for this loss?** ($^+3 + ^-6$) **Evaluate that expression.** ($^+3 + ^-6 = ^-3$) **How do you interpret that result?** (a loss of 3 yards)

- **How many yards did they gain on the next play?** (7) **What expression can you write for this gain?** ($^-3 + ^+7$) **Evaluate that expression.** ($^-3 + ^+7 = ^+4$) **Over the three plays, did the team gain or lose yards? How many?** (gain; 4 yards)

Choose a Strategy ✓

Strategies may vary. Possible strategies given.

Solve. Show your work. Tell what strategy you used.

8. **Estimate** Antarctica's climate is the harshest on Earth. The record low temperature there was about 70°F lower than the mean temperature of $^-58$°F. Is $^-130$°F a reasonable estimate for the record temperature? Explain.
See Additional Answers on Page 607.

9. **Calculator** A liquid lake lies miles below Antarctica's ice sheet. Lake Vostok is 250 kilometers long, 40 kilometers wide, and 0.4 kilometers deep. What is the lake's volume?
See Additional Answers on Page 607.

10. Jacqui, Ajay, Terri, and Mason are having a race. Jacqui is not riding a bike or roller-skating. Terri is on a skateboard. Mason will not roller-skate or use a scooter. Match each person with the correct mode of transportation.
See Additional Answers on Page 607.

PROBLEM-SOLVING Strategies

Use Models
Draw a Diagram
Find a Pattern
Guess and Check
Make an Organized List
Make a Table
Solve a Simpler Problem
Use Logical Reasoning
Work Backward
Write an Equation

Choose a Computation Method ✓

Mental Math • Estimation • Paper and Pencil • Calculator

 Data The table below shows wind chill temperatures for actual temperatures from $^+15$ to $^-10$°F. Use the table to solve Problems 11–14. Then explain which method you chose.

11. **Analyze** At which actual temperature does the wind chill temperature drop 11°F, then drops 5°, 3°, 3°, and 2° as the winds change from 0 miles per hour to 25 miles per hour? **0°F**

12. **Predict** What would be a reasonable prediction for the wind chill temperature at 10°F if the wind speed is 60 miles per hour? **Possible answer: $^-19$°F**

13. **You Decide** A school in the Northeast has outdoor recess if the temperature is not too low. Use the data in the table to create guidelines for the school to decide when to cancel outdoor recess.
Check guidelines. Answers will vary.

14. An old wind chill formula gave a wind chill index for $^+5$°F and a 5 mi/h wind that was about 5° higher than in this table. What was that wind chill index? **0°F**

Wind Chill Index

Wind (mi/h)	Temperature (°F)					
	+15	+10	+5	0	−5	−10
0	+15	+10	+5	0	−5	−10
5	7	1	−5	−11	−16	−22
10	3	−4	−10	−16	−22	−28
15	0	−7	−13	−19	−26	−32
20	−2	−9	−15	−22	−29	−35
25	−4	−11	−17	−24	−31	−37
30	−5	−12	−19	−26	−33	−39
35	−7	−14	−21	−27	−34	−41
40	−8	−15	−22	−29	−36	−43

604

Practice *continued*

Choose a Strategy

Assign **Problems 8–10** as independent work.

- *Problem Solving for Problems 8–10* Have students describe the strategies they used to solve each problem and share their solutions.

Choose a Computation Method

- *Problem Solving for Problems 11–14* Have students explain the method they used. For Problem 13, have students share and discuss each other's guidelines.

---

④ Assess and Close

- Have students discuss strategies that work in solving problems that include integers.

- **Which strategy is most helpful?** (Answers may vary, but Working Backward and Solving a Simpler Problem may often be useful.)

Assign the **LESSON QUIZ** on Transparency 22.6 to further assess student understanding.

Quick Check

Check your understanding for Lessons 4–6.

Use counters to subtract. (Lesson 4)

1.

   Take away 2 yellow counters.
   6 red counters or ⁻6

2.

   Take away 7 red counters.
   13 yellow counters or ⁺13

Decide whether the answer will be positive or negative. Then add or subtract. (Lesson 5)

3. ⁺7 + ⁻3
   positive; ⁺4

4. ⁻19 + ⁻5
   negative; ⁻24

5. ⁺27 − ⁻16
   positive; ⁺43

Solve. (Lesson 6)

6. On three consecutive plays, a football team gains 1 yard, gains 7 yards, and then loses 5 yards. Use integers to find the total number of yards lost or gained. **⁺3 yards or gained 3 yards**

Quick Check

Purpose: The Quick Check allows you to assess the students' understanding of the concepts presented in Lessons 4–6.

Items	Objectives Tested	Pages	Intervention
1–2	Use counters to model subtraction of integers.	596–597	Reteach Resource 22.4 *Ways to Success 22.4*
3–5	Use a number line to add and subtract integers.	598–601	Reteach Resource 22.5 *Ways to Success 22.5*
6	Solve problems that include integers.	602–605	Reteach Resource 22.6 *Ways to Success 22.6*

Patterns With Integers

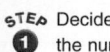 **Algebraic Thinking / Math Reasoning**

You can find and use patterns with integers.

Find the rule and the missing term for this pattern: ⁻19, ⁻15, ⁻11, ⁻7, ⁻3, ■

STEP 1 Decide whether the numbers increase or decrease.

The integers in this pattern increase.

STEP 2 Find a rule for the pattern.

⁻19 + what integer = ⁻15?

⁻19 + ⁺4 = ⁻15

Try adding ⁺4 to each term.

⁻15 + ⁺4 = ⁻11
⁻11 + ⁺4 = ⁻7
⁻7 + ⁺4 = ⁻3

STEP 3 Apply the rule to find terms in the pattern.

⁻3 + ⁺4 = ⁺1

Solution: The rule is to add ⁺4. The missing term is ⁺1.

Write the rule and name the missing term in the pattern.

1. 0, ■, ⁻10, ⁻15, ⁻20, ⁻25
   add negative 5; ⁻5

2. ⁺12, ⁺8, ⁺4, 0, ⁻4, ⁻8, ⁻12, ■
   subtract 4; ⁻16

3. $\frac{11}{2}, \frac{9}{2}, \frac{7}{2}, \frac{5}{2}, \frac{3}{2}, \frac{1}{2},$ ■ **subtract $\frac{2}{2}$; $-\frac{1}{2}$**

4. ⁻4.5, ⁻3, ⁻1.5, ■, ⁺1.5, ⁺3
   add ⁺1.5; 0

Keeping a Journal

Have students create a problem involving integers. Ask them to explain how the four problem-solving steps can be used to analyze and solve the problem.

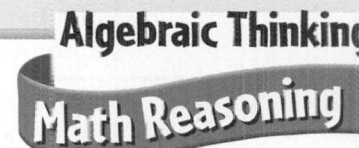 **Algebraic Thinking / Math Reasoning**

Patterns With Integers

- Have students discuss each step as you observe. Students should note that the integers increase.

- In Step 2, students find the difference between the first and second integers and then test that difference for the other terms.

- Step 3 involves extending the pattern to the sixth term. Have students take the pattern further.

Chapter Review/Test

Purpose: This test provides an informal assessment of the Chapter 22 objectives.

Chapter Test Items 1–20

To assign a numerical grade for this Chapter Test, use 5 points for each test item.

Check Understanding

You can use the **Write About It** question to assess student understanding of a key chapter concept.

Customizing Your Instruction

For students who have not yet mastered these objectives, you can use the Reteaching Resources listed in the chart below.

 Assessment Options

A summary test for this chapter is also provided in the Unit Resource Folder.

 Adequate Yearly Progress

Use the End of Grade Test Prep Assessment Guide to help familiarize your students with the format of standardized tests.

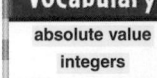 **Chapter Review/Test**

VOCABULARY

1. Counting numbers, their opposites, and zero are called ____. **integers**

2. Numbers to the left of 0 on a number line are called ____. **negative numbers**

3. The distance of a number from 0 on a number line is the ____ of that number. **absolute value**

> **Vocabulary**
> absolute value
> integers
> negative numbers
> opposite
> positive numbers

CONCEPTS AND SKILLS

Write the opposite of each integer. Then write the absolute value of each integer. (Lesson 1, pp. 586–587)

4. $^-98$ $^+98; 98$
5. $^+75$ $^-75; 75$
6. $^+629$ $^-629; 629$
7. $^-52$ $^+52; 52$

8. $^-31$ $^+31; 31$
9. $^-163$ $^+163; 163$
10. $^+312$ $^-312; 312$
11. $^+98$ $^-98; 98$

Draw a number line from $^-10$ to $^+10$ and label each integer. Write >, <, or = for each ●. (Lesson 2, pp. 588–591)

12. $^-9$ ● $^-4$ **<**
13. $^+3$ ● $^-1$ **>**
14. $^-6$ ● $^+4$ **<**
15. $^+2$ ● $^-10$ **>**

Decide whether the answer will be positive or negative. Then use the number line to add or subtract. (Lessons 3–5, pp. 592–601)

$^-10$ $^-8$ $^-6$ $^-4$ $^-2$ 0 $^+2$ $^+4$ $^+6$ $^+8$ $^+10$

16. $^-9 + ^+6$ **negative, $^-3$**
17. $^+7 - ^-2$ **positive, $^+9$**
18. $^-8 - ^+1$ **negative, $^-9$**
19. $^-3 - ^-1$ **negative, $^-2$**

Write About It *Possible answer:* No. Absolute value refers to the distance between the integer and 0. The distance is the same whether a given integer is positive or negative.

PROBLEM SOLVING

Solve. Use a number line to help you. (Lesson 6, pp. 602–605)

20. At noon on Monday, the temperature was $^-2$°F. By 6:00 P.M., the temperature had risen 10°. By midnight, the temperature had fallen 8°. What was the temperature at midnight? **0°F**

 Write About It

Show You Understand
From looking at the absolute value of an integer, can you tell whether that integer is positive or negative? Explain. *See above.*

Reteaching Support

Chapter Test Items	Summary Test Items	Chapter Objectives Tested	TE Pages	Use These Reteaching Resources
1–11	1–7	**22A** Locate integers on a number line and find the absolute value of integers.	586A–587	Reteach Resource 22.1 Ways to Success CD: 22.1 Skillsheet 175
12–15	8–10	**22B** Compare and order integers.	588A–591	Reteach Resource 22.2 Ways to Success CD: 22.2 Skillsheet 176
16–19	11–15	**22C** Add and subtract integers.	592A–601	Reteach Resource 22.3–22.5 Ways to Success CD: 22.3–22.5 Skillsheet 177, 178
20	16–20	**22D** Analyze and solve problems using integers.	602A–605	Reteach Resource 22.6 Ways to Success CD: 22.6 Skillsheet 179

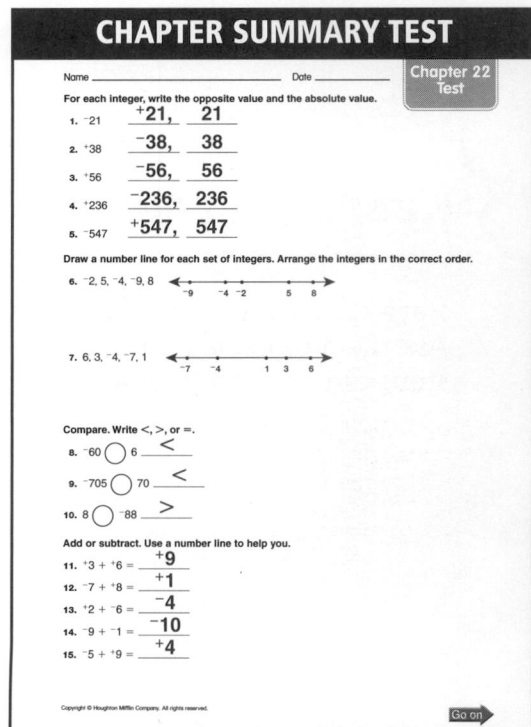

CHAPTER SUMMARY TEST

Set A (Lesson 1, pp. 586–587)

Write the opposite of each integer. Then write the absolute value of each integer.

1. $^+5$ $^-5, 5$ 2. $^-7$ $^+7, 7$ 3. $^+17$ $^-17, 17$ 4. $^+89$ $^-89, 89$ 5. $^-45$ $^+45, 45$

6. $^-72$ $^+72, 72$ 7. $^+100$ $^-100, 100$ 8. $^-36$ $^+36, 36$ 9. $^-29$ $^+29, 29$ 10. $^+55$ $^-55, 55$

11. $^-10$ $^+10, 10$ 12. $^+31$ $-31, 31$ 13. $^-127$ $^+127, 127$ 14. $^+66$ $^-66, 66$ 15. $^-64$ $^+64, 64$

Set B (Lesson 2, pp. 588–591)

Draw a number line from $^-8$ to $^+8$ and label each integer. Write >, <, or = for each ●.

1. $^+4$ > ● 0   2. $^+3$ < ● $^+5$ 3. $^-2$ > ● $^-5$ 4. $^-6$ < ● 0

5. $^-8$ < ● $^+8$ 6. $^-5$ < ● $^-4$ 7. $^+1$ > ● $^-2$ 8. $^+6$ < ● $^+7$

Write the integers in order from least to greatest.

9. 0, $^+7$, $^-5$, $^-3$
$^-5, ^-3, 0, ^+7$

10. $^+5$, $^+8$, $^-4$, $^-5$
$^-5, ^-4, ^+5, ^+8$

11. $^-2$, 0, $^+6$, $^-1$
$^-2, ^-1, 0, ^+6$

12. $^-4$, $^-8$, $^+5$, $^+2$
$^-8, ^-4, ^+2, ^+5$

13. $^-5$, 0, $^+5$, $^-7$
$^-7, ^-5, 0, ^+5$

14. $^+3$, $^-1$, $^-3$, $^+1$
$^-3, ^-1, ^+1, ^+3$

Set C (Lesson 5, pp. 598–601)

Decide whether the answer will be positive or negative. Then use the number line to add or subtract.

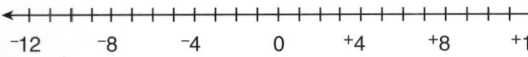

$^-12$ $^-8$ $^-4$ 0 $^+4$ $^+8$ $^+12$

1. $^+4 + ^+5$
positive; $^+9$

2. $^+6 + ^-8$
negative; $^-2$

3. $^-11 - ^+7$
negative; $^-4$

4. $^-6 + ^-2$
negative; $^-8$

5. $^+9 - ^+6$
positive; $^+3$

6. $^-4 - ^-2$
negative; $^-2$

7. $^+5 - ^-3$
positive; $^+8$

8. $^-7 - ^+5$
negative; $^-12$

9. $^+10 - ^-2$
positive; $^+12$

10. $^-8 + ^+3$
negative; $^-5$

11. $^+6 + ^-5$
positive; $^+1$

12. $^-4 - ^+4$
negative; $^-8$

13. $^+9 + ^-9$
neither; 0

14. $^+2 - ^+8$
negative; $^-6$

15. $^-7 - ^-5$
negative; $^-2$

16. $^-8 + ^+9$
positive; $^+1$

Chapter 22

Chapter Pretest, p. 585

20. 8° *Check drawings. Possible answer:* I can look at a thermometer and use it as a number line. Then I could count down by twos from 6°F to $^-2$°F.

Lesson 2, pp. 588–591

51. *Possible answer:* Debra wrote her number line with the positive integers on the left instead of on the right. The answer should be $^-5 < ^-4 < ^-3 < ^+2$.

52. *Possible answer:* You can see the order of the integers on the number line, so you can tell which integers are to the right of (greater than) other integers.

61. *Possible answer:* On a number line $^-4$ is to the right of $^-15$, so it is the greater temperature, so -15°C is the colder temperature.

Lesson 5, pp. 598–601

Explain Your Thinking: *Possible answer:* Subtracting an integer means reversing its direction (changing its sign); adding its opposite means to add the same integer with the sign changed.

Lesson 6, pp. 602–605

8. *Possible estimate:* yes; $6 + 7 = 13$ and $60 + 70 = 130$ and $^-6 + ^-7 = ^-13$, so $^-60 + ^-70 = ^-130$. (Solve a Simpler Problem)

9. 4,000 cubic kilometers (Write an Equation)

10. Jacqui, scooter; Ajay, roller-skate; Terri, skateboard; Mason, bike (Make a Table)

CHAPTER SUMMARY TEST

Name _____ Date _____

Chapter 22 Test continued

Solve. Use a number line to help you.

16. The temperature outside is 28°F. The wind chill makes it feel 30° colder. What is the wind chill temperature?
$^-2$°F

17. At 7:00 A.M., the temperature was $^-3$°F. At 2:00 P.M., the temperature was 12°F. How many degrees did the temperature change?
$^+15$°F

18. At 8:00 P.M., the temperature was $^-5$°F. Overnight the temperature dropped another 11°. What was the low temperature?
$^-16$°F

19. One night the temperature went down 12°. In the morning, the temperature went up 15°. If the final temperature was $^+9$°F, what was the temperature the night before?
$^+6$°F

20. Early in the day, the temperature was $^-3$°F. During the day, the temperature went up by 19° and then dropped 14°. What was the temperature at the end of the day?
$^+2$°F

STOP

Lesson By Lesson Overview
Coordinate Graphing

Lesson 1

- Students graph ordered pairs on a coordinate plane.
- Students identify the *x*-axis, the *y*-axis, the four quadrants, and the origin.
- Students locate and plot points in all four quadrants using ordered pairs.

Lesson 2

- Students use a function rule to find the value of ordered pairs where some of the values are negative.

Lesson 3

- Students complete function tables to show solutions (ordered pairs) to a function. They graph the function on a coordinate plane. The functions in this lesson are linear.
- Students use the graph of the function to predict other solutions.

Lesson 4

- Students read or make graphs on a coordinate plane to solve problems.

Lesson 5

- Students extend skills in identifying and describing transformations, or changes in the position of a figure, to figures graphed in the coordinate plane.

SKILLS TRACE: GRAPHING IN THE COORDINATE PLANE

Grade 4	Grade 5	Grade 6
• locate, identify points and graph points on a coordinate plane (ch. 24) • graph lines (ch. 24)	• graph ordered pairs in the four quadrants • complete function tables using integers and graph a line in the coordinate plane • identify and describe transformations on the coordinate plane	• graph points in all four quadrants (ch. 13) • investigate, represent, and graph functions (ch. 13)

Chapter Planner

Lesson	Objective	Vocabulary	Materials	✓ NCTM Standards
23.1 **Integers and the Coordinate Plane** p. 610A	Graph ordered pairs in the four quadrants of the coordinate plane.	coordinate plane x-axis y-axis quadrant ordered pair origin coordinates	Coordinate Plane Transparency, markers in two colors, grid paper	**Geometry:** Specify locations and describe spatial relationships using coordinate geometry and other representational systems.
23.2 **Algebra: Integers and Functions** p. 614A	Use a function rule to find the value of ordered pairs.	function	Table I Transparency and student copies of it, blank transparency	**Algebra:** Understand patterns, relations, and functions; Analyze change in various contexts
23.3 **Algebra: Use Functions and Graphs** p. 616A	Graph an equation on a coordinate plane.		Coordinate Plane Transparency, grid paper, student copies of Coordinate Plane Transparency	**Geometry:** Specify locations and describe spatial relationships using coordinate geometry and other representational systems.
23.4 **Algebra: Problem-Solving Application: Use a Graph** p. 620A	Use graphs to solve problems.		grid paper	**Algebra:** Understand patterns, relations, and functions.
23.5 **Transformations in the Coordinate Plane** p. 622A	Identify and describe transformations in the coordinate plane.	translation transformation reflection rotation	grid paper, Coordinate Plane Transparency, scissors	**Geometry:** Apply transformations and use symmetry to analyze mathematical situations; Specify locations and describe spatial relationships using coordinate geometry and other representational systems.

Resources For Reaching All Learners

LESSON RESOURCES: Reteach, Practice, Enrichment, Problem Solving, Homework, English Learners, Daily Routines, Transparencies, Math Center.

ADDITIONAL RESOURCES FROM HOUGHTON MIFFLIN: Combination Classroom Planning Guide, Chapter Challenges, Every Day Counts, Math at Hand (student handbook)

Every Day Counts

The **Daily Variable** activities in **Every Day Counts** support the math in this chapter.

Assessing Prior Knowledge

Before beginning the chapter, you can assess student understandings in order to assist you in differentiating instruction.

Complete Chapter Pretest in Unit Resource Folder

Use this test to assess both prerequisite skills (**Are You Ready?** — one page) and chapter content (**Check What You Know** — two pages).

Chapter 23 Prerequisite Skills Pretest

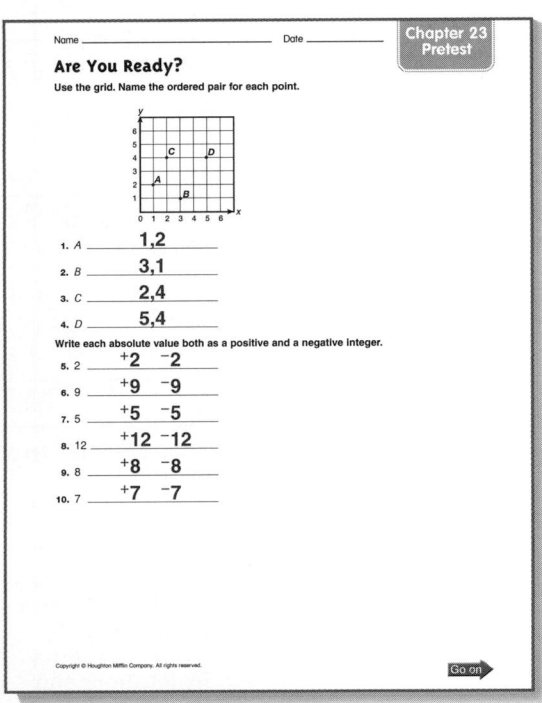

Chapter 23 New Content Pretest

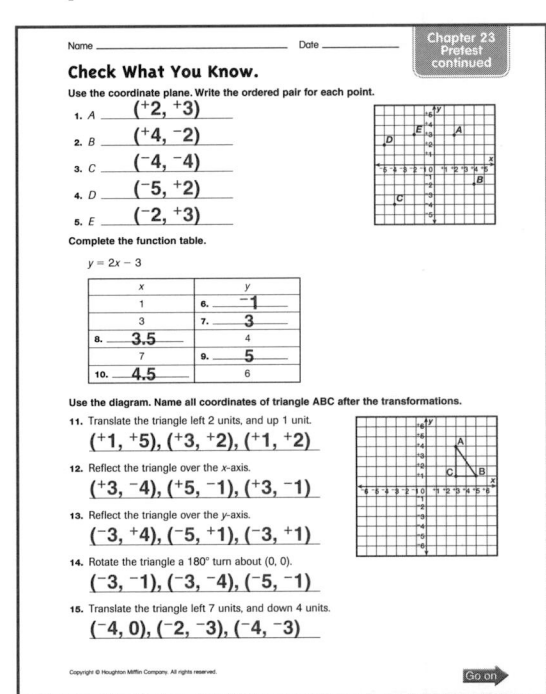

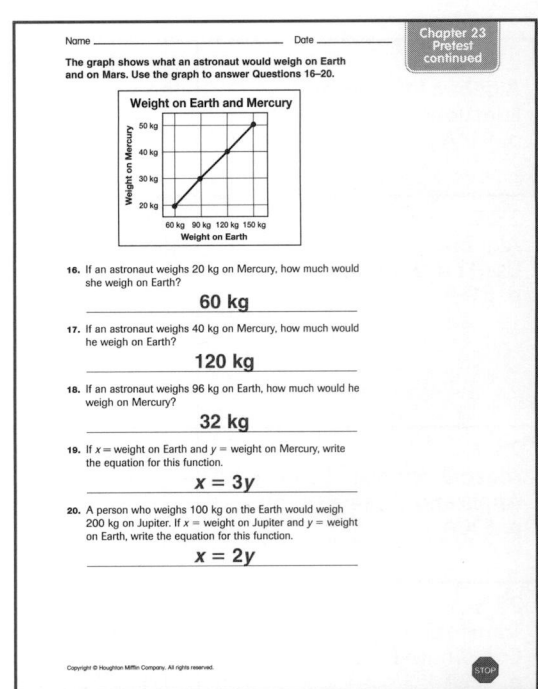

Customizing Instruction

For Students Having Difficulty

Items	Prerequisites	Ways to Success
1–4	Identify points on a coordinate plane	CD: 23a Skillsheet: 180
5–10	Write integers	CD: 23b Skillsheet: 181

Ways to Success: Intervention for every concept and skill (CD-ROM or Chapter Intervention Skillsheet).

For Students Having Success

Items	Objectives	Resources
1–5	**23A** Graph ordered pairs in the four quadrants of the coordinate plane.	Enrichment 23.1
6–10, 16–20	**23B** Complete functions tables using integers and graph a line in the coordinate plane.	Enrichment 23.2, 23.3
11–15	**23C** Identify and describe transformations on the coordinate plane.	Enrichment 23.5
16–20	**23D** Analyze and solve problems using a graph.	Enrichment 23.4

Other Pretest Options

Informal Pretest in Student Book

The student book pretest assesses vocabulary and prerequisite skills needed for success in this chapter.

Ways to Success CD-ROM

The *Ways to Success* chapter pretest has automatic assignment of appropriate review lessons.

Consider using **Knowing Mathematics** with any students who are working two or more years below grade level.

Use **Chapter Challenges** with any students who have success with all new chapter content.

Chapter Resources

Assessing Prior Knowledge

Input/Output (functions)

- Present a rule such as "Add ¯3" and have students make and complete an input/output table with five rows.
- Repeat with other rules.

Ongoing Skill Activity

Coordinate Desks (graphing, functions, and transformations in the coordinate grid)

- Have students arrange their desks in a rectangular array (with equal numbers of columns and rows, if possible).
- Illustrate each skill covered in the chapter on the "coordinate grid." To simulate each quadrant, alternate the location of the origin at each corner of the room.
- Students identify their coordinates after Lesson 1. After Lessons 3 and 4, they identify themselves as solutions to linear functions. For Lesson 6, pairs of students model translations of points.

Connecting to the Unit Project

- Have students develop a code based on points on the coordinate plane.
- Have them write a message using the code. They are to include hints to help others decode the message. Hints could be in the form of frequently used consonants and vowels, so that the decoder begins to get a sense of the encoded message.

Teacher Support

Professional Resources Handbook

Research, Mathematics Content, and Language Intervention

Research-Based Teaching

A number of researchers support an early introduction to the mathematics of change. They believe that early introduction of rate of change concepts is valuable–elementary students are clearly capable of thinking about and understanding concepts related to rate of change (Confrey, 2000). See *Professional Resources Handbook, Grade 5,* Unit 8.

For more ideas relating to Unit 8, see the Teacher Support Handbook at the back of this Teacher's Edition.

Language Intervention

Be sure students are correctly reading mathematical notation as they work in this chapter. (4, 6) is read as "four, six." Also be sure students are reading numbers correctly. Numbers greater than zero are positive numbers; so, +4 is read as "positive four," not "plus four." Numbers less than zero are negative numbers; so, –4 is read as "negative four," not "minus four."

Time Saving Technology Support

Ways to Assess Customized Spiral Review and Test Generator CD-ROM
Lesson Planner CD-ROM
Ways to Success Intervention CD-ROM
Math Tracks CD-ROM
Education Place: **www.eduplace.com/math/mw/**
Houghton Mifflin Math eBook CD-ROM
eManipulatives
eGames

Starting Chapter 23
Coordinate Graphing

Chapter Objectives

23A Graph ordered pairs in the four quadrants of the coordinate plane.

23B Complete functions tables using integers and graph a line in the coordinate plane.

23C Identify and describe transformations on the coordinate plane.

23C Analyze and solve problems using a graph.

Math Background

Coordinate Graphing

Graphing in the coordinate plane will help students visualize a relationship between two variables described as a rule. A coordinate plane is composed of a horizontal number line (the *x*-axis) and a vertical number line (the *y*-axis). The point where the two axes intersect is the origin. A location or point on the coordinate plane is identified by an ordered pair such as ($^+$3, $^+$2), which names the coordinates of the location. The first number, or the *x*-coordinate, tells how far to the right or left the number's location is in a horizontal direction. The second number, or the *y*-coordinate, tells how far up or down the number's location is in the vertical direction. The coordinates of the origin are (0, 0).

A common student error is confusing *x*-axis and *y*-axis. Remind students that in ordered pairs (*x*, *y*) the *x* and *y* are in alphabetical order. Also, *horizontal* is before *vertical* alphabetically, hence *x* is the horizontal axis and *y* is the vertical axis.

To graph a function, a table of values for *x* and *y* is completed and then the ordered pairs are graphed. Finally a line is drawn through the points. If the graph is a straight line, the function is called a linear equation.

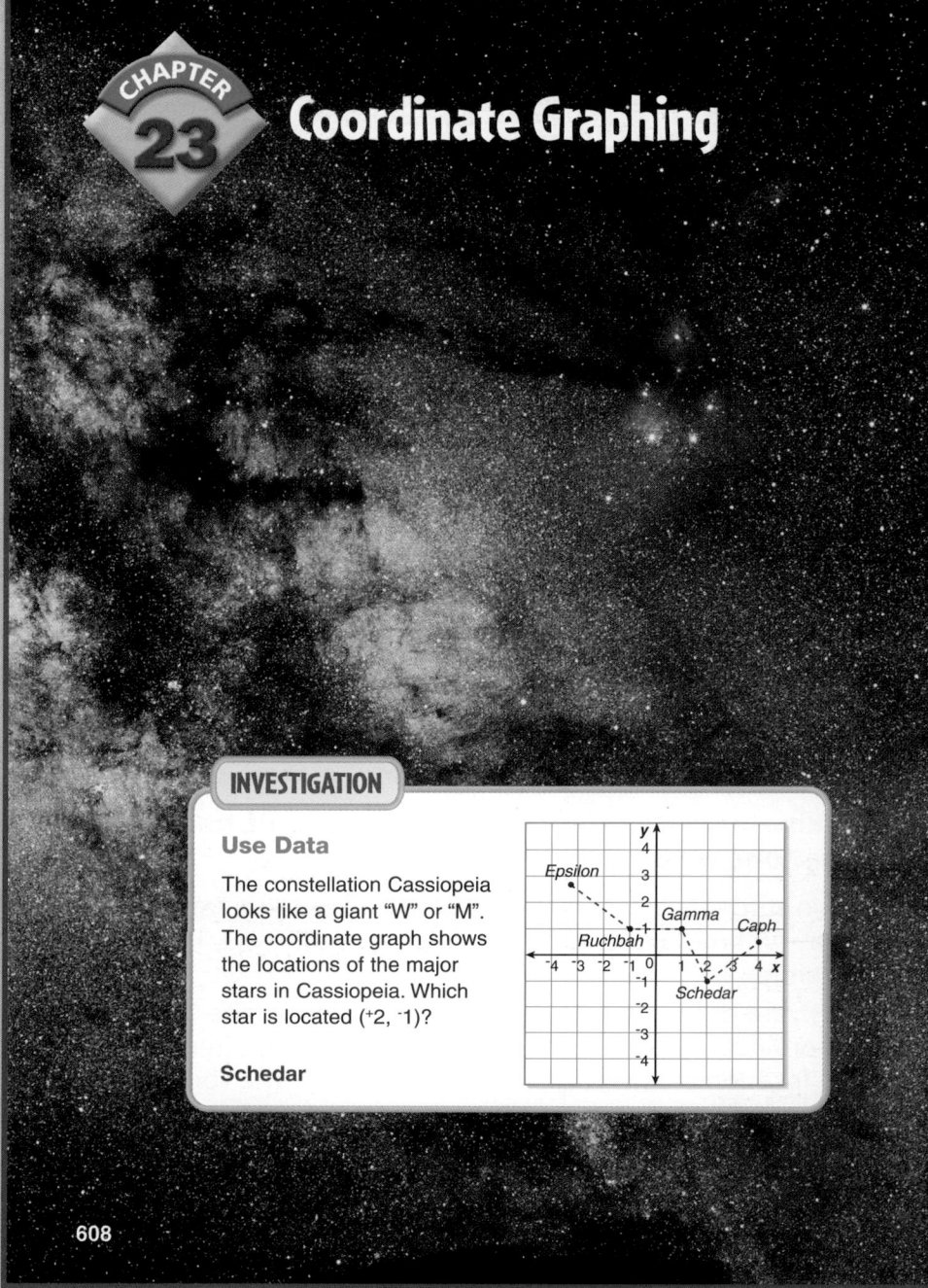

CHAPTER 23 — Coordinate Graphing

INVESTIGATION

Use Data

The constellation Cassiopeia looks like a giant "W" or "M". The coordinate graph shows the locations of the major stars in Cassiopeia. Which star is located ($^+$2, $^-$1)?

Schedar

608

Using the Investigation

Have students work in small groups to answer the question posed on page 608.

To extend the investigation, have students do the following activity.

- Use two different colored pencils. Graph (–1, 2), (2, 3), and (1, –1) on a coordinate plane and connect the points with one color. Multiply each coordinate by 2. Graph and connect the new ordered pairs with the other colored pencil. Compare the two figures. Describe how they are the same and how they are different. (Possible answer: The shapes are similar triangles. The lengths of the sides of the second triangle are double the corresponding sides of the first. Corresponding angles are equal.)

For more information about projects and investigations, visit **Education Place**.
eduplace.com/math/mw/

Use this page to review and remember
what you need to know for this chapter.

✓ VOCABULARY

Choose the best word to complete each sentence.

Vocabulary
function
ordered pair
opposite
positive

1. The number $^+5$ is a ____ number. **positive**

2. A(n) ____ is a rule that gives exactly one value
   of y for each value of x. **function**

✓ CONCEPTS AND SKILLS

Compare. Use the number line. Write $>$, $<$, or $=$ for each ●.

$$\begin{array}{ccccccccccccccccc} -8 & -7 & -6 & -5 & -4 & -3 & -2 & -1 & 0 & ^+1 & ^+2 & ^+3 & ^+4 & ^+5 & ^+6 & ^+7 & ^+8 \end{array}$$

3. $^-8$ $\overset{<}{●}$ $^-6$ 4. 0 $\overset{>}{●}$ $^-5$ 5. $^+3$ $\overset{>}{●}$ $^-7$

Add or subtract. You may use the number line above if you wish.

6. $^+4 + ^-8$ **-4**   7. $^+1 - ^-3$ **$^+4$**

8. $^-5 + ^+5$ **0**   9. $^-2 - ^+6$ **$^-8$**

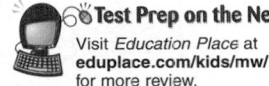 **Write About It**

10. Describe the pattern in the values of x
    and y in the function table below.

    Possible answer: As the values for x
    increase by 1 from 4 to 7, the values
    for y decrease by 3 from 18 to 9.

X	Y
4	18
5	15
6	12
7	9

Test Prep on the Net

Visit *Education Place* at
eduplace.com/kids/mw/
for more review.

 ✓ **Chapter Pretest**

Prerequisite Skills

Items	Skill
1–2	Vocabulary needed for this chapter
3–5	Comparing integers using a number line
6–9	Adding and subtracting integers
10	Understanding function tables

Chapter Challenges

For Mathematically Promising Students

Use the *Chapter Challenges* resource book.

Explore: Using Ordered Pairs in the Coordinate Plane, page 133, after Lesson 1

Extend: Graphing Linear Functions, page 135, after Lesson 3

Connect: Transformations in the Coordinate Plane, page 137, after Lesson 5

Using The Chapter Pretest

This page will help students review some of the prerequisite skills needed for this chapter. The chart above indicates which skills are covered on the pretest. If students need more help with these prerequisite skills use **Ways to Success,** Houghton Mifflin's intervention program that is available in CD-ROM and print formats.

 Students who need more review can visit **Education Place,** Houghton Mifflin's award-winning website.

NSF Children's Math Worlds

Using *Children's Math Worlds* helps develop student communication skills because of the daily work with Math Talk, a teaching practice that can be used with all lessons. The emphasis on building a helping community will also enhance student participation in all classroom discussion.

Lesson 23.1 — Integers and the Coordinate Plane

PLANNING THE LESSON

MATHEMATICS OBJECTIVE
Graph ordered pairs in the four quadrants of the coordinate plane.

Use Lesson Planner CD-ROM for Lesson 23.1.

Daily Routines

Vocabulary

Display a coordinate grid with *x*- and *y*-axes. Explain that the grid is called a **coordinate plane.** Draw two lines intersecting at right angles. **Two lines, or axes, separate the plane into four sectors, or quadrants.** Ask students what other word for *four* they can think of that has the root *quad* in it. (quadruple and quadralateral) Explain that each axis is a number line with intervals marked in integers.

Vocabulary Cards

Meeting North Carolina's Standards

Prepare for Grade 7 Objective **5.01** Identify, analyze, and create linear relations, sequences, and functions using symbols, graphs, tables, diagrams, and written descriptions.

Lesson Transparency 23.1

Problem of the Day
Franco, Will, and Tim each engage in a different sport. The sports are football, track, and wrestling. The name of the sport and the name of the boy do not begin with the same letter. Franco does not wrestle. Which is each boy's sport? (Franco, track; Will, football; Tim, wrestling)

Quick Review
Write the opposite and the absolute value of each integer.

1. $^{+}11$ ($^{-}11$, 11)   2. $^{+}8$ ($^{-}8$, 8)
3. $^{-}7$ ($^{+}7$, 7)   4. $^{-}5$ ($^{+}5$, 5)
5. $^{-}14$ ($^{+}14$, 14)

Lesson Quiz
In which quadrant would the coordinate pair ($^{+}8$, $^{+}10$) appear? (A)
A. Quadrant I   C. Quadrant III
B. Quadrant II   D. Quadrant IV

LEVELED PRACTICE

RETEACH 23.1

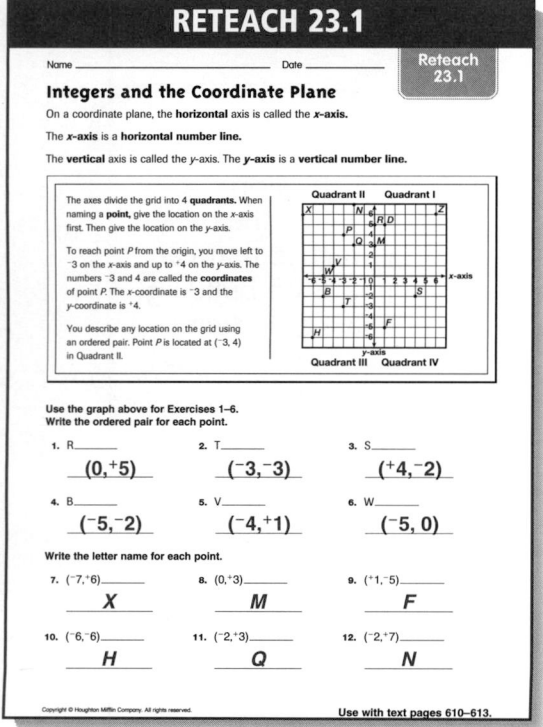

Integers and the Coordinate Plane

On a coordinate plane, the **horizontal** axis is called the **x-axis.**

The **x-axis** is a **horizontal number line.**

The **vertical** axis is called the **y-axis.** The **y-axis** is a **vertical number line.**

Use the graph above for Exercises 1–6.
Write the ordered pair for each point.

1. R ___ (0,$^{+}$5)
2. T ___ ($^{-}$3,$^{-}$3)
3. S ___ ($^{+}$4,$^{-}$2)
4. B ___ ($^{-}$5,$^{-}$2)
5. V ___ ($^{-}$4,$^{+}$1)
6. W ___ ($^{-}$5, 0)

Write the letter name for each point.

7. ($^{-}$7,$^{+}$6) ___ X
8. (0,$^{+}$3) ___ M
9. ($^{+}$1,$^{-}$5) ___ F
10. ($^{-}$6,$^{-}$6) ___ H
11. ($^{-}$2,$^{+}$3) ___ Q
12. ($^{-}$2,$^{+}$7) ___ N

Use with text pages 610–613.

PRACTICE 23.1

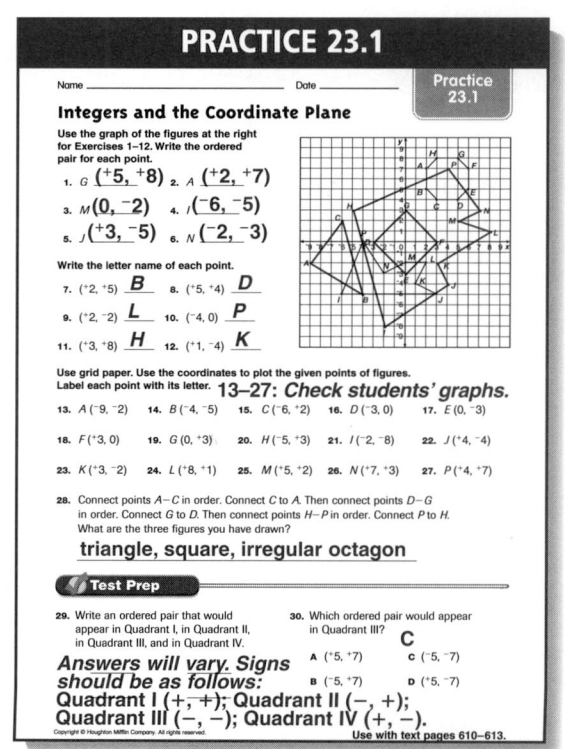

Integers and the Coordinate Plane

Use the graph of the figures at the right for Exercises 1–12. Write the ordered pair for each point.

1. G ($^{+}$5, $^{+}$8)   2. A ($^{+}$2, $^{+}$7)
3. M (0, $^{-}$2)   4. I ($^{-}$6, $^{-}$5)
5. J ($^{+}$3, $^{-}$5)   6. N ($^{-}$2, $^{-}$3)

Write the letter name of each point.

7. ($^{+}$2, $^{+}$5) **B**   8. ($^{+}$5, $^{+}$4) **D**
9. ($^{+}$2, $^{-}$2) **L**   10. ($^{-}$4, 0) **P**
11. ($^{+}$3, $^{+}$8) **H**   12. ($^{+}$1, $^{-}$4) **K**

Use grid paper. Use the coordinates to plot the given points of figures. Label each point with its letter. **13–27: Check students' graphs.**

13. A ($^{-}$9, $^{-}$2)   14. B ($^{-}$4, $^{-}$5)   15. C ($^{-}$6, $^{+}$2)   16. D ($^{-}$3, 0)   17. E (0, $^{-}$3)
18. F ($^{+}$3, 0)   19. G (0, $^{+}$3)   20. H ($^{-}$5, $^{+}$3)   21. I ($^{-}$2, $^{-}$8)   22. J ($^{+}$4, $^{-}$4)
23. K ($^{+}$3, $^{-}$2)   24. L ($^{+}$8, $^{+}$1)   25. M ($^{+}$5, $^{+}$2)   26. N ($^{+}$7, $^{+}$3)   27. P ($^{+}$4, $^{+}$7)

28. Connect points A–C in order. Connect C to A. Then connect points D–G in order. Connect G to D. Then connect points H–P in order. Connect P to H. What are the three figures you have drawn?

triangle, square, irregular octagon

Test Prep

29. Write an ordered pair that would appear in Quadrant I, in Quadrant II, in Quadrant III, and in Quadrant IV.
Answers will vary. Signs should be as follows:
Quadrant I (+, +); Quadrant II (−, +); Quadrant III (−, −); Quadrant IV (+, −).

30. Which ordered pair would appear in Quadrant III? **C**
A ($^{+}$5, $^{+}$7)   C ($^{-}$5, $^{-}$7)
B ($^{-}$5, $^{+}$7)   D ($^{+}$5, $^{-}$7)

Use with text pages 610–613.

ENRICHMENT 23.1

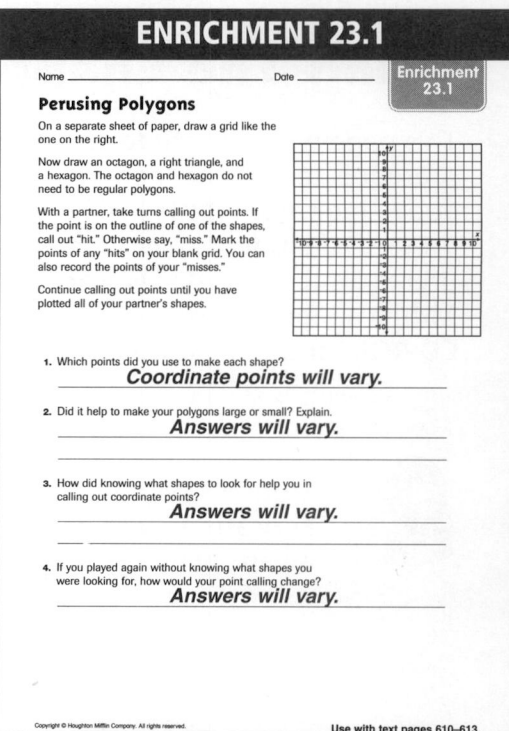

Perusing Polygons

On a separate sheet of paper, draw a grid like the one on the right.

Now draw an octagon, a right triangle, and a hexagon. The octagon and hexagon do not need to be regular polygons.

With a partner, take turns calling out points. If the point is on the outline of one of the shapes, call out "hit." Otherwise say, "miss." Mark the points of your "hits" on your blank grid. You can also record the points of your "misses."

Continue calling out points until you have plotted all of your partner's shapes.

1. Which points did you use to make each shape?
Coordinate points will vary.

2. Did it help to make your polygons large or small? Explain.
Answers will vary.

3. How did knowing what shapes to look for help you in calling out coordinate points?
Answers will vary.

4. If you played again without knowing what shapes you were looking for, how would your point calling change?
Answers will vary.

Use with text pages 610–613.

Practice Workbook Page 149

610A   CHAPTER 23   Lesson 1

Reaching All Learners

Differentiated Instruction

English Learners

Worksheet 23.1 uses text and an illustration to introduce the concept of a coordinate plane and related vocabulary. Students then answer questions about the sample coordinate plane.

Special Needs

VISUAL, AUDITORY

Materials: *Coordinate Plane Transparency*

- Display these points *without* their coordinates: A (2, 3), B (⁻2, 3), C (⁻2, ⁻3), D (2, ⁻3)
- **Find coordinates for A.** Repeat for *B, C,* and *D*. Explain that *A* is in Quadrant I, *B* is in II, *C* is in III, *D* in IV.

Gifted and Talented

VISUAL, AUDITORY

Materials: *grid paper*

- Have students use at least 8 points (2 in each Quadrant) to make a symmetrical design. On a separate sheet of paper, have them write down each point's coordinates. **Exchange papers.**
- Have them determine a design that fits the points. Compare results.

TECHNOLOGY

Spiral Review

Using the *Ways to Assess* CD-ROM, you can create **customized** spiral review worksheets covering any lessons you choose.

Education Place

Encourage students to visit Education Place at eduplace.com/kids/mw/ for more student activities.

Lesson Planner

Use the Lesson Planner CD-ROM to see how lesson objectives for this chapter are correlated to standards.

Social Studies Connection

Constellation Explanation

- Point out that many of the constellations are named for important figures in mythology or history. Have small groups of students choose a constellation and research the history and importance of the person or animal. Have students plot that constellation on a grid.
- Ask groups to report to the class on their findings and show their star plots. Challenge them to look in the night sky to find their constellations or the one on page 610.

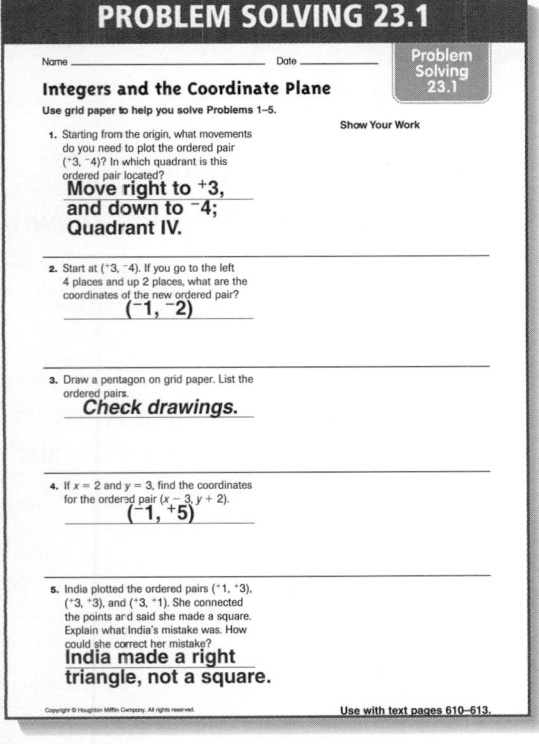

PROBLEM SOLVING 23.1

Name _____ Date _____

Integers and the Coordinate Plane

Use grid paper to help you solve Problems 1–5.

Show Your Work

1. Starting from the origin, what movements do you need to plot the ordered pair (⁺3, ⁻4)? In which quadrant is this ordered pair located?
   Move right to ⁺3, and down to ⁻4; Quadrant IV.

2. Start at (⁺3, ⁻4). If you go to the left 4 places and up 2 places, what are the coordinates of the new ordered pair?
   (⁻1, ⁻2)

3. Draw a pentagon on grid paper. List the ordered pairs.
   Check drawings.

4. If x = 2 and y = 3, find the coordinates for the ordered pair (x − 3, y + 2).
   (⁻1, ⁺5)

5. India plotted the ordered pairs (⁺1, ⁺3), (⁺3, ⁺3), and (⁺3, ⁺1). She connected the points and said she made a square. Explain what India's mistake was. How could she correct her mistake?
   India made a right triangle, not a square.

Use with text pages 610–613.

HOMEWORK 23.1

Name _____ Date _____

Integers and the Coordinate Plane

- In a coordinate plane, the horizontal axis is called the x-axis and the vertical axis is called the y-axis.
- The axes divide the grid into 4 quadrants, numbered I, II, III, and IV.
- Every point on a coordinate plane is named by an ordered pair, (x, y).
- The point named by the ordered pair (0, 0) is the origin.

Use the graph for Problems 1–12. Write the ordered pair for each point.

1. I **(⁻2, ⁻4)**
2. A **(⁺1, ⁺1)**
3. C **(⁺5, ⁻3)**
4. B **(⁻2, ⁺4)**
5. P **(⁻7, ⁻7)**
6. H **(⁺3, ⁻2)**

Write the letter name for each point.

7. (⁻9, ⁺3) **E**
8. (⁺4, ⁺5) **J**
9. (⁺3, ⁻4) **K**
10. (⁻4, ⁻4) **M**
11. (⁻3, ⁺9) **F**
12. (3, ⁻5) **D**

Problem Solving

13. If you plotted the points (⁻3, ⁻3), (⁻3, ⁺3), (⁺3, ⁺3), and (⁺3, ⁻3) and connected the points in that order, what shape would form?
    square

Use with text pages 610–613.

ENGLISH LEARNERS 23.1

Name _____ Date _____

Integers and the Coordinate Plane

In the Southwest United States, you can stand on a spot where four states meet. The name of that place is Four Corners. The map below shows Four Corners as a coordinate plane.

A **coordinate plane** is a flat surface formed by two intersecting, perpendicular lines. Each of these lines is called an **axis**. The horizontal line is called the **x-axis**. The vertical line is the **y-axis**. The x-axis and the y-axis divide the coordinate plane into four areas. These areas are called **quadrants**.

The x-axis and the y-axis meet at a point called the **origin**. To locate a point on a coordinate plane, use two numbers called an **ordered pair**. The first number tells how far to move horizontally or the x-axis. The second number tells how far to move up or down on the y-axis. The numbers in an ordered pair are called **coordinates**.

Find the ordered pair (6,1) on the map. Start at the origin, Four Corners. Now move 6 units to the right on the x-axis. Next, move one unit up. You'll find the coordinates in Quadrant I.

Use the map to answer the questions.

1. In which state are the coordinates (⁻3, 5)? **Utah**
2. Find (8, ⁻5) on the map. In which quadrant is (8, ⁻5)? **Quadrant II**
3. In which state are the coordinates (⁻4, ⁻6)? **Arizona**
4. Draw a line that connects (⁻4, ⁻6) to (6, 1). How many states does your line pass through? **3**

Use with text pages 610–613.

Homework Workbook Page 149

TEACHING LESSON 23.1

LESSON ORGANIZER

Objective Graph ordered pairs in the four quadrants of the coordinate plane.

Resources Reteach, Practice, Enrichment, Problem Solving, Homework, English Learners, Transparencies, Math Center

Materials Coordinate Plane Transparency, markers in two colors

Activity

Warm-Up Activity
Find the Sum of an Inverse Operation

 Whole Group 5 minutes | Visual, Auditory

Have students rewrite each subtraction sentence as an addition sentence and find the sum.

1. $^-4 - {^+5}$ ($^-9$)
2. $^+3 - {^-5}$ ($^+8$)
3. $^+6 - {^+2}$ ($^+4$)
4. $^+8 - {^-2}$ ($^+10$)
5. $^-2 - {^+7}$ ($^-9$)

Integers and the Coordinate Plane

Objective Graph ordered pairs in the four quadrants of the coordinate plane.

e Glossary
Vocabulary
coordinate plane
x-axis
y-axis
quadrant
ordered pair
origin
coordinates

Learn About It
MathTracks 2/34
Listen and Understand

Constellations are groups of stars that appear together in the sky. You can portray constellations on a **coordinate plane**.

A coordinate plane is formed by two perpendicular lines called axes, that lie in the plane. The horizontal axis is called the **x-axis**. The vertical axis is called the **y-axis**. These axes divide the plane into 4 **quadrants**, numbered I, II, III, and IV.

Some of the stars for the constellation Hercules are mapped on the coordinate plane at the right.

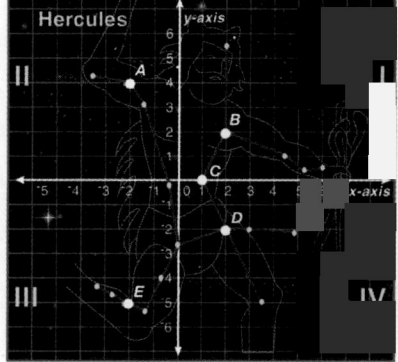

Constellation Hercules

What is another way to describe the location of the star at point A?

You can describe any location on the plane by using an **ordered pair** (x, y). The point named by the ordered pair (0, 0) is the **origin**.

- To reach point A, move left from the origin to $^-2$ and up to $^+4$.
- The numbers $^-2$ and $^+4$ are the **coordinates** of point A.

Solution: The location of the star at A is given as ($^-2$, $^+4$) in Quadrant II.

Other Examples

A. Point in Quadrant IV

- Point D is in Quadrant IV.
- To reach point D, start at the origin. Move right 2 units and down 2 units.
- Point D is at ($^+2$, $^-2$).

B. Distance Between Points

- Point A is at ($^-2$, 4) and point E is at ($^-2$, $^-5$).
- For two points, if the x-coordinates or the y-coordinates are the same, you can count to find the distance between those two points.
- The distance between A and E is 9 units.

610

---

1 Introduce

Materials: *Coordinate Plane Transparency, colored markers*

- Display the transparency. Have students work with you as you plot the point ($^+4$, $^+3$).
- Point out that each number in an ordered pair tells you how to move on the plane. **The x-coordinate is $^+4$. It tells us to move right 4 units.** Use one colored marker to draw a line segment from the origin 4 units right on the x-axis.
- **The y-coordinate is $^+3$. It tells us to move up 3 units.** Use the second colored marker to draw a line segment up 3 units from where the other line stops. Put a dot there. **That is the location of the point ($^+4$, $^+3$). Label the point ($^+4$, $^+3$).**
- Do the same for ($^-4$, $^+3$) in Quadrant II, ($^-4$, $^-3$) in Quadrant III, and ($^+4$, $^-3$) in Quadrant IV.

2 Develop

Guide students through the *Learn About It* section.

- Use the transparency, and draw dots for the points shown in the plane given on p. 610.
- In the examples on p. 610, students identify the coordinates of each point-star. The first example is point A, which is in Quadrant II at ($^-2$, $^+4$).
- Go through the *Other Examples*. Discuss Example A. **How do we locate D?** (Move 2 units right from 0 and 2 units down.) **What are the coordinates of D?** ($^+2$, $^-2$) In which quadrant is this point? (Quadrant IV)
- Do the same for Example B.

Materials: grid paper

Here is how to use ordered pairs to represent the major stars in the constellation Volans, or the Flying Fish.

Plot the star located at point V ($^-8$, $^+3$).

- Start at the origin (0, 0).
- Go left to $^-8$ and up to $^+3$.
- Mark a point at ($^-8$, $^+3$). Label it V.

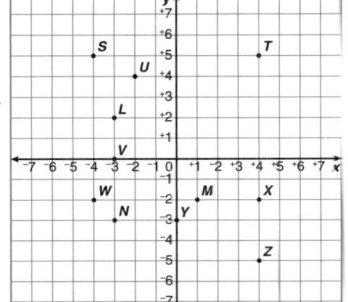

The Flying Fish

To plot the other stars in Volans, copy the graph and use these ordered pairs.

($^+3$, $^-3$) → (right 3, down 3) → point A
($^+6$, $^+3$) → (right 6, up 3) → point N
(0, $^+2$) → (no move, up 2) → point L
($^-3$, $^+4$) → (left 3, up 4) → point O
($^+7$, $^-1$) → (right 7, down 1) → point S

Remember
Always start at the origin. Move left or right along the x-axis first. Then up or down along the y-axis.

Guided Practice

Ask Yourself
- Do I move left or right from 0 to find the x coordinate?

Use the coordinate plane below for Exercises 1–6.

Write the ordered pair for each point.

1. L ($^-3$, $^+2$)   2. M ($^+1$, $^-2$)   3. N ($^-3$, $^-3$)

Write the letter name of each point.

4. ($^+4$, $^+5$) T   5. ($^-3$, 0) V   6. ($^-4$, $^-2$) W

Use the coordinates to plot each point. Label each point with its letter.
7–12. *See Additional Answers on Page 627.*
7. A ($^-2$, $^+3$)   8. B ($^+2$, $^+2$)

9. C ($^-1$, $^+1$)   10. D ($^-4$, $^-1$)

Find the distance between each pair of points.

11. X and Z   12. W and M
   3 units   5 units

Explain Your Thinking ▶ Is the location ($^-2$, $^-3$) the same as ($^+3$, $^-2$)? Why or why not?

Go On ▶

Chapter 23 Lesson 1   **611**

Reaching All Learners

Algebra

Functions Tell students that Mr. Willis bakes muffins for class parties. Using the equation $m = n + 2$, m represents the number of muffins, and n represents the number of students.

1. Have students write what the equation $m = n + 2$ means.

2. Have students use the equation to complete a table to find the number of muffins Mr. Willis will make for 3, 5, and 10 students.

3. Have students extend the table using random values of n up to 35. Ask: **How many students would be in the class if Mr. Willis made 18 muffins?**

Answers

1. The number of muffins equals to number of students plus 2.

2. 5; 7; 12

3. 16 students; Check students' tables.

Differentiated Assignments		
At Risk	**Average**	**Advanced**
Exercise 1	Exercises 1–2	Exercises 1–3

Guide students through the *Hands-on Math* section.

- You may wish to draw a plane on the chalkboard and have volunteers plot each point, or follow along on grid paper as you work on the transparency. Begin by having students explain how to plot the coordinates of V ($^-8$, $^+3$). **In which quadrant is the point ($^-8$, $^+3$)?** (Quadrant II)

- Have volunteers do the same for each of points A, N, and L. **In which quadrant is point A?** (Quadrant IV) **Point N?** (Quadrant I)

- **What do you notice about L?** (It is on the y-axis.) Explain that a point on either axis is not in any quadrant.

Guided Practice

Have students complete **Exercises 1–12** as you observe. Remind them to use the *Ask Yourself* question to help. Give students the opportunity to talk about the questions in *Explain Your Thinking*.

DAILY TEST PREP

Which of the following best describes how to locate the point $(^-8, ^-3)$? (A)

A. 8 units left, 3 units down

B. 3 units left, 8 units down

C. 3 units right, 8 units up

D. 8 units right, 3 units down

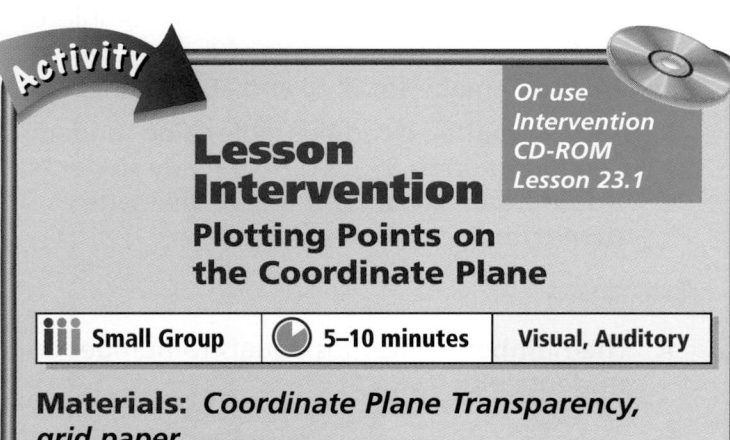

Activity

Or use Intervention CD-ROM Lesson 23.1

Lesson Intervention

Plotting Points on the Coordinate Plane

| 👤👤👤 Small Group | 🕐 5–10 minutes | Visual, Auditory |

Materials: *Coordinate Plane Transparency, grid paper*

- Have students use grid paper as you plot $(^-2, ^-4)$ on the transparency. **Which is the x-coordinate?** (-2) **Where does it go?** (left 2 units from 0) Which is the **y-coordinate?** (-4) **How do we move?** (down 4 units from -2)
- Students should have plotted the point $(^-2, ^-4)$ in Quadrant III.

Use the graph of the Big Dipper and Little Dipper asterisms for Exercises 13–24. Write the ordered pair for each point.

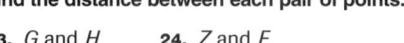

13. B $(^-5, ^-2)$ 14. D $(^-1.5, ^-5)$

15. F $(^+2, ^-8)$ 16. I $(^+9, ^+5)$

17. K $(^+5, ^+7)$ 18. L $(^+3, ^+6)$

Write the letter name of each point.

19. $(^-8, ^-1)$ **A**   20. $(^-3, ^-4)$ **C**

21. $(^-2, ^-7)$ **E**   22. $(^+3, ^-6)$ **G**

Find the distance between each pair of points.

23. G and H 24. Z and F
    3 units   **15 units**

Use grid paper. Plot points using the coordinates for stars in the constellation called the Whale, or the Sea Monster. Label each point with its letter. *See Additional Answers on Page 627.*

25. A $(^-12, ^+5)$ 26. B $(^-11, ^+8)$ 27. C $(^-9, ^+8)$ 28. D $(^-9, ^+4)$ 29. E $(^-8, ^+2)$

30. F $(^-4, 0)$ 31. G $(0, ^-4)$ 32. H $(^+4, ^-4)$ 33. I $(^+10, ^-5)$ 34. J $(^+7, ^-9)$

35. K $(^-2, ^-10)$ 36. L $(^-11, ^-4)$ 37. M $(^+1, ^-7)$ 38. N $(^+6, ^-5)$

39. Connect points A–L in order. Then connect L to E and M to J. Can you see the whale? Which point represents the eye of the whale? **point N**

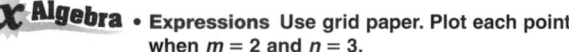

X Algebra • **Expressions** Use grid paper. Plot each point when $m = 2$ and $n = 3$.

40. P $(m + 1, n - 2)$ 41. Q $(m - 5, n + 6)$ 42. R $(m - 8, n - 3)$ 43. S $(m + 7; n + 5)$
    $(^+3, ^+1)$ $(^-3, ^+9)$ $(^-6, 0)$ $(^+9, ^+8)$

Solve.

47. Quadrant II: (−, +); Quadrant III: (−, −): Quadrant IV: (+, −); *Explanations will vary.*

44. **Write About It** Draw your own constellation on grid paper. List the ordered pairs. Write instructions for drawing your constellation.
See student drawings and instructions.

45. **Analyze** What pattern can you find in this group of ordered pairs: (0, 0), $(^+1, ^+2)$, $(^+2, ^+4)$, $(^+3, ^+6)$, $(^+4, ^+8)$, $(^+5, ^+10)$?
See Additional Answers on Page 627.

46. **Reasoning** The constellations Taurus, Cygnus, and Draco look like a swan, a dragon, and a bull. Cygnus is not a bull or a dragon. Taurus is not a dragon. Match each constellation to its animal. **Taurus: bull; Cygnus: swan; Draco: dragon**

47. **Explain** The coordinates of each point in Quadrant I are always positive: (+, +). Write rules for the coordinates in Quadrants II, III, and IV. Explain why your rules work. *See above.*

Extra Practice See page 627, Set A.

612

---

③ Practice

Assign **Exercises 13–50** as independent work.

- **Exercises 13–38** Have students explain their answers.
- *Algebra • Expressions for Problems 40–43* Have students discuss and explain their graphs.
- *Problem Solving for Problems 44, 46, and 47* Have students share their answers and discuss their work.

Common Error

Mistaking x-coordinates for y-coordinates When students plot the coordinates of a point, they sometimes forget that the x-coordinate is given first and the y-coordinate second. Remind them that this is a constant order.

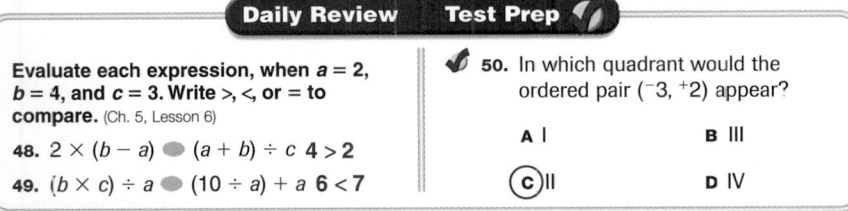

Daily Review   **Test Prep**

Evaluate each expression, when $a = 2$, $b = 4$, and $c = 3$. Write >, <, or = to compare. (Ch. 5, Lesson 6)

48. $2 \times (b - a)$ ● $(a + b) \div c$ **4 > 2**

49. $(b \times c) \div a$ ● $(10 \div a) + a$ **6 < 7**

50. In which quadrant would the ordered pair $(^-3, {}^+2)$ appear?

A   I   B   III

Ⓒ   II   D   IV

Practice GAME

Where's the Spaceship?

2 Players

What You'll Need • grid paper • colored pencils

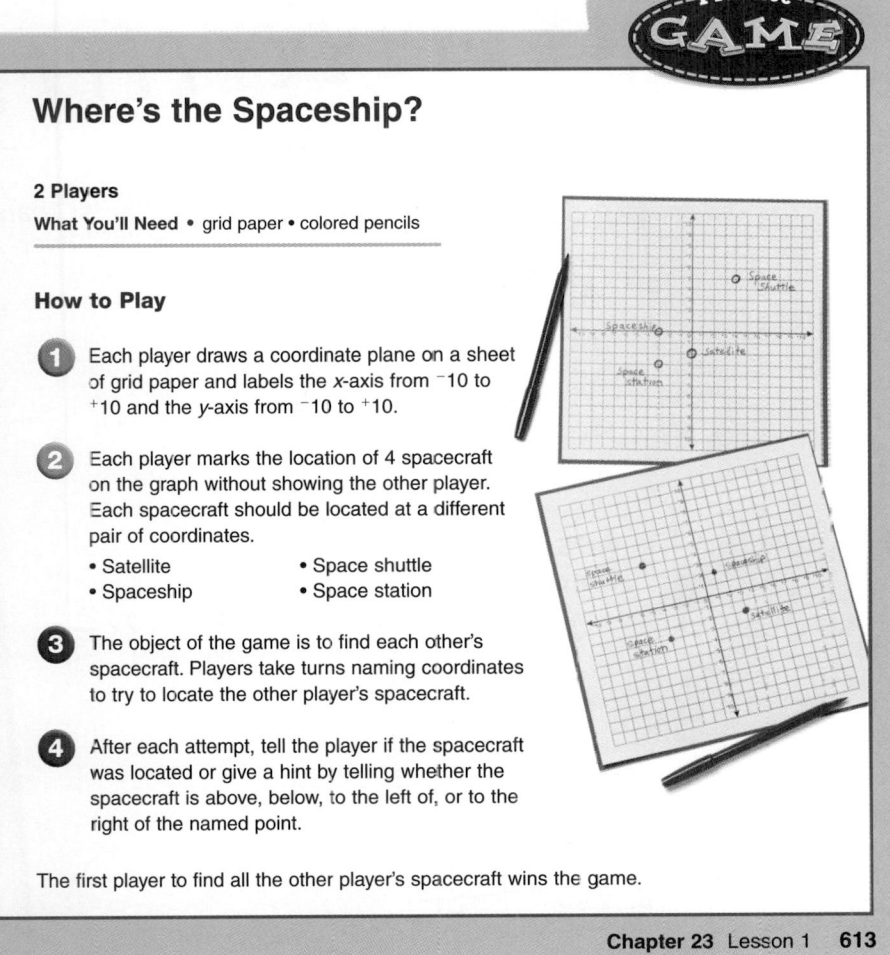

How to Play

1   Each player draws a coordinate plane on a sheet of grid paper and labels the x-axis from ⁻10 to ⁺10 and the y-axis from ⁻10 to ⁺10.

2   Each player marks the location of 4 spacecraft on the graph without showing the other player. Each spacecraft should be located at a different pair of coordinates.

- Satellite
- Spaceship
- Space shuttle
- Space station

3   The object of the game is to find each other's spacecraft. Players take turns naming coordinates to try to locate the other player's spacecraft.

4   After each attempt, tell the player if the spacecraft was located or give a hint by telling whether the spacecraft is above, below, to the left of, or to the right of the named point.

The first player to find all the other player's spacecraft wins the game.

Chapter 23 Lesson 1   **613**

Practice GAME

Where's the Spaceship?

Materials: *Grid paper, colored pencils*

- Students should begin by identifying the x-coordinate of the ordered pair that locates the spacecraft. To do this they should count the number of units left or right from the y-axis to the point.

- To identify the y-coordinate, they should count the number of units up or down from the x-axis to the point.

④ Assess and Close

- **How can you find the coordinates of a point on the coordinate plane?** (The distance from the origin *right or left* along the x-axis gives you the x-coordinate. The distance from the origin *up or down* along the y-axis gives you the y-coordinate.)

- **Explain how to plot a point, given its coordinates.** (Count left or right along the x-axis the number of units given in the x-coordinate. Then count up or down along the y-axis the number of units given in the y-coordinate.)

Assign the **LESSON QUIZ** on Transparency 23.1 to further assess student understanding.

 **Keeping a Journal**

Have students write a few sentences explaining how to identify which quadrant a point is in, based on the sign of its coordinates.

Integers and Functions

PLANNING THE LESSON

MATHEMATICS OBJECTIVE
Use a function rule to find the value of ordered pairs.

Use Lesson Planner CD-ROM for Lesson 23.2.

Daily Routines

Vocabulary
Review the definition of a *function:* a rule that relates the value of two variables, such as *x* and *y*. For each value of *x*, there is exactly one related value of *y*.

Vocabulary Cards

Meeting North Carolina's Standards
Prepare for Grade 7 Objective **5.01** Identify, analyze, and create linear relations, sequences, and functions using symbols, graphs, tables, diagrams, and written descriptions.

Lesson Transparency
23.2

Problem of the Day
What temperature is 12 degrees higher than $^-$5°F? What temperature is 9 degrees lower than 3°F? (7°F; $^-$6°F)

Quick Review
Find each sum.
1. $^+5 + ^-4$ ($^+1$)
2. $^-9 + ^-2$ ($^-11$)
3. $^+3 + ^-1$ ($^+2$)
4. $^-11 + ^+5$ ($^-6$)
5. $^-7 + ^-2$ ($^-9$)

Lesson Quiz
Complete the function table for $y = 2x - 1$.
(Tables may vary.)

	x	y
	$^+3$	$^+5$
1.	($^+2$)	($^+3$)
2.	($^+1$)	($^+1$)
3.	(0)	($^-1$)
4.	($^-1$)	($^-3$)
5.	($^-2$)	($^-5$)

LEVELED PRACTICE

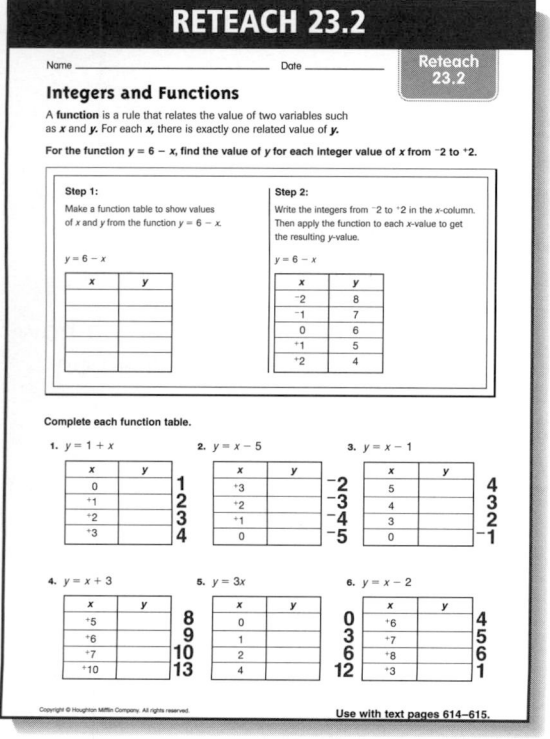

RETEACH 23.2

Name _____ Date _____   Reteach 23.2

Integers and Functions

A **function** is a rule that relates the value of two variables such as *x* and *y*. For each *x*, there is exactly one related value of *y*.

For the function $y = 6 - x$, find the value of *y* for each integer value of *x* from $^-2$ to $^+2$.

Step 1:	Step 2:
Make a function table to show values of *x* and *y* from the function $y = 6 - x$.	Write the integers from $^-2$ to $^+2$ in the *x*-column. Then apply the function to each *x*-value to get the resulting *y*-value.

$y = 6 - x$

x	y

$y = 6 - x$

x	y
$^-2$	8
$^-1$	7
0	6
$^+1$	5
$^+2$	4

Complete each function table.

1. $y = 1 + x$

x	y
0	1
$^+1$	2
$^+2$	3
$^+3$	4

2. $y = x - 5$

x	y
$^+3$	$^-2$
$^+2$	$^-3$
$^+1$	$^-4$
0	$^-5$

3. $y = x - 1$

x	y
5	4
4	3
3	2
0	$^-1$

4. $y = x + 3$

x	y
$^+5$	8
$^+6$	9
$^+7$	10
$^+10$	13

5. $y = 3x$

x	y
0	0
$^+6$	3
1	2
2	4

6. $y = x - 2$

x	y
$^+6$	4
$^+7$	5
$^+8$	6
$^+3$	1

Copyright © Houghton Mifflin Company. All rights reserved.   **Use with text pages 614–615.**

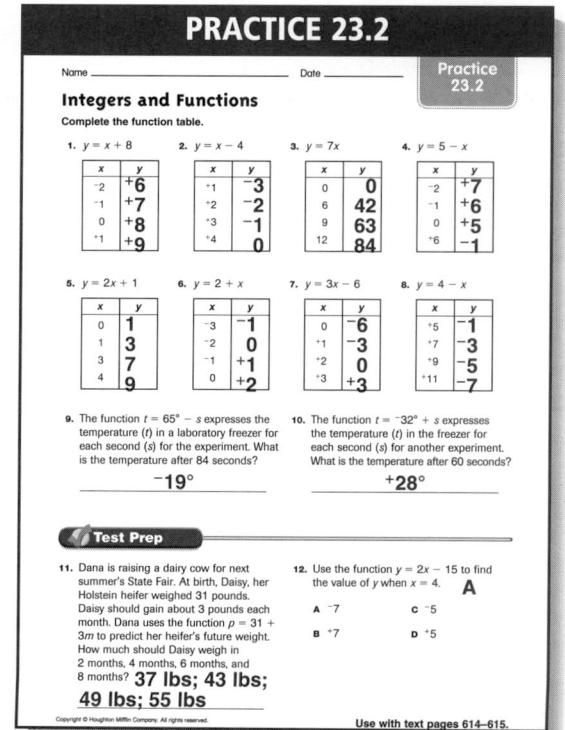

PRACTICE 23.2

Name _____ Date _____   Practice 23.2

Integers and Functions
Complete the function table.

1. $y = x + 8$

x	y
$^-2$	$^+6$
$^-1$	$^+7$
0	$^+8$
$^+1$	$^+9$

2. $y = x - 4$

x	y
$^+1$	$^-3$
$^+2$	$^-2$
$^+3$	$^-1$
$^+4$	0

3. $y = 7x$

x	y
0	0
6	42
9	63
12	84

4. $y = 5 - x$

x	y
$^-2$	$^+7$
$^-1$	$^+6$
0	$^+5$
$^+6$	$^-1$

5. $y = 2x + 1$

x	y
0	1
1	3
3	7
4	9

6. $y = 2 + x$

x	y
$^-3$	$^-1$
$^-2$	0
$^-1$	$^+1$
0	$^+2$

7. $y = 3x - 6$

x	y
0	$^-6$
$^+1$	$^-3$
$^+2$	0
$^+3$	$^+3$

8. $y = 4 - x$

x	y
$^+5$	$^-1$
$^+7$	$^-3$
$^+9$	$^-5$
$^+11$	$^-7$

9. The function $t = 65° - s$ expresses the temperature (*t*) in a laboratory freezer for each second (*s*) for the experiment. What is the temperature after 84 seconds?
$^-19°$

10. The function $t = ^-32° + s$ expresses the temperature (*t*) in the freezer for each second (*s*) for another experiment. What is the temperature after 60 seconds?
$^+28°$

Test Prep

11. Dana is raising a dairy cow for next summer's State Fair. At birth, Daisy, her Holstein heifer weighed 31 pounds. Daisy should gain about 3 pounds each month. Dana uses the function $p = 31 + 3m$ to predict her heifer's future weight. How much should Daisy weigh in 2 months, 4 months, 6 months, and 8 months? **37 lbs; 43 lbs; 49 lbs; 55 lbs**

12. Use the function $y = 2x - 15$ to find the value of *y* when $x = 4$. **A**

A $^-7$ C $^-5$
B $^+7$ D $^+5$

Copyright © Houghton Mifflin Company. All rights reserved.   **Use with text pages 614–615.**

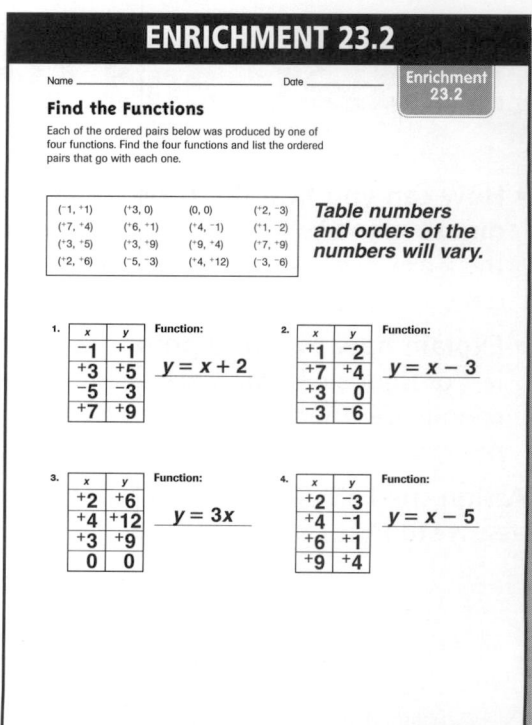

ENRICHMENT 23.2

Name _____ Date _____   Enrichment 23.2

Find the Functions

Each of the ordered pairs below was produced by one of four functions. Find the four functions and list the ordered pairs that go with each one.

($^-1, ^+1$) ($^+3, 0$) (0, 0) ($^+2, ^-3$)
($^+7, ^+4$) ($^+6, ^+1$) ($^+4, ^-1$) ($^+1, ^-2$)
($^+3, ^+5$) ($^+3, ^+9$) ($^+9, ^+4$) ($^+7, ^+9$)
($^+2, ^+6$) ($^-5, ^-3$) ($^+4, ^+12$) ($^-3, ^-6$)

Table numbers and orders of the numbers will vary.

1.
x	y	Function:
$^-1$	$^+1$	
$^+3$	$^+5$	$y = x + 2$
$^-5$	$^-3$	
$^+7$	$^+9$	

2.
x	y	Function:
$^+1$	$^-2$	
$^+7$	$^+4$	$y = x - 3$
$^+3$	0	
$^-3$	$^-6$	

3.
x	y	Function:
$^+2$	$^+6$	
$^+4$	$^+12$	$y = 3x$
$^+3$	$^+9$	
0	0	

4.
x	y	Function:
$^+2$	$^-3$	
$^+4$	$^-1$	$y = x - 5$
$^+6$	$^+1$	
$^+9$	$^+4$	

Copyright © Houghton Mifflin Company. All rights reserved.   **Use with text pages 614–615.**

Practice Workbook Page 150

Reaching All Learners

Differentiated Instruction

English Learners

Worksheet 23.2 defines *function* and shows students how to complete a function table. Students then translate information from a paragraph into a function table.

Inclusion
VISUAL, AUDITORY

Materials: *Table I Transparency*

- Display transparency. Label the left column *x*, the right *y*. Display $y = x + {}^+3$. In the *x*–column, write $^+3$, $^+2$, $^+1$, 0, $^-1$, $^-2$. **What is *y* when *x* is $^+3$?** ($^+6$) Write $^+3$ in the first *y*-cell.
- Repeat until table is full. Explain that the value of *y* depends on *x*.

Early Finishers
VISUAL, AUDITORY

- Have each student write a function rule. On separate paper, have them make a function table for the rule, using whole numbers from 0 to 5 for *x*-values to find *y*-values. Then have them work in pairs. Without sharing their function rule, have them exchange tables and try to find each other's rule.

TECHNOLOGY

Spiral Review

To reinforce skills on lessons taught earlier, create **customized** spiral review worksheets using the *Ways to Assess* CD-ROM.

Software

Use *Easy Sheet* or another spreadsheet to explore this lesson more fully.

Education Place

Visit Education Place at **eduplace.com/math/mw/** for teacher support materials.

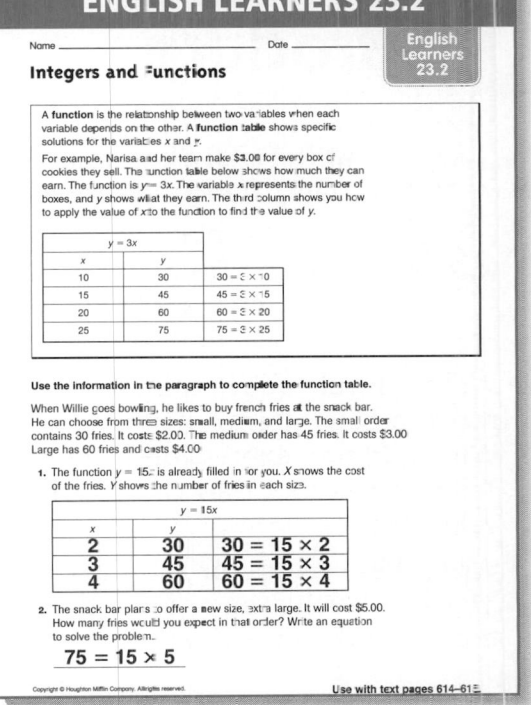

Science Connection

Temperature Table
Materials: *thermometer, hot plate, heating container, water*

- Bring water to a boil, then remove it from the burner. Have groups of students take the temperature every 2 minutes as it cools. Have them record the results in a function table, with time as the *x*-value and temperature the *y*-value.
- Have students graph the decrease in water temperature over time, then compare results.
- Challenge students to write a rule based on the results of the whole class.

PROBLEM SOLVING 23.2

Name _____ Date _____

Problem Solving 23.2

Integers and Functions

Show Your Work

1. The function $g = s + 30$ expresses Gloria's age (*g*) in terms of Stephanie's age (*s*). How old will Gloria be when Stephanie is 33?
63

2. Use the function from Problem 1. How old will Stephanie be when Gloria is 75?
45

3. The function $y = 2x - 1$ describes the path a storm is taking. At noon, $x = 0$. Find the value of *y* at noon.
$y = ^-1$

4. Use the function from Problem 3 to find the value of *y* when *x* = 1, 2, or 3.
$y = 1, 3, 5$

5. Explain the steps you used to solve Problem 2.
***Possible answer:* I substituted 75 for *g* to get $75 = s + 30$. I then subtracted 30 from both sides of the equation to get $45 = s$.**

Use with text pages 614–615.

HOMEWORK 23.2

Name _____ Date _____

Homework 23.2

Integers and Functions

$y = 3x - 4$

Step 1: Make a function table.

Step 2: Choose values for *x*. Write them in the table.

Step 3: Substitute each value of *x* into the function to find the value of *y*.

If $x = 1$, then $y = 3(1) - 4 = ^-1$
If $x = 2$, then $y = 3(2) - 4 = 2$
If $x = 3$, then $y = 3(3) - 4 = 5$
If $x = 4$, then $y = 3(4) - 4 = 8$

Function Table

x	y
1	$^-1$
2	2
3	5
4	8

Complete the function table.

1. Function: $y = x + 4$

x	y
$^-3$	$^+1$,
$^-2$	$^+2$,
$^-1$	$^+3$,
0	$^+4$

2. Function: $y = x - 3$

z	y
$^-2$	$^-5$,
0	$^-3$,
2	$^-1$,
5	$^+2$

3. Function: $y = 6 - x$

x	y
$^-2$	$^+8$,
$^-1$	$^+7$,
0	$^+6$,
3	$^+3$

4. Function: $y = 4x$

x	y
0	0,
1	4,
2	8,
3	12

5. Function: $y = x - 6$

z	y
$^-3$	$^-9$,
0	$^-6$,
3	$^-3$,
6	0

6. Function: $y = 7x$

x	y
0	0,
1	7,
2	14,
3	21

Problem Solving

Show Your Work

7. The first two set of ordered pairs in a function table are $(^-3, ^-2)$ and $(^-2, ^-1)$. What is the function?
$y = x + 1$

Use with text pages 614–615.

ENGLISH LEARNERS 23.2

Name _____ Date _____

English Learners 23.2

Integers and Functions

A function is the relationship between two variables when each variable depends on the other. A **function table** shows specific solutions for the variables *x* and *y*.

For example, Narisa and her team make $3.00 for every box of cookies they sell. The function table below shows how much they can earn. The function is $y = 3x$. The variable *x* represents the number of boxes, and *y* shows what they earn. The third column shows you how to apply the value of *x* into the function to find the value of *y*.

$y = 3x$

x	y	
10	30	$30 = 3 \times 10$
15	45	$45 = 3 \times 15$
20	60	$60 = 3 \times 20$
25	75	$75 = 3 \times 25$

Use the information in the paragraph to complete the function table.

When Willie goes bowling, he likes to buy french fries at the snack bar. He can choose from three sizes: small, medium, and large. The small order contains 30 fries. It costs $2.00. The medium order has 45 fries. It costs $3.00. Large has 60 fries and costs $4.00.

1. The function $y = 15x$ is already filled in for you. *X* shows the cost of the fries. *Y* shows the number of fries in each size.

$y = 15x$

x	y	
2	30	$30 = 15 \times 2$
3	45	$45 = 15 \times 3$
4	60	$60 = 15 \times 4$

2. The snack bar plans to offer a new size, extra large. It will cost $5.00. How many fries would you expect in that order? Write an equation to solve the problem.
$75 = 15 \times 5$

Use with text pages 614–615.

Homework Workbook Page 150

TEACHING LESSON 23.2

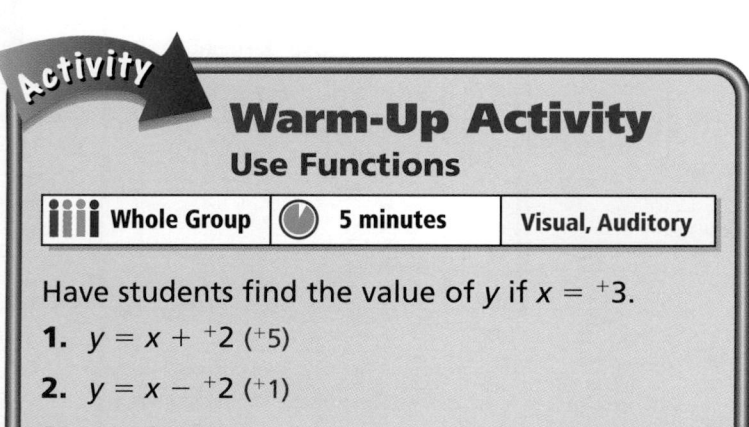

Warm-Up Activity
Use Functions

Whole Group	**5 minutes**	**Visual, Auditory**

Have students find the value of y if $x = {}^+3$.

1. $y = x + {}^+2$ $({}^+5)$

2. $y = x - {}^+2$ $({}^+1)$

3. $y = 2x$ $({}^+6)$

4. $y = x + {}^-5$ $({}^-2)$

5. $y = 3x + {}^+1$ (10)

Algebra
Integers and Functions

Objective Use a function rule to find the value of ordered pairs.

Learn About It 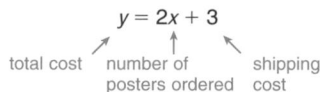 MathTracks 2/35
Listen and Understand

You learned that a **function** relates the value of two variables, such as x and y. For each value of x, there is exactly one related value of y.

Kirsten ordered some space posters. Each poster cost $2, and there was a shipping charge of $3 per order.

The total cost of Kirsten's order is a function of the number of posters she orders. She can use the equation $y = 2x + 3$, where x is the number of posters ordered.

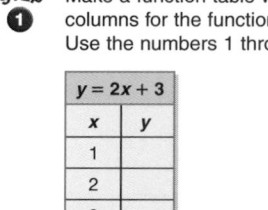

$$y = 2x + 3$$

total cost   number of posters ordered   shipping cost

Make a function table to show the possible total costs for Kirsten's order.

STEP 1 Make a function table with x and y columns for the function $y = 2x + 3$. Use the numbers 1 through 4 for x.

$y = 2x + 3$	
x	**y**
1	
2	
3	
4	

STEP 2 Substitute each value of x into the function to find the value of y.

$y = 2x + 3$		
x	**y**	
1	5	$(2 \times 1) + 3 = 2 + 3$
2	7	$(2 \times 2) + 3 = 4 + 3$
3	9	$(2 \times 3) + 3 = 6 + 3$
4	11	$(2 \times 4) + 3 = 8 + 3$

Positive 5 can be written as $^+5$ or 5

Another Example

Integers as values

In a function, the values for x and y also can be negative.

Substitute to find y.

$y = x - 6$		
x	**y**	
10	4	$10 - 6$
6	0	$6 - 6$
2	$^-4$	$2 - 6$
$^-2$	$^-8$	$^-2 - 6$

*Think
$2 + {}^-6$
$^-2 + {}^-6$*

614

---

1 Introduce

Materials: *blank transparency, Table I Transparency and student copies of it*

- Display blank transparency overlaid with Table I Transparency. Label left column x, right column y. Explain that a function rule may involve both positive and negative integers.

- Write this rule above the table: $y = x - 7$. Explain that $^+7$ can also be written 7. Rewrite the equation as $y = x - {}^+7$. **What addition expression is the same as $x - {}^+7$?** $(x + {}^-7)$ Tell students that they can use this expression to find the value of y.

- Write these values for x in the cells of the table: 2, 1, 0, $^-1$, $^-2$. Ask volunteers to use the rule $y = x + {}^-7$ to find the value of y for the value of x in each row.

2 Develop

Guide students through the *Learn About It* section.

- Discuss how the rule relates to the problem. Be sure students understand the meaning of each term.

- **Look at Step 1. What is written above the table?** (the function rule) **How are the columns labeled?** (left, x; right, y) **What values are in the cells in the x column?** (1, 2, 3, 4)

- **Look at Step 2. How are the values of y determined?** (by substituting values for x)

- **Another Example,** point out the negative values.

Guided Practice

Have students complete **Exercises 1–2** as you observe. Give students the opportunity to talk about the question in *Explain Your Thinking*. Remind them to use the *Ask Yourself* questions to help.

Complete the function table.

1. Function: $y = 3 - x$

x	y
-2	5
-1	■ 4
0	■ 3

2. Function: $y = 2x$

x	y
3	6
5	■ 10
10	■ 20

 Explain Your Thinking ▶ Why is it helpful to organize the x- and y-values in a function table? **It is easier to see patterns in this format.**

Practice and Problem Solving

Complete the function table.

3. $y = x + 5$

x	y
-2	■ 3
-1	■ 4
0	■ 5
1	■ 6

4. $y = x - 5$

x	y
3	■ -2
4	■ -1
5	■ 0
6	■ 1

5. $y = 5x$

x	y
3	■ 15
2	■ 10
1	■ 5
0	■ 0

Solve.

6. The cost for souvenir star charts is $12 each plus $5 shipping per order. Make a table to show the total cost for ordering 1, 2, 3, 4, or 5 charts.
$17; $29; $41; $53; $65

7. **Reasoning** Together Bob and Deb scored 28 points. Bob scored 4 more points than Deb. How many points did each person score?
Bob: 16 points; Deb: 12 points

8. Kirk puts money in his savings account each month and his father then adds $5. Write a function to describe how much money is put in the account each month.
$y = x + 5$

9. **Analyze** Who will win the game? Jodi started with 17 points, lost 6, and gained 4. Sara started with 11 points, gained 8, and lost 2?
Sara, with 17 points wins.

Daily Review   Test Prep ✔

Multiply or divide. (Ch. 12, Lessons 2–3, 5–6)

10. $\frac{2}{3} \times \frac{1}{2}$ $\frac{1}{3}$

11. $10\frac{4}{5} \times \frac{3}{4}$ $8\frac{1}{10}$

12. $6 \div \frac{2}{3}$ 9

13. $2\frac{1}{4} \div \frac{3}{4}$ 3

14. Free Response The function $a = e + {}^-4$ expresses Anne's age (a) in terms of Earl's age (e). How old will Anne be when Earl is 27? Explain how you found your answer.
See Additional Answers on Page 627.

Extra Practice See page 627, Set B.

DAILY TEST PREP

Which ordered pair makes the rule $y = x + ({}^-2)$ true? (C)

A. $({}^+2, {}^+4)$ C. $({}^+2, 0)$
B. $({}^+3, {}^+5)$ D. $({}^-3, {}^+1)$

Activity

Lesson Intervention

Or use Intervention CD-ROM Lesson 23.2

Finding y-Values from a Function Rule

iii Small Group	⏱ 5–10 minutes	Visual, Auditory

- Display a two-column function table. Above the table, write the rule $y = x + ({}^+2)$.
- **How should we label the columns in the table?** (Label the left column x and the right one y.) Suggest that they use positive integers as x-values. Write the values ${}^+1, {}^+2, {}^+3,$ and ${}^+4$ in order down the x-column.
- **How do we use the rule to find the y-value for each x-value?** (Substitute the x-value in the rule and calculate the y-value.) Ask a volunteer to do that for the first row, $x = {}^+1$. ($y = {}^+1 + ({}^+2) = {}^+3$)
- Follow the same procedure for the values of x in the other rows of the table.

---

3 Practice

Assign **Exercises 3–14** as independent work.

- *Problem Solving for Problems 6–9* Have volunteers share and discuss their work with the class.

Common Error

Calculating the y-value incorrectly Sometimes students substitute an incorrect value for x in the rule. In addition, sometimes they perform the wrong operation when finding the value of y.

4 Assess and Close

- **How do you find the value of y for each row of a function table?** (Substitute the value of x given in the row into the equation and calculate the value of the expression.)
- **Why is it helpful to organize x- and y-values in a table?** (It helps to see any pattern that is there in the relationship.)

Assign the **LESSON QUIZ** on Transparency 23.2 to further assess student understanding.

 **Keeping a Journal**

Have students explain what a function rule is and how to use a table to show the relationship between x- and y-values for the rule.

Lesson 23.3

Algebra: Use Functions and Graphs

PLANNING THE LESSON

MATHEMATICS OBJECTIVE
Graph an equation on a coordinate plane.

Use Lesson Planner CD-ROM for Lesson 23.3.

Daily Routines

Vocabulary
Ask students to tell you the meaning of **ordered pair.** (a pair of numbers in which one is considered to be first and the other second) Point out that in graphing a function on a coordinate plane, the first number in an ordered pair is the x-coordinate and the second is the y-coordinate. Both specify distance from the origin.

Vocabulary Cards

Meeting North Carolina's Standards
Prepare for Grade 7 Objective **5.01** Identify, analyze, and create linear relations, sequences, and functions using symbols, Graphs, tables, diagrams, and written descriptions.

Lesson Transparency **23.3**

Problem of the Day
The perimeter of Kristen's garden is 30 feet. The area is 50 square feet. What are the length and width of the garden? ($l = 10$ ft, $w = 5$ ft)

Quick Review
Identify the quadrant in which each point is located.
1. $(^+1, ^+4)$ (Quadrant I)
2. $(^+3, ^-3)$ (Quadrant IV)
3. $(^-6, ^+8)$ (Quadrant II)
4. $(^-3, ^-2)$ (Quadrant III)

Lesson Quiz
Find one ordered pair for each function.
1. $y = x + 2$ (Possible answer: $(^+1, ^+3)$)
2. $y = x - 4$ (Possible answer: $(^+1, ^-3)$)
3. $y = 2x$ (Possible answer: $(^+3, ^+6)$)
4. $y = 3x$ (Possible answer: $(^-2, ^-6)$)
5. $y = 2x + 3$ (Possible answer: $^-1, ^+1)$)

LEVELED PRACTICE

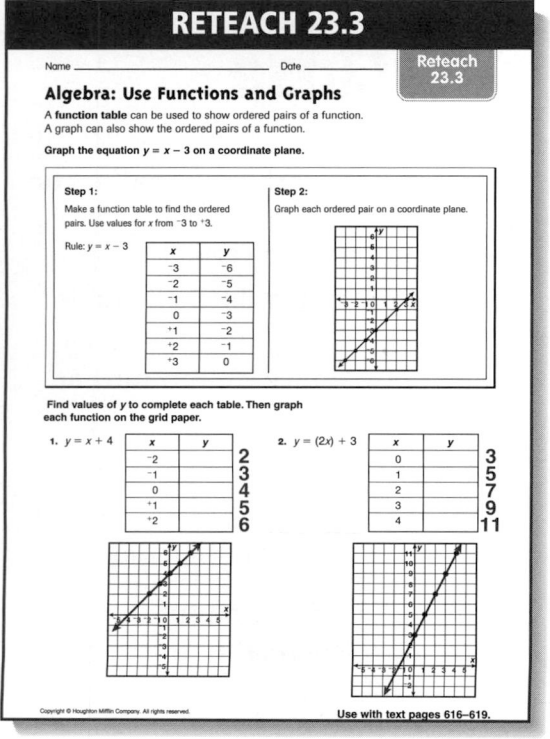

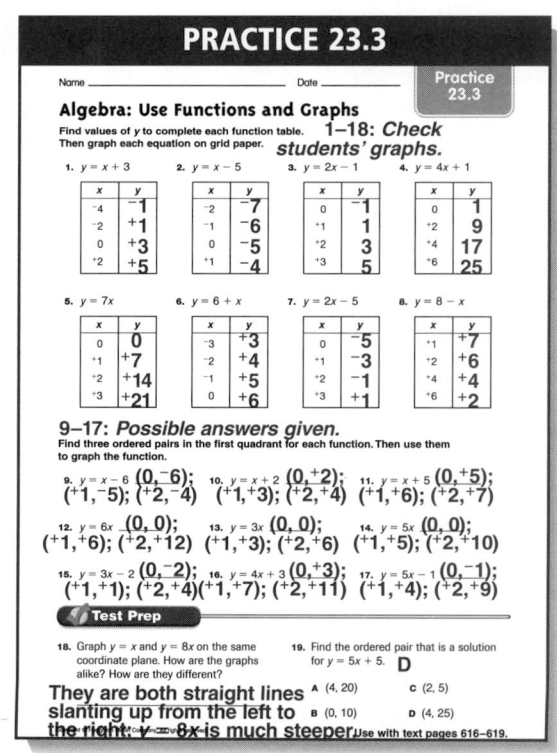

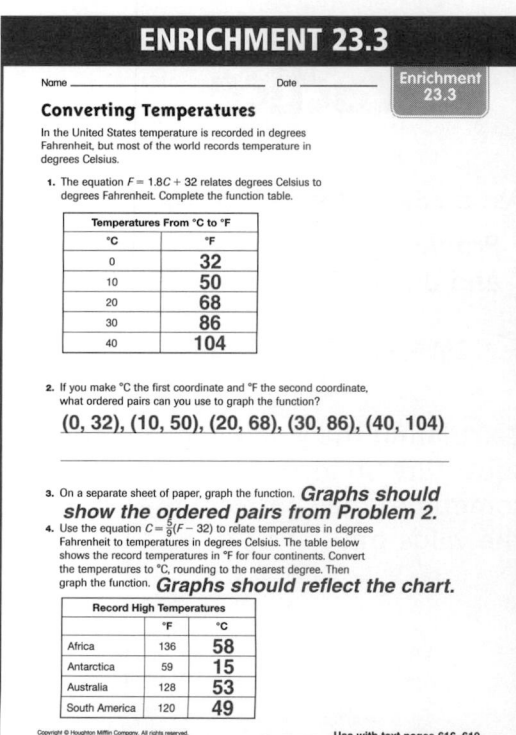

Practice Workbook Page 151

Reaching All Learners
Differentiated Instruction

English Learners

Worksheet 23.3 uses graphics and text to define *solution, graph,* and *grid*. Students then follow verbal instructions to graph solutions to a function and predict other solutions.

Special Needs
VISUAL, AUDITORY

Have each student write a function rule. On separate paper, have them make a function table for the rule, using whole numbers from 0 to 5 for *x*-values to find *y*-values. Then have them work in pairs. Without sharing their function rule, have them exchange tables and try to find each other's rule.

Gifted and Talented
VISUAL, AUDITORY

Materials: Grid paper

• Create a function rule. Make a table to produce 5 ordered pairs. Do not tell anyone your rule. Plot the pairs on a grid.

• Have them exchange grids. **Find the rule and extend the graph to include two more ordered pairs.**

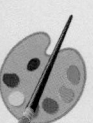

Art Connection
Create a Figure
Materials: Grid paper

Have students plot each set of ordered pairs on a separate coordinate grid. Then have them connect each pair of points sequentially with a straight line segment. Ask them to describe the figure that results.

1. (3, 3), (3, ⁻3), (⁻3, ⁻3), (⁻3, 3) (a square)

2. (⁻4, 6), (⁻2, 8), (4, 8), (2, 6) (a parallelogram)

3. (⁻4, ⁻5), (⁻2, 1), (2, ⁻1), (4, ⁻5) (a trapezoid)

4. (0, 6), (3, 0), (0, ⁻3), (⁻3, 0) (a kite)

TECHNOLOGY

Spiral Review

Help students remember skills they learned earlier by creating **customized** spiral review worksheets using the *Ways to Assess* CD-ROM.

Lesson Planner

You can use the Lesson Planner CD-ROM to create a report of the lessons and standards you have taught.

eBook

eMathBook allows students to review lessons and do homework without carrying their textbooks home.

Houghton Mifflin
Math

e**MathBook**

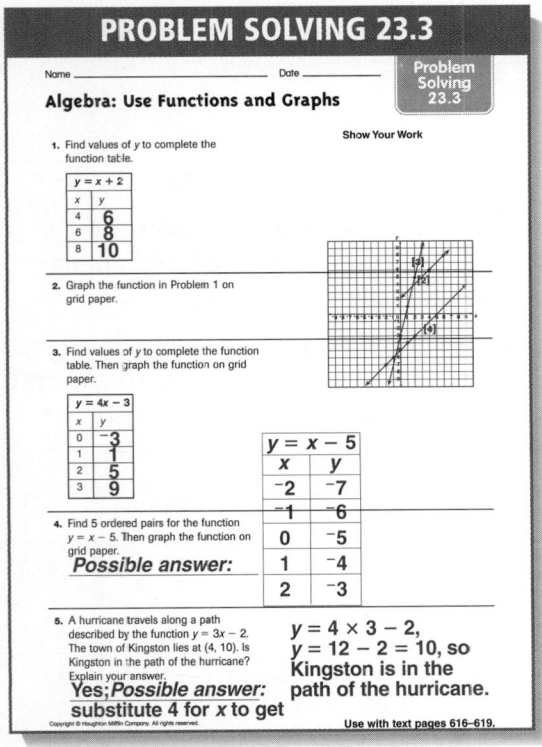

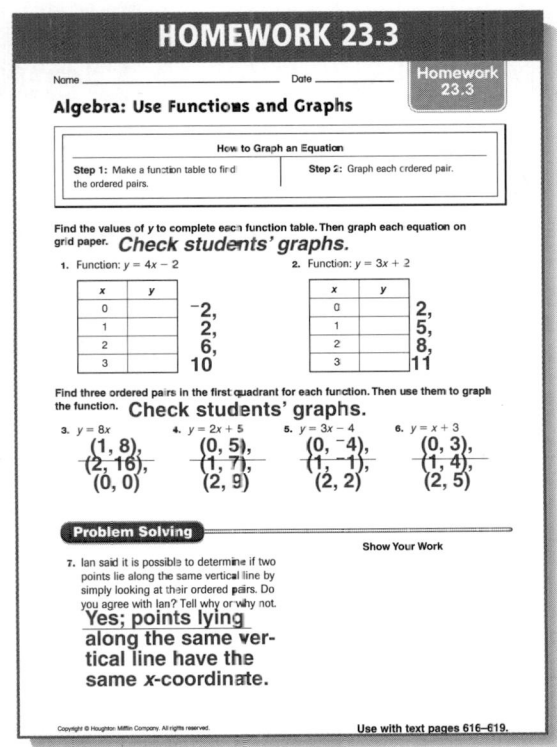

Homework Workbook Page 151

TEACHING LESSON 23.3

LESSON ORGANIZER

Objective Graph an equation on a coordinate plane.

Resources Reteach, Practice, Enrichment, Problem Solving, Homework, English Learners, Transparencies, Math Center

Materials Coordinate Plane Transparency and student copies of it, grid paper

Activity

Warm-Up Activity
Complete a Function Table

| Small Group | 5 minutes | Visual, Auditory |

Have students copy and complete the following function table for the rule $y = 2x + 1$.

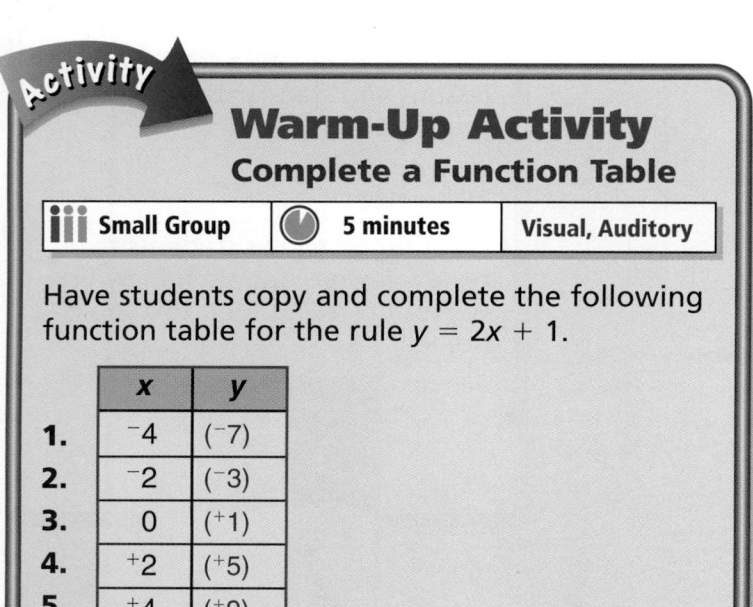

	x	y
1.	⁻4	(⁻7)
2.	⁻2	(⁻3)
3.	0	(⁺1)
4.	⁺2	(⁺5)
5.	⁺4	(⁺9)

Algebra
Use Functions and Graphs

Objective Graph an equation on a coordinate plane.

Learn About It

You can use both a function table and a graph to show the corresponding x- and y-values of a function rule.

In the last lesson, you saw that $y = 2x + 3$ shows the total cost (y) for the number of posters (x) that Kirsten ordered.

You can graph $y = 2x + 3$ to show the possible total costs for different orders.

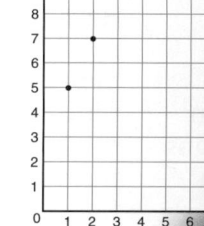

$y = 2x + 3$		**Ordered Pair**
x	**y**	
1	5	(1, 5)
2	7	(2, 7)
3	9	(3, 9)

Notice that since all values for x and y are positive, only the first quadrant of the coordinate plane is shown.

You can also graph functions that involve negative numbers. To do that, you need to show all quadrants of the coordinate plane.

Since you can only buy a whole number of posters, x must be a whole number. So only points are graphed.

Graph the equation $y = x - 2$ on a coordinate plane.

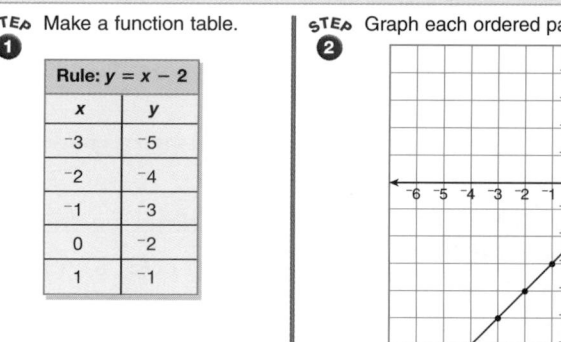

STEP 1 Make a function table.

Rule: $y = x - 2$	
x	**y**
⁻3	⁻5
⁻2	⁻4
⁻1	⁻3
0	⁻2
1	⁻1

STEP 2 Graph each ordered pair.

Since x can be a fraction or mixed number, a line can be drawn.

616

Activity

1 Introduce

| Whole Group | 5 minutes |

Materials: *Coordinate Plane Transparency, student copies of Coordinate Plane Transparency*

- At the bottom of the transparency, draw a function table. Label the first column x, and the second column y. Above the table write the rule $y = x - 3$.

- Enter these x-values: ⁺1, ⁺3, ⁺5. Have students use the rule to find the related y-values. (⁻2, 0, ⁺2)

- Explain that each of these pairs of values makes an ordered pair. Have students plot each ordered pair and connect each pair of dots. Ask students to discuss the result. (The dots appear to be on a straight line.)

2 Develop

Guide students through the *Learn About It* section.

- **Look at the graphs of the pairs of values in the table. What do you notice?** (The points are connected and appear to be on a straight line. They are all in the first quadrant.)

- Discuss the second example. Point out that the graphs of the ordered pairs in the table are in the first, third, and fourth quadrants. **What results when the points are connected?** (The points appear to be on a straight line.)

You can also use the graph of a function to predict what other pairs may be included in the function.

Graph the equation $y = x - 2$ on a coordinate plane, using the values $^-2$ to 2 for x. Use the graph to predict the value of y when $x = 5$.

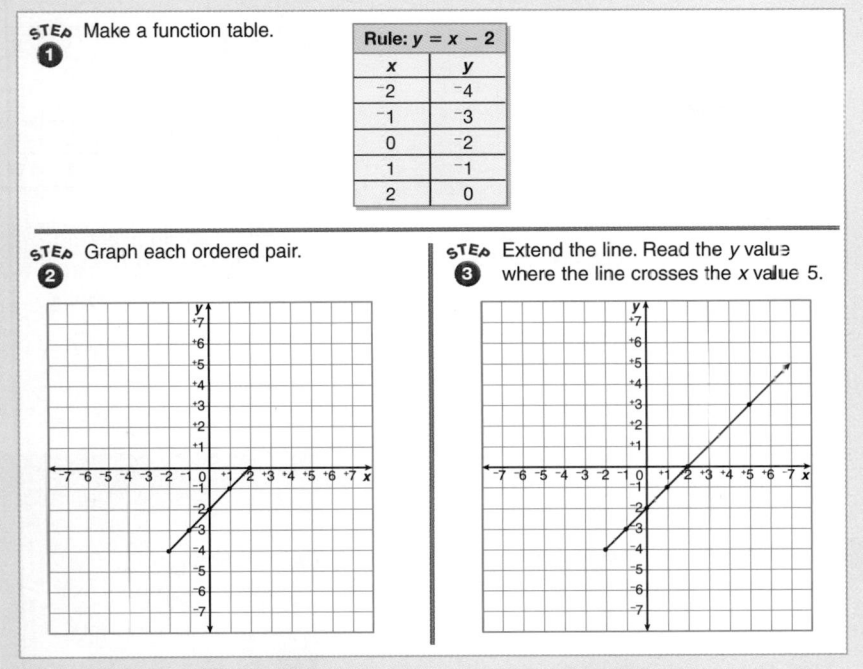

STEP 1 Make a function table.

Rule: $y = x - 2$

x	y
$^-2$	$^-4$
$^-1$	$^-3$
0	$^-2$
1	$^-1$
2	0

STEP 2 Graph each ordered pair.

STEP 3 Extend the line. Read the y value where the line crosses the x value 5.

Solution: For $y = x - 2$, when x is 5, y is 3.

Guided Practice

Find values of y to complete each function table. Then graph each function on grid paper.
See Additional Answers on Page T88.

1. $y = x - 2$ 2. $y = x + 3$ 3. $y = 2x - 1$

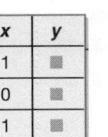
x	y
$^-1$	■
0	■
3	■

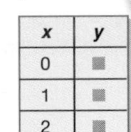
x	y
$^-1$	■
0	■
1	■

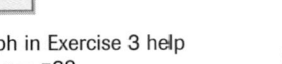
x	y
0	■
1	■
2	■

Ask Yourself
• Did I substitute each value for x in the equation to find y?
• Did I graph the equation as a straight line?

TEST TIPS

TEST TIPS **Explain Your Thinking** ▶ How could extending the graph in Exercise 3 help you find the value for y when $x = {}^-2$?
See Additional Answers on Page T88.

Go On ▶

Reaching All Learners

Algebra

Functions Copy the table on the board.

x	y	(x, y)	Answers:
1	2		(1, 2)
2	4		(2, 4)
3			6; (3, 6)
	8		4; (4, 8)

1. Have students use a pattern to complete the table.

2. Have students graph the ordered pairs from the complete table. Describe the relationship between x and y.

3. Have students write a function rule that describes the relationship between x and y.

Answers

1. See above.

2. Check students' graphs. Students should recognize that y is twice x.

3. $y = 2x$

Differentiated Assignments		
At Risk	**Average**	**Advanced**
Exercise 1	Exercises 1–2	Exercises 1–3

• **Look at Step 1.** Have students look at the function table for the rule $y = x - 2$.

• **Look at Step 2.** Have them compare the graphed points with the ordered pairs in the table.

• **Look at Step 3.** If you extend the line to the point where it intersects $x = {}^+5$, what will the corresponding y-value be? ($y = {}^+3$)

Guided Practice

Have students complete **Exercises 1–3** as you observe. Remind them to use the *Ask Yourself* questions to help. Give students the opportunity to talk about the question in *Explain Your Thinking*.

DAILY TEST PREP

Which is the function rule for this table? (D)

x	-2	-1	0	+1	+2
y	-4	-2	0	+2	+4

A. $y = x - 2$ C. $y = 4x$

B. $y = x + 2$ D. $y = 2x$

Activity

Or use Intervention CD-ROM Lesson 23.3

Lesson Intervention

Graphing an Equation

👥 Small Group	⏱ 5–10 minutes	Kinesthetic, Tactile

Materials: *Coordinate Plane Transparency, grid paper*

• Display a function table for $y = x + 1$, with the x-values +1, +2, +3. **Find the y-value related to each x-value.** (+2, +3, +4)

• Next, plot the ordered pairs. For each pair, ask: **How many units do we count right for x? How many units do we count up from there for y?** Have them name the ordered pair for each point. Place a dot at each point. **Let's connect the dots. What kind of graph is $y = x + 1$?** (straight line)

Practice and Problem Solving

Find values of *y* to complete each function table. Then graph each equation as a straight line on grid paper. *See Additional Answers on Page T88.*

4. $y = x - 1$

x	y
-2	■
-1	■
0	■
1	■

5. $y = x + 4$

x	y
-3	■
-2	■
-1	■
0	■

6. $y = 3x - 2$

x	y
0	■
1	■
2	■
3	■

7. $y = 3x + 1$

x	y
0	■
1	■
2	■
3	■

Find three ordered pairs for each function. 8–15. *See Additional Answers on* Then use them to graph the function as a straight line. *Page T88 and T89.*

8. $y = x + 1$ **9.** $y = x - 4$ **10.** $y = x + 6$ **11.** $x - 5 = y$

12. $y = 2x$ **13.** $y = 4x$ **14.** $y = 3x - 1$ **15.** $y = 2x + 2$

Solve. 16–18. *See Additional Answers on Page T89.*

16. Explain Graph $y = 2x$ and $y = 4x$ as straight lines on the same coordinate plane. How are the graphs alike? How are they different?

 17. Write About It Graph $y = x - 2$ and $y = x + 2$ as straight lines on the same coordinate plane. How are the graphs alike? How are they different?

18. Reasoning Explain how you can use the graph at the beginning of this lesson to find how much it would cost Kirsten for 8 posters.

19. Plot 3 or more points in a straight line on a coordinate plane. Find an equation for the line. Ask a partner to check the equation. *Check students' equations.*

Daily Review	Test Prep

Multiply or divide. (Ch. 13, Lessons 2–5; Ch. 14, Lessons 4–7)

20. 8×0.8
6.4

21. 0.4×0.05
0.02

22. $4 \div 0.8$
5

23. $2.8 \div 0.07$
40

24. Which of these ordered pairs is not a solution for $y = 4x + 2$?

Ⓐ (1, 4)   **B** (-1, -2)

C (0, 2)   **D** (1, 6)

Extra Practice See page 627, Set C.

---

③ Practice

Assign **Exercises 4–24** as independent work.

• *Problem Solving for Problems 16–19* Have volunteers share their work with the class. For Problem 19, have volunteers share their graphs and equations with the class.

Common Error

Ignoring negative signs When graphing ordered pairs, students sometimes forget to count left or down when graphing an ordered pair that contains one or more negative integers.

Where in the U.S.A.?

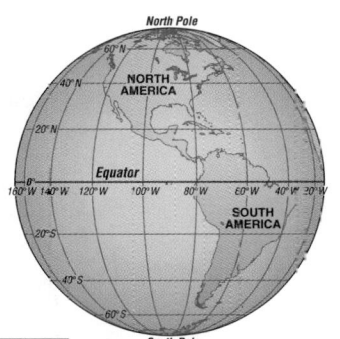

Mapmakers use a system very similar to a coordinate grid to identify positions of places on Earth. Latitude 0° is at the equator. Latitudes are North (N) or South (S) of the equator.

Longitude 0° passes through Greenwich, England. Longitudes are either West (W) or East (E) of 0°.

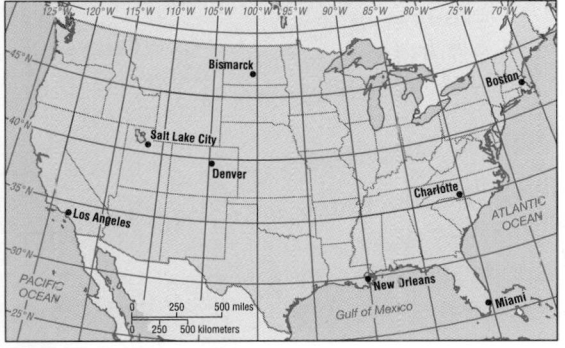

Estimate the latitude and longitude for each city.

1. Boston, MA
   40°N, 70°W

2. New Orleans, LA
   30°N, 90°W

3. Denver, CO
   40°N, 100°W

4. Los Angeles, CA
   35°N, 120°W

Use a map or an atlas.

5. Find the latitude and longitude for where you live. **Answers will vary.**

Find what city is at each location.

6. 25°N, 80°W
   Miami, FL

7. 45°N, 100°W
   Bismarck, ND

8. 40°N, 110°W
   Salt Lake City, UT

9. 35°N, 80°W
   Charlotte, NC

10. Explain the differences and similarities of locating and labeling a point on the coordinate plane and locating and labeling a city on a map. **See Additional Answers on Page T89.**

Chapter 23 Lesson 3 **619**

Social Studies Connection

Where in the U.S.A.?

- Have students examine the map of North America and identify lines of longitude and latitude. Explain that Latitude 0° passes through the equator. Lines of latitude are given in degrees North or South of 0°.

- Point out that the location of many places may be near but not on a particular line of longitude or latitude, and must be estimated to the line it is closest to.

4 Assess and Close

- **How can you use the graph of a set of ordered pairs to discover another ordered pair that satisfies the rule?**
  (Extend the graph in either direction to find an x-value. Then trace back to the y-axis to find the y-value for that point.)

Assign the **LESSON QUIZ** on Transparency 23.3 to further assess student understanding.

Keeping a Journal

Have students explain how the graphs of the equations $y = 2x$, $y = 3x$, and $y = 4x$ are similar and how they differ.

Problem-Solving Application: Use a Graph

PLANNING THE LESSON

MATHEMATICS OBJECTIVE
Use graphs to solve problems.

Use Lesson Planner CD-ROM for Lesson 23.4.

Daily Routines

Vocabulary
Ask students to give examples of ways they have used the word **coordinate** in everyday life. Challenge students to explain the meaning of **coordinates** given in an ordered pair of x- and y-values.

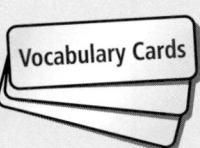
Vocabulary Cards

Meeting North Carolina's Standards
Prepare for Grade 7 Objective **5.01** Identify, analyze, and create linear relations, sequences, and functions using symbols, Graphs, tables, diagrams, and written descriptions.

Lesson
Transparency
23.4

Problem of the Day
The letters A, B, C, and D are arranged in a row. B is in front of A but behind C. D is behind A. Which letter is second? (B)

Quick Review
Given the function $y = 5x - 10$, find y for each value of x.

1. $x = {}^+2$ ($y = 0$)
2. $x = 0$ ($y = {}^-10$)
3. $x = {}^+5$ ($y = {}^+15$)
4. $x = {}^-1$ ($y = {}^-15$)
5. $x = {}^+1$ ($y = {}^-5$)

Lesson Quiz
Solve.

The temperature of the water in the pond in Green Park rose to 65°F at 3:00 P.M. The temperature dropped 3 degrees every hour after that. What will the temperature of the water be by 8:00 P.M.? What equation can you write? (50°F; $y = 65 - 3x$)

LEVELED PRACTICE

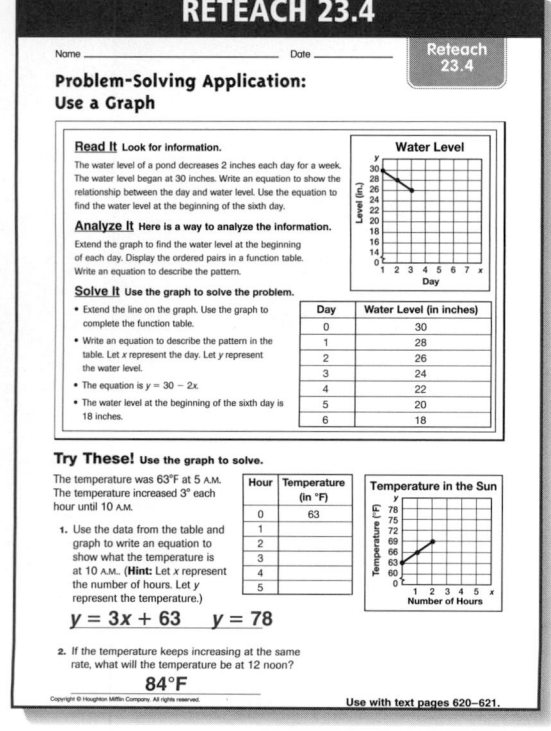

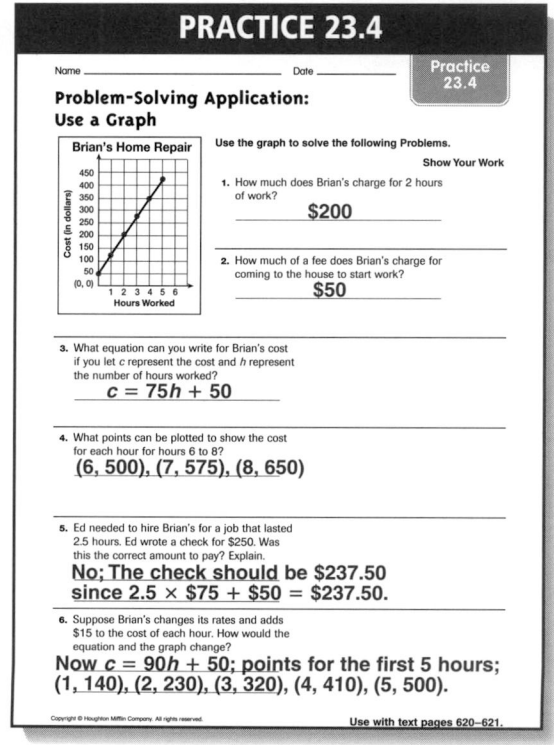

Reaching All Learners

Differentiated Instruction

English Learners

Worksheet 23.4 allows students to practice graphing data points to solve word problems.

Inclusion
VISUAL, AUDITORY

Materials: *Coordinate Plane Transparency, grid paper*

- Display a table with *x* values of 1, 2, and 3, and *y* values of 2, 4, and 6.
- Help students graph each pair. **Connect the points. What kind of graph is it?** (line) Extend the graph so that $x = 6$. What is the value of *y*? (12)

Early Finishers
VISUAL, AUDITORY

Materials: *Grid paper*

- Suppose you sell hats. Give the hats a price. Make a table for 4 hats. Have total hats equal *x* and total price equal *y*. Have them graph the ordered pairs and then connect points.
- Exchange tables and graphs. Extend the graph to include more hats than are in the table.

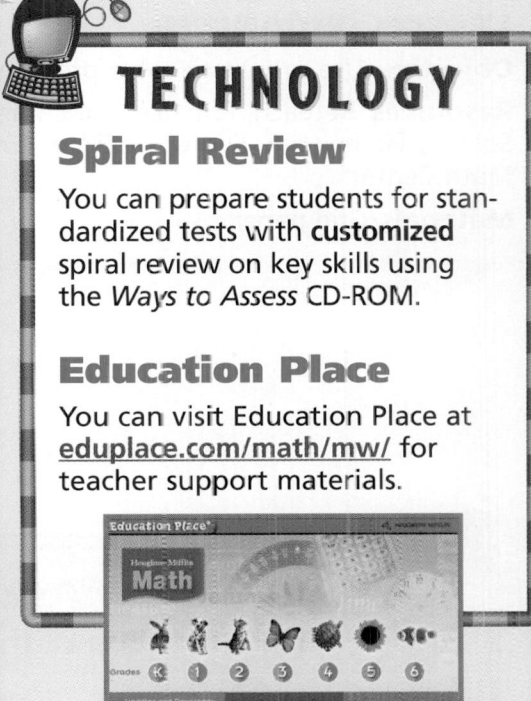

TECHNOLOGY

Spiral Review

You can prepare students for standardized tests with **customized** spiral review on key skills using the *Ways to Assess* CD-ROM.

Education Place

You can visit Education Place at eduplace.com/math/mw/ for teacher support materials.

Science Connection

Lighter Than Air

- Explain that on the Moon, a person weighs $\frac{1}{6}$ as much as on Earth. Have students write a function rule to relate weight on Earth (x) and weight on moon (y). ($y = \frac{1}{6} x$ or $y = \frac{x}{6}$) Then have them make a function table and find the value of y for x = 6, 9, 12, 15, and 30 lb.

- Have students graph and connect the ordered pairs, then find a point on their graph that represents the weight on Earth of a common object, such as a book, a brick, or a chair. Have them use the graph to find the weight on the Moon of that object.

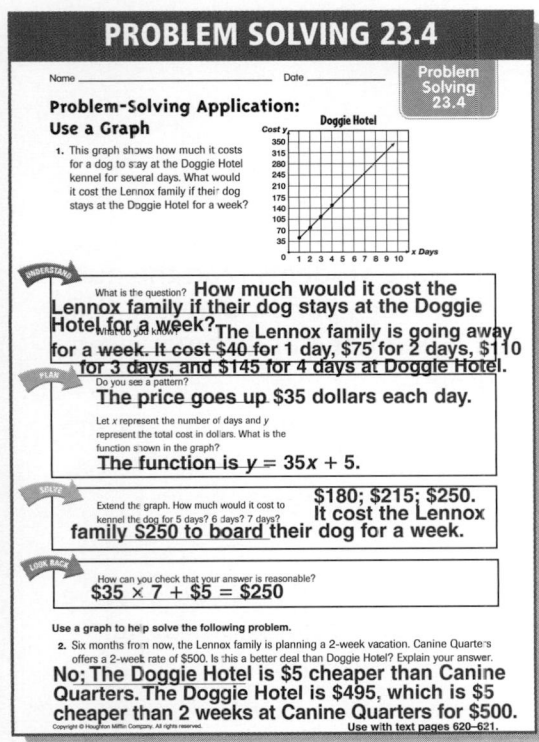

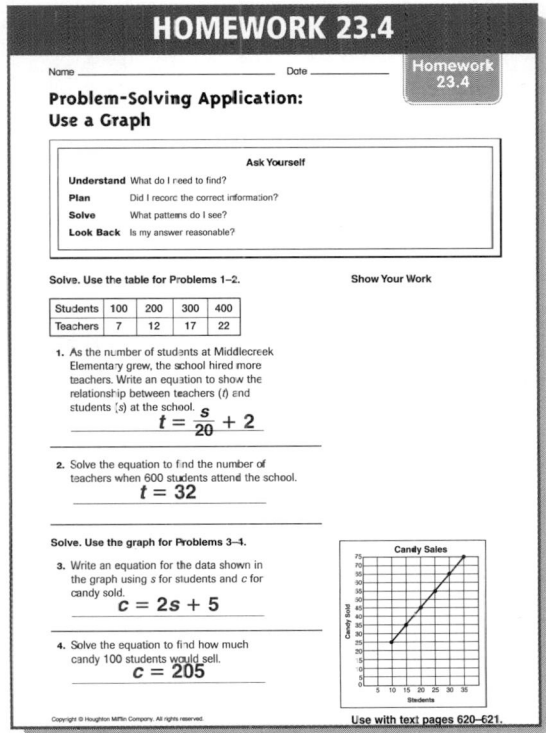

Homework Workbook Page 152

TEACHING LESSON 23.4

LESSON ORGANIZER

Objective Use graphs to solve problems.

Resources Reteach, Practice, Enrichment, Problem Solving, Homework, English Learners, Transparencies, Math Center

Materials Grid paper

Warm-Up Activity
Use Functions With Integers

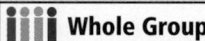 Whole Group 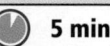 5 minutes | Visual, Auditory

Have students use the rule $y = 2x - 3$ to find the value of y for the given value of x.

1. $x = ^-4$ $(y = ^-11)$

2. $x = ^-2$ $(y = ^-7)$

3. $x = 0$ $(y = ^-3)$

4. $x = ^+2$ $(y = ^+1)$

5. $x = ^+4$ $(y = ^+5)$

Lesson 4
Problem-Solving Application
Use a Graph

Objective Use graphs to solve problems.

Sometimes you need to read the data in a graph to solve a problem.

How long does it take light to travel the mean distance of 93,000,000 miles from the Sun to Earth?

The original graph is shown in black. Since 93,000,000 miles is not shown on the graph, the graph was extended as shown in red.

Think: 93 million miles is between 90 million and 100 million miles.

A line is drawn horizontally from about 93,000,000 miles until it meets the graph. Then a vertical line is drawn to find the time.

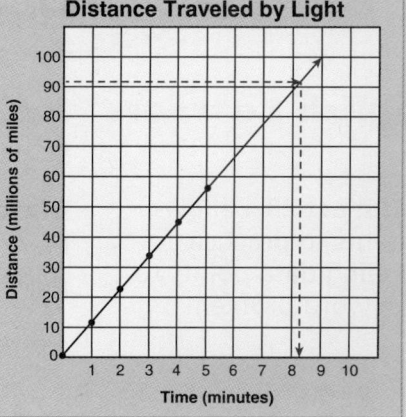

Distance Traveled by Light

Solution: It takes about $8\frac{1}{2}$ minutes for light to travel from the sun to Earth.

Sometimes you need to display data in a graph to help you solve a problem.

One planetarium uses the table at the right to determine the cost for a group to see a show. How much would it cost for a group of 9 people?

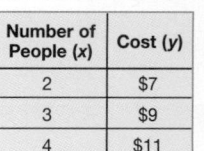

Number of People (x)	Cost (y)
2	$7
3	$9
4	$11

STEP 1 Use the table to write ordered pairs. (2, 7); (3, 9); (4, 11)

STEP 2 Graph the given coordinates.

STEP 3 Extend the graph with coordinates for 5 through 9 people, as shown in red.

Solution: The cost for 9 people is $21.

Since you cannot have part of a person, only the points are graphed for counting numbers 2 through 9.

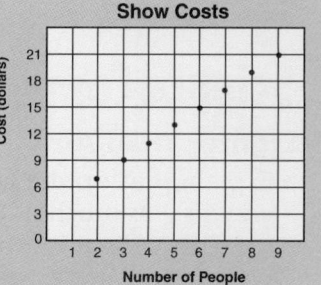

Show Costs

620

---

1 Introduce

- Have students write a function rule for this situation: **Renting a rowboat on Pine Lake costs $10 per hour.**

- **What will x represent?** (the number of hours) **What will y represent?** (the total cost for that number of hours) **What would the rule be?** ($y = 10x$)

- **If you set up a table, what would you use for values of x?** (Possible answer: 1, 2, 3, 4, 5) **What do each of these numbers represent?** (the number of hours) **How will you find related values for y?** (Use the rule to calculate it.) **What will those values be?** (10, 20, 30, 40, 50)

2 Develop

Guide students through the problem-solving steps on page 620.

- **Look at the first example.** Have students read the question and study the graph for each part. Make sure they understand how a graph is extended and how a given point is located on the graph.

- **Look at the second example. How could you check the solution for the second problem?** (Extend the table to 9 persons.)

Guided Practice

Have students complete **Exercises 1 and 2** as you observe. Remind them to use the *Ask Yourself* questions to help.

Use the graphs and the table on page 620 for Problems 1–2.

Ask Yourself
- What do I need to find?
- What patterns do I see?

TEST TIPS

1. It takes light about 6 minutes to reach Venus from the sun. About how far from the Sun is Venus? **about 67 million miles**

2. Using the data from table and its graph, write an equation that relates the number of people to the total cost of admission for the group. **y = 2x + 3**

(Hint) The equation is $y = (■ • x) + ■$. Look at the graph. If you extend the graph to the y-axis, what is the value of y for $x = 0$?

Independent Practice

Solve.

3. The gift shop at the planetarium marks up the cost of model solar systems as shown in the table. Write an equation to show how to find the store price (y) of any model solar system at cost x. **y = 2x**

Cost	Store Price
$20	$40
$25	$50
$30	$60
$35	$70

4. Solve the equation you wrote in Problem 3 to find the store price for a model that costs $120. **$240**

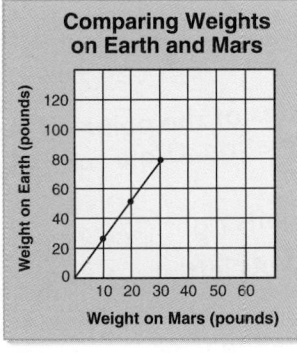

Comparing Weights on Earth and Mars

Weight on Earth (pounds) — vertical axis: 20, 40, 60, 80, 100, 120
Weight on Mars (pounds) — horizontal axis: 10 20 30 40 50 60

7. No. If the equation for the data was y = 4x, then the ordered pairs would be (10, 40), (20, 80), (30, 120).

5. **Estimate** The graph at the left shows the relationship between an object's weight on Earth and its weight on Mars. Suppose a rock weighs 15 pounds on Mars. About how much would that same rock weigh on Earth? **about 40 pounds**

6. On Earth an astronaut weighs 118 pounds. About how much would that astronaut weigh if she landed on Mars? **about 50 pounds**

7. **Explain** Martha says that the equation representing the data in the graph is y = 4x. If y is the weight on Earth and x is the weight on Mars, is Martha correct? Explain your reasoning. **See above.**

Chapter 23 Lesson 4 **621**

DAILY TEST PREP

Which is a rule for this function table? (D)

x	1	2	3	4
y	3	5	7	9

A. $y = x + 1$ C. $y = x - 1$

B. $y = 2x - 1$ D. $y = 2x + 1$

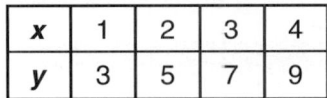 **Activity**

 Or use Intervention CD-ROM Lesson 23.4

Lesson Intervention

Plotting and Connecting Points

iii Small Group	⏱ 5–10 minutes	Visual, Kinesthetic

Materials: *grid paper*

- Draw an *x*- and *y*-axis. Number each axis from ⁻10 to ⁻10. Then have students plot and label (⁺1, ⁺2). Make sure they count right 1 unit from the origin and 2 units up from there. Repeat for (⁺2, ⁺3) and (⁺3, ⁺4). **Connect the three points. What graph do you see?** (a straight line)

- Have them extend the line so it meets the *y*-axis. **At what point does the line meet the *y*-axis?** (0, ⁺1) Extend the line in the other direction. **What is the next point it goes through in this direction?** (⁺4, ⁺5) **What equation fits these ordered pairs?** (y = x + 1)

3 Practice

Assign **Problems 3–7** as independent work. Have students share and discuss their work.

Problem-Solving Reminders

Have students review their answers to make sure they have done the following:

- expressed the solution properly
- used appropriate mathematical notation and terms
- supported their solution with verbal and symbolic work
- determined the reasonableness of the solution in the context of the original problem.

4 Assess and Close

- **How does extending a graph help you to solve problems?** (You can find an *x*-value that is not given on the graph and then read the related *y*-value.)

- **How can you find a value for a point that is between two plotted points?** (Find a point that has an *x*- or *y*-value close to the value you want and read the related value on the *y*- or *x*-axis.)

Assign the **LESSON QUIZ** on Transparency 23.4 to further assess student understanding.

 **Keeping a Journal**

Have students explain two ways that you could find *y*-values for *x*-values that are not in a table.

Transformations in the Coordinate Plane

PLANNING THE LESSON

MATHEMATICS OBJECTIVE
Identify and describe transformations in the coordinate plane.

Use Lesson Planner CD-ROM for Lesson 23.5.

Daily Routines

Vocabulary

Explain that the word *transformation* means "change." Explain that in mathematics, it means a change in the position of a figure on a coordinate plane. Have students look up the words *translation, reflection,* and *rotation* in the dictionary. Then discuss their meanings in mathematics.

Vocabulary Cards

Meeting North Carolina's Standards

Prepare for Grade 6 Objective **3.04** Solve problems involving geometric figures in the coordinate plane.

Lesson Transparency
23.5

Problem of the Day
Draw a circle and a square. How many points and lines of symmetry does each figure have? (A circle has 1 point (its center) and an infinite number of lines (its diameters). A square has one point (the intersection of diagonals) and 4 lines.)

Quick Review
Write the reciprocal of each fraction.
1. $\frac{3}{4}$ $\left(\frac{4}{3}\right)$
2. $\frac{8}{5}$ $\left(\frac{5}{8}\right)$
3. $\frac{1}{a}$ $\left(\frac{a}{1}$ or $a\right)$
4. $\frac{x}{y}$ $\left(\frac{y}{x}\right)$

Lesson Quiz
Name the coordinates of the point ($^+2$, $^+2$) after each transformation. Use a coordinate graph to help you.
1. A translation 5 units right ($^+7$, $^+2$)
2. A translation 6 units left and 1 unit down ($^-4$, $^+1$)
3. A reflection across the *y*-axis. ($^-2$, $^+2$)
4. A reflection across the *x*-axis ($^+2$, $^-2$)

LEVELED PRACTICE

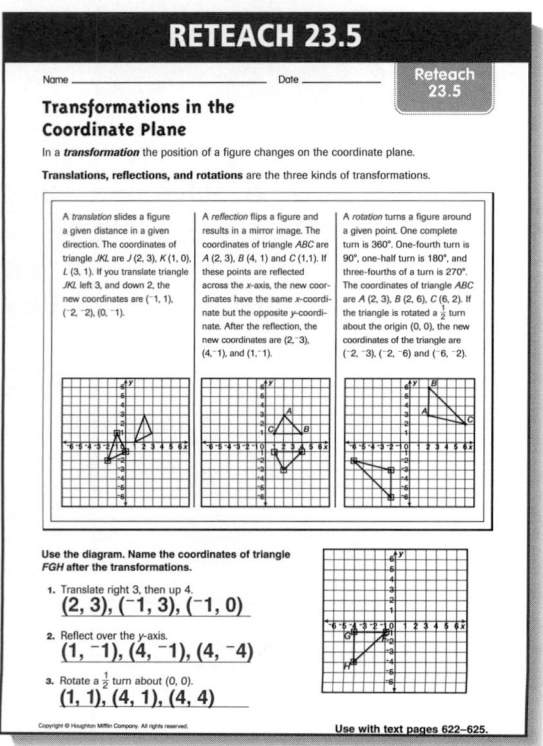

RETEACH 23.5

Name _____ Date _____ Reteach 23.5

Transformations in the Coordinate Plane

In a *transformation* the position of a figure changes on the coordinate plane.

Translations, reflections, and rotations are the three kinds of transformations.

Use the diagram. Name the coordinates of triangle *FGH* after the transformations.
1. Translate right 3, then up 4.
   (2, 3), ($^-1$, 3), ($^-1$, 0)
2. Reflect over the *y*-axis.
   (1, $^-1$), (4, $^-1$), (4, $^-4$)
3. Rotate a $\frac{1}{2}$ turn about (0, 0).
   (1, 1), (4, 1), (4, 4)

Use with text pages 622–625.

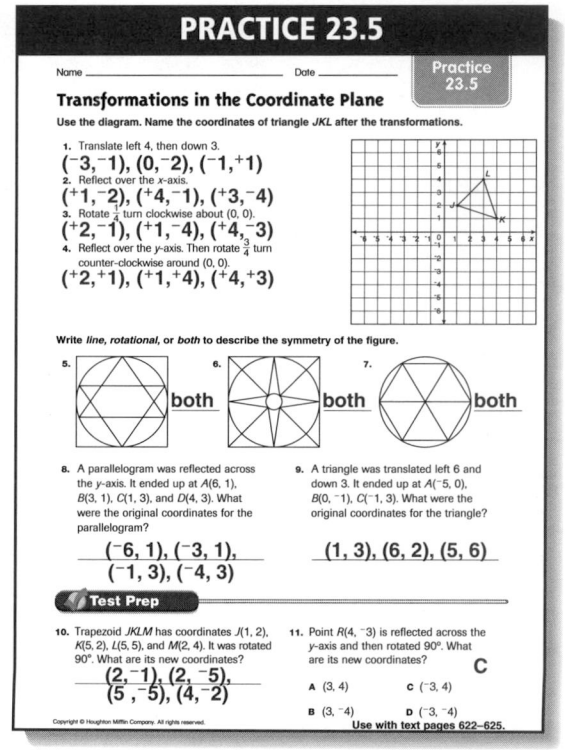

PRACTICE 23.5

Name _____ Date _____ Practice 23.5

Transformations in the Coordinate Plane

Use the diagram. Name the coordinates of triangle *JKL* after the transformations.
1. Translate left 4, then down 3.
   ($^-3$,$^-1$), (0,$^-2$), ($^-1$,$^+1$)
2. Reflect over the *x*-axis.
   ($^+1$,$^-2$), ($^+4$,$^-1$), ($^+3$,$^-4$)
3. Rotate $\frac{1}{4}$ turn clockwise about (0, 0).
   ($^+2$,$^-1$), ($^+1$,$^-4$), ($^+4$,$^-3$)
4. Reflect over the *y*-axis. Then rotate $\frac{1}{2}$ turn counter-clockwise around (0, 0).
   ($^+2$,$^+1$), ($^+1$,$^+4$), ($^+4$,$^+3$)

Write *line, rotational,* or *both* to describe the symmetry of the figure.
5. both
6. both
7. both

8. A parallelogram was reflected across the *y*-axis. It ended up at *A*(6, 1), *B*(3, 1), *C*(1, 3), and *D*(4, 3). What were the original coordinates for the parallelogram?
   ($^-6$, 1), ($^-3$, 1), ($^-1$, 3), ($^-4$, 3)

9. A triangle was translated left 6 and down 3. It ended up at *A*($^-5$, 0), *B*(0, $^-1$), *C*($^-1$, 3). What were the original coordinates for the triangle?
   (1, 3), (6, 2), (5, 6)

Test Prep

10. Trapezoid *JKLM* has coordinates *J*(1, 2), *K*(5, 2), *L*(5, 5), and *M*(2, 4). It was rotated 90°. What are its new coordinates?
    (2,$^-1$), (2,$^-5$), (5,$^-5$), (4,$^-2$)

11. Point *R*(4, $^-3$) is reflected across the *y*-axis and then rotated 90°. What are its new coordinates? **C**
    A (3, 4)   C $^-3$, 4)
    B (3, $^-4$)   D ($^-3$, $^-4$)

Use with text pages 622–625.

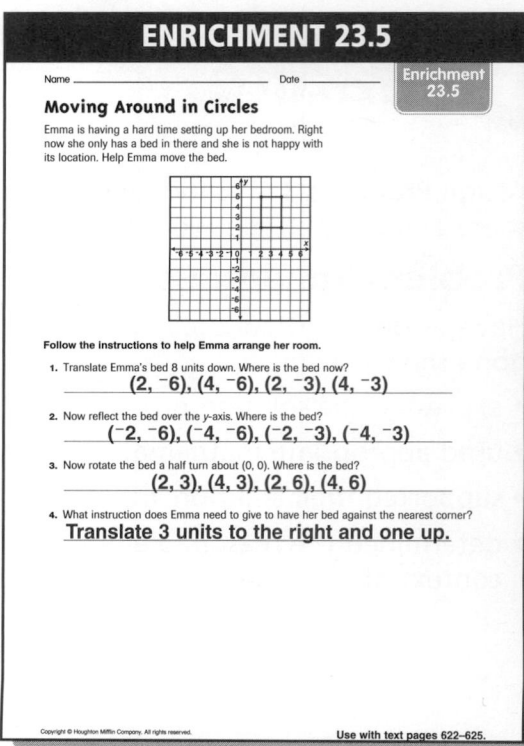

ENRICHMENT 23.5

Name _____ Date _____ Enrichment 23.5

Moving Around in Circles

Emma is having a hard time setting up her bedroom. Right now she only has a bed in there and she is not happy with its location. Help Emma move the bed.

Follow the instructions to help Emma arrange her room.
1. Translate Emma's bed 8 units down. Where is the bed now?
   (2, $^-6$), (4, $^-6$), (2, $^-3$), (4, $^-3$)
2. Now reflect the bed over the *y*-axis. Where is the bed?
   ($^-2$, $^-6$), ($^-4$, $^-6$), ($^-2$, $^-3$), ($^-4$, $^-3$)
3. Now rotate the bed a half turn about (0, 0). Where is the bed?
   (2, 3), (4, 3), (2, 6), (4, 6)
4. What instruction does Emma need to give to have her bed against the nearest corner?
   Translate 3 units to the right and one up.

Use with text pages 622–625.

Reaching All Learners

Differentiated Instruction

English Learners

Worksheet 23.5 uses pictures and text to reinforce the three kinds of transformation discussed in Lesson 5: reflection, rotation, and translation.

Special Needs
VISUAL, KINESTHETIC

Materials: *grid paper, color pencils*

- Help students plot: ($^+$3, $^+$3); ($^-$2, $^+$1); ($^+$3, $^-$1); ($^-$2, $^-$2); ($^-$6, $^+$3)

- **Now translate each point 3 units to the right and 3 units up. Mark the new points with a new color. What are the new coordinates of each?** (($^+$6, $^+$6), ($^+$1, $^+$4), ($^+$6, $^+$2), ($^+$1, $^+$1), ($^-$3, $^+$6))

Gifted and Talented
VISUAL, KINESTHETIC

- Have students graph either a square, a rectangle, a triangle, a parallelogram, or a trapezoid. **Do not write coordinates on the graph.**

- Have them write directions for a translation or a reflection. Have them exchange graphs and directions. **Draw the new figures and label the vertices.**

Social Studies Connection

Where We Live

- Have students create a map of three places in their neighborhoods (school, library, home, store, etc.), using points on a coordinate grid for each place. They should graph the points in the first quadrant, label

each point with a letter (e.g., *S* for *school*), and write the ordered pair for each point.

- Then ask them to reflect each point across the *x*-axis, using a pencil of a different color to graph the reflected points and write the ordered pair for each reflected point. Have students display and discuss their maps.

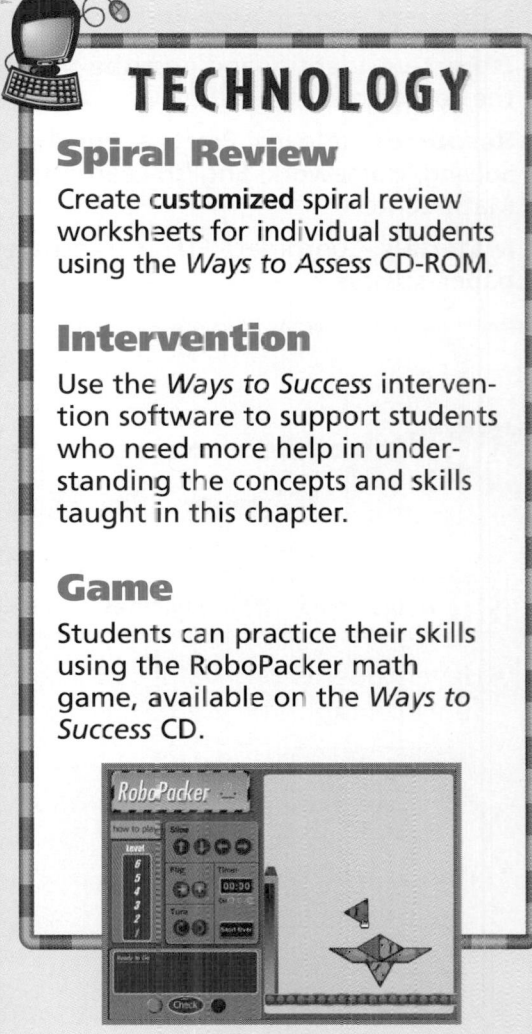

TECHNOLOGY

Spiral Review

Create customized spiral review worksheets for individual students using the *Ways to Assess* CD-ROM.

Intervention

Use the *Ways to Success* intervention software to support students who need more help in understanding the concepts and skills taught in this chapter.

Game

Students can practice their skills using the RoboPacker math game, available on the *Ways to Success* CD.

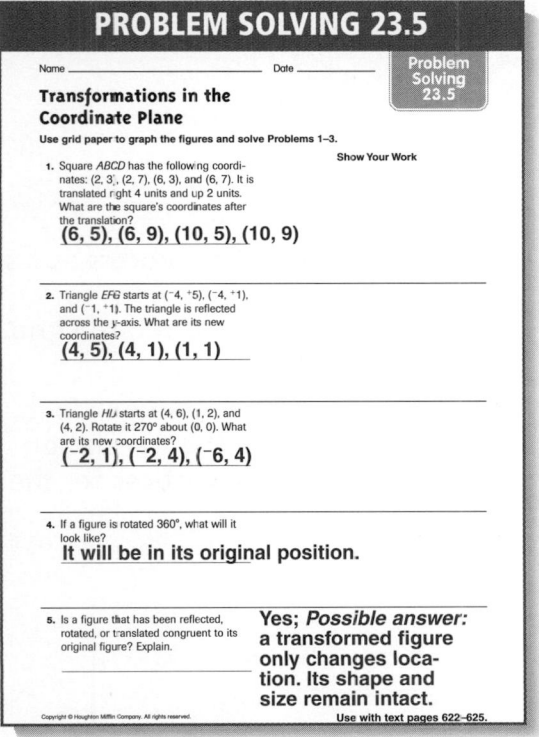

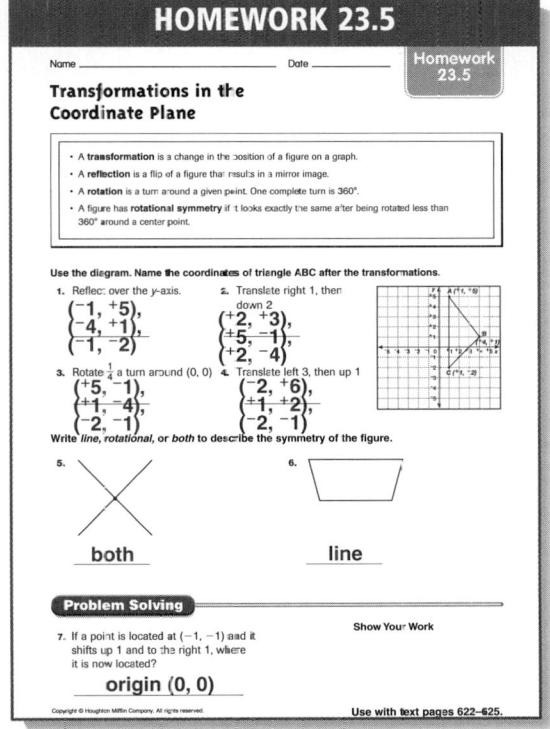

Homework Workbook Page 153

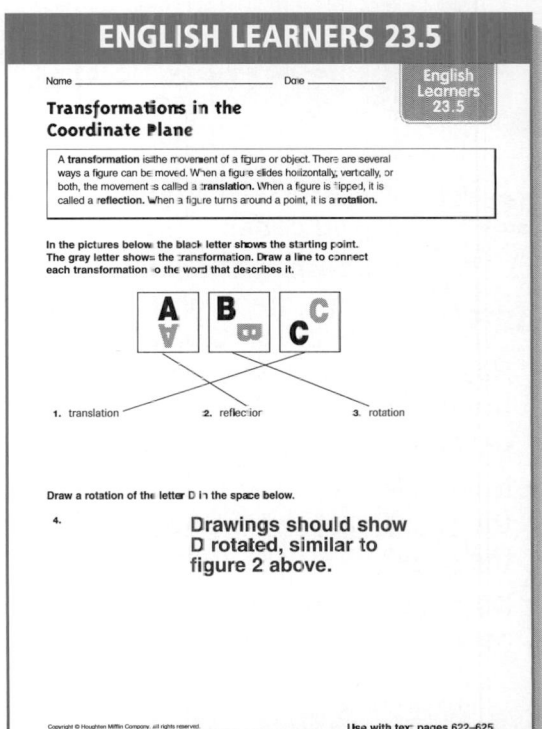

TEACHING LESSON 23.5

LESSON ORGANIZER

Objective Identify and describe transformations in the coordinate plane.

Resources Reteach, Practice, Enrichment, Problem Solving, Homework, English Learners, Transparencies, Math Center

Materials Coordinate Plane Transparency, grid paper, scissors

Warm-Up Activity
Complete a Function Table

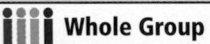 **Whole Group**   **5 minutes**   **Visual, Auditory**

- Have students find values of *y* to complete the function table for the rule $y = x + 4$.

	x	y
1.	⁻1	(⁺3)
2.	0	(⁺4)
3.	⁺1	(⁺5)
4.	⁺2	(⁺6)

- Ask students what the *y*-value would be for $x = 7$. (11)

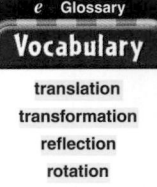
e Glossary
Vocabulary
translation
transformation
reflection
rotation

Transformations in the Coordinate Plane

Objective Identify and describe transformations in the coordinate plane.

Learn About It

On Miranda's map, her home is at point (0, 0). She leaves home and walks west 3 blocks and north 5 blocks. Where is she? What **translations** take her to this point? Remember that a translation slides a point or figure a given distance in a given direction.

Find Miranda's location after moving 3 blocks west and 5 blocks north.

After walking 3 blocks west, Miranda is at point (⁻3, 0). Walking 5 blocks north puts her at (⁻3, 15).

Solution: Miranda is at her school.

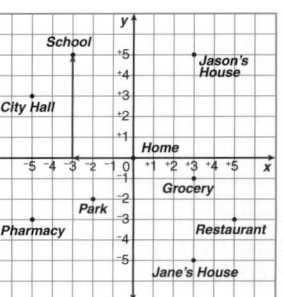

Try this activity to translate figures and points on a coordinate plane.

Materials: coordinate grid, scissors

STEP 1 Draw a rectangle in Quadrant I.

STEP 2 Trace the rectangle on another sheet of paper and cut it out.

STEP 3 Translate the rectangle and trace it.

STEP 4 Record the coordinates for each vertex.

STEP 5 Describe the translation you made.

A **transformation** is a change in the position of a figure on a graph. Transformations include translations, **reflections**, and **rotations**.

622

---

① Introduce   Whole Group   ⏱ 5 minutes

Teaching Transparency for 23.5

Materials: *Coordinate Plane Transparency, grid paper*

- Display the transparency. In the second quadrant, graph these points: (⁻5, ⁺2); (⁻2, ⁺2); (⁻2, ⁺6). Connect each pair to form a triangle. Have students draw the triangle on grid paper. Then trace the triangle on a sheet of paper and cut it out. Have students do the same.

- Now slide the paper triangle 3 units down. **What will be the coordinates of the vertices of the new triangle after the slide?** ((⁻5, ⁻1), (⁻2, ⁻1), (⁻2, ⁺3))

- Do the same for a slide 3 units to the right. **What will the new coordinates be?** ((⁻2, ⁺2), (⁺1, ⁺2), (⁺1, ⁺6))

② Develop

Guide students through the *Learn About It* portion of the lesson.

- Have students use grid paper and follow the process as it's described. Ask students to choose a slide they want to perform. Then have them draw a rectangle along the grid lines and record the coordinates of the vertices.

- Have them trace and cut out the rectangle shape, slide it, and record the new coordinates. **Describe the translation you made and give the coordinates of the vertices for the new position.**

Reflections and Line Symmetry

▶ A **reflection** is a flip of a figure that results in a mirror image.

Name the coordinates of points *A* and *B* after a reflection across the *y*-axis.

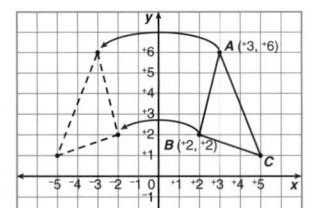

Reflect each vertex across the *y*-axis. The new points will be the same distance to the left of the *y*-axis as *A* and *B* are to its right.

The new points will be (⁻3, 6) and (⁻2, 2).

Use a reflection to decide whether the figure has line symmetry.

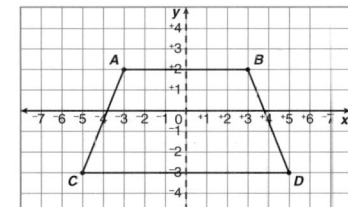

If an axis is a line of symmetry, then either its *x* or *y* coordinates will be opposites.

Point *A* (⁻3, 2) is opposite Point *B* (3, 2).

Point *C* (⁻5, ⁻3) is opposite Point *D* (5, ⁻3).

Rotations and Rotational Symmetry

▶ A **rotation** is a turn around a given point.

Name the coordinates of point *A* after a half-turn around the origin.

$\frac{1}{2}$ turn = 90° $\frac{1}{2}$ turn = 180°

$\frac{3}{2}$ turn = 270°   1 turn = 360°

Trace the axes, mark point *A*, and turn the tracing 180°.

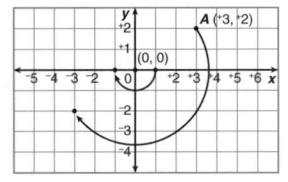

After the rotation, the new point is (⁻3, ⁻2.)

A figure has rotational symmetry if it looks exactly the same after being rotated less than 360° around a center point. When the figure turns 90°, it looks the same. The figure has rotational symmetry.

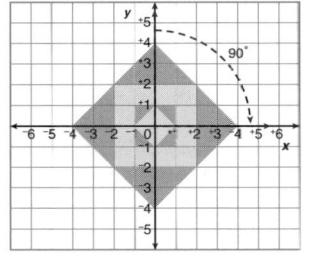

Go On ▶

Chapter 23 Lesson 5   **623**

- **For a reflection, any new points will be the same distance from the axis of reflection as the original points were.**
- **For points reflected over the *y*-axis, the *x*-coordinates will be opposites. For figures reflected over the *x*-axis, the *y*-coordinates will be opposites.**
- For another example of rotational symmetry, draw a rectangle with the intersection of its diagonals at the origin. **Does the figure have rotational symmetry?** (Yes; it looks the same after a rotation of 180°.)

Guided Practice

Have students complete **Exercises 1–5** as you observe. Remind them to use the *Ask Yourself* question to help. Give students an opportunity to talk about the question in *Explain Your Thinking*.

DAILY TEST PREP

What will the coordinates of the reflected point be if the point $(^-2, ^-4)$ is reflected over the *y*-axis? (B)

A. $(^+2, ^+4)$ C. $(^-2, ^+4)$

B. $(^+2, ^-4)$ D. $(^-2, ^-4)$

Activity

Lesson Intervention

Or use Intervention CD-ROM Lesson 23.5

Sliding Around

| 👥 Small Group | 🕐 5–10 minutes | Visual, Kinesthetic |

Materials: *Coordinate Plane Transparency*

- Use the Coordinate Plane Transparency. Graph the coordinates of these three points, one at a time: $(^+1, ^+2); (^+3, ^+4); (^-2, ^+3).$

- Ask volunteers to show where each point would be if it were translated 1 unit to the right and 1 unit down. Ask them to give the new coordinates. ((2, 1), (4, 3), $(^-1, 2)$)

- Using the same points, ask a volunteer to choose another translation. Have other volunteers show where each point would be and give the coordinates of the point for that translation.

Guided Practice

Ask Yourself
- Did I move each point in the correct direction?

TEST TIPS

Use the diagram. Name the coordinates of triangle *LMN* after the transformations.

1. Translate the triangle left 3 units, then down 1 unit.
   L $(^-1, 1)$; M $(^-1, 5)$; N $(3, 3)$

2. Reflect the triangle over the *x*-axis.
   L $(^+2, ^-2)$; M $(^+2, ^-6)$; N $(^+6, ^-4)$

3. Rotate the triangle a $\frac{3}{4}$ turn about (0, 0).
   L $(^-2, ^+2)$; M $(^-6, ^+2)$; N $(^-4, ^+6)$

Write *line, rotational,* or *both* to describe the symmetry of the figure.

4.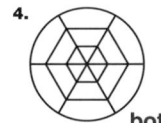
   both

5.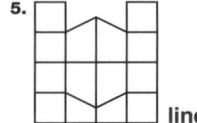
   line

TEST TIPS **Explain Your Thinking** ▶ Does a transformation change the shape of the original figure? Explain. **No; a transformation only changes the position of a figure.**

Practice and Problem Solving

Use the diagram. Name the coordinates of triangle *RST* after each transformation.

6. Translate right 4, then down 1.
   R $(6, 3)$; S $(8, 5)$; T $(10, 1)$

7. Reflect over the *y*-axis.
   R $(^-2, 4)$; S $(^-4, 6)$; T $(^-6, 2)$

8. Rotate a $\frac{1}{4}$ turn clockwise about (0, 0).
   R $(4, ^-2)$; S $(6, ^-4)$; T $(2, ^-6)$

9. Reflect over the *y*-axis. Then rotate counterclockwise a quarter turn around (0, 0).
   R $(^-4, ^-2)$; S $(^-6, ^-4)$; T $(^-2, ^-6)$

Write *line, rotational,* or *both* to describe the symmetry of each figure.

10. 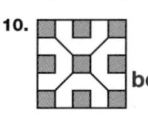 **both**

11. 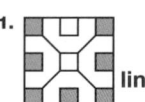 **line**

12. **both**

13. Triangle *ABC* was translated left 3 units and up 1 unit. It ended up at *A*(2, 4), *B*(2, 6), and *C* (6, 6). What were the original coordinates?
    A (5, 3); *B* (5, 5); *C* (9, 5)

Extra Practice See page 627, Set D.

---

3 Practice

Assign **Problems 6–13** as independent work.

- *Problem Solving for Problem 13* Have students share and discuss their work.

Common Error

Reflecting across the wrong axis Highlighting the axis of reflection in color can help students avoid this error.

4 Assess and Close

- **What is the difference between a translation and a reflection?** (A translation is a vertical or horizontal slide a given distance in a given direction. A reflection is a flip of a figure across an axis, which results in a mirror image.)

- **When does a figure have rotational symmetry?** (when the figure looks exactly the same after a rotation of less than 360° either clockwise or counterclockwise)

Assign the **LESSON QUIZ** on Transparency 23.5 to further assess student understanding.

Quick Check

4. (0,⁻4), (1,⁻3), (2,⁻2), (3,⁻1)
5. (0, 0), (1, 2), (2, 4), (3, 6)
6. (0, 1), (1, 3), (2, 5), (3, 7)

Check your understanding of Lessons 1–5.

Write the ordered pair for each point. (Lesson 1)

1. W (⁻3, 4)   2. X (⁻1, ⁻1)   3. Y (4, ⁻3)

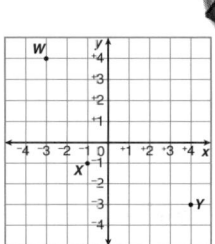

Make a table for each function. Use x = 0, 1, 2, and 3.
Write the ordered pairs and then graph the function.
(Lessons 2 and 3) **See above.**

4. $y = x - 4$ 5. $y = 2x$ 6. $y = 2x + 1$

4–6. See Additional Answers on Page T89.

Use the coordinate plane to solve Problems 7–9. (Lessons 4-5)

7. Make a function table for points A, B, C,
   and D. Write an equation for this function.
   $y = x - 3$

8. If you translate point A right 3 and up 2,
   what are the new coordinates for point A?
   (0, ⁻4)

9. If you rotate trapezoid MNOP 180°
   counterclockwise, what would be its
   new coordinates? **M (⁻4, ⁻6); N (⁻6, ⁻6);**
   O (⁻6, ⁻2); P (⁻2, ⁻2)

x	y
⁻3	⁻6
⁻2	⁻5
⁻1	⁻4
0	⁻3

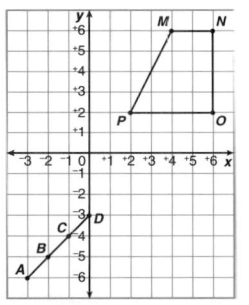

Trans Sym Club

BOB, AMY, TOMMY, BECKIE, MO

Can you discover the names of the members of Trans Sym Club?

Visual Thinking

Math Reasoning

How do you think the members decided on a name for their club?

Quick Check

Purpose: The Quick Check allows you to
assess the students' understanding of the
concepts presented in Lessons 1–5.

Items	Objectives Tested	Pages	Intervention
1–3	Graph ordered pairs in the four quadrants of the coordinate plane.	610–613	Reteach Resource 23.1 *Ways to Success* 23.1
4–6	Use a function rule to find the value of ordered pairs.	614–615	Reteach Resource 23.2 *Ways to Success* 23.2
4–6	Graph an equation or a coordinate plane.	616–619	Reteach Resource 23.3 *Ways to Success* 23.3
7–9	Use graphs to solve problems.	620–621	Reteach Resource 23.4 *Ways to Success* 23.4
7–9	Identify and describe transformations in the coordinate plane.	622–625	Reteach Resource 23.5 *Ways to Success* 23.5

Keeping a Journal

Have students draw and label examples of
translation, reflection, and rotation on grid paper.

Visual Thinking

Math Reasoning

Trans Sym Club

- Students should see that half of each letter in all the
  names is missing and is symmetrical to the half that is
  visible (except MO). The arrowed lines are lines of symmetry. Either the top or bottom half of the letters of
  each name is missing. Make sure students understand
  that the red dot is a point of rotational symmetry.

- Have students determine what each name is. (BOB,
  BECKIE, AMY, TOMMY, MO) Ask them to share their
  answers to the final question.

 **Chapter Review/Test**

Purpose: This test provides an informal assessment of the Chapter 23 objectives.

Chapter Test Items 1–20

To assign a numerical grade for this Chapter Test, use 5 points for each test item.

Check Understanding

You can use the **Write About It** question to assess student understanding of a key chapter concept.

Customizing Your Instruction

For students who have not yet mastered these objectives, you can use the Reteaching Resources listed in the chart below.

 ## Assessment Options

A summary test for this chapter is also provided in the Unit Resource Folder.

 ## Adequate Yearly Progress

Use the End of Grade Test Prep Assessment Guide to help familiarize your students with the format of standardized tests.

Chapter Review/Test

✔ VOCABULARY

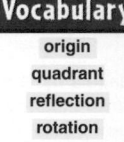

1. One of the four regions in a coordinate plane formed by the coordinate axes is called a(n) **quadrant**.

2. A figure that is flipped over a line shows a(n) **reflection**.

3. The **origin** is the point at which the x-axis and y-axis of a coordinate plane intersect.

4. A(n) **rotation** is a figure that is turned about a given point.

✔ CONCEPTS AND SKILLS

Use the coordinates to plot each point *See Additional Answers on Page T89.* on grid paper. Label. (Lesson 1, pp. 610–613)

5. $R(^-3, ^+3)$ 6. $M(^+2, ^-2)$ 7. $P(^-2, ^-4)$ 8. $N(^-5, 0)$

9. $O(^+4, ^+4)$ 10. $Q(0, ^+3)$ 11. $T(^+4, ^-3)$ 12. $S(^-3, ^-2)$

Find 4 ordered pairs for each function. Then use *See Additional Answers on Page T89.* them to graph each function. (Lessons 2–3, pp. 614–619)

13. $y = x + 4$ 14. $y = x - 5$ 15. $y = 2x + 1$ 16. $y = 2x - 6$

Use the diagram. Name the coordinates of triangle *DEF* after the transformations. (Lesson 5, pp. 622–625)

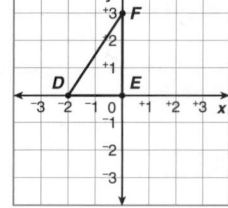

17. Translate right 4 units.
D (2, 0) E (4, 0) F (4, 3)

18. Rotate a $\frac{1}{4}$ turn clockwise about (0, 0).
D (0, 2) E (0, 0) F (3, 0)

19. Reflect over the y-axis.
D (2, 0) E (0, 0) F (0, 3)

✔ PROBLEM SOLVING

Use the table to solve. (Lesson 4, pp. 620–621)

20. Write an equation to show how to find the retail price of an item. $y = 2x + 1$

Wholesale Cost (x)	Retail Price (y)
$2	$5
$4	$9
$6	$13
$8	$17

Write About It

Show You Understand
Does a parallelogram have rotational symmetry? Explain.

Yes; *Possible answer:* It looks the same after a 180° rotation.

Reteaching Support

Chapter Test Items	Summary Test Items	Chapter Objectives Tested	TE Pages	Use These Reteaching Resources
1, 3, 5–12	1–5	**23A** Graph ordered pairs in the four quadrants of the coordinate plane.	610A–613	Reteach Resource 23.1 Ways to Success CD: 23.1 Skillsheet 182
13–16	6–10	**23B** Complete functions tables using integers and graph a line in the coordinate plane.	614A–619	Reteach Resource 23.2, 23.3 Ways to Success CD: 23.2, 23.3 Skillsheet 183, 184
2, 4, 17–19	11–15	**23C** Identify and describe transformations on the coordinate plane.	622A–625	Reteach Resource 23.5 Ways to Success CD: 23.5 Skillsheet 185
20	16–20	**23D** Analyze and solve problems using a graph.	620A–621	Reteach Resource 23.4 Ways to Success CD: 23.4 Skillsheet 186

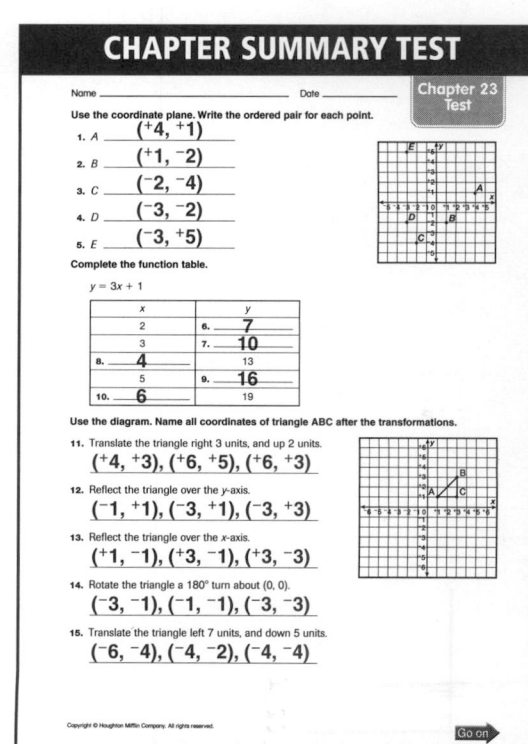

CHAPTER SUMMARY TEST

Set A (Lesson 1, pp. 610–613)

Use the coordinate plane at the right for Exercises 1–6. Write the ordered pair for each point.

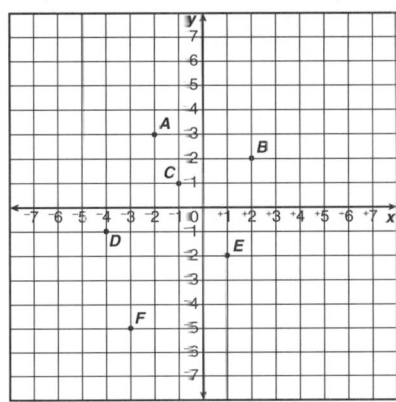

1. J
($^-5$, $^+2$)

2. E
($^+4$, $^-4$)

3. M
($^-2$, $^-5$)

4. B
($^+2$, $^+3$)

Write the letter name of each point.

5. ($^+1$, $^+1$) **L**

6. ($^-3$, $^-2$) **A**

7. ($^-2$, 0) **G**

Use grid paper. Use the coordinates to plot and label each point.
See Additional Answers on Page T90.

8. W ($^+3$, $^+5$)

9. X ($^-2$, $^-4$)

10. Y ($^+4$, $^-4$)

11. Z ($^-5$, $^+1$)

Set B (Lesson 2, pp. 614–615)

Make a function table for each of the following using 0, 4, 8, 12 for x.

1. $y = x + 4$
$^+4$, $^+8$, $^+12$, $^+16$

2. $y = 4x$
0, $^+16$, $^+32$, $^+48$

3. $y = x - 4$
$^-4$, 0, $^+4$, $^+8$

4. $y = 10 - x$
$^+10$, $^+6$, $^+2$, $^-2$

Set C (Lesson 3, pp. 616–619)

Find 4 sets of coordinates for each function. Then graph the functions on grid paper. *See Additional Answers on Page T90.*

1. $y = x - 6$

2. $y = x + 5$

3. $y = 2x + 2$

4. $y = 3x - 5$

Set D (Lesson 5, pp. 622–625)

Use the diagram. Name the coordinates of triangle ABC after the transformations.

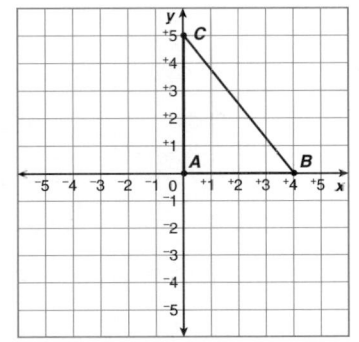

1. Translate left 5 units.
A ($^-5$, 0); B ($^-1$, 0); C ($^-5$, 5)

2. Reflect over the x-axis.
A (0, 0); B (4, 0); C (0, $^-5$)

3. Rotate a half turn about (0, 0).
A (0, 0); B ($^-4$, 0); C (0, $^-5$)

CHAPTER SUMMARY TEST

Name _____ Date _____

Chapter 23
Test
continued

The graph shows what an astronaut would weigh on Earth and on Io. Use the graph to answer Questions 16–20.

Weight on Earth and on Io

16. If an astronaut weighs 10 kg on Io, how much would she weigh on Earth?

60 kg

17. If an astronaut weighs 25 kg on Io, how much would he weigh on Earth?

150 kg

18. If an astronaut weighs 120 kg on Earth, how much would he weigh on Io?

20 kg

19. If x = weight on Earth and y = weight on Io, write the equation for this function.

$y = x \div 6$

20. A person who weighs 140 kg on the Earth would weigh 20 kg on Europa. If x = weight on Earth and y = weight on Europa, write the equation for this function.

$y = x \div 7$

Chapter 23

Lesson 1, pp. 611–612

7–12. Check grids.

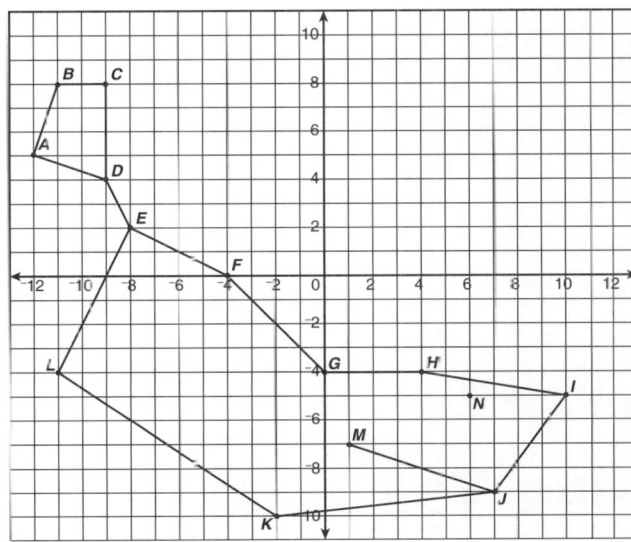

Explain Your Thinking: No. *Possible answer:* The first number indicates the position on the x-axis, and the second number indicates the position on the y-axis. The x-axis numbers do not match. Neither do the y-axis numbers.

25–39. Check grids.

45. The x-coordinate increases by 1. The y-coordinate increases by 2. The y-coordinate is twice or double the x-coordinate.

Lesson 2, p. 615

14. 23; substitute 27 for e in the equation and evaluate: $a = 27 + ^-4$.

See Additional Answers on p. T88.

Science Connection

PURPOSE

Students solve problems about the growth of bacteria by making function tables and graphing solutions to the equation $y = 2^x$.

Exponential Growth

Wash your hands! Rinse that apple! Don't eat food that has fallen on the floor!" Parents give these warnings all the time. Why? Although some bacteria that exist can actually help you stay healthy, certain harmful kinds of bacteria will make you really sick.

A bacterium is a living creature that is a single cell. However, one bacterium can reproduce rapidly. The first cell splits into two identical cells. Then each of the 2 cells splits, resulting in 4. Then each of 4 cells splits, so there are 8 bacteria. Each of the 8 cells splits, and so on. This kind of multiplication is called exponential growth.

628

Using The Science Connection

- Lead a discussion about the term exponential growth. Remind students that an exponent tells how many times a number is multiplied by itself. Have students recall that for 10^3 we say *ten to the third power.* **What does the expression 2^2 mean? 2^3?** (2 to the second power, or $2 \times 2 = 4$; 2 to the third power, or $2 \times 2 \times 2 = 8$) Point out that each time the bacteria divide, the resulting number of bacteria is a power of 2 and can be expressed in exponential form as 2^n.

- For Exercises 2–3, ask students to compare the graph of the exponential function to the graphs of the linear functions they learned in Chapter 23. Help them understand that the solutions to this exponential function ($y = 2^x$) are not on a straight line. **Why can't you simply connect the dots on your graph?** (Doing so would not show the true shape of the graph, which is a curve.)

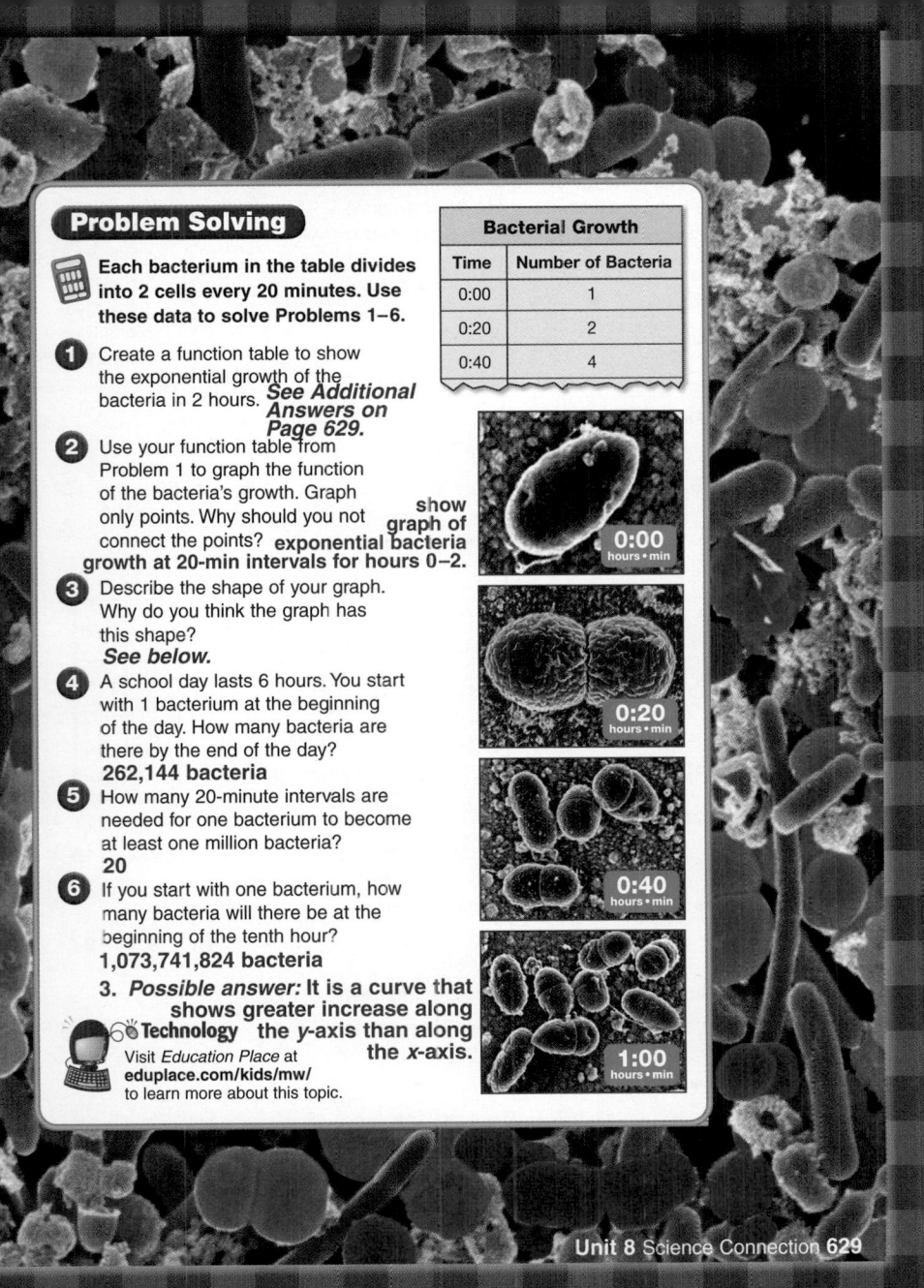

Problem Solving

Each bacterium in the table divides into 2 cells every 20 minutes. Use these data to solve Problems 1–6.

Bacterial Growth	
Time	Number of Bacteria
0:00	1
0:20	2
0:40	4

1. Create a function table to show the exponential growth of the bacteria in 2 hours. **See Additional Answers on Page 629.**

2. Use your function table from Problem 1 to graph the function of the bacteria's growth. Graph only points. Why should you not connect the points? *show graph of exponential bacteria growth at 20-min intervals for hours 0–2.*

3. Describe the shape of your graph. Why do you think the graph has this shape? **See below.**

4. A school day lasts 6 hours. You start with 1 bacterium at the beginning of the day. How many bacteria are there by the end of the day? **262,144 bacteria**

5. How many 20-minute intervals are needed for one bacterium to become at least one million bacteria? **20**

6. If you start with one bacterium, how many bacteria will there be at the beginning of the tenth hour? **1,073,741,824 bacteria**

3. *Possible answer:* It is a curve that shows greater increase along the *y*-axis than along the *x*-axis.

Technology Visit *Education Place* at eduplace.com/kids/mw/ to learn more about this topic.

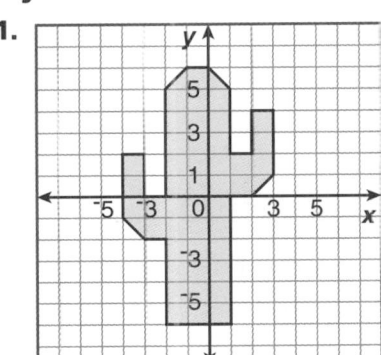

0:00 hours•min

0:20 hours•min

0:40 hours•min

1:00 hours•min

Performance Assessment, p. 632

Task 2

d. The triangle in Quadrant III is the image of the triangle in Quadrant I after a $\frac{1}{2}$ turn or 180° rotation about the origin.

Possible explanation: If I trace *ABC* on tracing paper and rotate the traced image 180°, it will coincide with the triangle in Quadrant III.

Enrichment, p. 633

Try These

1.
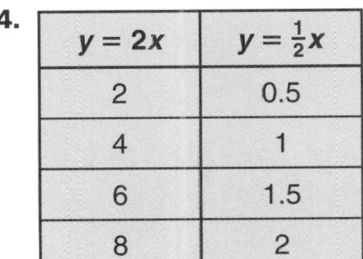

Cumulative Test Prep, p. 635

10B No; the surface area of the jumbo box is 944 square inches, which is more than 2 × 236.

10D *Possible answer:* 5 inches × 10 inches × 13 inches; 5 × 10 × 13 = 650. I used a guess-and-check strategy to find three factors whose product is greater than 600 and less than 700.

Technology Time, p. 636

4.

$y = 2x$	$y = \frac{1}{2}x$
2	0.5
4	1
6	1.5
8	2

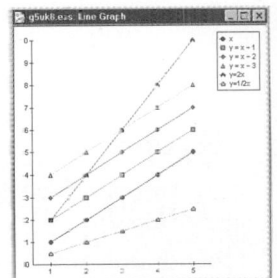

Weekly Reader, p. 629

1.

Time	Number of Bacteria
0:00	1
0:20	2
0:40	4
1:00	8
1:20	16
1:40	32
2:00	64

Additional Answers

Unit 8

Reading Words and Symbols, p. 562

1–3. *Possible answers are given.*

1. $17 = 4 + f$ where *f* represents the amount Frieda saved

2. $12 = h - 5$ where *h* represents the laps completed by Hal

3. $36 \div s = 4$ where *s* represents the number of equal shares

Decision Making, p. 631

Possible answer: Laura: ⁻8, ⁺1, ⁺7; Mitch: ⁻6, ⁺5, ⁺1; Natalie: ⁻4, ⁺3, ⁻1. The three integers must have a sum of zero.

Possible answer: A negative score; spinning a positive or a negative number is equally likely, but the sum of the positive scores (⁺16) has an absolute value less than the sum of the negative scores (⁻20).

PURPOSE

This test provides an informal assessment of the Unit 8 objectives.

Unit Test Items 1-33

To assign a numerical grade for this Unit Test, use 3 points for each test item.

Customizing Your Instruction

For students who have not yet mastered these objectives, you can use the **Reteaching Resources** listed in the chart below. *Ways to Success* is Houghton Mifflin's Intervention program, available in CD-ROM and blackline master formats.

 **VOCABULARY**

Vocabulary
origin
rotation
integers
reflection
translation
coordinates
absolute value

1. Opposite numbers have the same ■, or distance from zero. **absolute value**

2. A(n) ■ is a flip of a figure that results in a mirror image. **reflection**

3. The point named by the ordered pair (0, 0) is the ■ . **origin**

CONCEPTS AND SKILLS

Solve using inverse operations. (Chapter 21)

4. $9n = 495$
   $n = 55$

5. $m \div 8 = 43$
   $m = 344$

6. $372 = k - 138$
   $k = 510$

7. $68 + a = 172$
   $a = 104$

Copy and complete each function table. (Chapter 21)

8. $y = 36 \div x$

x	y
1	■
2	■
3	■
4	■

36; 18; 12; 9

9. $y = 21 - x$

x	y
0	■
1	■
2	■
3	■

21: 20; 19; 18

10. $y = 7x - 3$

x	y
0	■
2	■
■	32
■	53

x-values: 5, 8;
y-values: ⁻3, 11

11. $y = 32 - 5x$

x	y
0	■
■	17
■	12
6	■

x-values: 3, 4;
y-values: 32, 2

Write the opposite of each integer. (Chapter 22)

12. ⁺37   ⁻37

13. ⁻3   ⁺3

14. ⁻19   ⁺19

Write the absolute value of each integer. (Chapter 22)

15. ⁻22   22

16. 0   0

17. ⁺19   19

Write these integers in order from least to greatest. (Chapter 22)

18. 0, ⁻5, ⁻3, ⁺4
    ⁻5, ⁻3, 0, ⁺4

19. ⁻8, ⁻11, ⁻7, ⁺7
    ⁻11, ⁻8, ⁻7, ⁺7

20. ⁻6, ⁺7, ⁻8, ⁺9
    ⁻8, ⁻6, ⁺7, ⁺9

Add or subtract. (Chapter 22)

21. ⁺8 + ⁻3
    ⁺5

22. ⁻7 + ⁻8
    ⁻15

23. ⁺7 - ⁻5
    ⁺12

24. ⁻9 - ⁻5
    ⁻4

Reteaching Support

Unit Test Item pp. 630–631	Forms A & B		Unit Objectives Tested	TE Pages	Use These Reteaching Resources
4–7	1–4	8A	Write and solve equations.	568A–571	Reteach Resources and *Ways to Success*, 21.2
8–11	5–7	8B	Use functions and function tables to solve equations.	576A–577	Reteach Resources and *Ways to Success*, 21.4
1, 12–20	8–10	8C	Compare and order integers, and find the absolute value of integers.	586A–591	Reteach Resources and *Ways to Success*, 22.1–22.2
21–24	11–13	8D	Add and subtract integers.	598A–601	Reteach Resources and *Ways to Success*, 22.5
3, 25–27	14–16	8E	Graph ordered pairs in the four quadrants of the coordinate plane.	610A–613	Reteach Resources and *Ways to Success*, 23.1
8–11, 32–33	17–19	8F	Complete functions tables using integers and graph a line in the coordinate plane.	616A–619	Reteach Resources and *Ways to Success*, 23.3
2, 28–29	20–22	8G	Identify and describe transformations on the coordinate plane.	622A–625	Reteach Resources and *Ways to Success*, 23.5
30–33	23–25	8H	Solve problems, using skills and strategies.	568A–575, 602A–605, 620A–621	Reteach Resources and *Ways to Success*, 21.2 A–21.3, 22.6, 23.4

Use the coordinate plane for Exercises 25–29.
Name the coordinates for each. (Chapter 23)

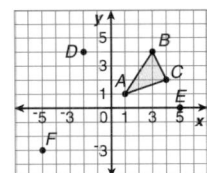

25. point D 26. point C 27. point E
(⁻2,⁺4)   (⁺4,⁺2)   (⁺5, 0)
28. triangle ABC after a translation 3 units left
(⁻2, 1), (0, 4), (1, 2)
29. triangle ABC after a reflection over the x-axis
(⁺1,⁻1), (⁺3,⁻4), (⁺4,⁻2)

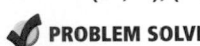 **PROBLEM SOLVING**

30. At sunrise, the temperature outdoors
was ⁻4°C. By the time school started,
the temperature had risen 6°. What
was the temperature when school
started?   **2°C**

Possible answer:
$\frac{1}{4} \times 124 = n$; $n = \$31$

31. A carpenter made $124 for building
a bookcase. She paid $\frac{1}{4}$ of that amount
to her assistant. Write and solve an
equation to find how much she paid
her helper.

Use the graph for Problems 32–33.
Alice charges a fee of $30 plus $5
per hour. Beth charges $10 per hour.

32. How many hours must Alice work to
make $70?   **8 hours**

33. After how many hours will they make
the same amount of money? After that,
who will make more? **6 hours; Beth**

**Amount Charged
for Yard Work**

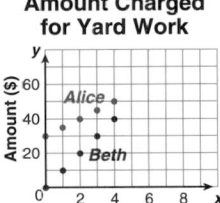

Decision Making
Extended Response

Task Laura, Mitch, and Natalie played
a game using the spinner base shown.
Each student spun a different set of
numbers, but each got a score of 0. What
numbers did each student spin? Is it more
likely that a person playing this game would
get a positive score or a negative score?
Explain your thinking.

Information You Need

* Each student got three spins.
* Each student's score was the sum
of his or her three spins.
* One of the numbers Laura spun was ⁻8.
* One of the numbers Mitch spun was ⁺5.

See Additional Answers on page 629.

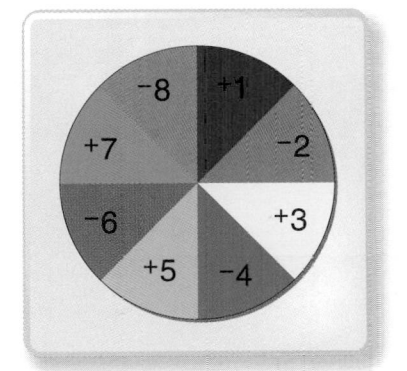

Unit 8 Test 631

 **Assessment Options**

Formal Tests for this unit are also provided in
the Unit Resource Folder.

● Unit 8 Open Response Test (Form A)
● Unit 8 Multiple Choice Test (Form B)

 **Performance Assessment**

You may want to use the Performance
Assessment instead of, or in addition to, the
Unit Test. Performance Assessment tasks for
this unit are on Student Book page 632.

 Adequate Yearly Progress Assessment Guide

Use the *End of Grade Test Prep Assessment
Guide* to help familiarize your students with
the format of standardized tests and to
monitor progress.

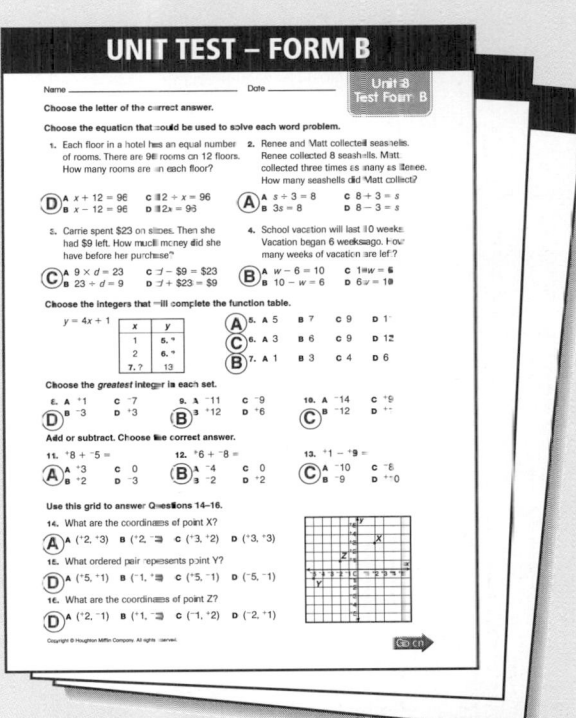

Unit 8 Test

See pages
632A–632B
for answers.

Algebra, Integers, and Coordinate Graphing   **631**

✔ Unit Test Answers: Form A

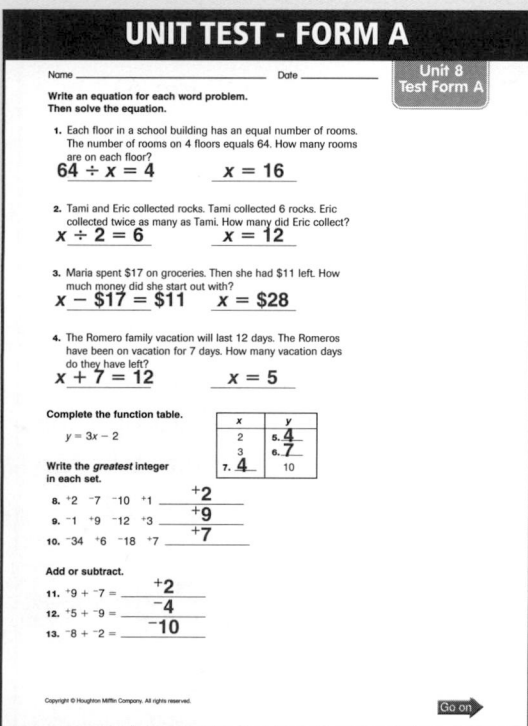

UNIT TEST - FORM A

Name _____ Date _____

Write an equation for each word problem. Then solve the equation.

1. Each floor in a school building has an equal number of rooms. The number of rooms on 4 floors equals 64. How many rooms are on each floor?

    $64 \div x = 4$ $x = 16$

2. Tami and Eric collected rocks. Tami collected 6 rocks. Eric collected twice as many as Tami. How many did Eric collect?

    $x \div 2 = 6$ $x = 12$

3. Maria spent $17 on groceries. Then she had $11 left. How much money did she start out with?

    $x - \$17 = \$11$ $x = \$28$

4. The Romero family vacation will last 12 days. The Romeros have been on vacation for 7 days. How many vacation days do they have left?

    $x + 7 = 12$ $x = 5$

Complete the function table.

$y = 3x - 2$

x	y
2	5. **4**
3	6. **7**
7. **4**	10

Write the *greatest* integer in each set.

8. $^+2$ $^-7$ $^-10$ $^+1$ **+2**

9. $^-1$ $^+9$ $^-12$ $^+3$ **+9**

10. $^-34$ $^+6$ $^-18$ $^+7$ **+7**

Add or subtract.

11. $^+9 + ^-7 =$ **+2**

12. $^+5 + ^-9 =$ **−4**

13. $^-8 + ^-2 =$ **−10**

Copyright © Houghton Mifflin Company. All rights reserved.

Go on →

UNIT TEST - FORM A

Name _____ Date _____

Write the ordered pair for each point.

14. A **(+4, +1)**

15. B **(+2, −3)**

16. C **(−4, +2)**

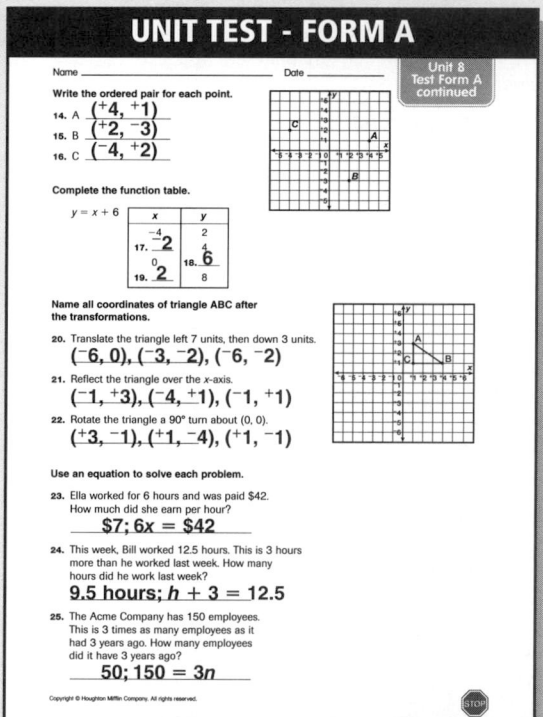

Complete the function table.

$y = x + 6$

x	y
−4	2
17. **−2**	4
0	18. **6**
19. **2**	8

Name all coordinates of triangle ABC after the transformations.

20. Translate the triangle left 7 units, then down 3 units.

    (−6, 0), (−3, −2), (−6, −2)

21. Reflect the triangle over the *x*-axis.

    (−1, +3), (−4, +1), (−1, +1)

22. Rotate the triangle a 90° turn about (0, 0).

    (+3, −1), (+1, −4), (+1, −1)

Use an equation to solve each problem.

23. Ella worked for 6 hours and was paid $42. How much did she earn per hour?

    $7; 6x = $42

24. This week, Bill worked 12.5 hours. This is 3 hours more than he worked last week. How many hours did he work last week?

    9.5 hours; $h + 3 = 12.5$

25. The Acme Company has 150 employees. This is 3 times as many employees as it had 3 years ago. How many employees did it have 3 years ago?

    50; $150 = 3n$

Copyright © Houghton Mifflin Company. All rights reserved.

STOP

Unit Test Answers: Form B

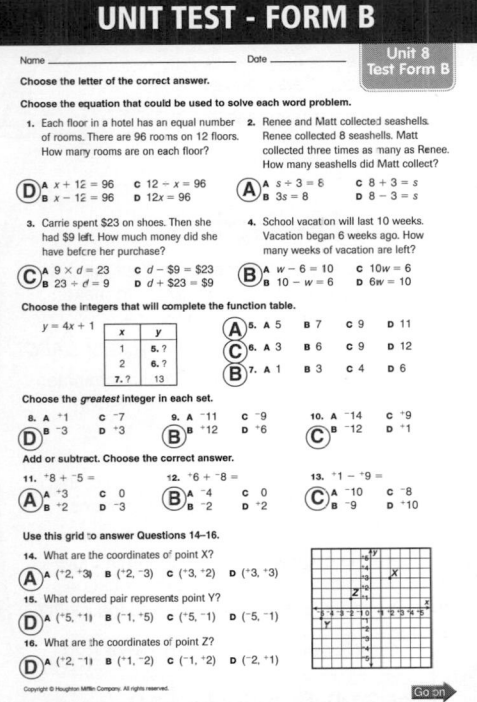

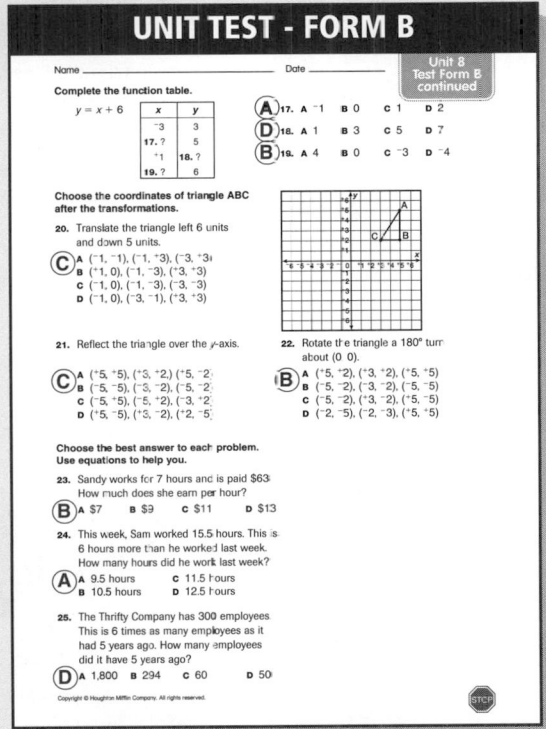

Performance Assessment

PURPOSE

In these assessments, students should be able to find absolute value, subtract integers, and draw transformations on a coordinate plane.

Scoring Rubric

4 EXEMPLARY

Fully completes each task, showing an understanding of integers, of absolute value, of writing and evaluating expressions, and of drawing transformations on a coordinate plane.

3 PROFICIENT

Fully completes each task, showing an understanding of integers and reflections on a coordinate plane, but needs help explaining absolute value and in describing the transformation.

2 ACCEPTABLE

Shows some understanding of integers and reflections, but has difficulty finding differences of integers, and gives incorrect or reversed coordinates and an incomplete or inaccurate description in 2d.

1 LIMITED

Shows a lack of understanding by erring when finding differences of integers, by omitting explanations, and by providing inaccurate reflections with incorrect coordinates.

---

c. *Possible answer: 1 − ⁻4 = 5*

Performance Assessment

TASK 1

A Cool Activity (Chapters 21, 22)

Karen's class recorded the 10:00 A.M. temperatures for one week during January. The table on the right shows the results.

10:00 A.M.	Temperatures
Monday	2°C
Tuesday	⁻3°C
Wednesday	1°C
Thursday	⁻4°C
Friday	3°C

a. What is the range of the recorded temperatures? **7 degrees**

b. Which temperature has the greatest absolute value? Explain. **See below.**

c. Write an expression to find the difference between the Wednesday temperature and the Thursday temperature. Then find the difference. **See above.**

b. ⁻4°; it has the greatest distance from zero on a number line.

TASK 2

A Moment of Reflection? (Chapter 23)

You are working as a wallpaper designer. Your job is to use transformations of a given triangle to make a design. Copy the coordinate grid on the left.

a. What are the coordinates of the vertices of △ABC?

b. Reflect △ABC over the y-axis. What coordinates do vertices of the new triangle have? Which quadrant contains the triangle?

c. Reflect the triangle you found in **b** over the x-axis. What coordinates do the vertices of this new triangle have? Which quadrant contains the triangle?

d. Compare the original triangle with the triangle you found in **c**. What transformation could be used to change the position of one to the other? Explain.
See Additional Answers on page 629.

a. *A*(⁺2,⁺4), *B*(⁺5,⁺3), *C*(⁺1,⁺1)
b. (⁻2,⁺4), (⁻5,⁺3), (⁻1,⁺1); **Quadrant II**
c. (⁻2,⁻4), (⁻5,⁻3), (⁻1,⁻1); **Quadrant III**

Self Check
• Did I answer the questions for each task?
• Did I check all my work?

Task One

Students find the range of a set of integers, find absolute value of integers, and write and evaluate an expression involving integers.

Task Two

Students draw a triangle on a coordinate plane, identify coordinates, reflect figures over the x- and y-axes, and describe a transformation.

GET THE PICTURE?

Computer programmers and designers use a grid system to draw the shapes that appear on your monitor's screen. You can use a similar process to create pictures on a coordinate grid.

Follow these steps to draw the rectangular prism on a coordinate grid.

STEP 1 Draw a square whose bottom left corner is at (1, 2) and whose top right corner is at (3, 4).

STEP 2 Draw a square whose bottom left corner is at (⁻3, ⁻1) and whose top right corner is at (⁻1, 1).

STEP 3 Draw three lines: from (⁻3, 1) to (1, 4); from (⁻1, 1) to (3, 4); and from (⁻1, ⁻1) to (1, 2).

STEP 4 Draw a dashed line from (⁻3, ⁻1) to (⁻1, 1).

Try These

1 On a coordinate grid, connect the following points in the order given. Name the object you drew.

(1, ⁻6)	(1, 0)	(2, 0)	(3, 1)	(3, 4)
(2, 4)	(2, 2)	(1, 2)	(1, 5)	(0, 6)
(⁻1, 6)	(⁻2, 5)	(⁻2, 0)	(⁻3, 0)	(⁻3, 2)
(⁻4, 2)	(⁻4, ⁻1)	(⁻3, ⁻2)	(⁻2, ⁻2)	(⁻2, ⁻6)

(1, ⁻6) *See Additional Answers on page 629.*

2 **Create Your Own** Write your own set of directions for drawing a picture on a coordinate grid. Give your directions to a partner to follow.

Answers will vary.

Unit 8 Enrichment **633**

Enrichment

▶ Picture Graphing

PURPOSE

On this page students plot points on a coordinate grid and connect them to draw two-dimensional representations of objects.

Using the Enrichment Activity

- Students apply the skills they learned in Chapter 23 Lessons 1 (Integers and the Coordinate Plane) and 5 (Transformations in the Coordinate Plane).

- Guide students in completing Steps 1 and 2. **Describe how you identified the coordinates for the other two vertices of each square.** (All the sides of a square are equal, so the other two vertices must be located to make each side two units long.)

- Before students begin Step 3, ask: **If the second square you drew is a transformed image of the first square, what transformation was performed?** (a translation 3 units down and 4 units to the left)

- Help students compare the drawings of the prism and the cactus. Both are two-dimensional representations of three-dimensional objects. While the drawing of the prism attempts to show depth, it does not have the vanishing-point perspective that an artist's drawing would have.

▶ Practice Test

PURPOSE

This page will familiarize students with the multiple-choice and open-response formats of many standardized state tests.

Cumulative Test Prep Practice

Solve Problems 1–10.

Test-Taking Tip

Sometimes when you take a test, you can circle important words that will help you understand what the question is asking.

Look at the example below.

Yuri collected these data on the weights, in pounds, of members of the basketball team:

122.8, $129\frac{1}{2}$, 122.75, $129\frac{1}{4}$, 128

He decided to list the weights from greatest to least. Which weight will be second on his list?

A 122.75   C 129 $\frac{1}{4}$

B 122.8   D 129 $\frac{1}{2}$

THINK

First circle the words "greatest to least," which mean that you have to order the given numbers. Another important word is "second," which indicates that you are looking for the second greatest weight, not the greatest.

The correct order is $129\frac{1}{2}$, $129\frac{1}{4}$, 128, 122.8, 122.75. So the correct answer is **C** $129\frac{1}{4}$.

634 For more Test-Taking Tips, see pages xxii–xxv.

Multiple Choice

1. Which numbers for *n* make this inequality true? $n > {}^-5$

   A ${}^-5, {}^-6, {}^-7$ C ${}^-5, {}^-4, {}^-3$

   B ${}^-6, {}^-7, {}^-8$ Ⓓ ${}^-4, {}^-3, {}^-2$

   (Chapter 22, Lesson 2)

2. The average temperature for January in Fairbanks, Alaska, is ${}^-10°$F. The average temperature for June is 60°F. What is the difference between these temperatures?

   F 50°   Ⓗ 70°

   G 60°   J 80°

   (Chapter 22, Lesson 5)

3. A hallway measures 3 feet by 9 feet. How many square yards of carpeting are needed to cover the floor of this hallway?

   Ⓐ 3   C 12

   B 9   D 27

   (Chapter 16, Lesson 3)

4. In a class of 30 fifth-graders, 20% of the students participated in the science fair. How many of the fifth-graders did not participate in the science fair?

   F 6   H 14

   G 10   Ⓙ 24

   (Chapter 19, Lesson 5)

Test-Taking TIPS

Review the test-taking tips with students before they begin the test. Discuss with students some of the ways they can check their work.

- When students have to compare a group of numbers listed horizontally, they can rewrite them in a vertical list to make it easier to compare the whole number parts. In the example test item, listing the numbers vertically and examining the whole-number parts makes it easy to see that the three least numbers are 122.75, 122.8, and 128.

Therefore, students need only compare $129\frac{1}{2}$ and $129\frac{1}{4}$ to determine which is the second greatest weight in the set.

- Remind students that there may be more than one way to solve a problem. If they are unable to solve a problem using one approach or strategy, encourage them to ask themselves what alternative strategies they could use.

5. A car service uses this formula to determine the cost of a ride. The variable *n* represents the number of miles.

Cost = $8 + $3 × (*n* − 1)

What is the cost of a 5-mile trip?

$20 (Chapter 5, Lesson 6)

6. Use the stem-and-leaf plot to identify the median of this set of data.

Hours Spent Training for Track Meet	
Stem	Leaf
1	2 3 4 5 5 9
2	0 1 6 6 6 9
3	0

Key: 3 | 0 means 30.

20 (Chapter 8, Lesson 3)

7. In a survey of 36 students, $\frac{1}{3}$ of the students said that their one favorite subject was math and $\frac{1}{4}$ said that their favorite subject was history. How many students in all reported that their favorite subject was either math or history?

21 (Chapter 12, Lesson 2)

8. A scale drawing has the scale $\frac{1}{4}$ inch: 1 foot. What is the actual length of a room that is $2\frac{3}{4}$ inches long in the drawing?

11 feet (Chapter 18, Lesson 5)

9. Ethan bought a sweater that had a price of $25. The sales tax was an additional 8% of the price of the sweater. How much did Ethan pay in all?

$27 (Chapter 19, Lesson 5)

10. The rectangular prism in the drawing above represents the box design for a new breakfast cereal.

A What is the least number of square inches of cardboard needed to build the box? Explain. **Find the surface area; 236 square inches.**

B The cereal company plans to produce a jumbo-sized box with dimensions that are twice those shown. Would twice as much cardboard be needed? Explain. **See Additional Answers on page 629.**

C Find the volume of the original cereal box and the volume of the jumbo-sized box. **240 cubic inches; 1,920 cubic inches**

D Suppose you are hired to design a new cereal box in the shape of a rectangular prism. The box must have a volume that is greater than 600 cubic inches but less than 700 cubic inches. What dimensions can you use? Explain how you decided. **See Additional Answers on page 629.** (Chapter 17, Lessons 4 and 6)

 Test Prep on the Net
Check out *Education Place* at **eduplace.com/kids/mw/** for test prep practice.

Unit 8 Cumulative Test Prep **635**

Test-Taking Vocabulary

- Display the following words: *inequality, average, actual, dimensions, survey,* and *scale.*

- Have students work in pairs to develop a list of synonyms for each. Have them rank the synonyms from those closest in meaning to the word to those most distant from the actual word meaning.

- Explain that substituting a synonym for a word in a test question may help to clarify what the question is asking. Have students substitute synonyms in the test questions that contain the listed words.

National and state assessments might also use these words to indicate finding *volume:*

- find the number of cubic units
- how many cubes will fill

GRAPH IT

PURPOSE

To provide students with an opportunity to graph and compare functions on a computer.

Graph It

You can use Easy Sheet to create and compare the graphs of equations in Quadrant I.

- Enter and complete the table shown at the right, starting in cell A1.
- Click on cell A1 and drag to cell C6.
- Click on 📊.

	A	B	C
1	x	y = x + 1	y = x + 2
2		1	2
3		2	
4		3	
5		4	
6		5	

Use Easy Sheet to answer the questions below.

1. How is the graph transformed each time you increase x by 1?

2. Predict what the graph for $y = x + 3$ will look like. Enter the values in column D and graph the line.

3. Based on the graphs you made above, predict what the lines will look like for the equations $y = 2x$ and $y = \frac{1}{2}x$. **See below right.**

4. Enter and complete the table shown at the right, starting in cell E1. Make a line graph of the data in cells A1 to F6.
See Additional Answers on page 629.

5. How is the graph transformed when you multiply by 2? By $\frac{1}{2}$? How do the graphs compare to your predictions?
See Additional Answers on page 629.

6. **Challenge** Predict what the graphs of $y = 2x + 1$ and $y = 2x + 2$ will look like based on the lines you have already graphed. Enter the equations and the first 5 values for each, in columns H and I. Make a new line graph of the data in cells H1 to I6.
The lines will have the same slope as $y = 2x$, but $y = 2x + 1$ will translate up 1 and $y = 2x + 2$ will translate up 2.

636 Unit 8 Technology Time

1. The graph translates up 1.

2. It will translate up 1 from the graph of $y = x + 2$, or up 3 from the graph of $y = x$.

	E	F
	$y = 2x$	$y = \frac{1}{2}x$
	2	0.5

3. *Possible answer:* The line for $y = 2x$ will translate up the graph. The graph of $y = \frac{1}{2}x$ will translate down the graph.

Using Technology Time

- You may wish to review how to find the value of a variable in a function. You may also wish to discuss how a function can be graphed on the coordinate plane.

- **Where does the value for *x* come from when using Easy Sheet?** (from the data inputted into column A)

- **How does Easy Sheet know to make 3 separate line graphs in the Example?** (because each column represents a different function)

- Have students solve Exercises 1–5 independently. Then have them work in pairs to solve the Challenge Problem.

Vocabulary Wrap-Up for **Unit 8**

Look back at the big ideas and vocabulary in this unit.

Big Ideas

2. *Possible answer:* Choose values for *x* and subtract 9 to find corresponding values of *y*.

You can use inverse operations to solve equations.

A function written in the form of an equation relates two variables, such as *x* and *y*.

You can add and subtract integers using counters or a number line.

Key Vocabulary
e Glossary

inverse operations

function

integer

1. *Possible answer:* Use the inverse operation of addition. *a* = 94

Math Conversations

Use your new vocabulary to discuss these big ideas.

I need to add ⁻6 and 4.

You could use a number line to show your work.

1. Explain how to solve this equation:
   $a - 47 = 47$ ***See above.***

2. Explain how to find values for *y* for the function $y = x - 9$. ***See above.***

3. Explain how to find this difference:
   $⁻18 - 7$ ***See below.***

4. Explain how to locate the point (5, ⁻3) on a coordinate plane. ***See below.***

5. **Write About It** Look for examples of integers in newspapers, magazines, and on television. List the different ways integers are used. Explain how integers are used in different occupations. ***Answers will vary.***

3. ***Possible answer:*** Use either counters or a number line to subtract. $⁻18 - 7 = ⁻25.$

4. ***Possible answer:*** Starting at the origin, move 5 units to the right and then 3 units down.

Unit 8 Vocabulary Wrap-Up **637**

Activity

Wrap Up The Unit Project

- Have pairs display their codes on large sheets of paper to form a class big book of codes. Have them include an introductory section to their codes that explained what they learned by doing this project.

- Display students' work in a "decoding area," an area of the classroom in which students can work to try to decode as many of the puzzles as possible.

- Students may wish to challenge another class to a code-breaking session.

Using the Vocabulary Wrap-Up

Purpose: Use this page to encourage students to use math vocabulary to talk about the important concepts they have learned in this unit.

Big Ideas and Key Vocabulary

Review and discuss with students the Big Ideas of this unit using the Key Vocabulary terms *inverse operations, function,* and *integer.*

Math Conversations

Have students work together in small groups to discuss Exercises 1–4. Check to see whether individual students understand the key concepts and are able to use the math vocabulary correctly. Clear up any misunderstandings students may have. After students have discussed the exercises in small groups, continue the conversation as a whole class. Have volunteers from each group share what their group talked about.

Write About It Ask for volunteers to read the occupations they listed as you or a student records them on the chalkboard. As a class, discuss how integers are used in these different occupations.

Algebra, Integers, and Coordinate Graphing 637

Literature Connections

As we talked with teachers about what to include in our new program, they asked for literature selections that connect to mathematics topics and concepts. The reasons for this request varied, from wanting to cover math and reading at the same time to needing to motivate students with real-world uses of mathematics.

A literature selection related to the mathematics content of each unit is presented in this section. Following each selection are questions designed to practice both mathematics and reading skills. Most selections were excerpted or adapted from trade books or children's magazines. Some were commissioned for use in these books. Although the selections can be used at any time during the unit, they may best be utilized as a part of your end-of-unit work.

Literature Connections

Unit 1 Literature Connection

THE MOST AMAZING Sights in Nature

SOURCE OF INFORMATION: THE WORLD ALMANAC AND BOOK OF FACTS

Topping the list of amazing natural sights is Mt. Everest. It sits on the border between Tibet and Nepal in Asia. Mt. Everest is the highest mountain in the world. However, nobody agrees about just how high it is. Edmund Hillary and Tenzing Norgay first climbed the mountain in 1953. They believed it was 29,002 feet high. Later, the Indian government measured it at 29,028 feet. Satellites have been used to measure the mountain. They suggest that Mount Everest could be more than 29,800 feet high.

Victoria Falls in Africa is no small wonder, either. It is the world's largest waterfall. At its widest point, Victoria Falls is more than a mile across. Its height ranges from 256 feet to about 400 feet at its center.

Arizona's Grand Canyon was slowly carved out of the earth by the Colorado River over the past million years. This wonder is both steep and deep — more than a mile deep, in fact. It runs some 217 miles long and up to 18 miles wide. It is one of the most popular places to visit in the United States.

The length of the Grand Canyon is small compared to the length of the Great Barrier Reef. It is the world's largest coral reef. It stretches 1,250 miles along the northeastern coast of Australia. What is a coral reef? It is formed by the bodies of tiny sea creatures called corals. The Great Barrier Reef is home to 1,500 kinds of fish and 215 types of birds. It also has 500 kinds of seaweed. Whales visit in the winter. You won't find many sharks, however, because they prefer the open sea.

638 Unit 1 Literature: Nonfiction

1. The selection tells how high Edmund Hillary believed Mt. Everest to be. What is the difference between his measurement and the Indian government's? What is the difference between Hillary's measurement and the satellite measurements?

2. What is the difference in height between Victoria Falls' lowest point and highest point?

3. How much longer than the Grand Canyon is the Great Barrier Reef?

4. What is the total number of types of fish and birds that live in the Great Barrier Reef? See below for answers to all questions.

Unit 1 Literature: Nonfiction **639**

Unit 1

Reading the Selection

Read the selection aloud to the class or ask students to read it themselves. Then have them work independently, in small groups, or as a whole class to answer questions.

Answers to Questions
1. 26 feet; 798 feet
2. 144 feet
3. 1,033 miles
4. 1,715

Literature Connections

Unit 2 Literature Connection

Ready for Anything

Ryan Shaw

My name is Jedediah, but people call me Jed. My story begins on March 5, 1849. That day, my family and I set out from St. Louis for California.

Our covered wagon, pulled by five yoke of oxen, was loaded with supplies. For you city folk, a yoke is a wood frame that fastens together two animals to pull a wagon or plow. We joined a train of 20 other wagons.

We thought we were ready for anything — huge deserts, fast rivers, and even bandits. Little did we know what was really in store for us.

It started one morning in May. The early sun gave way to dark skies, then a dead calm. Suddenly, a twister was spotted about 10 miles off. It looked like a long, dirty finger. And it was heading straight for us.

As luck would have it, the twister changed direction. We lost most of our belongings but we were alive. Some weren't as lucky. Two families had unknowingly headed right in the path of the twister.

1 In all, how many oxen pulled Jed's family's covered wagon? Write a multiplication sentence to solve. **See below for answers to all questions.**

2 Why, do you think, did Jed explain the meaning of the word *yoke* for "city folk"?

640 **Unit 2 Literature:** Historical Fiction

Unit 2

Unit 3 Literature Connection

Ships OF the Desert

Source of Information: The Information Please Almanac

Camels are made for the desert. They have broad, flat, leathery pads on each foot. As the camel walks, the pads spread, keeping the foot from sinking into the sand. Camels move both feet on one side of their body and then the feet on the other side. This makes them look as if they are rolling, the way a ship does in the ocean, and explains the nickname "ship of the desert."

Camels can go from 5 to 7 days on little or no food and water. They can also travel great distances, carrying loads ranging from 400 to almost 1,000 pounds. Their usual speed is about 3 miles per hour. However, when they gallop, they can go as fast as 12 miles per hour. Depending on their load, camels can travel between 25 and 50 miles a day.

How Fast Can Animals Run?

Animals	Speed (in Miles per Hour)
Cheetah	70
Zebra	40
Elephant	25
Grizzly bear	30
Lion	50
Camel	12

1 What's the mean, median, and range of the speed of the animals listed in the table?

2 How does the camel's speed affect the mean of the speeds shown in the table? **See below for answers to all questions.**

Unit 3 Literature: Nonfiction   641

Unit 3

Reading the Selection

Read the story aloud to the class or ask students to read it themselves. Then have them work independently, in small groups, or as a whole class to answer questions.

Answers to Questions

1. 5 yokes × 2 oxen = 10 oxen
2. Jed explained the meaning of the word *yoke* because he knew that people from the city would not be familiar with wagon trains and oxen.

Reading the Selection

Read the selection aloud to the class or ask students to read it themselves. Then have them work independently, in small groups, or as a whole class to answer questions.

Answers to Questions

1. mean: 37.8 miles per hour
   median: 35 miles per hour
   range: 58 miles per hour
2. It lowers the mean from 43 miles per hour to 37.8 miles per hour.

Literature Connections

Unit 4 Literature Connection

The Fruitomatic

HELEN STAKENICH

Darcy Devine was bored. Her parents had left for a day trip to Mars to celebrate her dad's birthday. Cousin Mindy was "babysitting" 12-year-old Darcy, as if Darcy wasn't old enough to take care of herself. Sixteen-year-old Mindy was no fun. All she wanted to do was talk on the disto-phone with her friends from the Andromeda Galaxy.

Darcy decided to check out Dad's latest kitchen invention, the Fruitomatic. Dad was always inventing cool, new gadgets for the kitchen — or at least Darcy thought they were cool.

The Fruitomatic could zap any fruit — well, just about any fruit. Watermelons and pineapples were too big to fit into the machine, and raspberries and blueberries were too small. Darcy pulled the Fruitomatic from under the sink, where Mom kept it. The Fruitomatic had two side-by-side chambers. You put the fruit into the chamber on the left, and you could get ice cream, juice, sliced fruit, fruit salad, and even cooked fruit in the chamber on the right.

642   **Unit 4 Literature:** Science Fiction

"That's it," thought Darcy. "I'll make fruit salad." Watching her dad fiddle with the Fruitomatic always eased her boredom. Now she would try the machine herself. But there was a problem; the fruit bowl was empty.

Darcy was about to give up all hope of improving her boring day when she spied lemons on the kitchen counter. She decided to make lemonade instead. She slipped the lemons into the left chamber of the Fruitomatic. Then she entered the number 4 and pressed the Enter button. Darcy looked into the right chamber. It was empty! She entered the number 6 and pressed Enter again. Still nothing. Then she remembered that Dad had said the machine could only make juice using prime numbers. She knew that 3 was a prime number. She entered three and — bingo! Out came more juice than she had ever seen. She entered 5, 7, and 9. Two of the three numbers worked!

By now, the lemon juice was pouring from the machine and Darcy was filling all the pitchers she could find. But she was having too much fun to stop. Darcy entered the number 12 and something strange happened. Out came a lemon cut into two halves. Then she entered 14 and got a lemon sliced into quarters. For some reason, the number 15 created a lemon cut into fifths. Darcy wasn't sure what was going on, but she was having a real blast. Before long, she had every pitcher in the kitchen filled with juice, and every bowl filled with lemon slices.

1 After Darcy entered the number 3, she entered three more numbers. Which two of those numbers produced lemon juice? Explain.

See below for answers to all questions.

2 What happened when Darcy started entering two-digit numbers? Suppose she entered the number 13, what would have happened? What might happen if Darcy entered the number 19?

Unit 4 Literature: Science Fiction   643

Unit 4

Reading the Selection

Read the story aloud to the class or ask students to read it themselves. Then have them work independently, in small groups, or as a whole class to answer questions.

Answers to Questions

1. 5 and 7 produced lemon juice, because they are prime numbers. 9 is not a prime number.

2. The Fruitomatic started cutting lemons into fractions; If she entered 13, the lemons would have been cut into thirds; If she entered 19, the lemons would have been cut into ninths.

Unit 5 Literature Connection

The World's Largest Trees

Source of Information: The National Park Service

The largest trees in the world are the giant sequoias. They grow on the western side of the Sierra Nevada Mountains in California. The tallest sequoias are as large as a 26-story building. At their base, they are wider than a city street. Sequoias are very old trees. Experts believe the largest of these trees may be as much as 2,700 years old.

In 1888, six loggers spent five days cutting down a giant sequoia. Walter Fry, one of the loggers, counted the growth rings on the tree stump. He knew that most trees add a ring to their circumference about once a year. When Fry finished counting, he was shocked and saddened. The tree they had just cut down was more than 3,000 years old!

Fry quit his job. He helped start a petition to save the sequoias. In 1890, the sequoia forests became a national park. It was named General Grant National Park, for Ulysses S. Grant, the 18th President of the United States. Years later, it was renamed Sequoia National Park. As for Walter Fry, he switched jobs and became a park ranger. Later, Fry became the park's first civilian superintendent.

The largest sequoia, the "General Sherman" is the largest known living thing on earth. The Sherman Tree weighs more than 6,167 tons, as much as 41 blue whales or 740 elephants.

The Five Largest Sequoias

Name	Height (feet)	Circumference (feet)	Volume (cubic feet)
General Sherman	274.9	102.6	52,508
Washington	254.7	101.1	47,850
General Grant	268.1	107.6	46,608
Lincoln	255.8	98.3	45,148
President	240.9	93.0	44,471

644 Unit 5 Literature: Nonfiction

1. If the General Sherman is as tall as a 26-story building, how many feet high would each story be? Express your answer to the nearest tenth.

2. Why might Walter Fry be pleased to know that we now protect endangered species and that we celebrate Earth Day?

See below for answers to all questions. Unit 5 Literature: Nonfiction **645**

Unit 5

Reading the Selection

Read the selection aloud to the class or ask students to read it themselves. Then have them work independently, in small groups, or as a whole class to answer questions.

Answers to Questions

1. Each story would be about 10.6 feet high.

2. *Answers may vary.*

Literature Connections

Unit 6 Literature Connection

No Place to Go
HELENA SERPA

Vanessa, Jen, Megan, and Natasha were 11 years old and friends. They had been looking forward to a summer of fun. Now their vacation was only a week old, and they were already bored.

"We need a place to play," Vanessa said.

"What, like a clubhouse?" Natasha asked.

Suddenly, the same idea struck the four girls. "The shed!" they shouted.

A wooden shed sat unused in the farthest corner of Natasha's back yard. With its triangle-shaped roof, it looked like a real cabin, only lots smaller. Was it too small for a clubhouse? Vanessa ran home and grabbed the tape measure from the toolbox. Minutes later, she was holding one end as Megan pulled the tape and measured the shed's outside dimensions. It was 10 feet long, and much to their surprise, 12 feet wide. And its walls were 7 feet tall.

The shed needed to be patched up and painted. But it was nothing the girls couldn't handle. That night, Natasha's parents quickly agreed to the deal.

Five days later, Natasha held open the freshly-painted door of the new clubhouse.

"Ladies first," she joked, as she waved her friends in.

1 Make a drawing of the clubhouse. Label the measurements of each dimension.

2 Calculate the area of a longer wall of the clubhouse. Then find the area of the clubhouse floor.

See below for answers to all questions.

646   Unit 6 Literature: Fiction

Unit 7 Literature Connection

NUMBERS
BY MARY CORNISH
from Sing a Song of Popcorn

I like the generosity of numbers.
The way, for example,
they are willing to count
anything or anyone:
two pickles, one door to the room,
eight dancers dressed as swans.

I like the domesticity of addition —
add two cups of milk and stir —
the sense of plenty: six plums
on the ground, three more
falling from the tree.

And multiplication's school
of fish times fish,
whose silver bodies breed
beneath the shadow
of a boat.

Even subtraction is never loss,
just addition somewhere else:
five sparrows take away two,
the two in someone else's
garden now.

There's an amplitude to long division,
as it opens Chinese take-out
box by paper box,
inside every folded cookie
a new fortune.

And I never fail to be surprised
by the gift of an odd remainder,
footloose at the end:
forty-seven divided by eleven equals four,
with three remaining.

Three boys beyond their mothers' call,
two Italians off to the sea,
one sock that isn't anywhere you look.

1 What does the poem say about numbers and what they do? **See below for answers to all questions.**

2 Why is counting important for working with ratio and probability?

3 Which verse describes an inverse relationship?

Unit 7 Literature: Poem   647

Unit 6

Unit 7

Reading the Selection

Read the story aloud to the class or ask students to read it themselves. Then have them work independently, in small groups, or as a whole class to answer questions.

Answers to Questions

1. *Drawings will vary. Drawings should show rectangular sides and a triangular roof, if shown from the front.*

2. The area of the longer wall is 84 square feet. The area of the floor is 120 square feet.

Reading the Selection

Read the poem aloud to the class or ask students to read it themselves. Then have them work independently, in small groups, or as a whole class to answer questions.

Answers to Questions

1. Numbers can count anything or anyone

2. Without being able to count things or outcomes exactly, neither ratio nor probability can be expressed.

3. The fourth verse describes the inverse relationship of addition and subtraction.

Unit 8 Literature Connection

Treasure Hunt

DOUGLAS COBLEIGH

The treasure hunt was Jack's bright idea. He and I had grown up near Boston. We went to different colleges but stayed close friends. After college, we decided to have some fun. So in December, we joined a company that was digging for treasure. Our destination: Oak Island, off the eastern coast of Nova Scotia, Canada.

Oak Island is 350 nautical miles northeast of Boston. Now, Boston winters can get pretty cold. But we soon discovered they were nothing compared to the damp cold of Nova Scotia. At first, we didn't mind it too much. After all, we were here to search for buried treasure.

We learned this search had been going on since 1795, when a Nova Scotia teenager had come across a sunken spot shaped like a circle. The boy had heard plenty of tales about pirates who had used the islands off Nova Scotia as secret hideouts. Legend had it that Captain Kidd and his crew had buried their treasure on one of these islands.

The next day, the boy returned to the spot with some friends. They started digging. And they continued to dig over the next year until they found a rather large stone with mysterious writing on it. By that time the hole was about 90 feet deep. When they returned the

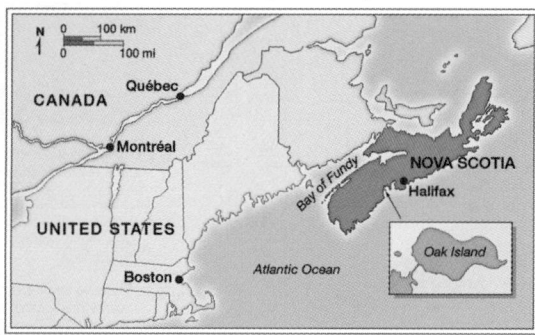

648 **Unit 8 Literature:** Realistic Fiction

following day, the hole was filled with water. When they removed the stone, they accidentally set off a trap that flooded the hole.

Over the years, various people have taken turns digging out the Money Pit, as the spot came to be called. Several were killed. But treasure hunters continued digging. Eventually, they dug down almost 190 feet. But they failed to find any treasure.

The company Jack and I worked for had a new idea. About 180 feet northeast of the Money Pit, engineers sank a steel tube more than 230 feet into the ground. Then they lowered a specially-made video camera. We could see what looked like three treasure chests and various tools.

The company decided to sink a second shaft close to where the cameras showed the three chests and tools. When we raised the chests, we found old china and glass in one, old bottles in another, and the remnants of what had been clothing in the third.

So much for the Money Pit!

1 What story information does each of the following integers stand for?
   A. ⁻190;   B. ⁺350;   C. ⁻230

2 List three details from the story that are facts. Explain why you think they are facts.

See below for answers to all questions.

Unit 8 Literature: Realistic Fiction   649

Unit 8

Reading the Selection

Read the article aloud to the class or ask students to read it themselves. Then have them work independently, in small groups, or as a whole class to answer questions.

Answers to Questions
1. a. the depth of the original hole
   b. the distance in nautical miles from Boston to Nova Scotia
   c. the depth of the shaft for the camera
2. *Answers may vary.*

Table of Measures / Glossary

Table Of Measures

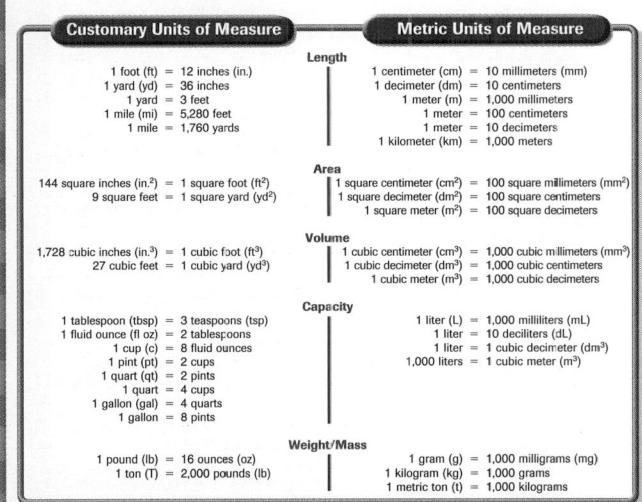

Customary Units of Measure

Length

1 foot (ft)	=	12 inches (in.)
1 yard (yd)	=	36 inches
1 yard	=	3 feet
1 mile (mi)	=	5,280 feet
1 mile	=	1,760 yards

Area

144 square inches (in.²)	=	1 square foot (ft²)
9 square feet	=	1 square yard (yd²)

Volume

1,728 cubic inches (in.³)	=	1 cubic foot (ft³)
27 cubic feet	=	1 cubic yard (yd³)

Capacity

1 tablespoon (tbsp)	=	3 teaspoons (tsp)
1 fluid ounce (fl oz)	=	2 tablespoons
1 cup (c)	=	8 fluid ounces
1 pint (pt)	=	2 cups
1 quart (qt)	=	2 pints
1 quart	=	4 cups
1 gallon (gal)	=	4 quarts
1 gallon	=	8 pints

Weight/Mass

1 pound (lb)	=	16 ounces (oz)
1 ton (T)	=	2,000 pounds (lb)

Metric Units of Measure

Length

1 centimeter (cm)	=	10 millimeters (mm)
1 decimeter (dm)	=	10 centimeters
1 meter (m)	=	1,000 millimeters
1 meter	=	100 centimeters
1 meter	=	10 decimeters
1 kilometer (km)	=	1,000 meters

Area

1 square centimeter (cm²)	=	100 square millimeters (mm²)
1 square decimeter (dm²)	=	100 square centimeters
1 square meter (m²)	=	100 square decimeters

Volume

1 cubic centimeter (cm³)	=	1,000 cubic millimeters (mm³)
1 cubic decimeter (dm³)	=	1,000 cubic centimeters
1 cubic meter (m³)	=	1,000 cubic decimeters

Capacity

1 liter (L)	=	1,000 milliliters (mL)
1 liter	=	10 deciliters (dL)
1 liter	=	1 cubic decimeter (dm³)
1,000 liters	=	1 cubic meter (m³)

Weight/Mass

1 gram (g)	=	1,000 milligrams (mg)
1 kilogram (kg)	=	1,000 grams
1 metric ton (t)	=	1,000 kilograms

Units of Time

1 minute (min)	=	60 seconds (s)
1 hour (h)	=	60 minutes
1 day	=	24 hours
1 week (wk)	=	7 days
1 year (yr)	=	12 months (mo)

1 year	=	365 days
1 leap year	=	366 days
1 decade	=	10 years
1 century	=	100 years
1 millennium	=	1,000 years

Glossary

absolute value The distance a number is from zero on a number line.

acute angle An angle with a measure less than that of a right angle.

acute triangle A triangle in which each of the three angles is acute.

addend A number to be added in an addition expression. In $7 - 4 + 8$, the numbers 7, 4, and 8 are addends.

algebraic expression An expression that consists of one or more variables. It could contain some constants and some operations. *Example: $2x + 3y + 6$.*

angle An angle is formed by two rays with a common endpoint.

area The number of square units that cover a surface with no overlap.

array An arrangement of objects, pictures, or numbers in columns and rows.

Associative Property of Addition Changing the grouping of addends does not change their sum. It is also called the *Grouping Property of Addition*. *Example:* For all numbers a, b and c, $a + (b + c) = (a + b) + c$.

Associative Property of Multiplication Changing the grouping of factors does not change their product. It is also called the *Grouping Property of Multiplication*. *Example:* For all numbers a, b and c, $a \times (b \times c) = (a \times b) \times c$.

average The number found by dividing the sum of a group of numbers by the number of addends. Also known as the *mean*.

bar graph A graph in which information is shown by means of rectangular bars.

base of a geometric figure A bottom side or face of a geometric figure.

base of a power A number used as a repeated factor in a product. *Example:* 10^3. 10 is the base of the power.

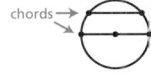

capacity The amount a container can hold.

Celsius The metric temperature scale with the freezing point of water set to 0 degrees, and the boiling point set to 100 degrees.

center of a circle A point that is the same distance from all points on a circle.

central angle An angle with a vertex at the center of a circle.

certain event An event that has a probability of 1.

chord Any segment within a circle that connects two points on the circle.

circle A closed figure in which every point is the same distance from a given point called the center of the circle.

Glossary

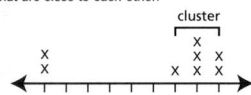

Glossary Pages 652, 653, 654, 655

---

circle graph A graph used for data that are parts of a whole.

circumference The distance around a circle.

cluster In a data display, a group of data points that are close to each other.

common denominator Any common multiple of the denominators of two or more fractions.

common factor A number that is a factor of two or more numbers.

common multiple A number that is shared as a multiple of two or more numbers.

Commutative Property of Addition Changing the order of addends does not change their sum. It is also called the *Order Property of Addition.*

Example: For all numbers *a* and *b*, $a + b = b + a$.

Commutative Property of Multiplication Changing the order of factors does not change their product. It is also called the *Order Property of Multiplication.*

Example: For all numbers *a* and *b*, $a \times b = b \times a$.

compatible numbers Numbers that close to the original numbers and are easy to divide.

composite number A whole number that has more than two factors.

compound event In probability, a combination of two or more events.

cone A solid that has a circular base and a surface from a boundary of the base to the vertex.

congruent figures Figures that have the same size and shape.

coordinate plane A plane formed by two perpendicular number lines in which every point is assigned an ordered pair of numbers.

coordinates An ordered pair of numbers that locates a point in the coordinate plane with reference to the x-axis and y-axis.

cross product A product obtained by multiplying the second term of one ratio by the first term of another.

cube A solid figure that has six square faces of equal size.

cubic unit A unit for measuring volume. A cube with sides one unit long.

customary system The measurement system that uses foot, quart, pound, and degrees Fahrenheit.

cylinder A solid with two circular faces that are congruent and a cylindrical surface connecting the two faces.

 D

data A set of numbers or pieces of information.

data set A collection of numbers or pieces of information.

decimal A number with one or more digits to the right of a decimal point.

decimal point A symbol used to separate the ones and tenths places in a decimal.

degrees A unit used to describe angle measures and also temperature. Its symbol is °.

denominator The number below the bar in a fraction.

diagonal A segment that joins two vertices of a polygon but is not a side.

diameter A chord that connects two points on the circle and passes through the center.

difference The result of subtraction.

discount A decrease in the price of an item.

Distributive Property When two addends are multiplied by a factor, the product is the same as if each addend was multiplied by the factor and those products were added.

Example: $a \times (b + c) = (a \times b) + (a \times c)$

dividend The number that is divided in a division problem.

divisible One number is divisible by another if the quotient is a whole number and there is a remainder of 0.

divisor The number by which a number is being divided.

double bar graph A graph in which data are compared by means of pairs of rectangular bars drawn next to each other.

double line graph A graph that is used to compare two or more sets of data over time.

E

edge The segment where two faces of a solid figure meet.

endpoint The point at either end of a line segment. The beginning point of a ray.

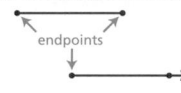
endpoints

equally likely Events which have the same chance of occurring.

equation A mathematical sentence that shows that two expressions are the same value.

equilateral triangle A triangle that has three congruent sides.

equivalent fractions Fractions that show different numbers with the same value.

equivalent ratios Ratios that show the same comparison.

estimate A number close to an exact amount. An estimate tells about how much or about how many.

evaluate To substitute the values given for the variables and perform the operations to find the value of the expression.

evaluating an expression For a numerical expression, performing the operations to find the value of the expression. For an algebraic expression, substituting number(s) for the variable(s) and then performing the operations to find the value of the expressions.

even number A whole number that is a multiple of 2. The ones digit in an even number is 0, 2, 4, 6, or 8. The numbers 56 and 48 are examples of even numbers.

event In probability, a result of an experiment that can be classified as certain, likely, unlikely, or impossible.

expanded form A way of writing a number as the sum of the values of its digits.

experimental probability The number of favorable outcomes in an event divided by the total number of completed trials of an experiment.

exponent The number in a power that tells the number of times the base is used as a factor.

base → 5^3 ← exponent

expression A number, variable, or any combination of numbers, variables, and operation signs.

 652 Glossary

Glossary 653

F

face A flat surface of a solid figure.

face →

fact family Facts that are related, using the same numbers.

Examples:
$1 + 4 = 5$	$4 + 1 = 5$
$5 - 1 = 4$	$5 - 4 = 1$
$3 \times 5 = 15$	$5 \times 3 = 15$
$15 \div 3 = 5$	$15 \div 5 = 3$

factor One of two or more numbers that are multiplied to give a product.

factor tree A diagram that is used to show the prime factorization of a number.

factorization A number written as a product of its factors.

Fahrenheit The customary temperature scale.

fraction A number that names a part of a whole, a part of a collection, or a part of a region.

frequency In surveys, the number of times a response is chosen.

frequency table A table used to record the number of times a response is chosen.

front-end estimation Estimation by looking at the digits in the greatest place of each number.

function A rule that gives exactly one value of *y* for every value of *x*.

function table A table that matches each input value with one output value.

G

gap In a data display, a large space between data points.

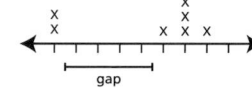
gap

greatest common divisor (GCD) The greatest whole number that is a common factor of two or more numbers. It is also called the *greatest common factor.*

greatest common factor (GCF) The greatest whole number that is a common factor of two or more numbers. It is also called the *greatest common divisor.*

H

histogram A graph in which bars are used to display how frequently data occurs within equal intervals.

horizontal axis The x-axis in a coordinate system. It is a number line that is used to locate points to the left or to the right of the origin.

I

Identity Property of Addition The property which states that the sum of any number and 0 is that number.

Example: $x + 0 = x$

Identity Property of Multiplication The property which states that the product of any number and 1 is that number.

Example: $a \times 1 = a$

impossible event An event that has a probability of 0.

improper fraction A fraction which has a numerator that is greater than or equal to its denominator.

inequality A relation that is expressed by placing an inequality symbol between two expressions.

Examples: $8 > 2, 2 < 8, 5 + 7 \neq 6 + 4$

integers The set of positive whole numbers, their opposites (negative numbers), and 0.

intersecting lines Lines that meet or cross at a common point.

interval A measure of space between two or more numbers.

inverse operations Operations that have opposite effects. Subtraction is the inverse operation of addition. Division is the inverse operation of multiplication.

invert To interchange the numerator and the denominator.

irregular polygon A polygon with at least one side or angle that is not congruent to the others.

isosceles triangle A triangle that has at least two congruent sides.

L

leaf The last digit of a number in a stem-and-leaf plot.

least common denominator (LCD) The least common multiple of two or more denominators.

least common multiple (LCM) The least number that is a multiple of two or more numbers.

line A straight, continuous, and unending set of points in a plane.

line graph A graph that uses a broken line to show changes in data. A line graph is often used to display data that vary with time.

line of symmetry The line along which a figure can be folded so that the two halves match exactly.

line plot A diagram that organizes data using a number line.

line segment A part of a line that has two endpoints.

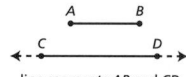
line segments *AB* and *CD*

line symmetry A figure has line symmetry if it can be folded in half and the two halves are congruent.

M

mass The amount of matter in an object.

mean The number found by dividing the sum of the numbers in a group by the number of addends. Also known as the *average.*

measures of central tendency The mean, median, and mode.

median The middle number when data are arranged in order.

metric system A system of measurement in which the basic units of length, mass and capacity are the meter, gram and liter.

midpoint The point that divides the segment into two congruent parts.

654 Glossary

Glossary 655

T58 **Glossary**

Glossary ....

mixed number A number made up of a whole number and a fraction.

whole number → 5 ⅔ ← fraction
mixed number

mode The number or numbers that occur most often in a set of data.

multiple A number that is the product of the given number and a counting number.

negative numbers Numbers that are less than 0.

net A flat pattern that can be folded to make a solid figure.

number line A line on which numbers are assigned points.

numerator The number above the bar in a fraction.

obtuse angle An angle with a measure greater than that of a right angle and less than 180°.

obtuse triangle A triangle that has one obtuse angle.

odd number A whole number that is not a multiple of 2. The ones digit in an odd number is 1, 3, 5, 7, or 9.

Examples: 67 and 493 are odd numbers.

opposite of a number The same number but of opposite sign. Also called the *additive inverse*.

order of operations Rules for performing operations in order to simplify expressions.

ordered pair A pair of numbers (x, y) indicating the x-coordinate and y-coordinates of a point on a graph.

origin The point where the x- and y-axis intersect in a coordinate plane.

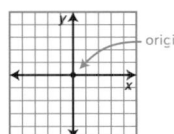
origin

outcome A single result in a probability experiment.

outlier A number or numbers whose values are much less or much greater than the other numbers in the data set.

parallel lines Lines that lie in the same plane and do not intersect. They are everywhere the same distance apart.

parallelogram A quadrilateral in which both pairs of opposite sides are parallel.

partial product In multiplication of numbers with two or more digits, the product of each digit in one factor and the other number.

```
    48
  × 23
   144  ← partial products
 + 960
 1,104
```

per Used in talking about rates. *Per* means "to each" or "for each."

percent Per hundred. A ratio of a number to 100.

period In a number, each group of three digits separated by a comma.

perimeter The distance around a plane figure.

656 Glossary

perpendicular Two lines or line segments that cross or meet to form right angles.

pi (π) A number defined by the ratio of the circumference of any circle to its diameter. Two common approximations used for pi are $\frac{22}{7}$ and 3.14.

pictograph A graph that uses pictures or symbols to represent data

place value The value of a digit determined by its place in a number.

plane A flat surface made up of a continuous and unending collection of points that are not all in the same line.

point An exact location in space, represented by a dot.

polygon A simple closed plane figure made up of three or more line segments.

positive number A number that is greater than 0.

power of ten A power with a base of 10.

precision A term used to refer to the accuracy of a measurement. A smaller unit produces a more precise measurement than a larger unit.

prime factorization Writing a number as the product of prime factors.

prime number A whole number greater than 1 that has exactly two factors.

prism A solid figure that has two parallel congruent bases and parallelograms for faces.

probability The chance of an event occurring. A probability can be any number from 0 through 1.

product The result in multiplication.

proper fraction A fraction in which the numerator is less than the denominator.

Example: $\frac{4}{7}$

proportion A statement that two ratios are equivalent.

pyramid A solid figure whose base can be any polygon and whose faces are triangles.

quadrant Each of the four parts into which a plane is separated by the x-axis and the y-axis. The axes are not parts of the quadrant.

quadrilateral A polygon with four sides.

quotient The result in division.

radius A segment that connects the center of a circle to any point on the circle.

range The difference between the greatest and least numbers in a set of data.

rate A ratio of two quantities using different units.

ratio A comparison of two numbers by division.

ray Part of a line that starts at an endpoint and goes on infinitely in one direction.

reciprocal The product of a number and its reciprocal is 1.

Glossary 657

rectangle A polygon with opposite sides parallel and four right angles.

rectangular prism A solid figure with six faces that are rectangles.

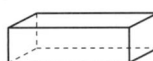

rectangular pyramid A solid figure whose base is a rectangle and whose faces are triangles.

reflection A transformation that flips a figure over a line.

regular polygon A polygon with all sides congruent and all angles congruent.

remainder The number that is left over after one whole number is divided by another.

repeating decimal A decimal quotient that contains a repeating block of digits.

rhombus A parallelogram with all four sides congruent.

right angle An angle that measures 90°.

right triangle A triangle that has one right angle.

rotation A transformation that turns a figure about a given point.

rotational symmetry If a figure can be turned less than a full turn about a given point and the figure looks exactly the way it did before the turn, that figure has rotational symmetry.

sale price The price of an item after the discount is subtracted.

sample space A list of all possible outcomes.

scale A ratio of the measurements in a drawing to actual measurements.

scale drawing A drawing created using a scale.

scalene triangle A triangle with no congruent sides.

sequence An ordered set of numbers.

side One of the line segments that make up a polygon.

similar figures Figures that have the same shape but not necessarily the same size.

simplest form A fraction is in simplest form when the GCF of the numerator and denominator is 1.

solid figure A three-dimensional figure in space.

speed A rate that shows distance per unit of time.

sphere A solid figure that is shaped like a round ball.

square A polygon with four right angles and four congruent sides.

square unit A square with sides one unit long.

standard form A way of writing a number using only digits.

stem The digit or digits to the left of the leaves in a stem-and-leaf plot.

stem-and-leaf plot A frequency distribution that arranges data in order of place value.

658 Glossary

straight angle An angle that measures 180°.

180°

sum The result in addition.

surface area The total area of the surface of a solid.

survey A method of collecting information about a group of people.

symmetric figure A figure that has line or rotational symmetry.

terms of a ratio The numerator and denominator of a ratio expressed as a fraction. The numerator is the first term, and the denominator is the second term.

tessellation A repeating pattern that covers a plane without gaps or overlaps.

theoretical probability For a single event, the probability calculated by dividing the number of favorable outcomes in the event by the total number of possible outcomes.

tip A percentage portion of a total bill, customarily left after service.

transformation A transformation changes the position of a plane figure.

translation A transformation that slides a figure a given distance in a given direction.

trapezoid A quadrilateral with exactly one pair of parallel sides.

tree diagram A diagram that shows combinations of outcomes of an event.

triangle A polygon with three sides.

triangular prism A prism whose bases are triangles.

triangular pyramid A pyramid whose base is a triangle.

unit cost The cost of a single item.

unit cube A cube with an edge length of 1.

unit fraction A fraction in which the numerator is 1.

unit lengths Standard lengths in the customary and metric systems of measurement.

unit rate A rate in which the second term is 1.

variable A letter that represents a number in an algebraic expression.

variable
↓
$6 + (r \div 2)$

vertex of an angle A point common to the two sides of an angle.

vertex

vertical axis The y-axis in the coordinate system. It is a number line used to locate points above or below the origin.

volume The number of cubic units that make up a solid figure.

Glossary 659

Glossary ....

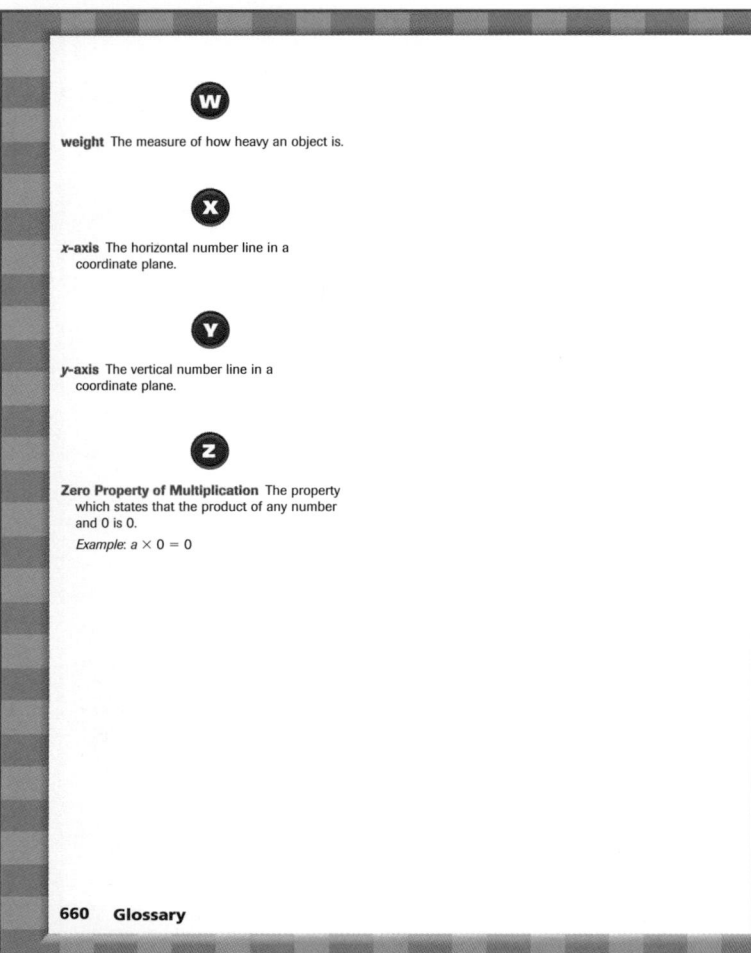

W

weight The measure of how heavy an object is.

X

x-axis The horizontal number line in a coordinate plane.

Y

y-axis The vertical number line in a coordinate plane.

Z

Zero Property of Multiplication The property which states that the product of any number and 0 is 0.

Example: $a \times 0 = 0$

Houghton Mifflin Math and *Weekly Reader* have worked together to provide you with enriching real-world activities and internet connections for your students. The *Weekly Reader Activity Almanac* includes a map activity designed to link math and map skills along with data-related information and activities for each unit.

The Weekly Reader Activity Almanac presents intriguing information about North Carolina and provides Data Hunt activities that encourage learning about historic sites, national and state parks, plants and animals, and other fascinating topics related to North Carolina. The Weekly Reader Web Connections found throughout the student book provide safe access to more information about many cross-curricular connections and math topics on Houghton Mifflin's Education Place Web site: **www.eduplace.com/kids/mw/**.

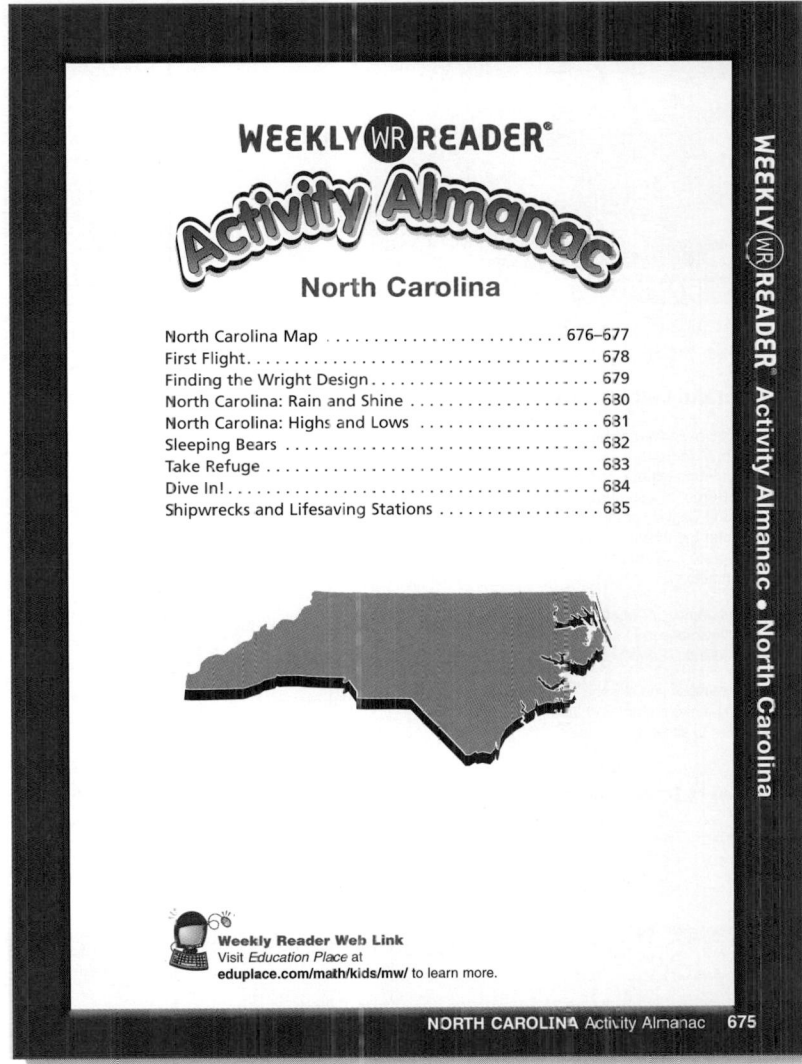

WEEKLY (WR) READER®
Activity Almanac
North Carolina

Weekly Reader Web Link
Visit *Education Place* at
eduplace.com/math/kids/mw/ to learn more.

NORTH CAROLINA Activity Almanac **675**

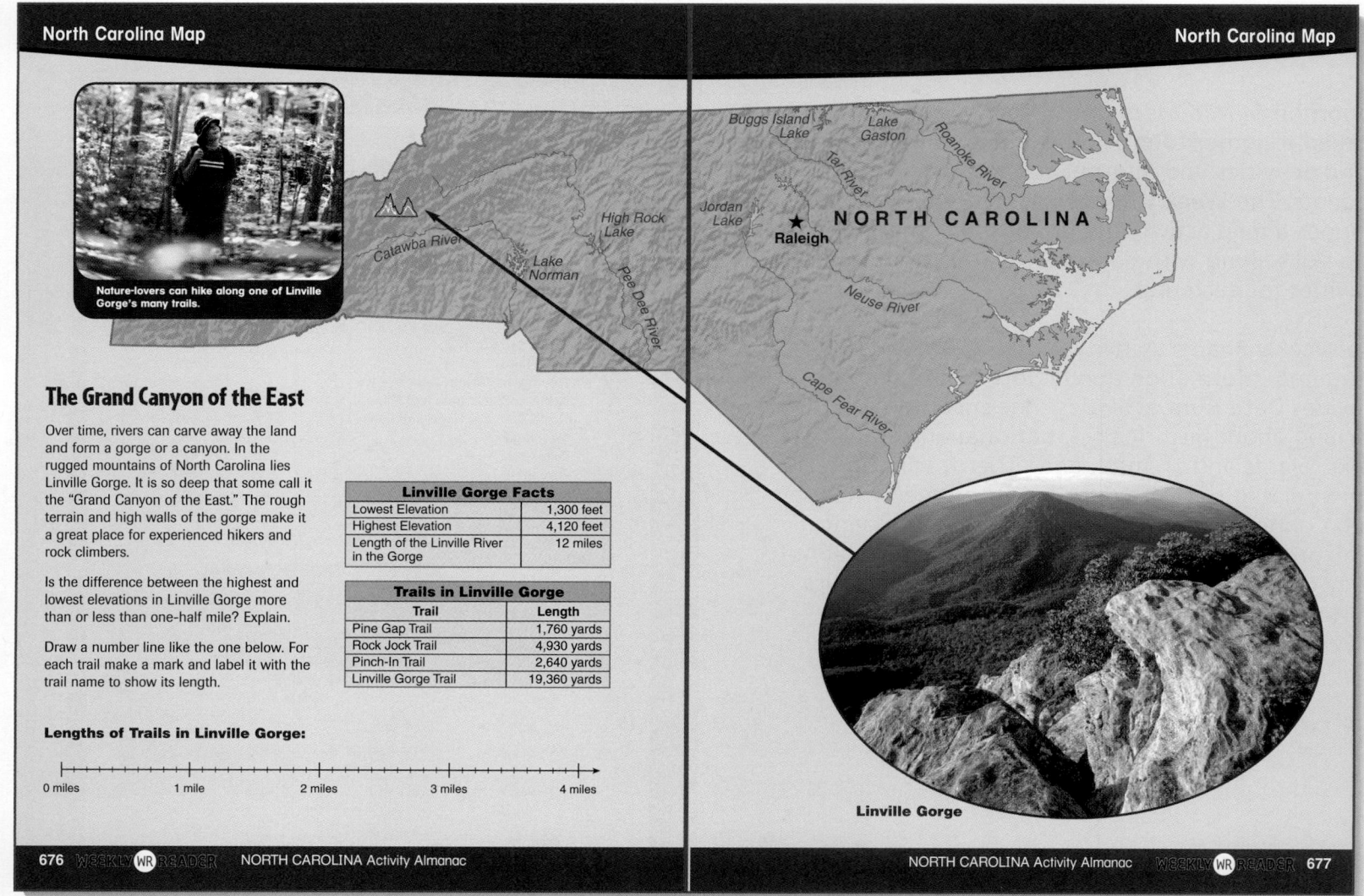

North Carolina Map

The Grand Canyon of the East

Over time, rivers can carve away the land and form a gorge or a canyon. In the rugged mountains of North Carolina lies Linville Gorge. It is so deep that some call it the "Grand Canyon of the East." The rough terrain and high walls of the gorge make it a great place for experienced hikers and rock climbers.

Is the difference between the highest and lowest elevations in Linville Gorge more than or less than one-half mile? Explain.

Draw a number line like the one below. For each trail make a mark and label it with the trail name to show its length.

Linville Gorge Facts	
Lowest Elevation	1,300 feet
Highest Elevation	4,120 feet
Length of the Linville River in the Gorge	12 miles

Trails in Linville Gorge	
Trail	Length
Pine Gap Trail	1,760 yards
Rock Jock Trail	4,930 yards
Pinch-In Trail	2,640 yards
Linville Gorge Trail	19,360 yards

Lengths of Trails in Linville Gorge:

0 miles — 1 mile — 2 miles — 3 miles — 4 miles

Nature-lovers can hike along one of Linville Gorge's many trails.

Linville Gorge

Teacher's Notes

The difference between the highest and lowest elevations in Linville Gorge is greater than one-half mile. The difference is 2,820 ft. One-half mile is half of 5,280 ft, or 2,640 ft. 2,820 ft is greater than 2,640 ft.

Students should mark the trails in order: Pine Gap Trail at 1 mi; Pinch-In Trail at 1.5 mi; Rock Jock Trail at 2.8 mi; and Linville Gorge Trail at 3.7 mi.

First Flight

In 1903 on a Kitty Hawk beach, the Wright brothers did what no one had ever done: They flew the first working airplane. The machine flew for an amazing 12 seconds!

Orville and Wilbur Wright made four flights before their plane fell apart. The fourth flight lasted almost one minute! Today, a national memorial stands where the historic flights took off.

The First Four Flights

Flight Number	Pilot	Distance
1	Orville	120 feet
2	Wilbur	175 feet
3	Orville	200 feet
4	Wilbur	852 feet

Data Hunt

Imagine you are giving a tour to people visiting the Wright Brothers National Memorial. Use the data on these pages to write a script for your tour.

• Use comparisons of data in your script, including distances of the flights.

• Use the timeline to write additional facts. Example: *The Wright brothers made their first successful flight 11 years after they opened a bicycle shop.*

THE HISTORY OF FLIGHT

1783
The first hot-air balloon flight takes place in France.

1892
The Wright brothers open a bicycle shop in Ohio.

1900
Orville and Wilbur start testing gliders in Kitty Hawk.

1903
The Wright brothers make their first successful flight.

Finding the Wright Design

The Wright brothers did not fly on their first try. They had to spend time testing different ideas first. They spent three years flying three different gliders. Their gliders looked like planes but had no motors. When they finished testing, the Wright brothers made their plane: the Flyer I.

Wright Brothers' Flyer I

Wright Brothers' Three Gliders

Year	Wingspan	Longest Flight
1900	17 feet	400 feet
1901	22 feet	390 feet
1902	32 feet	600 feet

Flyer I Facts

Wingspan	40 feet
Weight	605 pounds
Speed of first flight	6.8 miles per hour

Data Hunt

You have been asked to create math riddles for a booth at a school math fair. Use the data on these pages to prepare your questions.

• Your answers should be data about flights and the Wright brothers.

• At least two riddles must involve multiplication and at least two riddles must involve division. Be sure to provide answers to your riddles.

Example: *You must multiply 80 feet by 5 to get me. Which Wright brothers fact am I?*

Answer: The longest flight made with the 1900 glider was 400 feet.

1905
The Wright brothers build a plane that can stay in the sky for 39 minutes.

1911
Orville returns to Kitty Hawk to perform glider experiments.

1927
Charles Lindbergh flies alone across the Atlantic Ocean.

1969
Astronauts land on the moon.

Unit 1

Unit 2

Teacher's Notes

Student responses should include comparisons derived using addition and subtraction. Possible examples include: "Wilbur flew a total 1,027 feet on the first day, but Orville only flew 320 feet," and "Charles Lindbergh flew across the Atlantic Ocean 24 years after the Wright brothers' first successful flight."

Teacher's Notes

Riddles should focus on data about the Wright brothers and the planes and gliders they flew. Riddles should use both multiplication and division. Example: *You must divide 180 miles each hour by 6 to get me. What am I?* Answer: 30 miles each hour, the speed of Flyer I on its first flight.

Activity Almanac *(vertical sidebar)*

WEEKLY WR READER *(vertical sidebar)*

UNIT 3 · Measurement/Data and Graphing

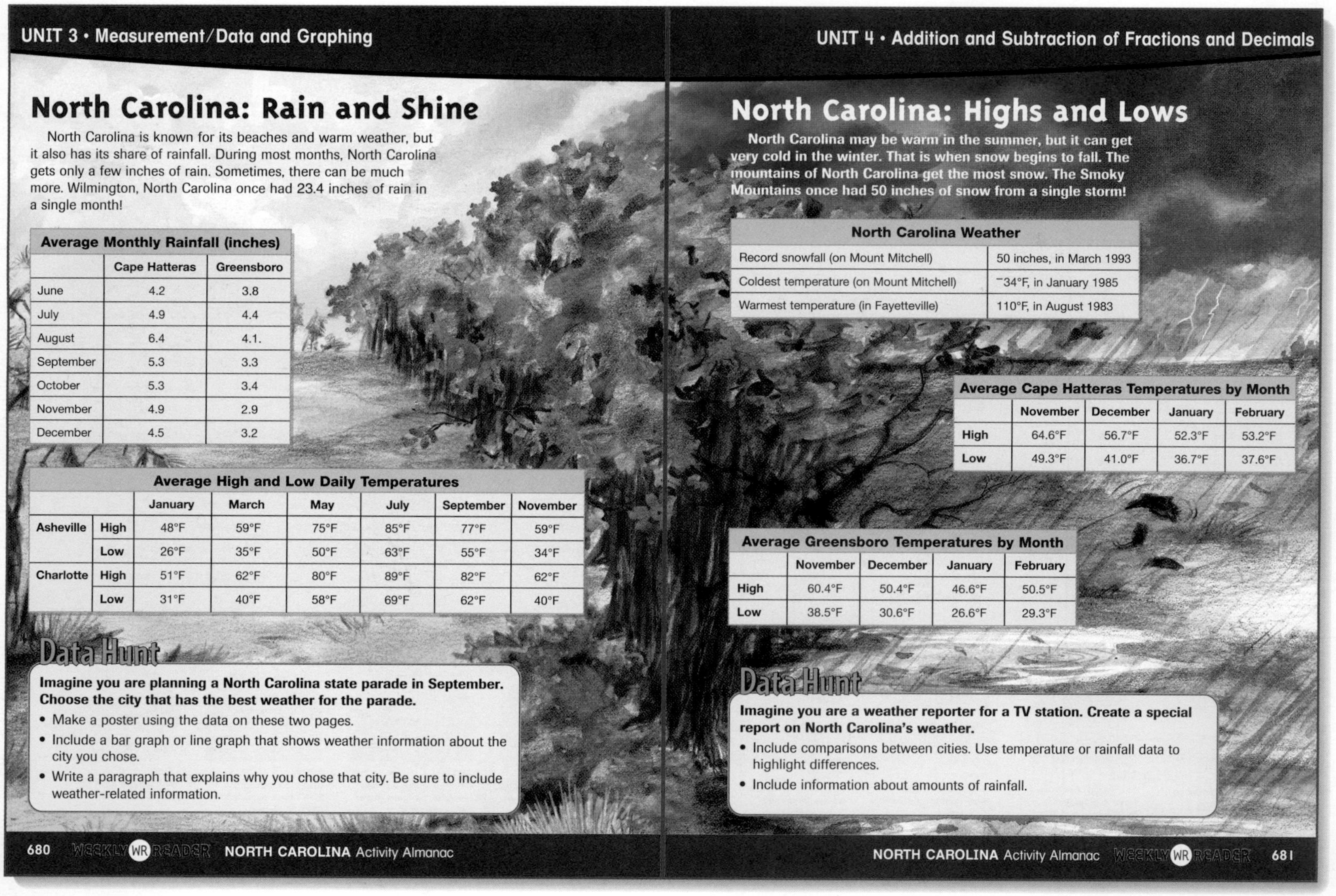

North Carolina: Rain and Shine

North Carolina is known for its beaches and warm weather, but it also has its share of rainfall. During most months, North Carolina gets only a few inches of rain. Sometimes, there can be much more. Wilmington, North Carolina once had 23.4 inches of rain in a single month!

Average Monthly Rainfall (inches)

	Cape Hatteras	Greensboro
June	4.2	3.8
July	4.9	4.4
August	6.4	4.1.
September	5.3	3.3
October	5.3	3.4
November	4.9	2.9
December	4.5	3.2

Average High and Low Daily Temperatures

		January	March	May	July	September	November
Asheville	High	48°F	59°F	75°F	85°F	77°F	59°F
	Low	26°F	35°F	50°F	63°F	55°F	34°F
Charlotte	High	51°F	62°F	80°F	89°F	82°F	62°F
	Low	31°F	40°F	58°F	69°F	62°F	40°F

Data Hunt

Imagine you are planning a North Carolina state parade in September. Choose the city that has the best weather for the parade.

- Make a poster using the data on these two pages.
- Include a bar graph or line graph that shows weather information about the city you chose.
- Write a paragraph that explains why you chose that city. Be sure to include weather-related information.

UNIT 4 · Addition and Subtraction of Fractions and Decimals

North Carolina: Highs and Lows

North Carolina may be warm in the summer, but it can get very cold in the winter. That is when snow begins to fall. The mountains of North Carolina get the most snow. The Smoky Mountains once had 50 inches of snow from a single storm!

North Carolina Weather

Record snowfall (on Mount Mitchell)	50 inches, in March 1993
Coldest temperature (on Mount Mitchell)	⁻34°F, in January 1985
Warmest temperature (in Fayetteville)	110°F, in August 1983

Average Cape Hatteras Temperatures by Month

	November	December	January	February
High	64.6°F	56.7°F	52.3°F	53.2°F
Low	49.3°F	41.0°F	36.7°F	37.6°F

Average Greensboro Temperatures by Month

	November	December	January	February
High	60.4°F	50.4°F	46.6°F	50.5°F
Low	38.5°F	30.6°F	26.6°F	29.3°F

Data Hunt

Imagine you are a weather reporter for a TV station. Create a special report on North Carolina's weather.

- Include comparisons between cities. Use temperature or rainfall data to highlight differences.
- Include information about amounts of rainfall.

Unit 3

Unit 4

Teacher's Notes

The poster should include a graph representing North Carolina weather data. Possible graphs include a line graph tracing the average daily high temperature in Charlotte or a bar graph showing the average rainfalls in Cape Hatteras. The poster should also include a short paragraph with weather data justifying their choice.

Teacher's Notes

Student reports should contain selected highlights of North Carolina weather data. Students' reports should compare rainfall amounts or temperatures in different cities. This activity engages students in calculations involving addition and subtraction of decimals. Possible example of comparison information: *On average, in the month of August there is 2.3 more inches of rainfall in Cape Hatteras than in Greensboro.*

WEEKLY WR READER Activity Almanac

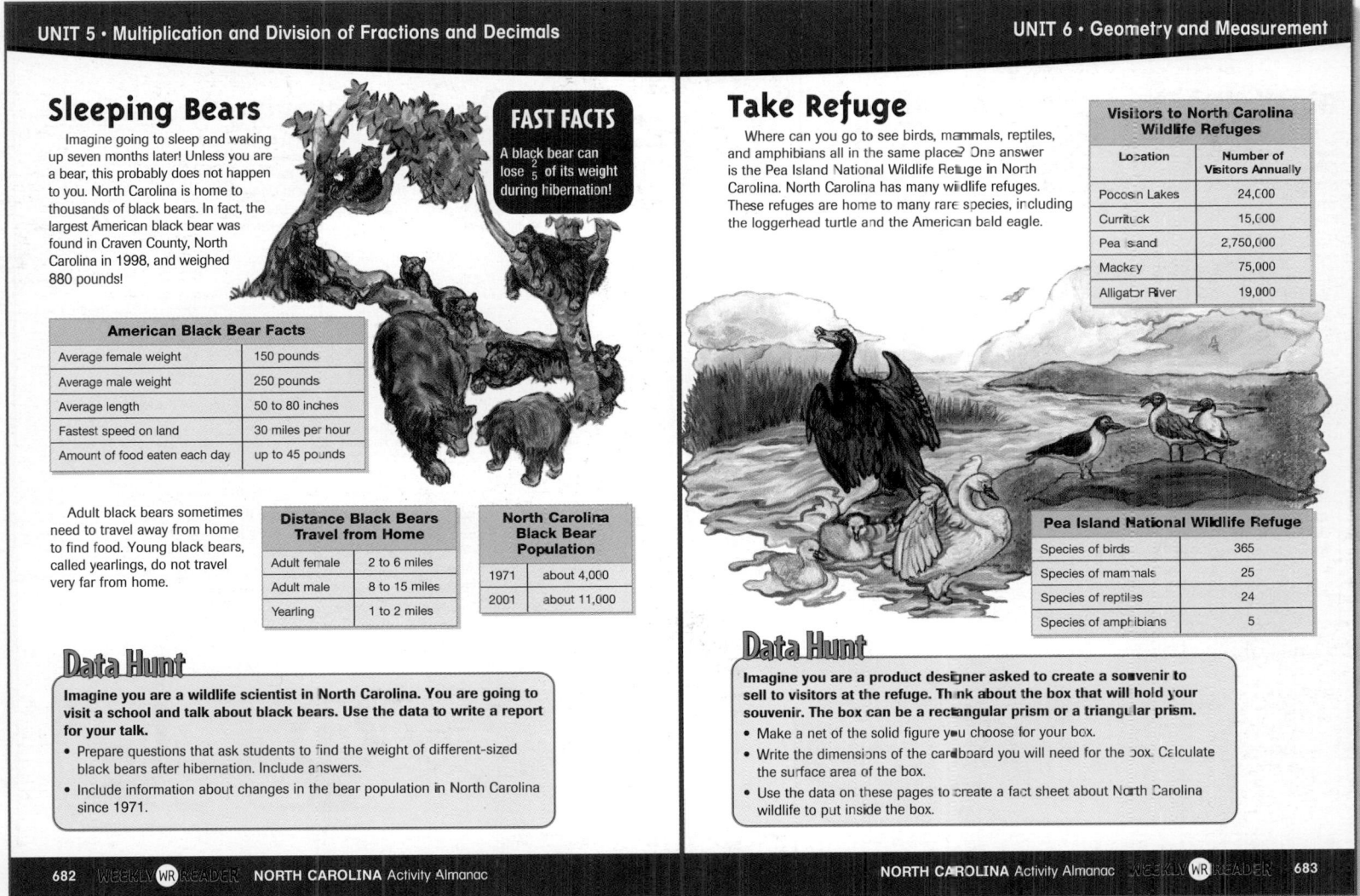

Sleeping Bears

Imagine going to sleep and waking up seven months later! Unless you are a bear, this probably does not happen to you. North Carolina is home to thousands of black bears. In fact, the largest American black bear was found in Craven County, North Carolina in 1998, and weighed 880 pounds!

FAST FACTS

A black bear can lose 2/5 of its weight during hibernation!

American Black Bear Facts

Average female weight	150 pounds
Average male weight	250 pounds
Average length	50 to 80 inches
Fastest speed on land	30 miles per hour
Amount of food eaten each day	up to 45 pounds

Adult black bears sometimes need to travel away from home to find food. Young black bears, called yearlings, do not travel very far from home.

Distance Black Bears Travel from Home

Adult female	2 to 6 miles
Adult male	8 to 15 miles
Yearling	1 to 2 miles

North Carolina Black Bear Population

1971	about 4,000
2001	about 11,000

Data Hunt

Imagine you are a wildlife scientist in North Carolina. You are going to visit a school and talk about black bears. Use the data to write a report for your talk.

- Prepare questions that ask students to find the weight of different-sized black bears after hibernation. Include answers.
- Include information about changes in the bear population in North Carolina since 1971.

Take Refuge

Where can you go to see birds, mammals, reptiles, and amphibians all in the same place? One answer is the Pea Island National Wildlife Refuge in North Carolina. North Carolina has many wildlife refuges. These refuges are home to many rare species, including the loggerhead turtle and the American bald eagle.

Visitors to North Carolina Wildlife Refuges

Location	Number of Visitors Annually
Pocosin Lakes	24,000
Currituck	15,000
Pea Island	2,750,000
Mackay	75,000
Alligator River	19,000

Pea Island National Wildlife Refuge

Species of birds	365
Species of mammals	25
Species of reptiles	24
Species of amphibians	5

Data Hunt

Imagine you are a product designer asked to create a souvenir to sell to visitors at the refuge. Think about the box that will hold your souvenir. The box can be a rectangular prism or a triangular prism.

- Make a net of the solid figure you choose for your box.
- Write the dimensions of the cardboard you will need for the box. Calculate the surface area of the box.
- Use the data on these pages to create a fact sheet about North Carolina wildlife to put inside the box.

Unit 5

Unit 6

Teacher's Notes

This activity requires students to use the information on the page to write a report on black bears. They should calculate the weight of the average black bear after hibernation using the fraction of weight bears lose. Students will also prepare questions that require other students to find the weight of different-sized black bears after hibernation.

Teacher's Notes

This activity requires students to design a box for a product for the refuge. They will need to decide what shape to make the box for the product as well as the amount of cardboard that will be needed. Students will make a net and calculate the surface area of a rectangular or triangular prism.

UNIT 7 • Ratio, Proportion, Percent, and Probability

Dive In!

There's no adventure quite like scuba diving. After plunging beneath the water's surface, divers enter a world completely different from the one above. They can encounter exotic fish, beautiful corals, and unusual reef formations. Many divers enjoy exploring one of the thousands of shipwrecks off the North Carolina coast.

FAST FACTS

Scuba divers usually wear wetsuits. That's because water conducts heat away from the human body 20 times faster than air does.

Popular Outer Banks Shipwrecks

Shipwreck	Type	Height of Vessel	Depth Below Surface
F.W. Abrahms	Tanker	31 feet	90 feet
Keshena	Tugboat	10 feet	90 feet
Suloide	Freighter	21 feet	65 feet
Tarpon	Submarine	15 feet	140 feet
Proteus	Passenger	29 feet	120 feet

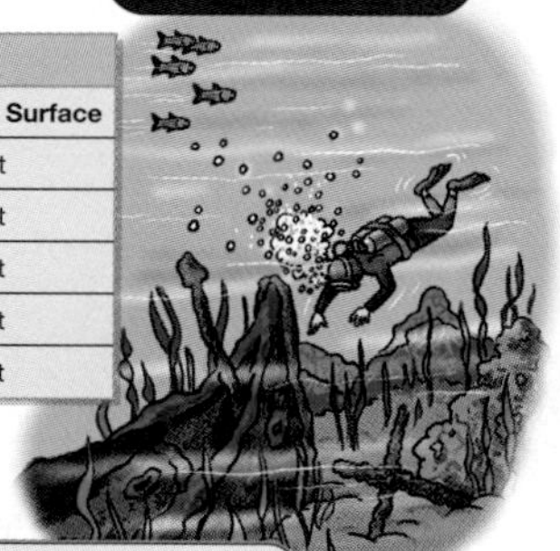

Data Hunt

Imagine you are working on an advertisement to tell people about diving in North Carolina. Your job is to design a poster that encourages divers to explore these shipwrecks.

- Use any of the data on these two pages.
- Highlight facts that you think would be interesting to divers.
- Compare vessel heights and depths using ratios or proportions.

FAST FACTS

Divers "talk" to each other underwater by using hand signals.

DIVING SIGNALS

Okay signal   Stop signal   Up signal

UNIT 8 • Algebra, Integers, and Coordinate Graphing

Shipwrecks and Lifesaving Stations

The early morning of November 24, 1877 was a difficult one for the USS *Huron*. This ship was sailing from Virginia to Cuba during a heavy storm when it ran aground 250 yards off Nags Head. As a result, Congress increased the number of lifesaving stations in North Carolina.

Now on the National Register of Historic Places, the USS *Huron* is one of the most popular shipwrecks for scuba divers and snorkelers to explore.

Wreck of the USS *Huron*

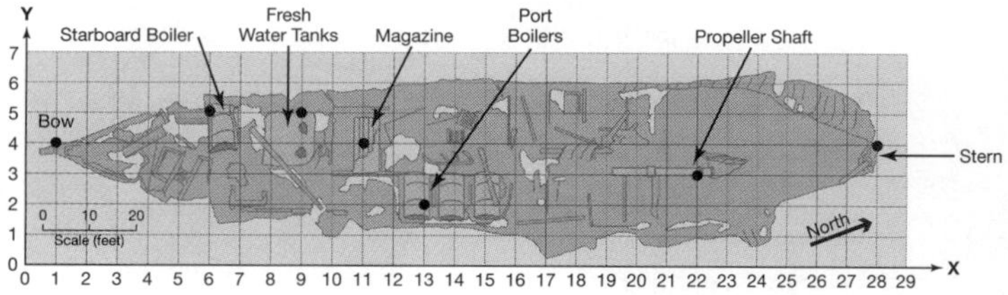

Data Hunt

A scuba diver might use a coordinate grid to explore the wreck of the *Huron*. Use a coordinate grid and some facts on these pages to create a game about the *Huron*.

- Draw a coordinate grid on graph paper and label the axes like the grid above.
- Plot the location of different parts of the wreck. Mark these locations on your grid and write down the ordered pairs.
- With a partner, take turns reading ordered pairs to each other and locating these points on the grid.

Down signal   Okay signal   Pick me up signal

Unit 7

Unit 8

Teacher's Notes

Students' posters should be visually appealing, and also include two facts in the form of ratio, proportion, percent, or estimation of probability.

Teacher's Notes

Check students' grids. The x-axis should be numbered from 0 to 29. The y-axis should be labeled from 0 to 7. At least 7 objects should be plotted.

Bow: (1,4)
Starboard Boiler: (6,5)
Fresh Water Tanks: (9,5)
Storeroom (11,4)
Port boilers: (13,2)
Propeller Shaft: (22,3)
Stern: (28,4)

The games students create should include rules that make significant use of a coordinate grid. Possible game themes might include a diver exploring the wreck of the Huron.

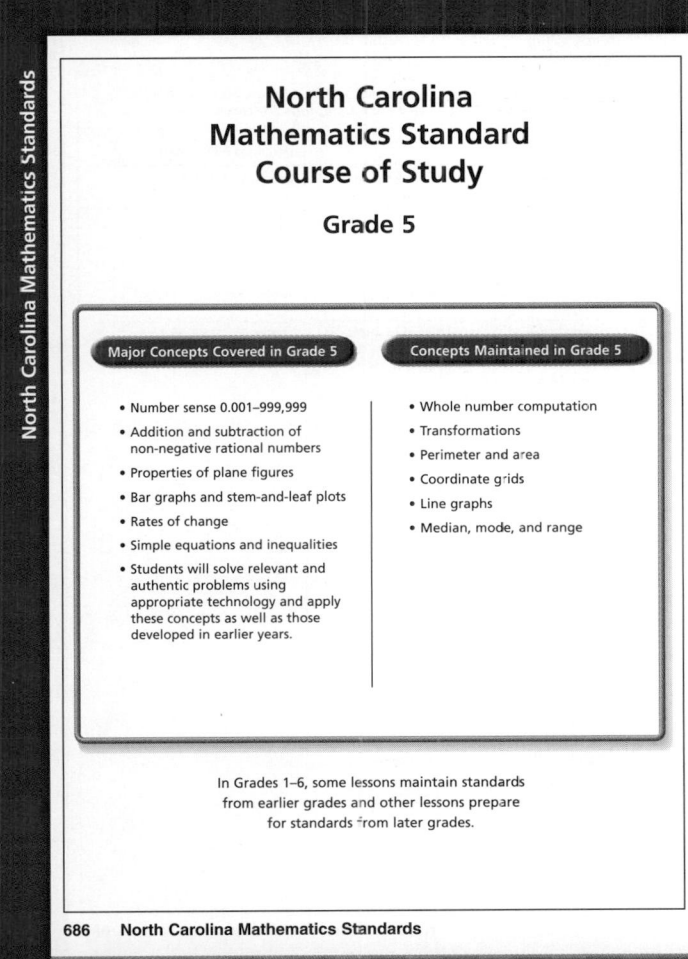

North Carolina Mathematics Standard Course of Study

Grade 5

Major Concepts Covered in Grade 5

- Number sense 0.001–999,999
- Addition and subtraction of non-negative rational numbers
- Properties of plane figures
- Bar graphs and stem-and-leaf plots
- Rates of change
- Simple equations and inequalities
- Students will solve relevant and authentic problems using appropriate technology and apply these concepts as well as those developed in earlier years.

Concepts Maintained in Grade 5

- Whole number computation
- Transformations
- Perimeter and area
- Coordinate grids
- Line graphs
- Median, mode, and range

In Grades 1–6, some lessons maintain standards from earlier grades and other lessons prepare for standards from later grades.

Strand: Number and Operations

Competency Goal 1: The learner will understand and compute with non-negative rational numbers.

Objectives	Houghton Mifflin Math
1.01 Develop number sense for rational numbers 0.001 through 999,999. • Connect model, number word, and number using a variety of representations. • Build understanding of place value (thousandths through hundred thousands). • Compare and order rational numbers. • Make estimates of rational numbers in appropriate situations.	Lessons 1.1–1.5, 1.7 Lessons 9.1, 9.8, 9.9
1.02 Develop fluency in adding and subtracting non-negative rational numbers (halves, fourths, eighths; thirds, sixths, twelfths; fifths, tenths, hundredths, thousandths; mixed numbers). • Develop and analyze strategies for adding and subtracting numbers. • Estimate sums and differences. • Judge the reasonableness of solutions.	Lessons 2.2–2.4 Lesson 10.1–10.8 Lessons 11.1–11.5
1.03 Develop flexibility in solving problems by selecting strategies and using mental computation, estimation, calculators or computers, and paper and pencil.	Lesson 2.6 Lesson 3.8 Lessons 4.3, 4.4, 4.6 Lessons 5.3, 5.7 Lesson 6.7 Lesson 7.6 Lesson 8.4 Lesson 9.7 Lesson 10.7 Lesson 12.7 Lesson 13.6 Lessons 17.5, 17.7 Lesson 18.6 Lesson 19.6

Meeting the Standards

The North Carolina Department of Education has developed the Mathematics Standard Course of Study for the teaching of mathematics across all grade levels. These standards reflect an approach for teaching mathematics that will prepare today's students for living and working in tomorrow's world.

These pages in the Student Book will help you show parents how your classroom teaching reflects the Strands and Competency Goals of the Standard Course of Study. This should help both parents and students understand how a particular lesson contributes to a student's overall achievement of the Competency Goals for Mathematics.

Strand: Measurement

Competency Goal 2: The learner will recognize and use standard units of metric and customary measurement.

Objectives	Houghton Mifflin Math
2.01 Estimate the measure of an object in one system given the measure of that object in another system.	Lesson 6.5 Lesson 12.3
2.02 Identify, estimate, and measure the angles of plane figures using appropriate tools.	Lesson 15.2

Strand: Geometry

Competency Goal 3: The learner will understand and use properties and relationships of plane figures.

Objectives	Houghton Mifflin Math
3.01 Identify, define, describe, and accurately represent triangles, quadrilaterals, and other polygons.	Lessons 15.3, 15.5
3.02 Make and test conjectures about polygons involving: • Sum of the measures of interior angles. • Lengths of sides and diagonals. • Parallelism and perpendicularity of sides and diagonals.	Lesson 15.3
3.03 Classify plane figures according to types of symmetry (line, rotational).	Lesson 15.9
3.04 Solve problems involving the properties of triangles, quadrilaterals, and other polygons. • Sum of the measures of interior angles. • Lengths of sides and diagonals. • Parallelism and perpendicularity of sides and diagonals.	Lessons 15.3, 15.5, 15.7

Strand: Data Analysis and Probability

Competency Goal 4: The learner will understand and use graphs and data analysis.

Objectives	Houghton Mifflin Math
4.01 Collect, organize, analyze, and display data (stem-and-leaf plots) to solve problems.	Lessons 7.1–7.4 Lessons 8.1, 8.3
4.02 Compare and contrast different representations of the same data; discuss the effectiveness of each representation.	Lesson 7.5 Lesson 8.2
4.03 Solve problems with data from a single set or multiple sets of data using median, range, and mode.	Lesson 8.5

Strand: Algebra

Competency Goal 5: The learner will demonstrate an understanding of patterns, relationships, and elementary algebraic representation.

Objectives	Houghton Mifflin Math
5.01 Describe, extend, and generalize numeric and geometric patterns using tables, graphs, words, and symbols.	Lesson 1.6 Lesson 5.1 Lesson 15.7 Lesson 16.2 Lessons 21.4, 21.5
5.02 Use algebraic expressions, patterns, and one-step equations and inequalities to solve problems.	Lessons 2.1, 2.5 Lesson 3.1 Lesson 4.7 Lessons 21.1–21.3
5.03 Identify, describe, and analyze situations with constant or varying rates of change.	Lesson 18.3 Lessons 21.4, 21.5

Teacher Support Handbook

References for a number of professional resources are presented in this section of your Teacher's Edition. These materials reflect the needs expressed by classroom teachers around the country for additional resources to help them enrich their teaching or enhance their understanding of mathematics.

Math and Literature Bibliography

The Adventures of Penrose the Mathematical Cat
  by Theoni Pappas
  Wide World Publishing/Tetra, 1997
A cat with a talent for math takes children on a tour of mathematical concepts.

Amazing Book of Shapes
  by Lydia Sharman
  DK Publishing, 1999
Geometric shapes and visual patterns are explored through colorful, sharply delineated photographs of objects and people.

Building Big
  by David Macaulay
  Houghton Mifflin, 2000
The structures we see and use every day are explored in this companion to the PBS series, helping students grasp the importance of measurement.

Cool Math
  by Christy Maganzini
  Putnam Publishing Group, 1997
Engaging games, quizzes, and amazing facts about mathematics and its history help to reinforce math skills in all areas.

Conned Again Watson! Cautionary Tales of Logic, Math, and Probability
  by Colin Bruce
  Perseus Publishing, 2002
Bruce uses drama, conflict, and familiar characters to bring logic and game theory to life.

Digging for Bird-Dinosaurs: An Expedition to Madagascar
  by Nic Bishop
  Houghton Mifflin, 2000
Clues to the mystery of bird evolution offer students opportunities to do calculations of greater numbers.

Discovering Graph Secrets
  by Sandra Markle
  Atheneum, 1997
Entertaining and informative book on four types of graphs: bar graphs, line graphs, circle graphs, and pictographs.

Do You Wanna Bet? Your Chance to Find Out About Probability
  by Jean Cushman
  Houghton Mifflin, 1991
Two boys become involved in everyday situations that involve probability.

Einstein Anderson, Science Detective: On-line Spacemen and Other Cases
  by Seymour Simon
  Avon Books, 1998
Einstein Anderson, a whiz at science, investigates the mysteries of the universe.

Flatland: A Romance of Many Dimensions
  by Edwin A. Abbot
  Penguin USA, 1998
A reprint of a classic about a flat world of two dimensions originally published in the 1880s.

The Fly on the Ceiling: A Math Myth
  by Julie Glass
  Random House, 1998
Combines math, history, and humor to tell the story of Rene Descartes, the father of analytic geometry.

Fractals, Googols and Other Mathematical Tales
  Wide World Publishing/Tetra, 1993
An unusual cast of characters bring mathematical concepts to life.

Math and Literature Bibliography

A Gebra Named Al
by Wendy Isdell
Free Spirit Publishing, 1993
A young girl's difficulty with algebra leads her to a journey through the "Land of Mathematics" where math and science are no longer mystifying.

If You Made a Million
by David M. Schwartz
William Morrow, 1994
Ways to earn and spend a penny, a nickel, and a million dollars are explored.

The Librarian Who Measured the Earth
by Kathryn Lasky
Little, Brown, 1994
Includes an explanation of math used by the ancient Greek astronomer Eratosthenes to calculate the earth's circumference.

The Man Who Counted: A Collection of Mathematical Adventures
by Malba Tahan
W.W. Norton, 1993
The tale of a humble sheepherder who, through the power and logic of mathematics, lives a life of great adventure.

Math Mysteries: Stories and Activities to Build Problem-Solving Skills
by Jack Silbert
Scholastic, 1996
The "Effective Detective Agency" introduces each reproducible story, presenting readers with engaging math problems to solve.

Also available
for purchase

*Math Trade Book
Literature Library*

Math Talk: Mathematical Ideas in Poems for Two Voices
by Theoni Pappas
Wide World Publishing/Tetra, 1991
Poetic dialogues, designed to be read by two people, present mathematical ideas in a novel way.

Neale S. Godfrey's Ultimate Kids' Money Book
Simon & Schuster Children's, 1998
From stressing the importance of knowing how to make change to establishing a checking account to investing in the stock market, money and its many uses are explained in terms children can understand.

On Beyond a Million: An Amazing Math Journey
by David M. Schwartz
Bantam Doubleday Dell Books for Young Readers, 1999
Amazing facts about numbers in the billions and trillions give children chances to practice using powers of ten.

Shaping the Earth
by Dorothy Hinshaw Patent
Houghton Mifflin, 2000
This natural history of the earth can be used to connect many of the major concepts of mathematics and science.

Sir Cumference and the First Round Table: A Math Adventure
by Cindy Neuschwander
Charlesbridge Publishing, 1997
The terms of geometry are brought to life, as problems with the Round Table force King Arthur and his knights to consider more suitable shapes.

What Are You Figuring Now? A Story About Benjamin Banneker
by Jeri Ferris
Lerner Publishing Group, 1990
A biography of the African American surveyor and self-taught mathematician who, in 1791, surveyed the site that would become our nation's capital.

Professional Resources Bibliography

Bresser, R., and C. Holtzman. *Developing Number Sense –Grades 3-6.* Math Solutions Publications, 1999.

Brodie, J. P. *Constructing Ideas About Large Numbers.* Creative Publications, 1995.

Burns, Marilyn. *About Teaching Mathematics: A K–8 Resource,* 2nd Ed. Sausalito, CA: Math Solutions Publications, 2000.

Butterworth, B. *The Mathematical Brain.* Macmillan, 1999.

Carpenter, Thomas P., Elizabeth Fennema, Megan Loef Franke, Linda Levi, and Susan P. Empson. *Children's Mathematics: Cognitively Guided Instruction.* Portsmouth, NH: Heinemann, 1999.

Cathcart. W., Y. Pothier, J. Vance, and N. Bezuk. *Learning Mathematics in Elementary and Middle Schools.* Merrill: Prentice-Hall, Inc., 2000.

Childs, L., and L Choate. *Nimble with Numbers.* Dale Seymour Publications, 1999.

Clapham, C. *Concise Dictionary of Mathematics.* Oxford University Press, 1996.

Coates, G., and J. Stenmark. *Family Math for Young Children.* Lawrence Hall of Science, 1997.

Cowan, T., and J. Maguire. *Timelines of African-American History: 500 Years of Black Achievement.* Berkley Publishing Group, 1994.

Crawford, M., and M. Witte. *"Strategies for Mathematics: Teaching in Context."* Educational Leadership, Vol. 57, ASCD, November 1999.

Eby, J., A. Herrell, and H. Hicks. *Reflective Planning, Teaching and Evaluation: K-12.* Merrill: Macmillan Publishing Company, 1994.

Flournoy, V., et al. *The Patchwork Quilt.* Scholastic, 1996.

Franco, B., et al. *Understanding Geometry.* Great Source Education Group, 1998.

Garland, T. Fibonacci *Fun: Fascinating Activities with Intriguing Numbers.* Dale Seymour Publications, 1998.

Geary, D. C. *Children's Mathematical Development: Research and Practical Applications.* Washington, D.C., 1994.

Gelfand, I., and A. Shen. *Algebra.* Birkhauser, 1993.

Ginsburg, H.P., Greenes, C., and Balfanz, R. *Big Math for Little Kids.* Dale Seymour Publications, 2003

Ginsburg, H. P., Greenes, C., Balfanz, R., Glassman, B., ed. *Macmillan Visual Almanac.* Blackbirch Press, 1996.

Greenes, C., and G. Immerzeel. *Problem Solving Focus: Time and Money.* Dale Seymour Publications, 1993.

Hiebert, J., T. Carpenter, E. Fennema, K. Fuson, D. Wearne, H. Murray, A. Olivier, and P. Humam. *Making Sense: Teaching and Learning Mathematics with Understanding.* Heinemann, 1997.

Hoffman, P. *The Man Who Loved Only Numbers: The Story of Paul Erdos and the Search for Mathematical Truth.* Hyperion, 1998.

Karp, Karen, E. Todd Brown, Linda Allen, and Candy Allen. *Feisty Females: Inspiring Girls to Think Mathematically.* Portsmouth, NH: Heinemann, 1998.

Kovalik, Susan J., and Karen D. Olsen. *Exceeding Expectations: A User's Guide to Implementing Brain Research in the Classroom,* 2nd Ed. Covington, WA: Books for Educators, Inc., 2001.

Lamon. Susan J. *Teaching Fractions and Ratios for Understanding.* Mahwah, NJ: Lawrence Erlbaum Associates, 1999.

Lee, M., and M. Miller. *Great Graphing.* Scholastic Professional Books, 1993.

Ma, Liping. *Knowing and Teaching Elementary Mathematics.* Lawrence Erlbaum Associates, 1999.

Mamchur, C. *A Teacher's Guide to Cognitive Type Theory and Learning Style.* ASCD, 1996.

The Math Learning Center. *"Fractions on a Geoboard,"* in *Opening Eyes to Mathematics,* Volume 3. 1995.

McIntosh, A., B. Reys, R. Reys, and J. Hope. *Number SENSE: Simple Effective Number Sense Experiences, Grades 4-6.* Dale Seymour Publications, 1997.

Means, B., C. Chelener, and M. Knapp. *Teaching Advanced Skills to At-Risk Students.* Jossey-Bass Inc., 1991.

Mendlesohn, E. *Teaching Primary Math with Music.* Dale Seymour Publications, 1990.

Miller, D., and A. McKinnon. *The Beginning School Mathematics Project.* ASCD, 1995.

Miller, E. *Read It! Draw It! Solve It! Problem Solving for Primary Grades.* Dale Seymour Publications, 1997.

Myren, C. *Posing Open-Ended Questions in the Primary Classroom.* Teaching Resource Center, 1997.

Professional Resources Bibliography

National Council of Teachers of Mathematics. Principles and Standards for School Mathematics (2000)
 See also these NCTM products:
  Addenda Series
  Navigations Series
  Yearbook

National Research Council. *Adding It Up: Helping Children Learn Mathematics.* Washington, DC, National Academy Press, 2001.

Newman, V. *Math Journals, Grades K-5.* Teaching Resource Center, 1994.

Norton-Wolf, S. *Base-Ten Block Activities.* Learning Resources, 1990.

Ohanian, S. *Garbage, Pizza, Patchwork Quilts, and Math Magic.* W. H. Freeman and Co., 1992.

Pappas, T. *The Magic of Mathematics – Discovering the Spell of Mathematics.* Wide World Publishing/Tetra, 1994.

Parker, M., ed. *She Does Math! – Real-Life Problems from Women on the Job.* The Mathematical Association of America, 1995.

Piccirilli, R. *Mental Math: Computation Activities for Anytime.* Scholastic Professional Books, 1996.

Rich, D. *MegaSkills.* Houghton Mifflin Company, 1992.

Salvin, R. E., N. L. Karweit, and B. A. Wasik, eds. *Preventing Early School Failure: Research, Policy, and Practice.* Boston: Allyn and Bacon. 1994.

Satariano, P. *Storytime, Mathtime: Math Explorations in Children's Literature.* Dale Seymour Publications, 1997.

Schechter, B. *My Brain Is Open: The Mathematical Journeys of Paul Erdos.* Simon & Schuster, 1998.

Schoenfeld, A. *"When Good Teaching Leads to Bad Results: The Disasters of Well-Taught Mathematics Courses,"* Educational Psychologist, Vol. 23, 145-66. 1998.

Schullman, D., and E. Rebeka. *Growing Mathematical Ideas in Kindergarten.* Math Solutions Publications, 1999.

Sheffield, Linda Jensen. *Extending the Challenge in Mathematics: Developing Mathematical Promise in K–8 Students.* Thousand Oaks, CA: Corwin Press, Inc., 2002.

Singer, Margie, et al. *Between Never and Always.* Dale Seymour Publications, 1997.

Skinner, P. *It All Adds Up! Math Solutions Publications* (Adapted by Permission of Addison-Wesley Longman, Australia), 1999.

Sparrow, Len, and Paul Swan. *Learning Math with Calculators: Activities for Grades 3–8.* Sausalito, CA: Math Solutions Publications, 2001.

Sternberg, R., and W. Williams. *How to Develop Student Creativity.* ASCD. 1996

Stewart, K., and K. Walker. *20 Thinking Questions for Base-Ten Blocks, Grades 3-6.* Creative Publications, 1995.

Tomlinson, Carol Ann. *How to Differentiate Instruction in Mixed-Ability Classrooms.* ASCD, 1995.

Trafton, P., and D. Thiesen. *Learning Through Problems: Number Sense and Computational Strategies/A Resource for Teachers.* Heinemann, 1999.

Van De Walle, J. *Elementary and Middle School Mathematics: Teaching Developmentally,* Fourth Edition. Dale Seymour Publications, 2000.

Wahl, Mark. *Math for Humans: Teaching Math Through 8 Intelligences,* 2nd Ed. Vernon Hills, IL: LivnLern Press, 1999.

Webb, N., and T. Romberg. *Reforming Mathematics Education in America's Cities: The Urban Mathematics Collaborative Project.* Teachers College Press, 1994.

Zaslavsky, C. *Fear of Math – How to Get Over It and Get On with Your Life.* Rutgers University Press, 1994.

Zemelman, S., H. Daniels, and A. Hyde. *Best Practice: New Standards for Teaching and Learning in America's Schools.* Heinemann, 1998.

Research Support* for Unit 1

TO: **Fifth Grade Teachers**

SUBJECT: **Planning Creative Number Sense Activities**

By Grade 5, students should be well on their way to developing their "number sense." The topics of this unit—place value and addition and subtraction—can contribute to the development of number sense as well as a review of prior content.

An important skill that contributes to number sense is the ability to decompose numbers to simplify the operations required or at least transform the problem to avoid facts that may not be remembered. For example, $8 + 7$ is a difficult basic fact for some children to recall. A "make-ten" decomposition is helpful:

$$8 + 7 = 8 + 2 + 5 = 10 + 5 = 15$$

One way to solve $73 - 36$ without using the usual algorithm with regrouping is to subtract 3 from both 73 and 36:

$$73 - 36 = (73 - 3) - (36 - 3) = 70 - 33 = 70 - 30 - 3 = 40 - 3 = 37.$$

Still another "number sense" approach is to add and subtract 3:

$$(73 + 3) - 36 - 3 = 76 - 36 - 3 = 40 - 3 = 37$$

Number sense that leads to solutions of this kind develops very slowly if it is not encouraged by the teacher. In Taiwan, where students are among the leaders in international comparisons, teachers and students rely on algorithmic methods and extensive drill. Reys and Yang (1998) found deficiencies in their number sense, however.

TRY IT OUT!

Plan number sense activities frequently. Ask for "clever" solutions rather than tedious calculated ones to produce answers to problems like these:

1. $162 - 63$ **2.** $245 + 156$ **3.** $\$20 + \$10.96$

Be sure to ask for more than one "clever" way to find each answer.

CHECK IT OUT!

Baroody, A. J. (1990). How and when should place-value concepts and skills be taught? *Journal for Research in Mathematics Education, 21*(4), 281-286.

Munakata, Mika and Esposito, Linda (2005). Place value, addition, and subtraction. *Professional Resources Handbook—Grade 5.* Boston: Houghton-Mifflin.

Sobel, M. S., & Maletsky, E. M. (1999). Teaching mathematics: *A source-book of aids, activities, and strategies.* Boston: Allyn & Bacon.

---

* For more information about the research base for this unit of *Houghton Mifflin Math,* see *Professional Resources Handbook, Grade 5.*

Research Support* for Unit 2

TO: **Fifth Grade Teachers**

SUBJECT: **The Distributive Principle in Action**

Place value numeration and the distributive principle are fundamental in performing multiplication and division of whole numbers with two or more digits:

$$
\begin{array}{ccccccccc}
963 & \rightarrow & 900 + 60 + 3 & \rightarrow & 900 & \rightarrow & 60 & \rightarrow & 3 \\
\times\ 3 & & \times\ \qquad\qquad 3 & & \times\ 3 & & \times\ 3 & & \times 3 \\
& & & & 2{,}700 & + & 180 & + & 9
\end{array}
$$

$$963 \div 3 \ \rightarrow \ (900 + 60 + 3) \div 3 \rightarrow (900 \div 3) + (60 \div 3) + (3 \div 3)$$
$$300 \quad + \quad 20 \quad + \quad 1$$

Note the important roles that place value and the distributive property play in each example. The symbol pattern for the distributive principle, $a \times (b + c) = (a \times b) + (a \times c)$, may become so familiar that students confuse similar patterns with the actual distributive principle. Expressions such as those shown below occur frequently in number theory and algebra.

$$\frac{6 \times 9}{3} = \tfrac{1}{3} \times (6 + 9) \qquad\qquad \frac{6 \times 9}{3} = \tfrac{1}{3} \times (6 \times 9)$$

Many students will divide *both* 6 and 9 by 3 in the second example and then multiply to obtain 6 rather than the correct answer, 18.

TRY IT OUT!

Give parallel problems involving the same numbers, in which the distributive principle applies in one example but not in the other. Compare and discuss students' answers.

1a) $3 \times (300 + 60)$ **1b)** $3 \times (300 \times 60)$

2a) $(70 \div 7) \div 7$ **2b)** $(70 - 7) \div 7$

3a) $\dfrac{100 + 40 + 5}{5}$ **3b)** $\dfrac{100 \times 40 \times 5}{5}$

Emphasize how important it is to know when the distributive principle applies and when it does not.

CHECK IT OUT!

Evered, Lisa (2005). Multiplication, division, and algebra. *Professional Resources Handbook—Grade 5.* Boston: Houghton-Mifflin.

Kieran, C. (1992). The learning and teaching of algebra. In D. A. Grouws (Ed.), *Handbook of research on mathematics teaching and learning* (pp. 390-419). New York: Macmillan Co.

Nickson, M. (2000). *Teaching and learning mathematics: A teacher's guide to recent research.* London: Cassell.

* For more information about the research base for this unit of *Houghton Mifflin Math,* see *Professional Resources Handbook, Grade 5.*

Research Support* for Unit 3

TO: **Fifth Grade Teachers**

SUBJECT: **Don't Miss Our Winter Sale!**

The ability to interpret data and to read graphs has become more and more important in American life. Middle school students need to develop these life skills and, in particular, to learn how to avoid being misled by displays of data that are intended to deceive.

Despite all the benefits the Internet and the World Wide Web have brought Americans, they also have made the uninformed citizen very vulnerable to misleading data. Teachers can begin to help children evaluate tables, graphs, and statistics intelligently.

TRY IT OUT!

Start a collection of misleading tables, graphs, and statistics that appear in newspapers, magazines, and on the Internet. Examples such as the following are ideal:

**"Drivers under 25 responsible for more than half
of all automobile accidents"**

"Stock prices rebound sharply"

"Don't miss out on our winter sale"
Price Reductions
Average 70% Off

	Regular Price	Sale Price
Blouses	$30	$28
Skirts	$45	$40
Bathing Suits	$75	$ 2

Discuss why these kinds of information are misleading. Divide the class into work groups of 3 or 4 students. Have each group make up an ad, graph, or table intended to mislead. Exchange the group's work to see if another group can detect and explain the deception.

CHECK IT OUT!

Cathcart, W. G., Pothier, Y. M., Vance, J. H., & Bezuk, H. S. (2003). *Learning mathematics in elementary and middle schools.* Englewood Cliffs, NJ: Merrill Prentice-Hall.

Friel, S. N., Curcio, F. R., & Bright, G. W. (2001). Making sense of graphs: Critical factors influencing comprehension and instructional implications. *Journal for Research in Mathematics Education, 32*, 124-158.

Maldonado, Luz (2005). Measurement, data, and graphing. *Professional Resources Handbook—Grade 5.* Boston: Houghton-Mifflin.

* For more information about the research base for this unit of *Houghton Mifflin Math*, see *Professional Resources Handbook, Grade 5.*

Research Support* for Unit 4

TO: **Fifth Grade Teachers**

SUBJECT: **Let's Play the Decimal Game!**

Fraction and decimal representations of rational numbers continue to confuse some students as they enter the middle grades. Sweeney and Quinn (2000) recommend that the teacher conduct an extensive pre-assessment of students' understanding of fractions and decimals through games rather than by written tests. The flexibility and variety of game activities allow the teacher to plan instruction in operations with rational numbers to take advantage of students' strengths and to remediate weaknesses. Comprehensive use of grid paper, diagrams, physical models, and number lines is recommended to develop deep understanding of fraction and decimal forms of rational numbers and operations with them.

In the case of decimal notation, the relation of decimals and base-ten place value must be stressed. Thompson and Walker (1996) recommend the use of calculators to associate decimals such as 1.1 appearing in the calculator's display with concrete materials or grid images modeling the same decimal.

TRY IT OUT!

Have students work in pairs—one student uses the calculator while the second has materials to model decimals. The second student models a decimal, say 1.1, on a grid or a place-value mat. The first student interprets the model and enters the interpretation on the calculator. Additional "places" are created on the grid or workmat while the student with the calculator enters the interpretation of the model to produce the decimal display. Students should be encouraged to verbalize their understanding. Calculator-materials roles should be shared by the pair. The calculator-materials activity can be extended to conceptualize addition and subtraction of decimals.

CHECK IT OUT!

Esposito, Linda (2005). Addition and subtraction of fractions and decimals. *Professional Resources Handbook—Grade 5.* Boston: Houghton-Mifflin.

Sweeney, E. S., & Quinn, R. J. (1999). Concentration: Connecting fractions, decimals, and percents. *Mathematics Teaching in the Middle School, 4*(5), 324-328.

Thompson, C. S., & Walker, V. (1996). Connecting decimals and other mathematical content. *Teaching Children Mathematics, 2,* 496-502.

* For more information about the research base for this unit of *Houghton Mifflin Math,* see *Professional Resources Handbook, Grade 5.*

Research Support* for Unit 5

TO: **Fifth Grade Teachers**

SUBJECT: **Grid Paper Multiplication**

It is in multiplying and dividing rational numbers that the characterizations of multiplication as repeated addition, and division as repeated subtraction, break down. For example, the description of $\frac{7}{8} \times \frac{2}{3}$ as an addition of $\frac{2}{3}$ "repeated" exactly $\frac{7}{8}$ times is meaningless. At least one factor must be a whole number for repeated addition to make intuitive sense!

Other means of conceptualizing multiplication of rational numbers must be found. Manipulative materials or a simple grid paper can be used effectively. Grid paper models have the added advantage of being easily extended from work with rational numbers in fraction form to rationals in decimal form.

TRY IT OUT!

Begin with the example $\frac{7}{8} \times \frac{2}{3}$. Draw a rectangle on grid paper that is 8 units long and 3 units wide.

Shade 7 of the 8 columns blue and 2 of the 3 rows yellow. The area of the green rectangle (shaded both yellow and blue) represents the numerator of the product of $\frac{7}{8}$ and $\frac{2}{3}$. The denominator is the area of the large rectangle or 24. Hence, $\frac{7}{8} \times \frac{2}{3} = \frac{14}{24}$ ($\frac{7}{12}$ reduced to lowest terms).

CHECK IT OUT!

Evered, Lisa and DeBello, Joan (2005). Multiplication and division of fractions and decimals. *Professional Resources Handbook—Grade 5.* Boston: Houghton-Mifflin.

Oppenheimer, L., & Hunting, R. P. (1999). Relating fractions and decimals: Listening to students talk. *Mathematics Teaching in the Middle School, 4*(5), 318-321.

Pitkethly, A., & Hunting, R. P. (1996). A review of recent research in the area of initial fraction concepts. *Educational Studies in Mathematics, 30,* 5-38.

---

* For more information about the research base for this unit of *Houghton Mifflin Math*, see *Professional Resources Handbook, Grade 5.*

Research Support* for Unit 6

TO: **Fifth Grade Teachers**

SUBJECT: **Girls Can Improve Their Spatial Abilities Too!**

Historically, geometry and measurement were closely related. The word "geometry" combines the Greek word "geo," meaning "land," and "metry," meaning "measure." Because of this historical connection, school geometry can provide many real-world situations and problems of interest to children in the middle grades. Further, geometry helps children develop spatial and visual thinking. Geometry provides girls with opportunities to improve their spatial abilities—the one area of mathematics where girls seem to lag behind boys.

The Dutch educators, Pierre and Dina Van Hiele, used their long experience as teachers to conjecture that geometric learning could be partitioned into five levels, with Level 3 the principal focus of the middle grades. Level 3 activities require understanding of the relationships between geometric figures and their properties, including measurements that distinguish various geometric figures.

TRY IT OUT!

Two important measurement concepts in geometry are perimeter and area. Here, visual thinking and number sense can be merged productively.

Question: Can two triangles have the same perimeter but not be congruent?

Answer: Of course they can! If the perimeter of a triangle is 12, the sides could be 3, 4, and 5 units long, since $3 + 4 + 5 = 12$. But the sides also could be 2, 5, and 5, since $2 + 5 + 5 = 12$. Could the sides be 2, 4, and 6? Why not?

CHECK IT OUT!

Clements, D. H., & Battista, M. T. (1992). Geometry and spatial reasoning. In D. A. Grouws (Ed.), *Handbook of research on mathematics teaching and learning* (pp. 420-464). New York: Macmillan Co.

Van Hiele, P. M. (1986). *Structure and insight.* Orlando, FL: Academic Press.

Walker, Erica and Maldonado, Luz (2005). Geometry and measurement. *Professional Resources Handbook—Grade 5.* Boston: Houghton-Mifflin.

* For more information about the research base for this unit of *Houghton Mifflin Math,* see *Professional Resources Handbook, Grade 5.*

Research Support* for Unit 7

TO: **Fifth Grade Teachers**

SUBJECT: **Basic Facts Are Still Fundamental**

Proportional reasoning has been called a "watershed concept" in the middle school grades. The foundation students receive in proportional reasoning prepares them for the study of higher-level mathematics.

Students may have been introduced informally to ratio and proportion earlier, but it is not until the fifth grade that difficulties with these concepts begin to appear. For example, 85% of fifth graders answered the following problem incorrectly:

> A class needs 5 leaves each day to feed 2 caterpillars.
>
> How many leaves would they need for 12 caterpillars?

A common mistake is to view the problem additively:

> 12 caterpillars is 10 more than 2, so add 10 to 5 leaves,
>
> and only 15 leaves are needed.

Mistakes like this stem from the fact that students do not really think about what is going on. Even in writing and using proportions, it is essential that students understand what the proportion says and why cross-multiplying is an effective way of finding an answer.

TRY IT OUT!

One important strategy for solving proportions that does not involve cross-multiplication directly is called "unitizing." Consider the following problem:

If Gary can buy 14 baseballs for $7, how much would 40 baseballs cost?

Rather than writing and solving a proportion, a student who can "unitize" would realize that $7 divided by 14 yields 50¢ per baseball, and that therefore 40 baseballs would cost 40×50¢, or $20.

CHECK IT OUT!

Goldberg, Adam (2005). Ratio, proportion, percent, and probability. *Professional Resources Handbook—Grade 5.* Boston: Houghton-Mifflin.

Kenney, P. A., Lindquist, M. M., & Heffernan, C. L. (2002). Butterflies and caterpillars: Multiplicative and proportional reasoning in early grades. In *Making sense of fractions, ratios, and proportions: 2002 NTM yearbook* (pp. 87-108). Reston, VA: National Council of Teachers of Mathematics.

Lo, J. J., & Watanabe, T. (1997). Developing ratio and proportion schemes: A story of a fifth grader. *Journal for Research in Mathematics Education, 28,* 216-236.

* For more information about the research base for this unit of *Houghton Mifflin Math,* see *Professional Resources Handbook, Grade 5.*

Research Support* for Unit 8

TO: **Fifth Grade Teachers**

SUBJECT: **Finding Patterns by "Growing Squares"**

According to various investigators, mathematics in Grades 5 and 6 must be extended beyond the traditional emphasis on number to include more preparation for algebra. Too many students do not survive the abrupt introduction of variables, integers, and equations in ninth grade algebra. The 1993 Algebra Initiative Colloquium recommended that algebra be "de-coursified," that is, algebra should not be treated as a unified set of topics, but rather treated throughout the elementary and middle school curricula.

In Grades 3–5, students were encouraged to investigate numerical and geometric patterns and express them mathematically. Often these investigations can take the form of games. The objectives of algebraic games should be to stimulate students' curiosity and problem-solving ability.

Many teachers use games more for their recreational value without realizing the considerable mathematical richness available in many games. *NCTM Standards* (1989) suggests a "growing squares" game in which students are encouraged to find patterns in the areas of squares from the first to later squares of the game (p. 159). The pattern can be expressed algebraically and used to predict the area of the 10th, 100th or an arbitrary square in the sequence.

TRY IT OUT!

Make a sequence of squares using squared paper.

Use grid paper to show this sequence of square numbers: 1, 4, 9, 25, ...

Various kinds of patterns can be observed:

1. The sequence of areas alternate from odd to even terms.

2. To obtain the second area, add 3 squares to the first area. To obtain the area of the third square, add 5 to the area of the second one, and so on.

Find any pattern...express it algebraically if you can, and use it to predict the area of, say, the 100th square.

CHECK IT OUT!

Crocker, D., & Long, B. (2002). Rice + technology = an exponential experience! *Mathematics Teaching in the Middle School, 7*(7), 404-407.

Shoaf, Mary Margaret (2005). Algebra, integers, and coordinate graphing. *Professional Resources Handbook—Grade 5.* Boston: Houghton-Mifflin.

Widmer, C. C., & Sheffield, L. J. (1994). Putting the fun into functions through the use of manipulatives, computers, and calculators. *School Science and Mathematics, 94*(7), 350-355.

* For more information about the research base for this unit of *Houghton Mifflin Math*, see *Professional Resources Handbook, Grade 5.*

Additional Answers

Chapter 1

Lesson 4, pp. 10–13

Explain Your Thinking: The hundreds place is the next greatest place. If a number has 5 or more hundreds, it rounds up to the next thousand. If a number has fewer than 5 hundreds, the number in the thousands place stays the same and the following digits become zeros.

Quick Check

4. $(5 \times 10^3) + (9 \times 10^2) + (5 \times 10^1) + (6 \times 10^0)$

5. $(7 \times 10^5) + (3 \times 10^4) + (4 \times 10^3) + (5 \times 10^2) + (8 \times 10^0)$

6. $(9 \times 10^4) + (5 \times 10^3) + (9 \times 10^1) + (6 \times 10^0)$

Lesson 5, pp. 14–15

33. Asia and Africa; *check students' place-value charts;* a good answer will include the following point:
- The place-value chart shows that Asia and Africa each has the digit two in the tenths place, and a digit or digits in places to the right of the two, which means that the decimal is greater than 0.2.

Lesson 6, pp. 16–19

13. Lisa rounded up all the numbers and got an overestimate. The cost of round-trip tickets to each city is $3,250. An estimate of $5,000 would mean that each ticket was about $1,000; and the highest ticket price is $900.

Chapter Review/Test and Extra Practice, pp. 24–25

7. $(7 \times 10^{10}) + (1 \times 10^9) + (9 \times 10^8) + (8 \times 10^7) + (3 \times 10^6) + (2 \times 10^5) + (3 \times 10^3) + (4 \times 10^2) + (3 \times 10^1) + (8 \times 10^0)$

8. $(1 \times 10^9) + (2 \times 10^8) + (3 \times 10^6) + (4 \times 10^5) + (8 \times 10^4) + (7 \times 10^3) + (3 \times 10^2) + (8 \times 10^1) + (6 \times 10^0)$

9. $(3 \times 10^1) + (8 \times 10^0)$

10. $(3 \times 10^3) + (4 \times 10^2) + (2 \times 10^0)$

Set A

1. sixteen thousand, three hundred sixty-two; 16 thousand, 362; $(1 \times 10,000) + (6 \times 1,000) + (3 \times 100) + (6 \times 10) + (2 \times 1)$

2. two hundred seventy-nine thousand, eighteen; 279 thousand, 18; $(2 \times 100,000) + (7 \times 10,000) + (9 \times 1,000) + (1 \times 10) + (8 \times 1)$

3. thirty-six thousand, one hundred nine, 36 thousand, 109; $(3 \times 10,000) + (6 \times 1,000) + (1 \times 100) + (9 \times 1)$

4. one hundred forty-eight thousand, three hundred, 148 thousand, 300; $(1 \times 100,000) + (4 \times 10,000) + (8 \times 1,000) + (3 \times 100)$

5. five hundred sixty-seven thousand, two hundred fifty-five; 567 thousand, 255; $(5 \times 100,000) + (6 \times 10,000) + (7 \times 1,000) + (2 \times 100) + (5 \times 10) + (5 \times 1)$

6. one hundred thousand, two; 100 thousand, 2; $(1 \times 100,000) + (2 \times 1)$

Set B

1. $(7 \times 10^3) + (9 \times 10^1) + (4 \times 10^0)$

2. $(4 \times 10^4) + (3 \times 10^3) + (7 \times 10^2) + (2 \times 10^1) + (9 \times 10^0)$

3. $(3 \times 10^5) + (9 \times 10^3) + (3 \times 10^2) + (9 \times 10^0)$

4. $(8 \times 10^5) + (7 \times 10^4) + (3 \times 10^3) + (2 \times 10^2) + (9 \times 10^0)$

Set C

3. $(3 \times 10^7) + (4 \times 10^6) + (5 \times 10^5) + (3 \times 10^3) + (5 \times 10^2) + (9 \times 10^1) + (8 \times 10^0)$

4. $(8 \times 10^{10}) + (1 \times 10^9) + (9 \times 10^7) + (4 \times 10^6) + (3 \times 10^5) + (8 \times 10^4) + (9 \times 10^3) + (2 \times 10^0)$

5. $(4 \times 10^{11}) + (3 \times 10^{10}) + (3 \times 10^8) + (9 \times 10^7) + (8 \times 10^6) + (2 \times 10^5) + (7 \times 10^4) + (8 \times 10^3) + (2 \times 10^1) + (1 \times 10^0)$

Chapter 2

Chapter Review/Test and Extra Practice, p. 44

20. Not enough information; missing how many cars were parked at 5:00 p.m.

Write About It: *Possible answer:* In addition, regroup when the digits being added have a sum of ten or greater. In subtraction, regroup when the digit being subtracted is greater than the digit it is being subtracted from.

Chapter 3

Lesson 4, p. 70

41. $(4 \times 90,000) + (4 \times 2,000) + (4 \times 100)$; 368,400

42. $(8 \times 900) + (8 \times 20) + (8 \times 5)$; 7,400

43. $(9 \times 400) + (9 \times 30)$; 3,870

44. $(8 \times 80,000) + (8 \times 2,000) + (8 \times 700) + (8 \times 50) + (8 \times 2)$; 662,016

45. $(4 \times 90,000) + (4 \times 2,000) + (4 \times 700) + (4 \times 50) + (4 \times 1)$; 371,004

Lesson 5, p. 73

37. *Answers will vary.* Find $9 \times 5 = 45$, then write a zero for each zero that appears in the factors: 450,000.

Lesson 6, p. 75

25. Rounding. *Possible answer:* The actual factors 49 and 28 are closer to rounded factors 50 and 30 then they are to the front-end estimate factors 40 and 20.

26. No. *Possible answer:* Using rounding, both factors are rounded up to give $30 \times 30 = 900$. Since both factors are rounded up, the actual answer is less than 900. So, Nina does not have enough prints to earn $1,000.

Lesson 7, p. 77

27. $(28 \times 70) + (28 \times 6)$, or $(20 \times 76) + (8 \times 76)$; 2,128

28. $(57 \times 10) + (57 \times 4)$, or $(50 \times 14) + (7 \times 14)$; 798

29. $(20 \times 206) + (9 \times 206)$; 5,974

30. $(30 \times 532) + (8 \times 532)$; 20,216

Chapter 4

Lesson 7, pp. 102–105

34. $n = 4$; check drawings. *Answers will vary. Possible answer:* The model showed that there are 4 groups of 6, or 24 in all.

39. $3n = 18$; $n \times 3 = 18$; $18 \div n = 3$; $18 \div 3 = n$; *Possible answer:* Once you write the fact family, you can use the fact $18 \div 3$ to find that $n = 6$.

40. $6 \times 12 = 72$. *Possible answer:* This equation is not the same as $6n = 12$. You need to find the number that when multiplied by 6 equals 12, not 72. $6 \times 2 = 12$

Lesson 7, page 105

Math Reasoning

Possible answer: All the numbers that are divisible by 10 also have a triangle on them. In addition, number 5 and the numbers in the column below it all have triangles in them.

1. *Possible answer:* Every other column in the chart (those that have 2, 4, 6, 8, and 10 at the top) has an X on them.

2. *Possible answer:* For numbers divisible by 4, alternate columns, those that begin with 4, 8, 12, 16, and 20, have squares in them. All the numbers divisible by 8 are in those columns too. The numbers divisible by 8 make alternate diagonal rows with numbers that are divisible by 4 only.

3. *Possible answer:* The numbers that are divisible by 3 make a right to left diagonal pattern. All the numbers that are divisible by 6 are part of that pattern too. The numbers that are divisible by 6 make alternate diagonal patterns that go left to right.

Chapter 6

Lesson 4, pp. 157–159

39. 6 m; 58 dm = 5.8 m and 5.8 m is closer to 6 m than to 5 m.

40. *Possible answer is:* To change metric units, you can multiply or divide, just as you do with customary units. Changing metric units is different than changing customary units because you can change metric units simply by moving the decimal point to the right or the left.

42. *Possible answer is:* Millimeter; since it is the smallest unit, it provides the greatest precision.

Lesson 5, pp. 161–162

28. *Possible answer is:* Deciliter or milliliter, because a glass holds less than 1 liter of water.

29. *Possible answer is:* Milliliter, because an eye dropper holds much less than 1 deciliter.

30. *Possible answer is:* Milligram or gram, because a hummingbird has a mass of less than 1 kilogram.

31. *Possible answer is:* Metric ton or kilogram, because an elephant might have a mass of over 1,000 kilograms.

32. more than 1 L; 3×350 mL = 1,050 mL; 1,050 mL $> +1$L

33. 2 1.5-L bottles; $2 \times \$1.79 = \$3.58$; $\$3.58 < \$3.68$ (the total price of a 1-L bottle and 2-L bottle) and $\$3.58 < \$3.87$ (the total price of a 3 1-L bottles)

34. yes; 6×350 mL = 2,100 mL or 2.1 L; 2.1 L for $2.39 is a better buy than 2 L for $2.39

36. *Possible answer:* 10 dL = 1 L, and 300 dL $\div$ 10 dL = 30 L

39. 15–27 kg is too light for a gorilla; the gorilla has a mass closer to 150–270 kg

Lesson 6, p. 164

Explain Your Thinking: When you add feet and inches, you regroup after you have found the sum if there are 12 or more inches in the sum.

Lesson 7, p.167

Science Connection

1. 12 h 46 min; found the elapsed time between 9:43 A.M. and noon, and the elapsed time between noon and 10:29 P.M., then added those two times.

2. 12:24 A.M. on Saturday morning; found the elapsed time between noon and 11:37 A.M. and subtracted that from 12 h 47 min, then added the difference to 12:00 to find the next high tide.

Chapter 7

10. five hundred eighty-six thousand, one hundred forty-seven

11. two thousand, three hundred forty-six

12. thirty-four thousand, five hundred one

13. two hundred fifty-seven thousand, eight hundred twenty-four

Lesson 5, p. 185

3. It looks like attendance is going up when it is really going down because years are reversed.

4. Even though 15 people chose Walrus and 10 chose Polar Bear, the bar for Walrus is more than twice as tall as the bar for Polar Bear.

5.
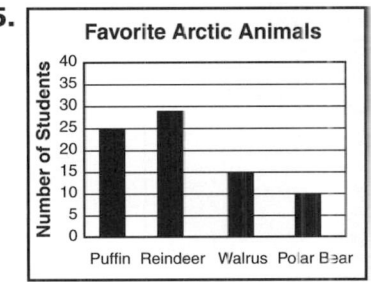

Lesson 6, p. 187

Quick Check

2. With a bar graph, you would only show the data for each month. January would show 2,000 pairs sold; February, 1,000; March, 2,000; April, 1,000.

3. The increase in sales would appear more gradual.

Chapter 7 *(continued)*

Chapter Review/Test and Extra Practice, pp. 188–189

3.

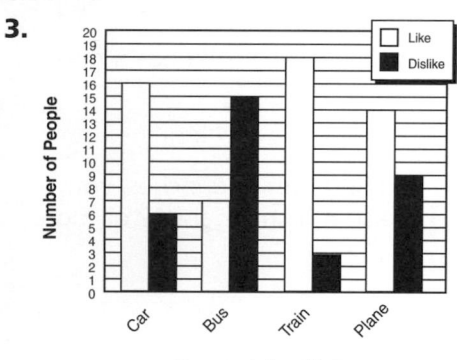

5.

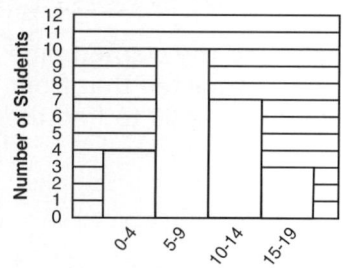

9. Ken: between Thursday and Friday; Kim: between Saturday and Sunday

10. *Possible answers:* Scale for *y*-axis uneven; some labels missing from *y*-axis; titles for *x*-axis and *y*-axis interchanged.

Set B

1.

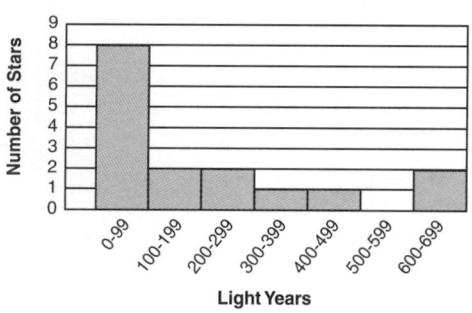

Set C

1.

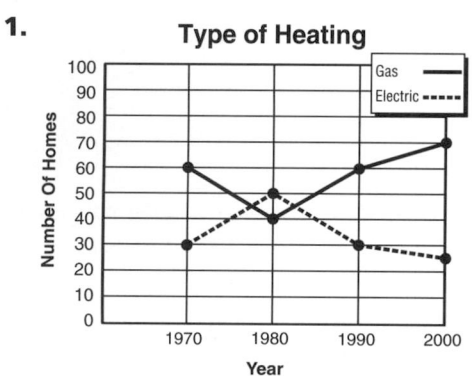

Set E

1. The vertical scale between 0 and 100 has been broken; making the increase in CD sales look greater than it really is.

Chapter 8

Lesson 2, p. 197

Take a Break:

1. Yes; since $5 \times 78 = 390$, $6 \times 80 = 480$, and $480 - 390 = 90$, you can raise your mean to 80 by getting a 90 on the sixth quiz.

2. No; since $6 \times 82 = 492$, $492 - 390 = 102$, and there are only 100 possible points on a quiz, you cannot score enough points on the sixth quiz to raise your mean to 82.

3. No; if you score 100 on each of your remaining quizzes, you will have 890 points. $890 \div 10 = 89$.

Lesson 3, pp. 198–199

Explain Your Thinking: *Possible answer:* I added all the numbers and divided by the number of addends to find the mean; I took the average of the tenth and eleventh numbers in the plot to find the median; I looked for the number repeated most often to find the mode; I subtracted the smallest number from the greatest number to find the range.

7. *Possible answer cluster:* 2–18, Most countries have between 2 and 18 amusement parks; only three countries have a large number of such parks: 38, 47, or 74.

14. John's median score is 17. Amy should score at least 18 points to have a better-than-even chance of beating John.

15. *Possible answer:* The median of John's scores, 17, is not a possible score, since each ring scores 2 points.

Lesson 4, p. 203

7. 73,600. *Possible answer:* The number increases by 4,000 every week.

Lesson 5, pp. 205–207

Explain Your Thinking: *Possible answer:* Because sometimes one statistic is not the best choice to describe the data.

2. *Possible answer:* You can expect to pay $10 because the mode of $10 accounts for seven of ten ticket prices. The median of $10 and the mode of $10 are better than the mean for predicting the amount you can expect to pay, because the mean of $9 is "pulled" lower by the few lower numbers.

3.

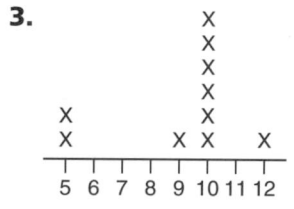

4. *Possible answer:* The median and mode are both $10. You can still expect to pay about $10 for a ticket.

6. *Possible answer:* 26; the median of 26 is a better statistic to use than the mean because most of the data cluster between 22 and 28.

7. *Possible answer:* The data would fall in two clusters: 22–28 and 48–52. The median, 38, would best describe the data because half of the numbers are less than 38 and half greater than 38.

13. *Possible answers:* The typical temperature is the mean temperature of 87°F because the data is spread evenly over a range and the mode is lower than most of the data. The typical temperature is the median temperature of 89° because half of the temperatures are lower than 89° and half are higher.

14. *Possible answer:* No, because 80°F is lower than most of the data. The brochure's writer used the mode to create the description.

Quick Check, p. 207

1. *Check tallies.* They should show the following: 4 years, 2; 5 years, 1; 6 years, 3; 7 years, 3; 8 years, 7; 9 years, 8; 10 years, 6.

5. *Possible answer:* The median, because the low score of 61 pulls the mean away from the rest of the data.

Chapter Review/Test and Extra Practice, pp. 208–209

3. cluster: 34–35; gaps: 32–33, 36–39; mean: 34.6; median: 35; mode: 35; range: 9

4. clusters: 51–53, 59–60; gap: 54–58; mean: 57.3; median: 59; mode: 60; range: 9

8. *Possible answer:* 35; since the mean, median, and mode are all around 35, the number of sit-ups the person typically does in 5 minutes is 35.

9. *Possible answer:* 59 or 60; the three low scores pull the mean away from the rest of the data, so the median and the mode best describe the person's typical score.

Set A

1–3 Check line plots.

1. mean, 16; median, 18; mode, 22; range, 20; there are clusters at 4–5, 14–15, 18–19, and 22–24; there are gaps between 6–9, 11–13, 16–17 and 20–21.

2. mean, 23; median, 24.5; modes, 14, 26, 29; range, 15; there are clusters at 23–26, and 28–29; there are gaps between 15–17 and 21–22.

3. mean, 98.3; median, 99.5; mode, 100; range, 16; there is a cluster at 97-101; there is a gap between 88–96.

4. mean, 44.4; median, 45.5; modes, 46, 49

5. mean, 64.5; median, 66; mode, 66, 67, 68

6. mean, 118.3; median, 119.5; mode, 120

Chapter 9

Lesson 3, pp. 229–230

14. 1, 13; 1, 19; GCF 1

15. 1, 2, 3, 4, 6, 12; 1, 2, 3, 4, 6, 8, 12, 24; GCF 12

16. 1, 2, 3, 4, 6, 9, 12, 18, 36; 1, 3, 5, 9, 15, 45; GCF 9

17. 2×5; $2^3 \times 3$; GCF 2

18. 2×3; 3×5; GCF 3

19. 3^2; $2^2 \times 7$; GCF 1

20. 2×5; 5×11; GCF 5

21. $2^2 \times 3$; $2 \times 3 \times 7$; GCF 6

22. 3×5^2; $2^3 \times 3 \times 5$; GCF 15

23. $2^2 \times 5$; 5^3; GCF 5

24. 5×7; $3 \times 5 \times 7$; GCF 35

25. 2×5; $2^4 \times 3 \times 5$; GCF 10

26. $2 \times 3 \times 5$; $2 \times 3 \times 5^2$; GCF 30

33. From left to right: Blue Bayou, Red River, Fink Plateau, Green Grass, Orange Outback

38. Yes. A prime number is a counting number greater than 1 with exactly two different factors − 1 and the number itself. 1×3; 1×5; 1×7; 1×11

Lesson 4, p. 233

Explain Your Thinking: *Possible answer:* Divide the number by each number and look for a remainder of zero; however, this method does not reveal if it is the least common multiple.

Lesson 5, pp. 237–238

Explain Your Thinking: *Possible answer:* If a fraction's numerator is greater than or equal to its denominator, it can be written as a mixed number or whole number.

28. $37 \div 4$. *Possible answer:* Find the quotient, 9 R1. Since the quotient represents 9 wholes with a remainder of $\frac{1}{4}$, the mixed number $\frac{37}{4}$ is equal to $9\frac{1}{4}$.

29.

Lesson 6, p. 241

Explain Your Thinking: *Possible answer:* Since the first denominator had to be multiplied by 6 to get the second denominator, the first numerator had to be multiplied by 6 to get the missing numerator.

15. *Possible answer:* An infinite number; you can multiply the numerator and denominator by an infinite number of numbers.

17. mean, 27; median, 26; mode, 24; range, 8

18. mean, 31; median, 20; mode, 20; range, 95

Lesson 7, p. 243

6. $\frac{6}{15}$; *Possible answer:* Use the factor tree to find the prime factors of 90: 5, 3, 3, 2. Use the Venn diagram to try arrangements of factors and find a pair of products with a difference of 9.

Lesson 8, p. 247

18. *Possible response:* It is important to use a denominator that is a power of 10 when writing a decimal in the form of an equivalent fraction because the place value of a decimal is in powers of 10.

19. *Possible response:* You use a power of 10 equivalent to the place value of the decimal you are writing as an equivalent fraction.

Chapter 9 *(continued)*

Lesson 9, p. 250

24. No; his total of $71 means he buys a weekly pass for $60 and a round trip ticket for $11, and to take 8 round trips on those tickets he must take 7 round trips one week and 1 round trip the next week.

25. *Possible response:* Either buy two 10-trip passes and 2 round-trip tickets or 12 round-trip tickets to make 3 round trips a week for 4 weeks during one month. Either way, the cost will be $132.

Chapter 10

Lesson 8, p. 277

Calculator Connection

2. the numerator remains 2 and the denominator doubles; $\frac{2}{80}$, $\frac{2}{160}$; each decimal is half the preceding decimal: 0.4, 0.2, 0.1, 0.05;0.025, 0.125

3. the numerator increases by one and the denominator increases by 25; $\frac{4}{100}$, $\frac{5}{125}$; each decimal remains 0.04: 0.04, 0.04;

Chapter Review/Test p. 278

Write About It: Mandy added the denominators instead of finding the least common denominator. Since the least common multiple of 5 and 15 is 15, the least common denominator would be 15.

$\frac{3}{5} = \frac{9}{15}$; $\frac{9}{15} + \frac{12}{15} = \frac{21}{15} = 1\frac{6}{15} = 1\frac{2}{5}$.

Chapter 11

Extra Practice, p. 295

Set A

1. $\frac{3}{10} + \frac{5}{10} = \frac{8}{10} = 0.8$

2. $5\frac{3}{10} + 6\frac{4}{10} = 11\frac{7}{10} = 11.7$

3. $\frac{31}{100} + \frac{52}{100} = \frac{83}{100} = 0.83$

4. $\frac{12}{100} + \frac{63}{100} = \frac{75}{100} = 0.75$

5. $\frac{83}{100} - \frac{60}{100} = \frac{23}{100} = 0.23$

6. $\frac{65}{100} - \frac{27}{100} = \frac{38}{100} = 0.38$

7. $1\frac{82}{100} - 1\frac{36}{100} = \frac{46}{100} = 0.46$

8. $1\frac{91}{100} - \frac{4}{100} = 1\frac{87}{100} = 1.87$

9. $\frac{85}{100} + \frac{90}{100} = \frac{175}{100} = 1\frac{75}{100} = 1.75$

10. $\frac{70}{100} + \frac{23}{100} = \frac{93}{100} = 0.93$

11. $2\frac{10}{100} - \frac{6}{100} = 2\frac{4}{100} = 2.04$

12. $1\frac{76}{100} - \frac{17}{100} = 1\frac{59}{100} = 1.59$

Chapter 15

Lesson 3, pp. 396–397

12. *Check students' drawings.* It is not possible to draw an equilateral, right triangle. An equilateral triangle has only 60° angles.

20. 45°; the two angles have equal measures and the third angle = 90° and 180° − 90° = 90°; 90° ÷ 2 = 45°

Lesson 4, pp. 398–399

1. *Check drawings.* **2.** *Check drawings.*

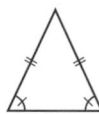 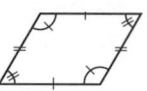

Explain Your Thinking: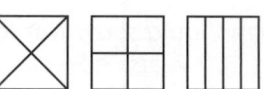

3. *Check drawings.* **4.** *Check drawings.*

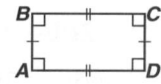 

5. *Check drawings.*

Lesson 5, p. 402

1. rectangle, parallelogram, quadrilateral, irregular polygon

2. trapezoid, quadrilateral, irregular polygon

3. octagon, regular polygon

4. quadrilateral, irregular polygon

5. pentagon, regular polygon

6. parallelogram, quadrilateral, irregular polygon

7. decagon, regular polygon

8. polygon, 149°; 360° − (63° + 68° + 80°)

9. polygon, 60°; 360° − (120° + 90° + 90°)

10. not a polygon

11. polygon, 58°; 360° − (122° + 122°) = 116°; 116° ÷ 2 = 58°

12. polygon, 90°; 360° − (3 × 90°)

13. not a polygon

14. polygon, 110°; 180° − (20° + 50°)

15. polygon, 140°; 360° − (90° + 60° + 70°)

18. Yes, every square is a rhombus since every square has 4 congruent sides. No, every rhombus is not a square because not every rhombus has 4 right angles.

Lesson 5, p. 403

1. perpendicular lines, intersecting lines

2. quadrilateral, parallelogram, irregular polygon

3. right triangle, scalene triangle, irregular polygon

4. obtuse angle

5. hexagon, regular polygon

10. Yes; *Possible explanation:* I traced one figure and it coincides with the other figure when I put one on top of the other.

Lesson 6, pp. 405–406

4. *Check drawings.*   **5.** *Check drawings.*

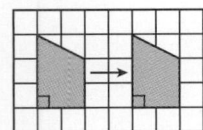   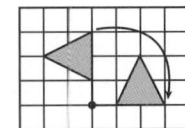

6. *Check drawings.*   **7–10.**

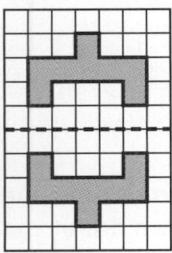   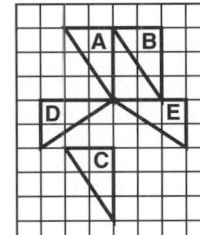

11. Rotate triangle *A* clockwise a quarter turn about point *O*.

17. Reflections and rotations can give the same result, depending on the figure, but they do not always do so.

18. By rotating, reflecting, or translating figures on top of one another, you can see if the sides and angles are congruent.

Lesson 7, pp. 409–411

4. Wrong; if you measure the angles of a regular octagon, you can see that each is 135°. There is no way to combine angles of 135° to equal 360°.

7. Bob is right. The sum of the angles that meet is 360°.

Problem-Solving Test Prep

6. Label the two circles *x* and *y*; write the GCF (4) in the intersection of the circles; find the other factors of 120 (2, 3, and 5); write one of the factors in the *x* circle and the other factors in the *y* circle. Multiply 4 times the *x* factor and then multiply 4 times the *y* factors; add the products and check to see if the sum is 52; if not, start over with a different *x* factor.

Lesson 8, p. 413

11–16. *Check drawings. Possible drawing shown.*

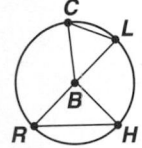

18. The length of a radius is half the length of a diameter; the length of a diameter is twice the length of a radius.

Lesson 9, p. 416

10. 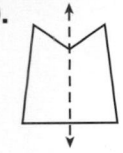   **12.**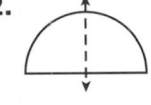

13. 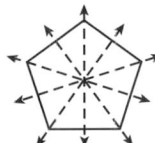   **14.** 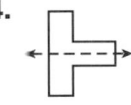   **16.**

Chapter 16

Lesson 5, pp. 434–437

Step 3: Decreasing the size of the squares increases the number of units in the perimeter, and the number of square units in the area.

16. *Possible answer:* To estimate perimeter, find the lengths of the straight side, and estimate the lengths of the curves by finding the number of vertical and horizontal units that the curves cover. Then add these lengths. To find the area, count the whole squares as 1 unit each, the partial squares as $\frac{1}{2}$ unit each, and find the total.

17. *Possible response:* Think of the figure as a large rectangle from which a smaller rectangle has been cut out. Find the area of the large rectangle, find the area of the small rectangle, and then subtract the area of the small rectangle from the area of the large rectangle.

Take a Break: *Estimates will vary. Estimates should reflect the following points.*
- The area of the tea room is equal to the area of a rectangle that is $15\frac{1}{12}$ ft. × $11\frac{1}{6}$ ft minus the area of the two small triangular regions that are outside of the left and right edges of the room. So, the area should be less than $168\frac{31}{72}$ ft
- The area of the dining room is equal to $18\frac{1}{2}$ ft × 18 ft = 333 ft²
- The area of the table is about $\frac{1}{6}$ of the area of the room.
- The long side of the rug will fit along the long side of the tea room, but the short side of the rug will not fit along the short side of the tea room. So, the rug probably will not fit.

Tetrominoes: There are 5 different tetrominoes. The 3 not shown are: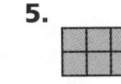

Lesson 6, pp. 438–441

Math Reasoning

Step 2: the radius; the length of the base of the parallelogram is about equal to $\frac{1}{2}$ the circumference of the circle; $A = \frac{1}{2}Cr$
Step 3: $A = \pi r^2$; $A = 50$ cm²; 28 m²

Chapter 17

Lesson 4, pp. 452–455

22. No; doubling the height only doubles the area of the front, back, and sides. It does not change the area of the top and bottom.

Quick Check

4.   **5.**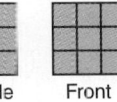

Chapter 17 *(continued)*

Lesson 4, pp. 452–455

Math Reasoning

1. *Accept reasonable answers.* A good answer will be in the range of 103 cm long by 60 cm wide.

2. *Accept reasonable answers.* A good answer will be in the range of 15 in. long by 10 in. wide.

3. *Accept reasonable answers.* A good answer will be in the range of 22 in. long by 18 in. wide.

Lesson 5, pp. 456–459

7.

14. A good response should include the following points:
    - Since earnings are increasing more than expenses are, there will probably be a profit in 2005.
    - For the same reason as above, the profit in 2005 will probably be greater than the profit in 2004, or greater than $1,750,000.

Lesson 6, pp. 460–463

24. 1,144 in.² Possible answer: Since the outside of the box is 28 in. × 46 in., and the sides are 1 in. thick, the inside of the box is 26 in. × 44 in.

29. A good response will relate the dimensions of the item being stored to the dimension of the container.

Chapter 20

Lesson 7, pp. 546–549

7. The number of pizza party winners in the first 50 tickets is greater than you would expect. *Possible answer:* There are 2 dinner winners in 50 tickets, giving an experimental probability of $\frac{1}{25}$. However, out of 800 winning tickets there are only 8 dinner winners, giving a theoretical probability of $\frac{1}{100}$. So, the number of dinner winners in the first 50 tickets is four times greater than you would expect.

Chapter Review/Test, p. 550

Write About It: *Possible answer:* Theoretical probability can be found by comparing the number of favorable outcomes with the number of all possible outcomes. In experimental probability, the number of favorable outcomes is compared to the total number of completed trials.

Chapter 23

Lesson 3, pp. 617–618

1. $^-3$; $^-2$; $^+1$;

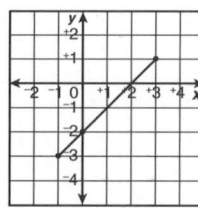

2. 2; 3; 4;

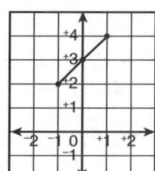

3. $^-1$, 1, 3;

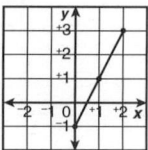

Explain Your Thinking: Find $^-2$ on the *x*-axis. Extend the line of the graph so it passes through that point. Draw a dot at that point and read across the *y*-axis to find the *y*-coordinate. The ordered pair is ($^-2$, $^-5$).

4. $^-3$; $^-2$; $^-1$; 0;

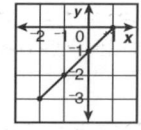

5. 1; 2; 3; 4;

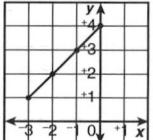

6. $^-2$; 1; 4; 7;

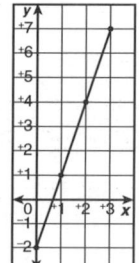

7. 1; 4; 7; 10;

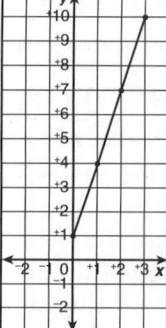

8–15. *Possible answers are shown.*

8. (0, 1); (1, 2); (2, 3);

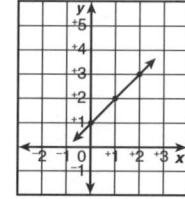

9. (0, $^-4$); (1, $^-3$); (2 ,$^-2$);

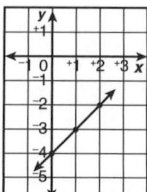

10. (0, 6); (1, 7); (2, 8);

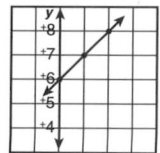

11. (0, $^-5$); (1, $^-4$); (2, $^-3$);

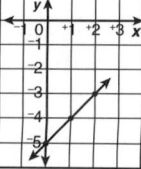

12. (0, 0); (1, 2); (2, 4);

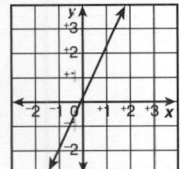

13. (0, 0); (1, 4); (2, 8);

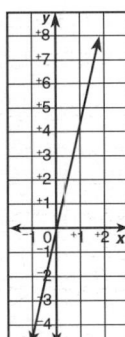

5–12.

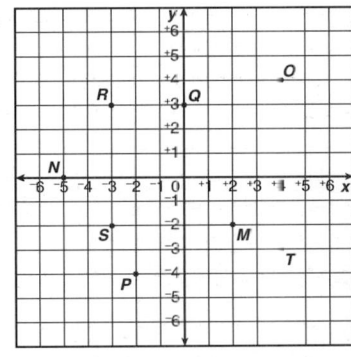

14. (0, ⁻1); (1, 2); (2, 5);

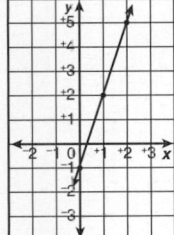

15. (0, 2); (1, 4); (2, 6);

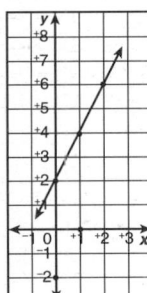

13–16. *See students' graphs. Examples given.*

13.

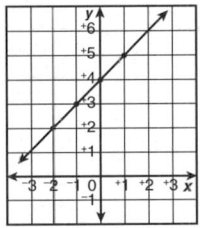

16. They are alike because they rise from left to right and pass through the origin. $y = 4x$ is steeper than $y = 2x$.

17. They both have the same steepness. $y = x - 2$ intersects the y-axis at ⁻2. $y = x + 2$ intersects the y-axis at 2.

18. Extend the line, find where $x = 8$ then find the y value. *Check students' graphs.*

14.

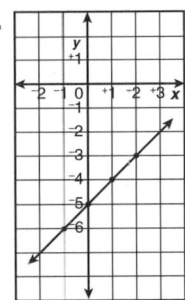

Social Studies Connection

10. *Answers will vary.* One similarity is that on both the location is described by a pair of coordinates. A difference is that on the coordinate plane the first coordinate is the x-coordinate which is to the left or right and the second is the y-coordinate which is up or down. The map's coordinates are listed north or south first and east or west second.

15.

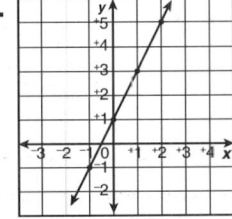

Lesson 5, p. 625

Quick Check

4.

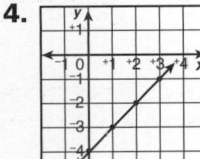

5.

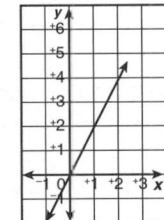

16.

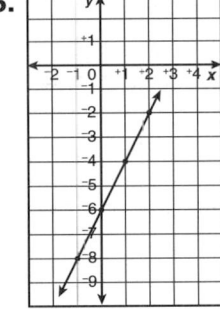

6.

Chapter 23 (continued)

Extra Practice, p. 627

Set A

8–11.

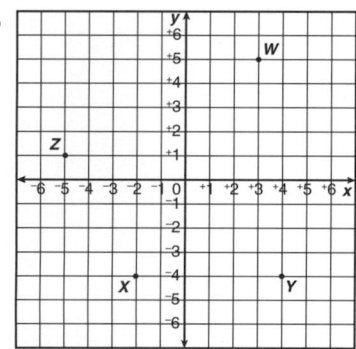

Set C

See students' graphs. Examples given.

1.

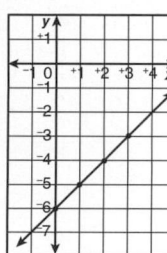

2.

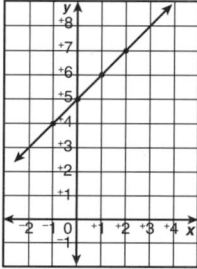

3.

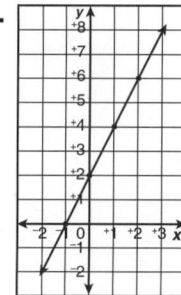

4.

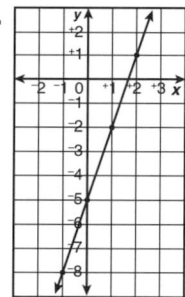

Grade 5 Index

Identity Property. *See* Properties.

Impossible events, 530

Improper fractions
dividing, 324A–327
mixed numbers as, 237–238, 316
multiplying, 316A–319

Inclusion. *See* Reaching All Learners.

Inequalities. *See* Comparing and ordering.

Input/Output tables. *See* Function tables.

Integers
absolute value and, 586A–587
adding, 598A–601
with models, 592A–595
comparing, 588A–591
coordinate plane and, 610A–613
functions and, 614A–615, 616A–619
ordering, 588A–591
patterns and, 605
subtracting, 598A–601
with models, 596A–597
using, to solve problems, 602A–605

Interest
compound, 474A–475
simple, 472A–473

Interest rate, 472

Interior, of an angle, 392

Internet. *See* Technology, Education Place.

Intersecting lines, 390A–391

Intervals
frequency table, 176A–177
graph, 172A–175, 177, 178A–181
misleading graphs and, 184A–185

Intervention. 1D, 56D, 144D, 220D, 306D, 386D, 480D, 562D; *See also* Language Intervention; Lesson Intervention.

Intervention Software. See Technology, *Ways to Success* Intervention CD-ROM.

Introduce *Found in every lesson in TE. See* for example, 4, 6, 8 in Chapter 1.

Introduction to *Houghton Mifflin Math,* T3–T32

Inverse operations
addition and subtraction, 568, 598
definition of, 562, 568
multiplication and division, 86, 569
to solve equations, 568A–571

Irregular polygons, 401

Isosceles triangles, 396A–397

Journals, keeping. *See* Keeping a Journal.

Keeping a Journal. *Found in every lesson in TE. See* for example, 5, 7, 9 in Chapter 1.

Key, for a graph, 172, 179

Language Intervention *Found on the fourth page (D) of each chapter in TE. See* for example, 2D, 26D, 58D.

Latitude, 619

Leaf, of a stem-and-leaf plot, 198

Least common denominator (LCD)
to add fractions, 260
to subtract fractions, 268

Least common multiple (LCM), 232A–235

Length. *See* Measurement.

Lesson-by-Lesson Overview. *Found on the first page (A) of each chapter in TE. See* for example, 2A, 26A, 58A.

Lesson Intervention Activities, *Found in every lesson in TE except Problem-Solving Decision. See* for example, 5, 7, 9 in Chapter 1.

Lesson Objectives. *See* Chapter Planner on second page (B) of each chapter; first page (A) of each lesson; and third page of each lesson in TE.

Lesson Organizers. *Found in every lesson in TE. See* for example, 4, 8, 10 in Chapter 1.

Lesson Planner *CD-ROM. See* Technology.

Lesson Quizzes. *Found in every lesson in TE. See* for example, 4A, 6A, 8A in Chapter 1.

Leveled practice. *Reteach, Practice, Enrichment, Problem Solving, Homework, and English Learners blackline masters are provided for every lesson. See* for example, 4A, 4B, 6A, 6B, 8A, 8B.

Likelihood of an event, 530A–531, 532

Linear functions, 616A–619

Line graph. *See* Graphs.

Line plot. *See* Graphs.

Lines
constructing perpendicular, 395
definition of, 390
intersecting, 390A–391
naming, 395
parallel, 390A–391
perpendicular, 390A–391
of symmetry, 415–416

Line segments, 386, 390A–391

Line of symmetry, 415–416

Line symmetry
exploring, 415–416
in the coordinate plane, 623–624

List
making an organized, 536A–539
making to find choices, 528A–529
making to find probability of compound events, 544A–545
making to find greatest common factor, 228A–231
making to find least common multiple, 232A–235
using, 58, 84, 222

Literature Connections
activities in TE, *See* Cross-curricular connections.
overview, 1, 57, 145, 221, 307, 387, 481, 563
selections, T50–T56

Logical Reasoning, Problem Solving Strategy, 64A–67, 242A–245

Logical thinking. *See* Math Challenge; Math Reasoning; Problem-Solving Strategies; Reasoning; Visual Thinking.

Longitude, 619

Low estimate, 338

Lowest terms fraction, 307

Magic squares, 265

Make a Model, Problem-Solving Strategy, 408A–411

Make an Organized List, Problem-Solving Strategy, 536A–539

Make a Table, Problem-Solving Strategy, 200A–203

Manipulatives, list, T3
balance scale, 160B, 163
circular objects, 438
coins, 173, 293
compass, 395, 412, 414
counters, 566, 592A–594, 596A–597
cubes, 448A–449, 460, 540
fraction strips, 249, 320A–321
grid paper, 320A–321, 510
measuring cups, 163
meter stick, 163, 438
number cards, 123, 293, 327
number cube, 197, 540
pattern blocks, 293, 408
protractor, 392A–395, 398
ruler, 148–149, 163, 173, 398, 414, 438, 499
scale, 163
straightedge, 62, 412, 506, 508, 510
tangrams, 407
tape measure, 148A–149, 163
yardstick, 163

Map scale, 499

Grade 5 Credits..

PERMISSIONS ACKNOWLEDGMENTS

Houghton Mifflin Mathematics © 2005, Grade 5 PE/TE

"Numbers," by Mary Cornish. Copyright © 2000 by the Modern Poetry Association. Reprinted by permission of the editor of *Poetry* and the author.

Cover © HMCo./Bruton Stroube Studios.

Credits

People Using Math
Rachel Carson

Rachel Carson loved nature and science. She also liked to write. When she was ten years old, she had a story published.

Rachel became a marine biologist, someone who studies plants and animals in the sea. She wrote many books about caring for our planet.

• •

Use tally marks to show how many people are in each family. Rachel lived with her mother, father, brother, and sister.

1.

Family Members	
Rachel's family	‖‖‖
My family	**Answers may vary.**

Use the tally chart to make a pictograph.

2.

Family Members	
Rachel's family	**5 symbols**
My family	**Answers may vary.**

3. Does one family have more people? _____ **Answers may vary.**

4. Write About It What can you and your family do to help care for our planet? _____ **Answers may vary.**

CHAPTER CHALLENGES

For Mathematically Promising Students

The Chapter Challenges resource book provides blackline masters for activities that explore, extend, and connect the mathematics in every chapter. To support this independent work, see the Teacher Notes for each activity.

Explore: Cube Colors, page 19, after Lesson 1
Extend: Line Plot Sums, page 21, after Lesson 3
Connect: Name Graphs, page 23, after Lesson 5

Using This Page

• Read the paragraph about Rachel Carson to children.

• Draw 3 tally marks on the board. Ask a volunteer to come up and add two tally marks to make 5. Remember to include Rachel when counting.

• Read the directions for Exercise 1 to children. Then have children tally how many family members are in their family.

• Read the directions for Exercise 2 to children. **Choose a symbol to represent each person in Rachel's family. Use the same symbol to show each person in your family. Remember to include yourself.**

• After children complete Exercises 3–4, have volunteers share their ideas for Exercise 4. Make a list on poster board of their suggestions and post it in the classroom.

NSF Children's Math Worlds

Using *Children's Math Worlds* helps develop student communication skills because of the daily work with Math Talk, a teaching practice that can be used with all lessons. The emphasis on building a helping community will also enhance student participation in all classroom discussion.

Hands-On: Make a Tally Chart

PLANNING THE LESSON

MATHEMATICS OBJECTIVE
Represent data with tally marks on a chart.

Use Lesson Planner CD-ROM for Lesson 4.1.

Meeting North Carolina's Standards

4.01 Collect, organize, describe and display data using line plots and tallies.

Daily Routines

Calendar

Refer to a class birthday list. Have a volunteer use tallies to record the number of birthdays for the current month. You can continue with other months.

Sunday	Monday	Tuesday	Wednesday	Thursday	Friday	Saturday
			1	2	3	4
5	6	7	8	9	10	11
12	13	14	15	16	17	18
19	20	21	22	23	24	25
26	27	28	29	30	31	

Vocabulary

Write the word **tally** on the board. Explain that people use the term **tally mark** to name the symbol. Ask a volunteer to use the word *tally* in a sentence.

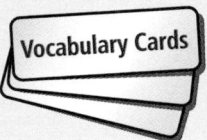

Vocabulary Cards

Lesson Transparency 4.1

Problem of the Day

Tyler buys 6 plants at the school sale. He gives 2 to his mother and 2 to his grandmother. How many plants does Tyler have left? (2)

Quick Review

$\begin{array}{r} 5 \\ -2 \\ \hline (3) \end{array}$ $\quad$ $\begin{array}{r} 7 \\ -4 \\ \hline (3) \end{array}$ $\quad$ $\begin{array}{r} 8 \\ -1 \\ \hline (7) \end{array}$ $\quad$ $\begin{array}{r} 4 \\ -3 \\ \hline (1) \end{array}$ $\quad$ $\begin{array}{r} 6 \\ -2 \\ \hline (4) \end{array}$

Lesson Quiz

Count how many.

1. ⅢⅡ (5)

2. ∥ (2)

3. Ⅲ∣ (6)

LEVELED PRACTICE

RETEACH 4.1

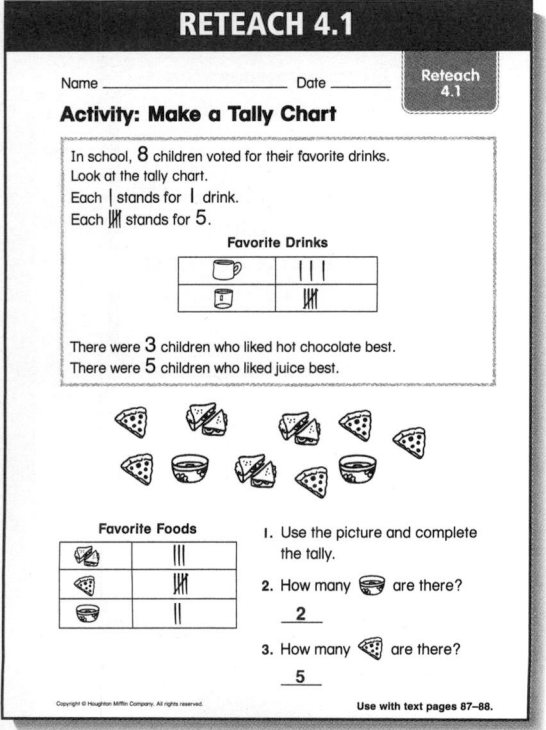

PRACTICE 4.1

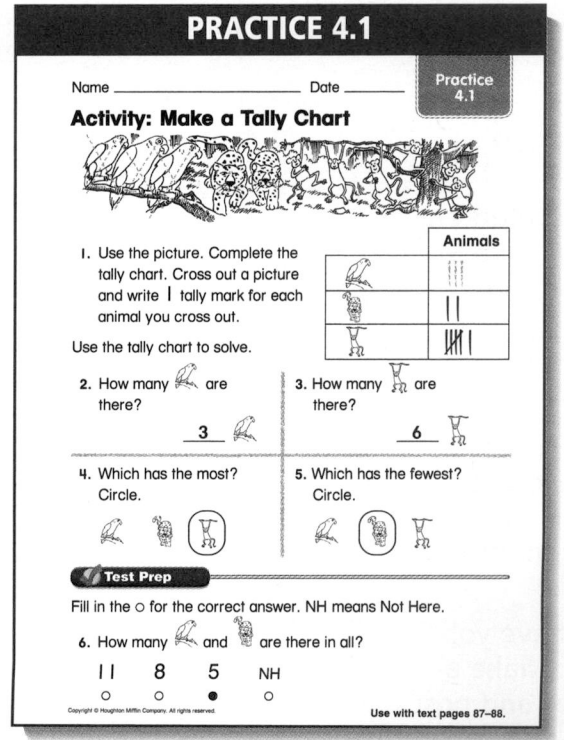

ENRICHMENT 4.1

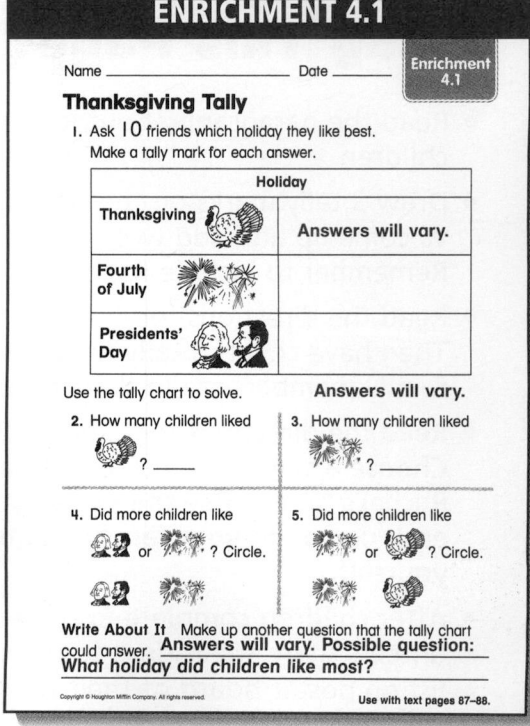

Practice Workbook Page 24

Reaching All Learners
Differentiated Instruction

English Learners

- In order to make comparisons of data in graphs, children will need to understand the words *fewest* and *most*. Use Worksheet 4.1 to help English-language learners understand and use these words.

Special Needs
VISUAL, TACTILE

Materials: *counters*

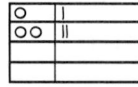

- Draw a tally chart.
- Display 1 counter in the first row, 2 counters in the second row and so on.
- Help the child draw tally marks for each row.
- Pay particular attention to 5 through 10.

Early Finishers
AUDITORY, VISUAL

Materials: *number cards 1–10 (LT 14), tally cards 1–10 (LT 18)*

- Have pairs put all cards face down in an array.
- Children turn over 2 cards at a time in an attempt to make a match. They pick up the cards if they match.
- Partners take turns until all cards have been collected.

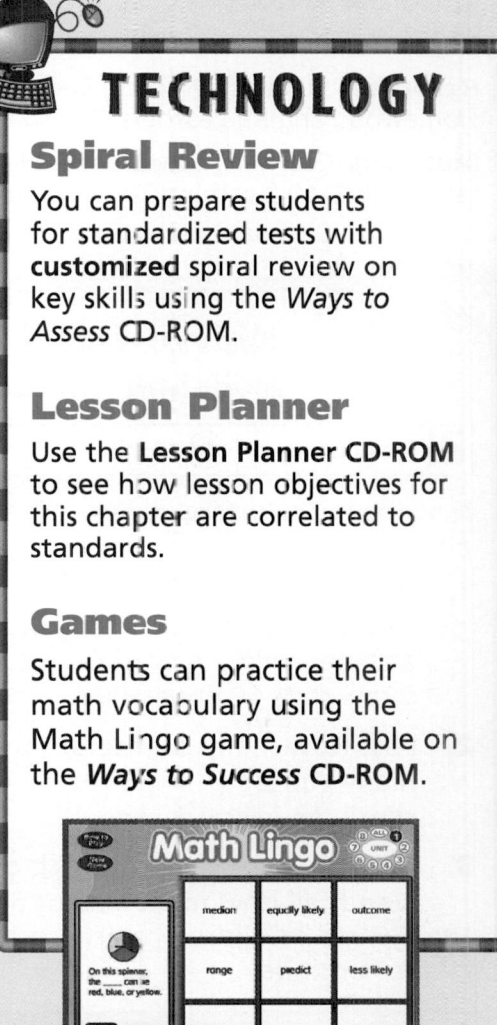

TECHNOLOGY

Spiral Review

You can prepare students for standardized tests with **customized** spiral review on key skills using the *Ways to Assess* CD-ROM.

Lesson Planner

Use the **Lesson Planner CD-ROM** to see how lesson objectives for this chapter are correlated to standards.

Games

Students can practice their math vocabulary using the Math Lingo game, available on the *Ways to Success* CD-ROM.

Social Studies Connection

Every ten years the number of people living in the United States are counted. This is called a census. How many men, women, boys, and girls are there? Make a tally chart to count the number of boys and girls in your class.

MATH CENTER

Basic Skills Activity

Motivate children to build basic skills. Use this activity to address multiple learning styles using hands-on activities related to the skills of this lesson.

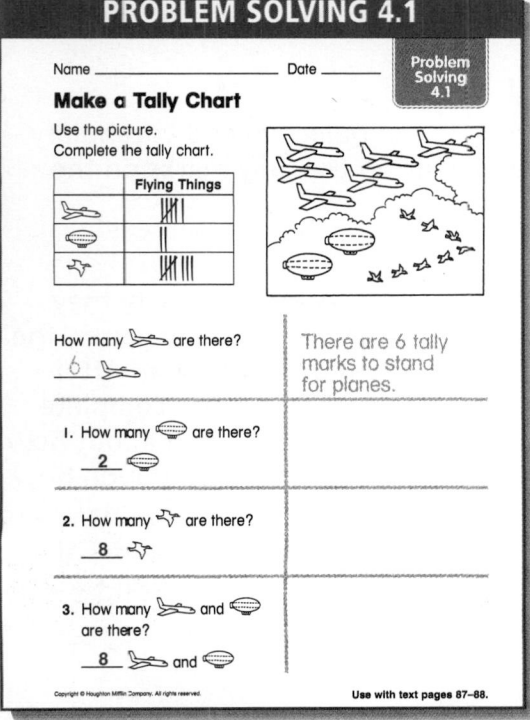

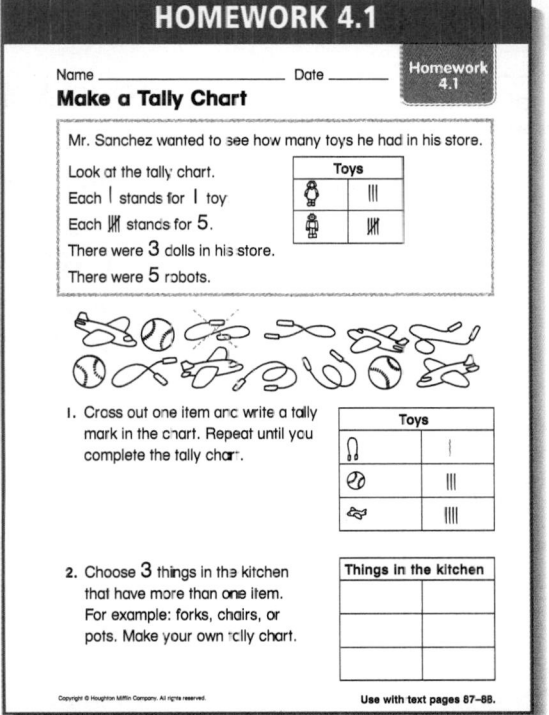

Homework Workbook Page 24

TEACHING LESSON 4.1

LESSON ORGANIZER

Objective Represent data with tally marks on a chart.

Resources Reteach, Practice, Enrichment, Problem Solving, Homework, English Learners, Transparencies, Math Center

Materials Counters, cubes, paper clips, blank transparency, tally cards 1–10 (Learning Tool (LT) 18), pencils, markers

Activity

Warm-Up Activity
Modeling Numbers

👤👤👤 Small Group	🕐 5 minutes	Tactile, Visual

Materials: *counters, cubes, paper clips*

1. Have one child make a row of 0-10 counters, another child a row of 0–10 cubes and a third child a row of 0–10 paper clips.

2. Ask: **How many counters?** (Answers will vary.) **How many cubes?** (Answers will vary.) **How many paper clips?** (Answers will vary.)

3. Have children separate each group into sets of 5 and tell how many sets of 5 and how many "extras." Children can reuse the chart and items to continue.

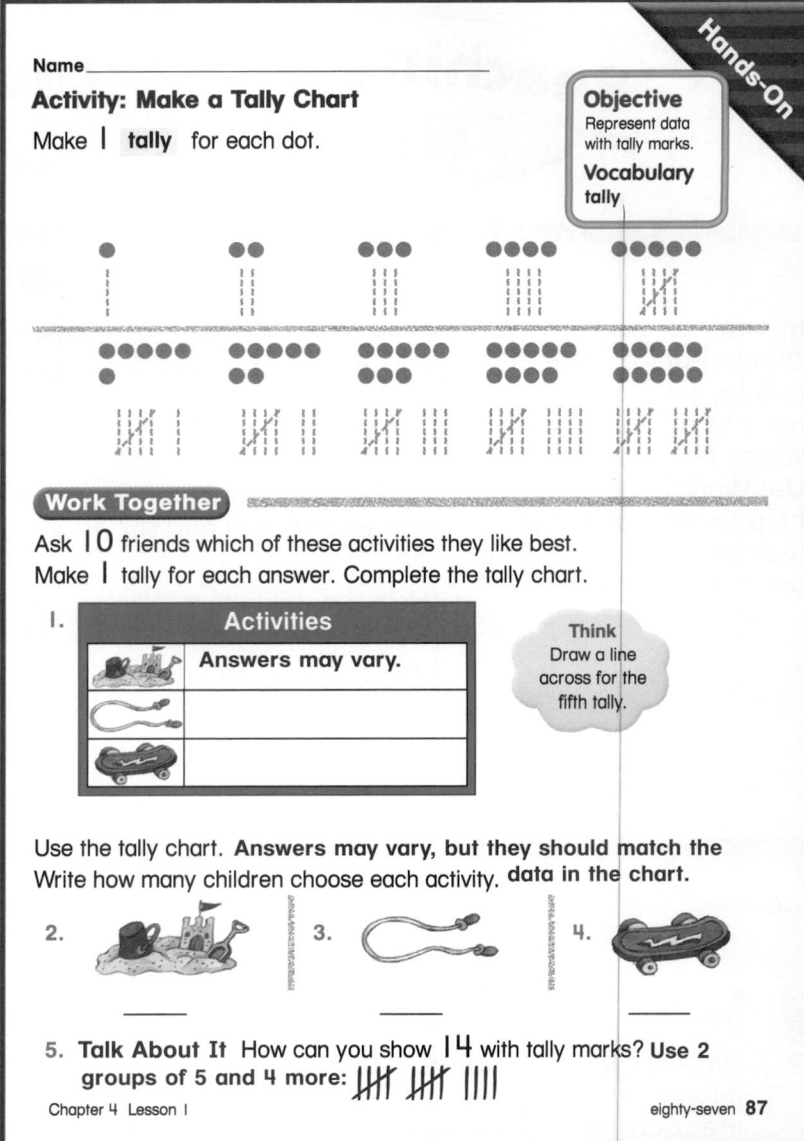

Hands-On

Name_____

Activity: Make a Tally Chart

Make **|** tally for each dot.

Objective Represent data with tally marks.

Vocabulary tally

Work Together

Ask 10 friends which of these activities they like best.
Make | tally for each answer. Complete the tally chart.

1.

Activities	
🏖️	Answers may vary.
〰️	
🛹	

Think Draw a line across for the fifth tally.

Use the tally chart. Write how many children choose each activity.
Answers may vary, but they should match the data in the chart.

2. 🏖️ _____

3. 〰️ _____

4. 🛹 _____

5. **Talk About It** How can you show 14 with tally marks? Use 2 groups of 5 and 4 more:  |||| |||| ||||

Chapter 4 Lesson 1

eighty-seven **87**

---

1 Introduce

Discuss Making a Tally Chart

👤👤👤👤 Whole Group	🕐 5–10 minutes	Visual, Tactile

Materials: *blank transparency, counters*

1. Have a child say a number from 1–4. Place that many counters on the transparency.

2. Have children count as you point to each counter.

3. Then have children count as you draw a tally mark under each counter.

4. Continue with numbers 5–10. Ask: **How is the fifth tally mark of each set different?** (It is drawn across as a diagonal.) Explain that the fifth mark makes it easy to see groups of 5.

2 Develop

Guided Learning

Teaching Example Introduce the objective and vocabulary to children. Guide them in tracing the tally marks on the page.

Work Together

Observe as children ask 10 classmates which activity they like best. Remind them that in a group of 5 tally marks, the fifth tally is a mark that goes across on a diagonal. After children record the data with tallies, have them complete **Exercises 2–4**. Ask children to make a prediction about how children in the class would vote or answer based upon how the group of 10 friends voted or answered. Discuss children's responses to the Talk About It question in Exercise 5. You may have the opportunity to discuss *mode* with some of the tally chart results.

On Your Own

1. Use the picture.
   Complete the tally chart.

   Cross out 1 child. Then make 1 tally.

Activities	
	IIII I
	I
	III

   Use the tally chart to solve.

2. How many are there? **6**

3. How many are there? **3**

4. Which has the most? Circle.

5. Which has the fewest? Circle.

6. How many and are there? **7** children

7. How many children are there in all? **10** children

8. **Talk About It** Explain how you found the answer for Exercise 7. **Possible answer: I counted all of the tally marks.**

88 eighty-eight

At Home Pick three foods. Help your child survey family members or friends to find their favorite. Use tally marks to record the results.

Daily Test Prep

Cindy saw 7 tulips growing in her garden on Monday. She saw 0 new tulips growing on Tuesday. How many tulips did Cindy see in all?

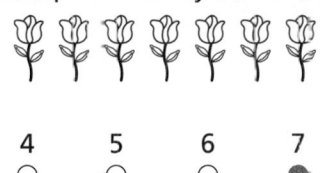

4	5	6	7
○	○	○	●

Activity

Lesson Intervention

Using Tally Marks

Or use Intervention CD-ROM Lesson 4.1

👤👤👤 Small Group	🕐 5–10 minutes	Auditory, Visual

Materials: *tally cards 1–10 (LT 18)*

1. Have one child choose a tally card. Ask children what number the tally marks show. Have children count the tally marks and write the number. Make certain children count the diagonal mark as a fifth tally.

2. Have children continue until all cards have been used.

---

3 Practice

On Your Own

Children complete **Exercises 1–7** independently. Explain that the first row in the tally chart is for walkers, the second row is for riders, and the third row is for skaters. Use the **Talk About It** in Exercise 8 to discuss how to read the tally chart.

Common Error

Writing Tally Marks Incorrectly

Some children may forget to group 5 tally marks for numbers greater than 5. Count aloud as you write tally marks to five, emphasize how a diagonal line is used for the fifth mark, and continue.

IIII

4 Assess and Close

Hold up a handful of pencils.

How can we use tally marks to show how many pencils? (Write 1 tally mark for each pencil.)

Ask a volunteer to do this at the board. Then repeat with a handful of markers.

How many markers do we have? (Answer will vary.)

Which do I have more of, pencils or markers? (Answer will vary.)

Keeping a Journal

Show how to make tally marks for 1, 2, 3, 4, 5, and 6.

Read a Pictograph

PLANNING THE LESSON

MATHEMATICS OBJECTIVE
Read and use a pictograph to compare information.

Use Lesson Planner CD-ROM for Lesson 4.2.

Daily Routines

Calendar
Have children identify any pictures used in the calendar (for example, autumn leaf, weather symbol). Discuss the idea that pictures can be used to show information.

Vocabulary
Draw a simple **pictograph**. Ask children what each picture on the graph is showing. Ask children to identify the graph by name.

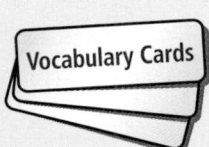
Vocabulary Cards

Meeting North Carolina's Standards
1.04 Create, model, and solve problems that use addition, subtraction, and fair shares (between two or three).

Also 1.01

Lesson Transparency **4.2**

Problem of the Day
Anne used tally marks to show how many friends buy milk. How many friends buy milk? (6)

milk | Ⅲ I

Quick Review

$$\begin{array}{ccccc} 8 & 5 & 0 & 7 & 3 \\ -0 & -0 & -0 & -0 & -0 \\ \hline (8) & (5) & (0) & (7) & (3) \end{array}$$

Lesson Quiz
Jenna made a pictograph. This row shows how many children are wearing shorts.

Each ⚲ stands for 1 child.
How many are wearing shorts? (8)

LEVELED PRACTICE

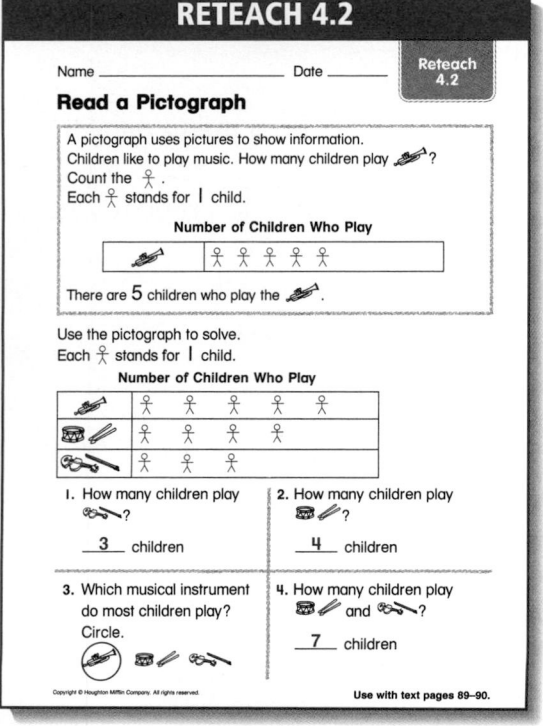

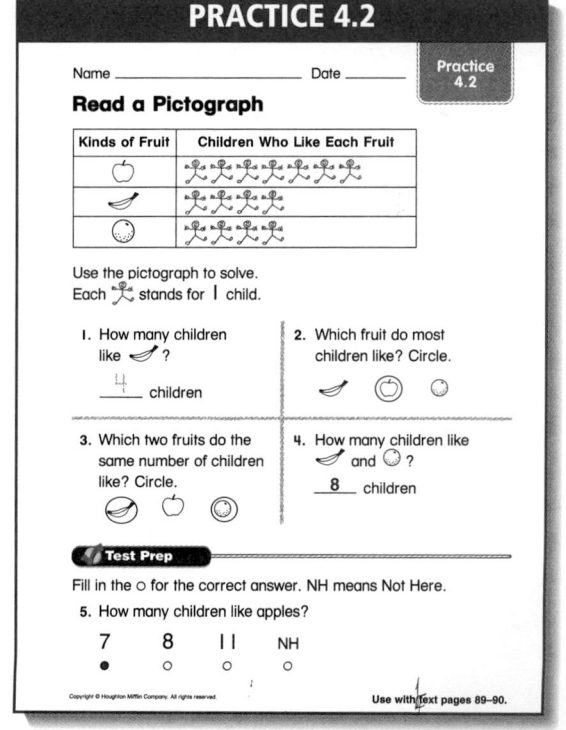

Practice Workbook Page 25

Reaching All Learners

Differentiated Instruction

English Learners

- In order to make comparisons of data in graphs, children will need to understand the words *more* and *fewer*. Use Worksheet 4.2 to help English-language learners understand and use these words.

Inclusion
VISUAL, TACTILE

Materials: *two types of small toys*

Give the child 5 of one type of toy and 3 of another type. Help the child sort the toys into two groups. Have the child place the toys in 2 rows, aligning one above the other. Ask which group has more and which has fewer. Make a pictograph of the toys and repeat the questions.

Gifted and Talented
VISUAL, TACTILE

- Give each child a list of their classmates' first names. Have them label the list "boy or girl" next to each name.
- Have children create a pictograph to show the number of boys and the number of girls.
- Have children share the results of their graph with a classmate.

TECHNOLOGY

Spiral Review

Create **customized** spiral review worksheets for individual students using the *Ways to Assess* CD-ROM.

Education Place

Encourage students to visit **Education Place** at eduplace.com/kids/mw/ for more student activities.

eBook

An electronic version of this lesson can be found in **eMathBook**.

 ## Literature Connection

In the story *Just One More* by Michelle Koch, each page adds on one more item than the previous page. The last page is a pictograph counting all the items. Children can choose a topic and create their own pictograph.

 **MATH CENTER**

Cross-Curricular Activity

As you use this activity to relate the mathematics of this lesson to another curriculum area, children will see how math can help them with other subjects.

Houghton Mifflin
Math

e **MathBook**

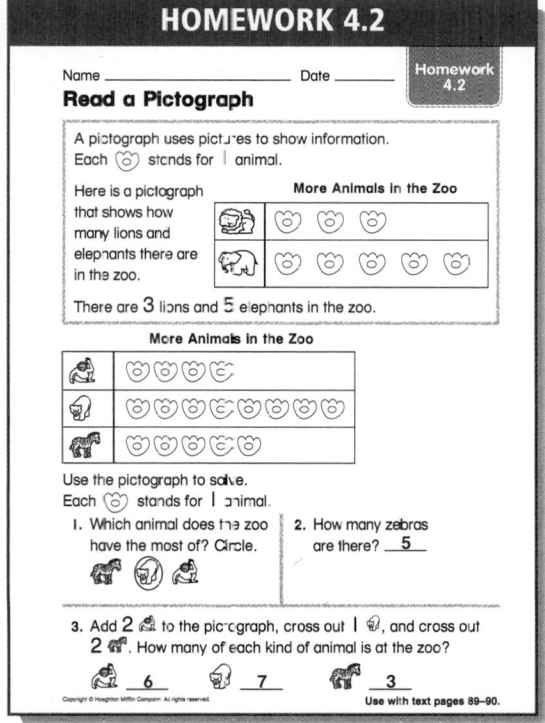

TEACHING LESSON 4.2

LESSON ORGANIZER

Objective Read and use a pictograph to compare information.

Resources Reteach, Practice, Enrichment, Problem Solving, Homework, English Learners, Transparencies, Math Center

Materials Old magazines, scissors

Activity

Warm-Up Activity
Modeling More and Fewer

👤👤👤 Small Group	⏱ 5 minutes	Visual, Tactile

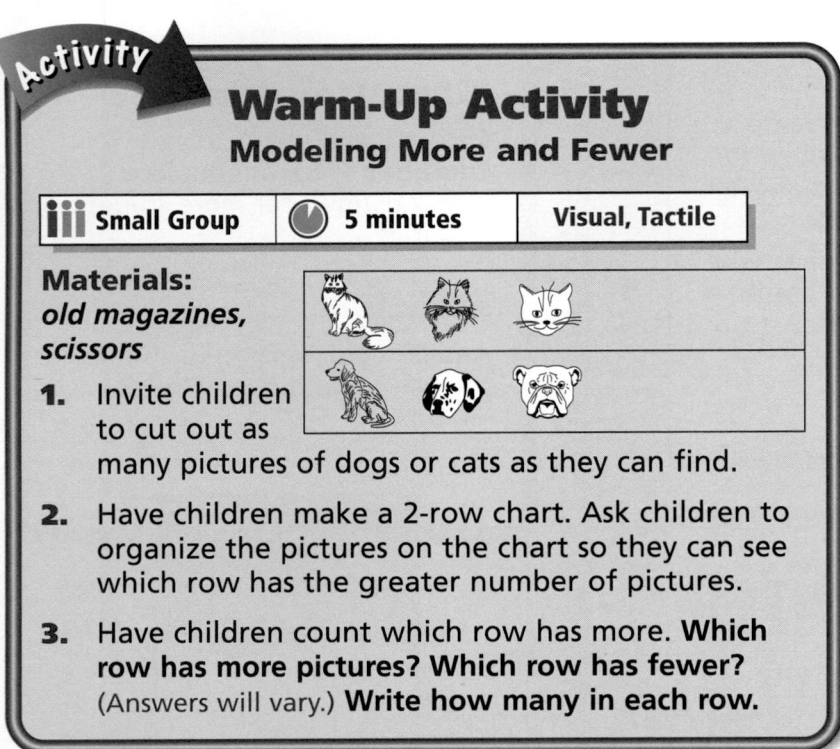

Materials:
old magazines, scissors

1. Invite children to cut out as many pictures of dogs or cats as they can find.

2. Have children make a 2-row chart. Ask children to organize the pictures on the chart so they can see which row has the greater number of pictures.

3. Have children count which row has more. **Which row has more pictures? Which row has fewer?** (Answers will vary.) **Write how many in each row.**

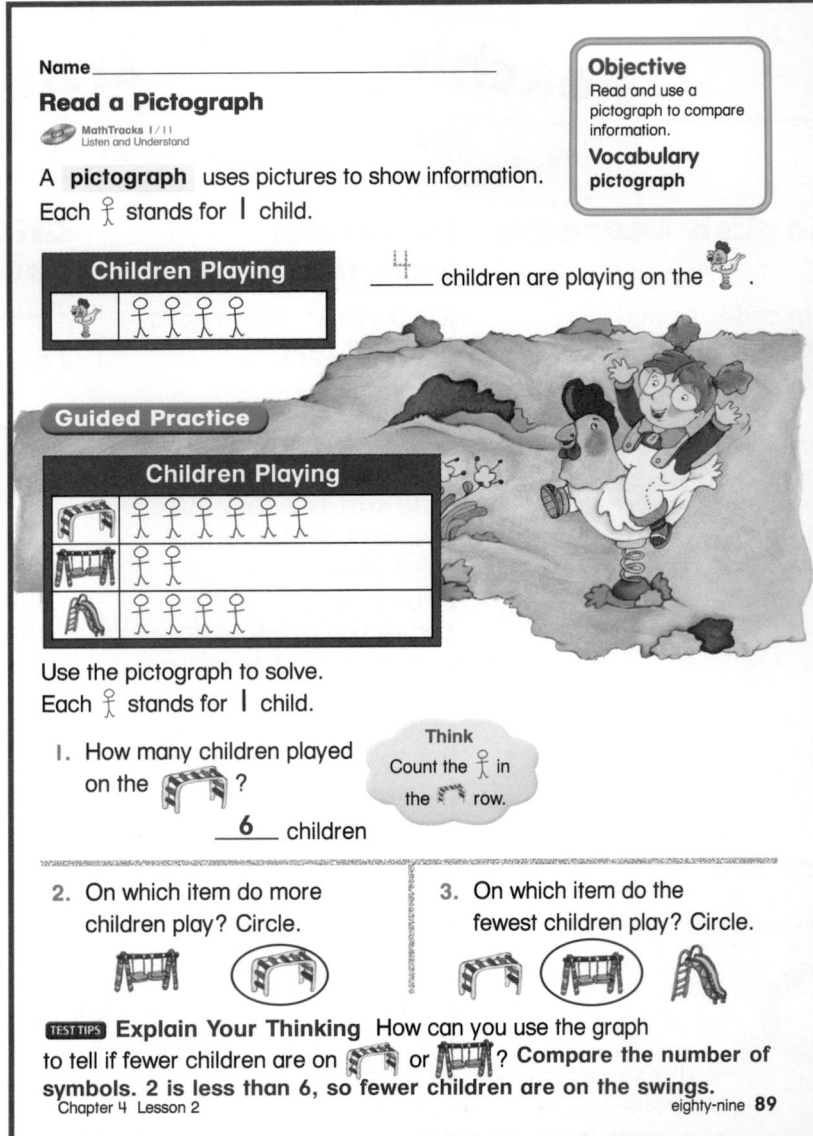

Name_____

Read a Pictograph

MathTracks 1 / 11
Listen and Understand

A **pictograph** uses pictures to show information. Each 👤 stands for 1 child.

> **Objective**
> Read and use a pictograph to compare information.
> **Vocabulary**
> pictograph

Children Playing

___4___ children are playing on the ____.

Guided Practice

Children Playing

Use the pictograph to solve. Each 👤 stands for 1 child.

1. How many children played on the [bars]?

   ___6___ children

   > **Think**
   > Count the 👤 in the [bars] row.

2. On which item do more children play? Circle.

3. On which item do the fewest children play? Circle.

TEST TIPS Explain Your Thinking How can you use the graph to tell if fewer children are on [bars] or [bars]? **Compare the number of symbols. 2 is less than 6, so fewer children are on the swings.**

Chapter 4 Lesson 2   eighty-nine **89**

1️⃣ Introduce

Model Reading a Pictograph

👤👤👤👤 Whole Group	⏱ 10–15 minutes	Visual, Auditory

1. Draw a pictograph on the board. Discuss each part with the class as you complete the pictograph.

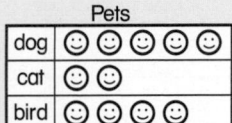

2. Explain: **You can use pictures, or symbols, to show information in a pictograph. This graph shows the pets owned by a group of children.**

3. **Each face on this pictograph stands for 1 child. How many children have a dog?** (5) **How many have a cat?** (2) **How many have a bird?** (4)

4. **Which pet do the most children have?** (dogs)

2️⃣ Develop

Guided Learning

Teaching Example Read the objective and vocabulary with the children. Guide them through the example so they understand that the graph shows 4 children playing. Explain that you can use symbols, like you used tallies, to show how many.

Guided Practice

Have children complete **Exercises 1–3** as you observe. Point out that the symbols on the graph align, and this helps them quickly get information from the pictograph. Give children the opportunity to answer the Explain Your Thinking question. Then have the class discuss the responses.

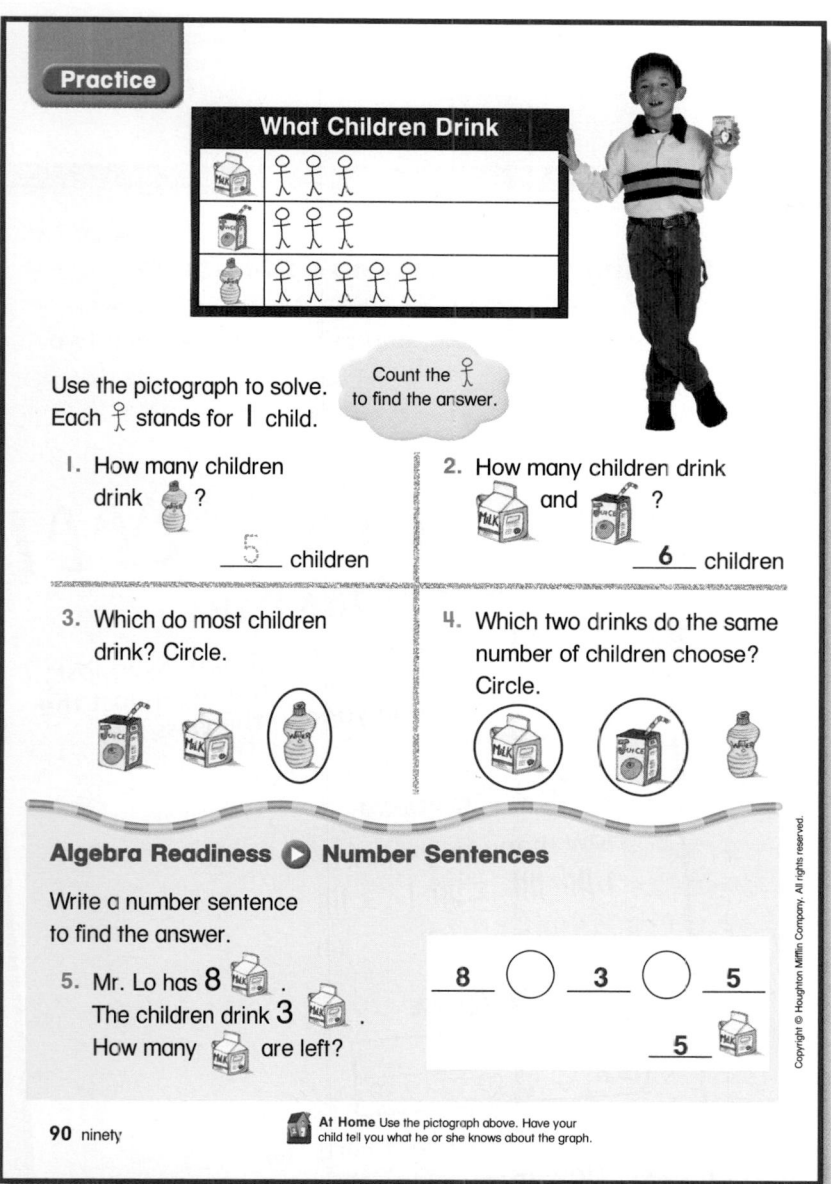

Practice

What Children Drink

Use the pictograph to solve.
Each ♀ stands for 1 child.

Count the ♀ to find the answer.

1. How many children drink 🥛?

   __5__ children

2. How many children drink 🧃 and 📦?

   __6__ children

3. Which do most children drink? Circle.

4. Which two drinks do the same number of children choose? Circle.

Algebra Readiness ▶ Number Sentences

Write a number sentence to find the answer.

5. Mr. Lo has 8 📦. The children drink 3 📦. How many 📦 are left?

   8 ◯ 3 ◯ 5

   __5__ 📦

At Home Use the pictograph above. Have your child tell you what he or she knows about the graph.

90 ninety

Daily Test Prep

How many children eat apples?

Each ♀ stands for 1 child.

6	5	4	NH
●	◯	◯	◯

Activity

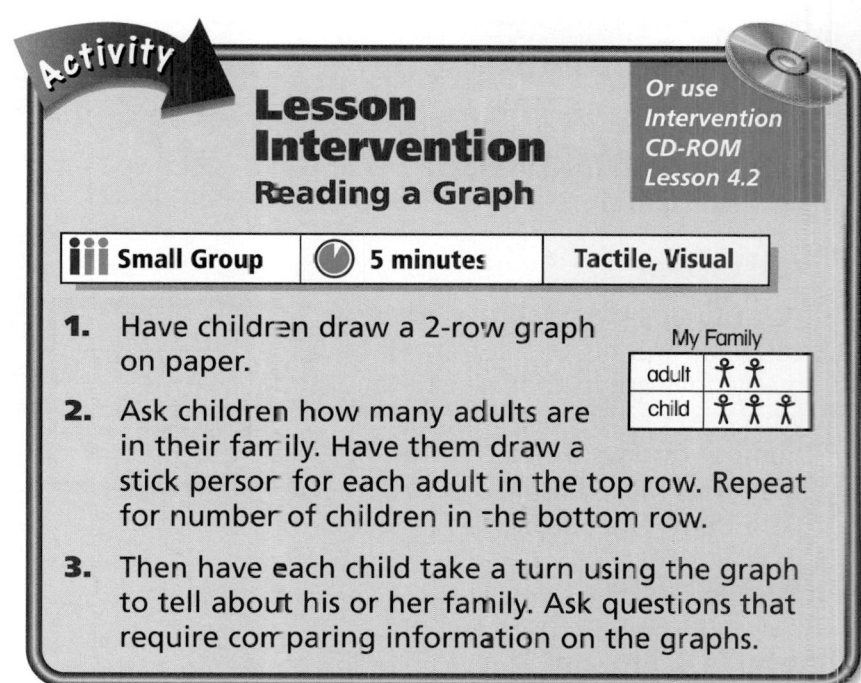

Lesson Intervention
Reading a Graph

Or use Intervention CD-ROM Lesson 4.2

👤👤👤 Small Group	🕐 5 minutes	Tactile, Visual

1. Have children draw a 2-row graph on paper.

   My Family

adult	♀♀
child	♀♀♀

2. Ask children how many adults are in their family. Have them draw a stick person for each adult in the top row. Repeat for number of children in the bottom row.

3. Then have each child take a turn using the graph to tell about his or her family. Ask questions that require comparing information on the graphs.

③ Practice

Independent Practice

Children complete **Exercises 1–4** independently. You may want to discuss *mode* with children using the pictograph.

Algebra Readiness

After children complete **Exercise 5**, call on volunteers to share their solutions. Then write the answer on the board so children can check their completed number sentence.

Common Error

Referring to the Wrong Row

Be sure children refer to the correct row when they answer the questions. Use top, middle, and bottom to describe the rows. Some children may benefit from using a strip of paper to focus on the designated row.

④ Assess and Close

Have children look at the pictograph on the page. **If 1 more child drinks milk, how would the pictograph change?** (There would be 4 people in the row for milk.)

Keeping a Journal

Draw pictures or symbols for a pictograph. Show people, pets, and toy cars.

Make a Pictograph

PLANNING THE LESSON

MATHEMATICS OBJECTIVE
Make and use a pictograph to compare information.

Use Lesson Planner CD-ROM for Lesson 4.3.

Daily Routines

Calendar

Point to one week on the monthly calendar and have children tell how many days are in that week. Repeat with a week that has a different number of days. Have children use the terms *more* and *fewer* to compare number of days in the weeks.

Vocabulary

Ask children how they would describe a **pictograph** to a child in kindergarten. Remind them that a pictograph is used to record and compare information.

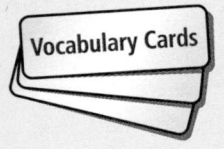

Vocabulary Cards

Meeting North Carolina's Standards

1.04 Create, model, and solve problems that use addition, subtraction, and fair shares (between two or three).

Also **1.01**

Lesson Transparency 4.3

Problem of the Day
Ryan's class made a tooth graph. Ryan lost 2 teeth. The graph shows that Ryan lost the most teeth. Did anyone in the class lose 3 teeth? (no)

Quick Review
How many tally marks?

1. (10) 2. (6) 3. (4)

Lesson Quiz

| red | ♡ ♡ ♡ ♡ |
| blue | ♡ ♡ ♡ ♡ ♡ ♡ |

1. How many blue hearts? (6)
2. How many red hearts? (4)
3. Which row has fewer hearts? (red)

LEVELED PRACTICE

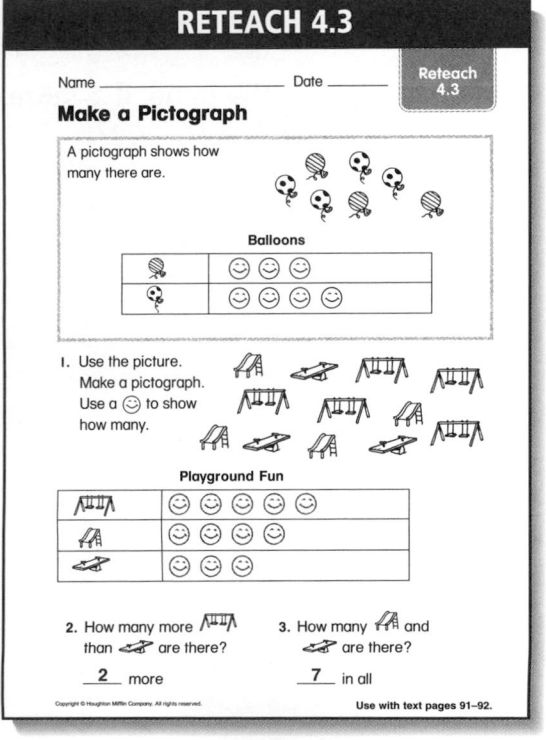

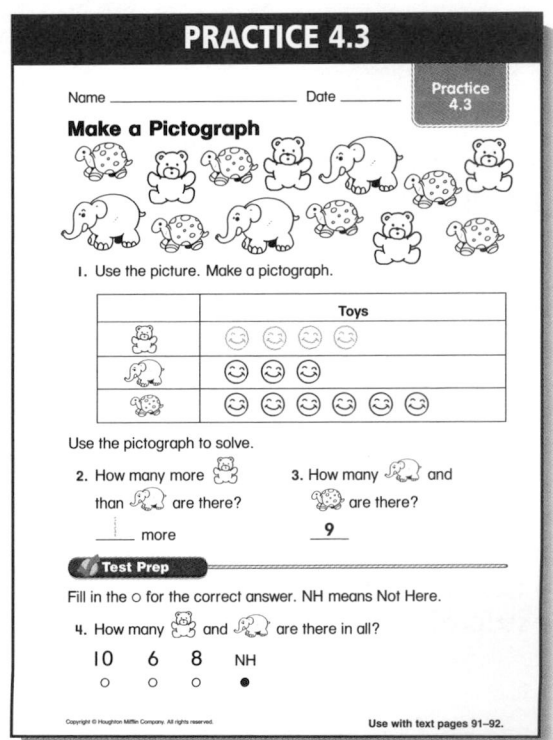

Practice Workbook Page 26

Reaching All Learners
Differentiated Instruction

English Learners

- English-language learners may not be familiar with the subject-verb agreement necessary to understand and write word problems. Use Worksheet 4.3 to develop children's knowledge of subject-verb agreement for the verb *to be*.

Special Needs
TACTILE, VISUAL

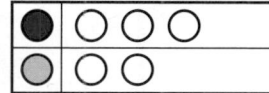

Materials: *counters*

- Have the child toss 5 counters and sort them by color.
- Help the child make a pictograph. Have the child draw a red and yellow circle and then circle symbols.
- Ask questions about the graph.

Early Finishers
VISUAL, TACTILE

- Have each child draw a group of ladybugs, bees, and dragonflies.
- Then have each child trade pictures with a partner. Have each child make a pictograph to show the number of bugs in the picture.
- Have partners share their graphs.

TECHNOLOGY

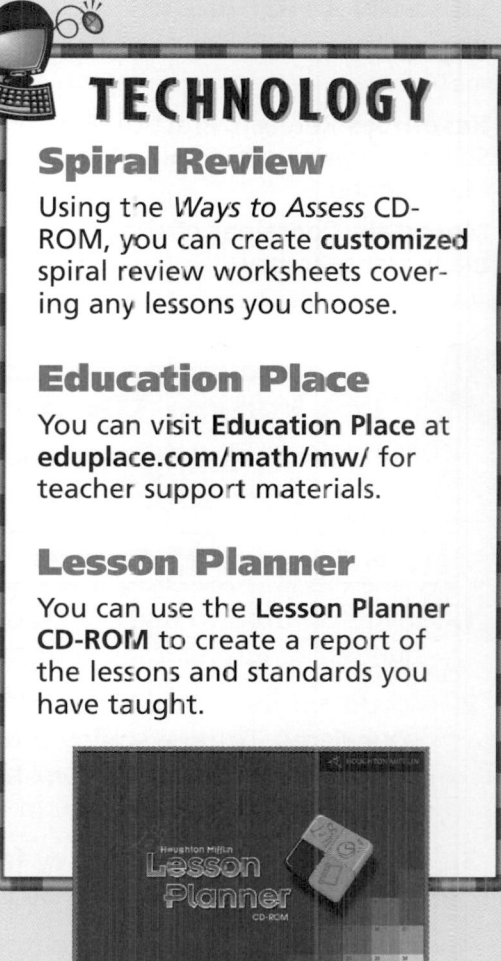

Spiral Review

Using the *Ways to Assess* CD-ROM, you can create **customized** spiral review worksheets covering any lessons you choose.

Education Place

You can visit **Education Place** at **eduplace.com/math/mw/** for teacher support materials.

Lesson Planner

You can use the **Lesson Planner CD-ROM** to create a report of the lessons and standards you have taught.

ScienceConnection

Make a list of farm animals. Discuss the number of legs found on each animal. Lead the class in creating a pictograph that shows the number of animals with 2 legs and 4 legs. Ask if more of the animals have 2 legs or 4 legs. (Answers may vary.)

MATH CENTER

Vocabulary Activity

This vocabulary-building activity helps children understand and remember new words. Encourage children to use the words in math discussion.

PROBLEM SOLVING 4.3

Name _____ Date _____ | Problem Solving 4.3

Make a Pictograph

Read the pictograph.
Then solve.
Each 🧍 stands for one child.

Children in Parade

📧	🧍 🧍 🧍 🧍 🧍 🧍
🥁	🧍 🧍 🧍 🧍
🎺	🧍 🧍 🧍 🧍 🧍

Draw or write to explain.

1. How many children carry 📧 ?

    6 children

2. How many children play 🥁 ?

    4 children

3. How many more 🎺 than 🥁 are there?

    1 more

4. How many 📧 and 🥁 are there in all?

    10 in all

Copyright © Houghton Mifflin Company. All rights reserved.   Use with text pages 91–92.

HOMEWORK 4.3

Name _____ Date _____ | Homework 4.3

Make a Pictograph

You can make a pictograph.
For each picture you cross out, draw a ∿ in the graph.

The child who is making this graph has just begun.
She needs to put 3 more robins and 4 more sparrows in the graph.

Birds

🐦	
🐦	∿

1. Use the picture.
Make a pictograph.
Show how many.

Birds

🐤	∿ ∿ ∿
🐤	∿ ∿ ∿ ∿ ∿ ∿

Use the pictograph to solve.

2. How many 🐤 are there?   **3**

3. How many 🐤 are there?   **6**

4. How many more 🐤 than 🐤 are there?   **3**

5. How many 🐤 and 🐤 are there in all?   **9**

Copyright © Houghton Mifflin Company. All rights reserved.   Use with text pages 91–92.

ENGLISH LEARNERS 4.3

Name _____ Date _____ | English Learners 4.3

Make a Pictograph

There is 1 broom. There are 2 brooms. There are 4 brooms.

Circle the correct word to complete the sentence.

1.

There is **are** 3 frogs.

2.

There is **are** 2 drums.

3.

There **is** are candle.

4.

There is **are** 5 cups.

To the Teacher: Use the examples at the top of the page to demonstrate the correct usage of *is* and *are*. Then read the sentences with children and have them circle the word to complete each sentence.

Copyright © Houghton Mifflin company. All rights reserved.   Use with text pages 91–53.

TEACHING LESSON 4.3

LESSON ORGANIZER

Objective Make and use a pictograph to compare information.

Resources Reteach, Practice, Enrichment, Problem Solving, Homework, English Learners, Transparencies, Math Center

Materials Container of cubes: red, green, and yellow; blank transparency

Warm-Up Activity

Modeling One-to-One Correspondence

 Small Group | 5 minutes | Visual, Tactile

1. Invite children to make a graph that shows the number of letters in each of their names.

2. Model on the board. **Cross off the first letter of your name. Draw a smiley face in the chart. Do this with each letter of your name.** Ask children how many faces they drew in their graphs.

3. **Check the number of smiley faces with the number of crossed out letters. Be sure they match.**

4. Have children compare their drawings with a neighbor's. **Who has fewer? Who has more?** (Answers will vary.)

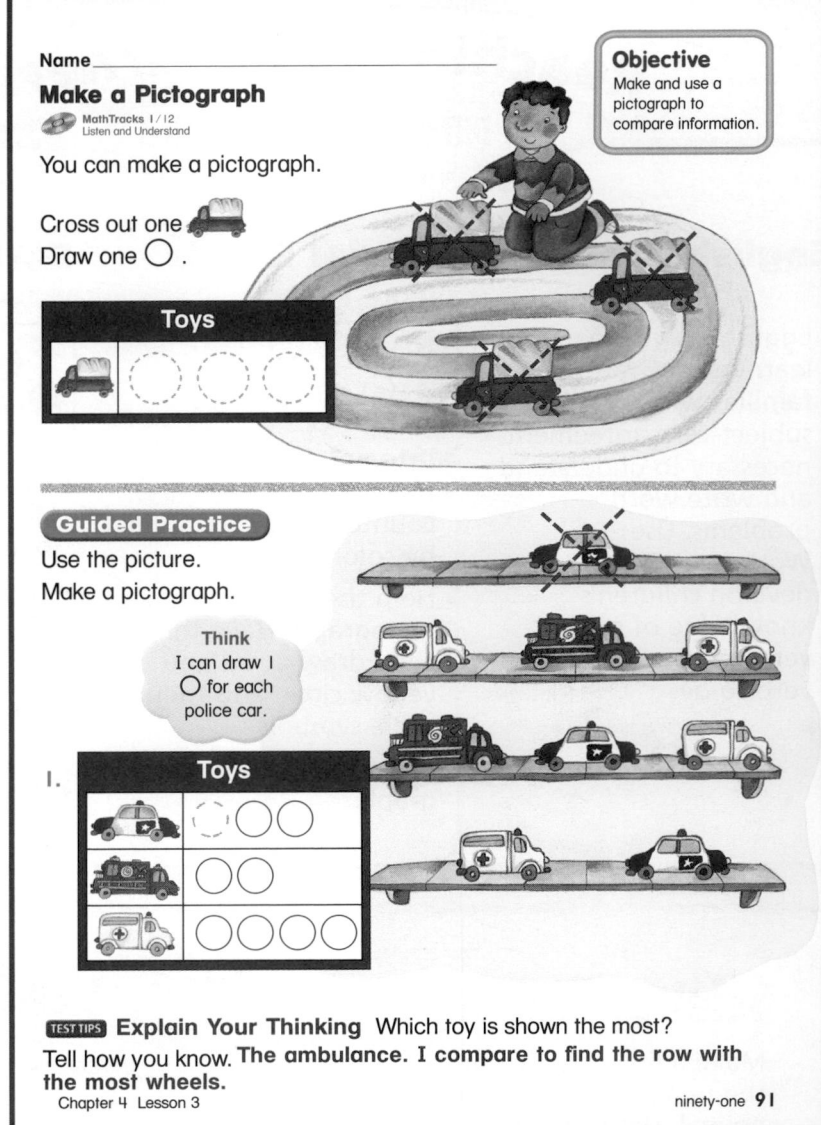

Name_____

Make a Pictograph

MathTracks 1 / 12
Listen and Understand

You can make a pictograph.

Cross out one 🚚
Draw one ○ .

Objective
Make and use a pictograph to compare information.

Toys

Guided Practice
Use the picture.
Make a pictograph.

Think
I can draw 1
○ for each
police car.

1. **Toys**

TEST TIPS **Explain Your Thinking** Which toy is shown the most?
Tell how you know. **The ambulance. I compare to find the row with the most wheels.**
Chapter 4 Lesson 3   ninety-one **91**

Introduce

Discuss Making a Pictograph

 Whole Group | 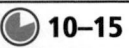 10–15 minutes | Visual, Tactile

Materials: *container of cubes: red, green, and yellow; blank transparency*

1. **How can we tell how many of each color cube we have in the bag?** (Answers may vary.) **We can compare how many by making a pictograph.**

2. **How many colors are in the bag?** (3) **Each color goes in one row.** Create the graph on the transparency. Label rows by color and title the graph. Use a square to stand for one cube.

3. Have children tell you what row each cube belongs in as you take it out of the bag. Draw a square in that row. Point out, as you draw the squares, that you are aligning each row top to bottom.

4. Ask volunteers to read the graph and tell you how many of each color. Compare the numbers in rows.

Develop

Guided Learning

Teaching Example Read the objective with children. Guide them through the example as they cross out 1 truck and draw 1 circle at a time to show the number of trucks.

Guided Practice

Have children complete the pictograph as you observe. Discuss children's responses to the Explain Your Thinking question to be sure they understand that the circles represent each vehicle.

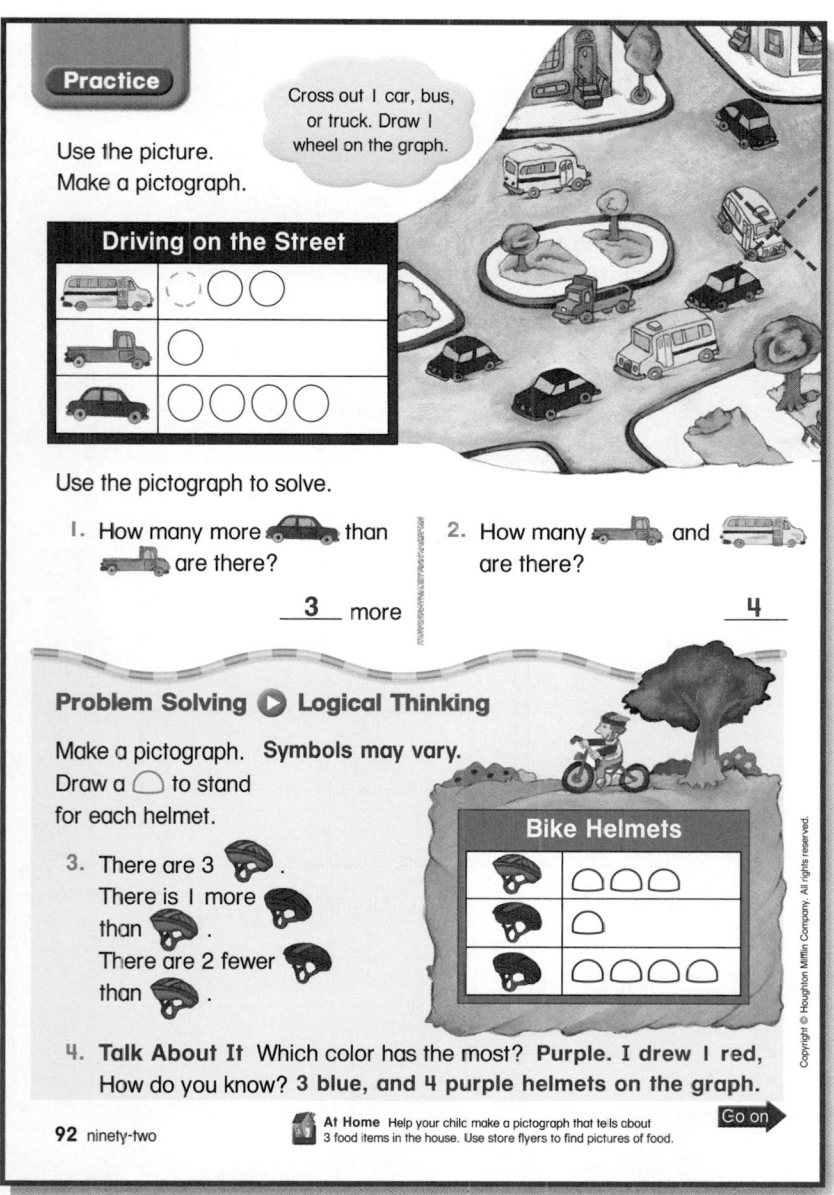

Practice

Cross out 1 car, bus, or truck. Draw 1 wheel on the graph.

Use the picture.
Make a pictograph.

Driving on the Street

Use the pictograph to solve.

1. How many more 🚗 than 🚚 are there?

_____3_____ more

2. How many 🚚 and 🚌 are there?

_____4_____

Problem Solving ▷ Logical Thinking

Make a pictograph. **Symbols may vary.**
Draw a ⬡ to stand
for each helmet.

3. There are 3 🪖.
There is 1 more 🪖
than 🪖.
There are 2 fewer 🪖
than 🪖.

Bike Helmets

4. **Talk About It** Which color has the most? **Purple. I drew 1 red,**
How do you know? **3 blue, and 4 purple helmets on the graph.**

92 ninety-two

At Home Help your child make a pictograph that tells about 3 food items in the house. Use store flyers to find pictures of food.

Go on ▶

Daily Test Prep

Emily draws a sun for each sunny day. Last week five days were sunny and two days were cloudy. How many suns will Emily draw?

4   5   6   NH
○   ●   ○   ○

Activity

Lesson Intervention

Or use
Intervention
CD-ROM
Lesson 4.3

Organizing Data for a Graph

| 👥 Small Group | ⏱ 5–10 minutes | Visual, Tactile |

Materials: *cubes (3 colors)*

1. Have children draw 1–10 flowers in 3 different colors at the top of a sheet of paper. Below this, guide them to draw a blank graph with 3 rows.

2. Place a cube of the same color on top of each flower. After children have covered all their flowers, say: **Now move all the cubes of one color to one row of the graph.** Have children count the cubes and then count the same color flower. The number should be the same. Have children repeat with the two remaining colors.

③ Practice

Independent Practice

Children complete **Exercises 1–2** independently.

Problem Solving

After children complete **Exercise 3**, call on a volunteer to share the graph. Use the **Talk About It** in **Exercise 4** to discuss how to read the graph.

Common Error

Incorrectly Transferring Data
Children may lose track of the number of items despite crossing out. Remind them to go back and count the items and the pictures they drew.

④ Assess and Close

If we need to graph 5 pieces of fruit, how many pictures will be on our graph in all? (5)

Suppose our graph shows 3 bananas and 2 apples. How could you use the graph to find out how many more bananas there are than apples?

(Compare and count the number of pictures in each row.)

✏ Keeping a Journal

Count how many windows and doors are in your classroom. Make a pictograph. Use pictures and words to explain the graph.

ACHIEVING Mathematical Proficiency

What Is Good Practice?

To become proficient in math, **children need to have many opportunities to use the computational methods, reasoning processes, and problem-solving strategies they are learning.** Children clearly profit when practice is accompanied by feedback, and when it is clearly tied to the content of the instruction. The topics of data and graphing lend themselves to daily practice of methods and reinforcement of vocabulary. Learning to use a tally chart provides practice in counting. Creating and interpreting pictographs and bar graphs provides practice in counting, ordering, and comparing numbers, and reinforces accompanying vocabulary words such as *fewer*, *more*, and *same*. **Effective practice facilitates gradual mastery of methods and content.** It also fosters independence in children and allows them to move on to more complex mathematical tasks.

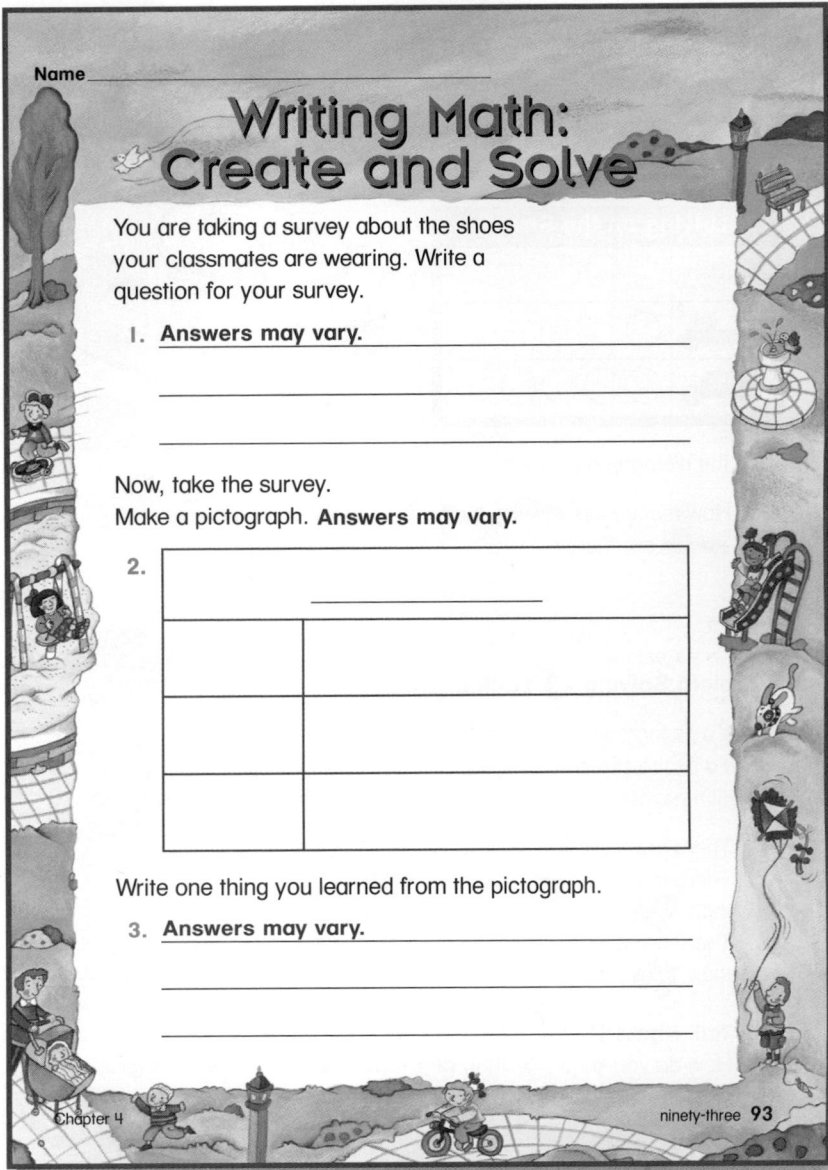

Name_____

Writing Math: Create and Solve

You are taking a survey about the shoes your classmates are wearing. Write a question for your survey.

1. **Answers may vary.**
_____
_____

Now, take the survey.
Make a pictograph. **Answers may vary.**

2.

Write one thing you learned from the pictograph.

3. **Answers may vary.**
_____
_____

Writing Math: Create and Solve

Discuss the different types of shoes children wear. Introduce the page and explain what it means to take a survey. Then ask children to write their survey question in **Exercise 1.**

How can you record the information you get from your survey? Children might draw pictures of the different shoes and use tally marks. Assist as children do the survey.

Then point to the work area for drawing a pictograph. Observe as children use the data to make a pictograph and complete question 3. Let children share their pictographs and what they learned. You may have the opportunity to discuss *mode* with the pictograph.

Finally, ask children to make a prediction about *how children in the school would vote or answer* based upon how the class voted or answered.

Quick Check

Use the picture.
Complete the tally chart.

I.

Crayons	
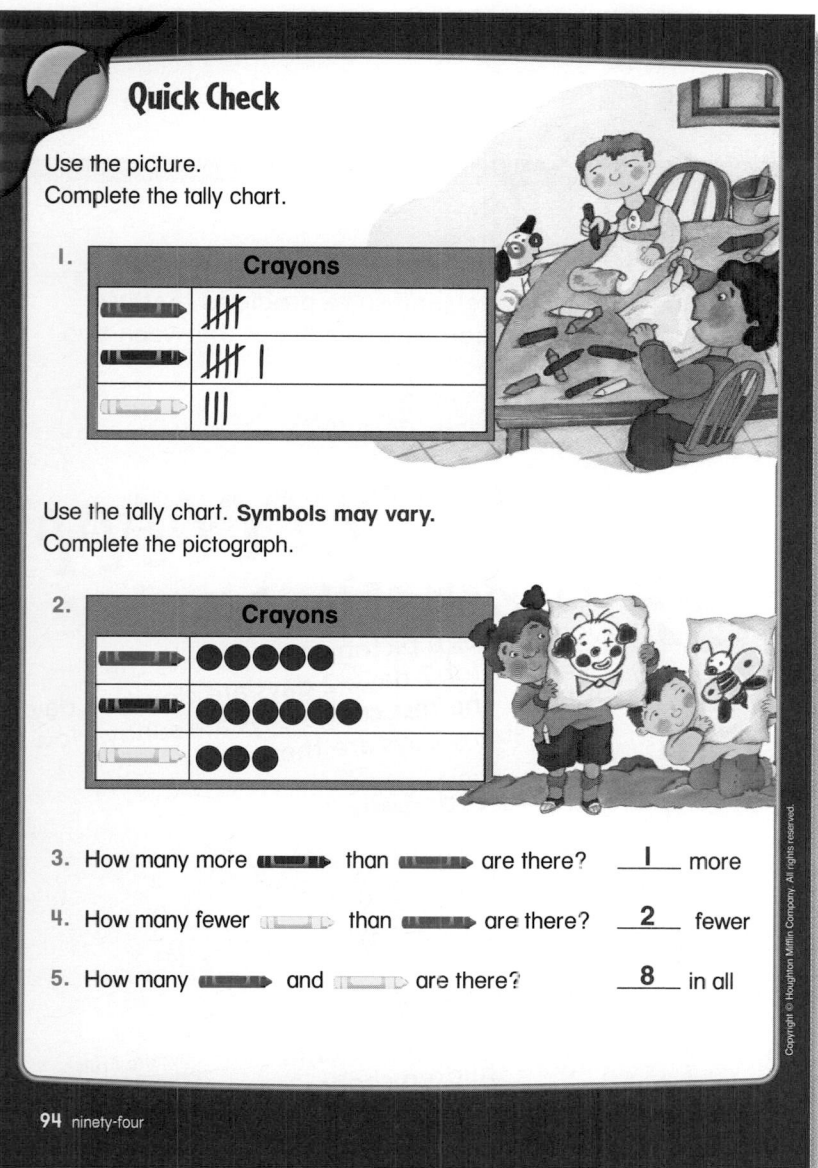	ЖН
	ЖН I
	III

Use the tally chart. **Symbols may vary.**
Complete the pictograph.

2.

Crayons	
	● ● ● ● ●
	● ● ● ● ●
	● ● ●

3. How many more ▬▬▶ than ▬▬▶ are there? __I__ more

4. How many fewer ▭▭▷ than ▬▬▶ are there? __2__ fewer

5. How many ▬▬▶ and ▭▭▷ are there? __8__ in all

Quick Check

Have children complete the Quick Check exercises independently to assess their understanding of concepts and skills taught in **Lessons 1–3**.

Item	Lesson	Error Analysis	Intervention
1	4.1	Children may forget to group 5 tally marks for numbers greater than 5.	Reteach Resource 4.1 *Ways to Success* 4.1
3–5	4.2	Children may refer to the wrong row or rows.	Reteach Resource 4.2 *Ways to Success* 4.2
2	4.3	Children may lose track of the data they transfer from one form to another.	Reteach Resource 4.3 *Ways to Success* 4.3

Read a Bar Graph

Lesson 4.4

PLANNING THE LESSON

MATHEMATICS OBJECTIVE

Read a bar graph and use it to compare information.

Use Lesson Planner CD-ROM for Lesson 4.4.

Daily Routines

Calendar

Have children look at the last week of the monthly calendar. Ask a volunteer to tell how many days are in that week. Point out that each box with a number is counted.

Vocabulary

Have children tell how a **bar graph** is the same and different from a pictograph. Encourage children to find one of each type of graph in the classroom or on the vocabulary cards.

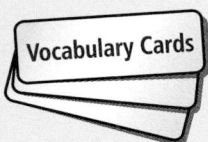
Vocabulary Cards

Meeting North Carolina's Standards

1.04 Create, model, and solve problems that use addition, subtraction, and fair shares (between two or three).

Also 1.01

Lesson Transparency 4.4

Problem of the Day

Jose makes a pictograph. It shows the weather for 7 days. 2 days are cloudy. 1 day it rains. The rest of the days are sunny. How many sunny days are there? (4)

Quick Review

$$5 - 4 \quad (1)$$
$$7 - 6 \quad (1)$$
$$1 - 0 \quad (1)$$
$$8 - 8 \quad (0)$$
$$4 - 0 \quad (4)$$

Lesson Quiz

1. Which kind of fruit did more children choose? (banana)

2. How many children chose apple as their favorite fruit? (4)

Favorite Fruit

Number of Children
0 1 2 3 4 5

LEVELED PRACTICE

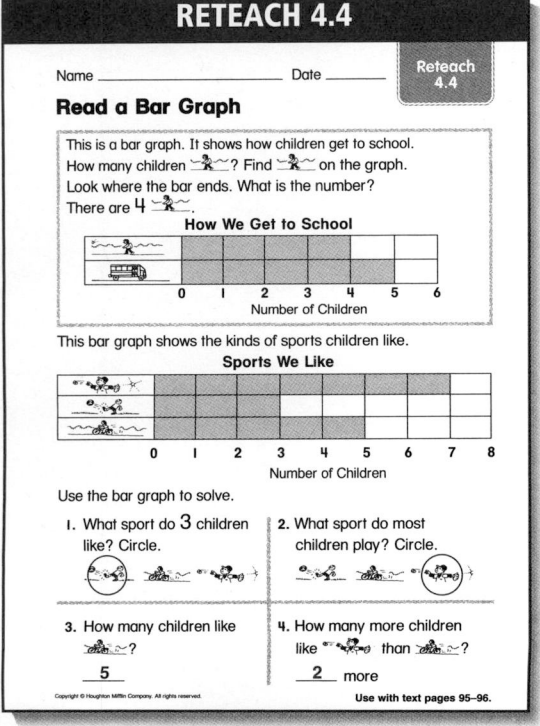

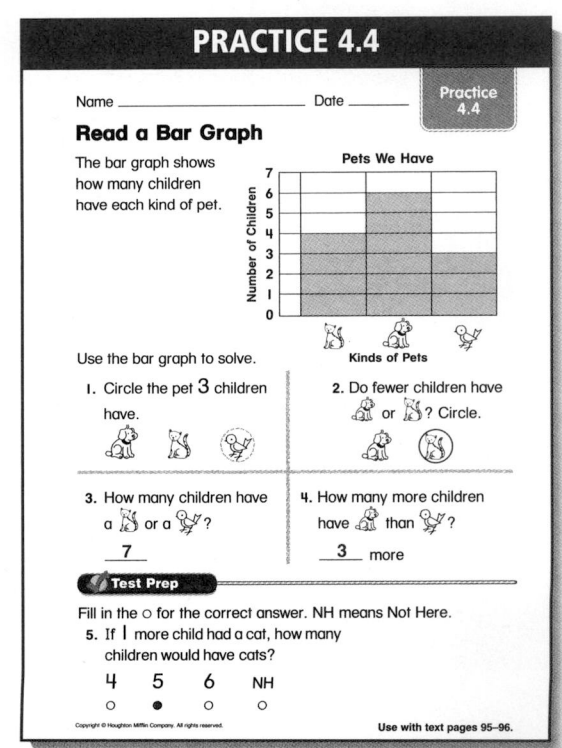

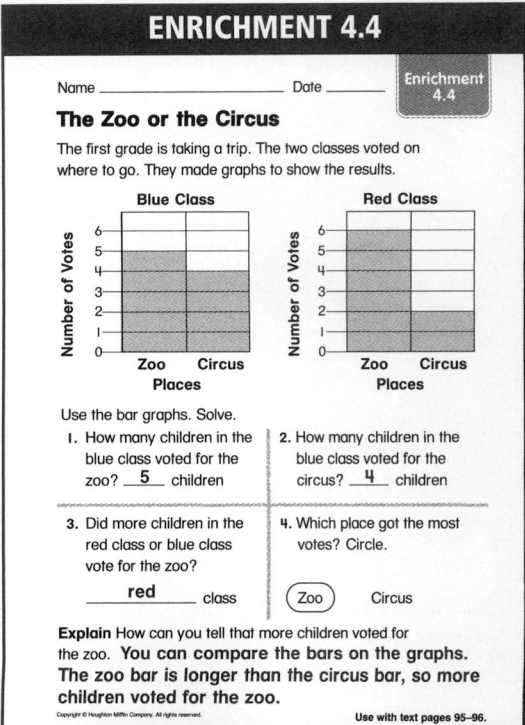

Practice Workbook Page 27

Reaching All Learners

Differentiated Instruction

English Learners

- English-language learners may not be familiar with different tenses of verbs they find in word problems. Use Worksheet 4.4 to develop children's knowledge of tenses for the verb *to choose*.

Inclusion
TACTILE, VISUAL

Materials: *cubes*

- Use cubes to replicate the graph on page 95.
- Ask the child questions based on those in the lesson.

Early Finishers
VISUAL, TACTILE

- Have children work in pairs to create a new version of the graph on page 96.
- They should use the following data:
  5 sailboats
  3 rowboats
  4 canoes
  5 motor boats
- When complete, children may write questions that can be answered using their graph.

TECHNOLOGY

Spiral Review

To reinforce skills on lessons taught earlier, create **customized** spiral review worksheets using the *Ways to Assess* CD-ROM.

Lesson Planner

You can customize your teaching plan or meet your curriculum requirements with the **Lesson Planner CD-ROM**.

eBook

eMathBook allows students to review lessons and do homework without carrying their textbooks home.

Literature Connection

Read the book *Lemonade for Sale*, by Stuart J. Murphy. Point out how the children are making their graph. You can have children help you make a graph that shows the number of cups sold.

MATH CENTER

Cross-Curricular Activity

As you use this activity to relate the mathematics of this lesson to another curriculum area, children will see how math can help them with other subjects.

PROBLEM SOLVING 4.4

Name _____ Date _____ | Problem Solving 4.4

Read a Bar Graph

Use the bar graph. Solve.

Favorite Zoo Animals

Number of Children

1. How many kinds of animals does the graph show?
   __4__

2. How many children chose 🐘?
   __4__

3. Circle the animal most children liked.

4. How many more children liked 🐘 than 🐻?
   __3__ more

Draw or write to explain.

Copyright © Houghton Mifflin Company. All rights reserved.

Use with text pages 95–96.

HOMEWORK 4.4

Name _____ Date _____ | Homework 4.4

Read a Bar Graph

This is a bar graph. It tells how many kinds of dogs are in the animal hospital.

Each box on the graph stands for one kind of dog.
There are 7 🐕.

Dogs in the Animal Hospital

Number of Dogs

Use the bar graph. Solve.

1. How many 🐕 are there?
   __5__

2. Are there fewer 🐕 or 🐑? Circle.

3. How many more 🐕 are there than 🐑?
   __1__ more

4. What kind of dog is there the most of? Circle.

5. Cross out 3 boxes from 🐕, add 2 boxes to 🐑, and leave 🐕 the same. How many dogs of each kind are in the hospital?
   🐑 4
   🐕 7
   🐕 6

Copyright © Houghton Mifflin Company. All rights reserved.

Use with text pages 95–96.

ENGLISH LEARNERS 4.4

Name _____ Date _____ | English Learners 4.4

Read a Bar Graph

Today I **choose** an apple for a snack.

Yesterday I **chose** a banana for a snack.

Circle the correct word to complete the sentence.

1. Last night I **choose** (**chose**) a crayon to draw with

2. Today the children (**choose**) **chose** a dog for a pet.

3. Today we (**choose**) **chose** the red paint.

4. Last week I **choose** (**chose**) a big flower.

To the Teacher: Use the example at the top of the page to demonstrate the present and past tense of the verb to choose. Then read the sentences with children and have them circle the correct word to complete each sentence.

Copyright © Houghton Mifflin Company. All rights reserved.

Use with text pages 95–96.

TEACHING LESSON 4.4

LESSON ORGANIZER

Objective Read a bar graph and use it to compare information.

Resources Reteach, Practice, Enrichment, Problem Solving, Homework, English Learners, Transparencies, Math Center

Materials Cubes of 2 colors, blank transparency, ruler

Activity

Warm-Up Activity
Modeling How to Read a Graph

| 👥 Small Group | 🕐 5–10 minutes | Visual, Tactile |

Materials: *cubes of 2 colors*

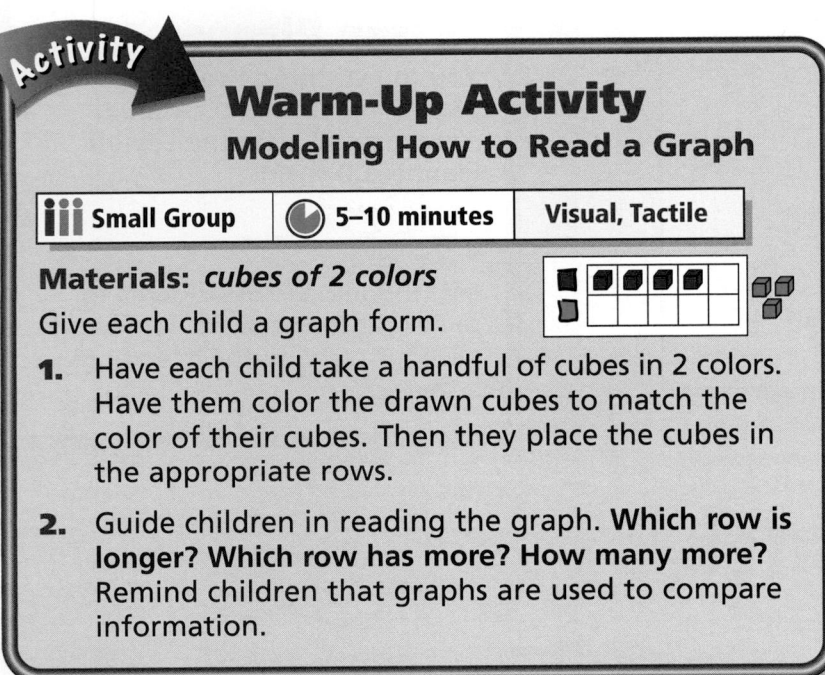

Give each child a graph form.

1. Have each child take a handful of cubes in 2 colors. Have them color the drawn cubes to match the color of their cubes. Then they place the cubes in the appropriate rows.

2. Guide children in reading the graph. **Which row is longer? Which row has more? How many more?** Remind children that graphs are used to compare information.

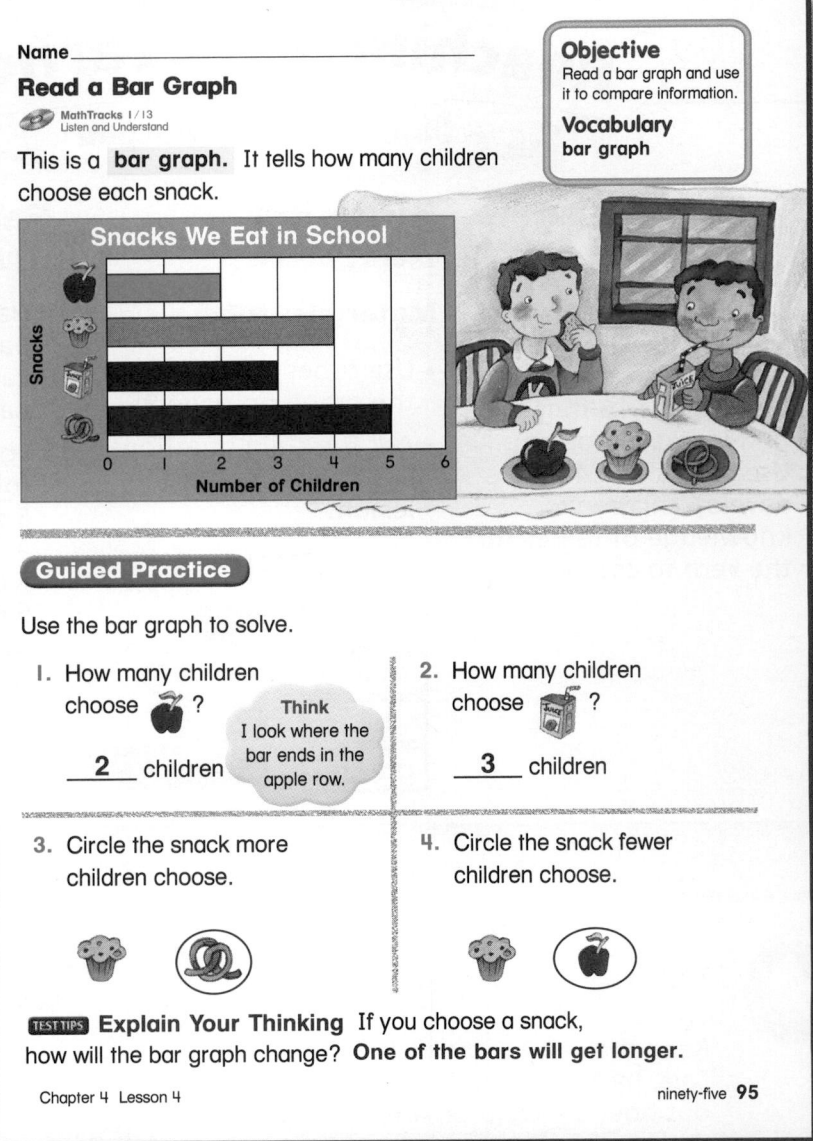

Name_____

Read a Bar Graph

MathTracks 1/13
Listen and Understand

This is a **bar graph.** It tells how many children choose each snack.

Snacks We Eat in School

Objective
Read a bar graph and use it to compare information.

Vocabulary
bar graph

Guided Practice

Use the bar graph to solve.

1. How many children choose 🍎 ?

   2 children

   Think
   I look where the bar ends in the apple row.

2. How many children choose 🧃 ?

   3 children

3. Circle the snack more children choose.

4. Circle the snack fewer children choose.

TEST TIPS **Explain Your Thinking** If you choose a snack, how will the bar graph change? **One of the bars will get longer.**

Chapter 4 Lesson 4

ninety-five **95**

---

1 Introduce

Discuss Reading a Bar Graph

| 👥 Whole Group | 🕐 10–15 minutes | Kinesthetic, Visual, |

Materials: *cubes of 2 colors, blank transparency*

Display a blank 2-row graph. Label increments 0–5 on the bottom of the graph.

1. Discuss how to read pictographs. **How do you know how many are in a row?** (Count the pictures.)

2. Take a handful of cubes and sort them by color. Tell children you are going to make another kind of graph. **I have 4 red cubes, so I will color 4 squares in the top row. How many boxes will I color in the bottom row?** Invite a volunteer to color the bottom row.

3. Have children read the bar graph. **How many red cubes?** Tell children they can look where the bar ends. Point as you say: **Place your finger at the end of the bar and drag it to the number at the bottom. This tells how many.** Invite volunteers to practice dragging fingers to the bottom.

2 Develop

Guided Learning

Teaching Example Read the objective and vocabulary with children. Guide them through the parts of the graph by reading the labels and pointing out the numbers on the bottom of the graph. Be sure children see that each bar ends at a different number.

Guided Practice

Have children complete **Exercises 1–4** as you observe. Give children the opportunity to answer the Explain Your Thinking question and have the class discuss each response.

Practice

The bar graph shows the boats Nara sees.

> Look at the number where the bar ends to know how many.

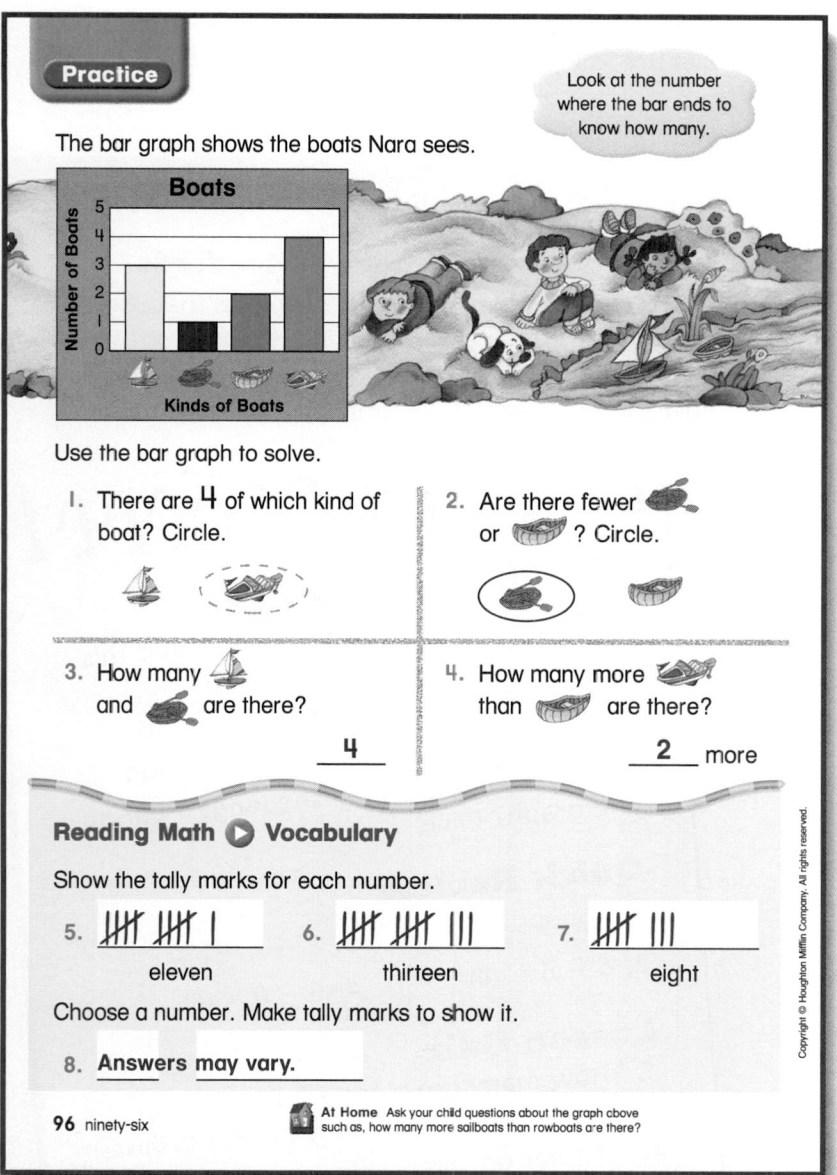

Use the bar graph to solve.

1. There are 4 of which kind of boat? Circle.

2. Are there fewer 🐢 or 🛶 ? Circle.

3. How many 🚤 and 🐢 are there?

___4___

4. How many more 🚤 than 🛶 are there?

___2___ more

Reading Math ▶ Vocabulary

Show the tally marks for each number.

5. IIII IIII I
   eleven

6. IIII IIII III
   thirteen

7. IIII III
   eight

Choose a number. Make tally marks to show it.

8. Answers may vary.

96 ninety-six

🏠 **At Home** Ask your child questions about the graph above such as, how many more sailboats than rowboats are there?

Daily Test Prep

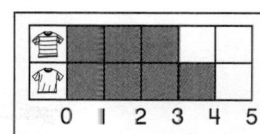

How many children wear striped T-shirts?

1   3   5   7
○   ●   ○   ○

Activity

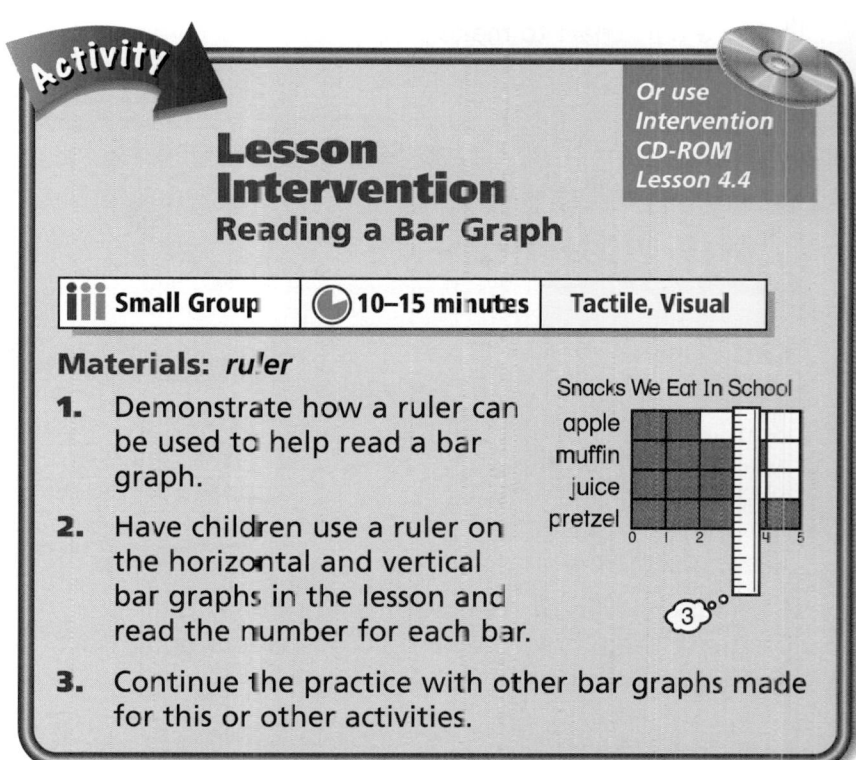

Lesson Intervention
Reading a Bar Graph

Or use Intervention CD-ROM Lesson 4.4

| 👥 Small Group | 🕐 10–15 minutes | Tactile, Visual |

Materials: *ruler*

1. Demonstrate how a ruler can be used to help read a bar graph.

2. Have children use a ruler on the horizontal and vertical bar graphs in the lesson and read the number for each bar.

3. Continue the practice with other bar graphs made for this or other activities.

---

3 Practice

Independent Practice

Discuss the vertical graph with children. Explain that these bars go up, but they show the same information as bars that go across. Children complete **Exercises 1–4** independently. Ask children how they found the answer for **Exercise 3**. If they counted, have them try adding to find the answer.

Reading Math

After children complete **Exercises 5–8**, invite volunteers to share their tally marks at the board.

Common Error

Incorrectly Reading the Bar

Some children may have difficulty following from the end of a bar to the number on the horizontal or vertical axis. Suggest that children check by counting the number of boxes in the row or column.

4 Assess and Close

Display the graph on page 96.

1 more sailboat appears on the lake. How does the graph change? (The first bar would be shaded to 4.)

Explain how you read a bar graph. (Answers may vary. Children may count the filled-in boxes in the bar, or just read the number at which the bar stops.)

 Keeping a Journal

Show how to make a bar graph.

Hands-On: Make a Bar Graph

Lesson 4.5

PLANNING THE LESSON

MATHEMATICS OBJECTIVE

Use a tally chart to make a bar graph and compare information.

Use Lesson Planner CD-ROM for Lesson 4.5.

Daily Routines

Calendar

Circle a full 7-day week. Ask children how they might use tally marks to show the number of days in a week.

Vocabulary

Remind children of their earlier work with tallies. Then ask them how they would describe a **tally chart**.

Vocabulary Cards

Meeting North Carolina's Standards

1.04 Create, model, and solve problems that use addition, subtraction, and fair shares (between two or three).

Also **1.01**

Lesson Transparency 4.5

Problem of the Day

Mrs. Lee makes a bar graph. It shows this information:

8 red crayons   17 blue crayons

4 green crayons   12 purple crayons

Which color crayon has the longest bar on the graph? (blue)

Quick Review

1. $8 - 5 = $ (3)   3. $8 - 3 = $ (5)
2. $6 - 6 = $ (0)   4. $6 - 0 = $ (6)

Lesson Quiz

1. How many boxes on a graph do you color if you have 3 tally marks? (3 boxes)
2. If a bar on the graph shows 5, how many tally marks are there? (5 tally marks)

LEVELED PRACTICE

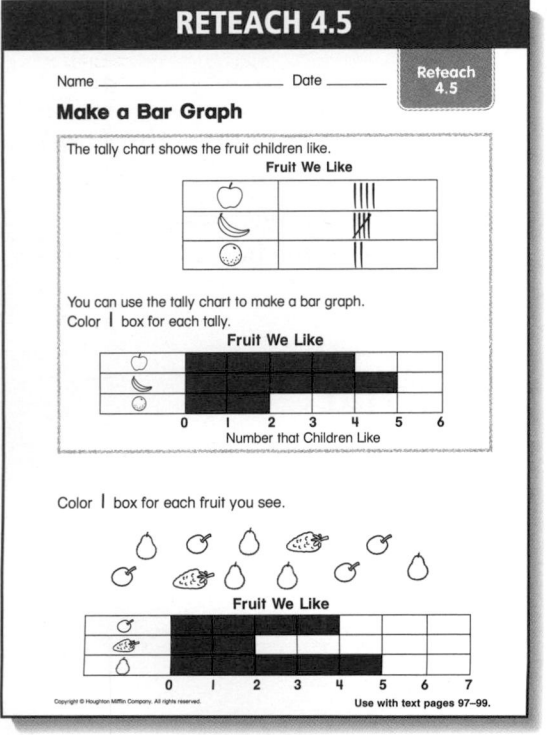

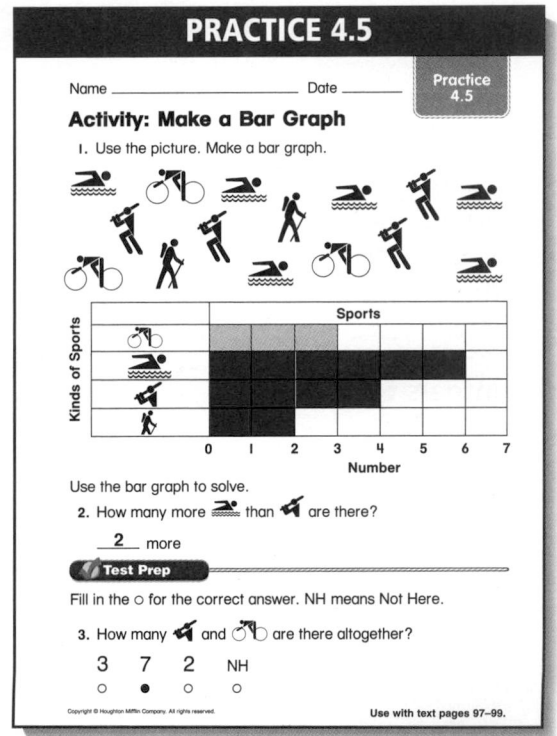

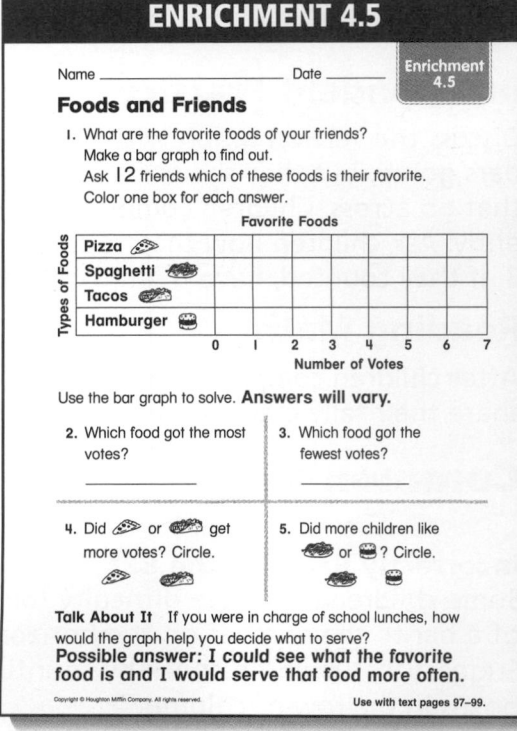

Practice Workbook Page 28

Reaching All Learners

Differentiated Instruction

English Learners

- In order to compare information in graphs, children will need to understand the words *least* and *greatest*. Use Worksheet 4.5 to help develop an understanding of these words.

Special Needs
TACTILE, VISUAL

Materials: *cubes*

- Have the child cover each car in the picture on page 98 with a cube of the same color.
- **How many greens are there?** (4) Move the cubes from the cars to cover the first 4 boxes on the top row of the graph.
- Continue with the blue, yellow, and red.

Gifted and Talented
VISUAL, AUDITORY

- Use the car graph on page 98. Have children work in pairs.
- Have each one ask their partner 2 questions about the graph that can be solved by adding.
- Then have the partner write the corresponding addition sentence.

How many liked red and yellow?

$2 + 3 = 5$

TECHNOLOGY

Spiral Review

Help students remember skills they learned earlier by creating **customized** spiral review worksheets using the *Ways to Assess* CD-ROM.

eBook

An electronic version of this lesson can be found in **eMathBook**.

Software

Use **Sunburst's** *Graphers* or another graphing program to explore this lesson's objectives more fully.

Social Studies Connection

Discuss the idea that most communities have places where people can play, exercise, relax. Brainstorm a list of places that are fun to go bicycling. Then help children make a graph that shows where they like to bicycle.

MATH CENTER

Real-Life Activity

Help children understand the usefulness of mathematics. This activity makes math come alive by connecting the lesson skills to a real-life situation.

Homework Workbook Page 28

TEACHING LESSON 4.5

LESSON ORGANIZER

Objective Use a tally chart to make a bar graph and compare information.

Resources Reteach, Practice, Enrichment, Problem Solving, Home work, Learners, Transparencies, Math Center

Materials Blank transparency, overhead squares, red and blue crayons, graph paper (LT 21), number cards 1–20 (LT 14 and 15)

Activity

Warm-Up Activity
Modeling Taking a Survey

Small Group	5 minutes	Visual, Auditory

Materials: *blank transparency*

1. Explain that you will demonstrate how to take a survey. Ask children what color bicycle helmet they use. Write the colors on the board.

   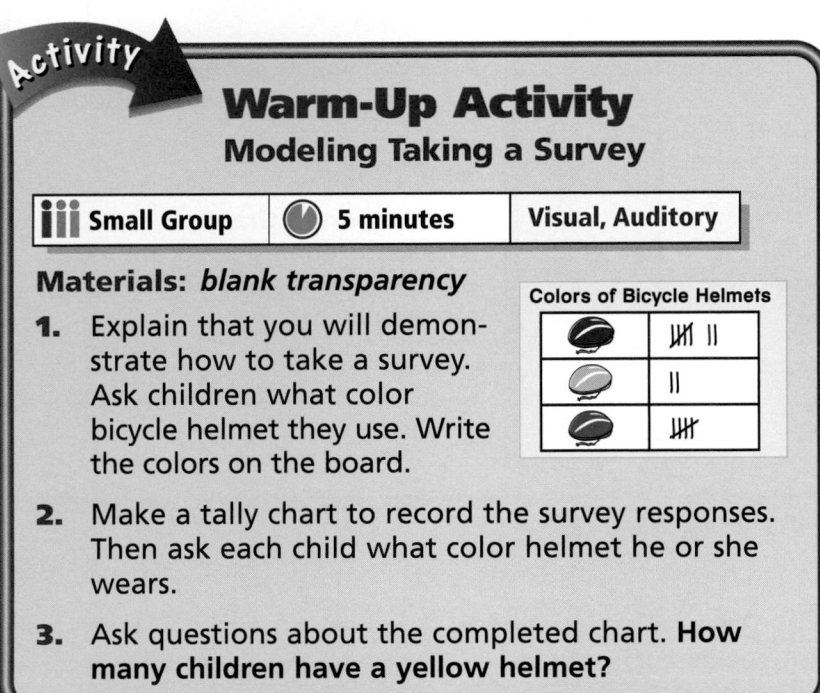

   Colors of Bicycle Helmets

2. Make a tally chart to record the survey responses. Then ask each child what color helmet he or she wears.

3. Ask questions about the completed chart. **How many children have a yellow helmet?**

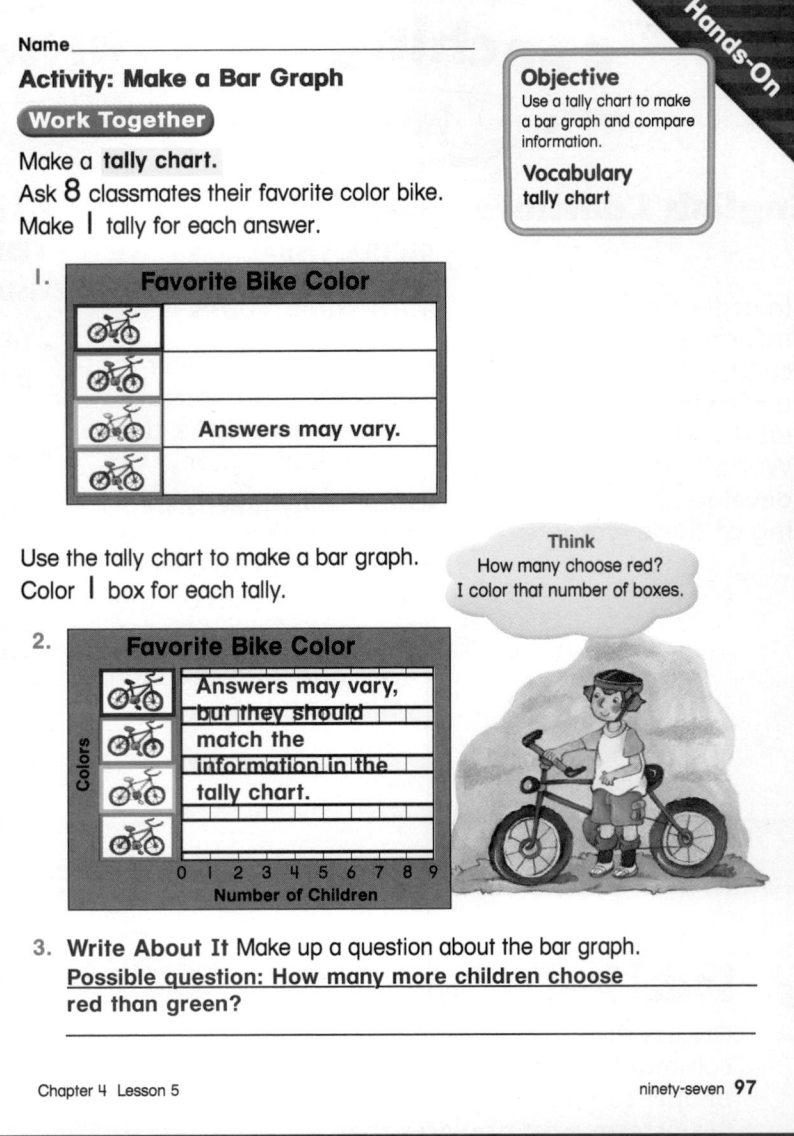

Name_____

Activity: Make a Bar Graph

Work Together

Make a **tally chart.**
Ask 8 classmates their favorite color bike.
Make 1 tally for each answer.

Objective
Use a tally chart to make a bar graph and compare information.

Vocabulary
tally chart

1. **Favorite Bike Color**

   Answers may vary.

Use the tally chart to make a bar graph.
Color 1 box for each tally.

Think
How many choose red?
I color that number of boxes.

2. **Favorite Bike Color**

   Colors

   Answers may vary, but they should match the information in the tally chart.

   0 1 2 3 4 5 6 7 8 9
   Number of Children

3. **Write About It** Make up a question about the bar graph.
   Possible question: How many more children choose red than green?

---

1 Introduce
Discuss Making a Bar Graph

Whole Group	10–15 minutes	Visual, Tactile

Materials: *blank transparency, overhead squares*

1. Place 3 different color squares on the transparency. Ask: **How many children like red the best?** Record the number in tally marks next to the red square. Continue with other colors.

2. Make a grid on the board. **One box on the grid equals 1 tally mark. How many boxes will I color in the red row on the graph?** Count the tally marks on the transparency with children. Continue until bar graph is complete.

3. **A bar graph is another way to compare information.** Model how to use the completed graph to answer questions.

2 Develop

Work Together

Read the objective with children and review the vocabulary.

Guide children in surveying 8 classmates and recording the responses in the tally chart for **Exercise 1**. You may have the opportunity to discuss mode with the tally chart. Then observe as children complete **Exercises 2–3**. Let volunteers share their responses to **Write About It** so that children see that many different questions apply to the graph.

Ask children to make a prediction about how children in the whole class would vote or answer based upon how the 8 classmates voted or answered.

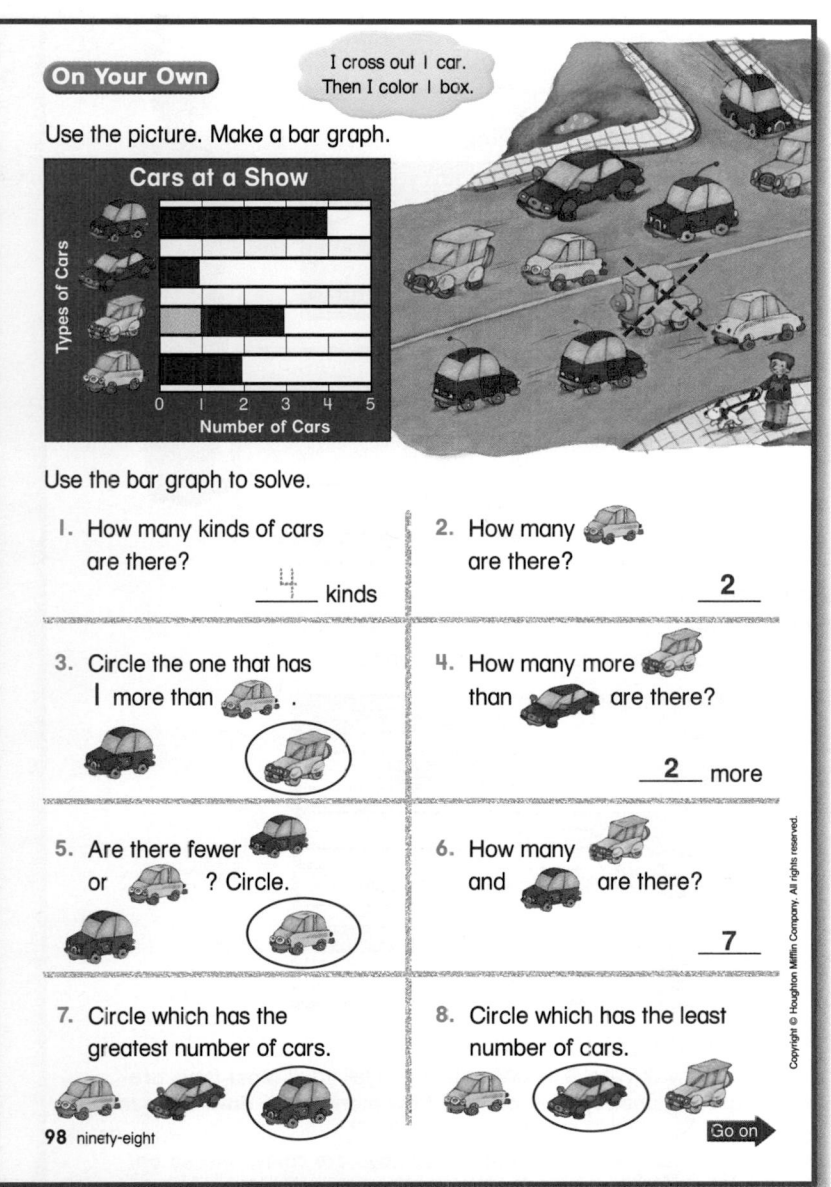

I cross out I car. Then I color I box.

Use the picture. Make a bar graph.

Cars at a Show

Types of Cars

0 1 2 3 4 5
Number of Cars

Use the bar graph to solve.

1. How many kinds of cars are there?

   _4_ kinds

2. How many [car] are there?

   2

3. Circle the one that has I more than [car].

4. How many more [car] than [car] are there?

   2 more

5. Are there fewer [car] or [car]? Circle.

6. How many [car] and [car] are there?

   7

7. Circle which has the greatest number of cars.

8. Circle which has the least number of cars.

98 ninety-eight

Go on ▶

Technology Connection
Use a Computer to Make a Bar Graph

Students gather and graph weather data using Graphers.

Have students make a tally chart with the following categories: sunny, partly cloudy, cloudy, rainy, and snowy. Have them record the weather each day for a week. Then have them follow the directions below to graph their data.

- Double-click **Work Out**, then **Create New Data**, then **Counting Data**. Choose **Weather**. Enter data in **Data Maker**.

- Click **Graphs**, then **Bar Graph**, then **Go**. Click **File** then **Save**. Enter your name and click **OK** to save your graph.

Have students record data for another week then add it to their saved graphs. Have students print and compare graphs.

Explain words like CD, software, mouse and boot. Have students use these terms to explain how they made their graphs.

---

③ Practice

On Your Own

Instruct children to count the number of cars of each color to make the bar graph. Remind them to cross out 1 car and then color 1 box to complete the bar graph. Then have children complete **Exercises 1–8** independently. You can discuss range on items 7 and 8.

Lesson continues ▶

Daily Test Prep

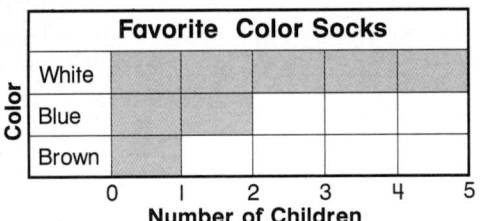

Favorite Color Socks

Color						
White						
Blue						
Brown						
	0	1	2	3	4	5

Number of Children

How many children like blue socks?

2   3   4   5
●   ○   ○   ○

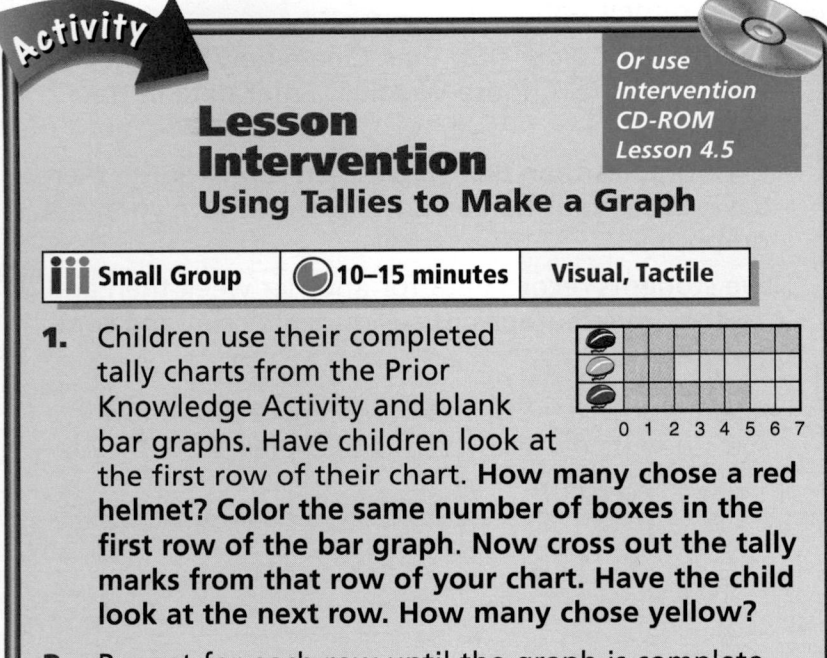

Activity

Or use Intervention CD-ROM Lesson 4.5

Lesson Intervention
Using Tallies to Make a Graph

👤👤👤 Small Group	⏱ 10–15 minutes	Visual, Tactile

1. Children use their completed tally charts from the Prior Knowledge Activity and blank bar graphs. Have children look at the first row of their chart. **How many chose a red helmet? Color the same number of boxes in the first row of the bar graph. Now cross out the tally marks from that row of your chart. Have the child look at the next row. How many chose yellow?**

0 1 2 3 4 5 6 7

2. Repeat for each row until the graph is complete.

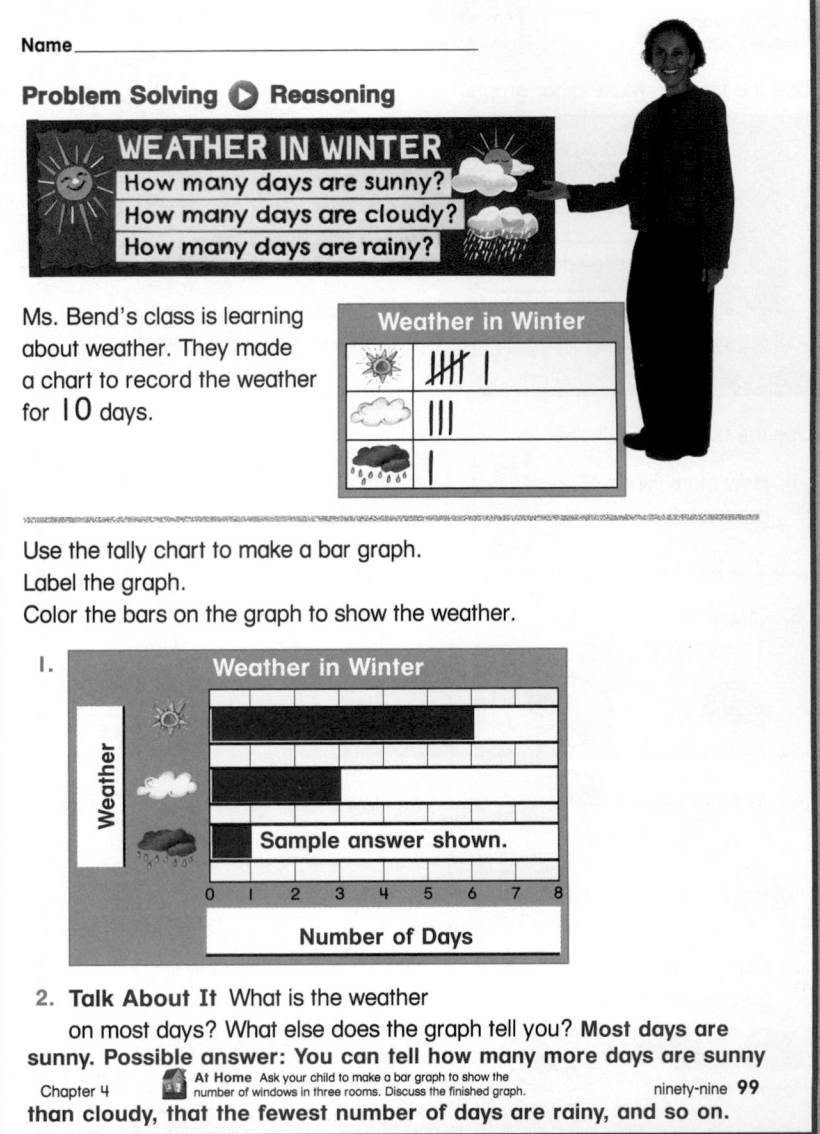

Name_____

Problem Solving ▶ Reasoning

WEATHER IN WINTER
How many days are sunny?
How many days are cloudy?
How many days are rainy?

Ms. Bend's class is learning about weather. They made a chart to record the weather for 10 days.

Weather in Winter

☀	卌 l
☁	lll
🌧	l

Use the tally chart to make a bar graph.
Label the graph.
Color the bars on the graph to show the weather.

1.

Weather in Winter

Weather

☀

☁

🌧   Sample answer shown.

0 1 2 3 4 5 6 7 8

Number of Days

2. Talk About It What is the weather on most days? What else does the graph tell you? **Most days are sunny. Possible answer: You can tell how many more days are sunny**

Chapter 4   🏠 **At Home** Ask your child to make a bar graph to show the number of windows in three rooms. Discuss the finished graph.   ninety-nine **99**

than cloudy, that the fewest number of days are rainy, and so on.

 **Practice**

Problem Solving

After children complete **Exercise 1**, call on volunteers to describe what each symbol in the chart represents. Use the **Talk About It** in **Exercise 2** to discuss the information in the graph.

Common Error

Omitting Boxes
Watch for children who skip boxes as they color. Remind them to color each box in order.

 **Assess and Close**

If you make a bar graph about bicycle colors, how will you show that 5 children have red bicycles? (color in 5 boxes)

What do the numbers at the bottom of a bar graph tell you? (How many boxes are colored.)

 **Keeping a Journal**

Draw a bar graph that shows three friends chose blue as their favorite color. Show that two friends chose red.

Numbers Are Great!

2 Players
What You Need: Number cards 1–20, blue crayon, red crayon

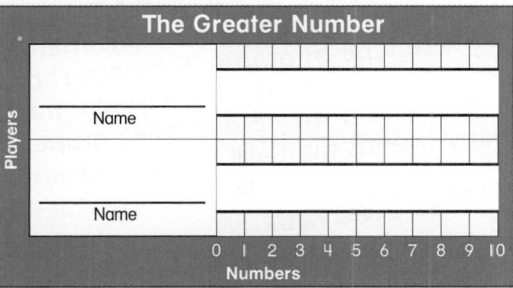

How to Play

1. Place the cards facedown in a pile.

2. Each player turns over a card.

3. The player with the greater number colors 1 box on the graph.

4. Play until all cards are used.

5. The player with the longer bar wins.

The Greater Number

Players	Name										
	Name										

0 1 2 3 4 5 6 7 8 9 10
Numbers

Other Ways to Play

A. Place the cards facedown. Play again. This time the player with the lesser number colors 1 box on the graph.

B. Use a 0–5 spinner. Each player spins twice and adds the two numbers. The greater sum colors 1 box on the graph.

Numbers Are Great!

Purpose: This game provides practice reading numbers to 20 and making a bar graph.

Materials: *For each pair: number cards 1–20 (LT 14 and 15), red and blue crayons, graph paper (LT 21)*

How to Play

- Children mix up the number cards and place them facedown between them. Have children take a blue or red crayon and write their names next to a row on the graph.

- Together players turn over a card and compare their numbers. The player with the greater number colors 1 box next to their name.

- Have each child count his or her colored-in boxes aloud to check who has more.

- If time allows, children may mix up the cards and continue playing until one of the bars on the graph is filled.

Other Ways to Play

A Children play as stated above. The player with the lesser number colors a box this time.

B Make a 0–5 spinner available. Each player spins twice. Have children write the addition sentences on paper. The player with the greater sum colors 1 box. Have children check each other's addition before coloring.

Literature Connection

Refer back to the unit story *Aunt Flossie's Hats (and Crab Cakes Later)* by Elizabeth Fitzgerald Howard.

Have children do the following exercises based on the passage that appears in the student book.

Aunt Flossie has so many colorful hats. Let's read and keep count by making a tally mark for each different color. How many tally marks in all? (6)

Let's pretend Aunt Flossie has 4 soft green hats and 3 floppy blue hats. Make a bar graph to compare how many.

Present similar problems to review children's knowledge of addition, comparing, tallies, and so on.

Problem Solving: Use a Graph

PLANNING THE LESSON

MATHEMATICS OBJECTIVE
Use a graph to solve a problem.

 *Use Lesson Planner CD-ROM for Lesson 4.6.*

Daily Routines

Point to two full weeks on the monthly calendar. Ask children how many school days are in the two weeks. Let a volunteer show how to count the days.

Sunday	Monday	Sunday	Wednesday	Thursday	Friday	Saturday
			1	2	3	4
5	6	7	8	9	10	11
12	13	14	15	16	17	18
19	20	21	22	23	24	25
26	27	28	29	30	31	

Vocabulary

Ask children what type of information is found on a **bar graph**. Discuss ways to use the information.

Vocabulary Cards

Meeting North Carolina's Standards
1.04 Create, model, and solve problems that use addition, subtraction, and fair shares (between two or three).

Lesson Transparency 4.6

Problem of the Day
Basil made a graph to show his friends' favorite type of grapes. 5 friends chose red grapes and 5 friends chose green grapes. 2 friends said they did not like grapes. How many friends did Basil ask? (12 friends)

Quick Review

$$
\begin{array}{ccccc}
4 & 5 & 4 & 3 & 2 \\
+5 & +2 & +3 & +5 & +4 \\
\hline
(9) & (7) & (7) & (8) & (6)
\end{array}
$$

Lesson Quiz

Favorite Fruit

1. To find how many children in all chose apples and grapes, do you add or subtract? (Add)

2. To find how many more children chose apples than grapes, do you add or subtract? (Subtract) Find how many more. (2)

LEVELED PRACTICE

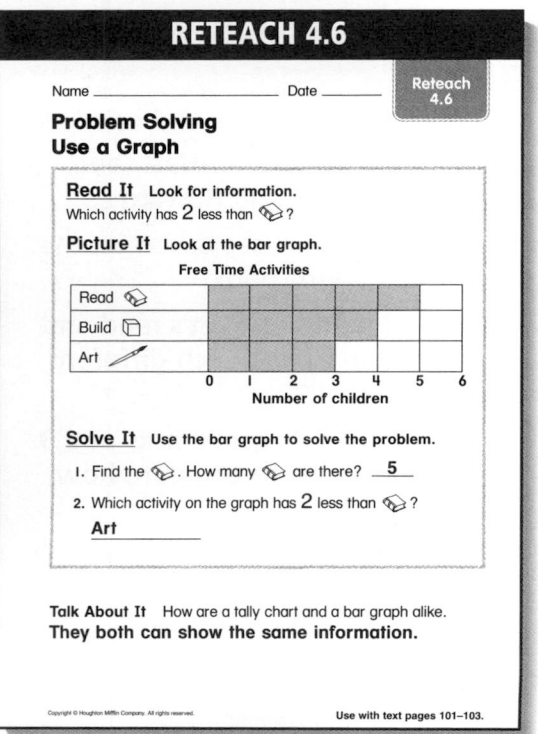

RETEACH 4.6

Name _____ Date _____ **Reteach 4.6**

Problem Solving
Use a Graph

Read It Look for information.
Which activity has 2 less than 🐾?

Picture It Look at the bar graph.

Free Time Activities

Read 🐾						
Build 🎲						
Art ✏						

0 1 2 3 4 5 6
Number of children

Solve It Use the bar graph to solve the problem.

1. Find the 🐾. How many 🐾 are there? **5**

2. Which activity on the graph has 2 less than 🐾? **Art**

Talk About It How are a tally chart and a bar graph alike.
They both can show the same information.

Copyright © Houghton Mifflin Company. All rights reserved.   Use with text pages 101–103.

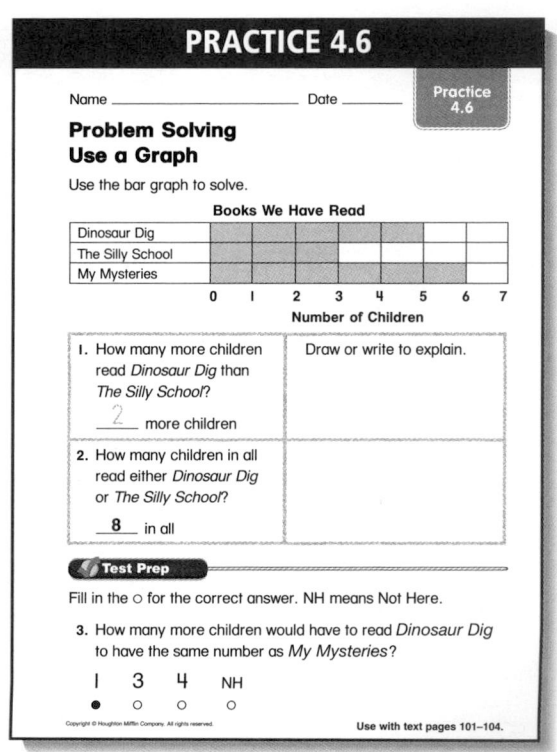

PRACTICE 4.6

Name _____ Date _____ **Practice 4.6**

Problem Solving
Use a Graph

Use the bar graph to solve.

Books We Have Read

Dinosaur Dig							
The Silly School							
My Mysteries							

0 1 2 3 4 5 6 7
Number of Children

1. How many more children read *Dinosaur Dig* than *The Silly School*?
   2 more children

   Draw or write to explain.

2. How many children in all read either *Dinosaur Dig* or *The Silly School*?
   8 in all

Test Prep

Fill in the ○ for the correct answer. NH means Not Here.

3. How many more children would have to read *Dinosaur Dig* to have the same number as *My Mysteries*?

   1 ● 3 ○ 4 ○ NH ○

Copyright © Houghton Mifflin Company. All rights reserved.   Use with text pages 101–104.

ENRICHMENT 4.6

Name _____ Date _____ **Enrichment 4.6**

Class Clubs

1. Read the problem.
   How many children are in ✏ club and 📷 club?

Class Clubs

Kinds of Clubs
Book 📖							
Camera 📷							
Art ✏							
Music 🎵							

0 1 2 3 4 5 6 7
Number of Children

Find the numbers in the graph. Then add.

$$
\begin{array}{rl}
4 & \text{book club} \\
+\; 4 & \text{art club} \\
\hline
8 & \text{children}
\end{array}
$$

2. Look back at the problem. How can you check your answer?
   Answers will vary.

3. Write your own problem that the graph can answer.
   Questions will vary.

Copyright © Houghton Mifflin Company. All rights reserved.   Use with text pages 101–103.

Practice Workbook Page 29

Reaching All Learners

Differentiated Instruction

English Learners

- To solve the multistep word problem, English-language learners will need to understand the words *on* and *off*. Use Worksheet 4.6 to help develop an understanding of these words.

Inclusion
VISUAL, TACTILE

Materials: *cubes in 3 colors*

- Review parts of a bar graph.
- Give the child cubes of 3 colors. Have the child sort the cubes by color. Guide the child to make a bar graph using this information.
- Then ask the child addition or subtraction questions relating to the bar graph.

Gifted and Talented
VISUAL, TACTILE

Children work in pairs.

- Give each pair blank sheets of paper. Have one child write an addition or a subtraction sentence on the paper.
- The partner creates a bar graph from the information in the addition or subtraction sentence.

TECHNOLOGY

Spiral Review

You can prepare students for standardized tests with **customized** spiral review on key skills using the *Ways to Assess* CD-ROM.

Intervention

Use the *Ways to Success* CD-ROM intervention software to support students who need more help in understanding the concepts and skills taught in this chapter.

Education Place

Recommend that parents visit **Education Place** at **eduplace.com/parents/mw/** for parent support activities.

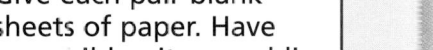

ScienceConnection

Discuss different types of boats with children. Encourage children to share information on the different ways boats move through the water. (Fuel for motorboats, wind for sailboats, etc.) Make a bar graph of the information.

MATH CENTER

Number of the Week Activity

Display the Number of the Week to motivate children to use their problem-solving skills. The exercises cover topics across all math strands.

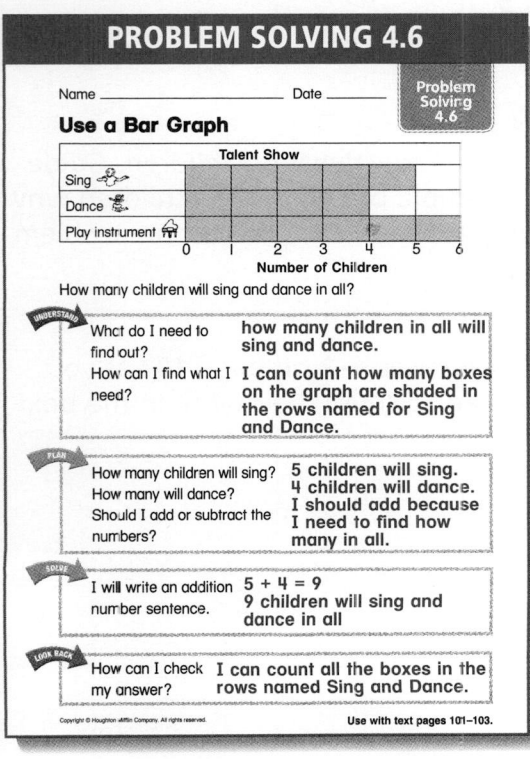

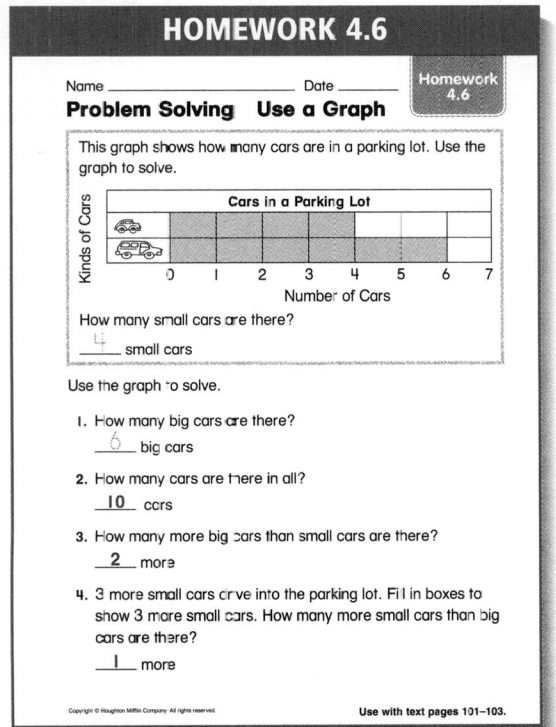

Homework Workbook Page 29

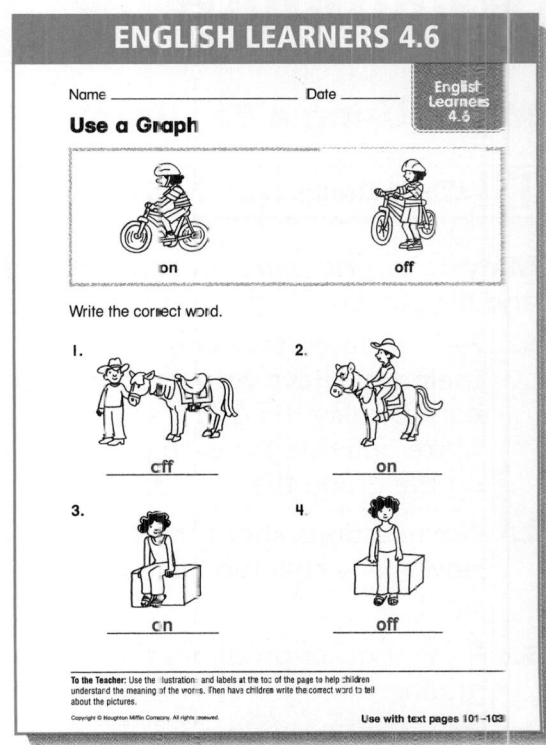

TEACHING LESSON 4.6

LESSON ORGANIZER

Objective Use a graph to solve a problem.

Resources Reteach, Practice, Enrichment, Problem Solving, English Learners, Transparencies, Math Center

Materials Number cards 0–9 (LT 14), 2-color counters, grid paper transparency; green, blue, brown, and black cubes

Activity

Warm-Up Activity
Solving Problems

👤👤👤 Small Group	🕐 5 minutes	Auditory, Visual

Materials: *number cards 0–9 (LT 14), cubes*

1. Give each group 3 number cards and cubes of 3 colors. Have them make a bar graph using the information on the card. Remind children: **Each color will be a different row on your graph.**

2. Have each child write an addition or subtraction problem that can be solved by using the information on the graph.

3. Children share their problems with the group.

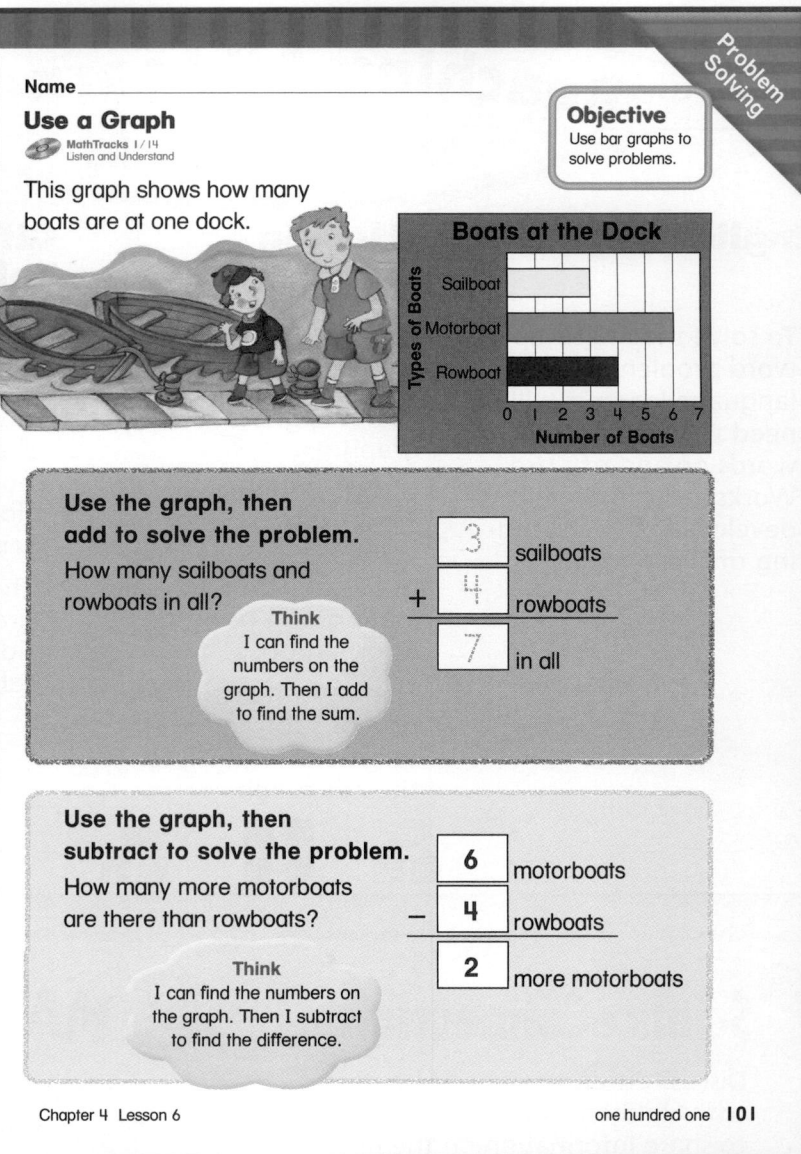

Use a Graph
MathTracks 1 / 14
Listen and Understand

Objective Use bar graphs to solve problems.

This graph shows how many boats are at one dock.

Boats at the Dock

Types of Boats: Sailboat, Motorboat, Rowboat
Number of Boats: 0 1 2 3 4 5 6 7

Use the graph, then add to solve the problem.
How many sailboats and rowboats in all?

> **Think**
> I can find the numbers on the graph. Then I add to find the sum.

3 sailboats
+ 4 rowboats
7 in all

Use the graph, then subtract to solve the problem.
How many more motorboats are there than rowboats?

> **Think**
> I can find the numbers on the graph. Then I subtract to find the difference.

6 motorboats
− 4 rowboats
2 more motorboats

Chapter 4 Lesson 6   one hundred one **101**

---

1 Introduce   Activity

Model Using a Bar Graph to Solve Problems

👤👤👤👤 Whole Group	🕐 10–15 minutes	Visual, Tactile

Materials: *grid paper transparency; green, blue, brown, and black cubes*

1. Have children take cubes that are the same color as their eyes. Have volunteers connect like cubes to make bars. Display the grid transparency and label the graph. Make one row for each eye color. Place the cube rows on the graph that match the color labeled.

2. Ask questions about the information on the graph. **How many children have brown eyes?** (Answers will vary.)

3. Present other problems that children can solve with the graph.

2 Develop

Guided Learning

Teaching Example Read the objective with children. Guide them through the two example problems. Ask children why the first problem requires addition and the second problem requires subtraction.

Guided Practice

Have children complete **Exercises 1–2 on page 102** as you observe. Encourage children to show their work in the box provided.

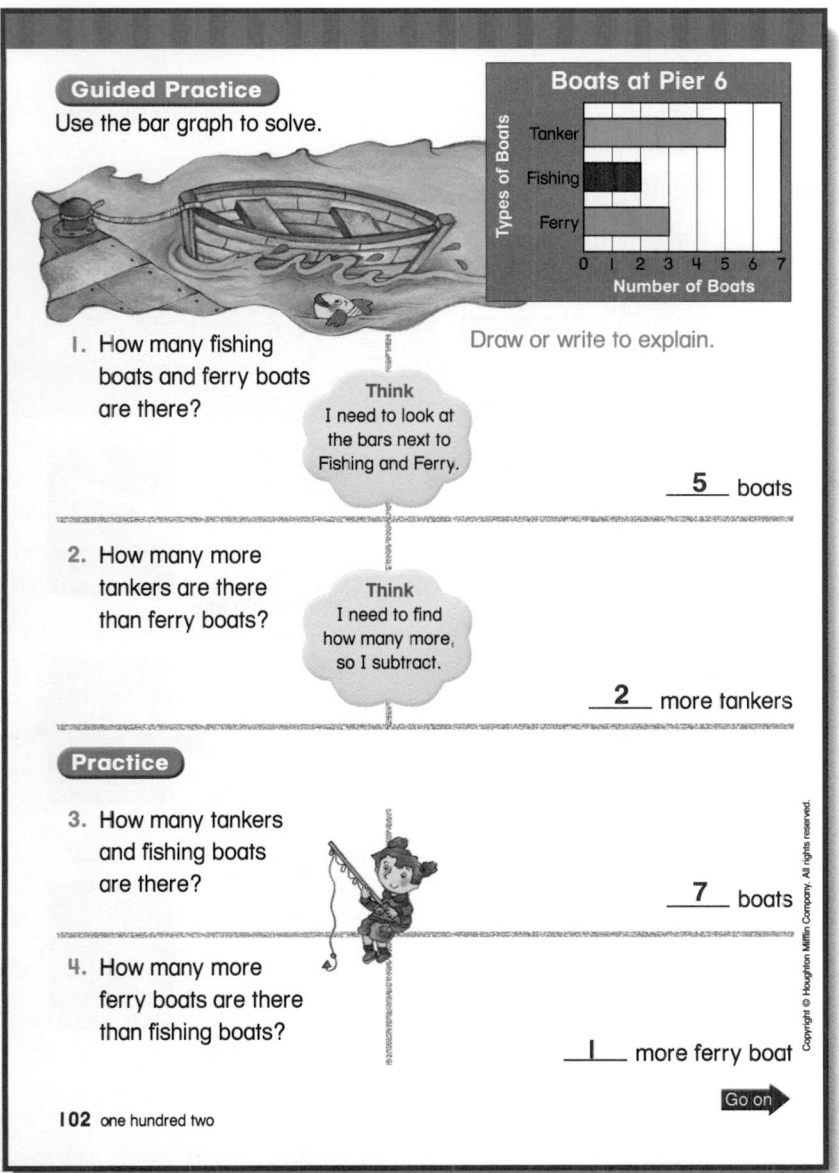

Use the bar graph to solve.

Boats at Pier 6

1. How many fishing boats and ferry boats are there?

Draw or write to explain.

Think
I need to look at the bars next to Fishing and Ferry.

_____5_____ boats

2. How many more tankers are there than ferry boats?

Think
I need to find how many more, so I subtract.

_____2_____ more tankers

Practice

3. How many tankers and fishing boats are there?

_____7_____ boats

4. How many more ferry boats are there than fishing boats?

_____I_____ more ferry boat

102 one hundred two

Go on

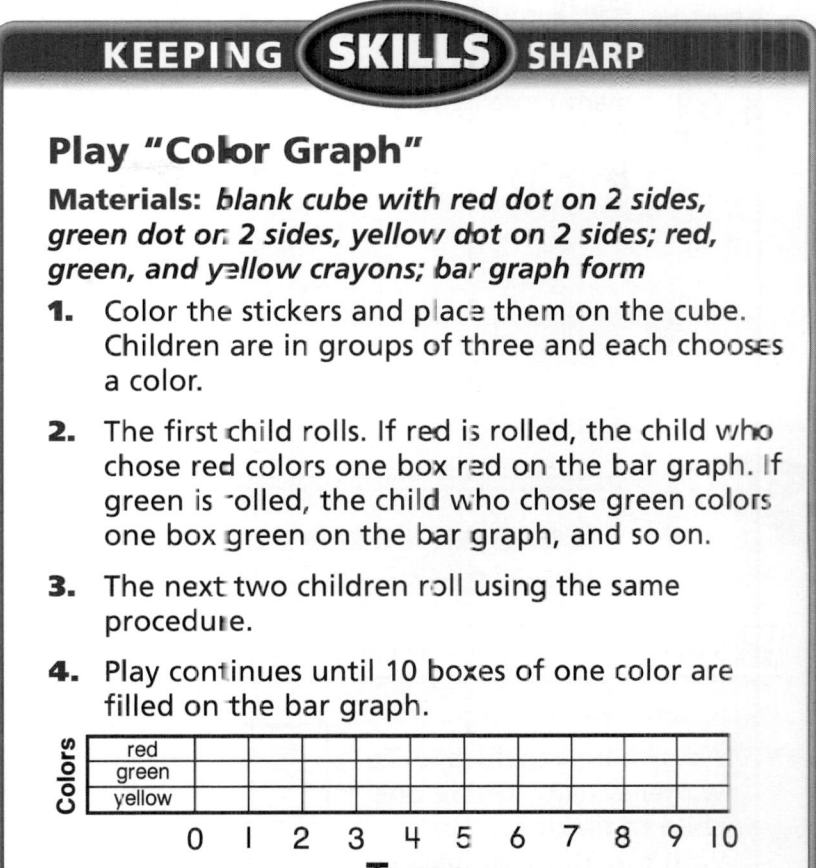

KEEPING SKILLS SHARP

Play "Color Graph"

Materials: *blank cube with red dot on 2 sides, green dot on 2 sides, yellow dot on 2 sides; red, green, and yellow crayons; bar graph form*

1. Color the stickers and place them on the cube. Children are in groups of three and each chooses a color.

2. The first child rolls. If red is rolled, the child who chose red colors one box red on the bar graph. If green is rolled, the child who chose green colors one box green on the bar graph, and so on.

3. The next two children roll using the same procedure.

4. Play continues until 10 boxes of one color are filled on the bar graph.

---

③ Practice

Independent Practice

Children complete **Exercises 3–4** on page 102 independently.

Lesson continues

Daily Test Prep

Jenna has 5 beach balls. Rimi has 4 water floats. How many more items does Jenna h

1	2	3	4
●	○	○	○

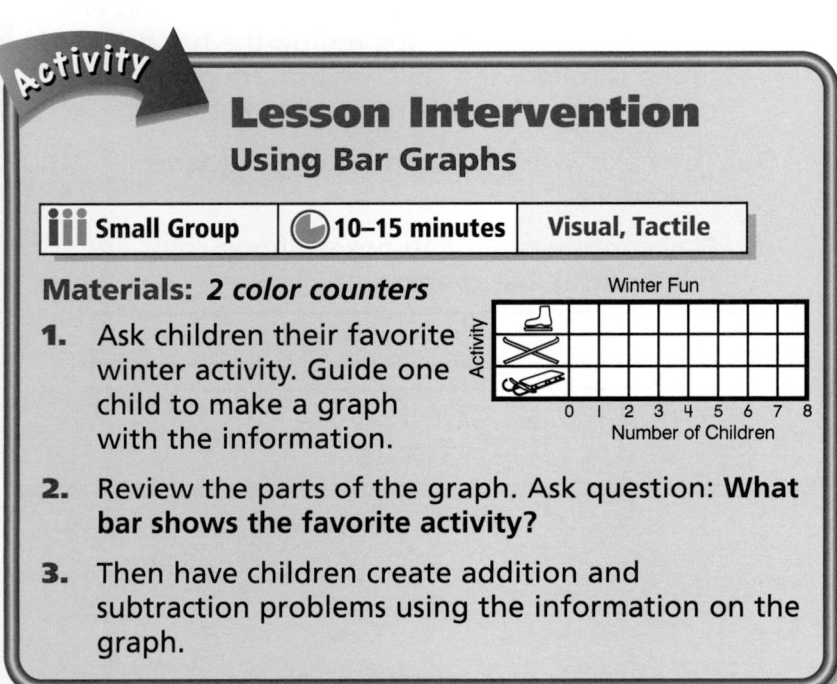

Activity

Lesson Intervention
Using Bar Graphs

👥 Small Group	⏱ 10–15 minutes	Visual, Tactile

Materials: *2 color counters*

1. Ask children their favorite winter activity. Guide one child to make a graph with the information.

2. Review the parts of the graph. Ask question: **What bar shows the favorite activity?**

3. Then have children create addition and subtraction problems using the information on the graph.

Winter Fun

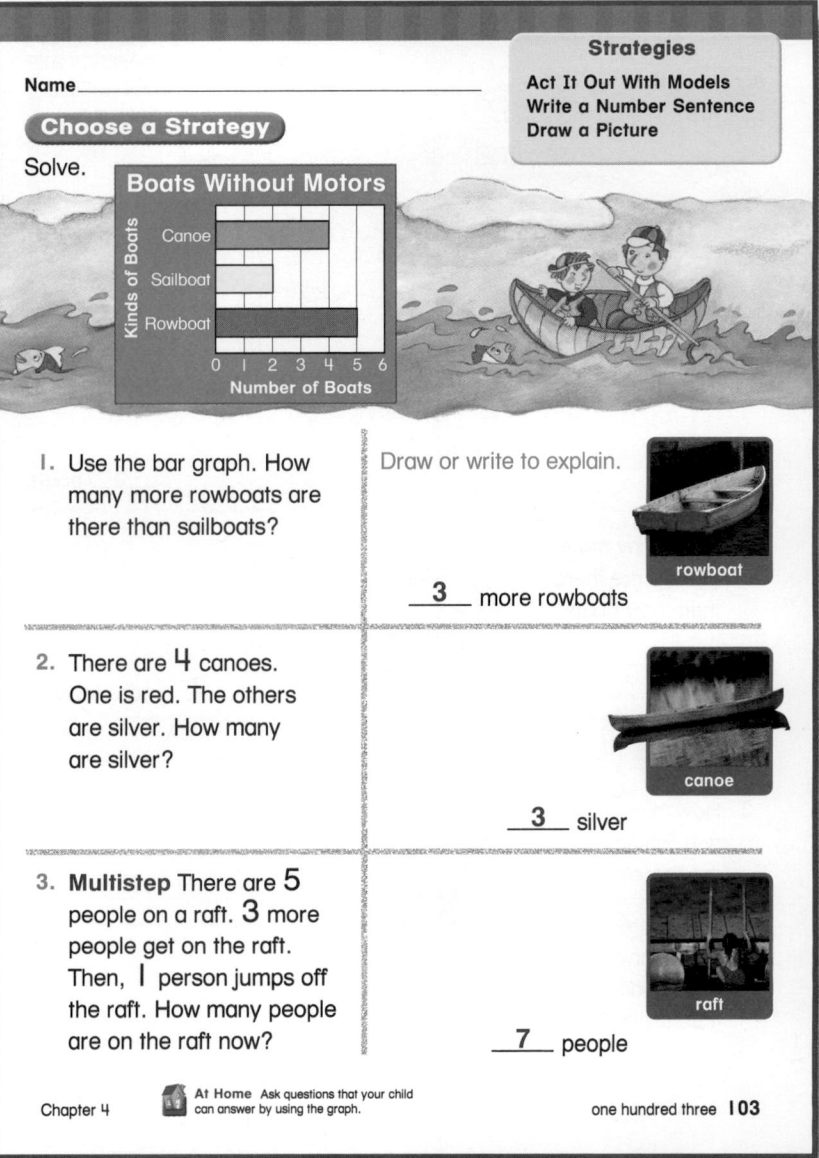

Name_____

Choose a Strategy

Solve.

Strategies
Act It Out With Models
Write a Number Sentence
Draw a Picture

Boats Without Motors

1. Use the bar graph. How many more rowboats are there than sailboats?

Draw or write to explain.

____3____ more rowboats

rowboat

2. There are 4 canoes. One is red. The others are silver. How many are silver?

____3____ silver

canoe

3. **Multistep** There are 5 people on a raft. 3 more people get on the raft. Then, 1 person jumps off the raft. How many people are on the raft now?

____7____ people

raft

Chapter 4

At Home Ask questions that your child can answer by using the graph.

one hundred three **103**

---

❸ Practice

Mixed Strategy Practice

Read the problem-solving strategies with children. Have children describe some problems they may have solved using one of the strategies. Children can also tell which strategy seems to help them the most. You might pair more proficient readers with less proficient readers to complete Exercises 1–3.

Common Error

Adding or Subtracting Incorrectly

Children may add or subtract information from the graph incorrectly. Encourage children to use strategies such as counting on or back and using counters to find and check answers.

❹ Assess and Close

What does the information on a graph help you do? (to see how many of each item and compare the items)

Look at the graph on page 103. What do you need to do to find how many canoes and sailboats in all? (Add 4 plus 2.)

Keeping a Journal

Write a problem that can be solved with a graph that shows the number of boys and girls in this class.

 **for Tests**   Listening Skills

Listen to your teacher read the problem.
Solve.

1. Frank's survey shows
that 4 children like red.
3 children like blue. 1 child
likes yellow. Show what his
pictograph looks like.

Favorite Colors	
red	
blue	
yellow	

2. Look at the pictograph.
How many children
answered the survey?

<u> 8 </u> children

Listen to your teacher read the problem.
Choose the correct answer.

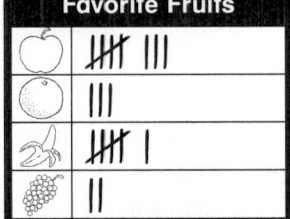

Favorite Fruits	
🍎	⊞⊞ |||
🍊	|||
🍌	⊞⊞	
🍇	||

3.    
   ●   ○   ○   ○

4.   1   3   4   7
     ○   ○   ○   ●

104   one hundred four

for Tests
Listening Skills

This page provides children practice with the oral
problem-solving format used in some standardized
test items.

You may want to read each item only once to model
the style of oral tests.

Use with Items 1 and 2

Listening Strategy: Read the problem silently as the
teacher reads it aloud.

• *When a problem is on the page, look at the problem when I'm reading it.*

• *Listen to the whole problem. Wait until I finish
reading.*

Use with Item 3

Listening Strategy: Listen to the problem and then
look at the graph.

• *Look at me when I read a problem that is not on
the page.*

Laura made a tally chart. Then she made a bar
graph. Which favorite fruit has the longest bar on
the graph?

• *Look at the tally chart. Mark your answer.*

Use with Item 4

Listening Strategy: Listen for important facts and
details.

• *Listen to the question so you will know how to
use the numbers.*

Carlos took a survey. He asked his friends a
question. Four children answered yes. Three
children answered no. How many children
answered Carlos's question?

• *Use the numbers to find the answer to the
question. Mark your answer.*

Quick Check

Have children complete the Quick Check exercises independently to assess their understanding of concepts and skills taught in **Lessons 4–6.**

Item	Lesson	Error Analysis	Intervention
1	4.5	Children may skip boxes as they color bars.	Reteach Resource 4.5 *Ways to Success* 4.5
2–3	4.4	Children may have difficulty reading the bars on a graph.	Reteach Resource 4.4 *Ways to Success* 4.4
4–5	4.6	Children may add or subtract incorrectly.	Reteach Resource 4.6 *Ways to Success* 4.6

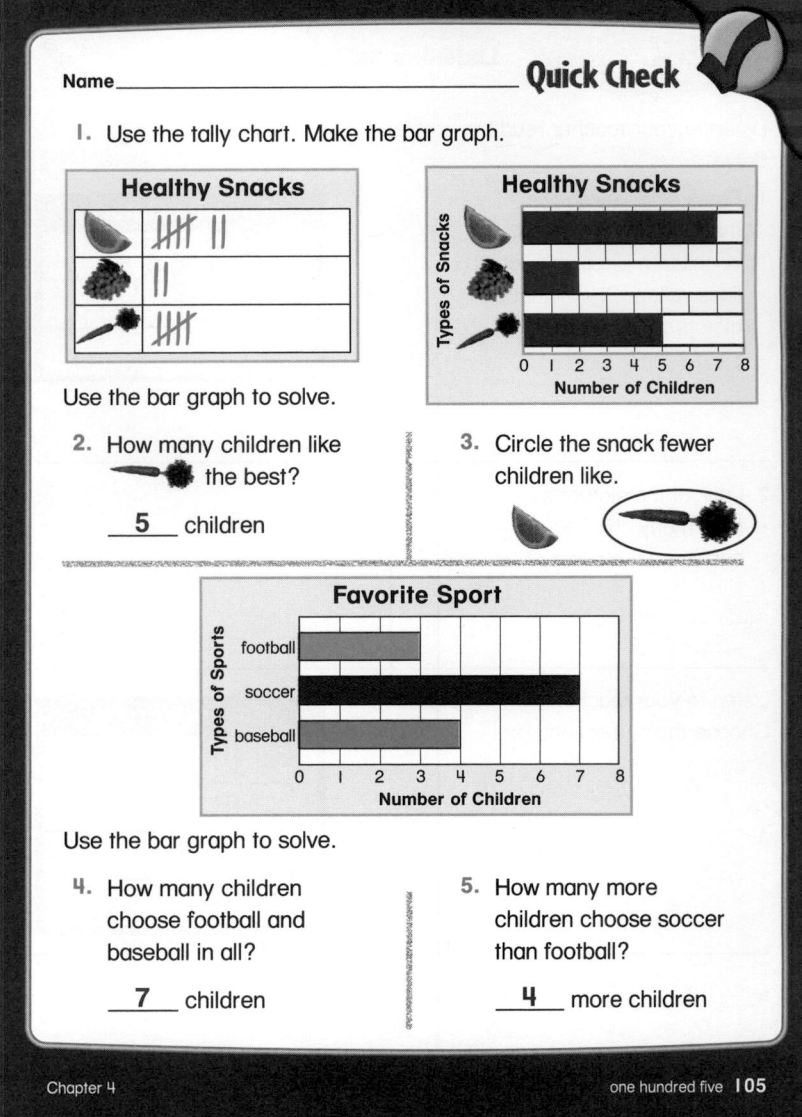

Name_____   **Quick Check**

1. Use the tally chart. Make the bar graph.

Healthy Snacks

Healthy Snacks

Use the bar graph to solve.

2. How many children like the best?

   __5__ children

3. Circle the snack fewer children like.

Favorite Sport

Use the bar graph to solve.

4. How many children choose football and baseball in all?

   __7__ children

5. How many more children choose soccer than football?

   __4__ more children

Chapter 4   one hundred five **105**

Key Topic Review

Write the sum.

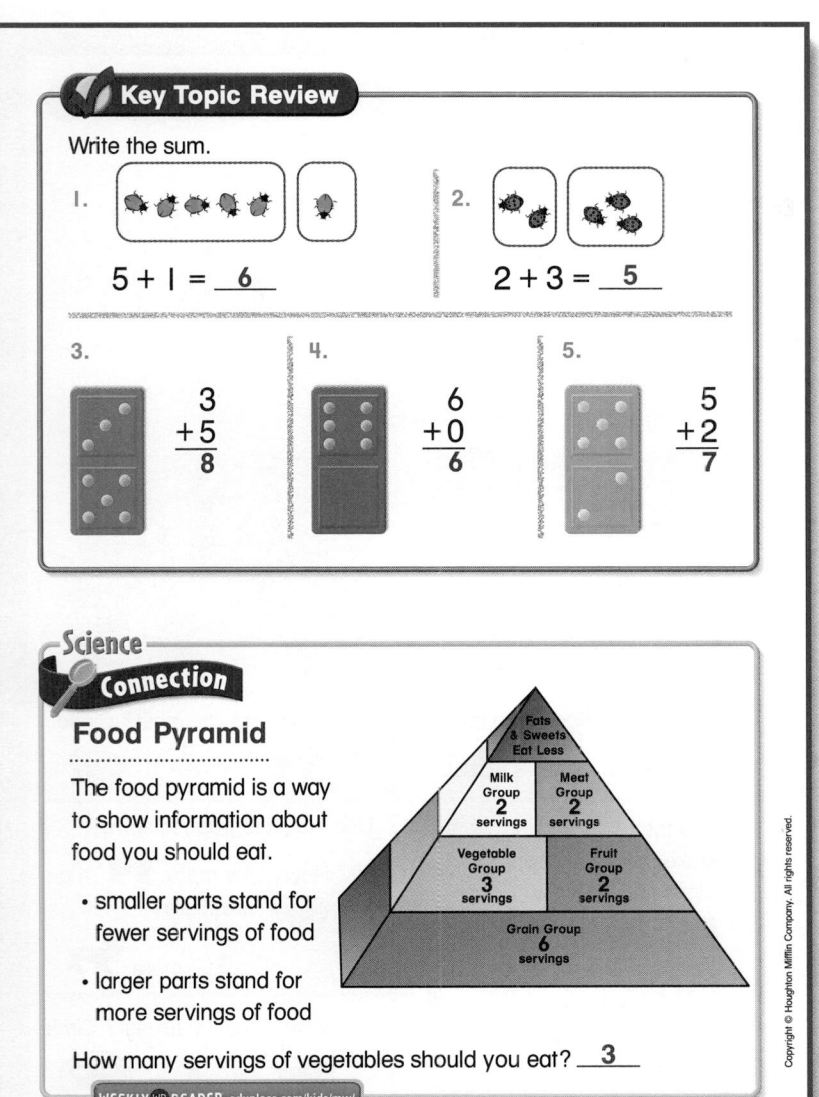

1. 5 + 1 = __6__

2. 2 + 3 = __5__

3.
$$\begin{array}{r} 3 \\ +5 \\ \hline 8 \end{array}$$

4.
$$\begin{array}{r} 6 \\ +0 \\ \hline 6 \end{array}$$

5.
$$\begin{array}{r} 5 \\ +2 \\ \hline 7 \end{array}$$

Science Connection

Food Pyramid

The food pyramid is a way to show information about food you should eat.

- smaller parts stand for fewer servings of food

- larger parts stand for more servings of food

How many servings of vegetables should you eat? __3__

WEEKLY WR READER eduplace.com/kids/mw/

Key Topic Review

This assessment provides a review of skills and concepts taught in Chapter 2.

Check to be sure that children:

- understand addition and how to find a sum
- are able to add horizontally and vertically

Science Connection

Food Pyramid

Discuss why fats, oils, and sweets are at the top of the pyramid. It is not healthy for people to eat too many of these types of foods. Have children check which food groups on the pyramid were in their last meal. How many different food groups did the entire class cover?

Note: The food pyramid shown is the Food Guide Pyramid for Young Children: A Daily Guide for 2-to-5-Year Olds. It is put out by the U.S. Department of Agriculture Center for Nutrition Policy and Promotion.

Monitoring Student Progress

Chapter Review/Test

Purpose: This test provides an informal assessment of the Chapter 4 objectives.

Chapter Test Items 1-15

To assign a numerical grade for this Chapter Test, use 6 points for each test item and add 10 to the score.

Check Understanding

Use children's work on word problems to informally assess progress on chapter content.

Customizing Your Instruction

For children who have not yet mastered these objectives, you can use the reteaching resources listed in the chart below.

 ## Assessment Options

A summary test for this chapter is also provided in the Unit Resource Folder.

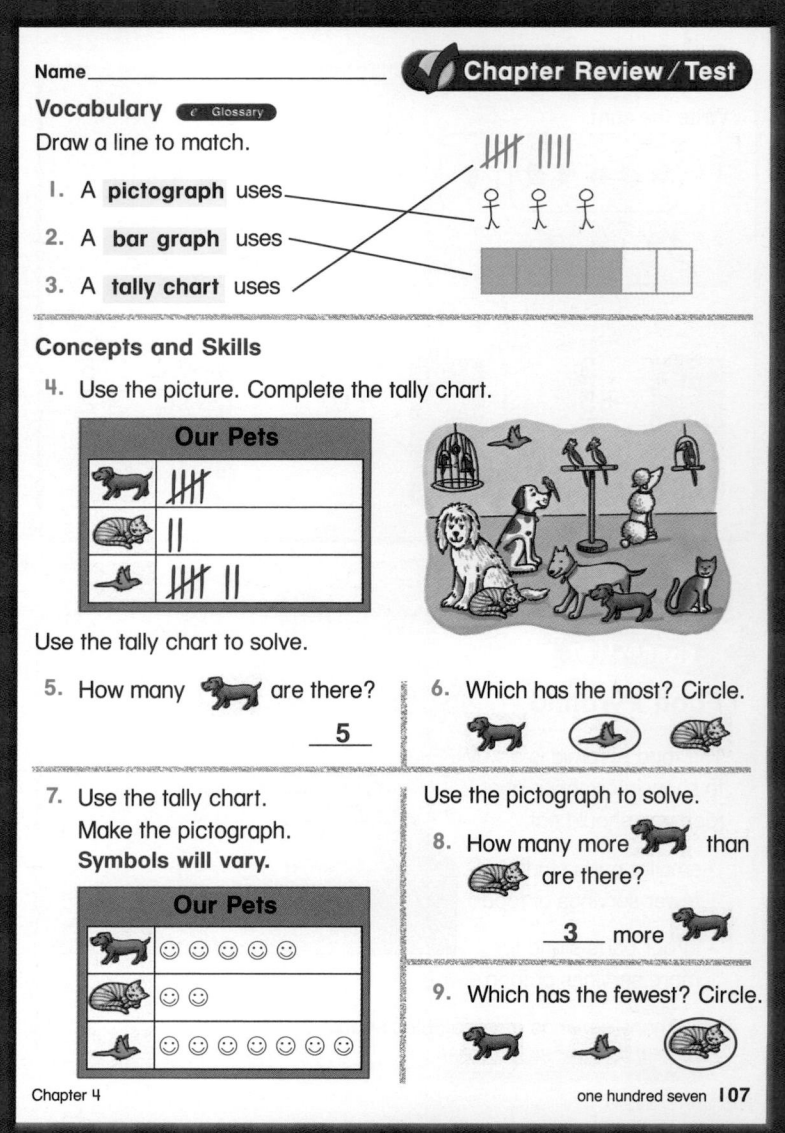

Reteaching Support

Chapter Test Items	Summary Test Items	Chapter Objectives Tested	TE Pages	Use These Reteaching Resources
1–3	1–3	**4A** Develop and use math vocabulary relating to data and graphing.	87A–90, 95A–96	Reteach Resources and *Ways to Success* CD: 4.1, 4.2, 4.4 Skillsheet 24
4–13	4–8	**4B** Read, make, and use tally charts, pictographs, and bar graphs to compare information.	89A–92, 95A–99	Reteach Resources and *Ways to Success* CD: 4.1-4.5 Skillsheet 25–27
14–15	9–10	**4C** Use graphs to solve problems.	101A–104	Reteach Resource and *Ways to Success* CD: 4.6 Skillsheet 28

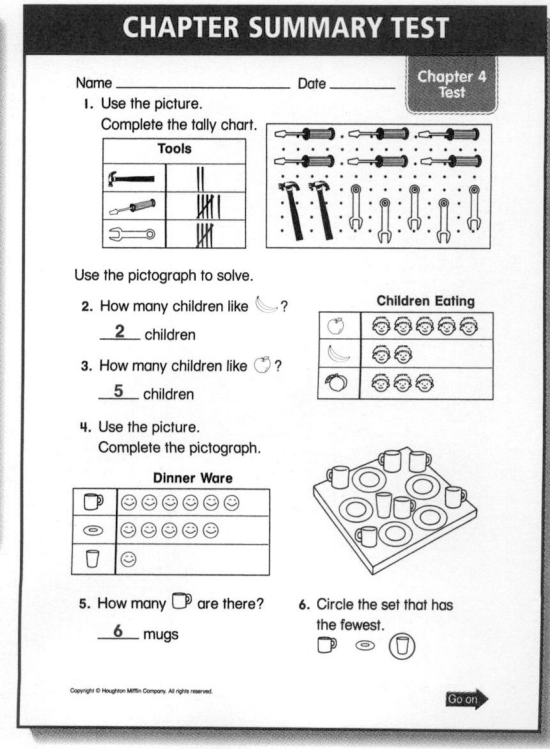

10. Use the tally chart.
    Make a bar graph.

Favorite Shoe Color

black	ⅧⅠ
white	ⅠⅠⅠ
blue	Ⅷ

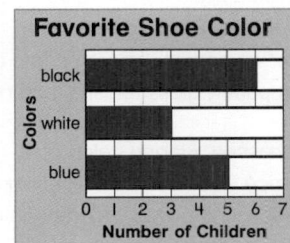

Favorite Shoe Color

11. How many children choose white shoes?   __3__ children

12. Do more children choose black or blue shoes?
    Circle.   (black)   blue

13. Circle the color fewer children choose.   black   (white)

Problem Solving

Use the bar graph to solve.

14. How many children like
    white and blue shoes?

    __8__ children

15. How many more
    children like black
    shoes than blue shoes?

    __1__ more

 Adequate Yearly Progress

Use the End of Grade Test Prep Assessment Guide
to help familiarize your children with the format
of standardized tests.

CHAPTER SUMMARY TEST

Name _____ Date _____   Chapter 4
Test
continued

Use the graph to solve.

Favorite Ball Game

Number of Children

7. How many children
   chose 🏈?

   __3__ children

8. Circle the game most
   children chose.

   ⚾ (⚽) 🏈

Use the graph, then add or subtract to solve the problems.

In the Garage

9. How many trucks and vans in
   all are there in the garage?

4	vans
+ 1	truck
5	in all

10. How many more cars than
    trucks are in the garage?

7	cars
− 1	truck
6	more cars

Social Studies Connection

PURPOSE

To write number sentences and read a chart for data.

Name_____

America Recycles

It is important to recycle trash. Recycled trash can be used to make new things. Some towns have recycling centers where people can bring paper, glass, plastic, and metal.

Tallahassee, Florida celebrates America Recycles Day. There are contests and prizes. In one contest people estimate how many cans are in a recycling bin. People learn about recycling and have fun at the festival.

Complete the number sentence to solve.

1. Joe brings 3 glass bottles to the recycling center. Sachi brings 2 cans. How many items do they bring in all?

   $\underline{3} + \underline{2} = \underline{5}$

   $\underline{5}$ items

2. Jean collects 5 bags of newspapers for recycling. Elias collects 2 bags. How many bags do they collect altogether?

   $\underline{5} + \underline{2} = \underline{7}$

   $\underline{7}$ bags

3. Mrs. Baker has 7 plastic bottles. She takes 4 of them to the center. How many bottles are left?

   $\underline{7} - \underline{4} = \underline{3}$

   $\underline{3}$ bottles

Unit 1   one hundred nine **109**

Using These Pages

Discussion Topics

- Tell children that in the United States, each person produces about 4 pounds of trash each day. **About how many pounds of trash does a person produce in two days?** (8 pounds)

- Refer children to the data in the pictograph. **How many people recycle paper and plastic?** (9) **Which item do people recycle the least?** (plastic)

- Have children brainstorm ideas for using recycled plastic bottles. Tell them that a company has found a way to turn plastic bottles into fabric! They use the fabric to make clothing and blankets.

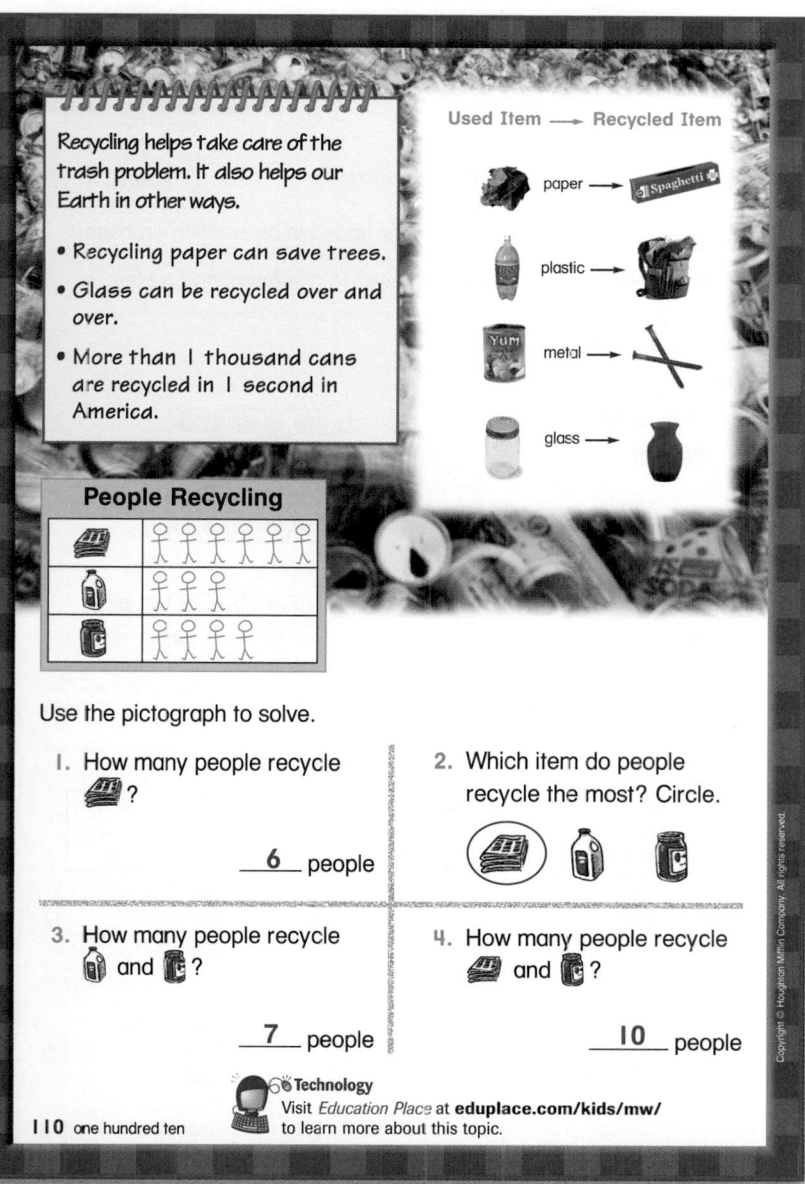

Recycling helps take care of the trash problem. It also helps our Earth in other ways.

- Recycling paper can save trees.
- Glass can be recycled over and over.
- More than 1 thousand cans are recycled in 1 second in America.

Used Item → Recycled Item

paper → Spaghetti

plastic →

metal →

glass →

People Recycling

Use the pictograph to solve.

1. How many people recycle ?

   ___6___ people

2. Which item do people recycle the most? Circle.

3. How many people recycle and ?

   ___7___ people

4. How many people recycle and ?

   ___10___ people

Technology
Visit *Education Place* at **eduplace.com/kids/mw/** to learn more about this topic.

110 one hundred ten

Wrap Up the Unit Project

- Create two separate display areas. Label each with a plus sign or a minus sign.

- As children complete their number sentences, have them place them under the appropriate symbol.

- Invite children to draw pictures of their favorite fruits and vegetables, then use their artwork to decorate the display areas.

PURPOSE

This test provides an informal assessment of the Unit 1 objectives.

Unit Test Items 1–20

To assign a numerical grade for this Unit Test, use 5 points for each test item.

Customizing Your Instruction

For children who have not yet mastered these objectives, you can use the Reteaching Resources listed in the chart below. **Ways to Success** is Houghton Mifflin's Intervention program available in CD-ROM and blackline master formats.

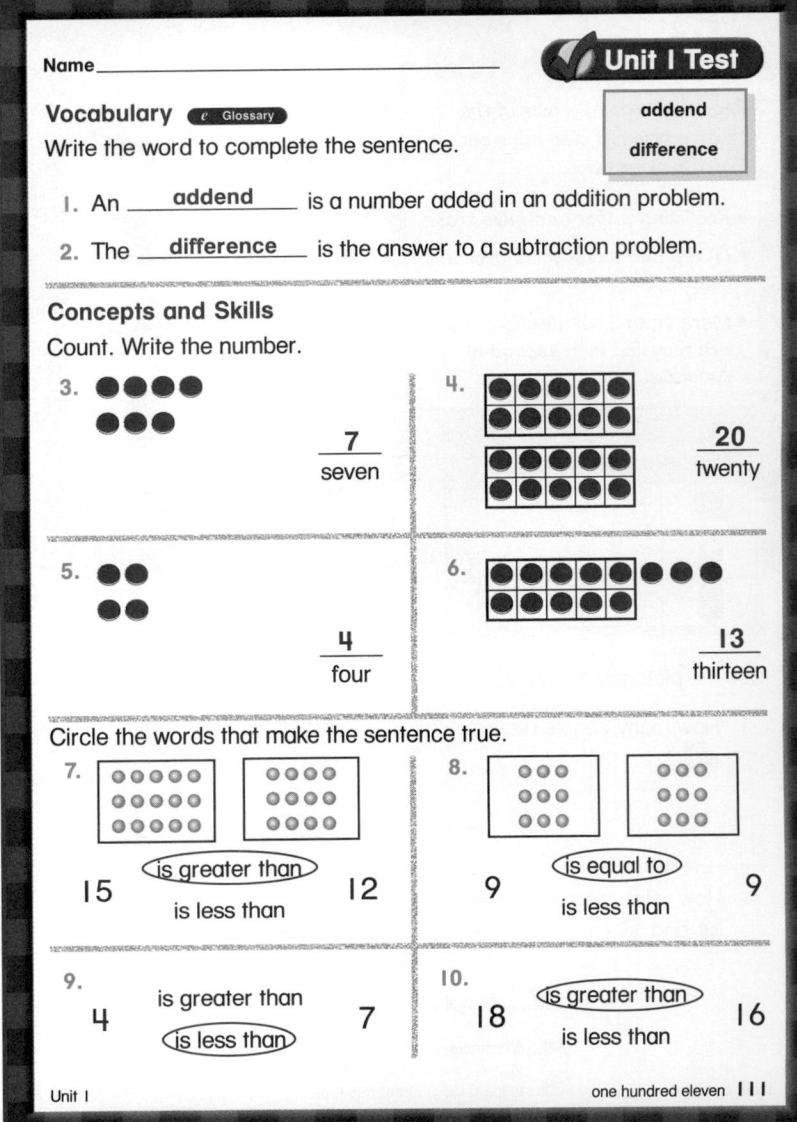

Reteaching Support

Unit Test Item		Unit Objectives Tested		TE Pages	Use These Reteaching Resources
p. 111–112 7–10	Tests A & B 3–4	1A	Recognize, count, order and compare numbers and sets through 20.	pp. 17A–22	Reteach Resources and *Ways to Success*, 1.4, 1.5
3–6	1–2	1B	Read and write numbers through 20.	pp. 7A–16	Reteach Resources and *Ways to Success*, 1.2, 1.3
1, 11–13	7–10	1C	Model addition concepts and use addition properties to solve problems and find sums through 8.	pp. 41A–50	Reteach Resources and *Ways to Success*, 2.4, 2.5, 2.6, 2.7
2, 14–16	5–6, 11–16	1D	Model subtraction concepts and use subtraction properties to solve problems and subtract from 8 or less.	pp. 61A–76	Reteach Resources and *Ways to Success*, 3.4, 3.5, 3.6, 3.7
17–19	19–25	1E	Read, make, and use graphs to compare information.	pp. 89A–92	Reteach Resources and *Ways to Success*, 4.2, 4.3
20	17–18	1F	Apply skills and strategies to solve problems.	pp. 51A–54	Reteach Resource and *Ways to Success*, 2.8

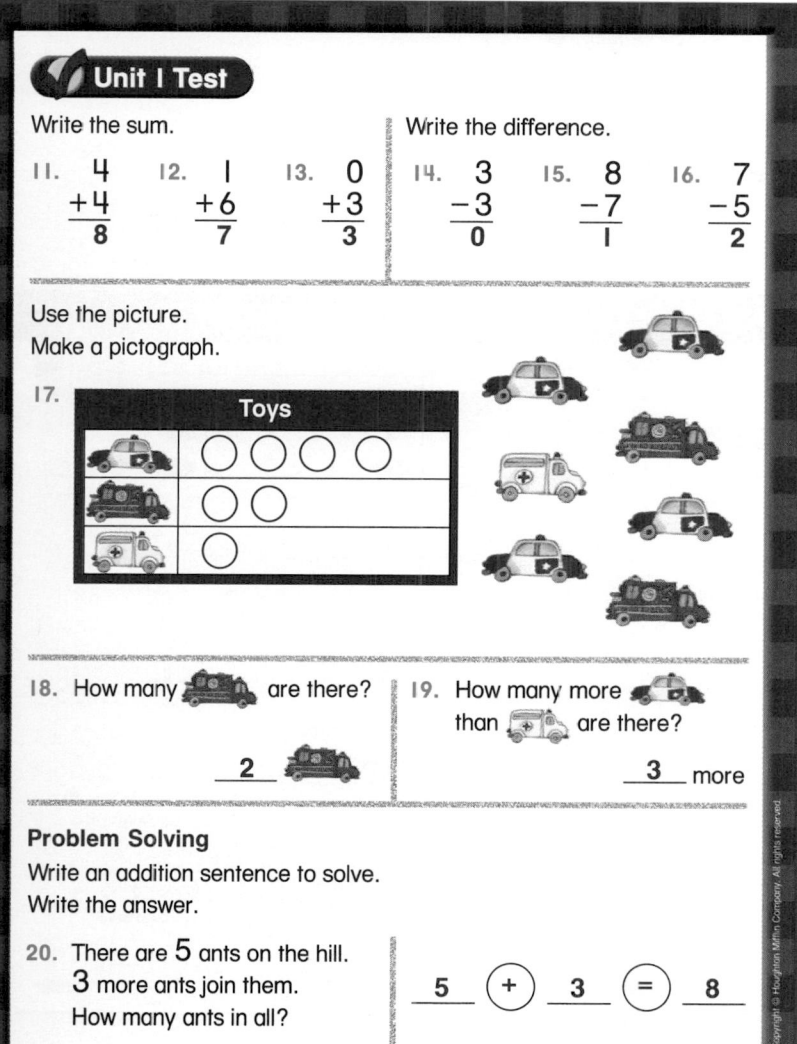

Unit 1 Test

Write the sum.

11.	12.	13.
4	1	0
+4	+6	+3
8	7	3

Write the difference.

14.	15.	16.
3	8	7
−3	−7	−5
0	1	2

Use the picture.
Make a pictograph.

17.

Toys
	○ ○ ○ ○
	○ ○
	○

18. How many  are there?

___2___

19. How many more  than are there?

___3___ more

Problem Solving

Write an addition sentence to solve.
Write the answer.

20. There are 5 ants on the hill.
3 more ants join them.
How many ants in all?

___5___ (+) ___3___ (=) ___8___

___8___ ants

112 one hundred twelve

Assessment Options

Formal Tests for this unit are also provided in the Unit Resource Folder.

- Unit 1 Test A (Open Response)
- Unit 1 Test B (Multiple Choice)

Performance Assessment

You may want to use the Performance Assessment instead of, or in addition to, the Unit Test. Three Performance Assessment tasks can be found on Student Book pages 113–114.

Adequate Yearly Progress

Use the *End of Grade Test Prep Assessment Guide* to help familiarize your children with the format of standardized tests.

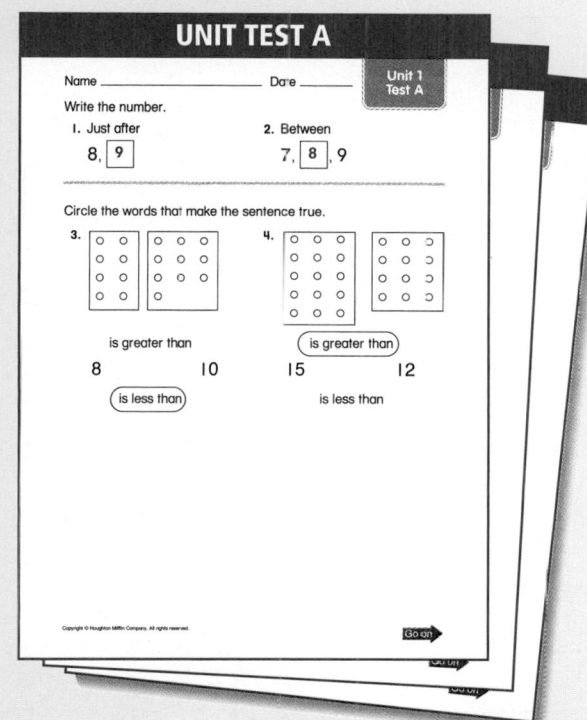

UNIT TEST A

Name _____ Date _____   Unit 1 Test A

Write the number.

1. Just after   2. Between
8, [9]   7, [8], 9

Circle the words that make the sentence true.

3. is greater than
   8   10
   is less than

4. **is greater than**
   15   12
   is less than

Unit 1 Tests

See pages
113A–113B
for answers.

UNIT TEST B

Name _____ Date _____   Unit 1 Test B

Fill in the ○ for the correct answer.
Choose the correct number.

1. Just after 7, [ ]   2. Between 8, [ ], 10
   ○ 6   ○ 8
   ● 8   ○ 7
   ○ 9   ● 9

Find the answer that matches the circles in the boxes.

3.
   ● 8 is greater than 5
   ○ 8 is less than 5
   ○ 8 is the same as 5

4.
   ○ 6 is greater than 10
   ● 6 is less than 10
   ○ 6 is the same as 10

Find the answer that shows the addition sentence in a different order.

5. 3 + 4 = 7   6. 0 + 7 = 7
   ○ 8 + 1 = 9   ○ 7 − 3 = 4
   ● 4 + 3 = 7   ○ 2 + 5 = 7
   ○ 7 − 4 = 3   ● 7 + 0 = 7

Unit Test Answers: Form A

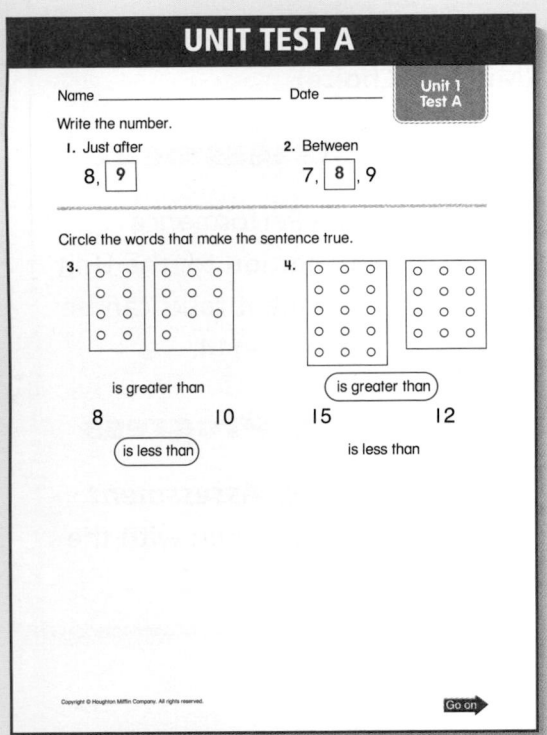

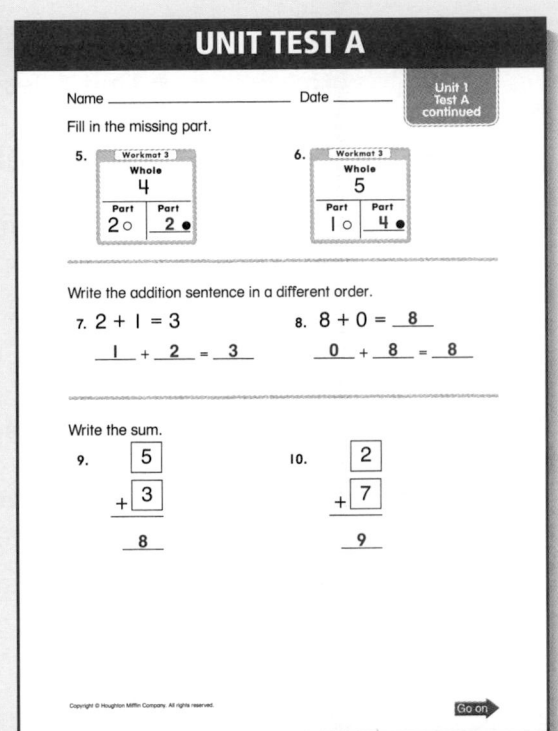

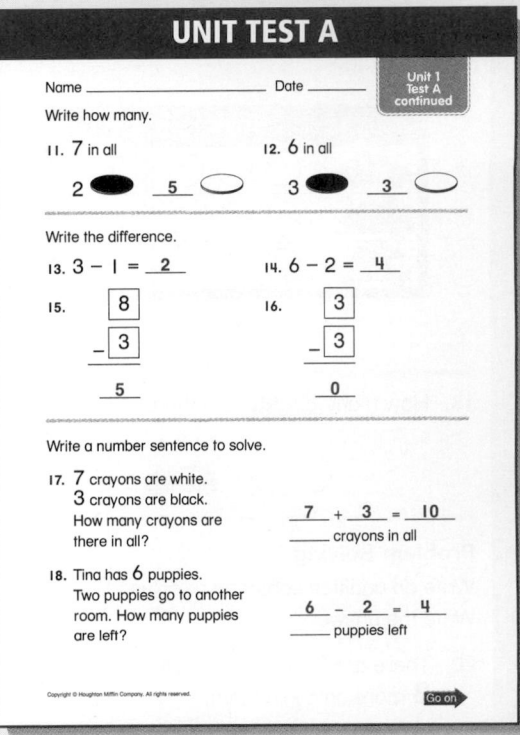

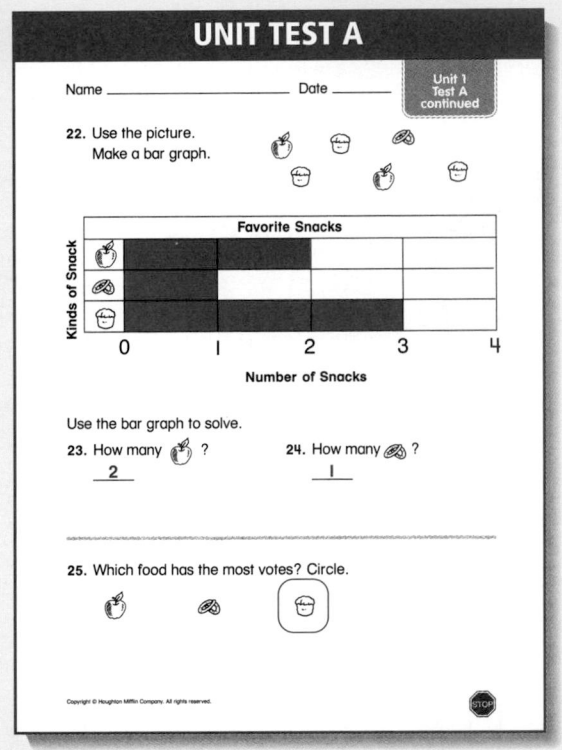

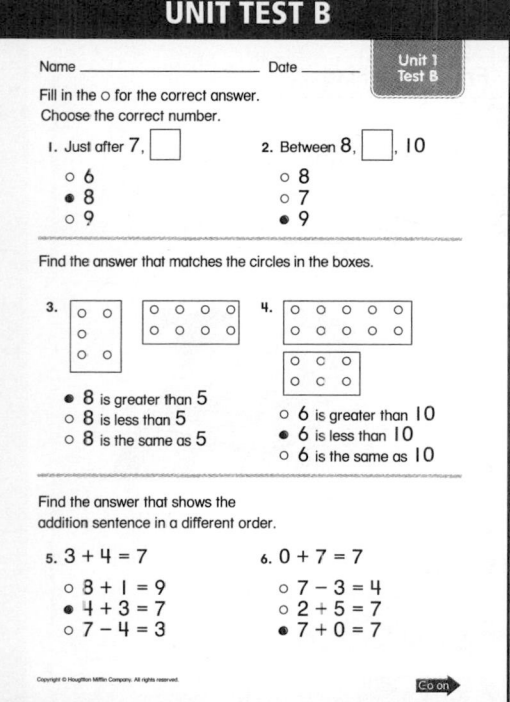

UNIT TEST B

Unit 1
Test B

Name _____ Date _____

Fill in the ○ for the correct answer.
Choose the correct number.

1. Just after 7, ☐
- ○ 6
- ● 8
- ○ 9

2. Between 8, ☐, 10
- ○ 8
- ○ 7
- ● 9

Find the answer that matches the circles in the boxes.

3. | 4.

- ● 8 is greater than 5
- ○ 8 is less than 5
- ○ 8 is the same as 5

- ○ 6 is greater than 10
- ● 6 is less than 10
- ○ 6 is the same as 10

Find the answer that shows the
addition sentence in a different order.

5. 3 + 4 = 7
- ○ 8 + 1 = 9
- ● 4 + 3 = 7
- ○ 7 − 4 = 3

6. 0 + 7 = 7
- ○ 7 − 3 = 4
- ○ 2 + 5 = 7
- ● 7 + 0 = 7

Go on

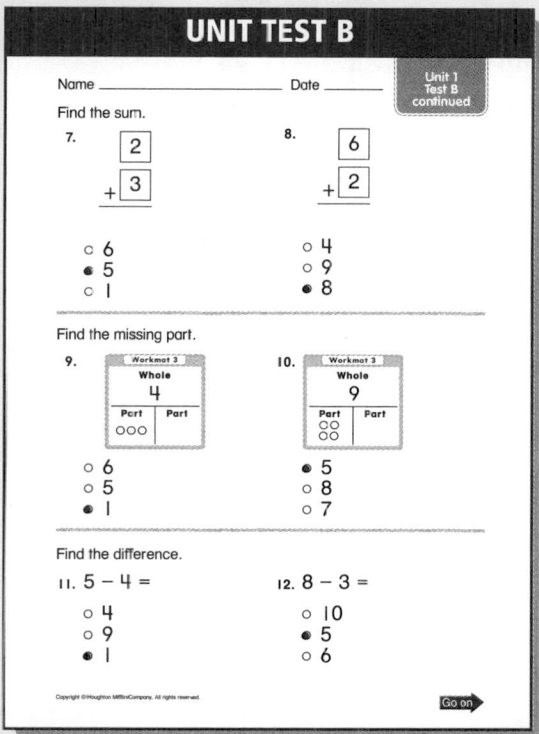

UNIT TEST B

Unit 1
Test B
continued

Name _____ Date _____

Find the sum.

7. 2 + 3
- ○ 6
- ● 5
- ○ 1

8. 6 + 2
- ○ 4
- ○ 9
- ● 8

Find the missing part.

9. Workmat 3
Whole 4
Part | Part
○○○ |
- ○ 6
- ○ 5
- ● 1

10. Workmat 3
Whole 9
Part | Part
○○ |
○○ |
- ● 5
- ○ 8
- ○ 7

Find the difference.

11. 5 − 4 =
- ○ 4
- ○ 9
- ● 1

12. 8 − 3 =
- ○ 10
- ● 5
- ○ 6

Go on

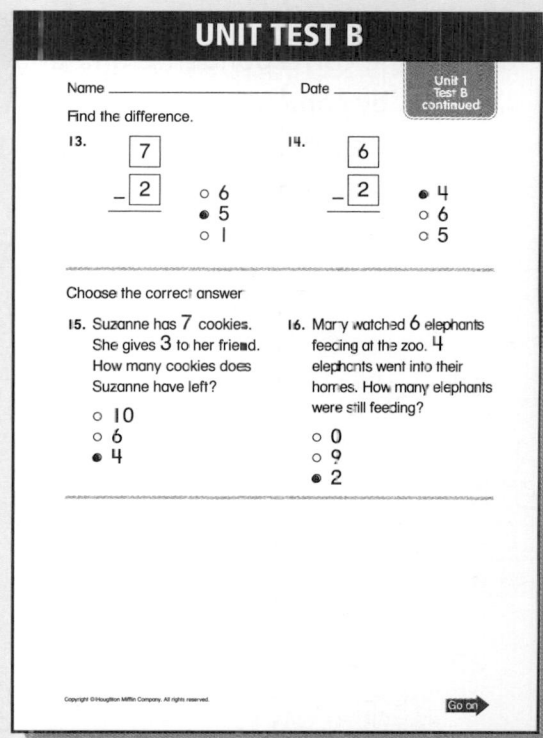

UNIT TEST B

Unit 1
Test B
continued

Name _____ Date _____

Find the difference.

13. 7 − 2
- ○ 6
- ● 5
- ○ 1

14. 6 − 2
- ● 4
- ○ 6
- ○ 5

Choose the correct answer

15. Suzanne has 7 cookies.
She gives 3 to her friend.
How many cookies does
Suzanne have left?
- ○ 10
- ○ 6
- ● 4

16. Mary watched 6 elephants
feeding at the zoo. 4
elephants went into their
homes. How many elephants
were still feeding?
- ○ 0
- ○ 9
- ● 2

Go on

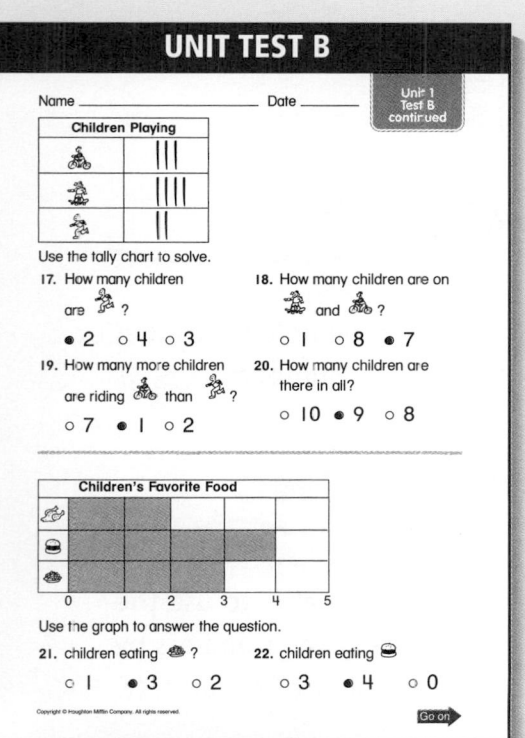

UNIT TEST B

Unit 1
Test B
continued

Name _____ Date _____

Children Playing	
🚲	|||
🛴	||||
⛸	||

Use the tally chart to solve.

17. How many children
are ⛸ ?
- ● 2 ○ 4 ○ 3

18. How many children are on
🛴 and 🚲 ?
- ○ 1 ○ 8 ● 7

19. How many more children
are riding 🚲 than ⛸ ?
- ○ 7 ● 1 ○ 2

20. How many children are
there in all?
- ○ 10 ○ 9 ○ 8

Children's Favorite Food					
🍕					
🍔					
🥪					
0	1	2	3	4	5

Use the graph to answer the question.

21. children eating 🍕 ?
- ○ 1 ● 3 ○ 2

22. children eating 🍔 ?
- ○ 3 ● 4 ○ 0

Go on

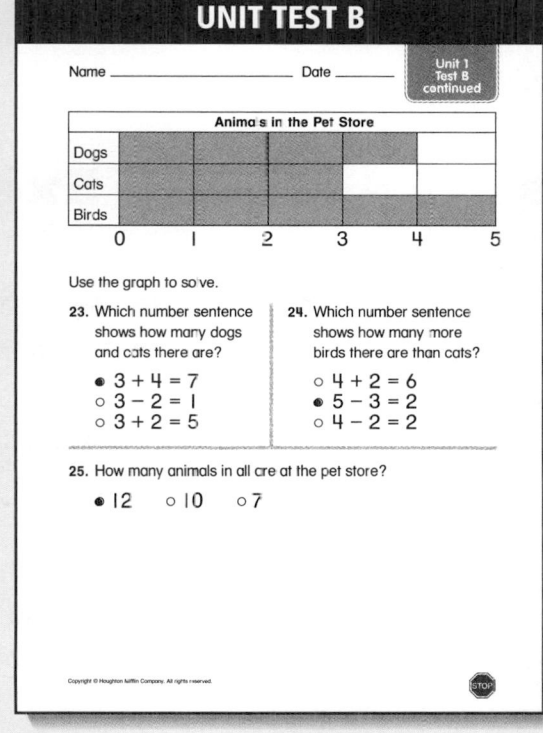

UNIT TEST B

Unit 1
Test B
continued

Name _____ Date _____

Animals in the Pet Store					
Dogs					
Cats					
Birds					
0	1	2	3	4	5

Use the graph to solve.

23. Which number sentence
shows how many dogs
and cats there are?
- ● 3 + 4 = 7
- ○ 3 − 2 = 1
- ○ 3 + 2 = 5

24. Which number sentence
shows how many more
birds there are than cats?
- ○ 4 + 2 = 6
- ● 5 − 3 = 2
- ○ 4 − 2 = 2

25. How many animals in all are at the pet store?
- ● 12 ○ 10 ○ 7

STOP

Performance Assessment

PURPOSE

This assessment focuses on graphing and addition. Children should be able to demonstrate one-to-one correspondence and understanding of numbers by completing the graphs. They should be able to apply skills and strategies to solve addition problems.

Name_____

Performance Assessment

Complete the pictograph.
Draw a 🧍 for each child.

1. 2 children like 🍎 best.
    5 children like 🍌 best.
    3 children like 🍇 best.

Fruits We Like

Complete the bar graph.

2. 2 children like green.
    6 children like blue.
    4 children like red.

Colors We Like

0 1 2 3 4 5 6 7 8
Number of Children

Unit 1   one hundred thirteen 113

Using These Pages

- Make a concrete graph using index cards. Each card represents one child in your class. Label the left column A–Z.

- **Ask, how many children have names that start with A?** Place that number of index cards in the "A" row.

- Continue to build a concrete graph. Have children compare the number of cards and the length of the bar. (Children should recognize that the longer bar represents the greater number.)

- Direct children's attention to assessment tasks.

- Observe children as they work to complete the tasks.

Exercise One

In Exercise 1, children should be able to draw stick figures to represent the given numbers. (2, 5, 3)

Exercise Two

In Exercise 2, children should be able to use the graph labels to represent the given numbers by coloring the appropriate number of squares. (2, 6, 4)

Performance Assessment

Solve.

3. There are 4 red flowers in a pot.
Taro plants 3 blue flowers in the pot.
How many flowers in all?

Show your work using pictures, numbers, or words.

_____7____ flowers

114 one hundred fourteen

Use the **Scoring Rubric** to evaluate children's performance on these tasks.

Scoring Rubric

4 EXEMPLARY

Represents the given numbers correctly on the graphs, finds the correct sum of 2 one-digit numbers with sums less than 8, and applies skills and strategies to solve the problem correctly.

3 PROFICIENT

Represents the given numbers correctly on the graphs, finds the correct sum of 2 one-digit numbers with sums less than 8. Solution to the problem demonstrates mathematical reasoning, although the reasoning is faulty.

2 ACCEPTABLE

Represents the given numbers correctly on one or both of the graphs, or finds the correct sum of 2 one-digit numbers with sums less than 8. Solution to the problem is incomplete.

1 LIMITED

Represents the given numbers incorrectly on the graphs and finds an incorrect sum of 2 one-digit numbers with sums less than 8. Solution to the problem shows no mathematica reasoning.

Exercise Three

In Exercise 3, children should be able to model the addition by drawing 3 more flowers in the pot and then find the sum. (7)

UNIT 1

Enrichment

▶ Estimation

PURPOSE

This page provides an opportunity for children to apply their understanding of subtraction concepts and number sense to help them estimate.

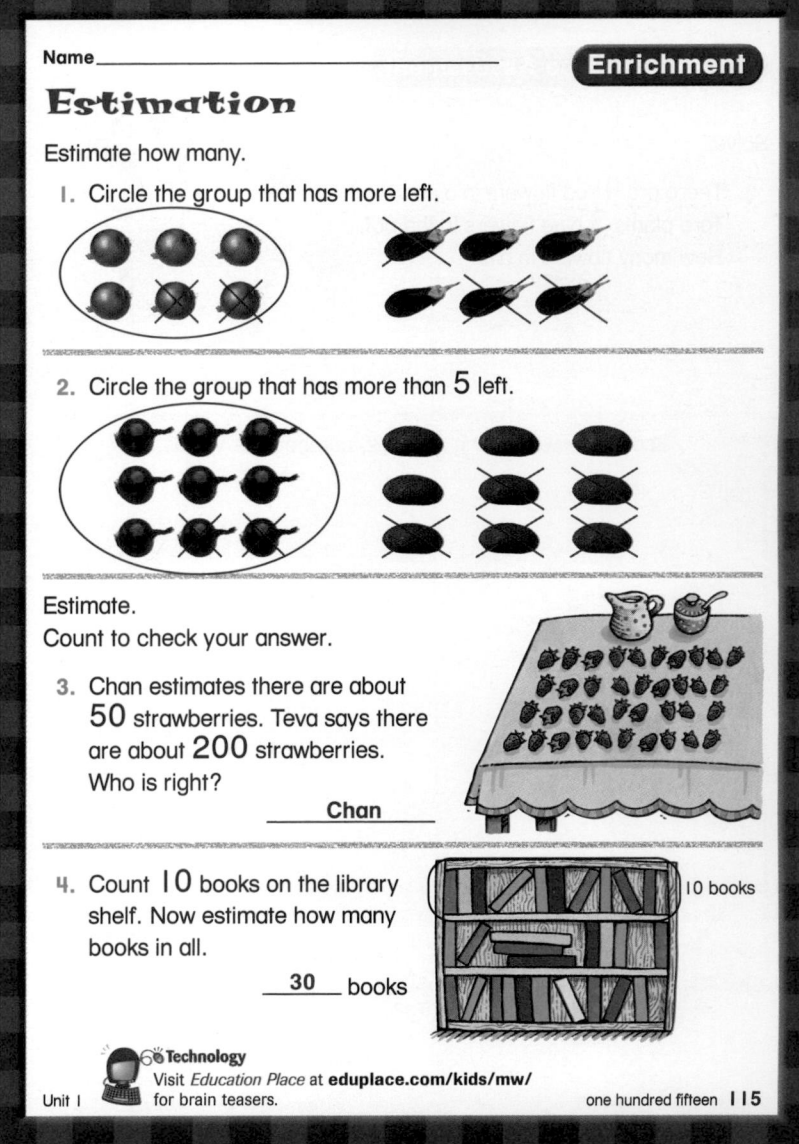

Using This Page

Discussion Topics

- Read the directions with children. Explain that an estimate is a good guess based on the information available. Remind children not to count the vegetables in Exercises 1 and 2, but to estimate how many there are.

- Tell children that when they are asked to look at how many are left, they should focus on the vegetables that are not crossed out.

- Remind children to estimate first in Exercise 3, and then count the strawberries to check their answer.

- Have children work individually or in pairs to complete Exercise 4. Then ask: **What is a good estimate?** (30) **How do you know?** (There are about 10 books on each shelf, so 10 + 10 + 10 = 30.) **Why is it easier to estimate than to count?** (It is faster.) In pairs, children can take turns solving the exercises, and then checking each other's work.

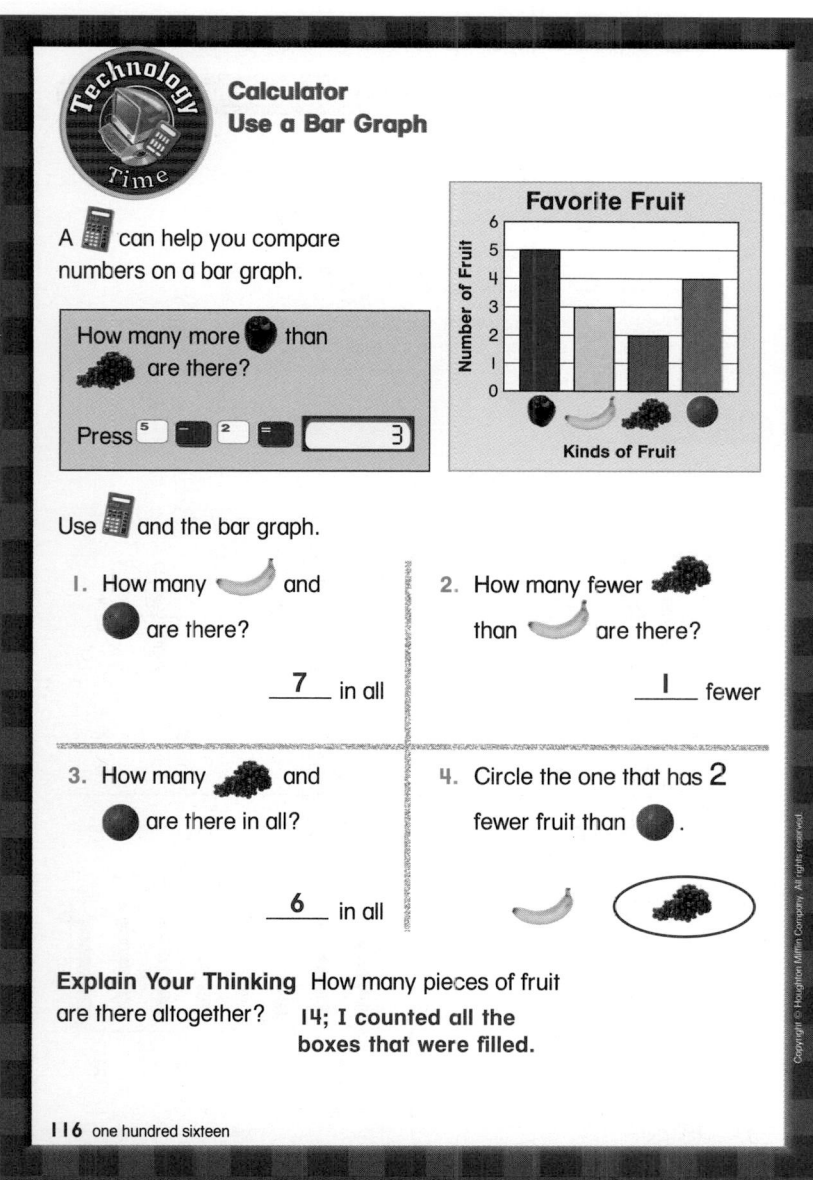

Calculator
Use a Bar Graph

A 🖩 can help you compare numbers on a bar graph.

How many more 🫐 **than** 🍇 **are there?**

Press ⁵ ☐ ➖ ² ☐ ➕ = ☐ 3

Favorite Fruit

Number of Fruit
6
5
4
3
2
1
0

Kinds of Fruit

Use 🖩 and the bar graph.

1. How many 🍌 and 🍊 are there?

   _7_ in all

2. How many fewer 🍇 than 🍌 are there?

   _1_ fewer

3. How many 🍇 and 🍊 are there in all?

   _6_ in all

4. Circle the one that has 2 fewer fruit than 🍊.

   🍌 (🍇)

Explain Your Thinking How many pieces of fruit are there altogether? **14; I counted all the boxes that were filled.**

116 one hundred sixteen

USE A BAR GRAPH

PURPOSE

To provide an opportunity for children to use a calculator when reading a bar graph.

Using This Page

Discussion Topics

- This is another way for the children to read a bar graph.

- You may want to guide children through adding and subtracting on a calculator. Remind children that certain words tell whether to add or subtract. **When asked to find how many in all, do we add or subtract?** (add)

- Read each question and allow time for children to complete it. Then have children share their work with the class.

Cumulative Test Prep

▶ Practice Test

PURPOSE

This page will familiarize children with the multiple-choice and open-response formats of many standardized state tests. Children can mark their responses directly on these pages. You may wish to read each test item and the multiple choice answer choices aloud to the children.

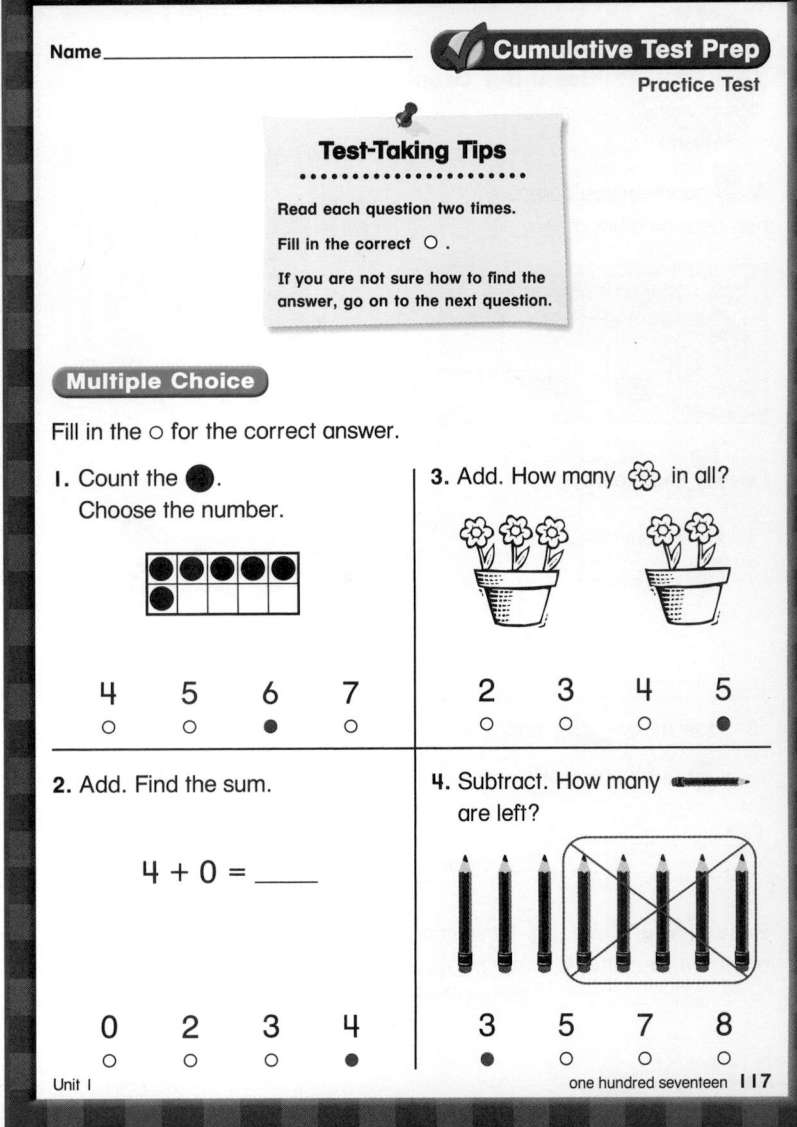

Name_____

Cumulative Test Prep
Practice Test

Test-Taking Tips

Read each question two times.

Fill in the correct ○ .

If you are not sure how to find the answer, go on to the next question.

Multiple Choice

Fill in the ○ for the correct answer.

1. Count the ●. Choose the number.

   4   5   6   7
   ○   ○   ●   ○

2. Add. Find the sum.

   4 + 0 = ____

   0   2   3   4
   ○   ○   ○   ●

3. Add. How many 🌸 in all?

   2   3   4   5
   ○   ○   ○   ●

4. Subtract. How many are left?

   3   5   7   8
   ●   ○   ○   ○

Unit 1   one hundred seventeen 117

Test-Taking TIPS

Review the test-taking tips with children before they begin the test. Remind children to read each question two times before they answer it.

- Remind children to look for word clues like *sum, in all,* and *left* to help them decide which operation to use.
- Remind children to pay close attention to operation signs.

- Remind children that each question has only one correct answer.
- Tell children they can draw a picture to help them solve a problem.

Fill in the ○ for the correct answer.
NH means Not Here.

5. Subtract. Find the difference.

$$\begin{array}{r} 7 \\ -5 \\ \hline \end{array}$$

2	3	4	NH
●	○	○	○

6. How many children have 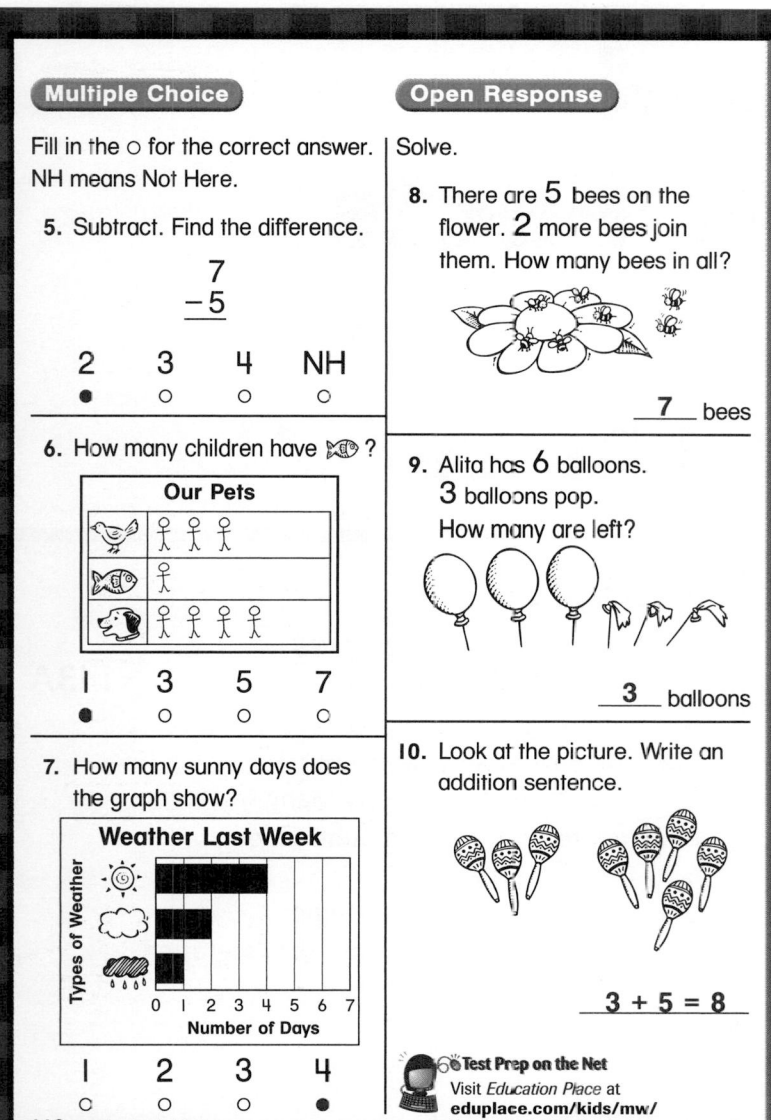 ?

Our Pets

1	3	5	7
●	○	○	○

7. How many sunny days does the graph show?

Weather Last Week

Types of Weather

Number of Days

1	2	3	4
○	○	○	●

118 one hundred eighteen

Solve.

8. There are 5 bees on the flower. 2 more bees join them. How many bees in all?

_____7_____ bees

9. Alita has 6 balloons. 3 balloons pop. How many are left?

_____3_____ balloons

10. Look at the picture. Write an addition sentence.

3 + 5 = 8

Test Prep on the Net
Visit *Education Place* at **eduplace.com/kids/mw/** for more test prep practice.

Test-Taking Vocabulary

- Review the terms *whole*, *parts*, *addends*, *sum*, and *difference* with children. Write an addition sentence and a subtraction sentence and ask volunteers to identify the part of the sentences that matches each term.

- Write the numbers 5 and 3 on the board. **Which symbols would you use to make an addition sentence?** (+ and =) **What is the sum?** (8)

- **Which symbols would you use to make a subtraction sentence?** (− and =) **What is the difference?** (2)

National and state tests may also use these words with addition problems:

- *together*
- *total*
- *altogether*
- *all together*

Number Concepts, Operations, and Graphing   118

Addition and Subtraction Facts Through 10

Unit at a Glance

Assessment System

Assessing Prior Knowledge

Check whether children understand the prerequisite concepts and skills.

- **CHAPTER PRETEST** (Unit Resource Folder or *Ways to Success* Intervention CD-ROM)
- **WARM-UP ACTIVITY:** Every TE Lesson
- **UNIT LITERATURE ACTIVITY:** PE p. 120

Ongoing Assessment

Monitor whether children are acquiring new concepts and skills.

- **PROBLEM OF THE DAY:** First page of every TE lesson
- **QUICK REVIEW:** First page of every TE lesson
- **LESSON QUIZ:** First page of every TE lesson
- **COMMON ERROR:** Every TE Lesson
- **QUICK CHECK:** PE pp. 132, 139, 152, 163
- **KEY TOPIC REVIEW:** PE pp. 140, 164

Test Prep and Practice

Help children prepare for state and standardized tests.

- **DAILY TEST PREP:** Every TE Lesson
- **CUMULATIVE TEST PREP:** PE p. 175–176
- **PROBLEM SOLVING FOR TESTS:** PE pp. 138, 162
- **TEST PREP ON THE NET:** eduplace.com/kids/mw
- **TEST-TAKING STRATEGIES:** eduplace.com/math/mw

Summary Assessment

Assess children's mastery of new concepts and skills.

- **CHAPTER TEST:**
  - ✔ PE pp. 141–142, 165–166
  - ✔ Unit Resource Folder
- **UNIT TEST:**
  - ✔ PE pp. 169–170
  - ✔ Test A, Unit Resource Folder
  - ✔ Test B, Unit Resource Folder

Student Self-Assessment

Allow children to evaluate their own understanding.

- **EXPLAIN YOUR THINKING:** PE pp. 125, 127, 129, 133, 145, 147, 149, 153, 155, 157

Performance Assessment

Evaluate children's ability to use mathematics in real-world situations.

PERFORMANCE ASSESSMENT: PE p. 171–172

WRITE ABOUT IT OR TALK ABOUT IT: in Hands-On lessons

WRITING MATH: CREATE AND SOLVE: PE p. 151

Technology Options

Use computer-based assessment to make testing and reporting easier.

- **WAYS TO ASSESS** (CD-ROM, LAN, or Web spiral review and test creation, administration, scoring, and report generation)
- **LEARNER PROFILE** (observations, evaluations, and reports from your handheld or desktop computer)

Reaching All Learners

Resources

Resources	On Level Students	Extra Support Students	English Learners	Inclusion/ Special Needs	Advanced Learners	Mathematically Promising
Student Editions						
Building Vocabulary	●	●	●	●	●	●
Guided Practice ✶	●	●	●	●	●	●
MathTracks MP3 Audio CD 💿	●	●	○	○		
Teacher's Editions						
Building Vocabulary Strategies	●	●	○	○	●	○
Teacher Support	●	○	●		○	○
Intervention Activities	○	●	●	●		
Other Resources						
Chapter Challenges	○				●	●
Combination Classroom Guide	●	●	●	●	●	●
English Learners Handbook	○	○	●	○		
Ways to Success CD-ROM 💿	○	●	●	●		

KEY   ● **Highly Appropriate**   ○ **Appropriate**   ✶ **Scaffolded Instruction**

Documenting Adequate Yearly Progress

National Test Correlation

UNIT 2 Objectives		ITBS	Terra Nova (CTBS)	CAT	SAT	MAT
2A	Use addition strategies to find sums through 10.	●	●	●	●	●
2B	Use subtraction strategies to subtract from 10 or less.	●	●	●	●	●
2C	Use related facts to solve addition and subtraction problems.	●	●	●	●	●
2D	Use related facts to write fact families.	●	●	●	●	●
2E	Apply skills and strategies to solve problems.	●	●	●	●	●

Activities for Reaching All Learners

Home-School Activity

Count to the End

Materials: 3 sets of count on/count back cards, 3 sets of number cards 1–3 for each pair; number line 10–20 for each child, counters

Shuffle sets of like cards and place them facedown in 2 piles. Children place a counter on the number 15 on their number line. Pairs take turns turning over the top card of each set and moving their counter as directed. (For example: Count back 2.) First child to reach either end on the number line wins.

Unit Vocabulary Activity

A Triple Double

Materials: 4 sets of number cards 1–5

Prepare 4 sets of number cards 1–5. Distribute 4 cards to each player. Place the remaining cards facedown in a stack. The first player takes a card from the pile, puts down any doubles, and records the sum. Then, the player discards 1 card face up. The next player can take the visible card or one from the facedown stack. Play continues until one person records 3 doubles facts.

Remediation

MathTracks Lessons: 5.3, 5.4, 6.3, 6.4, 6.5, 6.6, 6.7

Use the MathTracks CD-ROM to help children who need a quick review or extra support for the lesson, to provide children who were absent with a complete lesson presentation, or to assist children with reading difficulties.

Intervention

Ways to Success CD-ROM

Use the Ways to Success CD-ROM to help children who need extra help with lessons. This software is designed to reteach the lesson objective, provide extra guided and independent practice, and if needed, reteach a key prerequisite skill.

Unit Project

Sea Creature Number Stories

Math Topics

- find sums and differences to 10
- addition and subtraction strategies

To Begin

- Invite children to share what they know about the animals that live in the ocean. Explain that in this Unit Project, children will solve story problems about ocean animals.
- Read the problem aloud to children.

  5 whales swim in one group in the ocean. 3 whales swim in another group. How many whales swim in all?

  Have them model the problem with counters.
- Repeat the activity for a subtraction problem.

Ongoing

- Have children solve addition and subtraction story problems.
- Remind children of the different strategies they can use.
- For Connecting to the Unit Project, see page 123D for Chapter 5, and page 143D for Chapter 6.

To Finish

- Read an addition or subtraction story aloud and ask children to choose a strategy to solve the problem.
- Create a seashore scene display. Add a label for each strategy. Under the label, place a large envelope. Have children place their solution in the appropriate envelope.
- See page 168 to Wrap Up the Unit Project.

Starting Unit 2
Accessing Prior Knowledge

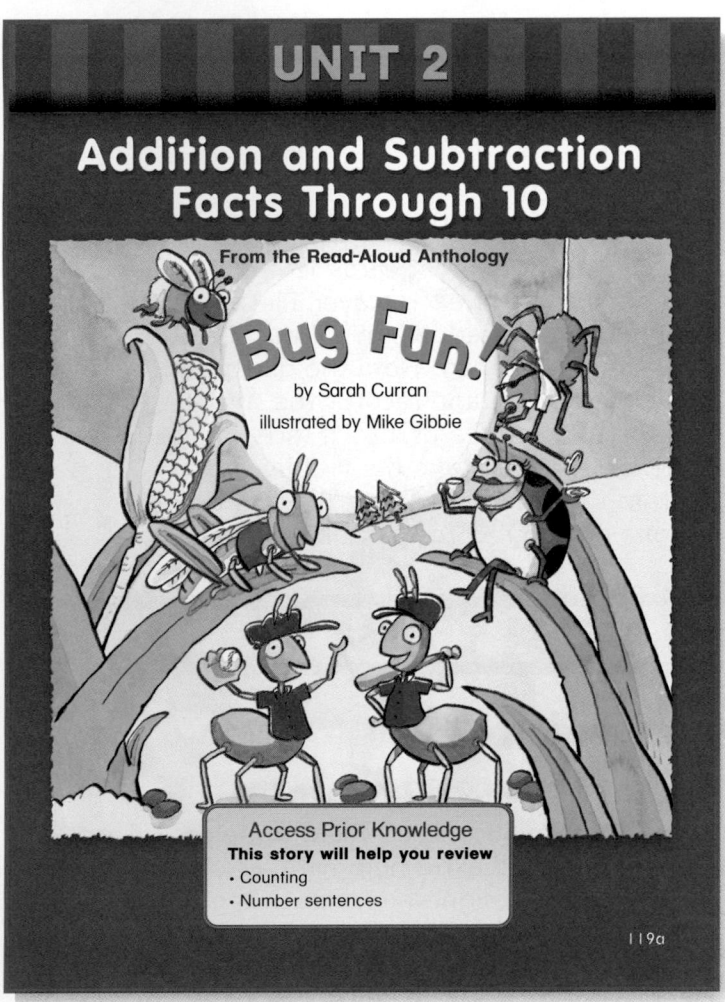

3 little ants soon strike out.
The others give a great big shout.
Now 4 ants wait to hit the ball.
How many ants are there in all?

$3 + 4 = \underline{7}$ ants

119b from *Bug Fun!*

Accessing Prior Knowledge

In Unit 1, children:

• read and write numbers through 20
• compare and order numbers
• model addition and subtraction
• write addition and subtraction sentences

This selection from the Unit Opener gives you the opportunity to review some of these prerequisite skills.

• You may also wish to review addition vocabulary by asking volunteers to write addition sentences for sums to 10 on the board, then identify the **addends** and **sums**.

• Review subtraction vocabulary by asking volunteers to write subtraction sentences on the board, then identify the **differences**.

Story Summary

Today you will be reading a story about bugs. The title of the story is *Bug Fun*. The author is Sarah Curran.

Reading the Story

You can find the entire text of the book at the end of the Teacher's Edition on page T53. Read the selection aloud to the children. Then read it again, having the children raise their hands whenever you come to a number word.

This story is available in the Read-Aloud Anthology, Volume 1

All the grasshoppers take a dip.
They are careful not to slip.
Then 2 grasshoppers hop away.
How many grasshoppers stay to play?

6 − 2 = __4__ grasshoppers

119c

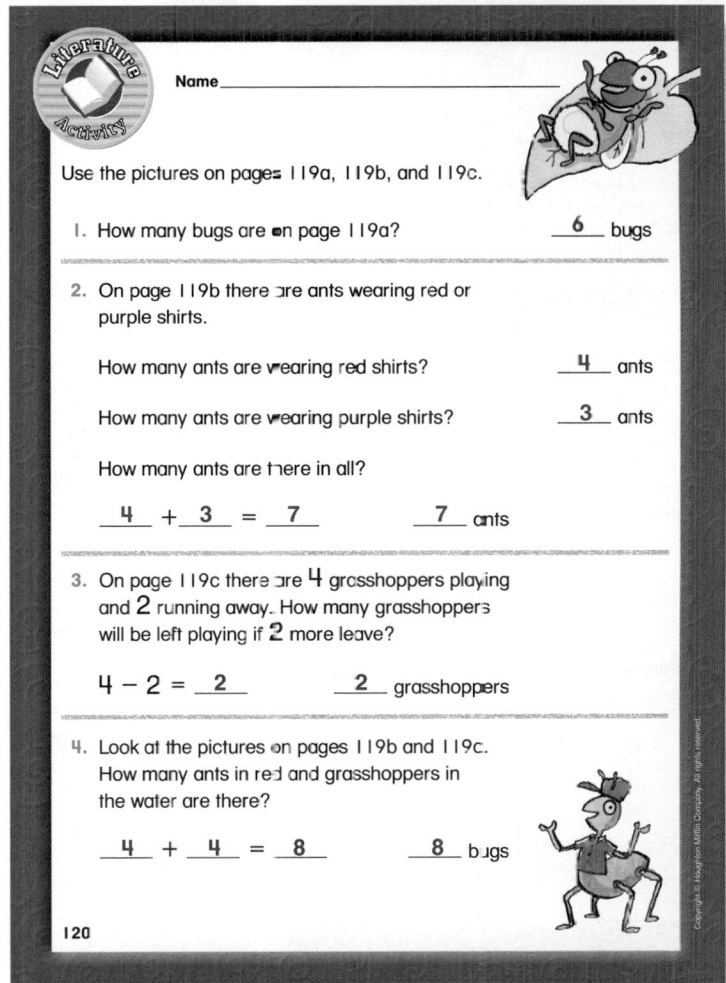

Name_____

Use the pictures on pages 119a, 119b, and 119c.

1. How many bugs are on page 119a?   __6__ bugs

2. On page 119b there are ants wearing red or purple shirts.

   How many ants are wearing red shirts?   __4__ ants

   How many ants are wearing purple shirts?   __3__ ants

   How many ants are there in all?

   __4__ + __3__ = __7__   __7__ ants

3. On page 119c there are 4 grasshoppers playing and 2 running away. How many grasshoppers will be left playing if 2 more leave?

   4 − 2 = __2__   __2__ grasshoppers

4. Look at the pictures on pages 119b and 119c. How many ants in red and grasshoppers in the water are there?

   __4__ + __4__ = __8__   __8__ bugs

120

Unit Bibliography

Addition Annie by David Gisler

Bug Fun by Sarah Curran
Illustrated by Mike Gibbie

How Many Feet In the Bed?
by Dianne Johnston Hamm

Musical Chairs and Dancing Bears
by J. Rocklin, L. deMatharel

One More Bunny by Rick Walton

1 + 1 Take Away Two! by Michael Berenstain

The Right Number of Elephants by Jeff Sheppard

Two of Everything by Lily Toy Hong

See also the **Math and Literature Bibliography** in the Teacher Support Handbook at the back of this Teacher's Edition.

Literature Activity

Purpose: This activity provides an opportunity to informally assess children's understanding of addition and subtraction facts through 10.

Using This Page
- Observe children as they work to complete Exercises 1–3. **What operation do we use to find how many in all?** (addition)
- Observe children as they work to complete Exercise 4. **What operation do we use to find how many are left?** (subtraction)
- For Exercise 5, be sure children count correctly to get the correct addends.

Math At Home

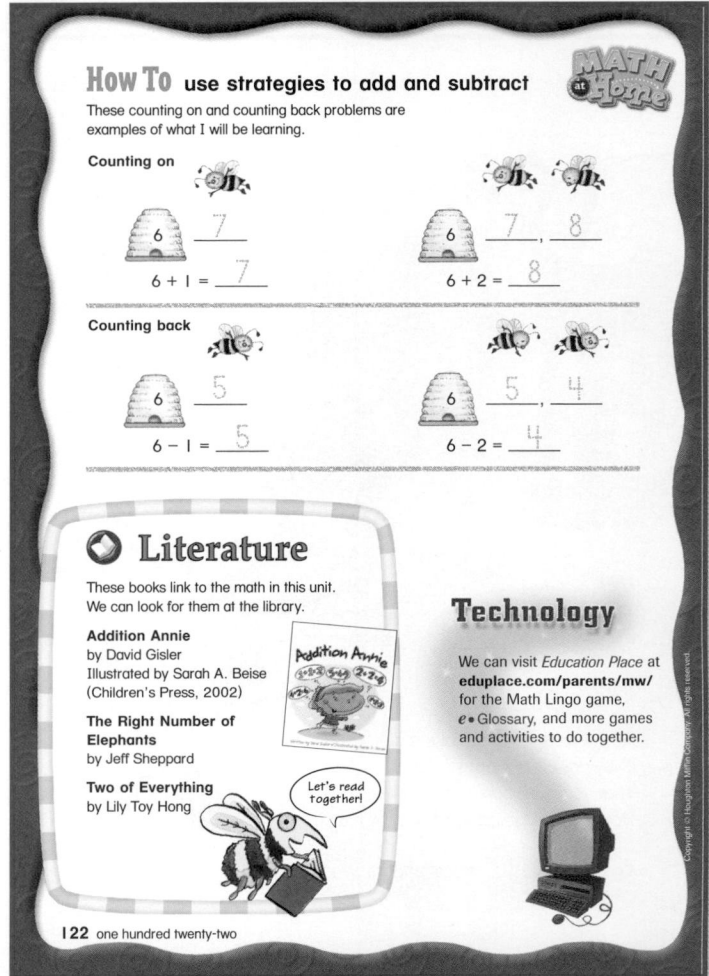

Discuss the letter to the family with children. You may want to use this letter as an introduction to the unit. Highlight for children what they will be learning in the unit. Tell children that as they go through the unit they will be able to answer the questions on these pages.

Math at Home is available in Spanish and other languages on Education Place.
www.eduplace.com/math/mw/

 Literature

Encourage parents to find the suggested books and read them with their children.

 Technology

Education Place is an award-winning website with engaging activities for students and helpful information for parents. Look for the eGlossary, the Math Lingo Game, and more.

Building Vocabulary

Strategies for Building Vocabulary

Counting On and Counting Back

Draw a 0–12 number line on the board. Write *Count On* and *Count Back*. Ask the children to find the sum for 2 + 3 and model **counting on**, saying 3, 4, 5 as you point to the number line. Ask children to decide if you are counting on or counting back. Ask, How do you know? (You count on to add.) What is the sum? (5)

Repeat the activity using 10 − 2 = 8 to **count back**. Invite children to draw arrows on the board to show which direction they will move along the number line for each strategy.

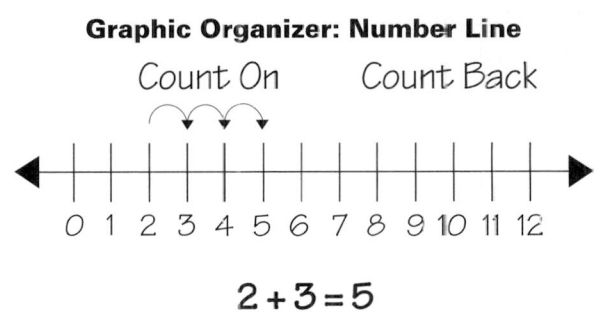

Graphic Organizer: Number Line

Count On   Count Back

0 1 2 3 4 5 6 7 8 9 10 11 12

2 + 3 = 5

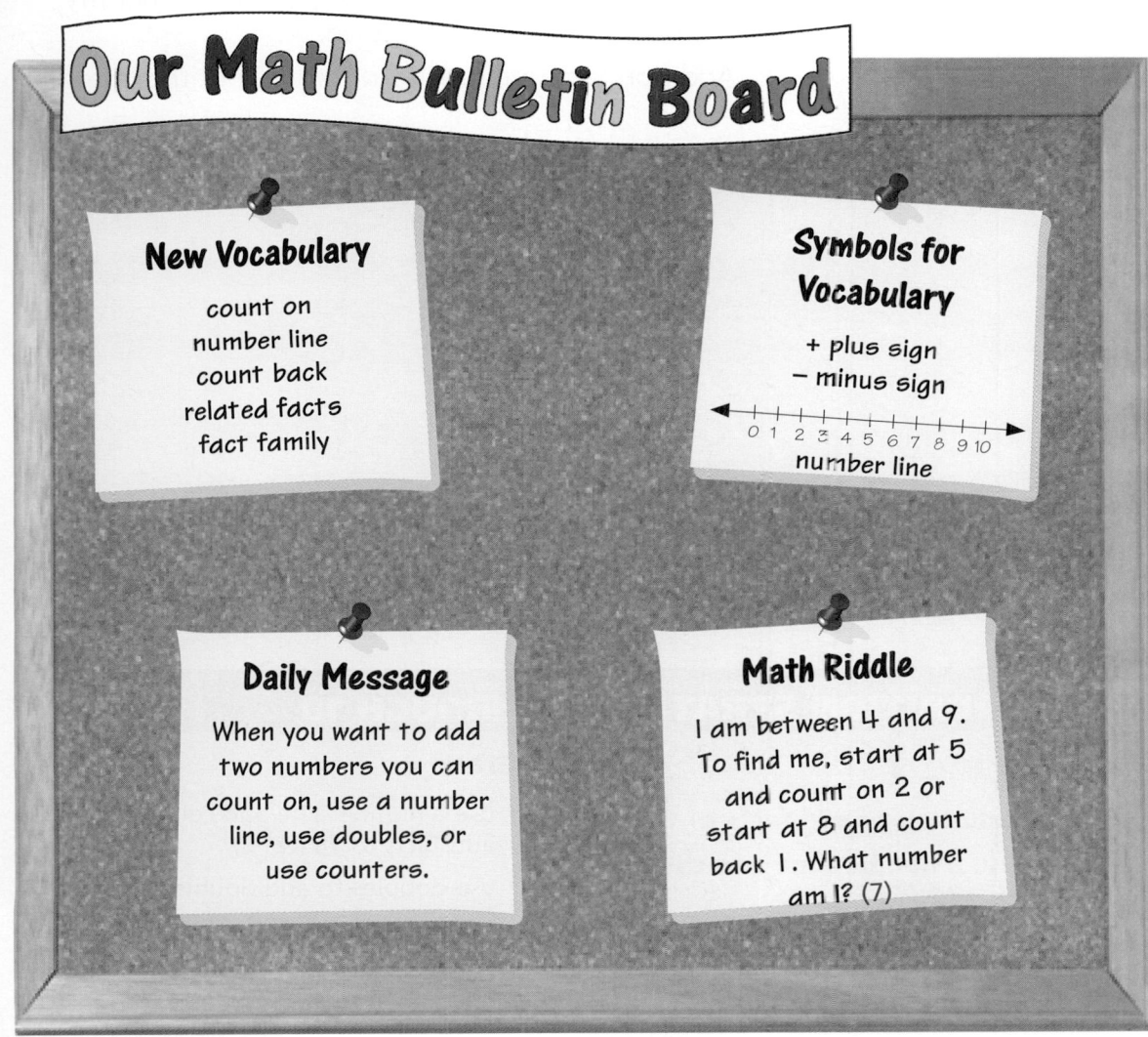

Our Math Bulletin Board

New Vocabulary

count on
number line
count back
related facts
fact family

Symbols for Vocabulary

+ plus sign
− minus sign

0 1 2 3 4 5 6 7 8 9 10
number line

Daily Message

When you want to add two numbers you can count on, use a number line, use doubles, or use counters.

Math Riddle

I am between 4 and 9. To find me, start at 5 and count on 2 or start at 8 and count back 1. What number am I? (7)

add

Vocabulary Cards

My Math Journal
Watch for **Keeping a Journal** entries in every lesson.

Lesson by Lesson Overview
Addition Strategies Through 10

Lesson 1

- Counting to add is a common strategy for children. Counting on 1, 2, or 3 requires some level of number sense.
- Showing the first addend as a numeral and modeling the second addend provides a pictorial representation of the strategy.
- Counting on is limited to 1, 2, or 3 because to count on greater numbers is not an efficient strategy.

Lesson 2

- Many children have success with using a number line to count on.
- This model reappears in Chapter 6 to develop subtraction as counting back.
- The problem solving set has children answer questions by identifying numbers that are 2 or 3 more than given numbers.

Lesson 3

- Doubles facts are easy for most children, so their use as a strategy can be helpful.
- The use of models clearly shows the *one more* in a double-plus-one fact.
- Children solve missing addend exercises by using doubles facts.

Lesson 4

- Children practice addition facts to 10 as they use the strategies taught in the previous lessons.
- They will use whatever strategy works best for them, but should try all strategies.

Lesson 5

- Children use a part-part-whole model to write an addition sentence to solve a story problem.
- The part-part-whole model helps children identify the operation needed to solve.
- Addition facts are practiced throughout the lesson.

SKILLS TRACE: ADDITION STRATEGIES THROUGH 10		
Grade K	**Grade 1**	**Grade 2**
• model addition (ch. 13)	• **count on to add facts to 10**	• use a number line and count on to add facts to 18 (ch. 2)
• complete addition sentences (ch. 13)	• **use a number line and count on to add**	• use doubles to add doubles plus one (ch. 2)
• add 1 to 0 through 9 (ch. 13)	• **use doubles to add doubles plus one**	• use properties to add (ch. 2)
• add 2 to 0 through 8 (ch. 13)	• **use different strategies to add**	• make a 10 to add 7, 8, or 9 (ch. 2)

Chapter Planner

Lesson	Objective	Vocabulary	Materials	✔ NCTM Standards
5.1 **Count On to Add** p. 125A	Write sums to 10 by counting on (increasing) 1, 2, or 3.	count on	paper cup, counters, number cards 0–20 (Learning Tools (LT) 14 and 15)	Develop and use strategies for whole-number computations, with a focus on addition and subtraction.
5.2 **Use a Number Line to Add** p. 127A	Find sums to 10 using a number line.	number line	red and blue cubes, blank transparency, counters, index cards (with addition exercises from the lesson without the sum), large strip of paper, markers	Develop and use strategies for whole-number computations, with a focus on addition and subtraction.
5.3 **Use Doubles to Add** p. 129A	Add using doubles and doubles plus one.	double addend	cubes, 2 number cubes 0–5, 2 game pieces	Develop and use strategies for whole-number computations, with a focus on addition and subtraction.
5.4 **Using Addition Strategies** p. 133A	Add using different strategies.		two-color counters, counters, blank transparency, hole punch, small pieces of paper	Develop and use strategies for whole-number computations, with a focus on addition and subtraction.
5.5 **Problem Solving:** **Write a Number Sentence** p. 135A	Use number sentences to solve problems.		part-part-whole transparency, counters, addition cards, cubes (two colors)	Understand various meanings of addition and subtraction of whole numbers and the relationship between the two operations.

Resources For Reaching All Learners

LESSON RESOURCES: Reteach, Practice, Enrichment, Problem Solving, Homework, English Learners, Daily Routines, Transparencies, Math Center.

ADDITIONAL RESOURCES FROM HOUGHTON MIFFLIN: Chapter Challenges, Combination Classroom Planning Guide, Every Day Counts, Math to Learn (Student Handbook)

Every Day Counts
The Totally Ten Count and Daily Depositor activities in Every Day Counts support the math in this chapter.

Assessing Prior Knowledge

Before beginning the chapter, you can assess student understandings in order to assist you in differentiating instruction.

Complete Chapter Pretest in Unit Resource Folder

Use this test to assess both prerequisite skills (**Are You Ready?** — one page) and chapter content (**Check What You Know** — two pages).

Chapter 5 Prerequisite Skills Pretest

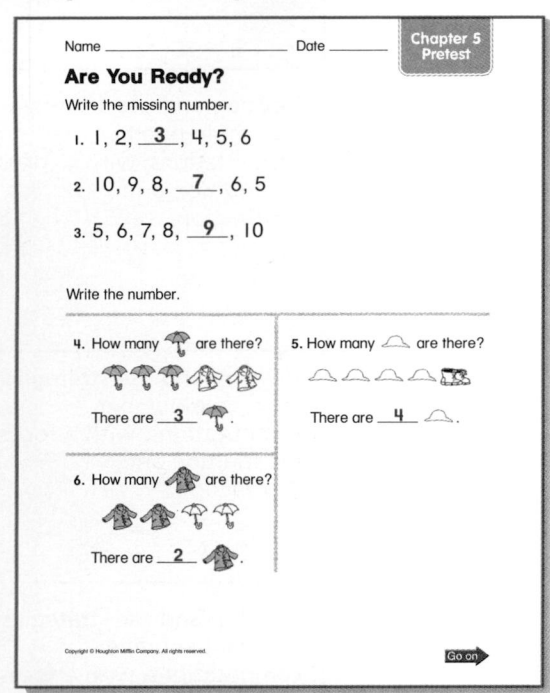

Chapter 5 New Content Pretest

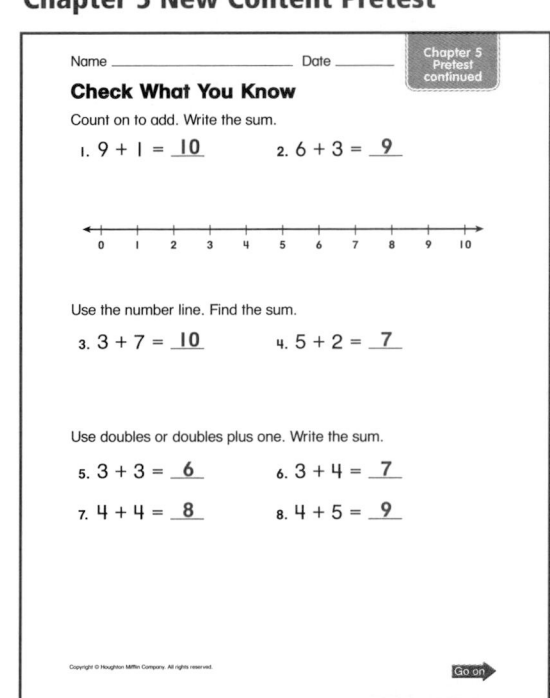

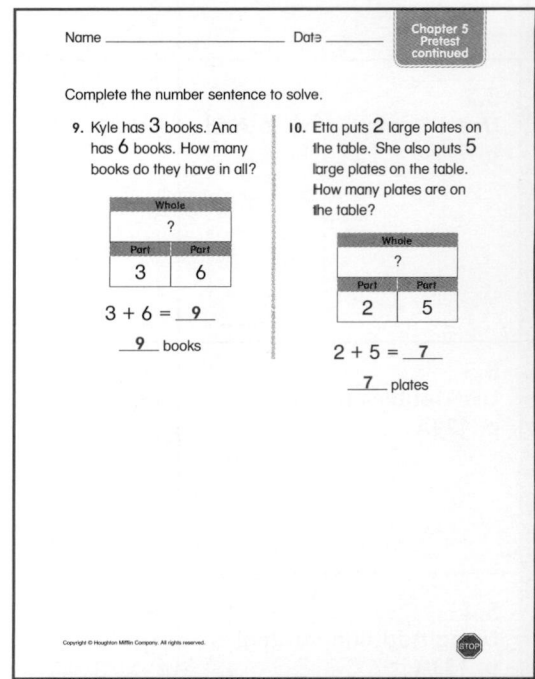

Customizing Instruction

For Students Having Difficulty

Items	Prerequisites	Ways to Success
1–3	Understands how to order numbers through 10.	CD: 1.4 Skillsheet 29
4–6	Understands how to count and compare through 10 using pictures.	CD: 1.2 Skillsheet 30

Ways to Success: Intervention for every concept and skill (CD-ROM or Chapter Intervention Skillsheets).

For Students Having Success

Items	Objectives	Resources
1–2	5A Develop and use math vocabulary relating to addition strategies.	Enrichment 5.1–5.3
3–8	5B Find sums through 10 using a number line, counting on, doubles, and doubles plus one.	Enrichment 5.1–5.4
9–10	5C Use parts and wholes and number sentences to solve problems.	Enrichment 5.5

Use **Chapter Challenges** with any students who have success with all new chapter content.

Other Pretest Options

Informal Pretest

The pretest assesses vocabulary and prerequisite skills needed for success in this chapter.

***Ways to Success* CD-ROM**

The ***Ways to Success*** chapter pretest has automatic assignment of appropriate review lessons.

Chapter Resources

Assessing Prior Knowledge

Make Equal Sets (number concepts, addition)

- Provide an egg carton and beans. Invite children to take a small handful of beans, place them in the egg carton, close the lid, and shake the carton. Children open the lid and note the arrangement of the beans.
- Children can take turns adding beans to make equal sets of beans on each side of the carton.

 Activity

Ongoing Skill Activity

Doubles Dominoes (number concepts, addition)

- Place number cards 1–5, drawing paper, and crayons or markers in the math center.
- Invite pairs of children to shuffle the number cards and place them facedown. Each child draws a card and reads the number.
- Children fold sheets of paper in half and open them. They draw the appropriate number of dots on each side of the paper. Then they write a number sentence.

 Activity

Connecting to the Unit Project

- Have children work in pairs.
- Tell children to create another addition problem.
- Have children use models to solve their partner's problem.
- Invite volunteers to explain how they solved the problem.

Teacher Support

Professional Resources Handbook

Research, Mathematics Content, and Language Intervention

Research-Based Teaching

The National Council of Teachers of Mathematics (2000) has emphasized the importance of children becoming proficient in the basic facts but cautions against placing too much emphasis on memorization before understanding is developed. Children also need to understand the inverse relationship between addition and subtraction. Using "fact families" for addition and subtraction can facilitate this process. Organizing facts into families makes it easier for children to learn them. See *Professional Resources Handbook, Grade 1, Unit 2.*

For more ideas relating to Unit 2, see the Teacher Support Handbook at the back of this Teacher's Edition.

Language Intervention

Research shows that it helps children to know many strategies for addition. It is important that children be flexible and not always try to use just one strategy. For further explanation, see "Mathematical Language and Addition Facts" in the *Professional Resources Handbook* Grade 1.

 **Technology**

Time-Saving Technology Support
Ways to Assess Customized Spiral Review
  Test Generator CD
Lesson Planner CD-ROM
Ways to Success Intervention CD-ROM
MathTracks CD-ROM
Education Place: www.eduplace.com/math/mw
Houghton Mifflin Math eBook CD-ROM
eManipulatives
eGames

Starting Chapter 5
Addition Strategies Through 10

Math Background

Addition Strategies Through 10

The basic facts of addition are all the combinations of numbers 0 through 9. The basic facts are defined as the combinations of numbers 0 through 9 because we have a base-ten numeration system with ten digits or numerals, 0 through 9. Knowledge of these facts provides children with a firm foundation and is essential for learning how to use and make sense of the standard addition algorithm.

There are several strategies children can use to learn their basic addition facts. Children may enter first grade with some strategies from kindergarten, such as drawing a picture, using counters, or even counting on.

The use of the number line also provides a concrete model for counting on. For example, for $5 + 2$, children start at 5 and count on 2. The strategy of using doubles to add is introduced at this level. It provides children practice in using basic addition facts and leads to a related strategy, doubles plus one. Use of addition strategies enables children to develop a sense of number relationships and helps them connect the relationships to the basic addition facts.

Addition Strategies Through 10

CHAPTER 5

INVESTIGATION
How many ants and bees are there altogether?

Chapter 5   one hundred twenty-three **123**

Using The Investigation

- Have children brainstorm things that people *join*. Write *join* on the board. Have volunteers offer synonyms for *join* (such as add, group, put together). Make a list of their suggestions.

- Read the question to children. **Look at the picture. How many ants and bees are there altogether?** $(6 + 3 = 9)$

- When children have completed the exercise, ask volunteers to tell how they found the sum.

For more information about projects and investigations, visit Education Place. **eduplace.com/math/mw/**

Flower Fun
∙∙∙∙∙∙∙∙∙∙
Listen to your teacher.

124 one hundred twenty-four

CHAPTER CHALLENGES

For Mathematically Promising Students

The *Chapter Challenges* resource book provides blackline masters for activities that explore, extend, and connect the mathematics in every chapter. To support this independent work, see the Teacher Notes for each activity.

Explore: 1, 2, 3 Cubes, page 25, after Lesson 1,
Extend: Find the Addends, page 27, after Lesson 3
Connect: Choose an Estimate, page 29, after Lesson 5

Using This Page

- Read these flower stories to the children.
- Have children model each story using counters and the workmat on this page.

Lila picked 2 flowers. She found 2 ladybugs on one flower and 6 ladybugs on the other. How many ladybugs did she find on her flowers? (8 ladybugs)

- Have each child put 2 counters on one flower on the mat and then place 6 more counters on the other flower on the mat. How many are there altogether?

Todd found 4 ladybugs on one flower and 3 ladybugs on the other flower. How many ladybugs did Todd find altogether? (7 ladybugs)

- Have the children use counters and explain how they found their answer. How many are there altogether?
- Create other flower addition stories and have children model with counters.

NSF Children's Math Worlds

Children's Math Worlds focuses on the use of models to represent mathematical situations. Thus, using a *Children's Math Worlds* lesson helps students develop a general facility with drawing models to support their thinking that will transfer to all their mathematical work.

Count On to Add

PLANNING THE LESSON

MATHEMATICS OBJECTIVE
Write sums to 10 by counting on (increasing) 1, 2, or 3.

Use Lesson Planner CD-ROM for Lesson 5.1

Daily Routines

Calendar
Point to today's day and date on the calendar. Ask children to point to the days and dates that are 1, 2, and 3 days after.

Vocabulary
Review **count on** by displaying a number card from 2–10 and asking children to count on with you from that number to 20.

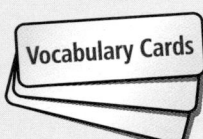
Vocabulary Cards

Meeting North Carolina's Standards

1.03 Develop fluency with single-digit addition and corresponding differences using strategies such as modeling, composing and decomposing quantities, using doubles, and making tens.

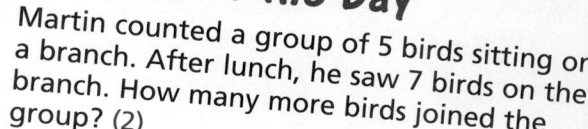

Lesson Transparency **5.1**

Problem of the Day
Martin counted a group of 5 birds sitting on a branch. After lunch, he saw 7 birds on the branch. How many more birds joined the group? **(2)**

Quick Review

6	0	2	0	0
+ 0	+ 4	+ 0	+ 4	+ 5
(6)	(4)	(2)	(4)	(5)

Lesson Quiz
1. $4 + 2 =$ ___ **(6)**
2. $6 + 3 =$ ___ **(9)**
3. $9 + 1 =$ ___ **(10)**

LEVELED PRACTICE

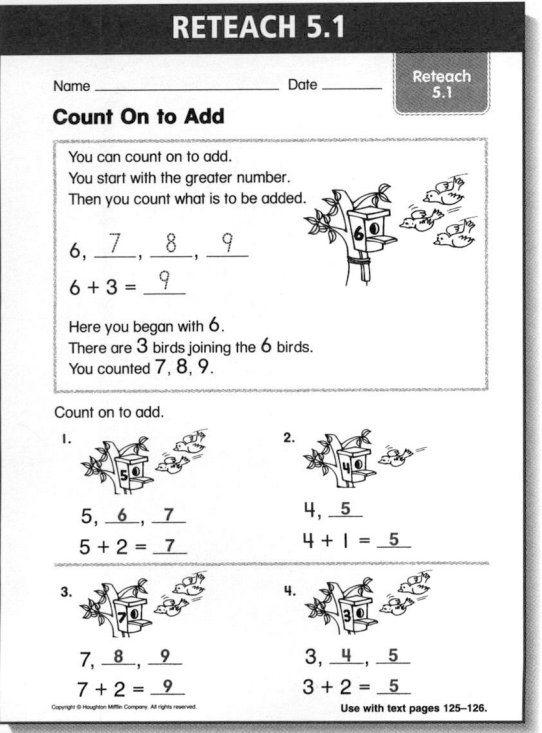

RETEACH 5.1

Name _____ Date _____ Reteach 5.1

Count On to Add

You can count on to add.
You start with the greater number.
Then you count what is to be added.

6, _7_, _8_, _9_
$6 + 3 =$ _9_

Here you began with 6.
There are 3 birds joining the 6 birds.
You counted 7, 8, 9.

Count on to add.

1.
5, _6_, _7_
$5 + 2 =$ _7_

2.
4, _5_
$4 + 1 =$ _5_

3.
7, _8_, _9_
$7 + 2 =$ _9_

4.
3, _4_, _5_
$3 + 2 =$ _5_

Copyright © Houghton Mifflin Company. All rights reserved.
Use with text pages 125–126.

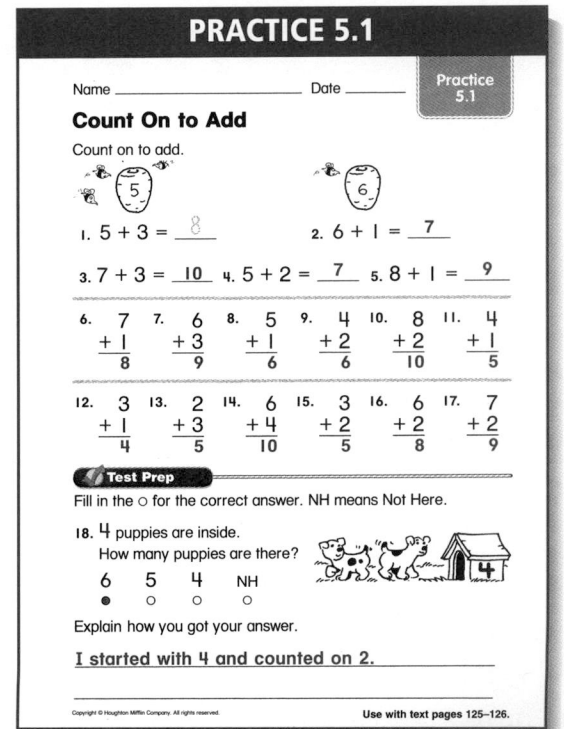

PRACTICE 5.1

Name _____ Date _____ Practice 5.1

Count On to Add

Count on to add.

1. $5 + 3 =$ _8_   2. $6 + 1 =$ _7_

3. $7 + 3 =$ _10_ 4. $5 + 2 =$ _7_ 5. $8 + 1 =$ _9_

6.	7.	8.	9.	10.	11.
7	6	5	4	8	4
+1	+3	+1	+2	+2	+1
8	9	6	6	10	5

12.	13.	14.	15.	16.	17.
3	2	6	3	6	7
+1	+3	+4	+2	+2	+2
4	5	10	5	8	9

Test Prep
Fill in the ○ for the correct answer. NH means Not Here.

18. 4 puppies are inside.
How many puppies are there?
6 ● 5 ○ 4 ○ NH ○

Explain how you got your answer.

I started with 4 and counted on 2.

Copyright © Houghton Mifflin Company. All rights reserved.
Use with text pages 125–126.

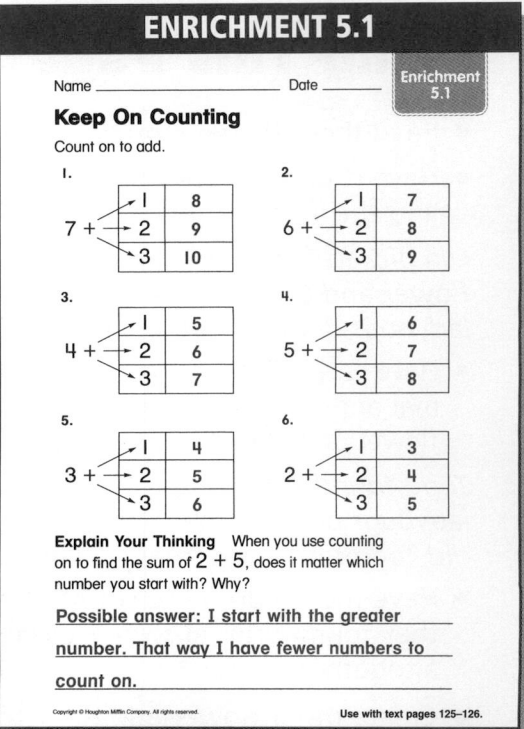

ENRICHMENT 5.1

Name _____ Date _____ Enrichment 5.1

Keep On Counting

Count on to add.

1.
$7 +$
1	8
2	9
3	10

2.
$6 +$
1	7
2	8
3	9

3.
$4 +$
1	5
2	6
3	7

4.
$5 +$
1	6
2	7
3	8

5.
$3 +$
1	4
2	5
3	6

6.
$2 +$
1	3
2	4
3	5

Explain Your Thinking When you use counting on to find the sum of $2 + 5$, does it matter which number you start with? Why?

Possible answer: I start with the greater
number. That way I have fewer numbers to
count on.

Copyright © Houghton Mifflin Company. All rights reserved.
Use with text pages 125–126.

Practice Workbook Page 30

Reaching All Learners
Differentiated Instruction

English Learners

English-language learners may not have the language skills to explain the process behind their thinking. Use Worksheet 5.1 to provide children with sentence frames they can use to complete the Explain Your Thinking activity.

Special Needs
VISUAL, TACTILE

Materials: *paper cup, counters*

- Have the child place 5 counters in the cup as she or he counts. Write 5 on the cup.

- Show 1 counter beside the cup. **How many counters in all?** Model how to begin with 5 then count on 1 to find the sum. Allow the child to recount all the counters to check.

Early Finishers
TACTILE, AUDITORY

Materials: *number cube, number cards 1–3 (LT 14)*

- Have children work in pairs. One child rolls the cube and then chooses a number card.

- The other child counts on to add and writes the sum.

- Children switch roles and continue.

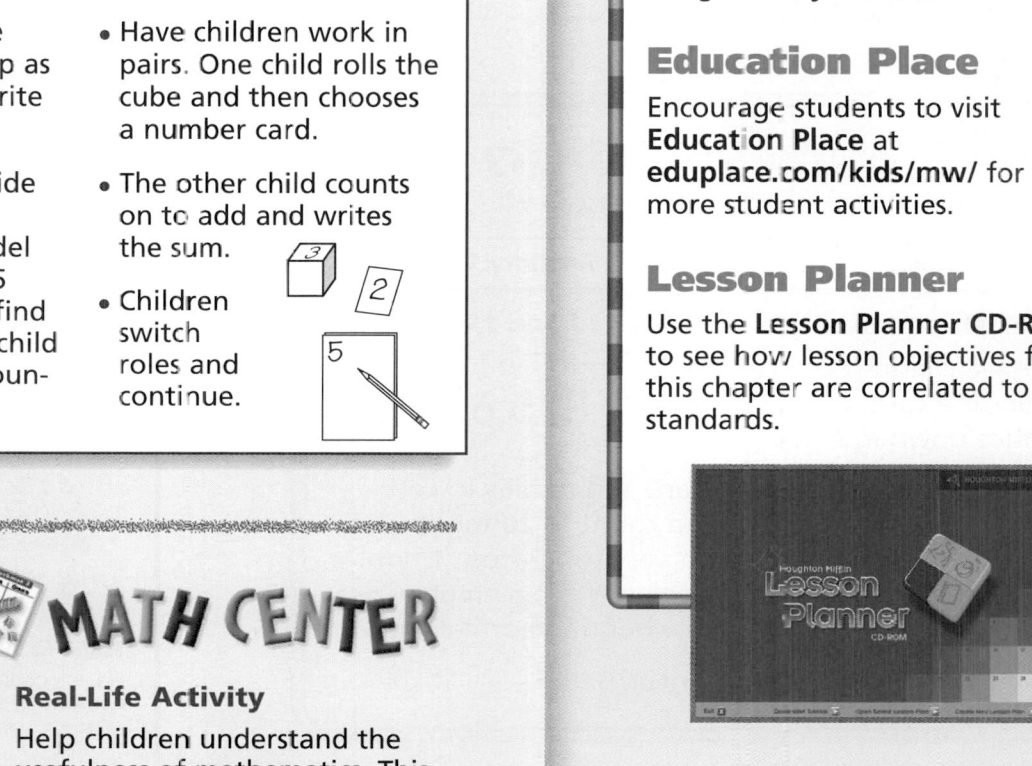

 ## Literature Connection

Read the story, *One More Bunny* by Rick Walton. As you read, pause before turning each page to have children predict how many bunnies will be on the next page by counting on 1.

MATH CENTER

Real-Life Activity

Help children understand the usefulness of mathematics. This activity makes math come alive by connecting the lesson skills to a real-life situation.

PROBLEM SOLVING 5.1

Name _____ Date _____ | Problem Solving 5.1

Count On to Add

Read to solve.
Count on to add.   Draw or write to explain.

1. There are 5 bees on a flower. Then 2 bees join them. How many bees are there in all?

   __7__ bees in all

2. There are 2 red roses in the vase. There are 3 white roses in the vase. How many roses are there in all?

   __5__ roses in all

3. 3 frogs jumped into the pond. 3 more frogs jumped in. How many frogs jumped in the pond?

   __6__ frogs in all

4. Amy found 3 pink shells. Then she found 4 yellow shells. How many shells did she find in all?

   __7__ shells in all

Use with text pages 125–126.

HOMEWORK 5.1

Name _____ Date _____ | Homework 5.1

Count On to Add

You can count on to add. Find $5 + 3$.

Start with 5. Count on 3.

| 5 | 6 | 7 | 8 |

$5 + 3 = 8$

Count on to add.

1. $4 + 2 = 6$ 2. $1 + 2 = 3$ 3. $4 + 3 = 7$

4.	5.	6.
3 +2 5	6 +2 8	2 +5 7

7.	8.	9.
8 +1 9	3 +5 8	4 +1 5

10. You have 4 new yellow pencils. Count on to add 3 red pencils. How many pencils do you have in all?

   __7__ pencils

Draw or write to explain.

Use with text pages 125–126.

ENGLISH LEARNERS 5.1

Name _____ Date _____ | English Learners 5.1

Count On to Add

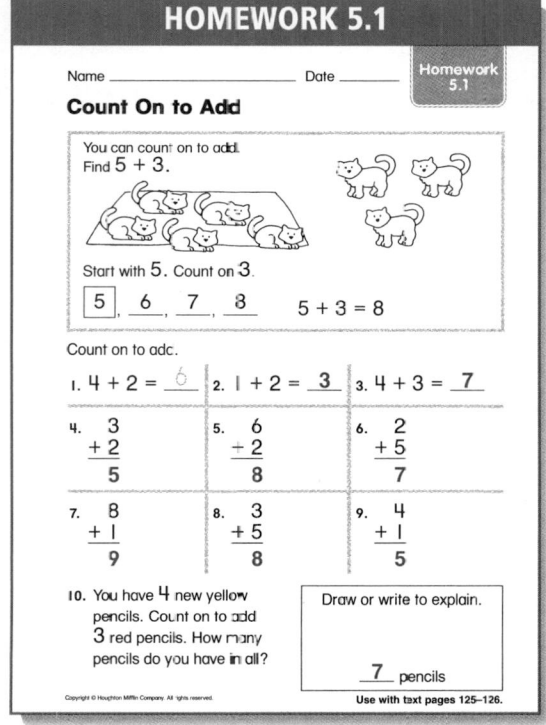

12 in all

Count on to find $9 + 3$. Do you get the same sum as when you count on to find $3 - 9$? Why?

First, I will count on to find __9__ + __3__.

$9 + 3 = $ __12__

Next, I will count on to find __3__ + __9__.

$3 + 9 = $ __12__

Both of them have the same sum because you are adding the same numbers. It doesn't matter which order they are in.

To the Teacher: Use the example at the top of the page to demonstrate how to add together two sets of bees. Then have children complete the sentence frames that provide the language needed to explain how to solve the word problem.

Use with text pages 125–126.

TEACHING LESSON 5.1

LESSON ORGANIZER

Objective Count on (increasing) 1, 2, or 3 to find sums through 10.

Resources Reteach, Practice, Enrichment, Problem Solving, Homework, English Learners, Transparencies, Math Center

Materials Number cards 0–20 (Learning Tools (LT) 14 and 15), counters, paper cup

Activity

Warm-Up Activity
Modeling Counting On

| 👤👤👤 Small Group | 🕐 5–10 minutes | Auditory, Visual |

Materials: *number cards 1–20 (LT 14 and 15)*

1. Have children sit in a circle. Shuffle cards and place them face down in a pile. $\boxed{4}$ 5,6,...20

2. Ask one child to draw a card and display it. **Let's start with this number and count to 20 together.** If needed, let children count very softly from 1 until they reach the number displayed, then emphasize that number and continue counting normally to 20.

3. Repeat with several other cards.

Name

Count On to Add

You can **count on** to add.

Objective
Count on 1, 2, or 3 to find sums through 10.

Vocabulary
count on

Find $7 + 2$.
Start with 7. Count on 2.

7 __8__ , __9__

$7 + 2 = $ __9__

Find $7 + 3$.
Start with 7. Count on 3.

7 __8__ , __9__ , __10__

$7 + 3 = $ __10__

Guided Practice

Count on to add.

Think
I start with 7.
I count on 1.

1. 7 __8__
   $7 + 1 = $ __8__

2. 8 __9__ , __10__
   $8 + 2 = $ __10__

3. 6 __7__ , __8__ , __9__
   $6 + 3 = $ __9__

4. 9 __10__
   $9 + 1 = $ __10__

TEST TIPS **Explain Your Thinking** Count on to find $9 + 3$.
Do you count on the same way to find $3 + 9$? Why? **Possible answer: Yes; because you are adding the same two numbers.**

---

1 Introduce

Discuss Counting On to Add

| 👤👤👤👤 Whole Group | 🕐 10–15 minutes | Visual, Auditory |

Materials: *counters, paper cup*

1. Show a cup. Drop 3 counters into the cup as children count. Write a 3 on the cup. Explain that it means there are 3 counters in the cup. Place a counter next to the cup.

2. **How many counters are in the cup?** (3) Point to the counter outside the cup as you ask: **How many more counters do we have?** (1) **How can we count on to find how many counters in all?** (Begin with 3, count on 1.) Count 3, **4**, emphasizing the 4. Write the addition sentence $3 + 1 = 4$.

3. Then repeat the activity with other numbers, counting on 1, 2, or 3.

2 Develop

Guided Learning

Teaching Example Introduce the objective and vocabulary to the children. Guide them through each example. Make sure children understand that the number on the beehive tells how many bees are in the beehive.

Guided Practice

Have children complete **Exercises 1–4** as you observe. Give children the opportunity to answer the Explain Your Thinking question. Then discuss the responses with the class.

Practice

Count on 1, 2, or 3.

Count on to add.

1.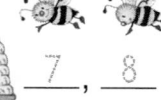

6 | 7, 8

6 + 2 = 8

2.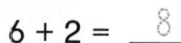

6 | 7

6 + 1 = 7

3. 5 + 1 = 6   4. 8 + 1 = 9   5. 4 + 2 = 6

6. 5 + 2 = 7   7. 6 + 3 = 9   8. 9 + 1 = 10

9. 16	10. 7	11. 3	12. 8	13. 4	14. 5
+2	+3	+1	+2	+1	+3
8	10	4	10	5	8

15. 3	16. 8	17. 2	18. 7	19. 9	20. 4
+2	+1	+1	+2	+1	+3
5	9	3	9	10	7

21. 7	22. 5	23. 6	24. 3	25. 5	26. 6
+1	+2	+1	+2	+1	+3
8	7	7	5	6	9

Problem Solving ▶ Visual Thinking

27. How many and  ?

10

126 one hundred twenty-six

At Home Say a number from 1 through 8. Have your child count on 2 and then say the addition fact.

Daily Test Prep

5 + 2

2 ○   5 ○   6 ○   NH ●

Activity

Lesson Intervention

Using Counters to Count On

Or use Intervention CD-ROM Lesson 5.1

👥 Small Group	🕐 5–10 minutes	Visual, Tactile

Materials: number cards 0–7 (LT 14), counters

1. Have one child display up to 7 counters.

6 | "7, 8"

2. Ask another child to count the counters and replace them with the matching number card. Then, have the child put 1, 2, or 3 counters next to the number card.

3. Have a third child count on from the number card to find out the total number of counters. If the child has difficulty finding the sum, he or she can exchange the number card for that number of counters and then count how many counters in all.

4. Children switch roles and repeat.

3 Practice

Independent Practice

Children complete **Exercises 1–26** independently.

Problem Solving

After children complete **Exercise 27**, call on volunteers to share their solutions. **Are there more black or red ants?** (black) **How do you know?** (Possible answer: if I draw lines to match the ants one-to-one there are two more black ants than red ants.)

Common Error

Counting On From the Wrong Number

Some children may begin counting from 1 as they count on. Have children circle the greater addend in each exercise in red pen or pencil and then count on from that number.

4 Assess and Close

Write 4 + 2 = _____.

How can you count on to find the sum?

(Begin with 4, then count on 2. Say 4. Count 5, 6.

 **Keeping a Journal**

Draw a picture or write about dogs in the park. Match the addition sentence 6 + 2 = _____. Write the sum.

Lesson 5.2

Use a Number Line to Add

PLANNING THE LESSON

MATHEMATICS OBJECTIVE

Find sums to 10 using a number line.

Use Lesson Planner CD-ROM for Lesson 5.2

Meeting North Carolina's Standards

1.03 Develop fluency with single-digit addition and corresponding differences using strategies such as modeling, composing and decomposing quantities, using doubles, and making tens.

Daily Routines

Calendar

Tell short calendar stories that focus on counting on: **It is [November] 3. Trisha's party is in 2 days. What is the date of her party?** (November 5)

Vocabulary

Review **number line** by helping children to make a number line. Give them a line with 11 tick marks. Have one or two children write the numbers 0–10 from left to right at the tick marks.

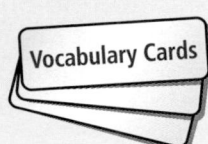
Vocabulary Cards

Lesson Transparency 5.2

Problem of the Day

There are 5 cars in the parking lot. Three cars leave. One more car parks. How many cars are in the lot now? (3)

Quick Review

$5 - 0 =$ ___ (5)
$0 - 0 =$ ___ (0)

$4 - 4 =$ ___ (0)

Lesson Quiz

1. What number is 2 more than 6? (8)
2. What number is 1 more than 9? (10)
3. What number is 3 more than 4? (7)

LEVELED PRACTICE

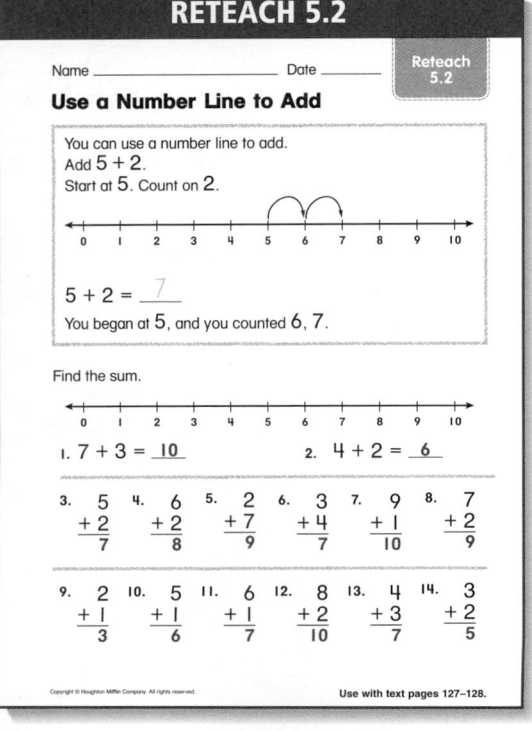

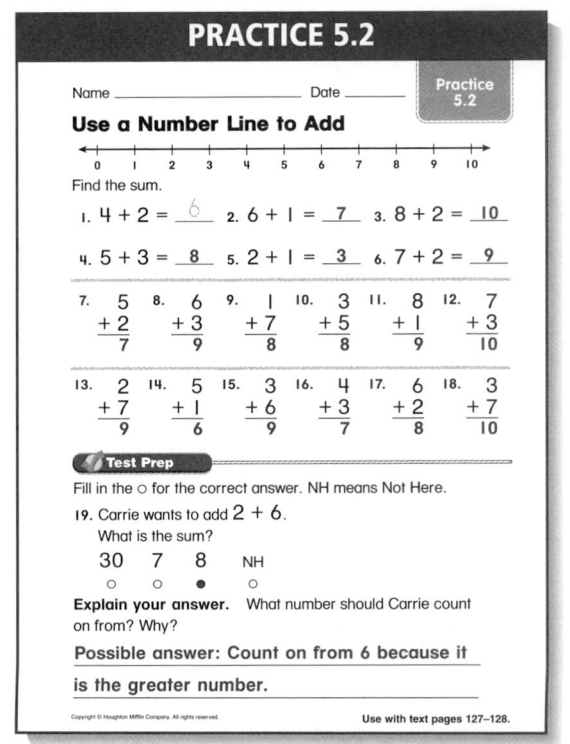

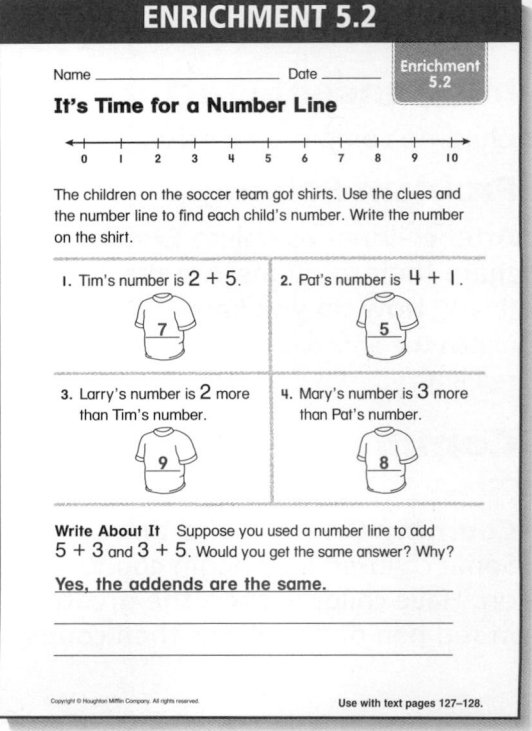

Practice Workbook Page 31

Reaching All Learners
Differentiated Instruction

English Learners

In order to find sums on a number line, children will need to understand the meaning of the term *greater*. Use Worksheet 5.2 to teach English-language learners the meaning of this term.

Inclusion
TACTILE, VISUAL

Materials: *number cards 0–10 (LT 14), yarn, number cube*

• Help the child make a number line with cards and yarn as shown.

• Have the child roll the number cube, point to the number, and count on 2. Continue with other numbers 1, 2, or 3.

Gifted and Talented
AUDITORY, VISUAL

Materials: *number lines (LT 8)*

• Provide exercises similar to those shown. Have children use 0–10 number lines to find the missing addends.

$5 + \square$ (3) $= 8$

$6 + \square$ (1) $= 7$

$3 + \square$ (2) $= 5$

$\square$ (8) $+ 1 = 9$

$\square$ (4) $+ 3 = 7$

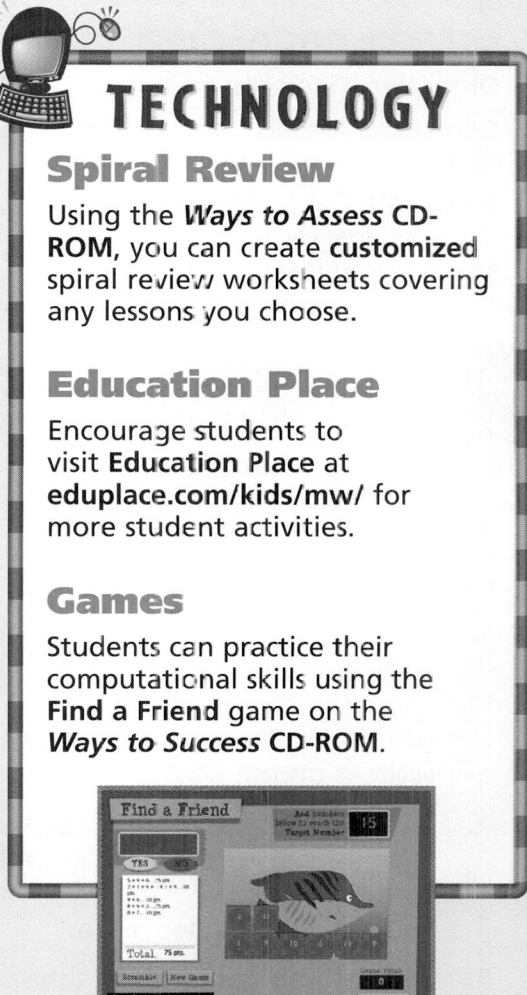

Literature Connection

Read the story *How Many Feet in the Bed?* by Dianne Johnston Hamm. Pause as you read to let children use a number line to predict how many feet are in the bed each time a family member joins. Then continue reading to confirm their predictions.

MATH CENTER

Basic Skills Activity

Motivate children to build basic skills. Use this activity to address multiple learning styles using hands-on activities related to the skills of this lesson.

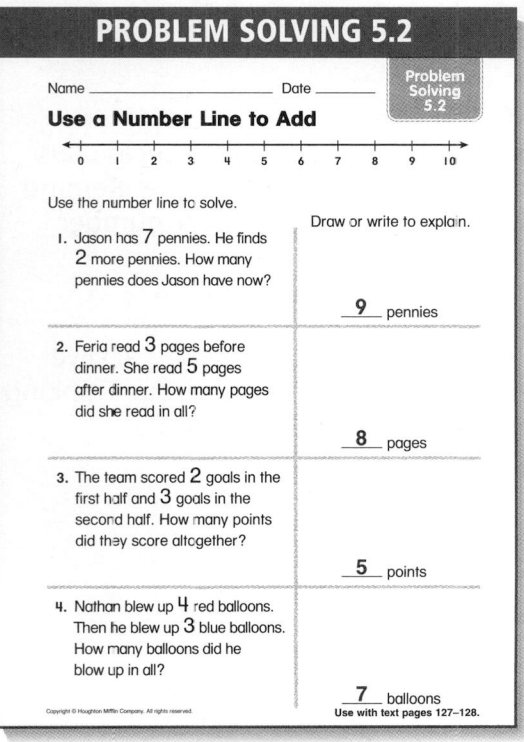

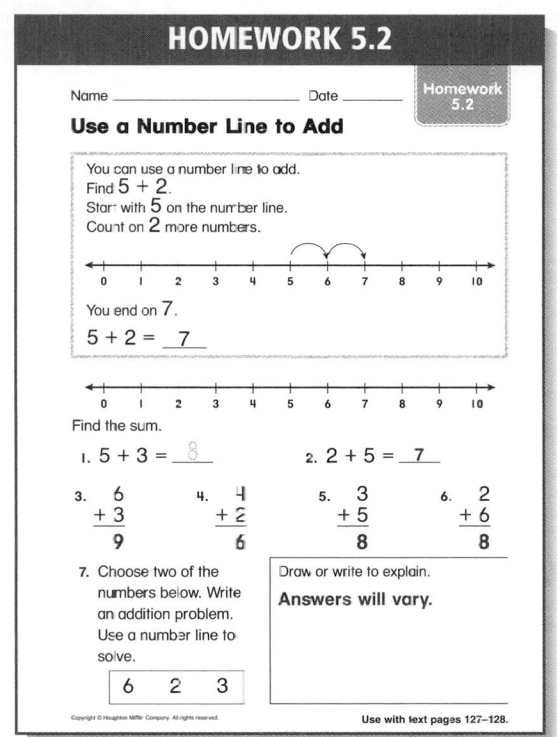

Homework Workbook Page 31

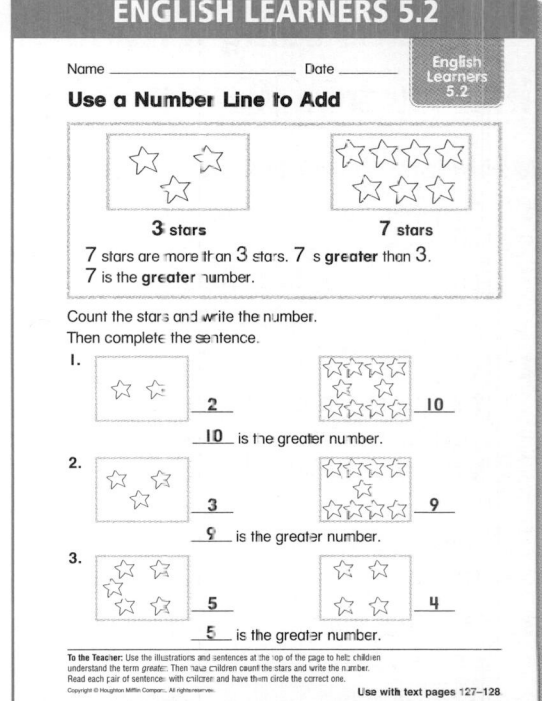

TEACHING LESSON 5.2

LESSON ORGANIZER

Objective Find sums to 10 using a number line.

Resources Reteach, Practice, Enrichment, Problem Solving, Homework, English Learners, Transparencies, Math Center

Materials Cubes, blank transparency, counter, large strip of paper, markers, index cards (with exercises from the lesson - no sums)

Activity

Warm-Up Activity
Modeling Adding in Any Order

| 👥 Small Group | 🕐 5–10 minutes | Visual, Tactile |

Materials: *red and blue cubes*

1. Ask children to make a cube train that shows 3 red cubes, then 1 blue cube. **What addition sentence describes your train?** (3 + 1 = 4) Write it on the board.

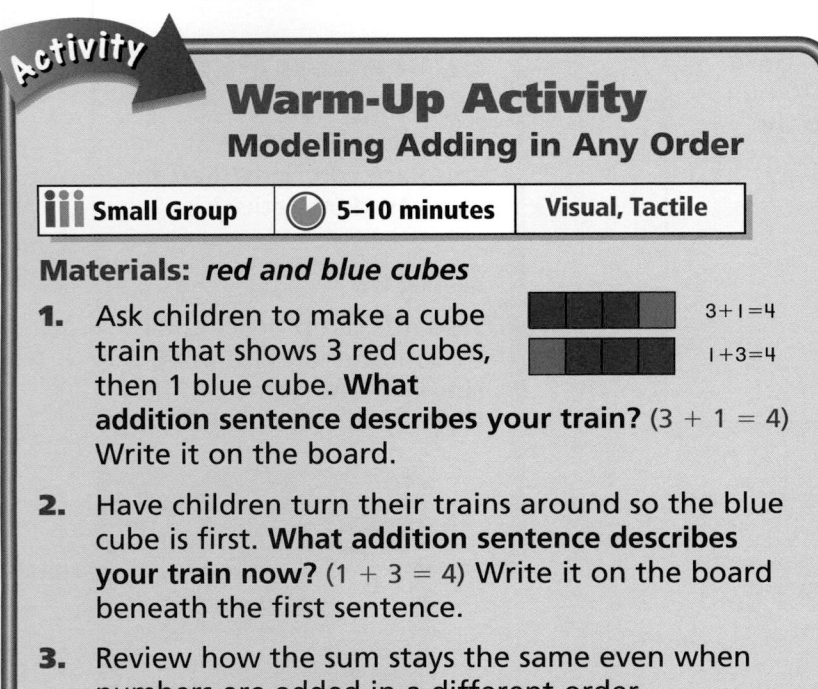

$3+1=4$
$1+3=4$

2. Have children turn their trains around so the blue cube is first. **What addition sentence describes your train now?** (1 + 3 = 4) Write it on the board beneath the first sentence.

3. Review how the sum stays the same even when numbers are added in a different order.

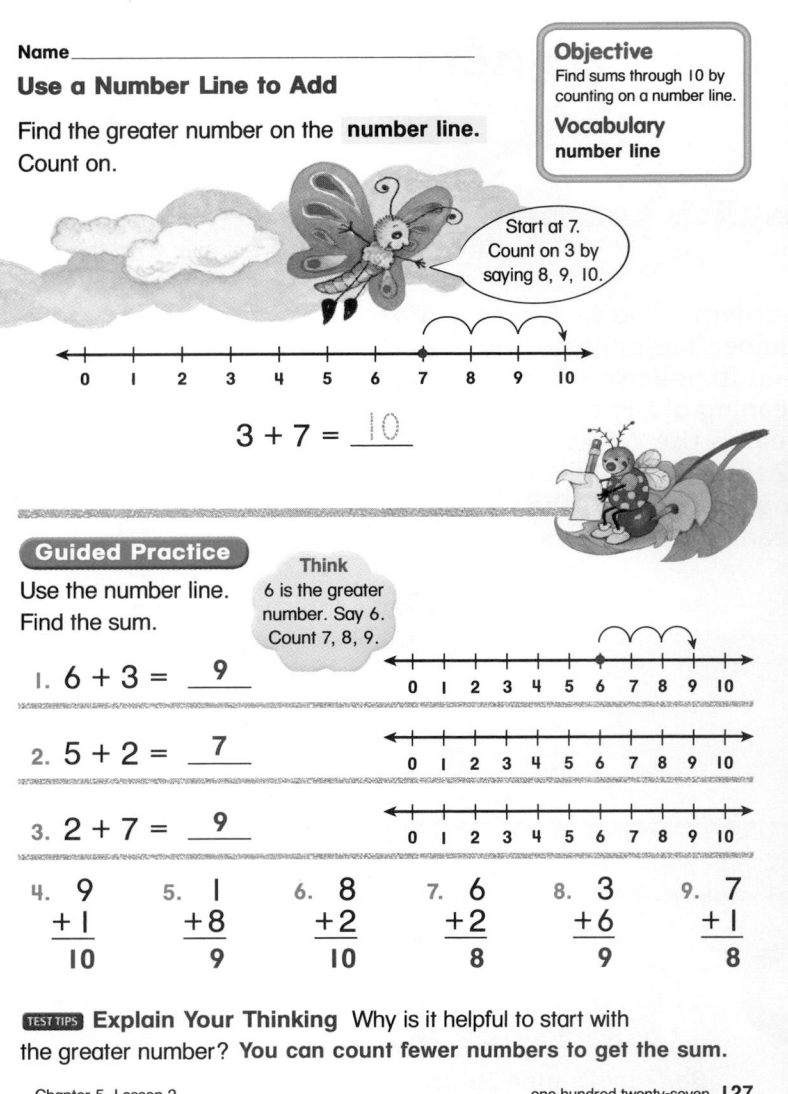

Name _____

Use a Number Line to Add

Find the greater number on the **number line.** Count on.

Start at 7. Count on 3 by saying 8, 9, 10.

$3 + 7 = \underline{10}$

Objective
Find sums through 10 by counting on a number line.

Vocabulary
number line

Guided Practice

Use the number line. Find the sum.

Think 6 is the greater number. Say 6. Count 7, 8, 9.

1. $6 + 3 = \underline{9}$
2. $5 + 2 = \underline{7}$
3. $2 + 7 = \underline{9}$

4. $\begin{array}{r} 9 \\ +1 \\ \hline 10 \end{array}$
5. $\begin{array}{r} 1 \\ +8 \\ \hline 9 \end{array}$
6. $\begin{array}{r} 8 \\ +2 \\ \hline 10 \end{array}$
7. $\begin{array}{r} 6 \\ +2 \\ \hline 8 \end{array}$
8. $\begin{array}{r} 3 \\ +6 \\ \hline 9 \end{array}$
9. $\begin{array}{r} 7 \\ +1 \\ \hline 8 \end{array}$

TEST TIPS Explain Your Thinking Why is it helpful to start with the greater number? **You can count fewer numbers to get the sum.**

Chapter 5 Lesson 2   one hundred twenty-seven **127**

---

1 Introduce
Activity
Discuss Using a Number Line to Add

| 👥 Whole Group | 🕐 10–15 minutes | Visual, Auditory |

Materials: *blank transparency, counter*

1. Draw a number line for 0–10. Place a counter on 5. Write 5 + 3 = ____. **You can use the number line to count on to find the sum.** Move the counter as you count on 3: **6, 7, 8. What is the sum?** (8)

2. Write 3 + 5 = ____. Place a counter on 3. **Will the sum be the same or different?** (same) Model counting on 5 as you move the counter along the number line to check. **Which was faster, starting at 3 or 5?** (5) **Why?** (You had to count on fewer numbers.) Lead children to see that because the order you add numbers doesn't matter, they should count on from the greater number.

3. Write 2 + 4 = ____ and have volunteers use the number line and counter to find the sum.

2 Develop

Guided Learning

Teaching Example Introduce the objective and vocabulary to the children. Guide them through the example. Remind children that they should start with the greater number when they count on.

Guided Practice

Have children complete **Exercises 1–9** as you observe. Give children the opportunity to answer the Explain Your Thinking question. Then discuss their responses with the class.

Practice

Start with the greater number.

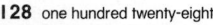

Use the number line.
Find the sum.

1. 4 + 2 = __6__ 2. 1 + 7 = __8__ 3. 8 + 2 = __10__

4. 3 + 5 = __8__ 5. 1 + 6 = __7__ 6. 2 + 3 = __5__

7. 2 + 4 = __6__ 8. 3 + 1 = __4__ 9. 1 + 9 = __10__

10. 2
 +1
 ‾3‾

11. 3
 +4
 ‾7‾

12. 7
 +3
 ‾10‾

13. 1
 +5
 ‾6‾

14. 5
 +2
 ‾7‾

15. 2
 +6
 ‾8‾

16. 9
 +1
 ‾10‾

17. 2
 +5
 ‾7‾

18. 1
 +4
 ‾5‾

19. 3
 +2
 ‾5‾

20. 2
 +8
 ‾10‾

21. 3
 +7
 ‾10‾

Problem Solving ▶ Number Sense

Use the number line.

22. What number is 2 more than 8? __10__

23. What number is 3 more than 7? __10__

24. What number is 2 more than 5? __7__

128 one hundred twenty-eight

🏠 **At Home** Have your child use the number line to add 1, 2, or 3 to any number less than 8.

Daily Test Prep

What number is missing?

6, 7, 8, _____, 10

7   8   9   NH
○   ○   ●   ○

Activity

Lesson Intervention

Using a Floor Number Line

Or use Intervention CD-ROM Lesson 5.2

👥 Small Group	🕐 10–15 minutes	Kinesthetic, Visual

Materials: *large strip of paper, markers, index cards (with addition exercises from the lesson without sums)*

1. Draw a 0–10 number line on large paper with a marker and make the addition cards.

4 5 6 7 8

2. Have one child choose an addition card and recite it aloud. Then have another child stand on the greater number and move on the number line as children count on to find the sum.

3. Continue until each child has had a turn.

---

3 Practice

Independent Practice

Children complete **Exercises 1–21** independently.

Problem Solving

After children complete **Exercises 22–24**, call on volunteers to share their solutions. **Which direction did you move on the number line to find your answers, right or left?** (right)

Common Error

Starting To Count On At Zero

Children may begin counting on the number line at 0. Have children place a counter on the greater number. Then have them move the counter as they count aloud.

4 Assess and Close

- **If you start at 6 and count on 3, what number will you land on?** (9)
- **Why should you start from the 6 when you count on to find the sum of 6 + 3?** (You will have to count on fewer numbers than if you started with 3.)

 **Keeping a Journal**

Draw a 0 to 10 number line. Show how to find the sum for 5 + 2 using the line.

Use Doubles to Add

PLANNING THE LESSON

MATHEMATICS OBJECTIVE
Add using doubles and doubles plus one.

Use Lesson Planner CD-ROM for Lesson 5.3

Daily Routines

Calendar
Point to the fourth day of the current month. Ask a volunteer to count 4 days ahead and name the date. Write the addition sentence: $4 + 4 = 8$.

Sunday	Monday	Tuesday	Wednesday	Thursday	Friday	Saturday
			1	2	3	4
5	6	7	8	9	10	11
12	13	14	15	16	17	18
19	20	21	22	23	24	25
26	27	28	29	30	31	

Vocabulary
Write $3 + 3 = 6$ on the board. Review **double** and **addend** by having a volunteer tell why this is a double. (Both addends are the same.)

Vocabulary Cards

Meeting North Carolina's Standards

1.03 Develop fluency with single-digit addition and corresponding differences using strategies such as modeling, composing and decomposing quantities, using doubles, and making tens.

Lesson Transparency **5.3**

Problem of the Day
Adam makes muffins and needs to double the recipe. The recipe calls for 2 cups of flour. How many cups of flour does he use? (4 cups)

Quick Review

$$\begin{array}{c} 3 \\ + 1 \\ \hline \end{array} \quad \begin{array}{c} 4 \\ + 2 \\ \hline \end{array} \quad \begin{array}{c} 2 \\ + 6 \\ \hline \end{array} \quad \begin{array}{c} 7 \\ + 1 \\ \hline \end{array} \quad \begin{array}{c} 2 \\ + 5 \\ \hline \end{array}$$
$$\quad (4) \qquad (6) \qquad (8) \qquad (8) \qquad (7)$$

Lesson Quiz
1. What doubles fact helps you add $3 + 4$? $(3 + 3 = 6)$
2. What is the same in the addition sentence $4 + 4 = 8$? (the addends or the numbers that are added)
3. What is the sum of $2 + 2$? (4)

LEVELED PRACTICE

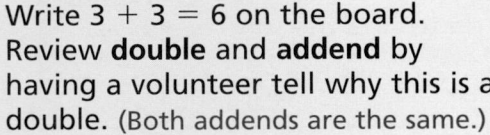

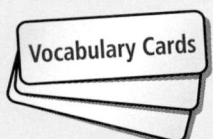

RETEACH 5.3

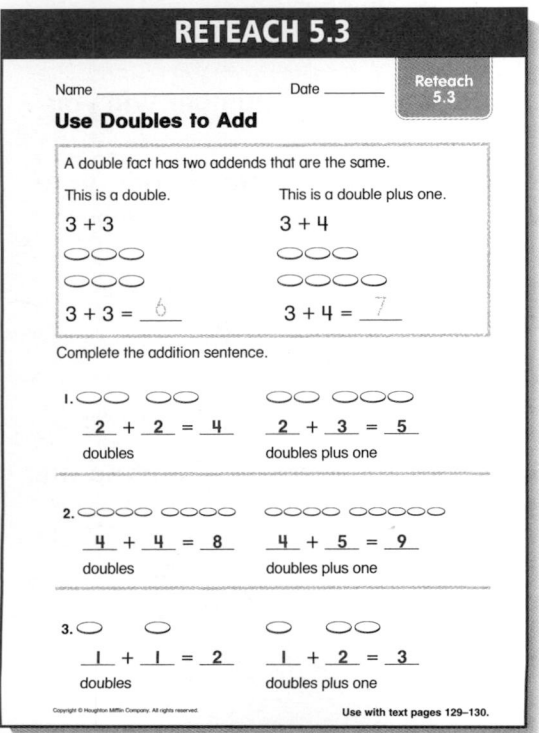

PRACTICE 5.3

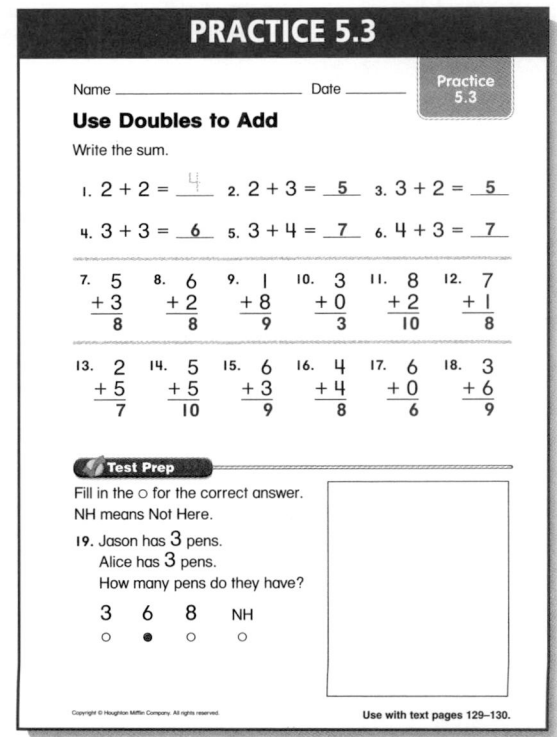

ENRICHMENT 5.3

Name _____ Date _____ Enrichment 5.3

Double Up!

When you double me, my sum is less than 7 and more than 4.

What numbers are less than 7 and more than 4? _6_ _5_

Is there a number you can double and get a sum of 5? _No_

Is there a number you can double and get a sum of 6? _Yes_

What is the number? _3_

Then the answer must be _3_.

1. When you double me, the sum is less than 9 and more than 6. I am number _4_. $4 + 4 = 8$	2. I am the double of 3 and 1 and more. I am number _7_. $3 + 4 = 7$
3. I am the double of 2 and 1 more. I am number _5_. $2 + 3 = 5$	4. When you double me, the sum is less than 11 and more than 8. I am number _5_. $5 + 5 = 10$

Write About It How do you know which addition facts are doubles?
<u>Possible answer: The two numbers added are</u>
<u>the same.</u>

Use with text pages 129–130.

Practice Workbook Page 32

Reaching All Learners

Differentiated Instruction

English Learners

English-language learners may not be familiar with the term *double*. Use Worksheet 5.3 to help children understand this term.

Special Needs
VISUAL, AUDITORY

Materials: *one inch grid paper (LT 28)*

Guide the child to color squares to show 3 + 3 and write the fact.

Add a square of a different color to show 3 + 4 and discuss. Ask what happened to the second tower. (1 more square was added.) Explain that the sum will be 1 greater as you count the squares. Write 3 + 4 = 7.

Early Finishers
AUDITORY, VISUAL

- Have pairs of children create stories that use doubles. For example: Robert has 5 baseball cards. Helen has the same number of cards. How many cards do they have in all? (10)

- Then have partners exchange their stories and write addition sentences for the doubles.

TECHNOLOGY

Spiral Review

To reinforce skills on lessons taught earlier, create customized spiral review worksheets using the *Ways to Assess* CD-ROM.

Lesson Planner

You can use the **Lesson Planner CD-ROM** to create a report of the lessons and standards you have taught.

eBook

eMathBook allows students to review lessons and do homework without carrying their textbooks home.

Education Place

You can visit **Education Place** at eduplace.com/math/mw/ for teacher support materials.

ScienceConnection

Display pictures of different insects. Show how the insects have matching parts on each side, such as wings, legs, antennae. Have children write doubles to describe the matching parts.

MATH CENTER

Basic Skills Activity

Motivate children to build basic skills. Use this activity to address multiple learning styles using hands-on activities related to the skills of this lesson.

PROBLEM SOLVING 5.3

Name _____ Date _____ | Problem Solving 5.3

Use Doubles to Add

Read to solve. Think about a double or double plus one.
Draw or write to explain.

1. Sally wears 2 rings on one hand and 2 rings on her other hand. How many rings does Sally wear?
   __4__ rings in all

2. Tony read 4 books this week and 5 books last week. How many books did Tony read in all?
   __9__ books in all

3. Josh packed 3 dishes in one box and 4 dishes in the other box. How many dishes did he pack in all?
   __7__ dishes in all

4. Delia saw 2 deer today and 2 deer yesterday. How many deer did she see in all?
   __4__ deer in all

Use with text pages 129–130.

HOMEWORK 5.3

Name _____ Date _____ | Homework 5.3

Use Doubles to Add

You can use doubles to add. This is a double.   This is a double plus one.

3 + 3 = 6
addend addend sum

3 + 4 = 7
addend addend sum

Write the sum.

1. 2 + 2 = __4__   2. 3 + 5 = __8__

3. 7   4. 6   5. 8   6. 4
   +3   +3   +1   +3
   10   9   9   7

7. 4 children are playing in the park. 4 more children join them. How many children are there in all?
   4 + 4 = __8__
   Circle how you solved the problem.
   (doubles)   doubles plus one

8. There are 4 children playing in the park. Then 5 more children join them. How many children are there in all?
   4 + 5 = __9__
   Circle how you solved the problem.
   doubles   (doubles plus one)

Use with text pages 129–130.

ENGLISH LEARNERS 5.3

Name _____ Date _____ | English Learners 5.3

Use Doubles to Add

doubles   not doubles

When there are two groups with the same number they are **doubles**.

Circle the doubles.

1.

2.

To the Teacher: Use the illustrations and sentences at the top of the page to help children understand the meaning of the word *doubles*. Then have children circle the doubles.

Use with text pages 129–132.

Homework Workbook Page 32

TEACHING LESSON 5.3

LESSON ORGANIZER

Objective Add using doubles and doubles plus one.

Resources Reteach, Practice, Enrichment, Problem Solving, Homework, English Learners, Transparencies, Math Center

Materials Cubes, 2 number cubes 0–5, 2 game pieces

Activity

Warm-Up Activity
Modeling One More Than

| ¡¡¡¡ Whole Group | ⏱ 5 minutes | Auditory, Visual |

Materials: *cubes*

1. Review **1 more than** with children. Show a 4-cube tower in one color.

2. **How many cubes?** (4) **What is one more than 4?** (5) Add a cube of a different color to the top. Have a volunteer count the cubes to check.

3. Repeat with other cube towers using 1–9 cubes.

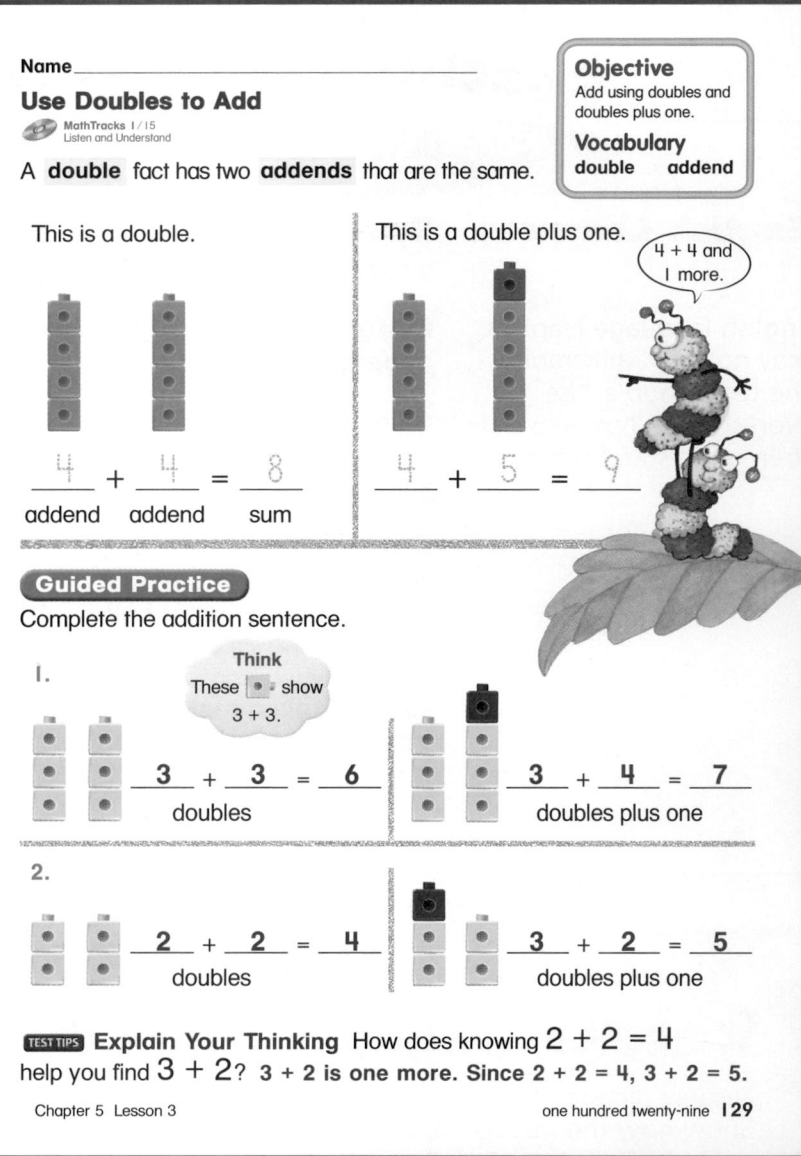

Name _____

Use Doubles to Add

MathTracks 1 / 15
Listen and Understand

Objective
Add using doubles and doubles plus one.

Vocabulary
double   addend

A **double** fact has two **addends** that are the same.

This is a double.

$$\underline{4} + \underline{4} = \underline{8}$$
addend   addend   sum

This is a double plus one.

$$\underline{4} + \underline{5} = \underline{9}$$

4 + 4 and 1 more.

Guided Practice

Complete the addition sentence.

1.

Think
These ▪▪ show 3 + 3.

$$\underline{3} + \underline{3} = \underline{6}$$
doubles

$$\underline{3} + \underline{4} = \underline{7}$$
doubles plus one

2.

$$\underline{2} + \underline{2} = \underline{4}$$
doubles

$$\underline{3} + \underline{2} = \underline{5}$$
doubles plus one

TEST TIPS **Explain Your Thinking** How does knowing $2 + 2 = 4$ help you find $3 + 2$? **3 + 2 is one more. Since 2 + 2 = 4, 3 + 2 = 5.**

Chapter 5 Lesson 3 ⸰⸰⸰⸰⸰⸰⸰⸰⸰⸰⸰⸰⸰⸰ one hundred twenty-nine **129**

---

① Introduce
Model Using Doubles to Add

| ¡¡¡¡ Whole Group | ⏱ 10–15 minutes | Visual, Auditory |

Materials: *cubes*

1. Display two blue 4-cube towers next to each other. **How many cubes are in each tower?** (4) Write 4 + 4 = ____ on the board. **What is the first addend?** (4) **What is the second addend?** (4) **What is the sum?** (8) **This is a doubles fact because the addends are the same.**

2. Add a red cube to the second tower. **What did I do to the second tower?** (added 1 more cube) Write the number sentence to read 4 + 5 = ____ beside the previous number sentence. **How will the sum change?** (The sum will be 1 more than the sum of 4 + 4.) Move the red cube to the first tower and write the number sentence 5 + 4 = ____. **Will the sum change?** (No, because you can add numbers in any order and the sum will stay the same.)

3. Continue, helping children understand the relationship between doubles and doubles plus one facts.

② Develop

Guided Learning

Teaching Example Introduce the objective and vocabulary to the children. Guide them through the examples. Help children to see that the first fact is a doubles fact because both addends are the same and that a doubles plus one fact is one more than the sum of a doubles fact.

Guided Practice

Have children complete **Exercises 1–2** as you observe.

You may need to remind children that they can add numbers in any order and the sum will stay the same.

Give children the opportunity to answer the Explain Your Thinking question. Then discuss their responses with the class.

Practice

Use doubles to help you find the sum.

Write the sum.

1. $3 + 3 = \underline{6}$ $3 + 4 = \underline{7}$ $4 + 3 = \underline{7}$

2. $4 + 4 = \underline{8}$ $4 + 5 = \underline{9}$ $5 + 4 = \underline{9}$

3. $\begin{array}{r} 2 \\ +2 \\ \hline 4 \end{array}$ $\begin{array}{r} 2 \\ +3 \\ \hline 5 \end{array}$ $\begin{array}{r} 3 \\ +2 \\ \hline 5 \end{array}$ 4. $\begin{array}{r} 1 \\ +1 \\ \hline 2 \end{array}$ $\begin{array}{r} 1 \\ +2 \\ \hline 3 \end{array}$ $\begin{array}{r} 2 \\ +1 \\ \hline 3 \end{array}$

5. $\begin{array}{r} 4 \\ +5 \\ \hline 9 \end{array}$ 6. $\begin{array}{r} 3 \\ +3 \\ \hline 6 \end{array}$ 7. $\begin{array}{r} 4 \\ +4 \\ \hline 8 \end{array}$ 8. $\begin{array}{r} 4 \\ +3 \\ \hline 7 \end{array}$ 9. $\begin{array}{r} 3 \\ +4 \\ \hline 7 \end{array}$ 10. $\begin{array}{r} 5 \\ +5 \\ \hline 10 \end{array}$

11. $\begin{array}{r} 0 \\ +8 \\ \hline 8 \end{array}$ 12. $\begin{array}{r} 1 \\ +5 \\ \hline 6 \end{array}$ 13. $\begin{array}{r} 5 \\ +3 \\ \hline 8 \end{array}$ 14. $\begin{array}{r} 2 \\ +4 \\ \hline 6 \end{array}$ 15. $\begin{array}{r} 7 \\ +2 \\ \hline 9 \end{array}$ 16. $\begin{array}{r} 5 \\ +4 \\ \hline 9 \end{array}$

17. $\begin{array}{r} 3 \\ +7 \\ \hline 10 \end{array}$ 18. $\begin{array}{r} 2 \\ +8 \\ \hline 10 \end{array}$ 19. $\begin{array}{r} 2 \\ +6 \\ \hline 8 \end{array}$ 20. $\begin{array}{r} 9 \\ +0 \\ \hline 9 \end{array}$ 21. $\begin{array}{r} 3 \\ +6 \\ \hline 9 \end{array}$ 22. $\begin{array}{r} 4 \\ +3 \\ \hline 7 \end{array}$

Algebra Readiness ▶ **Missing Addends**

Choose a number to make a double.

23. $\begin{array}{r} 4 \\ +\boxed{4} \\ \hline 8 \end{array}$ 24. $\begin{array}{r} \boxed{3} \\ +3 \\ \hline 6 \end{array}$ 25. $\begin{array}{r} \boxed{5} \\ +5 \\ \hline 10 \end{array}$ 26. $\begin{array}{r} 1 \\ +\boxed{1} \\ \hline 2 \end{array}$

$\boxed{1}\ \boxed{3}$
$\boxed{4}\ \boxed{5}$

130 one hundred thirty

At Home Say a doubles plus one fact such as $3 + 4$. Ask your child to name the double that helps find the sum.

Go on

Daily Test Prep

Mark under the answer that shows *eleven*.

8 ○   10 ○   11 ●   NH ○

Activity

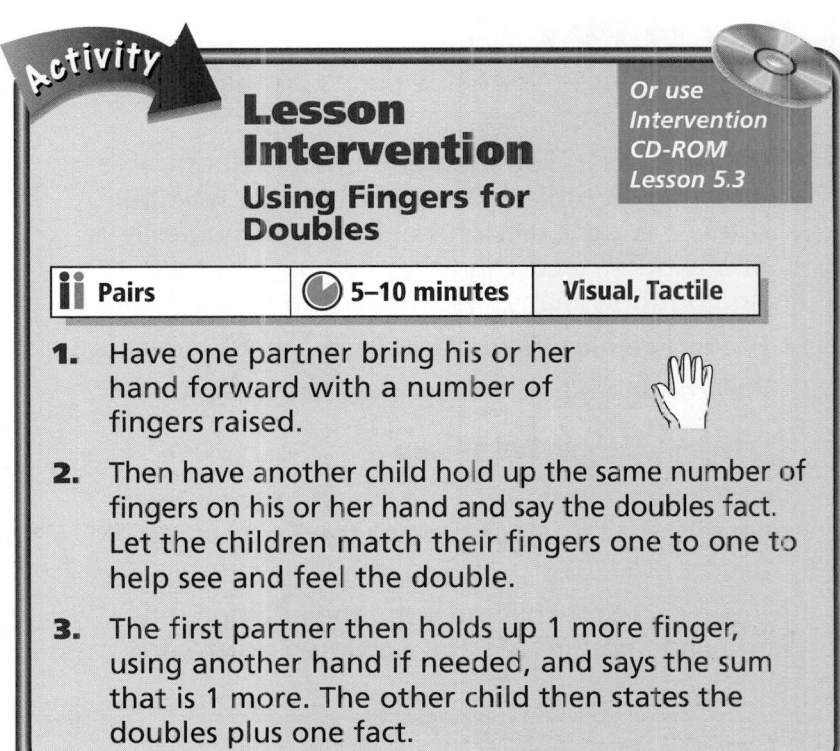

Lesson Intervention

Using Fingers for Doubles

Or use Intervention CD-ROM Lesson 5.3

| 👥 Pairs | 🕐 5–10 minutes | Visual, Tactile |

1. Have one partner bring his or her hand forward with a number of fingers raised.

2. Then have another child hold up the same number of fingers on his or her hand and say the doubles fact. Let the children match their fingers one to one to help see and feel the double.

3. The first partner then holds up 1 more finger, using another hand if needed, and says the sum that is 1 more. The other child then states the doubles plus one fact.

---

③ Practice

Independent Practice

Children complete **Exercises 1–22** independently.

Algebra Readiness

After children complete **Exercises 23–26**, call on volunteers to share their answers. Discuss why it is easy to find a missing addend when you know it is a doubles fact. (It is the same number as the addend you know.)

Common Error

Forgetting to Add 1

Watch for children who forget to add 1 more in the doubles plus one fact. Have children model the facts with cube towers.

---

④ Assess and Close

What doubles fact helps you add 5 + 6? ($5 + 5 = 10$)

Why is this a doubles fact? (Because both addends are the same.)

 **Keeping a Journal**

Draw doubles you see in real life. Write the matching doubles fact.

Lesson continues →

Doubles or Not

Purpose: This game provides practice identifying doubles and doubles plus one facts.

Materials: *2 number cubes 0-5, 2 game pieces*

How to Play

- Children place their game pieces on the game board at Start.

- In turn, players roll the two number cubes to create an addition fact. They must decide whether the fact is a doubles plus one fact, a doubles fact, or any other fact. Then they can use the table to find out how many spaces to move on the board.

- Encourage players to check each other's moves.

- Play continues until a player reaches the End.

Other Ways to Play

Children may continue to play during the same session, or this alternate version of the Practice Game could be used.

A After each roll, children write the addition sentence and find the sum. Have children check each other's addition sentences.

Refer back to the unit story *Bug Fun!* Have children replace both numbers in the verse on student book page 119b with the numbers given below. Reread the new verses you created together and have children write the matching addition sentences.
Do you see a pattern? (Possible answers: They are all doubles facts; the sums increase by 1s.)

- 1 (1 + 1)

- 2 (2 + 2)

- 3 (3 + 3)

- 4 (4 + 4)

- 5 (5 + 5)

If time permits, let children create a book of their new verses and title it "Double Bug Fun!"

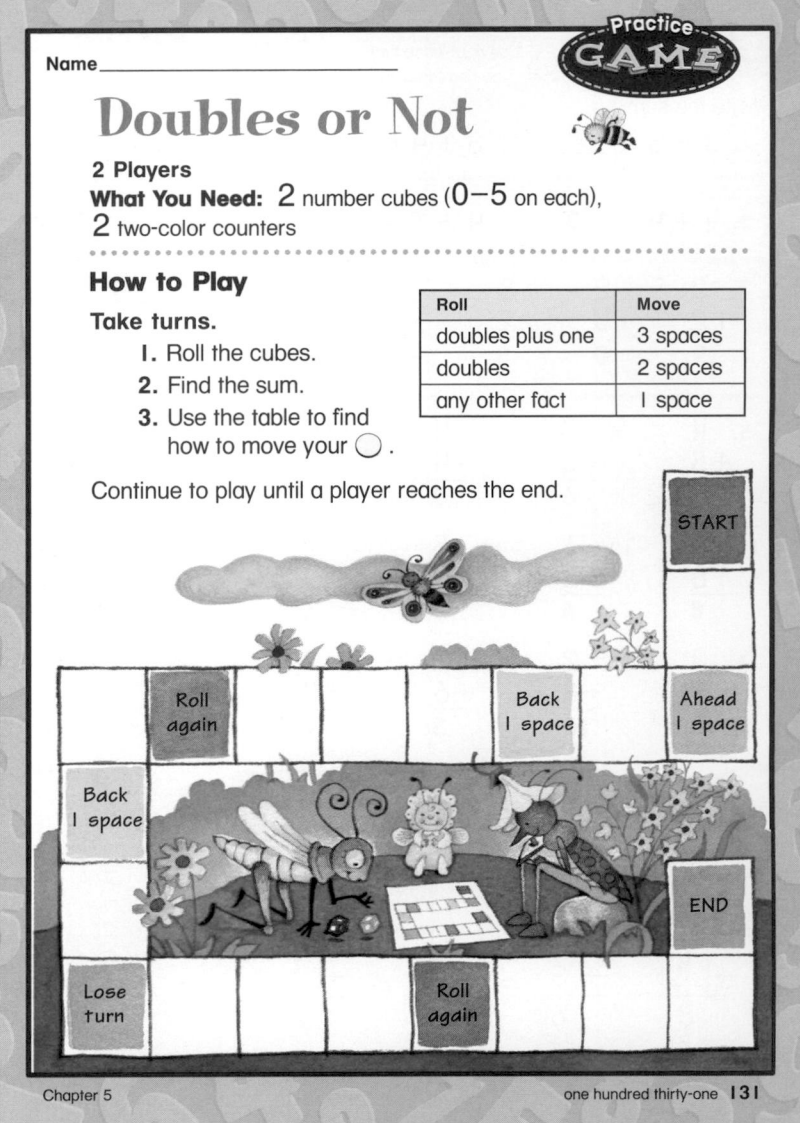

Name_____

Doubles or Not

2 Players
What You Need: 2 number cubes (0–5 on each), 2 two-color counters

How to Play
Take turns.

1. Roll the cubes.
2. Find the sum.
3. Use the table to find how to move your ○.

Roll	Move
doubles plus one	3 spaces
doubles	2 spaces
any other fact	1 space

Continue to play until a player reaches the end.

START

Roll again

Back 1 space

Ahead 1 space

Back 1 space

END

Lose turn

Roll again

Chapter 5   one hundred thirty-one 131

Quick Check

Count on to add.

1. $7 + 3 =$ __10__   2. $9 + 1 =$ __10__   3. $6 + 2 =$ __8__

Find the sum.

4. $\begin{array}{r} 1 \\ +5 \\ \hline 6 \end{array}$ 5. $\begin{array}{r} 2 \\ +7 \\ \hline 9 \end{array}$ 0 1 2 3 4 5 6 7 8 9 10

6. $\begin{array}{r} 4 \\ +4 \\ \hline 8 \end{array}$ 7. $\begin{array}{r} 5 \\ +4 \\ \hline 9 \end{array}$ 8. $\begin{array}{r} 3 \\ +3 \\ \hline 6 \end{array}$ 9. $\begin{array}{r} 4 \\ +3 \\ \hline 7 \end{array}$ 10. $\begin{array}{r} 4 \\ +5 \\ \hline 9 \end{array}$

Doubles Rule

Use the rule.
Complete the table.

Add the double.	
1	2
2	4
3	6
4	8

Add the double plus one.	
1	3
2	5
3	7
4	9

Quick Check

Have children complete the Quick Check exercises independently to assess their understanding of concepts and skills taught in **Lessons 1–3**.

Item	Lesson	Error Analysis	Intervention
1–3	5.1	Children may begin counting from 1 as they count on.	Reteach Resource 5.1 *Ways to Success* 5.1
4–5	5.2	Children may begin counting on from 0 rather than the greater addend	Reteach Resource 5.2 *Ways to Success* 5.2
6–10	5.3	Children may forget to add 1 more in the doubles plus one facts.	Reteach Resource 5.3 *Ways to Success* 5.3

Doubles Rule

Explain to children how to complete the function tables. Some children may need to use counters to find the sums.

Using Addition Strategies

PLANNING THE LESSON

MATHEMATICS OBJECTIVE
Add using different strategies.

Use Lesson Planner CD-ROM for Lesson 5.4.

Daily Routines

Calendar

Find today's date on the calendar. **What will the date be in 1 day? 2 days? Double the days?** Have children count to find the dates.

Sunday	Monday	Tuesday	Wednesday	Thursday	Friday	Saturday
			1	2	3	4
5	6	7	8	9	10	11
12	13	14	15	16	17	18
19	20	21	22	23	24	25
26	27	28	29	30	31	

Vocabulary

Write several addition facts on the board. Review **sum** and **add** by asking children to raise one hand when you point to the symbol that means add and two hands up when you point to a sum.

Vocabulary Cards

Meeting North Carolina's Standards

1.03 Develop fluency with single-digit addition and corresponding differences using strategies such as modeling, composing and decomposing quantities, using doubles, and making tens.

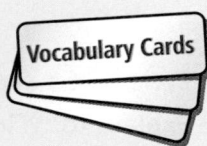

Lesson Transparency 5.4

Problem of the Day
Joan picked 6 flowers. Bob picked 4. Linda picked 3. Keesha picked 5. How many flowers did Linda and Keesha pick? (8 flowers)

Quick Review

$$\begin{array}{cccccc} 4 & 5 & 3 & 3 & 1 \\ +4 & +4 & +3 & +4 & +1 \\ \hline (8) & (9) & (6) & (7) & (2) \end{array}$$

Lesson Quiz
1. $4 + 6 =$ ___ (10)
2. $7 + 2 =$ ___ (9)
3. How did you add $7 + 2$? (Answers will vary. Possible answers: I just knew the fact; I counted on 2 from 7 to get 9.)

LEVELED PRACTICE

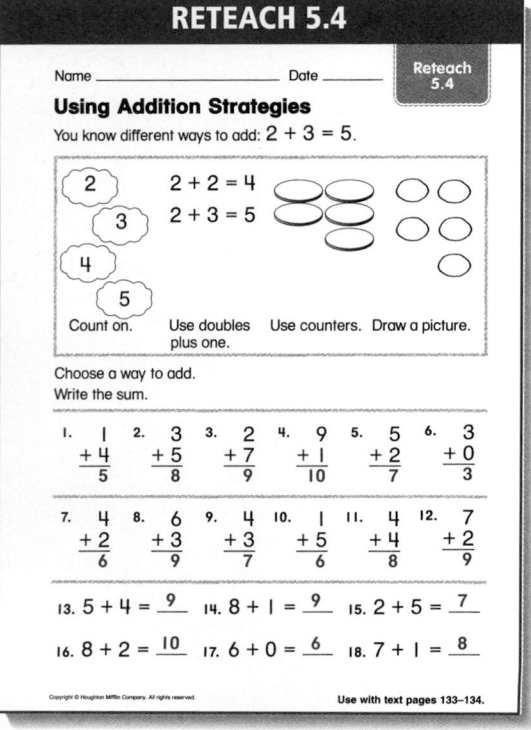

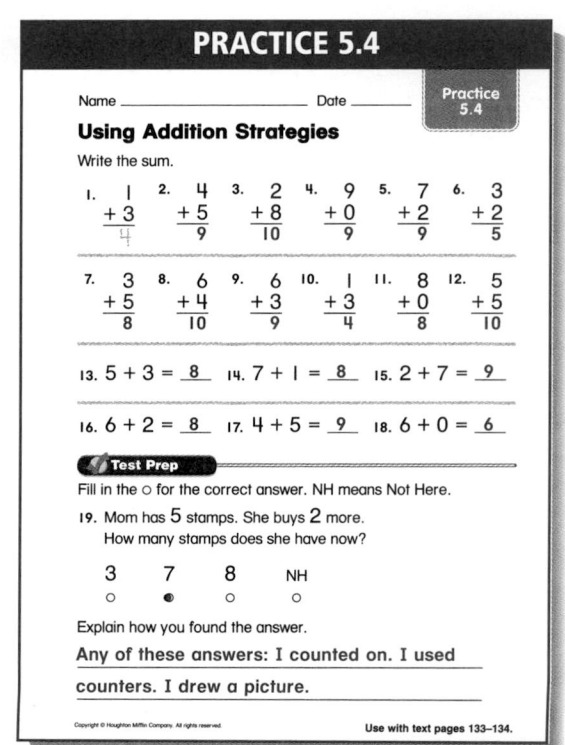

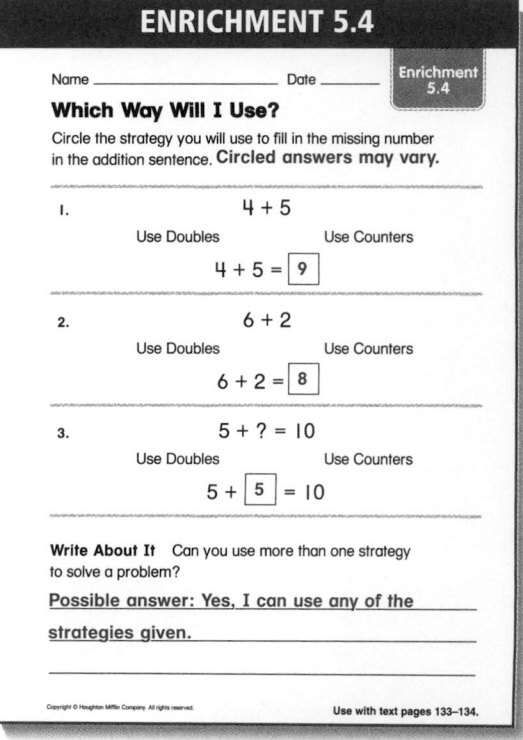

Practice Workbook Page 33

Reaching All Learners

Differentiated Instruction

English Learners

- Children will need to understand the phrase *different ways* in order to choose among different strategies to add. Use Worksheet 5.4 to help children understand this phrase.

Special Needs
TACTILE, AUDITORY

Materials: *teacher-made addition cards (with one addend 1, 2, or 3), number line (LT8)*

- Place cards face down.
- Ask the child to turn over the top card. Guide him or her to place a finger on the greater number on the number line and "finger walk" to count on.
- Repeat.

Gifted and Talented
TACTILE, VISUAL

Materials: *magazines*

- Have pairs of children find different animal pictures and make groups of each animal.
- Then have children write and solve addition problems using the pictures.

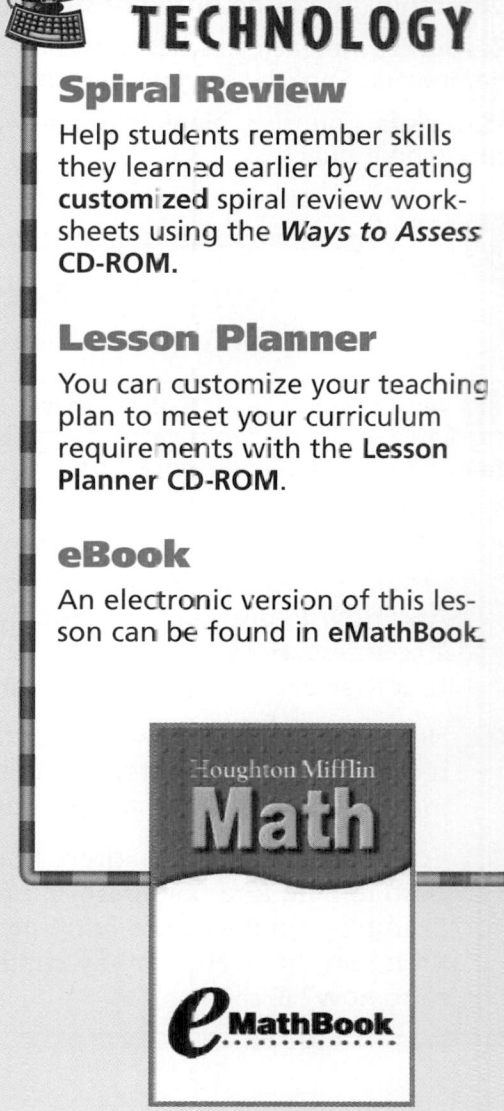

TECHNOLOGY

Spiral Review

Help students remember skills they learned earlier by creating **customized** spiral review worksheets using the *Ways to Assess* CD-ROM.

Lesson Planner

You can customize your teaching plan to meet your curriculum requirements with the **Lesson Planner CD-ROM.**

eBook

An electronic version of this lesson can be found in **eMathBook.**

Houghton Mifflin **Math**

e MathBook

Art Connection

Let pairs create "double designs on graph paper." They label their finished design with the matching doubles fact.

$4 + 4 = 8$

MATH CENTER

Basic Skills Activity

Motivate children to build basic skills. Use this activity to address multiple learning styles using hands-on activities related to the skills of this lesson.

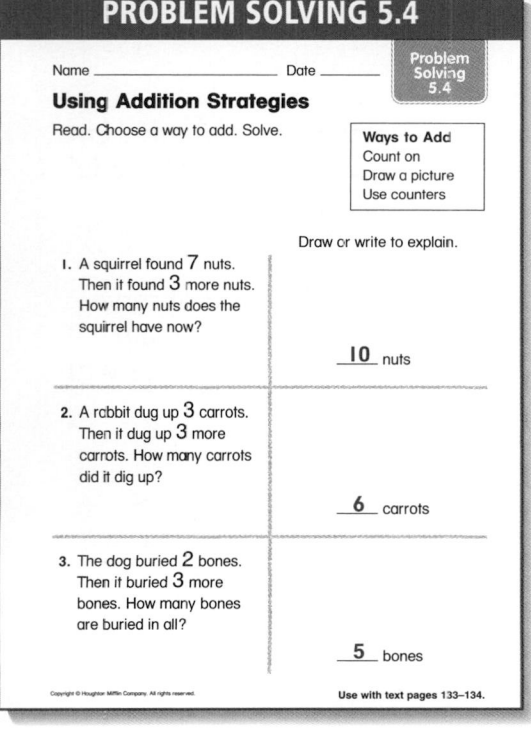

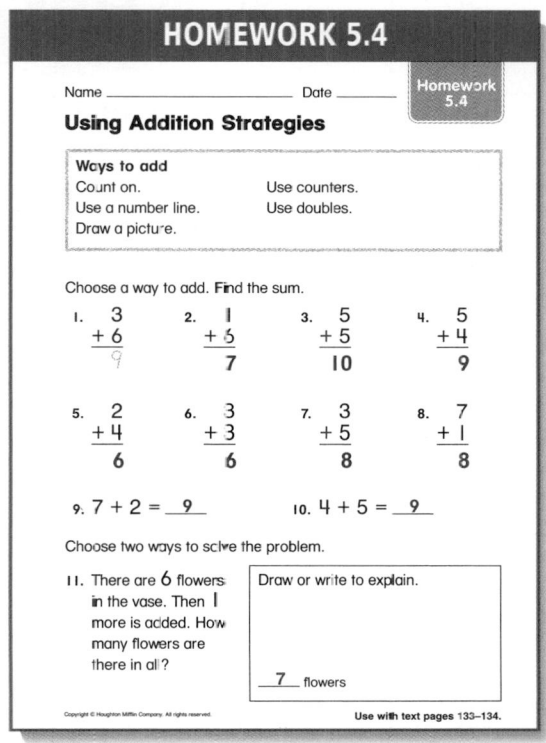

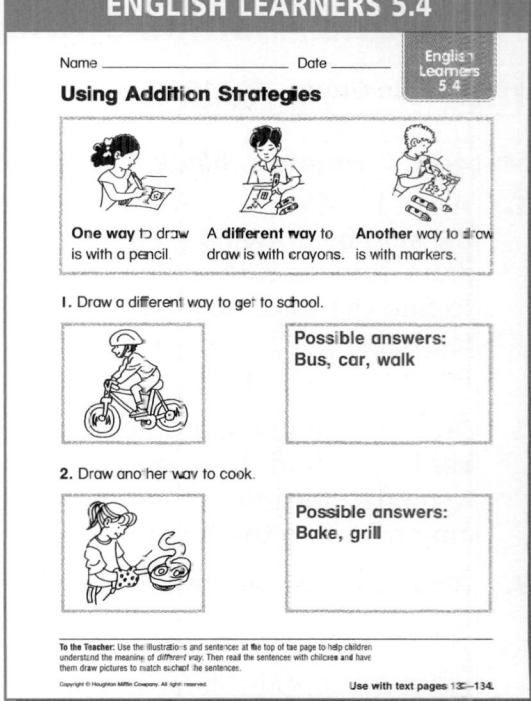

Homework Workbook Page 33

TEACHING LESSON 5.4

LESSON ORGANIZER

Objective Add using different strategies.

Resources Reteach, Practice, Enrichment, Problem Solving, Homework, English Learners, Transparencies, Math Center

Materials Counters, blank transparency, small pieces of paper, hole punch

Warm-Up Activity
Modeling Addition Concepts

iii Small Group	🕐 10–15 minutes	Visual, Tactile

Materials: *two-color counters*

1. Review the concept of addition. Remind children that sometimes when they add they join one group to another. Display 3 counters in one group. Ask: **How many?** (3) Then display another group of 2 counters. **How many?** (2) Now join the groups together. **How many counters are there in all?** (5)

2. Next model part-part-whole. Display one group of 5 red and 2 yellow counters. **How many red?** (5) **How many yellow?** (2) **How many counters in all?** (7)

3. Continue by having children model with counters both joining and part-part-whole addition stories. Example: **4 children are jumping rope. 2 more children join them. How many children are jumping rope now?** (6 children)

1 Introduce
Discuss Addition Strategies

iiii Whole Group	🕐 10–15 minutes	Visual, Auditory

Materials: *counters, blank transparency*

1. Write 3 + 4 = ____ on the overhead. **How can you find the sum by drawing pictures?** Call on a volunteer to draw dots for each addend and then to count the dots to find the sum. **How can you find the sum using counters?** Ask a different volunteer to demonstrate finding the sum by using counters.

2. Draw a 0–10 number line. **How can you use the number line to find the sum?** Call on a different volunteer to model starting at the greater addend (4) and counting on 3 using the line to find the sum.

3. **What doubles fact can help you find the sum?** (3 + 3)

2 Develop

Guided Learning

Teaching Example Read the objective and the different ways to add with the children. Ask volunteers to model each of the different ways to find a sum.

Guided Practice

Have children complete **Exercises 1–16** as you observe. Give children the opportunity to answer the Explain Your Thinking question. Then discuss the responses with the class.

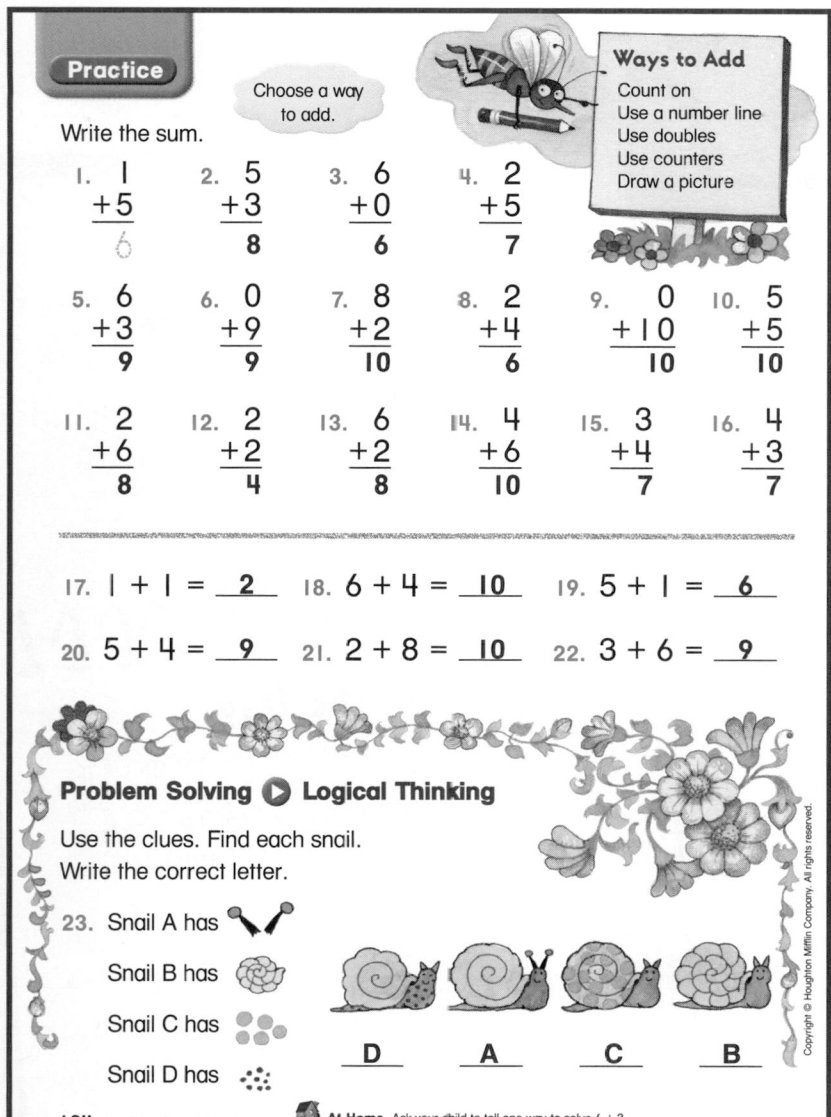

Practice

Choose a way to add.

Ways to Add
Count on
Use a number line
Use doubles
Use counters
Draw a picture

Write the sum.

1.	2.	3.	4.
1 +5 6	5 +3 8	6 +0 6	2 +5 7

5.	6.	7.	8.	9.	10.
6 +3 9	0 +9 9	8 +2 10	2 +4 6	0 +10 10	5 +5 10

11.	12.	13.	14.	15.	16.
2 +6 8	2 +2 4	6 +2 8	4 +6 10	3 +4 7	4 +3 7

17. 1 + 1 = __2__   18. 6 + 4 = __10__   19. 5 + 1 = __6__

20. 5 + 4 = __9__   21. 2 + 8 = __10__   22. 3 + 6 = __9__

Problem Solving ▶ Logical Thinking

Use the clues. Find each snail.
Write the correct letter.

23. Snail A has ✌
Snail B has 🐚
Snail C has ⚬⚬⚬
Snail D has ⋰

__D__   __A__   __C__   __B__

At Home Ask your child to tell one way to solve 6 + 3.

Daily Test Prep

Mark under the number that makes the sentence true.

☐ + 4 = 8

2	3	5	NH
○	○	○	●

Activity

Lesson Intervention
Practicing Facts

Or use Intervention CD-ROM Lesson 5.4

👥 Small Group	🕐 10–15 minutes	Tactile, Visual

Materials: *small pieces of paper, hole punch*

- Assign each child one or more addition facts that need practice. Write, or have the children write, that addition fact along the top edge of a paper.
- Then have children punch holes for each addend.

- Mix the cards and redistribute. Have children practice finding the sums by using the holes to count.

---

3 Practice

Independent Practice

Children complete **Exercises 1–22** independently.

Problem Solving

After children complete **Exercise 23,** call on volunteers to share their strategies and solutions.

Common Error

Miscounting When Finding a Sum
If errors occur during counting, have children draw pictures and count by pointing to each picture. Children may also benefit from continuing practice with models.

4 Assess and Close

What are the different ways you can find a sum? (count on, use doubles, use counters, use a number line, draw a picture)

✏️ Keeping a Journal

List addition facts that you know.

Problem Solving: Write a Number Sentence

PLANNING THE LESSON

MATHEMATICS OBJECTIVE

Use number sentences to solve problems.

Use Lesson Planner CD-ROM for Lesson 5.5.

Meeting North Carolina's Standards

1.04 Create, model, and solve problems that use addition, subtraction, and fair shares (between two or three).

Also 1.03

Daily Routines

Calendar

Count the number of school days in a week. Count the number of weekend days. Have a volunteer write an addition sentence that describes the days in a week. (5 + 2 = 7)

Vocabulary

Write several addition facts on the board. Review **plus sign** and **equal sign.** Ask a volunteer to name the sign that means *add* and circle it in one color. Ask another volunteer to name the sign that means *is the same as* and circle it in a different color.

Vocabulary Cards

Lesson Transparency 5.5

Problem of the Day

Rachel counts the dots on the wings of a butterfly. She counts 4 and 1 more on one wing and 5 on the other wing. How many dots does she count in all? (10 dots)

Quick Review

$$\begin{array}{r} 7 \\ + 1 \\ \hline (8) \end{array} \qquad \begin{array}{r} 4 \\ + 4 \\ \hline (8) \end{array} \qquad \begin{array}{r} 2 \\ + 6 \\ \hline (8) \end{array} \qquad \begin{array}{r} 3 \\ + 5 \\ \hline (8) \end{array} \qquad \begin{array}{r} 0 \\ + 8 \\ \hline (8) \end{array}$$

Lesson Quiz

Rebecca looks under a rock for beetles. She sees 4 black beetles and 2 brown beetles. How many beetles does she see? (6 beetles)

LEVELED PRACTICE

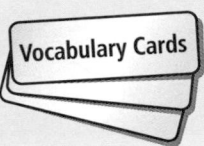

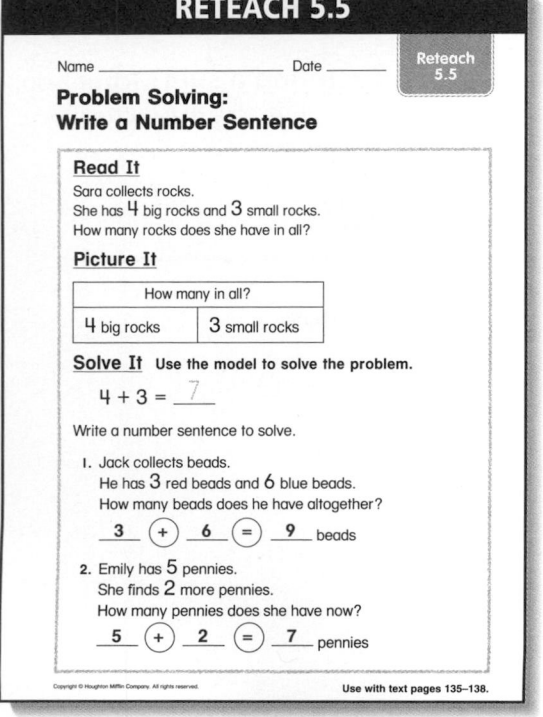

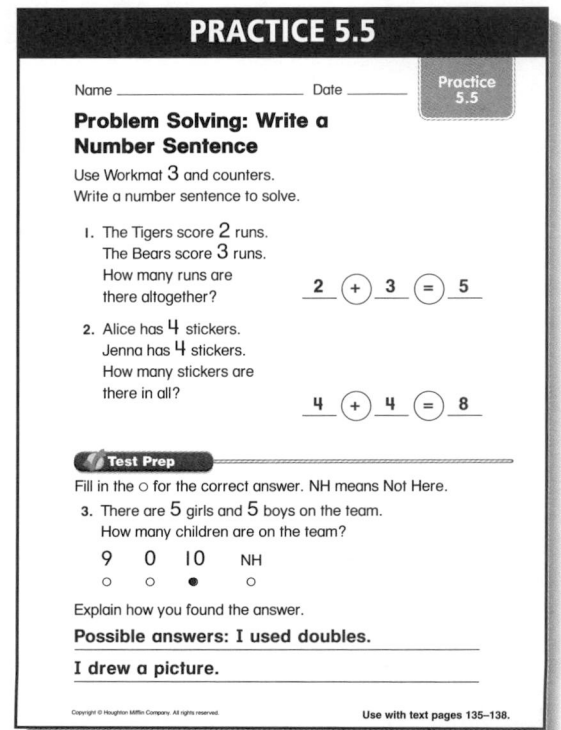

ENRICHMENT 5.5

Name _____ Date _____ Enrichment 5.5

A Sentence to Solve

1. **Read the problem.**

Dana read 5 books last night.
She read 4 books today.
How many books did Dana read?
Find the numbers you need.
Write a number sentence to solve.

__5__ (+) __4__ = __9__ books

2. **Write your own problem.**
Answers will vary. _____

_____

Write a number sentence to solve.

____ (+) ____ (=) ____ **Answers will vary.**

3. **Look back at the problem.**

How can I check my answer?
I can check that my sentence has the
numbers from the problem. Then, I can use
counters to check my addition.

Use with text pages 135–138.

Practice Workbook Page 34

Reaching All Learners

Differentiated Instruction

English Learners

- Children will need to understand the term *group* in order to solve some addition word problems. Use Worksheet 5.5 to develop children's understanding of this term.

Special Needs
VISUAL, TACTILE

Materials: *cup, two-color counters*

- Have the child put up to 10 counters in the cup, shake the cup, and then spill the counters out gently.

- Help the child write the matching number sentence. Relate the addends to each color of counter or parts of the group. Relate the sum to the whole group.

Gifted and Talented
AUDITORY, VISUAL

- Have children draw addition problems about their favorite book characters. For example, Goldilocks was sleeping when the three bears came home.

- Have partners solve the problems by writing the matching number sentence. (1 + 3 = 4)

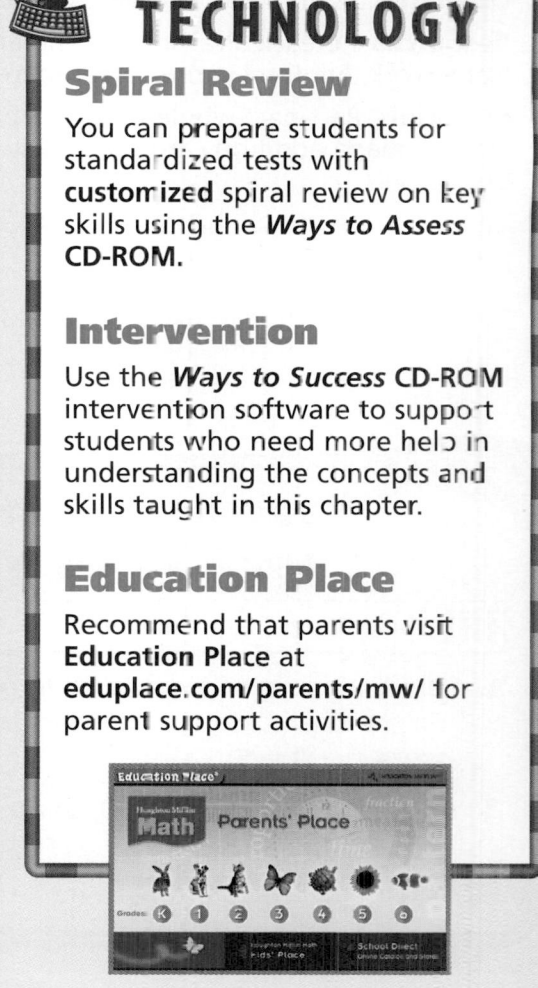

TECHNOLOGY

Spiral Review

You can prepare students for standardized tests with **customized** spiral review on key skills using the *Ways to Assess* CD-ROM.

Intervention

Use the *Ways to Success* CD-ROM intervention software to support students who need more help in understanding the concepts and skills taught in this chapter.

Education Place

Recommend that parents visit **Education Place** at **eduplace.com/parents/mw/** for parent support activities.

Social Studies Connection

People all over the world celebrate the New Year in different ways. In Vietnam the celebration is called *Tet.* Children receive small red envelopes with coins inside. Invite children to create addition stories about a special tradition they know.

MATH CENTER

Number of the Week Activity

Display the Number of the Week to motivate children to use their problem-solving skills. The exercises cover topics across all math strands.

PROBLEM SOLVING 5.5

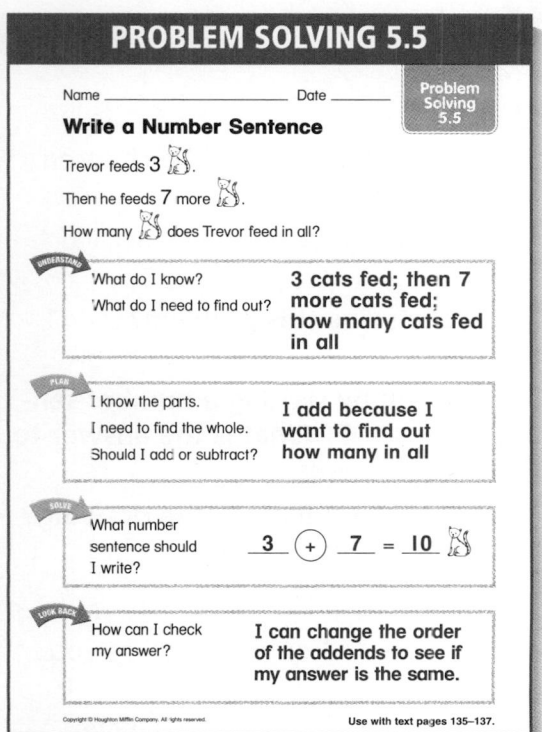

HOMEWORK 5.5

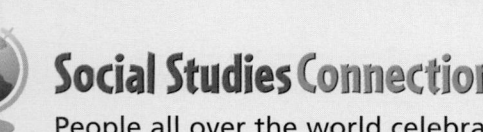

Homework Workbook Page 34

ENGLISH LEARNERS 5.5

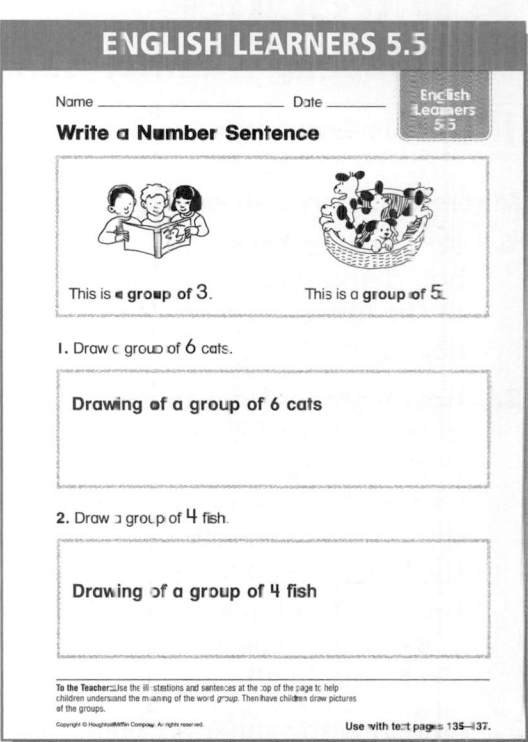

TEACHING LESSON 5.5

LESSON ORGANIZER

Objective Use number sentences to solve problems.

Resources Reteach, Practice, Enrichment, Problem Solving, Homework, English Learners, Transparencies, Math Center

Materials Part-part-whole mat transparency, counters, teacher-made addition cards with facts through 10, cubes in 2 colors

Activity

Warm-Up Activity
Modeling Using Symbols

| Whole Group | 5 minutes | Auditory, Visual |

1. Draw a group of 2 dots and then a group of 4 dots on the board. **How many dots in all?** (6) Then write 2 + 4 = 6.

2. Read the sentence as you point: **2 plus 4 equals 6.**

3. Write another addition sentence on the board and call on volunteers to read it.

Problem Solving

Name_____

Write a Number Sentence

Objective Use parts and wholes and number sentences to solve problems.

Erin looks for ants.
She finds a group of 3 red ants
and a group of 4 black ants.
How many ants does Erin find in all?

UNDERSTAND **What do you know?**
· Erin finds 3 red ants.
· Erin finds 4 black ants.

Whole

| Red | Black |

PLAN **You know the parts.**
You need to find the whole.
Circle how you would solve the problem.

add

subtract

SOLVE **Write a number sentence.**

3 + 4 = 7

Whole

7

| Part | Part |
| 3 | 4 |

Erin finds ___7___ ants in all.

LOOK BACK **How do you know your answer makes sense?**

Chapter 5 Lesson 5   one hundred thirty-five **135**

---

1 Introduce
Modeling Number Sentences to Solve

| Whole Group | 10–15 minutes | Visual, Auditory |

Materials: *part-part-whole mat transparency, counters*

1. *Write a number sentence*. Write the problem on the board and read it with children. **5 girls and 3 boys go to the library to read. How many children go to the library in all?**

2. **How many girls go to the library?** (5) Place 5 counters in the bottom left part of the mat. **How many boys go to the library?** (3) Place 3 counters in the bottom right part of the mat. **How many are in each part?** (5 and 3) Write 5 + 3 beneath the mat. **How many children go to the library in all?** (8) Push all the counters to the top of the mat. **How many are in the whole group?** (8) Write = 8 to complete the number sentence. **8 children go to the library in all.**

3. Repeat with similar problems asking volunteers to model the parts and the wholes on the overhead.

2 Develop

Guided Learning

Teaching Example Introduce the objective to the children. Guide them through the example problem.

Understand **What do you know?** (There are 3 red ants and 4 black ants.)

Plan **Do you add or subtract to solve this problem?** (Add.) Have children circle *add*.

Solve **You can solve this problem by writing a number sentence.** Have children trace 3 + 4 = 7. **What is the answer to the question?** (7 ants) Trace the answer.

Look Back **Does 3 plus 4 match the groups in the drawing?** (yes) **Does 7 show how many ants in all?** (yes)

Guided Practice

Have children complete **Exercises 1–2** on page 136 as you observe. Encourage children to use counters on the part-part-whole workmat to help them solve each problem.

135   **CHAPTER 5**   **Lesson 5**

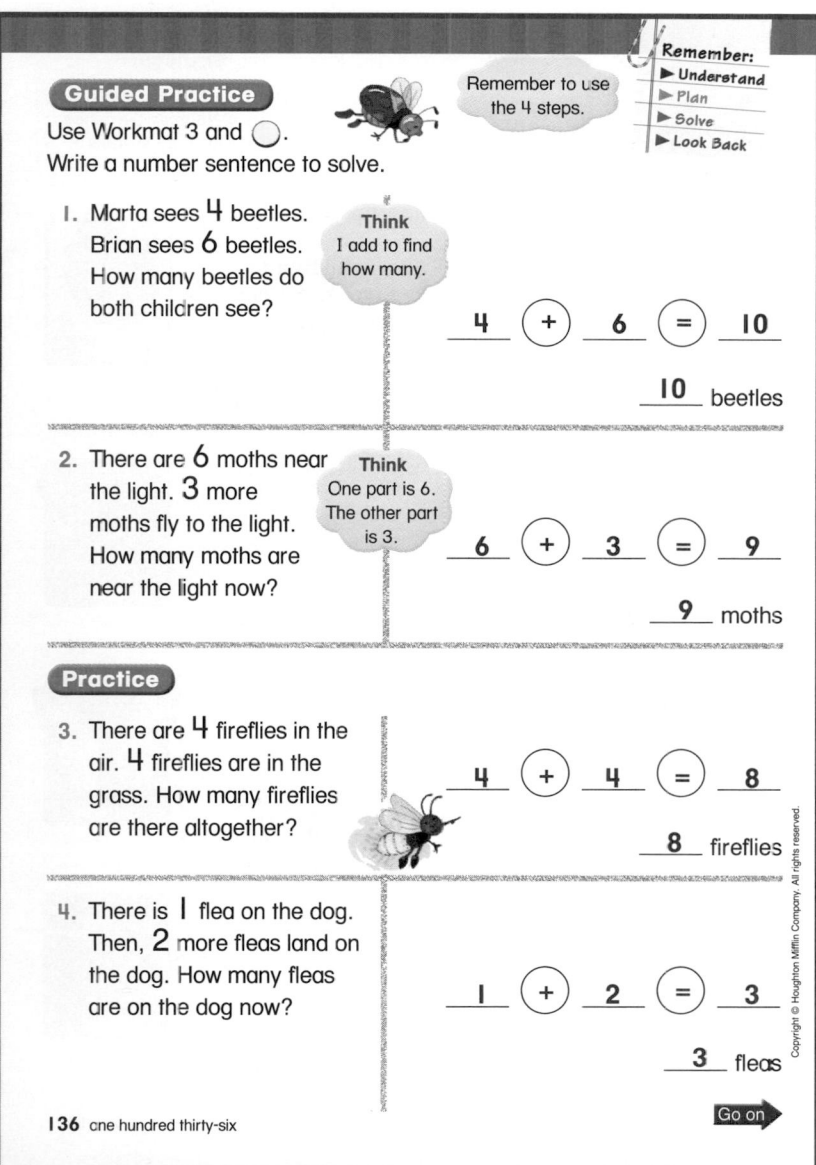

Guided Practice

Use Workmat 3 and ◯.
Write a number sentence to solve.

Remember to use the 4 steps.

Remember:
► Understand
► Plan
► Solve
► Look Back

1. Marta sees 4 beetles. Brian sees 6 beetles. How many beetles do both children see?

Think
I add to find how many.

__4__ (+) __6__ (=) __10__

__10__ beetles

2. There are 6 moths near the light. 3 more moths fly to the light. How many moths are near the light now?

Think
One part is 6. The other part is 3.

__6__ (+) __3__ (=) __9__

__9__ moths

Practice

3. There are 4 fireflies in the air. 4 fireflies are in the grass. How many fireflies are there altogether?

__4__ (+) __4__ (=) __8__

__8__ fireflies

4. There is 1 flea on the dog. Then, 2 more fleas land on the dog. How many fleas are on the dog now?

__1__ (+) __2__ (=) __3__

__3__ fleas

136 one hundred thirty-six

Go on ➡

Play "One, Two, Three Turn"

Materials: *number cards 0–5 (LT 14)*

Have children work in pairs. Place the number cards 0–5 face down in a row in front of both children. At the count of three, both partners turn over one card. The first to add the two numbers and say the correct sum takes both cards. Play continues until all the cards have been taken. The child with the most cards gets a point. Shuffle cards and repeat until one child gets 3 points.

ACHIEVING
Mathematical Proficiency

Learning Basic Facts

According to intervention studies, **an effective way to make single-digit addition accessible to children in first grade is by teaching counting on conceptually.**

Once children are comfortable counting out sets of objects and then counting the whole, they realize that they do not have to count the objects for the first addend. Rather, they can start with the greater addend and count on the objects in the other addend.

In this chapter, **children learn to start with a greater number and count on 1, 2, or 3 pictured objects. They also learn to count on using a number line.** Both of these methods give students a way to conceptualize single-digit addition.

Progressing from a concrete to a conceptual method of addition lays the groundwork for students' mastery of basic facts.

---

③ Practice

Independent Practice

Children complete **Exercises 3 and 4** on page 136 independently.

Daily Test Prep

5.5

Which number sentence shows how many in all?

$1 + 1 = \square$ $2 + 2 = \square$ $3 + 3 = \square$ NH
○   ○   ●   ○

Activity

Lesson Intervention
Using Cube Trains

Or use Intervention CD-ROM Lesson 5.5

| 👤👤👤 Small Group | 🕐 5–10 minutes | Visual, Tactile |

Materials: *teacher-made addition cards with facts through 10, cubes (2 colors)*

1. Place the cards face down in a pile. Give each child cubes of two different colors.

2. Have one child turn over the top card and read the addition. The other child makes a 2-color cube train to show the addends and finds the sum.

3. Children switch roles and repeat.

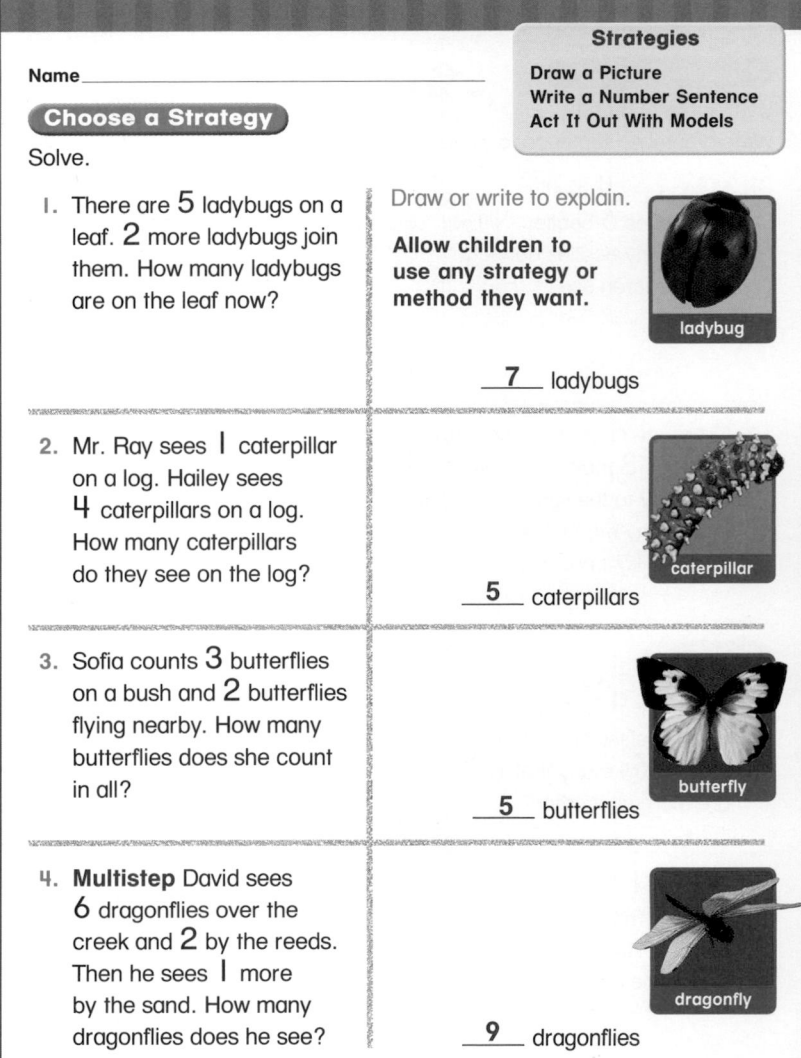

Name_____

Strategies
Draw a Picture
Write a Number Sentence
Act It Out With Models

Choose a Strategy
Solve.

1. There are 5 ladybugs on a leaf. 2 more ladybugs join them. How many ladybugs are on the leaf now?

   Draw or write to explain.
   Allow children to use any strategy or method they want.

   ladybug

   __7__ ladybugs

2. Mr. Ray sees 1 caterpillar on a log. Hailey sees 4 caterpillars on a log. How many caterpillars do they see on the log?

   caterpillar

   __5__ caterpillars

3. Sofia counts 3 butterflies on a bush and 2 butterflies flying nearby. How many butterflies does she count in all?

   butterfly

   __5__ butterflies

4. **Multistep** David sees 6 dragonflies over the creek and 2 by the reeds. Then he sees 1 more by the sand. How many dragonflies does he see?

   dragonfly

   __9__ dragonflies

🏠 **At Home** Use groups of 10 or fewer objects around you. Create addition problems that your child can solve.

one hundred thirty-seven **137**

③ Practice

Mixed Strategy Practice

Read the problem-solving strategies with children. Make sure children can read and comprehend the problems in **Exercises 1–4.** If necessary, pair more proficient readers with less proficient readers. Encourage them to discuss the problems before solving.

Common Error

Showing the Wrong Numbers

Children may show the wrong number of counters for each part. Have children count each counter as they point to it to check that the number matches the number in the problem.

④ Assess and Close

Have children tell an addition story that matches the number sentence 2 + 4 = 6. **How many are in each part?** (2, 4) **How many are in the whole?** (6)

Keeping a Journal

Draw a picture story that matches the number sentence 7 + 2 = 9.

Listen to your teacher read the problem.
Solve.

1. The class sees 6 bees on the hive. They see 2 bees on a flower. How many bees do they see altogether?

Show your work using pictures, numbers, or words.

___8___ bees

2. There are 2 crickets in the grass. 5 crickets are on the path. How many crickets are there?

___7___ crickets

Listen to your teacher read the problem.
Choose the correct answer.

3.   1   5   6   10
     ○   ○   ●   ○

4.   5   8   9   10
     ○   ○   ○   ●

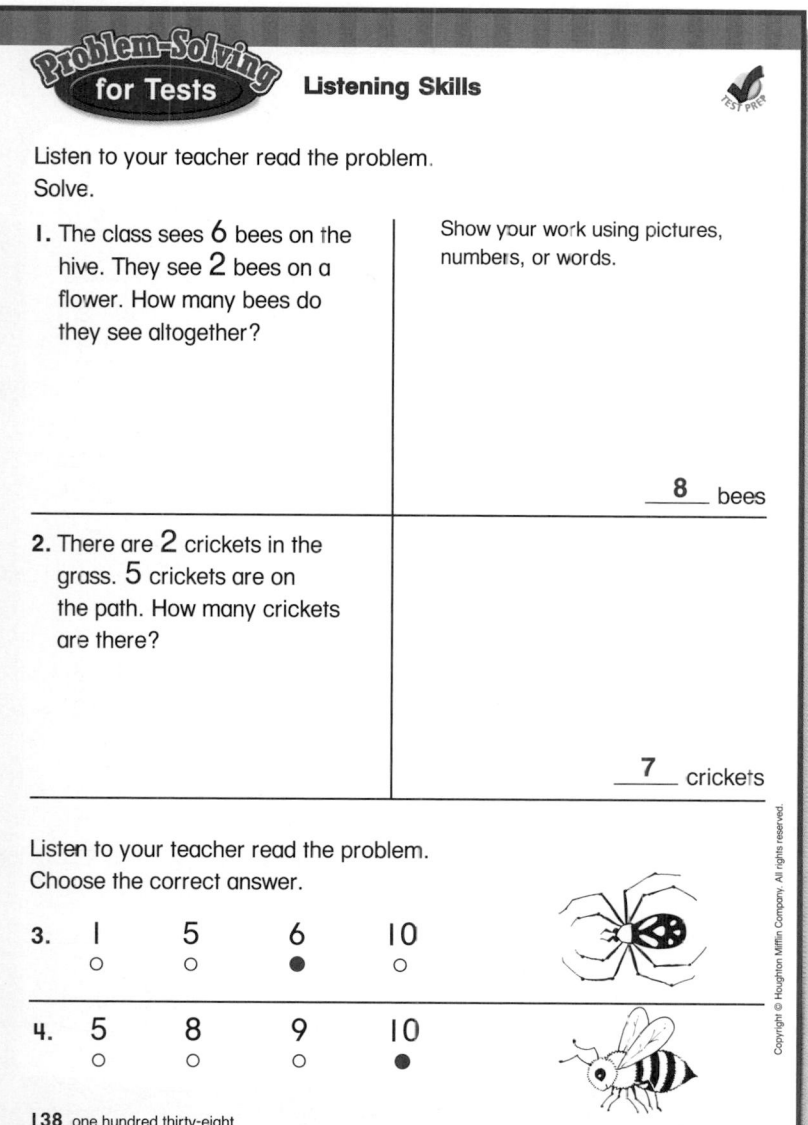

138 one hundred thirty-eight

This page provides practice with the oral problem-solving format used in some standardized test items.

You may want to read each item only once to mimic the style of oral tests.

Use with Items 1 and 2

Listening Strategy: Read the problem silently as the teacher reads it aloud.

- *If a problem is on the page, look at the problem while I'm reading it aloud.*
- *Listen to the whole problem. Do not start writing until I finish reading.*

Use with Item 3

Listening Strategy: Listen for important details.

- *Write down important numbers.*

   There are 5 spiders spinning webs. 1 spider joins them. How many spiders are spinning webs now?

- *Use the numbers to find the answer. Mark your answer.*

Use with Item 4

Listening Strategy: Listen for important details.

- *Listen to the question so you will know what to do with the numbers.*

   Jeff sees 5 bees in the field. Gina sees the same number of bees by the tree. How many bees do they see in all?

- *Use the numbers to find the answer. Mark your answer.*

Lesson continues

Quick Check

Have children complete the Quick Check exercises independently to assess their understanding of concepts and skills taught in **Lessons 4–5**.

Item	Lesson	Error Analysis	Intervention
1-19	5.4	Children may miscount when counting on.	Reteach Resource 5.4 *Ways to Success* 5.4
20	5.5	Children may show or use the wrong numbers.	Reteach Resource 5.5 *Ways to Success* 5.5

Name_____   **Quick Check**

Write the sum.

1. $8 + 2 =$ __10__   2. $1 + 4 =$ __5__   3. $6 + 3 =$ __9__

4. $\begin{array}{r} 1 \\ +9 \\ \hline 10 \end{array}$ 5. $\begin{array}{r} 5 \\ +2 \\ \hline 7 \end{array}$ 6. $\begin{array}{r} 7 \\ +2 \\ \hline 9 \end{array}$ 7. $\begin{array}{r} 3 \\ +5 \\ \hline 8 \end{array}$ 8. $\begin{array}{r} 2 \\ +4 \\ \hline 6 \end{array}$

9. $0 + 6 =$ __6__   10. $4 + 5 =$ __9__   11. $3 + 6 =$ __9__

12. $3 + 4 =$ __7__   13. $4 + 4 =$ __8__   14. $3 + 0 =$ __3__

15. $\begin{array}{r} 5 \\ +5 \\ \hline 10 \end{array}$ 16. $\begin{array}{r} 9 \\ +0 \\ \hline 9 \end{array}$ 17. $\begin{array}{r} 5 \\ +3 \\ \hline 8 \end{array}$ 18. $\begin{array}{r} 4 \\ +6 \\ \hline 10 \end{array}$ 19. $\begin{array}{r} 7 \\ +3 \\ \hline 10 \end{array}$

Write a number sentence to solve.

20. Jessie finds 6 small rocks and 1 large rock. How many rocks does he find in all?

__6__ (+) __1__ (=) __7__

__7__ rocks

Key Topic Review

Use the picture. Complete the tally chart.

1.

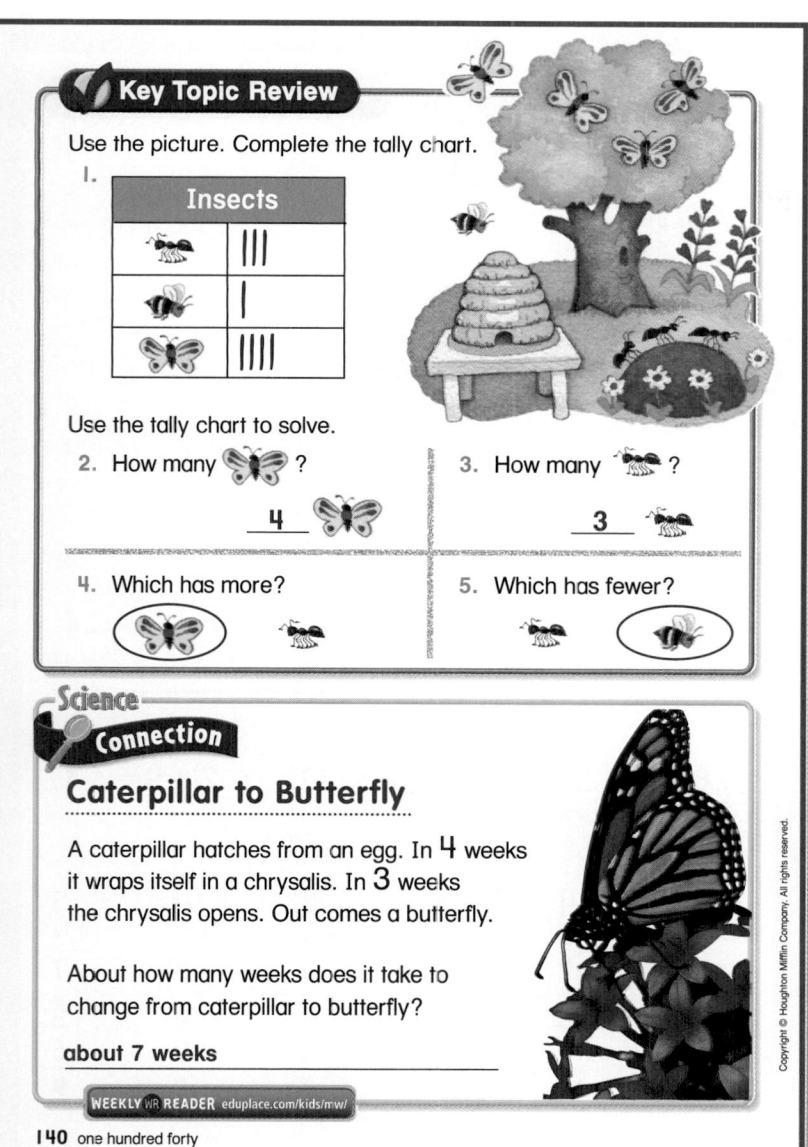

Insects	
🐜	|||
🐝		
🦋	||||

Use the tally chart to solve.

2. How many 🦋 ?

___4___ 🦋

3. How many 🐜 ?

___3___ 🐜

4. Which has more?

(🦋)   🐜

5. Which has fewer?

🐜   (🐝)

Science Connection

Caterpillar to Butterfly

A caterpillar hatches from an egg. In 4 weeks it wraps itself in a chrysalis. In 3 weeks the chrysalis opens. Out comes a butterfly.

About how many weeks does it take to change from caterpillar to butterfly?

about 7 weeks

Key Topic Review

This assessment provides a review of skills and concepts taught in Chapter 4.

Check to be sure that children:
• Enter tally marks in correct row
• Count tally marks correctly
• Understand difference between more and fewer

Science Connection

Caterpillar to Butterfly

Discuss the answer the children found. **What number sentence would be written for this problem?** (4 + 3 = 7) Talk about caterpillars. **What do caterpillars eat?** (leaves) **Has anyone seen a cocoon? Where?** (usually attached to twigs and branches) **What happens inside the cocoon?** (caterpillar is changing into a butterfly)

Monitoring Student Progress

Chapter Review/Test

Purpose: This test provides and informal assessment of the Chapter 5 objectives.

Chapter Test Items 1–25

To assign a numerical grade for this Chapter Test, use 4 points for each test item.

Check Understanding

Use children's work on word problems to informally assess progress on chapter content.

Customizing Your Instruction

For children who have not yet mastered these objectives, you can use the reteaching resources listed in the chart below.

 ## Assessment Options

A summary test for this chapter is also provided in the Unit Resource Folder.

Name_____

Chapter Review/Test

Vocabulary *e* Glossary

1. Circle the **addends** in this fact.

$$⑤ + ④ = 9$$

2. How do you use a **number line**?
   Circle.

   (to count on)   to add doubles

3. Write a **double** fact. **Sample answer is given.**

   $$2 + 2 = 4$$

Concepts and Skills

Count on to add.

4. $9 + 1 = \underline{10}$ 5. $5 + 2 = \underline{7}$ 6. $6 + 2 = \underline{8}$

Find the sum.

0 1 2 3 4 5 6 7 8 9 10

7. $8 + 1 = \underline{9}$ 8. $1 + 9 = \underline{10}$ 9. $2 + 4 = \underline{6}$

Write the sum.

10. $\begin{array}{r} 4 \\ +4 \\ \hline 8 \end{array}$ 11. $\begin{array}{r} 4 \\ +5 \\ \hline 9 \end{array}$ 12. $\begin{array}{r} 5 \\ +4 \\ \hline 9 \end{array}$ 13. $\begin{array}{r} 3 \\ +3 \\ \hline 6 \end{array}$ 14. $\begin{array}{r} 4 \\ +3 \\ \hline 7 \end{array}$ 15. $\begin{array}{r} 3 \\ +4 \\ \hline 7 \end{array}$

16. $\begin{array}{r} 0 \\ +9 \\ \hline 9 \end{array}$ 17. $\begin{array}{r} 6 \\ +4 \\ \hline 10 \end{array}$ 18. $\begin{array}{r} 7 \\ +3 \\ \hline 10 \end{array}$ 19. $\begin{array}{r} 5 \\ +4 \\ \hline 9 \end{array}$ 20. $\begin{array}{r} 8 \\ +2 \\ \hline 10 \end{array}$ 21. $\begin{array}{r} 3 \\ +6 \\ \hline 9 \end{array}$

Chapter 5   one hundred forty-one **141**

Reteaching Support

Chapter Test Items	Summary Test Items	Chapter Objectives Tested	TE Pages	Use These Reteaching Resources
1–3	1–2	**5A** Develop and use math vocabulary relating to addition strategies.	125A–130	Reteach Resources and *Ways to Success* CD: 5.1–5.3 Skillsheet 31
4–21	3–8	**5B** Find sums through 10 using a number line, counting on, doubles, and doubles plus one.	125A–130, 133A–134	Reteach Resources and *Ways to Success* CD: 5.1–5.4 Skillsheets 32–34
22–25	9–10	**5C** Use parts and wholes and number sentences to solve problems.	135A–138	Reteach Resources and *Ways to Success* CD: 5.5 Skillsheet 35

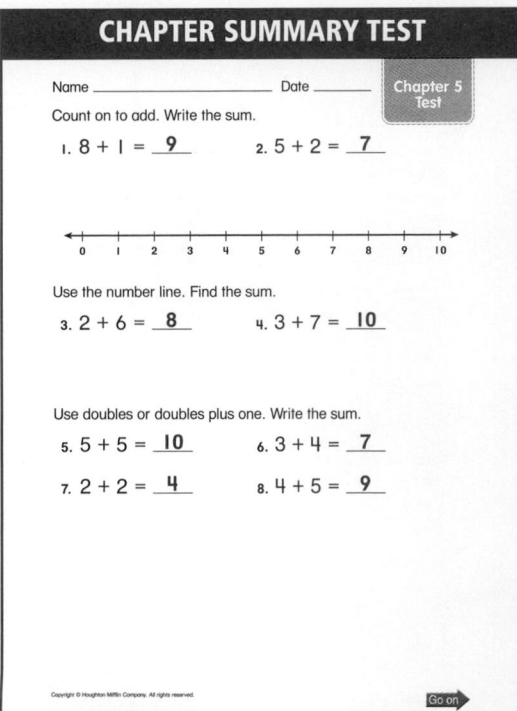

CHAPTER SUMMARY TEST

Name_____ Date_____ Chapter 5 Test

Count on to add. Write the sum.

1. $8 + 1 = \underline{9}$ 2. $5 + 2 = \underline{7}$

0 1 2 3 4 5 6 7 8 9 10

Use the number line. Find the sum.

3. $2 + 6 = \underline{8}$ 4. $3 + 7 = \underline{10}$

Use doubles or doubles plus one. Write the sum.

5. $5 + 5 = \underline{10}$ 6. $3 + 4 = \underline{7}$

7. $2 + 2 = \underline{4}$ 8. $4 + 5 = \underline{9}$

Go on

Problem Solving

Write a number sentence to solve.

22. Gia sees 7 bumble bees and 1 honey bee. How many bees does she see in all?

$7 \;(+)\; 1 \;=\; 8$

___8___ bees

23. There are 5 red ants and 4 black ants. How many ants are there altogether?

$5 \;(+)\; 4 \;=\; 9$

___9___ ants

24. Jon finds 1 beetle. Then he finds 5 more. How many beetles does Jon find?

$1 \;(+)\; 5 \;=\; 6$

___6___ beetles

25. There are 3 ladybugs on one leaf. There are 2 ladybugs on another. How many ladybugs are there in all?

$3 \;(+)\; 2 \;=\; 5$

___5___ ladybugs

Adequate Yearly Progress

Use the End of Grade Test Prep Assessment Guide to help familiarize your children with the format of standardized tests.

CHAPTER SUMMARY TEST

Name _____ Date _____

Chapter 5 Test continued

Complete the number sentence to solve.

9. Tanya has 5 bracelets. She buys 3 more. How many bracelets does she have in all?

Whole	
?	
Part	Part
5	3

$5 + 3 = $ ___8___

___8___ bracelets

10. Manny has 4 blue socks and 6 red socks. How many socks does he have altogether?

Whole	
?	
Part	Part
4	6

$4 + 6 = $ ___10___

___10___ socks

STOP

Lesson by Lesson Overview
Subtraction Strategies Through 10

Lesson 1

- Counting back to subtract can be difficult for some children.
- Showing the starting number as a numeral and modeling the number being subtracted provides a pictorial representation of the strategy.
- Counting back is limited to 1, 2, or 3 because to count back greater numbers is not an efficient strategy.

Lesson 2

- Using a number line to count back is a model that can easily be related to counting on to add.
- Showing the counting back jumps on the page helps to reinforce the need to count the spaces back to find the difference.
- The problem solving set presents problems that illustrate the *doing and undoing* nature of addition and subtraction.

Lesson 3

- Subtracting to compare is introduced with models to help children find *how many more* and *how many fewer*.
- Children use one-to-one correspondence to match objects in two sets and count to find the difference.
- The lesson provides an opportunity for children to write a subtraction story problem based on an illustration.

Lesson 4

- This lesson uses part-part-whole to relate addition and subtraction.
- Children show the parts on a workmat and write the addition sentence. Then they write the related subtraction sentence from the same model.

Lesson 5

- Part-part-whole is the model used to find fact families.
- Children write addition and subtraction sentences for the models.
- Algebra readiness features missing addends.

Lesson 6

- Children practice subtraction facts to 10 as they use the strategies taught in the previous lessons.
- They will use whatever strategy works best for them, but should try all strategies.

Lesson 7

- Children use a part-part-whole model to help them choose the operation to solve a story problem.
- The part-part-whole model helps children interpret the problem in terms of what is given and what is to be found.
- Subtraction and addition facts are practiced throughout the lesson.

SKILLS TRACE: SUBTRACTION STRATEGIES THROUGH 10

Grade K	Grade 1	Grade 2
• model subtraction (ch. 14)	• **count back to subtract facts to 10**	• use a number line and count back to subtract facts to 18 (ch. 3)
• complete subtraction sentences (ch. 14)	• **use a number line and count back to subtract**	• subtract to compare (ch. 3)
• subtract 1 from 1 through 10 (ch. 14)	• **subtract to compare**	• use related addition facts to subtract (ch. 3)
• subtract 2 from 2 through 10 (ch. 14)	• **solve related addition and subtraction facts; fact families**	• identify and write addition and subtraction expressions that name the same number
	• **use different strategies to subtract**	• identify and write fact families
		• find the missing number in addition and subtraction sentences

Chapter Planner

Lesson	Objective	Vocabulary	Materials	✓ NCTM Standards
6.1 **Count Back to Subtract** p. 145A	Find differences by counting back (taking away) 1, 2, or 3.	count back	small cup, counters, number cards 5–10 (Learning Tool (LT) 14), blank transparency	Develop and use strategies for whole-number computations, with a focus on addition and subtraction.
6.2 **Use a Number Line to Subtract** p. 147A	Subtract using a number line.	number line	clothesline, clothespins, number cards 0–10 (LT 14), number lines (LT 8)	Use a variety of methods and tools to compute, including objects, mental computation, estimation, paper and pencil, and calculators.
6.3 **How Many More? How Many Fewer?** p. 149A	Show the meaning of subtraction by comparing.		blank transparency	Use a variety of methods and tools to compute, including objects, mental computation, estimation, paper and pencil, and calculators.
6.4 **(Hands-On)** **Relate Addition and Subtraction** p. 153A	Write and solve number sentences using related addition and subtraction facts (inverse operations).	related facts	cubes, part-part-whole transparency, number cards 1–9 (LT 14), Workmat 3	Understand various meanings of addition and subtraction of whole numbers and the relationship between the two operations.
6.5 **Fact Families** p. 155A	Write fact families using related facts (inverse operations).	fact family	part-part-whole transparency, cubes, Workmat 3	Understand various meanings of addition and subtraction of whole numbers and the relationship between the two operations.
6.6 **Use Subtraction Strategies** p. 157A	Subtract using different strategies.		counters	Use a variety of methods and tools to compute, including objects, mental computation, estimation, paper and pencil, and calculators.
6.7 **Problem Solving: Choose the Operation** p. 159A	Solve problems by choosing the correct operation.		counters, part-part-whole transparency, Workmat 3	Solve problems that arise in mathematics and in other contexts.

Resources For Reaching All Learners

LESSON RESOURCES: Reteach, Practice, Enrichment, Problem Solving, Homework, English Learners, Daily Routines, Transparencies, Math Center.

ADDITIONAL RESOURCES FROM HOUGHTON MIFFLIN: Chapter Challenges, Combination Classroom Planning Guide, Every Day Counts, Math to Learn (Student Handbook)

Every Day Counts
The Daily Depositor and Number Stories Activities in Every Day Counts support the math in this chapter.

Assessing Prior Knowledge

Before beginning the chapter, you can assess student understandings in order to assist you in differentiating instruction.

Complete Chapter Pretest in Unit Resource Folder

Use this test to assess both prerequisite skills (**Are You Ready?** — one page) and chapter content (**Check What You Know** — two pages).

Chapter 6 Prerequisite Skills Pretest

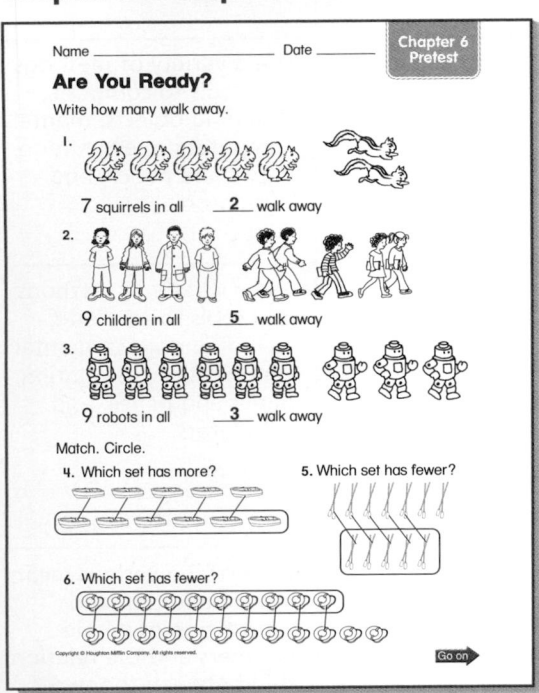

Chapter 6 New Content Pretest

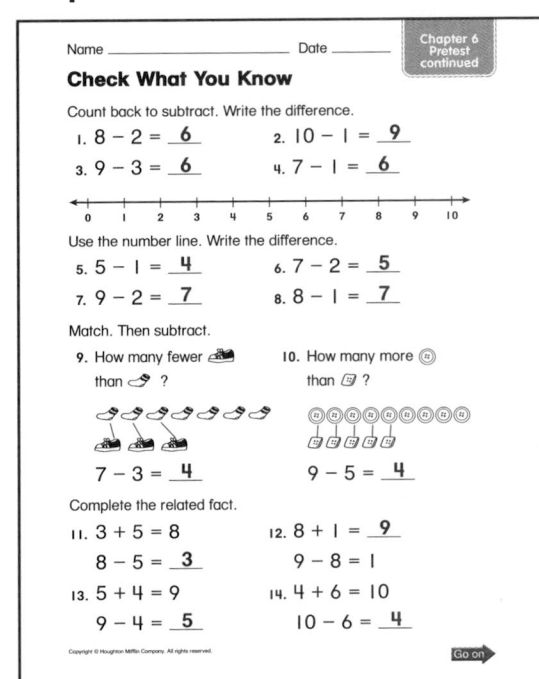

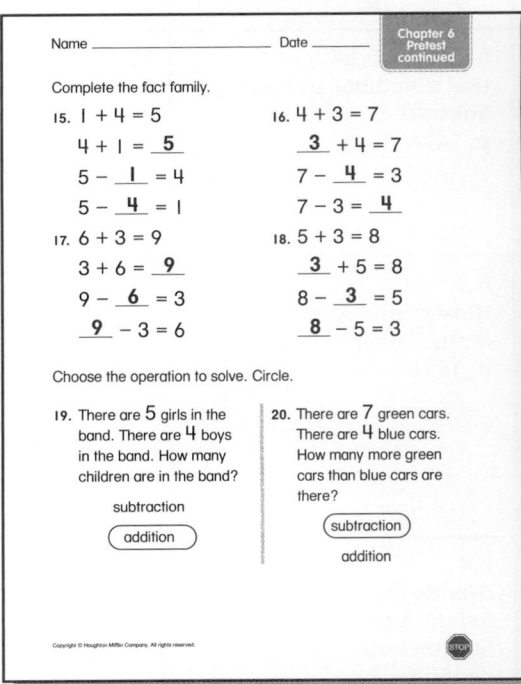

Customizing Instruction

For Students Having Difficulty

Items	Prerequisites	*Ways to Success*
1–3	Understand how to count back from 10 using pictures.	Skillsheet 36
4–6	Understand more and fewer.	CD: 1.1 Skillsheet 37

Ways to Success: Intervention for every concept and skill (CD-ROM or Chapter Intervention Skillsheets).

For Students Having Success

Items	Objectives	Resources
1–2	Use vocabulary relating to subtraction strategies.	Enrichment 6.1, 6.2, 6.4
3–4	6B Find differences from 10 using a number line and counting back.	Enrichment 6.1, 6.2
5–8	6C Write fact families and solve related addition and subtraction facts.	Enrichment 6.3–6.6
9–10	6D Solve problems by choosing the correct operation.	Enrichment 6.7

Other Pretest Options

Informal Pretest

The pretest assesses vocabulary and prerequisite skills needed for success in this chapter.

***Ways to Success* CD-ROM**

The *Ways to Success* chapter pretest has automatic assignment of appropriate review lessons.

Consider using **Chapter Challenges** with any students who have success with all new chapter content.

Chapter Resources

 Activity

Assessing Prior Knowledge

Count Backwards (number concepts)

- Place an egg carton with 10 sections, counters, and number cards 1–10 in the math center. Have each child choose a card and place that many counters in the egg carton, one in each section.
- Children remove one counter at a time and count backwards to 0.

 Activity

Ongoing Skill Activity

How Many More? Fewer? (number concepts, subtraction)

- Place two-color counters in a bag. Direct children to take a handful of counters and drop them on a table.
- Tell children to count the number of red and yellow counters. Then have them tell how many more or fewer counters there are of one color than another.

 Activity

Connecting to the Unit Project

- Have children work in pairs.
- Ask each child to create a subtraction story problem.
- Have partners write a number sentence to show the subtraction.
- Have children describe what strategy they used to solve the problem.
- Then have them write a related addition sentence.

Teacher Support

Professional Resources Handbook

Research, Mathematics Content, and Language Intervention

Research-Based Teaching

By working with numbers and using basic facts, children refine their mathematical thinking. Rathmell (1978) has analyzed a number of important *thinking strategies* used by children to learn addition and subtraction facts. These thinking strategies can be defined as mental strategies employed to relate known facts to unknown facts. Thinking strategies let children discover answers to facts problems without using concrete materials by providing structure for organizing facts so that recall is easier. See *Professional Resources Handbook, Grade 1,* Unit 2.

For more ideas relating to Unit 2, see the Teacher Support Handbook at the back of this Teacher's Edition.

Language Intervention

Chinese teachers emphasize using the "add up" strategy to teach subtraction. They feel that this more clearly shows the close relationship between addition and subtraction. For further explanation, see "Mathematical Language and Fractions", "Mathematical Language and Measurement", "Mathematical Language and Addition Facts" and "Mathematical Language and Subtraction Facts" in the *Professional Resources Handbook Grade 1.*

Technology

Time-Saving Technology Support
Ways to Assess Customized Spiral Review
  Test Generator CD
Lesson Planner CD-ROM
Ways to Success Intervention CD-ROM
MathTracks CD-ROM
Education Place: www.eduplace.com/math/mw
Houghton Mifflin Math eBook CD-ROM
eManipulatives
eGames

Starting Chapter 6
Subtraction Strategies Through 10

INVESTIGATION

When this girl takes her lamb away, how many lambs will be left?

CHAPTER OBJECTIVES

6A Develop and use math vocabulary relating to subtraction strategies.

6B Find differences from 10 using a number line and counting back 1, 2, or 3.

6C Write fact families and write and solve related addition and subtraction facts.

6D Solve problems by choosing the correct operation.

Math Background

Subtraction Strategies Through 10

Subtraction is one of the four basic operations that form the foundation of arithmetic, and it is an essential part of the computation work of the elementary school grades.

There are several strategies children can use to learn their basic subtraction facts. Drawing a picture, counting back by 1, 2, or 3, using a number line, and using related addition facts are all strategies for finding the answers to subtraction facts. The last strategy is the most mathematically powerful strategy since it is based on the inverse relationship between addition and subtraction. Since addition and subtraction are inverse operations, there are "families of facts" for addition and subtraction. Most fact families consist of four related facts. Using variables, the four members of a family can be shown as follows:

$$a + b = c$$
$$b + a = c$$
$$c - a = b$$
$$c - b = a$$

Fact families are useful for finding the answers to subtraction facts by using a related addition fact.

Using The Investigation

- Have children brainstorm things that people *separate*. Write *separate* on the board. Have volunteers offer synonyms for *separate* (such as split, take away, take apart). Make a list of their suggestions.

- Read the question to children. **Look at the picture. When this girl takes her lamb away, how many lambs will be left?** $(4 - 1 = 3)$

- When children have completed the exercise, ask volunteers to tell how they found the difference.

- Have children create problems using other farm animals.

 For more information about projects and investigations, visit Education Place. **eduplace.com/math/mw/**

People Using Math
James Herriot

James Herriot was a man who loved animals. He became a veterinarian, a doctor that takes care of animals. He took care of farm animals and pets. Dogs were his favorite animals, and he had many dogs during his life.

James Herriot, author of *All Creatures Great and Small*

Use the picture to solve the problems.

1. How many dogs are there?   __3__ dogs

2. How many ears are there altogether?   __6__ ears

    If one dog walks away, how many ears are left?

    $$\underline{6} \; \ominus \; \underline{2} \; \oplus \; \underline{4} \qquad \underline{4} \text{ ears}$$

3. How many tails are there altogether?   __3__ tails

    If one dog walks away, how many tails are left?

    $$\underline{3} \; \ominus \; \underline{1} \; \oplus \; \underline{2} \qquad \underline{2} \text{ tails}$$

4. **Talk About It** If you could choose any animal for a pet, what would you choose?

144 one hundred forty-four

CHAPTER CHALLENGES

For Mathematically Promising Students

The *Chapter Challenges* resource book provides blackline masters for activities that explore, extend, and connect the mathematics in every chapter. To support this independent work, see the Teacher Notes for each activity.

Explore: Find the Number, page 31, after Lesson 1
Extend: Mr. Brown's Pet Store, page 33, after Lesson 3
Connect: Related Story Facts, page 35, after Lesson 5

Using This Page

- Read the paragraph about James Herriot to children.
- Tell children that they will look at the picture of the dogs to answer the questions.
- Remind them to look for clue words like *altogether* and *are left* to help them decide which operation to use.
- After children have completed the exercises, take a poll about the different types of pets children have. Use the numbers to make subtraction sentences. Write the sentences on the board and have volunteers solve.

NSF Children's Math Worlds

Using *Children's Math Worlds* helps develop student communication skills because of the daily work with Math Talk, a teaching practice that can be used with all lessons. The emphasis on building a helping community will also enhance student participation in all classroom discussion.

Count Back to Subtract

Lesson 6.1

PLANNING THE LESSON

MATHEMATICS OBJECTIVE
Find differences by counting back (taking away) 1, 2, or 3.

 *Use Lesson Planner CD-ROM for Lesson 6.1.*

Meeting North Carolina's Standards
1.03 Develop fluency with single-digit addition and corresponding differences using strategies such as modeling, composing and decomposing quantities, using doubles, and making tens.

Daily Routines

Calendar
Have children name today's date. Then present a problem that requires children to count back 1, 2, or 3 to find yesterday's date, the date two days ago, etc.

Sunday	Monday	Tuesday	Wednesday	Thursday	Friday	Saturday
			1	2	3	4
5	6	7	8	9	10	11
12	13	14	15	16	17	18
19	20	21	22	23	24	25
26	27	28	29	30	31	

Vocabulary
Use the vocabulary cards for **count on** and **count back** to help children understand the difference between the two concepts. Emphasize that you subtract when you **count back**.

Vocabulary Cards

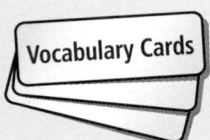

Lesson Transparency 6.1

Problem of the Day
The team had 5 goals. Then Maria scored 1 goal, and Lily scored 1 goal. How many goals did the team score in all? (7 goals)

Quick Review
$\begin{array}{c} 4 \\ +2 \\ \hline (6) \end{array}$ $\begin{array}{c} 5 \\ +1 \\ \hline (6) \end{array}$ $\begin{array}{c} 8 \\ +2 \\ \hline (10) \end{array}$ $\begin{array}{c} 7 \\ +3 \\ \hline (10) \end{array}$ $\begin{array}{c} 6 \\ +1 \\ \hline (7) \end{array}$

Lesson Quiz
1. $\begin{array}{c} 6 \\ -2 \\ \hline (4) \end{array}$ **2.** $\begin{array}{c} 5 \\ -1 \\ \hline (4) \end{array}$ **3.** $\begin{array}{c} 8 \\ -3 \\ \hline (5) \end{array}$ **4.** $\begin{array}{c} 9 \\ -2 \\ \hline (7) \end{array}$ **5.** $\begin{array}{c} 7 \\ -1 \\ \hline (6) \end{array}$

LEVELED PRACTICE

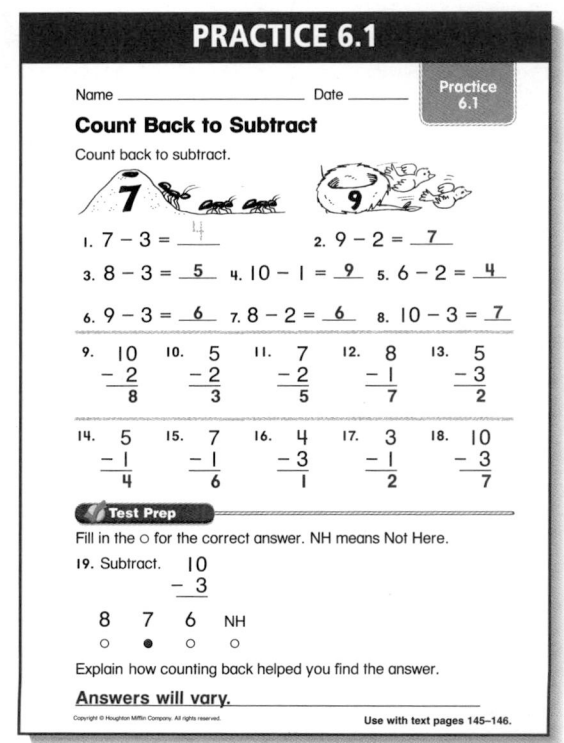

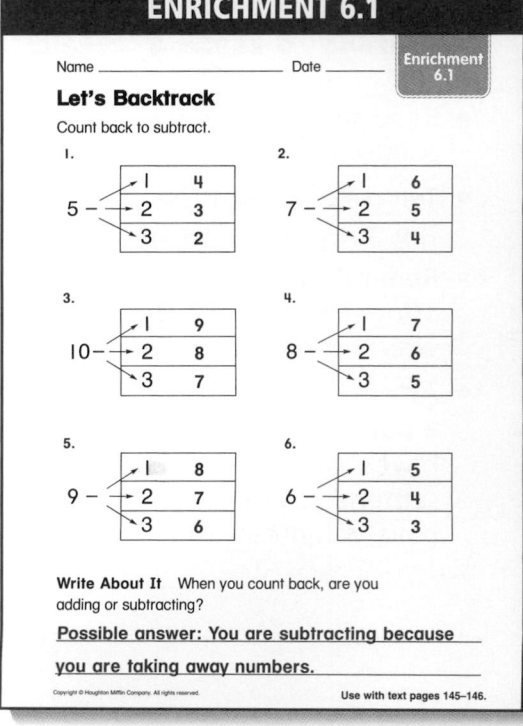

Practice Workbook Page 35

Reaching All Learners

Differentiated Instruction

English Learners

English-language learners may not have the language skills to explain the process behind their thinking. Use Worksheet 6.1 to provide children with sentence frames they can use to complete the Explain Your Thinking activity.

Inclusion

TACTILE, AUDITORY

Materials: *number cards 2–10 (LT 14), counters*

- Display the number card 10. Have the child count as he or she places 10 counters under the card. Write $10 - 3 = $ ___.
- Model how to count back 9, 8, 7. Move one counter from under the number card as you count each number.
- Ask the child to say the difference. Then count the counters remaining.

Gifted and Talented

VISUAL, TACTILE

Materials: *number cards 5–10 (LT 14)*

- Place number cards face down. Have one child at a time choose 1 card.
- Ask the child to count back 3 from that number and write the fact.
- Repeat until all the cards are turned over.
- Have children place the facts in order. Discuss the pattern.

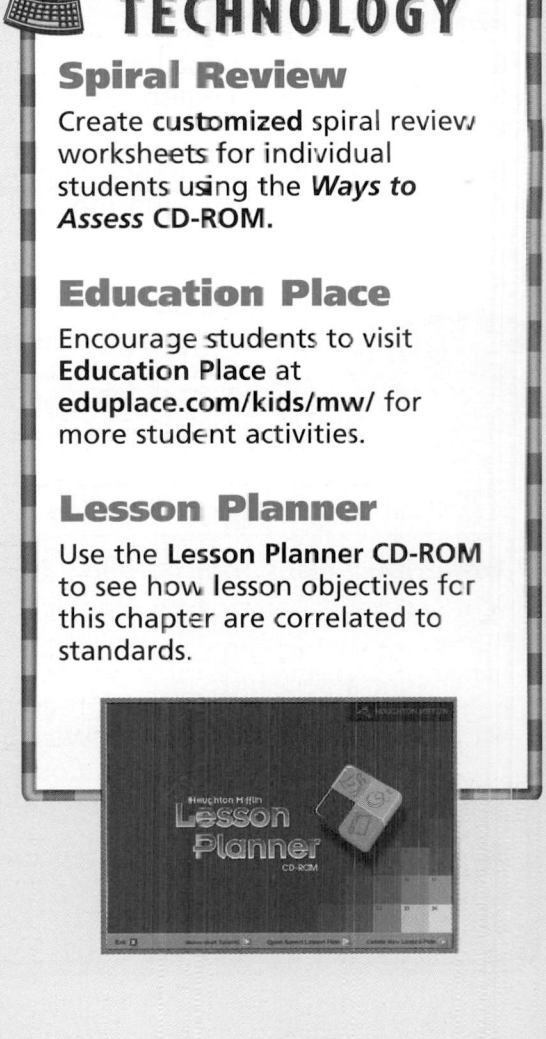

TECHNOLOGY

Spiral Review

Create customized spiral review worksheets for individual students using the *Ways to Assess CD-ROM.*

Education Place

Encourage students to visit **Education Place** at eduplace.com/kids/mw/ for more student activities.

Lesson Planner

Use the **Lesson Planner CD-ROM** to see how lesson objectives for this chapter are correlated to standards.

 **Literature Connection**

Share the book *1 + 1 Take Away Two!* by Michael Berenstain. Involve children in counting the number of animals and predicting the math solutions.

 **MATH CENTER**

Basic Skills Activity

Motivate children to build basic skills. Use this activity to address multiple learning styles using hands-on activities related to the skills of this lesson.

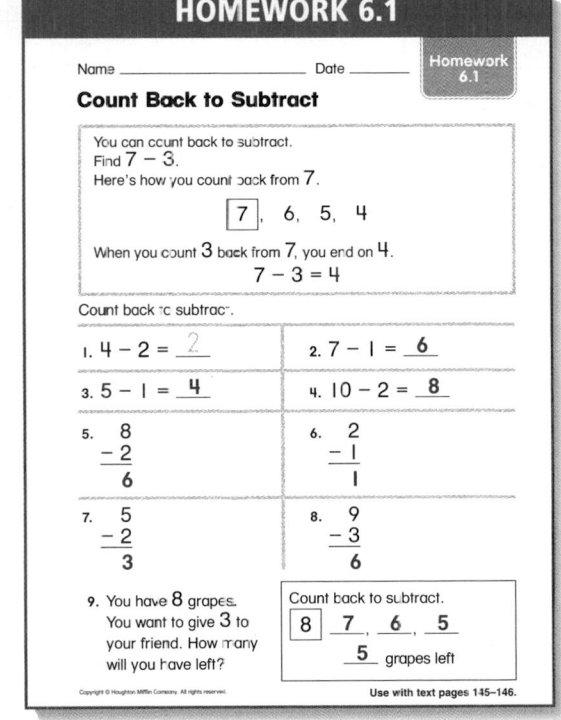

PROBLEM SOLVING 6.1

Name _____ Date _____

Problem Solving 6.1

Count Back to Subtract

Read and solve.   Draw or write to explain.

1. There are 8 bees in a hive. Then 3 bees fly away. How many bees are left?

___5___ bees

2. There are 5 birds sitting in a tree. Then 3 fly away. How many birds are left?

___2___ birds

3. The squirrel finds 8 nuts. It eats 2 of the nuts. How many nuts does the squirrel have left?

___6___ nuts

4. The dog buries 6 bones. It digs up 3 of them. How many bones are still buried?

___3___ bones

Copyright © Houghton Mifflin Company. All rights reserved.

Use with text pages 145–146.

HOMEWORK 6.1

Name _____ Date _____

Homework 6.1

Count Back to Subtract

You can count back to subtract. Find $7 - 3$. Here's how you count back from 7.

| 7 | 6, 5, 4 |

When you count 3 back from 7, you end on 4. $7 - 3 = 4$

Count back to subtract.

1. $4 - 2 = $ __2__   2. $7 - 1 = $ __6__

3. $5 - 1 = $ __4__   4. $10 - 2 = $ __8__

5. 8
   $- 2$
    6

6. 2
   $- 1$
    1

7. 5
   $- 2$
    3

8. 9
   $- 3$

9. You have 8 grapes. You want to give 3 to your friend. How many will you have left?

Count back to subtract.
| 8 | 7, 6, 5 |

___5___ grapes left

Copyright © Houghton Mifflin Company. All rights reserved.

Use with text pages 145–146.

ENGLISH LEARNERS 6.1

Name _____ Date _____

English Learners 6.1

Count Back to Subtract

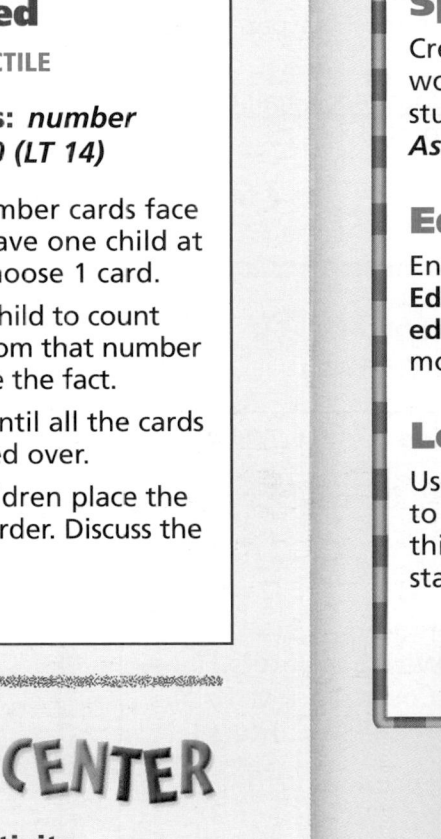

$5 - 1 = $ ___

How do you count back to find $8 - 2$?

I start with __8__.

I count back __2__.

I stop at __6__.

$8 - 2 = $ __6__

To the Teacher: Use the example at the top of the page to demonstrate how to count back to subtract. Then have children complete the sentence frames that provide the language needed to explain how to solve the word problem.

Copyright © Houghton Mifflin Company. All rights reserved.

Use with text pages 145–146.

TEACHING LESSON 6.1

LESSON ORGANIZER

Objective Find differences by counting back (taking away) 1, 2, or 3.

Resources Reteach, Practice, Enrichment, Problem Solving, Homework, English Learners, Transparencies, Math Center

Materials Blank transparency, counters, small cup, number cards 5–10 (Learning Tool (LT) 14)

Activity

Warm-Up Activity
Modeling Subtraction

| iii Small Group | ⏱ 5–10 minutes | Visual, Auditory |

Materials: *blank transparency, 10 counters*

1. Make a row of 7 counters. Point to each one as children count aloud with you.

   7 – 2 = 5

2. Tell children **I am taking away 2 counters.** Take away 1 counter at a time. **Count back with me. Start at 7. Count 6, 5. There are 5 counters left.**

3. Write the subtraction sentence. Point to it as you say **7 – 2 = 5.**

Name _____

Count Back to Subtract

You can **count back** to subtract.

> **Objective**
> Find differences by counting back 1, 2, or 3.
> **Vocabulary**
> count back

Start with 9. Count back 2.

9   _8_ , _7_

9 – 2 = _7_

Start with 9. Count back 3.

9   _8_ , _7_ , _6_

9 – 3 = _6_

Guided Practice
Count back to subtract.

> **Think**
> I start with 10.
> I count back 2.

1.   10   _9_ , _8_
   10 – 2 = _8_

2.   10   _9_ , _8_ , _7_
   10 – 3 = _7_

3.   10   _9_
   10 – 1 = _9_

4.   9   _8_
   9 – 1 = _8_

TEST TIPS **Explain Your Thinking** How do you count back to find 8 – 2? **You start at 8 and count back 7, 6.**

Chapter 6 Lesson 1   one hundred forty-five **145**

---

1 Introduce   Activity
Model Counting Back

| iiii Whole Group | ⏱ 10–15 minutes | Tactile, Visual |

Materials: *small cup, counters*

1. *Subtract 8 – 2.* Place 8 counters in a cup as children count and write 8 on the cup.

2. Tell children you will begin with 8. Take one counter out of the cup. **Take away 1 counter, so now there are 7 counters in the cup.** Take another counter out of the cup. **I take away 1 more, so now I have 6 counters in the cup.** Say: **8 – 2 = 6.** Check by counting how many are in the cup.

3. Repeat. This time have children identify how many are left in the cup at each step as you count back 3. Then say and write the subtraction sentence.

4. Continue counting back 1, 2, and 3 from different starting numbers.

2 Develop

Guided Learning

Teaching Example Introduce the objective and vocabulary to children. Guide them through the 2 examples. Have children count back aloud as they point to the animals walking away.

Guided Practice

Have children complete **Exercises 1–4** as you observe. Discuss children's responses to the Explain Your Thinking question.

Practice

Count back to subtract.

Count back 1, 2, or 3.

1.
8
7, 6, 5
8 − 3 = 5

2.
8
7, 6
8 − 2 = 6

3. 10 − 3 = 7   4. 10 − 2 = 8   5. 10 − 1 = 9

6. 7 − 2 = 5   7. 9 − 1 = 8   8. 2 − 2 = 0

9.	10.	11.	12.	13.	14.
6	10	7	6	5	7
−3	−1	−1	−2	−1	−2
3	9	6	4	4	5

15.	16.	17.	18.	19.	20.
9	10	8	9	8	7
−3	−2	−3	−2	−2	−3
6	8	5	7	6	4

Problem Solving ▶ Reasoning

21. There are 4 sheep.
2 of the sheep are black.
How many sheep are white?

Draw or write to explain.

2 white sheep

At Home Say a number from 4 through 10. Have your child use counting back to subtract 1, 2, or 3.

Daily Test Prep

Subtract.
9
− 3

12   7   6   NH
○   ○   ●   ○

Activity

Or use
Intervention
CD-ROM
Lesson 6.1

Lesson Intervention

Counting Back

👥 Small Group	⏱ 5–10 minutes	Auditory, Visual

Materials: *number cards 5–10 (LT 14)*

1. Lead children in a shuttle launch countdown from 10: **10, 9, 8, 7, 6, 5, 4, 3, 2, 1, Blast Off!**

5
5 − 1 = 4
5 − 2 = 3

7
7 − 1 = 6
7 − 2 = 5

2. Give each child a number card (5–10). Have each child count back 1 from the number. Repeat, and have each child count back 2. Point out that each number is 1 less than the number before.

3. Have children trade cards and count back 3 from the new number.

4. Write subtraction sentences on the board and relate the counting back to the subtraction.

---

③ Practice

Independent Practice

Children complete **Exercises 1–20** independently.

Problem Solving

After children complete **Exercise 21**, call on volunteers to share their solutions. Discuss how children solved the problem and whether or not they counted back.

Common Error

Counting Back Incorrectly

Some children may include the starting number when they count back to subtract. Suggest they point to the starting number as they whisper it, then count back by saying the count back numbers aloud.

---

④ Assess and Close

Explain how you can count back to subtract 5 minus 2. (Count back: 4, 3.)

How many did you count back? (2)

What is the difference? (3)

Keeping a Journal

Draw a picture that shows how you can count back to subtract 10 − 3.

Use a Number Line to Subtract

PLANNING THE LESSON

MATHEMATICS OBJECTIVE
Subtract using a number line.

Use Lesson Planner CD-ROM for Lesson 6.2.

Daily Routines

Calendar

Point to the 10th of the current month. Have children count back 3 days. What is that date? Discuss likenesses and differences in counting back on a calendar and a number line.

Sunday	Monday	Tuesday	Wednesday	Thursday	Friday	Saturday
			1	2	3	4
5	6	7	8	9	10	11
12	13	14	15	16	17	18
19	20	21	22	23	24	25
26	27	28	29	30	31	

Vocabulary

Point to a **number line**. Have volunteers tell what kind of information is on a number line and how it is used. Lead children in counting on and back from various numbers.

Vocabulary Cards

Meeting North Carolina's Standards
1.03 Develop fluency with single-digit addition and corresponding differences using strategies such as modeling, composing and decomposing quantities, using doubles, and making tens.

Problem of the Day
Brian's class is making number cards. Brian needs to make cards for the number just before 8 and the number just after 8. Which two cards does he make? (7, 9)

Quick Review
Count on to find the sum.

7	5	9	6	8
$+1$	$+2$	$+1$	$+3$	$+2$
(8)	(7)	(10)	(9)	(10)

Lesson Quiz
Count back to find the difference.

1. 7	**2.** 9	**3.** 10	**4.** 8	**5.** 6
-2	-1	-3	-2	-2
(5)	(8)	(7)	(6)	(4)

LEVELED PRACTICE

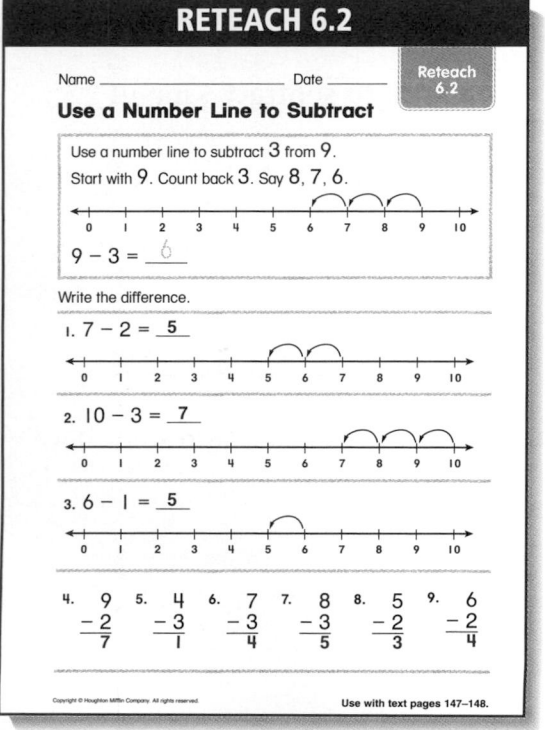

RETEACH 6.2

Name _____ Date _____

Reteach 6.2

Use a Number Line to Subtract

Use a number line to subtract 3 from 9.
Start with 9. Count back 3. Say 8, 7, 6.

$9 - 3 = \underline{6}$

Write the difference.

1. $7 - 2 = \underline{5}$

2. $10 - 3 = \underline{7}$

3. $6 - 1 = \underline{5}$

4. 9	5. 4	6. 7	7. 8	8. 5	9. 6
-2	-3	-3	-3	-2	-2
7	1	4	5	3	4

Use with text pages 147–148.

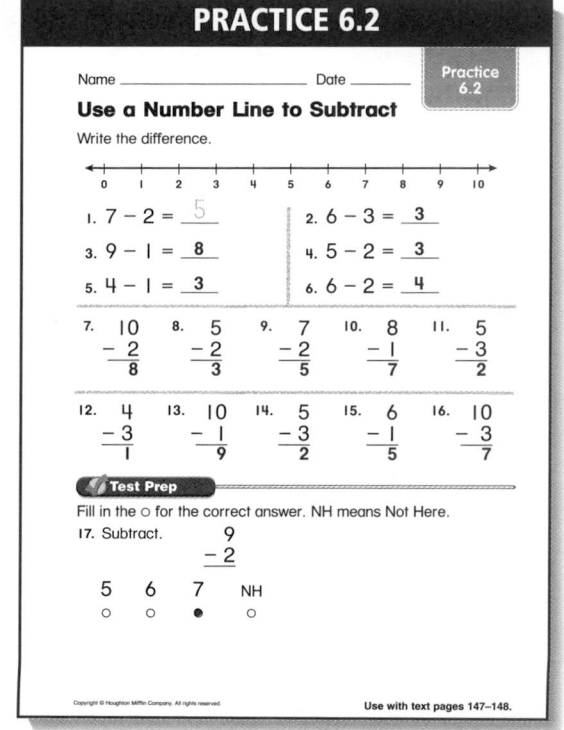

PRACTICE 6.2

Name _____ Date _____

Practice 6.2

Use a Number Line to Subtract

Write the difference.

1. $7 - 2 = \underline{5}$ 2. $6 - 3 = \underline{3}$

3. $9 - 1 = \underline{8}$ 4. $5 - 2 = \underline{3}$

5. $4 - 1 = \underline{3}$ 6. $6 - 2 = \underline{4}$

7. 10	8. 5	9. 7	10. 8	11. 5
-2	-2	-2	-1	-3
8	3	5	7	2

12. 4	13. 10	14. 5	15. 6	16. 10
-3	-1	-3	-1	-3
1	9	2	5	7

Test Prep
Fill in the ○ for the correct answer. NH means Not Here.

17. Subtract.

9
-2

5 ○   6 ○   7 ●   NH ○

Use with text pages 147–148.

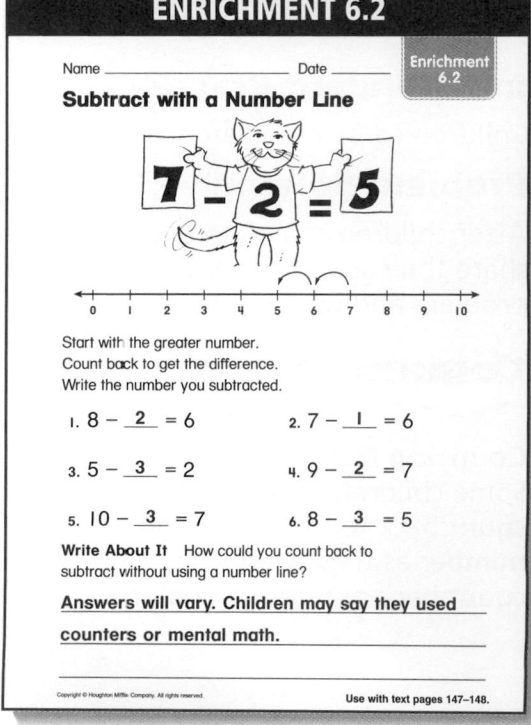

ENRICHMENT 6.2

Name _____ Date _____

Enrichment 6.2

Subtract with a Number Line

$7 - 2 = 5$

Start with the greater number.
Count back to get the difference.
Write the number you subtracted.

1. $8 - \underline{2} = 6$ 2. $7 - \underline{1} = 6$

3. $5 - \underline{3} = 2$ 4. $9 - \underline{2} = 7$

5. $10 - \underline{3} = 7$ 6. $8 - \underline{3} = 5$

Write About It How could you count back to subtract without using a number line?

Answers will vary. Children may say they used counters or mental math.

Use with text pages 147–148.

Practice Workbook Page 36

Reaching All Learners

Differentiated Instruction

English Learners

English-language learners may not have the language skills to explain the process behind their thinking. Use Worksheet 6.2 to provide children with sentence frames they can use to complete the Explain Your Thinking activity.

Special Needs
TACTILE, VISUAL

Materials: *sheets of number lines 0–10 (LT 8), number cube 5–10*

- Have the child roll the cube. Circle that number on the number line.
- Guide the child to count back 3 from that number and draw arrows to show the jumps.

Gifted and Talented
VISUAL, TACTILE

- Provide open number sentences as shown below.
- Each child decides whether the sentence can be completed by counting on or counting back, then writes the appropriate sign.

$$7 \bigcirc 3 = 10$$
$$5 \bigcirc 2 = 3$$
$$6 \bigcirc 1 = 5$$
$$6 \bigcirc 2 = 8$$

TECHNOLOGY

Spiral Review

Using the *Ways to Assess* CD-ROM, you can create **customized** spiral review worksheets covering any lessons you choose.

eBook

An electronic version of this lesson can be found in **eMathBook**.

Education Place

You can visit **Education Place** at **eduplace.com/math/mw/** for teacher support materials.

Music Connection

Introduce children to the scale of music by singing do, re, mi, fa, so, la, ti, do. Write each pitch syllable name on an index card and place in ascending order. Compare this to the order of numbers in a number line.

MATH CENTER

Basic Skills Activity

Motivate children to build basic skills. Use this activity to address multiple learning styles using hands-on activities related to the skills of this lesson.

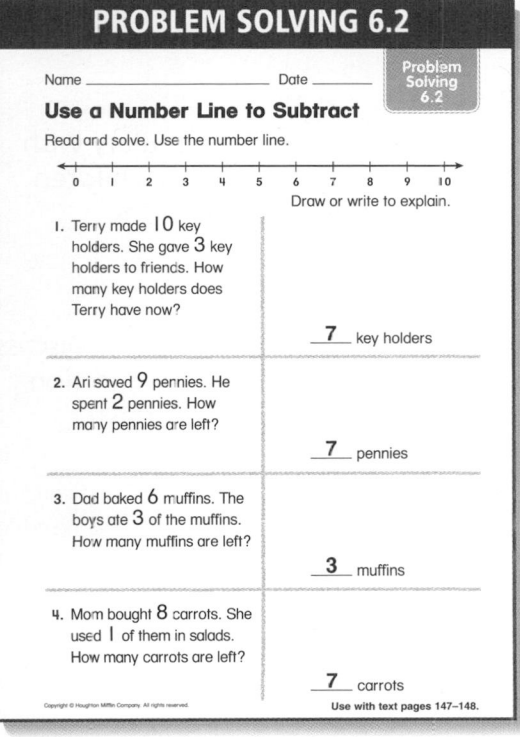

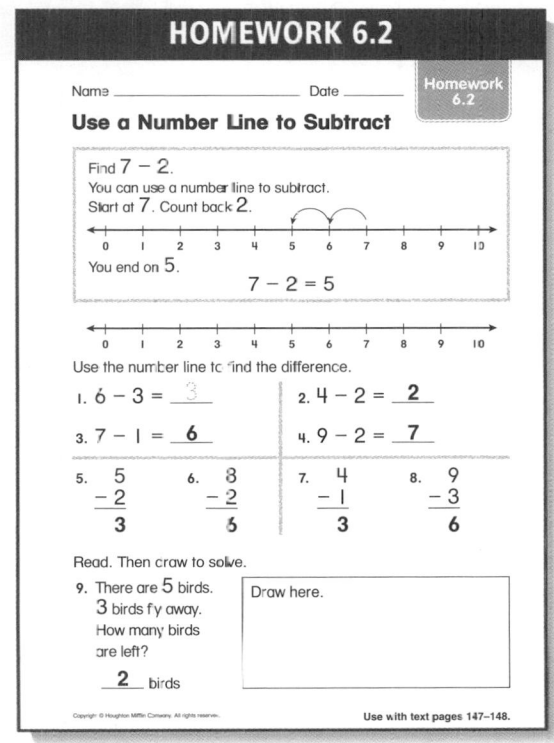

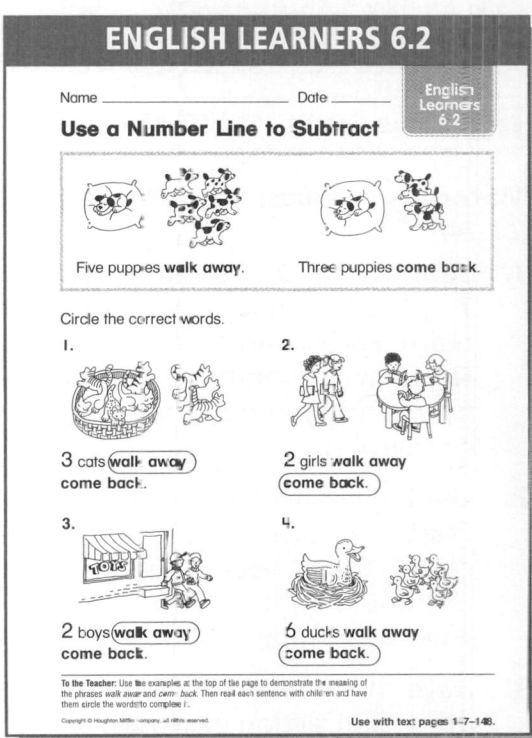

Homework Workbook Page 36

TEACHING LESSON 6.2

LESSON ORGANIZER

Objective Subtract using a number line.

Resources Reteach, Practice, Enrichment, Problem Solving, Homework, English Learners, Transparencies, Math Center

Materials Clothesline, clothespins, number cards 0–10 (LT 14), number lines (LT 8)

 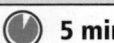 **Warm-Up Activity**
Modeling Counting Back

👤👤👤 Small Group	⏱ 5 minutes	Auditory, Kinesthetic

1. Ask 5 volunteers to help you demonstrate how to count back to subtract 5 minus 2.

2. Place the children in a single line. **We have 5 children in line. Let's take away 2 children. How can we count back to subtract?**
(Silently move 1 child away at a time as you count back to show the number of children left: 4, 3.)

$5 - 2 = 3$

3. Repeat with other volunteers. This time let children demonstrate the counting back.

Name _____

Use a Number Line to Subtract

Use a **number line** to find $10 - 3$.

Objective Subtract using a number line.
Vocabulary number line

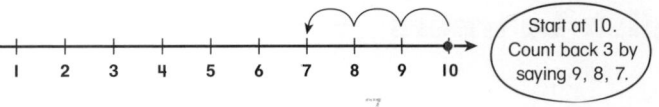

Start at 10. Count back 3 by saying 9, 8, 7.

$10 - 3 = \underline{7}$

Think
9 is the greater number. Say 9. Count 8, 7.

Guided Practice

Write the difference.

1. $9 - 2 = \underline{7}$

2. $10 - 1 = \underline{9}$

3. $8 - 3 = \underline{5}$

4. $\begin{array}{r} 10 \\ -2 \\ \hline 8 \end{array}$
5. $\begin{array}{r} 9 \\ -3 \\ \hline 6 \end{array}$
6. $\begin{array}{r} 7 \\ -1 \\ \hline 6 \end{array}$
7. $\begin{array}{r} 6 \\ -3 \\ \hline 3 \end{array}$
8. $\begin{array}{r} 5 \\ -1 \\ \hline 4 \end{array}$
9. $\begin{array}{r} 8 \\ -2 \\ \hline 6 \end{array}$

TEST TIPS **Explain Your Thinking** Tell how you can use the number line to find $8 - 3$. Start at 8. Count back 3 by saying 7, 6, 5. 8 minus 3 equals 5.

Chapter 6 Lesson 2   one hundred forty-seven **147**

---

① Introduce

Model Counting Back on a Number Line

👤👤👤👤 Whole Group	⏱ 10–15 minutes	Kinesthetic, Visual

Materials: *clothesline, clothespins, number cards 0–10 (LT 14)*

1. *Subtract $7 - 3$.* We can use a number line to show $7 - 3 = 4$. Hang the clothesline low so children can reach. For example, between 2 chairs, 2 doorknobs, etc. Now have children help you make a 0–10 number line by attaching number cards on a piece of string with clothespins.

2. Use the line to model counting back to subtract $7 - 3$. **Start at 7.** Have a child hold the bottom of the number card 7. **Count back 3.** As you point, have a child clip a clothespin on the bottom of each number card, **6, 5, 4. 7 minus 3 equals 4.**

3. Have children take turns modeling counting back for other subtraction exercises.

② Develop

Guided Learning

Teaching Example Read the objective and vocabulary with children. Guide them through the example. Have children count back aloud as they follow the 3 arrows on the number line.

Guided Practice

Have children complete **Exercises 1–9** as you observe. Discuss children's responses to the Explain Your Thinking question and have volunteers model the subtraction on a class number line.

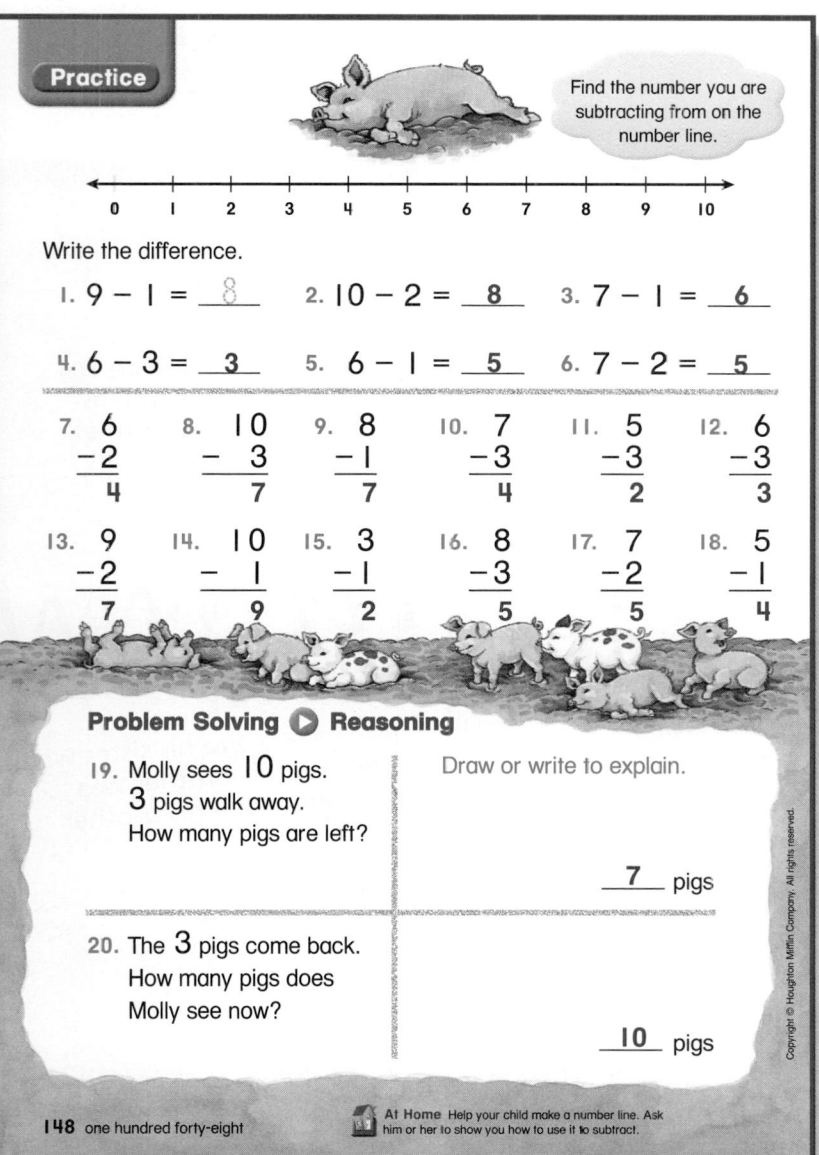

Practice

Find the number you are subtracting from on the number line.

```
0  1  2  3  4  5  6  7  8  9  10
```

Write the difference.

1. $9 - 1 = \underline{8}$ 2. $10 - 2 = \underline{8}$ 3. $7 - 1 = \underline{6}$

4. $6 - 3 = \underline{3}$ 5. $6 - 1 = \underline{5}$ 6. $7 - 2 = \underline{5}$

7. 6	8. 10	9. 8	10. 7	11. 5	12. 6
$\underline{-2}$	$\underline{-3}$	$\underline{-1}$	$\underline{-3}$	$\underline{-3}$	$\underline{-3}$
4	7	7	4	2	3

13. 9	14. 10	15. 3	16. 8	17. 7	18. 5
$\underline{-2}$	$\underline{-1}$	$\underline{-1}$	$\underline{-3}$	$\underline{-2}$	$\underline{-1}$
7	9	2	5	5	4

Problem Solving ▶ Reasoning

19. Molly sees 10 pigs.
3 pigs walk away.
How many pigs are left?

Draw or write to explain.

_____7_____ pigs

20. The 3 pigs come back.
How many pigs does
Molly see now?

_____10_____ pigs

148 one hundred forty-eight

At Home Help your child make a number line. Ask him or her to show you how to use it to subtract.

Daily Test Prep

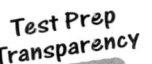
6.2

$9 - 2 = \square$

8   7   6   5
○   ●   ○   ○

Activity

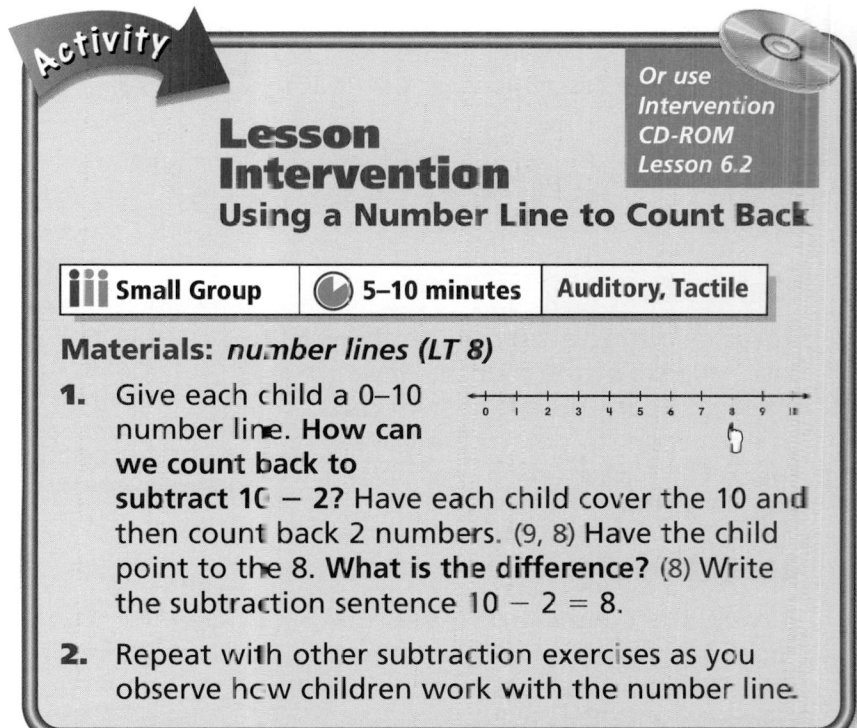

Or use Intervention CD-ROM Lesson 6.2

Lesson Intervention
Using a Number Line to Count Back

👤👤👤 Small Group	🕐 5–10 minutes	Auditory, Tactile

Materials: *number lines (LT 8)*

1. Give each child a 0–10 number line. **How can we count back to subtract 10 – 2?** Have each child cover the 10 and then count back 2 numbers. (9, 8) Have the child point to the 8. **What is the difference?** (8) Write the subtraction sentence 10 – 2 = 8.

2. Repeat with other subtraction exercises as you observe how children work with the number line.

---

3 Practice

Independent Practice

Children complete **Exercises 1–18** independently.

Problem Solving

After children complete **Exercises 19 and 20**, call on volunteers to share their solutions and ways of solving each problem.

Common Error

Starting on the Incorrect Number
Some children may have difficulty finding the starting number when they count back. Have children circle the first number in the exercise and then point to the same number on the number line.

---

4 Assess and Close

If you start on 9 and count back 3, what number will you land on? (6)

What if you only counted back 2 from 9, what number would you land on? (7)

 **Keeping a Journal**

Draw a number line. Show how to subtract 6 – 2.

How Many More? How Many Fewer?

PLANNING THE LESSON

MATHEMATICS OBJECTIVE
Show the meaning of subtraction by comparing.

Use Lesson Planner CD-ROM for Lesson 6.3.

Meeting North Carolina's Standards
1.03 Develop fluency with single-digit addition and corresponding differences using strategies such as modeling, composing and decomposing quantities, using doubles, and making tens.

Daily Routines

Calendar
Focus children's attention on the last 2 weeks of the month. Have them compare the number of days in each week to determine how many more days are in one week than another.

Vocabulary
Review the meaning of the terms **more** and **fewer**. Model sentences that use each word to compare the number of objects in two groups, or **sets**. Then invite volunteers to use the words in sentences.

Vocabulary Cards

Lesson Transparency **6.3**

Problem of the Day
Sam is 7 years old. 2 years ago his sister was born. 1 year before that his brother was born. How old was Sam when his brother was born? (4 years old)

Quick Review
10 − 3 = (7)   9 − 2 = (7)
8 − 3 = (5)   7 − 1 = (6)

Lesson Quiz
1. How many more □ than ○?
   □□□□□   5 − 2 = (3)
   ○○
2. How many fewer ○ than △?
   △△△
   ○○   3 − 2 = (1)

LEVELED PRACTICE

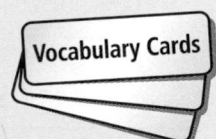

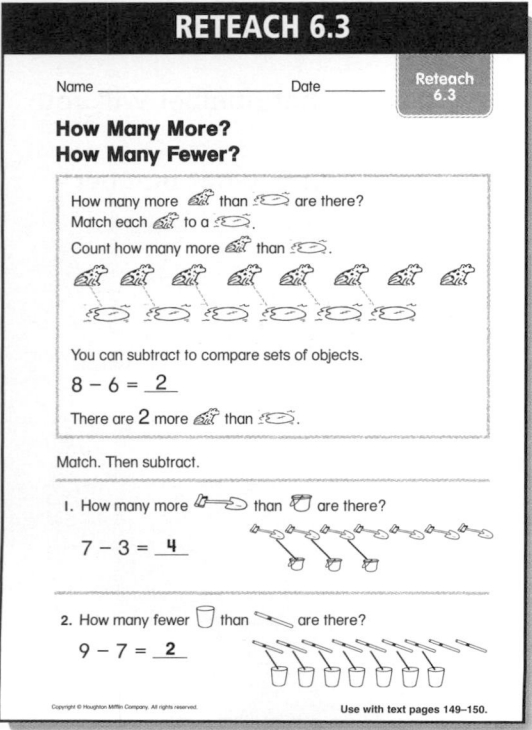

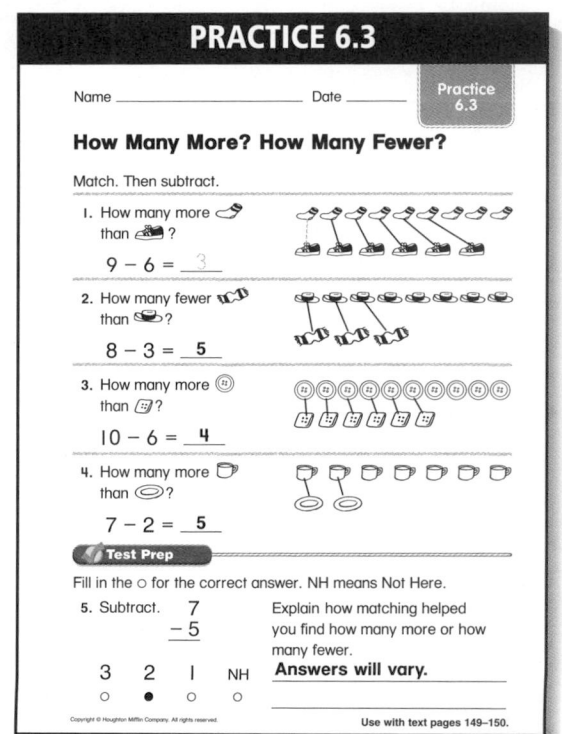

RETEACH 6.3

Name _____ Date _____ | Reteach 6.3

How Many More? How Many Fewer?

How many more 🐕 than 🐁 are there?
Match each 🐕 to a 🐁.
Count how many more 🐕 than 🐁.

You can subtract to compare sets of objects.
8 − 6 = **2**
There are 2 more 🐕 than 🐁.

Match. Then subtract.

1. How many more 🥄 than 🍴 are there?
   7 − 3 = **4**

2. How many fewer 🥛 than 🥄 are there?
   9 − 7 = **2**

Copyright © Houghton Mifflin Company. All rights reserved.   **Use with text pages 149–150.**

PRACTICE 6.3

Name _____ Date _____ | Practice 6.3

How Many More? How Many Fewer?

Match. Then subtract.

1. How many more 🧦 than 👟?
   9 − 6 = **3**

2. How many fewer 🥄 than ☕?
   8 − 3 = **5**

3. How many more ○ than ▢?
   10 − 6 = **4**

4. How many more ☕ than ○?
   7 − 2 = **5**

Test Prep

Fill in the ○ for the correct answer. NH means Not Here.

5. Subtract.   7
              − 5

   3 2 1 NH
   ○ ● ○ ○

Explain how matching helped you find how many more or how many fewer. **Answers will vary.**

Copyright © Houghton Mifflin Company. All rights reserved.   **Use with text pages 149–150.**

ENRICHMENT 6.3

Name _____ Date _____ | Enrichment 6.3

Take Away and Find More—or Fewer

Read the problem.
Complete the subtraction sentence.
Draw a picture to check.

1. Jane has 8 🦴. She has 6 🐕.
   How many more 🦴 than 🐕 are there?
   8 − **6** = **2** more

   Draw here.
   Check children's drawings.

2. Dan has 4 🦴. He has 7 🐕.
   How many fewer 🦴 than 🐕 are there?
   7 − **4** = **3** fewer

Write About It Why do you subtract to find how many more or how many fewer?
Possible answer: By matching the groups you can compare the numbers to find how many fewer.

Copyright © Houghton Mifflin Company. All rights reserved.   **Use with text pages 149–150.**

Practice Workbook Page 37

Reaching All Learners
Differentiated Instruction

English Learners

In order to subtract by comparing, English-language learners will need to understand the phrases *more ___ than ___* and *fewer ___ than ___*. Use Worksheet 6.3 to help children understand and use these phrases.

Inclusion
TACTILE, VISUAL

Materials: *cubes*

- Place 8 orange cubes in a row above 6 yellow cubes.

- Point out the 1-to-1 correspondence. Have the child tell how many orange cubes do not have a yellow cube to match. (2) Write $8 - 6 = 2$.

Early Finishers
VISUAL, TACTILE

- Invite children to draw 3 picture problems that compare sets of objects.
- Have them exchange problems with a partner. Partners write a subtraction sentence and solve.

How many more 🌷 than 🌱?

TECHNOLOGY

Spiral Review

To reinforce skills on lessons taught earlier, create **customized** spiral review worksheets using the *Ways to Assess* CD-ROM.

Lesson Planner

You can use the **Lesson Planner CD-ROM** to create a report of the lessons and standards you have taught.

eBook

eMathBook allows students to review lessons and do homework without carrying their textbooks home.

 Literature Connection

Introduce the book *Musical Chairs and Dancing Bears* by Joanne Rocklin. Children will soon see that there is always one more bear than chair. Challenge children to make a list of the subtraction in the story.

MATH CENTER

Basic Skills Activity

Motivate children to build basic skills. Use this activity to address multiple learning styles using hands-on activities related to the skills of this lesson.

PROBLEM SOLVING 6.3

Name _____ Date _____

Problem Solving 6.3

How Many More? How Many Fewer?

Read and solve. Compare sets of objects.

Draw or write to explain.

1. Jim read 8 books. Don read 6 books. How many more books did Jim read than Don?
   __2__ more books

2. Kala saw 7 red birds. Deena saw 4 red birds. How many fewer birds did Deena see?
   __3__ fewer birds

3. Basil collected 9 toy cars. Lacy collected 8 toy cars. How many more toy cars did Basil collect?
   __1__ more toy car

4. Rosa walks 6 blocks to school. Lance walks 2 blocks to school. How many fewer blocks does Lance walk?
   __4__ fewer blocks

Use with text pages 149–150.

HOMEWORK 6.3

Name _____ Date _____

Homework 6.3

How Many More? How Many Fewer?

To compare numbers, subtract.

How many more 🐦 than 🐕 are there?
Match each 🐕 to one 🐦. Then subtract.
$6 - 3 = 3$ There are 3 more dogs than cats.

Match. Then subtract.

1. How many more ○ than △ are there?
   $7 - 2 = $ __5__

2. How many fewer ◇ than ☐ are there?
   $8 - 3 = $ __5__

3. How many fewer △ than ○ are there?
   $9 - 4 = $ __5__

Use with text pages 149–150.

ENGLISH LEARNERS 6.3

Name _____ Date _____

English Learners 6.3

How Many More? How Many Fewer?

eggs | 3 chicks

There are **more** eggs **than** chicks.
There are **fewer** chicks **than** eggs.

Circle the correct word.

1. There are (more) fewer bees than flowers.

2. There are (more) fewer cats than dogs.

3. There are more (fewer) nests than birds.

4. There are (more) fewer chairs than tables.

To the Teacher: Use the illustrations and sentences at the top of the page to help children understand the comparative phrases. Then read each sentence with children and have them circle the word that completes it.

Use with text pages 149–151.

Homework Workbook Page 37

TEACHING LESSON 6.3

LESSON ORGANIZER

Objective Show the meaning of subtraction by comparing.

Resources Reteach, Practice, Enrichment, Problem Solving, Homework, English Learners, Transparencies, Math Center

Materials Blank transparency

Warm-Up Activity
How Many

👥 Small Group	🕐 5 minutes	Tactile, Visual

1. Take several strips of paper and a handful of pencils. **Do we have enough strips of paper to match each pencil?**

2. Line up the strips of paper in a row. Line up the pencils in a row below the paper. Count the strips. Then count the pencils. Have children first identify the group that has more. Then identify the group that has fewer.

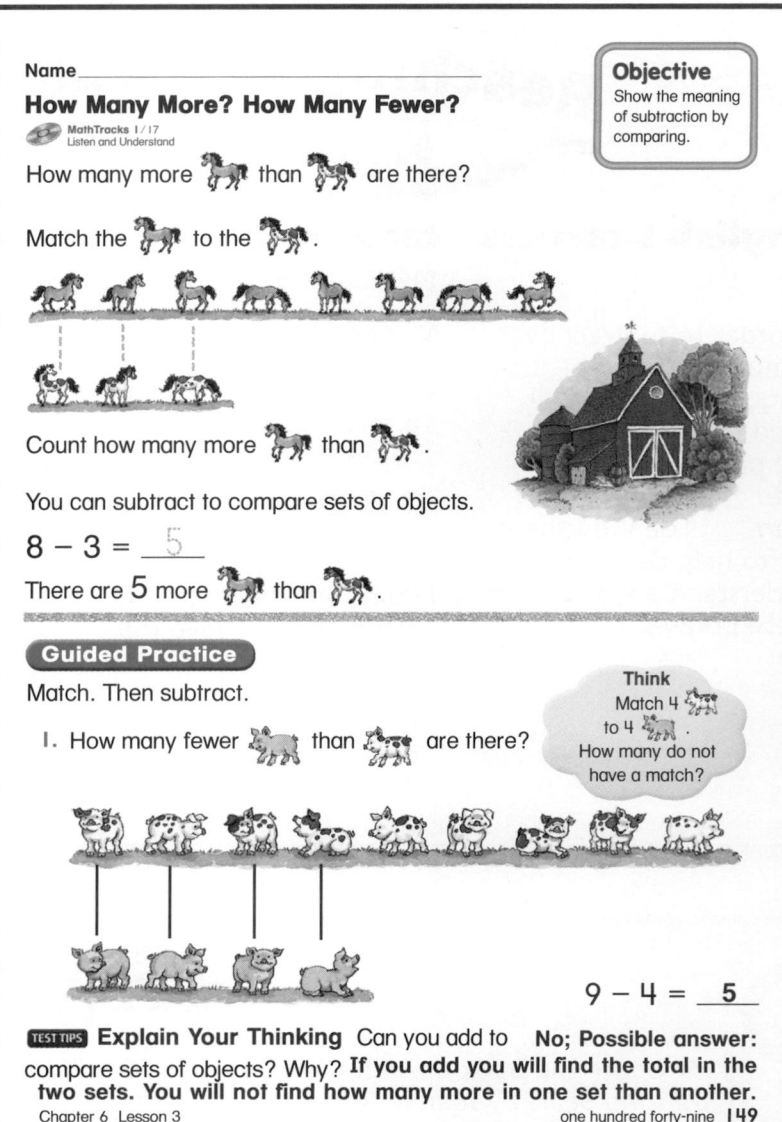

---

1 Introduce
Model Comparing

👥 Whole Group	🕐 10–15 minutes	Kinesthetic, Visual

1. *Subtract 5 − 4*. Place 4 chairs in a row and ask for 5 volunteers. Have 4 of the volunteers each stand behind a chair. One child will be without a chair.

2. **How many more children than chairs are there?** (1) Reinforce the language: **There is 1 more child than chair.** Write 5 − 4 = 1 on the board and relate it to the 5 children and 4 chairs.

3. Repeat with 5 new volunteers and 3 chairs. **How many more children are there than chairs?** (2) **How many fewer chairs are there than children?** (2) Write 5 − 3 = 2 on the board and relate it to the 5 children and 3 chairs.

2 Develop

Guided Learning

Teaching Example Read the objective with children. Guide them through the example as they match brown horses to spotted horses using one-to-one correspondence.

Guided Practice

Have children complete **Exercise 1** as you observe. Give children the opportunity to answer the Explain Your Thinking question. Then discuss why you can subtract to compare.

Count how many do not have a match.

Match. Then subtract.

1. How many more 🦆 than 🦅 are there?

   $8 - 6 = \underline{2}$

2. How many fewer 🐄 than 🐄 ?

   $9 - 5 = \underline{4}$

3. How many more 🐓 than 🐤 are there?

   $10 - 4 = \underline{6}$

Problem Solving ▶ Reasoning

4. Ratta sees 6 cows. Then she sees 4 more. How many cows does Ratta see?

   Draw or write to explain.

   $\underline{10}$ cows

At Home Make two sets of objects; one with 10 and one with less than 10. Have your child subtract to compare the sets.

Go on ▶

Test Prep Transparency

6.3

Daily Test Prep

Subtract.
How many more 🌼 than 🎩 ?

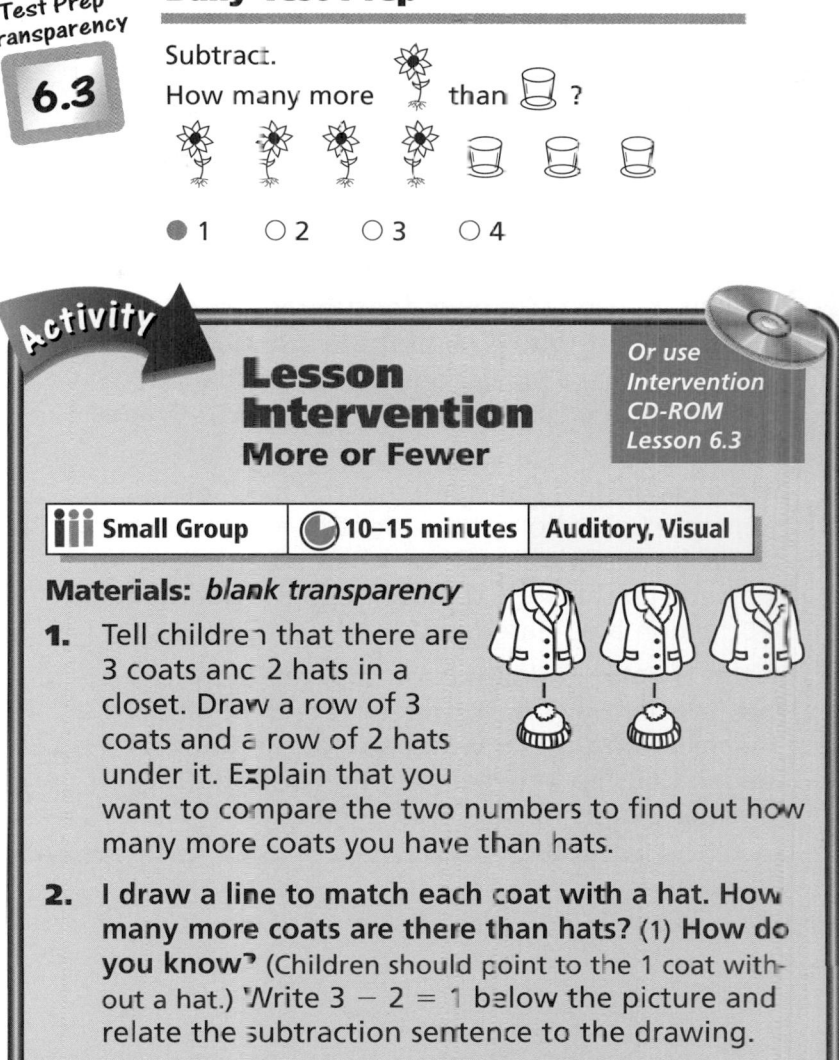

● 1   ○ 2   ○ 3   ○ 4

Activity ↗

Lesson Intervention
More or Fewer

Or use Intervention CD-ROM Lesson 6.3

| 👥 Small Group | ⏱ 10–15 minutes | Auditory, Visual |

Materials: *blank transparency*

1. Tell children that there are 3 coats and 2 hats in a closet. Draw a row of 3 coats and a row of 2 hats under it. Explain that you want to compare the two numbers to find out how many more coats you have than hats.

2. I draw a line to match each coat with a hat. How many more coats are there than hats? **(1) How do you know?** (Children should point to the 1 coat without a hat.) Write $3 - 2 = 1$ below the picture and relate the subtraction sentence to the drawing.

3. Repeat by presenting a different problem that compares finding how many fewer.

---

③ Practice

Independent Practice

Children complete **Exercises 1–3** independently.

Problem Solving

After children complete **Exercise 4**, call on volunteers to share their solutions. **Then ask; If Ratta sees 4 cows first then 6 more, will she still see 10 cows in all?** (Yes, because changing the order of the addends does not change the sum.)

Common Error

Counting the Matched Pairs

Children may count the matched pairs instead of the extras. Remind them that when they are looking for how many more or fewer, they should count the unmatched objects.

④ Assess and Close

How can you compare 3 bicycles with 2 helmets to tell how many more bicycles than helmets? (Match each helmet with a bicycle to find 1 extra bicycle. Subtract $3 - 2 = 1$.)

If you caught 10 blue butterflies and 1 red butterfly, what subtraction sentence tells how many more blue than red? $(10 - 1 = 9)$

✎ Keeping a Journal

Count your fingers and ears. How many more fingers do you have than ears? Draw a picture to show how many and write a number sentence.

Lesson continues ▶

Understanding Algebraic Thinking

Learning experiences that focus on part-part-whole relations have been shown to help students develop efficient thinking strategies for subtraction. **Learning to see the part-whole relations in addition and subtraction situations is one of the most significant mathematical achievements for children in Grades K–2.**

When children are presented with "join" or "separate" situations, they identify which number stands for the whole and which numbers stand for the parts. In this way, children see how addition and subtraction are related.

In this chapter, **children learn that related facts in fact families have the same parts and wholes.** This understanding, along with an understanding of the relationship between addition and subtraction, provides a basis for algebraic thinking.

Name _____

Writing Math: Create and Solve

Write a subtraction story that compares the birds.

1. Answers may vary. Possible answer: There are
   4 red birds and 2 blue birds. How many more
   red birds than blue birds?

Write the subtraction sentence.

2. __4__ ⊖ __2__ ⊜ __2__

Tell a story to match the number sentence.   7 − 4 = 3
Draw a picture to show your story.

3. Stories and pictures may vary. Children may show comparing 7 and 4 or 7 take away 4.

Chapter 6 Lesson 3   one hundred fifty-one 151

Writing Math: Create and Solve

Direct children to the picture of the birds on the page as you read the directions. Discuss the picture for **Exercises 1 and 2.** Be sure children understand that they are to write a story problem that ends in a question. The question should ask *how many more* **or** *how many fewer.* Then children should write a subtraction sentence for the picture.

Explain that for **Exercise 3**, children will tell a subtraction story problem to match the number sentence. Then they will draw a picture to show the story. Children may tell their story problem to a partner.

When all children are finished, let them share their work.

Quick Check

Count back to subtract.

1. $10 - 1 = \underline{9}$ 2. $8 - 2 = \underline{6}$ 3. $9 - 3 = \underline{6}$

Write the difference.

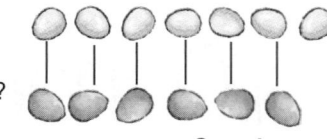

4. $\begin{array}{r} 8 \\ -3 \\ \hline 5 \end{array}$ 5. $\begin{array}{r} 6 \\ -2 \\ \hline 4 \end{array}$ 6. $\begin{array}{r} 7 \\ -1 \\ \hline 6 \end{array}$ 7. $\begin{array}{r} 10 \\ -3 \\ \hline 7 \end{array}$ 8. $\begin{array}{r} 5 \\ -1 \\ \hline 4 \end{array}$ 9. $\begin{array}{r} 9 \\ -2 \\ \hline 7 \end{array}$

Match.
Then subtract.

10. How many more ⬭ than ⬭ ?

$8 - 6 = \underline{2}$

Math Challenge

Duck Feet

Leon counts 10 feet.
How many ducks are there?

$\underline{5}$ ducks

152 one hundred fifty-two

Quick Check

Have children complete the Quick Check exercises independently to assess their understanding of concepts and skills taught in **Lessons 1–3.**

Item	Lesson	Error Analysis	Intervention
1–3	6.1	Children may mistakenly count the starting number as they count back.	Reteach Resource 6.1 *Ways to Success* 6.1
4–9	6.2	Children may start with an incorrect number.	Reteach Resource 6.2 *Ways to Success* 6.2
10	6.3	Children may count the matched pairs instead of the extras.	Reteach Resource 6.3 *Ways to Success* 6.3

Math Challenge

Draw 10 duck feet on the board. Have volunteers share the methods they used to solve the question. You may want to display the chart below as one method. Discuss the number pattern.

Number of Ducks	Number of Feet
1	2
2	4
3	6
4	8
5	10

Lesson 6.4

Hands-On: Relate Addition and Subtraction

PLANNING THE LESSON

MATHEMATICS OBJECTIVE
Write and solve related addition and subtraction facts (inverse operations).

Use Lesson Planner CD-ROM for Lesson 6.4.

Meeting North Carolina's Standards
1.03 Develop fluency with single-digit addition and corresponding differences using strategies such as modeling, composing and decomposing quantities, using doubles, and making tens.

Daily Routines

Calendar
Ask children to identify the number of weekdays in a week and the number of weekend days in a week. Discuss how this could be shown in an addition sentence $(5 + 2 = 7)$, and then a subtraction sentence to compare $(7 - 2 = 5)$.

Sunday	Monday	Tuesday	Wednesday	Thursday	Friday	Saturday
			1	2	3	4
5	6	7	8	9	10	11
12	13	14	15	16	17	18
19	20	21	22	23	24	25
26	27	28	29	30	31	

Vocabulary
Introduce the term **related facts** by first discussing the word *related*. Explain that people in a family are related and sometimes we call them *relatives.* Then give examples of addition and subtraction facts that are related.

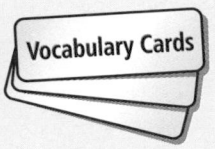
Vocabulary Cards

Lesson Transparency 6.4

Problem of the Day
Bobby has 10 pairs of socks. 5 pairs are white, 1 pair is black, and the rest are blue. How many pairs are blue? (4)

Quick Review
$3 + 4 =$ (7) $4 + 3 =$ (7)
$5 + 2 =$ (7) $2 + 5 =$ (7)

Lesson Quiz
1. $\begin{array}{r} 3 \\ + 6 \\ \hline (9) \end{array}$ $\begin{array}{r} 9 \\ - 6 \\ \hline (3) \end{array}$ **2.** $\begin{array}{r} 4 \\ + 4 \\ \hline (8) \end{array}$ $\begin{array}{r} 8 \\ - 4 \\ \hline (4) \end{array}$

LEVELED PRACTICE

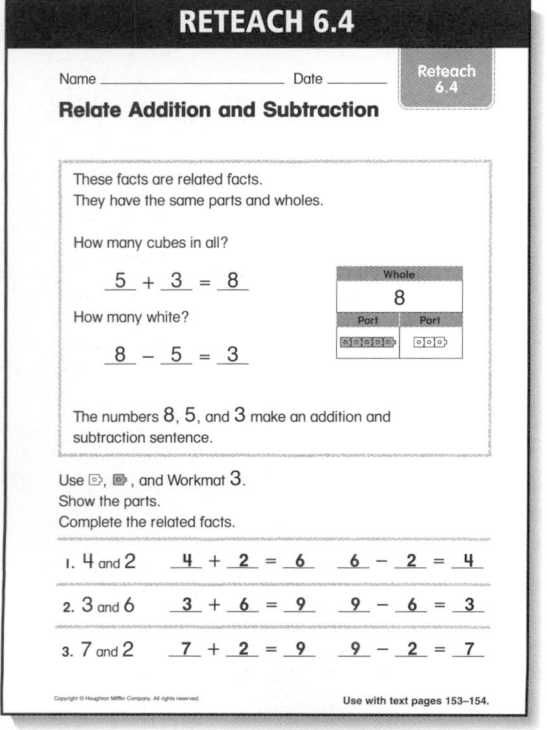

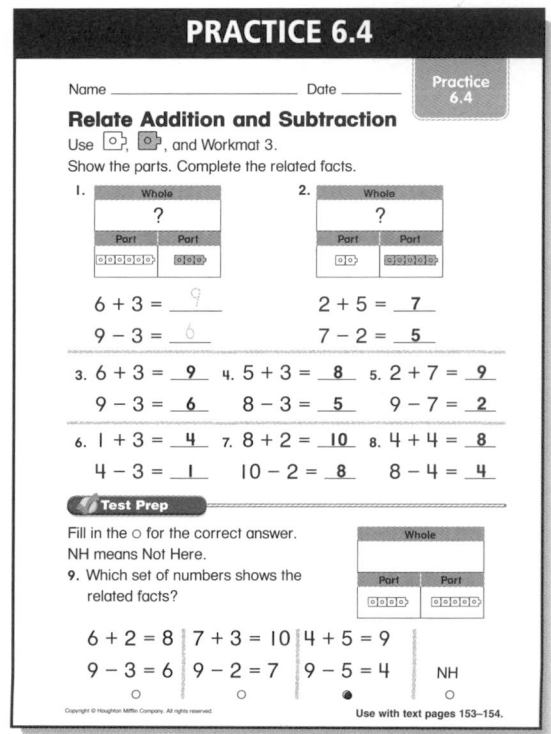

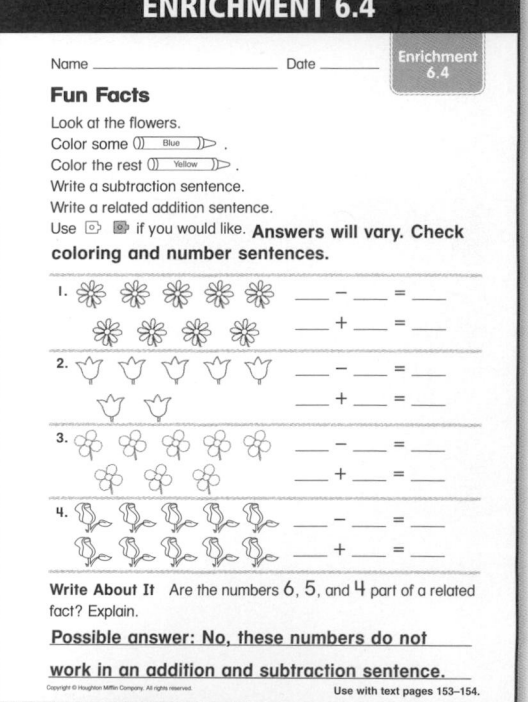

Practice Workbook Page 38

Reaching All Learners

Differentiated Instruction

English Learners

In order to write and solve related addition and subtraction facts, children will need to understand the meaning of the words *part* and *whole*. Use Worksheet 6.4 to develop their understanding of these words.

Special Needs
TACTILE, VISUAL

Materials: *cubes*

- Have the child build a train of 7 cubes and a train of 2 cubes. Have the child identify the number in each part and the whole as you record 7 + 2 = 9.
- Have have the child say the subtraction as you write 9 − 2 = 7.
- Relate the *doing* and *undoing* of the facts.

Early Finishers
VISUAL, TACTILE

- Have pairs of children use the exercises on the page to write missing addend exercises.
- Then have the children trade papers and solve the exercises.
- Then have the partner write the related subtraction fact. Partners check each others work.

| 8 and 2 | 8 + ___ = 10 |
| 9 and 1 | 9 + ___ = 10 |

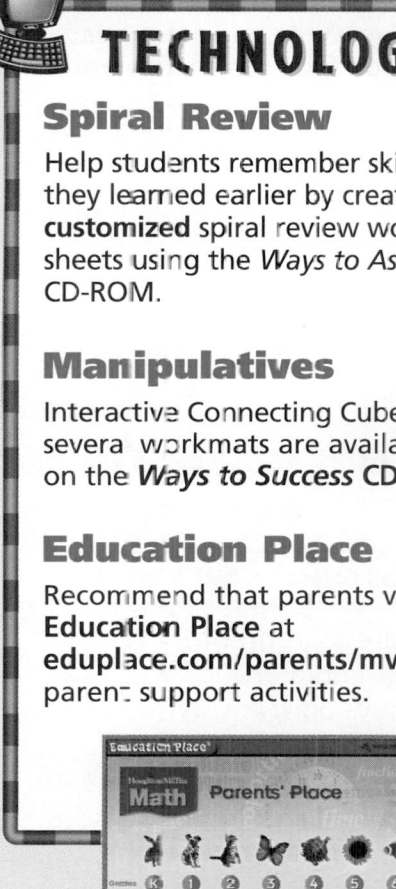
 ## Literature Connection   ## MATH CENTER

Read the story *1 + 1 Take Away Two!* by Michael Berenstain. Invite children to look for the related facts presented. Make a list of these facts. Have children tell animal stories for the related facts.

Cross-Curricular Activity

As you use this activity to relate the mathematics of this lesson to another curriculum area, children will see how math can help them with other subjects.

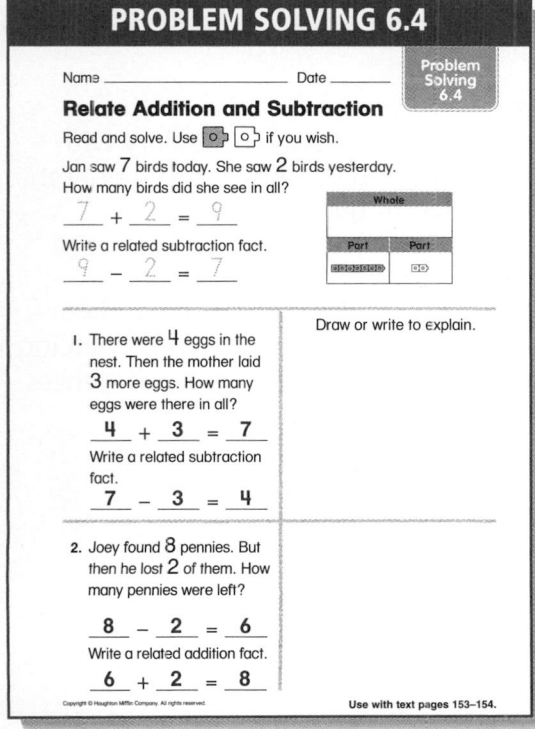

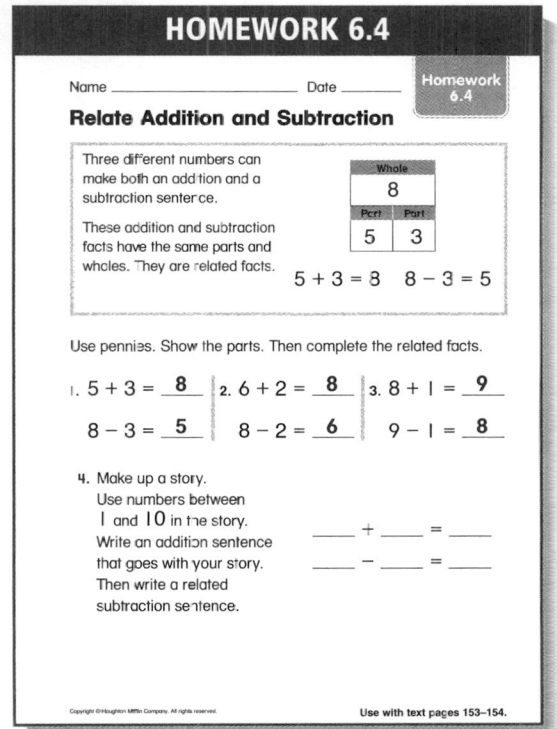

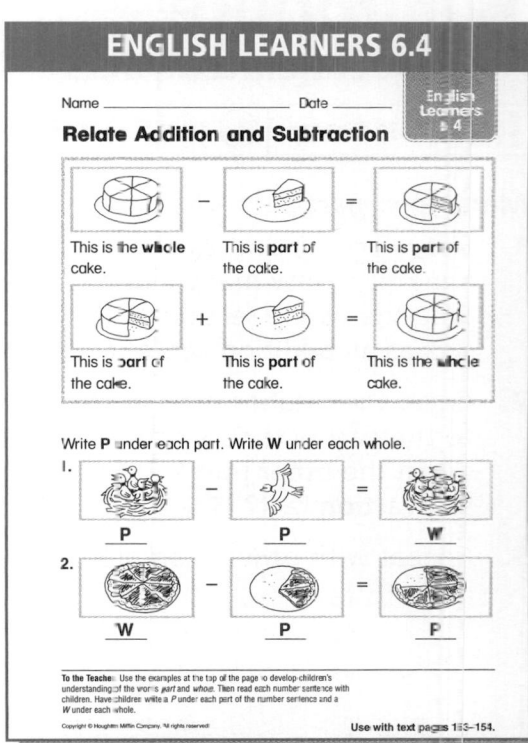

Homework Workbook Page 38

TEACHING LESSON 6.4

LESSON ORGANIZER

Objective Write and solve related addition and subtraction facts (inverse operations).

Resources Reteach, Practice, Enrichment, Problem Solving, Homework, English Learners, Transparencies, Math Center

Materials Part-part-whole transparency, cubes, number cards 1–9 (LT 14), Workmat 3

Activity

Warm-Up Activity
Modeling Part-Part-Whole

| iii Small Group | ⏱ 5 minutes | Kinesthetic, Visual |

1. Invite a group of 3 girls and a group of 2 boys up front. **We have 3 girls and 2 boys. How many children are there in all?** (5)

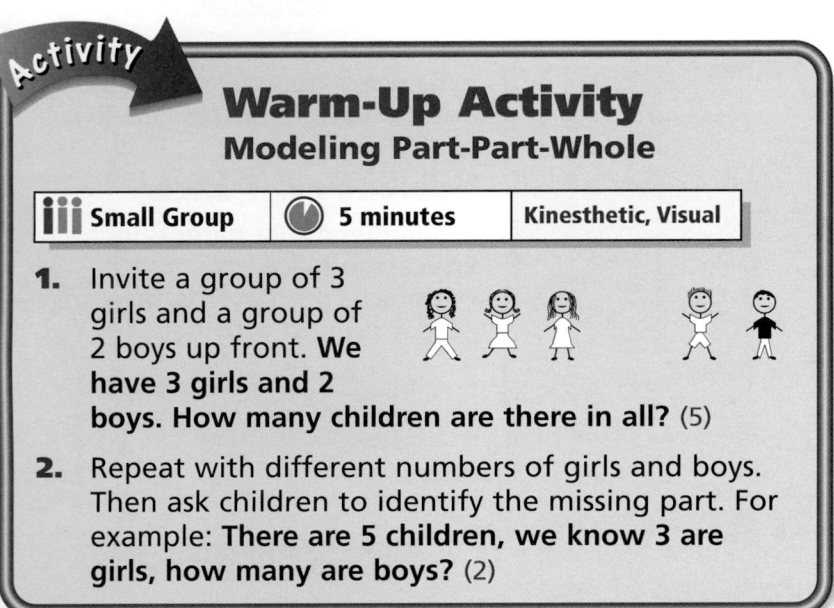

2. Repeat with different numbers of girls and boys. Then ask children to identify the missing part. For example: **There are 5 children, we know 3 are girls, how many are boys?** (2)

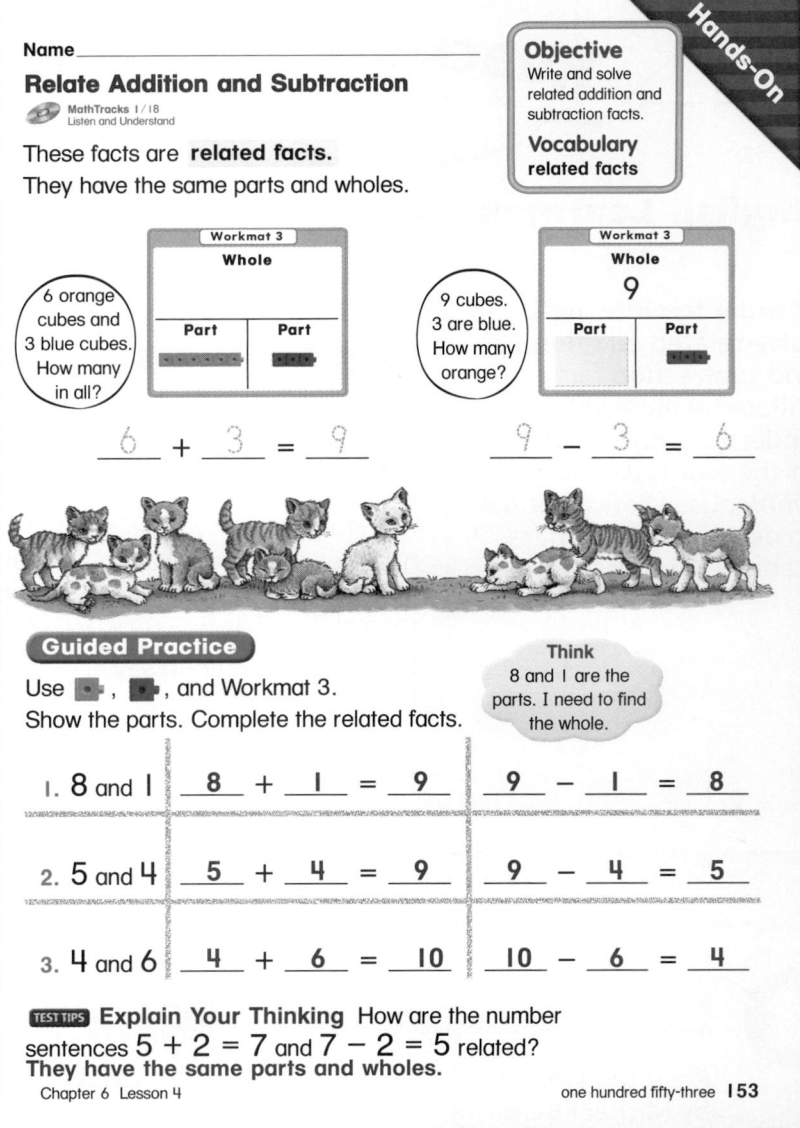

Name _____

Relate Addition and Subtraction

MathTracks 1/18
Listen and Understand

Objective
Write and solve related addition and subtraction facts.

Vocabulary
related facts

These facts are **related facts.**
They have the same parts and wholes.

$6 + 3 = 9$ $9 - 3 = 6$

Guided Practice

Use ▪, ▪, and Workmat 3.
Show the parts. Complete the related facts.

Think
8 and 1 are the parts. I need to find the whole.

1. 8 and 1 $8 + 1 = 9$ $9 - 1 = 8$

2. 5 and 4 $5 + 4 = 9$ $9 - 4 = 5$

3. 4 and 6 $4 + 6 = 10$ $10 - 6 = 4$

TEST TIPS **Explain Your Thinking** How are the number sentences $5 + 2 = 7$ and $7 - 2 = 5$ related?
They have the same parts and wholes.

Chapter 6 Lesson 4   one hundred fifty-three **153**

---

1 Introduce
Model Related Facts

| iiii Whole Group | ⏱ 10–15 minutes | Tactile, Visual |

Materials: *part-part whole transparency, cubes*

1. Show 3 cubes and 2 cubes on the part-part-whole workmat. **How many cubes do I have in all?** (5) Write 5 on the whole section of the mat. **How can I show this as an addition sentence?** ($3 + 2 = 5$)

2. Cover the 3 cubes with paper. **There are 5 cubes.** Point to the part with 2. **2 cubes are in this part. How many are in the other part?** (3) **How could we write this as a subtraction fact?** ($5 - 2 = 3$)

3. Repeat with other examples.

2 Develop

Guided Learning

Teaching Example Read the objective and vocabulary with children. Have children use cubes on Workmat 3 to model the addition and subtraction shown in the example.

Guided Practice

Have children complete **Exercises 1–3** as you observe. Give children the opportunity to answer the Explain Your Thinking question. Then have volunteers model the number sentences with cubes as you discuss the children's responses.

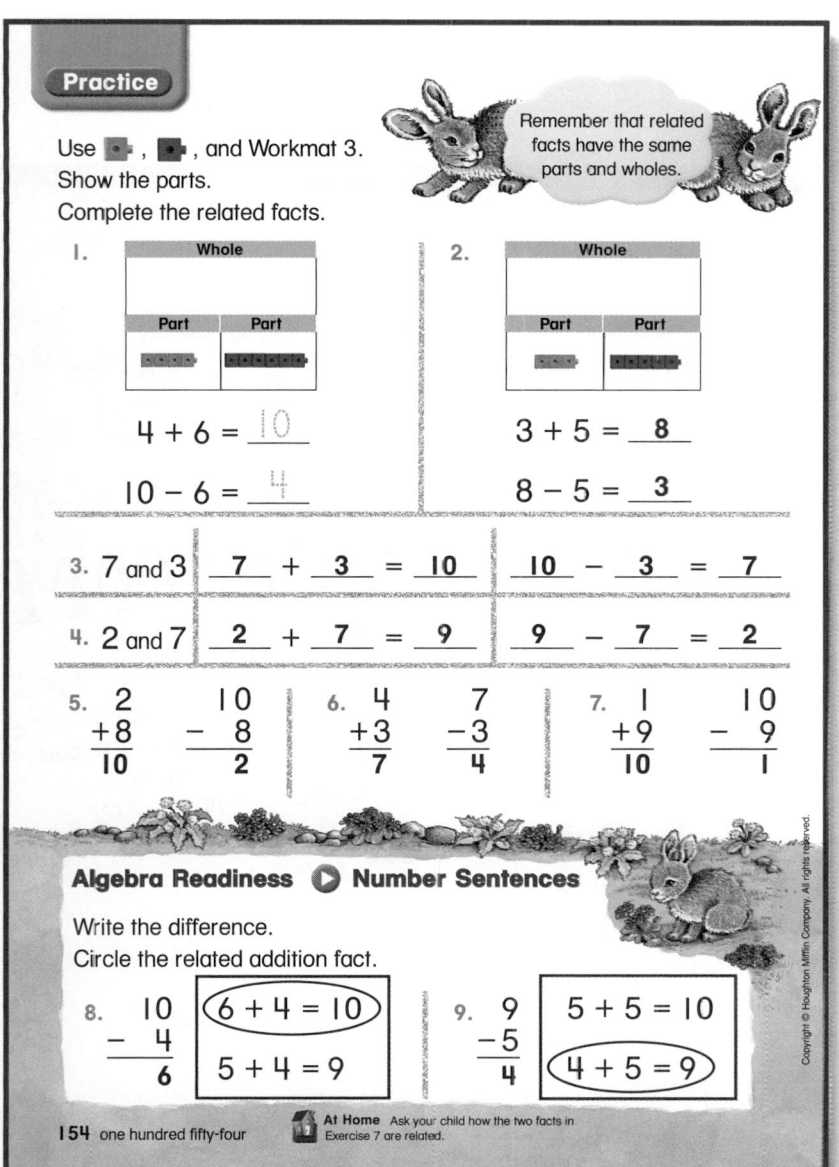

Practice

Use ▣, ▣, and Workmat 3.
Show the parts.
Complete the related facts.

Remember that related facts have the same parts and wholes.

1.

Whole	
Part	Part

$4 + 6 = \underline{10}$

$10 - 6 = \underline{4}$

2.

Whole	
Part	Part

$3 + 5 = \underline{8}$

$8 - 5 = \underline{3}$

3. 7 and 3 $\underline{7} + \underline{3} = \underline{10}$ $10 - \underline{3} = \underline{7}$

4. 2 and 7 $\underline{2} + \underline{7} = \underline{9}$ $9 - \underline{7} = \underline{2}$

5.
$\begin{array}{r} 2 \\ +8 \\ \hline 10 \end{array}$
$\begin{array}{r} 10 \\ -8 \\ \hline 2 \end{array}$

6.
$\begin{array}{r} 4 \\ +3 \\ \hline 7 \end{array}$
$\begin{array}{r} 7 \\ -3 \\ \hline 4 \end{array}$

7.
$\begin{array}{r} 1 \\ +9 \\ \hline 10 \end{array}$
$\begin{array}{r} 10 \\ -9 \\ \hline 1 \end{array}$

Algebra Readiness ▶ Number Sentences

Write the difference.
Circle the related addition fact.

8.
$\begin{array}{r} 10 \\ -4 \\ \hline 6 \end{array}$
| (6 + 4 = 10) |
| 5 + 4 = 9 |

9.
$\begin{array}{r} 9 \\ -5 \\ \hline 4 \end{array}$
| 5 + 5 = 10 |
| (4 + 5 = 9) |

154 one hundred fifty-four

At Home Ask your child how the two facts in Exercise 7 are related.

Copyright © Houghton Mifflin Company. All rights reserved.

Test Prep Transparency 6.4

Daily Test Prep

Which fact has the same parts as 5 + 4 = 9?

$5 + 3 = 8$ ○ $3 + 6 = 9$ ○ $9 - 6 = 3$ ○ $9 - 4 = 5$ ●

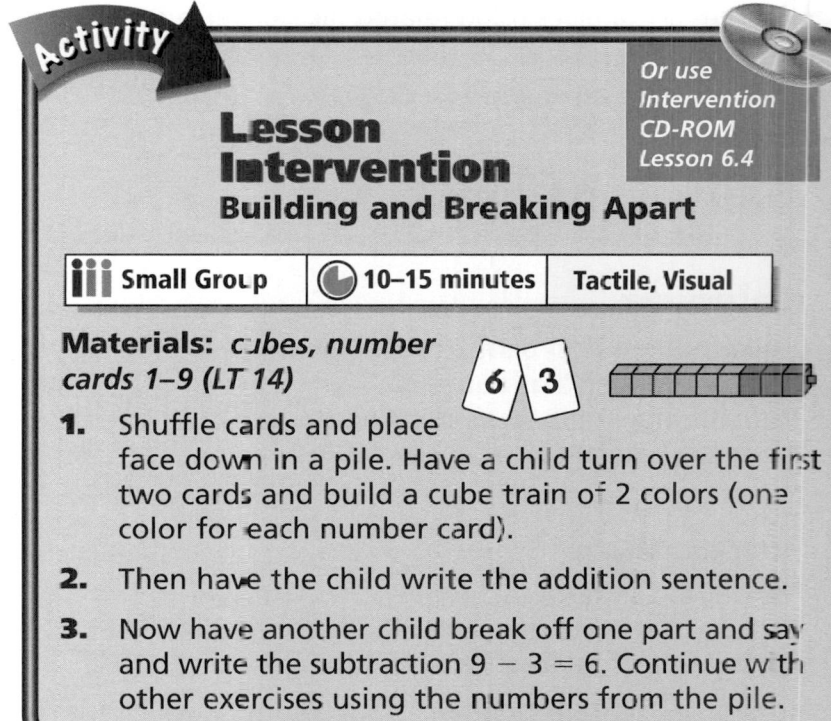

Activity

Lesson Intervention
Building and Breaking Apart

Or use Intervention CD-ROM Lesson 6.4

Small Group   **10–15 minutes**   **Tactile, Visual**

Materials: cubes, number cards 1–9 (LT 14)

1. Shuffle cards and place face down in a pile. Have a child turn over the first two cards and build a cube train of 2 colors (one color for each number card).

2. Then have the child write the addition sentence.

3. Now have another child break off one part and say and write the subtraction 9 − 3 = 6. Continue with other exercises using the numbers from the pile.

---

3 Practice

Independent Practice

Children complete **Exercises 1–7** independently.

Algebra Readiness

After children complete **Exercises 8–9,** call on volunteers to share their solutions. Discuss the related addition and subtraction.

Common Error

Confusing Parts and Whole
Some children may confuse the parts and whole when they go to subtract the related fact. Demonstrate how the sum in the addition fact is the same as the number they subtract from. Then relate the parts.

4 Assess and Close

How are 7 + 2 = 9 and 9 − 2 = 7 the same? (They have the same parts and wholes.)

If you know 8 + 1 = 9, how can it help you subtract 9 − 1? (The facts are related, so the parts are the same.)

Keeping a Journal

Write two related facts. Draw a picture to show how the facts are related.

CHAPTER 6   Lesson 4   154

Fact Families

Lesson 6.5

PLANNING THE LESSON

MATHEMATICS OBJECTIVE
Write fact families using related facts (inverse operations).

Use Lesson Planner CD-ROM for Lesson 6.5.

Daily Routines

Calendar
Have children find pairs of numbers on the calendar that equal 10. Describe the numbers as parts and 10 as the whole. ($1 + 9, 2 + 8, 3 + 7, 4 + 6$)

Sunday	Monday	Tuesday	Wednesday	Thursday	Friday	Saturday
			1	2	3	4
5	6	7	8	9	10	11
12	13	14	15	16	17	18
19	20	21	22	23	24	25
26	27	28	29	30	31	

Vocabulary
Introduce the term **fact family**. Explain that a fact family is made up of two sets of **related facts**. Use the vocabulary cards for fact family and related facts to help children understand the two terms.

Vocabulary Cards

Meeting North Carolina's Standards

1.03 Develop fluency with single-digit addition and corresponding differences using strategies such as modeling, composing and decomposing quantities, using doubles, and making tens.

Lesson Transparency 6.5

Problem of the Day
Jade wants to take 5 picture books and 3 chapter books home from the library. She can only take 6 books home. How many books does Jade need to leave at the library? (2)

Quick Review
$4 + 5 = $ (9) $9 - 5 = $ (4)
$3 + 6 = $ (9) $9 - 6 = $ (3)

Lesson Quiz
Complete the fact family.
___ (4) + ___ (3) = ___ (7)
___ (3) + ___ (4) = ___ (7)
___ (7) − ___ (3) = ___ (4)
___ (7) − ___ (4) = ___ (3)

Whole	
7	
Part	Part
4	3

LEVELED PRACTICE

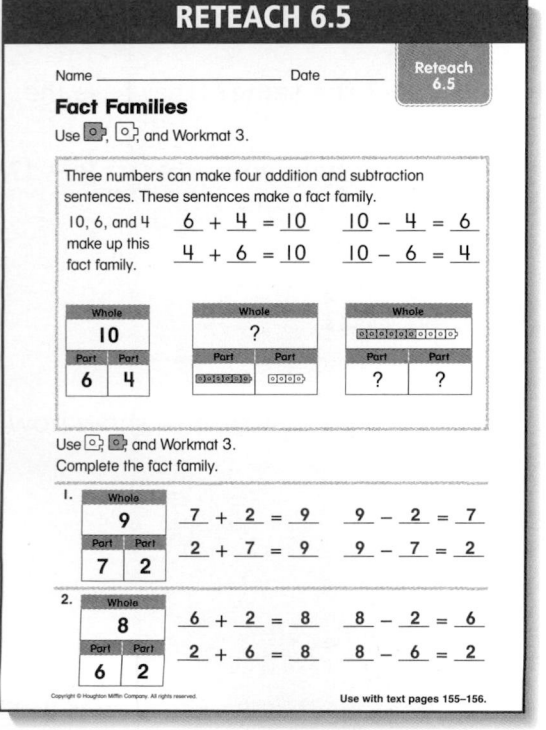

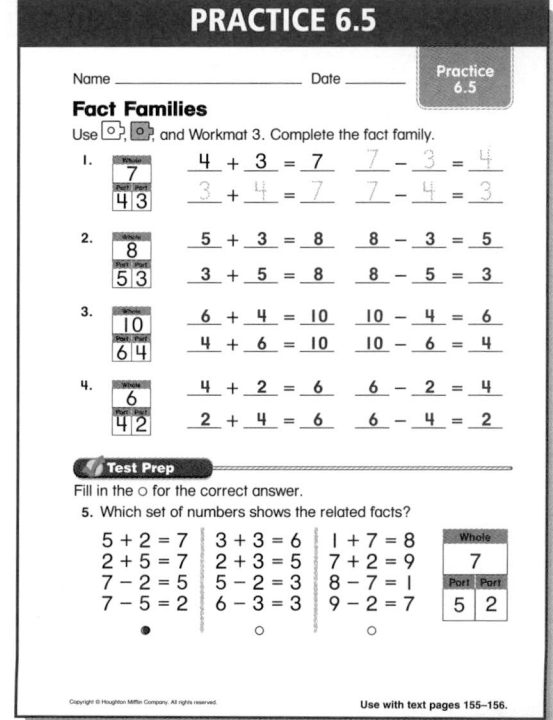

ENRICHMENT 6.5

Name _____ Date _____ **Enrichment 6.5**

All in the Family

Choose one number from the ☾.
Choose one number from the ☆.
Use the numbers to complete the fact family for each ✿.

☾ 1, 2, 3, 4   ☆ 3, 4, 5, 6

1. ✿   **2.** ✿ **Answers will vary.**

___ + ___ = ___   ___ + ___ = ___
___ + ___ = ___   ___ + ___ = ___
___ − ___ = ___   ___ − ___ = ___
___ − ___ = ___   ___ − ___ = ___

3. ✿   **4.** ✿

___ + ___ = ___   ___ + ___ = ___
___ + ___ = ___   ___ + ___ = ___
___ − ___ = ___   ___ − ___ = ___
___ − ___ = ___   ___ − ___ = ___

Write About It How many addition and subtraction facts are there for the numbers 3, 3, and 6? Why?
Possible answer: There is just one addition and one subtraction fact. There are two 3s so the numbers can't be reversed.

Practice Workbook Page 39

Reaching All Learners
Differentiated Instruction

English Learners

English-language learners may not have the language skills to explain the process behind their thinking. Use Worksheet 6.5 to provide children with sentence frames they can use to complete the Explain Your Thinking activity.

Inclusion
VISUAL, AUDITORY

Materials: Workmat 3

- Write numbers for a fact on a part-part-whole mat. Help the child use the numbers to name 2 addition facts, then 2 subtraction facts. Record each fact on paper.

Whole	
10	
Part	Part
6	4

Early Finishers
VISUAL, TACTILE

- Have children draw a picture that shows why doubles facts only have 2 facts in a fact family.
- Then have each child share the drawing with a classmate and work together to make a list of fact families for doubles facts to 10.

$$1 + 1 = 2 \qquad 2 - 1 = 1$$
$$2 + 2 = 4 \qquad 4 - 2 = 2$$
$$4 + 4 = 8 \qquad 8 - 4 = 4$$
$$5 + 5 = 10 \qquad 10 - 5 = 5$$

TECHNOLOGY

Spiral Review

You can prepare students for standardized tests with **customized** spiral review on key skills using the *Ways to Assess* CD-ROM.

Education Place

Visit **Data Place** at eduplace.com/dataplace/ to take a survey and see graphs of the results.

Manipulatives

Interactive Connecting Cubes with several workmats are available on the *Ways to Success* CD-ROM.

 ## Social Studies Connection

Discuss how families may differ in the number of adults and children. Record the fact family for 2 adults and 3 children. $(2 + 3 = 5, 3 + 2 = 5, 5 - 3 = 2, 5 - 2 = 3.)$

 ## MATH CENTER

Vocabulary Activity

This vocabulary-building activity helps children understand and remember new words. Encourage children to use the words in math discussion.

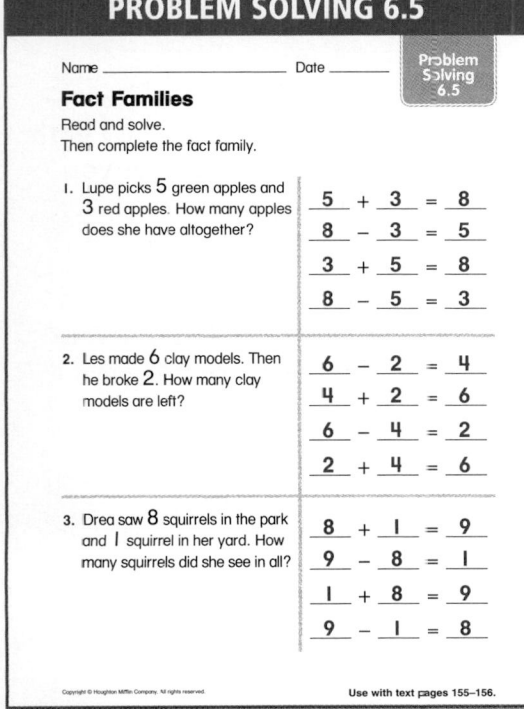

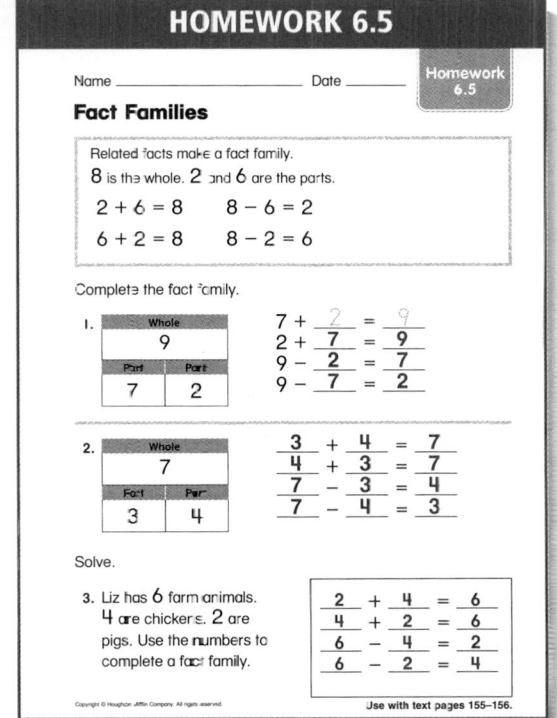

Homework Workbook Page 39

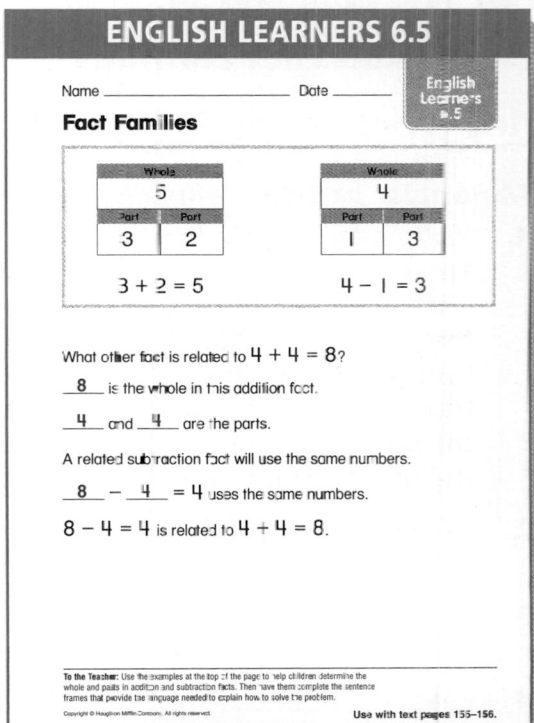

TEACHING LESSON 6.5

LESSON ORGANIZER

Objective Write fact families using related facts (inverse operations).

Resources Reteach, Practice, Enrichment, Problem Solving, Homework, English Learners, Transparencies, Math Center

Materials Part-part-whole transparency, cubes, Workmat 3

Activity

Warm-Up Activity
Modeling Related Facts

| 👤👤👤 Small Group | ⏱ 5 minutes | Visual, Auditory |

Materials: *part-part-whole transparency, cubes*

1. Review how cube trains can show related addition and subtraction facts. Place a train of 2 cubes and a train of 4 cubes on the part-part-whole mat. **What addition fact do you see?** (2 + 4 = 6) Write 6 in the whole section and cover the 2 cubes. **What subtraction fact do you see?** (6 − 4 = 2)

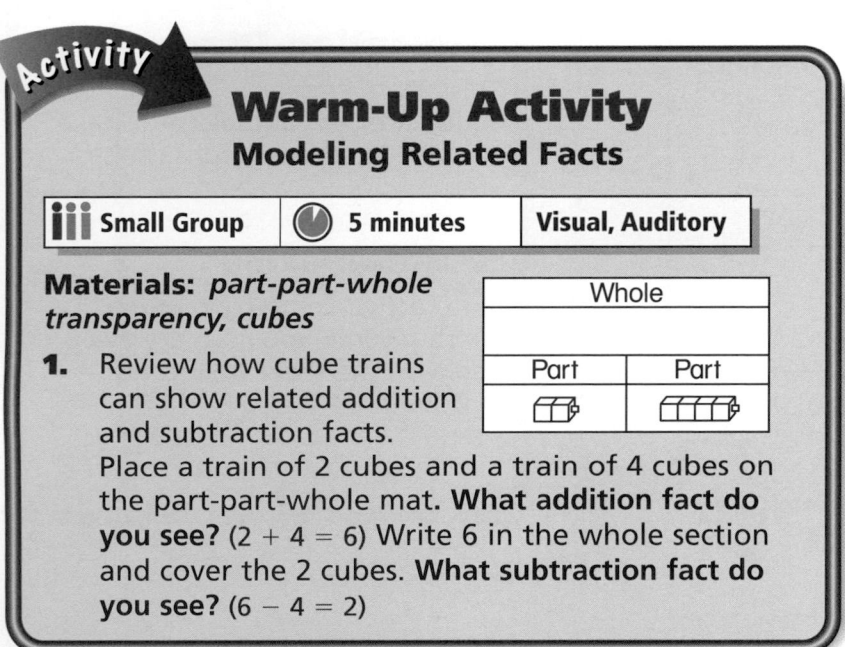

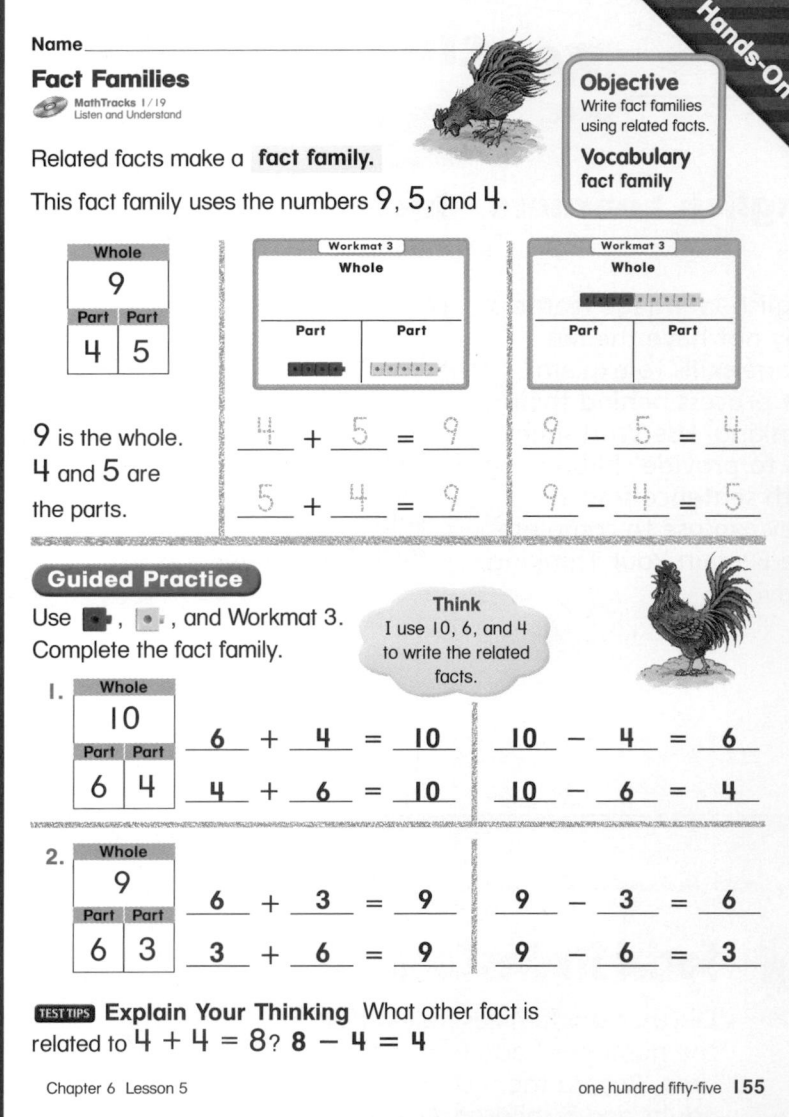

---

1 Introduce
Model Fact Families

| 👤👤👤👤 Whole Group | ⏱ 10–15 minutes | Tactile, Visual |

Materials: *part-part whole transparency, cubes*

1. *Write a fact family for 2, 4, and 6.* Discuss what children know about related addition and subtraction facts. Then place 2 cubes and 4 cubes on the part-sections of the part-part-whole mat. **What addition fact do you see?** (2 + 4 = 6) Then switch the placement of the cube trains and have children name the addition fact now shown. (4 + 2 = 6) Write 6 under the word Whole on the mat and write the facts on the board.

2. Use the mat and cube trains to model the 2 subtraction facts and write them on the board.

3. **How many facts are in this fact family?** (4) Point out that there are 2 addition facts and 2 subtraction facts.

4. Repeat with another example.

2 Develop

Guided Learning

Teaching Example Read the objective and vocabulary with children. Have children use cubes and Workmat 3 as you guide them through each step of the example.

Guided Practice

Have children complete **Exercises 1–2** as you observe. Give children the opportunity to answer the Explain Your Thinking question. Then discuss why there are only two facts in a doubles fact family.

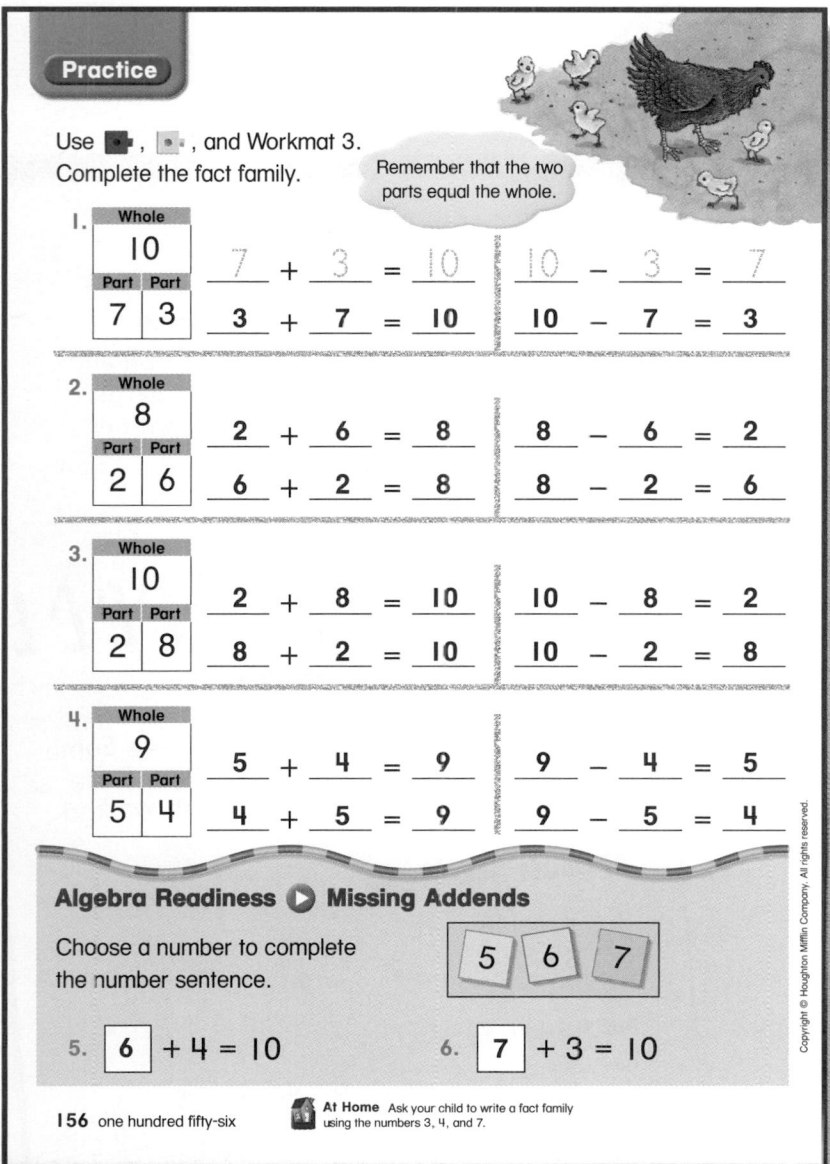

Practice

Use ■, ▪, and Workmat 3.
Complete the fact family.

Remember that the two parts equal the whole.

1.

Whole
10

Part	Part
7	3

$7 + 3 = 10$ $10 - 3 = 7$
$3 + 7 = 10$ $10 - 7 = 3$

2.

Whole
8

Part	Part
2	6

$2 + 6 = 8$ $8 - 6 = 2$
$6 + 2 = 8$ $8 - 2 = 6$

3.

Whole
10

Part	Part
2	8

$2 + 8 = 10$ $10 - 8 = 2$
$8 + 2 = 10$ $10 - 2 = 8$

4.

Whole
9

Part	Part
5	4

$5 + 4 = 9$ $9 - 4 = 5$
$4 + 5 = 9$ $9 - 5 = 4$

Algebra Readiness ▶ Missing Addends

Choose a number to complete
the number sentence.

5	6	7

5. $\boxed{6} + 4 = 10$ **6.** $\boxed{7} + 3 = 10$

156 one hundred fifty-six

At Home Ask your child to write a fact family using the numbers 3, 4, and 7.

Daily Test Prep

Which fact completes the fact family shown?

$8 + 2 = 10$
$2 + 8 = 10$
$10 - 2 = 8$

$7 + 3 = 10$ $10 - 8 = 2$ $8 - 2 = 6$ $10 - 5 = 5$
   ○   ●   ○   ○

Activity

Lesson Intervention
Domino Families

Or use Intervention CD-ROM Lesson 6.5

i Individual	⏱ 5 minutes	Tactile, Visual

1. Children may benefit from using a different model. Help the group create paper domino representations for some of the exercises.

$2 + 6 = 8$
$6 + 2 = 8$

2. Have children place the domino on the table and explain how to use the domino. Now have children turn the domino to show the related addition fact. Have children take turns presenting an exercise. Suggest they cover parts of the domino as they identify the subtraction facts.

3. Have children write each related fact as it is presented.

---

3 Practice

Independent Practice

Children complete **Exercises 1–4** independently.

Algebra Readiness

After children complete **Exercises 5–6**, call on volunteers to share their solutions. Encourage children to share how they solved each problem.

Common Error

Incomplete Fact Families

Some children may mistakenly write the same fact twice. Tell children to check that the numbers of each fact are in a different order.

4 Assess and Close

If 5 is the whole and 4 and 1 are the parts, what addition sentences and subtraction sentences can you write? ($4 + 1 = 5, 1 + 4 = 5, 5 - 1 = 4, 5 - 4 = 1$)

Why are these 4 facts called a fact family? (The facts are related, the parts and wholes are the same.)

 **Keeping a Journal**

Write a fact family you know. Draw a picture to show the facts.

Use Subtraction Strategies

PLANNING THE LESSON

MATHEMATICS OBJECTIVE
Subtract using different strategies.

Use Lesson Planner CD-ROM for Lesson 6.6.

Meeting North Carolina's Standards

1.03 Develop fluency with single-digit addition and corresponding differences using strategies such as modeling, composing and decomposing quantities, using doubles, and making tens.

Daily Routines

Calendar

Have children name the date that is 1 week from today, the day before yesterday, and a week ago. Discuss the different strategies or ways to find dates on a calendar.

Sunday	Monday	Tuesday	Wednesday	Thursday	Friday	Saturday
			1	2	3	4
5	6	7	8	9	10	11
12	13	14	15	16	17	18
19	20	21	22	23	24	25
26	27	28	29	30	31	

Vocabulary

Say a subtraction fact and label the **difference**. Repeat with an addition problem and review the term **sum**. Have volunteers name other facts and identify the number that is the sum or difference.

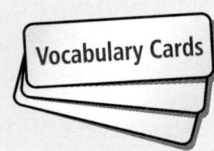
Vocabulary Cards

Lesson Transparency 6.6

Problem of the Day

8 horses are in the field on a hot day. Some walk away to stand under the trees. 5 are left on the field. How many horses walked away? (3)

Quick Review

$8 + 2 =$ (10) $\quad 10 - 2 =$ (8)
$6 + 3 =$ (9) $\quad 9 - 3 =$ (6)

Lesson Quiz

1. $\begin{array}{r} 7 \\ -3 \\ \hline (4) \end{array}$ **2.** $\begin{array}{r} 5 \\ -1 \\ \hline (4) \end{array}$ **3.** $\begin{array}{r} 8 \\ -3 \\ \hline (5) \end{array}$ **4.** $\begin{array}{r} 9 \\ -5 \\ \hline (4) \end{array}$ **5.** $\begin{array}{r} 6 \\ -0 \\ \hline (6) \end{array}$

LEVELED PRACTICE

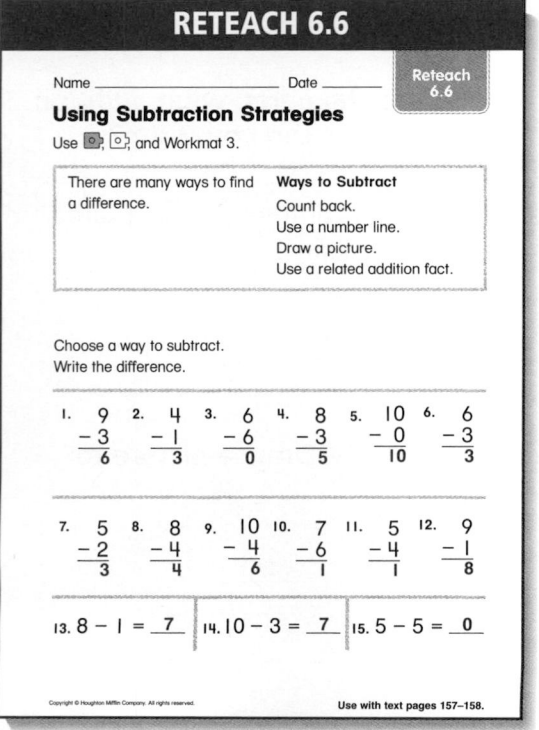

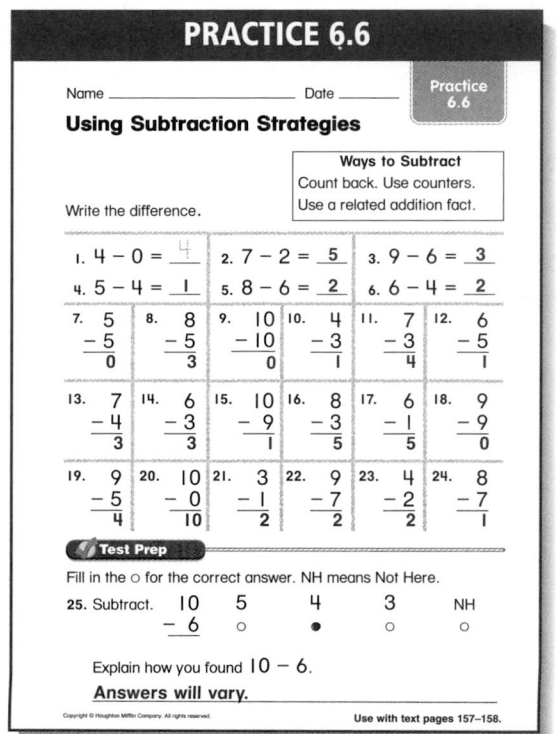

ENRICHMENT 6.6

Name _____ Date _____ Enrichment 6.6

It's All Good

Read the problem. Use the different ways to subtract.

Donna had 8 🎈. She gave 3 🎈 to Lyn. How many 🎈 does she have left?

Ways to Subtract
Count back
Use a number line
Draw a picture
Use a related addition fact

1. Count back.
8 _7_ , _6_ , _5_

2. Use a number line.

3. Draw a picture.
Check children's drawings.

4. Use a related fact.
_3_ (+) _5_ (=) _8_

Write About It Is there more than one way to solve the problem. Explain.
Yes, I could use any of the strategies.

Use with text pages 157–158.

Practice Workbook Page 40

Reaching All Learners

Differentiated Instruction

English Learners

In order to complete some word problems, children will need to understand the meaning of the words *inside* and *outside*. Use Worksheet 6.6 to develop children's understanding of these words.

Inclusion

TACTILE, AUDITORY

Materials: *cubes, number line 0–10 (LT 8)*

- Write 8 − 3 = ___. Help the child place a cube on the numbers 1–8 on the number line.
- Have the child take away the last 3 cubes as he or she counts back.
- Complete the subtraction.

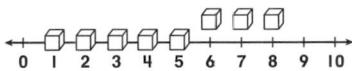

Early Finishers

VISUAL, TACTILE

- Have children write the related addition, without the sum, for 4 of the subtraction exercises on the page.
- Then each child can exchange papers with a classmate and find the sums of the related facts.

$$\begin{array}{cccc} 3 & 6 & 1 & 3 \\ +7 & +4 & +6 & +3 \end{array}$$

Science Connection

Discuss what children know about the moon. Explain that we see Earth's moon and that other planets also have moons.

Pluto also has 1, Mars has 2, and Neptune has 13. Pose problems comparing the number of moons.

MATH CENTER

Basic Skills Activity

Motivate children to build basic skills. Use this activity to address multiple learning styles using hands-on activities related to the skills of this lesson.

TECHNOLOGY

Spiral Review

Create **customized** spiral review worksheets for individual students using the *Ways to Assess* CD-ROM.

eBook

An electronic version of this lesson can be found in **eMathBook**.

Games

Students can practice their skills using the **Rock Hopper** math game, available on the *Ways to Success* CD-ROM.

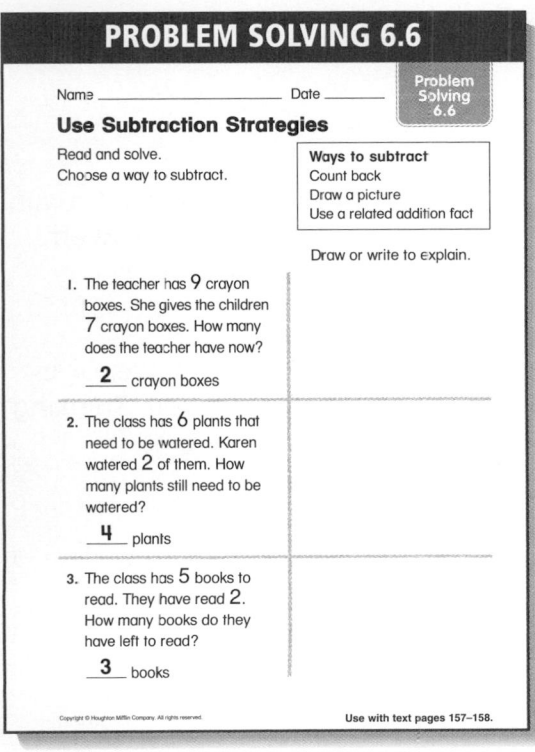

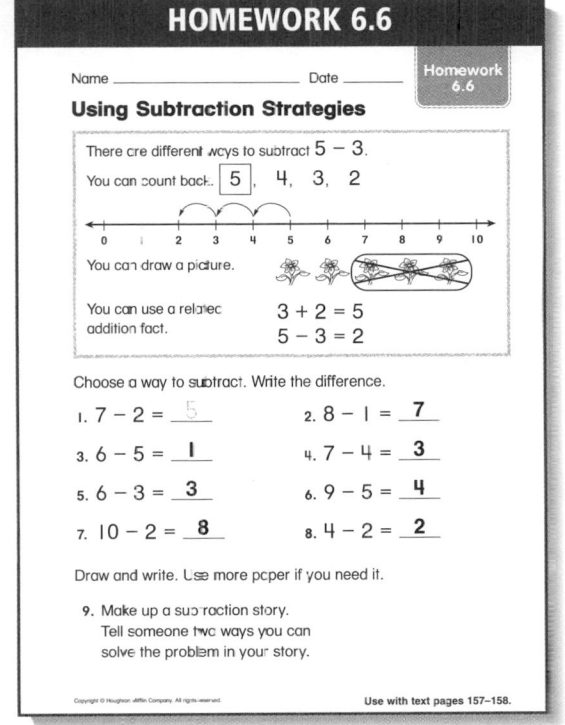

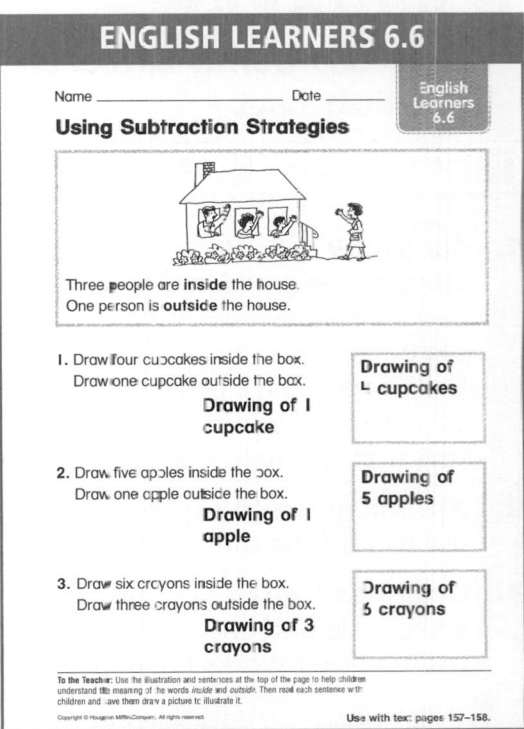

TEACHING LESSON 6.6

Warm-Up Activity
Modeling Subtraction on a Number Line

| 👥 **Small Group** | ⏱ **5 minutes** | **Visual, Auditory** |

1. Review how to count back on a number line. **We will subtract 10 minus 3. We can use the number line.** Point to 10 on the number line. **Start at 10. Count back 3.** Point at each number as you say: **9, 8, 7.** Say the subtraction sentence: **10 minus 3 equals 7.**

2. Ask if any child counts back without using the number line. Have volunteers tell how they count back mentally. Explain that the process is the same, except they don't use the number line.

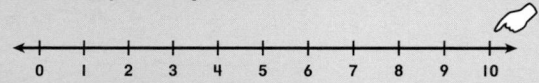

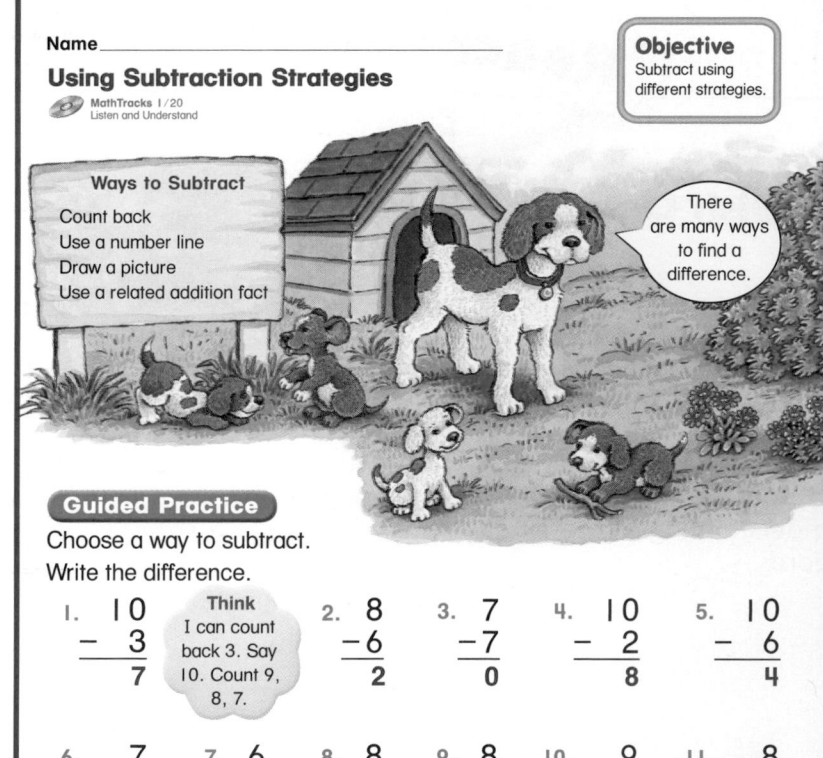

Name_____

Using Subtraction Strategies

Objective Subtract using different strategies.

MathTracks 1 / 20
Listen and Understand

Ways to Subtract
Count back
Use a number line
Draw a picture
Use a related addition fact

There are many ways to find a difference.

Guided Practice

Choose a way to subtract.
Write the difference.

| 1. | 10 − 3 = 7 | *Think I can count back 3. Say 10. Count 9, 8, 7.* | 2. | 8 − 6 = 2 | 3. | 7 − 7 = 0 | 4. | 10 − 2 = 8 | 5. | 10 − 6 = 4 |

| 6. | 7 − 6 = 1 | 7. | 6 − 3 = 3 | 8. | 8 − 0 = 8 | 9. | 8 − 7 = 1 | 10. | 9 − 4 = 5 | 11. | 8 − 4 = 4 |

12. $7 - 2 = \underline{5}$ 13. $10 - 4 = \underline{6}$ 14. $9 - 9 = \underline{0}$

15. $10 - 5 = \underline{5}$ 16. $10 - 1 = \underline{9}$ 17. $9 - 5 = \underline{4}$

TEST TIPS Explain Your Thinking How did you find $9 - 5$? **Answers may vary. Children may use counters or draw a picture because this is a harder fact.**

Chapter 6 Lesson 6   one hundred fifty-seven **157**

 **Introduce**

Discuss Using Different Strategies to Subtract

| 👥 **Whole Group** | ⏱ **10–15 minutes** | **Auditory, Tactile** |

1. *Subtract 9 − 3.* Write 9 − 3 on the board. **What is one strategy we could use to solve this exercise?** (Count back on number line.) **What other ways could we subtract?** (Children might suggest using counters, counting back, or drawing a picture.) Point out that you can also use a related addition fact. **Do you know an addition fact that will help you solve 9 − 3?** (6 + 3)

2. Ask volunteers to explain a different strategy they may use to find the difference.

3. Discuss each strategy. Point out that any strategy is acceptable and encourage children to choose the strategy that works for them for a given exercise.

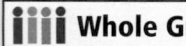 **Develop**

Guided Learning

Teaching Example Read the objective with children. Explain the meaning of strategy as a way to do something. Read aloud the text in the list as you discuss each strategy.

Guided Practice

Have children complete **Exercises 1–17** as you observe. Give children the opportunity to answer the Explain Your Thinking question. Then discuss their responses with the class.

Practice

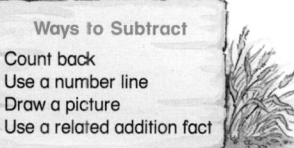

Choose a way to subtract.

Ways to Subtract
- Count back
- Use a number line
- Draw a picture
- Use a related addition fact

Write the difference.

1. 3
   −3
   ___
   0

2. 5
   −0
   ___
   5

3. 2
   −1
   ___
   1

4. 8
   −5
   ___
   3

5. 7
   −5
   ___
   2

6. 6
   −6
   ___
   0

7. 9
   −7
   ___
   2

8. 7
   −3
   ___
   4

9. 9
   −0
   ___
   9

10. 5
    −4
    ___
    1

11. 10
    −10
    ___
    0

12. 9
    −8
    ___
    1

13. 9
    −3
    ___
    6

14. 4
    −0
    ___
    4

15. 6
    −4
    ___
    2

16. 1
    −0
    ___
    1

17. 9
    −6
    ___
    3

18. 7
    −4
    ___
    3

19. 7 − 0 = __7__   20. 5 − 1 = __4__   21. 10 − 8 = __2__

22. 3 − 2 = __1__   23. 6 − 5 = __1__   24. 6 − 2 = __4__

Problem Solving ▶ Logical Thinking

Use clues to find the number.

25. I am inside a shape.
    I am greater than 5.
    I am less than 9.
    I am not in the triangle.

    Which number am I? __8__

158 one hundred fifty-eight

At Home Ask your child to explain how to subtract 10 − 4 using different strategies.

Daily Test Prep

Subtract.

8 − 1 = ___

7   8   9   10
●   ○   ○   ○

Activity

Or use Intervention CD-ROM Lesson 6.6

Lesson Intervention
Using Counters to Subtract

| iii Small Group | ⏱ 10–15 minutes | Tactile, Visual |

Materials: *counters*

1. Provide several exercises and have children use counters to find the differences.

2. As children work, introduce one strategy to each child. For example, model how using the number line might be quicker than showing 10 counters to subtract 2. Or that the child could draw a picture to show 8, then cross out 6.

3. Conclude by encouraging children to share the strategies they tried with other members of the group.

---

3 Practice

Independent Practice

Children complete **Exercises 1–24** independently.

Problem Solving

After children complete **Exercise 25**, call on volunteers to share their answers. Draw the picture on the board and encourage children to use it as they discuss how they solved the problem.

Common Error

Incorrectly Applying a Strategy
Children may confuse parts and wholes when trying to use addition to find a difference. Provide additional practice with part-part-whole mats and counters.

4 Assess and Close

Which strategy did you use to solve 6 − 2? (Answers may vary.)

Why is it good to know several ways to subtract? (Answers may vary. I can choose the way that works best for different facts.)

Keeping a Journal

Write about a subtraction strategy you use. Show how you use it.

Problem Solving: Choose the Operation

PLANNING THE LESSON

MATHEMATICS OBJECTIVE
Solve problems by choosing the correct operation.

Use Lesson Planner CD-ROM for Lesson 6.7.

Meeting North Carolina's Standards
1.04 Create, model, and solve problems that use addition, subtraction, and fair shares (between two or three).

Also 1.03

Daily Routines

Calendar
Point to two weeks with a different number of days in the month. Ask children how they can find out how many more days are in one week than the other. Have children identify whether they subtracted or added to solve.

Vocabulary
Review the meaning of the terms **addition** and **subtraction**. Ask children to describe situations when they use addition and when they use subtraction.

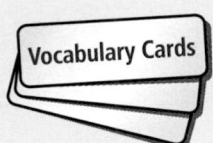
Vocabulary Cards

Lesson Transparency
6.7

Problem of the Day
The Yen farm has 5 cows, 10 chickens, and 3 pigs. How many more animals at the farm have 2 legs than 4 legs? (2 more animals)

Quick Review

$$\begin{array}{ccccc} 10 & 7 & 5 & 8 & 9 \\ -0 & -7 & -1 & -3 & -4 \\ \hline (10) & (0) & (4) & (5) & (5) \end{array}$$

Lesson Quiz
Add or subtract to solve.

There are 6 chickens inside the coop and 3 chickens outside.

How many chickens are there in all? (9 chickens)

LEVELED PRACTICE

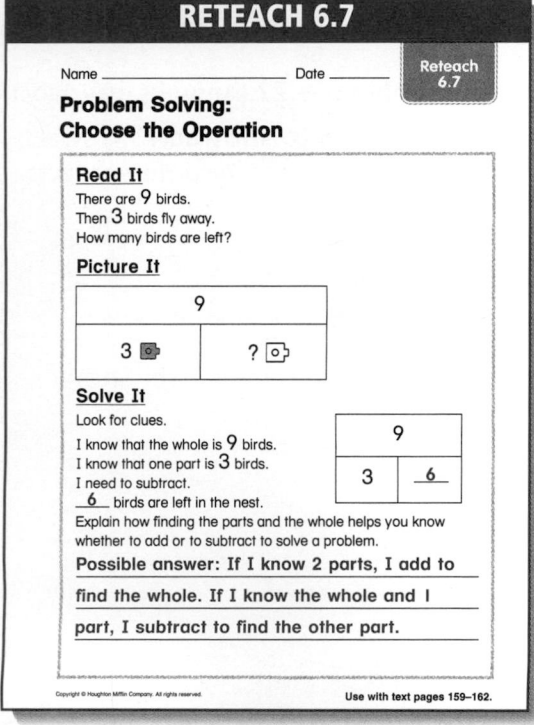

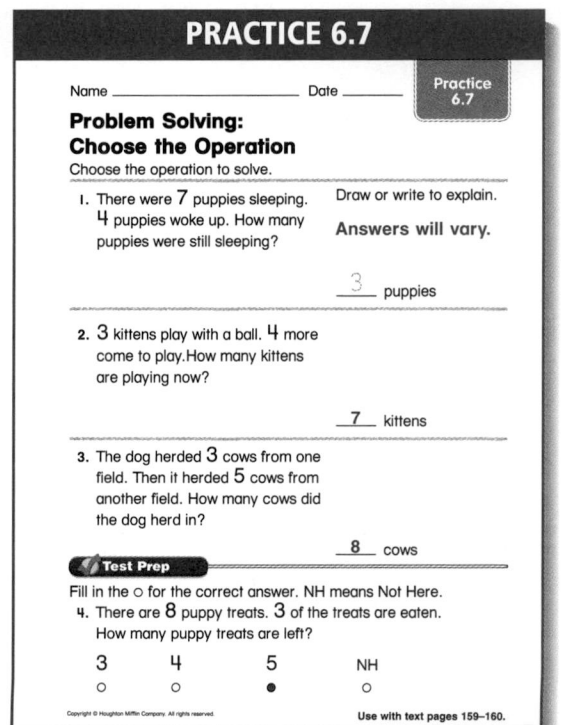

Reaching All Learners

Differentiated Instruction

English Learners

English-language learners may not know the correct subject-verb agreement in order to understand word problems. Use Worksheet 6.7 to develop children's understanding of subject-verb agreement for the verb *go*.

Inclusion

TACTILE, VISUAL

Materials: *Workmat 3, counters*

- Present a simple problem. There are 8 dogs. 3 leave. How many dogs are left?
- Show 8 counters on the part-part-whole mat, move 3 to make a part. **There are 5 dogs left.**
- Repeat with similar addition problems.

Gifted and Talented

VISUAL, TACTILE

- Have children work in pairs. Each child writes the first two sentences of a problem; such as: There are 6 cows in the barn. 2 cows leave.
- They exchange papers and write the question for their partner's problem; such as: How many cows are left?
- They exchange papers once again and solve the problem.

TECHNOLOGY

Spiral Review

Using the *Ways to Assess* CD-ROM, you can create **customized** spiral review worksheets covering any lessons you choose.

Education Place

Encourage students to visit **Education Place** at eduplace.com/kids/mw/ for more student activities.

Intervention

Use the *Ways to Success* CD-ROM intervention software to support students who need more help in understanding the concepts and skills taught in this chapter.

Ways to Success

Social Studies Connection

Help children name all the farm animals mentioned in the lesson. Write each name on an index card.

Discuss ways to classify farm animals (such as number of legs). Create simple addition and subtraction problems.

MATH CENTER

Number of the Week Activity

Display the Number of the Week to motivate children to use their problem-solving skills. The exercises cover topics across all math strands.

PROBLEM SOLVING 6.7

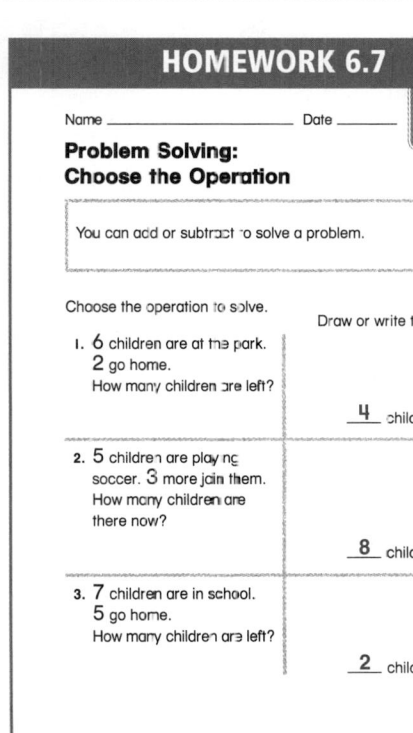

Homework Workbook Page 41

HOMEWORK 6.7

ENGLISH LEARNERS 6.7

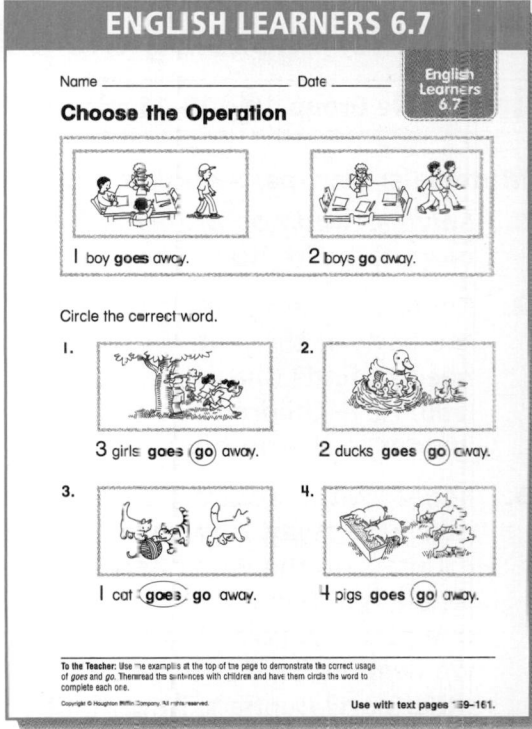

TEACHING LESSON 6.7

LESSON ORGANIZER

Objective Solve problems by choosing the correct operation.

Resources Reteach, Practice, Enrichment, Problem Solving, Homework, English Learners, Transparencies, Math Center

Materials Part-part-whole transparency, counters, Workmat 3

Activity

Warm-Up Activity
Modeling Addition and Subtraction

👥 Small Group	🕐 5 minutes	Auditory, Visual

1. Present an addition problem using things from your class-room. For example, **I have 2 red markers and 3 blue markers on my desk. How many markers do I have in all?** (5 markers) **Did you use addition or subtraction to solve?** (addition) Discuss why addition was used to solve.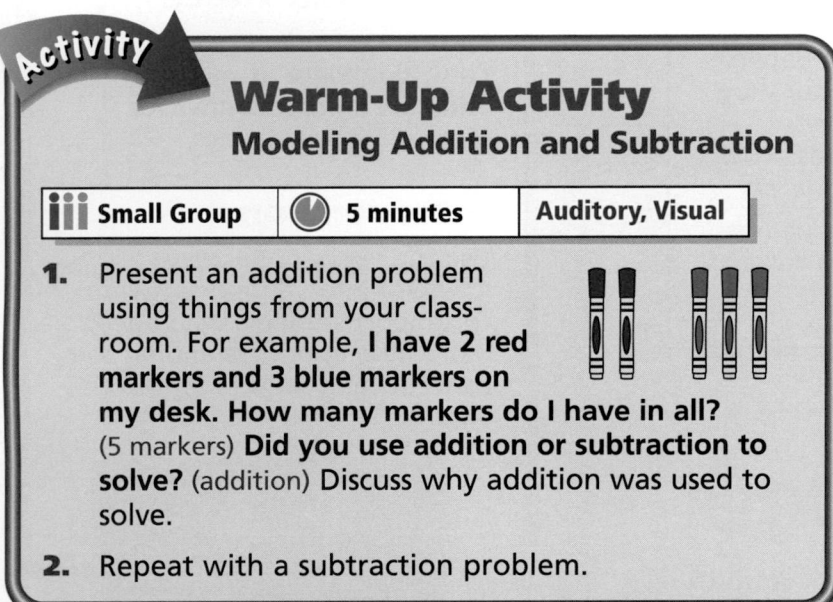

2. Repeat with a subtraction problem.

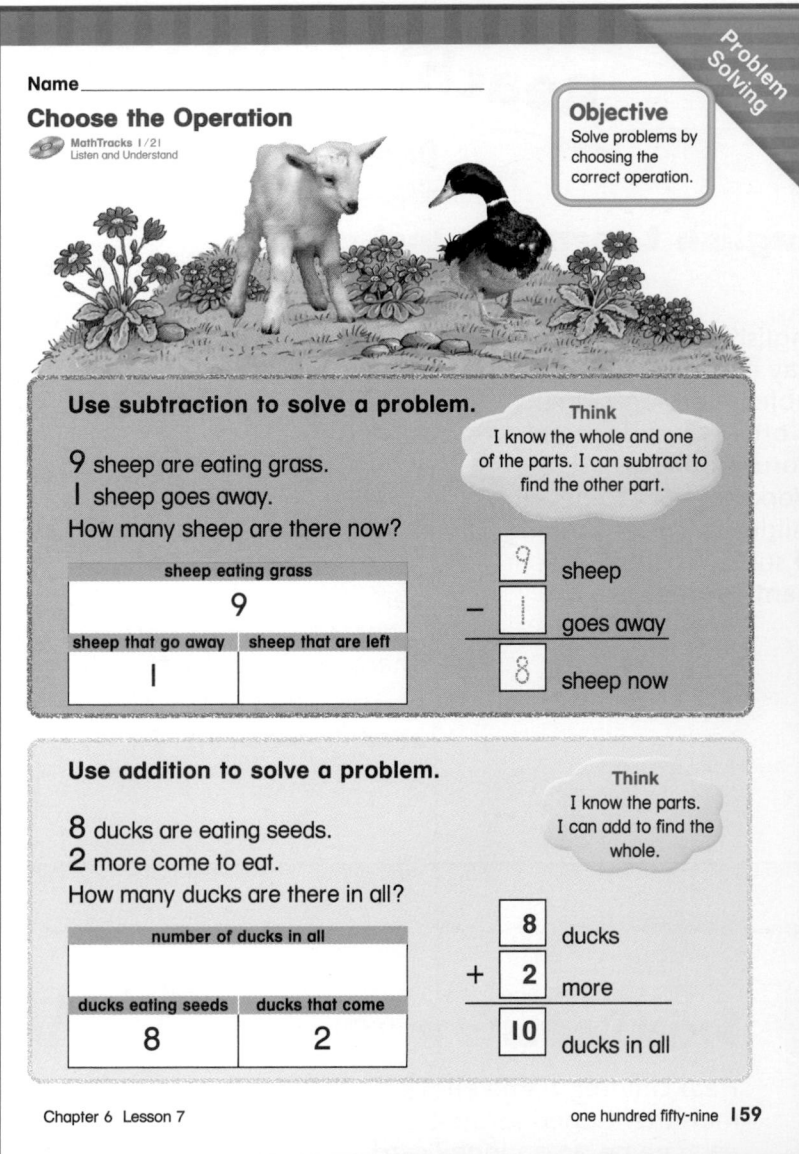

Name_____

Choose the Operation

MathTracks 1/21
Listen and Understand

Objective
Solve problems by choosing the correct operation.

Use subtraction to solve a problem.

9 sheep are eating grass.
1 sheep goes away.
How many sheep are there now?

Think
I know the whole and one of the parts. I can subtract to find the other part.

sheep eating grass
9

sheep that go away	sheep that are left
1	

9 sheep
− 1 goes away
8 sheep now

Use addition to solve a problem.

8 ducks are eating seeds.
2 more come to eat.
How many ducks are there in all?

Think
I know the parts. I can add to find the whole.

number of ducks in all

ducks eating seeds	ducks that come
8	2

8 ducks
+ 2 more
10 ducks in all

Chapter 6 Lesson 7   one hundred fifty-nine **159**

① Introduce
Model Choosing the Operation

👥 Whole Group	🕐 10–15 minutes	Visual, Auditory

Materials: *part-part-whole transparency, counters*

1. *Solve an addition problem.* 5 roosters are in the barn. 2 more come in. How many roosters are there now?

2. Represent the numbers by placing 5 and 2 counters on the parts of the mat. **We know the parts. What do we need to find?** (the whole) **How can we find the whole?** (add) Have children add to find 7. Emphasize that the answer to the problem is *7 roosters.*

3. Repeat with a subtraction problem. **5 pigs are in the pen. 2 go away. How many pigs are there now?** Place 5 counters on the whole section of the mat. **We know the whole is 5.** Move 2 counters to the first part. **We know one part is 2.** Point to the other part and say: **What do we need to find?** (the other part) **How can we find the other part?** (subtract) Have children subtract to find 3. Emphasize that the answer to the problem is *3 pigs.*

② Develop

Guided Learning

Teaching Example Read the objective with children. Guide them through the two example problems. Reinforce the tips in the Think clouds. Ask the questions in the problems again and have children state the answers as sentences.

Guided Practice

Have children complete **Exercises 1–2** on page 160 as you observe. Encourage children to show their work in the box provided.

Choose the operation to solve.

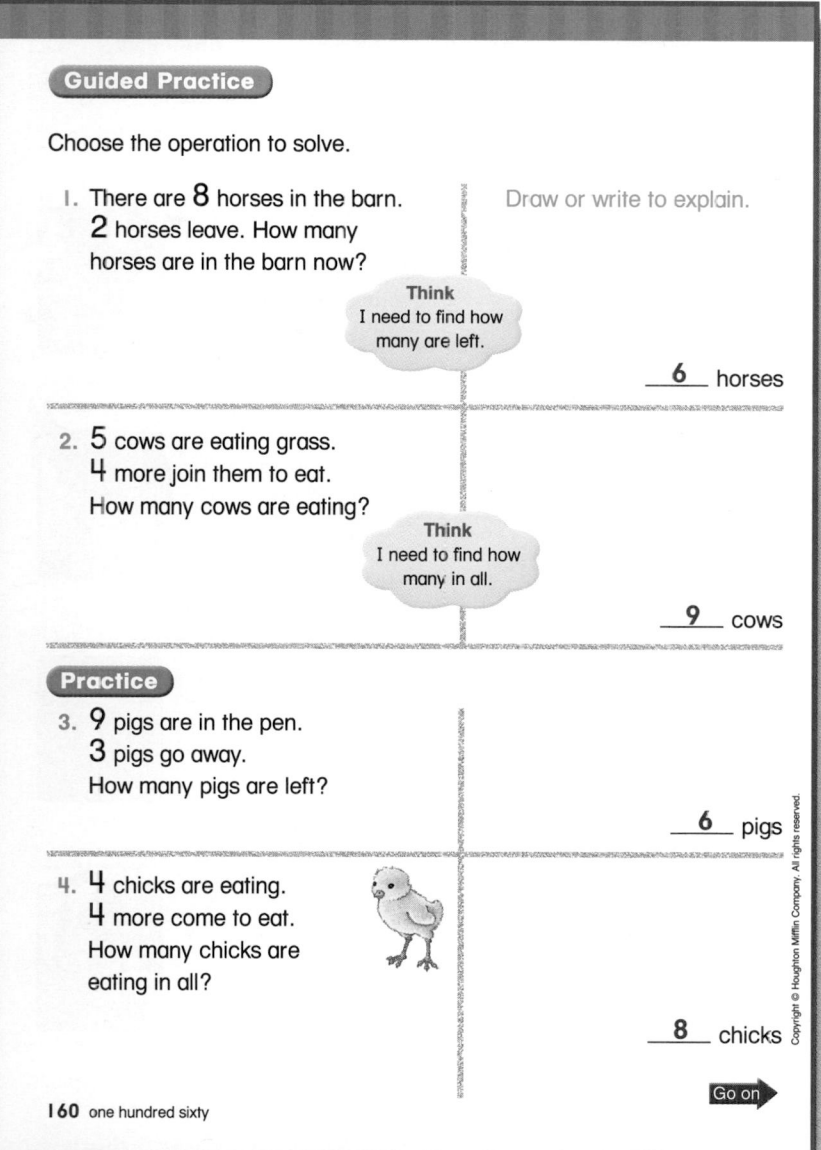

1. There are 8 horses in the barn. 2 horses leave. How many horses are in the barn now?

Draw or write to explain.

Think
I need to find how many are left.

__6__ horses

2. 5 cows are eating grass. 4 more join them to eat. How many cows are eating?

Think
I need to find how many in all.

__9__ cows

Practice

3. 9 pigs are in the pen. 3 pigs go away. How many pigs are left?

__6__ pigs

4. 4 chicks are eating. 4 more come to eat. How many chicks are eating in all?

__8__ chicks

160 one hundred sixty

Go on ▶

KEEPING **SKILLS** SHARP

Play "How Many More Points?"

Assign children partners and give each pair score cards numbered from 0 to 10. Children place the cards in a pile face down. To play, each child takes a score card and turns it face up. The child with the higher score subtracts the partner's score to find how many more points he or she has than the other child. Write the subtraction to check. The cards are placed aside and play continues until all cards are played.

③ Practice

Independent Practice

Children complete **Exercises 3–4** on page 160 independently.

Lesson continues ▶

Daily Test Prep

7 kittens rest in the basket.
2 run away to play.
How many kittens are still in the basket?

2　　4　　**5**　　6
○　　○　　●　　○

Activity

Lesson Intervention

Or use Intervention CD-ROM Lesson 6.7

| 👥 Small Group | 🕐 10–15 minutes | Visual, Tactile |

Materials: *Workmat 3, counters*

| Whole |
| ○○○○○ |

| Part | Part |
| ○○ | |

1. Present a problem such as, **There are 7 horses in the barn. 2 horses are taken outside. How many horses are in the barn now?** Guide children through the problem by using the part-part-whole mat. **What is the whole, the number we start with?** (7) Have children place 7 counters in the whole section of the mat and write 7 under the mat. **A part of the whole is taken away. How many are taken away?** (2) Have children move 2 counters to one part and write 2 under the mat. **Now we need to find the other part. Do we add or subtract?** (subtract) **What number will you write as the difference?** (5) **What is the answer to the problem?** (5 horses)

2. Repeat the procedure with an addition problem.

Name _____

Strategies
Act It Out With Models
Draw a Picture

Choose a Strategy

Solve.

	Draw or write to explain.
1. There are 2 brown cows. There are 5 black cows. How many cows are there in all?	Allow children to use any strategy or method they want. 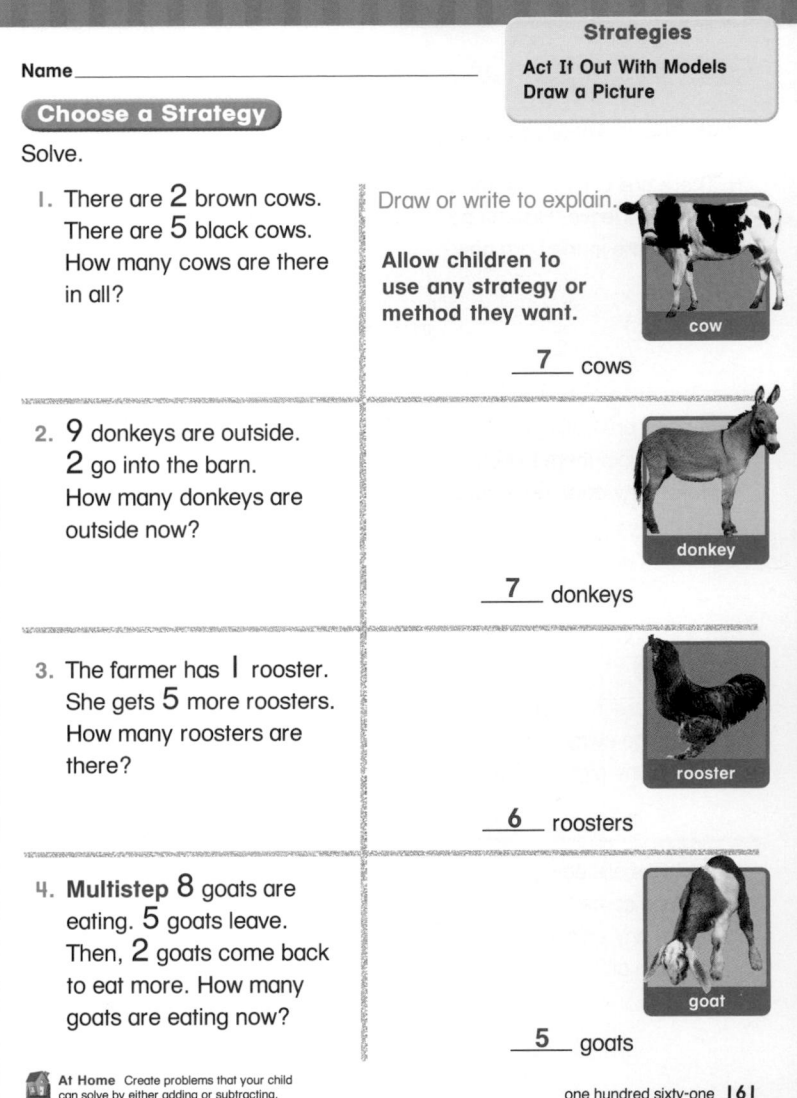 cow
	___7___ cows
2. 9 donkeys are outside. 2 go into the barn. How many donkeys are outside now?	donkey
	___7___ donkeys
3. The farmer has 1 rooster. She gets 5 more roosters. How many roosters are there?	rooster
	___6___ roosters
4. **Multistep** 8 goats are eating. 5 goats leave. Then, 2 goats come back to eat more. How many goats are eating now?	goat
	___5___ goats

🏠 **At Home** Create problems that your child can solve by either adding or subtracting.

one hundred sixty-one 161

---

③ Practice

Mixed Strategy Practice

Read the problem-solving strategies with children. Make sure children can read and comprehend the problems in **Exercises 1–4** on page 161. You might pair more proficient readers with less proficient readers. Encourage them to discuss the problems before solving.

Common Error

Using the Wrong Operation

Provide practice where children use counters to show the problem. Demonstrate that by knowing the parts a child can add to find the whole. Demonstrate that by knowing the whole and one part a child can subtract to find the other part.

④ Assess and Close

3 pigs are in the mud. 2 pigs join them. Do you add or subtract to find how many pigs are in the mud now? (add)

Share a problem about pigs that you can solve with subtraction. (Answers will vary.)

✏️ Keeping a Journal

Draw a picture that shows adding to solve a problem about your favorite farm animal. Write the addition sentence.

Listen to your teacher read the problem.
Solve.

1. There are 4 horses in one stable. There are 6 horses in another stable. How many horses are there in both stables?

Show your work using pictures, numbers, or words.

___10___ horses

2. There are 6 horses in the barn. 2 are taken out for a run. How many horses are still in the barn?

___4___ horses

Listen to your teacher read the problem.
Choose the correct answer.

3. 2   6   8   14
   ●   ○   ○   ○

4. 5   6   9   10
   ○   ○   ●   ○

162 one hundred sixty-two

Problem-Solving for Tests

Listening Skills

This page provides children practice with the oral problem-solving format used in some standardized test items.

You may want to read each item only once to mimic the style of oral tests.

Use with Items 1 and 2

Listening Strategy: Read the problem silently as the teacher reads it aloud.

• *When a problem is on the page, look at the problem as I read it.*

• *Do not start writing until I finish reading the whole problem.*

Use with Item 3

Listening Strategy: Listen to the problem carefully to help you find the answer.

• *Look at me when I read a problem that is not on the page.*

The Dawsons have a horse farm.

They have 8 white horses and 6 spotted horses.

How many more white horses than spotted horses are there?

• *Mark your answer.*

Use with Item 4

Listening Strategy: Listen for important facts and details.

• *Listen to the question so you will know how to use the numbers.*

Aaron brushes the horses at camp.

On Monday he brushes 7 horses.

On Tuesday he brushes 2.

How many horses does he brush on Monday and Tuesday?

• *Use the numbers to solve the problem. Then mark your answer.*

Quick Check

Have children complete the Quick Check exercises independently to assess their understanding of concepts and skills taught in **Lessons 4–7.**

Item	Lesson	Error Analysis	Intervention
1–2	6.4	Children may not understand which number is the whole.	Reteach Resource 6.4 *Ways to Success* 6.4
3	6.5	Children may write the same fact twice when listing a fact family.	Reteach Resource 6.5 *Ways to Success* 6.5
4–8	6.6	Children may incorrectly apply subtraction strategies.	Reteach Resource 6.6 *Ways to Success* 6.6
9	6.7	Children may choose the wrong operation to solve a problem.	Reteach Resource 6.7 *Ways to Success* 6.7

Name _____   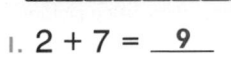 **Quick Check**

Find the sum and the difference.

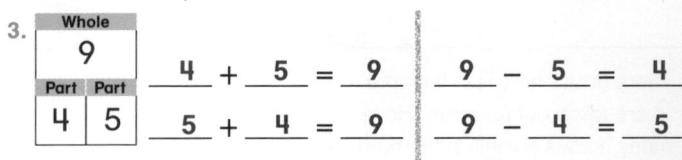

1. 2 + 7 = __9__

   9 − 7 = __2__

2. 5 + 3 = __8__

   8 − 3 = __5__

Write the fact family.

3.

Whole
9

Part	Part
4	5

4 + 5 = 9   9 − 5 = 4

5 + 4 = 9   9 − 4 = 5

Write the difference.

4. 6
  −0
  ‾‾
   6

5. 7
  −2
  ‾‾
   5

6. 10
  − 5
  ‾‾
   5

7. 5
  −1
  ‾‾
   4

8. 4
  −4
  ‾‾
   0

Choose the operation to solve.

9. Rosita has 6 animal cards. Mark gives her 2 more animal cards. How many animal cards does Rosita have now?

   Draw or write to explain.

   __8__ cards

Key Topic Review

This assessment provides a review of skills and concepts taught in Chapter 5.

Check to be sure that children:

• use strategies to find unknown sums
• understand horizontal and vertical form of addition

Science Connection

Have children share their solutions to the problem.

What do red pandas eat? (bamboo)

When do they eat? (in the morning and in the afternoon)

Red pandas are much smaller than the giant black and white pandas. Why do you think some people call red pandas *red cat bears*? (They are about the size of large house cats.)

 **Chapter Review/Test**

Purpose: This test provides an informal assessment of the Chapter 6 objectives.

Chapter Test Terms 1–20

To assign a numerical grade for this Chapter Test, use 5 points for each test item.

Check Understanding

Use children's work on word problems to informally assess progress on chapter content.

Customizing Your Instruction

For children who have not yet mastered these objectives, you can use the reteaching resources listed in the chart below.

 Assessment Options

A summary test for this chapter is also provided in the Unit Resource Folder.

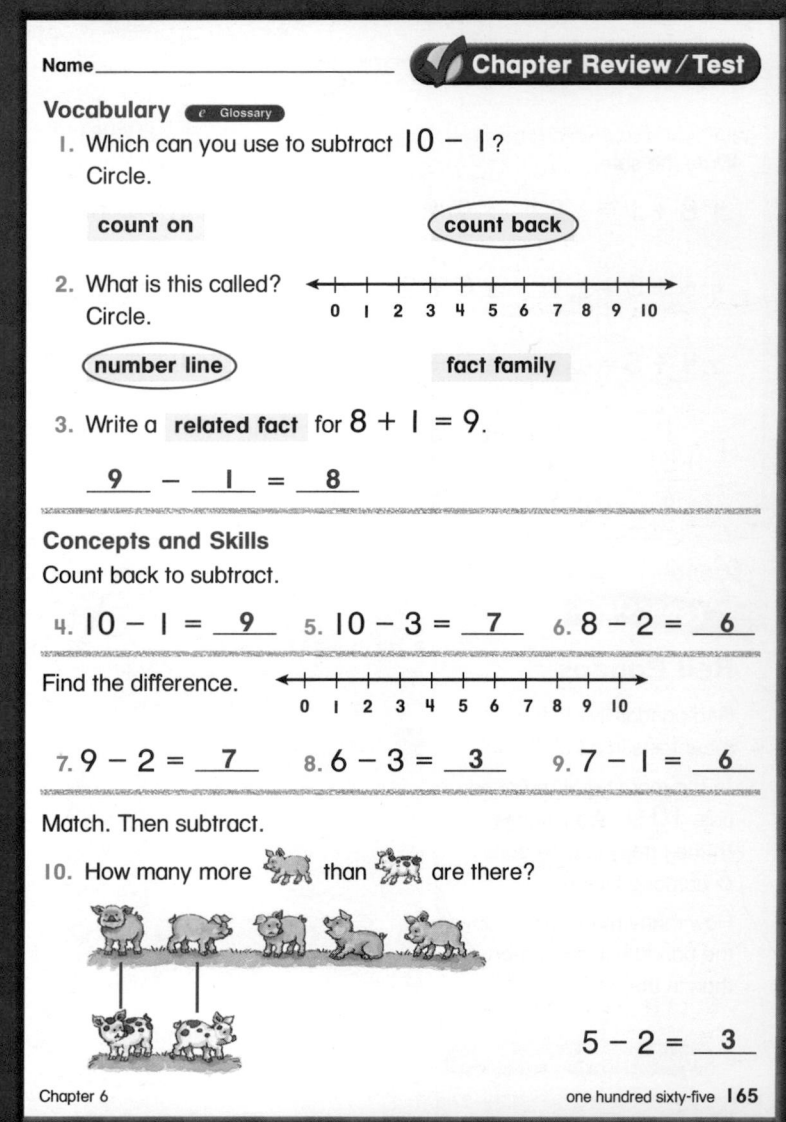

Reteaching Support

Chapter Test Items	Summary Test Items	Chapter Objectives Tested	TE Pages	Use These Reteaching Resources
1–3	1–2	**6A** Develop and use math vocabulary relating to subtraction strategies.	145A–148, 153A–154	Reteach Resources and *Ways to Success* CD: 6.1, 6.2, 6.4 Skillsheet 38
4–10	3–4	**6B** Find differences from 10 using a number line and counting back 1, 2, or 3.	145A–148	Reteach Resource and *Ways to Success* CD: 6.1, 6.2 Skillsheet 39
11–18	5–8	**6C** Write fact families and write and solve related addition and subtraction facts.	149A–150, 153A–158	Reteach Resource and *Ways to Success* CD: 6.3–6.6 Skillsheets 40–41
19–20	9–10	**6D** Solve problems by choosing the correct operation.	159A–160	Reteach Resources and *Ways to Success* CD: 6.7 Skillsheet 42

Complete the related facts.

11. $\begin{array}{r} 7 \\ +2 \\ \hline 9 \end{array}$ $\begin{array}{r} 9 \\ -2 \\ \hline 7 \end{array}$ 12. $\begin{array}{r} 6 \\ +4 \\ \hline 10 \end{array}$ $\begin{array}{r} 10 \\ -4 \\ \hline 6 \end{array}$ 13. $\begin{array}{r} 5 \\ +4 \\ \hline 9 \end{array}$ $\begin{array}{r} 9 \\ -4 \\ \hline 5 \end{array}$

Complete the fact family.

14.

Whole	
10	
Part	Part
3	7

$7 + 3 = 10$ $10 - 3 = 7$

$3 + 7 = 10$ $10 - 7 = 3$

Write the difference.

15. $\begin{array}{r} 7 \\ -2 \\ \hline 5 \end{array}$ 16. $\begin{array}{r} 10 \\ -1 \\ \hline 9 \end{array}$ 17. $\begin{array}{r} 5 \\ -1 \\ \hline 4 \end{array}$ 18. $\begin{array}{r} 8 \\ -4 \\ \hline 4 \end{array}$

Problem Solving

Choose the operation to solve.   Draw or write to explain.

19. Kate sees 10 baby chicks. 6 chicks run away. How many chicks are left?

_4_ chicks

20. On Monday Luca milks 3 cows. On Tuesday he milks 4 cows. How many cows does he milk in all?

_7_ cows

✓ **Adequate Yearly Progress**

Use the End of Grade Test Prep Assessment Guide to help familiarize your children with the format of standardized tests.

CHAPTER SUMMARY TEST

Name _____ Date _____

Complete the fact family.

15. $3 + 1 = 4$
$1 + 3 = \underline{4}$
$4 - \underline{1} = 3$
$\underline{4} - 3 = 1$

16. $2 + 4 = 6$
$4 + \underline{2} = 6$
$6 - 4 = \underline{2}$
$\underline{6} - 2 = 4$

17. $7 + 3 = 10$
$3 + 7 = \underline{10}$
$10 - \underline{7} = 3$
$\underline{10} - 3 = 7$

18. $2 + 5 = 7$
$5 + 2 = \underline{7}$
$\underline{7} - 2 = 5$
$7 - \underline{5} = 2$

Choose the operation to solve. Circle.

19. In the morning, Emma reads 6 pages in her book. At night, she reads 4 pages. How many more pages does she read in the morning?

(subtraction)

addition

20. Toma went to the beach 4 days last week. She is going to the beach 5 days this week. How many days will she go in all?

subtraction

(addition)

STOP

Subtraction Strategies Through 10

Science Connection

Name_____

WEEKLY WR READER®
Science Connection

National Zoo

Our country has a zoo called the National Zoo. Each animal has a home like the one it lived in before it came to the zoo.

This chart gives information about animals that live at the National Zoo.

Type of Animal	Number of Animals	Name of Zoo Home
Lowland gorilla	9	The Great Ape House
Ring-tailed lemur	8	Lemur Island
Giant panda	2	Asia Trail

Lowland Gorilla, National Zoo

Use the table to solve.   Draw or write to explain.

1. How many more animals live in The Great Ape House than on Lemur Island?

    __1__ more animal

2. How many lemurs and pandas live at the zoo in all?

    __10__ lemurs and pandas

3. How many more lemurs than pandas live at the zoo?

    __6__ more lemurs

Using These Pages
Discussion Topics

- Tell children that the giant pandas at the National Zoo are named Mei Xiang (may-SHONG) and Tian Tian (t-YEN t-YEN). Explain that the pandas are visiting from China. They will live in the United States for 10 years. **If the pandas have been in the United States for 2 years, how many more years will they be here?** (8 years)

- Refer children to the table. **How many more gorillas than pandas live at the zoo?** (7 more)

- Tell children that the 9 lowland gorillas at the zoo live in two groups. **One group has 6 gorillas. How many gorillas are in the other group?** (3 gorillas)

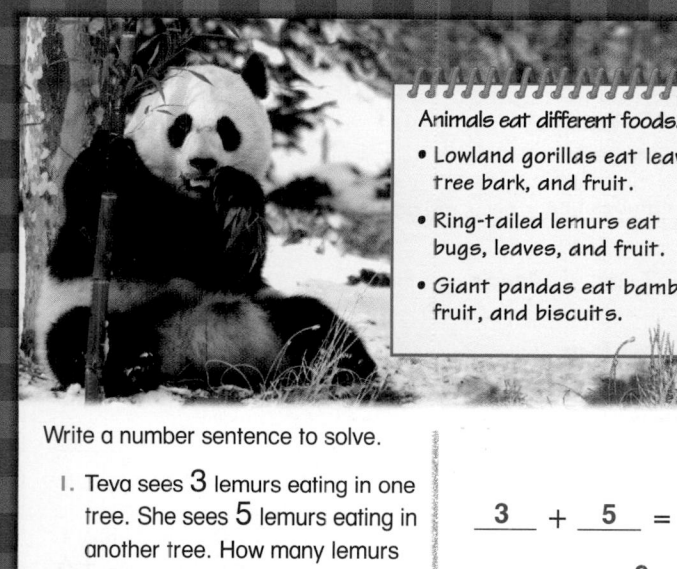

Animals eat different foods.
- Lowland gorillas eat leaves, tree bark, and fruit.
- Ring-tailed lemurs eat bugs, leaves, and fruit.
- Giant pandas eat bamboo, fruit, and biscuits.

Write a number sentence to solve.

1. Teva sees 3 lemurs eating in one tree. She sees 5 lemurs eating in another tree. How many lemurs does she see altogether?

$$\underline{3} + \underline{5} = \underline{8}$$

$\underline{8}$ lemurs

2. There are 9 gorillas eating in The Great Ape House. 3 gorillas walk away. How many gorillas are still eating?

$$\underline{9} - \underline{3} = \underline{6}$$

$\underline{6}$ gorillas

3. Jamal sees 2 giant pandas and 4 ring-tailed lemurs. How many animals does he see in all?

$$\underline{2} + \underline{4} = \underline{6}$$

$\underline{6}$ animals

4. There are 9 gorillas at a zoo. 2 gorillas go to a zoo in another state. How many gorillas are left?

$$\underline{9} - \underline{2} = \underline{7}$$

$\underline{7}$ gorillas

Technology
Visit *Education Place* at **eduplace.com/kids/mw/** to learn more about this topic.

168 one hundred sixty-eight

Wrap Up the Unit Project

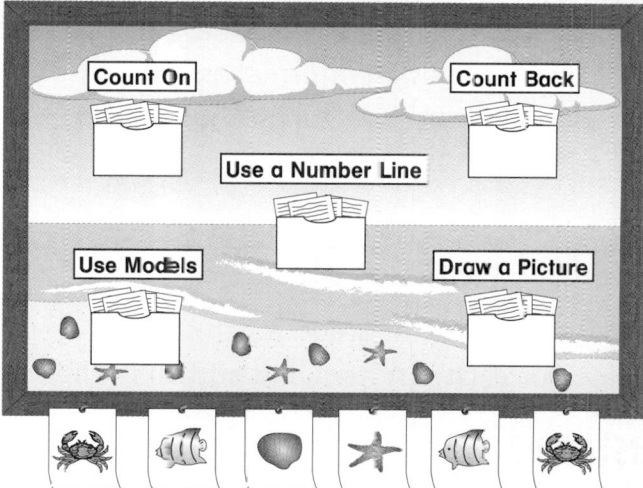

- Before children place their story solutions in the appropriate place on the display, you might want to have them share their solutions with a partner. Encourage children to tell what strategy they used and describe what they did to solve the problem. Children can compare their work to see if they came up with the same solution.

- Invite children to draw pictures of ocean animals to add to the display.

Unit 2 Test

PURPOSE

This test provides an informal assessment of the Unit 2 objectives.

Unit Test Items 1–30

To assign a numerical grade for this Unit Test, use 3 points for each test item and add 10 to the score.

Customizing Your Instruction

For children who have not yet mastered these objectives, you can use the **Reteaching Resources** listed in the chart below. *Ways to Success* is Houghton Mifflin's Intervention program available in CD-ROM and blackline master formats.

Name_____   Unit 2 Test

Vocabulary *Glossary*

Complete the sentence.

| double |
| number line |
| related fact |

1. A __number line__ helps me add and subtract.

2. $2 + 2$ is a __double__ fact.

3. __Related facts__ have the same parts and whole.

Concepts and Skills

Use an addition strategy.
Write the sum.

4. 8   5. 2   6. 9   7. 5   8. 1
   +2   +2   +1   +4   +6
  ————   ————   ————   ————   ————
   10   4   10   9   7

9. 7   10. 6   11. 3   12. 8   13. 2
   +2   +0   +3   +1   +6
  ————   ————   ————   ————   ————
    9   6   6   9   8

Use a subtraction strategy.
Write the difference.

14. 10   15. 7   16. 8   17. 4   18. 9
    −0   −5   −8   −3   −4
  ————   ————   ————   ————   ————
   10   2   0   1   5

19. 5   20. 9   21. 7   22. 6   23. 7
    −1   −6   −4   −3   −6
  ————   ————   ————   ————   ————
    4   3   3   3   1

Unit 2   one hundred sixty-nine **169**

Reteaching Support

Unit Test Item		Unit Objectives Tested	TE Pages	Use These Reteaching Resources
169–170 1, 2, 4–13	Tests A & B 1–8	**2A** Use addition strategies to find sums through 10.	127A–130, 133A–134	Reteach Resources and *Ways to Success*, 5.2, 5.3, 5.4
14–23	9–19	**2B** Use subtraction strategies to subtract from 10 or less.	145A–148, 157A–158	Reteach Resources and *Ways to Success*, 6.1, 6.2, 6.6
3, 24–28	20–21	**2C** Use related facts to solve addition and subtraction problems.	153A–154	Reteach Resource and *Ways to Success*, 6.4
29	22–23	**2D** Use related facts to write fact families.	155A–156	Reteach Resource and *Ways to Success*, 6.5
30	24–25	**2E** Apply skills and strategies to solve problems.	159A–162	Reteach Resource and *Ways to Success*, 6.7

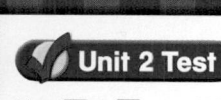 **Unit 2 Test**

Use , , and Workmat 3.
Show the parts. Complete the related facts.

24. 6 and 1   __6__ + __1__ = __7__   __7__ − __1__ = __6__

25. 2 and 7   __2__ + __7__ = __9__   __9__ − __7__ = __2__

26. 8 and 2   __8__ + __2__ = __10__   __10__ − __2__ = __8__

27. 5 + 3 = __8__   28. 1 + 9 = __10__

    8 − 3 = __5__   10 − 1 = __9__

Use , 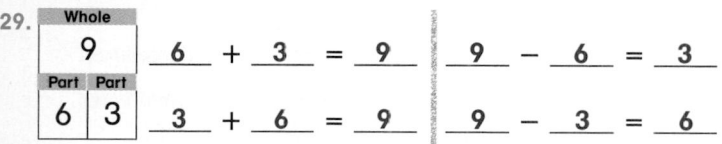, and Workmat 3.
Complete the fact family.

29.

Whole
9

Part	Part
6	3

__6__ + __3__ = __9__   __9__ − __6__ = __3__

__3__ + __6__ = __9__   __9__ − __3__ = __6__

Problem Solving

Choose the operation to solve.   Draw or write to explain.

30. Rae sees 5 chickens eating. 3 more chickens come to eat. How many chickens are eating now?

                       __8__ chickens

170 one hundred seventy

 Assessment Options

Formal Tests for this unit are also provided in the Unit Resource Folder.

- Unit 2 Test A (Open Response)
- Unit 2 Test B (Multiple Choice)

Performance Assessment

You may want to use the Performance Assessment instead of, or in addition to, the Unit Test. Three Performance Assessment tasks can be found on Student Book pages 265–266.

Adequate Yearly Progress

Use the *End of Grade Test Prep Assessment Guide* to help familiarize your children with the format of standardized tests.

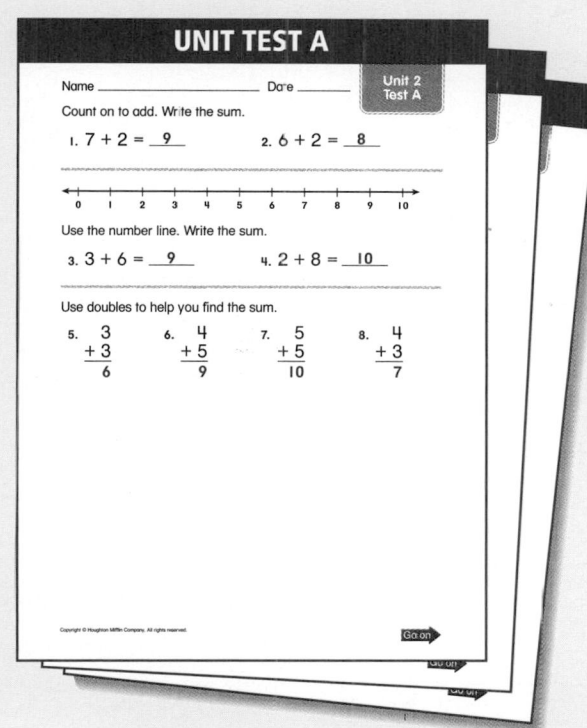

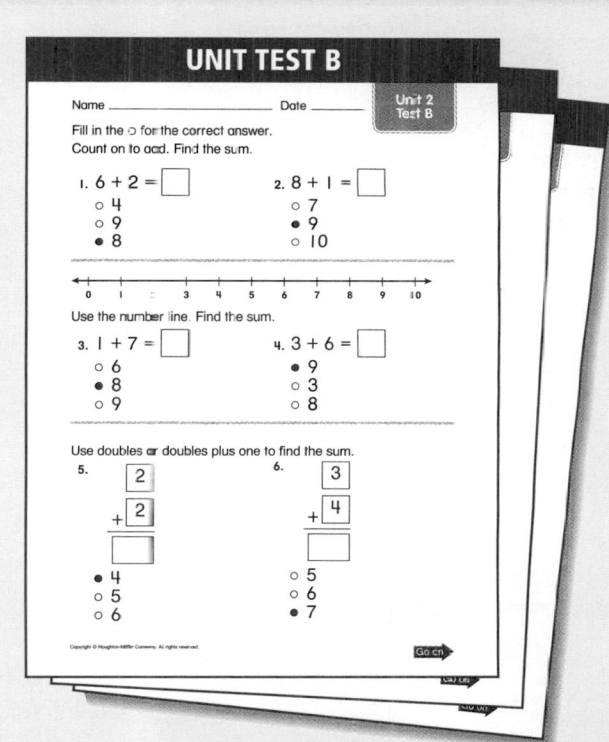

Unit 2
Tests
See pages
171A–171B
for answers.

Addition and Subtraction Facts Through 10   **170**

Unit Test Answers: Form A

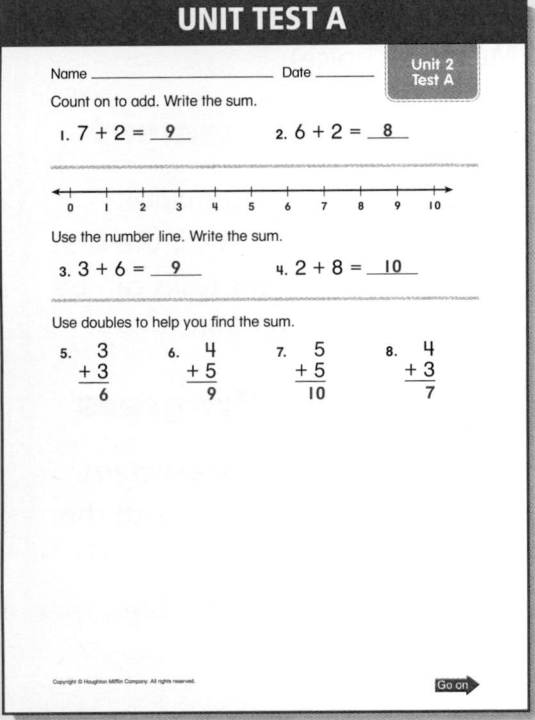

UNIT TEST A

Name _____ Date _____

Unit 2
Test A

Count on to add. Write the sum.

1. $7 + 2 = \underline{9}$　　　2. $6 + 2 = \underline{8}$

```
◄——┼——┼——┼——┼——┼——┼——┼——┼——┼——┼——►
   0   1   2   3   4   5   6   7   8   9   10
```

Use the number line. Write the sum.

3. $3 + 6 = \underline{9}$　　　4. $2 + 8 = \underline{10}$

Use doubles to help you find the sum.

5. $\begin{array}{r} 3 \\ +3 \\ \hline 6 \end{array}$　6. $\begin{array}{r} 4 \\ +5 \\ \hline 9 \end{array}$　7. $\begin{array}{r} 5 \\ +5 \\ \hline 10 \end{array}$　8. $\begin{array}{r} 4 \\ +3 \\ \hline 7 \end{array}$

Go on ►

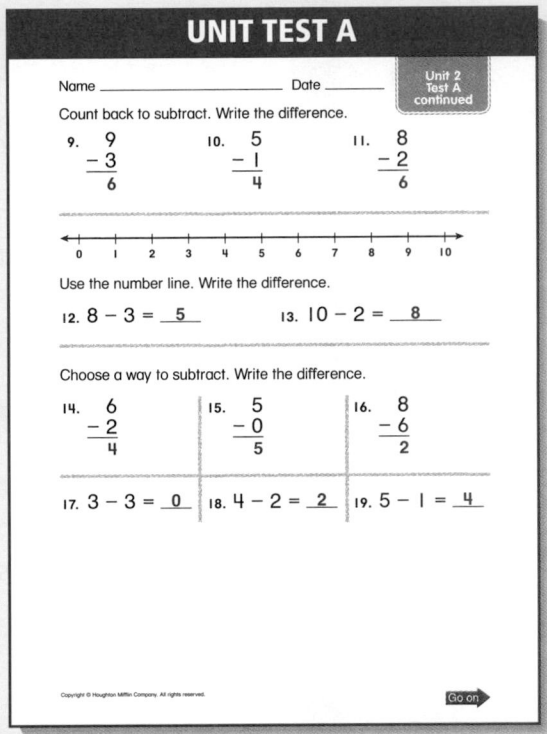

UNIT TEST A

Name _____ Date _____

Unit 2
Test A
continued

Count back to subtract. Write the difference.

9. $\begin{array}{r} 9 \\ -3 \\ \hline 6 \end{array}$　10. $\begin{array}{r} 5 \\ -1 \\ \hline 4 \end{array}$　11. $\begin{array}{r} 8 \\ -2 \\ \hline 6 \end{array}$

```
◄——┼——┼——┼——┼——┼——┼——┼——┼——┼——┼——►
   0   1   2   3   4   5   6   7   8   9   10
```

Use the number line. Write the difference.

12. $8 - 3 = \underline{5}$　　　13. $10 - 2 = \underline{8}$

Choose a way to subtract. Write the difference.

14. $\begin{array}{r} 6 \\ -2 \\ \hline 4 \end{array}$　15. $\begin{array}{r} 5 \\ -0 \\ \hline 5 \end{array}$　16. $\begin{array}{r} 8 \\ -6 \\ \hline 2 \end{array}$

17. $3 - 3 = \underline{0}$　18. $4 - 2 = \underline{2}$　19. $5 - 1 = \underline{4}$

Go on ►

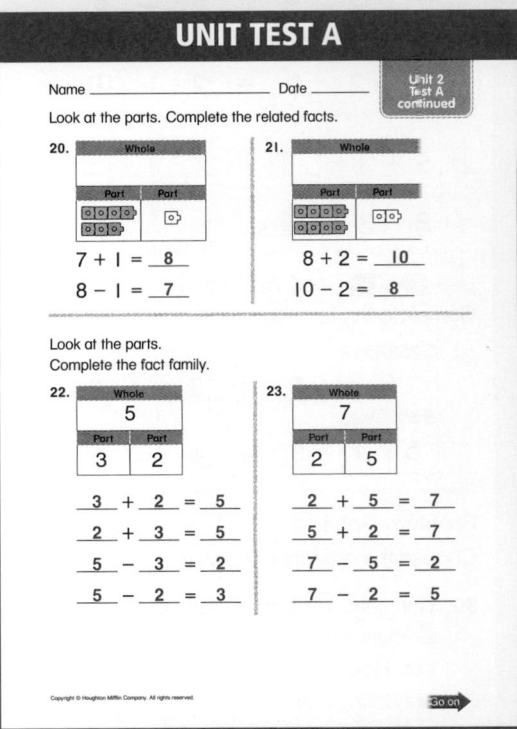

UNIT TEST A

Name _____ Date _____

Unit 2
Test A
continued

Look at the parts. Complete the related facts.

20.

Whole	
Part	Part

$7 + 1 = \underline{8}$
$8 - 1 = \underline{7}$

21.

Whole	
Part	Part

$8 + 2 = \underline{10}$
$10 - 2 = \underline{8}$

Look at the parts.
Complete the fact family.

22.

Whole	
5	
Part	Part
3	2

$3 + 2 = \underline{5}$
$2 + 3 = \underline{5}$
$5 - 3 = \underline{2}$
$5 - 2 = \underline{3}$

23.

Whole	
7	
Part	Part
2	5

$2 + 5 = \underline{7}$
$5 + 2 = \underline{7}$
$7 - 5 = \underline{2}$
$7 - 2 = \underline{5}$

Go on ►

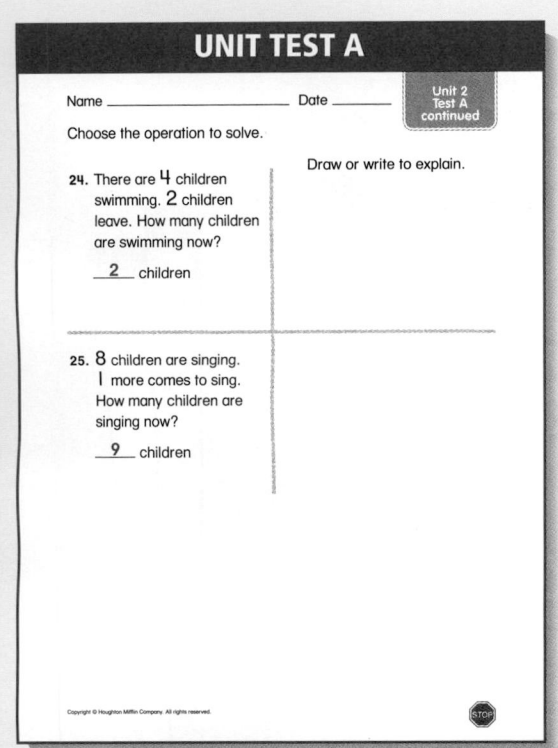

UNIT TEST A

Name _____ Date _____

Unit 2
Test A
continued

Choose the operation to solve.

Draw or write to explain.

24. There are 4 children swimming. 2 children leave. How many children are swimming now?

　$\underline{2}$ children

25. 8 children are singing. 1 more comes to sing. How many children are singing now?

　$\underline{9}$ children

STOP

Unit Test Answers: Form B

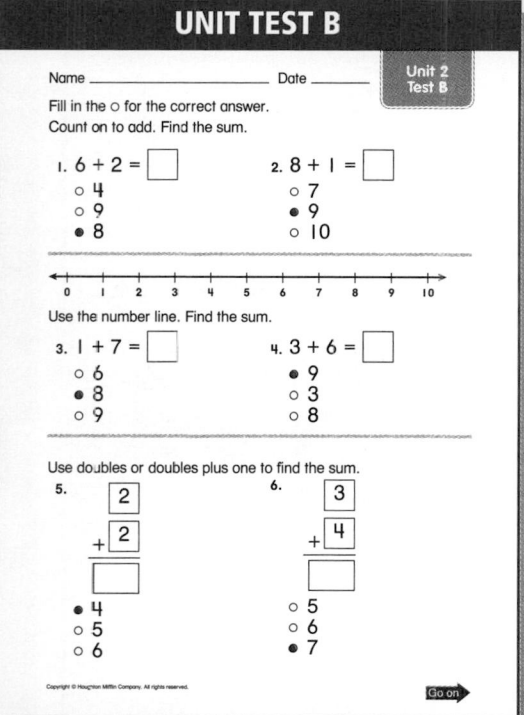

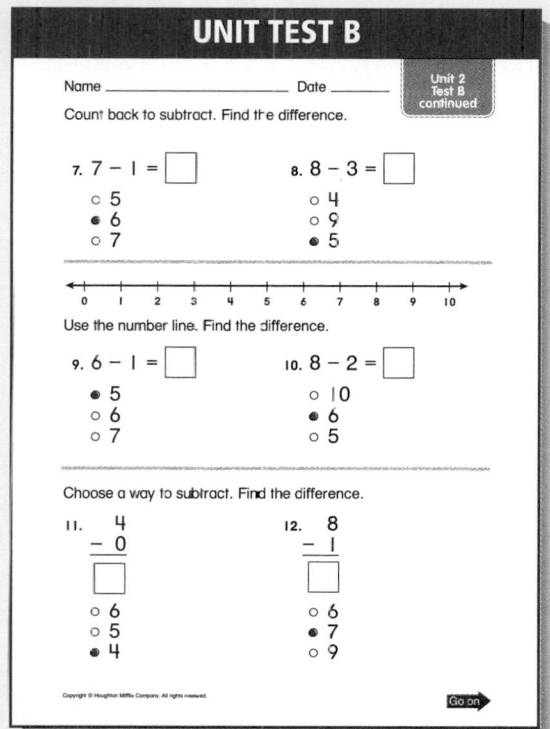

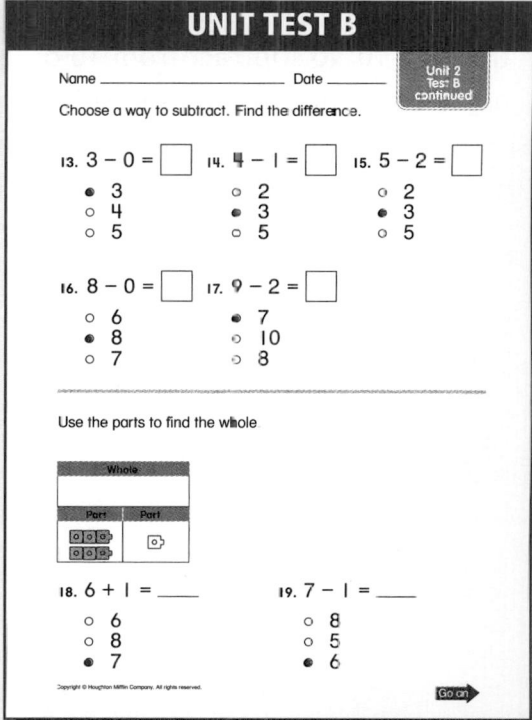

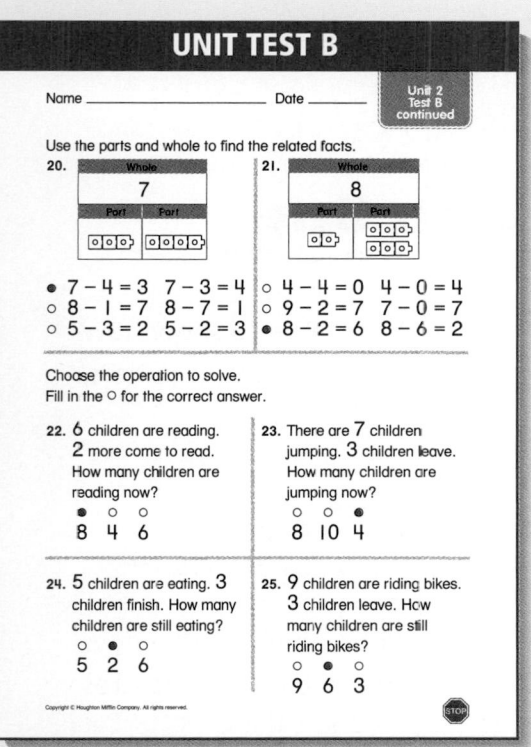

 # Performance Assessment

PURPOSE

This assessment focuses on addition and subtraction strategies. Children should be able to find sums through 10, to subtract from 10 or less, and to apply skills and strategies to solve problems.

Name_____

Performance Assessment

Find the sum.

1. $4 + 2$

Show your work using pictures, numbers, or words.

$4 + 2 = \underline{6}$

Find the difference.

2. $7 - 3$

Show your work using pictures, numbers, or words.

$7 - 3 = \underline{4}$

Using These Pages

- Write $6 + 2$ and $8 - 2$ on the board and model the addition with counters. **How many counters do you have in all when you add 6 plus 2?** (8 counters) **Explain how you added.** (Children may use different strategies.)

- **If I take 2 counters away from the 8 counters, how many counters do I have left?** Demonstrate the subtraction with counters. (6 counters) **Explain how you subtracted.** (Children may use different strategies.)

- Direct children's attention to assessment tasks. You may wish to read the directions aloud.

- Observe children as they work to complete the tasks.

 ## Exercise One

In Exercise 1, children should be able to show how to add to find the sum by using pictures, numbers, or words. (6)

 ## Exercise Two

In Exercise 2, children should be able to show how to subtract to find the difference by using pictures, numbers, or words. (4)

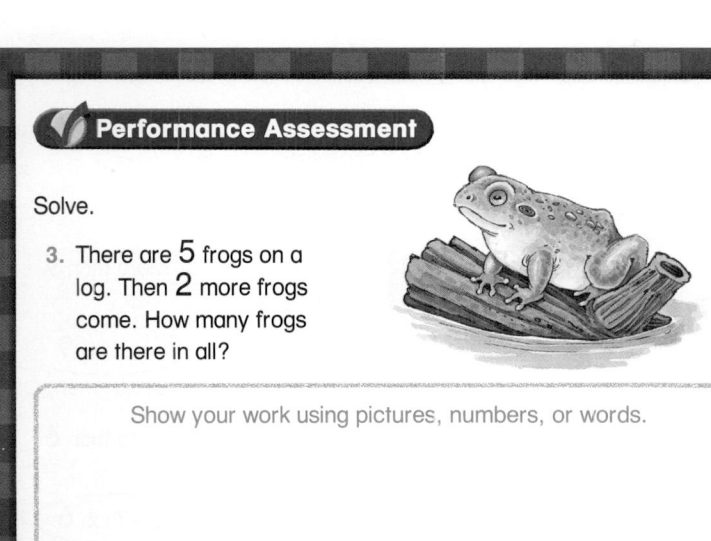

Performance Assessment

Solve.

3. There are **5** frogs on a log. Then **2** more frogs come. How many frogs are there in all?

Show your work using pictures, numbers, or words.

_____7_____ frogs

172 one hundred seventy-two

Assessing Student Work

Use the **Scoring Rubric** to evaluate children's performance on these tasks.

Scoring Rubric

4 EXEMPLARY

Represents the addition and subtraction correctly and finds the correct sum and difference, and applies skills and strategies to solve problems correctly.

3 PROFICIENT

Represents the addition and subtraction correctly and finds the correct sum and difference. Solution to problems demonstrates mathematical reasoning, although the picture or the number sentence is faulty.

2 ACCEPTABLE

Represents the addition and subtraction correctly and finds the correct sum and difference. Solution to problems is incorrect or incomplete.

1 LIMITED

Represents the addition and subtraction incorrectly or finds the incorrect sum and difference. Solution to problems shows no mathematical reasoning.

Exercise Three

In Exercise 3, children should be able to represent the addition story by drawing a picture and writing the corresponding number sentence.

(5 + 2 = 7)

UNIT 2

Enrichment

▶ Estimating Sums and Differences

PURPOSE

This page provides an opportunity for children to apply their understanding of addition and subtraction to help them estimate sums and differences.

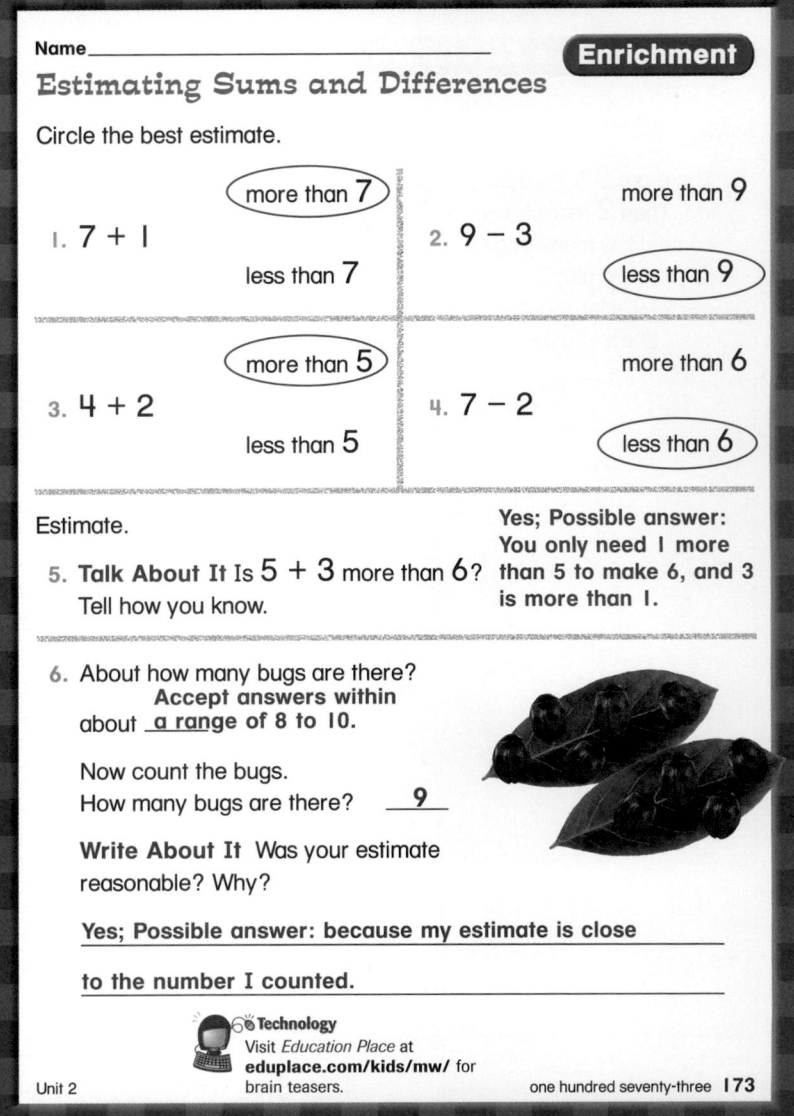

Name_____

Enrichment

Estimating Sums and Differences

Circle the best estimate.

1. 7 + 1 — (more than 7) / less than 7

2. 9 − 3 — more than 9 / (less than 9)

3. 4 + 2 — (more than 5) / less than 5

4. 7 − 2 — more than 6 / (less than 6)

Estimate.

5. **Talk About It** Is 5 + 3 more than 6? Tell how you know.

Yes; Possible answer: You only need 1 more than 5 to make 6, and 3 is more than 1.

6. About how many bugs are there? **Accept answers within** about _a range of 8 to 10._

Now count the bugs. How many bugs are there? ___9___

Write About It Was your estimate reasonable? Why?

Yes; Possible answer: because my estimate is close to the number I counted.

Technology
Visit *Education Place* at **eduplace.com/kids/mw/** for brain teasers.

Unit 2   one hundred seventy-three **173**

Using This Page

Discussion Topics

- This page extends children's understanding of addition and subtraction by having them estimate sums and differences.

- **What is an estimate?** (A best guess based on available information.) Tell children that they do not need to find the exact answer, but should estimate the sum or difference in each exercise.

- Explain that when you add, the sum is greater than either addend; when you subtract, the difference is less than the first number.

- Remind children to check the operation in each exercise before they estimate.

- Have children work individually or in pairs to complete the page. In pairs, children can take turns solving the exercises, and then check each other's work.

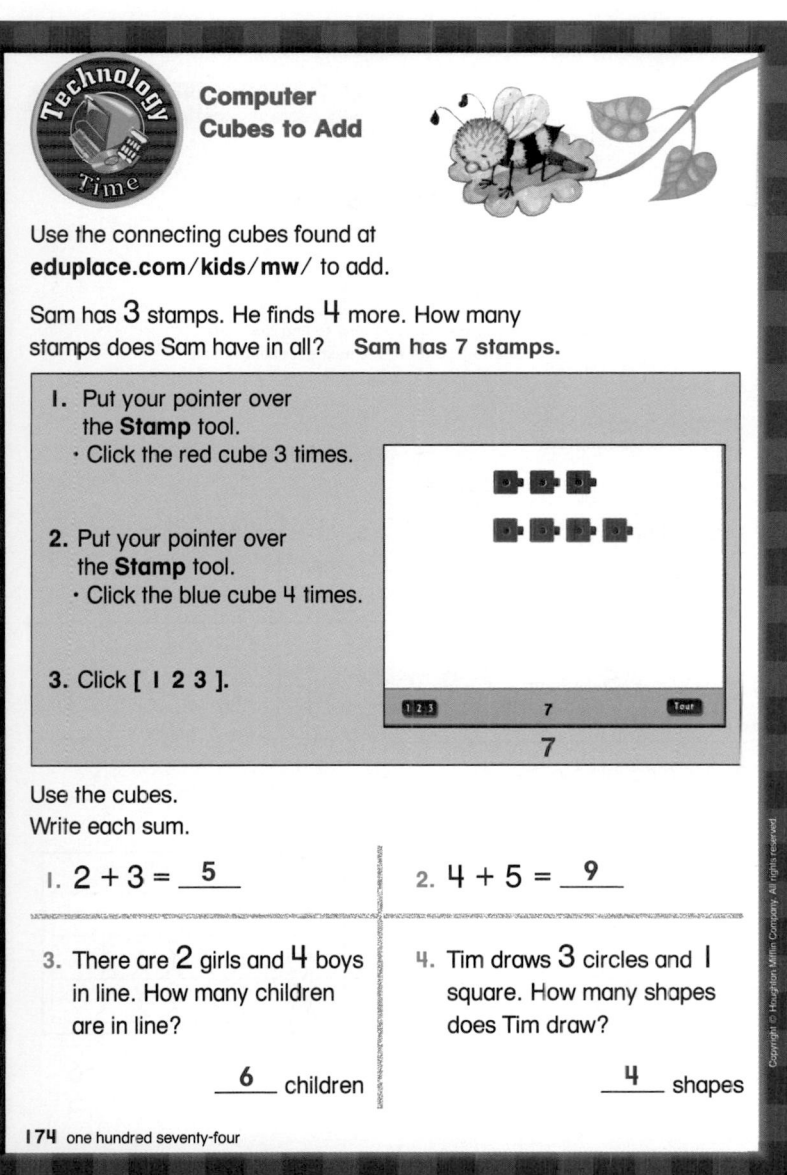

Computer
Cubes to Add

Use the connecting cubes found at
eduplace.com/kids/mw/ to add.

Sam has **3** stamps. He finds **4** more. How many
stamps does Sam have in all?   Sam has 7 stamps.

1. Put your pointer over
   the **Stamp** tool.
   · Click the red cube 3 times.

2. Put your pointer over
   the **Stamp** tool.
   · Click the blue cube 4 times.

3. Click [1 2 3].

7

Use the cubes.
Write each sum.

1. $2 + 3 = \underline{5}$

2. $4 + 5 = \underline{9}$

3. There are **2** girls and **4** boys
   in line. How many children
   are in line?

   $\underline{6}$ children

4. Tim draws **3** circles and **1**
   square. How many shapes
   does Tim draw?

   $\underline{4}$ shapes

174 one hundred seventy-four

PURPOSE

To provide an opportunity for children to use a
computer to find sums.

Using This Page

Discussion Topics

● This is another way for the children to practice
addition.

● You may want to review how to move the cursor
with the children.

● Work through the example with the children.

Remind children that when adding numbers, the
answer is called the sum.

● Read the remaining questions and allow time for
children to complete. When the page is
complete, have children share their answers with
a partner.

Cumulative Test Prep

▶ Practice Test

PURPOSE

This page will familiarize children with the multiple-choice and open-response formats of many standardized state tests. Children can mark their responses directly on these pages. You may wish to read each multiple choice test item and the answer choices aloud to the children.

Name_____

✓ **Cumulative Test Prep**
Practice Test

📌

Test-Taking Tips
. . . .

Work slowly.

Check your work.

If you are not sure how to find the answer, go on to the next question.

Multiple Choice

Fill in the ○ for the correct answer.

1. Count on to add.

$$7$$
$$+2$$

3	5	7	9
○	○	○	●

2. Use a double fact to add.

$$4$$
$$+5$$

6	7	8	9
○	○	○	●

3. What number is 2 more than 4?

0 1 2 3 4 5 6 7 8 9 10

4	6	7	8
○	●	○	○

4. Look at the pictograph. How many children choose bears?

Favorite Animals

🐯	유 유 유
🐶	유 유 유 유 유
🦍	유 유 유 유 유

3	4	5	6
○	○	●	○

Unit 2   one hundred seventy-five **175**

Test-Taking TIPS

Review the test-taking tips with children before they begin the test. Remind children to work slowly and carefully.

- Remind children to answer every question, even if they are unsure of the correct answer.

- Remind children to pay close attention to operation signs.

- Remind children to fill in each answer bubble completely.

- Emphasize that children should always go back and check their work.

Fill in the ○ for the correct answer.
N means here.

5. Count back to subtract.

10 − 3

7   6   5   N
●   ○   ○   ○

6. How many more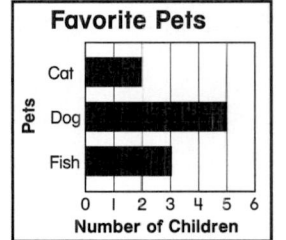
than ?

1   2   3   4
○   ●   ○   ○

7. Which number is greater than 7?

9   7   5   3
●   ○   ○   ○

Solve.

8. There are 2 ducks in the water. 3 more ducks come. How many ducks are there in all?

    5 ducks

Write the number sentence.

2 + 3 = 5

9. Write this fact another way.

6 + 2 = 8

2 + 6 = 8

10. How many children choose fish?

Favorite Pets

Pets: Cat, Dog, Fish

Number of Children
0 1 2 3 4 5 6

    3 children

Test Prep on the Net
Visit *Education Place* at
eduplace.com/kids/mw/
for more test prep practice.

Test-Taking Vocabulary

- Ask volunteers to define the terms *sum* and *difference*.
- Have volunteers define the terms *more than* and *fewer than*, and use them in sentences.
- Review *doubles facts* with children. **What is a doubles fact for 6?** (3 + 3 = 6) **For 10?** (5 + 5 = 10)

National and state tests may use these words when asking children to find a difference:

- *how many more than*
- *how many fewer than*

UNIT 3

Geometry and Fractions

Unit at a Glance

Assessment System

Assessing Prior Knowledge

Check whether children understand the prerequisite concepts and skills.

- **CHAPTER PRETEST** (Unit Resource Folder or *Ways to Success* Intervention CD-ROM)
- **WARM-UP ACTIVITY:** Every TE Lesson
- **UNIT LITERATURE ACTIVITY:** PE p. 178

Ongoing Assessment

Monitor whether children are acquiring new concepts and skills.

- **PROBLEM OF THE DAY:** First page of every TE lesson
- **QUICK REVIEW:** First page of every TE lesson
- **LESSON QUIZ:** First page of every TE lesson
- **COMMON ERROR:** Every TE Lesson
- **QUICK CHECK:** PE pp. 190, 201, 214, 231, 244, 255
- **KEY TOPIC REVIEW:** PE pp. 202, 232, 256

 ## Test Prep and Practice

Help children prepare for state and standardized tests.

- **DAILY TEST PREP:** Every TE Lesson
- **CUMULATIVE TEST PREP:** PE pp. 269–270
- **PROBLEM SOLVING FOR TESTS:** PE pp. 200, 230, 254
- **TEST PREP ON THE NET:** eduplace.com/kids/mw
- **TEST-TAKING STRATEGIES:** eduplace.com/math/mw

Summary Assessment

Assess children's mastery of new concepts and skills.

- **CHAPTER TEST:**
  - ✔ PE pp. 203–204, 233–234, 257–258
  - ✔ Unit Resource Folder
- **UNIT TEST:**
  - ✔ PE pp. 263–264
  - ✔ Test A, Unit Resource Folder
  - ✔ Test B, Unit Resource Folder

 ## Student Self-Assessment

Allow children to evaluate their own understanding.

- **EXPLAIN YOUR THINKING:** PE pp. 183, 185, 187, 193, 195, 207, 209, 211, 219, 221, 223, 237, 239, 241, 245

Performance Assessment

Evaluate children's ability to use mathematics in real-world situations.

PERFORMANCE ASSESSMENT: PE pp. 265–266
WRITE ABOUT IT or TALK ABOUT IT: in Hands-On lessons
WRITING MATH: CREATE AND SOLVE: PE p. 213

 ## Technology Options

Use computer-based assessment to make testing and reporting easier.

- **WAYS TO ASSESS** (CD-ROM, LAN, or Web spiral review and test creation, administration, scoring, and report generation)
- **LEARNER PROFILE** (observations, evaluations, and reports from your handheld or desktop computer)

Reaching All Learners

Resources	On Level Students	Extra Support Students	English Learners	Inclusion/ Special Needs	Advanced Learners	Mathematically Promising
Student Editions						
Building Vocabulary	●	●	●	●	●	●
Guided Practice ★	●	●	●	●	●	●
MathTracks MP3 Audio CD 💿	●	●	○	○		
Teacher's Editions						
Building Vocabulary Strategies	●	●	○	○	●	○
Alternate Teaching Strategies	●	○			○	○
Intervention Activities	○	●	●	●		
Other Resources						
Chapter Challenges	○				●	●
Combination Classroom Guide	●	●	●	●	●	●
English Learners Handbook	○	○	●	○		
Ways to Success CD-ROM 💿	○	●	●	●		

KEY   ● **Highly Appropriate**   ○ **Appropriate**   ★ **Scaffolded Instruction**

Documenting Adequate Yearly Progress

National Test Correlations

UNIT 3 Objectives		ITBS	Terra Nova (CTBS)	CAT	SAT	MAT
3A	Identify, describe, classify, compare, and sort plane and solid shapes.	●	●	●	●	●
3B	Use position words and grids to describe and locate objects.	●	●	●	●	●
3C	Identify transformations of shapes and symmetry in shapes.	●	●	●	●	●
3D	Identify, create, and extend patterns.	●	●	●	●	●
3E	Identify and name $\frac{1}{2}$, $\frac{1}{3}$, and $\frac{1}{4}$ of a region or set.	●	●	●	●	●
3F	Apply skills and strategies to solve problems.	●	●	●	●	●

Activities for Reaching All Learners

Home-School Activity

Sort of a Mystery

Materials: paper pattern blocks (2 sets)

Prepare 2 identical sets of pattern blocks that can be sorted by shape, size, and color. Each player takes one set. With a book placed between them to block the view, players independently sort their own blocks.

Then they compare the sets and discuss whether they used the same or different attributes to sort.

Unit Vocabulary Activity

Over or Under?

Materials: item cards, position cards

Prepare cards showing 8 identical items, each a different color. Write the direction words *next to, to the left, to the right, under, over,* and *between* on individual cards (2 of each).

One child picks a card and uses the word or phrase in a direction, such as *"Point to the balloon over the red balloon."*

Players switch roles and repeat for 5 rounds.

Remediation

MathTracks Lessons: 7.2, 7.4, 7.6, 7.7, 8.4, 8.5, 8.7, 9.1, 9.4, 9.5

Use the MathTracks CD-ROM to help children who need a quick review or extra support for the lesson, to provide children who were absent with a complete lesson presentation, or to assist children with reading difficulties.

Intervention

Ways to Success CD-ROM

Use the Ways to Success CD-ROM to help children who need extra help with lessons. This software is designed to reteach the lesson objective, provide extra guided and independent practice, and if needed, reteach a key prerequisite skill.

Unit Project

Flags: Shapes and Patterns

Math Topics:

- identify and sort plane shapes
- create patterns
- identify $\frac{1}{2}$ and $\frac{1}{4}$ of a whole

To Begin

- Ask children to share what they know about flags. Show an American flag and explain that the 50 stars stand for the 50 states in our country.
- In this Unit Project children will make flags. The flags will show shapes and fractions.

Ongoing

- Give each group a piece of fabric (about 24" x 24").
- Supply scraps of colored fabric, felt, and glue. Give the directions shown. Have children follow the directions to design, and create a flag.

> 1. Cut out ☐s, △s, ◯s and ☐s.
> 2. Make a pattern with shapes.
> 3. Decorate flag with more shapes.
> 4. Color $\frac{1}{2}$ of a ◯ black.
> 5. Color $\frac{1}{4}$ of a ☐ red.

- For Connecting to the Unit Project, see page 181D for Chapter 7, page 205D for Chapter 8, and page 235D for Chapter 9.

To Finish

- Display the flags each group has created.
- See page 262 to Wrap Up the Unit Project.

Starting Unit 3
Accessing Prior Knowledge

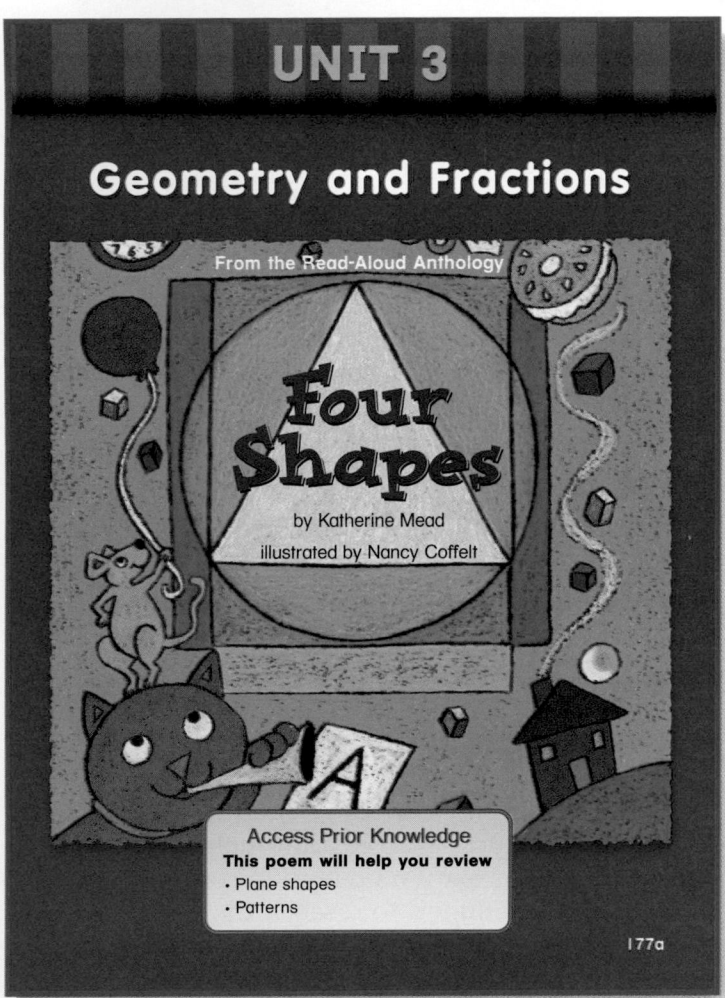

UNIT 3

Geometry and Fractions

From the Read-Aloud Anthology

Four Shapes

by Katherine Mead

illustrated by Nancy Coffelt

Access Prior Knowledge
This poem will help you review
• Plane shapes
• Patterns

177a

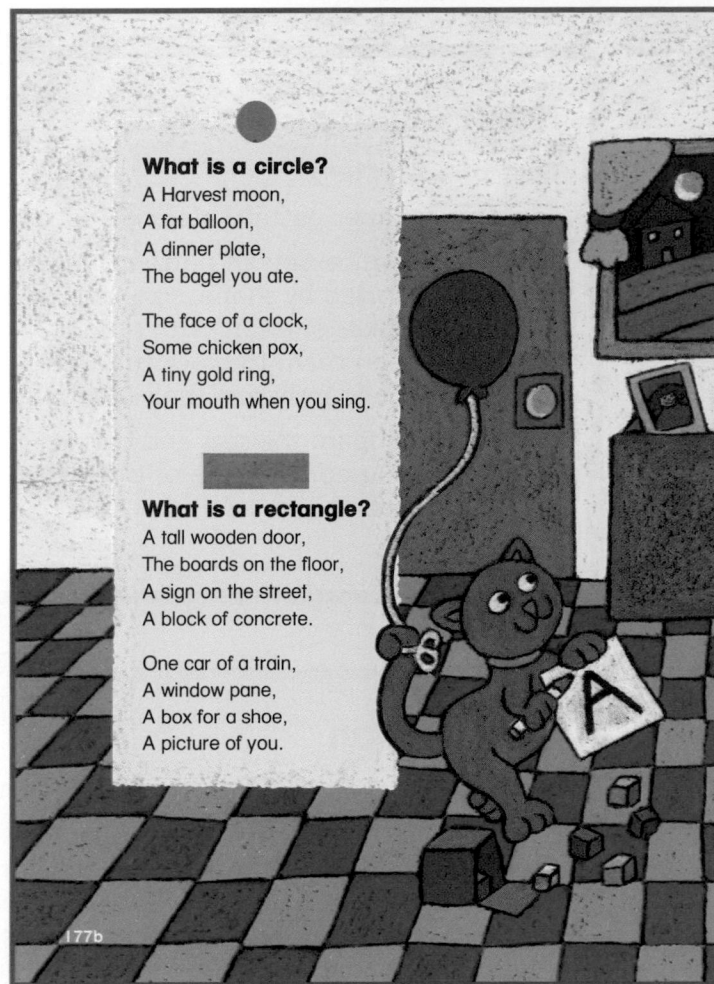

What is a circle?
A Harvest moon,
A fat balloon,
A dinner plate,
The bagel you ate.

The face of a clock,
Some chicken pox,
A tiny gold ring,
Your mouth when you sing.

What is a rectangle?
A tall wooden door,
The boards on the floor,
A sign on the street,
A block of concrete.

One car of a train,
A window pane,
A box for a shoe,
A picture of you.

177b

Accessing Prior Knowledge

In Kindergarten, children:
• identify and describe circles, squares, rectangles, and triangles
• identify and describe solid shapes
• sort plane and solid shapes
• create and identify patterns
• identify halves of a whole

This selection from the Unit Opener gives you the opportunity to review some of these prerequisite skills.

• You may wish to review plane and solid shapes by having volunteers identify plane and solid shapes around the classroom.

• Then review patterns by having children arrange themselves into a boy-girl pattern.

Poem Summary

Today you will be reading a poem about four different shapes. The title of the poem is *Four Shapes*. The author is Katherine Mead.

Reading the Poem

Read the poem aloud to the children. Then read it again, having the children draw and hold up a picture of each shape they hear.

This poem is available in the Read-Aloud Anthology, Volume 2

What is a triangle?
The roof of a house,
The ear of a mouse,
The top of an A
When you print a neat way.

The nose of a cat,
An old soldier's hat,
An instrument made
For a rhythm parade.

What is a square?
Some buttons on coats,
Some cards and some notes,
A picture frame,
A place for a name.

One side of a box,
The shape of some blocks,
A part of a door,
The tiles on the floor.

177c

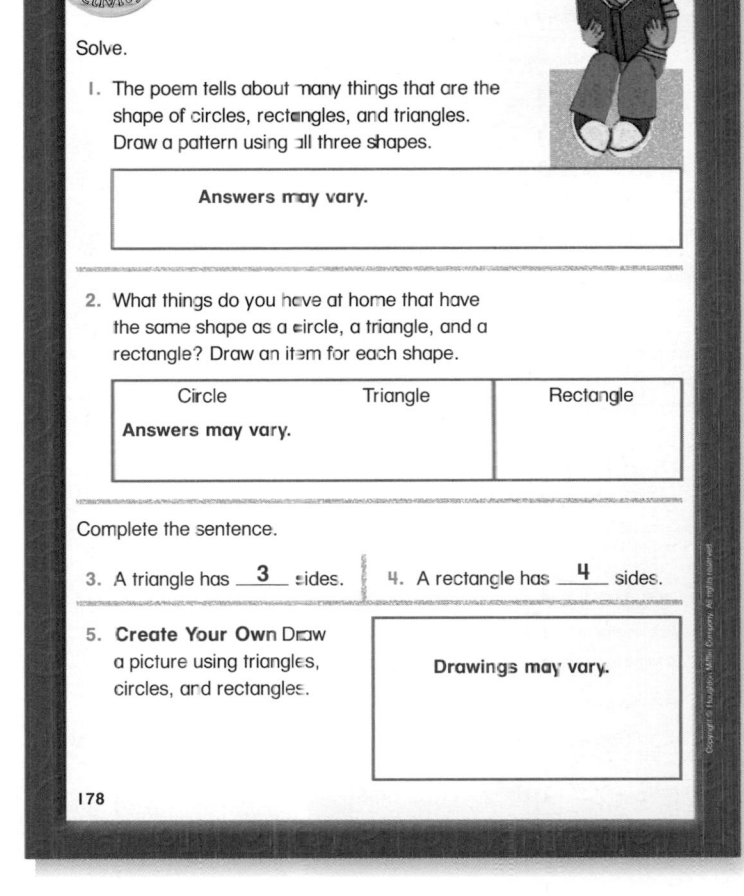

Name _____

Solve.

1. The poem tells about many things that are the shape of circles, rectangles, and triangles. Draw a pattern using all three shapes.

> Answers may vary.

2. What things do you have at home that have the same shape as a circle, a triangle, and a rectangle? Draw an item for each shape.

Circle	Triangle	Rectangle
Answers may vary.		

Complete the sentence.

3. A triangle has __3__ sides.

4. A rectangle has __4__ sides.

5. **Create Your Own** Draw a picture using triangles, circles, and rectangles.

> Drawings may vary.

178

Unit Bibliography

The Doorbell Rang by Pat Hutchins

Eating Fractions by Bruce McMillan

Four Shapes by Katherine Mead

Gator Pie by Louise Mathews

Let's Fly a Kite by Stuart J. Murphy

Probably Pistachio by Stuart J. Murphy

Shape (Math Counts) by Henry Pluckrose

Where's That Bone? by Lucille Recht Penner

See also the **Math and Literature Bibliography** in the Teacher Support Handbook at the back of this Teacher's Edition.

Literature Activity

Purpose: This activity provides an opportunity to informally assess children's understanding of plane shapes and patterns.

Using This Page

• Observe children as they work to complete Exercise 1. **How many shapes are in your pattern?** (3) Ask volunteers to describe their patterns.

• Observe children as they work to complete Exercises 2–4. **Does a circle have sides?** (no)

• For Exercise 5, be sure children can identify the shapes they draw.

Math At Home

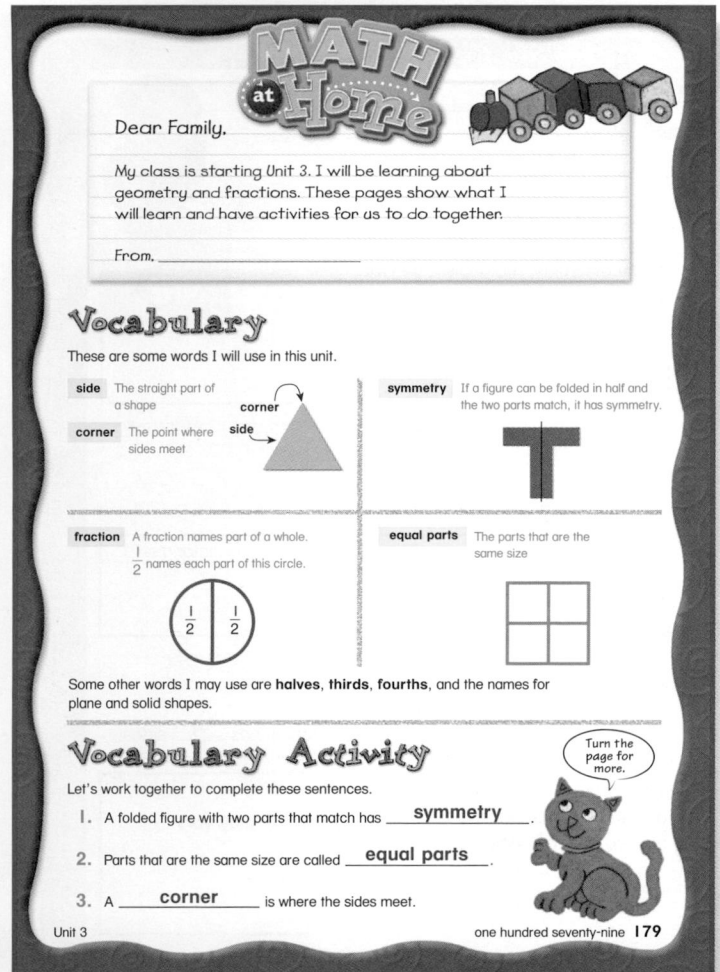

MATH at Home

Discuss the letter to the family with children. You may want to use this letter as an introduction to the unit. Highlight for children what they will be learning in the unit. Tell children that as they go through the unit they will be able to answer the questions on these pages.

Math at Home is available in Spanish and other languages on Education Place.

www.eduplace.com/math/mw/

Literature

Encourage parents to find the suggested books and read them with their children.

 Technology

Education Place is an award-winning website with engaging activities for students and helpful information for parents. Look for the eGlossary, the Math Lingo Game, and more.

Building Vocabulary

Strategies for Building Vocabulary

Solid Shapes

Create a chart showing names and drawings of a **sphere, cylinder, pyramid, rectangular prism, cone,** and **cube.** Point out that the names for solid shapes are different from the names of their related plane shapes.

Help children to read the names of the solids listed on the chart. Have children choose a solid shape. Then have them describe a real object that has the same shape.

Solid Shapes

cube	
cylinder	
cone	
rectangular prism	
sphere	
pyramid	

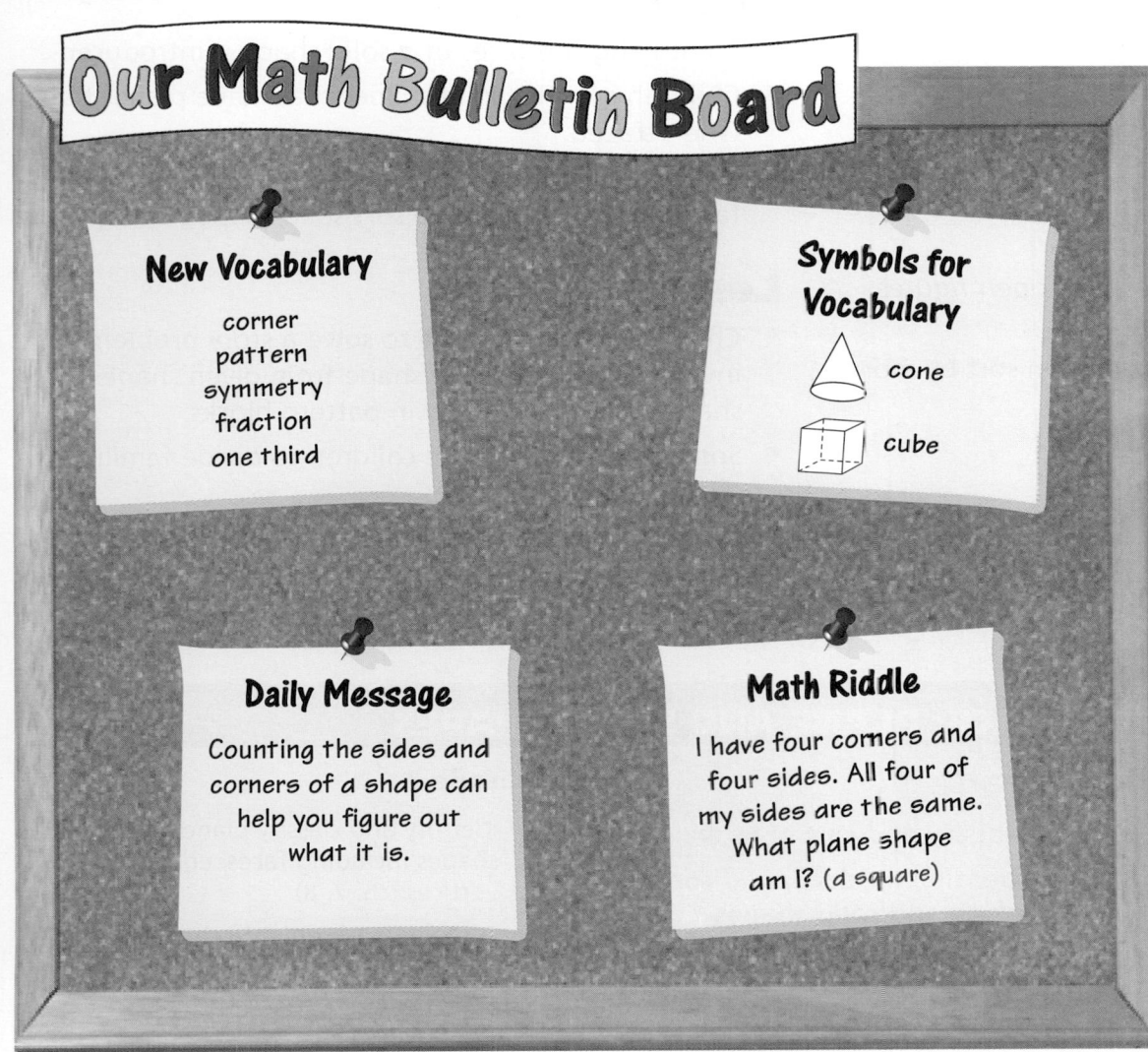

Our Math Bulletin Board

New Vocabulary

corner
pattern
symmetry
fraction
one third

Symbols for Vocabulary

cone

cube

Daily Message

Counting the sides and corners of a shape can help you figure out what it is.

Math Riddle

I have four corners and four sides. All four of my sides are the same. What plane shape am I? (a square)

Vocabulary Cards

add

My Math Journal
Watch for **Keeping a Journal** entries in every lesson.

Lesson by Lesson Overview
Plane and Solid Shapes

Lesson 1

- This lesson has children sort real-life objects by *size, color,* or *shape.*
- Classifying and sorting are basic skills that children use, even before they enter school.
- These are skills that children will use when they work with patterns, geometry, graphing, and other concepts.

Lesson 2

- Children identify, describe, and compare the attributes of plane shapes. They also draw shapes.
- Children count the number of *sides* and *corners* and learn that sides are straight.
- At this grade level, square and rectangle are classified as different shapes.

Lesson 3

- This lesson focuses on classifying and sorting shapes using the concepts taught in the two previous lessons.
- Children sort by various attributes, such as number of sides, corners, or no sides and corners.
- A problem solving activity introduces *open figures* and *closed figures.*
- The lesson is extended to have children sort by more than one attribute.

Lesson 4

- Children identify, describe, and compare solid shapes.
- Shapes are classified by how they can move: *slide, stack,* and/or *roll.*
- Shapes are also classified by *number of faces, number of edges,* and *number of corners.*

Lesson 5

- This lesson focuses on classifying and sorting shapes using concepts taught in previous lessons.
- Children sort by various attributes, such as number of faces, corners, or edges; and shapes with curved parts.
- Children also sort plane and solid shapes into two groups.

Lesson 6

- Identifying the faces of a solid shape is introduced.
- Children identify solid shapes that make plane shapes when traced.
- The problem solving activity has children use the faces of plane shapes to sort solid shapes into groups.

Lesson 7

- Children draw a picture to solve a story problem that involves making a new shape from given shapes. The shapes are those found in pattern blocks.
- Some problems require children to divide familiar shapes into new shapes.
- Shape names are used throughout to provide additional practice.

SKILLS TRACE: PLANE AND SOLID SHAPES

Grade K	Grade 1	Grade 2
• sort by alike/different, color, size, shape, own rule (ch. 1) • identify circle and rectangle (ch. 5) • identify square and triangle (ch. 5) • combine plane shapes (ch. 5)	• classify and sort objects • identify, describe, and compare plane and solid shapes • classify and sort plane and solid shapes • identify faces of solid shapes	• identify and classify plane and solid shapes including faces, edges, and vertices (ch. 7, 8) • combine and separate shapes (ch. 7) • make plane shapes from solid (ch. 8) • compare solid shapes (ch. 8)

Chapter Planner

Lesson	Objective	Vocabulary	Materials	✓ NCTM Standards
7.1 Classifying and Sorting Objects p. 183A	Classify, sort, and compare objects by one attribute such as color, size, or shape.		teacher-made cut-out mittens, paper in different colors	Describe attributes and parts of two- and three-dimensional shapes.
7.2 Plane Shapes p. 185A	Identify, describe, and compare attributes of triangles, rectangles, squares, and circles; find plane shapes in the environment.	side corner names for plane shapes	plane shapes (Learning Tool (LT) 22 and 23), paper bag	Describe attributes and parts of two- and three-dimensional shapes.
7.3 Classifying and Sorting Shapes p. 187A	Classify and sort plane shapes; identify open and closed shapes; sort objects by more than one attribute.		pattern blocks, plane shapes (LT 22 and 23), attribute blocks or LT 26 and 27	Recognize, name, build, draw, compare, and sort two- and three-dimensional shapes.
7.4 Solid Shapes (Hands-On) p. 191A	Identify, describe, and compare solid shapes.	face edge corner names for solid shapes	set of solid shapes, real-life objects	Recognize, name, build, draw, compare, and sort two- and three-dimensional shapes.
7.5 Classifying and Sorting Solid Shapes p. 193A	Classify and sort solid shapes.		sets of solid shapes, real-life solids (shoe box, crayon box, soup can), bag	Recognize, name, build, draw, compare, and sort two- and three-dimensional shapes.
7.6 Identify Faces of a Solid Shape p. 195A	Identify the faces of a solid shape.		sets of solid shapes, blank transparency	Recognize, name, build, draw, compare, and sort two- and three-dimensional shapes.
7.7 Problem Solving: Draw a Picture p. 197A	Draw pictures to solve problems.		pattern blocks, teacher-made pattern block cards	Solve problems that arise in mathematics and in other contexts.

Resources For Reaching All Learners

LESSON RESOURCES: Reteach, Practice, Enrichment, Problem Solving, Homework, English Learners, Daily Routines, Transparencies, Math Center.

ADDITIONAL RESOURCES FROM HOUGHTON MIFFLIN: Chapter Challenges, Combination Classroom Planning Guide, Every Day Counts, Math to Learn (Student Handbook)

Every Day Counts
The Calendar and Graph activities in **Every Day Counts** support the math in this chapter.

Assessing Prior Knowledge

Before beginning this chapter, you can assess student understandings in order to assist you in differentiating instruction.

Complete Chapter Pretest in Unit Resource Folder

Use this test to assess both prerequisite skills (**Are You Ready?** — one page) and chapter content (**Check What You Know** — two pages).

Chapter 7 Prerequisite Skills Pretest

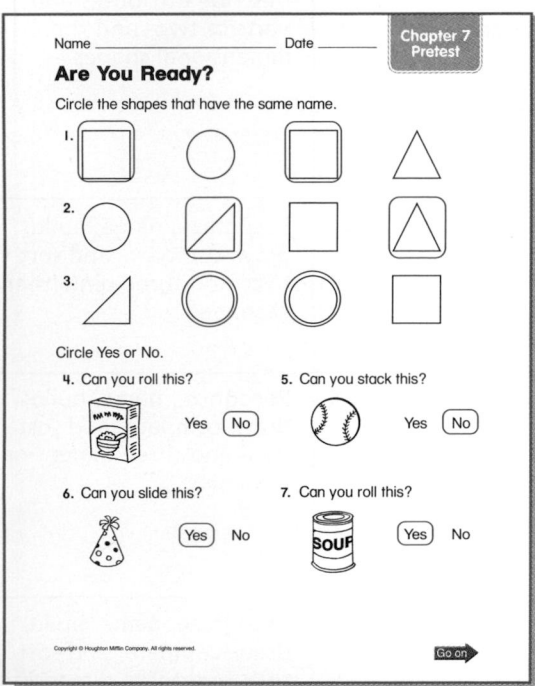

Chapter 7 New Content Pretest

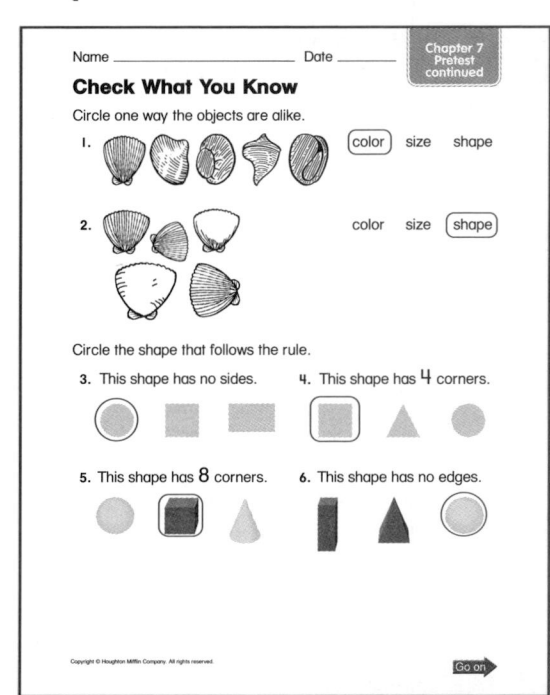

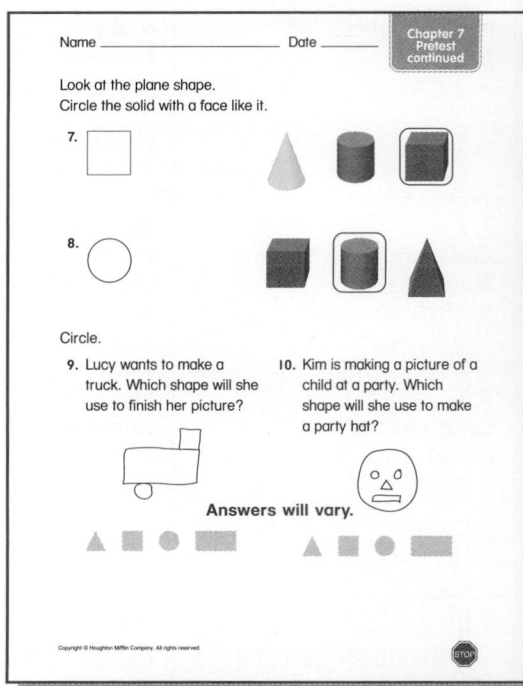

Customizing Instruction

For Students Having Difficulty

Items	Prerequisites	Ways to Success
1–3	Identify shapes that are the same and different.	CD: 7b Skillsheet 43
4–7	Describe solid shapes.	CD: 7c Skillsheet 44

Ways to Success: Intervention for every concept and skill (CD-ROM or Chapter Intervention Skillsheets).

For Students Having Success

Items	Objectives	Resources
3–4	7A Use vocabulary relating to plane and solid shapes.	Enrichment 7.2
5–6	7B Classify, sort, and compare objects using one attribute.	Enrichment 7.1, 7.3
1–2, 7–8	7C Identify, describe, compare, classify, and sort plane shapes and solid shapes.	Enrichment 7.3–7.6
9–10	7D Draw pictures to solve problems.	Enrichment 7.7

Use **Chapter Challenges** with any students who have success with all new chapter content.

Other Pretest Options

Informal Pretest

The pretest assesses vocabulary and prerequisite skills needed for success in this chapter.

***Ways to Success* CD-ROM**

The *Ways to Success* chapter pretest has automatic assignment of appropriate review lessons.

Chapter Resources

Assessing Prior Knowledge

Shapes Spies (identify plane shapes)

- Draw a circle, a square, a rectangle, and triangle on the board or on a sheet of poster paper.
- On the first day of the activity, have children name a few objects that are these shapes.
- Tell children to keep an eye out for things they see that are these shapes. Each day, provide a time when children can add items to the lists.

Ongoing Skill Activity

Sort Containers in the Class Store (classify and sort solid shapes)

- Create a class store. Stock the store with containers of various shapes, such as cans, cereal boxes, oatmeal boxes, aluminum foil boxes, and tissue boxes.
- Have partners work together to sort the containers by one attribute.
- Have them make a list of containers with like attributes.

Connecting to the Unit Project

- Tell children to listen carefully as you say this riddle about plane shapes.

  My flag has two shapes. One shape has 3 sides and 3 corners. The other shape has 0 sides and 0 corners. What 2 shapes are on my flag?
  (triangle and circle)

- Call on a volunteer to answer the riddle.
- Have children create their own shape riddles. Allow time for children to share their riddles.

Teacher Support

Professional Resources Handbook

Research, Mathematics Content, and Language Intervention

Research-Based Teaching

The Van Hieles conducted a number of research projects resulting in the Van Hiele theory of development (1959) in geometric thinking. They believe that children progress through five levels of thought in learning geometry. Researchers have discovered that "phases of instruction linked to the levels have proven to be effective in classroom teaching" (Nickson, 2000). See *Professional Resources Handbook, Grade 1,* Unit 3.

For more ideas relating to Unit 3, see the Teacher Support Handbook at the back of this Teacher's Edition.

Language Intervention

In East Asian countries, children learn that just as numbers can be composed and decomposed as sets and subsets, geometric figures can be composed and decomposed as well. Consistency and application of mathematical language across topics and strands reinforces understanding. For further explanation, see "Mathematical Language and Geometry" in the *Professional Resources Handbook Grade 1.*

 **Technology**

Time-Saving Technology Support
Ways to Assess Customized Spiral Review
  Test Generator CD
Lesson Planner CD-ROM
Ways to Success Intervention CD-ROM
MathTracks CD-ROM
Education Place: www.eduplace.com/math/mw
Houghton Mifflin Math eBook CD-ROM
eManipulatives
eGames

Starting Chapter 7
Plane and Solid Shapes

CHAPTER OBJECTIVES

7A Develop and use math vocabulary relating to plane and solid shapes.

7B Classify, sort, and compare objects using one attribute.

7C Identify, describe, compare, classify, and sort plane shapes and solid shapes.

7D Draw pictures to solve problems.

Math Background

Plane and Solid Shapes

The study of geometry focuses on space and the figures and shapes that are a part of space. Geometric representations often take the form of drawing a picture in the primary grades and are very useful when modeling and solving a variety of real-world problems. The fundamental concepts of elementary geometry, sometimes called Euclidian geometry, are the point, the line, and the plane. Plane geometry concerns itself with the study of figures that lie in a plane, or two-dimensional figures. The square, triangle, and rectangle have line segments for sides and are all polygons. A circle is not a polygon because it has no line segments for sides. Solid geometry concerns itself with the study of shapes of three dimensions. Some shapes children study are the sphere, cylinder, rectangular prism, pyramid, and cone. In first grade, fundamental new learning should focus on the properties and relationships of these figures and shapes. A second goal of the study of geometry should be the use of conventional terminology when children describe and discuss plane and solid shapes.

Plane and Solid Shapes

CHAPTER 7

INVESTIGATION

Name the plane shapes you see in the picture.

Using The Investigation

- Review plane shapes with children. Ask volunteers to identify objects in the classroom that have the shape of a *square, circle, triangle,* and *rectangle.*

- Invite volunteers to draw plane shapes on the board as you name them.

- Read the question to children. **Look at the picture. Name the plane shapes you see in the picture.** (circles, squares, rectangles, triangles)

 For more information about projects and investigations, visit Education Place. **eduplace.com/math/mw/**

Toy Shelf
....
Listen to your teacher.

182 one hundred eighty-two

For Mathematically Promising Students

The *Chapter Challenges* resource book provides blackline masters for activities that explore, extend, and connect the mathematics in every chapter. To support this independent work, see the Teacher Notes for each activity.

Explore: Paper Shape Sort, page 37, after Lesson 1
Extend: Shape Designs, page 39, after Lesson 3
Connect: Tangram Shapes, page 41, after Lesson 5

Using This Page

- Use a set of solids to review their names.
- Tell children that the story names real-life objects. Explain that you will ask a volunteer to find a solid shape to match the shape of each object. Then children draw the object from the story on the correct shelf. Read the story.
- *The children are putting toys on the shelf. Manuel puts his book on the bottom shelf.* **What solid matches the book?** (rectangular prism) Check that children draw the book on the bottom shelf.
- *He puts his soccer ball on the middle shelf.* **What solid matches the ball?** (sphere) Check that children have drawn the ball on the middle shelf.
- *Sandy puts her party hat on the top shelf.* **What solid matches the party hat?** (cone) Check that children have drawn the hat on the top shelf.

NSF Children's Math Worlds

Build stronger conceptual understanding of plane and solid shapes with *Children's Math Worlds* lessons. The most effective approach is to use the *Children's Math Worlds* lessons along with the lessons in the chapter.

Plane and Solid Shapes   **182**

Classifying and Sorting Objects

PLANNING THE LESSON

MATHEMATICS OBJECTIVE

Classify, sort, and compare objects by one attribute such as color, size, or shape.

Use Lesson Planner CD-ROM for Lesson 7.1.

Meeting North Carolina's Standards

5.01 Sort and classify objects by two attributes.

Daily Routines

Calendar

Discuss with children ways to sort the dates on the calendar into 2 groups. For example, they could sort by dates with and without 2s. Ask children to demonstrate different ways to sort.

Vocabulary

Write the word **sort** on the board. Remind children that to sort means putting things that are alike into groups. Sort children by age, color of shoes, or other attributes.

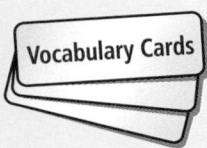
Vocabulary Cards

Lesson Transparency **7.1**

Problem of the Day

How many children have pet dogs? Three fewer children have pet cats. How many have cats? (2)

Quick Review

$$\begin{array}{ccccc} 7 & 5 & 4 & 2 & 9 \\ +3 & +2 & +3 & +6 & +0 \\ \hline (10) & (7) & (7) & (8) & (9) \end{array}$$

Lesson Quiz

How are these objects alike? (all are triangles)

LEVELED PRACTICE

RETEACH 7.1

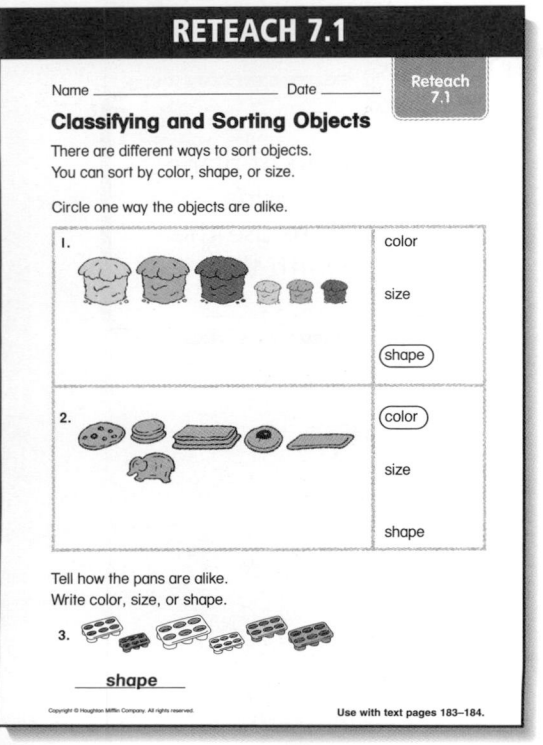

PRACTICE 7.1

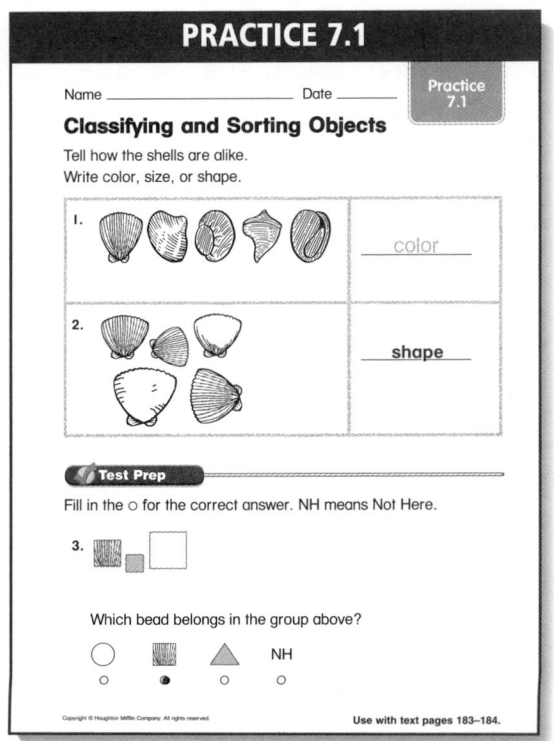

ENRICHMENT 7.1

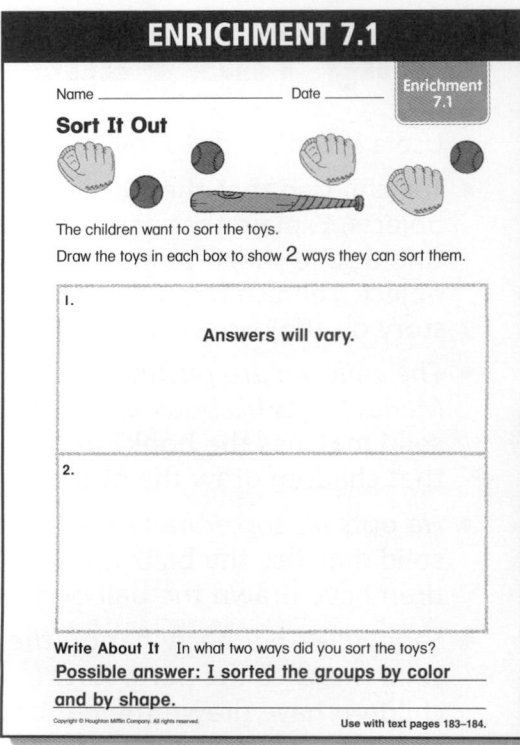

Practice Workbook Page 42

Reaching All Learners
Differentiated Instruction

English Learners

Children will need to understand the meaning of the word *alike* in order to classify and sort objects. Use Worksheet 7.1 to develop children's understanding of this word.

Special Needs
TACTILE, VISUAL

Materials: *crayons, sorting mat, cup*

Give the child a sorting mat with 3 rings: red, blue, and green. Also give the child a cup of crayons in red, blue, and green. Have the child sort the crayons by color onto the rings. Have the child tell you by what attribute she or he is sorting. (color)

Gifted and Talented
TACTILE, VISUAL

Materials: *objects to sort*

Give children a collection of classroom objects. For example: paper clips, cubes, and buttons. Have children sort the objects by an attribute of their choice. Then have them draw or write to explain how they sorted.

I sorted by shape.

TECHNOLOGY

Spiral Review

To reinforce skills on lessons taught earlier, create **customized** spiral review worksheets using the *Ways to Assess* CD-ROM.

Lesson Planner

Use the **Lesson Planner CD-ROM** to see how lesson objectives for this chapter are correlated to standards.

eBook

An electronic version of this lesson can be found in **eMathBook**.

Education Place

You can visit **Education Place** at **eduplace.com/math/mw/** for teacher support materials.

ScienceConnection

Give children a collection of items from nature, such as shells, leaves, or pine cones of different sizes and shapes. Children can sort them by attributes. For example: things that have patterns and no patterns or, things that are smooth and rough.

MATH CENTER

Basic Skills Activity

Motivate children to build basic skills. Use this activity to address multiple learning styles using hands-on activities related to the skills of this lesson.

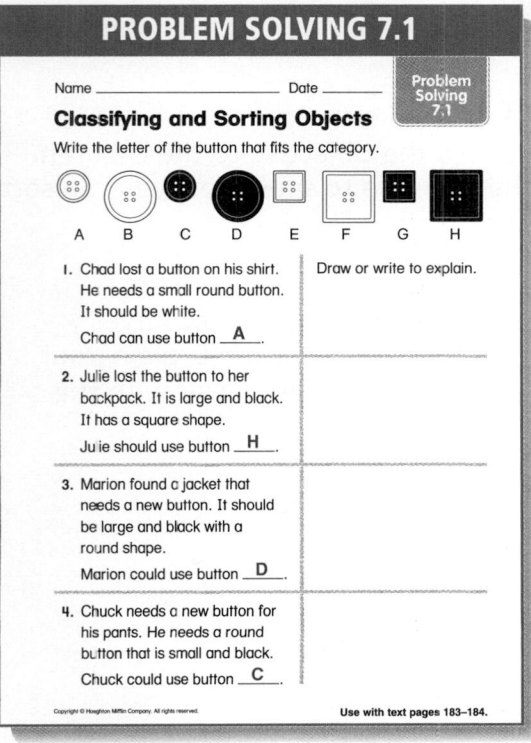

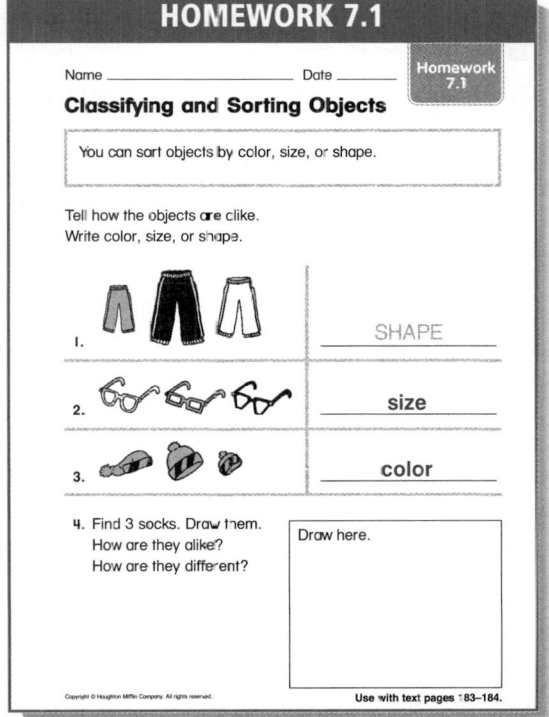

Homework Workbook Page 42

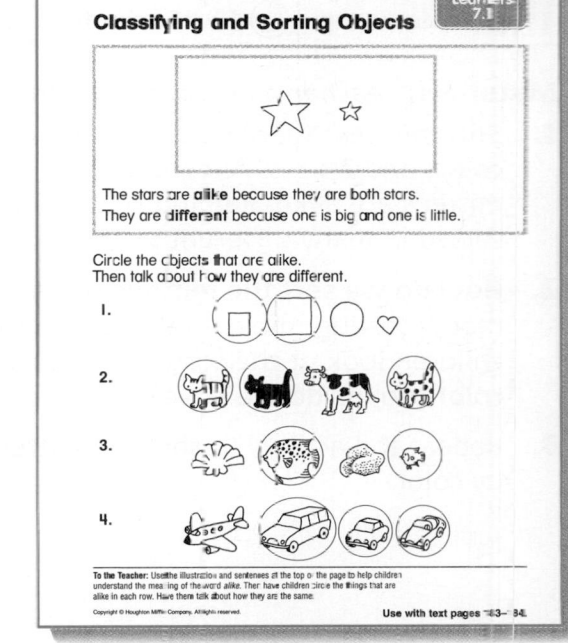

TEACHING LESSON 7.1

LESSON ORGANIZER

Objective Classify, sort, and compare objects by one attribute such as color, size, or shape.

Resources Reteach, Practice, Enrichment, Problem Solving, Homework, English Learners, Transparencies, Math Center

Materials Teacher-made cut-out mittens, paper in different colors

Activity

Warm-Up Activity
Identifying Objects

iiii Whole Group	⏲ 5 minutes	Visual, Auditory

1. Review how to sort objects by color. Hold up a brown crayon. Ask children to find objects in the classroom that are brown. As children give suggestions, list them on the board. **What is the same about all of these things?** (color)

2. Hold up a cube. Ask children to find objects in the classroom that are the same shape. **What is alike about all of these objects?** (shape)

Name_____

Classifying and Sorting Objects

Objective Classify, sort, and compare objects by one attribute.

There are different ways to sort objects.

The shirts in each group are alike in one way.

color   shape   size

Guided Practice

Circle one way the objects are alike.

1.
   Think
   The color and shape are different.

   color (size) shape

2.
   (color) size shape

Tell how the hats are alike.
Write color, size, or shape.

3.
   _____ shape

TEST TIPS **Explain Your Thinking** Describe how the objects in Exercise 3 are different. **They are different sizes and colors.**

Chapter 7 Lesson 1   one hundred eighty-three **183**

---

①Introduce   Activity

Model Classifying and Sorting Objects

iiii Whole Group	⏲ 10–15 minutes	Visual, Tactile

Materials: *teacher-made cut-out mittens*

1. *Sort mittens.* Supply a group of cut-out mittens in 3 colors and 2 sizes. Ask children to find one way the mittens are alike. Remind children that objects can be sorted in many different ways.

2. **How do we sort the mittens by color?** Ask a child to model sorting mittens into groups by color. Have children look at the sorted groups and ask: **What color groups do we have?**

3. Repeat the activity to sort the mittens by size and again by color.

②Develop

Guided Learning

Teaching Example Introduce the objective to the children. Guide them through the example to show how you can sort the shirts in different ways.

Guided Practice

Have children complete **Exercises 1–3** as you observe. Give children the opportunity to answer the Explain Your Thinking question. Then discuss their responses with the class.

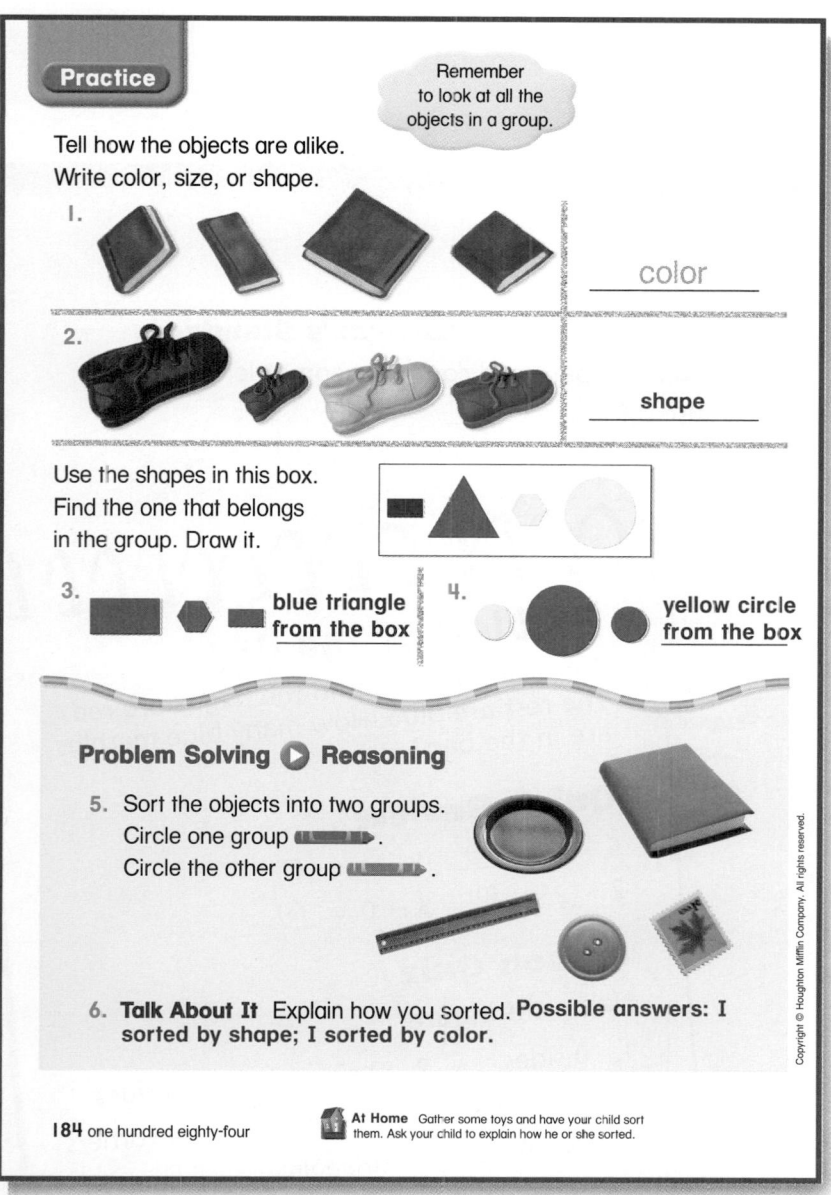

Remember to look at all the objects in a group.

Tell how the objects are alike.
Write color, size, or shape.

1. _____ color _____

2. _____ shape _____

Use the shapes in this box.
Find the one that belongs
in the group. Draw it.

3. ▮ ⬡ ▮ blue triangle from the box

4. ○ ● ● yellow circle from the box

Problem Solving ▶ Reasoning

5. Sort the objects into two groups.
   Circle one group ▬▬▬.
   Circle the other group ▬▬▬.

6. **Talk About It** Explain how you sorted. **Possible answers: I sorted by shape; I sorted by color.**

184 one hundred eighty-four

At Home Gather some toys and have your child sort them. Ask your child to explain how he or she sorted.

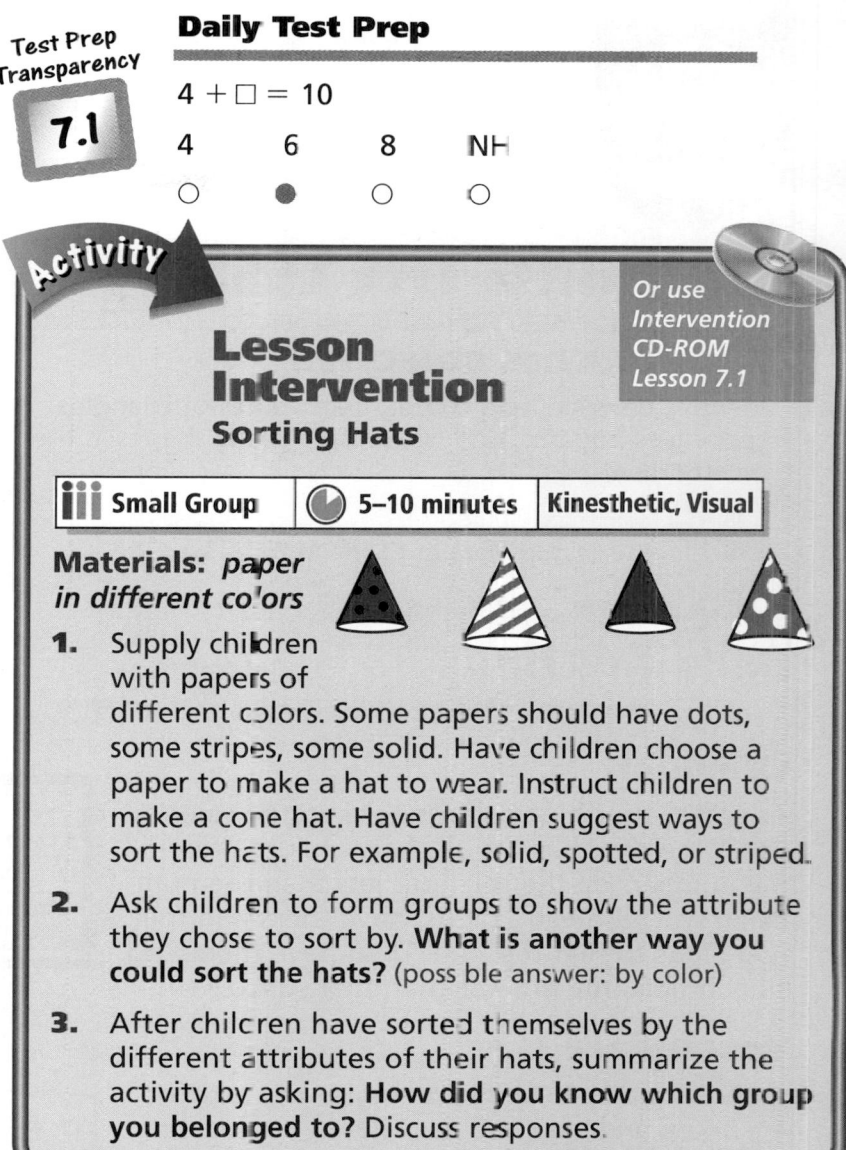

Daily Test Prep

$4 + \square = 10$

4 ○   6 ●   8 ○   NH ○

Activity

Or use Intervention CD-ROM Lesson 7.1

Lesson Intervention
Sorting Hats

| 👥 Small Group | 🕐 5–10 minutes | Kinesthetic, Visual |

Materials: paper in different colors

1. Supply children with papers of different colors. Some papers should have dots, some stripes, some solid. Have children choose a paper to make a hat to wear. Instruct children to make a cone hat. Have children suggest ways to sort the hats. For example, solid, spotted, or striped.

2. Ask children to form groups to show the attribute they chose to sort by. **What is another way you could sort the hats?** (possible answer: by color)

3. After children have sorted themselves by the different attributes of their hats, summarize the activity by asking: **How did you know which group you belonged to?** Discuss responses.

---

3 Practice

Independent Practice

Children complete **Exercises 1–4** independently.

Problem Solving

After children complete **Exercises 5 and 6**, call on volunteers to share how they sorted the objects.

You may want to draw a Venn diagram (two circles) on the board to illustrate the different ways to sort the objects.

Common Error

Misidentifying Attributes

Have children name the attribute by which they are sorting and then identify that attribute in each object.

4 Assess and Close

How could we sort the children in the class? (possible responses: by boy/girl, by height, by age)

How could we sort the books on the shelves? (possible responses: by subject, by size)

Keeping a Journal

Draw a picture to show how you would sort a group of red and blue balls.

Plane Shapes

PLANNING THE LESSON

MATHEMATICS OBJECTIVE
Identify, describe, and compare attributes of triangles, rectangles, squares, and circles; find plane shapes in the environment.

 Use Lesson Planner CD-ROM for Lesson 7.2.

Daily Routines

Calendar
Ask children to find today's date on the calendar. If the date has 1 digit, have children find all the numbers on the calendar less than the number. If the date has 2 digits, have them add the two digits to find the sum. Then have them find all numbers that are less than that sum.

Vocabulary
Draw a **square**, **rectangle**, **triangle**, and **circle** on the board and label. Guide children in reading the names. Identify the **sides** and the **corners** of the square. Call on volunteers to identify the sides and corners of the rectangle and triangle.

Vocabulary Cards

Meeting North Carolina's Standards
3.03 Compare and contrast geometric figures.
Also 3.01

Lesson Transparency
7.2

Problem of the Day
There are 5 marbles in the bag. 2 are red. The rest are blue. How many blue marbles are in the bag? (3)

Quick Review
$6 - 0 =$ (6) $1 - 1 =$ (0)
$2 - 2 =$ (0) $3 - 0 =$ (3)

Lesson Quiz
Name the figure.

1. 0 sides
    0 corners
    (circle)

2. 3 sides
    3 corners
    (triangle)

3. 4 sides
    4 corners
    (square or rectangle)

LEVELED PRACTICE

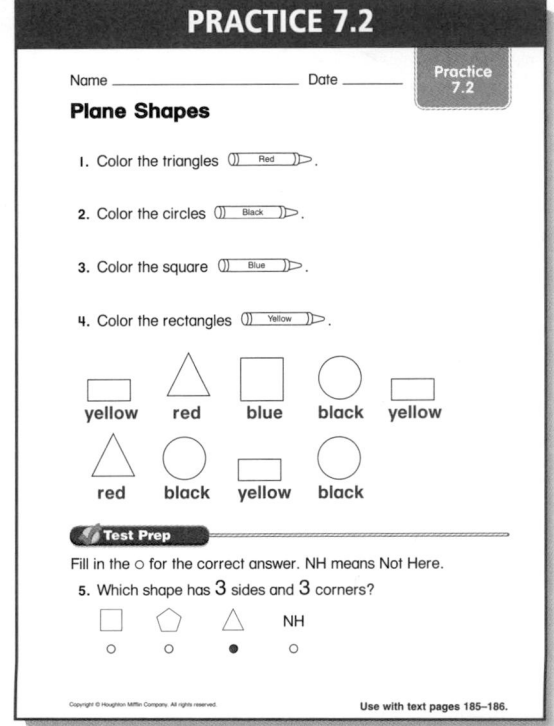

Practice Workbook Page 43

Reaching All Learners

Differentiated Instruction

English Learners

In order to identify plane shapes, children will need to know the meaning of the words *side* and *corner*. Use Worksheet 7.2 to develop children's understanding of these words.

Inclusion

TACTILE, VISUAL

Materials: *attribute blocks or LT 26 and 27*

Give the child several triangle and square attribute blocks. Have the child find all of the blocks with 3 sides. Count the 3 corners. Have the child count the sides. Now have the child find all the blocks with 4 corners. Then count the 4 sides of the squares together.

Early Finishers

TACTILE, VISUAL

Materials: *pattern blocks*

Give each child 3 pattern blocks. Ask children to put the blocks together to form a new shape with the fewest possible sides. Then have children trace around their blocks to draw the new shape.

TECHNOLOGY

Spiral Review

Help students remember skills they learned earlier by creating **customized** spiral review worksheets using the *Ways to Assess* CD-ROM.

Education Place

Encourage students to visit **Education Place** at **eduplace.com/kids/mw/** for more student activities.

Social Studies Connection

Describe a shape search. Tell children that they will hunt in the classroom to find as many square objects as possible. Have children keep a list or drawing of all the square objects they find.

MATH CENTER

Vocabulary Activity

This vocabulary-building activity helps children understand and remember new words. Encourage children to use the words in math discussion.

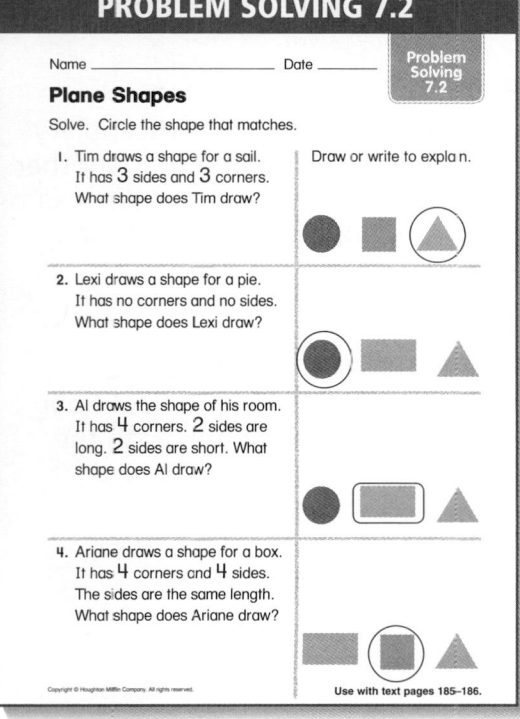

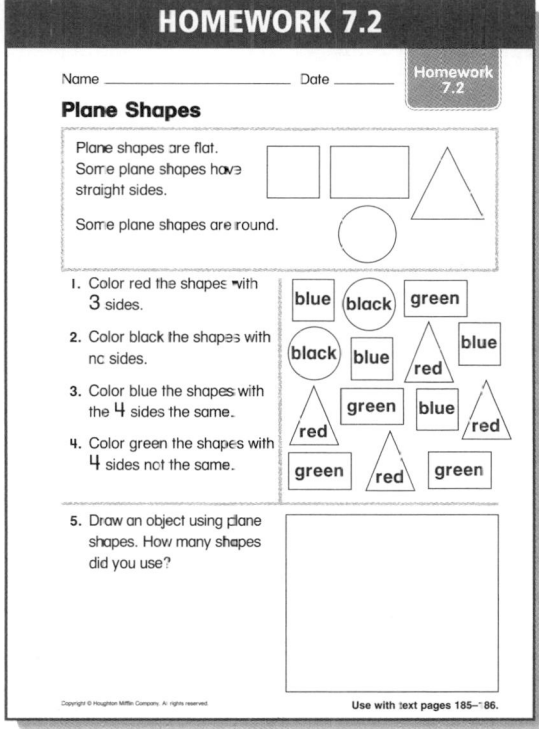

Homework Workbook Page 43

TEACHING LESSON 7.2

LESSON ORGANIZER

Objective Identify, describe, and compare attributes of triangles, rectangles, squares, and circles; find plane shapes in the environment.

Resources Reteach, Practice, Enrichment, Problem Solving, Homework, English Learners, Transparencies, Math Center

Materials Plane shapes (Learning Tool (LT) 22 and 23), paper bag

Warm-Up Activity
Identifying Plane Shapes

👥 Whole Group	🕐 5 minutes	Visual, Auditory

Materials: *cut-out plane shapes (LT 22 and 23), bag*

1. Review the words circle, square, triangle, and rectangle. Draw a triangle on the board. **What is the name of this shape?** Repeat until all of the shapes have been reviewed.

2. Put a set of plane shapes in a bag. Have a volunteer pull one shape from the bag and hold it up. Ask the child to name the shape. Have children raise their hands if they agree. Continue with different volunteers until there are no shapes left in the bag.

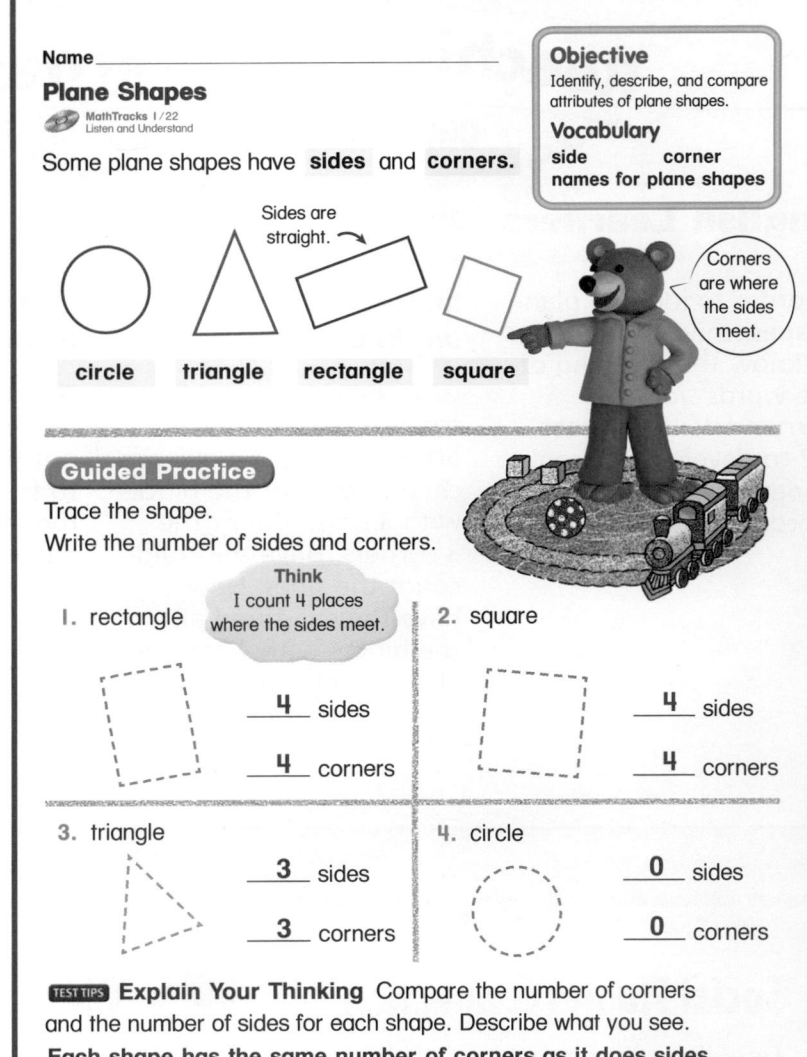

---

1 Introduce

Discuss Identifying Plane Shapes

👥 Whole Group	🕐 10–15 minutes	Visual, Tactile

1. ***Count corners and sides.*** Introduce the words corner and side. You may want to tell children that another word for *corner* is *vertex*. Draw a triangle on the board. Identify the corners as you point. Have children hold up the correct number of fingers as you ask: **How many corners does this shape have?** (3) Explain that a side is a straight line. Then point to and identify the sides. Ask: **How many sides does this shape have?** Have children hold up the number of fingers. (3)

2. Repeat with a rectangle and then a square. **How are a rectangle and a square alike? How are they different?** (Answers will vary.) Explain to children that a square is a special rectangle.

3. Draw a circle. **How many straight sides?** (0) **How many corners?** (0)

2 Develop

Guided Learning

Teaching Example Introduce the objective and vocabulary to the children. You may want to tell children that another word for *corner* is *vertex*. Guide children through the example by showing how to find the number of sides and corners of each shape.

Guided Practice

Have children complete **Exercises 1–4** as you observe. Give children the opportunity to answer the Explain Your Thinking question. Then discuss their responses with the class.

Practice

Answer the question.
Color the shapes on the bus.

Remember the shapes.

circle   square   rectangle   triangle

1. How many shapes have **0** sides? __3__
   Color the circles ▬▬.

2. How many shapes have **3** sides? __2__
   Color the triangles ▬▬.

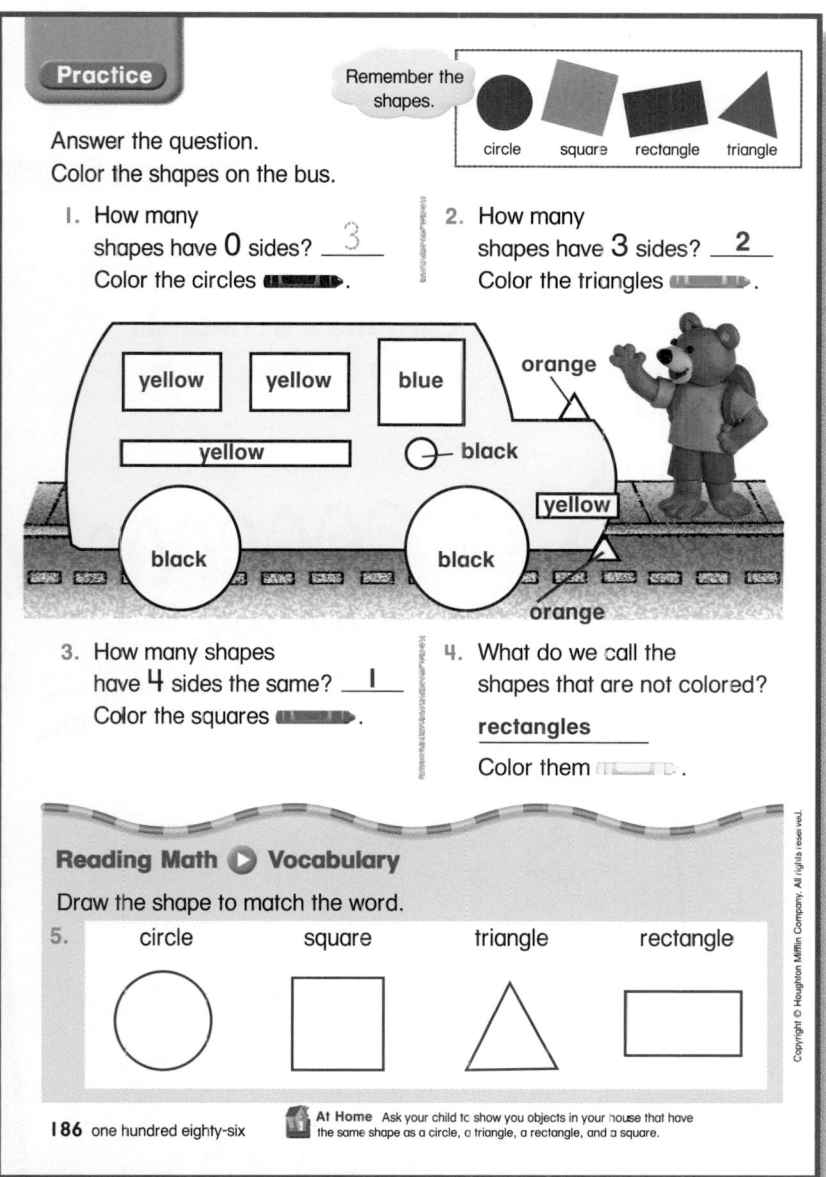

3. How many shapes have **4** sides the same? __1__
   Color the squares ▬▬.

4. What do we call the shapes that are not colored?
   rectangles
   Color them ▬▬.

Reading Math ▶ Vocabulary

Draw the shape to match the word.

5.   circle   square   triangle   rectangle

186 one hundred eighty-six

 **At Home** Ask your child to show you objects in your house that have the same shape as a circle, a triangle, a rectangle, and a square.

Daily Test Prep

Which shape is a square?

○   □   ▭   △

○   ●   ○   ○

Activity

Lesson Intervention

Naming and Describing Figures

Or use Intervention CD-ROM Lesson 7.2

| Small Group | 5–10 minutes | Visual, Tactile |

1. Tell children that a rectangle has 4 sides and 4 corners. Remind them that a square is a special type of rectangle since all 4 of its sides are the same.

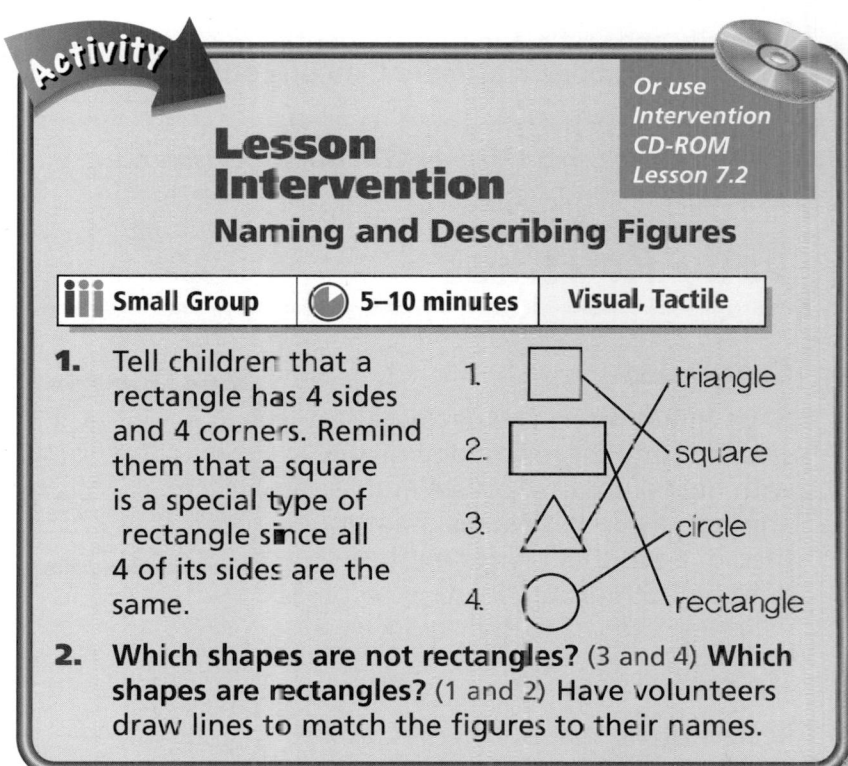

1. ☐ —— triangle
2. ▭ —— square
3. △ —— circle
4. ○ —— rectangle

2. **Which shapes are not rectangles?** (3 and 4) **Which shapes are rectangles?** (1 and 2) Have volunteers draw lines to match the figures to their names.

---

③ Practice

Independent Practice

Children complete **Exercises 1–4** independently.

Reading Math

After children complete **Exercise 5**, call on volunteers to share their drawings. Encourage them to explain how they knew what shape to draw.

Common Error

Miscounting Sides

Children may lose their place when counting sides of a shape. Have children mark the side where they begin counting or put a finger on it to keep their place.

④ Assess and Close

How many sides and corners does a rectangle have? (4)

If you draw a shape with 0 sides and 0 corners, what shape do you draw? (circle)

Keeping a Journal

Use words and pictures to show whether a square, rectangle, circle, or triangle has the same number of sides and corners.

Classifying and Sorting Shapes

PLANNING THE LESSON

MATHEMATICS OBJECTIVE

Classify and sort plane shapes; identify open and closed figures; sort objects by more than one attribute.

Use Lesson Planner CD-ROM for Lesson 7.3.

Daily Routines

Calendar

Have children sort the dates on the calendar into 2 groups: one group with digit sums of 5 or less and another group with sums greater than 5. Have them write all the dates in each group. Invite volunteers to share their work.

Vocabulary

Review plane shape names as well as the terms **side** and **corner**. Call on volunteers to demonstrate the terms using attribute blocks.

Vocabulary Cards

Meeting North Carolina's Standards

3.03 Compare and contrast geometric figures. Also 3.01, 5.01

Lesson Transparency
7.3

Problem of the Day

4 boys had a race. Josh was not first or third. Pete was last. In what place did Josh finish? (second)

Quick Review

$3 + 5 =$ (8) $9 + 0 =$ (9)
$7 - 2 =$ (5) $6 - 5 =$ (1)

Lesson Quiz

The rule is shapes with 4 sides.
Circle the shape that does not belong.
(triangle)

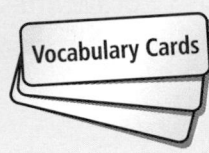

LEVELED PRACTICE

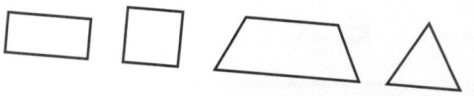

RETEACH 7.3

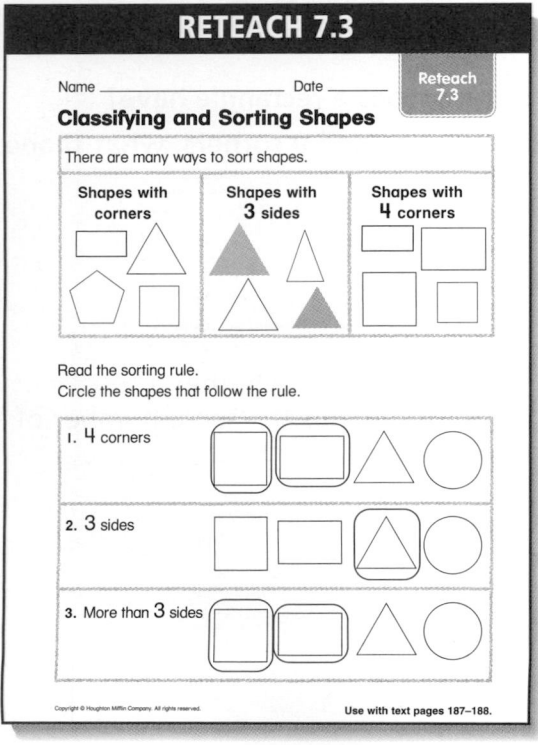

PRACTICE 7.3

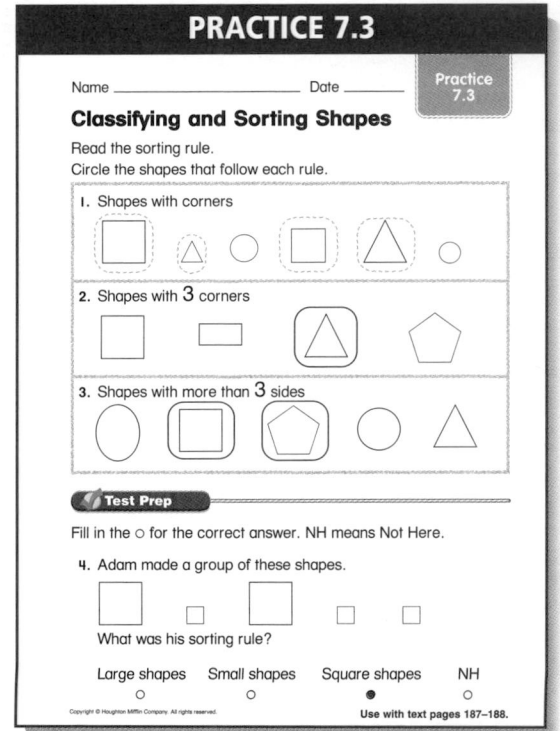

ENRICHMENT 7.3

Practice Workbook Page 44

Reaching All Learners

Differentiated Instruction

English Learners

To classify and sort plane shapes, children will need to know the concept of sorting. Worksheet 7.3 will help them develop this concept.

Special Needs

VISUAL, TACTILE

Materials: *pattern blocks: squares, triangles; small box*

Display squares and triangles. Have the child sort the shapes by putting all the squares in the box. Use the same blocks and put all the triangles in the box. Repeat the sorting by number of sides and then number of corners.

Gifted and Talented

TACTILE, VISUAL

Materials: *cutouts of plane shapes*

Give each group a set of plane shape cutouts.

Ask children to sort the shapes in different ways. Have children draw or write to record each sorting.

TECHNOLOGY

Spiral Review

You can prepare students for standardized tests with **customized** sp ral review on key skills using the *Ways to Assess CD-ROM.*

eBook

eMathBook allows students to review lessons and do homework without carrying their textbooks home.

Geometry Software

Use **Sunburst's Shape Up!** or another shapes program to explore this lesson's objectives more fully.

Social Studies Connection

The Chinese people invented a 7-piece puzzle of different shapes that fit together and make a square. It is called a tangram. Prepare tagboard tangrams for children to cut out and use.

MATH CENTER

Basic Skills Activity

Motivate children to build basic skills. Use this activity to address multiple learning styles using hands-on activities related to the skills of this lesson.

PROBLEM SOLVING 7.3

Name _____ Date _____ | Problem Solving 7.3

Classifying and Sorting Shapes

Circle to follow the sorting rule.

1. Austin is putting away shapes that have no corners. Which shapes should he put into the box? | Draw or write to explain.

2. Teela is putting away shapes that have 3 corners. Which shapes should she put into the box?

3. Tighe is putting away shapes with 4 corners. Which shapes should he put into the box?

4. Lynda is putting away shapes with more than 2 sides. Which shapes should she put into the box?

Copyright © Houghton Mifflin Company. All rights reserved.   Use with text pages 187–188.

HOMEWORK 7.3

Name _____ Date _____ | Homework 7.3

Classifying and Sorting Shapes

You can sort shapes in many ways.
Some shapes have 3 or 4 corners. ← corner
Some shapes have 3 or 4 sides. ← side

Circle the shapes that follow the rule.

1. 3 sides

2. 4 sides the same

3. More than 3 sides

4. No corners

5. David drew a picture with a shape with 4 sides inside a shape with 3 sides inside a shape with no sides. What picture did David draw? | Draw here.

Copyright © Houghton Mifflin Company. All rights reserved.   Use with text pages 187–188.

ENGLISH LEARNERS 7.3

Name _____ Date _____ | English Learners 7.3

Classifying and Sorting Shapes

Tim can **sort** the toys into two groups.

Sort the objects by drawing in the different boxes.

1.

| Drawing of 2 hearts | Drawing of 3 stars |

2.

| Drawing of 4 squares | Drawing of 4 circles |

3.

X Z X Z
Z X Z

| Drawing of 3 X's | Drawing of 4 Z's |

4.

| Drawing of 5 eggs | Drawing of 2 chicks |

To the Teacher: Use the illustration and sentence at the top of the page to help children understand the concept of sorting. Then have children draw pictures to sort the objects.

Copyright © Houghton Mifflin Company. All rights reserved.   Use with text pages 187–189.

TEACHING LESSON 7.3

LESSON ORGANIZER

Objective Classify and sort plane shapes; identify open and closed figures; sort objects by more than one attribute.

Resources Reteach, Practice, Enrichment, Problem Solving, Homework, English Learners, Transparencies, Math Center

Materials Plane shapes (LT 22 and 23), pattern blocks, attribute blocks or LT 26 and 27

Activity

Warm-Up Activity
Identifying Plane Shapes

| ▮▮▮▮ Whole Group | ⏱ 5 minutes | Visual, Auditory |

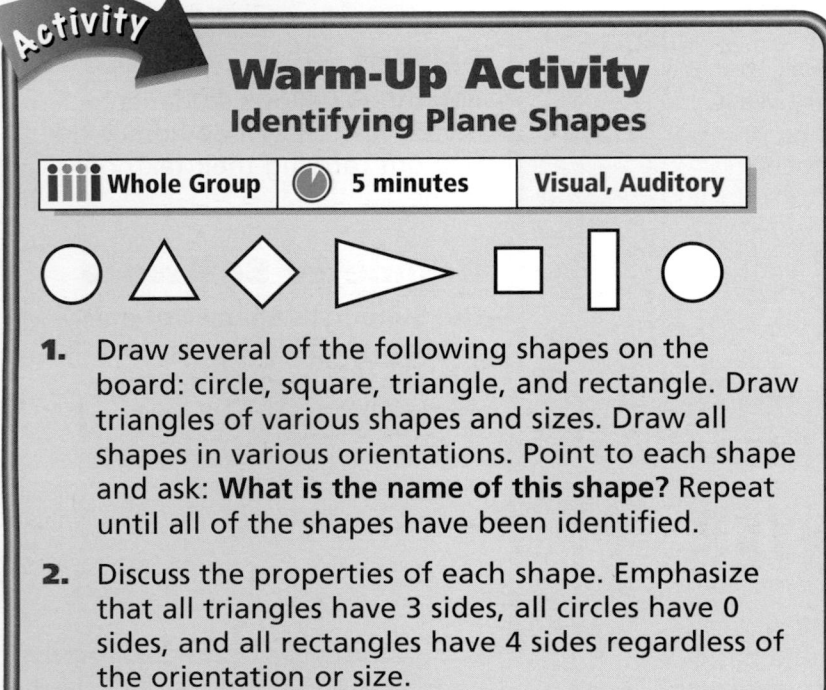

1. Draw several of the following shapes on the board: circle, square, triangle, and rectangle. Draw triangles of various shapes and sizes. Draw all shapes in various orientations. Point to each shape and ask: **What is the name of this shape?** Repeat until all of the shapes have been identified.

2. Discuss the properties of each shape. Emphasize that all triangles have 3 sides, all circles have 0 sides, and all rectangles have 4 sides regardless of the orientation or size.

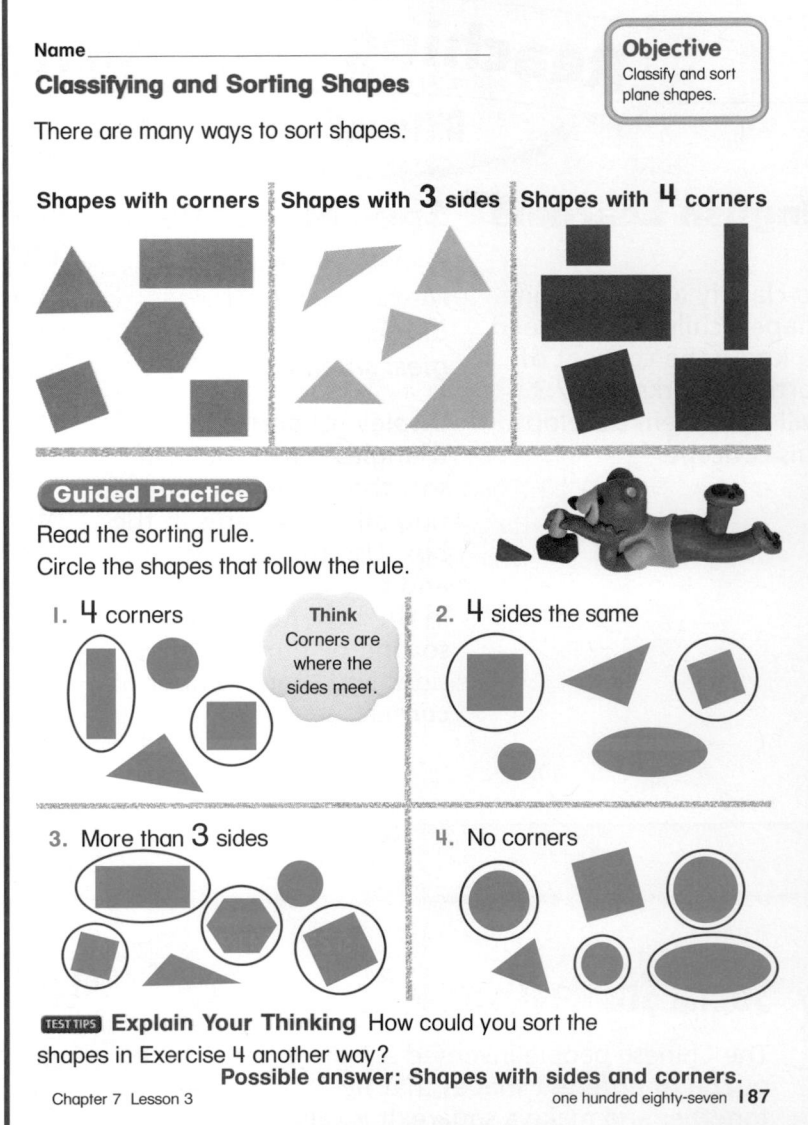

Name_____

Classifying and Sorting Shapes

Objective Classify and sort plane shapes.

There are many ways to sort shapes.

| Shapes with corners | Shapes with 3 sides | Shapes with 4 corners |

Guided Practice

Read the sorting rule.
Circle the shapes that follow the rule.

1. 4 corners

Think Corners are where the sides meet.

2. 4 sides the same

3. More than 3 sides

4. No corners

TEST TIPS **Explain Your Thinking** How could you sort the shapes in Exercise 4 another way?
Possible answer: Shapes with sides and corners.

Chapter 7 Lesson 3   one hundred eighty-seven **187**

---

1 Introduce
Classifying and Sorting Shapes

| ▮▮▮▮ Whole Group | ⏱ 10–15 minutes | Visual, Tactile |

Materials: *plane shapes (LT 22 and 23)*

1. **Sort shapes.** Review the term *sorting rule*. Display a set of plane shapes and ask volunteers to suggest a sorting rule. Prompt children to identify one way some of the shapes are alike. Explain that finding one way shapes are alike helps you decide on a sorting rule.

2. **What is one way you can sort these shapes?** (Answers will vary.) Have a volunteer sort the shapes by his or her sorting rule. Write the sorting rule on the board and relate it to how the shapes were sorted. Repeat with another volunteer, modeling another sorting rule.

3. Make sure children understand that the number of sides and corners can be used to sort shapes. Relate this to the sorting rules and figures in the demonstration.

2 Develop

Guided Learning

Teaching Example Introduce the objective to the children. Guide them through the example to show the different sorting rules. You may want to remind children that another word for *corner* is *vertex*.

Guided Practice

Have children complete **Exercises 1–4** as you observe. Give children the opportunity to answer the Explain Your Thinking question. Then discuss their responses with the class.

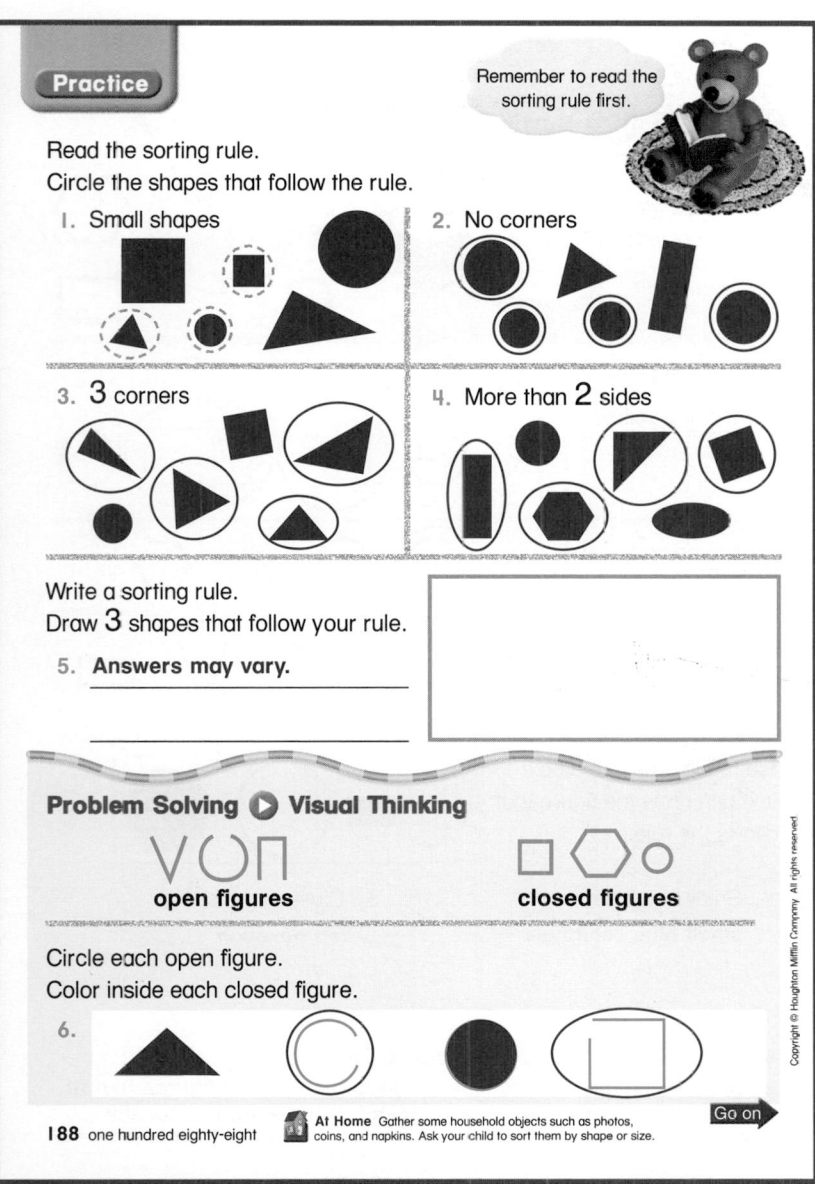

Practice

Remember to read the sorting rule first.

Read the sorting rule.
Circle the shapes that follow the rule.

1. Small shapes

2. No corners

3. 3 corners

4. More than 2 sides

Write a sorting rule.
Draw **3** shapes that follow your rule.

5. **Answers may vary.**

Problem Solving ▶ Visual Thinking

V ∩ ∩ **open figures**

□ ⬡ ○ **closed figures**

Circle each open figure.
Color inside each closed figure.

6.

At Home Gather some household objects such as photos, coins, and napkins. Ask your child to sort them by shape or size.

Go on

ACHIEVING
Mathematical Proficiency

Developing Geometric Sense

Recent studies in the area of geometric reasoning reinforce the idea that appropriate activities can help children move from simple to more advanced levels of reasoning. Research has shown that children come to school with a certain amount of knowledge about shapes. Meaningful instruction should build on this informal knowledge and then move beyond it.

When children learn how to identify and compare attributes of plane shapes, they are ready to extend this knowledge to attributes of solid shapes. Similarly, classifying and sorting plane shapes extends readily to classifying and sorting solid shapes.

Children develop their geometric sense as they progress from an understanding of two-dimensional shapes to an understanding of three-dimensional solids.

---

3 Practice

Independent Practice

Children complete **Exercises 1–4** independently. Remind children how to write a sorting rule before they complete **Exercise 5.**

Problem Solving

After children complete **Exercise 6,** call on volunteers to share their solutions. Encourage them to explain how they knew which figures were open and which were closed.

Common Error

Misapplying the Sorting Rule

Have children say the rule aloud before sorting. Then provide simple sorting exercises. Have them identify the sorting attribute in each shape.

4 Assess and Close

Explain what you know about how to sort shapes. (You can sort by finding one thing alike in the shapes.)

What shape has 3 sides and 3 corners? (triangle)

 **Keeping a Journal**

Draw a group of shapes. Write a sorting rule and show a way the shapes can be sorted.

Lesson continues ▶

Daily Test Prep

Which fact does **not** belong?

5 + 2 = 7   7 − 2 = 5   7 − 5 = 2   7 = 2 − 9
   ○   ○   ○   ●

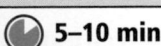

Activity

Or use Intervention CD-ROM Lesson 7.3

Lesson Intervention
Naming and Describing Figures

Small Group	5–10 minutes	Visual, Tactile

Materials: *pattern blocks*

1. Allow groups time to explore the shapes. **Do all your shapes have corners?** (yes) **Do all your shapes have 4 sides?** (no)

2. Ask groups to sort their shapes by number of corners. **What do we call the shapes with 3 corners?** (triangles)

3. Ask children to make a group of shapes with 4 equal sides. **What is the name of the shapes in this group?** (possible answer: squares)

4. Allow children to sort the shapes. Then have each group share their work. Encourage children to describe how the shapes have been sorted.

Name_____

Now Try This Sort by Two Attributes

Small and yellow

Sometimes we use more than one sorting rule to make a set.

Circle the figure that follows the rule.

1. Big and yellow

2. Round and blue

3. Open and red

Use the figures in the box. Find and draw the figure that follows the rule.

4. Small and blue

   small blue rectangle

5. Closed and red

   red hexagon

6. **Talk About It** How did you choose figures for Exercises 4 and 5? **Possible answer: I looked for figures that fit the first word in the rule. Then I looked at those figures for the second word.**

Chapter 7 Lesson 3   one hundred eighty-nine **189**

Now Try This

Materials: *attribute blocks or LT 26 and 27*

Introduce Use attribute blocks to review how to find things that are alike about shapes. Tell children that they can sort shapes using 2 rules. Guide children through the Venn diagram example at the top. Point out that the sorting rule uses two words—small and yellow. **The only shapes that belong in the circle are small, yellow shapes. Why are the small shapes outside the ring?** (They are not yellow.) **Why are the yellow shapes outside the ring?** (They are not small.)

Develop Children complete Exercises 1–3 as you observe. Help children as necessary to identify the open shape in **Exercise 3**.

Practice Children complete Exercises 4–5 independently. Give children the opportunity to answer the **Talk About It** question in **Exercise 6**. Discuss their responses with the class.

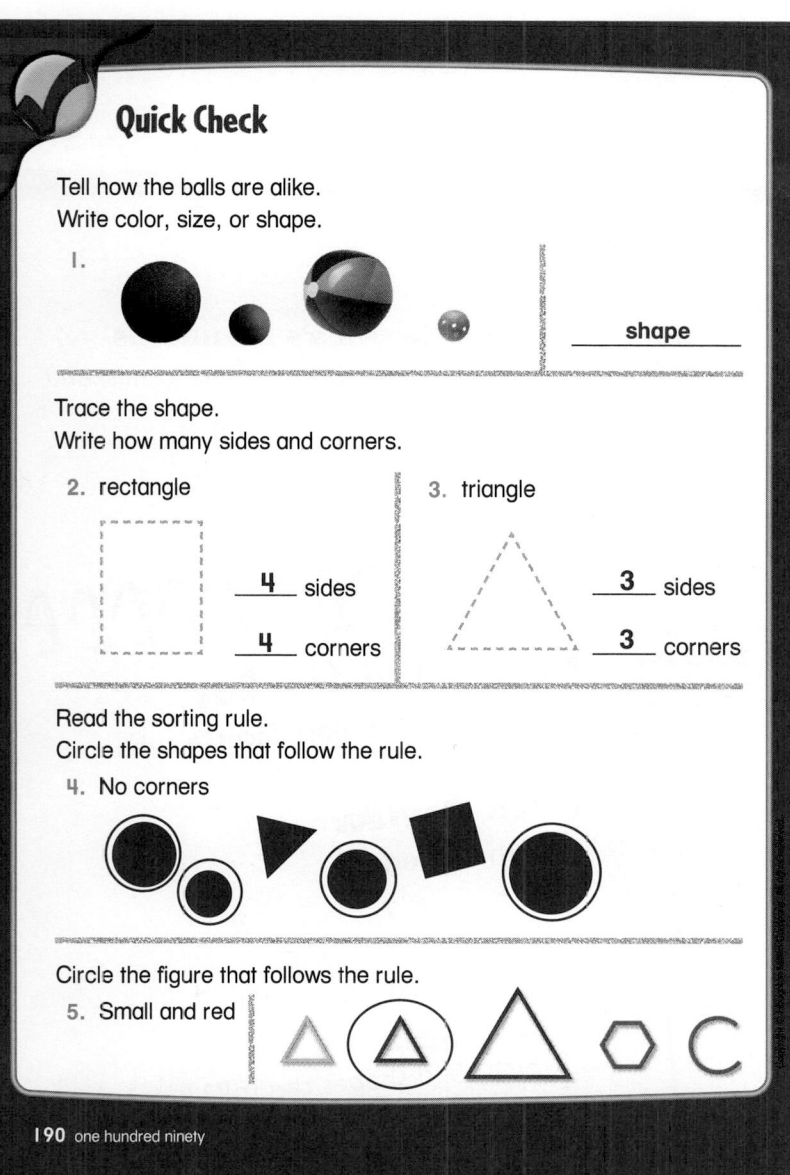

Quick Check

Tell how the balls are alike.
Write color, size, or shape.

1.

_____ **shape** _____

Trace the shape.
Write how many sides and corners.

2. rectangle

__4__ sides

__4__ corners

3. triangle

__3__ sides

__3__ corners

Read the sorting rule.
Circle the shapes that follow the rule.

4. No corners

Circle the figure that follows the rule.

5. Small and red

Quick Check

Have children complete the Quick Check exercises independently to assess their understanding of concepts and skills taught in **Lessons 1–3**.

Item	Lesson	Error Analysis	Intervention
1	7.1	Children may not be able to identify attributes.	Reteach Resource 7.1 *Ways to Success* 7.1
2–3	7.2	Children may miscount the number of sides and corners.	Reteach Resource 7.2 *Ways to Success* 7.2
4–5	7.3	Children may misapply the sorting rule.	Reteach Resource 7.3 *Ways to Success* 7.3

Hands-On: Solid Shapes

PLANNING THE LESSON

MATHEMATICS OBJECTIVE
Identify, describe, and compare solid shapes.

Use Lesson Planner CD-ROM for Lesson 7.4.

Daily Routines

Calendar
Have children say and write all the dates that include a 5. Ask children what pattern they see. (Each number is 10 more.) Point to the calendar as you have children say the pattern. (5, 15, 25) Now ask children to extend the pattern as far as they can: 35, 45, 55, ...

Vocabulary
Display a set of solid shapes. Write the words cube, cone, cylinder, rectangular prism, pyramid, sphere and identify each solid. Now write **face, edge, corner.** Point out the **corners, faces,** and **edges** on each solid.

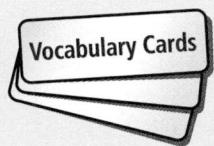

Vocabulary Cards

Meeting North Carolina's Standards
3.02 Identify, build, and name cylinders, cones, and rectangular prisms.
Also 3.03

Lesson Transparency
7.4

Problem of the Day
Which shape has more faces, a cube or a pyramid? (cube)

Quick Review
Write the difference.

$$8 - 0 = (8)$$
$$7 - 4 = (3)$$
$$8 - 7 = (1)$$
$$6 - 6 = (0)$$

Lesson Quiz
1. Which solid shapes can roll? (sphere, cylinder, and cone)
2. Which solid shapes can stack? (rectangular prism, cube, and cylinder)

LEVELED PRACTICE

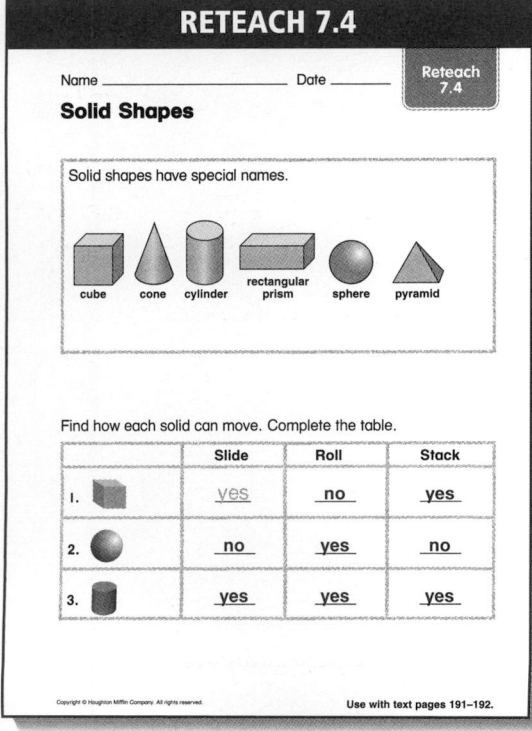

RETEACH 7.4

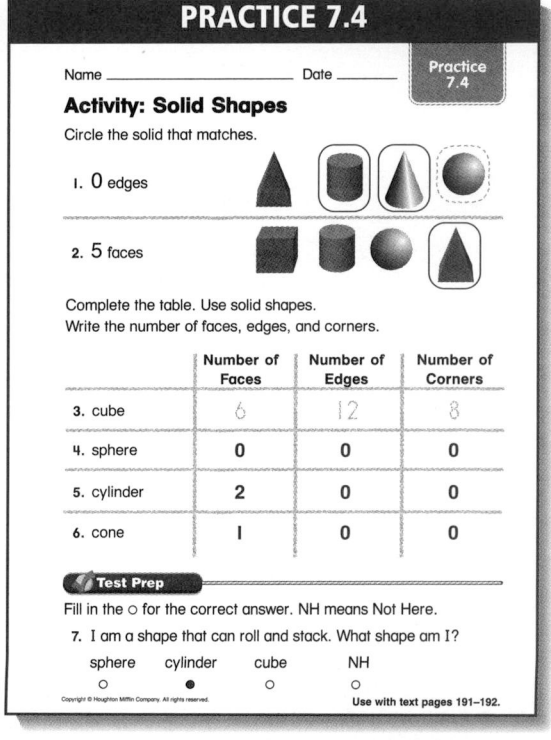

PRACTICE 7.4

Practice Workbook Page 45

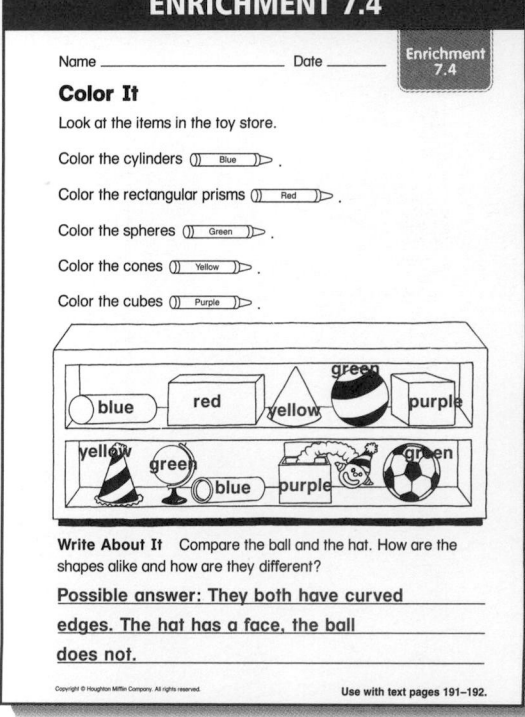

ENRICHMENT 7.4

Reaching All Learners
Differentiated Instruction

English Learners

English-language learners will need to know the meaning of the words *slide*, *stack*, and *roll* in order to discuss how solids move. Use Worksheet 7.4 to develop their understanding of these words.

Special Needs
VISUAL, TACTILE

Materials: *set of solid shapes*

- Display a set of geometric solids.
- Hold up the sphere and ask the child if the shape can roll. Have the child try it. Repeat with the remaining shapes.
- Hold up the cube and ask if the shape can stack. Continue with all the shapes.

Gifted and Talented
TACTILE, VISUAL

Materials: *solids, straws, clay*

Have children select a solid. Instruct children to use straws and clay to build a model of the solid. Have children exchange their models with a partner, identify the solid shape and write how many corners, edges, and faces.

Science Connection

Discuss how people use their senses to understand things in our world. Discuss each sense: touch, smell, hearing, sight, and taste. Then ask children to identify solids using only their sense of touch.

MATH CENTER

Basic Skills Activity

Motivate children to build basic skills. Use this activity to address multiple learning styles using hands-on activities related to the skills of this lesson.

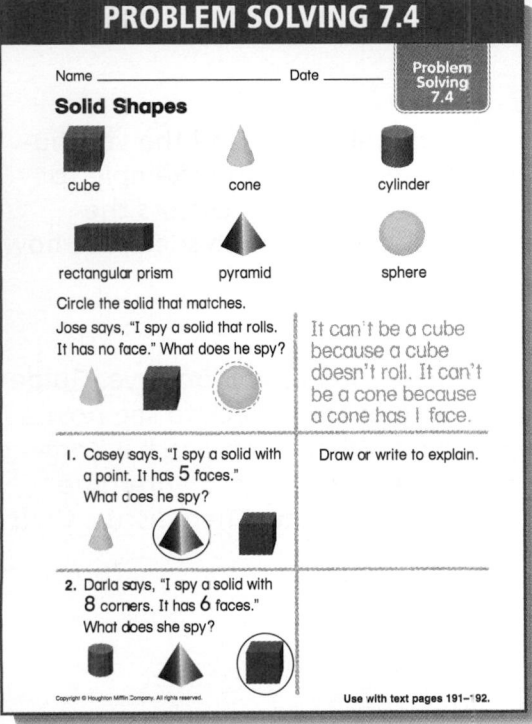

PROBLEM SOLVING 7.4

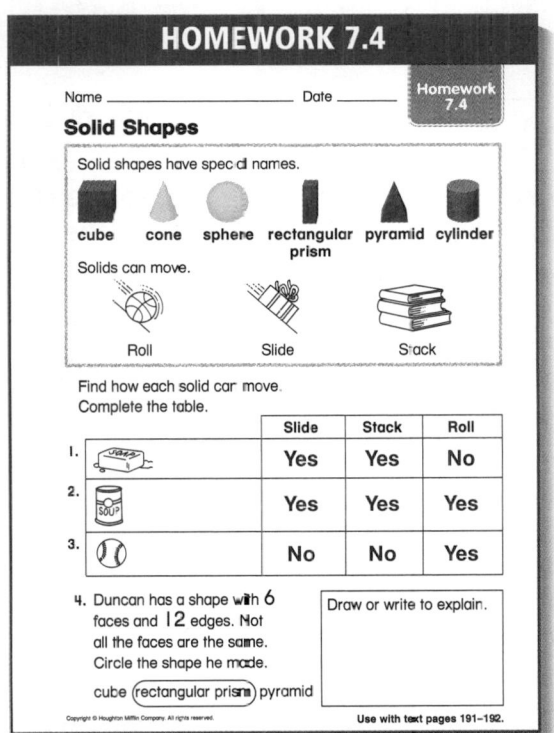

HOMEWORK 7.4

Homework Workbook Page 45

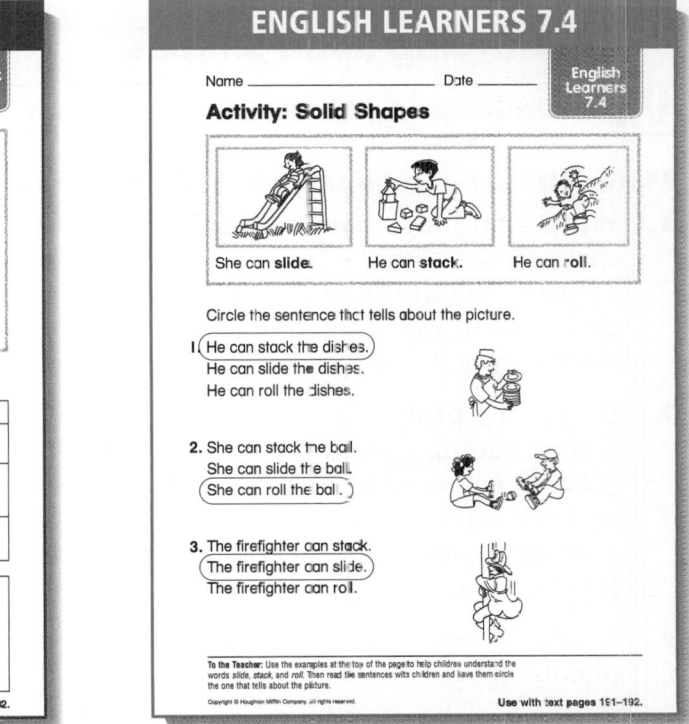

ENGLISH LEARNERS 7.4

TEACHING LESSON 7.4

LESSON ORGANIZER

Objective Identify, describe, and compare solid shapes.

Resources Reteach, Practice, Enrichment, Problem Solving, Homework, English Learners, Transparencies, Math Center

Materials Set of solid shapes, real-life objects

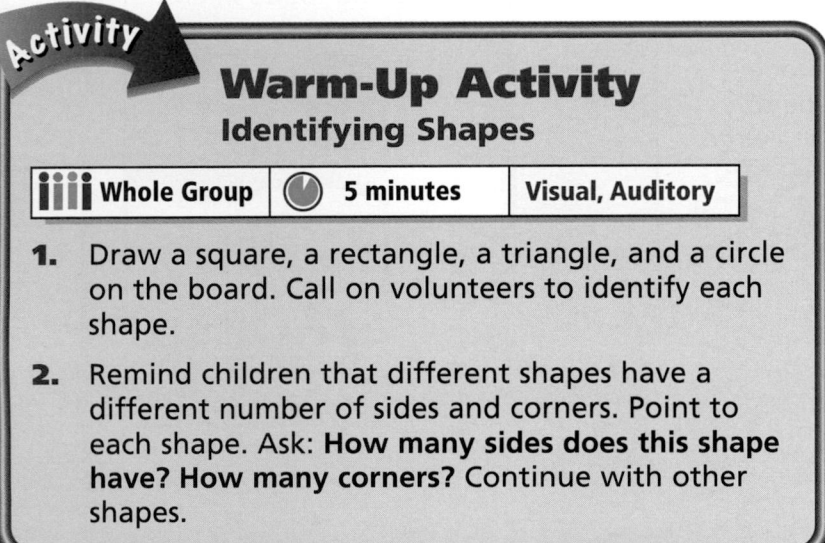

Activity

Warm-Up Activity
Identifying Shapes

👥 Whole Group	⏱ 5 minutes	Visual, Auditory

1. Draw a square, a rectangle, a triangle, and a circle on the board. Call on volunteers to identify each shape.

2. Remind children that different shapes have a different number of sides and corners. Point to each shape. Ask: **How many sides does this shape have? How many corners?** Continue with other shapes.

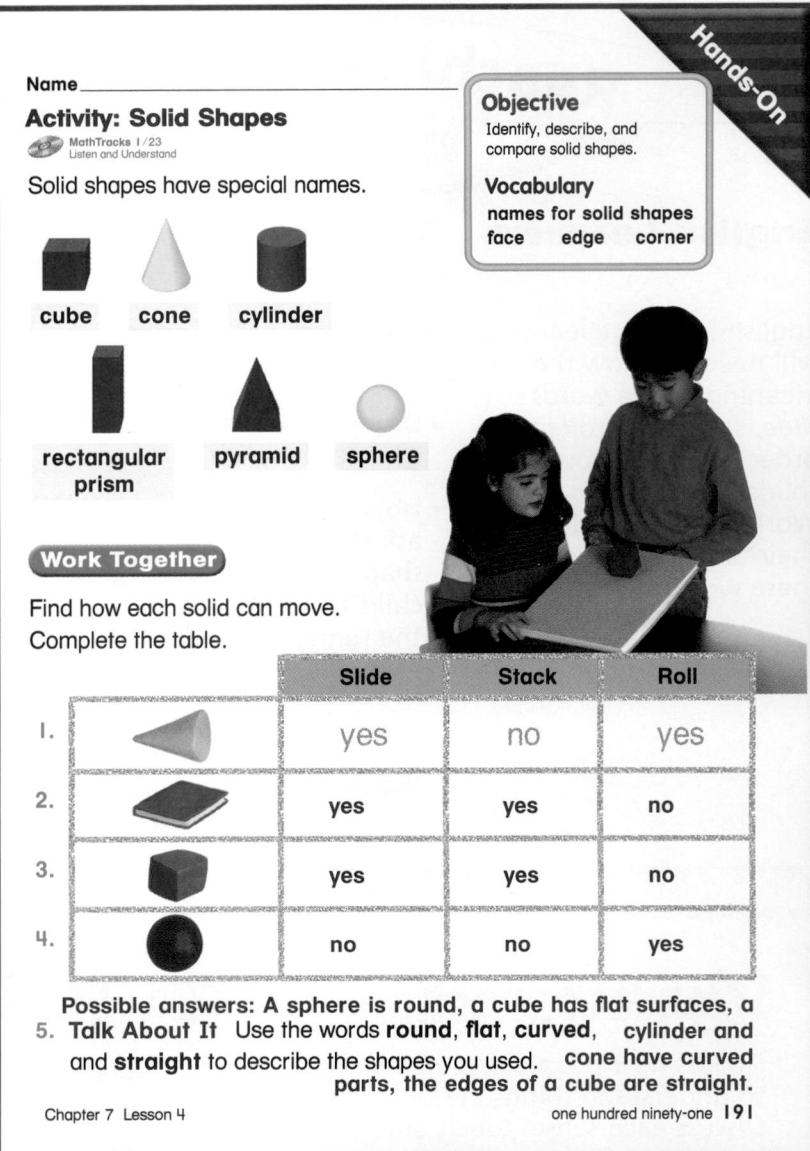

Name_____

Activity: Solid Shapes
MathTracks 1/23
Listen and Understand

Solid shapes have special names.

cube   cone   cylinder

rectangular prism   pyramid   sphere

Objective
Identify, describe, and compare solid shapes.

Vocabulary
names for solid shapes
face   edge   corner

Work Together

Find how each solid can move.
Complete the table.

		Slide	Stack	Roll
1.		yes	no	yes
2.		yes	yes	no
3.		yes	yes	no
4.		no	no	yes

5. **Talk About It** Use the words **round**, **flat**, **curved**, and **straight** to describe the shapes you used.

Possible answers: A sphere is round, a cube has flat surfaces, a cylinder and cone have curved parts, the edges of a cube are straight.

Chapter 7 Lesson 4   one hundred ninety-one **191**

---

① Introduce
Identifying Solid Shapes

👥 Whole Group	⏱ 10–15 minutes	Visual, Tactile

Materials: *set of solid shapes, real-life objects*

1. Write solid shape names on the board. Display a solid shape. Have a volunteer identify the matching real-life object. Have the child say the name of the solid as you point to the word. Repeat until all of the shapes and matching real-life objects have been identified.

2. Discuss the properties of each solid shape. Use words such as **round, curved surfaces, and faces**. Make sure children can connect the language you are using to the faces being described. Show how some shapes can roll and some cannot. Show how some shapes can stack and some cannot.

3. Finally, have volunteers identify the edges and corners of each solid.

② Develop

Guided Learning

Teaching Example Introduce the objective and the vocabulary to the children. Guide them through the example to review the names and shapes of the solids. Discuss the properties of the solids and ask volunteers to speculate how the figures can move.

Work Together

Have children complete **Exercises 1–4** as you observe. Guide them through the first example as they check to see how a cone can move down an incline. When everyone has completed the exercises, discuss **Exercise 5**. Give children the opportunity to describe what they wrote. Then discuss their responses with the class.

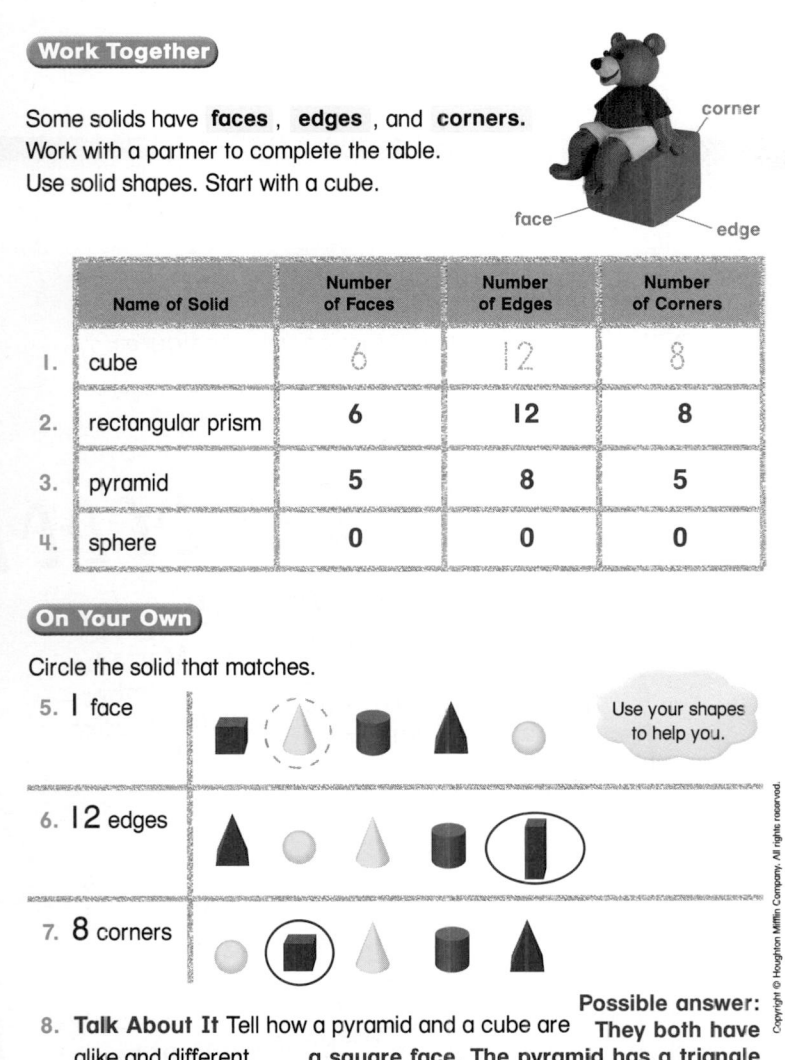

Work Together

Some solids have **faces**, **edges**, and **corners**.
Work with a partner to complete the table.
Use solid shapes. Start with a cube.

corner

face

edge

	Name of Solid	Number of Faces	Number of Edges	Number of Corners
1.	cube	6	12	8
2.	rectangular prism	6	12	8
3.	pyramid	5	8	5
4.	sphere	0	0	0

On Your Own

Circle the solid that matches.

5. 1 face

Use your shapes to help you.

6. 12 edges

7. 8 corners

8. **Talk About It** Tell how a pyramid and a cube are alike and different.

Possible answer: They both have a square face. The pyramid has a triangle face and a point at the top.

At Home Ask your child to find an object in your house that will slide, stack, and roll.

192 one hundred ninety-two

Test Prep Transparency

7.4

Which object has the same shape?

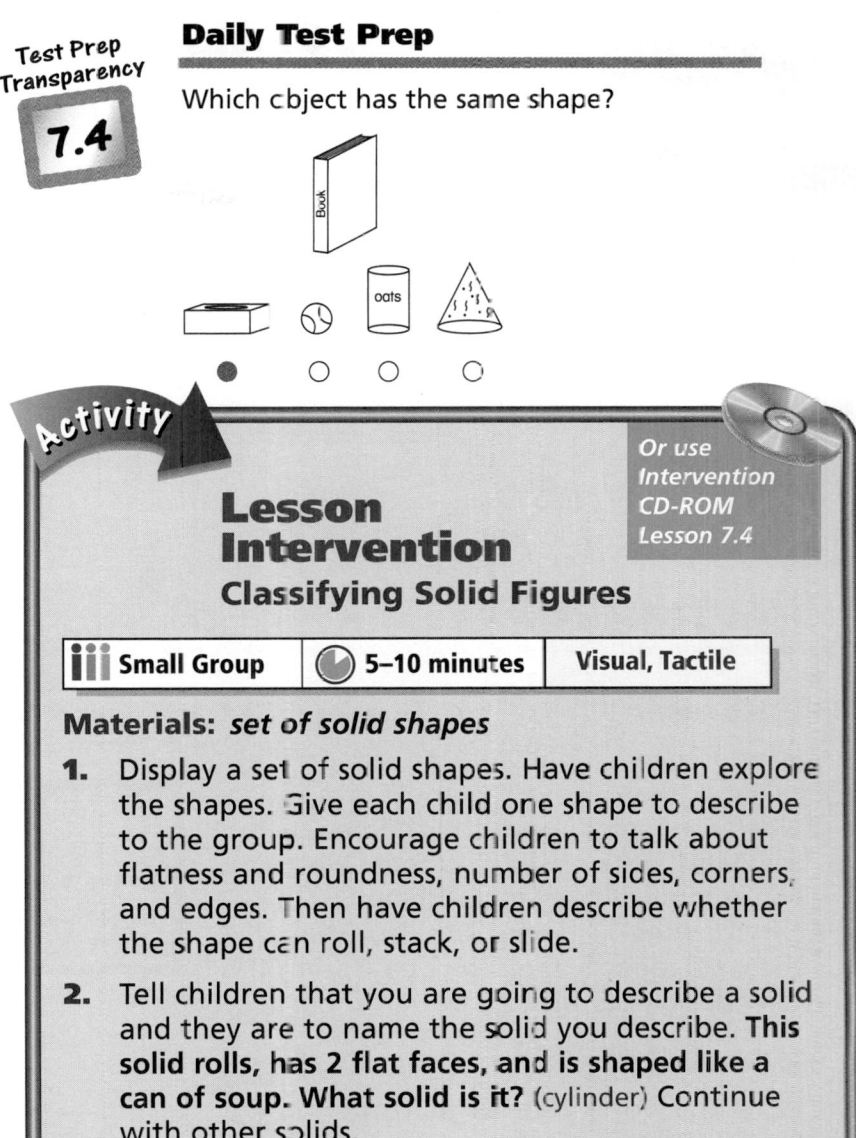

Book

oats

● ○ ○ ○

Activity

Lesson Intervention
Classifying Solid Figures

Or use Intervention CD-ROM Lesson 7.4

👤👤👤 Small Group	🕐 5–10 minutes	Visual, Tactile

Materials: *set of solid shapes*

1. Display a set of solid shapes. Have children explore the shapes. Give each child one shape to describe to the group. Encourage children to talk about flatness and roundness, number of sides, corners, and edges. Then have children describe whether the shape can roll, stack, or slide.

2. Tell children that you are going to describe a solid and they are to name the solid you describe. **This solid rolls, has 2 flat faces, and is shaped like a can of soup. What solid is it?** (cylinder) Continue with other solids.

③ Practice

Work Together

Work through **Exercise 1** with the class. Count the faces. Write 6 in the table. Count the edges. Write 12 in the table. Count the corners. Write 8 in the table. Have children complete **Exercises 2–4** with a partner.

On Your Own

Children complete **Exercises 5–7** independently. After children complete **Exercise 8**, call on volunteers to share their answers. Encourage children to use geometric terms to describe the differences between the solids.

Common Error

Miscounting the Number of Edges

Have children place a numbered sticker on each edge as it is counted. This can also be done for counting faces or corners.

④ Assess and Close

Explain what you know about solid shapes. (Answers may vary. They have different faces, edges, and corners; they can move in different ways.)

What solid shape has 0 faces, 0 edges, and 0 sides? (sphere)

✏️ Keeping a Journal

Draw a solid shape. Describe how the shape can move. Explain why it can move that way.

Classifying and Sorting Solid Shapes

PLANNING THE LESSON

MATHEMATICS OBJECTIVE
Classify and sort solid shapes.

Use Lesson Planner CD-ROM for Lesson 7.5.

Meeting North Carolina's Standards

3.03 Compare and contrast geometric figures.
Also 3.02, 3.04

Daily Routines

Calendar

Have volunteers name four dates on the calendar that form a rectangle or a square when connected. Have the child point to the dates as he or she says them aloud. For example: Friday the 10th and 17th, Saturday the 11th and 18th. Now have the child identify the shape by tracing the calendar blocks with his or her finger.

Sunday	Monday	Tuesday	Wednesday	Thursday	Friday	Saturday
			1	2	3	4
5	6	7	8	9	10	11
12	13	14	15	16	17	18
19	20	21	22	23	24	25
26	27	28	29	30	31	

Vocabulary

Write the words **face, edge, corner** on the board. Call on volunteers to find examples from a set of items with solid shapes. Also review the terms *solid shape, plane shape,* and shape names.

Vocabulary Cards

Lesson
Transparency
7.5

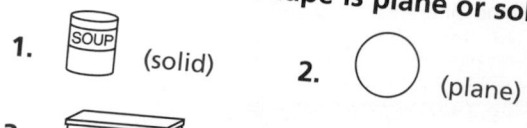

Problem of the Day
Nina has six boxes of crayons. Marta has nine boxes of crayons. Write a number sentence to show how many more boxes Marta has than Nina. $(9 - 6 = 3)$

Quick Review

$\begin{array}{r} 10 \\ -5 \\ \hline \end{array}$	$\begin{array}{r} 9 \\ -3 \\ \hline \end{array}$	$\begin{array}{r} 8 \\ -1 \\ \hline \end{array}$	$\begin{array}{r} 7 \\ -6 \\ \hline \end{array}$	$\begin{array}{r} 6 \\ -4 \\ \hline \end{array}$
(5)	(6)	(7)	(1)	(2)

Lesson Quiz
Tell whether the shape is plane or solid.

1. 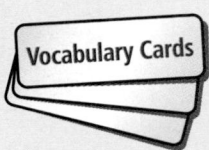 SOUP (solid)   2. ◯ (plane)

3. Sneakers (solid)

LEVELED PRACTICE

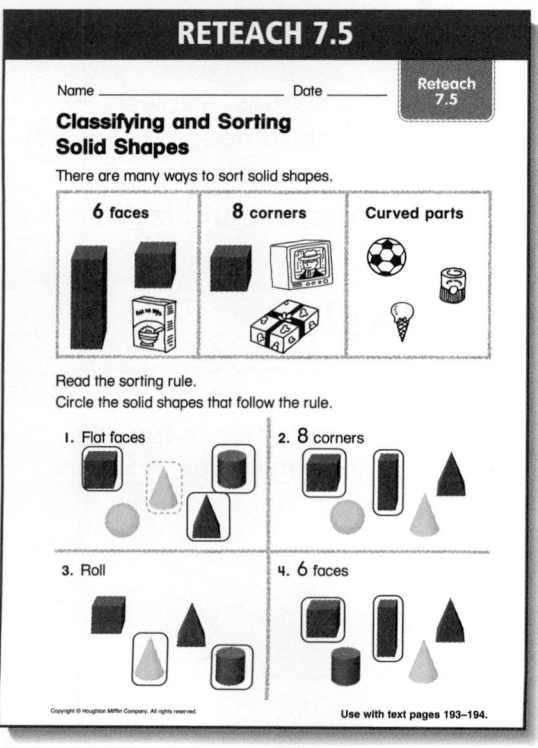

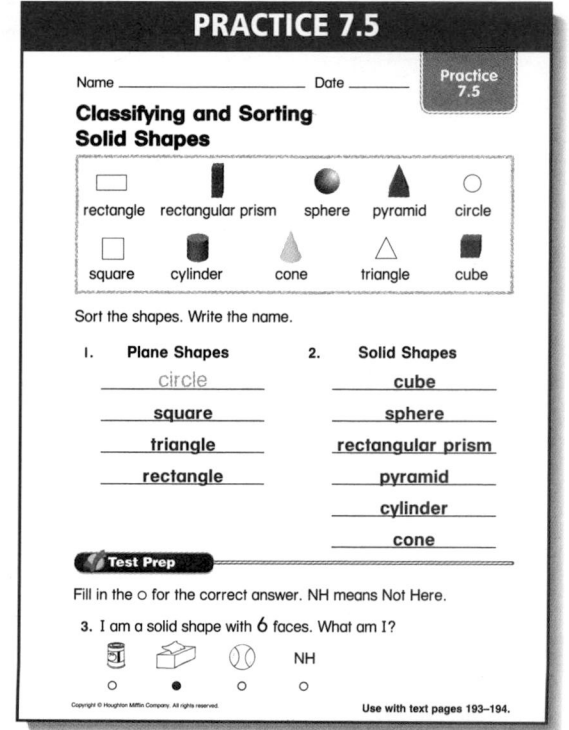

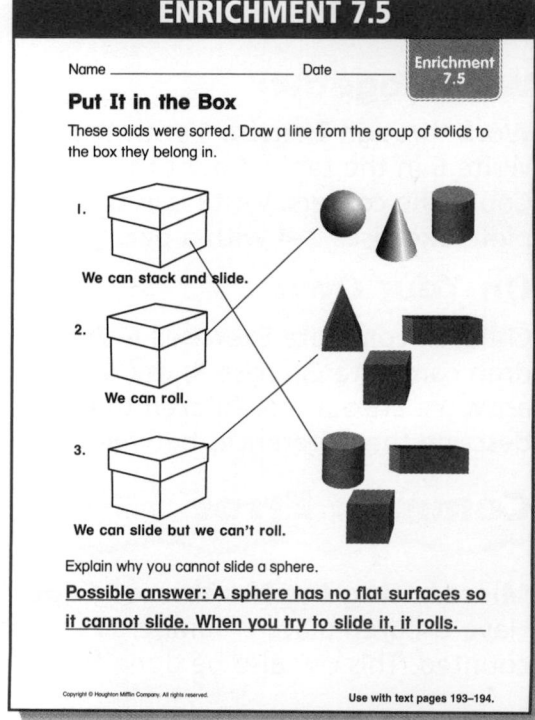

Practice Workbook Page 46

Reaching All Learners
Differentiated Instruction

English Learners

Children wil need to know the meaning of the words *flat* and *curved* in order to explain how solid shapes are alike and different. Worksheet 7.5 will develop children's ability to understand and use these words.

Inclusion
TACTILE, VISUAL

Materials: *real-life objects, solid shapes*

Display real-life objects. Give the child a solid shape. Ask the child to find an object from the set of real-life objects that matches the solid. Repeat with other solid shapes and objects.

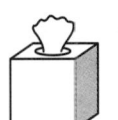

Early Finishers
VISUAL, TACTILE

Materials: *magazines*

Give children magazines, glue, scissors, and paper. Have children cut out examples of solids from the magazines. Now have children sort and glue the pictures into groups. Then have children exchange their pictures with a partner. The partner labels each group.

Art Connection

Materials: *recycled materials such as paper towel rolls or tissue boxes*

Have a variety of recycled materials available for children. Have them make a sculpture by gluing different shapes together. Then use markers to decorate the sculptures.

MATH CENTER

Real-Life Activity

Help children understand the usefulness of mathematics. This activity makes math come alive by connecting the lesson skills to a real-life situation.

PROBLEM SOLVING 7.5

Name _____ Date _____
Problem Solving 7.5

Classifying and Sorting Solid Shapes

Solve. Circle the shapes that follow the rule.

1. Sam is looking for 2 solids that roll. Which shapes should he choose?

   Draw or write to explain.

2. Corrine is looking for 2 solids that have 8 corners. Which shapes should she choose?

3. Julio is looking for 2 solids that come to a point. Which shapes shoulc he choose?

4. Tara is looking for 2 solids that have 8 or more edges. Which shapes should she choose?

Copyright © Houghton Mifflin Company. All rights reserved.
Use with text pages 193–194.

HOMEWORK 7.5

Name _____ Date _____
Homework 7.5

Classifying and Sorting Solid Shapes

You can sort solid shapes many ways.
6 faces   Curved parts   5 corners

Look at the picture below. Then sort the solid shapes according to the rule.

1. Draw a line under the shapes with 0 faces.
2. Circle the shapes with 6 faces.
3. Draw a box around the shapes with 1 face.
4. Draw an X through the shapes with 2 faces.

5. Look in your kitchen. Draw a solid shape that can roll.

   Draw here.

Copyright © Houghton Mifflin Company. All rights reserved.
Use with text pages 193–194.

ENGLISH LEARNERS 7.5

Name _____ Date _____
English Learners 7.5

Classifying and Sorting Solid Shapes

The ball is **curved.**   The book is **flat.**

Circle the word that e is about the picture.

1. curved (flat)
2. (curved) flat
3. curved (flat)
4. (curved) flat
5. curved (flat)

To the Teacher: Use the examples at the top of the page to help children understand the words *curved* and *flat*. Then have children circle the word that describes the shape of each pictured item.

Copyright © Houghton Mifflin Company. All rights reserved.
Use with text pages 193–194.

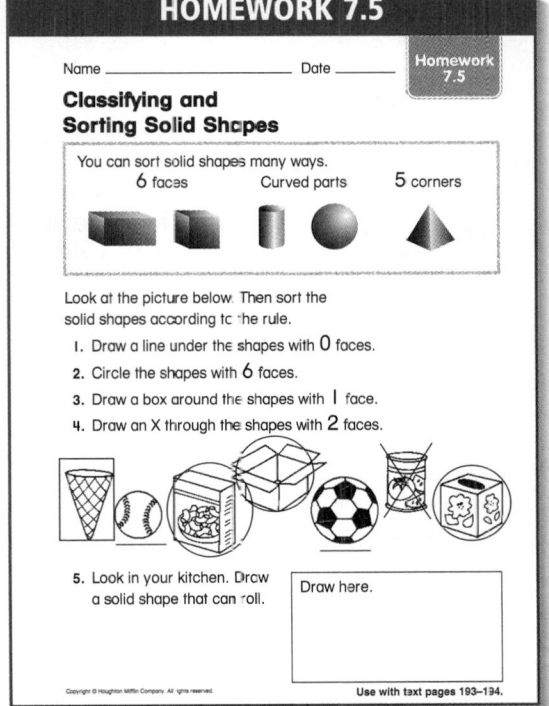

TEACHING LESSON 7.5

LESSON ORGANIZER

Objective Classify and sort solid shapes.

Resources Reteach, Practice, Enrichment, Problem Solving, Homework, English Learners, Transparencies, Math Center

Materials Sets of solid shapes, real-life solids (shoebox, crayon box, soup can)

Activity

Warm-Up Activity
Sorting Shapes

| 👥 Small Group | ⏱ 5 minutes | Visual, Auditory |

Materials: *sets of solid shapes*

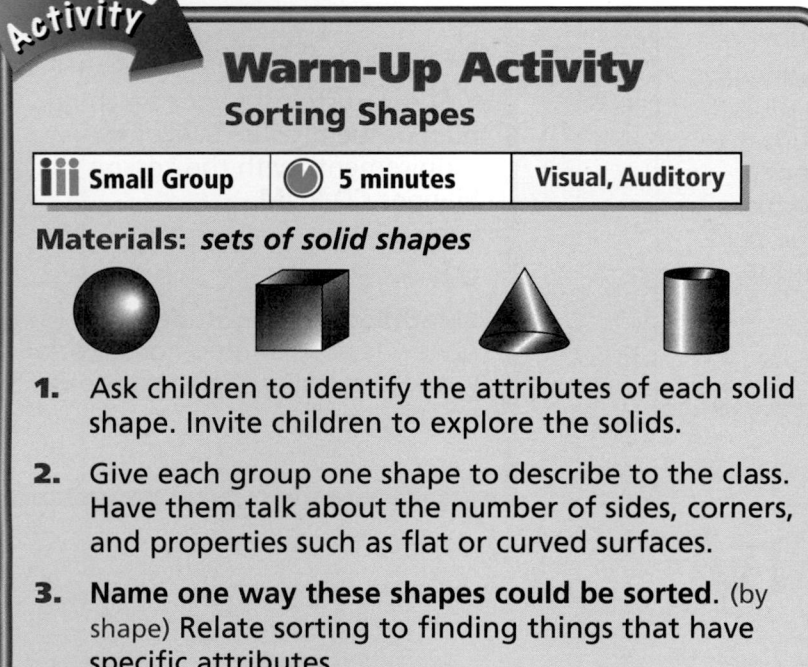

1. Ask children to identify the attributes of each solid shape. Invite children to explore the solids.

2. Give each group one shape to describe to the class. Have them talk about the number of sides, corners, and properties such as flat or curved surfaces.

3. **Name one way these shapes could be sorted.** (by shape) Relate sorting to finding things that have specific attributes.

Name_____

Classifying and Sorting Solid Shapes

Objective Classify and sort solid shapes.

There are many ways to sort solid shapes.

6 faces | Curved parts | 8 corners

Guided Practice

Read the sorting rule.
Circle the solid shapes that follow the rule.

1. All faces

Think
The cup and cone have curved parts.

2. Roll

3. Has edges

TEST TIPS **Explain Your Thinking** Tell how the solid shapes in Exercise 2 are alike and different. **Possible answer: The can and hat have curved parts; the can and hat can roll but the crayon box cannot.**

Chapter 7 Lesson 5   one hundred ninety-three **193**

---

1 Introduce

Activity

Model Classifying and Sorting Solid Shapes

| 👥 Whole Group | ⏱ 10–15 minutes | Visual, Tactile |

Materials: *sets of solids, real-life solids (shoe box, crayon box, soup can)*

1. Display the solid shapes. Tell children to look at the solids and find one way that they are alike or different. Remind children that objects can be sorted in many different ways.

2. **What objects in the classroom look like the solid shapes?** Ask a child to choose a solid shape. Draw a circle on the board and label it with the name of the shape. Then have the children look around the classroom to find real-life objects that are the same shape and tell why they are like the solid. Write the names of the objects in the circle.

2 Develop

Guided Learning

Teaching Example Introduce the objective to the children. Guide them through the example to show how to sort solids in different ways.

Guided Practice

Have children complete **Exercises 1–3** as you observe. Give children the opportunity to answer the Explain Your Thinking question. Then discuss their responses with the class.

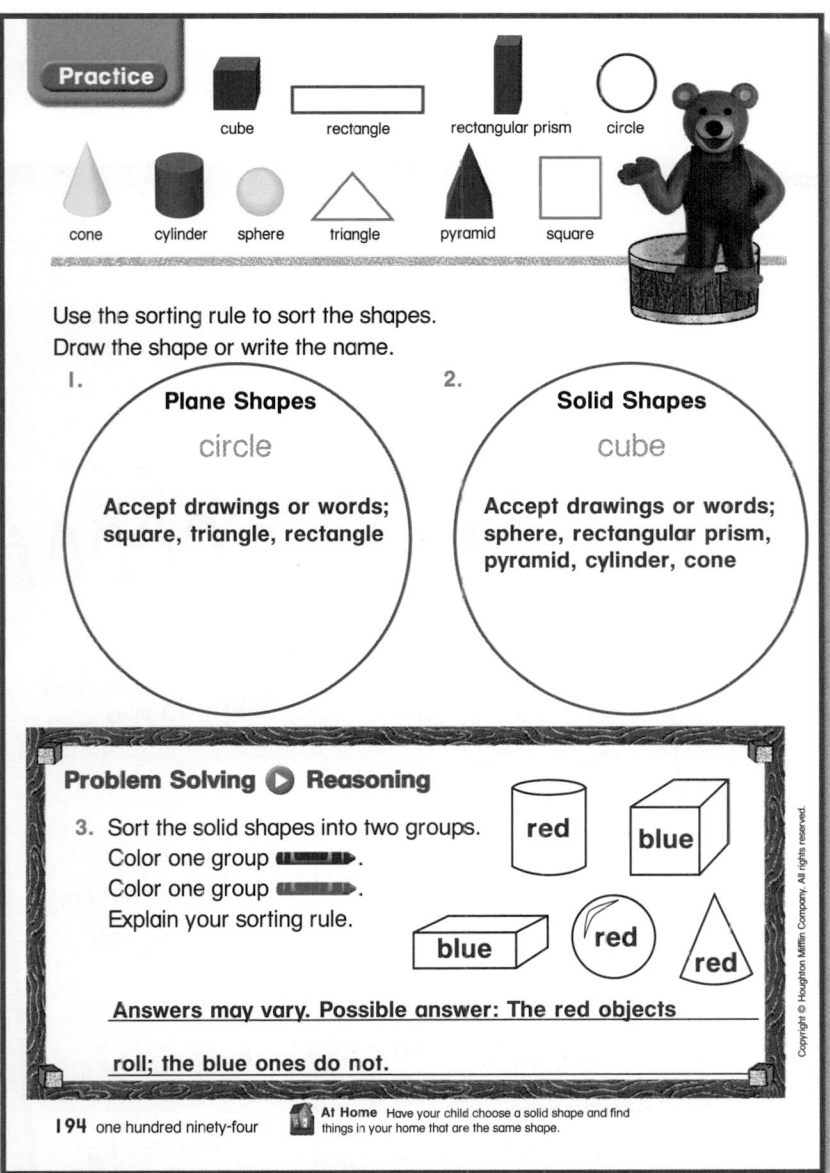

Practice

cube · rectangle · rectangular prism · circle

cone · cylinder · sphere · triangle · pyramid · square

Use the sorting rule to sort the shapes.
Draw the shape or write the name.

1. **Plane Shapes**

circle

Accept drawings or words; square, triangle, rectangle

2. **Solid Shapes**

cube

Accept drawings or words; sphere, rectangular prism, pyramid, cylinder, cone

Problem Solving ▶ Reasoning

3. Sort the solid shapes into two groups.
Color one group ▬▬▬.
Color one group ▬▬▬.
Explain your sorting rule.

red · blue
blue · red · red

Answers may vary. Possible answer: The red objects roll; the blue ones do not.

At Home Have your child choose a solid shape and find things in your home that are the same shape.

194 one hundred ninety-four

Test Prep Transparency

Daily Test Prep

7.5

Lin had 9 seeds to plant. She has already planted 3. Which number sentence can you use to find how many more seeds she has to plant?

○ $9 + 3 = \square$ ● $9 - 3 = \square$
○ $3 + 9 = \square$ ○ $12 - 9 = \square$

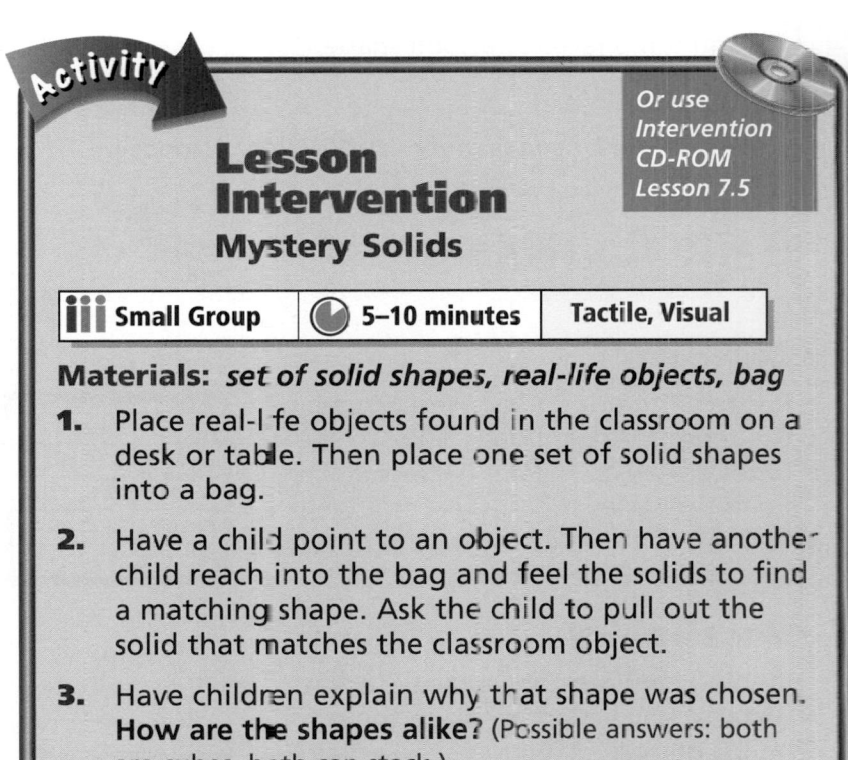

Activity

Lesson Intervention

Mystery Solids

Or use Intervention CD-ROM Lesson 7.5

| 👥 Small Group | ⏱ 5–10 minutes | Tactile, Visual |

Materials: *set of solid shapes, real-life objects, bag*

1. Place real-life objects found in the classroom on a desk or table. Then place one set of solid shapes into a bag.

2. Have a child point to an object. Then have another child reach into the bag and feel the solids to find a matching shape. Ask the child to pull out the solid that matches the classroom object.

3. Have children explain why that shape was chosen. **How are the shapes alike?** (Possible answers: both are cubes, both can stack.)

---

③ Practice

Independent Practice

Children complete **Exercises 1–2** independently.

Problem Solving

After children complete **Exercise 3**, call on volunteers to share how they sorted the shapes and why.

Common Error

Misidentifying Attributes

Some children may not understand that cubes are a special kind of rectangular prism. Have children compare the shapes and their attributes. Help them to see that a rectangular prism has pairs of faces that are the same size and a cube not only has pairs of faces that are the same, but all the faces are the same.

④ Assess and Close

If spheres and cylinders are in the same sorting ring, how did you sort? (by shapes that roll)

What is the difference between a circle and a sphere? (A circle is flat; a sphere is curved like a ball. A circle is a plane shape and a sphere is a solid shape.)

Keeping a Journal

Draw a cone. Then describe what it looks like.

Identify Faces of a Solid Shape

PLANNING THE LESSON

MATHEMATICS OBJECTIVE
Identify the faces of a solid shape.

Use Lesson Planner CD-ROM for Lesson 7.6.

Daily Routines

Calendar
Recite all the dates for Wednesday in the month. Ask children how all the dates are alike. (All are Wednesdays.) Read the dates for the first full week in the month. Ask how all the dates are alike. (All are in the same week.)

Vocabulary
Remind children that a **face** is a flat surface. Have children place their hands on top of their desks. Explain that the top of the desk is a face. Then ask them to look around the room for other flat surfaces that are faces of objects.

Vocabulary Cards

Meeting North Carolina's Standards
3.02 Identify, build, and name cylinders, cones, and rectangular prisms.
Also 3.03

Lesson Transparency **7.6**

Problem of the Day
You have 1 square, 2 circles, 3 triangles and 5 rectangles. How many shapes do you have? (11 shapes)

Quick Review
Identify the solid figure.
No flat surface and does not stack (sphere)
6 equal flat surfaces and does not roll (cube)

Lesson Quiz
1. Which solid has a face in the shape of a triangle? (pyramid)
2. Which solid has a face in the shape of a square? (Possible answers: cube, rectangular prism, pyramid)
3. Which solid has a face in the shape of a circle? (Possible answers: cone, cylinder)

LEVELED PRACTICE

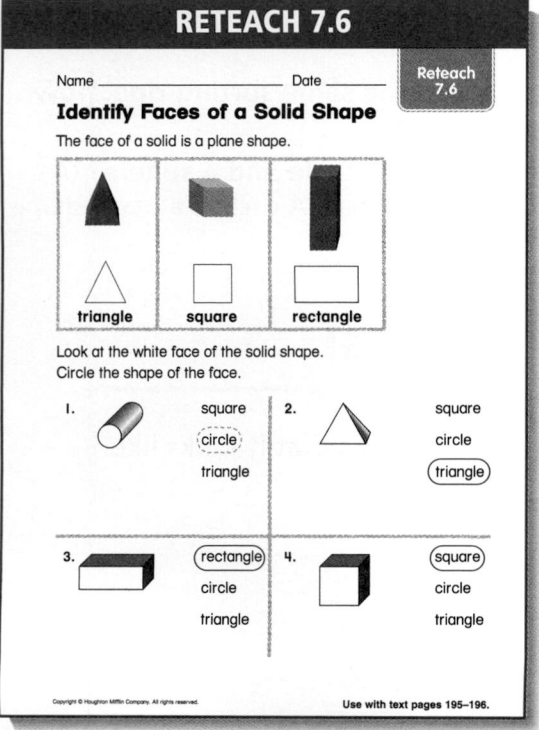

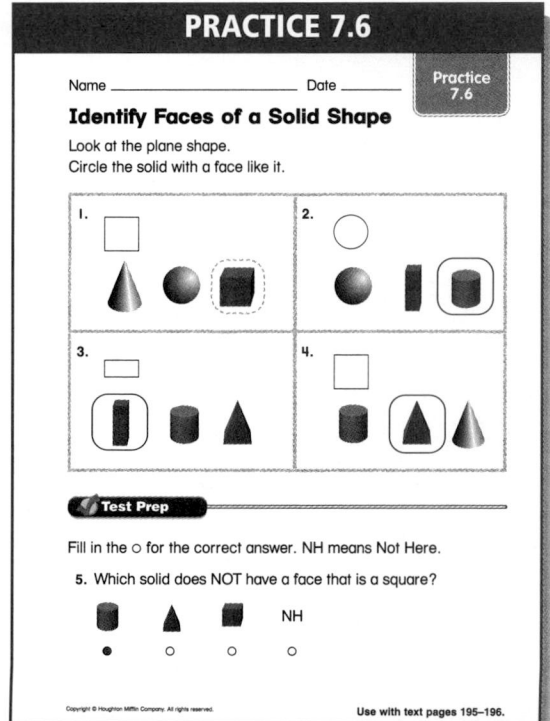

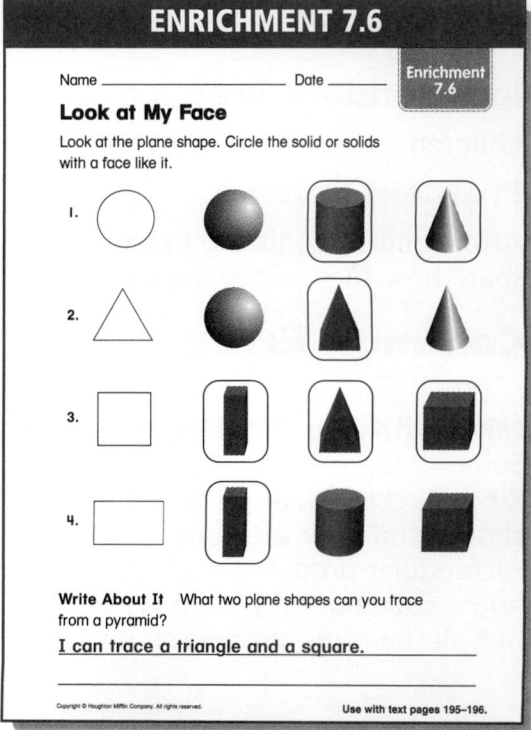

Practice Workbook Page 47

Reaching All Learners

Differentiated Instruction

English Learners

The word *like* has several meanings in English. English-language learners will need to understand how the word is used to compare objects in order to group solids. Use Worksheet 7.6 to develop children's understanding of this meaning.

Inclusion
VISUAL, TACTILE

Materials: *solid shapes, index cards*

Prepare index cards with plane shapes traced from solid shapes. Have the child choose an index card. Have the child find the solid shape with a face that matches the plane shape on each card. Continue until all cards are identified.

Early Finishers
TACTILE, VISUAL

Materials: *real-life objects*

Display several objects. Have the child choose one object to use as a template for making a picture. Have the child create a drawing made of shapes traced from the object they selected.

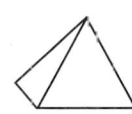 

TECHNOLOGY

Spiral Review

To reinforce skills on lessons taught earlier, create **customized** spiral review worksheets using the *Ways to Assess* CD-ROM.

Education Place

Recommend that parents visit **Education Place** at **eduplace.com/parents/mw/** for parent support activities.

Games

Students can practice their skills using the **RoboPacker** math game, available on the *Ways to Success* CD-ROM.

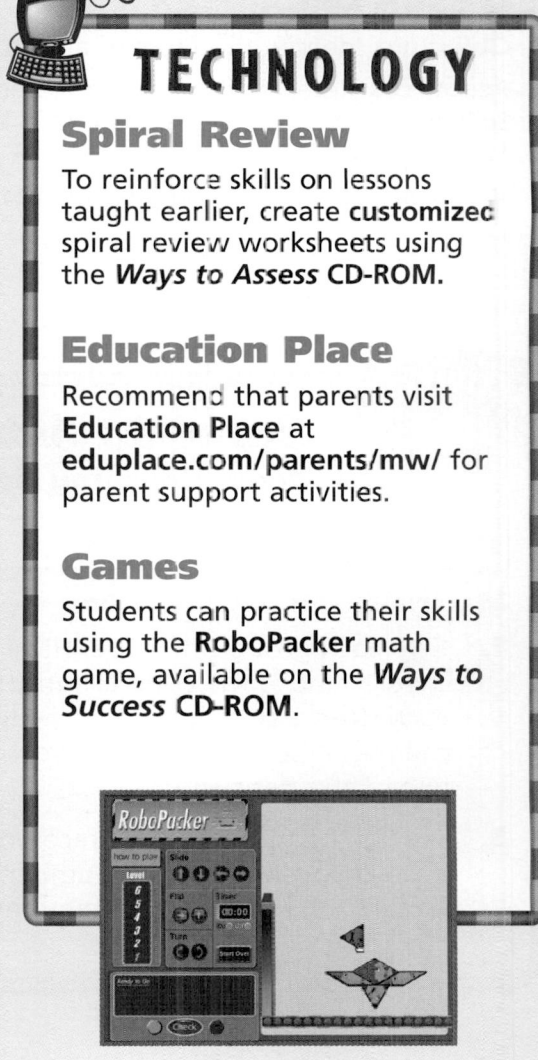

Music Connection

Provide each child with a cylinder, for example, an oatmeal container, or a soup can. Help children make a drum. Stretch a piece of thin fabric across the open end and fasten with rubber bands. Have children create rhythm patterns.

MATH CENTER

Cross-Curricular Activity

As you use this activity to relate the mathematics of this lesson to another curriculum area, children will see how math can help them with other subjects.

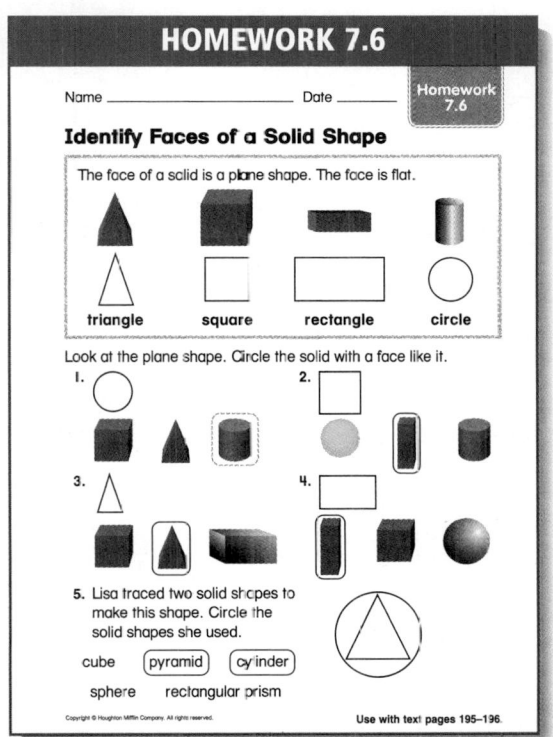

PROBLEM SOLVING 7.6

Name _____ Date _____

Problem Solving 7.6

Identify Faces of a Solid Shape

Solve. Write the name of the child who holds the matching solid.

	Draw or write to explain.
1. Who has a solid with a face that is circle?	
Ben	
2. Who has a solid with a face that is a triangle?	
Alice	
3. Who has a solid with a face that is a rectangle?	
Otis	
4. Who has a solid with a face that is a square?	
Olga	

Copyright © Houghton Mifflin Company. All rights reserved.

Use with text pages 195–196.

HOMEWORK 7.6

Name _____ Date _____

Homework 7.6

Identify Faces of a Solid Shape

The face of a solid is a plane shape. The face is flat.

triangle   square   rectangle   circle

Look at the plane shape. Circle the solid with a face like it.

1.   2.

3.   4.

5. Lisa traced two solid shapes to make this shape. Circle the solid shapes she used.

cube   (pyramid)   (cylinder)
sphere   rectangular prism

Copyright © Houghton Mifflin Company. All rights reserved.

Use with text pages 195–196.

ENGLISH LEARNERS 7.6

Name _____ Date _____

English Learners 7.6

Identify Faces of a Solid Shape

One clown has a smile **like** the other clown.

Circle the object that is like the one in the box.

1.

2.

3.

4.

To the Teacher: Use the example at the top of the page to help children understand the meaning of the word *like*. Then have children circle the object that is like the one in the box for each exercise.

Copyright © Houghton Mifflin Company. All rights reserved.

Use with text pages 195–196.

TEACHING LESSON 7.6

LESSON ORGANIZER

Objective Identify the faces of a solid shape.

Resources Reteach, Practice, Enrichment, Problem Solving, Homework, English Learners, Transparencies, Math Center

Materials Sets of solid shapes, blank transparency

Activity

Warm-Up Activity
Model Counting the Flat Surfaces

👥 Small Group	🕐 5 minutes	Visual, Tactile

Materials: *sets of solid shapes*

1. Give each group one cube. Have the children move the cube around. Ask: **How does a cube move?** (It slides.) Tell children when they slide the cube they are using one of the flat surfaces.

2. Discuss the meaning of a face on a solid figure. Have children count the number of flat surfaces or faces on the cube. **How many faces does a cube have?** (six)

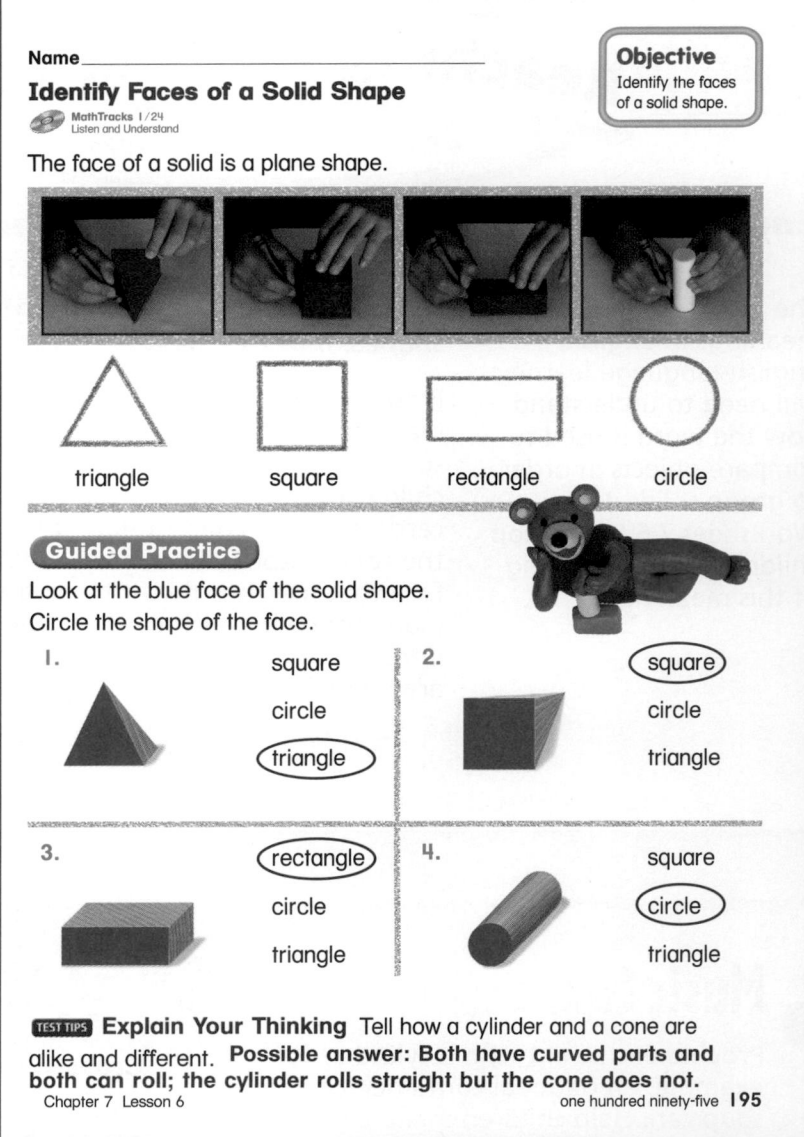

1 Introduce

Activity

Discuss Faces of a Solid Shape

👥 Whole Group	🕐 10–15 minutes	Visual, Tactile

Materials: *blank transparency*

1. *Trace faces.* Review the term face. **Which solid has a face that is a square?** (cube, rectangular prism, pyramid) **Which solid has a face that is a triangle?** (pyramid) **Which solid has a face that is a circle?** (cylinder, cone)

2. Trace squares, triangles, circles, and rectangles from the faces of various solid shapes onto the transparency. Mix up the solid shapes. Ask a volunteer to place the solid on the matching plane shape. Have volunteers match each plane figure with the face of the solid figure.

3. Allow time for children to trace one or more faces from a solid shape.

2 Develop

Guided Learning

Teaching Example Introduce the objective to the children. Guide them through the example to show how to trace one face on a solid figure.

Guided Practice

Have children complete **Exercises 1–4** as you observe. Give children the opportunity to answer the Explain Your Thinking question. Discuss their responses with the class.

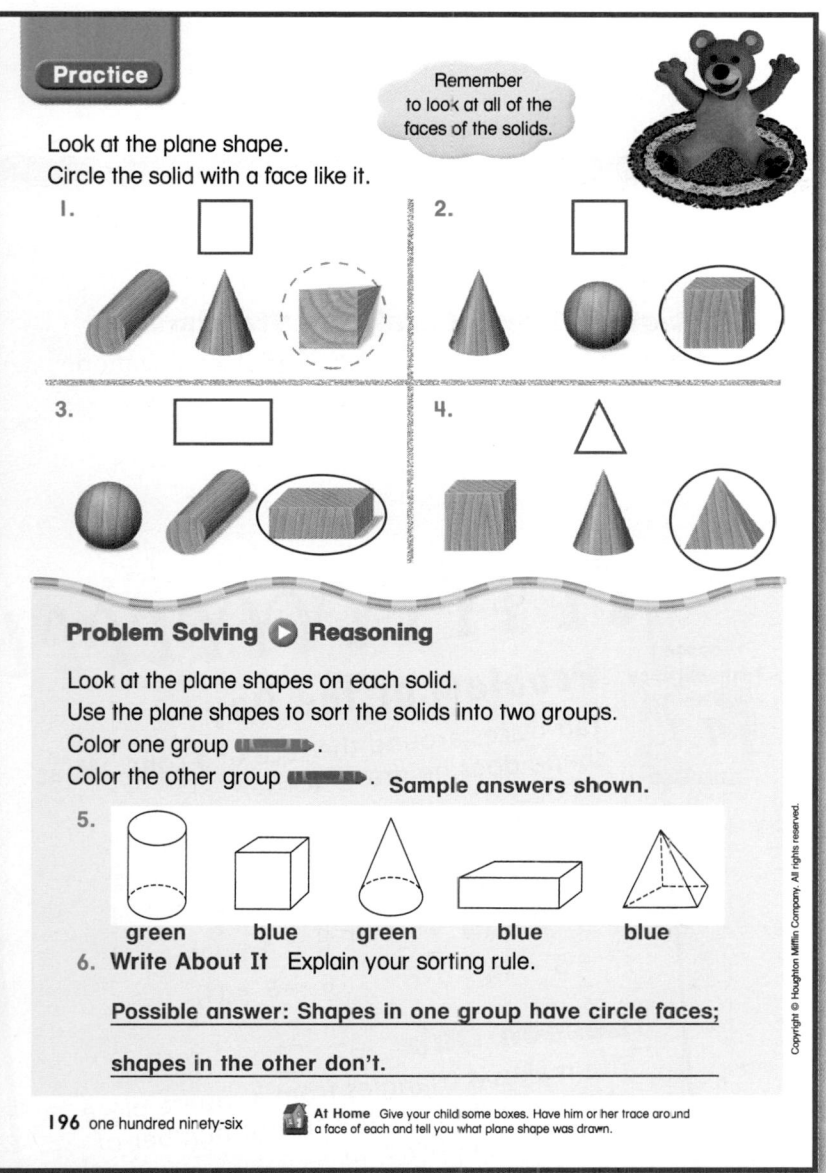

Practice

Remember to look at all of the faces of the solids.

Look at the plane shape.
Circle the solid with a face like it.

1.

2.

3.

4.

Problem Solving ▶ Reasoning

Look at the plane shapes on each solid.
Use the plane shapes to sort the solids into two groups.
Color one group ▬▬▬.
Color the other group ▬▬▬. **Sample answers shown.**

5.

| green | blue | green | blue | blue |

6. **Write About It** Explain your sorting rule.

Possible answer: Shapes in one group have circle faces;

shapes in the other don't.

At Home Give your child some boxes. Have him or her trace around a face of each and tell you what plane shape was drawn.

Test Prep Transparency

7.6

6 + 2 + 4

| 6 | 8 | 12 | NH |
| ○ | ○ | ● | ○ |

Activity

Or use Intervention CD-ROM Lesson 7.6

Lesson Intervention
Making Faces

| 👥 Small Group | 🕐 5–10 minutes | Visual, Tactile |

Materials: *pyramid, cube, rectangular prism, cylinder*

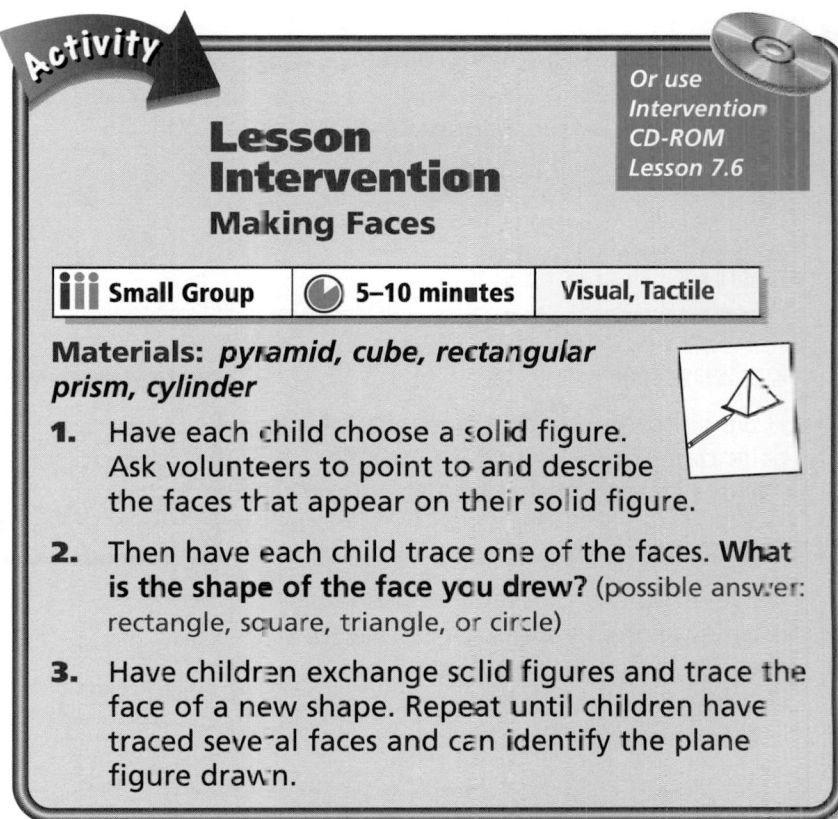

1. Have each child choose a solid figure. Ask volunteers to point to and describe the faces that appear on their solid figure.

2. Then have each child trace one of the faces. **What is the shape of the face you drew?** (possible answer: rectangle, square, triangle, or circle)

3. Have children exchange solid figures and trace the face of a new shape. Repeat until children have traced several faces and can identify the plane figure drawn.

---

③ Practice

Independent Practice

Children complete **Exercises 1–4** independently.

Problem Solving

After children complete **Exercise 5**, use the **Write About It** in **Exercise 6** to discuss different sorting rules for the shapes.

Common Error

Mismatching Pictures of Solids and Plane Shapes
Have children trace the face of the solid and compare it to the plane shape on the page.

④ Assess and Close

Which solid has the face of a triangle? (pyramid)
Which solid has the face of a circle? (cone, cylinder)

✏ Keeping a Journal

Draw two solid shapes. Write about how they are alike and how they are different.

Lesson 7.7

Problem Solving: Draw a Picture

PLANNING THE LESSON

MATHEMATICS OBJECTIVE
Draw pictures to solve problems.

Use Lesson Planner CD-ROM for Lesson 7.7.

Daily Routines

Calendar
Have children decide the shape of the calendar. Then have them look for various shapes found on the calendar.

Vocabulary
Review the words used for the four problem-solving steps: *Understand, Plan, Solve,* and *Look Back.* Ask children to give examples of the use of these words.

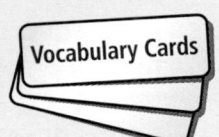
Vocabulary Cards

Meeting North Carolina's Standards
3.04 Solve problems involving spatial visualization.
Also 1.04

Lesson Transparency 7.7

Problem of the Day
Tad traces around the face of a cone. What shape does he draw? (circle)

Quick Review
Find the difference.

$10 - 2 = $ (8) $8 - 3 = $ (5)

$7 - 3 = $ (4) $6 - 5 = $ (1)

Lesson Quiz
Tita makes 4 triangles from a square piece of paper. What are the fewest number of lines she can draw? (2)

LEVELED PRACTICE

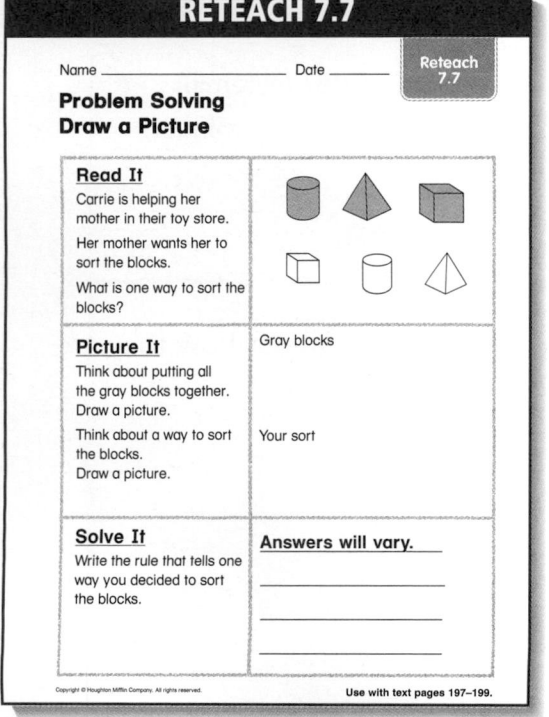

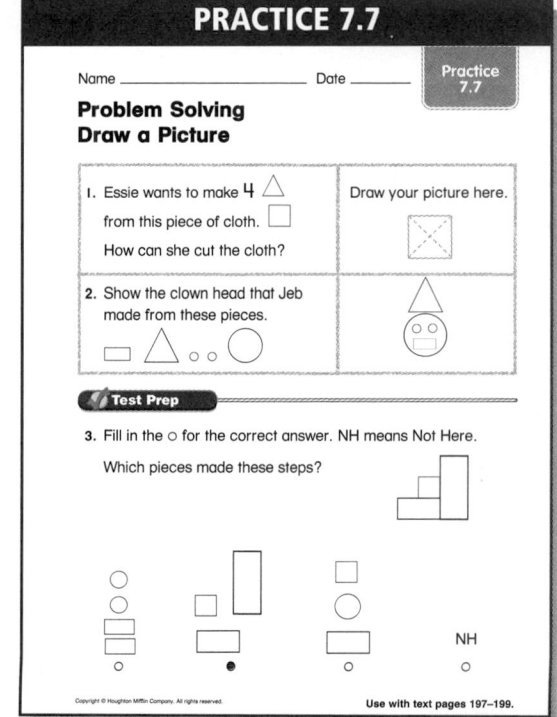

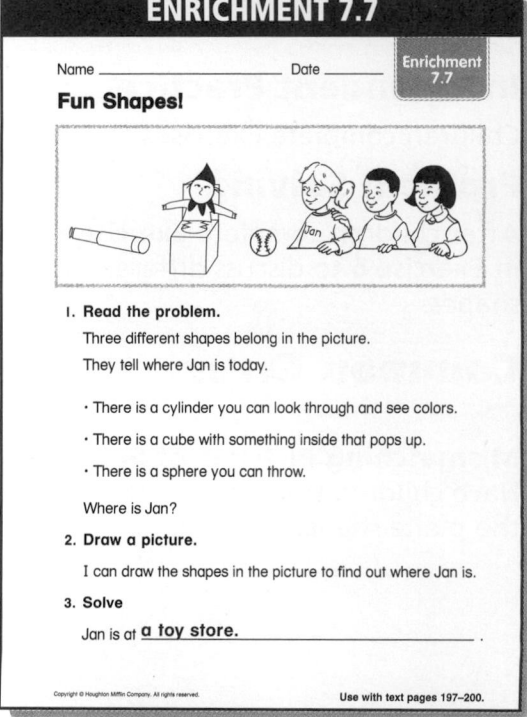

Practice Workbook Page 48

Reaching All Learners
Differentiated Instruction

English Learners

English-language learners may not be familiar with the subject-verb agreement necessary to understand word problems. Use Worksheet 7.7 to develop children's knowledge of subject-verb agreement for the verb *use*.

Special Needs
TACTILE, VISUAL

Materials: *sponges, paint*

Cut out sponge shapes: a square, a triangle, and a rhombus. Give the child the sponges to use as stamps. Have the child stamp and identify individual shapes. Have the child combine the shapes to create a picture.

Gifted and Talented
TACTILE, VISUAL

Materials: *pattern blocks*

Have children combine shapes of the same type to make a new shape. Then have children draw a picture of the shape and write the name of the new shape.

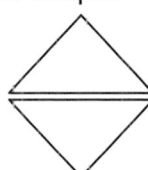

TECHNOLOGY

Spiral Review

Help students remember skills they learned earlier by creating customized spiral review worksheets using the *Ways to Assess CD-ROM.*

Intervention

Use the *Ways to Success CD-ROM* intervention software to support students who need more help in understanding the concepts and skills taught in this chapter.

Lesson Planner

Use the **Lesson Planner CD-ROM** to see how lesson objectives for this chapter are correlated to standards.

Literature Connection

Read *Shape* by Henry Pluckrose. Have each child make a picture of a rectangle used in a different way. Put together a "Class Rectangle Book."

MATH CENTER

Number of the Week Activity

Display the Number of the Week to motivate children to use their problem-solving skills. The exercises cover topics across all math strands.

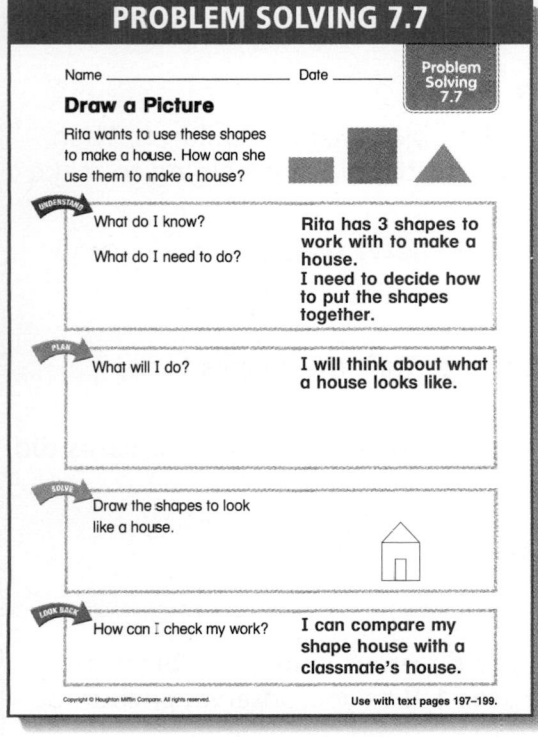

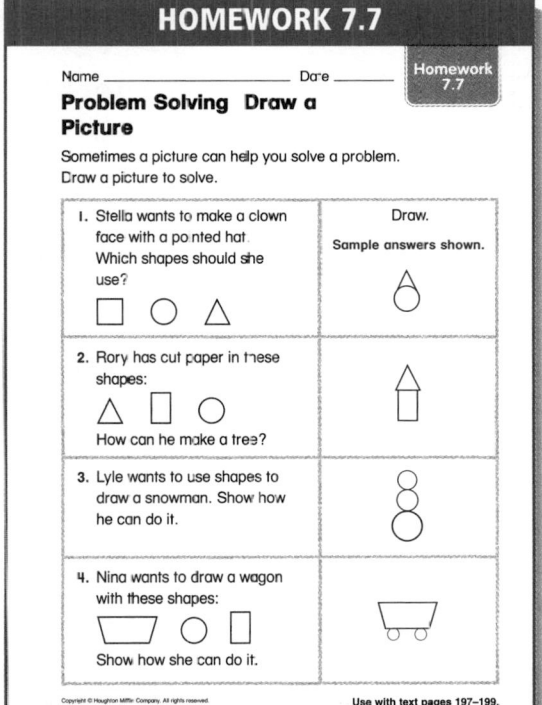

Homework Workbook Page 48

TEACHING LESSON 7.7

LESSON ORGANIZER

Objective Draw pictures to solve problems.

Resources Reteach, Practice, Enrichment, Problem Solving, Homework, English Learners, Transparencies, Math Center

Materials Pattern blocks, teacher-made pattern block cards

Warm-Up Activity
Modeling New Shapes

| 👥 Whole Group | ⏱ 10 minutes | Visual, Auditory |

Materials: *pattern blocks*

1. Draw a hexagon on the board. Have a volunteer name the shape. Demonstrate how to combine 3 blue parallelograms to make the same shape. Call on a volunteer to combine 2 red trapezoids to make the same shape.

2. Now, show 6 green triangles. Ask a volunteer to show you how to arrange the 6 triangles to make the shape that is on the board.

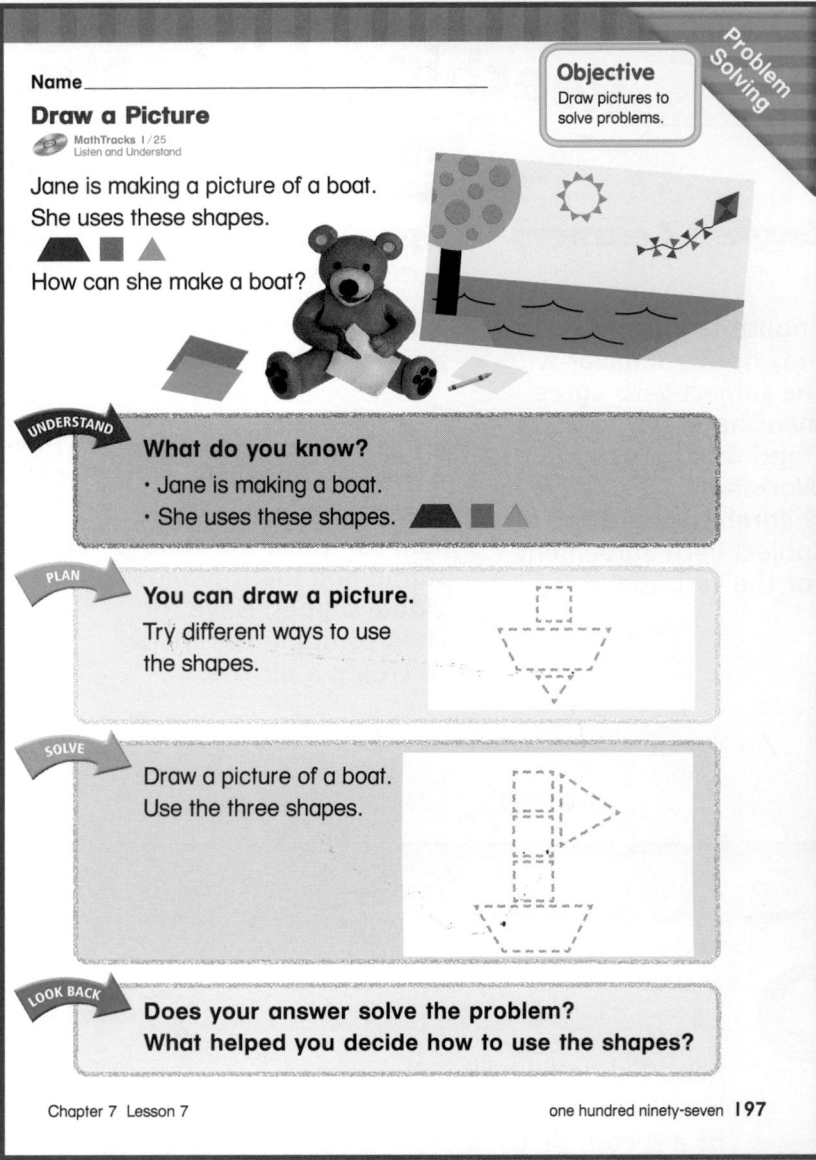

Name _____

Draw a Picture

🔵 MathTracks 1/25
Listen and Understand

Jane is making a picture of a boat.
She uses these shapes.

How can she make a boat?

Objective
Draw pictures to solve problems.

UNDERSTAND
What do you know?
• Jane is making a boat.
• She uses these shapes.

PLAN
You can draw a picture.
Try different ways to use the shapes.

SOLVE
Draw a picture of a boat.
Use the three shapes.

LOOK BACK
Does your answer solve the problem?
What helped you decide how to use the shapes?

Chapter 7 Lesson 7   one hundred ninety-seven **197**

---

1 Introduce

Model: Drawing a Picture

| 👥 Whole Group | ⏱ 10–15 minutes | Visual, Tactile |

1. Use shapes to draw a picture. Present the problem: **Rose is drawing a flag. She only has 2 square pattern blocks. How can Rose use the squares to draw a flag?**

2. After you tell the story, have a volunteer use pattern blocks to model the flag. Ask: **What shape is the flag?** (rectangle)

3. Guide the child to place the 2 squares side by side and then trace around them to make a rectangle.

4. Present another problem. Have a volunteer use pattern blocks to draw the solution.

2 Develop

Guided Learning

Teaching Example Read the objective with children. Then read the problem and explain that Jane is helping to make a classroom mural.

UNDERSTAND What do you know? (Jane will use shapes to help her draw a boat. She will use only 3 shapes; a trapezoid, a square, a rectangle.)

PLAN You can draw a picture. Turn the shapes to try different ways.

SOLVE Trace the picture of the boat. How many squares did you use? (3)

LOOK BACK Did you use all the shapes? (yes) **Does the picture look like a boat?** (yes)

Guided Practice

Explain that **Exercise 2** is a different kind of problem. Have children complete **Exercises 1–2** as you observe. Encourage children to explain how they found their answers.

Remember:
► Understand
► Plan
► Solve
► Look Back

Remember to use the four steps.

Draw a picture to solve.

Draw or write to explain.

1. Nico wants to make a picture of a house. He uses these shapes.

■ ▲

How can he make a house?

Answers may vary. Sample answer shown.

Think
I start by thinking about the shape of a whole house.

2. Millie wants to make **2** triangles from this piece of paper. Draw a line to show how she can do it.

Think
A triangle has 3 sides and 3 corners.

3. Don wants to make a picture of a rocket. He uses these shapes.

▲ ■ ▲

How can he make a rocket?

Answers may vary. Sample answer is shown.

4. Tarika wants to make **6** triangles from this shape. Draw lines to show how she can do it.

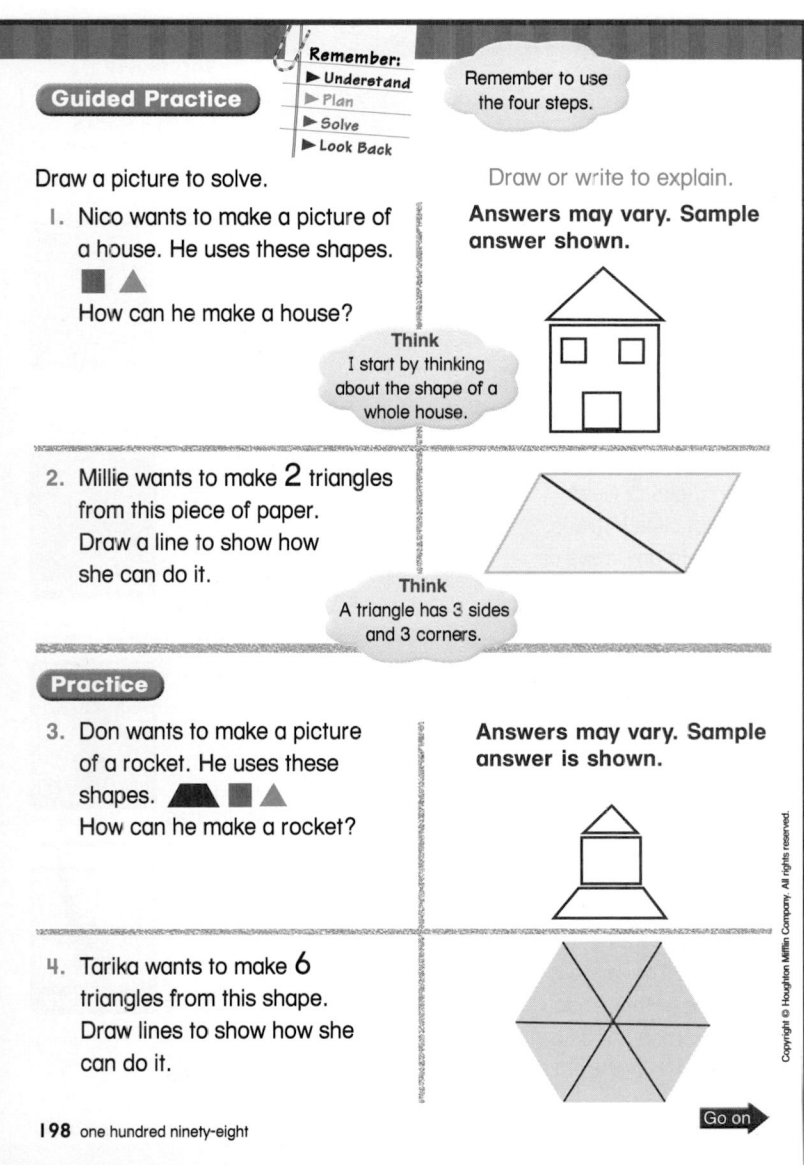

198 one hundred ninety-eight

Go on ►

Play "Shape Bingo"

Supply one teacher-made game board and counters for each child. Make shape index cards to match the shapes on the board. Have children try to cover four shapes in a row, in any direction. Invite one volunteer to choose the cards.

1. The volunteer holds up one card as he or she says the name of the shape.

2. The volunteer draws another card when everyone is ready.

3. Play continues until one child covers four shapes in a row.

4. Repeat with a new volunteer.

---

3 Practice

Independent Practice

Children complete **Exercises 3–4** independently.

TechnologyConnection

Use Technology to Explore the Faces of Solid Figures

In this activity, students investigate the faces of both familiar and unfamiliar solid figures.

Have students follow the directions below in Shape Up! 3D World.

• Have students click the right **Paging Arrow** twice. Have them stamp down the top three solids.

• Have students use the **Hand Rotate** tool to view different sides of the solids. Have them give each face a different color or make opposite faces the same color.

• Next to each solid, have students stamp down the plane shape that is the face for that solid.

• Have students click **Text** and record how many of each face are found on each solid.

Daily Test Prep

7 + 6

12   13   14   NH
○   ●   ○   ○

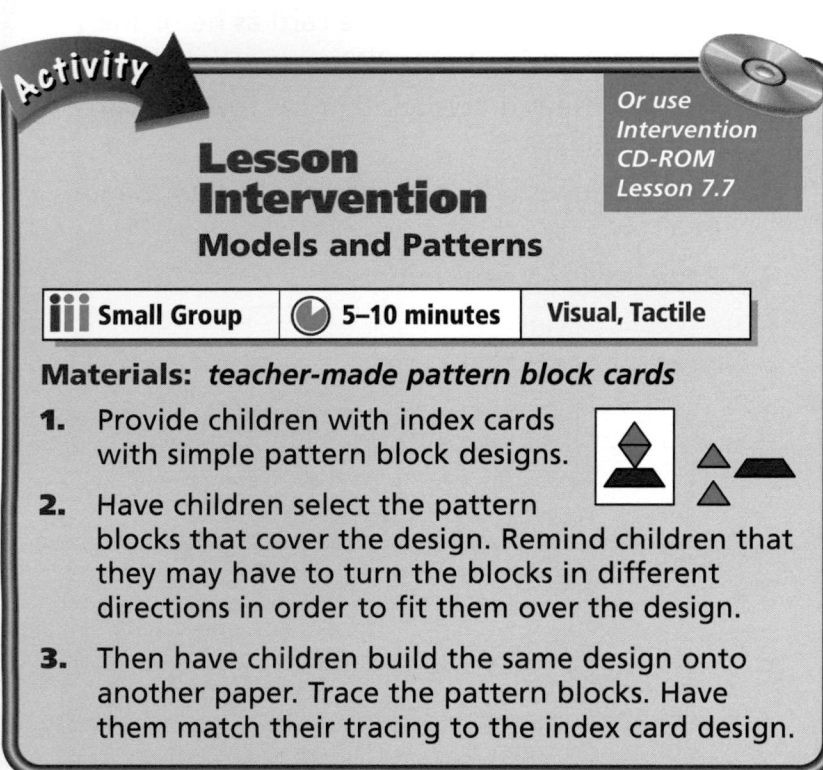

Activity

Or use
Intervention
CD-ROM
Lesson 7.7

Lesson Intervention

Models and Patterns

| 👥 Small Group | ⏱ 5–10 minutes | Visual, Tactile |

Materials: *teacher-made pattern block cards*

1. Provide children with index cards with simple pattern block designs.

2. Have children select the pattern blocks that cover the design. Remind children that they may have to turn the blocks in different directions in order to fit them over the design.

3. Then have children build the same design onto another paper. Trace the pattern blocks. Have them match their tracing to the index card design.

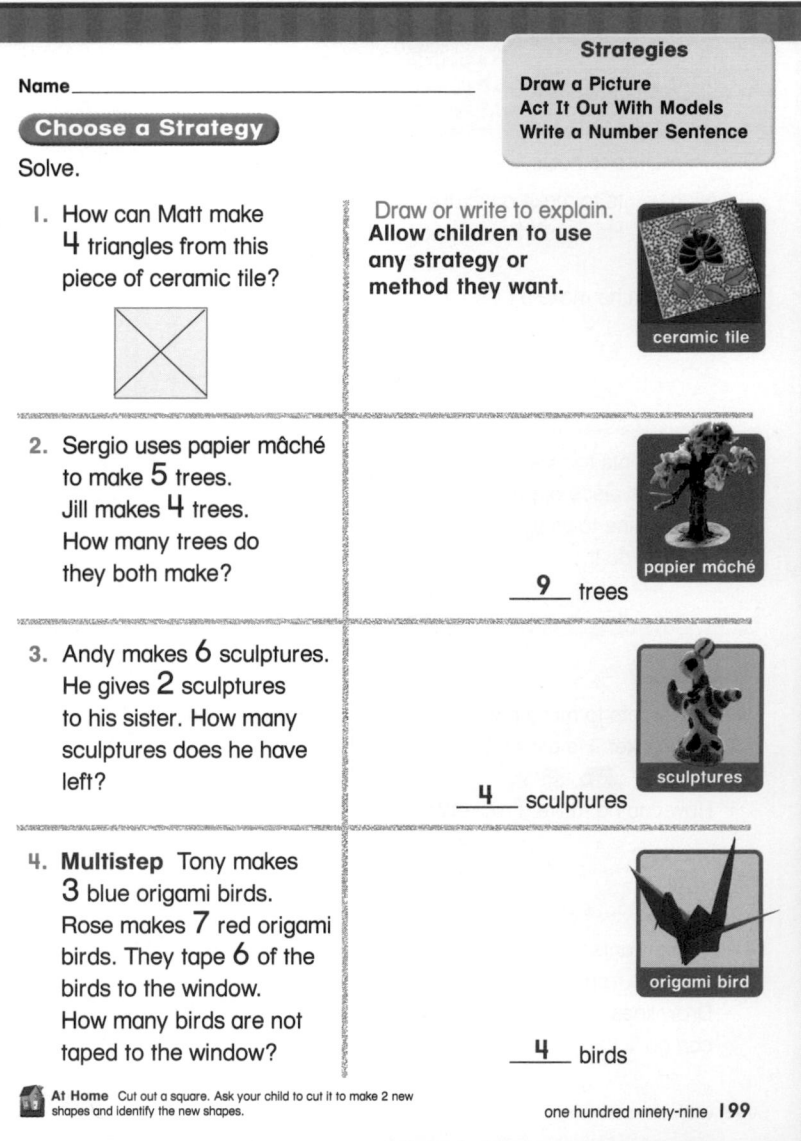

Strategies
Draw a Picture
Act It Out With Models
Write a Number Sentence

Name_____

Choose a Strategy

Solve.

1. How can Matt make 4 triangles from this piece of ceramic tile?

   Draw or write to explain.
   Allow children to use any strategy or method they want.

   ceramic tile

2. Sergio uses papier mâché to make 5 trees. Jill makes 4 trees. How many trees do they both make?

   ___9___ trees

   papier mâché

3. Andy makes 6 sculptures. He gives 2 sculptures to his sister. How many sculptures does he have left?

   ___4___ sculptures

   sculptures

4. **Multistep** Tony makes 3 blue origami birds. Rose makes 7 red origami birds. They tape 6 of the birds to the window. How many birds are not taped to the window?

   ___4___ birds

   origami bird

At Home Cut out a square. Ask your child to cut it to make 2 new shapes and identify the new shapes.

one hundred ninety-nine **199**

3 Practice

Mixed Strategy Practice

Read the problem-solving strategies with children. Make sure children can read and comprehend the problems in **Exercises 1–4** on page 199. If necessary, pair more proficient readers with less proficient readers. Encourage them to discuss the problems before solving.

Common Error

Drawings Are Not Recognizable

Children may choose shapes that create drawings that are not recognizable. Provide templates that allow them to trace the shapes.

4 Assess and Close

How can drawing a picture help you solve a problem?
(Possible answer: you can use information about shapes from the picture to help you solve the problem.)

 **Keeping a Journal**

Draw a picture to show how you can make a diamond with triangles.

Listen to your teacher read the problem.
Solve.

1. Rosa makes this picture of a boat. How many triangles are in the picture?

Show your work using pictures, numbers, or words.

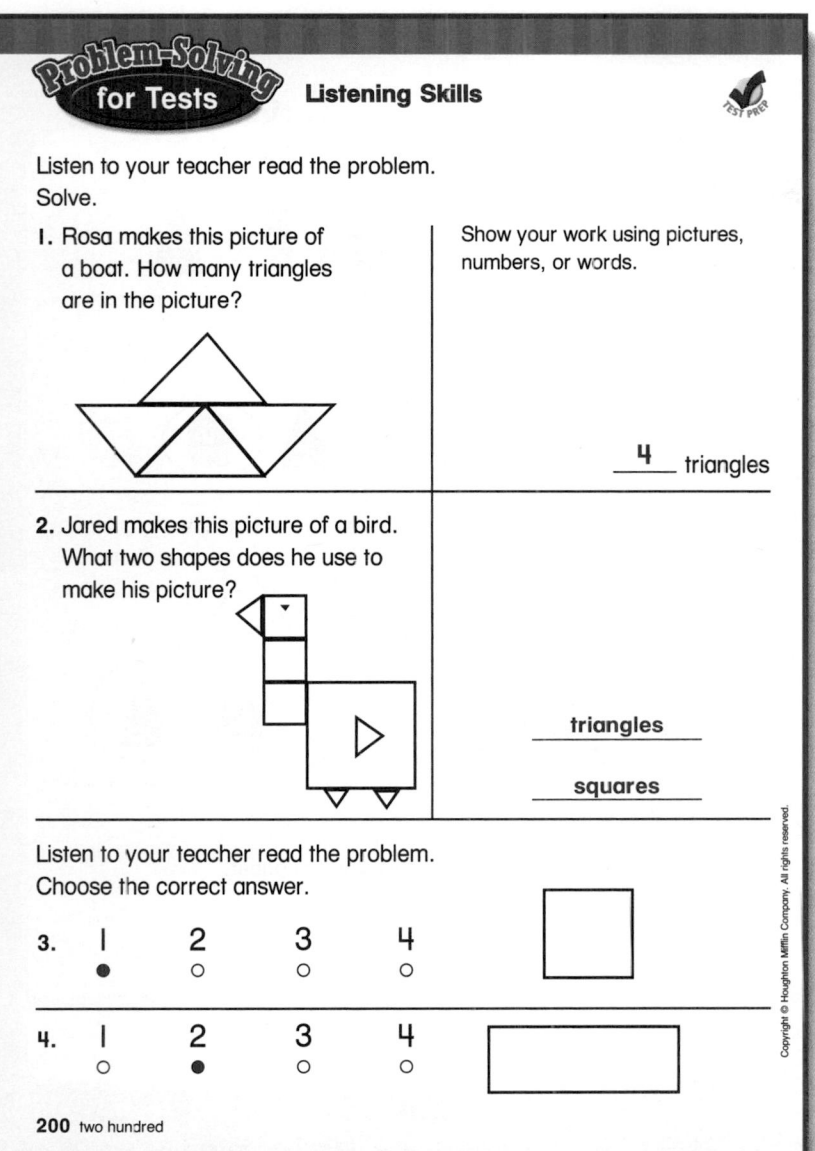

__4__ triangles

2. Jared makes this picture of a bird. What two shapes does he use to make his picture?

_____ triangles

_____ squares

Listen to your teacher read the problem.
Choose the correct answer.

3. 1   2   3   4
       ●   ○   ○   ○

4. 1   2   3   4
       ○   ●   ○   ○

Problem-Solving for Tests

Listening Skills

This page provides children practice with the oral problem-solving format used in some standardized test items.

You may want to read each item only once to mimic the style of oral tests.

Use with Items 1 and 2

Listening Strategy: Listen for important words and numbers in the problem.

* **When a problem is on the page, look at the problem while I am reading it.**
* **Wait until I finish reading the problem before you start writing.**

Use with Item 3

Listening Strategy: Listen to the problem and then look at the picture.

* **Look at the picture as I read the problem.** How many lines would you have to draw to make a square into 2 rectangles?
* **Look at the picture. Mark your answer.**

Use with Item 4

Listening Strategy: Listen for important facts and details.

* **Listen for the question the problem asks. Look at the picture.** How many triangles can you make if you draw 1 line through the rectangle?
* **Use the picture to solve your problem. Then mark your answer.**

Quick Check

Have children complete the Quick Check exercises independently to assess their understanding of concepts and skills taught in **Lessons 4–7**.

Item	Lesson	Error Analysis	Intervention
1	7.4	Children may miscount the number of corners.	Reteach Resource 7.4 ***Ways to Success* 7.4**
2	7.5	Children may misidentify the number of faces.	Reteach Resource 7.5 ***Ways to Success* 7.5**
3–4	7.6	Children may misidentify the faces of solids.	Reteach Resource 7.6 ***Ways to Success* 7.6**
5	7.7	Children may draw the wrong shape.	Reteach Resource 7.7 ***Ways to Success* 7.7**

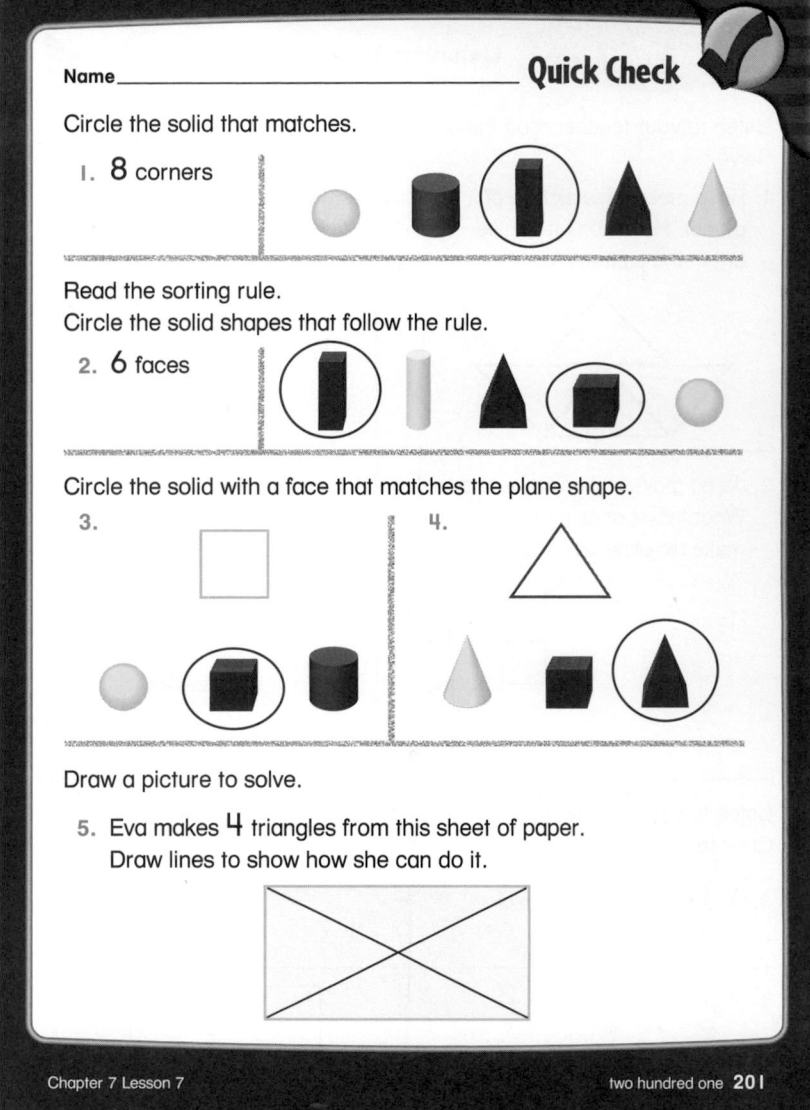

Write the difference.

1. $10 - 4 = \underline{6}$ 2. $9 - 2 = \underline{7}$ 3. $7 - 5 = \underline{2}$

4. $8 - 4 = \underline{4}$ 5. $9 - 6 = \underline{3}$ 6. $8 - 5 = \underline{3}$

7. $10 - 7 = \underline{3}$ 8. $7 - 2 = \underline{5}$ 9. $9 - 5 = \underline{4}$

10.	11.	12.	13.	14.	15.
8	7	9	10	8	10
-3	-4	-3	-8	-2	-2
5	3	6	2	6	8

Social Studies
Connection

Keys

People have been using keys for a long time. Keys are used to keep things safe. They come in many shapes and sizes.

Circle one way the keys are the same.

(color)

size

shape

Talk About It What do you think the key at the top could open?

WEEKLY WR READER eduplace.com/kids/mw/ **Possible answer: an old-fashioned door**

This Assessment provides a review of skills and concepts taught in Chapter 3.

Check to be sure that children:

• can subtract in both horizontal and vertical forms.

• use strategies to find unknown facts.

Social Studies
Connection

Keys

Discuss how the keys are alike and different. (alike in color, different in sizes and shapes) Ask children if they have seen any keys that are similar. Do they know what the keys opened? Many homes have old keys around the house, but people may not remember what they open. **What can you do with your old keys? Use your imagination.** (make a necklace, string together for paperweight, make loads for toy trucks)

Chapter Review/Test

Purpose: This test provides an informal assessment of the Chapter 7 objectives.

Chapter Test Items 1–15

To assign a numerical grade for this Chapter Test, use 6 points for each test item and add 10 to the score.

Check Understanding

Use children's work on word problems to informally assess progress on chapter content.

Customizing Your Instruction

For children who have not yet mastered these objectives, you can use the reteaching resources listed in the chart below.

 ### Assessment Options

A summary test for this chapter is also provided in the Unit Resource Folder.

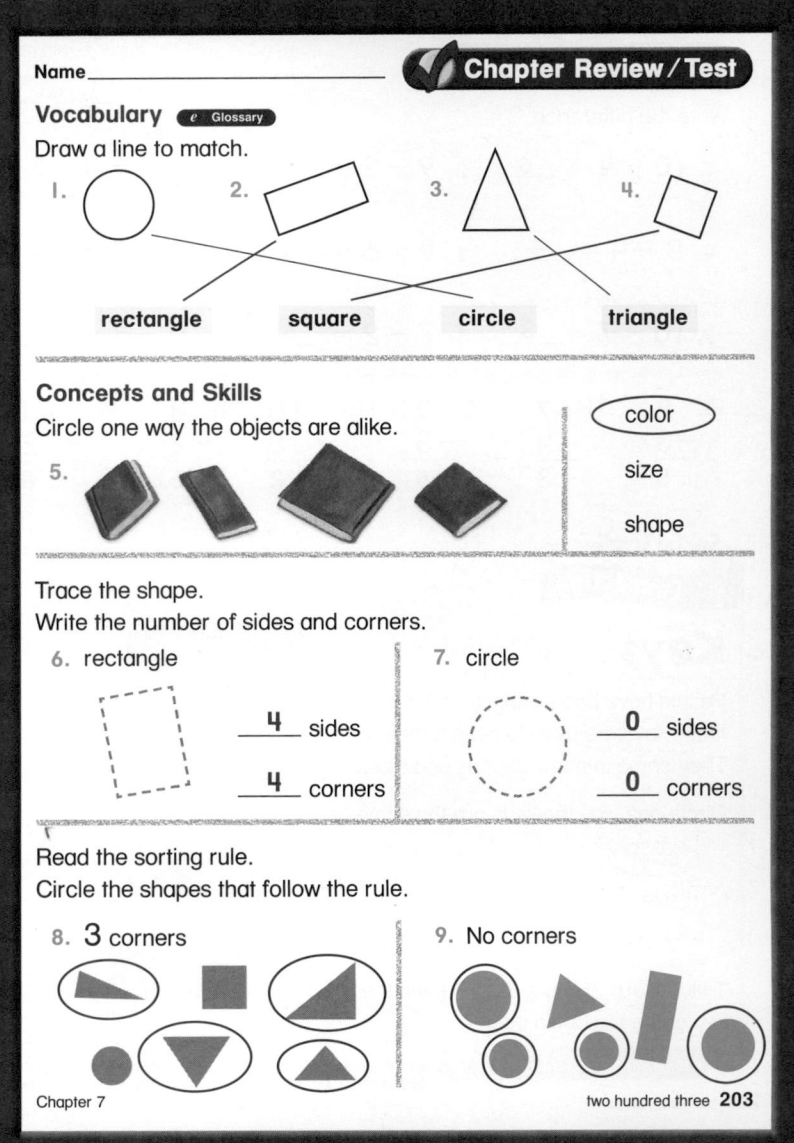

Name _____

Chapter Review/Test

Vocabulary *e* Glossary

Draw a line to match.

1. 2. 3. 4.

rectangle   square   circle   triangle

Concepts and Skills

Circle one way the objects are alike.

5.

color
size
shape

Trace the shape.
Write the number of sides and corners.

6. rectangle   ___4___ sides   ___4___ corners

7. circle   ___0___ sides   ___0___ corners

Read the sorting rule.
Circle the shapes that follow the rule.

8. 3 corners

9. No corners

Chapter 7   two hundred three **203**

Reteaching Support

Chapter Test Items	Summary Test Items	Chapter Objectives Tested	TE Pages	Use These Reteaching Resources
1–4	3–4	**7A** Develop and use math vocabulary relating to plane and solid shapes.	185A–186	Reteach Resource and *Ways to Success* CD:7.2 Skillsheet 45
5	5–6	**7B** Classify, sort, and compare objects using one attribute.	183A–184, 187A–188	Reteach Resources and *Ways to Success* CD: 7.1, 7.3 Skillsheet 46
6–14	1–2, 7–8	**7C** Identify, describe, compare, classify, and sort plane shapes and solid shapes.	187A–188, 191A–196	Reteach Resources and *Ways to Success* CD: 7.3–7.6 Skillsheet 47–49
15	9–10	**7D** Draw pictures to solve problems.	197A–200	Reteach Resource and *Ways to Success* CD: 7.7 Skillsheet 50

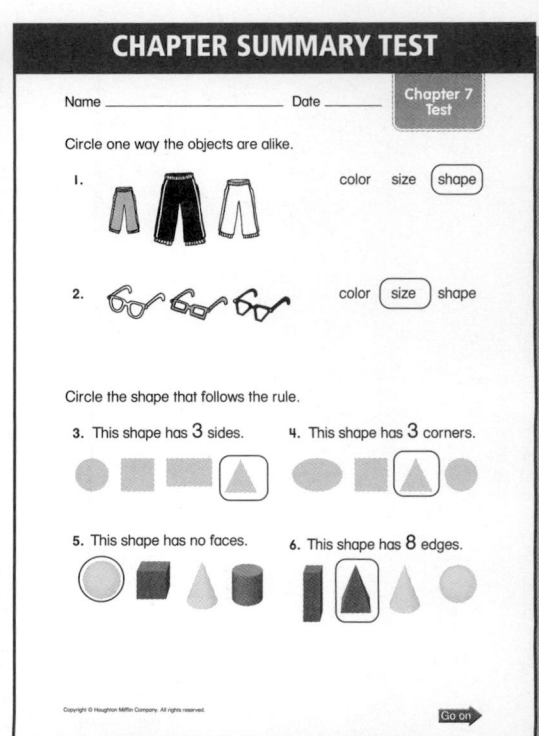

CHAPTER SUMMARY TEST

Name _____ Date _____   Chapter 7 Test

Circle one way the objects are alike.

1.   color   size   shape

2.   color   size   shape

Circle the shape that follows the rule.

3. This shape has 3 sides.

4. This shape has 3 corners.

5. This shape has no faces.

6. This shape has 8 edges.

Copyright © Houghton Mifflin Company. All rights reserved.   Go on

Circle the solid that matches.

10. **2 faces**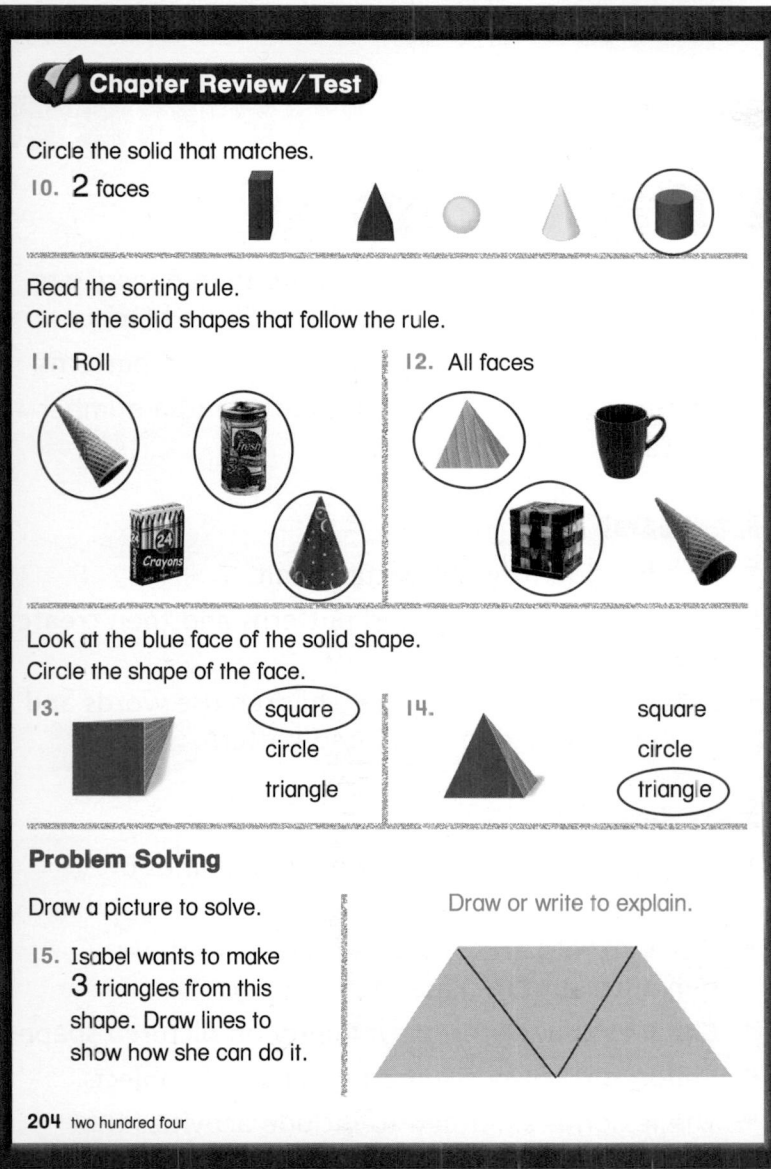

Read the sorting rule.
Circle the solid shapes that follow the rule.

11. Roll

12. All faces

Look at the blue face of the solid shape.
Circle the shape of the face.

13.
~~square~~
circle
triangle

14.
square
circle
~~triangle~~

Problem Solving

Draw a picture to solve.

Draw or write to explain.

15. Isabel wants to make **3** triangles from this shape. Draw lines to show how she can do it.

204 two hundred four

Adequate Yearly Progress

Use the End of Grade Test Prep Assessment Guide to help familiarize your children with the format of standardized tests.

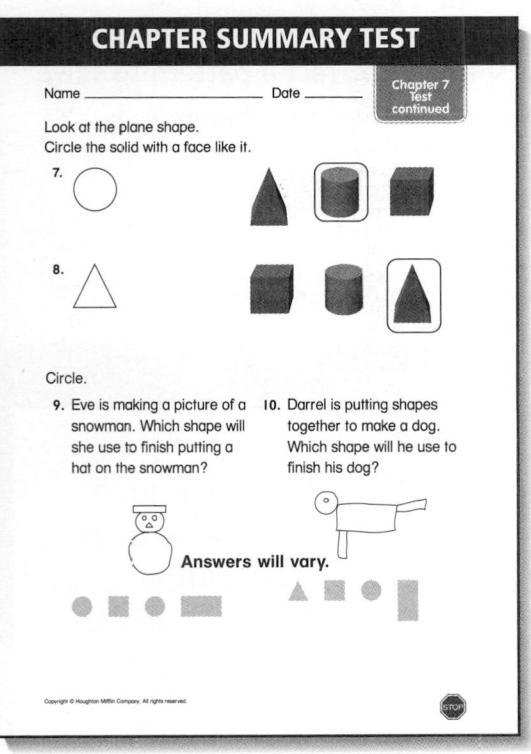

CHAPTER SUMMARY TEST

Name _____ Date _____

Chapter 7 Test continued

Look at the plane shape.
Circle the solid with a face like it.

7.

8.

Circle.

9. Eve is making a picture of a snowman. Which shape will she use to finish putting a hat on the snowman?

10. Darrel is putting shapes together to make a dog. Which shape will he use to finish his dog?

Answers will vary.

Lesson by Lesson Overview
Spatial Sense and Patterns

Lesson 1

- This lesson teaches children to follow directions about position and location of objects in space.
- Children identify images in pictures using the words *over, under, left, between, right*.
- Following directions to draw at a position indicated is a basic skill applied in later lessons.

Lesson 2

- In this lesson, children use the words *behind, in front, up, down, near, far*, and *next to* to describe positions.
- Children complete descriptions of pictured positions by choosing the correct term. Vocabulary is extended to use the words *above, below*, and *beside*.

Lesson 3

- This lesson introduces coordinate grids.
- Children identify points on a grid by following directions. At this grade level, *ordered pairs* are not recorded as such.
- A problem requires children to write directions to tell how to get from one point to another.

Lesson 4

- Children use pattern blocks in an introduction to *slides, flips*, and *turns*. Pictures of models enable children to put a block on the page, move it, and trace the move.

Lesson 5

- This lesson focuses on describing, predicting, and extending patterns.

- Children learn that there is more than one way to describe a pattern made with attribute blocks.
- Blocks are used to copy and then extend patterns.
- Children also translate a dot pattern to a number pattern.

Lesson 6

- Children identify the pattern unit.
- Children copy and extend patterns and then create their own patterns.
- In the problem-solving set, children use words and actions to describe a pictured pattern.

Lesson 7

- This lesson introduces *symmetry* and *lines of symmetry*.
- Children fold and cut paper shapes to show symmetry and the line of symmetry.
- Children draw lines of symmetry on pictured shapes.
- Children identify symmetry on real-life objects.
- The lesson is extended to include activities that explore *same size* and *same shape*.

Lesson 8

- Using a pattern to solve problems is presented in real-life contexts.
- Children identify and write the pattern unit. They choose the next shape or correct a pattern to solve.
- Children use strategies to solve problems.

SKILLS TRACE: SPATIAL SENSE AND PATTERNS

Grade K	Grade 1	Grade 2
• identify and use position words (ch. 2)	• use position words	• identify congruent shapes (ch. 7)
• extend and transfer patterns (ch. 2)	• find locations on a grid	• identify lines of symmetry (ch. 7)
• extend and create patterns with shapes and positions (ch. 5)	• identify slides, flips, and turns	• use a coordinate grid (ch. 4)
• identify and make symmetrical figures (ch. 5)	• describe, extend, predict, and create geometric patterns	• identify slides, flips, and turns (ch. 7)
	• identify symmetry in shapes	• identify and create geometric patterns (ch. 7)

Chapter Planner

Lesson	Objective	Vocabulary	Materials	✔ NCTM Standards
8.1 **Position Words** p. 207A	Give and follow directions about position and location of objects in space.	position words	cubes, two-color counters	Describe, name, and interpret relative positions in space and apply ideas about relative position.
8.2 **More Position Words** p. 209A	Arrange and describe the location of objects in space by position, proximity, and direction.	position words	index cards, plane shapes (Learning Tool (LT) 22 and 23)	Describe, name, and interpret relative positions in space and apply ideas about relative position.
8.3 **Give and Follow Directions** p. 211A	Give and follow directions to find locations on a grid.		two-color counters, one-inch grid paper (LT 28)	Find and name locations with simple relationships such as "near to" and in coordinate systems such as maps.
8.4 **Slides, Flips, and Turns** (Hands-On) p. 215A	Identify slides, flips, and turns of figures.	flip turn slide	pattern blocks	Recognize and apply slides, flips, and turns.
8.5 **Patterns** (Hands-On) p. 219A	Describe, extend, predict, and reproduce a pattern.	pattern	overhead pattern blocks, blank transparency, attribute-blocks (LT 26 and 27)	Recognize, describe, and extend patterns such as sequences of sounds and shapes or simple numeric patterns and translate from one representation to another.
8.6 **Create Patterns** (Hands-On) p. 221A	Identify and create patterns.		attribute blocks (LT 26 and 27), cubes	Recognize, describe, and extend patterns such as sequences of sounds and shapes or simple numeric patterns and translate from one representation to another.
8.7 **Symmetry** (Hands-On) p. 223A	Identify lines of symmetry and make symmetrical figures.	symmetry, line of symmetry	plane shapes (LT 22 and 23), scissors, construction paper, paint	Recognize and create shapes that have symmetry.
8.8 **Problem Solving: Find a Pattern** p. 227A	Use patterns to solve problems.			Apply and adapt a variety of appropriate strategies to solve problems.

Resources For Reaching All Learners

LESSON RESOURCES: Reteach, Practice, Enrichment, Problem Solving, Homework, English Learners, Daily Routines, Transparencies, Math Center.

ADDITIONAL RESOURCES FROM HOUGHTON MIFFLIN: Chapter Challenges, Combination Classroom Planning Guide, Every Day Counts, Math to Learn (Student Handbook)

Every Day Counts
The Calendar activities in *Every Day Counts* support the math in this chapter.

Assessing Prior Knowledge

Before beginning this chapter, you can assess student understandings in order to assist you in differentiating instruction.

Complete Chapter Pretest in Unit Resource Folder

Use this test to assess both prerequisite skills (**Are You Ready?** — one page) and chapter content (**Check What You Know** — two pages).

Chapter 8 Prerequisite Skills Pretest

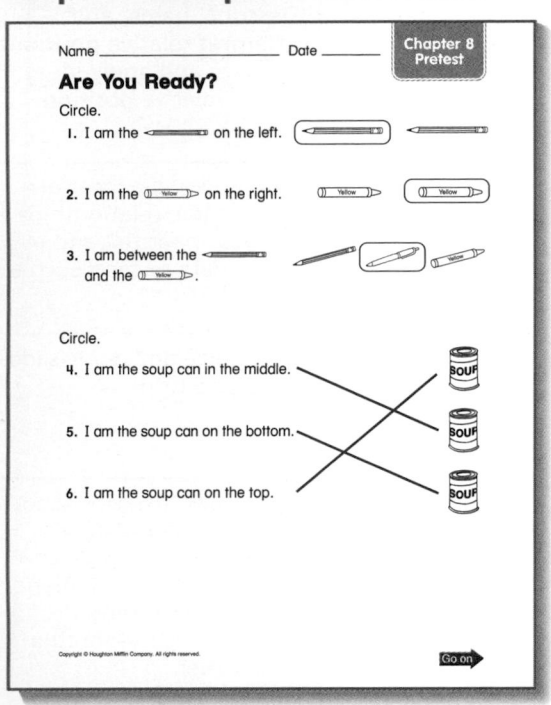

Chapter 8 New Content Pretest

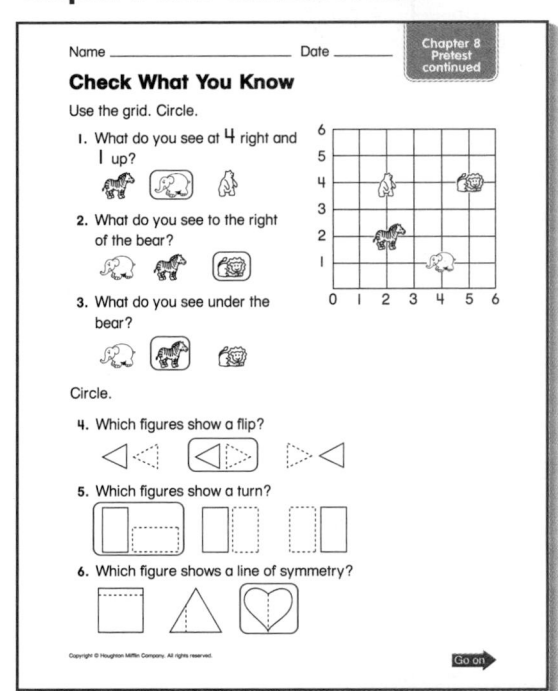

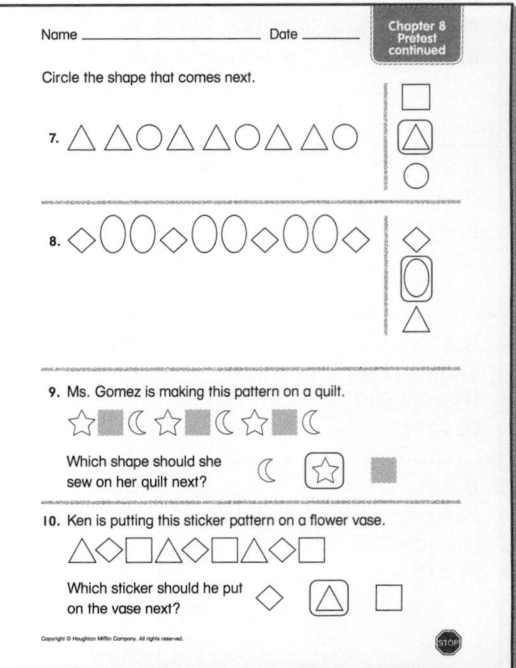

Customizing Instruction

For Students Having Difficulty

Items	Prerequisites	Ways to Success
1–3	Use position words.	CD: 8a Skillsheet 51
4–6	Use position words.	CD: 8a Skillsheet 52

Ways to Success: Intervention for every concept and skill (CD-ROM or Chapter Intervention Skillsheets).

For Students Having Success

Items	Objectives	Resources
3	8A Use vocabulary relating to spatial sense and patterns.	Enrichment 8.1
1–2	8B Use position words.	Enrichment 8.1–8.3
4–6	8C Find transformations and symmetry in shapes.	Enrichment 8.4–8.7
7–8	8D Describe, predict, extend and create patterns.	Enrichment 8.5, 8.6
9–10	8E Use patterns to solve problems.	Enrichment 8.8

Other Pretest Options

Informal Pretest

The pretest assesses vocabulary and prerequisite skills needed for success in this chapter.

Ways to Success CD-ROM

The *Ways to Success* chapter pretest has automatic assignment of appropriate review lessons.

Consider using **Chapter Challenges** with any students who have success with all new chapter content.

Chapter Resources

Assessing Prior Knowledge

Spelling Bee (use terms before, after, between)

- Each day give children directions similar to the following example. Display an alphabet chart as a resource.
- *The first letter of the word comes after e.*
  The second letter comes before s
  The third letter comes between n and p.
  The last letter comes before h.
  What is the word? (frog)

Ongoing Skill Activity

**Paint Symmetrical Designs
(make symmetrical shapes)**

- Give children pieces of paper folded in half.
- Have children drip small dots of paint along the fold of the paper to create a design.
- While the paint is wet, have children fold the paper onto the design and press down onto the paint. Then have them unfold their papers and observe the symmetry in their artwork.

Connecting to the Unit Project

- Tell children this problem is about patterns.
- Draw a triangle, circle, square, triangle, circle, square pattern on the board.
- Tell children that you are thinking about a pattern to put on a flag. Ask children to draw the next three shapes in the pattern.

Teacher Support

Professional Resources Handbook

Research, Mathematics Content, and Language Intervention

Research-Based Teaching

Friedrich Froebel (1782-1852), building on the ideas of Pestalozzi (1746-1827) and others, emphasized the development of teaching methods that draw upon children's concrete experiences with everyday objects. Froebel recognized spatial understanding and manipulation as an integral part of children's intellectual development. Piaget's work further underscored the importance of building upon children's experiences with shape in the real world. See *Professional Resources Handbook, Grade 1*, Unit 3.

For more ideas relating to Unit 3, see the Teacher Support Handbook at the back of this Teacher's Edition.

Language Intervention

In East Asian countries, children learn that just as numbers can be composed and decomposed as sets and subsets, geometric figures can be composed and decomposed as well. For further explanation, see "Mathematical Language and Geometry" in the *Professional Resources Handbook* Grade 1.

Technology

Time-Saving Technology Support
Ways to Assess Customized Spiral Review
  Test Generator CD
Lesson Planner CD-ROM
Ways to Success Intervention CD-ROM
MathTracks CD-ROM
Education Place: www.eduplace.com/math/mw
Houghton Mifflin Math eBook CD-ROM
eManipulatives
eGames

Starting Chapter 8
Spatial Sense and Patterns

CHAPTER OBJECTIVES

8A Develop and use math vocabulary relating to spatial sense and patterns.

8B Use position words to locate, arrange, and describe objects in space and locations on a grid.

8C Identify transformations and symmetry in shapes.

8D Describe, predict, extend, and create patterns.

8E Use patterns to solve problems.

Math Background

Spatial Sense and Patterns

Knowledge of spatial sense is essential as people communicate in the classroom and the real world. Knowledge of positional words such as *next to, in front, far, near, up,* and *down* enhances children's ability to follow and give directions and to use language precisely. It is important to remember that a variety of positional words may apply to a situation: A book may be above another toy, on the top shelf, between two objects, near another toy, and so on. Using words in connection with concrete objects and situations helps children develop their vocabulary.

Pattern is a powerful idea in mathematics because so many situations in the real world occur in patterns. In this chapter, children learn to recognize, describe, and extend simple patterns. Working with patterns draws on children's skills in recognizing similarities and differences and leads to the ability to generalize about pattern situations. Basic concepts of symmetry and transformations, including slides, flips, and turns, are also introduced in this chapter.

Spatial Sense and Patterns CHAPTER 8

INVESTIGATION

Use the words **inside** and **outside** to talk about the picture.

Chapter 8   two hundred five **205**

Using The Investigation

- Ask volunteers to define the terms *inside* and *outside.* Have children identify objects that are inside and outside the classroom. Discuss the weather. **Is today a good day to play outside?** (Answers will vary.)

- Read the question to children. **Look at the picture of the city. Use the words *inside* and *outside* to talk about the picture.** (Answers will vary. Possible answers: There is a cat inside the building. There is trash inside the can. All of the people in the picture are outside.)

 For more information about projects and investigations, visit Education Place. **eduplace.com/math/mw/**

You will learn about grids in this chapter. People who plan parks use grids. Frederick Law Olmsted planned parks.

People Using Math

Frederick Law Olmsted

Central Park, New York

When Frederick Law Olmsted was a boy, he loved to be outdoors. He liked to see the wildflowers and hear the birds sing.

When Frederick went to cities, he did not see open spaces with grass and trees, or places to walk and play. He believed that everyone should have open spaces to visit.

Frederick decided to become a landscape architect, someone who plans parks. He helped create many beautiful places, like Central Park in New York City and the land around the Capitol building in Washington, D.C. His work as a park planner changed many cities.

Frederick Law Olmsted was in charge of planning Central Park until 1861. He had been in charge for 3 years. What year did he start?

Draw or write to explain.

_____1858_____

206 two hundred six

Meeting the Needs of Mathematically Promising Students

The *Chapter Challenges* resource book provides blackline masters for activities that explore, extend, and connect the mathematics in every chapter. To support this independent work, see the Teacher Notes for each activity.

Explore: Number Position, page 43, after Lesson 1
Extend: City Grid, page 45, after Lesson 3
Connect: Navajo Blankets, page 47, after Lesson 5

Using This Page

- Read about Frederick Law Olmstead to children.

- Ask the children why Olmstead wanted to build parks. (Possible answer: He liked flowers, walking, grass, and being outdoors)

- Explain to children that a landscape architect plans where to plant flowers and trees, or where to place streams and ponds within a park.

- Give each child a piece of paper and explain that they are going to design a park. Have them draw their plans for a park.

- Have children share their plans. Note that while many children drew the same things, each park looks different.

- In this chapter you will learn about grids. You can use a grid to follow someone else's plans.

NSF Children's Math Worlds

Using the lessons from the *Children's Math Worlds* is a good way to ensure that your students will develop a deep understanding of spatial sense and patterns. The most effective approach is to use the *Children's Math Worlds* lessons along with the lessons in this chapter.

Position Words

PLANNING THE LESSON

MATHEMATICS OBJECTIVE
Give and follow directions about position and location of objects in space.

 *Use Lesson Planner CD-ROM for Lesson 8.1.*

Daily Routines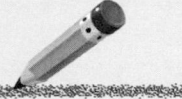

Calendar
Say a date and have children name dates on the calendar that are above, below, to the right, and to the left of that date. Say two dates and have children name the date that is between.

Sunday	Monday	Tuesday	Wednesday	Thursday	Friday	Saturday
			1	2	3	4
5	6	7	8	9	10	11
12	13	14	15	16	17	18
19	20	21	22	23	24	25
26	27	28	29	30	31	

Vocabulary
Demonstrate the meaning of the words **over, under, between, right,** and **left.** As you say each word, place your hand over a desk, then under a desk, between two books, to the right and to the left of a book.

Vocabulary Cards

Meeting North Carolina's Standards
Maintain Grade K Standard 3.03 Model and use directional and positional vocabulary.

Lesson Transparency **8.1**

Problem of the Day
Sandy's friends were picking numbers from a bag. Sandy's number was between 14 and 16. What number did Sandy pick? (15) Connie's number was just before 11. What number did Connie pick? (10)

Quick Review

$$8 - 3 \quad (5)$$

$$4 - 2 \quad (2)$$

$$9 - 6 \quad (3)$$

$$7 - 7 \quad (0)$$

$$5 - 0 \quad (5)$$

Lesson Quiz
Use **under, left, between,** or **over.**

1. The circle is _____ the triangle. (under)

2. The triangle is to the _____ of the square. (left)

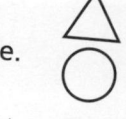

LEVELED PRACTICE

RETEACH 8.1

Name _____ Date _____   Reteach 8.1

Position Words

These words tell where objects are.

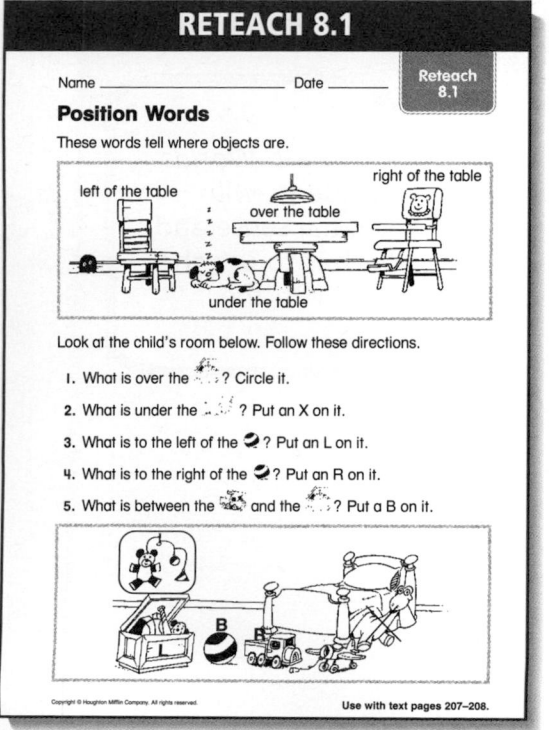

left of the table   over the table   right of the table
under the table

Look at the child's room below. Follow these directions.

1. What is over the 🛏? Circle it.
2. What is under the 🛏? Put an X on it.
3. What is to the left of the 🪑? Put an L on it.
4. What is to the right of the 🪑? Put an R on it.
5. What is between the 🧸 and the 🪑? Put a B on it.

Copyright © Houghton Mifflin Company. All rights reserved.   **Use with text pages 207–208.**

PRACTICE 8.1

Name _____ Date _____   Practice 8.1

Position Words

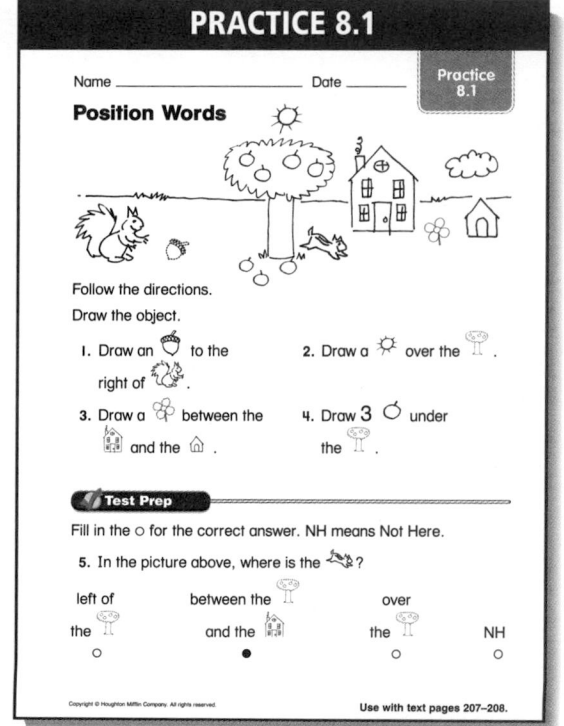

Follow the directions.
Draw the object.

1. Draw an 🌰 to the right of 🐿.
2. Draw a ☀ over the 🌳.
3. Draw a 🍀 between 🏠 and the 🏠.
4. Draw 3 🍎 under the 🌳.

Test Prep

Fill in the ○ for the correct answer. NH means Not Here.

5. In the picture above, where is the 🐿?

left of the 🌳   between the 🌳 and the 🏠   over the 🌳   NH
○   ●   ○   ○

Copyright © Houghton Mifflin Company. All rights reserved.   **Use with text pages 207–208.**

ENRICHMENT 8.1

Name _____ Date _____   Enrichment 8.1

At the Pet Store

What pet did Megan get?
Read the clues.
Cross out the pet Megan did not get.
Write the name on the line.

bird	fish	cat
dog	snake	hamster

1. It is not the pet over the 🐕. ___**fish**___
2. It is not the pet to the left of the 🐠. ___**bird**___
3. It is not the pet between the 🐦 and the 🐠. ___**snake**___
4. It is not the pet under the 🐦. ___**hamster**___
5. It is not the pet to the right of the 🐍. ___**cat**___
6. What pet did Megan get? She got the ___**dog**___

Talk About It Use the words over, between, and under to describe where you are sitting.
Answers will vary.

Copyright © Houghton Mifflin Company. All rights reserved.   **Use with text pages 207–208.**

Practice Workbook Page 49

Reaching All Learners
Differentiated Instruction

English Learners

Children will need to understand position words in order to give and follow directions about objects in space. Use Worksheet 8.1 to help children learn to understand and use these words when giving or following directions.

Special Needs
AUDITORY, TACTILE

Materials: *cubes of 2 colors*

- Have the child put a red cube on the table. Place a green cube to the right of the red cube.

- Ask the child to use the word right to describe where the green cube is. (It is to the right of the red cube.)

- Repeat using other position words.

Early Finishers
TACTILE, VISUAL

- Provide children with geometric shapes cut from colored paper.

- Have children glue shapes so they are positioned above, between, below, to the left of, and to the right of another object in the collage.

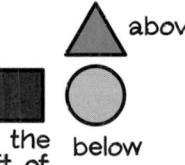

above
to the left of
below

TECHNOLOGY

Spiral Review

You can prepare students for standardized tests with **customized** spiral review on key skills using the *Ways to Assess* CD-ROM.

eBook

An electronic version of this lesson can be found in **eMathBook**.

Lesson Planner

Use the **Lesson Planner CD-ROM** to see how lesson objectives for this chapter are correlated to standards.

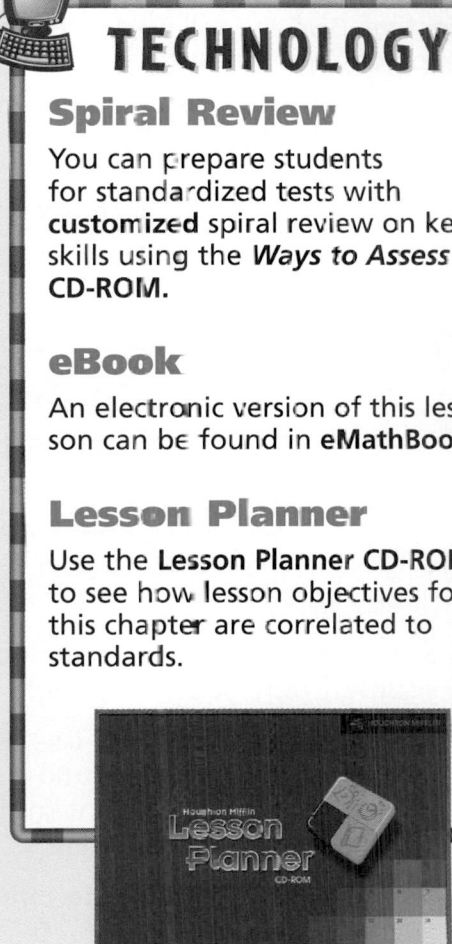

Social Studies Connection

Show children a map of the United States. Point to and identify a state. Give directions such as: Point to the state under this state. Point to the state to the left.

MATH CENTER

Basic Skills Activity

Motivate children to build basic skills. Use this activity to address multiple learning styles using hands-on activities related to the skills of this lesson.

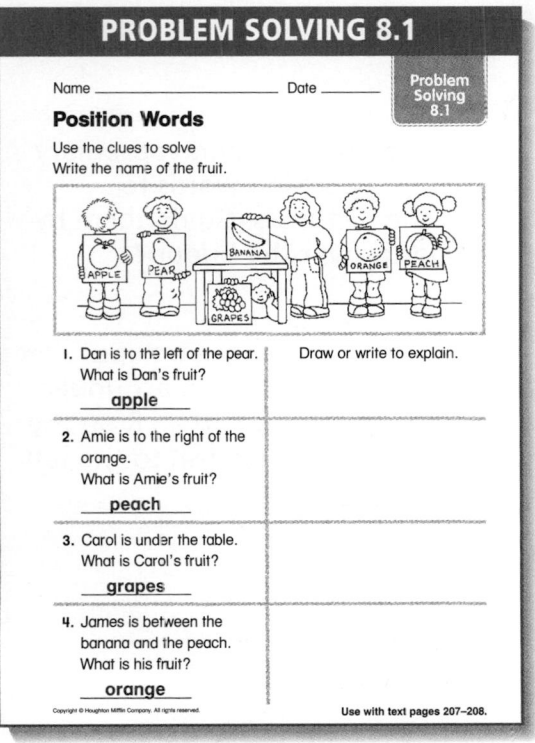

PROBLEM SOLVING 8.1

Name _____ Date _____

Problem Solving 8.1

Position Words

Use the clues to solve
Write the name of the fruit.

1. Dan is to the left of the pear. What is Dan's fruit?
   apple

   Draw or write to explain.

2. Amie is to the right of the orange. What is Amie's fruit?
   peach

3. Carol is under the table. What is Carol's fruit?
   grapes

4. James is between the banana and the peach. What is his fruit?
   orange

Use with text pages 207–208.

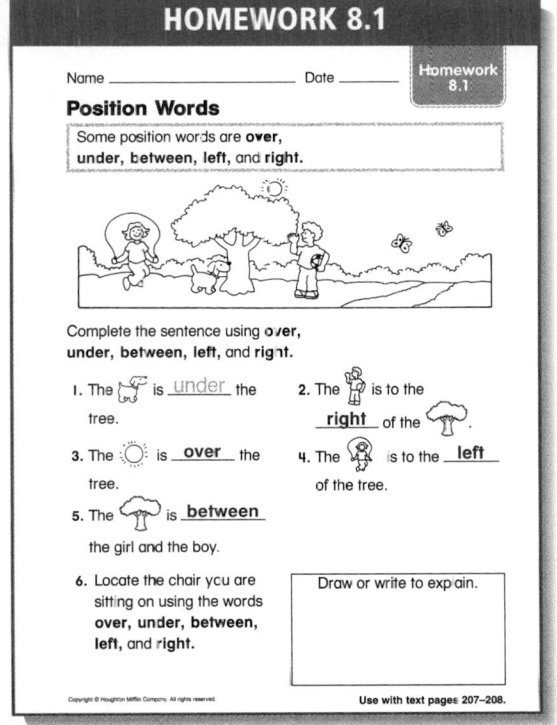

HOMEWORK 8.1

Name _____ Date _____

Homework 8.1

Position Words

Some position words are **over, under, between, left, and right.**

Complete the sentence using **over, under, between, left, and right.**

1. The 🐕 is **under** the tree.

2. The 🧍 is to the **right** of the tree.

3. The ☀ is **over** the tree.

4. The 🐦 is to the **left** of the tree.

5. The 🌳 is **between** the girl and the boy.

6. Locate the chair you are sitting on using the words **over, under, between, left, and right.**

Draw or write to explain.

Use with text pages 207–208.

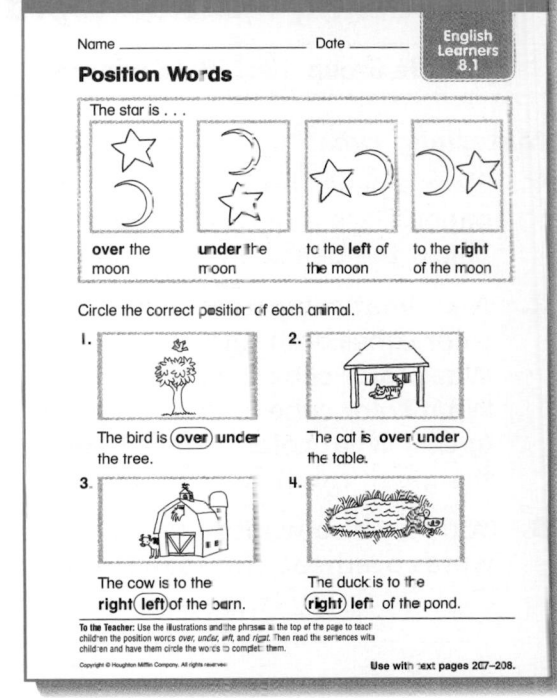

ENGLISH LEARNERS 8.1

Name _____ Date _____

English Learners 8.1

Position Words

The star is . . .

over the moon | **under** the moon | to the **left** of the moon | to the **right** of the moon

Circle the correct position of each animal.

1. The bird is (over) under the tree.

2. The cat is over (under) the table.

3. The cow is to the right (left) of the barn.

4. The duck is to the (right) left of the pond.

To the Teacher: Use the illustrations and the phrases at the top of the page to teach children the position words over, under, left, and right. Then read the sentences with children and have them circle the words to complete them.

Use with text pages 207–208.

Homework Workbook Page 49

TEACHING LESSON 8.1

LESSON ORGANIZER

Objective Give and follow directions about position and location of objects in space.

Resources Reteach, Practice, Enrichment, Problem Solving, Homework, English Learners, Transparencies, Math Center

Materials Cubes, two-color counters

Warm-Up Activity
Model Using Position Words

iiii Whole Group	⏱ 5 minutes	Auditory, Kinesthetic

1. Ask children to listen carefully and follow these directions.

2. **Shake your left hand. Shake your right leg. Raise your left foot. Touch your right ear.**

3. Have 4 volunteers form a line. **Point to the child in front of you in line; the child is before you in line.** Now have volunteers point to the child behind. **This child is after you in line.**

4. Now instruct all children to point to the space between their eyes.

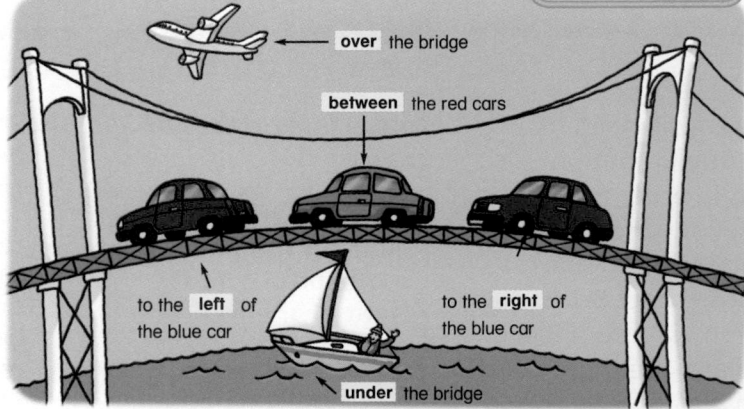

Name_____

Position Words

These words tell where objects are.

Objective
Give and follow directions about position and location of objects in space.
Vocabulary
position words

over the bridge
between the red cars
to the left of the blue car
to the right of the blue car
under the bridge

Guided Practice

Listen. Follow the directions.

I.

TEST TIPS **Explain Your Thinking** Tell how you know something is to the left or to the right of you. **Possible answer: I remember which hand I use to hold my pencil. I use that as a clue.**

Chapter 8 Lesson I   two hundred seven **207**

---

1 Introduce
Modeling Position Words

iiii Whole Group	⏱ 10–15 minutes	Visual, Auditory

Materials: *cubes*

1. Place a pencil horizontally in the middle of a sheet of paper. Place a red cube above the pencil. Place 3 cubes below the pencil, in a row: blue, yellow, green.

2. Ask: **What color cube is over the pencil?** (red) **What color cubes are under the pencil?** (blue, yellow, green) **What color cube is to the left of the yellow cube?** (blue) **What color cube is to the right of the yellow cube?** (green) **What color cube is between the blue cube and the green cube?** (yellow)

3. You may also want to use the 5 different position words overhead transparencies during this lesson.

2 Develop

Guided Learning

Teaching Example Introduce the objective and vocabulary to the children. Help children use position words to describe where each item in the picture is. Guide them by asking questions such as: **What is over the bridge?**

Guided Practice

Have children circle the object that is over the octopus. (the swimmer) Then have them draw an X on the object under the swimmer. (the octopus) Have children write an R on the fish to the right of the octopus, an L on the fish to the left of the octopus.

207   **CHAPTER 8**   **Lesson 1**

Practice

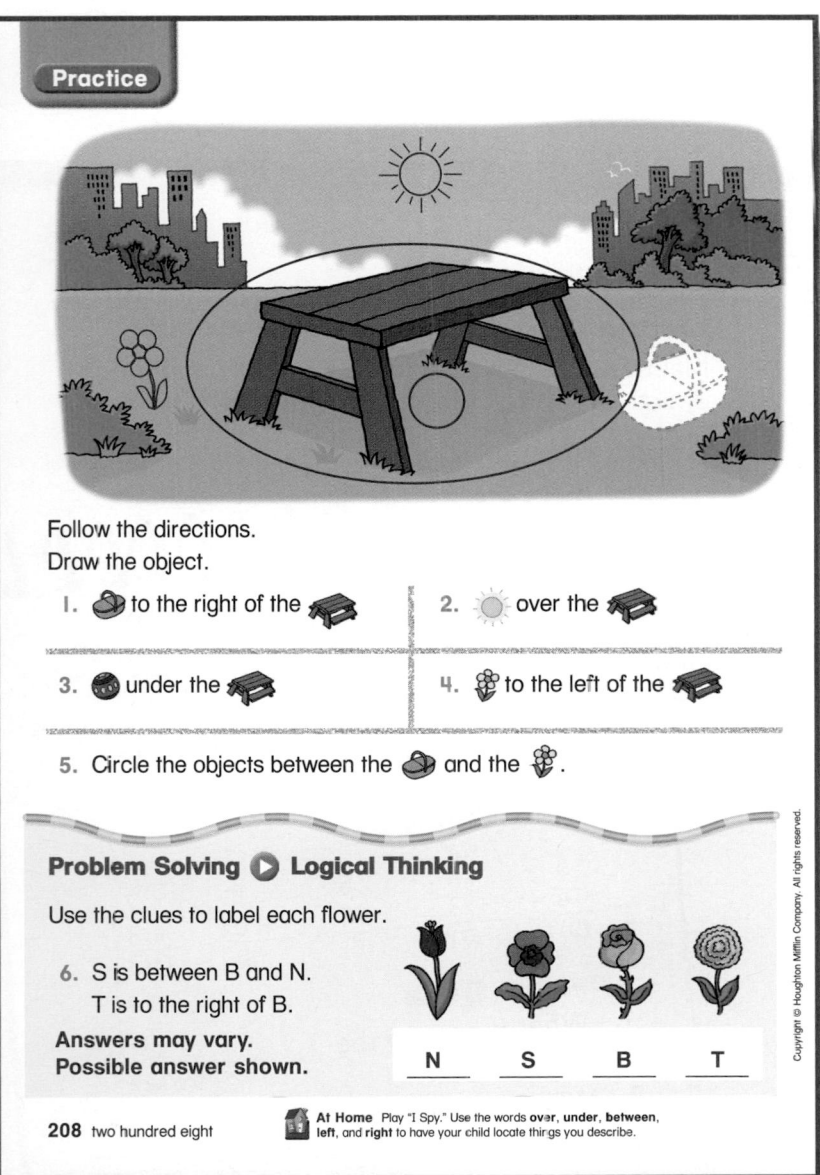

Follow the directions.
Draw the object.

1. 🥧 to the right of the 🪑
2. ☀ over the 🪑
3. 🥧 under the 🪑
4. 🌷 to the left of the 🪑

5. Circle the objects between the 🥧 and the 🌼.

~~~~~~

Problem Solving ▶ **Logical Thinking**

Use the clues to label each flower.

6. S is between B and N.
   T is to the right of B.

   Answers may vary.
   Possible answer shown.

N	S	B	T

208 two hundred eight

At Home Play "I Spy." Use the words **over**, **under**, **between**, **left**, and **right** to have your child locate things you describe.

Test Prep
Transparency
8.1

Daily Test Prep

   10
 − 3
_____

   5   6   7   8
   ○   ○   ●   ○

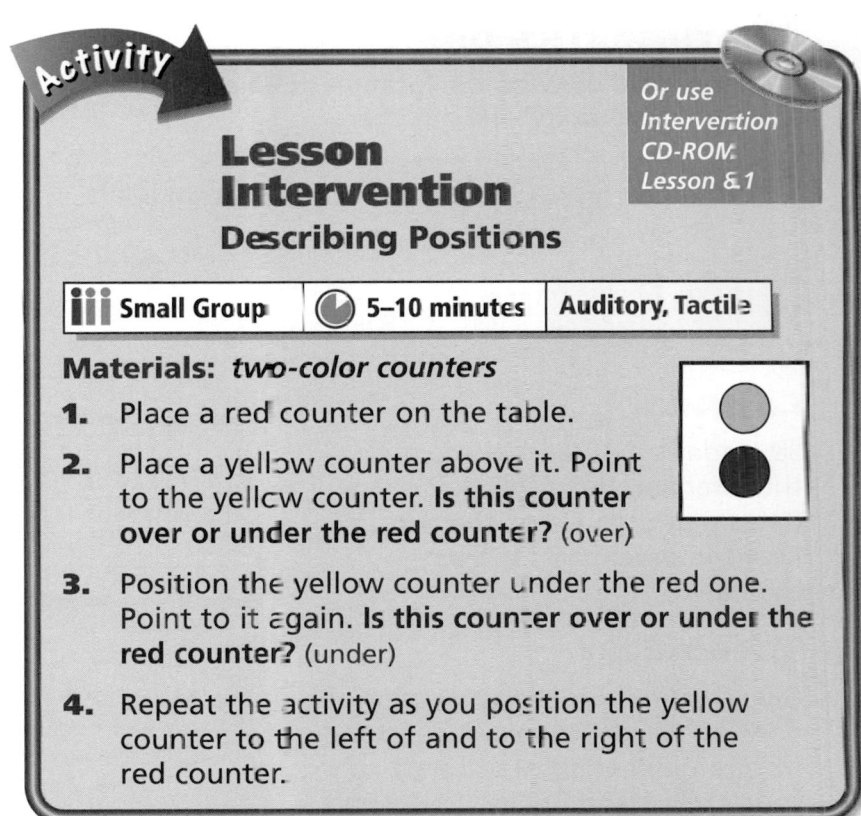

Activity

Or use Intervention CD-ROM Lesson 8.1

Lesson Intervention
Describing Positions

| 👥 Small Group | 🕐 5–10 minutes | Auditory, Tactile |

Materials: *two-color counters*

1. Place a red counter on the table.

2. Place a yellow counter above it. Point to the yellow counter. **Is this counter over or under the red counter?** (over)

3. Position the yellow counter under the red one. Point to it again. **Is this counter over or under the red counter?** (under)

4. Repeat the activity as you position the yellow counter to the left of and to the right of the red counter.

3 Practice

Independent Practice

Children complete **Exercises 1–5** independently.

Problem Solving

After children complete **Exercise 6**, call on volunteers to share their answers. Other possible answers include: BSNT, BTSN, BSTN.

Common Error

Confusing Left and Right

Children may not remember which direction is left and which is right. Have right-handed children sit on the hand they do not write with to find left. Instruct left-handed children to sit on the hand they do not write with to find right.

4 Assess and Close

Draw a birdhouse. Draw a red bird over it. Draw a blue bird under it. Draw a yellow bird to the right of it.

✏ Keeping a Journal

Draw a circle in the middle of your page. Write the position words you learned in the correct places around the circle.

8.2

More Position Words

PLANNING THE LESSON

MATHEMATICS OBJECTIVE
Arrange and describe the location of objects in space by position, proximity, and direction.

Use Lesson Planner CD-ROM for Lesson 8.2.

Daily Routines

Calendar
Say today's date and locate it on the calendar. Have children name dates that are next to the date, near the date, and far from the date.

Vocabulary
Give children directions by using the position words. For example: stand in front of your chair, stand next to your chair, stand behind your chair, put your right hand up, put your right hand down.

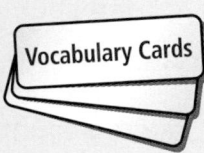
Vocabulary Cards

Meeting North Carolina's Standards
Maintain Grade K Standard 3.03 Model and use directional and positional vocabulary.

Lesson Transparency

8.2

Problem of the Day
Carlos is to the right of Hannah. Gabi is between Carlos and Alana. Write the names to show where each child is sitting. (Hannah, Carlos, Gabi, Alana)

Quick Review
$$\begin{array}{c} 5 \\ +4 \\ \hline (9) \end{array} \quad \begin{array}{c} 4 \\ +3 \\ \hline (7) \end{array} \quad \begin{array}{c} 6 \\ +4 \\ \hline (10) \end{array} \quad \begin{array}{c} 8 \\ +0 \\ \hline (8) \end{array} \quad \begin{array}{c} 7 \\ +3 \\ \hline (10) \end{array}$$

Lesson Quiz
1. What is next to the pond? (duck)

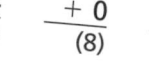

2. What is behind the tree? (table)

3. What is far from the pond? (tree, table)

LEVELED PRACTICE

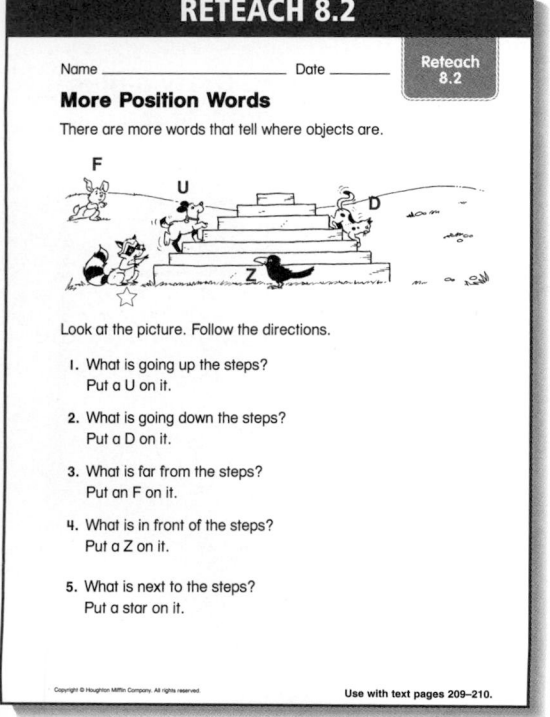

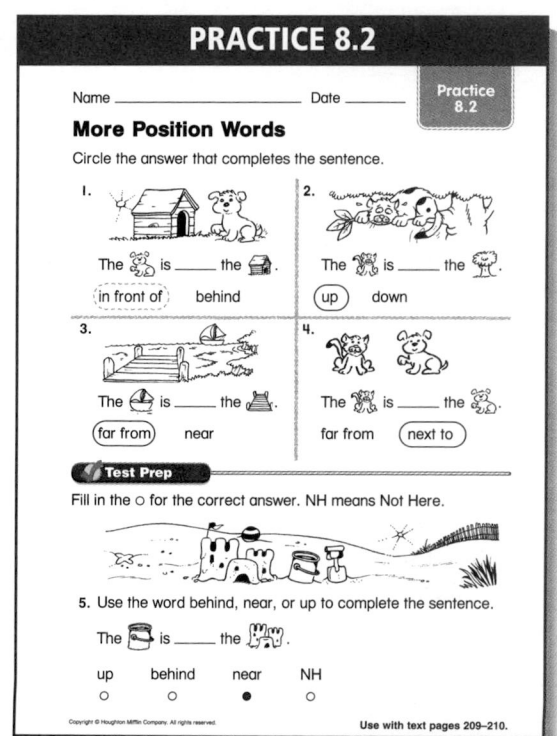

Practice Workbook Page 50

Reaching All Learners

Differentiated Instruction

English Learners

Children will need to understand position words in order to give and follow directions about objects in space. Use Worksheet 8.2 to help children learn to understand and use these words when giving or following directions.

Inclusion

VISUAL, TACTILE

Have the child hold up a sheet of paper. Direct the child to put his or her hand behind the paper. Where is your hand? (behind the paper)

Then tell him or her to move the hand in front of the paper. Where is your hand now? (in front of the paper) Continue with other positions.

Early Finishers

VISUAL, AUDITORY

Materials: *index cards*

Write each position word: over, under, left, right, between, behind, in front, far, near, next, up, and down on an index card. Place them face down. Children take turns choosing a card. Have children use the word to describe the location of one object relative to another object. For example, "The clock is over the door."

TECHNOLOGY

Spiral Review

Create **customized** spiral review worksheets for individual students using the *Ways to Assess* CD-ROM.

eBook

An electronic version of this lesson can be found in **eMathBook**.

Education Place

Encourage students to visit **Education Place** at eduplace.com/kids/mw/ for more student activities.

Science Connection

Draw a simple diagram of the solar system showing the relative distance of each planet from the sun. (Sun, Mercury, Venus, Earth, Mars, Jupiter, Saturn, Uranus, Neptune, Pluto) Ask questions that use the words next to, far, and near.

MATH CENTER

Real-Life Activity

Help children understand the usefulness of mathematics. This activity makes math come alive by connecting the lesson skills to a real-life situation.

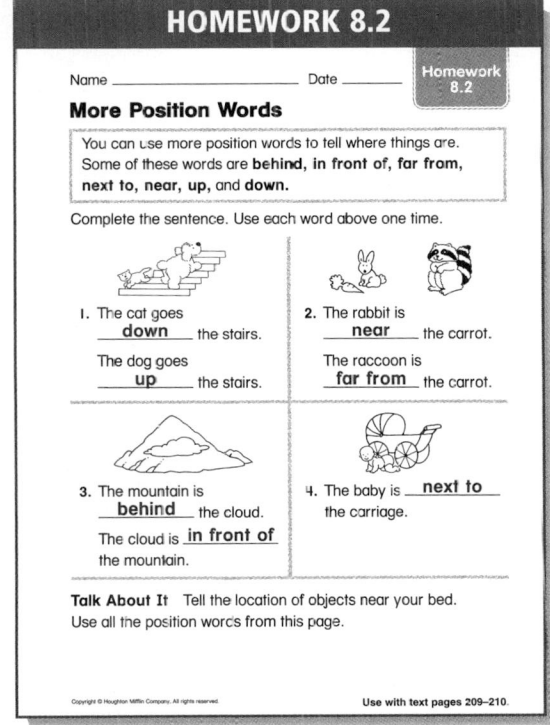

Homework Workbook Page 50

TEACHING LESSON 8.2

LESSON ORGANIZER

Objective Arrange and describe the location of objects in space by position, proximity, and direction.

Resources Reteach, Practice, Enrichment, Problem Solving, Homework, English Learners, Transparencies, Math Center

Materials Plane shapes (Learning Tool (LT) 22 and 23), index cards

Activity

Warm-Up Activity
Discuss Using Position Words

iii Small Group	⊙ 5 minutes	Auditory, Visual

1. Line up 6 crayons of different colors in two rows of 3 each.

2. Use the words over, under, to the right of, to the left of, and between to describe the location of the orange crayon. **It is over the blue crayon.**

3. Have volunteers point to the crayon you are describing.

Name_____

More Position Words

These words tell the location of objects.

Objective Arrange and describe the location of objects.

Vocabulary position words

behind the cloud
far from the slide
in front of the sun
down the slide
next to the tree
up the ladder
near the slide

Guided Practice

Listen. Follow the directions.

I.

TEST TIPS **Explain Your Thinking** Use some words from this page. Tell how to find your desk in the classroom. **Possible answer: I sit in front of the bookshelves near the sink.**

Chapter 8 Lesson 2   two hundred nine **209**

---

① Introduce
Modeling Position Words

iiii Whole Group	⊙ 10–15 minutes	Visual, Auditory

Materials: *Plane shapes (LT 22 and 23), index cards*

1. Display paper shapes. Place an index card next to each shape.

2. Guide children to identify the position of shapes relative to other shapes. As each position is agreed upon, write it on the index card next to the shape. **Is the square near the large circle or far from it? Is the triangle in front of or behind the square? Where is the large rectangle? Where is the small rectangle?** (Answers will vary.)

3. Call on volunteers to reposition shapes and identify the new positions. You may also want to use the 5 different position words overhead transparencies during the lesson.

② Develop

Guided Learning

Teaching Example Introduce the objective and vocabulary to the children. As you read each position word, have children explain the location using the object's name and the position word.

Guided Practice

Have children follow these directions: **draw an X on the object that is behind the sandbox** (pail); **write an F on the object in front of the climbing structure** (ball); **write an N on the object that is near the slide** (book bag); **circle the object that is far from the climbing structure** (turtle); **put a U on the child's arm that is up in the air and a D on the arm that is down.**

Continue giving directions. **Draw a shovel next to the pail. Then draw a rock in front of the turtle.**

Help children focus on their position in the room in order to answer the Explain Your Thinking question.

Practice

Circle the answer that completes the sentence.

1. The ☁ is _____ the 🏢 .

   (in front of)   behind

2. The 🐿 goes _____ the 🌳 .

   (up)   down

3. The ⚾ is _____ the 🐕 .

   far from   (near)

4. The 🐦 is _____ the ☀ .

   (far from)   next to

Reading Math ▶ **Vocabulary**

Use the word **above**, **below**, or **beside**.
Complete the sentence.

5. The rabbit is ___**below**___ the swing.

6. The butterfly is ___**above**___ the swing.

7. The flower is ___**beside**___ the rabbit.

8. Draw a picture on another piece of
   paper. Use **above**, **below**, and **beside**
   to tell where things are.

210 two hundred ten

🏠 **At Home** Have your child use words from this
lesson to describe the location of things in the kitchen.

Daily Test Prep

Test Prep
Transparency

8.2

$$\begin{array}{r} 9 \\ -\ 6 \\ \hline \end{array}$$

3   4   5   6
●   ○   ○   ○

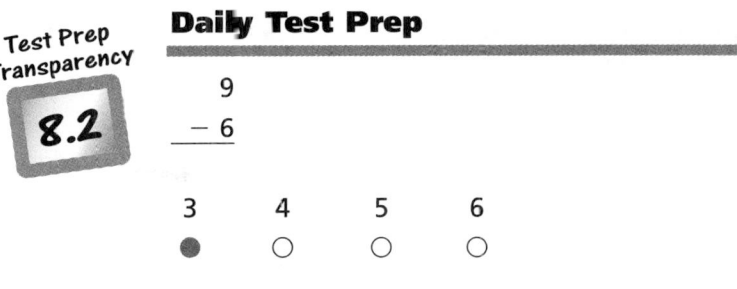

Activity

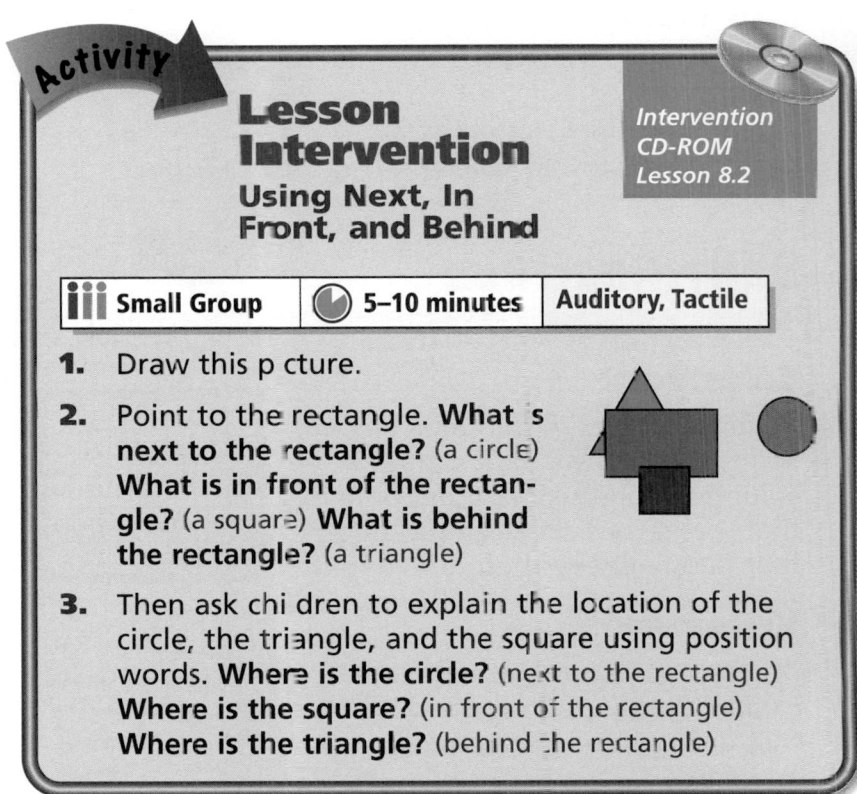

Lesson Intervention
Using Next, In Front, and Behind

Intervention CD-ROM Lesson 8.2

| iii Small Group | 🕐 5–10 minutes | Auditory, Tactile |

1. Draw this picture.

2. Point to the rectangle. **What is
   next to the rectangle?** (a circle)
   **What is in front of the rectan-
   gle?** (a square) **What is behind
   the rectangle?** (a triangle)

3. Then ask children to explain the location of the
   circle, the triangle, and the square using position
   words. **Where is the circle?** (next to the rectangle)
   Where is the square? (in front of the rectangle)
   Where is the triangle? (behind the rectangle)

---

③ Practice

Independent Practice

Children complete **Exercises 1–4** independently.

Reading Math

After children complete **Exercises 5–8** invite volunteers to
share their completed sentences. Discuss their solutions
with the class.

Common Error

Confusing *In Front* and *Behind*
Children may not be able to interpret position in a picture.
Provide models to place in the same positions found in the
pictures as they solve problems.

④ Assess and Close

Who is sitting next to you? (Answers will vary.)

Who is sitting near you? (Answers will vary.)

Is someone sitting in front of you? Who is it? (Answers will
vary.)

 **Keeping a Journal**

Look out the window. Draw a picture of what you
see. Then label the picture using the words next, in
front, and behind.

Give and Follow Directions

PLANNING THE LESSON

MATHEMATICS OBJECTIVE

Give and follow directions to find locations on a grid.

Use Lesson Planner CD-ROM for Lesson 8.3.

Daily Routines

Calendar

Name two dates in the same week. Point to one of the dates. Have a volunteer point to the other date in that week. Have children say a date that falls between those two dates.

Sunday	Monday	Tuesday	Wednesday	Thursday	Friday	Saturday
			1	2	3	4
5	6	7	8	9	10	11
12	13	14	15	16	17	18
19	20	21	22	23	24	25
26	27	28	29	30	31	

Vocabulary

Draw a 4 × 4 grid on the board. Explain that a **grid** is formed by lines that go across and lines that go up and down.

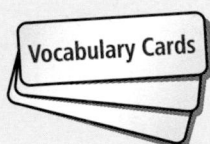

Vocabulary Cards

Meeting North Carolina's Standards

3.04 Solve problems involving spatial visualization.

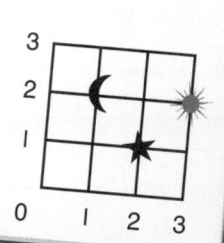

Lesson Transparency 8.3

Problem of the Day

Luc had 5 dimes on Sunday. On Monday he found 2 dimes. On Tuesday his mother gave him 1 dime. How many dimes does Luc have now? (8 dimes)

Quick Review

$$2 + 2 \quad (4)$$
$$5 + 5 \quad (10)$$
$$3 + 3 \quad (6)$$
$$10 + 0 \quad (10)$$
$$4 + 4 \quad (8)$$

Lesson Quiz

1. Go right 2 spaces. Go up 1 space. What did you find? (star)

LEVELED PRACTICE

RETEACH 8.3

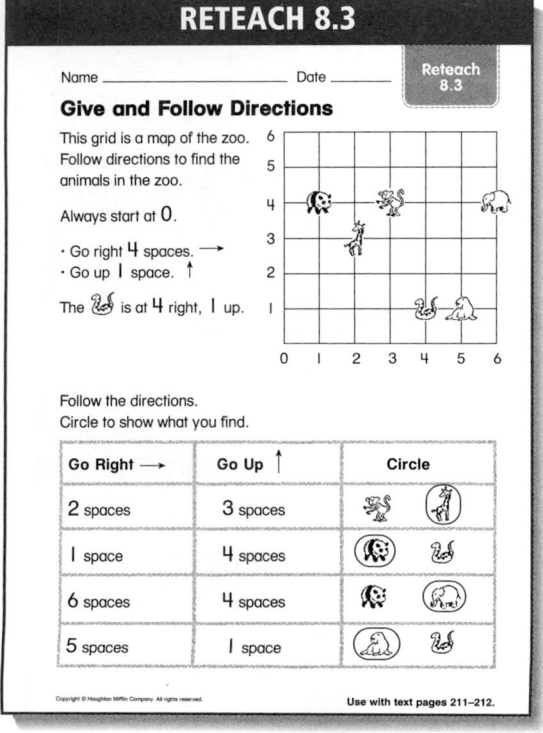

Name _____ Date _____

Reteach 8.3

Give and Follow Directions

This grid is a map of the zoo. Follow directions to find the animals in the zoo.

Always start at 0.

· Go right 4 spaces. →
· Go up 1 space. ↑

The 🦁 is at 4 right, 1 up.

Follow the directions. Circle to show what you find.

Go Right →	Go Up ↑	Circle
2 spaces	3 spaces	
1 space	4 spaces	
6 spaces	4 spaces	
5 spaces	1 space	

Copyright © Houghton Mifflin Company. All rights reserved.

Use with text pages 211–212.

PRACTICE 8.3

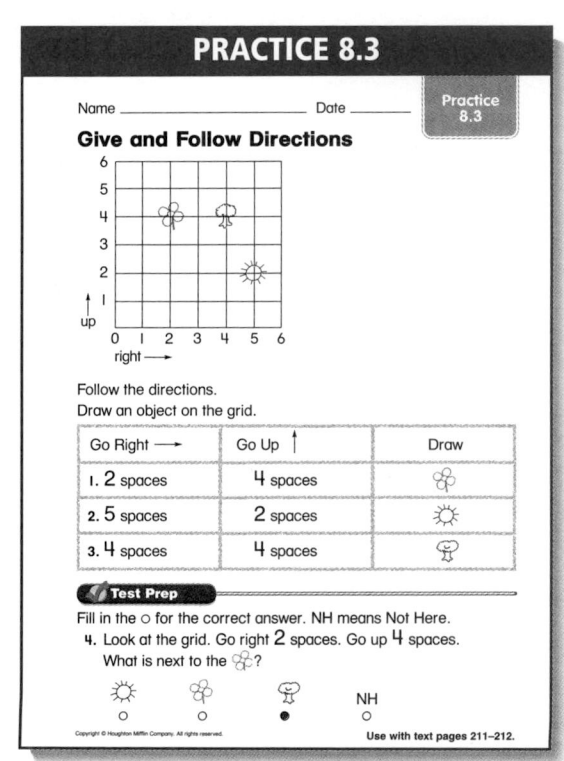

Name _____ Date _____

Practice 8.3

Give and Follow Directions

Follow the directions. Draw an object on the grid.

Go Right →	Go Up ↑	Draw
1. 2 spaces	4 spaces	🌸
2. 5 spaces	2 spaces	☀
3. 4 spaces	4 spaces	🌷

Test Prep

Fill in the ○ for the correct answer. NH means Not Here.

4. Look at the grid. Go right 2 spaces. Go up 4 spaces. What is next to the 🌸?

○ ☀   ○ 🌷   ● 🍄   ○ NH

Copyright © Houghton Mifflin Company. All rights reserved.

Use with text pages 211–212.

ENRICHMENT 8.3

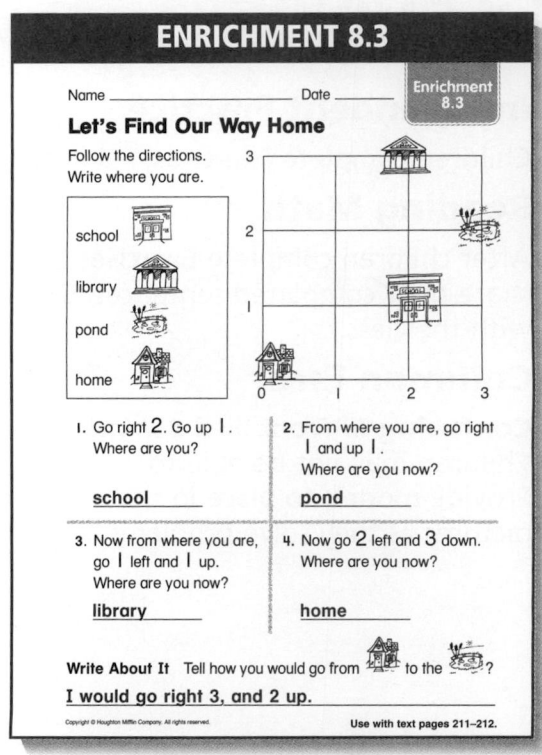

Name _____ Date _____

Enrichment 8.3

Let's Find Our Way Home

Follow the directions. Write where you are.

1. Go right 2. Go up 1. Where are you?

school

2. From where you are, go right 1 and up 1. Where are you now?

pond

3. Now from where you are, go 1 left and 1 up. Where are you now?

library

4. Now go 2 left and 3 down. Where are you now?

home

Write About It Tell how you would go from 🏠 to the 🏫?

I would go right 3, and 2 up.

Copyright © Houghton Mifflin Company. All rights reserved.

Use with text pages 211–212.

Practice Workbook Page 51

Reaching All Learners
Differentiated Instruction

English Learners

The word *space* has several meanings in English. In order to find locations on a grid, English-language learners will need to understand the meaning within the context of a grid. Use Worksheet 8.3 to develop children's understanding of this meaning.

Inclusion
VISUAL, TACTILE

Materials: *one-inch grid (LT 28)*

Draw a 4 × 4 grid. Draw a blue baseball cap at (3, 2). Instruct the child to: Go right 3 spaces. Have the child use a crayon to draw the horizontal line as he or she counts across. Then say: Go up 2 spaces. Count and draw the vertical line. The cap is at (3, 2).

Gifted and Talented
TACTILE, VISUAL

Materials: *one-inch grid (LT 28)*

Have children outline a 6 × 6 grid on grid paper. Label bottom and side with numbers. Remind them to begin with zero. Have children draw 4 stick figures at intersecting points on their grids. Partners ask questions to find a figure on the grid. For example: Is it at right 2 and up 3?

TECHNOLOGY

Spiral Review

Using the *Ways to Assess* CD-ROM, you can create customized spiral review worksheets covering any lessons you choose.

eBook

eMathBook allows students to review lessons and do homework without carrying their textbooks home.

Lesson Planner

You can customize your teaching plan to meet your curriculum requirements with the **Lesson Planner CD-ROM**.

Art Connection

Draw a large grid on paper and display it on a wall. Ask each child to draw a small picture at a point on the grid. Have children draw two pictures from the grid on their own papers and write directions to each location.

MATH CENTER

Real-Life Activity

Help children understand the usefulness of mathematics. This activity makes math come alive by connecting the lesson skills to a real-life situation.

PROBLEM SOLVING 8.3

Name _____ Date _____

Problem Solving 8.3

Give and Follow Directions

Use the grid.
Finish the directions.

Draw or write to explain.

1. Jeni wants to find the squirrel. She goes right __4__ spaces and up __2__ spaces.

2. Gary wants to find the rabbit. He goes right __3__ spaces and up __1__ space.

3. Roy wants to find the fox. He goes right __2__ spaces and up __5__ spaces.

4. Barb wants to find the owl. She goes right __5__ spaces and up __3__ spaces.

Use with text pages 211–212.

HOMEWORK 8.3

Name _____ Date _____

Homework 8.3

Give and Follow Directions

This grid shows places in the garden.

Follow the directions.
Circle the flower or animal you find.

1. Go right 3 spaces. Go up 2 spaces. What do you find?

2. Go right 2 spaces. Go up 4 spaces. What do you find?

3. Go right 4 spaces. Go up 1 space. What do you find?

4. Go right 1 space. Go up 3 spaces. What do you find?

5. Draw a flower on the grid. Write where the flower is.

_____ spaces to the right
_____ spaces up

Use with text pages 211–212.

Homework Workbook Page 51

ENGLISH LEARNERS 8.3

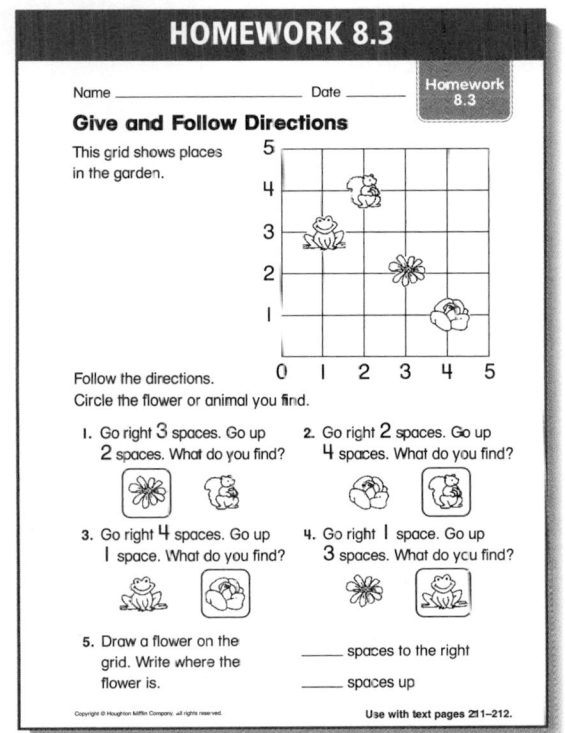

Name _____ Date _____

English Learners 8.3

Give and Follow Directions

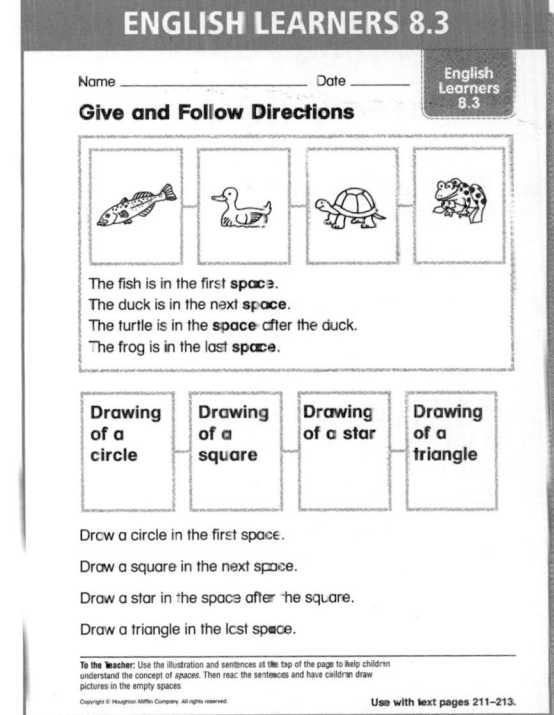

The fish is in the first **space**.
The duck is in the next **space**.
The turtle is in the **space** after the duck.
The frog is in the last **space**.

Drawing of a circle	Drawing of a square	Drawing of a star	Drawing of a triangle

Draw a circle in the first space.

Draw a square in the next space.

Draw a star in the space after the square.

Draw a triangle in the last space.

To the Teacher: Use the illustration and sentences at the top of the page to help children understand the concept of spaces. Then read the sentences and have children draw pictures in the empty spaces.

Use with text pages 211–213.

TEACHING LESSON 8.3

LESSON ORGANIZER

Objective Give and follow directions to find locations on a grid.

Resources Reteach, Practice, Enrichment, Problem Solving, Homework, English Learners, Transparencies, Math Center

Materials Two-color counters, one-inch grid paper (LT 28)

Activity

Warm-Up Activity
Following Directions for Right and Up

iii Small Group	⏱ 5 minutes	Auditory, Tactile

1. Review the direction words right and up. Have children draw to follow your directions. Remind children to begin drawing at the bottom left corner of their papers.

2. **Draw a short line to the right. Draw a short line up. Draw a short line to the right. Draw a short line up.**

3. Continue until children reach the top right corner of their papers. **What does your drawing look like?** (stairs)

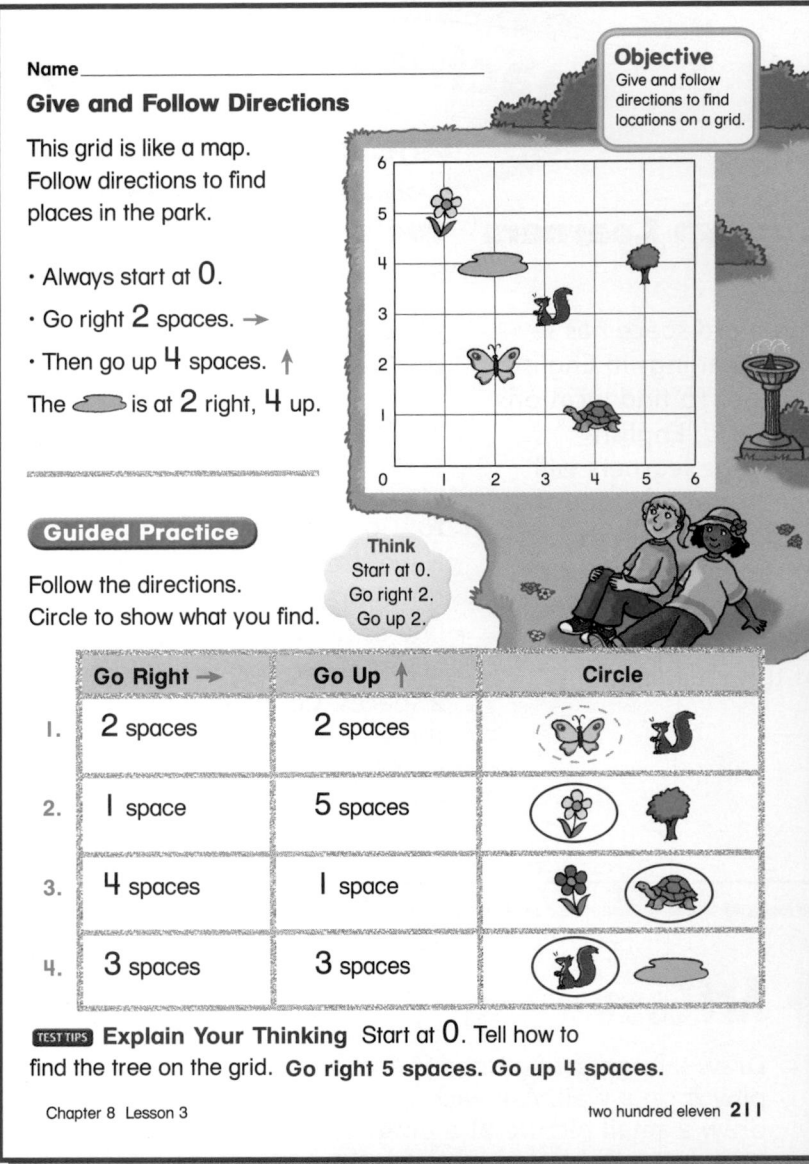

Name _____

Give and Follow Directions

This grid is like a map. Follow directions to find places in the park.

- Always start at 0.
- Go right 2 spaces. →
- Then go up 4 spaces. ↑

The ⬭ is at 2 right, 4 up.

Objective Give and follow directions to find locations on a grid.

Guided Practice

Follow the directions. Circle to show what you find.

Think Start at 0. Go right 2. Go up 2.

	Go Right →	Go Up ↑	Circle
1.	2 spaces	2 spaces	
2.	1 space	5 spaces	
3.	4 spaces	1 space	
4.	3 spaces	3 spaces	

TEST TIPS Explain Your Thinking Start at 0. Tell how to find the tree on the grid. **Go right 5 spaces. Go up 4 spaces.**

Chapter 8 Lesson 3

two hundred eleven **211**

1 Introduce
Modeling Following Directions

iiii Whole Group	⏱ 10–15 minutes	Visual, Auditory

1. Draw a 4 × 4 grid on the board. Draw a flower at (2, 1); draw a sun at (1, 3); draw a house at (4, 3) on the grid.

2. Move your finger along the grid as you give these directions. **I start at 0. I move my finger 2 spaces to the right.** Have children count as you move. **Then I move my finger up 1 space. What picture is here?** (a flower) **The flower is at 2 right, 1 up.**

3. Repeat the process as you locate the sun and the house on the grid. Emphasize that the point is created by the intersection of the two lines.

2 Develop

Guided Learning

Teaching Example Introduce the objective to the children. Guide them through the example to show them how to follow the directions to find the pond on the grid.

Guided Practice

Have children complete **Exercises 1–4** as you observe. Remind them to go right first, then up. Give children the opportunity to answer the Explain Your Thinking question. Then discuss their responses with the class.

Practice

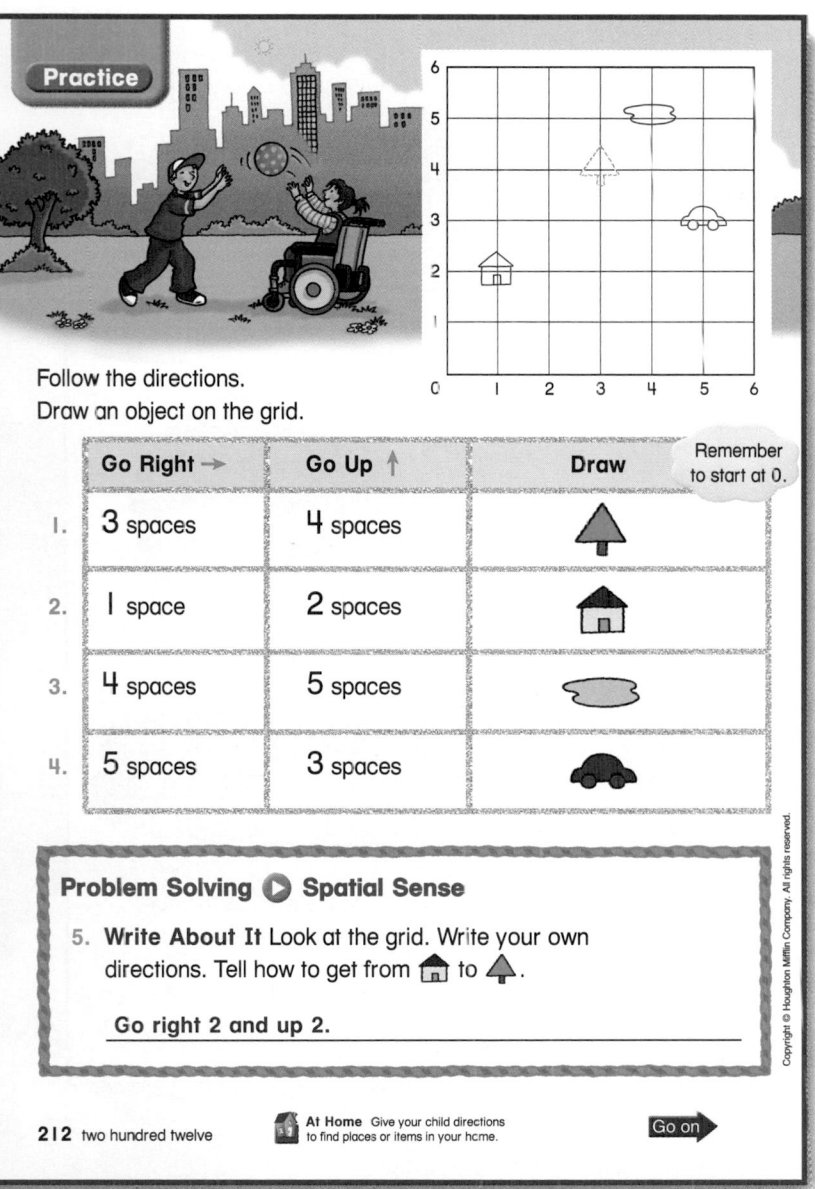

Follow the directions.
Draw an object on the grid.

Remember to start at 0.

	Go Right →	Go Up ↑	Draw
1.	3 spaces	4 spaces	
2.	1 space	2 spaces	
3.	4 spaces	5 spaces	
4.	5 spaces	3 spaces	

Problem Solving ▶ Spatial Sense

5. **Write About It** Look at the grid. Write your own directions. Tell how to get from 🏠 to 🔺.

Go right 2 and up 2.

212 two hundred twelve

At Home Give your child directions to find places or items in your home.

Go on →

Daily Test Prep

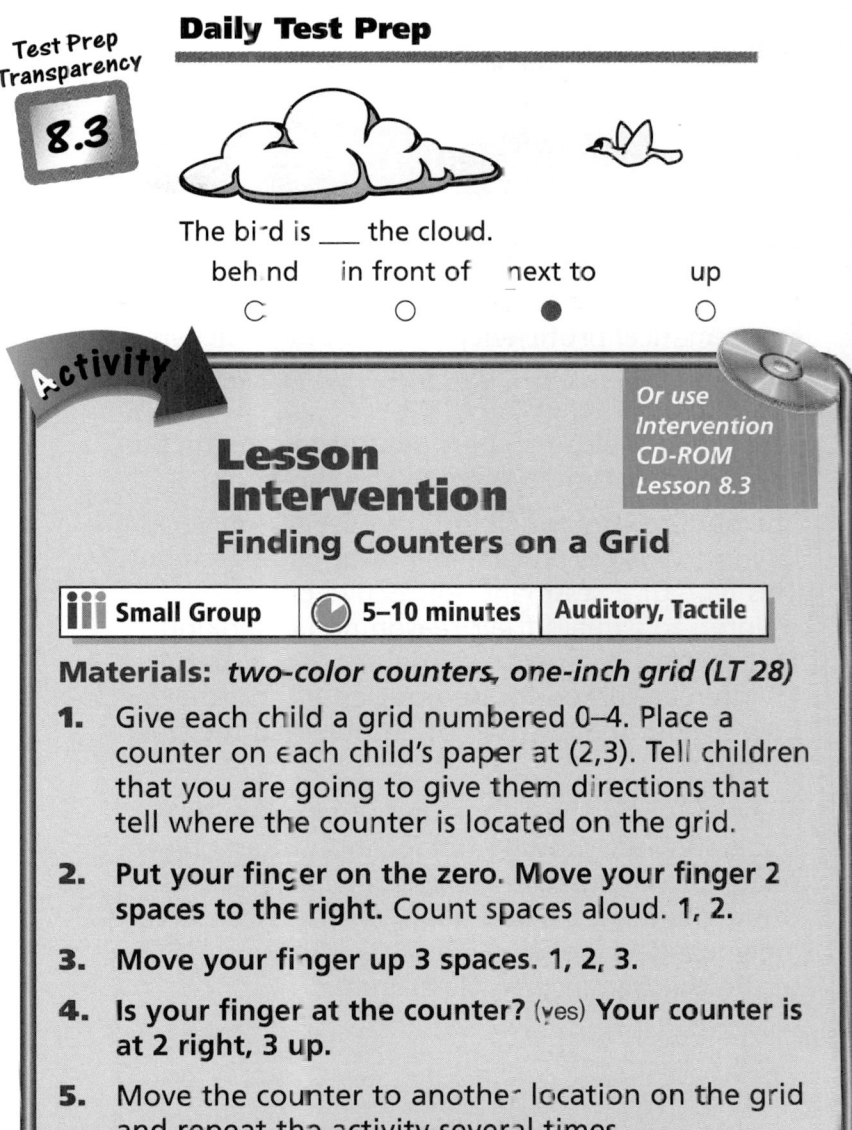

The bird is ___ the cloud.

behind   in front of   next to   up
○   ○   ●   ○

Activity

Lesson Intervention
Finding Counters on a Grid

Or use Intervention CD-ROM Lesson 8.3

👥 Small Group	🕐 5–10 minutes	Auditory, Tactile

Materials: *two-color counters, one-inch grid (LT 28)*

1. Give each child a grid numbered 0–4. Place a counter on each child's paper at (2,3). Tell children that you are going to give them directions that tell where the counter is located on the grid.

2. **Put your finger on the zero. Move your finger 2 spaces to the right. Count spaces aloud. 1, 2.**

3. **Move your finger up 3 spaces. 1, 2, 3.**

4. **Is your finger at the counter?** (yes) **Your counter is at 2 right, 3 up.**

5. **Move the counter to another location on the grid and repeat the activity several times.**

---

3 Practice

Independent Practice

Children complete **Exercises 1–4** independently.

Problem Solving

After children complete **Exercise 5**, call on volunteers to share their responses. Use the **Write About It** in Exercise 5 to discuss how to get from the house to the tree.

Common Error

Counting the Wrong Number of Spaces
Children may lose track of the number of spaces they move. Have children count aloud as they move their fingers on the grid.

4 Assess and Close

Where do you begin counting spaces on a grid? (at zero)

If you had a grid that was 4 spaces across and 3 spaces up, could you follow these directions: Go right 4 spaces and up 4 spaces? (no) **Why not?** (because there are not enough spaces to go up 4 spaces)

Keeping a Journal

Draw a grid in your journal. Draw 1 house on the grid. Write directions that tell how to get to the house.

Lesson continues →

What Is Good Assessment?

Good assessment supports the development of mathematical proficiency by providing teachers with valuable information and children with opportunities to learn. When used appropriately, **assessment helps teachers adapt their instruction to support better learning in the classroom.**

The opportunity for children to use lesson vocabulary in context is an example of good assessment. This type of assessment is effective because it allows children to explain their reasoning or thinking. This chapter deals with spatial sense and patterns. Children are asked to use position words to explain how to find the location of an object in the classroom.

They are given the opportunity to explain their thinking when judging the location of an object relative to themselves. Teachers who can **assess these explanations and adapt their lessons accordingly** are developing the mathematical proficiency of the children in their classrooms.

Name_____

Writing Math: Create and Solve

Draw items in the picture to show these words. Label the picture with the words.
Answers may vary. Sample answer is shown.

| in front |
| over |
| under |

1.

over

under

in front

2. **Write About It** Tell where to draw a ☁ in your picture. Use a position word in your sentence.

  Possible answer: Draw a cloud above the tree.

_____

Writing Math: Create and Solve

Guide children through the activity.

Discuss the picture for **Exercise 1** and be sure children understand the position words listed. Have volunteers name the objects in the scene.

Then tell children to trace the dashed outline of the ball and point to the word under. Tell children the ball is under the table.

If children have difficulty beginning **Exercise 1**, prompt their thinking with questions. For example: **What is something that could be in front of the tree?** After children draw and label their items, have them write a sentence for **Exercise 2**. Remind them to use position words in their sentences. Children who will have difficulty writing a response can tell a classmate where to draw a cloud.

Quick Check

Follow the directions.
Draw the object.

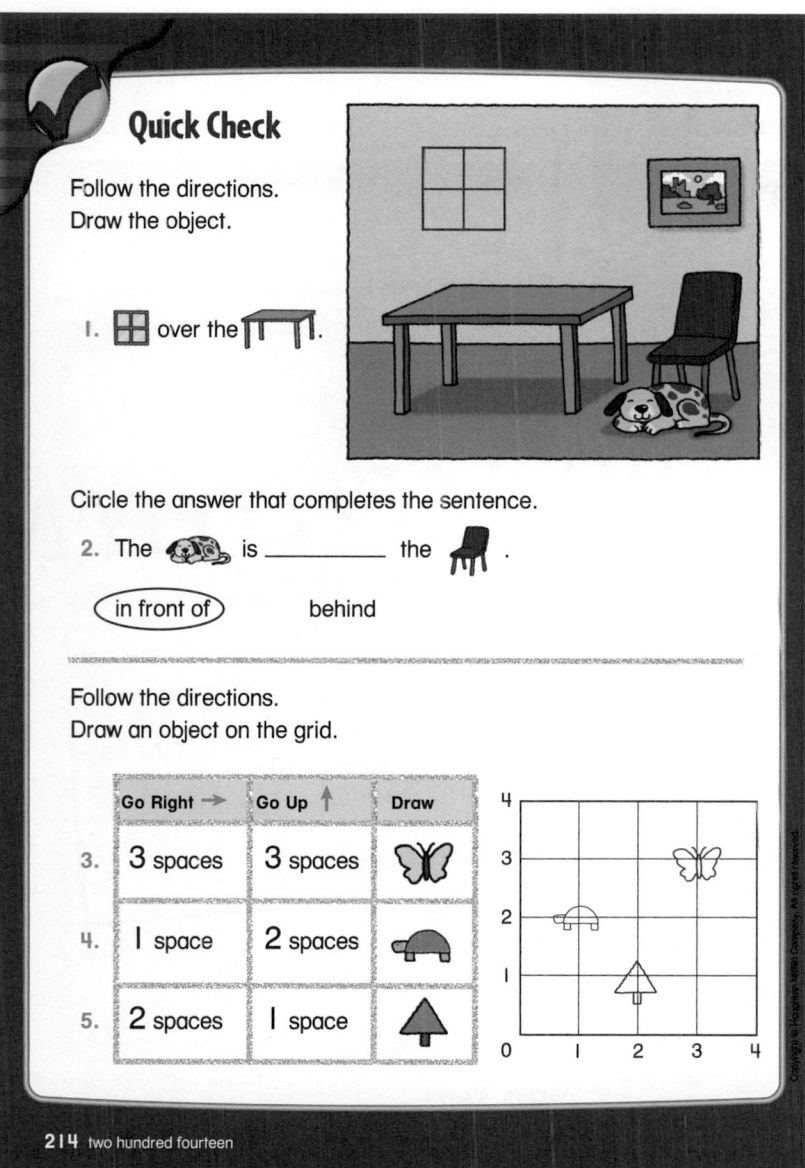

1. over the .

Circle the answer that completes the sentence.

2. The is ________ the .

(in front of) behind

Follow the directions.
Draw an object on the grid.

	Go Right →	Go Up ↑	Draw
3.	3 spaces	3 spaces	butterfly
4.	1 space	2 spaces	turtle
5.	2 spaces	1 space	tree

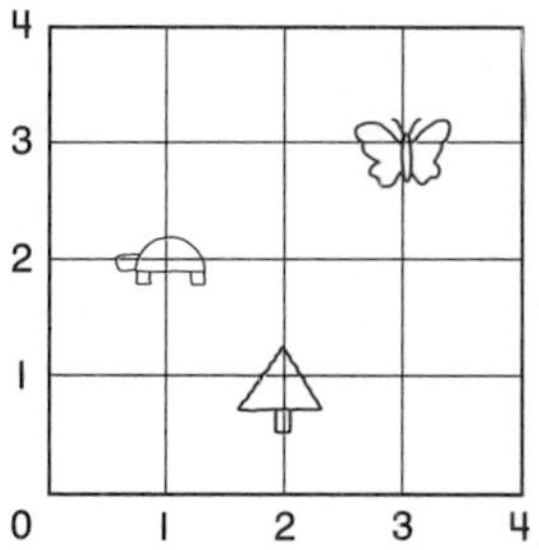

Quick Check

Have children complete the Quick Check exercises independently to assess their understanding of concepts and skills taught in **Lessons 1–3**.

Item	Lesson	Error Analysis	Intervention
1	8.1	Children may confuse over and under.	Reteach Resource 8.1 ***Ways to Success*** 8.1
2	8.2	Children may confuse in front and behind.	Reteach Resource 8.2 ***Ways to Success*** 8.2
3–5	8.3	Children may lose track of the number of spaces they move right and up.	Reteach Resource 8.3 ***Ways to Success*** 8.3

Hands-On: Slides, Flips, and Turns

PLANNING THE LESSON

MATHEMATICS OBJECTIVE
Identify slides, flips, and turns of figures.

Use Lesson Planner CD-ROM for Lesson 8.4.

Daily Routines

Calendar

Have a volunteer locate the 10th of the month. Ask children to think of all the number combinations that have a sum of 10.

Sunday	Monday	Tuesday	Wednesday	Thursday	Friday	Saturday
				1	2	3	4
5	6	7	8	9	10	11
12	13	14	15	16	17	18
19	20	21	22	23	24	25
26	27	28	29	30	31	

Vocabulary

Demonstrate the meaning of the terms **flip, slide,** and **turn** by having children move their closed math books as you direct.

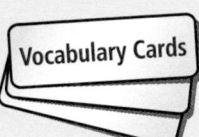
Vocabulary Cards

Meeting North Carolina's Standards

3.04 Solve problems involving spatial visualization.
Also 3.01

Lesson Transparency **8.4**

Problem of the Day

Alexa made these tally marks as she sold balloons at the fair. Martin sold 6 balloons. He said he sold more balloons than Alexa. Was he right? (no)

balloons I sold
‖‖‖ ‖‖

Quick Review

How many sides?

□ (4)   △ (3)   ○ (0)

Lesson Quiz

Does this show a flip or a turn? (flip)

LEVELED PRACTICE

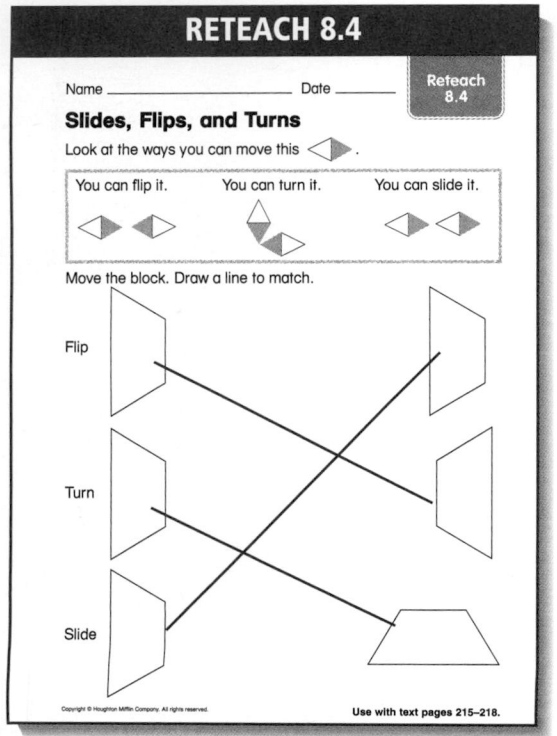

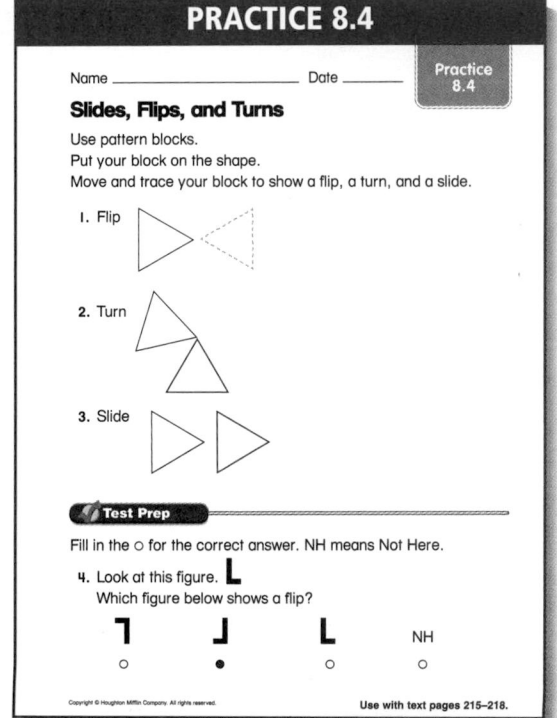

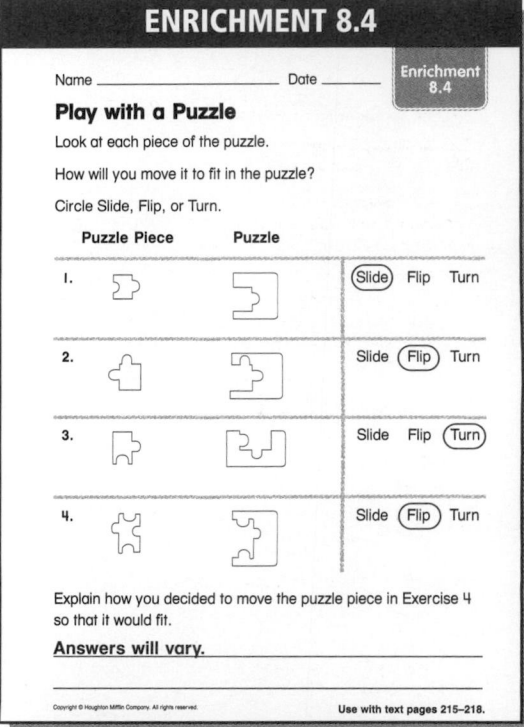

Practice Workbook Page 52

Reaching All Learners

Differentiated Instruction

English Learners

In order to move pattern blocks, children will need to understand the terms *slide*, *flip*, and *turn*. Use Worksheet 8.4 to develop children's ability to move pattern blocks in different ways.

Special Needs

VISUAL, TACTILE

Put the book on the table. Have the child slide it to the right as you say the word slide. Repeat the activity for flips and turns. Move on to shapes that clearly look different after each movement.

Early Finishers

VISUAL, TACTILE

Materials: *puzzle pieces*

Provide children with old, simple puzzle pieces. Have them trace the piece. Then have them flip the piece, turn it, and slide it, tracing the puzzle piece each time.

TECHNOLOGY

Spiral Review

To reinforce skills on lessons taught earlier, create **customized** spiral review worksheets using the *Ways to Assess* CD-ROM.

Geometry Software

Use Sunburst's **Shape Up!** or another shapes program to explore this lesson more fully.

Social Studies Connection

Show children pictures of signs they would see around their neighborhood, such as a stop sign and a school zone sign. Make a cut out of each shape. Have children match the shape to the sign, then flip, turn, and slide the shapes.

MATH CENTER

Vocabulary Activity

This vocabulary-building activity helps children understand and remember new words. Encourage children to use the words in math discussion.

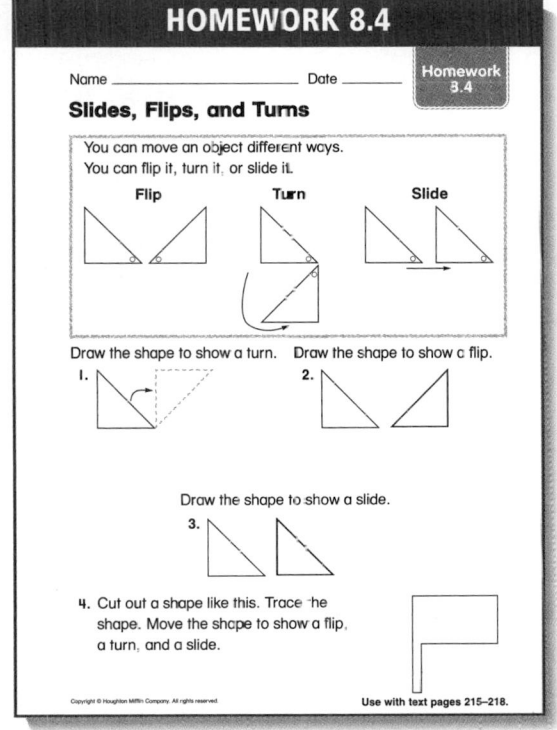

Homework Workbook Page 52

TEACHING LESSON 8.4

LESSON ORGANIZER

Objective Identify slides, flips, and turns of figures.

Resources Reteach, Practice, Enrichment, Problem Solving, Homework, English Learners, Transparencies, Math Center

Materials Pattern blocks

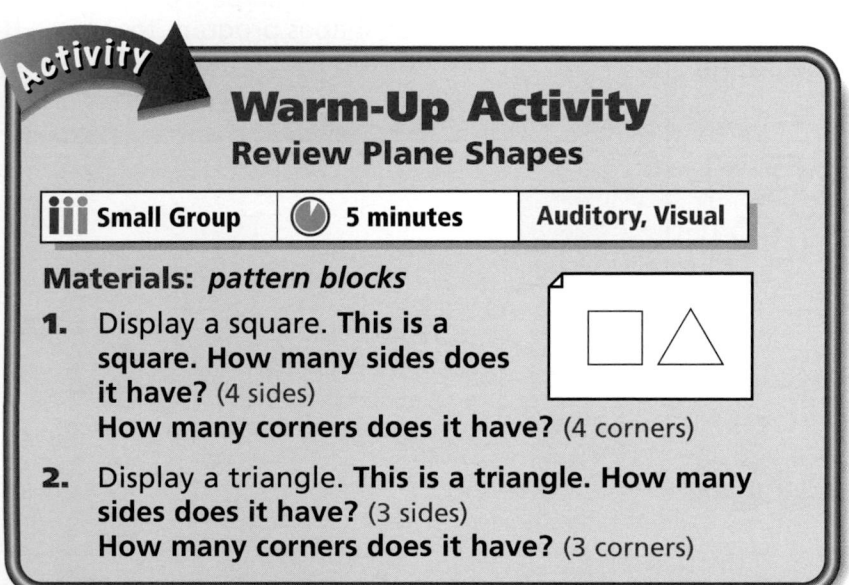

Activity

Warm-Up Activity
Review Plane Shapes

iiii Small Group	**⏱** 5 minutes	Auditory, Visual

Materials: *pattern blocks*

1. Display a square. **This is a square. How many sides does it have?** (4 sides) **How many corners does it have?** (4 corners)

2. Display a triangle. **This is a triangle. How many sides does it have?** (3 sides) **How many corners does it have?** (3 corners)

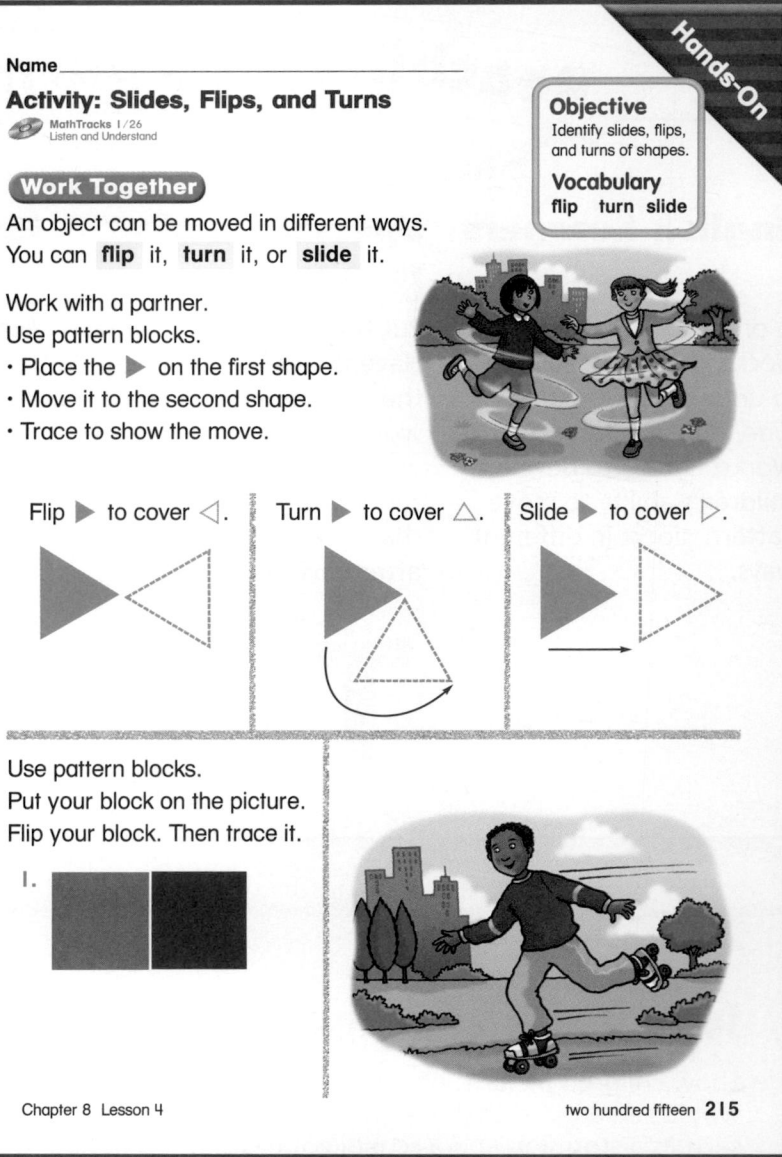

Name_____

Activity: Slides, Flips, and Turns

MathTracks 1/26
Listen and Understand

Objective
Identify slides, flips, and turns of shapes.

Vocabulary
flip turn slide

Work Together

An object can be moved in different ways. You can **flip** it, **turn** it, or **slide** it.

Work with a partner.
Use pattern blocks.
• Place the ▶ on the first shape.
• Move it to the second shape.
• Trace to show the move.

Flip ▶ to cover ◁.   Turn ▶ to cover △.   Slide ▶ to cover ▷.

Use pattern blocks.
Put your block on the picture.
Flip your block. Then trace it.

1.

Chapter 8 Lesson 4   two hundred fifteen **215**

---

1 Introduce
Model Flips, Turns, and Slides

iiii Whole Group	**⏱** 10–15 minutes	Visual, Auditory

Materials: *pattern blocks*

1. Display a blue parallelogram pattern block. Model how to trace it. **I am going to flip the block. Watch how I pick it up, flip it, and put it down.** Flip the pattern block and trace it in the new position. **After I flip it, the shape is the same, but it is like a mirror image.**

2. **This is how I turn the block. I turn it like a handle.** Turn the pattern block and trace it in the new position. **After I turn it, it is still the same shape, but it is in a different position.** Point out how the points and sides of the triangle have changed position again.

3. **This is how I slide the triangle. I don't pick it up, I just slide it over.** Slide the pattern block and trace it in the new position. **After I slide it, it looks the same, but it is in a different place.**

2 Develop

Work Together

Introduce the objective and vocabulary to the children. As they work with partners, help children flip, turn, and slide their triangle pattern blocks into the positions indicated on the page. After children complete **Exercise 1**, call on volunteers to share their response.

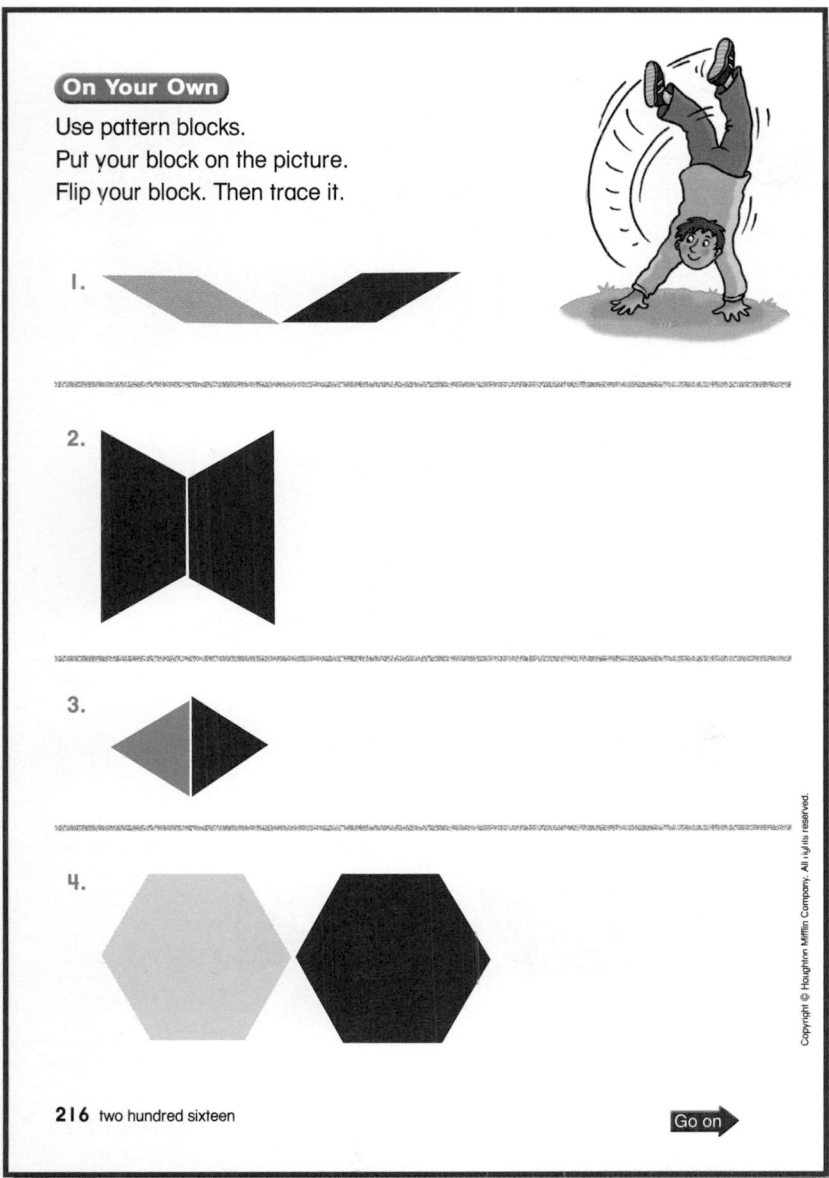

On Your Own

Use pattern blocks.
Put your block on the picture.
Flip your block. Then trace it.

1.

2.

3.

4.

Go on ▶

Literature Connection

Have children look through the book *Where's That Bone?* by Lucille Recht Penner to find pictures of the bone. Using the bone in the book as a model, have each child draw a large bone on construction paper. Then have them cut out the bones. Tell children to trace their bones on paper and then flip, turn, and slide the bones, tracing them each time.

❸ Practice

On Your Own

Have children work together to flip pattern blocks to complete **Exercises 1–4** on page 216.

Lesson continues ▶

Technology Connection
Use Technology to Create Patterns

In this activity, students preview the content of the next lesson by using Shape Up! to create patterns.

Have students work in Shape Up! 2D World to create the patterns described below.

1. A pattern involving one shape and 2 colors.

2. A pattern involving 3 shapes and 3 colors.

3. A pattern involving turns with 1 shape. Tell students to use the **z-Axis Rotation** button.

4. A pattern involving different sizes of 1 shape. Tell students to use the **Enlarge** and **Reduce** buttons.

5. Have students create their own patterns. Have them click **Text** and describe their pattern.

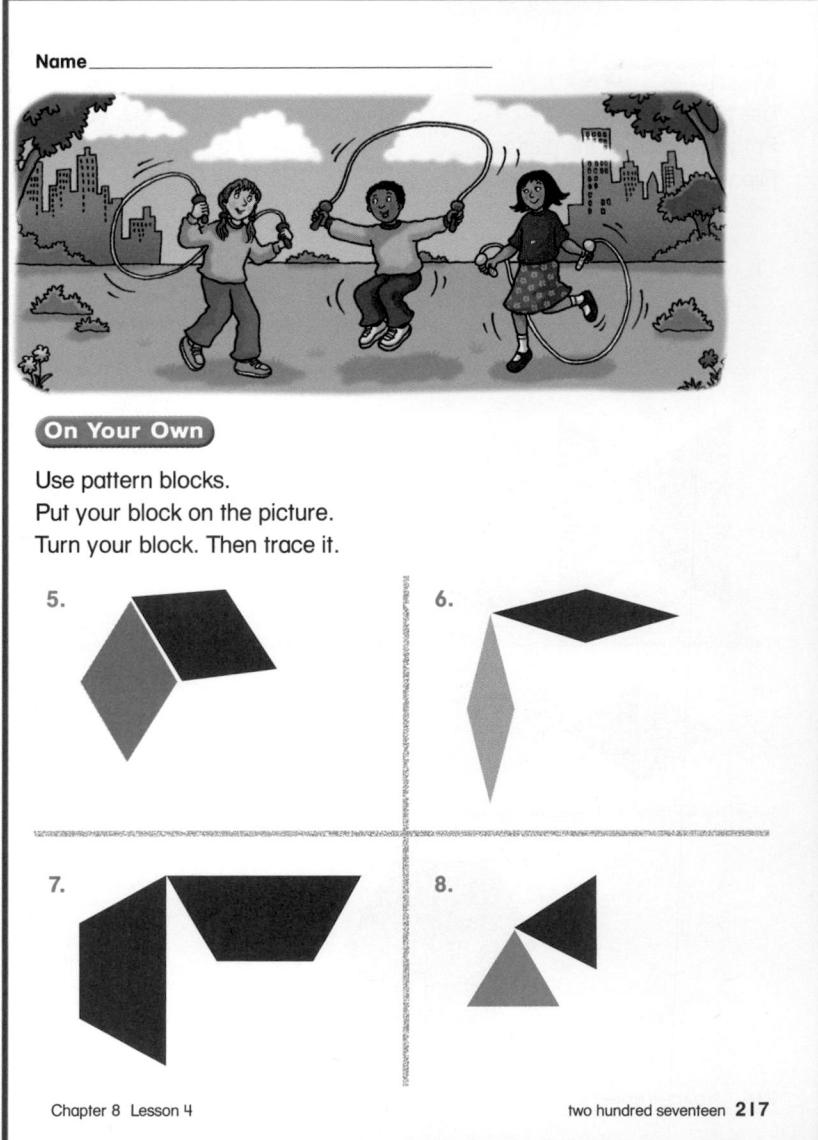

Name_____

On Your Own

Use pattern blocks.
Put your block on the picture.
Turn your block. Then trace it.

5.

6.

7.

8.

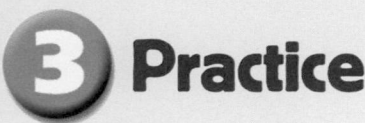 **Practice**

On Your Own

Have children work together to complete **Exercises 5–8** on page 217. Children may turn blocks in either a clockwise or counter clockwise direction. On page 218, children continue to work together to slide blocks for **Exercises 9–11**. After children complete **Exercise 12**, call on volunteers to share their ideas about the two moves that resulted in the picture. Explain to children that there may be more than one correct answer: Note that it is acceptable if a child states a flip as a turn ($\frac{1}{2}$ turn).

Common Error

Confusing Flips and Turns
Children may confuse the actions of flipping and turning objects. To help them remember the difference, brainstorm things that turn, but do not flip, such as a doorknob and a steering wheel.

Use pattern blocks.
Put your block on the picture.
Slide your block. Then trace it.

9.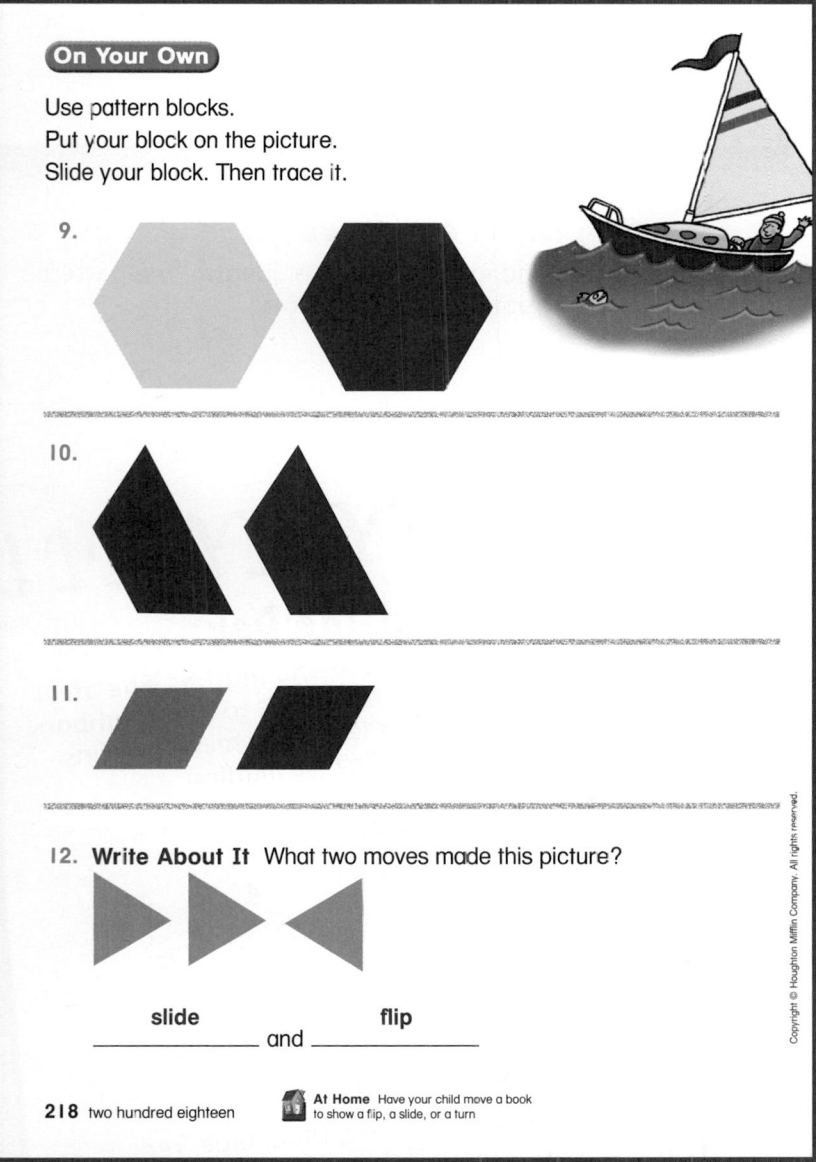

10.

11.

12. **Write About It** What two moves made this picture?

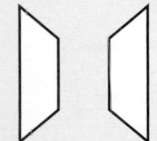

_____ and _____
　　slide　　　　　flip

Daily Test Prep

Which fact has the same **difference** as $9 - 3 = 6$?

$7 - 3 = 4$　　$8 - 2 = 6$　　$6 + 3 = 9$　　$3 + 3 = 6$

○　　　　　●　　　　　○　　　　　○

Activity

Lesson Intervention

Model Turning an Object

CD-ROM Lesson 8.4

| 👥 Small Group | 🕐 5–10 minutes | Visual, Tactile |

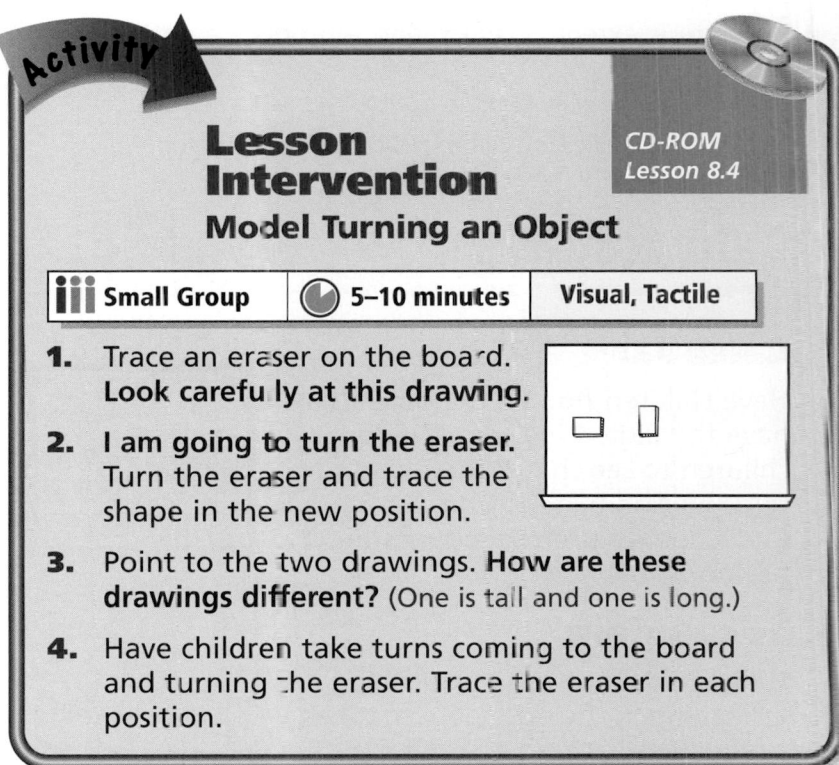

1. Trace an eraser on the board. **Look carefully at this drawing.**

2. **I am going to turn the eraser.** Turn the eraser and trace the shape in the new position.

3. Point to the two drawings. **How are these drawings different?** (One is tall and one is long.)

4. Have children take turns coming to the board and turning the eraser. Trace the eraser in each position.

---

4 Assess and Close

Does this show a flip or a turn? (a flip)

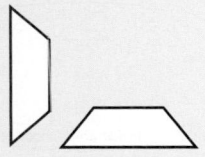

Does this show a turn or a slide? (a turn)

Keeping a Journal

Look around the room. Write the names of things you could flip. Draw to show how to flip a shape.

Hands-On: Patterns

PLANNING THE LESSON

Meeting North Carolina's Standards

5.03 Create and extend patterns, identify the pattern unit, and translate into other forms.

MATHEMATICS OBJECTIVE

Describe, extend, predict, and reproduce a pattern.

Use Lesson Planner CD-ROM for Lesson 8.5

Daily Routines

Calendar

Have children find all the dates that have the digit 4 in them. Guide children to see that 4, 14, 24, is skipcounting by tens from 4. Challenge children to extend the pattern: 34, 44, 54, . . .

Sunday	Monday	Tuesday	Wednesday	Thursday	Friday	Saturday
			1	2	3	4
5	6	7	8	9	10	11
12	13	14	15	16	17	18
19	20	21	22	23	24	25
26	27	28	29	30	31	

Vocabulary

Show children an item of clothing or something in the classroom that has a repeating pattern. Identify the elements in the pattern and tell children that the repeating design is a **pattern**.

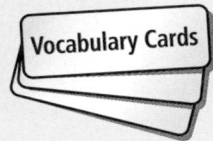

Vocabulary Cards

Lesson Transparency 8.5

Problem of the Day

Ms. Green baked banana muffins. She ate 1 muffin and gave 4 muffins to her neighbor. She has 5 muffins left. How many muffins did Ms. Green make? (10 muffins)

Quick Review

$$\begin{array}{cc} 7 \\ -\ 5 \\ \hline (2) \end{array} \qquad \begin{array}{cc} 8 \\ -\ 3 \\ \hline (5) \end{array} \qquad \begin{array}{cc} 5 \\ +\ 5 \\ \hline (10) \end{array} \qquad \begin{array}{cc} 4 \\ +\ 3 \\ \hline (7) \end{array} \qquad \begin{array}{cc} 4 \\ -\ 2 \\ \hline (2) \end{array}$$

Lesson Quiz

What comes next in the pattern?

1. 2, 1, 2, 1, 2, 1, __(2)__

2. red, blue, blue, red, blue, blue, red, blue, blue, red, blue, __(blue)__

3. snap, slap, stamp, snap, slap, stamp, snap, slap, stamp, __(snap)__

LEVELED PRACTICE

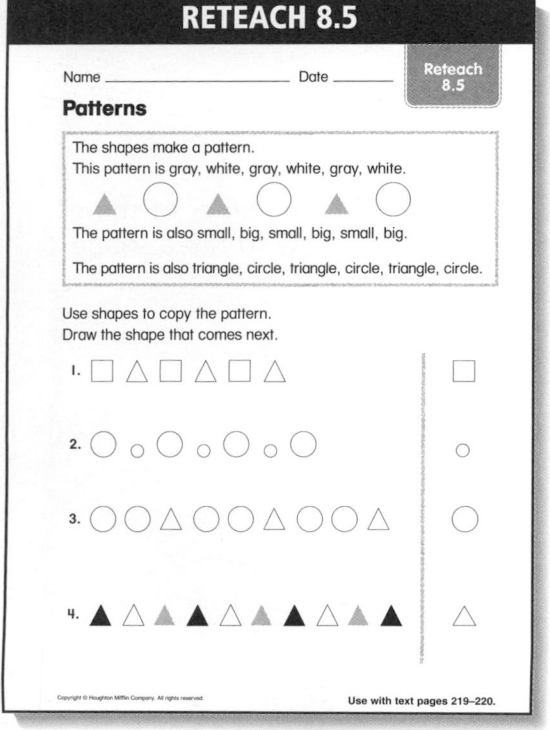

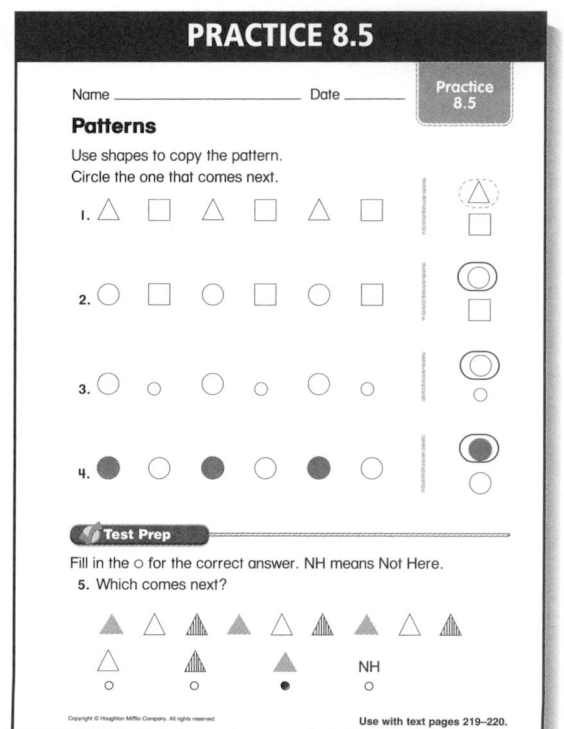

Reaching All Learners
Differentiated Instruction

English Learners

Children will need to understand the concept *alike/different* in order to understand patterns. Worksheet 8.5 will help children to understand how sets of shapes are *alike* and *different*.

Inclusion
TACTILE, VISUAL

Materials: *red and blue crayons*

Create a pattern by alternating the red and blue crayons. Have the child say each color as you point to it. Identify this as a red and blue pattern.

Draw a row of circles. Have the child color the circles to show the pattern.

Have the child explain the pattern.

Early Finishers
TACTILE, VISUAL

Materials: *cubes or counters*

• Have children work with partners. Write number patterns on strips of paper, such as 1, 2, or 2, 1 and give patterns to each pair.

• Have children use cubes or counters to model and extend each pattern.

TECHNOLOGY

Spiral Review

Help students remember skills they learned earlier by creating **customized** spiral review worksheets using the *Ways to Assess* CD-ROM.

Lesson Planner

You can customize your teaching plan or meet your curriculum requirements with the **Lesson Planner CD-ROM.**

Education Place

You can visit **Education Place** at **eduplace.com/math/mw/** for teacher support materials.

Literature Connection

Refer to the shapes described in the unit literature, *Four Shapes* by Katherine Mead. Have children find shapes. Then choose a shape to create a "shape rubbing" design by placing paper over a shape and rubbing a crayon over it.

MATH CENTER

Cross-Curricular Activity

As you use this activity to relate the mathematics of this lesson to another curriculum area, children will see how math can help them with other subjects.

PROBLEM SOLVING 8.5

Name _____ Date _____ Problem Solving 8.5

Patterns
Circle the shape that comes next.

Randy is making a belt. His pattern is ○○□○○□○○□. What shape comes next?
Draw or write to explain. ○ □ △

1. Suzie is making a necklace. Her pattern is ◇○□◇○□◇○□. What shape comes next?
Draw or write to explain. ○ □ ◎

2. Enrique is making a quilt. His pattern is □○□◇□○□◇. What shape comes next?
○ ⊡ ◇

3. Kara is making a scarf. Her pattern is △○○△○○△○○. What shape comes next?
○ □ △

Copyright © Houghton Mifflin Company. All rights reserved.   Use with text pages 219–220.

HOMEWORK 8.5

Name _____ Date _____ Homework 8.5

Hands-On Lesson: Patterns

You can make a pattern with shapes.
□ ○ □ ○ □ ○
This is a square, circle, square, circle, square, circle pattern.
Circle the shape that comes next.
□ ○

Draw the shape that comes next.

1. ♡ ♦ ♡ ♦ ♡ ♦ ♡   ♦
2. ▮ ▼ ▮ ▼ ▮ ▼ ▮   ▼
3. ▲ ▲ ▲ ▲ ▲ ▲ ▲   ▲
4. ▮ ● ▮ ● ▮ ● ▮   ▮

5. Draw a pattern for beads using 2 shapes.

Copyright © Houghton Mifflin Company. All rights reserved.   Use with text pages 219–220.

ENGLISH LEARNERS 8.5

Name _____ Date _____ English Learners 8.5

Patterns

| Alike | Different |

Draw a circle around the things that are alike.
Draw a line under things that are different.

1. △ △
2. ○ □
3. △ ○
4. □ □
5. ○ □
6. □ □

To the Teacher: Use the examples at the top of the page to help children understand the terms alike and different. Then have children follow the directions to tell if the shapes are alike or different.

Copyright © Houghton Mifflin Company. All rights reserved.   Use with text pages 219–220.

TEACHING LESSON 8.5

LESSON ORGANIZER

Objective Describe, extend, predict, and reproduce a pattern.

Resources Reteach, Practice, Enrichment, Problem Solving, Homework, English Learners, Transparencies, Math Center

Materials Overhead pattern blocks, blank transparency, attribute blocks (LT 26 and 27)

Activity

Warm-Up Activity
Modeling Patterns

| 👤👤👤👤 Whole Group | 🕐 5 minutes | Kinesthetic, Visual |

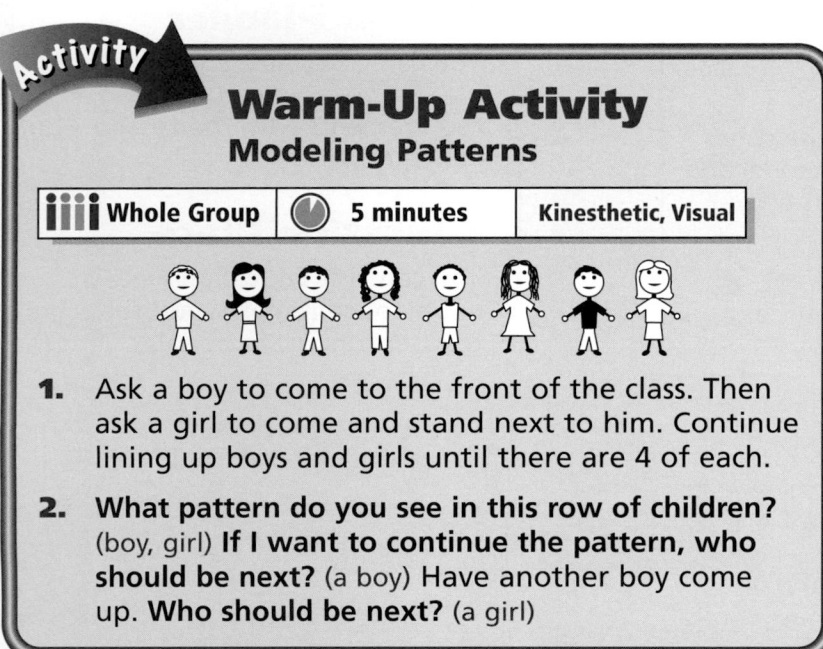

1. Ask a boy to come to the front of the class. Then ask a girl to come and stand next to him. Continue lining up boys and girls until there are 4 of each.

2. **What pattern do you see in this row of children?** (boy, girl) **If I want to continue the pattern, who should be next?** (a boy) Have another boy come up. **Who should be next?** (a girl)

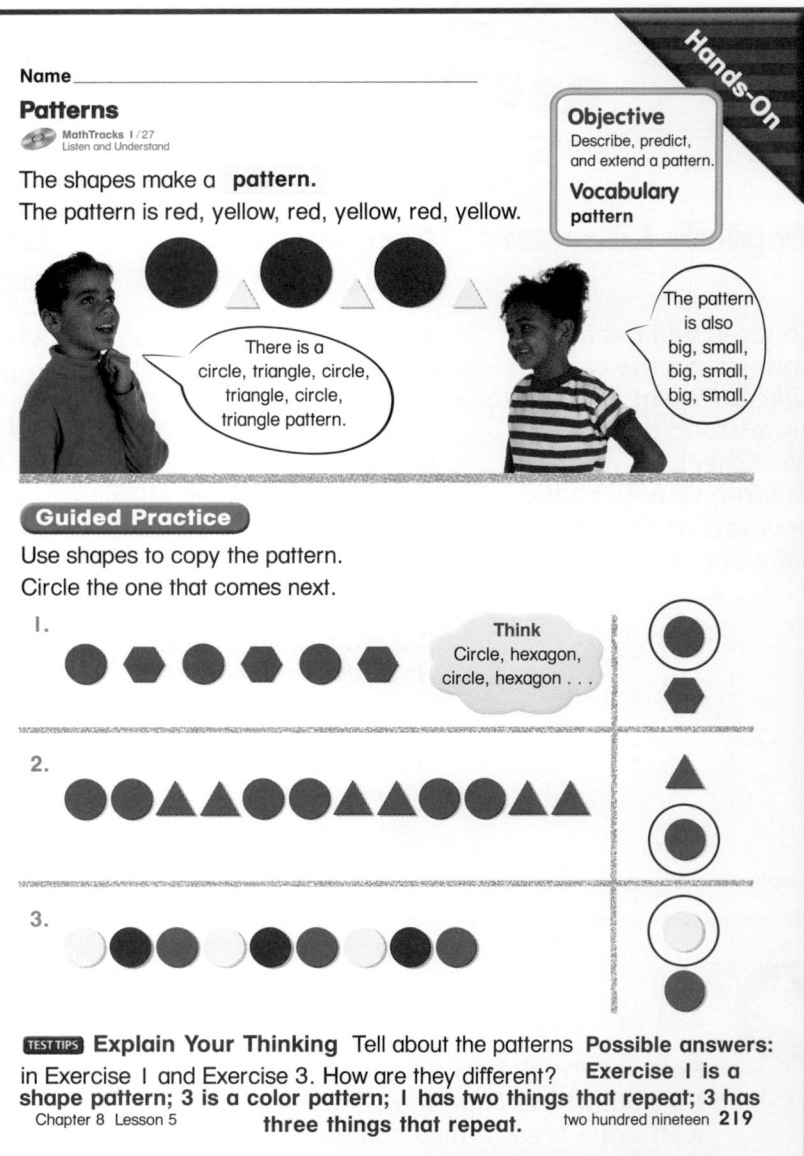

Name_____

Patterns

MathTracks 1 / 27
Listen and Understand

The shapes make a **pattern.**
The pattern is red, yellow, red, yellow, red, yellow.

Objective
Describe, predict, and extend a pattern.

Vocabulary
pattern

There is a circle, triangle, circle, triangle, circle, triangle pattern.

The pattern is also big, small, big, small, big, small.

Guided Practice

Use shapes to copy the pattern.
Circle the one that comes next.

1.

Think
Circle, hexagon, circle, hexagon . . .

2.

3.

TEST TIPS **Explain Your Thinking** Tell about the patterns in Exercise 1 and Exercise 3. How are they different? **Possible answers: Exercise 1 is a shape pattern; 3 is a color pattern; 1 has two things that repeat; 3 has three things that repeat.**

Chapter 8 Lesson 5   two hundred nineteen **219**

---

1 Introduce
Discuss Extending Patterns

| 👤👤👤👤 Whole Group | 🕐 10–15 minutes | Visual, Auditory |

Materials: *overhead pattern blocks, blank transparency*

1. Place pattern blocks on the overhead: triangle, triangle, square, triangle, triangle, square, triangle, triangle, square. Have children say the shape pattern. (triangle, triangle, square, triangle, triangle, square, triangle, triangle, square) **There is also a color pattern. What is it?** (green, green, orange)

2. Tell children that you want to continue the pattern. **What shape should I place next?** (triangle) **What is the part that repeats?** (triangle, triangle, square)

3. Continue with other shape and color patterns. **How can you tell what a pattern is?** (Look at the shapes or colors and find the part that repeats.)

2 Develop

Guided Learning

Teaching Example Introduce the objective and vocabulary to the children. Guide them through the example by having groups of children copy the pattern with shapes. Discuss the different ways to describe a pattern.

Guided Practice

Prepare Attribute Blocks LT26 and LT27 for each child. Have children use the cut out blocks to complete **Exercises 1–3** as you observe. Point out that the patterns on pages 219 and 220 only have one attribute. Give children the opportunity to answer the Explain Your Thinking question. Then discuss their responses with the class.

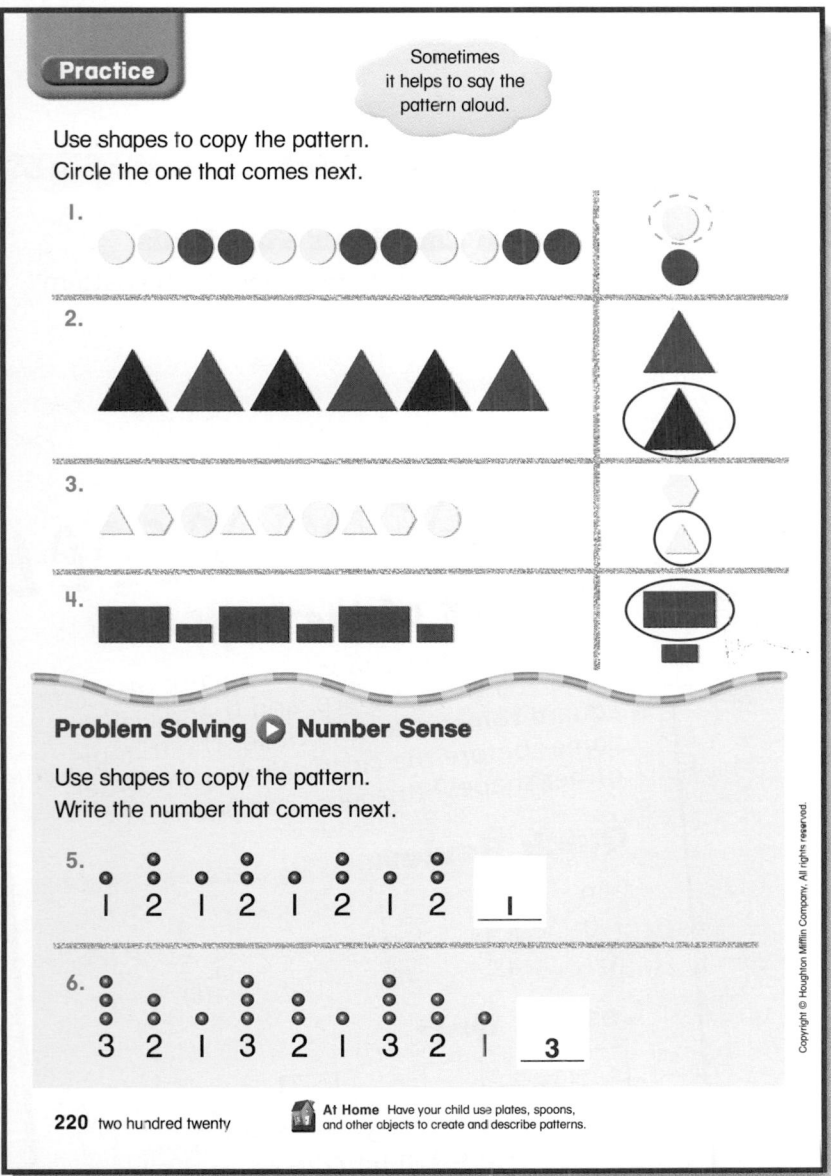

Practice

Sometimes it helps to say the pattern aloud.

Use shapes to copy the pattern.
Circle the one that comes next.

1.

2.

3.

4.

Problem Solving ▶ Number Sense

Use shapes to copy the pattern.
Write the number that comes next.

5.

1 2 1 2 1 2 1 2 **1**

6.

3 2 1 3 2 1 3 2 1 **3**

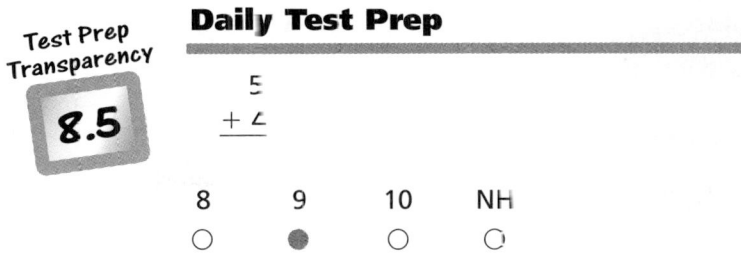

220 two hundred twenty

At Home Have your child use plates, spoons, and other objects to create and describe patterns.

Daily Test Prep

$$\begin{array}{r} 5 \\ +\ 4 \\ \hline \end{array}$$

8	9	10	NH
○	●	○	○

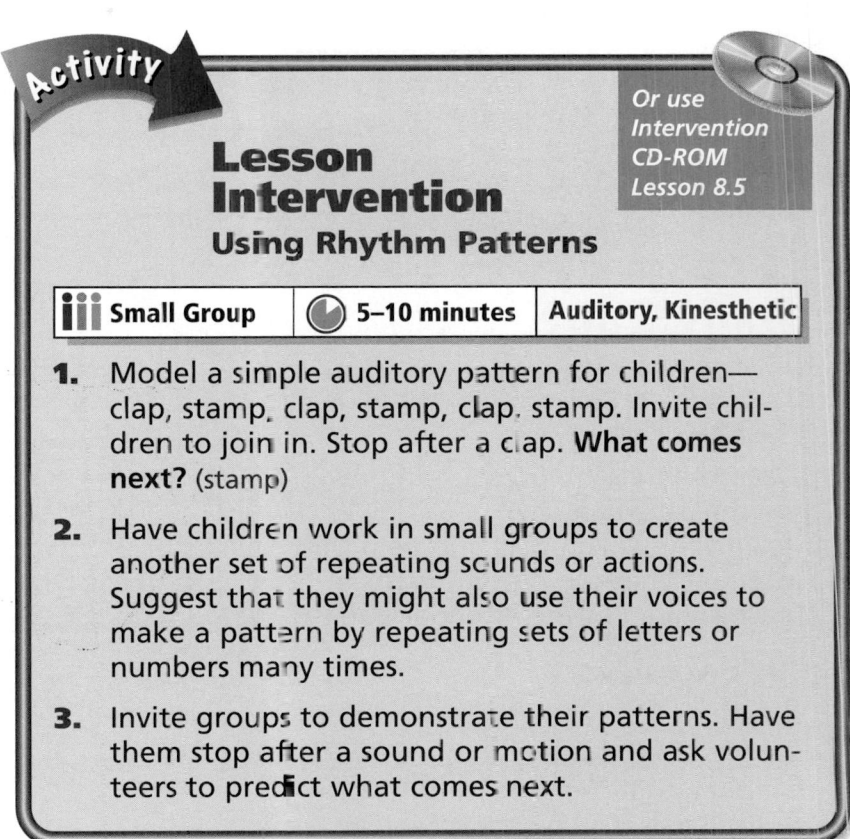

Activity

Or use Intervention CD-ROM Lesson 8.5

Lesson Intervention
Using Rhythm Patterns

| 👥 Small Group | ⏱ 5–10 minutes | Auditory, Kinesthetic |

1. Model a simple auditory pattern for children— clap, stamp, clap, stamp, clap, stamp. Invite children to join in. Stop after a clap. **What comes next?** (stamp)

2. Have children work in small groups to create another set of repeating sounds or actions. Suggest that they might also use their voices to make a pattern by repeating sets of letters or numbers many times.

3. Invite groups to demonstrate their patterns. Have them stop after a sound or motion and ask volunteers to predict what comes next.

3 Practice

Independent Practice

Have children use cut out Attribute Blocks LT26 and LT27 to complete **Exercises 1–4** independently. They can use a variety of materials to model the patterns, such as buttons, cubes, pattern blocks, or attribute blocks.

Problem Solving

After children complete **Exercises 5 and 6**, call on volunteers to share their solutions.

Common Error

Circling the Wrong Picture

Children may circle the wrong picture. Suggest that they draw the picture they choose at the end of the row to see if it continues the pattern before circling it.

4 Assess and Close

What is the pattern? (triangle, triangle, circle)

Tell what comes next in this pattern. (yellow)

✏ Keeping a Journal

Look for a pattern in your classroom or at home. Draw a picture of the pattern.

Hands-On: Create Patterns

Lesson 8.6

PLANNING THE LESSON

MATHEMATICS OBJECTIVE
Identify and create patterns.

Use Lesson Planner CD-ROM for Lesson 8.6

Daily Routines

Calendar
Lead children in skip-counting by 2s on the calendar. Then count by 7s from various numbers and help children see that the pattern exists in each column of the calendar page.

Vocabulary
Draw a pattern on the board, such as A B C A B C A B C. Remind children that the repeating letters form a **pattern**. Ask volunteers to predict what comes next.

Vocabulary Cards

Lesson Transparency 8.6

Problem of the Day
Emma has three shapes on a piece of paper—a circle, square, and triangle. The square comes after the circle. The triangle comes before the circle. What is the order of her shapes? (triangle, circle, square)

Quick Review

$$\begin{array}{ccccc} 9 & 1 & 4 & 3 & 3 \\ +0 & +1 & +4 & +2 & +5 \\ \hline (9) & (2) & (8) & (5) & (8) \end{array}$$

Lesson Quiz

What is the pattern unit? (large square, small square, small square)

What comes next? (large square)

LEVELED PRACTICE

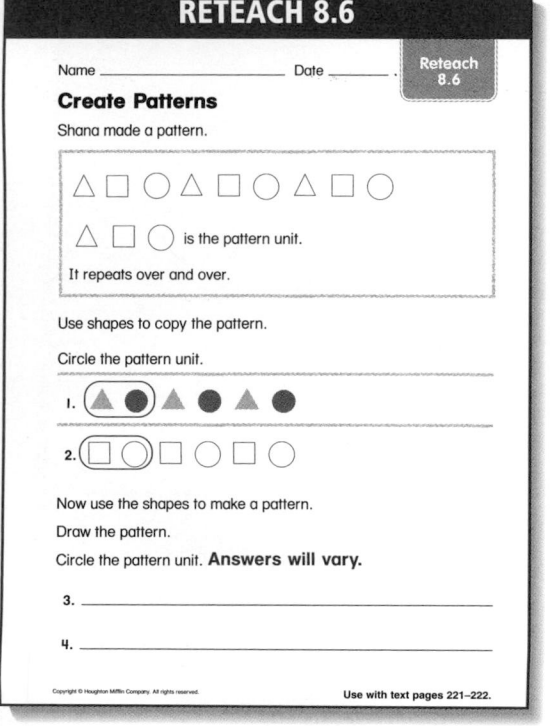

RETEACH 8.6

Name _____ Date _____ **Reteach 8.6**

Create Patterns

Shana made a pattern.

△ □ ○ △ □ ○ △ □ ○

△ □ ○ is the pattern unit.

It repeats over and over.

Use shapes to copy the pattern.

Circle the pattern unit.

1. ▲ ● ▲ ● ▲ ●

2. □ ○ □ ○ □ ○

Now use the shapes to make a pattern.
Draw the pattern.
Circle the pattern unit. **Answers will vary.**

3. _____

4. _____

Copyright © Houghton Mifflin Company. All rights reserved.   Use with text pages 221–222.

PRACTICE 8.6

Name _____ Date _____ **Practice 8.6**

Create Patterns

Use the shapes to draw a pattern.
Answers will vary.

1. △ ○ □

2. △ □ ○

3. ▯ □ △

Test Prep

Fill in the ○ for the correct answer. NH means Not Here.

4. Which might come next?

D D D D D D D D

○ D   ○ D   ○ D   ● NH

Copyright © Houghton Mifflin Company. All rights reserved.   Use with text pages 221–222.

ENRICHMENT 8.6

Name _____ Date _____ **Enrichment 8.6**

Create Your Own Fun Patterns

You can make your own ～～ with beads.
Use some of the beads to make a pattern unit.
Draw the bracelet.
Color the bracelet if you wish.
Answers will vary.

1. You have: 6 ⊙ and 6 □.	Pattern
	Bracelet
2. You have: 1 □, 4 ⊙, and 4 △.	Pattern
	Bracelet
3. You have 4 □, 4 △, and 4 ⊙	Pattern
	Bracelet

Write About It Compare two of your patterns. How are they the same? How are they different?

Answers will vary.

_____

Copyright © Houghton Mifflin Company. All rights reserved.   Use with text pages 221–222.

Practice Workbook Page 54

Reaching All Learners

Differentiated Instruction

English Learners

In order to identify and create patterns, children will need to understand the word *repeat*. Use Worksheet 8.6 to help English-language learners understand how this word relates to patterns.

Special Needs
TACTILE, VISUAL

Materials: *sponges, paint*

Cut sponges into circle and square shapes. Help the child create a pattern with sponges dipped into paint. First, guide the child to make a pattern of different shapes in one color. As the child shows understanding of patterns, expand the activity by adding another color of paint. Model saying the pattern.

Early Finishers
TACTILE, VISUAL

Materials: *index cards*

- Draw pattern units on index cards. Have children choose a card, use shapes to copy the pattern, and then extend it.

- Have children explain their patterns and check each other's work.

TECHNOLOGY

Spiral Review

You can prepare students for standardized tests with **customized** spiral review on key skills using the *Ways to Assess CD-ROM.*

eBook

An electronic version of this lesson can be found in **eMathBook.**

Games

Students can practice their math vocabulary using the Math Lingo game, available on the *Ways to Success* CD.

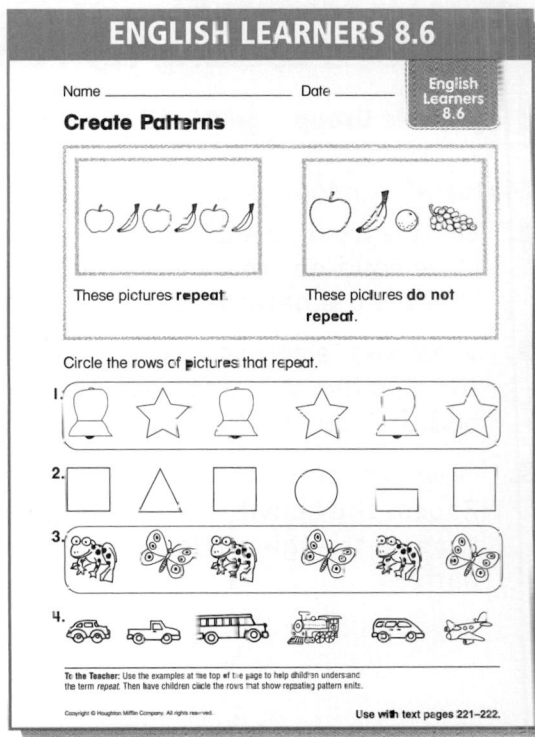

Art Connection

Make pattern necklaces. Model making a repeating pattern necklace. Then invite children to try a few patterns and decide on one they like. They can thread beads, colored macaroni, and colored paper shapes on yarn.

MATH CENTER

Basic Skills Activity

Motivate children to build basic skills. Use this activity to address multiple learning styles using hands-on activities related to the skills of this lesson.

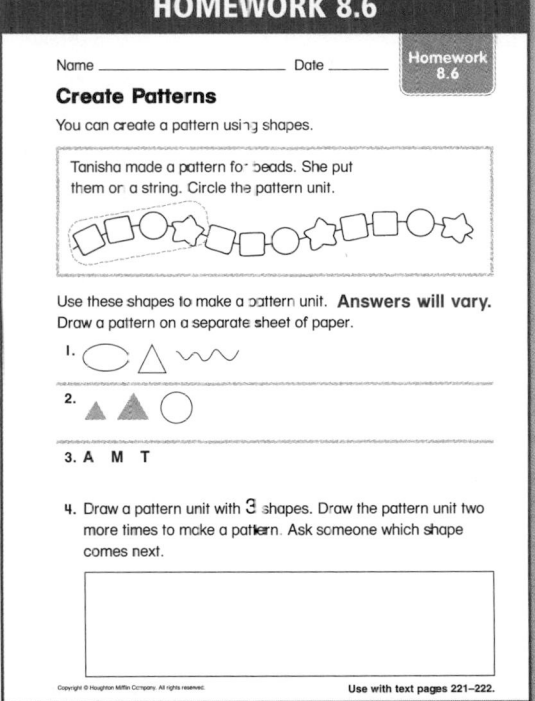

Homework Workbook Page 54

TEACHING LESSON 8.6

LESSON ORGANIZER

Objective Identify and create patterns.

Resources Reteach, Practice, Enrichment, Problem Solving, Homework, English Learners, Transparencies, Math Center

Materials Attribute blocks (LT 26 and 27), cubes

Activity

Warm-Up Activity
Modeling Identifying Patterns

| 👥 Whole Group | ⏱ 5 minutes | Auditory, Kinesthetic |

1. Review patterns by having children identify rhythmic patterns. Create a one-two pattern of beats with your hand on a desk or other surface. **What is the pattern?** (1 beat, 2 beats)

2. Then create a one-two-two pattern with claps. **What is the pattern?** (1 clap, 2 claps, 2 claps) Ask volunteers to clap or beat a pattern and have others identify it.

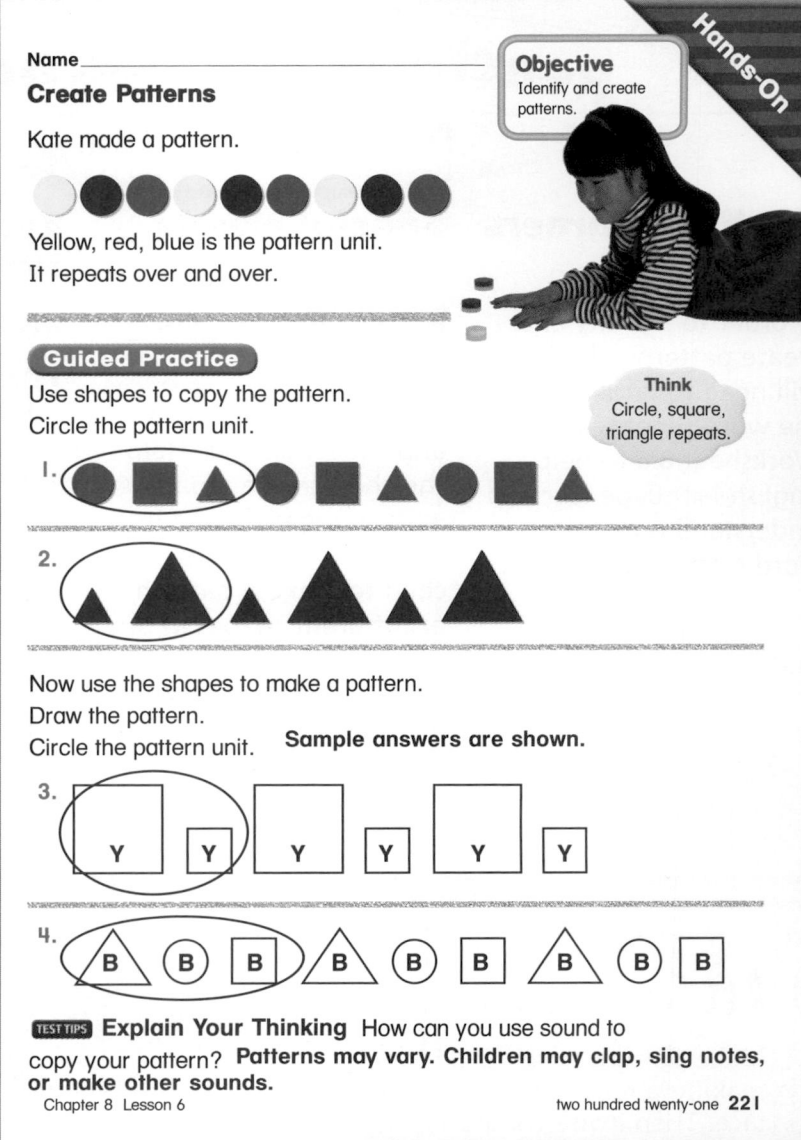

Name _____

Create Patterns

Objective
Identify and create patterns.

Kate made a pattern.

Yellow, red, blue is the pattern unit.
It repeats over and over.

Guided Practice

Use shapes to copy the pattern.
Circle the pattern unit.

Think
Circle, square, triangle repeats.

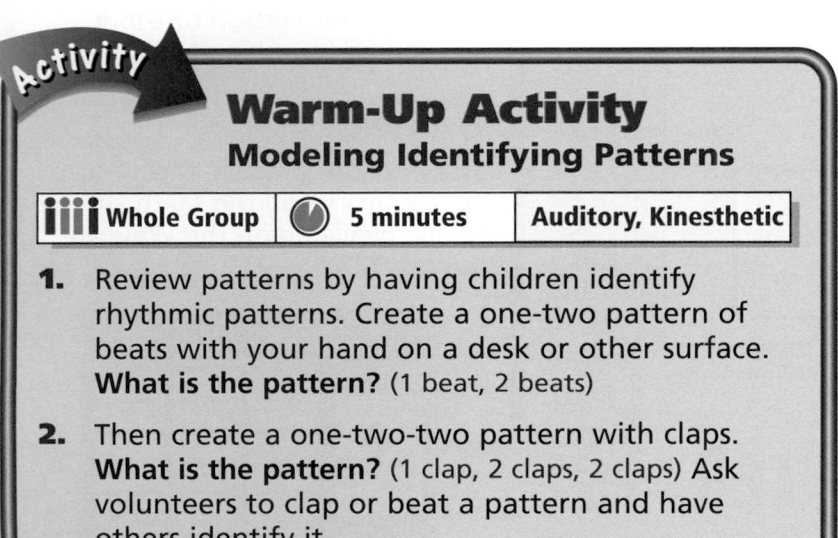

Now use the shapes to make a pattern.
Draw the pattern.
Circle the pattern unit.   **Sample answers are shown.**

3.

4.

TEST TIPS **Explain Your Thinking** How can you use sound to copy your pattern? **Patterns may vary. Children may clap, sing notes, or make other sounds.**

Chapter 8 Lesson 6   two hundred twenty-one **221**

1 Introduce   Activity

Discuss Looking for Patterns

| 👥 Whole Group | ⏱ 10–15 minutes | Visual, Auditory |

Materials: *attribute blocks (LT 26 and 27)*

1. Draw a triangle-square-circle pattern on the board. Have children create the pattern with attribute blocks. **What is the pattern?** (triangle, square, circle)

2. **What shape comes next?** (triangle) Have children add the triangle. **What comes next?** (square) Have children add the square. **What comes next?** (circle)

3. Draw a triangle-triangle-circle pattern on the board. Repeat the activity above. Suggest that children say triangle-triangle-circle aloud to help identify the pattern.

2 Develop

Guided Learning

Teaching Example Introduce the objective to the children. Guide them through the example by having them copy the pattern and then identify the pattern unit.

Guided Practice

Prepare Attribute Blocks LT 26 and LT 27 for each child. Have children use the cut out blocks to complete **Exercises 1–2** as you observe them copy the pattern and circle the pattern unit. For **Exercises 3–4,** some children may need more room to draw or trace their patterns, so provide drawing paper. Give children the opportunity to answer the Explain Your Thinking question. Then discuss their responses with the class. For example, children might clap their hands and touch their knees for an AB pattern.

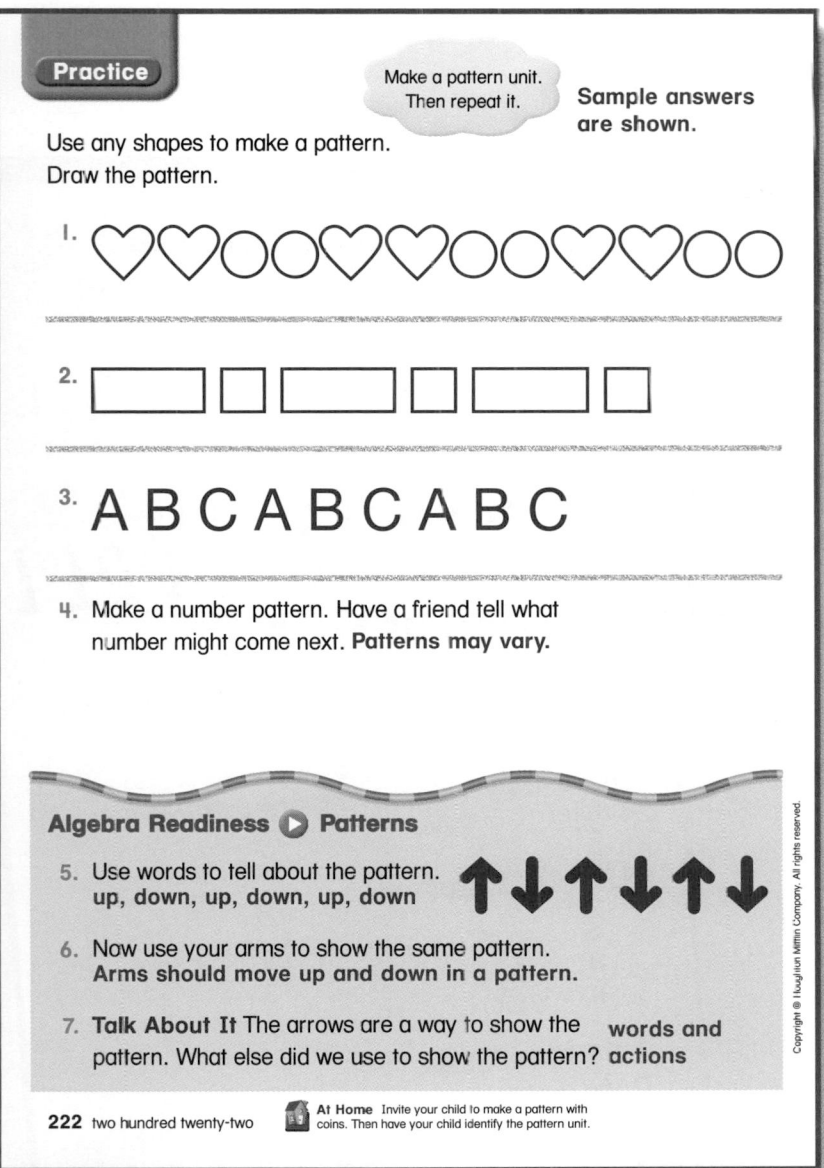

Practice

Make a pattern unit. Then repeat it.

Sample answers are shown.

Use any shapes to make a pattern. Draw the pattern.

1. ♡♡○○♡♡○○♡♡○

2. ▭ ▭ ▭ ▭ ▭ ▭

3. **A B C A B C A B C**

4. Make a number pattern. Have a friend tell what number might come next. **Patterns may vary.**

Algebra Readiness ▶ Patterns

5. Use words to tell about the pattern.
   up, down, up, down, up, down   ↑↓↑↓↑↓

6. Now use your arms to show the same pattern. Arms should move up and down in a pattern.

7. **Talk About It** The arrows are a way to show the pattern. What else did we use to show the pattern? **words and actions**

222 two hundred twenty-two

At Home Invite your child to make a pattern with coins. Then have your child identify the pattern unit.

Test Prep Transparency

8.6

Daily Test Prep

$3 + 2 = \square + 3$

3   5   2   NH
○   ○   ●   ○

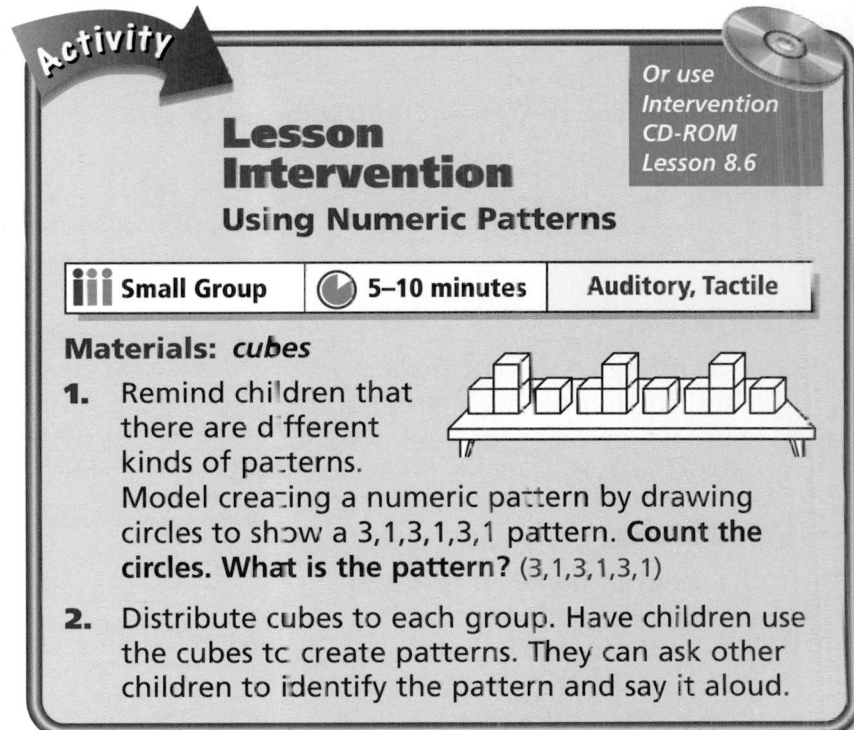

Activity

Lesson Intervention
Using Numeric Patterns

Or use Intervention CD-ROM Lesson 8.6

👥 Small Group	🕐 5–10 minutes	Auditory, Tactile

Materials: *cubes*

1. Remind children that there are different kinds of patterns. Model creating a numeric pattern by drawing circles to show a 3,1,3,1,3,1 pattern. **Count the circles. What is the pattern?** (3,1,3,1,3,1)

2. Distribute cubes to each group. Have children use the cubes to create patterns. They can ask other children to identify the pattern and say it aloud.

---

③ Practice

Independent Practice

Children complete **Exercises 1–4** independently. Children can use a variety of materials when modeling patterns, such as buttons, cubes, blocks, long and short pasta, magnetic letters, and so on. Allow children to use drawing paper if necessary.

Problem Solving

After children complete **Exercise 5–6**, call on volunteers to share their responses. Use the **Talk About It** in Exercise 7 to discuss ways to show a pattern.

Common Error

Failing to Recognize a Pattern

Children may fail to recognize that a pattern has a unit of repeating elements. Have them choose two or three shapes, make a pattern unit, say the names of the shapes, and repeat the pattern.

---

④ Assess and Close

What is the pattern unit?   ◇◇○◇◇○◇◇○
(diamond, diamond, circle)

Make up a pattern using 2 numbers. (Patterns may vary.)

 ### Keeping a Journal

Create a pattern. Use shapes, colors, or numbers. Tell what the pattern unit is.

Hands-On: Symmetry

Lesson 8.7

PLANNING THE LESSON

Meeting North Carolina's Standards
3.04 Solve problems involving spatial visualization.

MATHEMATICS OBJECTIVE
Identify lines of symmetry and make symmetrical figures.

 *Use Lesson Planner CD-ROM for Lesson 8.7.*

Daily Routines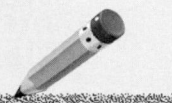

Calendar
Look at today's date. Discuss if the numeral is symmetrical. Ask children to check other dates for lines of symmetry. (Possible dates: 3, 8, 11)

Sunday	Monday	Tuesday	Wednesday	Thursday	Friday	Saturday
			1	2	3	4
5	6	7	8	9	10	11
12	13	14	15	16	17	18
19	20	21	22	23	24	25
26	27	28	29	30	31	

Vocabulary
Fold a sheet of paper in half and open it up. Tell children that if a shape can be folded in half to make two parts that match, it has **symmetry**. Tell them that the fold line is the **line of symmetry**.

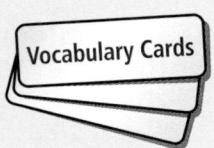 Vocabulary Cards

Lesson Transparency 8.7

Problem of the Day
Jenny plants a flower garden of tulips and pansies. She plants this pattern.

What flower does she plant to continue the pattern? (a tulip)

Quick Review

$$\begin{array}{ccccc} 8 & 10 & 7 & 5 & 9 \\ -4 & -0 & -6 & -2 & -4 \\ \hline (4) & (10) & (1) & (3) & (5) \end{array}$$

Lesson Quiz
Does the shape have a line of symmetry?

 (yes)

LEVELED PRACTICE

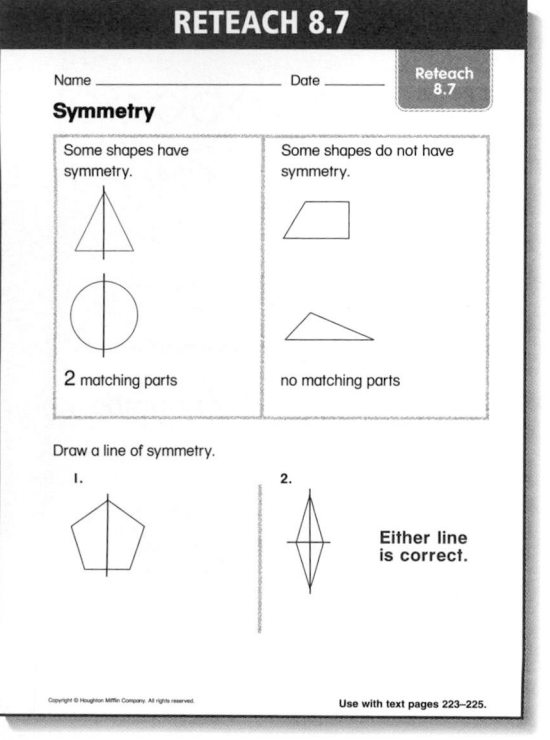

RETEACH 8.7

Name _____ Date _____ **Reteach 8.7**

Symmetry

Some shapes have symmetry.

Some shapes do not have symmetry.

2 matching parts

no matching parts

Draw a line of symmetry.

1.

2. Either line is correct.

Use with text pages 223–225.

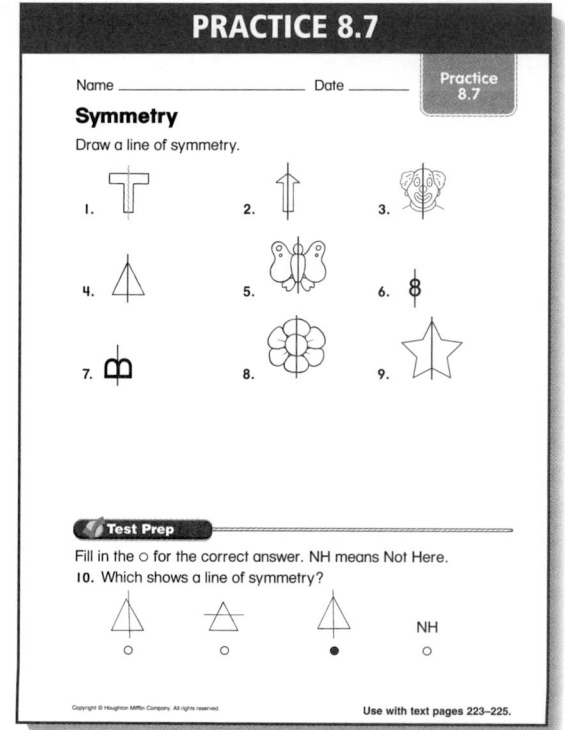

PRACTICE 8.7

Name _____ Date _____ **Practice 8.7**

Symmetry
Draw a line of symmetry.

1.   2.   3.

4.   5.   6.

7.   8.   9.

Test Prep
Fill in the ○ for the correct answer. NH means Not Here.
10. Which shows a line of symmetry?

○   ○   ●   ○ NH

Use with text pages 223–225.

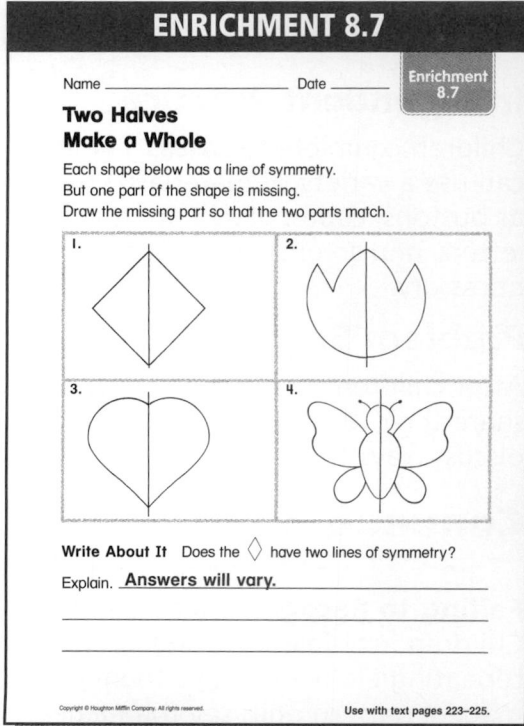

ENRICHMENT 8.7

Name _____ Date _____ **Enrichment 8.7**

Two Halves Make a Whole

Each shape below has a line of symmetry. But one part of the shape is missing. Draw the missing part so that the two parts match.

1.   2.

3.   4.

Write About It Does the ◇ have two lines of symmetry?
Explain. **Answers will vary.**

Use with text pages 223–225.

Practice Workbook Page 55

Reaching All Learners

Differentiated Instruction

English Learners

Children will need to understand the term *matching* in order to understand symmetry. Use Worksheet 8.7 to develop children's understanding of this term.

Special Needs
TACTILE, VISUAL

Materials: *plane shapes (LT 22 and 23)*

Choose one shape and fold it in half. Have the child open the shape and tell if the two parts look the same. Repeat the activity with the other shapes. Reinforce that since both parts match the shape has symmetry.

Gifted and Talented
TACTILE, VISUAL

Materials: *plastic mirror, pattern blocks (LT 25)*

Model placing a mirror along one side of a block so it is reflected in the mirror. Explain that where the two images meet is a line of symmetry. Have partners explore ways to make symmetrical images with the mirror.

TECHNOLOGY

Spiral Review

Create **customized** spiral review worksheets for individual students using the *Ways to Assess* CD-ROM.

Lesson Planner

Use the **Lesson Planner CD-ROM** to see how lesson objectives for this chapter are correlated to standards.

Education Place

Recommend that parents visit **Education Place** at eduplace.com/parents/mw/ for parent support activities.

ScienceConnection

Explain that many items in nature have lines of symmetry. Discuss examples, such as butterflies, leaves, snowflakes, and pieces of fruit. Provide illustrations and invite children to find the line of symmetry.

MATH CENTER

Cross-Curricular Activity

As you use this activity to relate the mathematics of this lesson to another curriculum area, children will see how math can help them with other subjects.

PROBLEM SOLVING 8.7

Name _____ Date _____
Problem Solving 8.7

Symmetry

Circle the shape that has symmetry.

Duke is looking for a shape with symmetry to use for an art project. Which shape should he choose? | Draw or write to explain.

1. Nikki wants to find a shape with symmetry for a necklace. Which shape should she choose? | Draw or write to explain.

2. Irving needs a shape with symmetry for a belt he's making. Which shape should he choose?

3. Mel would like a shape with symmetry for his costume. Which shape should he choose?

Use with text pages 223–225.

HOMEWORK 8.7

Name _____ Date _____
Homework 8.7

Symmetry

Some shapes have symmetry. They have 2 matching parts.

Some shapes do not have symmetry. They have no matching parts.

Draw a line of symmetry. Remember, the 2 parts must match.

1.   2.

3.   4.

5. The shape has 4 lines of symmetry. Draw all 4 lines of symmetry. | Draw here.

Use with text pages 223–225.

ENGLISH LEARNERS 8.7

Name _____ Date _____
English Learners 8.7

Symmetry

These are **matching** shoes. They **go together**. | These are **not matching** shoes. They **do not go together**.

Circle the objects that match.

1.   2.

3.   4.

To the Teacher: Use the sentences and pictures at the top of the page to help children understand the term *matching*. Then have children circle the matching parts.

Use with text pages 223–226.

Homework Workbook Page 55

TEACHING LESSON 8.7

LESSON ORGANIZER

Objective Identify lines of symmetry and make symmetrical figures.

Resources Reteach, Practice, Enrichment, Problem Solving, Homework, English Learners, Transparencies, Math Center

Materials Plane shapes (LT 22 and 23), construction paper, scissors, paint

Activity
Warm-Up Activity
Identifying Shapes

| 👥 Small Group | 🕐 5 minutes | Visual, Tactile |

Materials: *cut-out plane shapes (LT 22 and 23)*

1. Display a variety of paper shapes and have children identify each shape by name.

2. Call on volunteers to sort the shapes. Have children put all the squares together, all the circles, and so on.

3. Then have children sort the shapes by size. Encourage children to suggest and sort by other attributes.

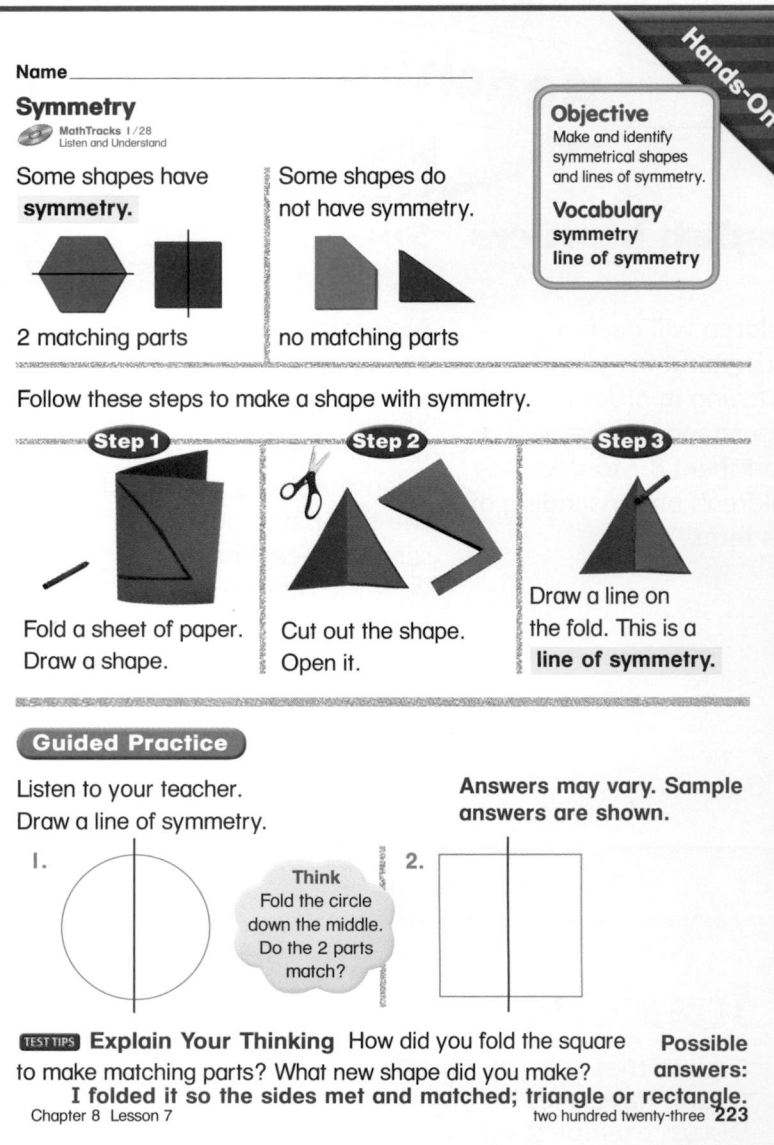

Name_____

Symmetry

MathTracks 1/28
Listen and Understand

Some shapes have **symmetry.**   Some shapes do not have symmetry.

2 matching parts   no matching parts

Objective
Make and identify symmetrical shapes and lines of symmetry.

Vocabulary
symmetry
line of symmetry

Follow these steps to make a shape with symmetry.

Step 1 Fold a sheet of paper. Draw a shape.

Step 2 Cut out the shape. Open it.

Step 3 Draw a line on the fold. This is a **line of symmetry.**

Guided Practice

Listen to your teacher. Draw a line of symmetry.

Answers may vary. Sample answers are shown.

1.

Think Fold the circle down the middle. Do the 2 parts match?

2.

TEST TIPS **Explain Your Thinking** How did you fold the square to make matching parts? What new shape did you make?   **Possible answers:** I folded it so the sides met and matched; triangle or rectangle.

Chapter 8 Lesson 7   two hundred twenty-three **223**

---

1 Introduce
Discuss Symmetry

| 👥 Whole Group | 🕐 10–15 minutes | Visual, Tactile |

Materials: *construction paper, scissors*

1. Introduce the word symmetry. Fold a sheet of paper and discuss how the fold divides the paper into 2 matching parts. Point out that the matching parts are the same size and shape.

2. Ask children to fold a piece of construction paper in half and then cut out a shape around the fold. Remind them not to cut the fold.

3. **Who has a shape with symmetry? How do you know?** Have volunteers share their symmetrical shapes with the class. Have them fold their shapes closed again to show that the two parts are the same size and shape.

2 Develop

Guided Learning

Teaching Example Introduce the objective and vocabulary to the children. Discuss the example to show how to recognize and identify shapes with symmetry. Then guide children through the steps of the activity. Be sure that children draw the triangle on the fold and do not cut the fold.

Guided Practice

Prepare large circle and square from LT 22 and LT 23 for each child. Have children fold the shapes to make two matching parts. Direct them to use the shapes to complete **Exercises 1–2** as you observe. Give children the opportunity to answer the Explain Your Thinking question. Then discuss their responses with the class.

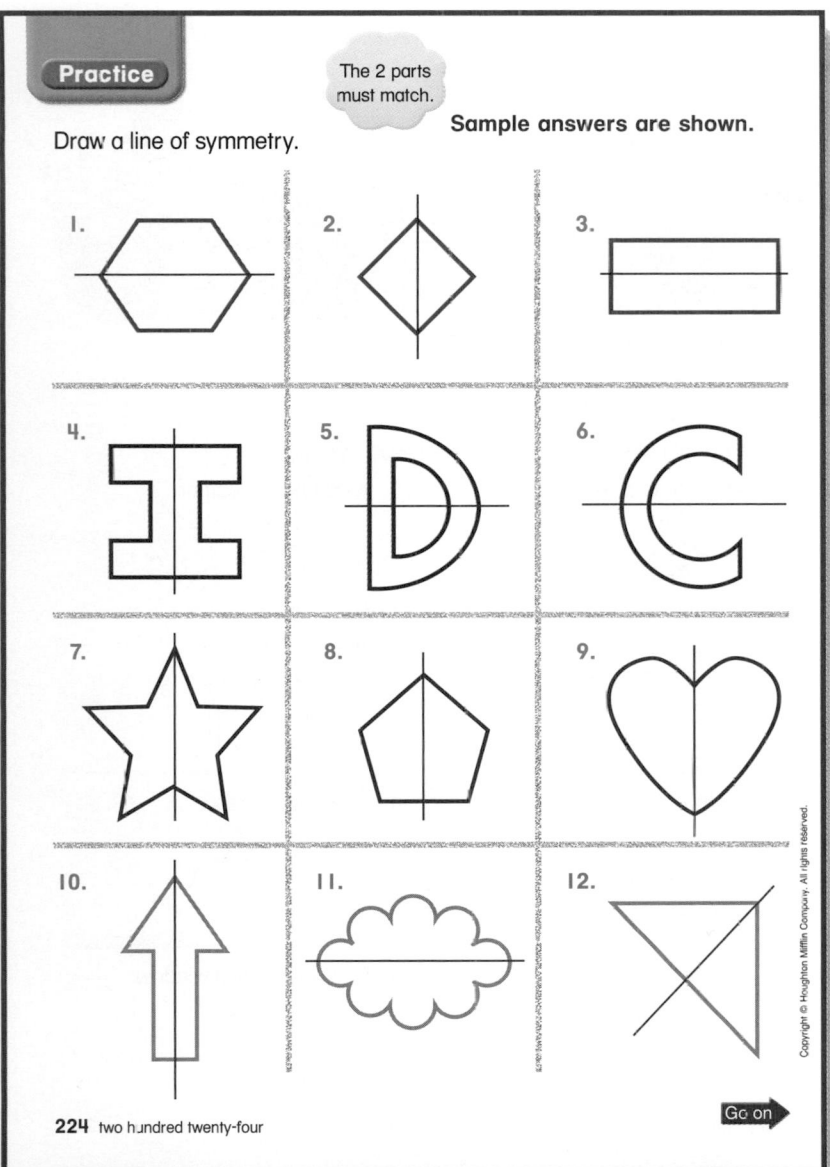

Learning to Communicate

Research highlights several features that distinguish certain mathematics classrooms as true communities of learners. One important feature of such classrooms is that they provide an environment in which teachers give children sufficient opportunities to answer questions, offer solutions, and provide explanations.

Developing mathematical proficiency requires children to explain their thinking and reasoning verbally and in written form. It requires them to make comparisons, defend their reasoning, and evaluate their responses.

In this chapter, children are given the opportunity to describe the movement of shapes in terms of slides, flips, and turns. They compare and contrast geometric patterns. They explain how to identify lines of symmetry. Their verbal explanations help form a community of learners.

③ Practice

Independent Practice

Children complete **Exercises 1–12** on page 224 independently. Encourage children to share their responses while you emphasize that some shapes have more than one line of symmetry.

Lesson continues

Literature Connection

Refer back to the unit selection, *Four Shapes.*

Have children answer these questions, based on the poem.

- **What shape is a dinner plate?** (circle)

- **What shape is a door?** (rectangle)

- **How many sides does a triangle have?** (3)

- **How many corners does a rectangle have?** (4)

- **If you fold a circle shape in half, does it have a line of symmetry? Explain.** (Yes, because both parts are the same size and shape.)

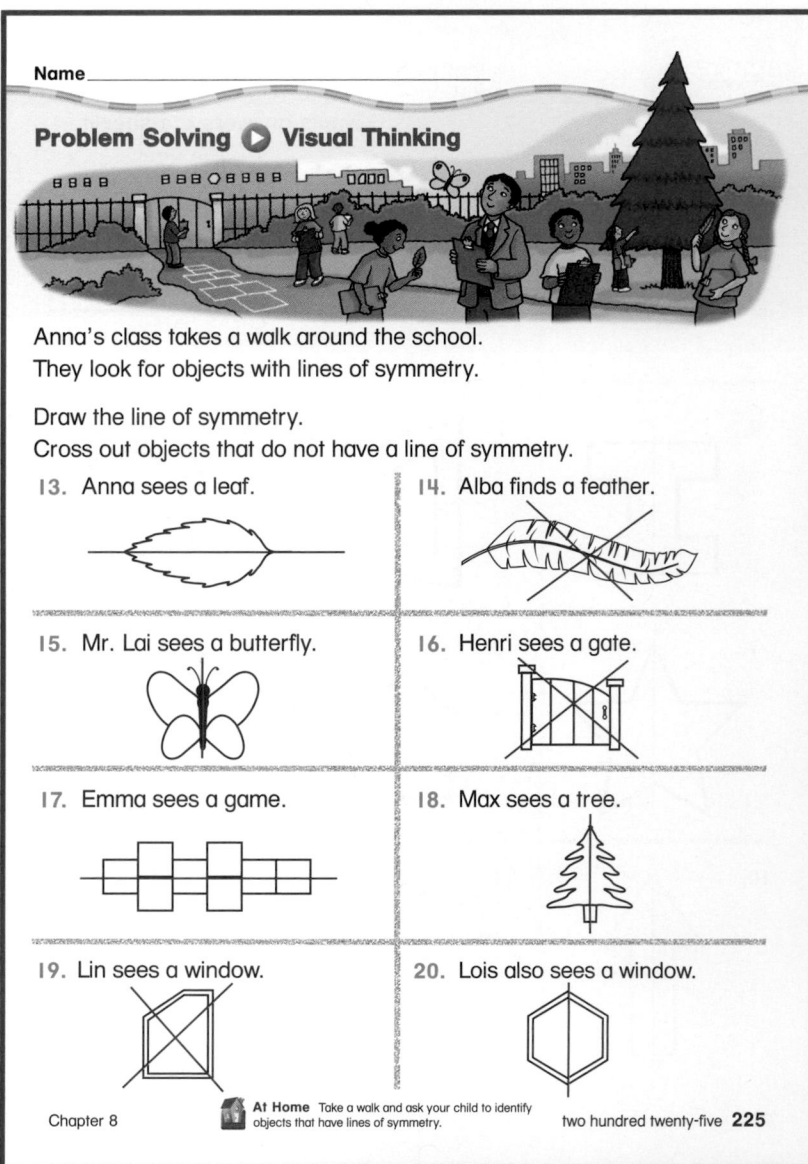

Name _____

Problem Solving ▶ Visual Thinking

Anna's class takes a walk around the school.
They look for objects with lines of symmetry.

Draw the line of symmetry.
Cross out objects that do not have a line of symmetry.

13. Anna sees a leaf.

14. Alba finds a feather.

15. Mr. Lai sees a butterfly.

16. Henri sees a gate.

17. Emma sees a game.

18. Max sees a tree.

19. Lin sees a window.

20. Lois also sees a window.

Chapter 8

At Home Take a walk and ask your child to identify objects that have lines of symmetry.

two hundred twenty-five **225**

 **Practice**

Problem Solving

After children complete **Exercises 13–20,** call on volunteers to share their solutions. Discuss why one window has a line of symmetry and the other does not.

Common Error

Failing to See Symmetry

Children may not see that a line of symmetry can be drawn horizontally or vertically. Have them try both with paper folding before they decide that an object does or does not have a line of symmetry.

 **Assess and Close**

Do all circles have a line of symmetry? (yes)

How many lines of symmetry does this shape have? (4)

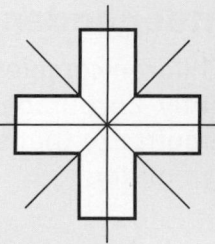

 **Keeping a Journal**

Write your name in uppercase letters. Find a letter that has a line of symmetry. Draw the line of symmetry.

Now Try This — Same Size, Same Shape

Some objects are the same size and shape.

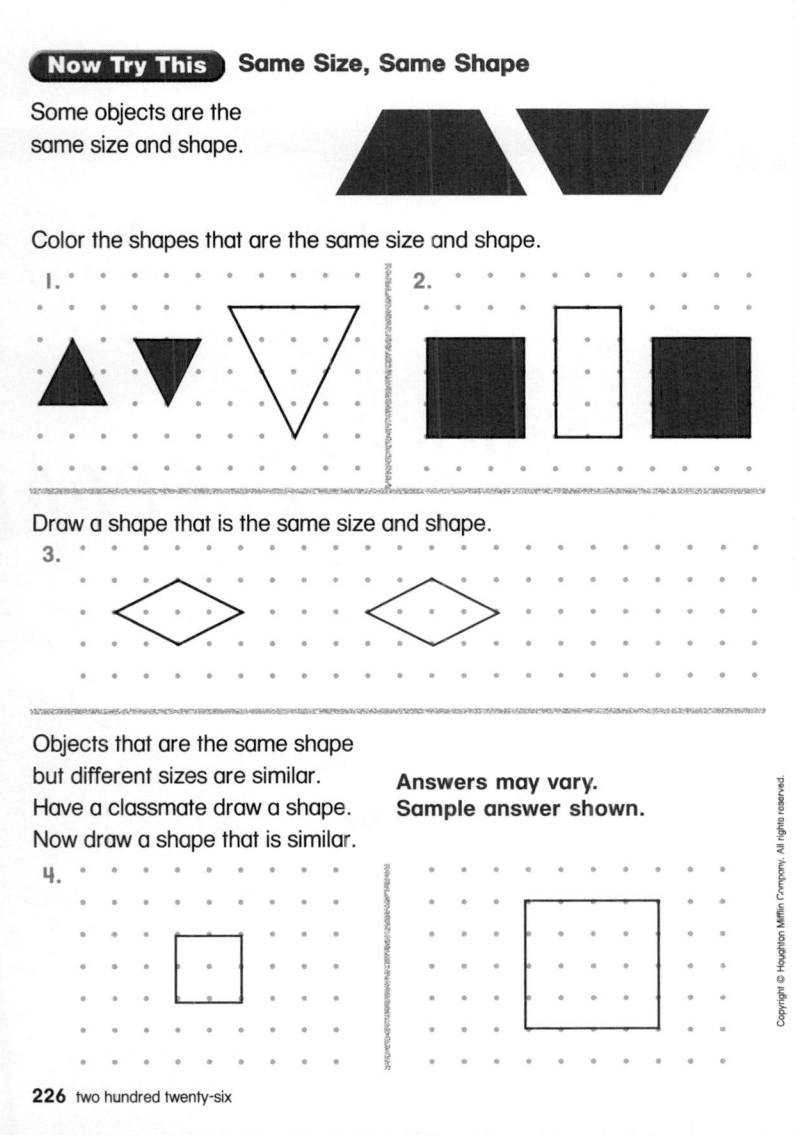

Color the shapes that are the same size and shape.

1.

2.

Draw a shape that is the same size and shape.

3.

Objects that are the same shape but different sizes are similar. Have a classmate draw a shape. Now draw a shape that is similar.

Answers may vary. Sample answer shown.

4.

226 two hundred twenty-six

Daily Test Prep

Which one is correct?

3 > 4   9 < 6   9 > 6   NH
  ○   ○   ●   ○

Activity

Lesson Intervention
Creating Symmetrical Designs

Or use Intervention CD-ROM Lesson 8.7

| 👥 Small Group | 🕐 10–15 minutes | Visual, Tactile |

Materials: *construction paper, paint*

1. Have children fold construction paper in half to create a fold line, then open the paper.

2. Invite children to drip small dots of paint onto one side of the fold line. While the paint is still wet, have them fold the paper again and press down on the paper with their hands. Have them open the paper and see the duplicate design.

3. **Does your painting have a line of symmetry?** Elicit from children that the designs on both sides of the paper are the same.

Now Try This

Introduce Point out that the objects are in different positions but they are the same size and shape.

Develop Have children complete **Exercises 1–3** as you observe.

Practice Tell children that shapes are **similar** if they have the same shape but are a different size. Have children complete **Exercise 4**.

Explore Have children match cereal boxes to find those with matching shapes and sizes. Help children realize that the back of the box must also be congruent with the front of the box.

Problem Solving: Find a Pattern

PLANNING THE LESSON

MATHEMATICS OBJECTIVE
Use patterns to solve problems.

Use Lesson Planner CD-ROM for Lesson 8.8.

Daily Routines

Calendar
Present problems for children to solve. For example, I am going shopping next Monday. On what date will I go shopping?

Vocabulary
Draw a circle-square-circle-square-circle-square **pattern** on the board. Have children say the pattern in words. Elicit that the pattern unit is circle-square and that the pattern repeats.

Vocabulary Cards

Meeting North Carolina's Standards
5.03 Create and extend patterns, identify the pattern unit, and translate into other forms.
Also 1.04

Lesson Transparency **8.8**

Problem of the Day
Carrie drew this pattern.

☆ ◇ ◇ ♡ ☆ ◇ ◇ ♡

What shape comes next? (a star)

Quick Review

$$\begin{array}{r} 5 \\ +\ 3 \\ \hline (8) \end{array} \quad \begin{array}{r} 8 \\ -\ 5 \\ \hline (3) \end{array} \quad \begin{array}{r} 4 \\ +\ 3 \\ \hline (7) \end{array} \quad \begin{array}{r} 7 \\ -\ 4 \\ \hline (3) \end{array} \quad \begin{array}{r} 7 \\ -\ 3 \\ \hline (4) \end{array}$$

Lesson Quiz
Look at the pattern. Which shape does not belong? (square) What is the correct shape? (triangle)

○ △ △ ○ △ △ ○ □ △

LEVELED PRACTICE

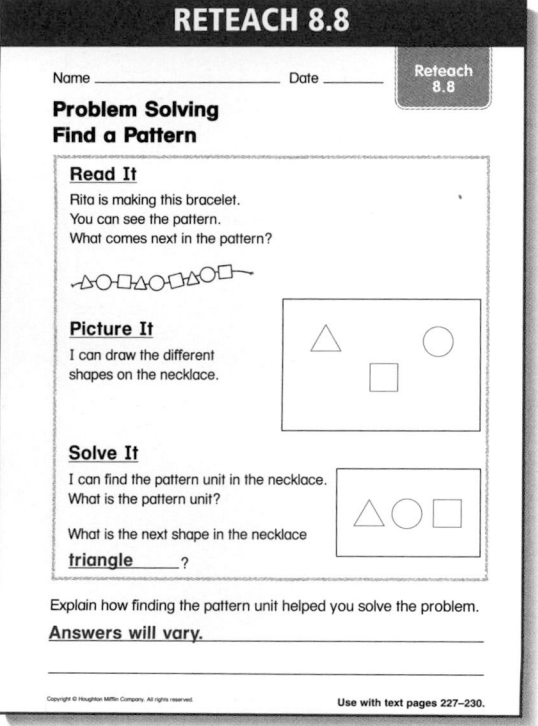

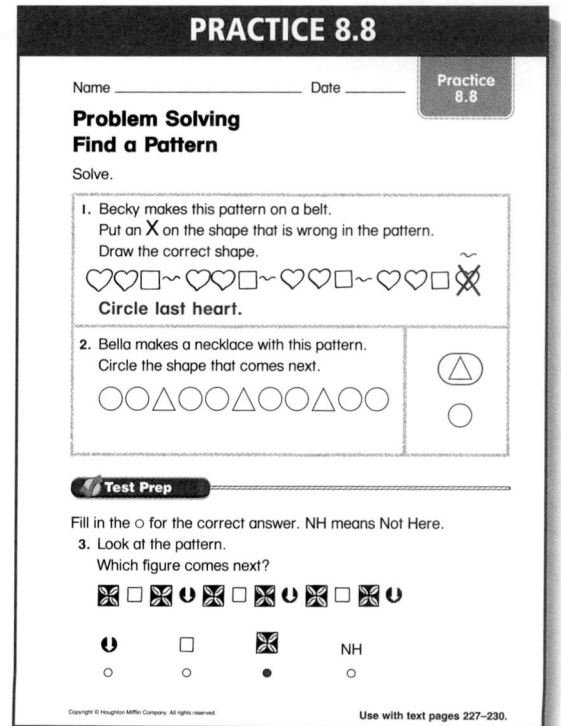

ENRICHMENT 8.8

Name _____ Date _____   Enrichment 8.8

What Comes Next?

1. Read the problem.
   Dad is painting a pattern on the wall.
   What comes next in the pattern?

Look for a pattern.
Circle the flower that comes next.

2. Make your own pattern. Use 🌷 and 🌼.

3. Look back at the pattern you made.
   What is your pattern unit?
   <u>Answers will vary.</u>

Use with text pages 227–230.

Practice Workbook Page 56

Reaching All Learners

Differentiated Instruction

English Learners

Children will need to understand the term *wrong* in order to solve some word problems involving shapes. Worksheet 8.8 will help children understand this term.

Special Needs
TACTILE, VISUAL

Materials: *pattern blocks*

Make a triangle-rhombus pattern. Repeat the pattern unit several times. Then use a square instead of a triangle. If the child notices the "error," have him or her correct it before you continue. If the error is not seen, lead the child in saying the pattern until the error is obvious.

Gifted and Talented
TACTILE, VISUAL

Materials: *buttons*

Give children buttons of various sizes and shapes. Ask one child to make a pattern with the buttons. Have him or her use 3 or 4 buttons in a pattern unit. Have the partner identify and describe the pattern. Then the partner makes a different pattern. The first child identifies the

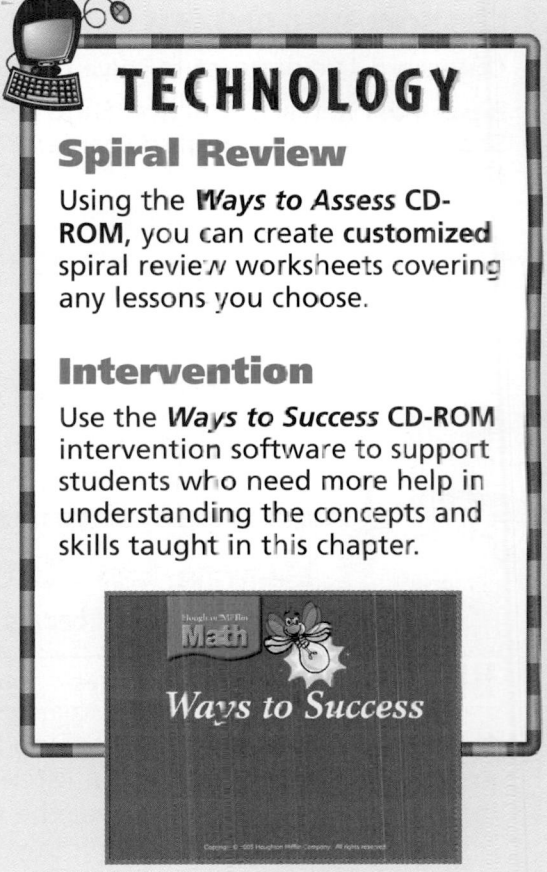

TECHNOLOGY

Spiral Review

Using the *Ways to Assess* CD-ROM, you can create customized spiral review worksheets covering any lessons you choose.

Intervention

Use the *Ways to Success* CD-ROM intervention software to support students who need more help in understanding the concepts and skills taught in this chapter.

Ways to Success

Social Studies Connection

Explain that many Amish people live in Pennsylvania and Ohio. They are well known for their beautiful quilts. Show a picture of an Amish quilt. Ask children to identify the shapes they see. Have them describe the patterns.

MATH CENTER

Number of the Week Activity

Display the Number of the Week to motivate children to use their problem-solving skills. The exercises cover topics across all math strands.

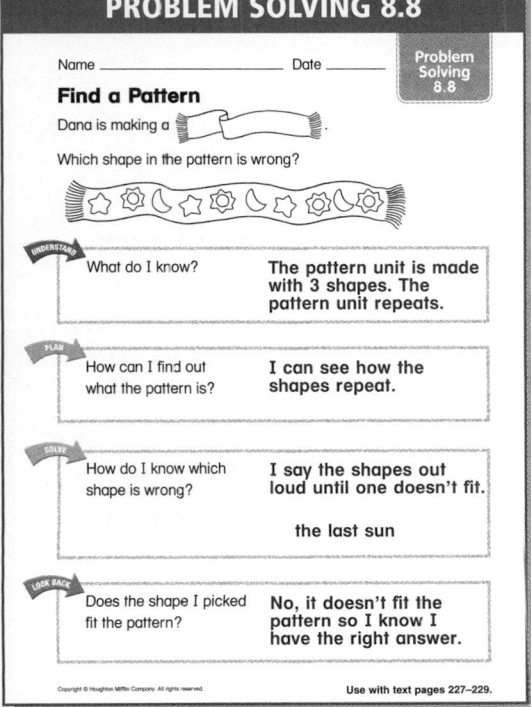

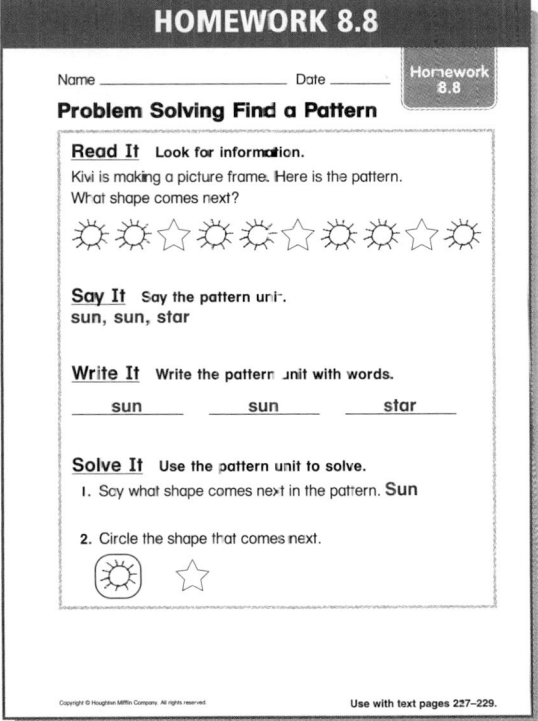

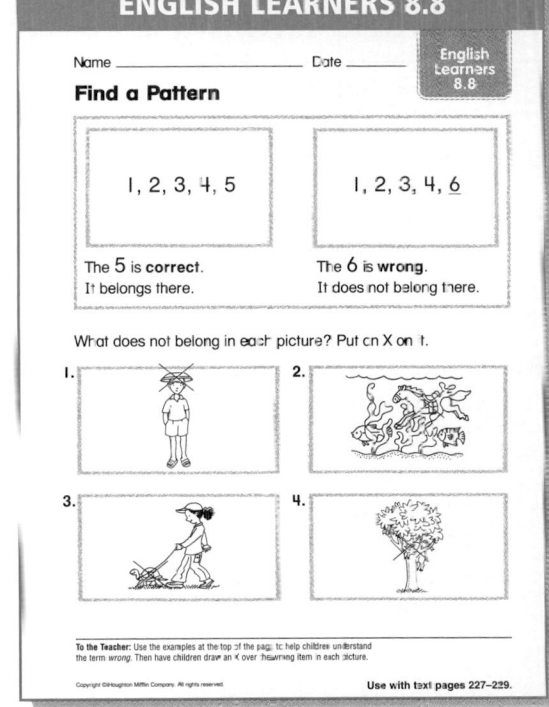

Homework Workbook Page 56

TEACHING LESSON 8.8

LESSON ORGANIZER

Objective Use patterns to solve problems.

Resources Reteach, Practice, Enrichment, Problem Solving, Homework, English Learners, Transparencies, Math Center

Activity

Warm-Up Activity
Modeling Patterns

| 🚹🚹🚹🚹 Whole Group | ⏱ 5 minutes | Auditory, Kinesthetic |

1. Tell children that you are going to create a sound pattern. Have the children listen as you clap, stomp, and "beep." Repeat the pattern three times, then have children join you.

2. **What is the pattern?** (clap-stomp-beep) Repeat the entire pattern again. **What sound comes next in the pattern?** (clap)

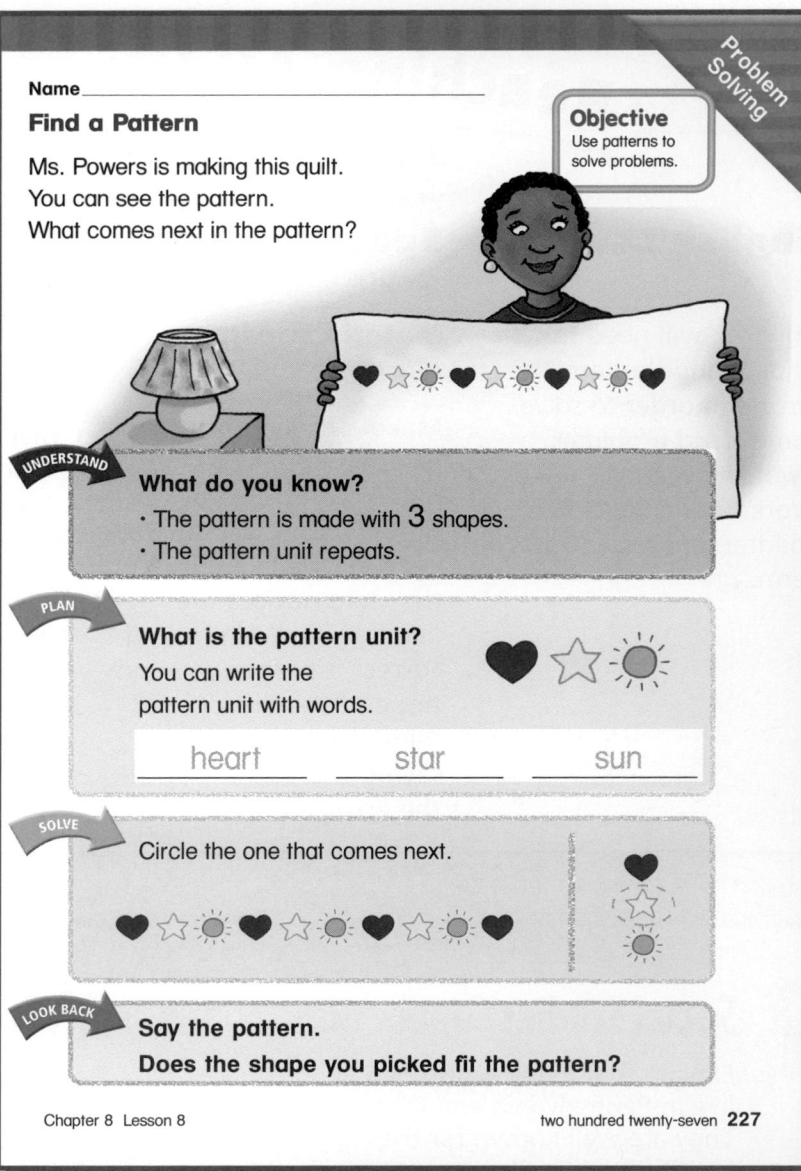

Find a Pattern

Objective
Use patterns to solve problems.

Ms. Powers is making this quilt.
You can see the pattern.
What comes next in the pattern?

UNDERSTAND

What do you know?
· The pattern is made with 3 shapes.
· The pattern unit repeats.

PLAN

What is the pattern unit?
You can write the pattern unit with words.

| heart | star | sun |

SOLVE

Circle the one that comes next.

LOOK BACK

Say the pattern.
Does the shape you picked fit the pattern?

Chapter 8 Lesson 8   two hundred twenty-seven **227**

---

1 Introduce

Discuss Finding a Pattern

| 🚹🚹🚹🚹 Whole Group | ⏱ 10–15 minutes | Visual, Auditory |

1. Draw a star-star-moon pattern on the board.

2. **What shapes are in the pattern?** (star, moon) Then point out that the pattern repeats. **How many shapes in each pattern unit?** (2 shapes) **What is the pattern?** (star, star, moon)

3. **What shape comes next in the pattern?** (star) **How do you know?** (The pattern is star-star-moon. The next shape after the moon will be a star.)

2 Develop

Guided Learning

Teaching Example Introduce the objective to the children, read the problem, and discuss the picture. Guide them through the example.

UNDERSTAND **How many different shapes are in the pattern unit?** (3 shapes)

PLAN **What are the names of the shapes in the pattern?** (heart, star, sun) Trace the picture as you say the words to show the pattern unit.

SOLVE Say the pattern aloud: **heart, star, sun, heart, star, sun, heart, star, sun, heart. What comes next?** (star)

LOOK BACK Say the pattern again. **Did you choose the correct shape?**

Guided Practice

Have children complete **Exercises 1–2** on page 228 as you observe. Point out that the task on Exercise 2 is different than Exercise 1.

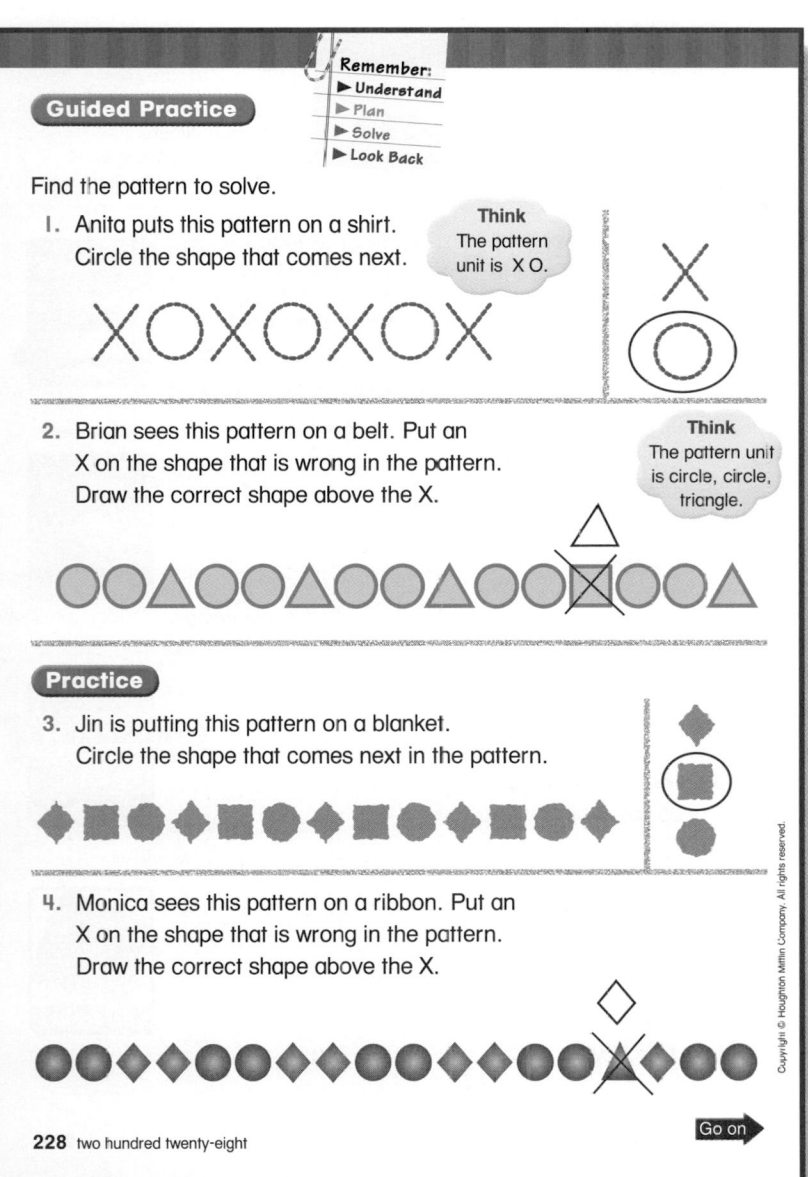

Guided Practice

Remember:
► Understand
► Plan
► Solve
► Look Back

Find the pattern to solve.

1. Anita puts this pattern on a shirt. Circle the shape that comes next.

Think
The pattern unit is X O.

XOXOXOX

2. Brian sees this pattern on a belt. Put an X on the shape that is wrong in the pattern. Draw the correct shape above the X.

Think
The pattern unit is circle, circle, triangle.

Practice

3. Jin is putting this pattern on a blanket. Circle the shape that comes next in the pattern.

4. Monica sees this pattern on a ribbon. Put an X on the shape that is wrong in the pattern. Draw the correct shape above the X.

228 two hundred twenty-eight

Go on ►

KEEPING SKILLS SHARP

Play "Pattern Baseball"

Separate the class into two teams. Have a child from each team roll a number cube to determine which team goes first.

- Model a pattern with sounds and/or actions. Have a child from the first team tell what comes next in the pattern. If the child's response is correct, the child "goes to first base." If the response is incorrect, the child is "out."

- When the team has four correct responses, they score a "run." If the team has three incorrect responses, they are "out." The other team is "up."

3 Practice

Independent Practice

Children complete **Exercises 3–4** on page 228 independently.

Lesson continues ►

$2 + 3 = 5$

Which of the following is in the same fact family?

$3 + 5 = 8$ $2 + 2 = 4$ $5 - 3 = 2$ NH

○   ○   ●   ○

Activity

Or use Intervention CD-ROM Lesson 8.8

Lesson Intervention
Using Patterns

| 👥 Small Group | ⏱ 5–10 minutes | Visual, Tactile |

1. Have children draw a pattern. Tell them to include three or four items in the pattern. Suggest that they look around the classroom for ideas. Remind children that they can use shapes, colors, sizes, and numbers to create a pattern.

2. When children complete their patterns, have them exchange their drawings with a classmate. Have children describe the pattern and tell what comes next.

3. Ask children to compare their patterns. **What is the same about your patterns? What is different?**

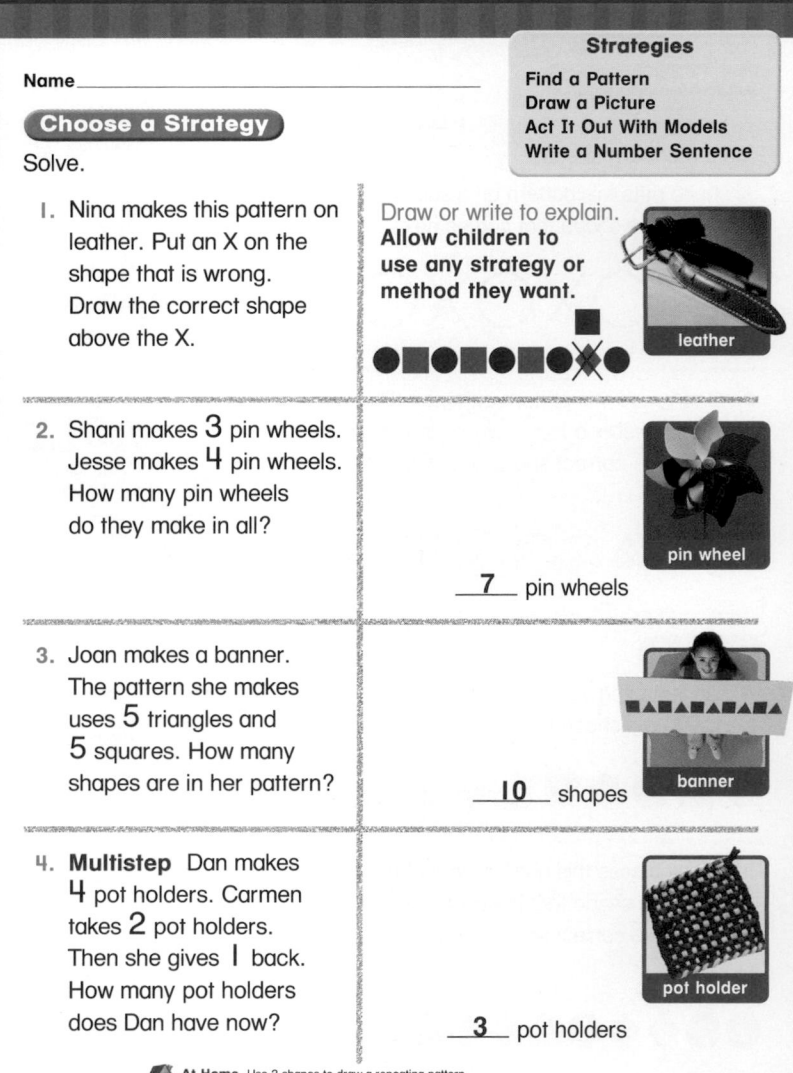

Name _____

Strategies
Find a Pattern
Draw a Picture
Act It Out With Models
Write a Number Sentence

Choose a Strategy

Solve.

1. Nina makes this pattern on leather. Put an X on the shape that is wrong. Draw the correct shape above the X.

   Draw or write to explain. **Allow children to use any strategy or method they want.**

   leather

2. Shani makes 3 pin wheels. Jesse makes 4 pin wheels. How many pin wheels do they make in all?

   ___7___ pin wheels

   pin wheel

3. Joan makes a banner. The pattern she makes uses 5 triangles and 5 squares. How many shapes are in her pattern?

   ___10___ shapes

   banner

4. **Multistep** Dan makes 4 pot holders. Carmen takes 2 pot holders. Then she gives 1 back. How many pot holders does Dan have now?

   ___3___ pot holders

   pot holder

At Home Use 3 shapes to draw a repeating pattern. Ask your child to describe the pattern and tell what comes next.

Chapter 8   two hundred twenty-nine **229**

3️⃣ Practice

Mixed Strategy Practice

Read the problem-solving strategies with children. Make sure children can read and comprehend the problems in **Exercises 1–4** on page 229. If necessary, pair more proficient readers with less proficient readers. Encourage them to discuss the problems before solving.

Common Error

Missing the Incorrect Shape
Children may become confused and have difficulty finding the incorrect shape. Have them say the pattern aloud to reinforce the repeated shapes.

4️⃣ Assess and Close

Which shape comes next in the pattern? (triangle)

Is this a pattern? How do you know? (Yes, the pattern is 3-1, and it repeats.)

✏️ Keeping a Journal

Draw a pattern you would like to have on a T-shirt. Write about the pattern.

Listen to your teacher read the problem.
Solve.

1. Larry saw this dot pattern on a plate.
Use numbers to show the same pattern.

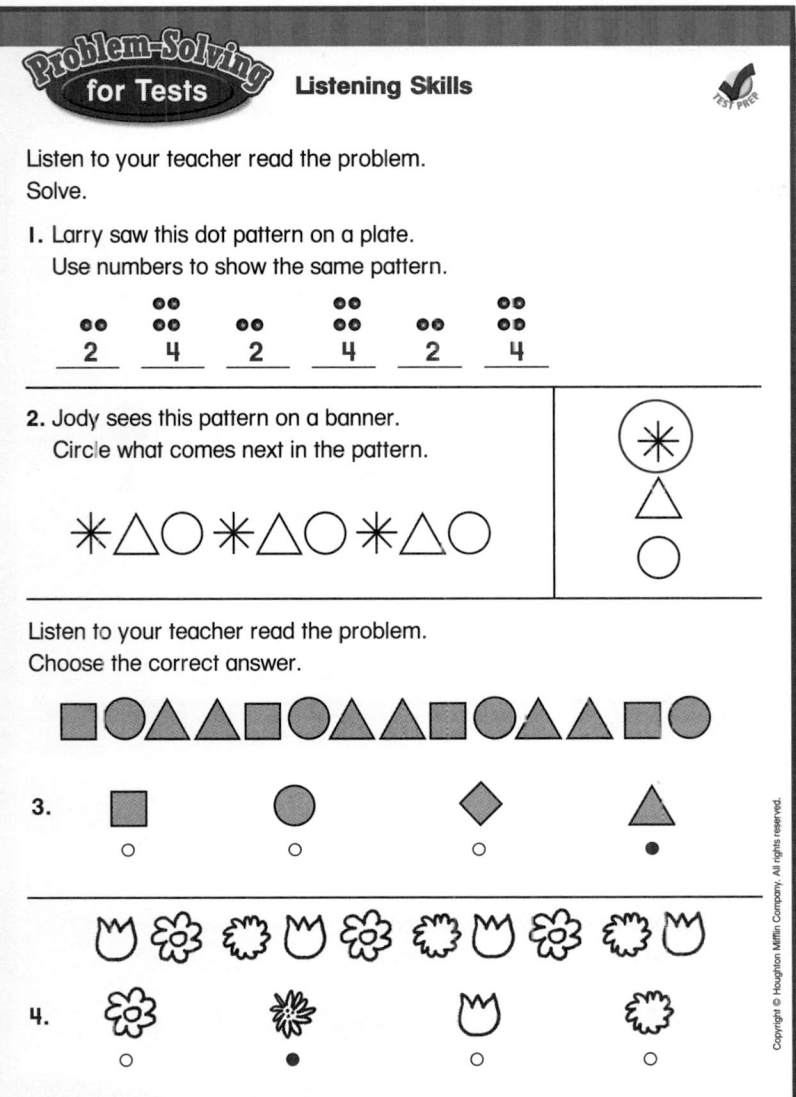

2   4   2   4   2   4

2. Jody sees this pattern on a banner.
Circle what comes next in the pattern.

Listen to your teacher read the problem.
Choose the correct answer.

3.   ○ ○ ○ ●

4.   ○ ● ○ ○

This page provides children practice with the oral problem-solving format used in some standardized test items.

You may want to read each item only once to mimic the style of oral tests.

Use With Items 1 and 2

Listening Strategy: Read the problem silently as the teacher reads it aloud.

- *When a problem is on the page, look at the problem while I read it aloud.*

- *Listen to the whole problem. Wait until I finish reading to start writing.*

Use With Item 3

Listening Strategy: Listen to the problem and then look at the picture.

- *When a problem is not on the page, look at me and listen as I read the problem.*

  Samantha is painting this pattern on a sweatshirt. Which shape comes next in the pattern?

- *Now look at the picture. Mark your answer.*

Use With Item 4

Listening Strategy: Listen to the problem and think about what it asks.

- *Listen to the problem so you will know how to find the answer.*

  Tony is planting flowers in this pattern. Which flower would not have a place in the pattern?

- *Look at the choices. Then mark your answer.*

Quick Check

Have children complete the Quick Check exercises independently to assess their understanding of concepts and skills taught in **Lessons 4–8**.

Item	Lesson	Error Analysis	Intervention
1	8.4	Children may confuse the terms flip and turn.	Reteach Resource 8.4 ***Ways to Success*** 8.4
2	8.5	Children may circle the wrong picture.	Reteach Resource 8.5 ***Ways to Success*** 8.5
3	8.6	Children may have difficulty creating a repeating pattern.	Reteach Resource 8.6 ***Ways to Success*** 8.6
4	8.7	Children may fail to see where the line of symmetry can be drawn.	Reteach Resource 8.7 ***Ways to Success*** 8.7
5	8.8	Children may have difficulty finding the incorrect shape.	Reteach Resource 8.8 ***Ways to Success*** 8.8

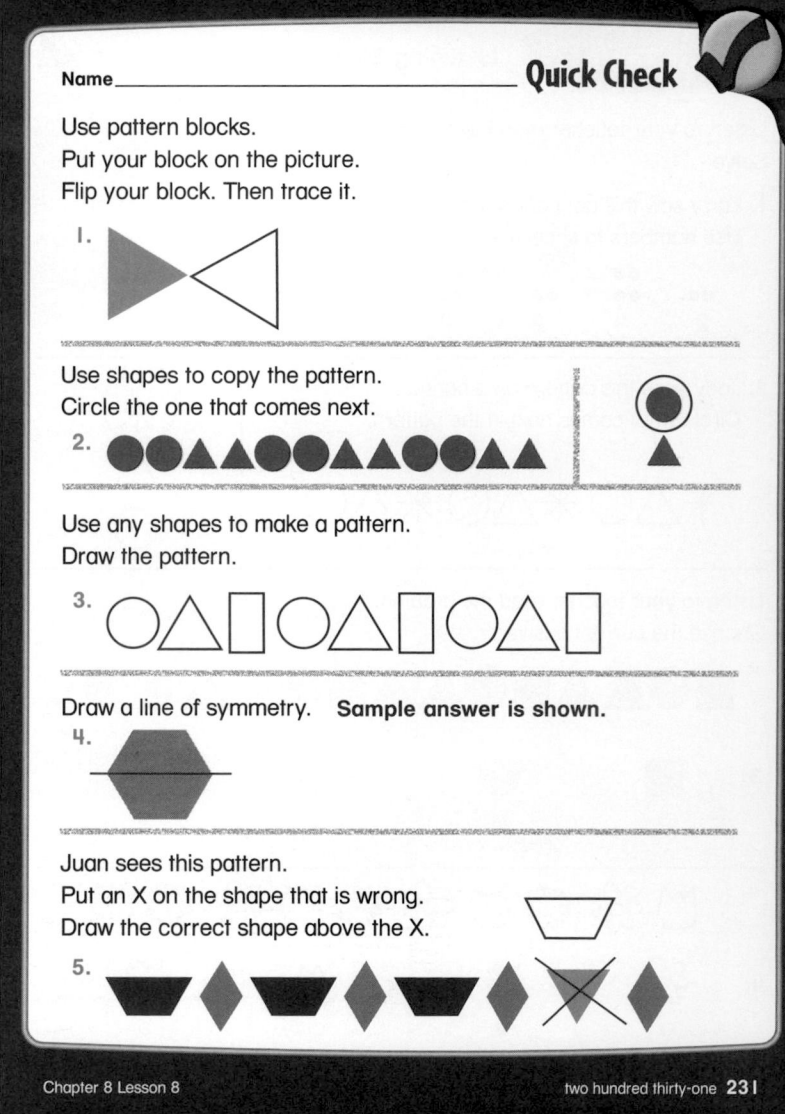

Key Topic Review

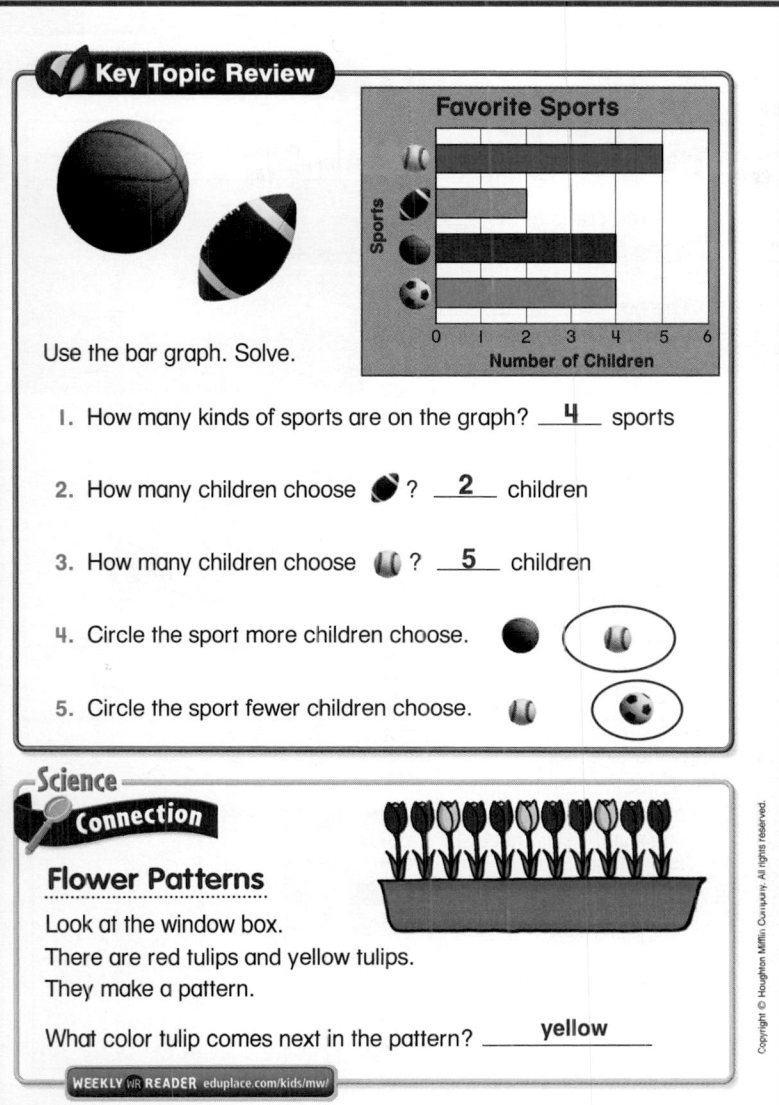

Favorite Sports

Sports

Number of Children

Use the bar graph. Solve.

1. How many kinds of sports are on the graph? __4__ sports

2. How many children choose 🏈 ? __2__ children

3. How many children choose 🎾 ? __5__ children

4. Circle the sport more children choose. ⚫ (🎾)

5. Circle the sport fewer children choose. 🎾 (⚽)

Science
Connection

Flower Patterns

Look at the window box.
There are red tulips and yellow tulips.
They make a pattern.

What color tulip comes next in the pattern? _____yellow_____

WEEKLY WR READER eduplace.com/kids/mw/

232 two hundred thirty-two

This assessment provides a review of the skills and concepts taught in Chapter 4.

Check to be sure children understand that:

• the topic is stated in the title of the graph.

• sports are listed on the vertical axis.

• the numbers are shown along the horizontal axis.

• each box stands for one child.

Science

Connection

Ask children to tell if they have ever seen tulips, and if so, where they have seen them. Ask children if they have seen tulips in their neighborhood or in a park. Tell children that tulips can be different colors, such as red, yellow, white, and pink.

Help children follow the directions to complete the questions.

Chapter Review/Test

Purpose: This test provides an informal assessment of the Chapter 8 objectives.

Chapter Test Items 1–15

To assign a numerical grade for this Chapter Test, use 6 points for each test item and add 10 to the score.

Check Understanding

Use children's work on word problems to informally assess progress on chapter content.

Customizing Your Instruction

For children who have not yet mastered these objectives, you can use the reteaching resources listed in the chart below.

 ## Assessment Options

A summary test for this chapter is also provided in the Unit Resource Folder.

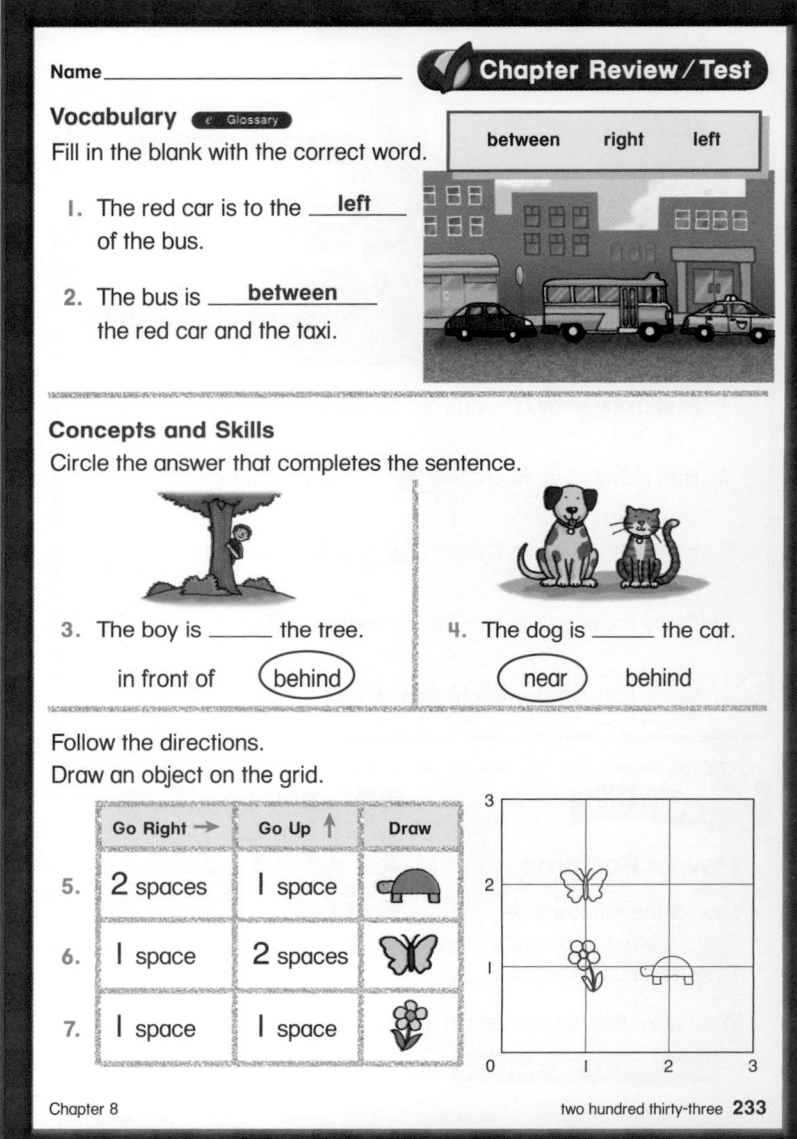

Reteaching Support

Chapter Test Items	Summary Test Items	Chapter Objectives Tested	TE Pages	Use These Reteaching Resources
1–2	3	**8A** Use math vocabulary relating to spatial sense and patterns.	207A–208	Reteach Resource and *Ways to Success* CD: 8.1, Skillsheet 53
3–7	1–2	**8B** Use position words to locate, arrange, and describe objects in space and locations on a grid.	207A–212	Reteach Resources and *Ways to Success* CD: 8.1–8.3 Skillsheets 54–55
8–9, 12–14	4–6	**8C** Identify transformations and symmetry in shapes.	215A–218, 223A–225	Reteach Resources and *Ways to Success* CD: 8.4, 8.7, Sheets 56–57
10–11	7–8	**8D** Describe, predict, extend and create patterns.	219A–222	Reteach Resources and *Ways to Success* CD: 8.5, 8.6, Skillsheet 58
15	9–10	**8E** Use patterns to solve problems.	227A–230	CD: 8.8, Skillsheet 59

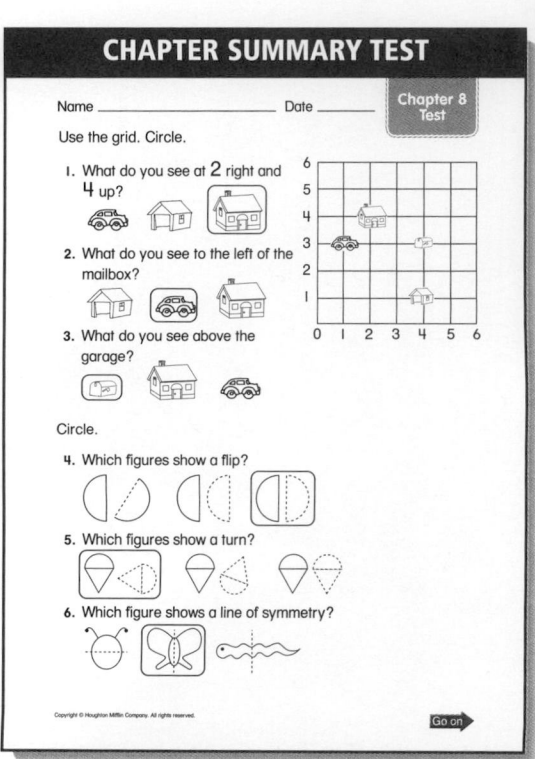

Draw to show a flip.

8.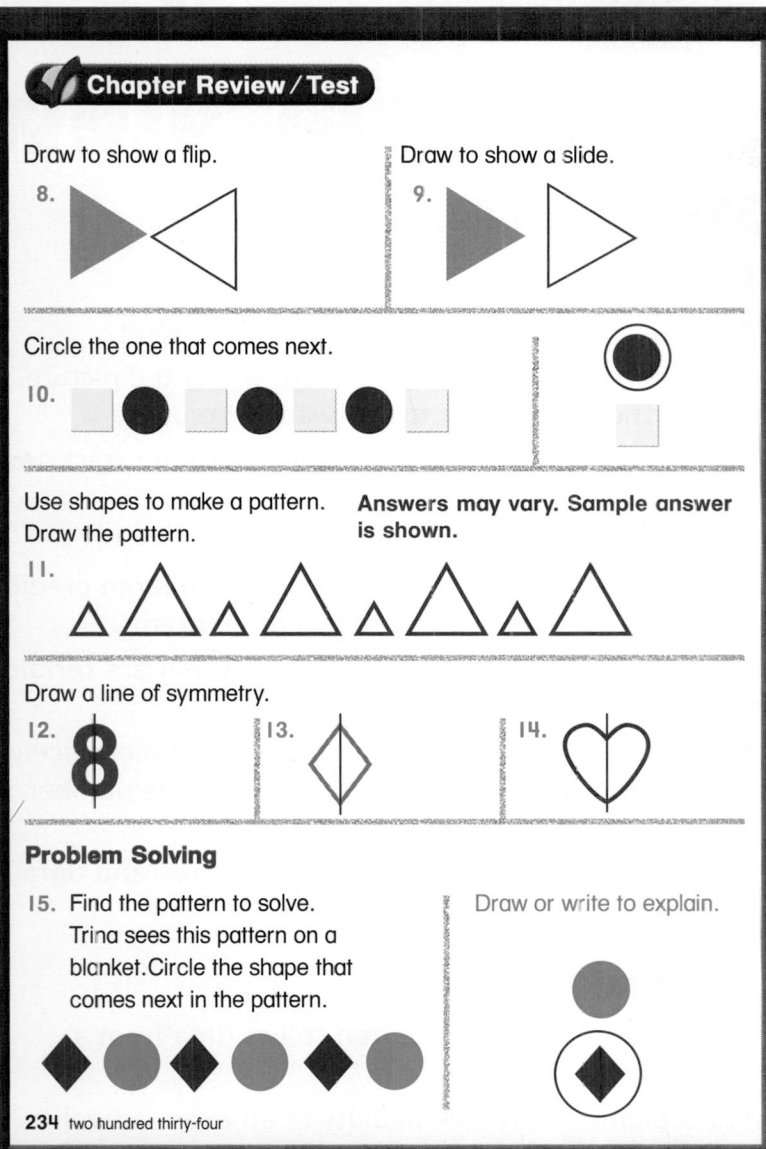

Draw to show a slide.

9.

Circle the one that comes next.

10.

Use shapes to make a pattern.
Draw the pattern.

Answers may vary. Sample answer is shown.

11.

Draw a line of symmetry.

12.   13.   14.

Problem Solving

15. Find the pattern to solve.
Trina sees this pattern on a blanket. Circle the shape that comes next in the pattern.

Draw or write to explain.

Use the End of Grade Test Prep Assessment Guide to help familiarize your children with the format of standardized tests.

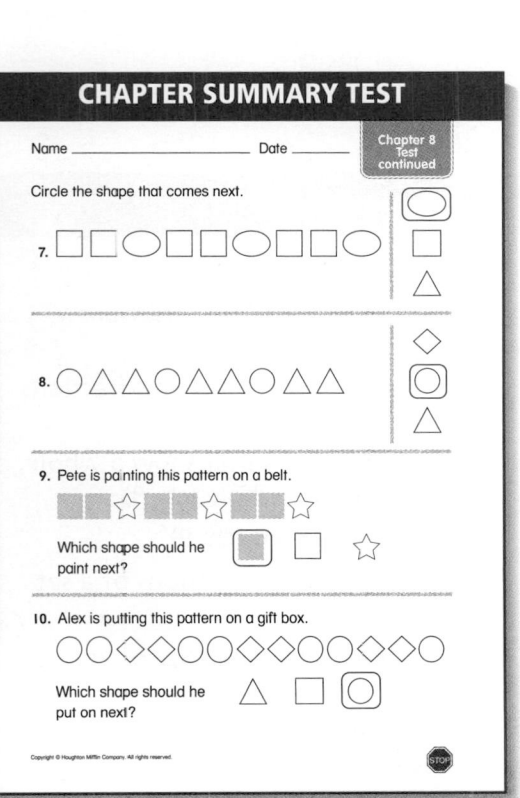

CHAPTER SUMMARY TEST

Name _____ Date _____

Chapter 8 Test continued

Circle the shape that comes next.

7.

8.

9. Pete is painting this pattern on a belt.

Which shape should he paint next?

10. Alex is putting this pattern on a gift box.

Which shape should he put on next?

Lesson by Lesson Overview
Fractions and Probability

Lesson 1

- This lesson reviews equal parts and children identify shapes with equal parts.
- They also count and record the number of equal parts in a shape.
- A problem solving activity has children draw to show equal parts.

Lesson 2

- In this lesson, children learn that a *fraction* is used to name equal parts.
- At this grade level, the parts of a fraction are not named, however, children are taught that $\frac{1}{2}$ means 1 out of 2 parts.
- Children identify shapes that show two halves and color $\frac{1}{2}$.
- They also draw lines on pictures to show halves and color $\frac{1}{2}$.

Lesson 3

- Children identify shapes that show fourths and color $\frac{1}{4}$.
- They also draw lines on pictures to show fourths and color $\frac{1}{4}$.
- Children identify shapes that show thirds and color $\frac{1}{3}$.
- The lesson is extended to have children choose the fraction for a picture; color to show a fraction and write the fraction.

Lesson 4

- Fraction of a set is introduced in this lesson.
- Children choose the fraction shown by the picture and then they color to show a fraction.
- The problem solving set explores non-unit fractions.

Lesson 5

- This lesson introduces probability as children predict and determine the probability of an event.
- Children use spinners to find events that are *certain, impossible,* and *probable.*
- Children also determine events that are *more likely, less likely,* and *equally likely* based on the number and color of cubes in various sets.
- Practice games help children explore *fair* and *unfair* games.

Lesson 6

- This lesson teaches children to use data from a picture to solve problems.
- Problems involve probability of an event as well as subtraction to compare.
- Combining these two concepts provides experience with ideas that will be presented formally in later grades.

SKILLS TRACE: FRACTIONS AND PROBABILITY

Grade K	Grade 1	Grade 2
• identify and make equal parts, including fourths (ch. 5)	• identify and count equal parts	• identify and write unit fractions (ch. 9)
• identify and make halves (ch. 5)	• identify halves and $\frac{1}{2}$ of a whole	• identify and write non-unit fractions (ch. 9)
• explore probability through likely and unlikely; predict and record outcomes (ch. 5)	• identify fourths and $\frac{1}{4}$ of a whole; thirds and $\frac{1}{3}$ of a whole	• identify fractions that show a whole; more than one whole (ch. 9)
	• identify and represent $\frac{1}{2}$, $\frac{1}{3}$, and $\frac{1}{4}$ of a set	• compare fractions (ch. 9)
	• predict and determine the probability of an event	• identify and write fractions of a set (ch. 9)
		• determine the probability of an event (ch. 4)
		• predict and record the outcome of an event (ch. 4)

Chapter Planner

Lesson	Objective	Vocabulary	Materials	✓ NCTM Standards
9.1 **Equal Parts** p. 237A	Identify and count equal parts.	equal parts	pattern blocks, plane shapes (Learning Tool (LT) 22 and 23)	Understand and represent commonly used fractions, such as $\frac{1}{4}$, $\frac{1}{3}$, and $\frac{1}{2}$.
9.2 **One-Half** p. 239A	Use fractions to name parts of a whole; identify one half of a whole.	fraction one half halves	paper shapes (LT 22 and 23), teacher-made symmetrical object pictures cut in half	Understand and represent commonly used fractions, such as $\frac{1}{4}$, $\frac{1}{3}$, and $\frac{1}{2}$.
9.3 **One-Fourth** p. 241A	Identify one fourth and one third of a whole.	fourths one fourth thirds one third	paper shapes (LT 22 and 23), teacher-made paper fraction circles	Understand and represent commonly used fractions, such as $\frac{1}{4}$, $\frac{1}{3}$, and $\frac{1}{2}$.
9.4 **Fractions of a Set** p. 245A	Identify and represent $\frac{1}{2}$, $\frac{1}{3}$, and $\frac{1}{4}$ of a set.		paper shapes (LT 22 and 23), cubes	Understand and represent commonly used fractions, such as $\frac{1}{4}$, $\frac{1}{3}$, and $\frac{1}{2}$.
9.5 **Probability** **(Hands-On)** p. 247A	Predict and determine the probability of an event.	certain impossible probable predict	spinners (LT 38), paper clips, pennies, cup, colored cubes, bag, ten frame	Discuss events related to students' experiences as likely and unlikely.
9.6 **Problem Solving:** **Use a Picture** p. 251A	Use data from a picture to solve problems.		blank transparency, 3 clear bags, counters, connecting cubes	Solve problems that arise in mathematics and in other contexts.

Resources For Reaching All Learners

LESSON RESOURCES: Reteach, Practice, Enrichment, Problem Solving, Homework, English Learners, Daily Routines, Transparencies, Math Center.

ADDITIONAL RESOURCES FROM HOUGHTON MIFFLIN: Chapter Challenges, Combination Classroom Planning Guide, Every Day Counts, Math to Learn (Student Handbook)

Every Day Counts
The Daily Domino activities in Every Day Counts support the math in this chapter.

Assessing Prior Knowledge

Before beginning the chapter, you can assess student understandings in order to assist you in differentiating instruction.

Complete Chapter Pretest in Unit Resource Folder

Use this test to assess both prerequisite skills (**Are You Ready?** — one page) and chapter content (**Check What You Know** — two pages).

Chapter 9 Prerequisite Skills Pretest

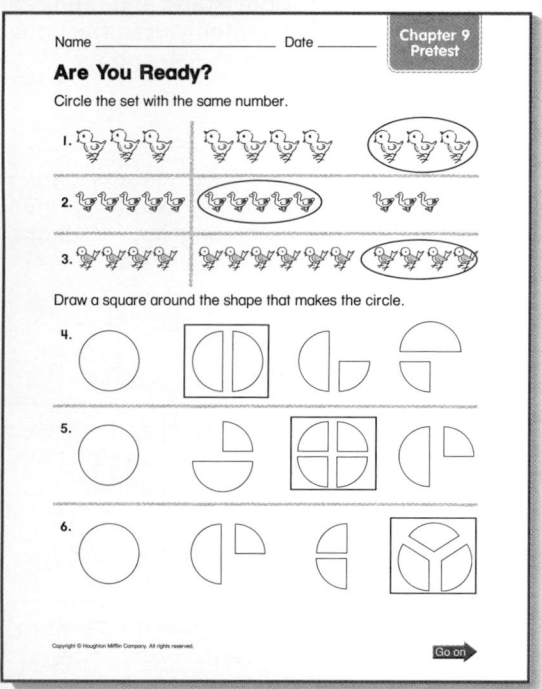

Chapter 9 New Content Pretest

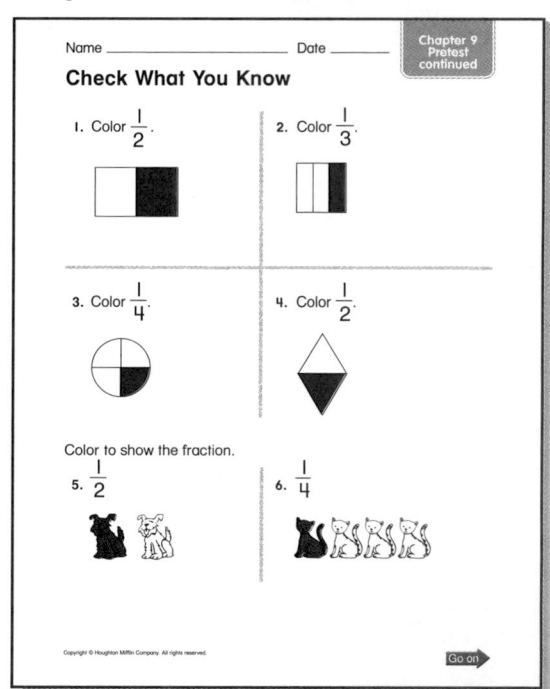

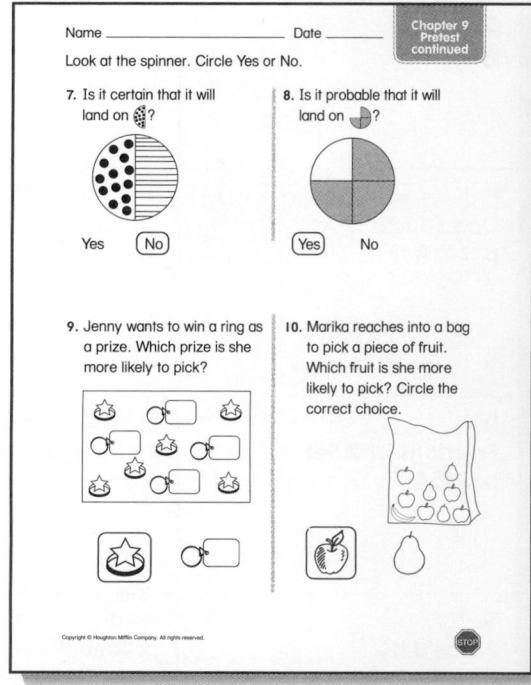

Customizing Instruction

For Students Having Difficulty

Items	Prerequisites	Ways to Success
1–6	Identify and count equal parts.	CD: 9a Skillsheet 60

Ways to Success: Intervention for every concept and skill (CD-ROM or Chapter Intervention Skillsheets).

For Students Having Success

Items	Objectives	Resources
1	9A Use vocabulary relating to fractions and probability.	Enrichment 9.2, 9.3
2–6	9B Identify, name, and represent $\frac{1}{2}$, $\frac{1}{3}$, and $\frac{1}{4}$ of a region and of a set.	Enrichment 9.1–9.4
7–8	9C Use probability to determine the likelihood of an event.	Enrichment 9.5
9–10	9D Use data from a picture to solve problems.	Enrichment 9.6

Other Pretest Options

Informal Pretest

The pretest assesses vocabulary and prerequisite skills needed for success in this chapter.

Ways to Success CD-ROM

The *Ways to Success* chapter pretest has automatic assignment of appropriate review lessons.

Use **Chapter Challenges** with any students who have success with all new chapter content.

Chapter Resources

Assessing Prior Knowledge

Make Number Puzzles (recognize and count sets of 1–9, read and write numbers)

- On paper strips, have each child draw sets of 1–9 objects and the number that names each set.
- Have children cut apart their strips between the pictures and the number.
- Place each child's work in an envelope. Have children choose an envelope and put the puzzle pieces together by counting the objects and reading the numbers.

Ongoing Skill Activity

What Are Your Chances? (predict and determine probability)

- Place 6 blue cubes and 1 yellow cube in a bag. Have children check the contents of the bag and guess which color they will choose most often.
- Then have them draw a cube from the bag 20 times. Have them use tally marks to track results.

Connecting to the Unit Project

- Tell children in this activity they will work with fractions.
- Draw a square, a rectangle, and a circle on the board.
- Have children create a drawing using these shapes. Then have them draw lines to show halves on each shape.

Professional Resources Handbook

Research, Mathematics Content, and Language Intervention

Research-Based Teaching

Language is important as children begin to learn about fractions. Research has found that in languages, such as Korean, Chinese, and Japanese the concept of fractions is built into the language. In Korea, $\frac{1}{4}$ is read as "of four parts, one." (Miura et al. 1999). Encouraging the use of phrases such as one out of 4 parts are blue, helps children understand what the fraction $\frac{1}{4}$ represents. See *Professional Resources Handbook, Grade 1,* Unit 3.

For more ideas relating to Unit 3, see the Teacher Support Handbook at the back of this Teacher's Edition.

Language Intervention

In East Asian countries, children learn that just as whole numbers can be composed and decomposed as sets and subsets, fractions can be composed and decomposed as well. For further explanation, see "Mathematical Language and Fractions" in the *Professional Resources Handbook Grade 1.*

Technology

Time-Saving Technology Support

Ways to Assess Customized Spiral Review
  Test Generator CD
Lesson Planner CD-ROM
Ways to Success Intervention CD-ROM
MathTracks CD-ROM
Education Place: www.eduplace.com/math/mw
Houghton Mifflin Math eBook CD-ROM
eManipulatives
eGames

Starting Chapter 9
Fractions and Probability

CHAPTER OBJECTIVES

9A Develop and use math vocabulary relating to fractions and probability.

9B Identify, name, and represent $\frac{1}{2}$, $\frac{1}{3}$, and $\frac{1}{4}$ of a region and of a set.

9C Use probability to determine the likelihood of an event.

9D Use data from a picture to solve problems.

Math Background

Fractions and Probability

A fraction can be used to represent a part of a whole or part of a collection of things or sets. The parts into which the whole is divided must be of equal size.

Study of two equal parts or halves helps children understand that a shape can also be separated into three or more equal parts. Children learn to associate $\frac{1}{2}$ with 1 out of 2 equal parts of a figure. This is extended to the study of $\frac{1}{3}$ and $\frac{1}{4}$ as being 1 out of 3 equal parts and 1 out of 4 equal parts, respectively.

The concept of equal parts as used with fractions can be extended to a brief introduction to probability. At this grade level, children need to understand the language of probability. For example, more likely, less likely, and certain. If a spinner is separated into two equal parts, the probability of the pointer landing on either section is equal. If one section is much larger than the other section, the pointer is more likely to land on the larger section.

INVESTIGATION

Which picture shows the paper folded in half?

Chapter 9   two hundred thirty-five **235**

Using The Investigation

- Discuss fractions with children. Have them suggest times they divide objects into equal parts or pieces. Draw three circles on the board. Divide one circle in half, one in quarters, and one in thirds. Write the appropriate fraction word below each circle.

- Read the question to children. **These pictures show *origami*, which is the Japanese art of folding paper into shapes. Look at the pictures. Which picture shows the paper folded in half?** (Check children's answers.)

 For more information about projects and investigations, visit Education Place. **eduplace.com/math/mw/**

How Many Parts?

First, fold a square piece of paper in half.

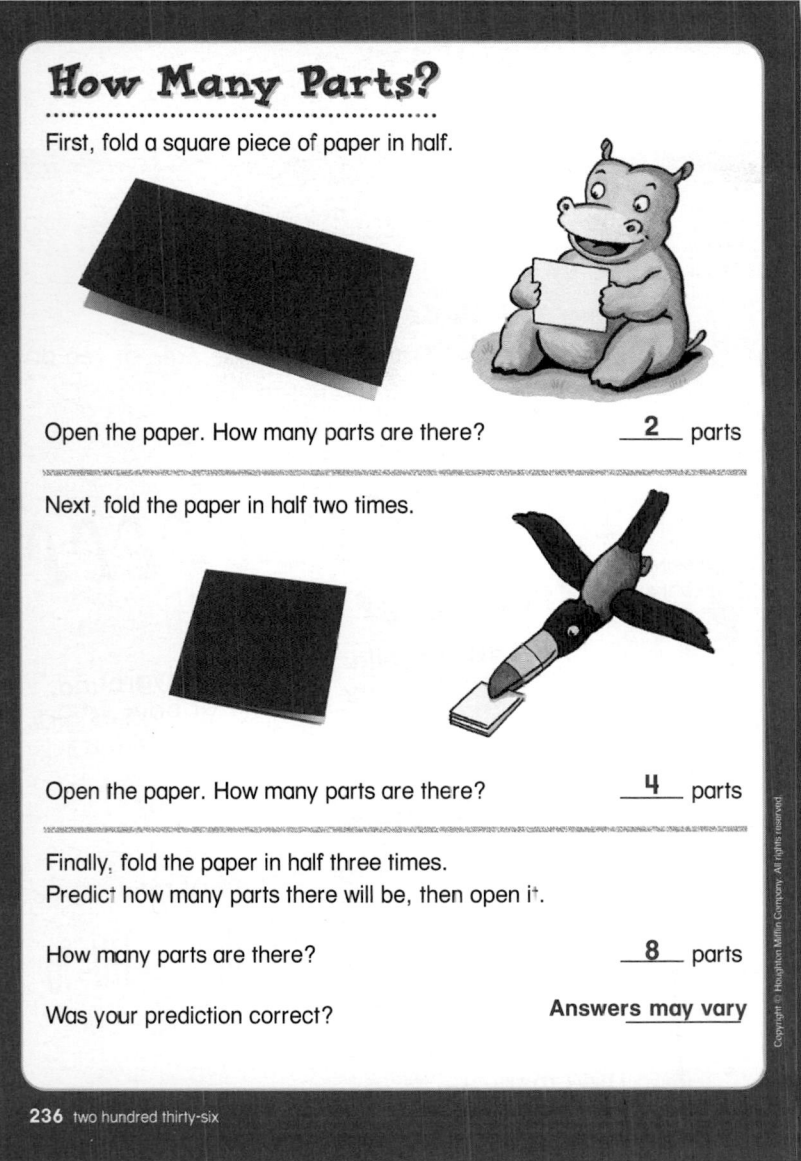

Open the paper. How many parts are there? ___2___ parts

Next, fold the paper in half two times.

Open the paper. How many parts are there? ___4___ parts

Finally, fold the paper in half three times.
Predict how many parts there will be, then open it.

How many parts are there? ___8___ parts

Was your prediction correct? **Answers may vary**

Meeting the Needs of Mathematically Promising Students

The *Chapter Challenges* resource book provides blackline masters for activities that explore, extend, and connect the mathematics in every chapter. To support this independent work, see the Teacher Notes for each activity.

Explore: Parts of Squares, page 49, after Lesson 1
Extend: Cut the Fraction, page 51, after Lesson 3
Connect: Predict and Pick, page 53, after Lesson 5

Using This Page

Tell the children that they are now going to fold a piece of paper to make equal parts.

- Hold up a square piece of paper and demonstrate folding it in half. Remind the children that the corners should be even before they crease the paper.
- Open the paper and count how many parts of equal size. (2 parts)
- Demonstrate folding the paper in half two times. The first fold is the previous fold. Open and count how many parts of equal size. (4 parts)
- Demonstrate folding the paper in half three times. Ask children to predict how many equal parts. Open and count. (8 equal parts) **How many predictions are correct?**

NSF Children's Math Worlds

Children's Math Worlds focuses on the use of models to represent mathematical situations. Thus, using a *Children's Math Worlds* lesson helps students develop a general facility with drawing models to support their thinking that will transfer to their mathematical work.

Equal Parts

PLANNING THE LESSON

MATHEMATICS OBJECTIVE
Identify and count equal parts.

Use Lesson Planner CD-ROM for Lesson 9.1.

Daily Routines

Calendar

Ask children to name pairs of dates in which the sum of the digits is the same, for example, the 15th and the 24th. $(1 + 5 = 6, 2 + 4 = 6)$

Sunday	Monday	Tuesday	Wednesday	Thursday	Friday	Saturday
			1	2	3	4
5	6	7	8	9	10	11
12	13	14	15	16	17	18
19	20	21	22	23	24	25
26	27	28	29	30	31	

Vocabulary

Introduce **equal parts** by telling children that equal parts are the same size. Draw plane shapes on the board. Divide some into equal parts and some into unequal parts. Ask children to shake their heads "yes" when you point to a shape with equal parts. Ask them to shake their heads "no" when you point to a shape that does not have equal parts.

Vocabulary Cards

Meeting North Carolina's Standards

Prepare for Grade 2 Standard 1.02 Use area or region models and set models of fractions to explore part-whole relationships in contexts.

Lesson Transparency **9.1**

Problem of the Day
There are 16 children on the playground. There are the same number of boys as girls. How many boys are on the playground? (8 boys)

Quick Review
Write the number for each set of tally marks.

꠸꠸꠸꠸꠸ ꠸꠸꠸꠸꠸ | ꠸꠸꠸꠸꠸ ꠸꠸꠸   ꠸꠸꠸꠸꠸ ꠸꠸꠸

(eleven, thirteen, eight)

Lesson Quiz
How many equal parts?

1. (4)　　2. (3)

LEVELED PRACTICE

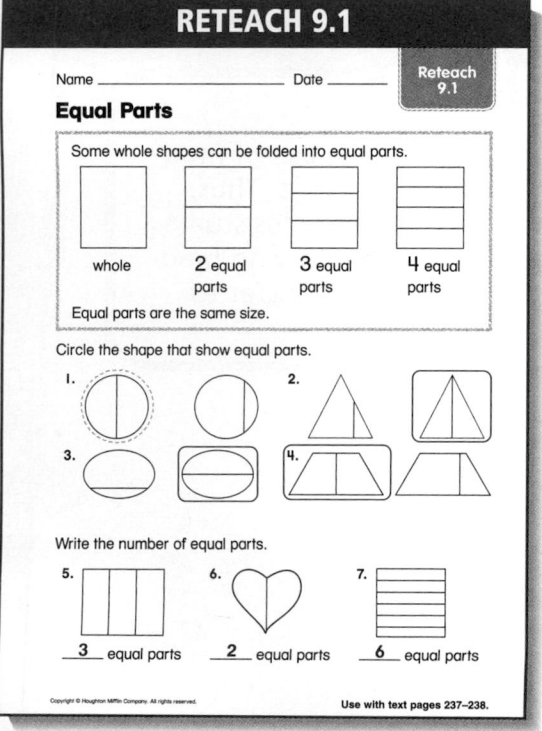

RETEACH 9.1

Name _____ Date _____   Reteach 9.1

Equal Parts

Some whole shapes can be folded into equal parts.

whole | 2 equal parts | 3 equal parts | 4 equal parts

Equal parts are the same size.

Circle the shape that show equal parts.

1.   2.
3.   4.

Write the number of equal parts.

5. ___ 3 ___ equal parts
6. ___ 2 ___ equal parts
7. ___ 6 ___ equal parts

Copyright © Houghton Mifflin Company. All rights reserved.   Use with text pages 237–238.

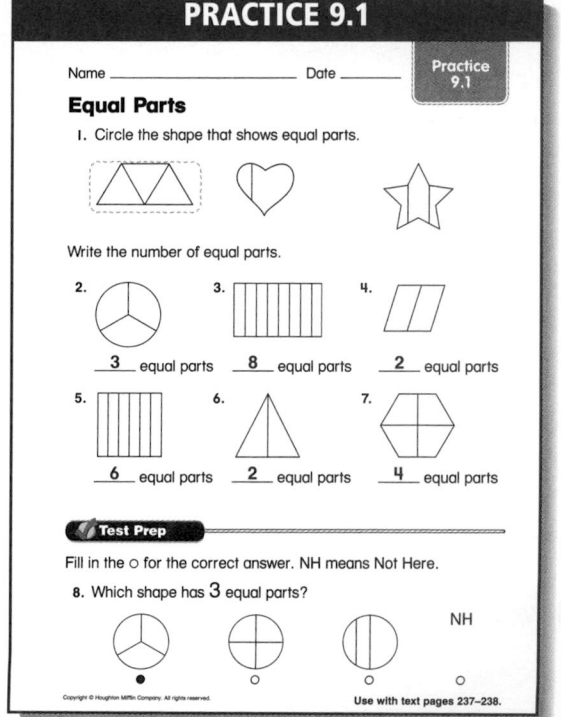

PRACTICE 9.1

Name _____ Date _____   Practice 9.1

Equal Parts

1. Circle the shape that shows equal parts.

Write the number of equal parts.

2. ___ 3 ___ equal parts
3. ___ 8 ___ equal parts
4. ___ 2 ___ equal parts
5. ___ 6 ___ equal parts
6. ___ 2 ___ equal parts
7. ___ 4 ___ equal parts

Test Prep

Fill in the ○ for the correct answer. NH means Not Here.

8. Which shape has 3 equal parts?

  NH

Copyright © Houghton Mifflin Company. All rights reserved.   Use with text pages 237–238.

ENRICHMENT 9.1

Name _____ Date _____   Enrichment 9.1

Put parts Back Together

Circle the equal part to complete the shape.

1.
2.
3.

Write About It If you make equal parts, can one part be bigger than another part? Explain.

_____
_____

Copyright © Houghton Mifflin Company. All rights reserved.   Use with text pages 237–238.

Reaching All Learners

Differentiated Instruction

English Learners

In order to identify and count equal parts, English-language learners will need to understand the term *equal*. Worksheet 9.1 will develop children's understanding of this term.

Special Needs
TACTILE, VISUAL

Show a circle with 3 unequal parts. Cut the pieces apart. Is each piece an equal part? (No, they are different sizes.) Discuss the meaning of *equal parts*. Show a circle with 4 equal parts. Cut it apart and show how to stack them to see if they are the same size.

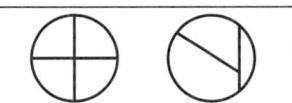

Gifted and Talented
TACTILE, VISUAL

Materials: *pattern blocks*

Have each child make a design using 4 to 8 pattern blocks. Then have the child trace the design. Have children write a sentence about their designs. For example, "My design has 6 equal parts."

TECHNOLOGY

Spiral Review

To reinforce skills on lessons taught earlier, create **customized** spiral review worksheets using the *Ways to Assess* CD-ROM.

eBook

An electronic version of this lesson can be found in **eMathBook**.

Lesson Planner

Use the **Lesson Planner CD-ROM** to see how lesson objectives for this chapter are correlated to standards.

Music Connection

Tell children that in music some notes are held longer than other notes. Demonstrate the length of different notes. Clap and sing a **whole** note for 4 beats; 2 **half** notes for 2 beats each, and 4 **quarter** notes for one beat each.

MATH CENTER

Basic Skills Activity

Motivate children to build basic skills. Use this activity to address multiple learning styles using hands-on activities related to the skills of this lesson.

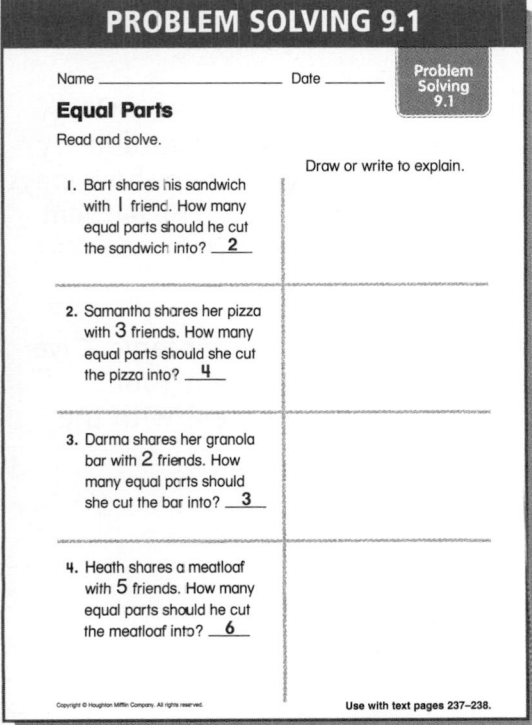

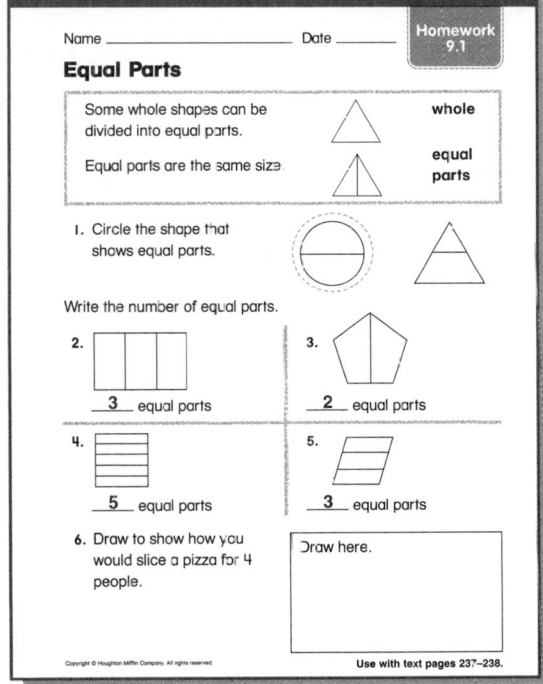

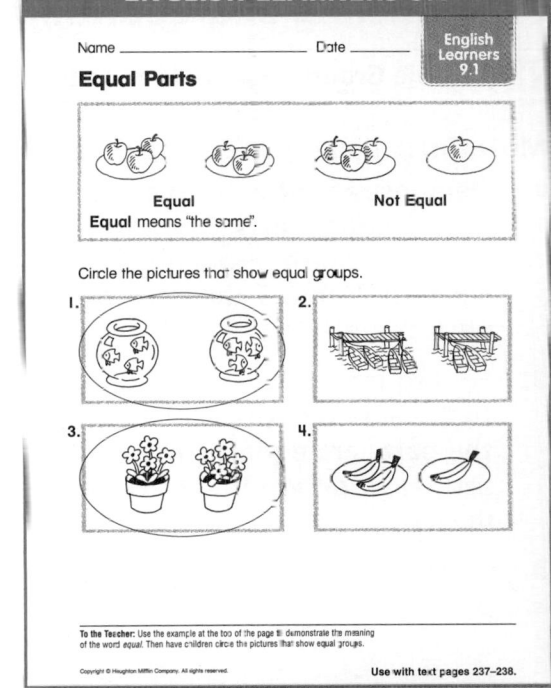

TEACHING LESSON 9.1

LESSON ORGANIZER

Objective Identify and count equal parts.

Resources Reteach, Practice, Enrichment, Problem Solving, Homework, English Learners, Transparencies, Math Center

Materials Plane shapes (Learning Tool (LT) 22 and 23), pattern blocks

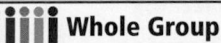

Warm-Up Activity
Identifying Symmetric Shapes

👤👤👤👤 Whole Group	🕐 5 minutes	Auditory, Tactile

Materials: *plane shapes (LT 22 and 23)*

1. Review **symmetry**. Fold a regular shape to form 2 equal parts. Open the shape. **Does this folded shape have matching parts?** (yes) Fold another shape to form 2 unequal parts. **Do these parts match?** (no)

2. Call on volunteers to fold shapes with equal parts and parts that are not equal.

3. **How do we know if a shape has symmetry?** (It can be folded to make matching parts.)

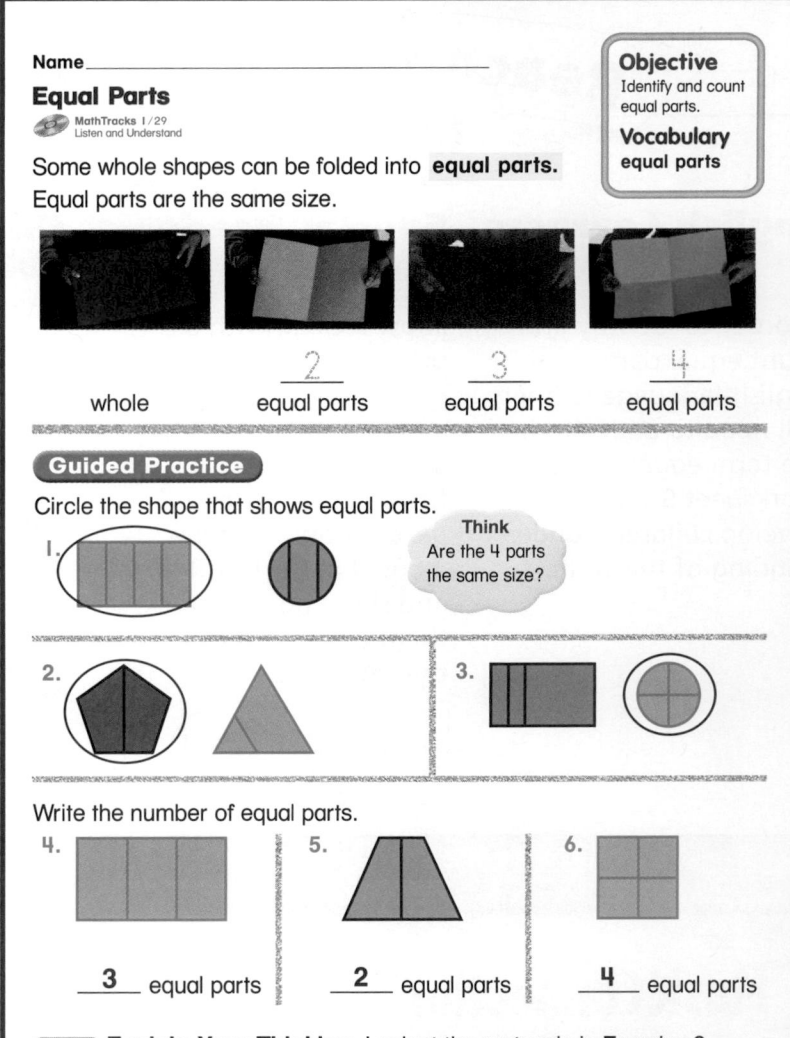

Name_____

Equal Parts

MathTracks 1/29
Listen and Understand

Some whole shapes can be folded into **equal parts.**
Equal parts are the same size.

Objective Identify and count equal parts.

Vocabulary equal parts

whole | 2 equal parts | 3 equal parts | 4 equal parts

Guided Practice

Circle the shape that shows equal parts.

1.

Think Are the 4 parts the same size?

2.

3.

Write the number of equal parts.

4. _3_ equal parts

5. _2_ equal parts

6. _4_ equal parts

TEST TIPS **Explain Your Thinking** Look at the rectangle in Exercise 3. Explain why the shape does not show 3 equal parts. **All of the parts are not the same size.**

Chapter 9 Lesson 1

two hundred thirty-seven **237**

1 Introduce
Modeling and Counting Equal Parts

👤👤👤👤 Whole Group	🕐 10–15 minutes	Visual, Auditory

Materials: *paper circles, paper squares (LT 22 and 23)*

1. Demonstrate how to fold a paper square in half to form 2 equal parts. Open to show children. Now fold another square into 4 equal parts. Open it and have children decide if the parts are equal and how many parts there are.

2. Fold squares into 2 and 4 unequal parts. Compare them to the squares with equal parts. **How do we know if the parts are equal?** (They are equal if they are the same size.) **How do we find how many equal parts?** (Count them.)

3. Have children fold paper circles into 2 and into 4 equal parts.

2 Develop

Guided Learning

Teaching Example Introduce the objective and vocabulary to children. Guide them through the example to show ways a whole shape can be folded into equal parts. Have them trace to show there are 2, 3, and 4 equal parts.

Guided Practice

Have children complete **Exercises 1–6** as you observe. Give children the opportunity to answer the Explain Your Thinking question. Then discuss their responses with the class.

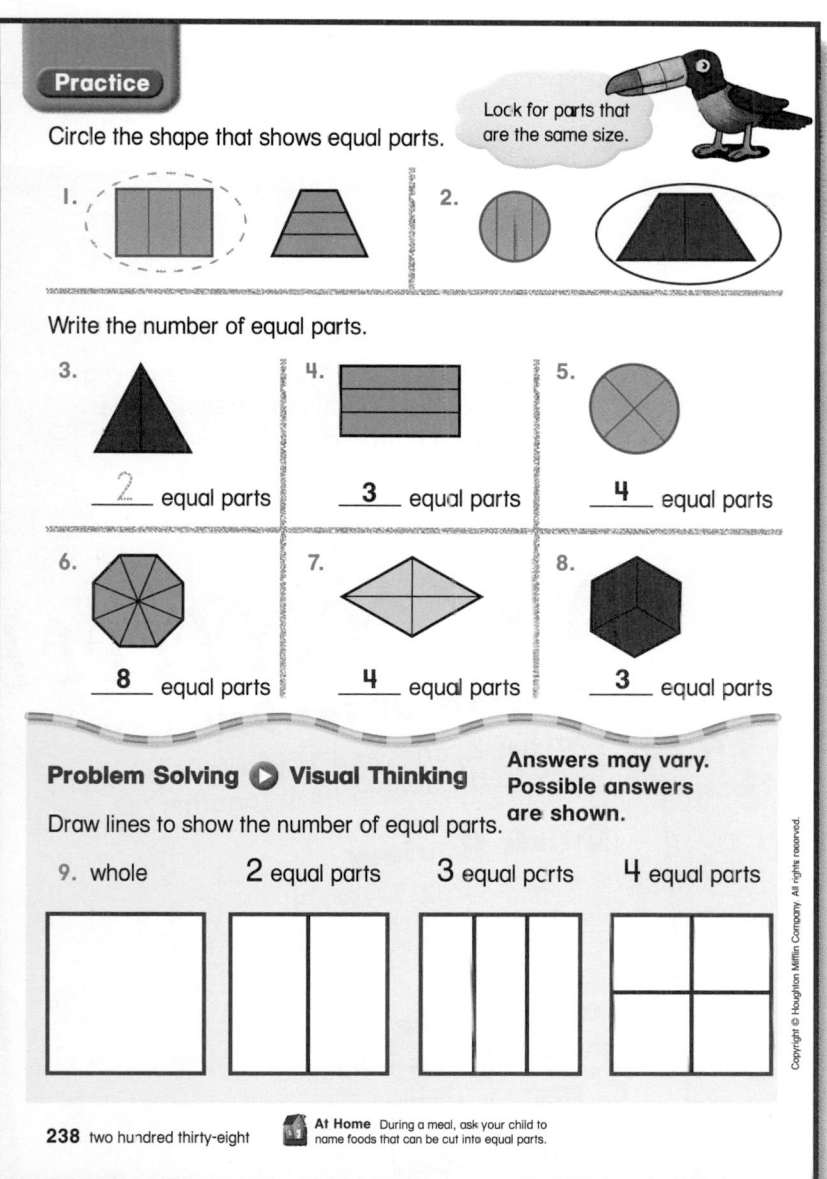

Practice

Circle the shape that shows equal parts.

Lock for parts that are the same size.

1.

2.

Write the number of equal parts.

3. _2_ equal parts

4. _3_ equal parts

5. _4_ equal parts

6. _8_ equal parts

7. _4_ equal parts

8. _3_ equal parts

Problem Solving ▶ Visual Thinking

Draw lines to show the number of equal parts.

Answers may vary. Possible answers are shown.

9. whole | 2 equal parts | 3 equal parts | 4 equal parts

238 two hundred thirty-eight

At Home During a meal, ask your child to name foods that can be cut into equal parts.

Daily Test Prep

Sue gives Mia 3 clips. Lee gives Mia 4 clips. How many clips does Mia have now?

7   8   9   NH
●   ○   ○   ○

Activity

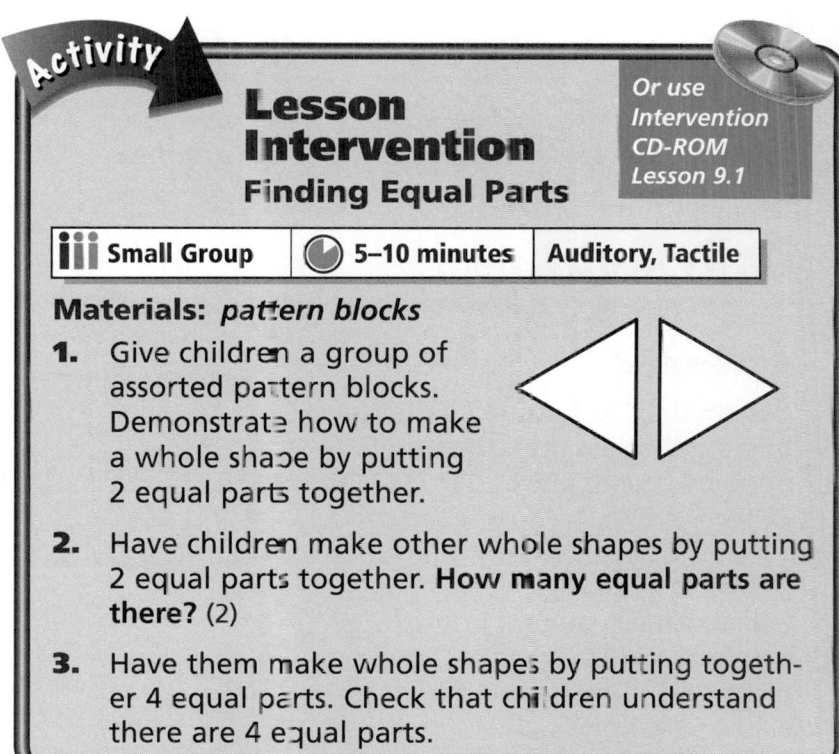

Lesson Intervention

Finding Equal Parts

Or use Intervention CD-ROM Lesson 9.1

👥 Small Group   🕐 5–10 minutes   Auditory, Tactile

Materials: pattern blocks

1. Give children a group of assorted pattern blocks. Demonstrate how to make a whole shape by putting 2 equal parts together.

2. Have children make other whole shapes by putting 2 equal parts together. **How many equal parts are there?** (2)

3. Have them make whole shapes by putting together 4 equal parts. Check that children understand there are 4 equal parts.

---

3 Practice

Independent Practice

Children complete **Exercises 1–8** independently.

Problem Solving

After children complete **Exercise 9**, call on volunteers to share their solutions.

Common Error

Difficulty Identifying Equal Parts

Children may have difficulty identifying parts that match. Have them trace one part and place it over the other parts to see if they match.

4 Assess and Close

Explain how you know a shape has unequal parts. (The parts are not the same size.)

How many equal parts? (3)

 **Keeping a Journal**

Draw a shape. Draw lines to show equal parts. Write how many equal parts your shape has. Describe how you know.

One Half

PLANNING THE LESSON

MATHEMATICS OBJECTIVE
Use fractions to name parts of a whole; identify one half of a whole.

Use Lesson Planner CD-ROM for Lesson 9.2.

Daily Routines

Calendar
Ask children to find dates that have one digit that is the other digit doubled. (for example: 12th, 21st, and 24th)

Sunday	Monday	Tuesday	Wednesday	Thursday	Friday	Saturday
			1	2	3	4
5	6	7	8	9	10	11
12	13	14	15	16	17	18
19	20	21	22	23	24	25
26	27	28	29	30	31	

Vocabulary
Explain that two equal parts of a whole are called **halves**. Draw a picture to show halves. Further explain that **one half** is a **fraction**, or part, of the whole. Draw other pictures to show one half.

Vocabulary Cards

Meeting North Carolina's Standards
Prepare for Grade 2 Standard 1.02 Use area or region models and set models of fractions to explore part-whole relationships in contexts.

Lesson Transparency 9.2

Problem of the Day
Josh has 2 cones and 1 cylinder. How many faces do the shapes have together? (4 faces)

Quick Review

$$\begin{array}{ccccc} 1 & 2 & 3 & & \\ +1 & +2 & +3 & 4 & 5 \\ \hline (2) & (4) & +3 & +4 & +5 \\ & & (6) & (8) & (10) \end{array}$$

Lesson Quiz
Which shape has $\frac{1}{2}$ shaded?

1.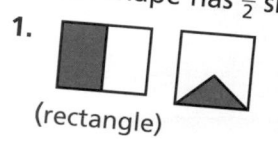

(rectangle)

LEVELED PRACTICE

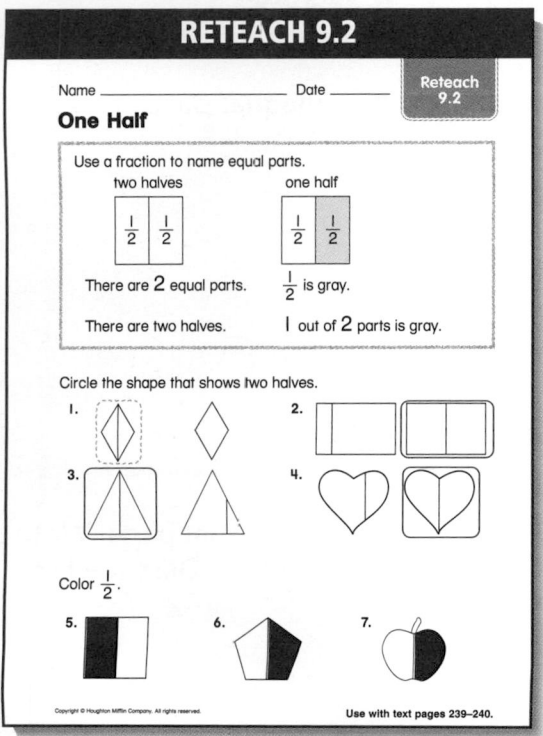

RETEACH 9.2

Name _____ Date _____   Reteach 9.2

One Half

Use a fraction to name equal parts.

two halves   one half

There are **2** equal parts. $\frac{1}{2}$ is gray.

There are two halves.   1 out of 2 parts is gray.

Circle the shape that shows two halves.

1.   2.
3.   4.

Color $\frac{1}{2}$.

5.   6.   7.

Use with text pages 239–240.

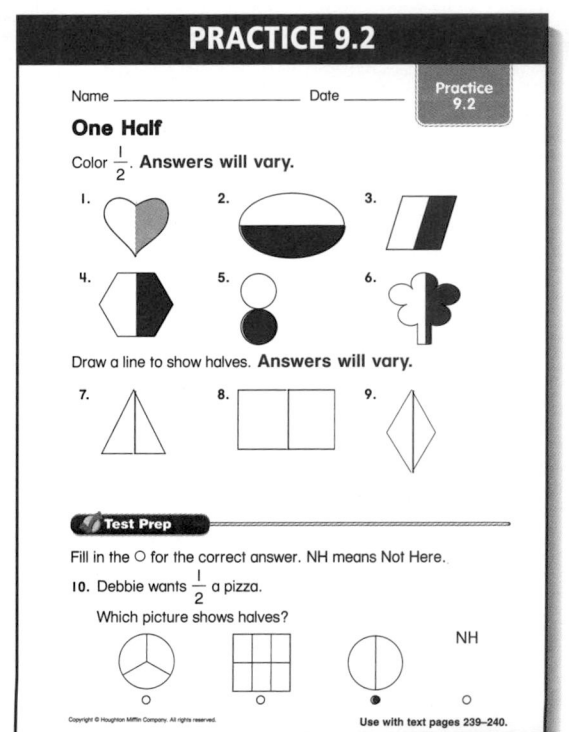

PRACTICE 9.2

Name _____ Date _____   Practice 9.2

One Half

Color $\frac{1}{2}$. **Answers will vary.**

1.   2.   3.
4.   5.   6.

Draw a line to show halves. **Answers will vary.**

7.   8.   9.

Test Prep

Fill in the ○ for the correct answer. NH means Not Here.

10. Debbie wants $\frac{1}{2}$ a pizza.
    Which picture shows halves?

    NH

Use with text pages 239–240.

ENRICHMENT 9.2

Name _____ Date _____   Enrichment 9.2

Cut in Half

Circle the object that shows two halves.

1.   2.   3.   4.
5.   6.   7.   8.
9.   10.   11.   12.

Write About It How could you show one half of a piece of paper?

Answers will vary. _____

Use with text pages 239–240.

Practice Workbook Page 58

Reaching All Learners

Differentiated Instruction

English Learners

English-language learners may not be familiar with the singular and plural form of *half*, which they will need to know to solve some word problems with fractions. Use Worksheet 9.2 to teach these forms.

Inclusion

TACTILE, VISUAL

Materials: *apple*

- Cut the apple in half.
- Tell the child that each half is one part of the whole apple.
- Have the child draw an apple and color $\frac{1}{2}$. Ask the child how much of the apple is colored. (one half)

Early Finishers

TACTILE, VISUAL

Materials: *index cards*

- Draw symmetrical shapes on index cards and cut the cards along the line of symmetry.
- Have pairs of children mix the cards and spread them out face up.
- Children work together to find the matching halves.

TECHNOLOGY

Spiral Review

Help students remember skills they learned earlier by creating **customized** spiral review worksheets using the *Ways to Assess* CD-ROM.

eBook

eMathBook allows students to review lessons and do homework without carrying their textbooks home.

Education Place

Encourage students to visit **Education Place** at eduplace.com/kids/mw/ for more student activities.

Art Connection

Give children clay and a craft stick. Have them flatten the clay into a circle and use the craft stick to divide it into halves. Ask children to make a square from the clay and divide it into halves. How many ways can you divide a square into halves?

MATH CENTER

Vocabulary Activity

This vocabulary-building activity helps children understand and remember new words. Encourage children to use the words in math discussion.

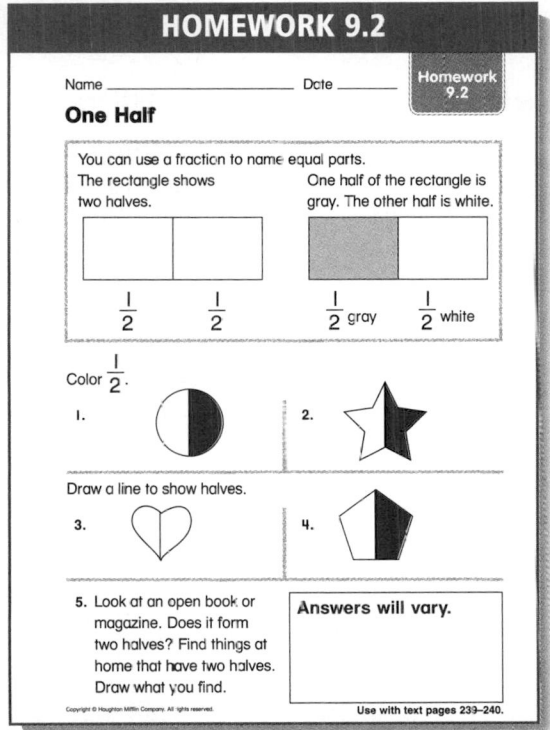

Homework Workbook Page 58

TEACHING LESSON 9.2

LESSON ORGANIZER

Objective Use fractions to name parts of a whole; identify one half of a whole.

Resources Reteach, Practice, Enrichment, Problem Solving, Homework, English Learners, Transparencies, Math Center

Materials Paper shapes (LT 22 and 23), teacher-made symmetrical object pictures (cut in halves)

Activity

Warm-Up Activity
Identifying Equal Parts

iii Small Group	⏱ 5 minutes	Visual, Tactile

Materials: *paper shapes (LT 22 and 23)*

1. Review equal parts. Fold a square in half to form 2 equal parts. Open the shape and show it to children. Have children say the number of parts. (2)

2. Give children a shape to fold into 2 equal parts. Ask volunteers to share their shapes and tell if the parts are equal.

3. **How do we know if a shape has equal parts?** (If the parts match, they are equal.)

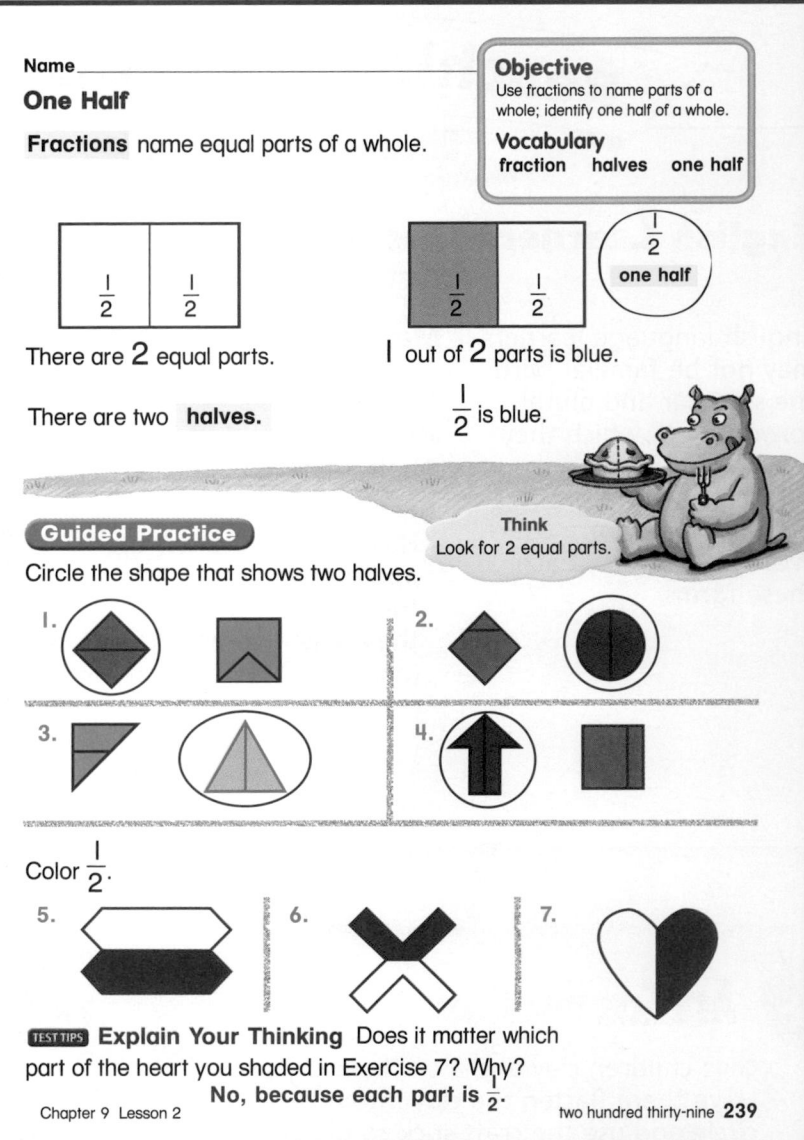

Name _____

One Half

Fractions name equal parts of a whole.

Objective
Use fractions to name parts of a whole; identify one half of a whole.
Vocabulary
fraction   halves   one half

There are **2** equal parts.

There are two **halves**.

1 out of **2** parts is blue.

$\frac{1}{2}$ is blue.

Guided Practice

Think
Look for 2 equal parts.

Circle the shape that shows two halves.

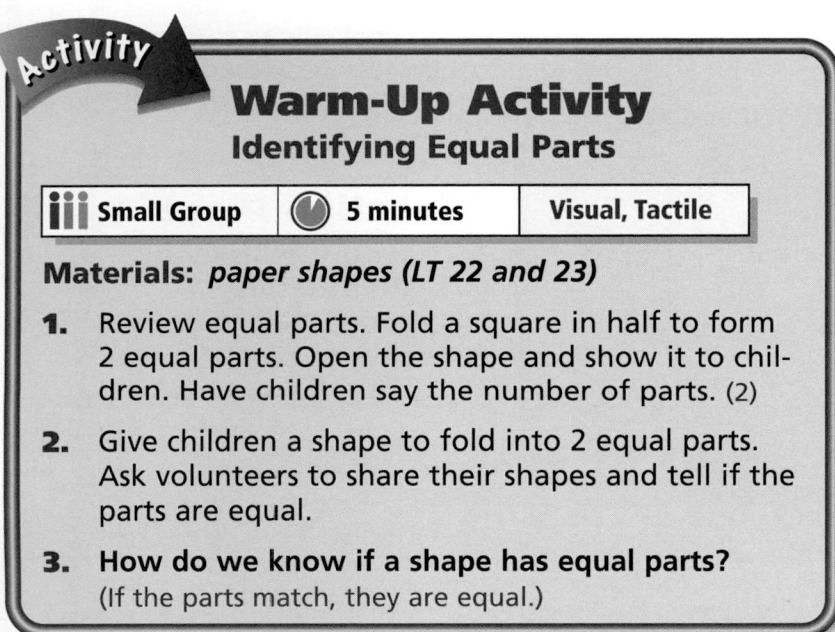

Color $\frac{1}{2}$

TEST TIPS **Explain Your Thinking** Does it matter which part of the heart you shaded in Exercise 7? Why? **No, because each part is $\frac{1}{2}$.**

Chapter 9 Lesson 2   two hundred thirty-nine **239**

---

① Introduce   *Activity*

Discuss Using a Fraction to Name Equal Parts

iiii Whole Group	⏱ 10–15 minutes	Visual, Auditory

Materials: *paper circles (LT 22 and 23)*

1. Have children fold a paper circle in half to form 2 equal parts. Have them unfold their circles. **How many equal parts?** (2 parts)

2. Tell children to color one part of their circles blue. **How many parts are blue?** (1 part) **What part of the whole circle is blue?** (one half)

3. Write the fraction $\frac{1}{2}$ on the board. Explain that the 2 stands for 2 equal parts and the 1 stands for 1 out of the 2 equal parts.

② Develop

Guided Learning

Teaching Example Introduce the objective and vocabulary to children. Show children how to fold a square paper into halves. Color $\frac{1}{2}$ blue. Write $\frac{1}{2}$ on the board. Explain that $\frac{1}{2}$ is a fraction. Discuss what each number in the fraction means and relate it to the parts of the square.

Guided Practice

Have children complete **Exercises 1–4** as you observe. Be sure they understand that they are to color $\frac{1}{2}$ of the shapes for **Exercises 5–7**. Give children the opportunity to answer the Explain Your Thinking question. Then discuss their responses with the class.

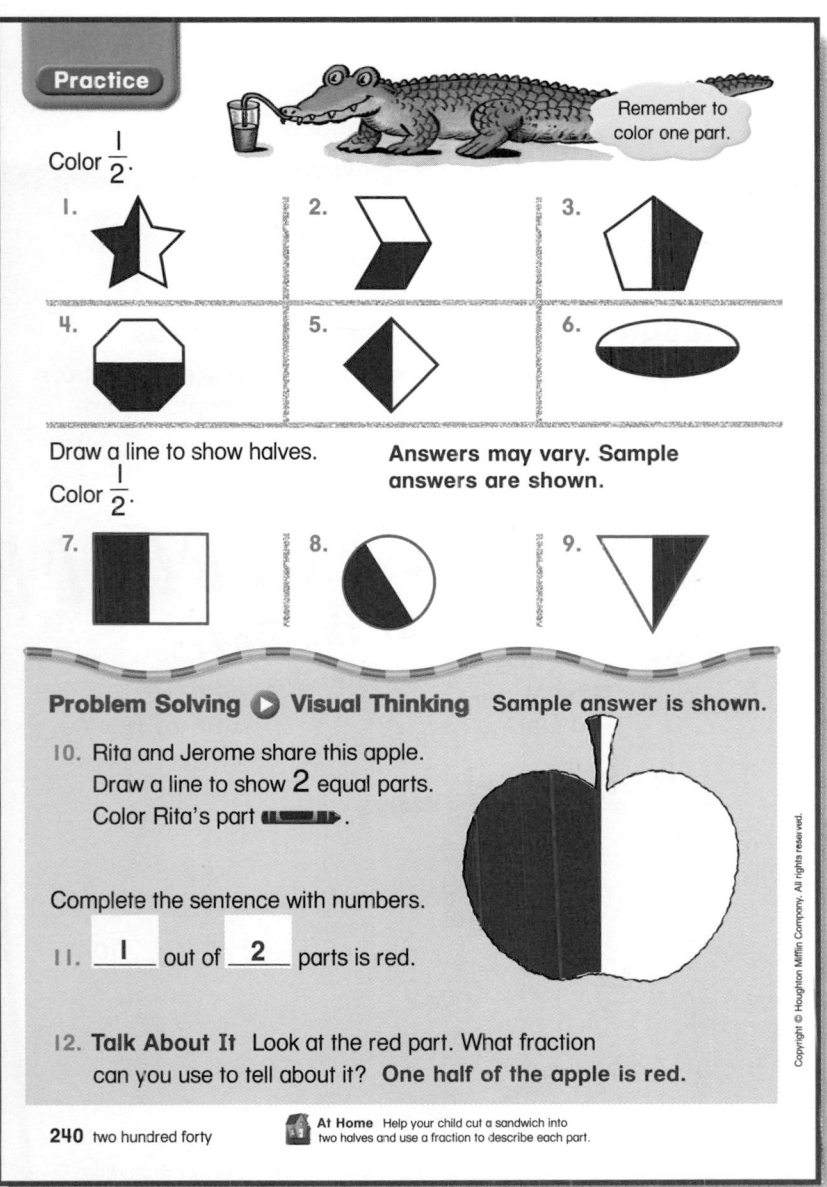

Practice

Remember to color one part.

Color $\frac{1}{2}$.

1. 2. 3.

4. 5. 6.

Draw a line to show halves.
Color $\frac{1}{2}$.

Answers may vary. Sample answers are shown.

7. 8. 9.

Problem Solving ▶ Visual Thinking Sample answer is shown.

10. Rita and Jerome share this apple.
Draw a line to show **2** equal parts.
Color Rita's part 🖍.

Complete the sentence with numbers.

11. | 1 | out of | 2 | parts is red.

12. **Talk About It** Look at the red part. What fraction can you use to tell about it? **One half of the apple is red.**

240 two hundred forty

At Home Help your child cut a sandwich into two halves and use a fraction to describe each part.

Daily Test Prep

Test Prep Transparency
9.2

$5 \square 3 = 8$

$-$ $+$ $=$

○   ●   ○

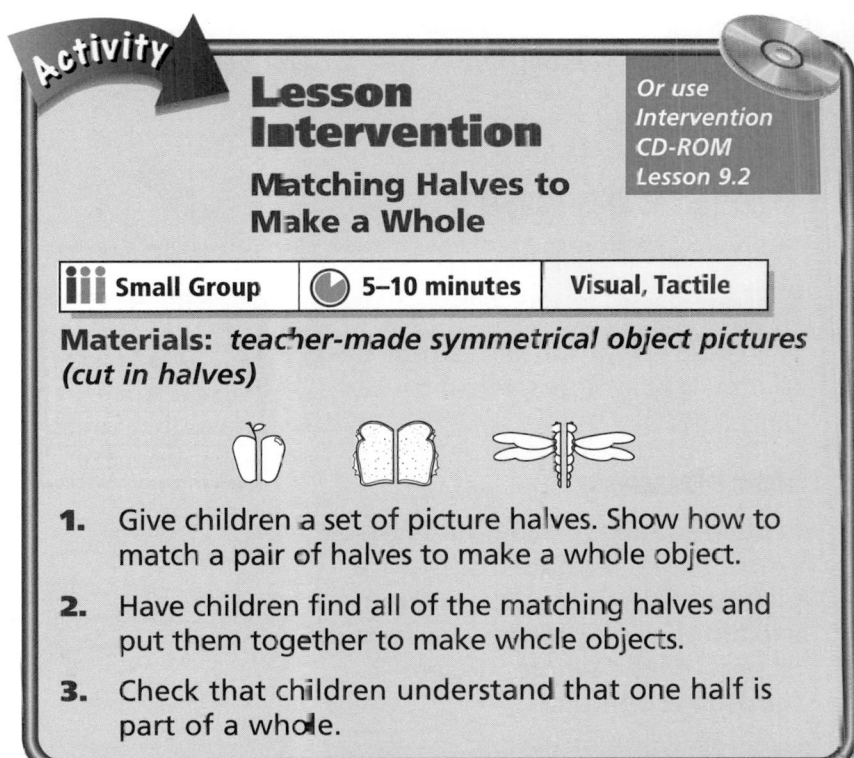

Activity

Lesson Intervention

Or use Intervention CD-ROM Lesson 9.2

Matching Halves to Make a Whole

| 👥 Small Group | ⏱ 5–10 minutes | Visual, Tactile |

Materials: *teacher-made symmetrical object pictures (cut in halves)*

1. Give children a set of picture halves. Show how to match a pair of halves to make a whole object.

2. Have children find all of the matching halves and put them together to make whole objects.

3. Check that children understand that one half is part of a whole.

---

❸ Practice

Independent Practice

Children complete **Exercises 1–9** independently.

Problem Solving

After children complete **Exercises 10–11**, call on volunteers to share their solutions. Use the **Talk About It** in **Exercise 12** to discuss how to use the fraction to describe a picture.

Common Error

Coloring Two Halves

Children may forget that the 1 in $\frac{1}{2}$ represents 1 part. Remind them that it means 1 out of 2 equal parts.

❹ Assess and Close

What fraction of an orange is left if you eat $\frac{1}{2}$? ($\frac{1}{2}$)

Explain what the numbers in $\frac{1}{2}$ mean. (The 1 means 1 part. The 2 means 2 equal parts.)

Keeping a Journal

Draw a shape. Color $\frac{1}{2}$ red. Explain how to tell that one half of your shape is red.

One Fourth

Lesson 9.3

PLANNING THE LESSON

MATHEMATICS OBJECTIVE
Identify one fourth and one third of a whole.

 *Use Lesson Planner CD-ROM for Lesson 9.3.*

Daily Routines

Calendar
Ask children to find dates that have two matching digits. (the 11th and the 22nd)

Vocabulary
Explain that four equal parts of a whole are called **fourths**. Draw a picture to show fourths. Further explain that **one fourth** is a fraction, or part, of the whole. Repeat for **thirds** and **one third**.

Vocabulary Cards

Meeting North Carolina's Standards
Prepare for Grade 2 Standard 1.02 Use area or region models and set models of fractions to explore part-whole relationships in contexts.

Lesson Transparency 9.3

Problem of the Day
Danny cut a rope into 2 equal parts. He gave 1 part to Al. What fraction of the rope did Danny give to Al? ($\frac{1}{2}$)

Quick Review

$$\begin{array}{r} 2 \\ +8 \\ \hline (10) \end{array} \qquad \begin{array}{r} 7 \\ +3 \\ \hline (10) \end{array} \qquad \begin{array}{r} 1 \\ +9 \\ \hline (10) \end{array} \qquad \begin{array}{r} 6 \\ +4 \\ \hline (10) \end{array} \qquad \begin{array}{r} 5 \\ +5 \\ \hline (10) \end{array}$$

Lesson Quiz
Which shape shows $\frac{1}{4}$?

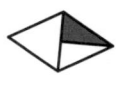

(circle)

LEVELED PRACTICE

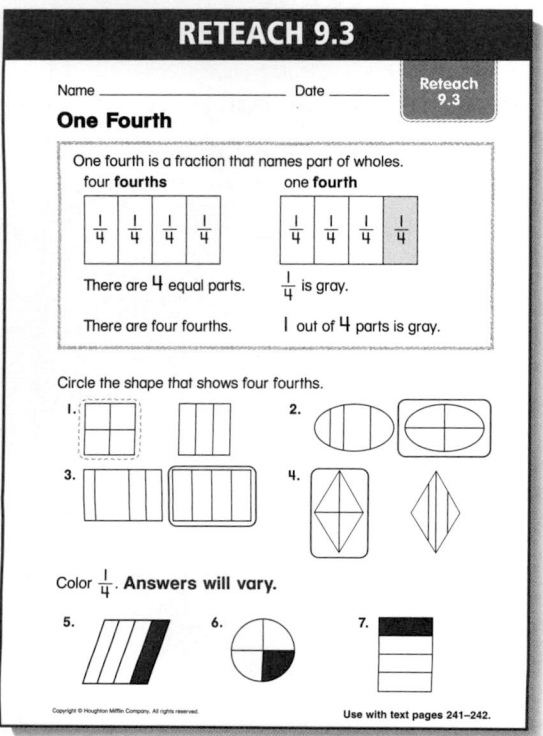

RETEACH 9.3

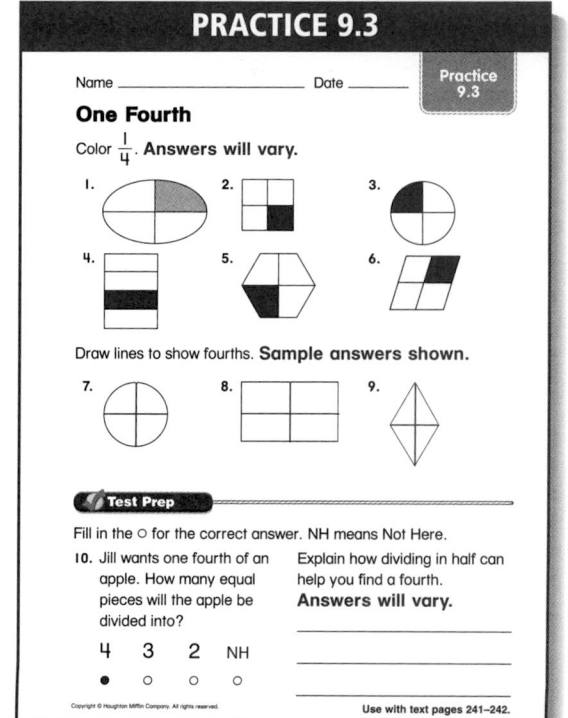

PRACTICE 9.3

Practice Workbook Page 59

ENRICHMENT 9.3

Reaching All Learners
Differentiated Instruction

English Learners

English-language learners may be confused by similar words representing fractions and ordinal positions. Use Worksheet 9.3 to help them understand the differences between these words.

Special Needs
VISUAL, TACTILE

Materials: *fraction cards for $\frac{1}{2}$, $\frac{1}{3}$, $\frac{1}{4}$; index cards of fraction shapes (teacher-made)*

Have the child place shape cards in a pile. Place the fraction cards face up in rows. Have the child turn over the top picture card. Direct the child to match the fraction cards. Continue with remaining cards.

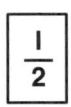 

Early Finishers
TACTILE, VISUAL

Materials: *game cards, counters, bag*

Make 3 × 3 game cards. Write $\frac{1}{2}$, $\frac{1}{3}$, $\frac{1}{4}$ on paper and place into a bag. Have the child pull a fraction from the bag. Place a counter on the shape that shows that fraction. Play continues until 3 shapes are covered in a row.

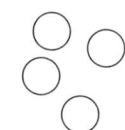

Literature Connection

In the story *Gator Pie,* by Louise Matthews, two gators think they have to share a pie with other gators. Have children draw a picture of the pie if it is to be shared with 2, 3, and 4 gators.

MATH CENTER

Vocabulary Activity

This vocabulary-building activity helps children understand and remember new words. Encourage children to use the words in math discussion.

TECHNOLOGY

Spiral Review

You can prepare students for standardized tests with **customized** spiral review on key skills using the *Ways to Assess* CD-ROM.

Education Place

You can visit **Education Place** at eduplace.com/math/mw/ for teacher support materials.

Games

Students can practice their skills using the Rock Hopper math game, available on the *Ways to Success* CD-ROM.

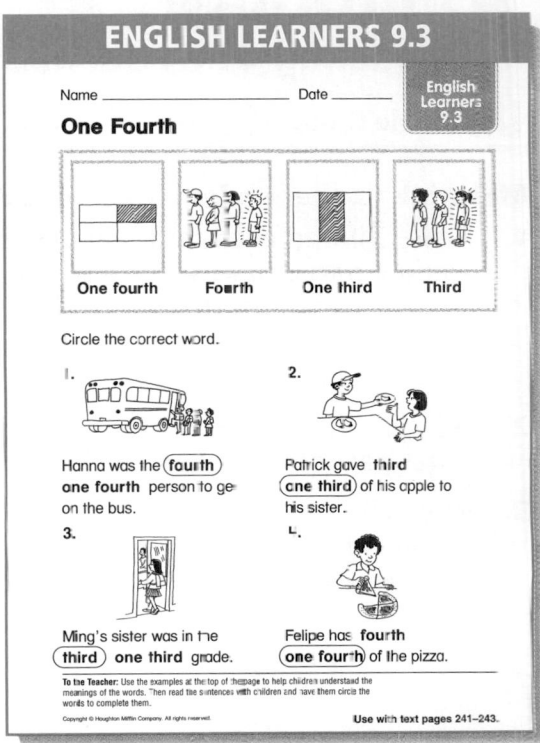

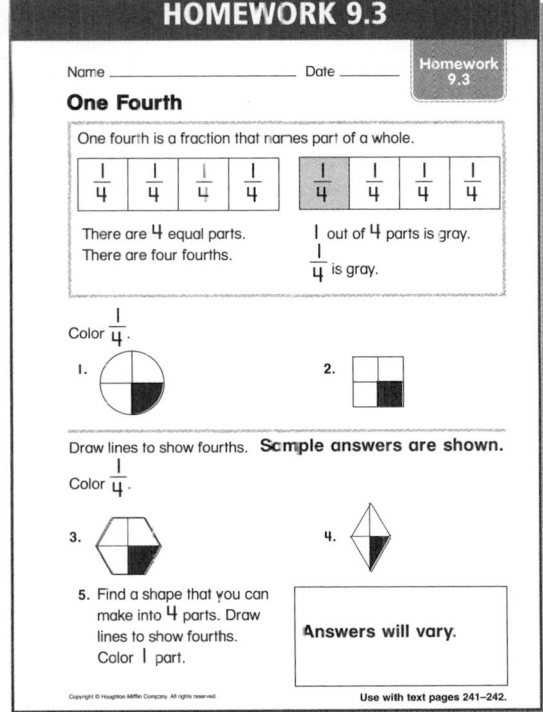

Homework Workbook Page 59

CHAPTER 9   Lesson 3   **241B**

TEACHING LESSON 9.3

Objective Identify one fourth and one third of a whole.

Resources Reteach, Practice, Enrichment, Problem Solving, Homework, English Learners, Transparencies, Math Center

Materials Paper shapes (LT 22 and 23), teacher-made paper fraction circles

Activity
Warm-Up Activity
Model and Identify One Half of a Whole

| 👤👤👤👤 Whole Group | 🕐 5 minutes | Visual, Tactile |

Materials: *paper squares (LT 22 and 23)*

1. Review one half. Draw a square and divide it into halves. Shade one half. Emphasize that $\frac{1}{2}$ is part of a whole.

2. Give children each a paper square. Have them fold their squares in half. Have them color one half of their squares. Have volunteers share their squares and write the fraction on the board.

3. **How do we know that $\frac{1}{2}$ names the colored part of our squares?** (The 1 in $\frac{1}{2}$ stands for 1 colored part of 2 equal parts. The 2 means there are 2 parts.)

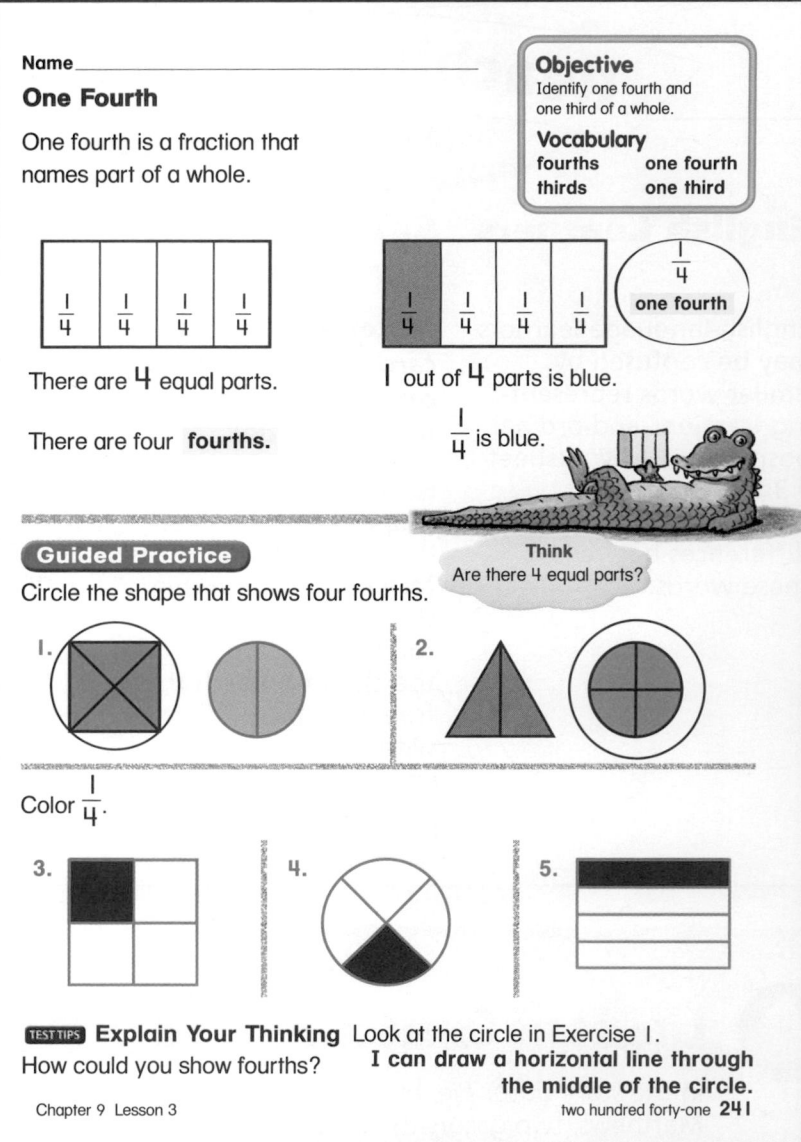

Name_____

One Fourth

One fourth is a fraction that names part of a whole.

> **Objective**
> Identify one fourth and one third of a whole.
> **Vocabulary**
> fourths   one fourth
> thirds   one third

There are 4 equal parts.

There are four **fourths.**

1 out of 4 parts is blue.

$\frac{1}{4}$ is blue.

Guided Practice

> **Think**
> Are there 4 equal parts?

Circle the shape that shows four fourths.

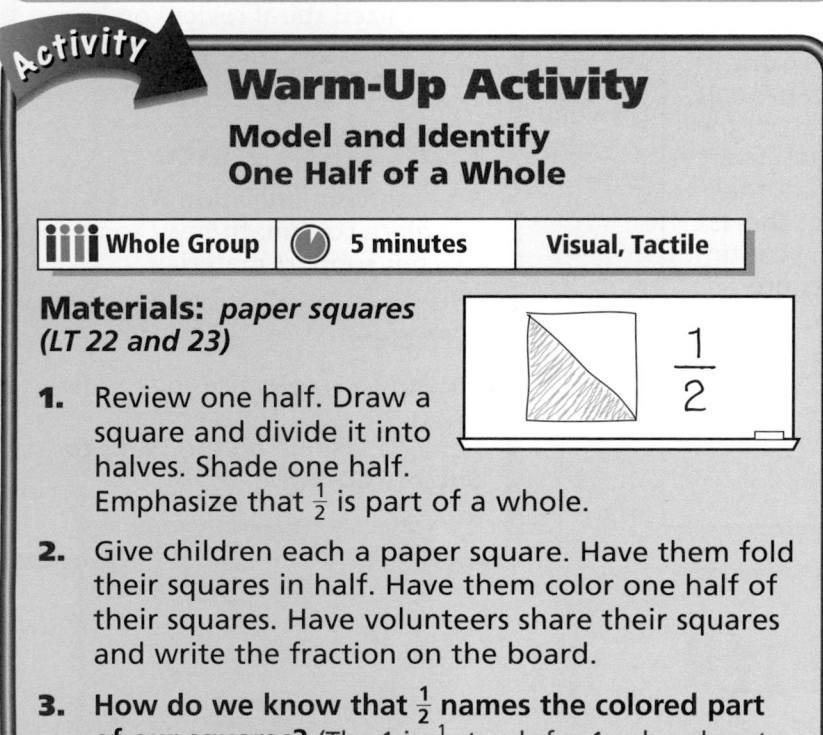

1.

2.

Color $\frac{1}{4}$.

3.

4.

5.

TEST TIPS **Explain Your Thinking** Look at the circle in Exercise 1. How could you show fourths?   *I can draw a horizontal line through the middle of the circle.*

Chapter 9 Lesson 3

two hundred forty-one **241**

---

① Introduce
Activity
Modeling One Fourth of a Whole

| 👤👤👤👤 Whole Group | 🕐 10–15 minutes | Visual, Auditory |

Materials: *paper circles (LT 22 and 23)*

1. Have children each fold a paper circle in half to form 2 equal parts. Have them fold it in half again to form 4 equal parts. Tell them to unfold their circle. **How many parts equal the whole circle?** (4 parts) **Are the parts equal?** (yes)

2. Tell children to color one part of their circles blue. **What part of the whole circle is blue?** (1 part)

3. Write the fraction $\frac{1}{4}$ on the board. Explain that the 4 stands for 4 equal parts and the 1 stands for 1 of the 4 equal parts. Help children read the fraction $\frac{1}{4}$.

② Develop

Guided Learning

Teaching Example Introduce the objective and vocabulary to children. Show children how to fold a rectangle into fourths. Color $\frac{1}{4}$ blue. Write $\frac{1}{4}$ on the board. Explain that $\frac{1}{4}$ is the fraction that names 1 part of 4 equal parts. Discuss what each number in the fraction means and relate it to the parts of the rectangle.

Guided Practice

Have children complete **Exercises 1–5** as you observe. Give children the opportunity to answer the Explain Your Thinking question. Then discuss their responses with the class.

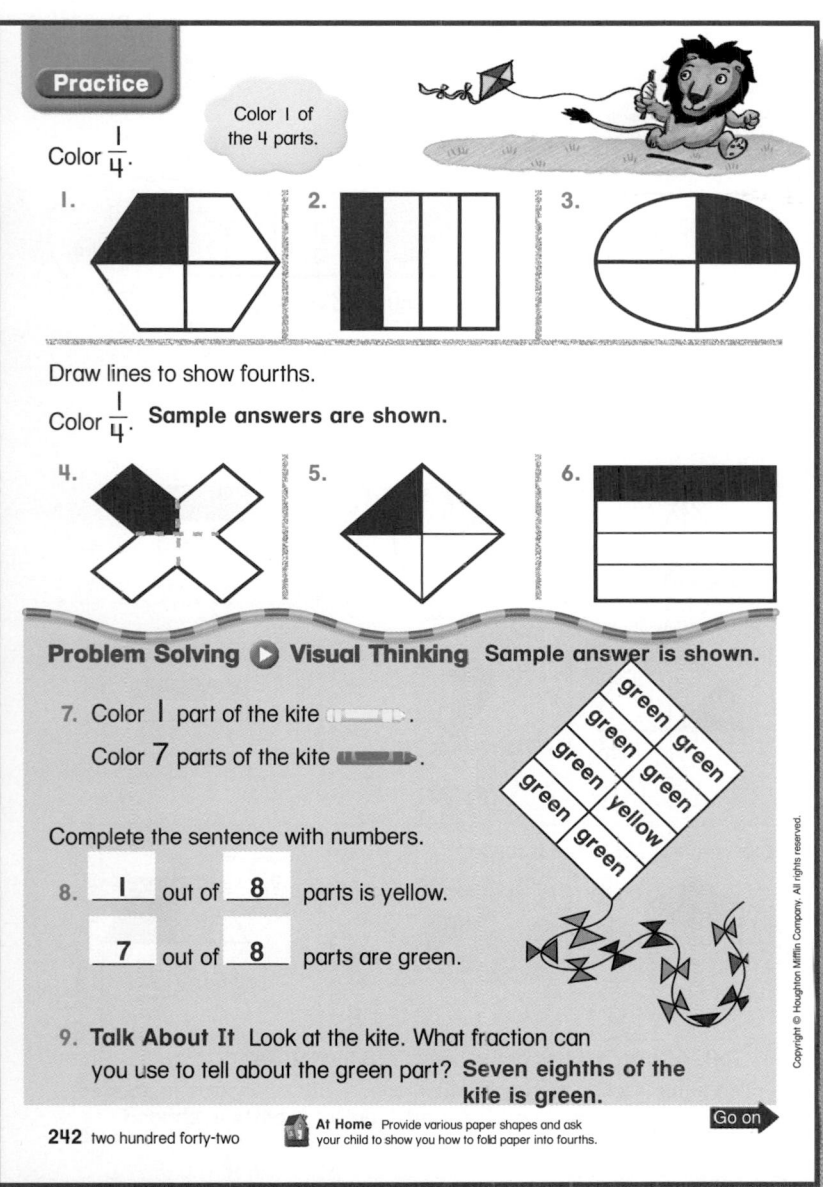

Color $\frac{1}{4}$.

Color 1 of the 4 parts.

1.   2.   3.

Draw lines to show fourths.

Color $\frac{1}{4}$. **Sample answers are shown.**

4.   5.   6.

Problem Solving ▶ Visual Thinking Sample answer is shown.

7. Color **1** part of the kite

   Color **7** parts of the kite

Complete the sentence with numbers.

8. **1** out of **8** parts is yellow.

   7 out of **8** parts are green.

9. **Talk About It** Look at the kite. What fraction can you use to tell about the green part? **Seven eighths of the kite is green.**

At Home Provide various paper shapes and ask your child to show you how to fold paper into fourths.

Go on ▶

ACHIEVING
Mathematical Proficiency

Understanding Proportional Reasoning

Research has shown that the development of math proficiency depends on consistent instruction that engages children as learners. They must be consistently encouraged to see mathematical concepts as something they use on an everyday basis. Many children pick up useful informal knowledge of fractions through activities and experiences in their daily lives. This can occur both inside and outside of school.

Most children inherently grasp the idea of fair shares. This idea can be used as a basis for introducing the concept of fractions. In this chapter, children are actively involved in lessons about fractions.

The challenge of instruction is to engage students in learning activities that support and develop the informal knowledge they bring to the classroom.

---

3 Practice

Independent Practice

Children complete **Exercises 1–6** independently.

Problem Solving

After children complete **Exercises 7–8**, call on volunteers to share their solutions. Use the **Talk About It** in **Exercise 9** to discuss seven eighths as a fraction.

You may want to return to Exercises 1–6 and ask children to talk about the white part of the shape. In each exercise 3 out of 4 parts is white.

Common Error

Coloring the Whole Shape

Children may forget that the 1 in $\frac{1}{4}$ represents 1 part of 4. Remind them to color only 1 out of 4 parts to show $\frac{1}{4}$.

4 Assess and Close

A pizza has 4 slices. How many slices are left if you eat $\frac{1}{4}$? (3 slices)

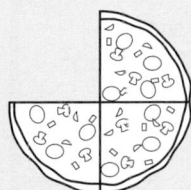

How many slices equal the whole pizza? (4 slices)

 **Keeping a Journal**

Draw a shape. Color $\frac{1}{4}$ red. Write a sentence to describe what you drew.

Daily Test Prep

8 □ 3 = 5

  −   +   =
  ●   ○   ○

*Or use
Intervention
CD-ROM
Lesson 9.3*

Activity

Lesson Intervention
Modeling Fourths

| 👤👤👤 Small Group | ⏱ 5–10 minutes | Visual, Tactile |

Materials: *paper fraction circles (teacher-made)*

1. Give children fraction circles. Have them use 2 pieces to make a circle. Discuss equal parts (2) and discuss the name for each part. (half) Make sure children understand that one part is one half.

2. Have children use 4 pieces to make a circle. Discuss the number of equal parts (4) and the name for the parts. (fourths) Make sure children understand that one part is one fourth.

3. Check that children understand that 2 halves make a whole and 4 fourths make a whole.

Name_____

Now Try This One Third

A shape can have 3 equal parts called thirds.

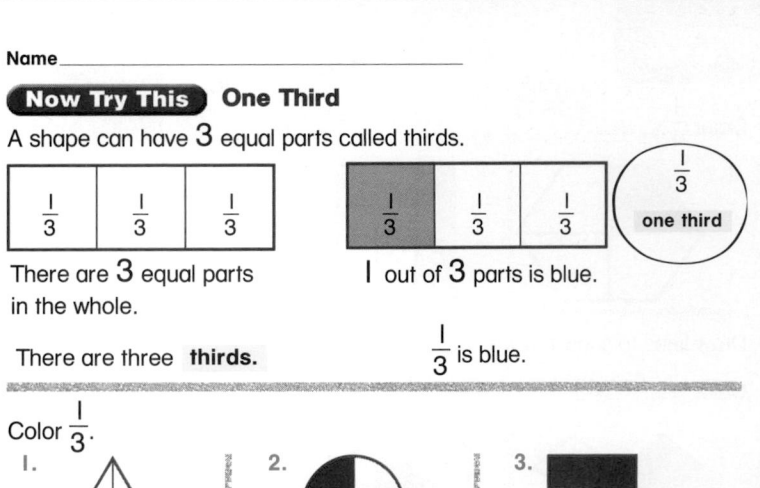

There are 3 equal parts in the whole.

1 out of 3 parts is blue.

There are three **thirds**.

$\frac{1}{3}$ is blue.

Color $\frac{1}{3}$.

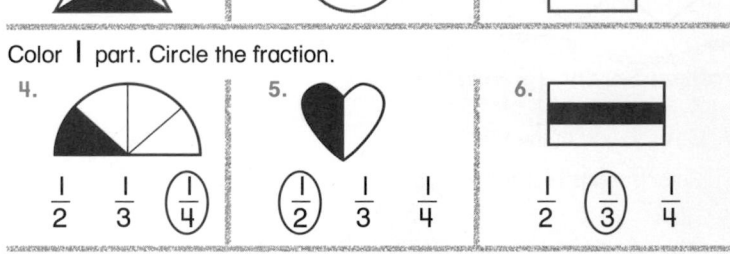

Color 1 part. Circle the fraction.

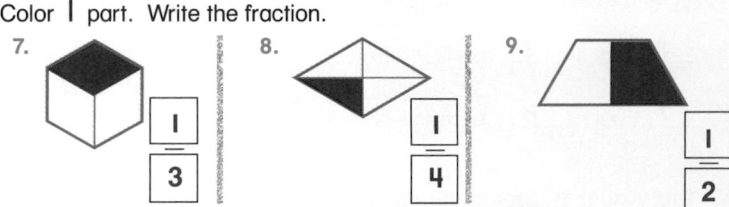

Color 1 part. Write the fraction.

7. [cube figure] $\frac{1}{3}$

8. [diamond figure] $\frac{1}{4}$

9. [trapezoid figure] $\frac{1}{2}$

10. **Talk About It** Look at Exercises 7, 8, and 9. Tell what the fraction means for each one. **1 out of 3 parts is shaded, 1 out of 4 parts is shaded, and 1 out of 2 parts is shaded.**

Chapter 9 Lesson 3   two hundred forty-three **243**

Now Try This

Introduce Remind children that fractions name parts of a whole. Explain to children that you can divide a rectangle into a different numbers of parts.

- Guide children through the example. **The whole rectangle has how many equal parts?** (3) Point out that the whole rectangle has three thirds.

- **What part of the rectangle is blue?** ($\frac{1}{3}$) Explain that 1 out of 3 equal parts is blue.

Develop Have children complete **Exercises 1–3** as you observe. Discuss any questions.

Practice Have children complete **Exercises 4–9** independently. Give children the opportunity to answer the **Talk About It** question in **Exercise 10**. Then discuss their responses with the class.

Quick Check

Write the number of equal parts.

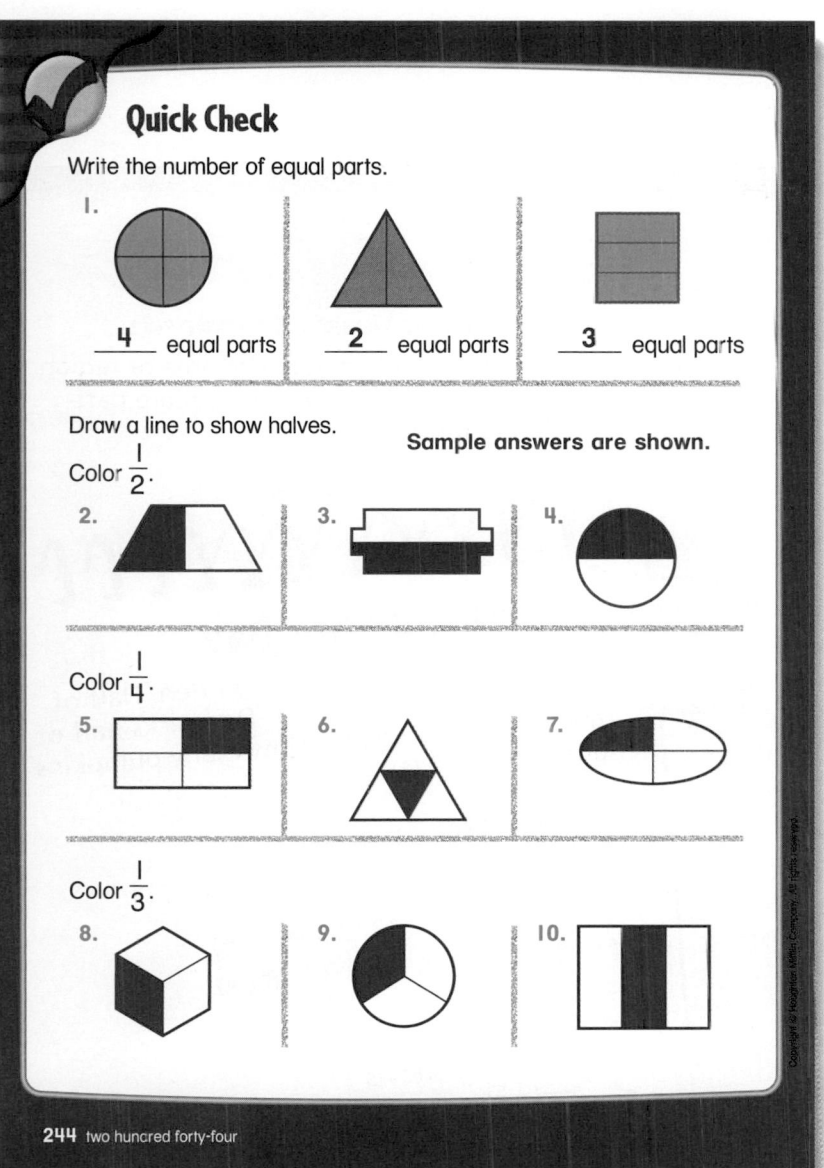

1.

__4__ equal parts   __2__ equal parts   __3__ equal parts

Draw a line to show halves.

Color $\frac{1}{2}$.   **Sample answers are shown.**

2.   3.   4.

Color $\frac{1}{4}$.

5.   6.   7.

Color $\frac{1}{3}$.

8.   9.   10.

Quick Check

Have children complete the Quick Check exercises independently to assess their understanding of concepts and skills taught in **Lessons 1–3.**

Item	Lesson	Error Analysis	Intervention
1	9.1	Children may have difficulty identifying equal parts.	Reteach Resource 9.1 *Ways to Success* 9.1
2–4	9.2	Children may color both halves.	Reteach Resource 9.2 *Ways to Success* 9.2
5–10	9.3	Children may color the whole shape.	Reteach Resource 9.3 *Ways to Success* 9.3

Math Challenge

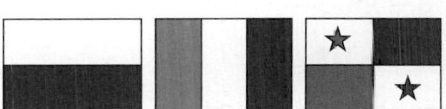

Display pictures of flags from different countries with equal parts that are halves, thirds or fourths. For example, Poland, (halves), Italy (thirds), or Panama (fourths). Discuss the parts of each flag in relation to the whole. $(\frac{1}{2}, \frac{1}{3}, \frac{1}{4})$ Tell children the name of the country from which each flag comes. Discuss any facts the children know about these countries.

Lesson 9.4

Fractions of a Set

PLANNING THE LESSON

MATHEMATICS OBJECTIVE
Identify and represent $\frac{1}{2}$, $\frac{1}{3}$, and $\frac{1}{4}$ of a set.

 *Use Lesson Planner CD-ROM for Lesson 9.4.*

Daily Routines

Calendar
Ask students to name pairs of dates in which the sum of the digits is 2, 3, or 4. (11th, 12th, 13th, 20th, 21st, 22nd, 30th, 31st)

Vocabulary
Review the meanings of **one half, one third, and one fourth.** Emphasize how each fraction names part of a set. Have children draw pictures to show each fraction.

Vocabulary Cards

Meeting North Carolina's Standards
Prepare for Grade 2 Standard 1.02 Use area or region models and set models of fractions to explore part-whole relationships in contexts.

Lesson Transparency **9.4**

Problem of the Day
There are 8 pumpkins in a garden. Half of the pumpkins are orange. Don picks half of the orange pumpkins. How many pumpkins does he pick? (2)

Quick Review
Choose + or −.
$7 \bigcirc 3 = 4$ (−) $12 \bigcirc 9 = 3$ (−)
$4 \bigcirc 0 = 4$ (+,−) $9 \bigcirc 1 = 8$ (−)

Lesson Quiz
Which picture shows $\frac{1}{4}$?

1.  (triangles)

2. (circles)

LEVELED PRACTICE

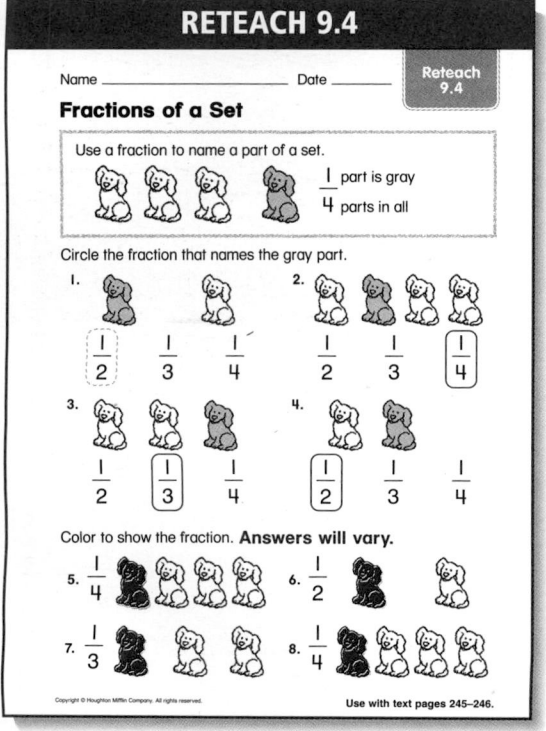

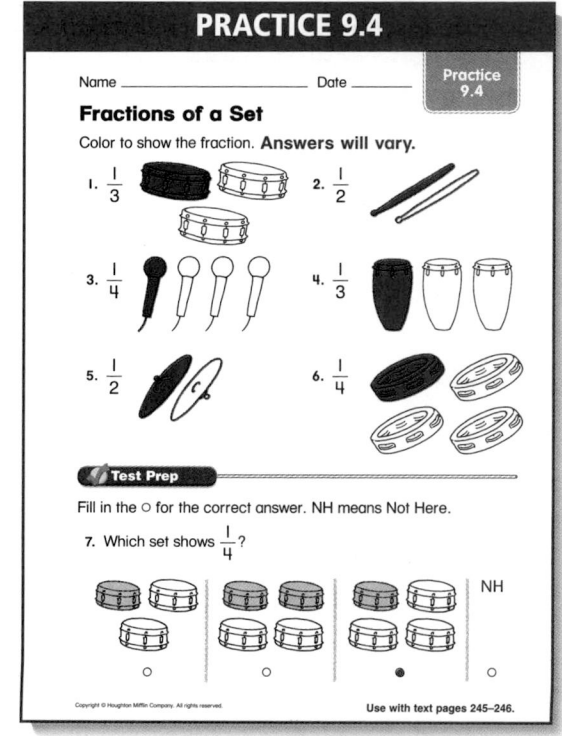

Practice Workbook Page 60

ENRICHMENT 9.4

Name _____ Date _____ Enrichment 9.4

Name a Part

Color one toy.
Write the fraction.

Write About It How is $\frac{1}{3}$ of a set and $\frac{1}{3}$ of a whole the same? How is it different?

Answers will vary.

Reaching All Learners
Differentiated Instruction

English Learners

Children will need to understand the term *set* in order to name parts of a *set*. Use Worksheet 9.4 to help children develop an understanding of this term.

Special Needs
VISUAL, TACTILE

Materials: *dot stickers (teacher-made)*

Give the child paper and dot stickers of 2 colors. Have the child put 1 dot of each color on the paper. Relate the 2 dots to the fraction $\frac{1}{2}$. Explain the meaning of set and parts of a set. Emphasize why the 2 in the fraction relates to the number of dots in the whole set. Repeat with 3 and 4 dots.

Early Finishers
TACTILE, VISUAL

Materials: *fraction cards, set cards (teacher-made)*

Have children draw 2–4 like items on a card. Now have them write $\frac{1}{2}$, $\frac{1}{2}$, $\frac{1}{3}$ on different cards. Arrange cards face down in an array. One child turns over two cards and tries to match a set to a fraction. Play until all the matches are made.

TECHNOLOGY
Spiral Review

Create **customized** spiral review worksheets for individual students using the *Ways to Assess* CD-ROM.

Lesson Planner

You can customize your teaching plan to meet your curriculum requirements with the **Lesson Planner CD-ROM**.

Science Connection

Humans share the Earth with many different animals. Some animals have 4 legs, others have none. Some fly, others walk. Create a mural that includes sets such as:

- $\frac{1}{2}$ walk; $\frac{1}{2}$ fly or swim

MATH CENTER
Real-Life Activity

Help children understand the usefulness of mathematics. This activity makes math come alive by connecting the lesson skills to a real-life situation.

PROBLEM SOLVING 9.4

Name _____ Date _____ Problem Solving 9.4

Fractions of a Set

Write the fraction. | Draw or write to explain.

1. David has 3 apples. He gives 2 to his friend Helena. He eats the 1 that is left. What fraction names the part David ate? → $\frac{1}{3}$

2. Gary draws 4 leaves. He colors 3 leaves orange. He colors 1 red. What fraction names the orange part? → $\frac{3}{4}$

3. Grace makes 3 placemats. She makes 1 green. She makes 2 blue. What fraction names the green part? → $\frac{1}{3}$

4. Frank makes a picture with 3 flowers. He makes 1 red flower. He makes 2 yellow flowers. What fraction names the red part of the picture? → $\frac{1}{3}$

Use with text pages 245–246.

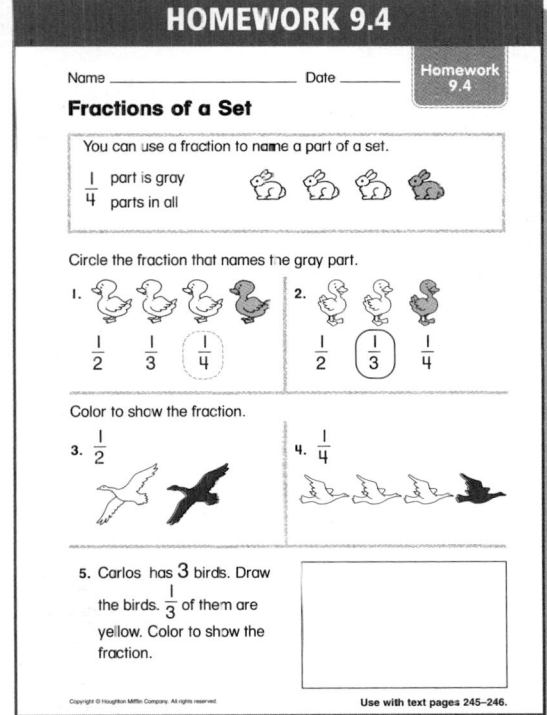

HOMEWORK 9.4

Name _____ Date _____ Homework 9.4

Fractions of a Set

You can use a fraction to name a part of a set.

$\frac{1}{4}$ part is gray, parts in all

Circle the fraction that names the gray part.

1. $\frac{1}{2}$ $\frac{1}{3}$ $\frac{1}{4}$
2. $\frac{1}{2}$ $\frac{1}{3}$ $\frac{1}{4}$

Color to show the fraction.

3. $\frac{1}{2}$
4. $\frac{1}{4}$

5. Carlos has 3 birds. Draw the birds. $\frac{1}{3}$ of them are yellow. Color to show the fraction.

Use with text pages 245–246.

Homework Workbook Page 60

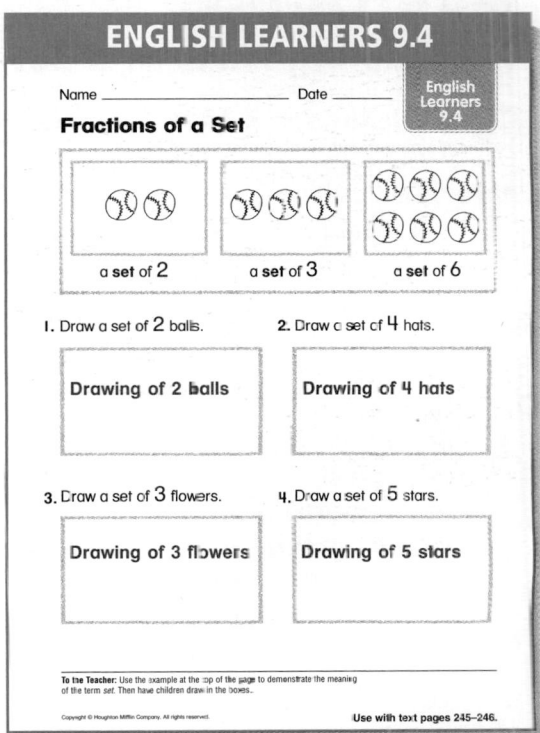

ENGLISH LEARNERS 9.4

Name _____ Date _____ English Learners 9.4

Fractions of a Set

a set of 2 | a set of 3 | a set of 6

1. Draw a set of 2 balls.
   [Drawing of 2 balls]
2. Draw a set of 4 hats.
   [Drawing of 4 hats]
3. Draw a set of 3 flowers.
   [Drawing of 3 flowers]
4. Draw a set of 5 stars.
   [Drawing of 5 stars]

To the Teacher: Use the example at the top of the page to demonstrate the meaning of the term *set*. Then have children draw in the boxes.

Use with text pages 245–246.

TEACHING LESSON 9.4

LESSON ORGANIZER

Objective Identify and represent $\frac{1}{2}$, $\frac{1}{3}$, and $\frac{1}{4}$ of a set.

Resources Reteach, Practice, Enrichment, Problem Solving, Homework, English Learners, Transparencies, Math Center

Materials Paper shapes (LT 22 and 23), cubes

Warm-Up Activity
Identifying Parts of a Whole

| iiii Whole Group | ⏱ 5 minutes | Visual, Tactile |

Materials: *paper shapes (LT 22 and 23)*

1. Review parts of a whole. Give children paper shapes. Have them fold the paper to make equal parts. **Are the parts in your shape equal?** (yes)

2. Tell children to color some of the parts. Have volunteers tell what fraction their shape shows. Ask a volunteer to display his or her shape.

3. Write the fraction on the board. **How do we read the fraction?** Have a volunteer read the fraction. Continue with other shapes.

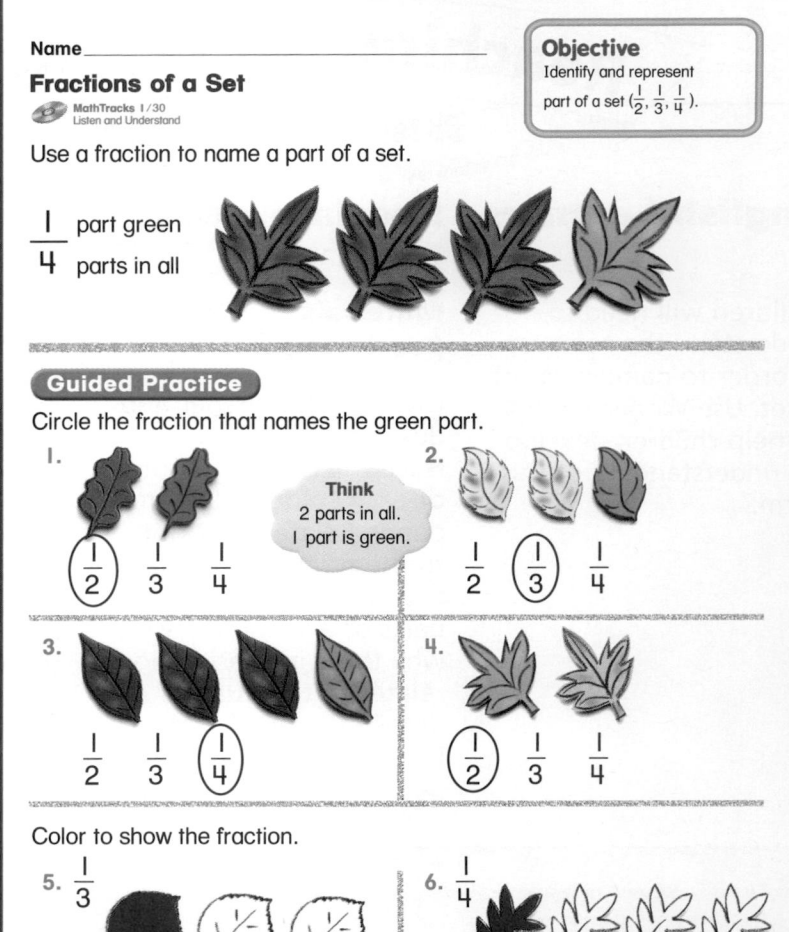

Name_____

Fractions of a Set

MathTracks 1/30
Listen and Understand

Objective
Identify and represent part of a set ($\frac{1}{2}$, $\frac{1}{3}$, $\frac{1}{4}$).

Use a fraction to name a part of a set.

$\frac{1}{4}$ part green
parts in all

Guided Practice

Circle the fraction that names the green part.

1. $\frac{1}{2}$ $\frac{1}{3}$ $\frac{1}{4}$

Think
2 parts in all.
1 part is green.

2. $\frac{1}{2}$ $\frac{1}{3}$ $\frac{1}{4}$

3. $\frac{1}{2}$ $\frac{1}{3}$ $\frac{1}{4}$

4. $\frac{1}{2}$ $\frac{1}{3}$ $\frac{1}{4}$

Color to show the fraction.

5. $\frac{1}{3}$

6. $\frac{1}{4}$

TEST TIPS **Explain Your Thinking** Look at Exercise 4. What does the fraction $\frac{1}{2}$ tell you about the leaves? **Possible answers: 1 out of 2 leaves is green; $\frac{1}{2}$ of the leaves are green.**

Chapter 9 Lesson 4

two hundred forty-five **245**

---

1 Introduce
Modeling Parts of a Set

| iiii Whole Group | ⏱ 10–15 minutes | Visual, Auditory |

Materials: *cubes*

1. Show 2 red cubes and 1 green cube. Describe the cubes as a set.

2. **How are the items in the set alike?** (all cubes) **How are they different?** (different colors)

3. Point out that there are 3 parts in the set. Tell children that just as in naming parts of a whole, the number of parts in a set is the bottom number of a fraction. Write 3 at the bottom of a fraction on the board. **How many parts are green?** (1) Have volunteers tell where to write the 1 to name the green part of the set. (on the top) Write the 1 in the fraction on the board.

2 Develop

Guided Learning

Teaching Example Introduce the objective to children. Guide them through the example to show how parts of sets can be colored. Be sure children understand that $\frac{1}{4}$ stands for the green leaf which is 1 out of the 4 parts.

Guided Practice

Have children complete **Exercises 1–6** as you observe. Give children the opportunity to answer the Explain Your Thinking question. Then discuss their responses with the class.

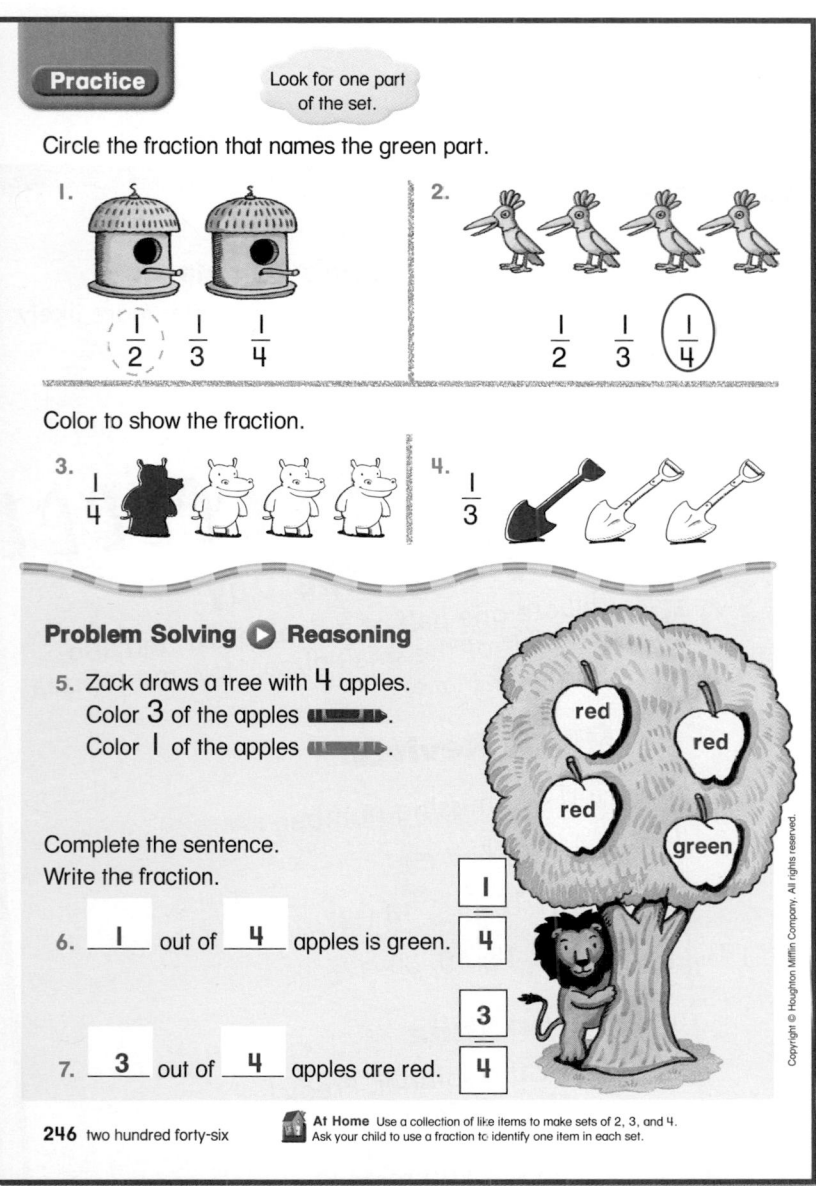

Practice

Look for one part of the set.

Circle the fraction that names the green part.

1. $\frac{1}{2}$ $\frac{1}{3}$ $\frac{1}{4}$

2. $\frac{1}{2}$ $\frac{1}{3}$ $\frac{1}{4}$

Color to show the fraction.

3. $\frac{1}{4}$

4. $\frac{1}{3}$

Problem Solving ▶ Reasoning

5. Zack draws a tree with 4 apples.
Color 3 of the apples ■■■■■.
Color 1 of the apples ■■■■■.

Complete the sentence.
Write the fraction.

6. __1__ out of __4__ apples is green. $\frac{1}{4}$

7. __3__ out of __4__ apples are red. $\frac{3}{4}$

246 two hundred forty-six

At Home Use a collection of like items to make sets of 2, 3, and 4. Ask your child to use a fraction to identify one item in each set.

Daily Test Prep

Tom has 3 cats. Jo gives Tom another cat.
How many cats does Tom have now?

2 ○ 3 ○ 4 ● NH ○

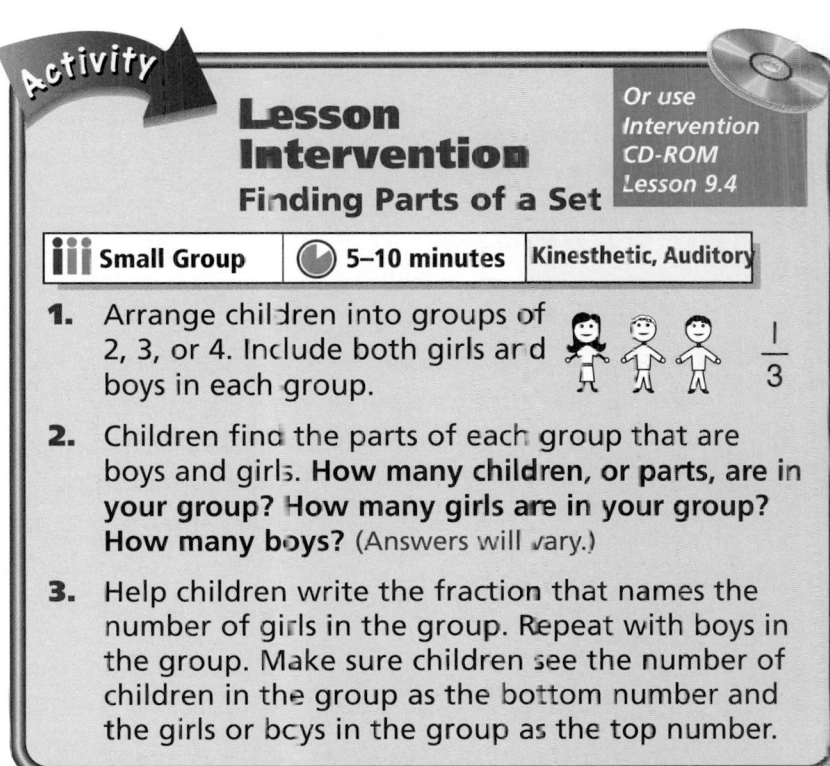

Activity

Lesson Intervention
Finding Parts of a Set

Or use Intervention CD-ROM Lesson 9.4

| Small Group | 5–10 minutes | Kinesthetic, Auditory |

1. Arrange children into groups of 2, 3, or 4. Include both girls and boys in each group. $\frac{1}{3}$

2. Children find the parts of each group that are boys and girls. **How many children, or parts, are in your group? How many girls are in your group? How many boys?** (Answers will vary.)

3. Help children write the fraction that names the number of girls in the group. Repeat with boys in the group. Make sure children see the number of children in the group as the bottom number and the girls or boys in the group as the top number.

---

③ Practice

Independent Practice

Children complete **Exercises 1–4** independently.

Problem Solving

After children complete **Exercises 5–7**, call on volunteers to share their solutions.

Extend this problem by discussing fair shares. Tell children that Zack picks the 4 apples and wants to share them equally with a friend. How many apples will each child get? (2 apples)

Common Error

Difficulty Identifying Parts and the Whole
Children may compare the parts of a set instead of a part to the whole set. Emphasize that the number of parts in the whole set names the number of parts in the fraction.

④ Assess and Close

Tell what parts of a set you read on the bottom of a fraction. (The number of parts in a set is the bottom number.)

Draw a set of leaves that is $\frac{1}{3}$ red.

Keeping a Journal

Draw a picture of a set with a part that would be named $\frac{1}{4}$. Describe how many parts your set has. Tell how you know the part shows $\frac{1}{4}$.

Lesson 9.5

Hands-On: Probability

PLANNING THE LESSON

MATHEMATICS OBJECTIVE

Predict and determine the probability of an event.

Use Lesson Planner CD-ROM for Lesson 9.5.

Daily Routines

Calendar

Have children find today's date on the calendar. Using position words, have them take turns finding and naming dates on the calendar that are above, below, to the right or to the left of today's date.

Vocabulary

Have a discussion with the class about daily events that are **certain**, **impossible**, or **probable**. Extend the discussion to include situations that are **more likely**, **less likely**, and **equally likely**.

Vocabulary Cards

Meeting North Carolina's Standards
4.02 Describe events as certain, impossible, more likely or less likely to occur.

Lesson Transparency **9.5**

Problem of the Day

Jill ate one half of a small pizza. Ted also ate half of the small pizza. How much pizza was left? (none)

Quick Review

Find the missing number.

3, 4, ___, 6, 7 (5)

10, 11, 12, ___, 14 (13)

16, ___, 18, 19, 20 (17)

Lesson Quiz

Look at the spinner. Predict.

1. What are you most likely to spin? (dots)

LEVELED PRACTICE

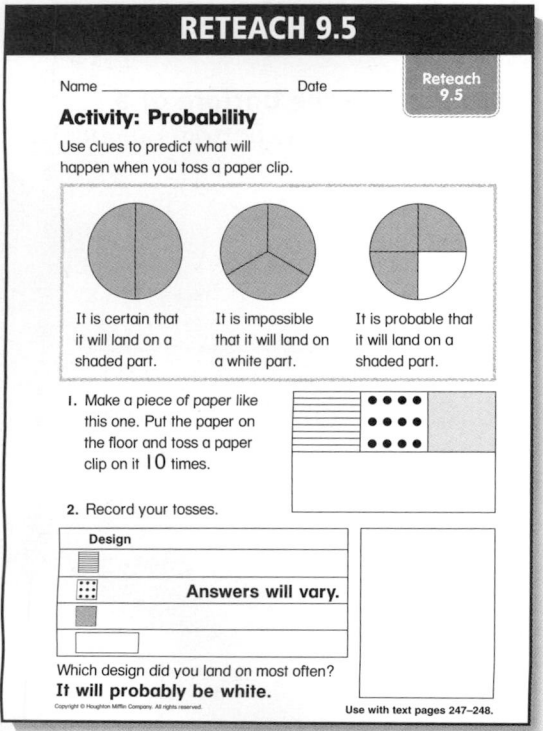

RETEACH 9.5

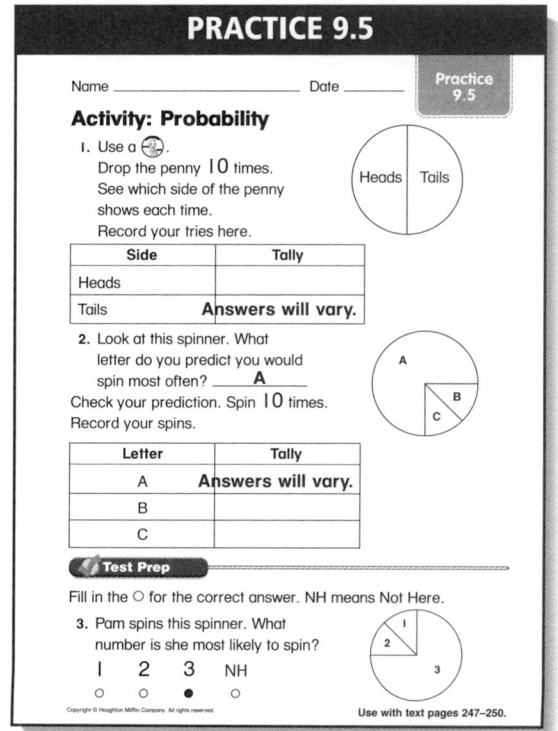

PRACTICE 9.5

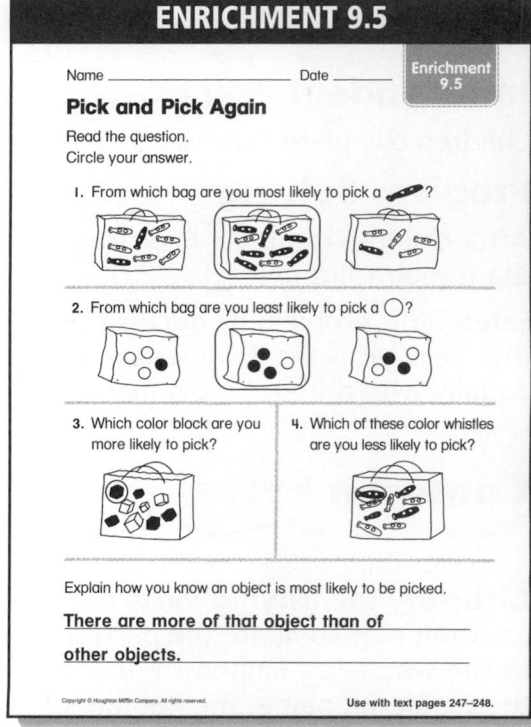

ENRICHMENT 9.5

Practice Workbook Page 61

Reaching All Learners
Differentiated Instruction

English Learners

In order to make predictions, English-language learners will need to understand verbs in the future tense. Worksheet 9.5 will give children practice in reading future tense verbs.

Special Needs
AUDITORY, VISUAL

Materials: *index cards*

Make a set of event cards. Include everyday situations that are more likely to happen, (waking up, eating dinner) or less likely to happen (see the circus, have no homework). Have the child choose a card from each pile and tell whether the event is more likely or less likely to happen today.

Gifted and Talented
VISUAL, TACTILE

Materials: *four-part blank spinners (LT 38), crayons*

Have partners color two parts of the spinner green, one part purple, and one part orange. Have children predict how many times they will spin a certain color. Have partners take turns spinning the spinner and recording the results in a tally chart.

TECHNOLOGY

Spiral Review

Using the *Ways to Assess* CD-ROM, you can create **customized** spiral review worksheets covering any lessons you choose.

Education Place

Recommend that parents visit **Education Place** at eduplace.com/parents/mw/ for parent support activities.

Social Studies Connection

Discuss how many children go to school in the town where they were born – their *birthplace*. Have partners survey 10 children. Make a tally chart of the results. Is it less likely or more likely that the person asked was born in your town?

MATH CENTER

Real-Life Activity

Help children understand the usefulness of mathematics. This activity makes math come alive by connecting the lesson skills to a real-life situation.

PROBLEM SOLVING 9.5

Name _____ Date _____ | Problem Solving 9.5

Probability

Marc has 5 marbles.

Marc wants to be **certain** that his friend picks a blue marble from the bag. What marbles should be in the bag?

Draw or write to explain.

(B B B B B)

__5 blue__ marbles

1. Marc wants to make it **probable** that his friend picks a green marble from the bag. What marbles should be in the bag?

   __4 green__ marbles
   __1 blue__ marble

2. Marc wants to make it **impossible** to pick a blue marble. What marbles should be in the bag?

   __5 green__ marbles

Use with text pages 247–248.

HOMEWORK 9.5

Name _____ Date _____ | Homework 9.5

Probability

When you predict, you tell what may happen.

There are more 🐟 in the jar than 🐱.

So, it is more likely that you would pick a 🐟.

How likely is it that you will pick a star? Circle.

1. more equally (less)
2. (more) equally less
3. more (equally) less
4. more equally (less)

5. Draw any number of Xs and Zs in the jar. Are you more likely or less likely to pick an X or a Z?

   ____ likely

   Draw here. **Answers will vary.**

   Answers will vary.

Use with text pages 247–250.

ENGLISH LEARNERS 9.5

Name _____ Date _____ | English Learners 9.5

Probability

I **wrote** a story last night.

Lilli **will write** a story tomorrow.

Circle the correct answer for each sentence.

1. We ate (will eat) sandwiches tomorrow.
2. I (rode) will ride a bus last week.
3. Pedro played (will play) next weekend.
4. Hideki (sang) will sing yesterday.
5. My father made (will make) dinner tomorrow.
6. He (helped) will help me yesterday.

To the Teacher: Use the example at the top of the page to help children understand future tense verbs. Then read the sentences with children and have them circle the word or words that complete each sentence.

Use with text pages 247–249.

TEACHING LESSON 9.5

LESSON ORGANIZER

Objective Predict and determine the probability of an event.

Resources Reteach, Practice, Enrichment, Problem Solving, Homework, English Learners, Transparencies, Math Center

Materials Paper clips, spinners (LT 38), pennies, cup, connecting cubes, bag, ten frame

Activity

Warm-Up Activity
Model Tally Marks

 Whole Group | ⏱ **10 minutes** | **Visual, Tactile**

Materials: *large and small paper clips*

1. Review with children how to sort and classify real objects.

2. Have children sort their paper clips into sets of large clips and small clips.

3. Draw a tally chart on the board. Write the labels *large* and *small*. Have children come to the board and draw a tally mark in the correct row for each large or small paper clip. Observe children as they mark the tallies on the chart.

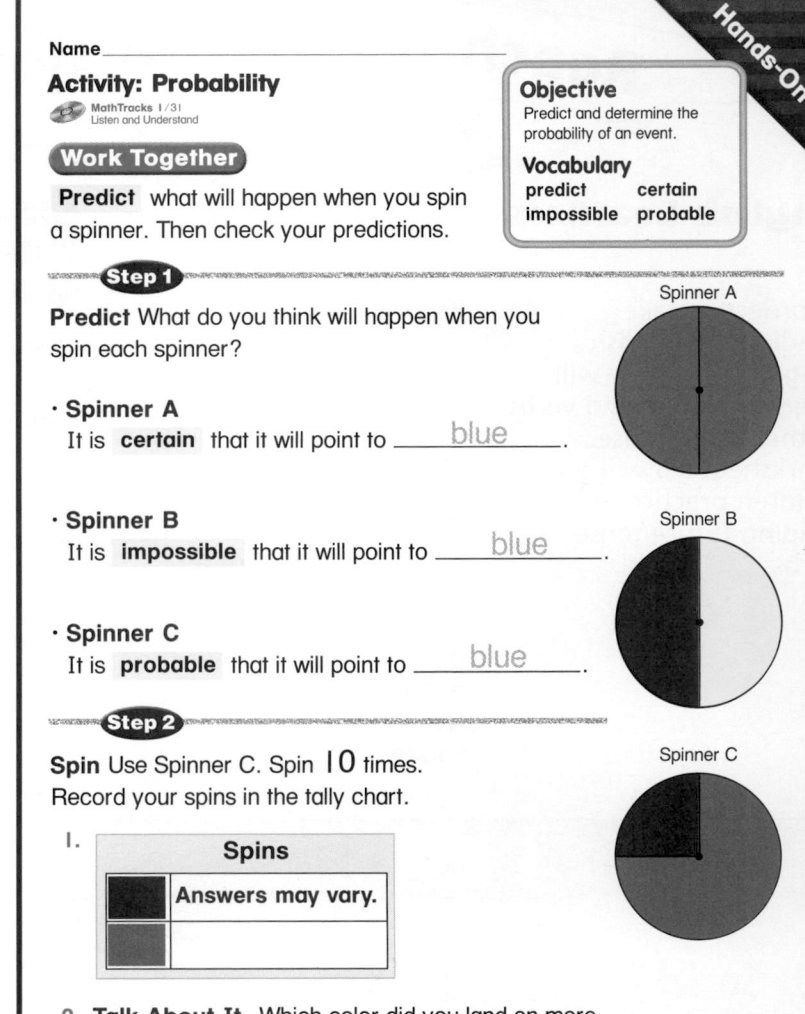

Name_____

Activity: Probability
MathTracks 1/31
Listen and Understand

Hands-On

Objective
Predict and determine the probability of an event.

Vocabulary
predict   certain
impossible probable

Work Together

Predict what will happen when you spin a spinner. Then check your predictions.

Step 1

Predict What do you think will happen when you spin each spinner?

Spinner A

· **Spinner A**
It is **certain** that it will point to ____blue____.

Spinner B

· **Spinner B**
It is **impossible** that it will point to ____blue____.

Spinner C

· **Spinner C**
It is **probable** that it will point to ____blue____.

Step 2

Spin Use Spinner C. Spin 10 times.
Record your spins in the tally chart.

1.

Spins	
	Answers may vary.

2. **Talk About It** Which color did you land on more often? Why? **Answers may vary, but it will probably be blue because more of the spinner is blue.**

Chapter 9 Lesson 5   two hundred forty-seven **247**

1 Introduce
Discuss Probability

Whole Group | ⏱ **10–15 minutes** | **Visual, Tactile**

Materials: *spinners (LT 38), paper clips*

1. Introduce the terms *certain*, *impossible*, and *probable*. Use the words to describe real-life situations: it is *certain* that the sun will rise tomorrow, it is *impossible* to have a lion read you a story, it is *probable* that we will have homework.

2. Show three 4-section spinners. Spinner 1 has a circle in each section. Spinner 2 has a star in 2 sections and a square in 2 sections. Spinner 3 has a circle in 3 sections and a star in 1 section. **Is it certain that spinner 3 will point to a circle?** (no) **What do you predict will happen?** (It is probable that it will point to a circle because 3 sections have circles.) **What do you predict will happen when you spin spinner 1?** (It is certain it will point to a circle.)

2 Develop

Work Together

Teaching Example Guide children through Step 1. **On which spinner is it certain to spin blue?** (Spinner A) **On which spinner is it impossible to spin blue?** (Spinner B)

For Step 2, have children work in pairs to spin the spinner. Have one child hold the pencil and the other child spin the paper clip. Have children record each spin on the tally chart. Have a volunteer explain whether his or her prediction about Spinner C was correct in Step 1. Have children complete the **Talk About It in Exercise 2.** Encourage children to share their results.

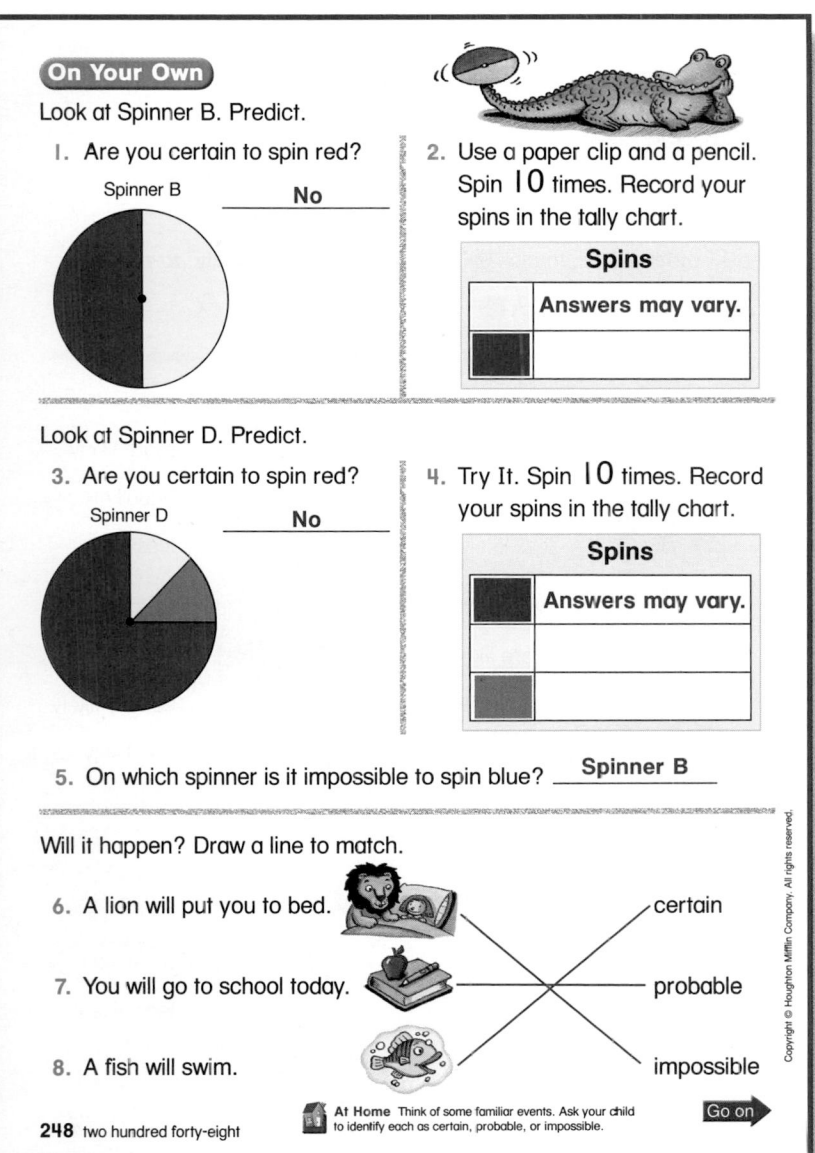

On Your Own

Look at Spinner B. Predict.

1. Are you certain to spin red?

   Spinner B   **No**

2. Use a paper clip and a pencil. Spin 10 times. Record your spins in the tally chart.

Spins
Answers may vary.

Look at Spinner D. Predict.

3. Are you certain to spin red?

   Spinner D   **No**

4. Try It. Spin 10 times. Record your spins in the tally chart.

Spins
Answers may vary.

5. On which spinner is it impossible to spin blue? _____**Spinner B**_____

Will it happen? Draw a line to match.

6. A lion will put you to bed.   certain

7. You will go to school today.   probable

8. A fish will swim.   impossible

At Home Think of some familiar events. Ask your child to identify each as certain, probable, or impossible.

Go on →

248 two hundred forty-eight

ACHIEVING
Mathematical Proficiency

Helping Children Become Learners

One goal in teaching math proficiency is to **help children become independent learners.** Homework is often given for that purpose. Before homework is given, however, children should understand a skill well enough that they do not practice it incorrectly on their own.

There are other **settings in which children can begin to learn on their own.** Children can work individually, in pairs, or in groups within the classroom. One scenario involves children learning about probability. As children predict and determine the probability of an event, they can **question each other, discuss a point of view, and explain** what they are doing.

Children become **better learners when they talk with each other about mathematical ideas** in addition to practicing math skills independently.

---

3 Practice

On Your Own

Have children complete **Exercises 1–8** on page 248 as you observe. Encourage children to explain how they found their answers.

Common Error

Making Unlikely Predictions

Remind children that a prediction is based on knowledge of a situation. Guide them to examine the spinner closely and help them understand why some predictions are better than others.

4 Assess and Close

A spinner is divided into four equal parts. 2 of the parts are yellow, the other parts are green and blue. Predict what color is the most probable to spin? (yellow) **Why?** (more of the spinner is yellow)

 **Keeping a Journal**

Draw a bag with 5 green marbles and 2 white marbles. Write to explain what you think will happen when you draw a marble from the bag.

Lesson continues →

Activity

Lesson Intervention

Predicting Probability

Or use Intervention CD-ROM Lesson 9.5

👤👤👤 Small Group	🕐 5–10 minutes	Visual, Tactile

Materials: *pennies, cup*

	heads	tails

1. Give each group a penny. Be sure they know which side is "heads" and which is "tails." Have them discuss whether the penny will land with heads or tails facing up if tossed.

2. Have one child shake the penny out of a small cup onto the table. Have another child make a tally mark for each toss.

3. After several tries, discuss with children how collecting data could help them decide whether it is certain, impossible, or probable that the coin will land heads up or tails up.

4. Tell children that collecting data can help them predict the outcome of an event.

Name _____

Now Try This How Likely?

Keesha's bag has . She will pick one cube.

She is **more likely** to pick ▪.

She is **less likely** to pick ▪.

Tu's bag has . He will pick one cube.

He is **equally likely** to pick  as ▪.

How likely is it that you will pick blue? Circle.

1. (more likely) / equally likely / less likely

2. more likely / (equally likely) / less likely

3. more likely / equally likely / (less likely)

4. (more likely) / equally likely / less likely

When there are more than **2** colors, you need to say **most likely** and **least likely**. How likely is it that you will pick blue? Circle.

5. most likely / (least likely)

6. (most likely) / least likely

Chapter 9 Lesson 5

two hundred forty-nine **249**

Now Try This

Materials: *connecting cubes*

Introduce Discuss the meaning of **more likely, less likely, equally likely, most likely,** and **least likely**.

• Put 3 blue cubes and 1 red cube in a bag.

• **Which color is more likely to be drawn from the bag?** Be sure children understand that since there are more blue cubes in the bag, it is more likely a blue cube will be picked.

• Allow each child a chance to draw a cube from the bag.

• **Record with tallies the number of times a blue cube and a red cube is drawn**.

• Repeat the activity modeling less likely, equally likely, most likely, and least likely.

Develop Have children complete **Exercises 1–2** as you observe.

Practice Children complete **Exercises 3–6** independently.

Blue Wins

2 Players

What You Need:

Bag with  and ,
Workmat 1, Bag with and

How to Play

1. Each player takes a bag and a ten frame workmat.

2. You each pick a cube from your bag.

3. Color 1 square the same color as the cube.

4. Put the cube back in the bag.

5. Keep playing until both players color all their squares.

6. The player with more blue than red wins.

Blue Wins

Purpose: This game provides practice with finding the probability of events.

Materials: *a bag, red cubes, blue cubes, ten frame*

How to Play

- Children work in pairs.

- Explain that children try to pick the most blue cubes from their bag.

- Children take turns picking cubes from their bag without looking.

- **Talk About It** Look inside your bag. Who is more likely to win? Is the game fair? (The player with 5 blues and 1 red is more likely to pick blue. The game is not fair.)

Another Way to Play

Children may use this alternate version in the Math Center.

Children decide who will pick red and blue. As they take turns, they record their results on a tally chart. If they pick their color, they mark the chart. After 10 picks, the player with the most tallies wins. Have them switch colors and begin again.

Literature Connection

Read the book *Probably Pistachio* by Stuart J. Murphy. Have children answer these questions.

- After reading page 8 ask: **Was Emma more likely or less likely to have a pastrami sandwich for lunch?** (more likely) Have children explain why Emma was more likely to have a pastrami sandwich.

- Show the picture on page 17 and ask: **Which snack is Jack less likely to choose and why?** (popcorn, because there are only 3 bags) **Which snack is Jack more likely to choose and why?** (pretzels, because there are 7 bags)

- Have children predict whether it is more likely or less likely that everyone will be in class the next day.

Problem Solving: Use a Picture

PLANNING THE LESSON

MATHEMATICS OBJECTIVE
Use data from a picture to solve problems.

Use Lesson Planner CD-ROM for Lesson 9.6.

Meeting North Carolina's Standards
4.02 Describe events as certain, impossible, more likely or less likely to occur.

Also 4.01, 5.03

Daily Routines

Calendar
Show 2 calendar months. Have children compare data in the 2 months. For example: How many Mondays are in each month?

Vocabulary
Review the terms **predict, chance, more likely, equally likely,** and **less likely.** Call on volunteers to use each term in a sentence or phrase.

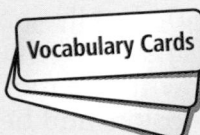
Vocabulary Cards

Lesson Transparency 9.6

Problem of the Day
A cow jumps over the moon. Tell whether the event is certain, impossible, or probable. (impossible)

Quick Review
$7 + 2 + 1 = \square$ (10) $3 + 1 + 4 = \square$ (8)
$6 + 1 + 2 = \square$ (9) $5 + 2 + 2 = \square$ (9)

Lesson Quiz
1. Henry picks a marble from the bag. Which color marble is he less likely to pick? (white) Which color will he probably pick? (black)

LEVELED PRACTICE

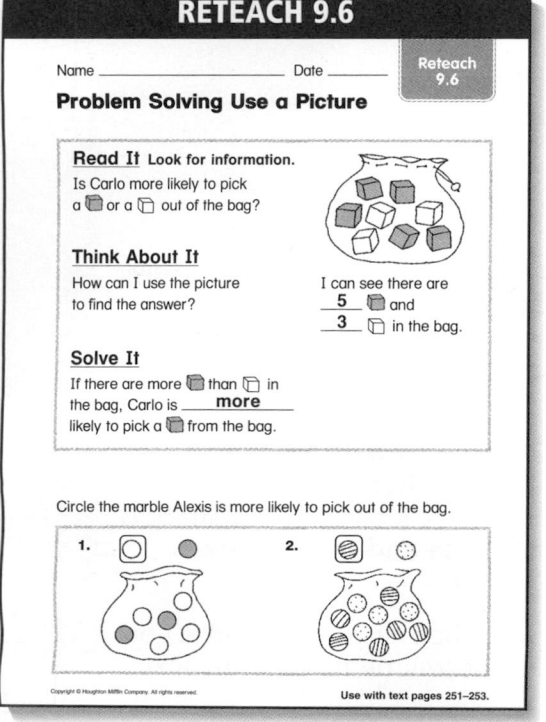

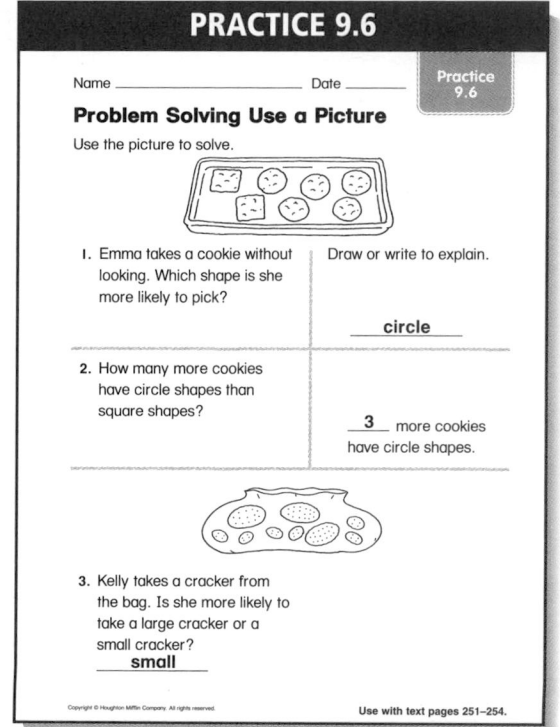

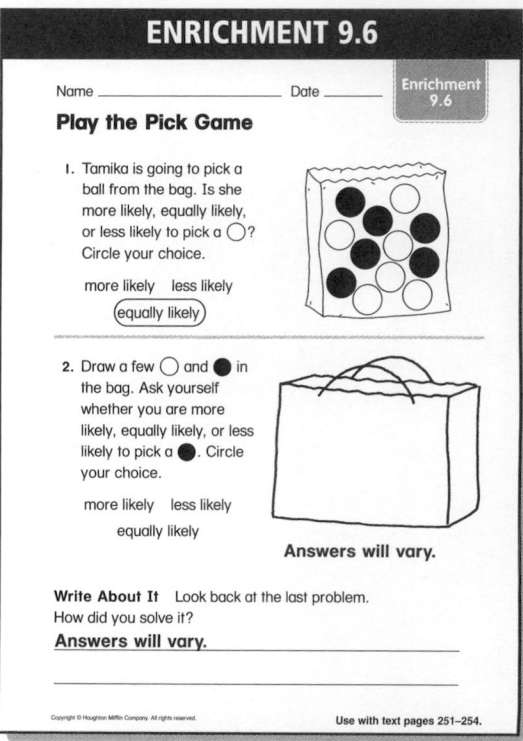

Practice Workbook Page 62

Reaching All Learners

Differentiated Instruction

English Learners

In order to compare groups when solving problems, English-language learners will need to understand the comparative phrase *more than*. Use Worksheet 9.6 to help children learn how to understand and use this phrase when solving problems.

Inclusion
TACTILE, VISUAL

Materials: *cubes, bag*

Prepare a bag with 5 red and 2 blue cubes. Have the child predict which color he or she is more likely to take out of the bag. Have the child take 1 cube out of the bag. Record the color with a tally mark. Return the cube to the bag. Continue drawing 10 cubes. Count the tally marks. If the guess was incorrect, repeat process.

Early Finishers
AUDITORY, VISUAL

Materials: *magazines*

Have pairs of children find pictures to create a story. Have each pair show their pictures and ask questions. Model asking questions: How many birds are in the picture? Are there more birds than people? Have children record answers on a tally chart. Ask pairs to share their data with the class.

Social Studies Connection

Have groups collect data about their relatives such as: Do their relatives live in another town or state? Have children record the data on a tally chart. Then have them use the data to make a pictograph.

MATH CENTER

Number of the Week Activity

Display the Number of the Week to motivate children to use their problem-solving skills. The exercises cover topics across all math strands.

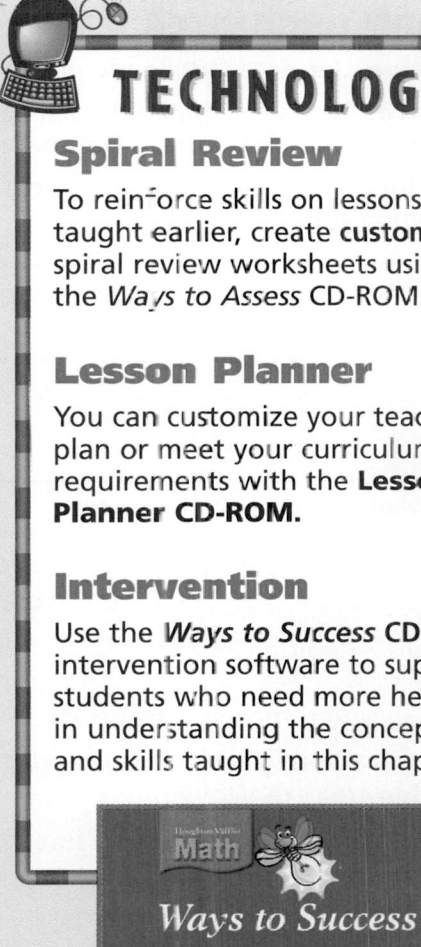

TECHNOLOGY

Spiral Review

To reinforce skills on lessons taught earlier, create **customized** spiral review worksheets using the *Ways to Assess* CD-ROM.

Lesson Planner

You can customize your teaching plan or meet your curriculum requirements with the **Lesson Planner CD-ROM.**

Intervention

Use the *Ways to Success* CD-ROM intervention software to support students who need more help in understanding the concepts and skills taught in this chapter.

Ways to Success

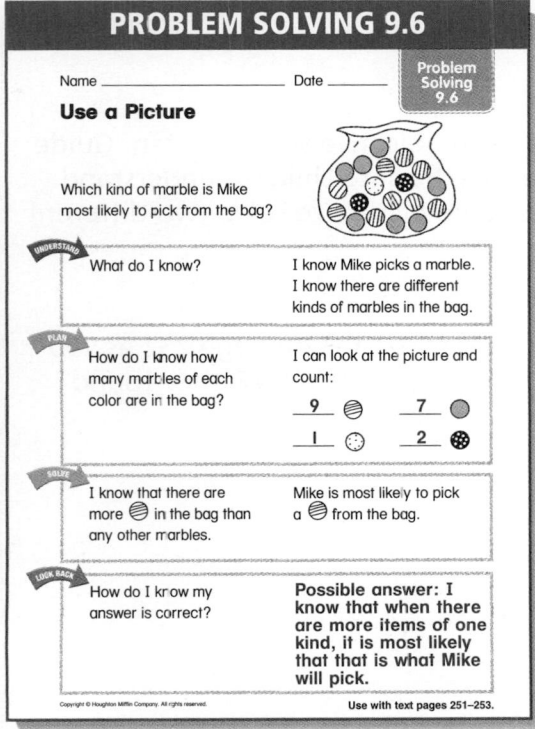

Homework Workbook Page 62

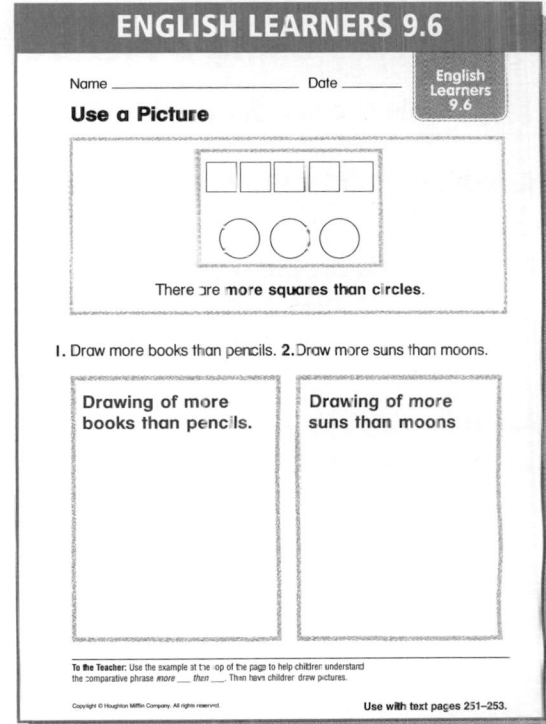

TEACHING LESSON 9.6

LESSON ORGANIZER

Objective Use data from a picture to solve problems.

Resources Reteach, Practice, Enrichment, Problem Solving, Homework, English Learners, Transparencies, Math Center

Materials Blank transparency, 3 clear bags, counters, connecting cubes

Warm-Up Activity

Model Using Data from a Picture

Whole Group	10 minutes	Visual, Auditory

Materials: Blank transparency

- Draw 4 bags of marbles on a transparency. Bag A has 1 red and 8 green marbles. Bag B has 5 red and 5 green marbles. Bag C has 10 red marbles and Bag D has 10 green marbles. Have volunteers respond:

- **From which bag would you be certain to choose a red marble?** (Bag C) **Why?** (All the marbles in Bag C are red.)

- **From which bag would you have an equal chance of getting a red or green marble?** (Bag B) **Why?** (The number of red and green marbles is the same.)

- **Would you choose from Bag A or Bag B if you wanted the best chance of getting a red marble?** (Bag B) **Why?** (Bag B has more red marbles.)

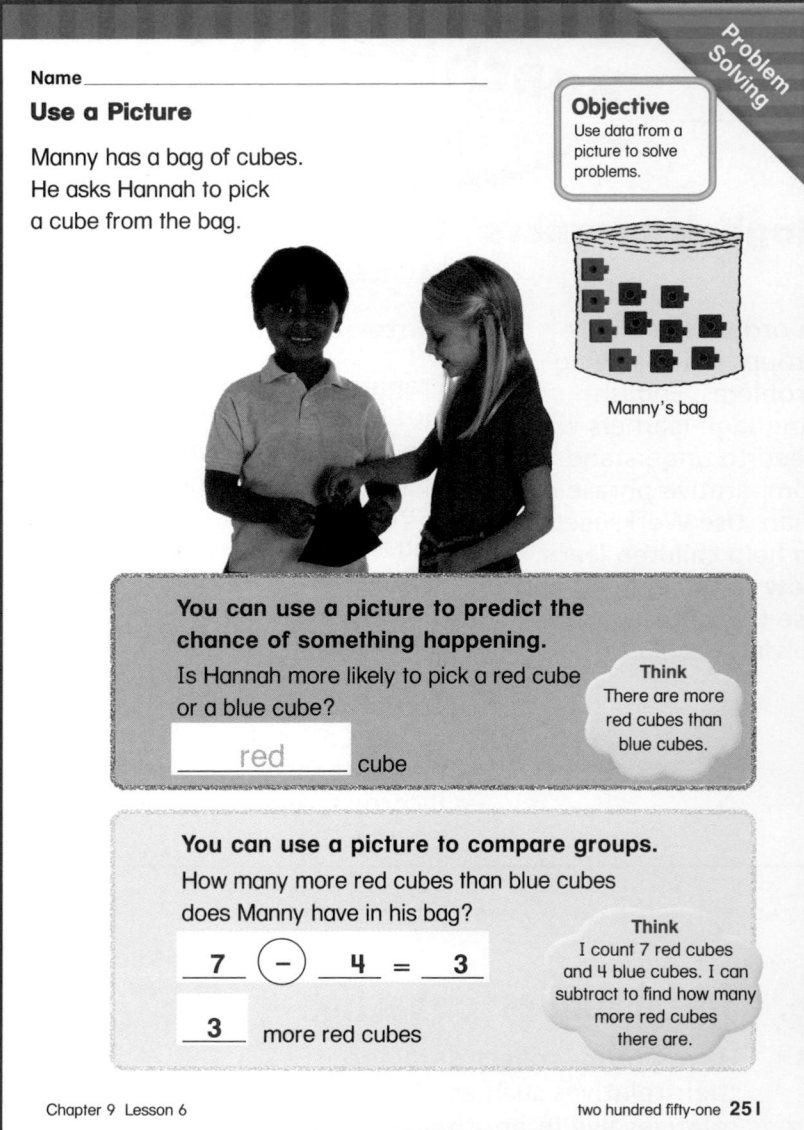

Name _____

Use a Picture

Manny has a bag of cubes. He asks Hannah to pick a cube from the bag.

> **Objective**
> Use data from a picture to solve problems.

Manny's bag

You can use a picture to predict the chance of something happening.
Is Hannah more likely to pick a red cube or a blue cube?

___red___ cube

> **Think**
> There are more red cubes than blue cubes.

You can use a picture to compare groups.
How many more red cubes than blue cubes does Manny have in his bag?

7 − 4 = 3

___3___ more red cubes

> **Think**
> I count 7 red cubes and 4 blue cubes. I can subtract to find how many more red cubes there are.

Chapter 9 Lesson 6   two hundred fifty-one **251**

 **Introduce**

Discuss Using a Picture

Whole Group	10–15 minutes	Visual, Auditory

1. Draw a bag with 7 green and 3 yellow marbles on the board.

2. Read this problem to the children. **Kate has a bag of green marbles and yellow marbles. Is she more likely to pick a green or a yellow marble from the bag?** (green)

3. **How can you use the picture on the board to help you solve the problem?** (Possible answer: count to see if there are more green or yellow marbles.)

4. Invite a volunteer to explain how he or she would use the picture to solve the problem.

 **Develop**

Guided Learning

Teaching Example Read the objective with children. Guide them through the example. Be sure children understand that they are using the same picture to solve two different problems.

Guided Practice

Have children complete **Exercises 1–2** on page 252 as you observe. Encourage children to explain how they found their answers.

Guided Practice

Use the picture to solve.

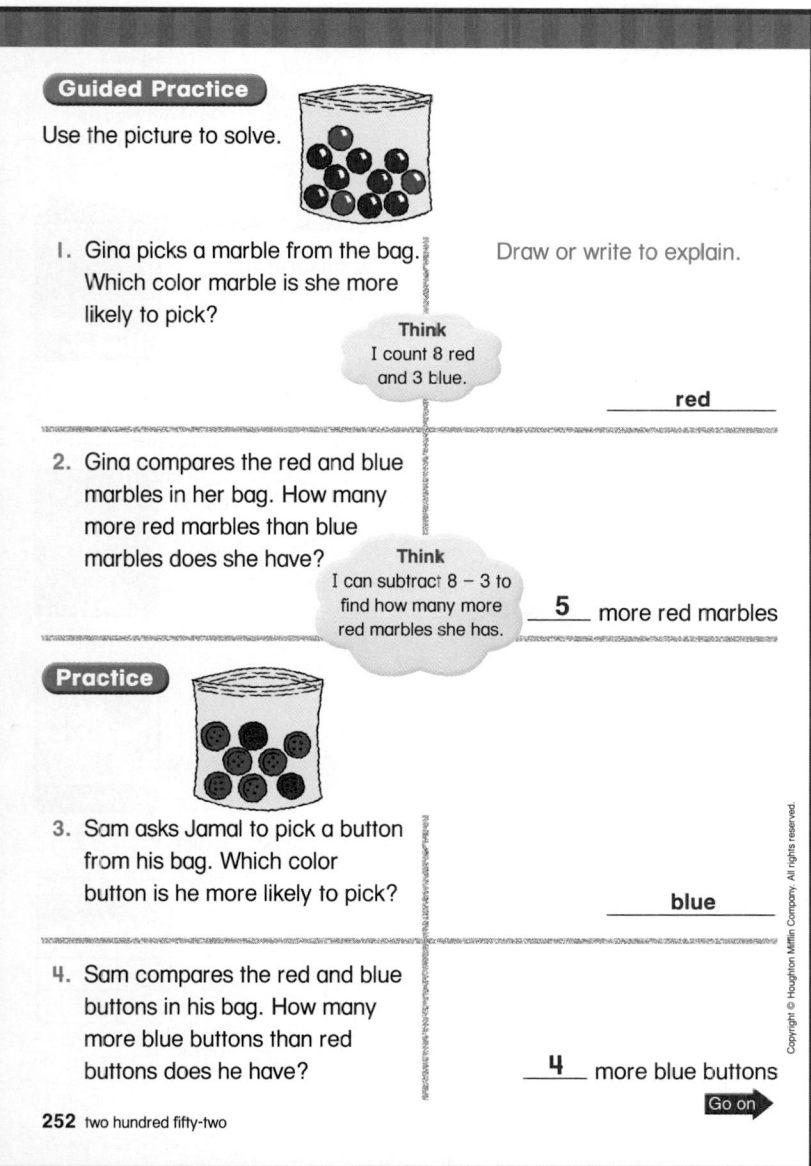

1. Gina picks a marble from the bag. Which color marble is she more likely to pick?

Draw or write to explain.

> **Think**
> I count 8 red and 3 blue.

_____red_____

2. Gina compares the red and blue marbles in her bag. How many more red marbles than blue marbles does she have?

> **Think**
> I can subtract 8 – 3 to find how many more red marbles she has.

__5__ more red marbles

Practice

3. Sam asks Jamal to pick a button from his bag. Which color button is he more likely to pick?

_____blue_____

4. Sam compares the red and blue buttons in his bag. How many more blue buttons than red buttons does he have?

__4__ more blue buttons

Go on

252 two hundred fifty-two

Play "Picture It"

Separate the class into two teams. Decide which team goes first. Have a volunteer from the second team draw a picture on the board as you tell a story.

Jenna has a box of 6 striped rocks and 2 solid rocks. Which rock will she most likely choose if she pulls one from the box?

A child from the first team predicts which type of rock Jenna will most likely choose. If the answer is correct, the team gets 1 point. If not, then the other team has a chance to answer. Then tell the teams to switch roles. Continue as time allows.

---

③ Practice

Independent Practice

Have children complete **Exercises 3–4** on page 252 independently.

Lesson continues

Daily Test Prep

Find the missing number.

21, 22, ____, 24, 25

21	22	24	NH
○	○	○	●

Activity

Lesson Intervention

Certain, Probable, or Impossible

Or use Intervention CD-ROM Lesson 9.6

iii Small Group	⏱ 5–10 minutes	Visual, Auditory

Materials: *3 clear bags, counters, connecting cubes*

1. Place connecting cubes in the first bag, links in the second bag, and a mix of cubes and links in the third bag. Write *always*, *never*, and *sometimes* on a separate piece of paper. Underneath write *certain*, *impossible*, and *probable*.

2. Hold up the bag with connecting cubes. Guide children to hold up the correct paper as they answer. **Will you always, sometimes, or never pick a cube from this bag?** (always/certain) Explain that if you always pick a cube then it is certain you will pick a cube each time. Continue holding up bags and emphasizing the connection between never, impossible and sometimes, probable.

3. Continue the activity with different items until children are comfortable deciding.

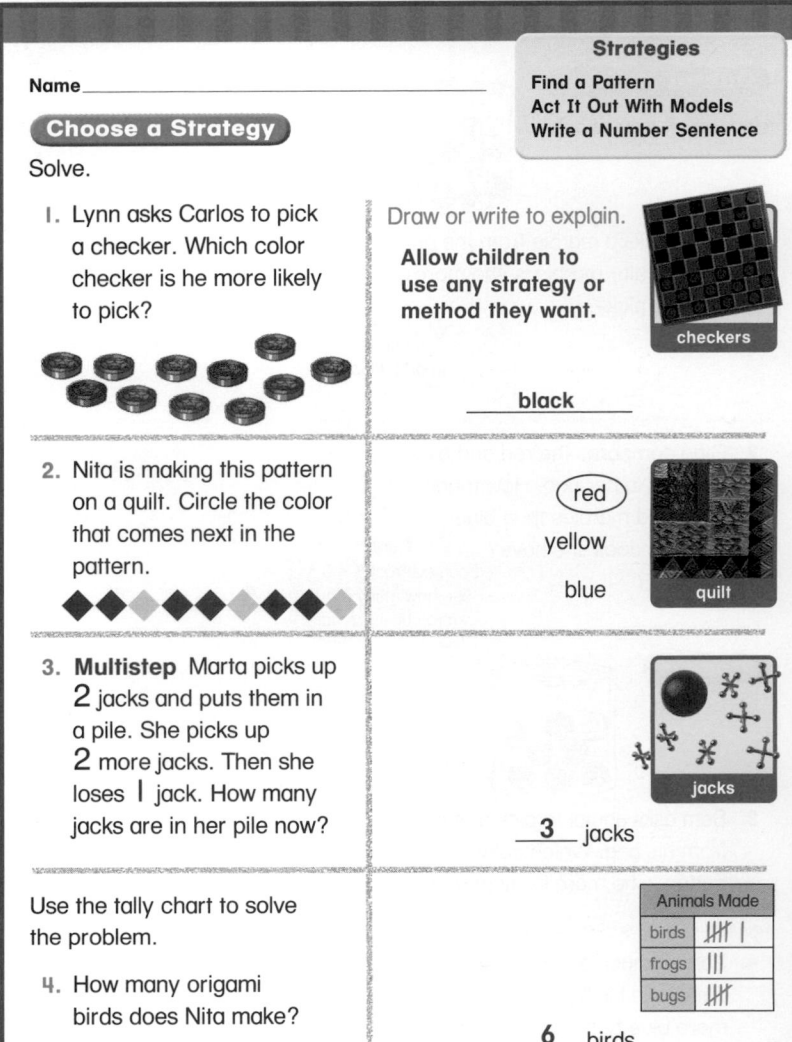

Strategies
Find a Pattern
Act It Out With Models
Write a Number Sentence

Name_____

Choose a Strategy

Solve.

1. Lynn asks Carlos to pick a checker. Which color checker is he more likely to pick?

   Draw or write to explain. Allow children to use any strategy or method they want.

   checkers

   _____ black _____

2. Nita is making this pattern on a quilt. Circle the color that comes next in the pattern.

   (red) yellow blue

   quilt

3. **Multistep** Marta picks up 2 jacks and puts them in a pile. She picks up 2 more jacks. Then she loses 1 jack. How many jacks are in her pile now?

   jacks

   __3__ jacks

Use the tally chart to solve the problem.

4. How many origami birds does Nita make?

Animals Made	
birds	JHT I
frogs	III
bugs	JHT

   __6__ birds

At Home Put two colors of like objects in a bag as shown in the lesson. Ask your child to predict which color he or she is more likely to pick. Take turns picking and returning the object to bag.

two hundred fifty-three **253**

---

③ Practice

Mixed Strategy Practice

Read the problem-solving strategies with children. Make sure children can read and comprehend the problems in **Exercises 1–4** on page 253. If necessary, pair more proficient readers with less-proficient readers. Encourage them to discuss the problems before solving.

Common Error

Misreading Problems

Some children may become confused by the language used in the problems. Discuss such problems with children and provide tips for solving.

④ Assess and Close

How can you use the data in a picture to help you solve a problem? (Possible answer: A picture can show what the problem is asking. You can count the marbles in the picture to find or check your answer.)

 **Keeping a Journal**

Tell or show how drawing a picture can help you solve a problem.

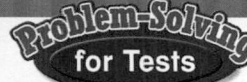 **Listening Skills**

Listen to your teacher read the problem.
Use the picture to solve.

Show your work using pictures, numbers, or words.

1. Pretend it is your turn to pick a cube from the bag. Which color are you more likely to pick?

gray

2. Compare the cubes in the bag. How many more gray cubes than white cubes are in there?

4 more gray cubes

Listen to your teacher read the problem.
Choose the correct answer.

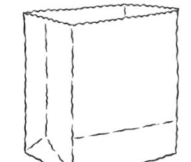

3.   red   blue   yellow   green
    ○   ○   ●   ○

4.   red   blue   yellow   green
    ●   ○   ○   ○

254 two hundred fifty-four

Problem-Solving for Tests

Listening Skills

This page provides children practice with the oral problem-solving format used in some standardized test items.

You may want to read each item only once to mimic the style of oral tests.

Use with Items 1 and 2

Listening Strategy: Listen for important words and numbers in the problem.

• *When a problem is on the page, look at the problem while I am reading it.*

• *Wait until I finish reading the problem before you start writing.*

Use with Item 3

Listening Strategy: Listen to the problem and then look at the picture.

Sue has a bag with 2 red and 7 yellow beads. She asks Missy to pick a bead from the bag. Which color bead is Missy more likely to pick?

• *Look at the picture. Mark your answer.*

Use with Item 4

Listening Strategy: Listen for important facts and details.

Ted has a bag with 3 yellow and 8 red beads. He asks Missy to pick a bead from the bag. Which color bead is Missy more likely to pick?

• *Look at the picture. Mark your answer.*

Quick Check

Have children complete the Quick Check exercises independently to assess their understanding of concepts and skills taught in **Lessons 4–6**.

Item	Lesson	Error Analysis	Intervention
1–2	9.4	Children may have difficulty identifying the parts of the set.	Reteach Resource 9.4 *Ways to Success* 9.4
3–4	9.5	Children may make faulty predictions.	Reteach Resource 9.5 *Ways to Success* 9.5
5	9.6	Children may be confused by the language in the problems.	Reteach Resource 9.6 *Ways to Success* 9.6

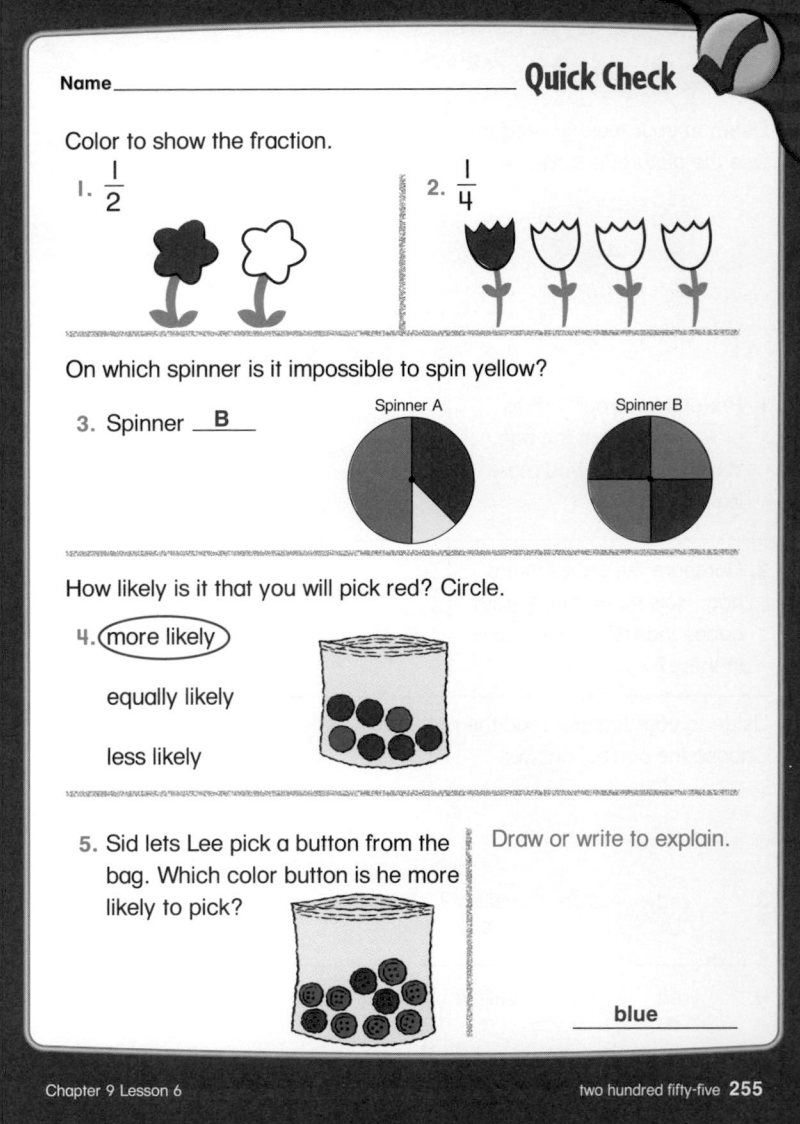

Name _____   **Quick Check**

Color to show the fraction.

1. $\frac{1}{2}$

2. $\frac{1}{4}$

On which spinner is it impossible to spin yellow?

3. Spinner __B__   Spinner A   Spinner B

How likely is it that you will pick red? Circle.

4. (more likely)

   equally likely

   less likely

5. Sid lets Lee pick a button from the bag. Which color button is he more likely to pick?

Draw or write to explain.

___blue___

 **Key Topic Review**

Key Topic Review

Trace the shape.
Write how many sides and corners.

1. triangle

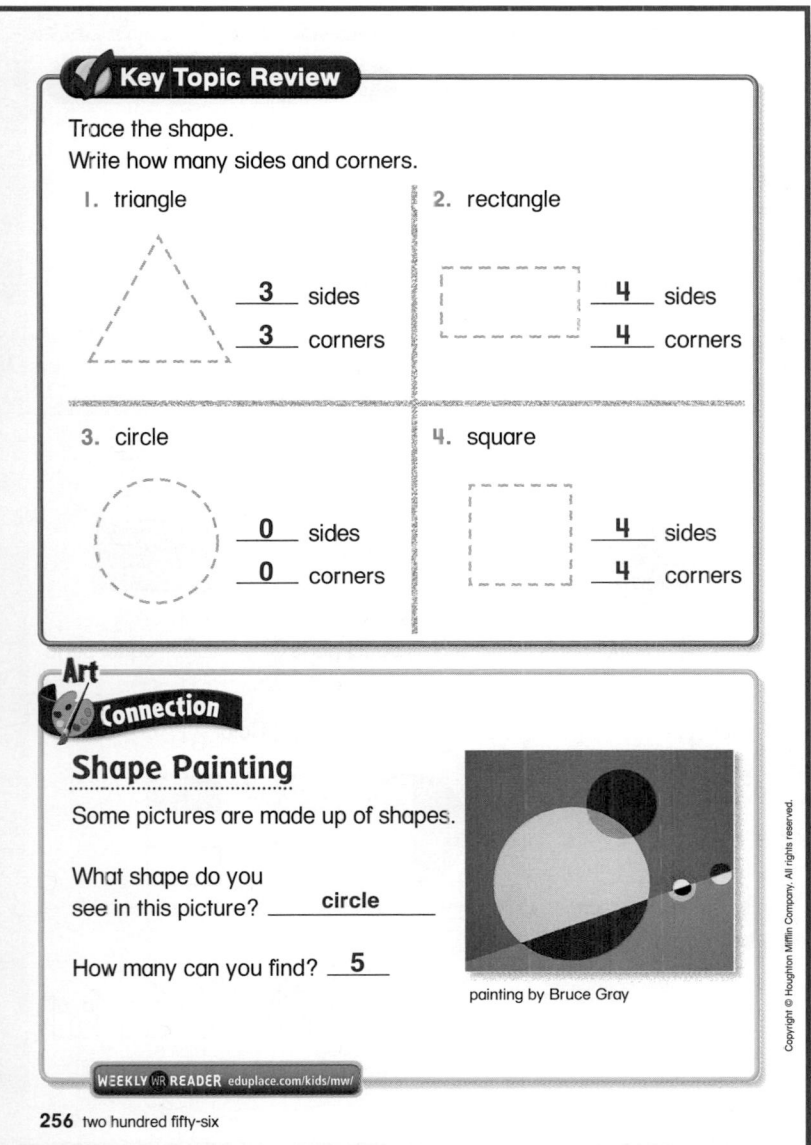

    __3__ sides

    __3__ corners

2. rectangle

    __4__ sides

    __4__ corners

3. circle

    __0__ sides

    __0__ corners

4. square

    __4__ sides

    __4__ corners

Art Connection

Shape Painting

Some pictures are made up of shapes.

What shape do you
see in this picture? ___circle___

How many can you find? __5__

painting by Bruce Gray

WEEKLY WR READER eduplace.com/kids/mw/

Key Topic Review

This assessment provides a review of skills and concepts taught in Chapter 7.

Check to be sure that children

• can identify the number of sides and corners of plane shapes correctly.

Art Connection

Shape Paintings

Direct children to look at the shape painting by Bruce Gray on page 256. Have volunteers describe the shapes in the painting. Encourage children to use language such as "part of the circle." Have them see how many shapes they can find. Then have children make a drawing using the same shapes.

Chapter Review/Test

Purpose: This test provides an informal assessment of the Chapter 9 objectives.

Chapter Test Items 1–15

To assign a numerical grade for this Chapter Test, use 6 points for each test item and add 10 to the score.

Check Understanding

Use children's work on word problems to informally assess progress on chapter content.

Customizing Your Instruction

For children who have not yet mastered these objectives, you can use the reteaching resources listed in the chart below.

 Assessment Options

A summary test for this chapter is also provided in the Unit Resources Folder.

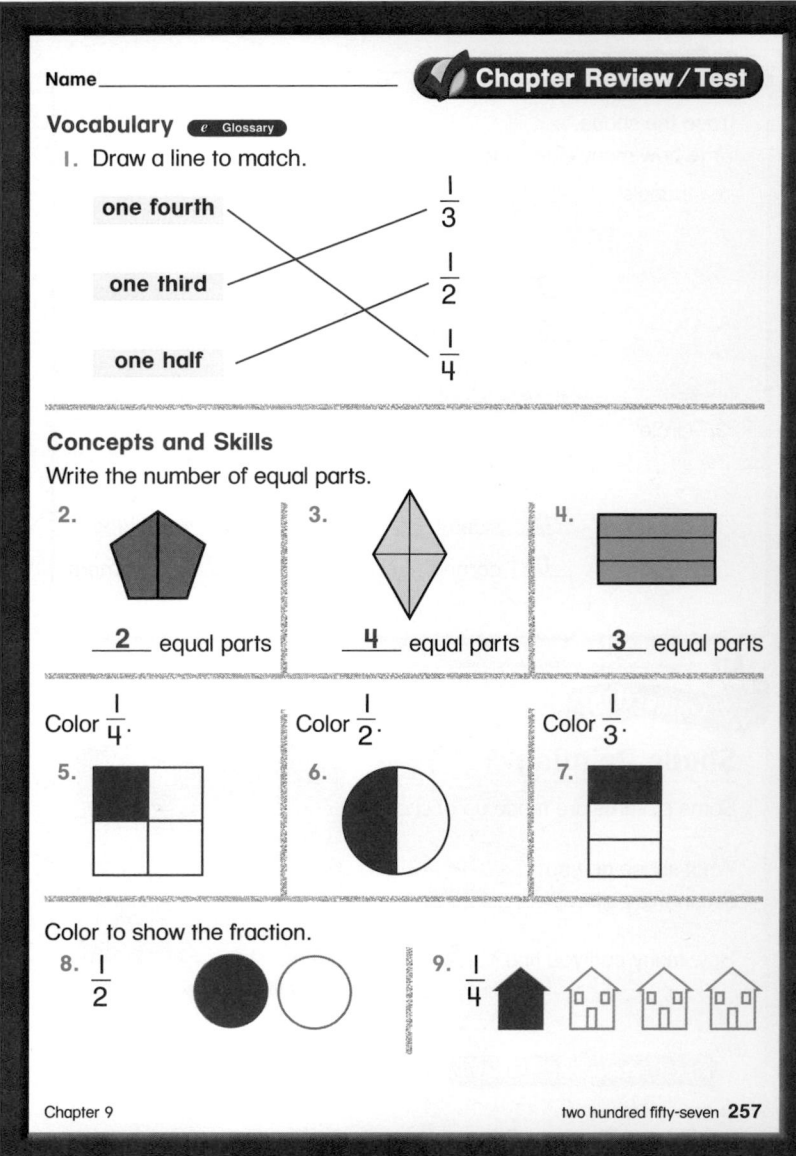

Reteaching Support

Chapter Test Items	Summary Test Items	Chapter Objectives Tested	TE Pages	Use These Reteaching Resources
1	1	**9A** Develop and use math vocabulary relating to fractions and probability.	239A–242	Reteach Resources and *Ways to Success* CD: 9.2, 9.3 Skillsheet 62
2–9	2–6	**9B** Identify, name, and represent $\frac{1}{2}$, $\frac{1}{3}$, and $\frac{1}{4}$ of a region and of a set.	237A–242, 245A–246	Reteach Resources and *Ways to Success* CD: 9.1–9.4 Skillsheet 63–64
10–14	7–8	**9C** Use probability to determine the likelihood of an event.	247A–249	Reteach Resource and *Ways to Success* CD: 9.5 Skillsheet 65
15	9–10	**9D** Use data from a picture to solve problems.	251A–254	Reteach Resource and *Ways to Success* CD: 9.6 Skillsheet 66

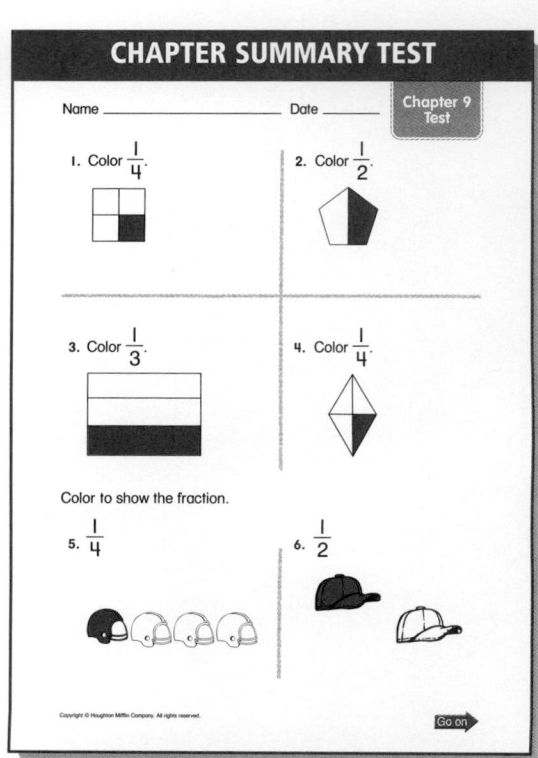

Will it happen?
Draw a line to match.

10. The sun shines on you at night. — certain

11. You sing during music time. — probable

12. Puppies will grow. — impossible

How likely is it that you will pick red?
Circle.

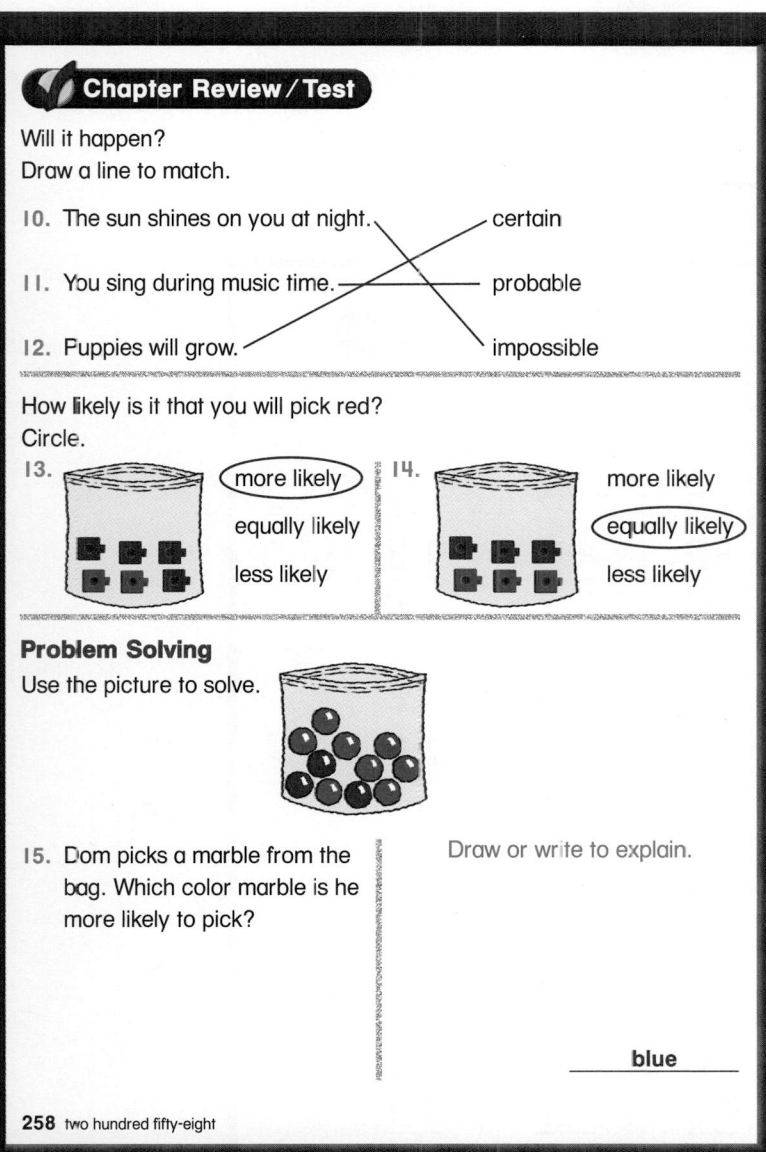

13. (more likely)

equally likely

less likely

14. more likely

(equally likely)

less likely

Problem Solving

Use the picture to solve.

15. Dom picks a marble from the bag. Which color marble is he more likely to pick?

Draw or write to explain.

_____ **blue** _____

Adequate Yearly Progress

Use the End of Grade Test Prep Assessment Guide to help familiarize your children with the format of standardized tests.

CHAPTER SUMMARY TEST

Name _____ Date _____

Chapter 9
Test
continued

Look at the spinner. Circle.

7. Is it certain that it will land on ▌ ?

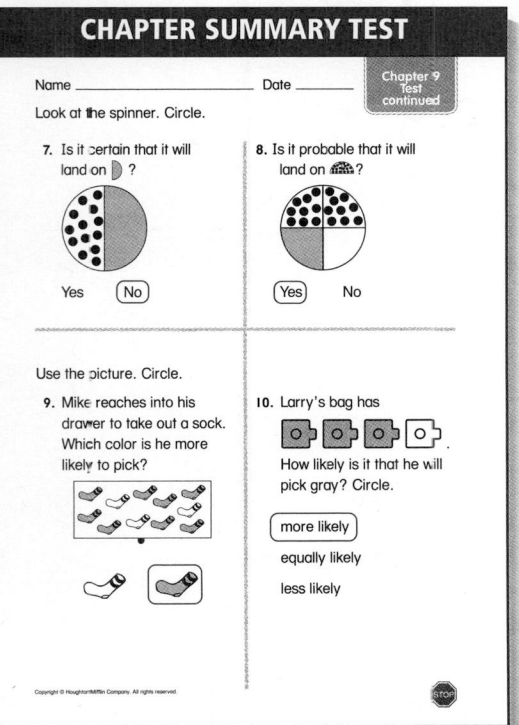

Yes   (No)

8. Is it probable that it will land on ▦ ?

(Yes)   No

Use the picture. Circle.

9. Mike reaches into his drawer to take out a sock. Which color is he more likely to pick?

10. Larry's bag has

.

How likely is it that he will pick gray? Circle.

(more likely)

equally likely

less likely

STOP

Facts Practice ....

Facts Practice

Add.
Write the sum.

1.
2	4	5	0	5	7	1
+2	+2	+3	+0	+2	+0	+3
4	6	8	0	7	7	4

2.
3	2	0	2	1	3	2
+5	+5	+1	+3	+1	+2	+6
8	7	1	5	2	5	8

3.
7	2	9	6	3	1	3
+1	+4	+0	+4	+1	+4	+4
8	6	9	10	4	5	7

4.
6	4	2	9	0	5	5
+0	+1	+7	+1	+6	+1	+4
6	5	9	10	6	6	9

5.
2	0	5	8	1	6	3
+8	+7	+5	+1	+5	+3	+6
10	7	10	9	6	9	9

6.
7	4	8	6	4	4	5
+2	+0	+2	+2	+6	+5	+0
9	4	10	8	10	9	5

7.
7	1	3	3	5	7	1
+3	+6	+7	+4	+3	+0	+7
10	7	10	7	8	7	8

Facts Practice

Subtract.
Write the difference.

1.
$$\begin{array}{r} 10 \\ -\ 9 \\ \hline 1 \end{array}$$
$$\begin{array}{r} 7 \\ -4 \\ \hline 3 \end{array}$$
$$\begin{array}{r} 3 \\ -2 \\ \hline 1 \end{array}$$
$$\begin{array}{r} 4 \\ -4 \\ \hline 0 \end{array}$$
$$\begin{array}{r} 9 \\ -8 \\ \hline 1 \end{array}$$
$$\begin{array}{r} 4 \\ -0 \\ \hline 4 \end{array}$$
$$\begin{array}{r} 8 \\ -5 \\ \hline 3 \end{array}$$

2.
$$\begin{array}{r} 9 \\ -7 \\ \hline 2 \end{array}$$
$$\begin{array}{r} 2 \\ -2 \\ \hline 0 \end{array}$$
$$\begin{array}{r} 6 \\ -4 \\ \hline 2 \end{array}$$
$$\begin{array}{r} 9 \\ -4 \\ \hline 5 \end{array}$$
$$\begin{array}{r} 0 \\ -0 \\ \hline 0 \end{array}$$
$$\begin{array}{r} 4 \\ -2 \\ \hline 2 \end{array}$$
$$\begin{array}{r} 4 \\ -3 \\ \hline 1 \end{array}$$

3.
$$\begin{array}{r} 9 \\ -5 \\ \hline 4 \end{array}$$
$$\begin{array}{r} 10 \\ -\ 8 \\ \hline 2 \end{array}$$
$$\begin{array}{r} 2 \\ -0 \\ \hline 2 \end{array}$$
$$\begin{array}{r} 8 \\ -6 \\ \hline 2 \end{array}$$
$$\begin{array}{r} 7 \\ -6 \\ \hline 1 \end{array}$$
$$\begin{array}{r} 10 \\ -\ 5 \\ \hline 5 \end{array}$$
$$\begin{array}{r} 7 \\ -5 \\ \hline 2 \end{array}$$

4.
$$\begin{array}{r} 10 \\ -\ 0 \\ \hline 10 \end{array}$$
$$\begin{array}{r} 9 \\ -1 \\ \hline 8 \end{array}$$
$$\begin{array}{r} 5 \\ -2 \\ \hline 3 \end{array}$$
$$\begin{array}{r} 7 \\ -2 \\ \hline 5 \end{array}$$
$$\begin{array}{r} 8 \\ -1 \\ \hline 7 \end{array}$$
$$\begin{array}{r} 7 \\ -3 \\ \hline 4 \end{array}$$
$$\begin{array}{r} 7 \\ -0 \\ \hline 7 \end{array}$$

5.
$$\begin{array}{r} 6 \\ -5 \\ \hline 1 \end{array}$$
$$\begin{array}{r} 10 \\ -\ 2 \\ \hline 8 \end{array}$$
$$\begin{array}{r} 8 \\ -3 \\ \hline 5 \end{array}$$
$$\begin{array}{r} 8 \\ -7 \\ \hline 1 \end{array}$$
$$\begin{array}{r} 9 \\ -3 \\ \hline 6 \end{array}$$
$$\begin{array}{r} 7 \\ -1 \\ \hline 6 \end{array}$$
$$\begin{array}{r} 6 \\ -2 \\ \hline 4 \end{array}$$

6.
$$\begin{array}{r} 9 \\ -2 \\ \hline 7 \end{array}$$
$$\begin{array}{r} 5 \\ -3 \\ \hline 2 \end{array}$$
$$\begin{array}{r} 6 \\ -3 \\ \hline 3 \end{array}$$
$$\begin{array}{r} 1 \\ -1 \\ \hline 0 \end{array}$$
$$\begin{array}{r} 9 \\ -6 \\ \hline 3 \end{array}$$
$$\begin{array}{r} 9 \\ -9 \\ \hline 0 \end{array}$$
$$\begin{array}{r} 5 \\ -5 \\ \hline 0 \end{array}$$

7.
$$\begin{array}{r} 8 \\ -4 \\ \hline 4 \end{array}$$
$$\begin{array}{r} 5 \\ -4 \\ \hline 1 \end{array}$$
$$\begin{array}{r} 8 \\ -2 \\ \hline 6 \end{array}$$
$$\begin{array}{r} 2 \\ -1 \\ \hline 1 \end{array}$$
$$\begin{array}{r} 9 \\ -0 \\ \hline 9 \end{array}$$
$$\begin{array}{r} 6 \\ -6 \\ \hline 0 \end{array}$$
$$\begin{array}{r} 10 \\ -\ 6 \\ \hline 4 \end{array}$$

Social Studies Connection

PURPOSE

To identify and describe triangles, rectangles, and circles.

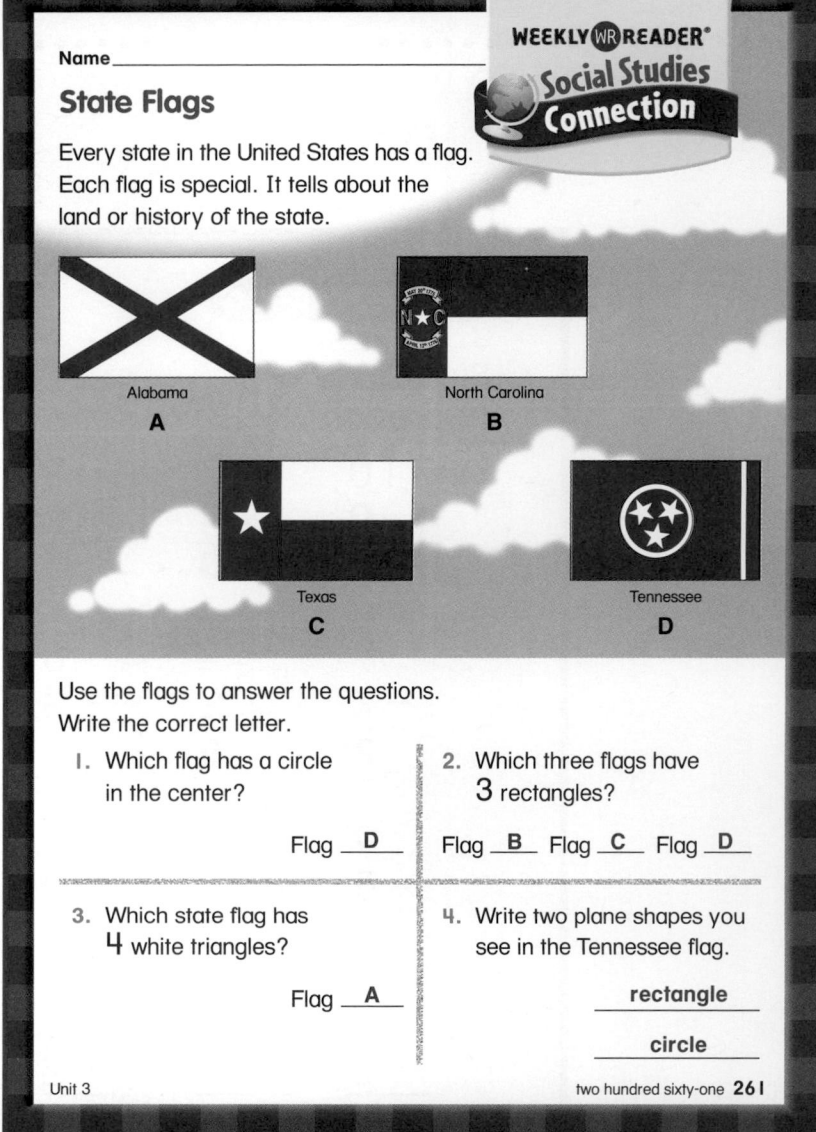

Name_____

State Flags

Every state in the United States has a flag. Each flag is special. It tells about the land or history of the state.

Alabama
A

North Carolina
B

Texas
C

Tennessee
D

Use the flags to answer the questions.
Write the correct letter.

1. Which flag has a circle in the center?

   Flag __D__

2. Which three flags have **3** rectangles?

   Flag __B__ Flag __C__ Flag __D__

3. Which state flag has **4** white triangles?

   Flag __A__

4. Write two plane shapes you see in the Tennessee flag.

   rectangle

   circle

Unit 3
two hundred sixty-one **261**

Using These Pages

Discussion Topics

- Refer children to the four flags on page 261. **What plane shape are all the flags?** (rectangle) Read and discuss Exercises 1–4 at the bottom of the page.

- Then refer children to the four flags on page 262. **Which flag has a circle in the center?** (A; Florida)

- **Find the flag with the palm tree and moon on it.** (B; South Carolina) **What shape is that flag?** (rectangle) Read and discuss Exercises 1–4 at the bottom of the page.

Here are four more state flags.

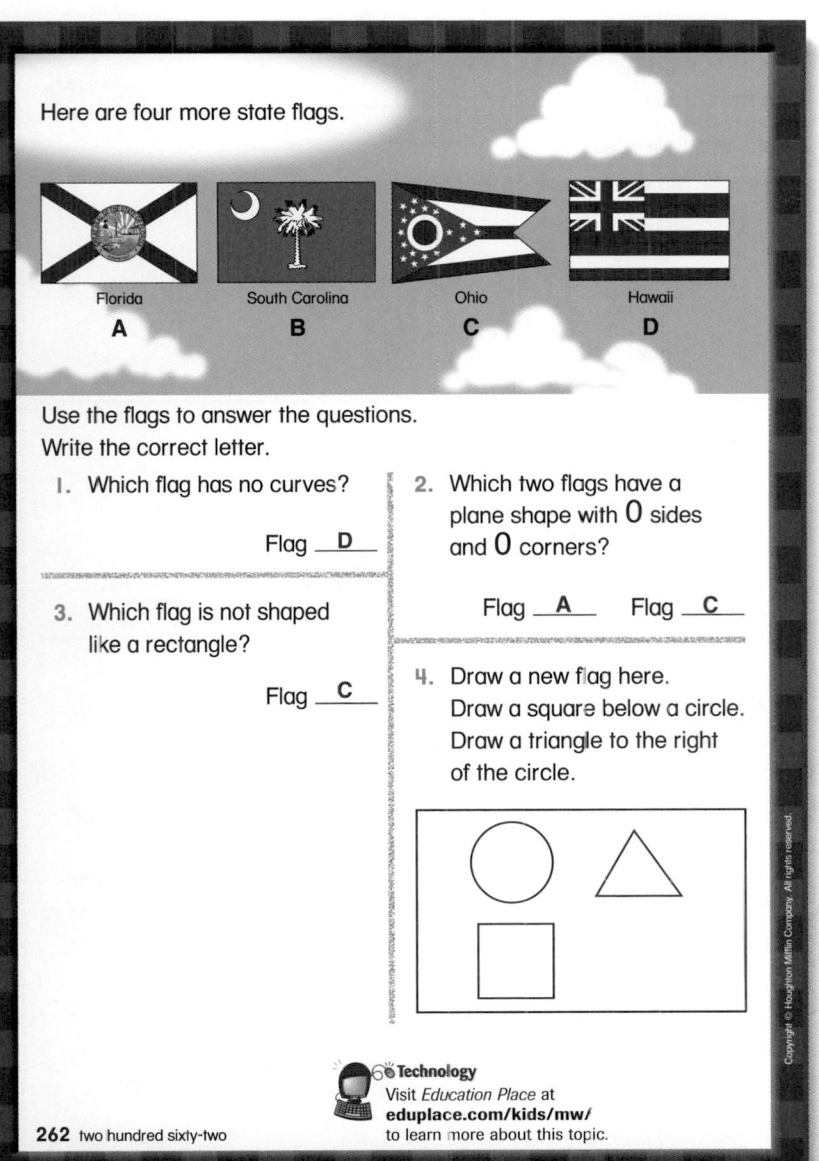

Florida	South Carolina	Ohio	Hawaii
A	**B**	**C**	**D**

Use the flags to answer the questions.
Write the correct letter.

1. Which flag has no curves?

   Flag __D__

3. Which flag is not shaped
   like a rectangle?

   Flag __C__

2. Which two flags have a
   plane shape with 0 sides
   and 0 corners?

   Flag __A__   Flag __C__

4. Draw a new flag here.
   Draw a square below a circle.
   Draw a triangle to the right
   of the circle.

Technology
Visit *Education Place* at
eduplace.com/kids/mw/
to learn more about this topic.

Wrap Up the Unit Project

The Shapes on Our Flags

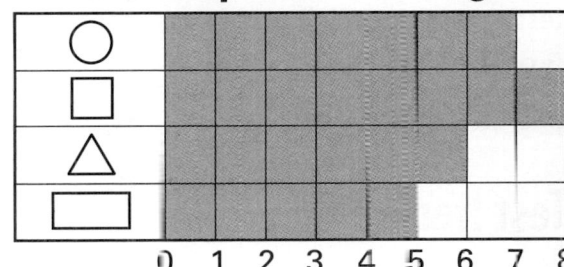

0 1 2 3 4 5 6 7 8

- Use the flags to review shapes. For example,
  invite children to count the squares, rectangles,
  triangles, and circles on the flags and use
  tally marks to record the data. Then help them
  convert the information into a bar graph.

- Remind children that symbols and pictures
  on flags often give information. **If a visitor
  came to our room and saw our flags, what
  information could he or she learn?**

Unit 3 Test

PURPOSE

This test provides an informal assessment of the Unit 3 objectives.

Unit Test Items 1–15

To assign a numerical grade for this Unit Test, use 6 points for each test item and add 10 to the score.

Customizing Your Instruction

For children who have not yet mastered these objectives, you can use the **Reteaching Resources** listed in the chart below. *Ways to Success* is Houghton Mifflin's Intervention program available in CD-ROM and blackline master formats.

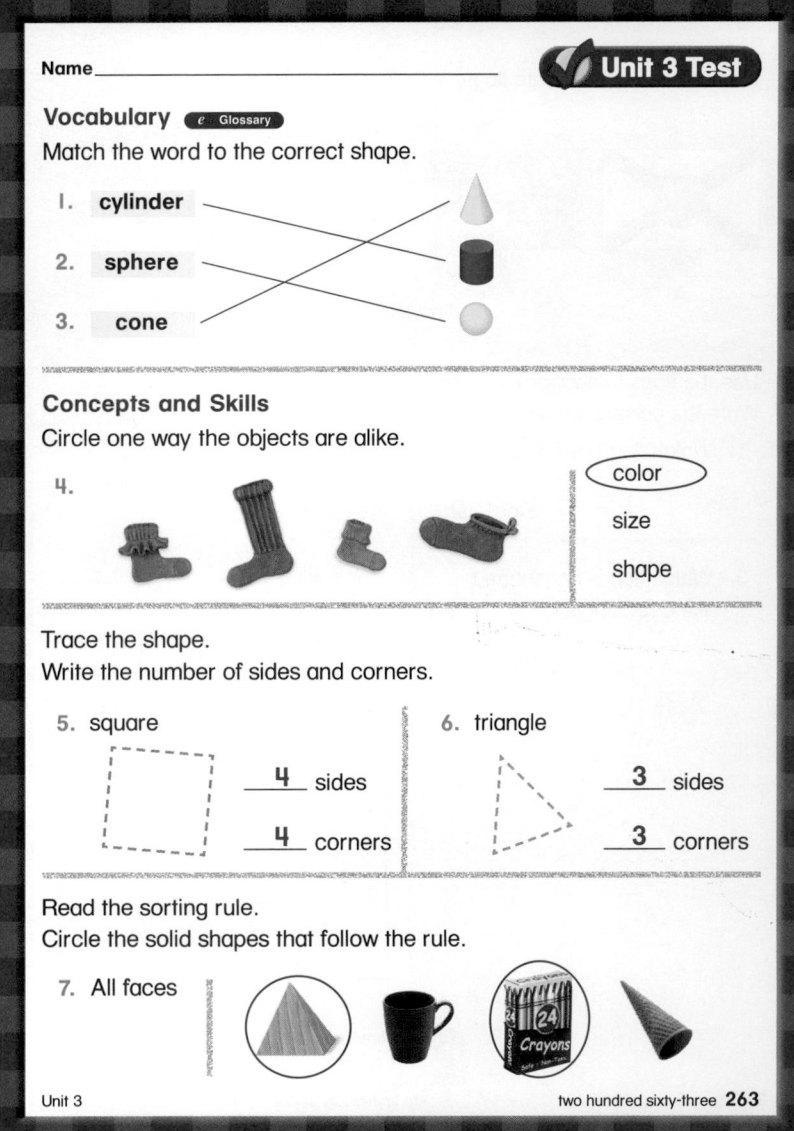

Reteaching Support

Unit Test Item		Unit Objectives Tested	TE Pages	Use These Reteaching Resources
p. 263–264 1–7	Tests A & B 1–4	**3A** Identify, describe, classify, compare, and sort plane and solid shapes.	183A–188, 191A–196	Reteach Resources and *Ways to Success*, 7.1–7.4
8–9	5–8	**3B** Use position words and grids to describe and locate objects.	207A–212, 215A–218	Reteach Resources and *Ways to Success*, 8.1–8.4
10–11	9–12	**3C** Identify transformations of shapes and symmetry in shapes.	223A–225	Reteach Resource and *Ways to Success*, 8.7
12	13–14	**3D** Identify, create, and extend patterns.	221A–222	Reteach Resource and *Ways to Success*, 8.6
13–14	15–18	**3E** Identify and name $\frac{1}{2}$, $\frac{1}{3}$, and $\frac{1}{4}$ of a region or set.	239A–242, 245A–246	Reteach Resources and *Ways to Success*, 9.2–9.4
15	19–20	**3F** Apply skills and strategies to solve problems.	227A–230	Reteach Resource and *Ways to Success*, 8.8

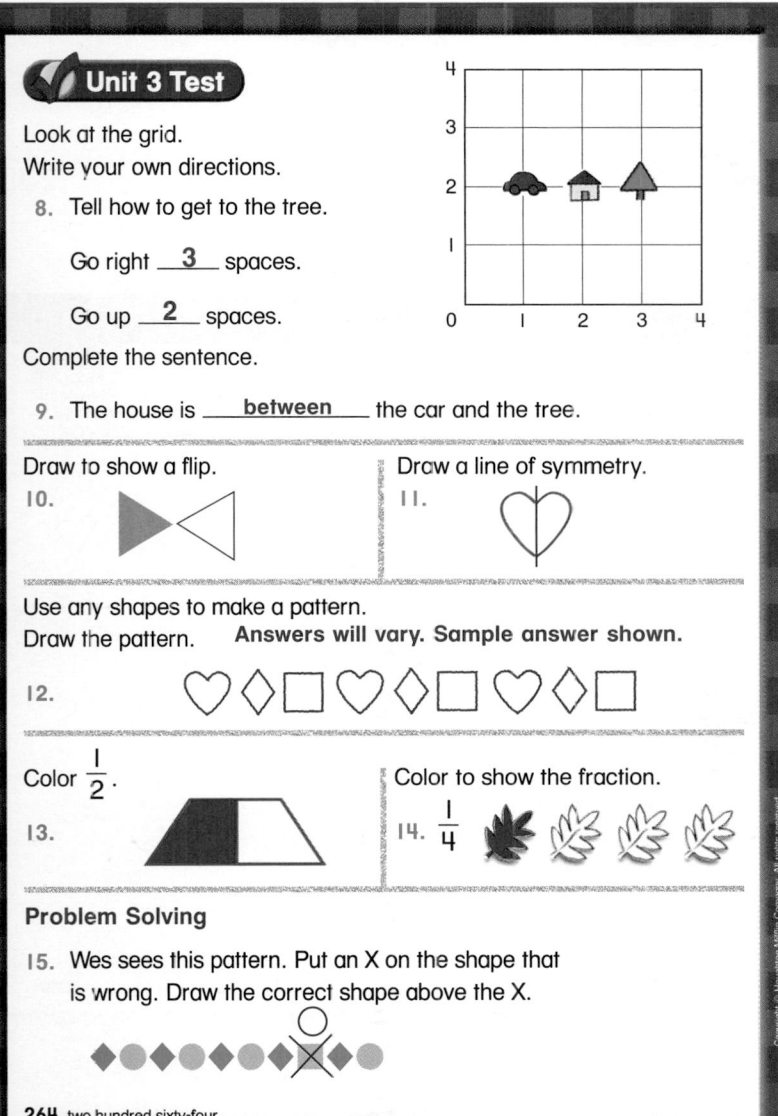

Unit 3 Test

Look at the grid.
Write your own directions.

8. Tell how to get to the tree.

    Go right __3__ spaces.

    Go up __2__ spaces.

Complete the sentence.

9. The house is __between__ the car and the tree.

Draw to show a flip.

10.

Draw a line of symmetry.

11.

Use any shapes to make a pattern.
Draw the pattern. **Answers will vary. Sample answer shown.**

12. ♡ ◇ □ ♡ ◇ □ ♡ ◇ □

Color $\frac{1}{2}$.

13.

Color to show the fraction.

14. $\frac{1}{4}$

Problem Solving

15. Wes sees this pattern. Put an X on the shape that is wrong. Draw the correct shape above the X.

264 two hundred sixty-four

Assessment Options

Formal Tests for this unit are also provided in the Unit Resource Folder.

- **Unit 3 Test A (Open Response)**
- **Unit 3 Test B (Multiple Choice)**

Performance Assessment

You may want to use the Performance Assessment instead of, or in addition to, the Unit Test. Three Performance Assessment tasks can be found on Student Book pages 265–266.

Adequate Yearly Progress

Use the *End of Grade Test Prep Assessment Guide* to help familiarize your children with the format of standardized tests.

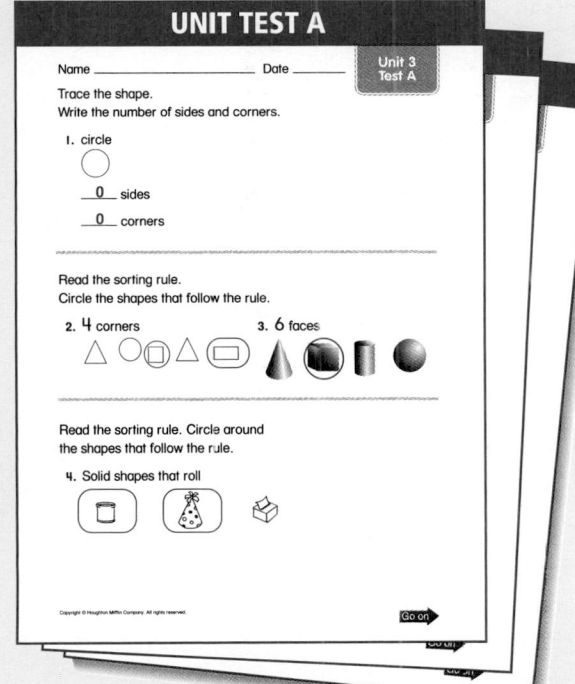

Unit 3 Tests

See pages 265A–265B for answers.

Unit Test Answers: Form A

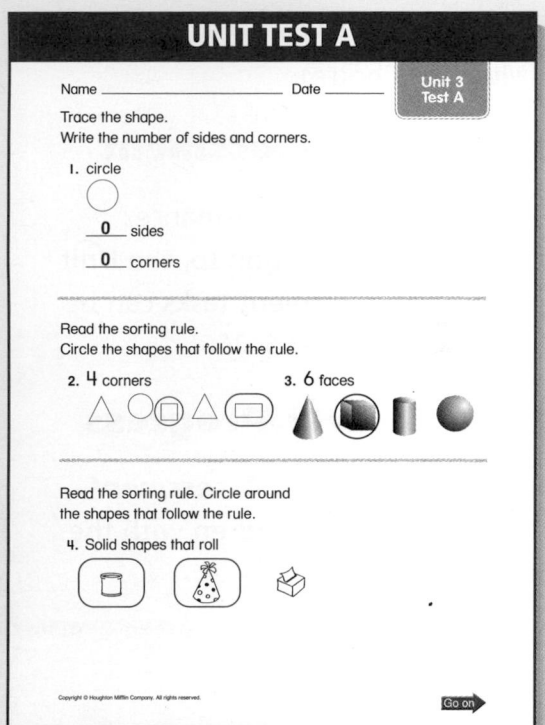

UNIT TEST A

Name _____ Date _____ | Unit 3 Test A

Trace the shape.
Write the number of sides and corners.

1. circle

◯

0 sides

0 corners

Read the sorting rule.
Circle the shapes that follow the rule.

2. 4 corners   3. 6 faces

Read the sorting rule. Circle around
the shapes that follow the rule.

4. Solid shapes that roll

Go on ▶

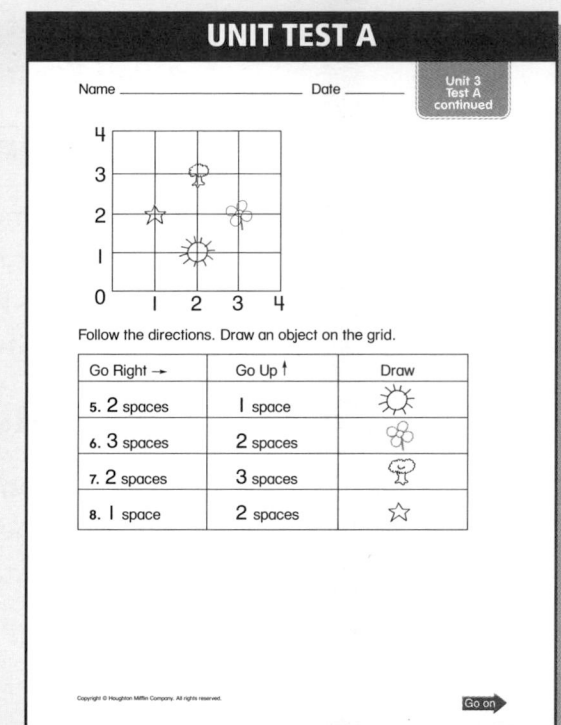

UNIT TEST A

Name _____ Date _____ | Unit 3 Test A continued

Follow the directions. Draw an object on the grid.

Go Right →	Go Up ↑	Draw
5. 2 spaces	1 space	☀
6. 3 spaces	2 spaces	🌼
7. 2 spaces	3 spaces	🌳
8. 1 space	2 spaces	☆

Go on ▶

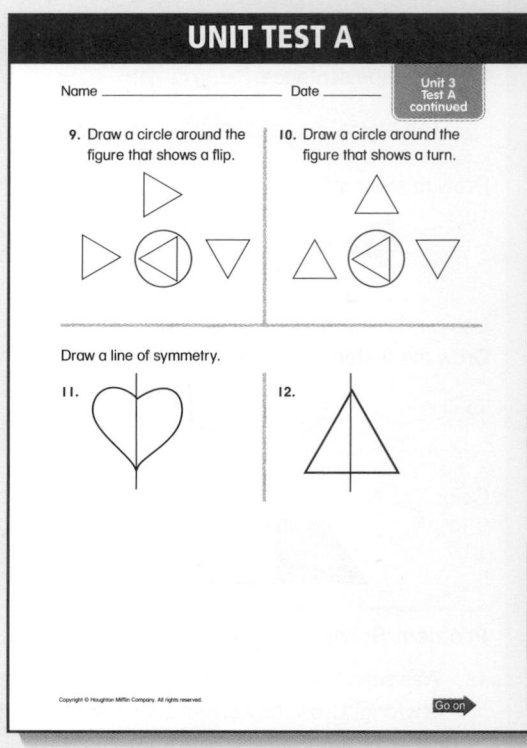

UNIT TEST A

Name _____ Date _____ | Unit 3 Test A continued

9. Draw a circle around the figure that shows a flip.

10. Draw a circle around the figure that shows a turn.

Draw a line of symmetry.

11.   12.

Go on ▶

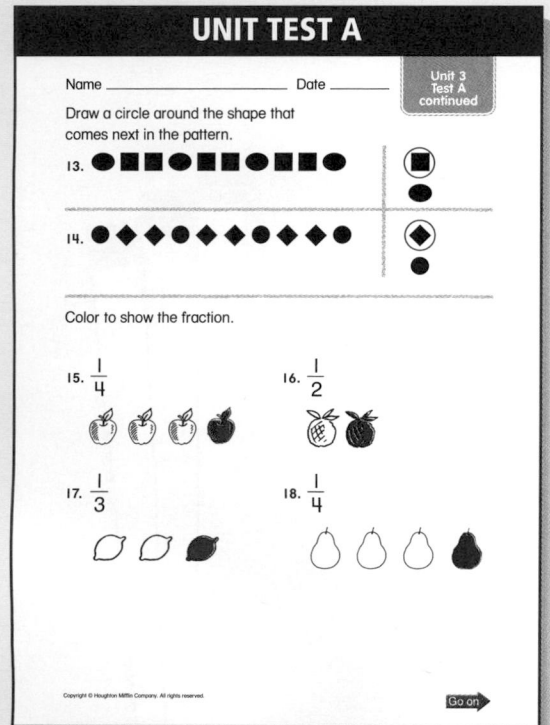

UNIT TEST A

Name _____ Date _____ | Unit 3 Test A continued

Draw a circle around the shape that
comes next in the pattern.

13. ●■●■●■●●■

14. ●◆●◆●◆●◆●◆

Color to show the fraction.

15. $\frac{1}{4}$ 16. $\frac{1}{2}$

17. $\frac{1}{3}$ 18. $\frac{1}{4}$

Go on ▶

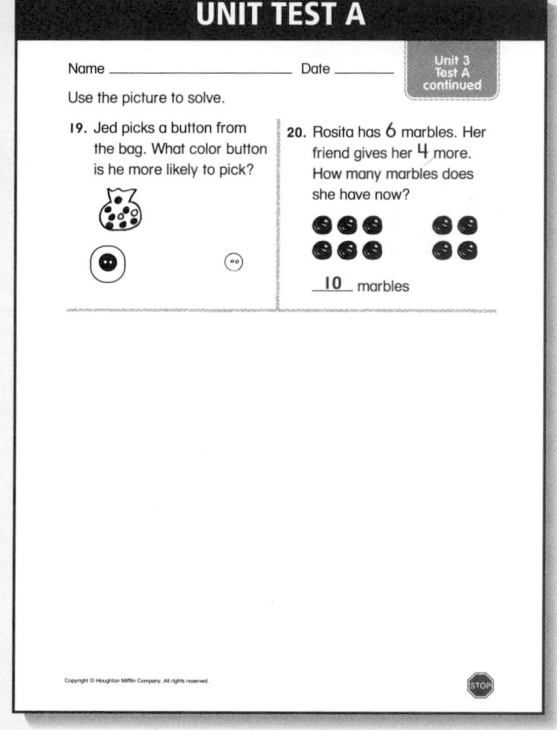

UNIT TEST A

Name _____ Date _____ | Unit 3 Test A continued

Use the picture to solve.

19. Jed picks a button from
the bag. What color button
is he more likely to pick?

20. Rosita has 6 marbles. Her
friend gives her 4 more.
How many marbles does
she have now?

10 marbles

STOP

Unit Test Answers: Form B

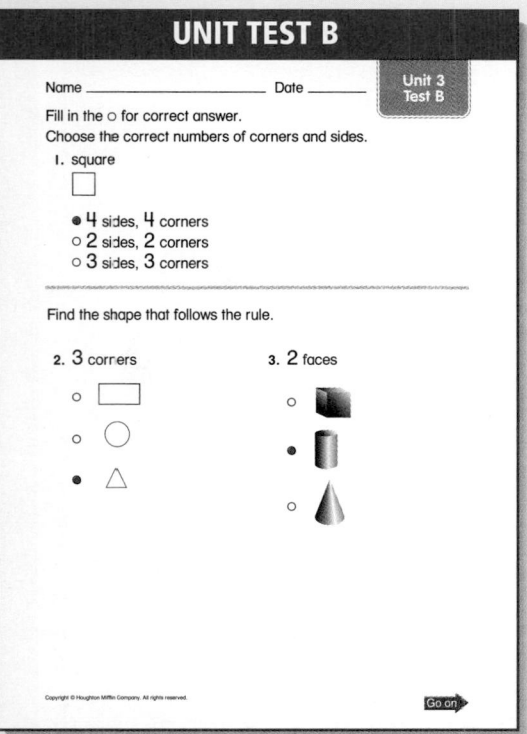

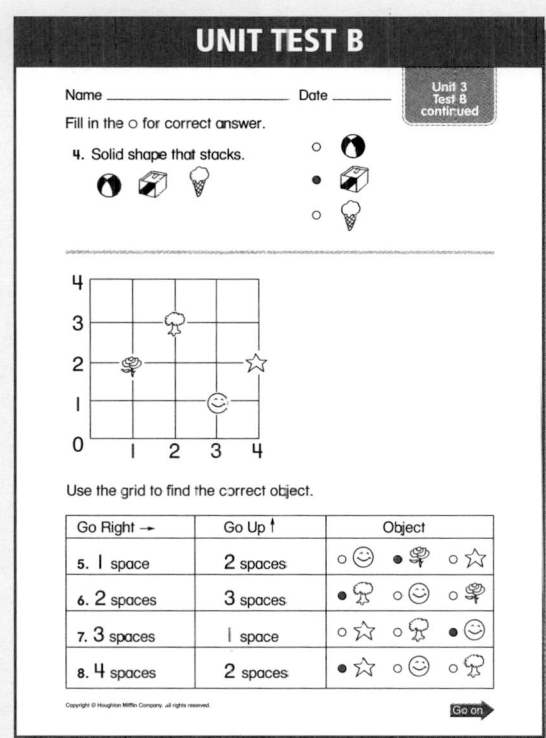

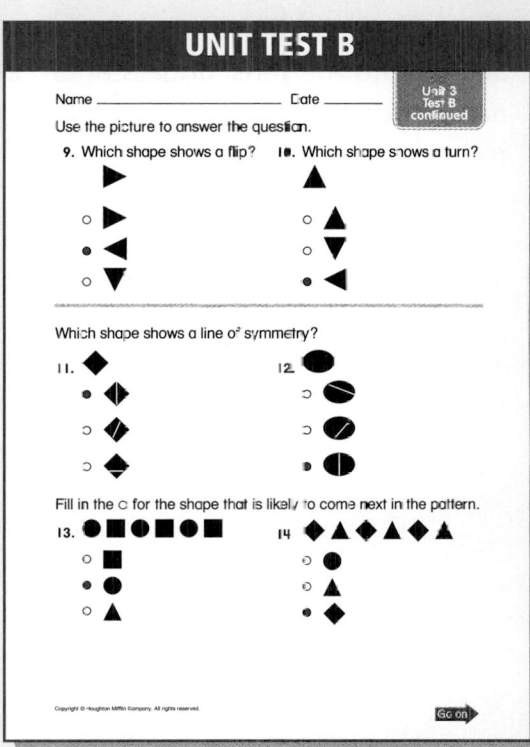

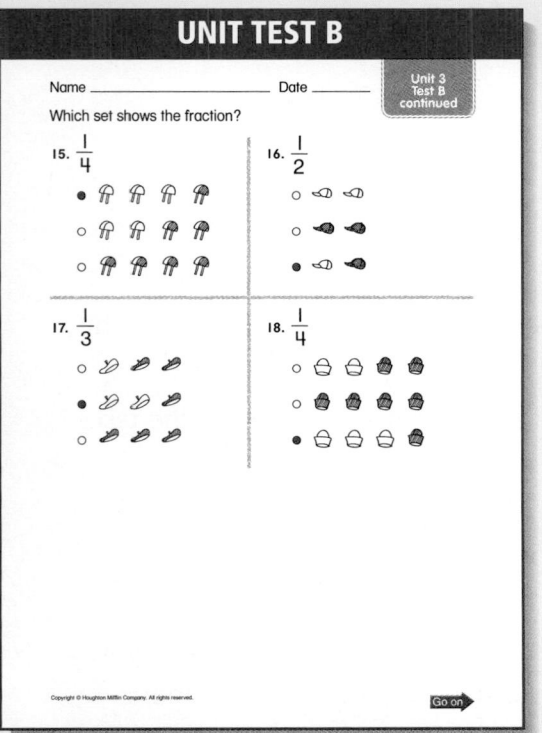

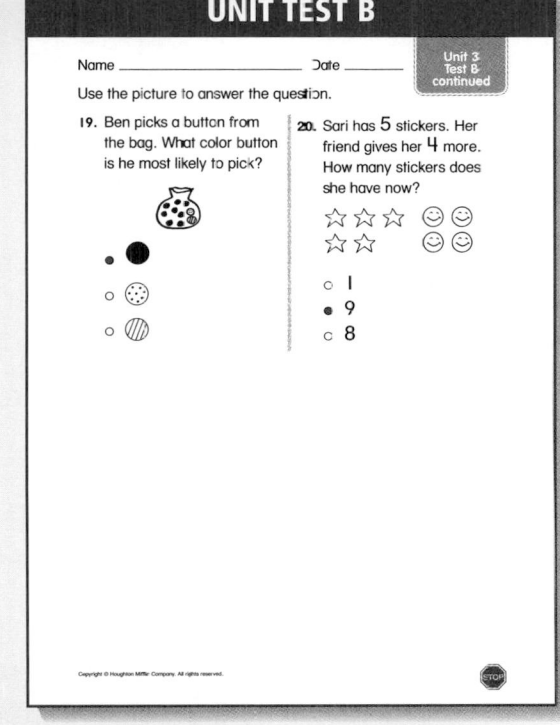

Performance Assessment

PURPOSE

This assessment focuses on geometry and fractions. Children should be able to identify plane shapes and transformations, understand position words, name a fraction of a set, and apply skills and strategies to solve problems.

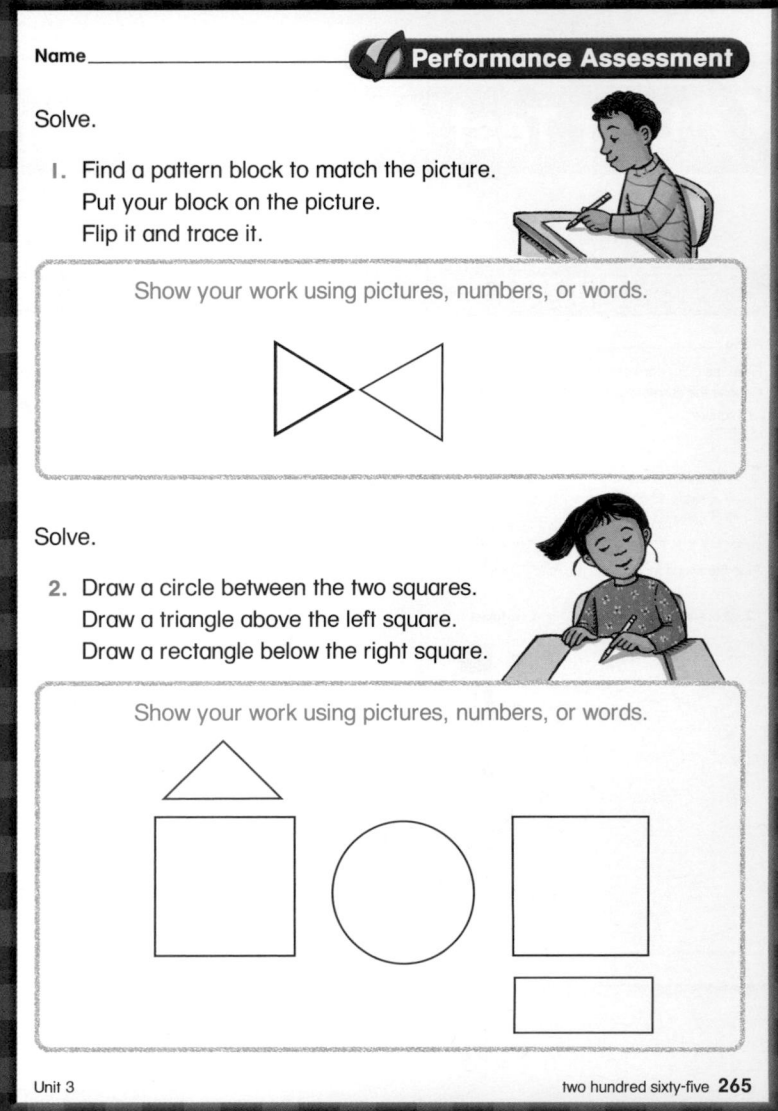

Name_____

✔ Performance Assessment

Solve.

1. Find a pattern block to match the picture.
   Put your block on the picture.
   Flip it and trace it.

Show your work using pictures, numbers, or words.

Solve.

2. Draw a circle between the two squares.
   Draw a triangle above the left square.
   Draw a rectangle below the right square.

Show your work using pictures, numbers, or words.

Unit 3   two hundred sixty-five **265**

Using These Pages

- Show children a set of pattern blocks. **What shapes in this set of blocks are triangles? Squares?** (Children should identify all squares and triangles within the set and give reasons for their selections, such as number of sides.)

- **Can you make a pattern showing a triangle between a hexagon and a square?** (Children should use pattern blocks to show the position of the shapes.)

- Select 2 squares and 2 triangles from the pattern block set. **How many shapes do I have in this set?** (4 shapes) **Are there an equal number of triangles and squares?** (Yes, there are 2 of each.) **What fraction can I write to describe the number of triangles in the set?** ($\frac{1}{2}$ are triangles.)

- Direct children's attention to assessment tasks. You may wish to read the directions aloud to the children.

- Observe children as they work to complete the tasks.

Exercise One

In Exercise 1, children should be able to identify a triangle of the same size, and identify and make the transformation. (flip)

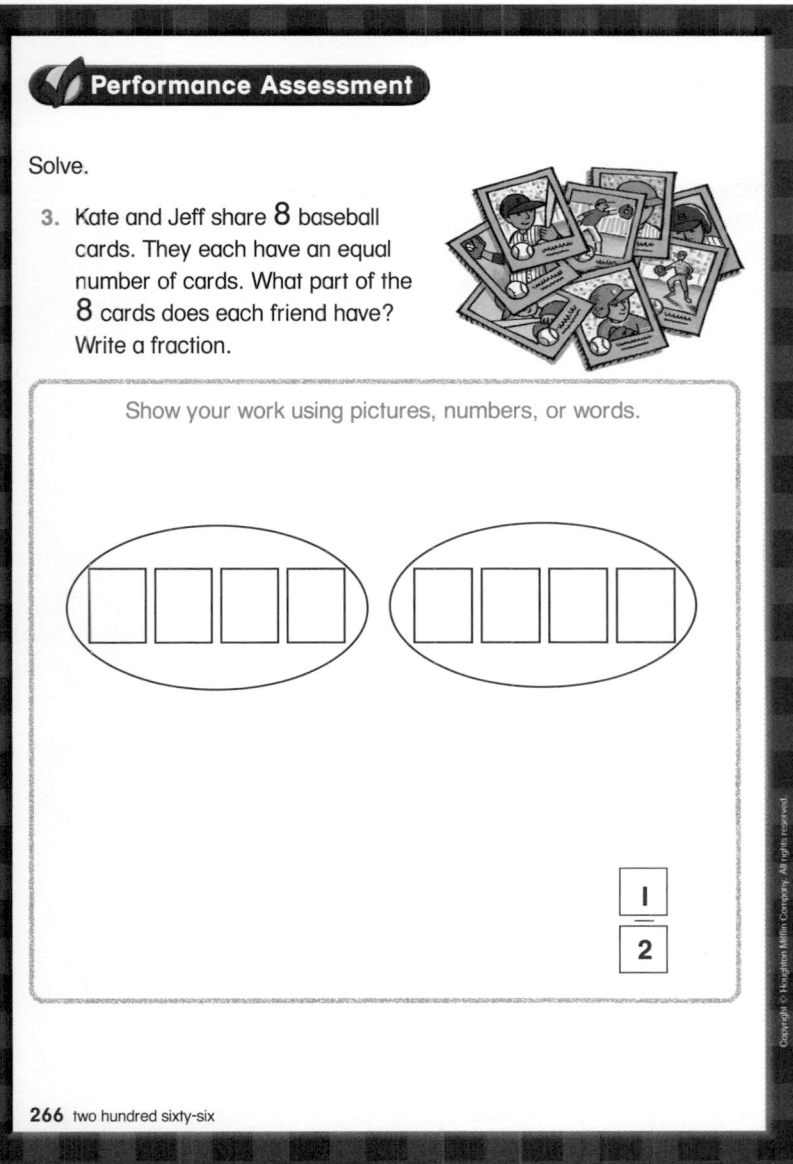

Performance Assessment

Solve.

3. Kate and Jeff share 8 baseball cards. They each have an equal number of cards. What part of the 8 cards does each friend have? Write a fraction.

Show your work using pictures, numbers, or words.

$\frac{1}{2}$

266 two hundred sixty-six

Assessing Student Work

Use the **Scoring Rubric** to evaluate children's performance on these tasks.

Scoring Rubric

4 EXEMPLARY

Identifies shapes, transformation, and position correctly, and applies skills and strategies to solve problem and write fractions correctly.

3 PROFICIENT

Identifies shapes, transformation, and position correctly. Solution to problem demonstrates mathematical reasoning, although the picture or the written fraction is faulty.

2 ACCEPTABLE

Identifies shapes, transformation, and position correctly. Solution to problem is incorrect or incomplete.

I LIMITED

Identifies shapes, transformation, or position incorrectly. Solution to problem shows no mathematical reasoning.

 **Exercise Two**

In Exercise 2 children should be able to identify and draw the shapes in the positions given.

Exercise Three

In Exercise 3, children should be able to represent equal parts using a picture of 8 cards and writing the fraction $\frac{1}{2}$.

This problem presents an opportunity to discuss fair shares with children. Kate and Jeff share the 8 baseball cards equally, 4 each, so this is a case of fair shares.

Geometry and Fractions   266

UNIT 3

Enrichment

► Growing Patterns

PURPOSE

This page provides an opportunity for children to apply their understanding of patterns by extending a growing pattern.

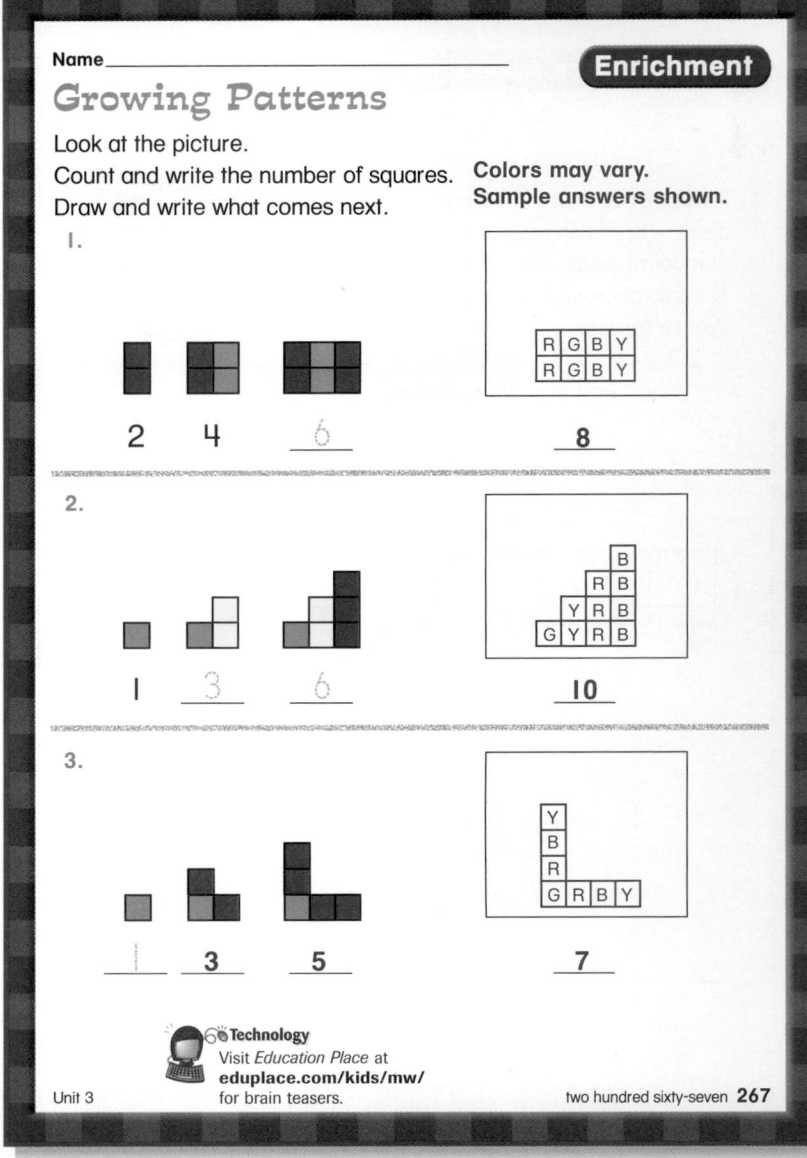

Growing Patterns

Look at the picture.
Count and write the number of squares.
Draw and write what comes next.

Colors may vary.
Sample answers shown.

1.

2   4   6   8

| R | G | B | Y |
| R | G | B | Y |

2.

1   3   6   10

3.

1   3   5   7

Technology
Visit *Education Place* at
eduplace.com/kids/mw/
for brain teasers.

Unit 3

two hundred sixty-seven **267**

Using This Page

Discussion Topics

- This page extends children's understanding of patterns by having them identify how a pattern grows and then extending the pattern.

- Explain that they need to look at each piece of the pattern carefully to decide how the pattern is growing. **Remember to count and write the number of squares in each piece of the pattern. This will help you decide what comes next.**

- Have children work individually or in pairs to complete the page. In pairs, children can work together to decide how the patterns grow and how to extend them correctly.

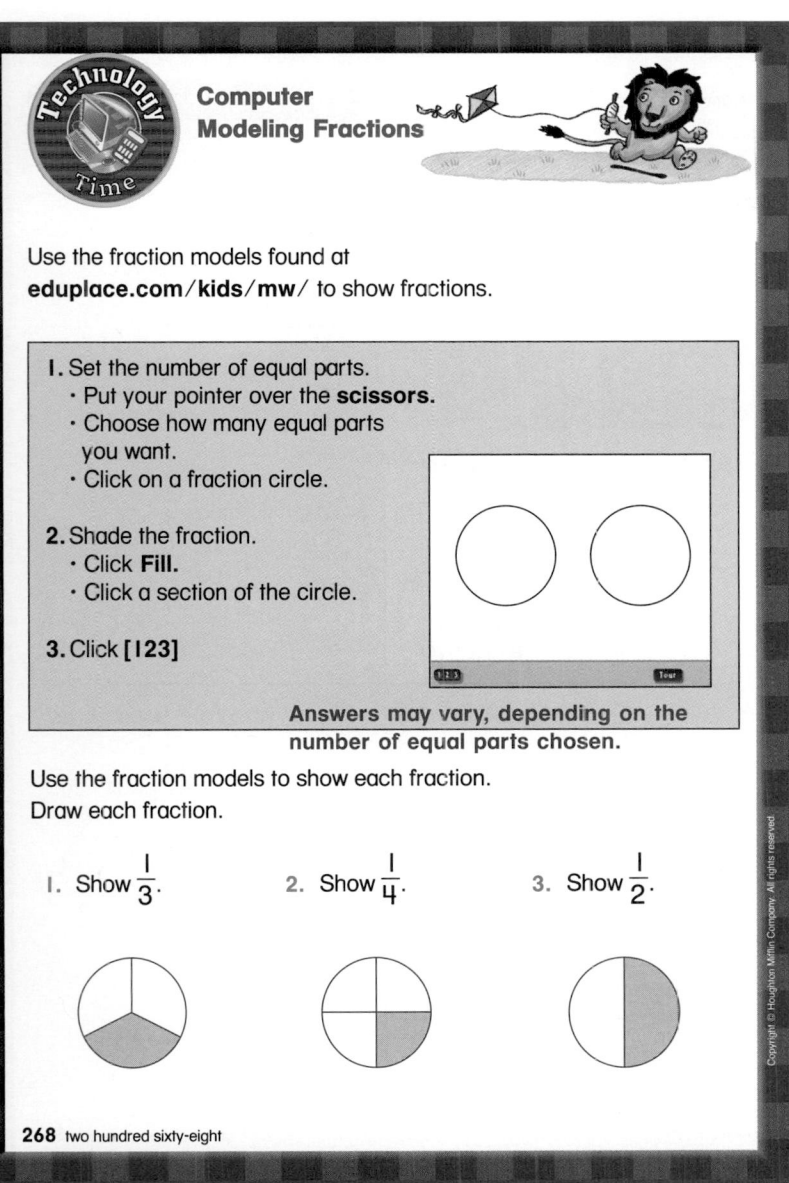

Computer
Modeling Fractions

Use the fraction models found at
eduplace.com/kids/mw/ to show fractions.

1. Set the number of equal parts.
   - Put your pointer over the **scissors**.
   - Choose how many equal parts you want.
   - Click on a fraction circle.

2. Shade the fraction.
   - Click **Fill**.
   - Click a section of the circle.

3. Click **[123]**

Answers may vary, depending on the number of equal parts chosen.

Use the fraction models to show each fraction.
Draw each fraction.

1. Show $\frac{1}{3}$.

2. Show $\frac{1}{4}$.

3. Show $\frac{1}{2}$.

MODELING FRACTIONS

PURPOSE

To provide an opportunity for children to use a computer to work with fractions.

Using This Page

Discussion Topics

- This is another way for the children to practice identifying fractions.

- You may want to review how to move the cursor to click on fraction parts that need to be filled in.

- Work through the example with the children. Remind children that fractions are equal parts of a whole. The part that is shaded represents the fraction.

- Read the remaining questions and allow time for the children to complete. When the page is completed, have children check the fraction parts that are shaded with a partner.

Cumulative Test Prep

▶ Practice Test

PURPOSE

This page will familiarize children with the multiple-choice and open-response formats of many standardized state tests. Children can mark their responses directly on these pages. You may wish to read each multiple-choice test item and the answer choices aloud to the children.

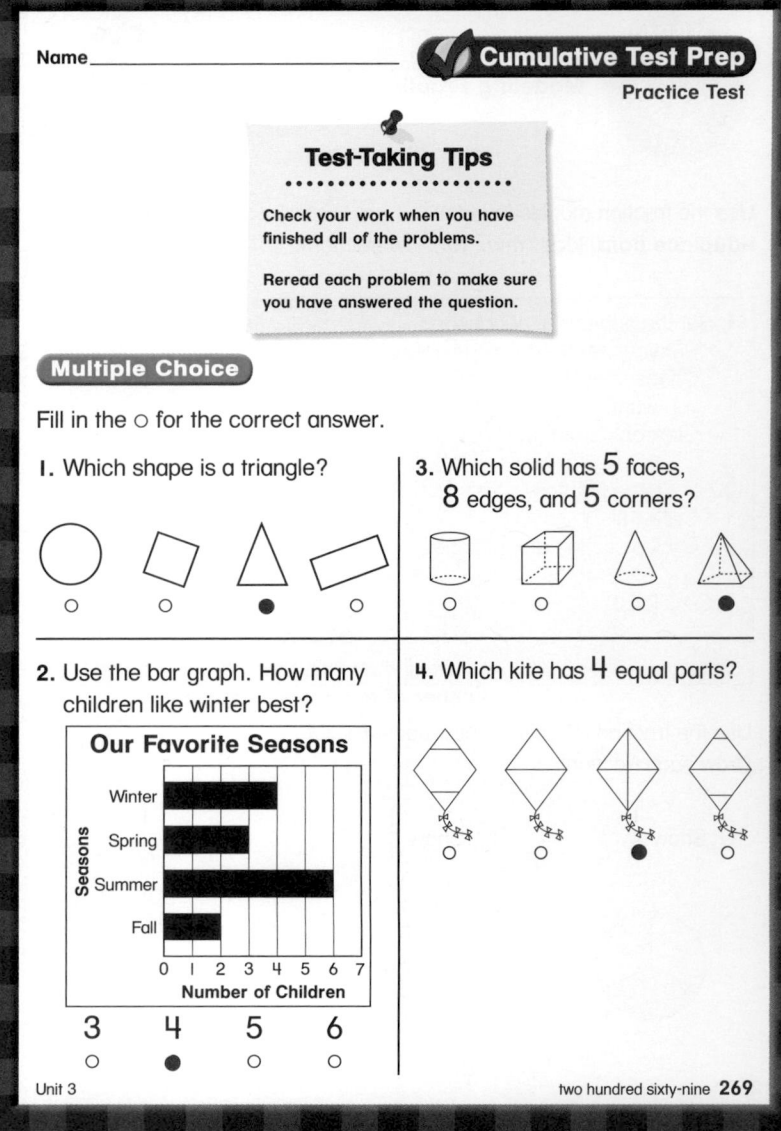

Name _____

Cumulative Test Prep
Practice Test

Test-Taking Tips

Check your work when you have finished all of the problems.

Reread each problem to make sure you have answered the question.

Multiple Choice

Fill in the ○ for the correct answer.

1. Which shape is a triangle?

3. Which solid has 5 faces, 8 edges, and 5 corners?

2. Use the bar graph. How many children like winter best?

Our Favorite Seasons

3   4   5   6

4. Which kite has 4 equal parts?

Unit 3   two hundred sixty-nine **269**

Test-Taking TIPS

Review the test-taking tips with children before they begin the test. Remind children to reread each problem to be sure they answered the question.

- Remind children that there is only one correct answer for each question.
- Encourage children to rule out answers they know are wrong.

- Remind children that if they make a mistake and change their answer, to erase the incorrect answer completely.
- Encourage children to draw or write on scrap paper to help them find the correct answer.

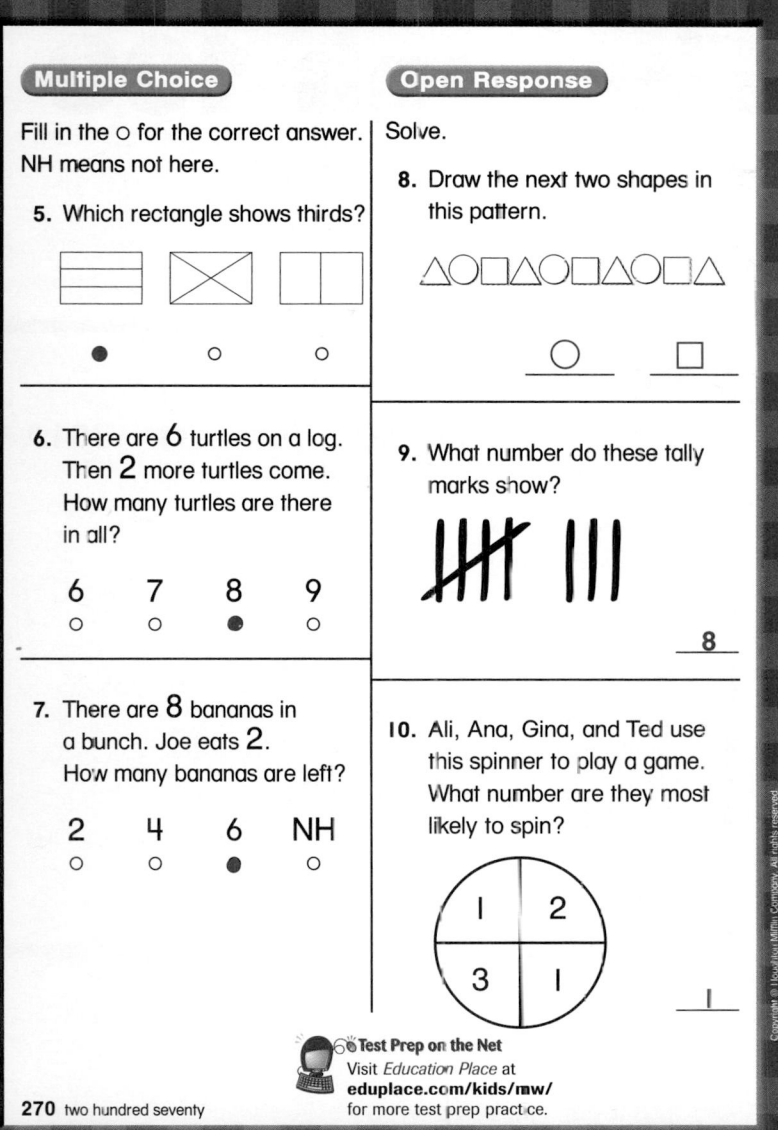

Multiple Choice

Fill in the ○ for the correct answer.
NH means not here.

5. Which rectangle shows thirds?

●   ○   ○

6. There are 6 turtles on a log.
Then 2 more turtles come.
How many turtles are there
in all?

6   7   8   9
○   ○   ●   ○

7. There are 8 bananas in
a bunch. Joe eats 2.
How many bananas are left?

2   4   6   NH
○   ○   ●   ○

Open Response

Solve.

8. Draw the next two shapes in
this pattern.

△○□△○□△○□△

○   □

9. What number do these tally
marks show?

|||| |||

___8___

10. Ali, Ana, Gina, and Ted use
this spinner to play a game.
What number are they most
likely to spin?

1	2
3	1

___1___

Test Prep on the Net
Visit *Education Place* at
eduplace.com/kids/mw/
for more test prep practice.

270 two hundred seventy

Test-Taking Vocabulary

- Ask a volunteer to give an example of a pattern. Have him or her describe or draw the pattern for the class.

- Have a volunteer define *sides, corners,* and *faces.* Have children give examples of plane shapes with 3, 4, and 6 sides and corners. Then have them describe solid shapes with circle faces.

- Review fraction words with children. Draw circles divided into halves, thirds, and fourths, and shade one part of each. Have volunteers name the fractions shown.

National and state tests may use these words when talking about geometry and fractions:

- *figures*
- *fractional*

UNIT 4

Numbers Through 100

Unit at a Glance

UNIT 4 NUMBERS THROUGH 100

Assessment System

Assessing Prior Knowledge

Check whether children understand the prerequisite concepts and skills.

- **CHAPTER PRETEST** (Unit Resource Folder or Ways to Success Intervention CD-ROM)
- **WARM-UP ACTIVITY:** Every TE Lesson
- **UNIT LITERATURE ACTIVITY:** PE p. 272

Ongoing Assessment

Monitor whether children are acquiring new concepts and skills.

- **PROBLEM OF THE DAY:** First page of every TE lesson
- **QUICK REVIEW:** First page of every TE lesson
- **LESSON QUIZ:** First page of every TE lesson
- **COMMON ERROR:** Every TE Lesson
- **QUICK CHECK:** PE pp. 286, 297, 310, 317, 330, 337
- **KEY TOPIC REVIEW:** PE pp. 298, 318, 338

 Test Prep and Practice

Help children prepare for state and standardized tests.

- **DAILY TEST PREP:** Every TE Lesson
- **CUMULATIVE TEST PREP:** PE page 351–352
- **PROBLEM SOLVING FOR TESTS:** PE pp. 296, 336
- **TEST PREP ON THE NET:** eduplace.com/kids/mw
- **TEST-TAKING STRATEGIES:** eduplace.com/math/mw

Summary Assessment

Assess children's mastery of new concepts and skills.

- **CHAPTER TEST:**
  - ✔ PE pp. 299–300, 319–320, 339–340
  - ✔ Unit Resource Folder
- **UNIT TEST:**
  - ✔ PE pp. 345–346
  - ✔ Test A, Unit Resource Folder
  - ✔ Test B, Unit Resource Folder

Student Self-Assessment

Allow children to evaluate their own understanding.

- **EXPLAIN YOUR THINKING:** PE pp. 277, 279, 281, 283, 287, 289, 291, 303, 305, 307, 311, 313, 323, 325, 327, 331

Performance Assessment

Evaluate children's ability to use mathematics in real-world situations.

PERFORMANCE ASSESSMENT: PE p. 347–348

WRITE ABOUT IT OR TALK ABOUT IT: in Hands-On lessons

 Technology Options

Use computer-based assessment to make testing and reporting easier.

- **WAYS TO ASSESS** (CD-ROM, LAN, or Web spiral review and test creation, administration, scoring, and report generation)
- **LEARNER PROFILE** (observations, evaluations, and reports from your handheld or desktop computer)

Reaching All Learners

Resources	On Level Students	Extra Support Students	English Learners	Inclusion/ Special Needs	Advanced Learners	Mathematically Promising
Student Editions						
Building Vocabulary	●	●	●	●	●	●
Guided Practice *	●	●	●	●	●	●
MathTracks MP3 Audio CD	●	●	○	○		
Teacher's Editions						
Building Vocabulary Strategies	●	●	●	○	●	○
Teacher Support	●	○	●		○	○
Intervention Activities	○	●	●	●		
Other Resources						
Chapter Challenges	○				●	●
Combination Classroom Guide	●	●	●	●	●	●
English Learners Handbook	○	○	●	○		
Ways to Success CD-ROM	○	●	●	●		

KEY ● Highly Appropriate   ○ Appropriate   * Scaffolded Instruction

Documenting Adequate Yearly Progress
National Test Correlations

UNIT 4 Objectives		ITBS	Terra Nova (CTBS)	CAT	SAT	MAT
4A	Identify, read, write, order, and compare numbers through 100.	●	●	●	●	●
4B	Count and regroup tens and ones.		●	●	●	●
4C	Identify place value through 99.	●	●	●	●	●
4D	Identify ordinal numbers 1st-10th.	●	●	●	●	●
4E	Use a 100 chart to skip count by 2s and 5s to 100.		●	●	●	●
4F	Identify odd and even numbers.				●	
4G	Apply skills and strategies to solve problems.	●	●	●	●	●

Activities for Reaching All Learners

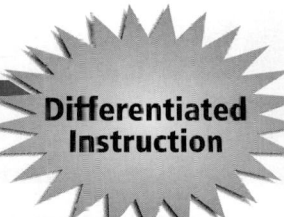

Differentiated Instruction

Home-School Activity

Place Value Challenge

Materials: number cube (1–6), tens and ones chart for each player

One player rolls the number cube and writes the number in the tens or ones column. The other player repeats the activity. The first player rolls the cube again and writes the number in the empty column. The second player repeats. The players compare their numbers. The player who has the greater number wins the round. Children repeat the activity for five rounds.

Unit Vocabulary

Cover It Up

Materials: game board (4 columns, 4 rows), 2 sets of number cards (numbers on the board), counters

Shuffle cards and place them facedown. Write 16 numbers on the board (1–99). Children write one number in each square on their gameboard. One child picks a card and reads it. Each child covers that number on their gameboard. Game continues until one child has covered 4 numbers in a row.

Remediation

MathTracks Lessons: 10.2, 10.5, 10.6, 10.8, 11.2, 11.3, 11.5, 12.3, 12.4, 12.5

Use the MathTracks CD-ROM to help children who need a quick review or extra support for the lesson, to provide children who were absent with a complete lesson presentation, or to assist children with reading difficulties.

Intervention

Ways to Success CD-ROM

Use the Ways to Success CD-ROM to help children who need extra help with lessons. This software is designed to reteach the lesson objective, provide extra guided and independent practice, and if needed, reteach a key prerequisite skill.

Unit Project

Count 100 Rocks
Math Topics:

- count tens
- place value through 99
- compare numbers
- count by twos, and fives

To Begin

- Display a collection of 20–30 rocks. Explain to children that they will collect, count, and make a grid of 100 rocks.
- Have children count the rocks into groups of 10. Have them count and record the tens and ones.

Ongoing

- Ask children to collect and bring small pebbles to school.
- Have children place each group of 10 pebbles in a clear bag. Then have children count the groups and write the number.
- Now have them count the rocks by 10s to 100.
- For Connecting to the Unit Project see page 275D for Chapter 10, page 301D for Chapter 11, and page 321D for Chapter 12.

To Finish

- Tell children that they will make a grid of 100 rocks. Use a 10 x 10 square of tile and model gluing rocks onto the tile. Then have children work with partners to glue rows of 10. Encourage them to place one rock right next to the previous one. Use the display as a counting tool in the classroom.
- See page 344 to Wrap Up the Unit Project.

Starting Unit 4
Accessing Prior Knowledge

UNIT 4

Numbers Through 100
From the Read-Aloud Anthology

100 Days of School

Trudy Harris

illustrations by
Beth Griffis
Johnson

Access Prior Knowledge
This story will help you review
• Counting through 20
• Addition and subtraction
  strategies through 10

271a

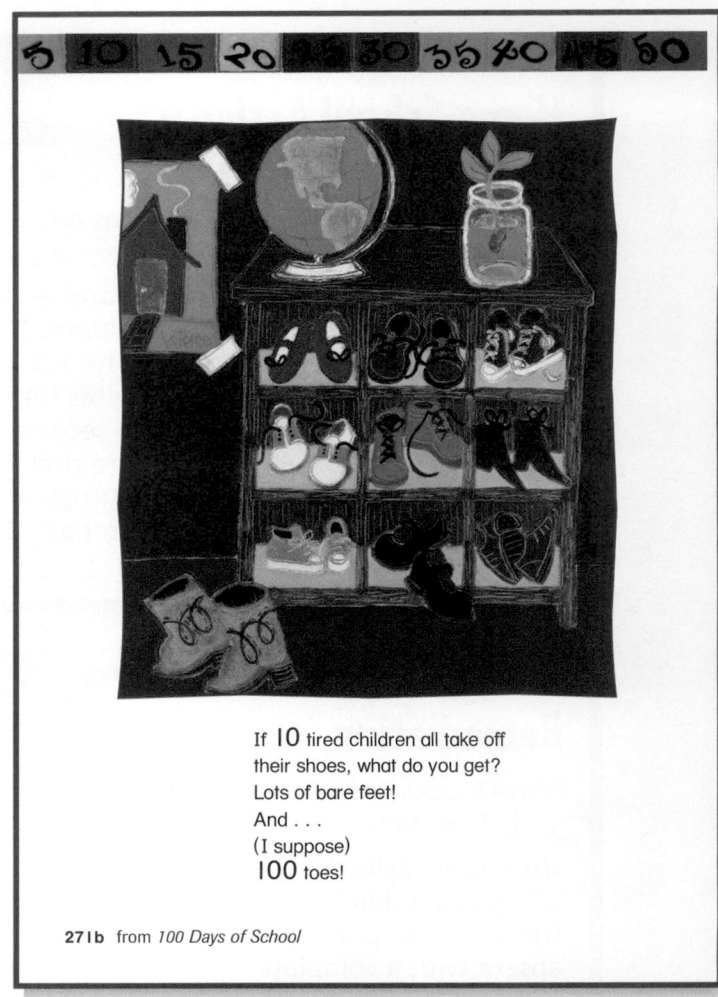

If 10 tired children all take off
their shoes, what do you get?
Lots of bare feet!
And . . .
(I suppose)
100 toes!

271b from *100 Days of School*

Accessing Prior Knowledge

In Units 1 and 2, children:

• read, write, order, and compare numbers through 20
• write number sentences
• use addition strategies
• use subtraction strategies

This selection from the Unit Opener gives you the opportunity to review some of these prerequisite skills.

• You may wish to review number sentences by writing the numbers 4 and 5 on the board. Have a volunteer use the numbers in an addition sentence and a subtraction sentence.

• You may also wish to have a volunteer tell how he or she adds 2 to 8 by counting on a number line.

Story Summary

Today you will be reading a story about children counting. The title of the story is *100 Days of School*. The author is Trudy Harris.

Reading the Story

You can find the entire text of the book at the end of the Teacher's Edition on page T 54.

Read the selection aloud to the children. Then count the children in the class. Have the class work together to tell how many bare feet there would be if everyone removed his or her shoes.

**This story is available in the
Read-Aloud Anthology, Volume 2**

55 60 65 70 75 80 85 90 95 100

If 20 children each
drop 5 papers on the
floor, what do you get?
100 papers.
And . . .
(I would guess)
an awful mess.

271c

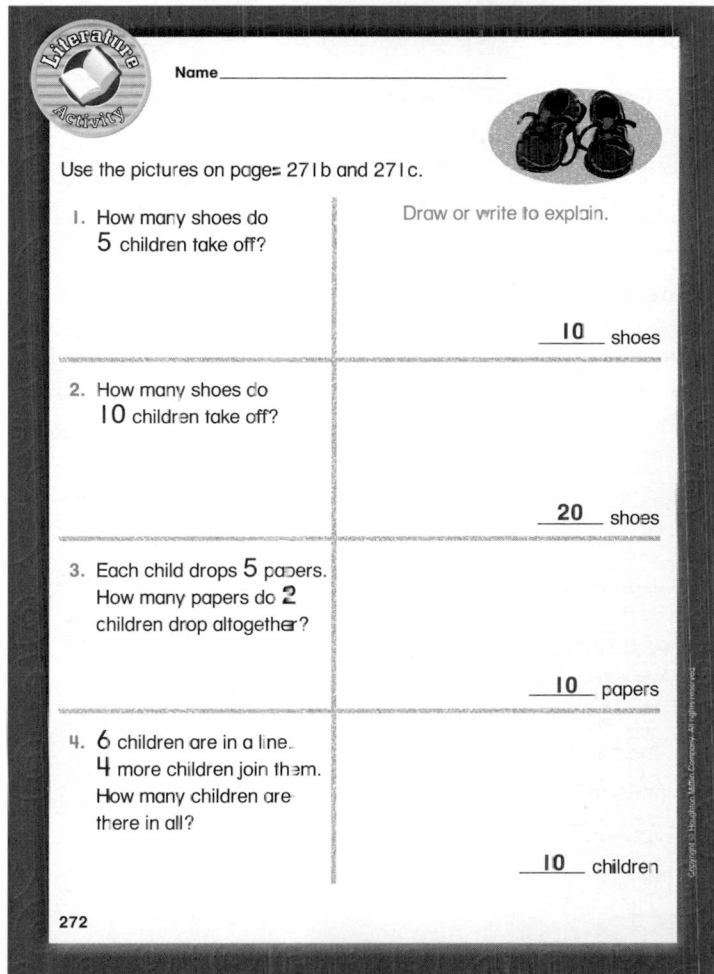

Name_____

Use the pictures on pages 271b and 271c.

Draw or write to explain.

1. How many shoes do
5 children take off?

_____10_____ shoes

2. How many shoes do
10 children take off?

_____20_____ shoes

3. Each child drops 5 papers.
How many papers do 2
children drop altogether?

_____10_____ papers

4. 6 children are in a line.
4 more children join them.
How many children are
there in all?

_____10_____ children

272

Unit Bibliography

Unit Literature

100 Days of School by Trudy Harris

Count on Pablo by Barbara deRubertis

Each Orange Had 8 Slices: A Counting Book
by Paul Giganti, Jr.

Missing Mittens by Stuart J. Murphy

One Hundred Is a Family by Pam Muñoz Ryan

Take Off with Numbers by Sally Hewitt

What's a Pair? What's a Dozen?
by Stephen R. Swinburne

See also the **Math and Literature Bibliography**
in the Teacher Support Handbook at the back
of this Teacher's Edition.

Literature Activity

Purpose: This activity provides an
opportunity to informally assess
children's understanding of numbers through 20 and
number patterns.

Using This Page

- Observe children as they work to complete
  Exercises 1–2. **How many feet does each child
  have?** (2) **What number will you skip count with?** (2)
- For Exercise 3, be sure children understand that
  they need to use the number sentence 5 + 5, not
  5 + 2.
- For Exercise 4, observe what strategy children use
  to solve the addition of 6 + 4.

Math At Home

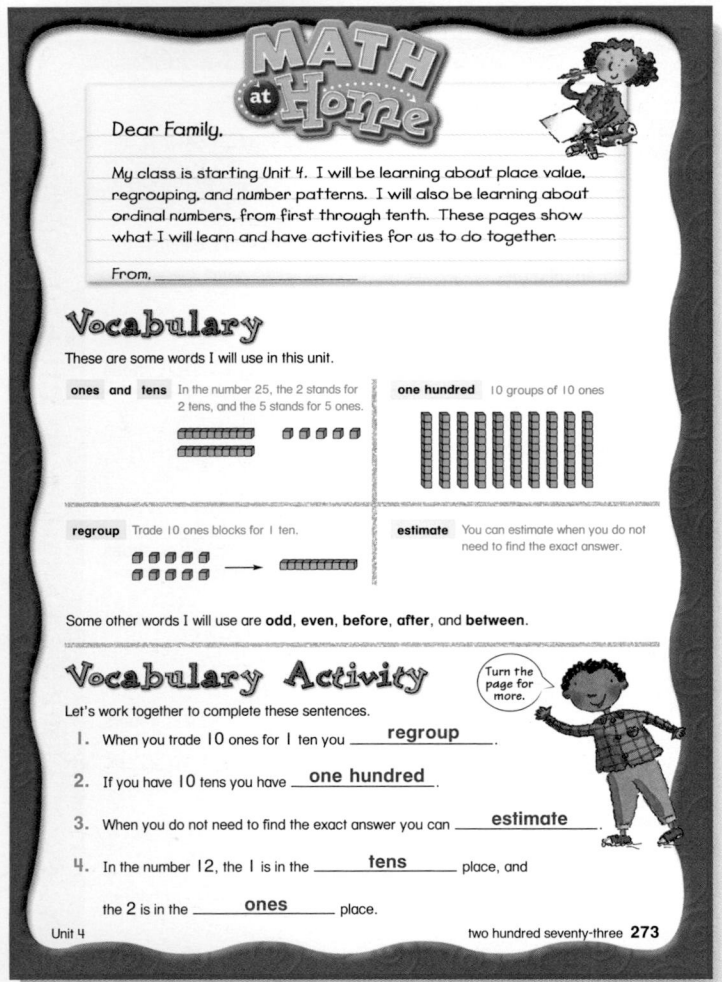

Dear Family,

My class is starting Unit 4. I will be learning about place value, regrouping, and number patterns. I will also be learning about ordinal numbers, from first through tenth. These pages show what I will learn and have activities for us to do together.

From. _____

Vocabulary

These are some words I will use in this unit.

ones and tens In the number 25, the 2 stands for 2 tens, and the 5 stands for 5 ones.	**one hundred** 10 groups of 10 ones
regroup Trade 10 ones blocks for 1 ten.	**estimate** You can estimate when you do not need to find the exact answer.

Some other words I will use are **odd**, **even**, **before**, **after**, and **between**.

Vocabulary Activity

Let's work together to complete these sentences.

Turn the page for more.

1. When you trade 10 ones for 1 ten you ____regroup____.

2. If you have 10 tens you have ____one hundred____.

3. When you do not need to find the exact answer you can ____estimate____.

4. In the number 12, the 1 is in the ____tens____ place, and the 2 is in the ____ones____ place.

Unit 4   two hundred seventy-three **273**

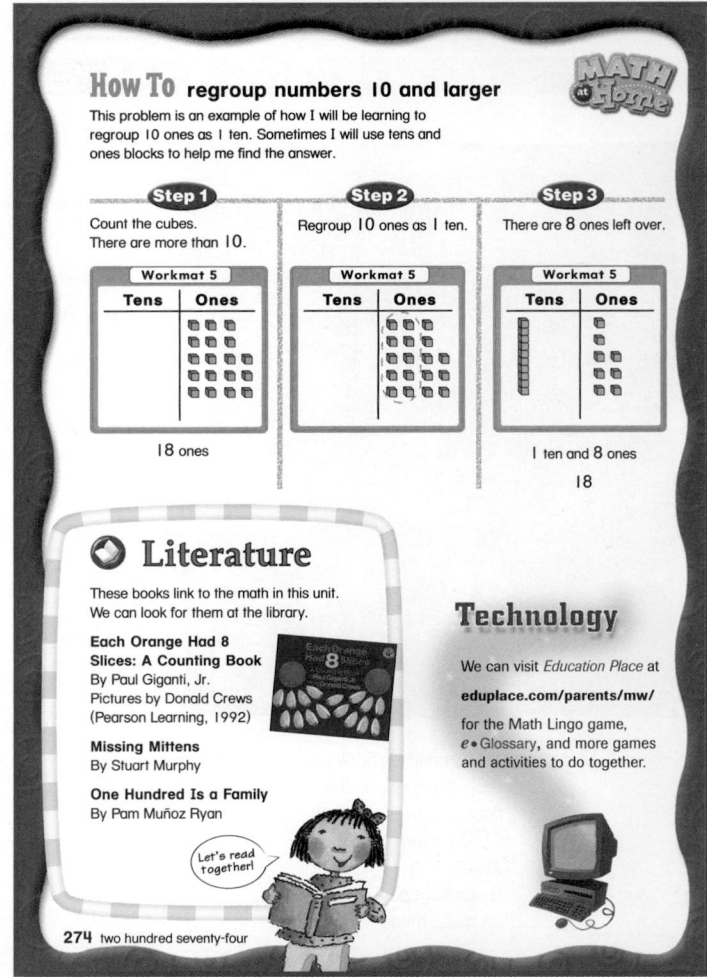

How To regroup numbers 10 and larger

This problem is an example of how I will be learning to regroup 10 ones as 1 ten. Sometimes I will use tens and ones blocks to help me find the answer.

Step 1
Count the cubes. There are more than 10.

Workmat 5	
Tens	**Ones**

18 ones

Step 2
Regroup 10 ones as 1 ten.

Workmat 5	
Tens	**Ones**

Step 3
There are 8 ones left over.

Workmat 5	
Tens	**Ones**

1 ten and 8 ones
18

Literature

These books link to the math in this unit. We can look for them at the library.

Each Orange Had 8 Slices: A Counting Book
By Paul Giganti, Jr.
Pictures by Donald Crews
(Pearson Learning, 1992)

Missing Mittens
By Stuart Murphy

One Hundred Is a Family
By Pam Muñoz Ryan

Let's read together!

Technology

We can visit *Education Place* at

eduplace.com/parents/mw/

for the Math Lingo game, e•Glossary, and more games and activities to do together.

274 two hundred seventy-four

Discuss the letter to the family with children. You may want to use this letter as an introduction to the unit. Highlight for children what they will be learning in the unit. Tell children that as they go through the unit they will be able to answer the questions on these pages.

Math at Home is available in Spanish and other languages on Education Place.

www.eduplace.com/math/mw/

 ## Literature

Encourage parents to find the suggested books and read them with their children.

Technology

Education Place is an award-winning website with engaging activities for students and helpful information for parents. Look for the eGlossary, the Math Lingo Game, and more.

Building Vocabulary

Strategies for Building Vocabulary

Understanding How to Estimate

Discuss the meaning of the word **estimate** as a thoughtful guess, not an exact count. Ask children to think about times they might estimate a total instead of counting the actual number. Record their responses in a word web.

Graphic Organizer: Word Web

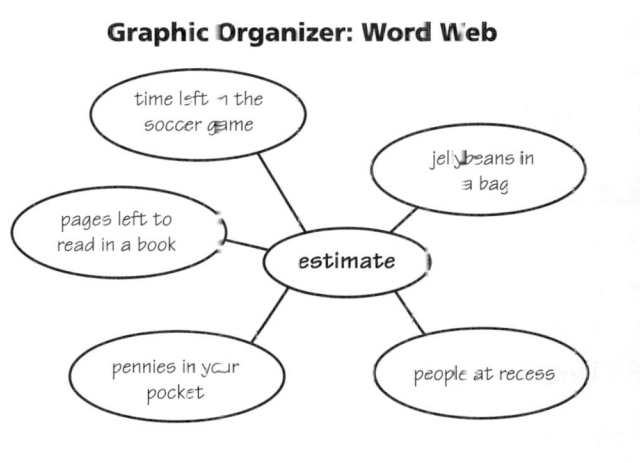

- time left in the soccer game
- jelly beans in a bag
- pages left to read in a book
- estimate
- pennies in your pocket
- people at recess

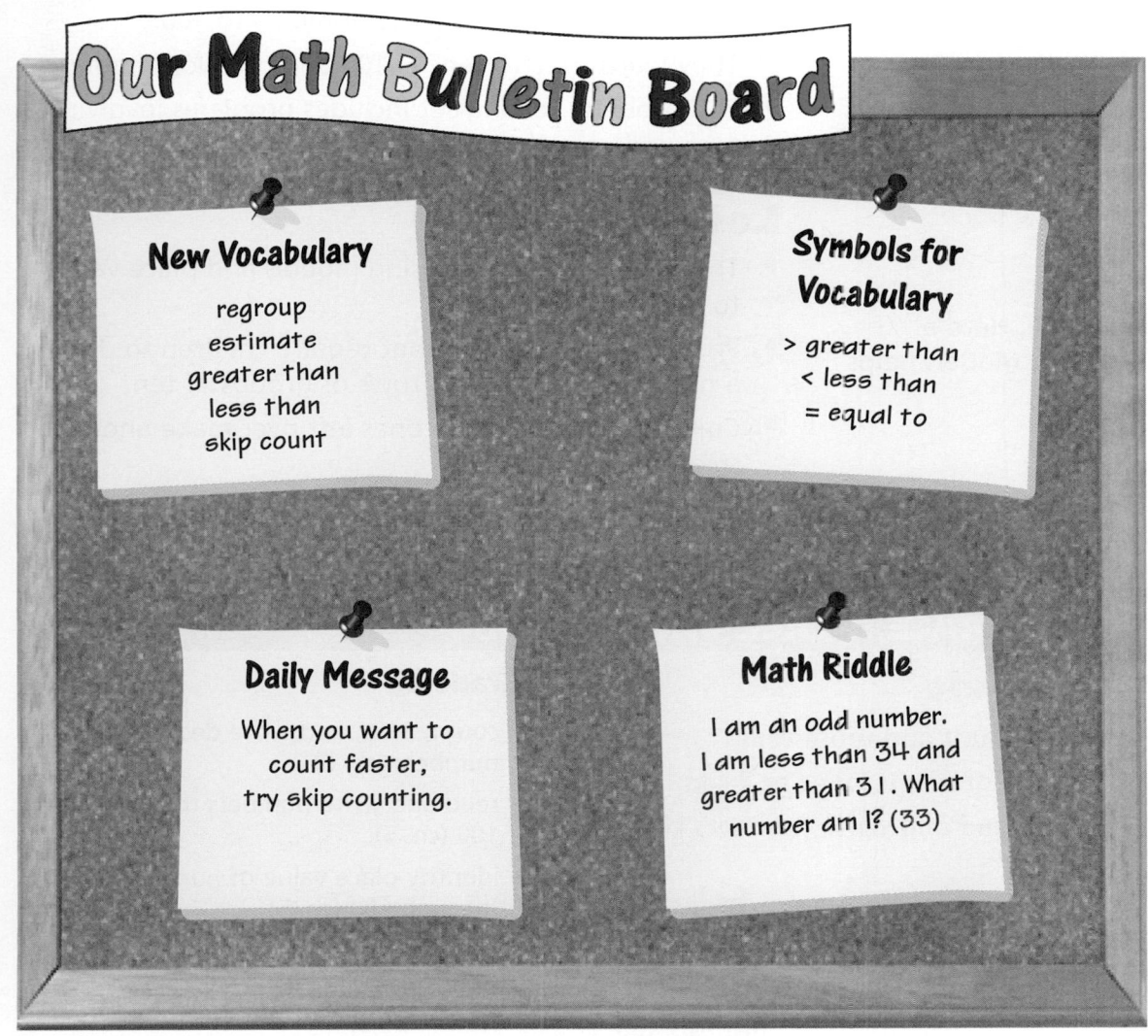

Our Math Bulletin Board

New Vocabulary
regroup
estimate
greater than
less than
skip count

Symbols for Vocabulary
> greater than
< less than
= equal to

Daily Message
When you want to count faster, try skip counting.

Math Riddle
I am an odd number. I am less than 34 and greater than 31. What number am I? (33)

add

Vocabulary Cards

My Math Journal

My Math Journal
Watch for **Keeping a Journal** entries in every lesson.

Lesson by Lesson Overview
Place Value to 100

Lesson 1

- This lesson introduces the concept of tens, making tens, and counting by tens.
- Children make groups of tens and write the number.
- They also count pictured tens and write the number.
- The problem solving presents a problem that can be solved by counting tens.

Lesson 2

- In this lesson, children regroup 10 ones as 1 ten.
- Children show a number of cubes as ones, snap together 10 to make a tens train.
- They write the number of tens and ones and then write the number.

Lesson 3

- Children model tens and ones on workmats, write the number of tens and ones and the number.
- They read word names as well as numerals for numbers to 50.
- The problem solving presents a problem that requires children to circle groups of ten, write the number of tens and ones, and the number.

Lesson 4

- Children read and write numbers to 99. Here a pictorial model is used. Using different models helps children develop number sense.

- A full-page problem solving set uses a variety of models, including tally marks. Children write the numbers and identify those that are between two given numbers.

Lesson 5

- This lesson introduces place value through 99.
- Children write the number of tens in the tens place and the number of ones in the ones place. Then they write the number.

Lesson 6

- This lesson teaches different ways to show numbers.
- Children count and write pictured tens and ones models. Then they write the number in expanded form.

Lesson 7

- Children identify and write numbers to 100.
- They learn that 10 tens = 100 and the word name.
- The problem solving set includes problems involving tens and ones.

Lesson 8

- This lesson focuses on using models and place value to act out problems.
- Problems are the type that require children to divide a number of items into rows or groups of ten.
- Children learn that the ones left over make another smaller group.

SKILLS TRACE: PLACE VALUE TO 100

Grade K	Grade 1	Grade 2
• count and show numbers to 25 (ch. 16)	• **count and write tens**	• count, read, and write decade numbers (ch. 5)
• order numbers to 31 (ch. 16)	• **regroup 10 ones as 1 ten**	• read and write numbers through 100 (ch. 5)
• count orally by tens to 100 (ch. 16)	• **read and write numbers through 99**	• identify place value of numbers through 100 (ch. 5)
	• **identify place value of numbers through 99**	• regroup tens as ones (ch. 5)
	• **show numbers in different ways**	• represent numbers in different forms (ch. 5)
	• **identify numbers through 100**	

Chapter Planner

Lesson	Objective	Vocabulary	Materials	✔ NCTM Standards
10.1 Count Tens (Hands-On) p. 277A	Count and write tens.	ones tens	cubes, blank transparency, craft sticks, rubber bands, spinner 1–6 (Learning Tool (LT) 38)	Use multiple models to develop initial understandings of place value and the base-ten number system.
10.2 Tens and Ones (Hands-On) p. 279A	Regroup ten ones as one ten and write the number.	regroup	cubes, Workmat 5, tens and ones chart transparency, paper clips, number cards with 2-digit numbers to 30 (teacher-made)	Use multiple models to develop initial understandings of place value and the base-ten number system.
10.3 Numbers Through 50 (Hands-On) p. 281A	Read and write numbers through 50.		egg cartons, counters, paper bag, place-value blocks, tens and ones chart transparency, overhead place-value blocks, Workmat 5	Use multiple models to develop initial understandings of place value and the base-ten number system.
10.4 Numbers Through 99 p. 283A	Read and write numbers through 99.		counters, paper cups, overhead counters, blank transparency, number cards 61–79 (teacher-made)	Use multiple models to develop initial understandings of place value and the base-ten number system.
10.5 Place Value Through 99 p. 287A	Identify the place value of numbers through 99.		overhead place-value blocks, tens and ones chart transparency two-color counters, Workmat 5, place-value blocks	Use multiple models to develop initial understandings of place value and the base-ten number system.
10.6 Different Ways to Show Numbers p. 289A	Show two-digit numbers in different ways.		overhead place-value blocks, place-value blocks, connecting cubes, counters, blank transparency, tens and ones chart (LT6)	Develop a sense of whole numbers and represent and use them in flexible ways, including relating, composing, and decomposing numbers.
10.7 Numbers Through 100 p. 291A	Identify numbers through 100.	one hundred	cubes, Workmat 6, penny, tens and ones chart (LT6)	Connect number words and numerals to the quantities they represent, using various physical models and representations.
10.8 Problem Solving: Act It Out With Models p. 293A	Use models and place value to solve problems.		counters, paper clips, tens and ones chart (LT6), blank transparency	Use multiple models to develop initial understandings of place value and the base-ten number system.

Resources For Reaching All Learners

LESSON RESOURCES: Reteach, Practice, Enrichment, Problem Solving, Homework, English Learners, Daily Routines, Transparencies, Math Center.

ADDITIONAL RESOURCES FROM HOUGHTON MIFFLIN: Chapter Challenges, Combination Classroom Planning Guide, Every Day Counts, Math to Learn (Student Handbook)

Every Day Counts
The Totally Ten Count and Birthday Data activities in Every Day Counts support the math in this chapter.

Assessing Prior Knowledge

Before beginning the chapter, you can assess student understandings in order to assist you in differentiating instruction.

Complete Chapter Pretest in Unit Resource Folder

Use this test to assess both prerequisite skills (**Are You Ready?** — one page) and chapter content (**Check What You Know** — two pages).

Chapter 10 Prerequisite Skills Pretest

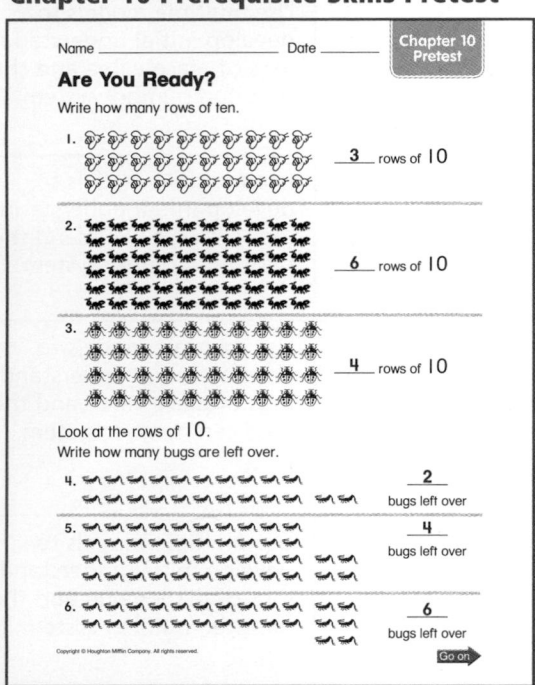

Chapter 10 New Content Pretest

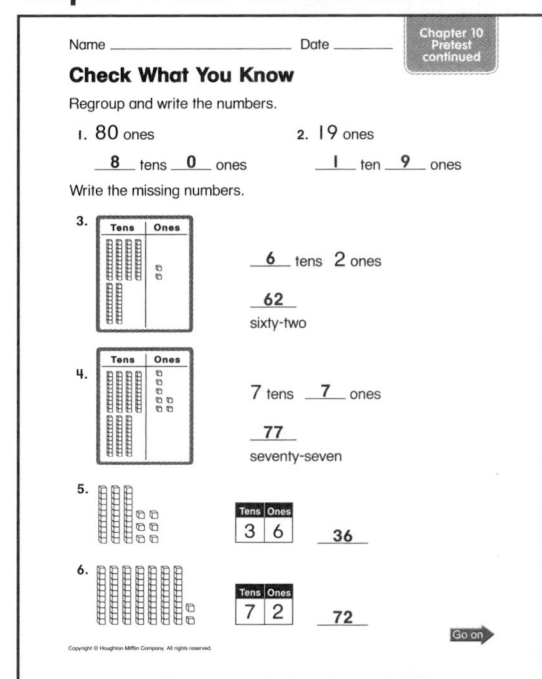

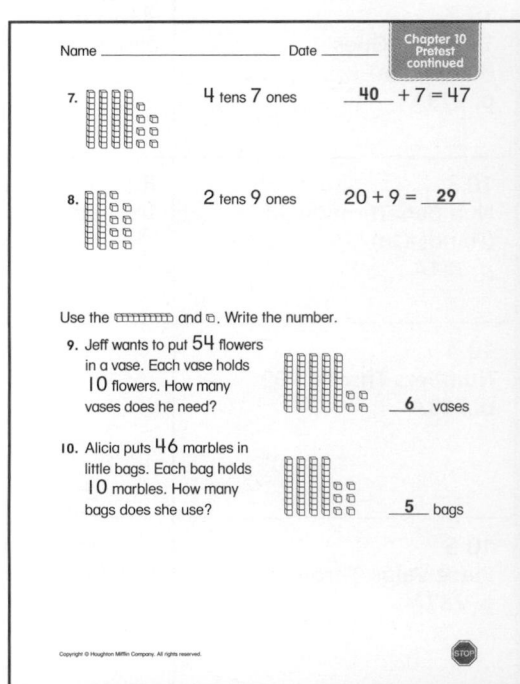

Customizing Instruction

For Students Having Difficulty

Items	Prerequisites	Ways to Success
1–3	Understand how to count by 10s.	Skillsheet 67
4–6	Can recognize unequal groups.	CD: 1.1 Skillsheet 68

Ways to Success: Intervention for every concept and skill (CD-ROM or Chapter Intervention Skillsheets).

For Students Having Success

Items	Objectives	Resources
1–4	10A Use vocabulary relating to place value to 100.	Enrichment 10.1–10.2
5–6	10B Identify, read and write numbers through 100.	Enrichment 10.1, 10.3, 10.4
7–8	10C Write and identify the place value of numbers through 99.	Enrichment 10.2, 10.5–10.7
9–10	10D Use place value to solve problems.	Enrichment 10.8

Use **Chapter Challenges** with any students who have success with all new chapter content.

Other Pretest Options

Informal Pretest

The pretest assesses vocabulary and prerequisite skills needed for success in this chapter.

Ways to Success CD-ROM

The *Ways to Success* chapter pretest has automatic assignment of appropriate review lessons.

Chapter Resources

Assessing Prior Knowledge

Regrouping Ones (number concepts)

- You might want to include a container of craft sticks in the math center for children to use as a counting tool.
- Each day, post a number from 11–19.
- Have children take that many craft sticks, make a group of ten and a group of ones. Have them write the number as "____ tens ____ ones."

Ongoing Skill Activity

Counting School Days (number concepts)

- Have children keep track of the number of days they have been in school.
- Each day have a child put a cube into a container. Then, ask a volunteer to count all the cubes in the container and write the number on the board.
- Periodically, have the children connect the cubes and count by 10s. For example, on the 40th day of school, have a volunteer connect the cubes in groups of 10s, then count by 10s to 40.

Connecting to the Unit Project

- Tell children the following problem: **Jason and Caroline collected rocks at the beach. They counted the rocks into groups of ten. They counted 5 groups of ten and 8 more rocks. How many rocks did they collect in all?**
- Tell children to record the number of tens and ones. Then have them record the number. (5 tens 8 ones; 58)
- Ask a volunteer to tell how many rocks Jason and Caroline collected.

Teacher Support

Professional Resources Handbook

Research, Mathematics Content, and Language Intervention

What Research and Practice Tell Us

Children must earn the numbers greater than 12 in order to achieve mastery in more complex mathematical topics later on (NCTM, 2000). Place value is perhaps one of the most challenging concepts in mathematical development learned after the concept of number. See *Professional Resources Handbook, Grade 1,* Unit 4.

For more ideas relating to Unit 4, see the Teacher Support Handbook at the back of this Teacher's Edition.

Language Intervention

Researchers have found that children's spoken language affects how they think and thus can affect the learning of the basic facts (Miura et al., 1994). "The consensus is that the Chinese number-word system illustrates the relationship between numbers and their names more straightforwardly than the English number-word system" (Ma, 1999, p. xix). For further explanation, see "Mathematical Language and Place Value" in the *Professional Resources Handbook Grade 1.*

Technology

Time-Saving Technology Support

Ways to Assess Customized Spiral Review
  Test Generator CD
Lesson Planner CD-ROM
Ways to Success Intervention CD-ROM
MathTracks CD-ROM
Education Place: www.eduplace.com/math/mw
Houghton Mifflin Math eBook CD-ROM
eManipulatives
eGames

Starting Chapter 10
Place Value to 100

Math Background

Place Value to 100

The Hindu-Arabic number system can be described as a base-ten positional number system. It begins with special symbols called digits that represent the first nine counting numbers, 1, 2, 3, 4, 5, 6, 7, 8, 9. There is also a very important tenth digit, 0, that represents an empty column. Hindus are credited with the development of this system, and Arabs introduced it to Western Europe.

The importance and power of a positional numeration system cannot be understated. In future chapters the importance of this base-ten positional system will become apparent. All computational algorithms for whole numbers and decimals that children learn in elementary school are based on and work because of the base-ten positional numeration system.

In a whole number, the digit farthest to the right is in the ones place. Moving to the left, each digit has a place value 10 times that of the digit to its right. The place-value chart below shows the first two places. A place-value chart can be made with as many places as needed.

Tens	Ones
10 x 1 10	1

Using The Investigation

- Draw a group of 10 circles and a group of 3 circles on the board. **Which group shows 10?** Ask a volunteer to circle the group of 10.

- Point to the group of 3. **How many in this group?** (3) **How many in all?** (13)

- Read the question to children. **Look at the picture. How many different groups of 10 objects can you find?** (6; 10 fish, 10 pencils, 10 crayons, 10 buttons, 10 noodles, 10 books)

 For more information about projects and investigations, visit Education Place. **eduplace.com/math/mw/**

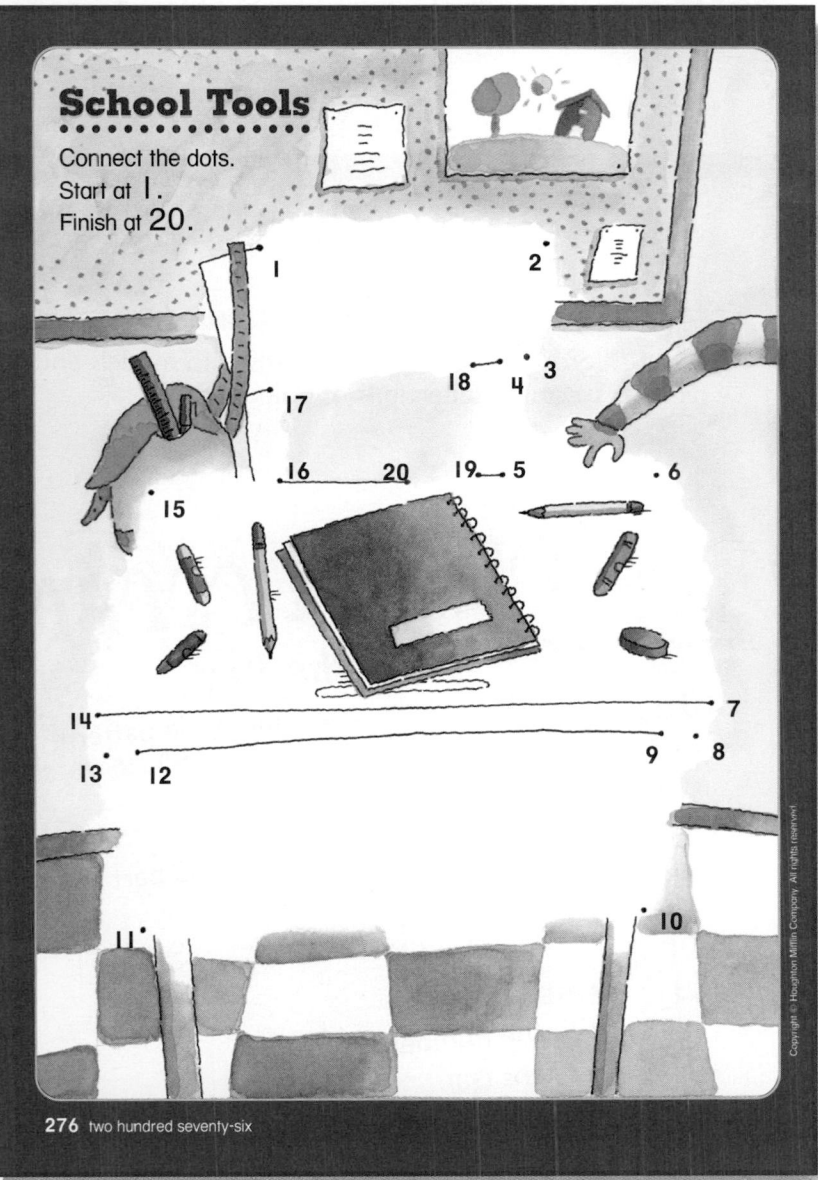

School Tools

Connect the dots.
Start at 1.
Finish at 20.

CHAPTER CHALLENGES

For Mathematically Promising Students

The *Chapter Challenges* resource book provides blackline masters for activities that explore, extend, and connect the mathematics in every chapter. To support this independent work, see the Teacher Notes for each activity.

Explore: Estimate Tens, page 55, after Lesson 1
Extend: Guess My Number, page 57, after Lesson 3
Connect: Counting by 10s, page 59, after Lesson 5

Using This Page

- Tell children that when they connect the dots on page 276, they will make a picture.

- **Put your pencil on dot 1. Then draw a line to dot 2. Keep connecting the dots in order until you reach dot 20.**

- Ask a volunteer to tell about the picture the connected dots make. (The completed picture is of a school desk and chair.)

- Have children create their own connect-the-dot pictures using numbers 1 to 20. Have them trade papers with a partner and connect the dots.

NSF Children's Math Worlds

Using lessons from the *Children's Math Worlds* is a good way to ensure that your students will develop a deep understanding of place value to 100. The most effective approach is to use the *Children's Math Worlds* lessons along with the lessons in the chapter.

Hands On: Count Tens

Lesson 10.1

PLANNING THE LESSON

MATHEMATICS OBJECTIVE
Count and write tens.

Use Lesson Planner CD-ROM for Lesson 10.1.

Daily Routines

Calendar
Have children place a sticker on every date that ends in zero. Ask children to tell how many dates this month end in zero. (Most months have 3 dates ending in zero.)

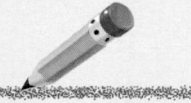

Sunday	Monday	Tuesday	Wednesday	Thursday	Friday	Saturday
			1	2	3	4
5	6	7	8	9	10	11
12	13	14	15	16	17	18
19	20	21	22	23	24	25
26	27	28	29	30	31	

Vocabulary
Place a pile of cubes on a table. Pick up 5 cubes and count the cubes aloud. Point out that there are 5 single cubes. Then make 2 rods of 10 cubes each. Tell children that you can count these cubes by tens. Repeat for other numbers, reinforcing the words **ones** and **tens**.

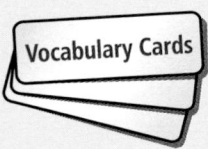

Vocabulary Cards

Meeting North Carolina's Standards
1.02 Use groupings of 2s, 5s, and 10s with models and pictures to count collections of objects.

Lesson Transparency 10.1

Problem of the Day
Fill in the blanks to complete the pattern.
10, 20, ___, 40, 50, 60, ___, ___, 90 (30, 70, 80)

Quick Review
Write the fraction for the shaded part in each set.
($\frac{1}{4}$) ($\frac{1}{3}$) ($\frac{1}{2}$)

Lesson Quiz
Write the number.
1. 3 tens (30)
2. 6 tens (60)
3. 8 tens (80)

LEVELED PRACTICE

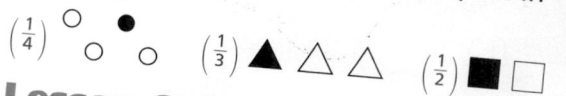

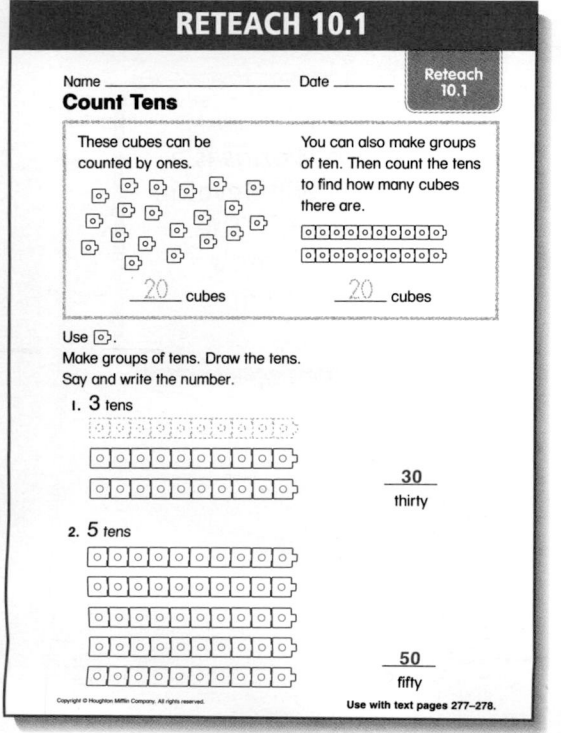

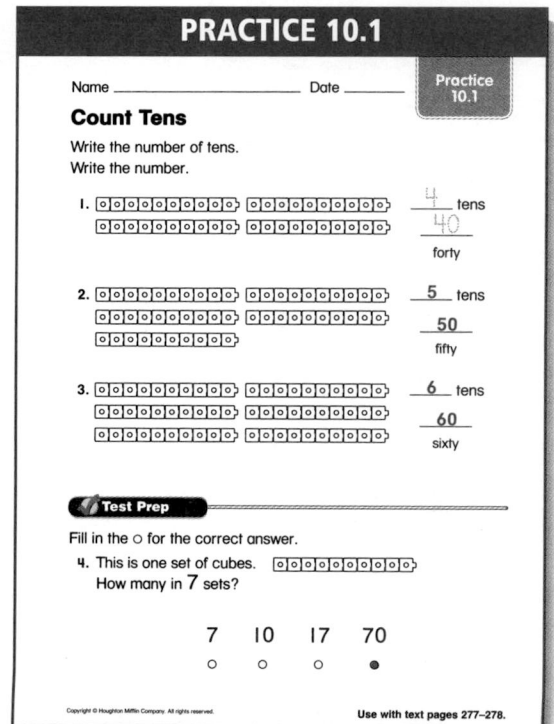

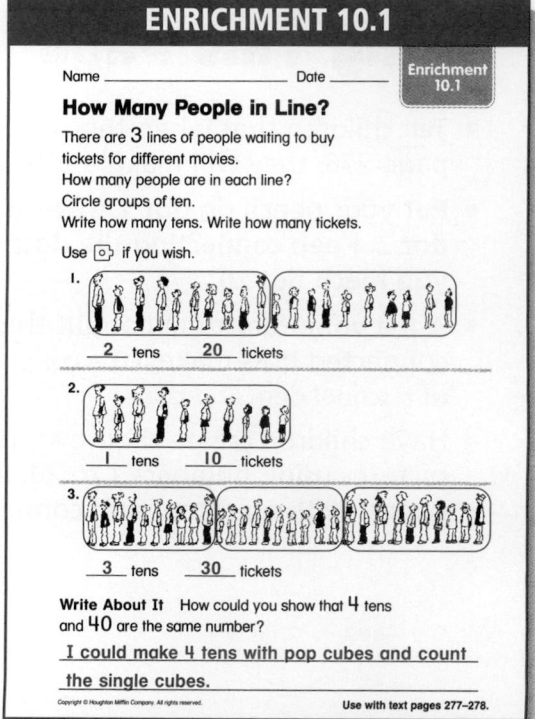

Practice Workbook Page 63

Reaching All Learners
Differentiated Instruction

English Learners

English-language learners may not have the language skills to explain the process behind their thinking. Use Worksheet 10.1 to provide children with sentence frames they can use to complete the Explain Your Thinking activity.

Inclusion
VISUAL, TACTILE

Materials: *stackable objects*

- Start with ten objects. Ask the child to stack the objects, count, and write the number 10.
- Then give the child another ten to develop 20, then 30, and so on. Model how to write 2 tens as 20 and 3 tens as 30.

Early Finishers
TACTILE, VISUAL

Materials: *tens number cards (LT 16), beans*

- Place the number cards facedown in a pile. Have one child at a time turn over the top card and make groups of ten beans to correspond to the number on the card.
- Have the other child write the number of tens and write the number.

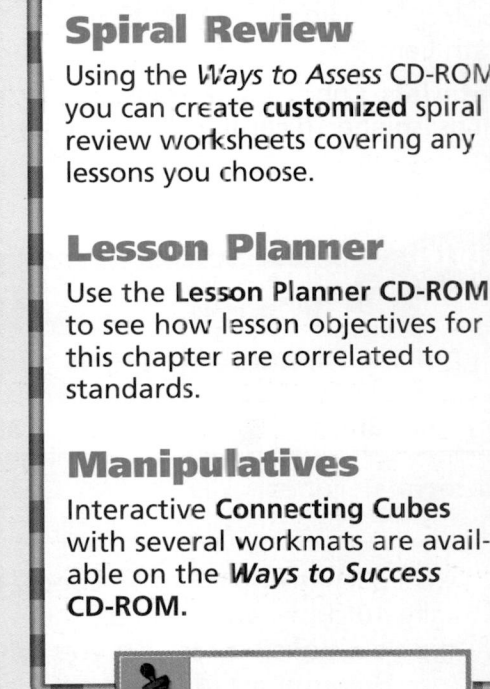

TECHNOLOGY

Spiral Review

Using the *Ways to Assess* CD-ROM, you can create **customized** spiral review worksheets covering any lessons you choose.

Lesson Planner

Use the **Lesson Planner CD-ROM** to see how lesson objectives for this chapter are correlated to standards.

Manipulatives

Interactive **Connecting Cubes** with several workmats are available on the *Ways to Success* CD-ROM.

Social Studies Connection

Explain that there is one star on the flag for every state in the United States. Have children count orally as you point to each star. Ask how many states are in the United States. (50) Ask children to tell how many tens in 50. (5 tens)

MATH CENTER

Real-Life Activity

Help children understand the usefulness of mathematics. This activity makes math come alive by connecting the lesson skills to a real-life situation.

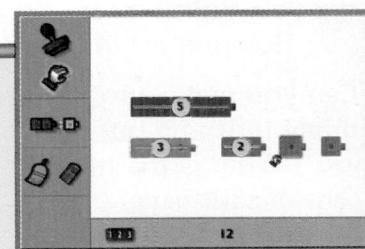

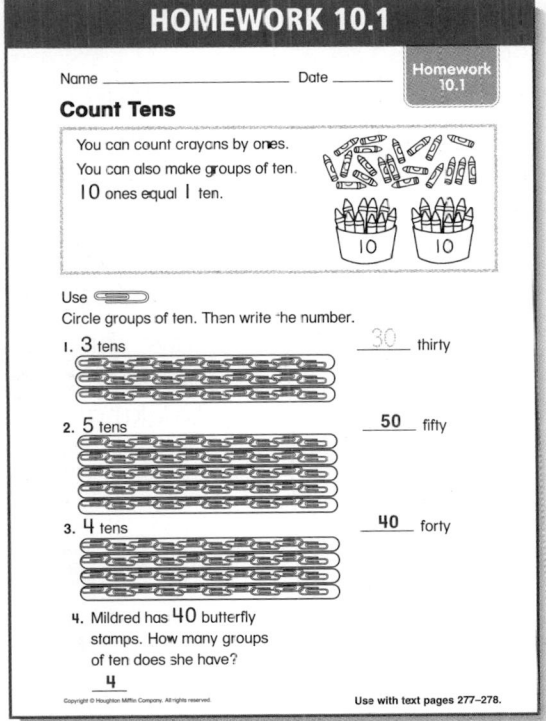

PROBLEM SOLVING 10.1

Name _____ Date _____

Problem Solving 10.1

Count Tens

Read and solve.
Use ⬜, if you wish.

Dana is taking 4 boxes of muffins to the bake sale. Each box has 10 muffins. How many muffins are in 4 boxes?

Draw or write to explain.

__40__ muffins

1. Richard is sorting his pennies into piles of 10. He has 6 piles. How many pennies does he have?

Draw or write to explain.

__60__ pennies

2. Lian is packing cans for the food drive. There are 10 cans in each box. How many cans can she put into 3 boxes?

__30__ cans

3. Tom is arranging tables for a party. There are 4 tables. 10 people can sit at each table. How many people can be seated?

__40__ people

Use with text pages 277–278.

HOMEWORK 10.1

Name _____ Date _____

Homework 10.1

Count Tens

You can count crayons by ones.
You can also make groups of ten.
10 ones equal 1 ten.

Use 🖇
Circle groups of ten. Then write the number.

1. 3 tens _____ __30__ thirty

2. 5 tens _____ __50__ fifty

3. 4 tens _____ __40__ forty

4. Mildred has 40 butterfly stamps. How many groups of ten does she have?

__4__

Use with text pages 277–278.

Homework Workbook Page 63

ENGLISH LEARNERS 10.1

Name _____ Date _____

English Learners 10.1

Count Tens

10 ones equal 1 ten.

How would you show the number sixty with cubes?

I can make groups of 10 with cubes.

__10__ ones equal 1 ten.

I know that there are __6__ tens in 60.

I will need to make __6__ groups of ten.

__6__ tens make 60.

To the Teacher: Use the example at the top of the page to demonstrate how to make groups of ten. Then read the sentences with children and have them complete each one.

Use with text pages 277–278.

TEACHING LESSON 10.1

LESSON ORGANIZER

Objective Make, count and write tens.

Resources Reteach, Practice, Enrichment, Problem Solving, Homework, English Learners, Transparencies, Math Center

Materials Cubes, blank transparency, craft sticks, rubber bands, spinner, (Learning Tool (LT) 38)

Activity

Warm-Up Activity
Modeling Teens

| iii Small Group | ⏱ 5 minutes | Auditory, Tactile |

Materials: *cubes*

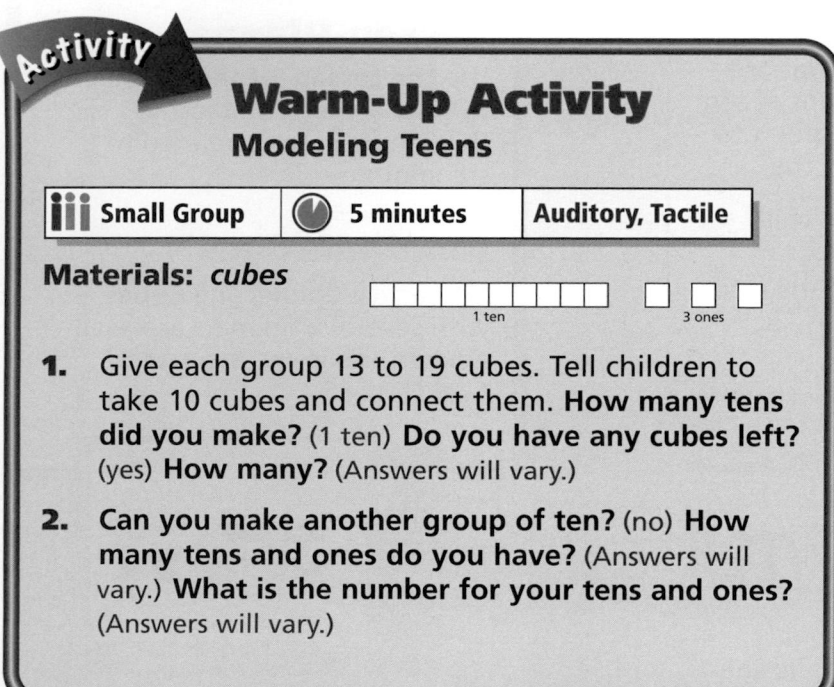

1 ten   3 ones

1. Give each group 13 to 19 cubes. Tell children to take 10 cubes and connect them. **How many tens did you make?** (1 ten) **Do you have any cubes left?** (yes) **How many?** (Answers will vary.)

2. **Can you make another group of ten?** (no) **How many tens and ones do you have?** (Answers will vary.) **What is the number for your tens and ones?** (Answers will vary.)

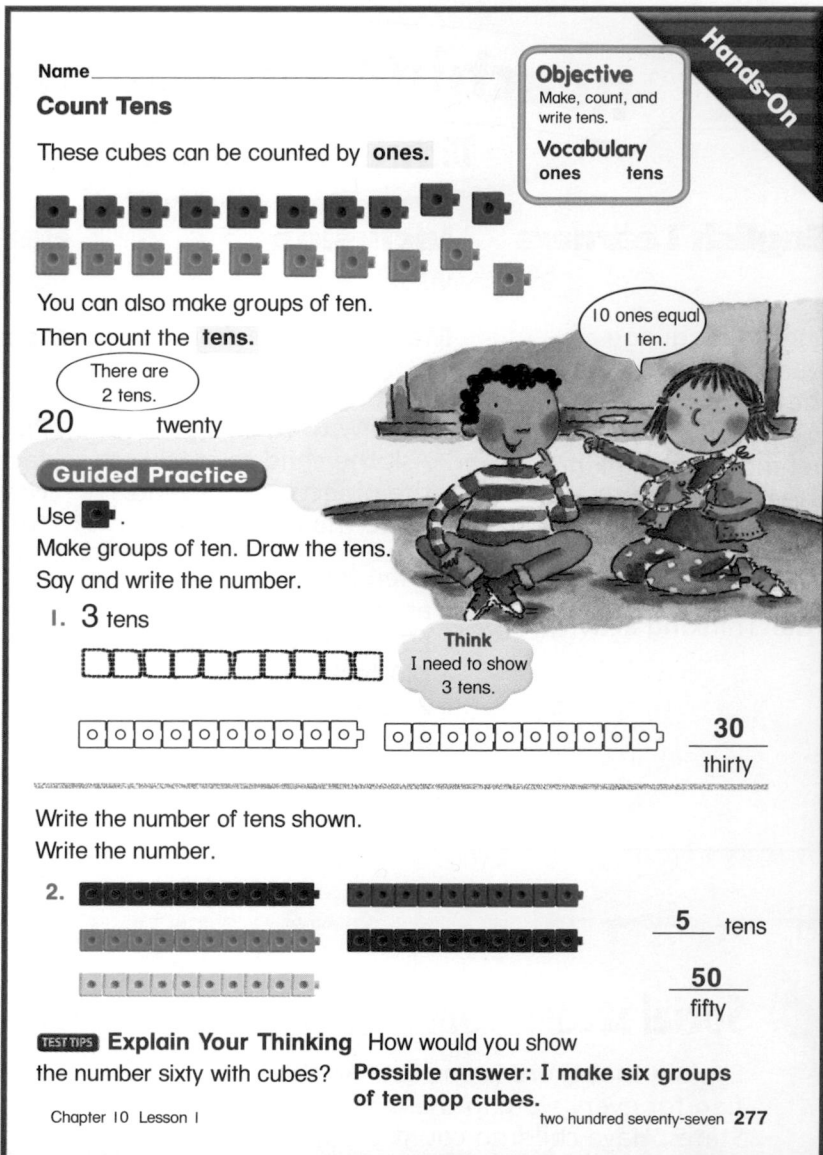

Name_____

Count Tens

These cubes can be counted by **ones.**

You can also make groups of ten. Then count the **tens.**

There are 2 tens.

20   twenty

10 ones equal 1 ten.

Guided Practice

Use ⬛.
Make groups of ten. Draw the tens.
Say and write the number.

1. **3 tens**

Think
I need to show 3 tens.

<u>30</u>
thirty

Write the number of tens shown.
Write the number.

2.

<u>5</u> tens

<u>50</u>
fifty

TEST TIPS **Explain Your Thinking** How would you show the number sixty with cubes? **Possible answer: I make six groups of ten pop cubes.**

Chapter 10 Lesson 1   two hundred seventy-seven **277**

---

1 Introduce

Activity

Model Tens

| iiii Whole Group | ⏱ 10–15 minutes | Visual, Tactile |

Materials: *blank transparency, cubes*

1. *Build 90.* Build a train of 10 cubes. Have children build one along with you. Place your train of 10 cubes on the overhead. **How many tens are shown?** (1 ten) **How many ones?** (0)

2. Write *1 ten* on the transparency. **How do we write the number ten?** Have a volunteer write *10* on the transparency.

3. Have a volunteer place his or her train of 10 cubes on the overhead. **How many tens are there now?** (2 tens) **How many ones?** (0) Write *2 tens* on the transparency. **What number is the same as 2 tens?** (20) Have a child write *20* on the transparency.

4. Repeat the activity, adding 1 cube train at a time until there are 9 trains. Each time, write the number of tens and have a volunteer write the number.

2 Develop

Guided Learning

Teaching Example Introduce the objective and vocabulary to the children. Guide them through the example by having them count loose cubes and then make two 10-cube trains for 20. Emphasize that 10 ones equal 1 ten.

Guided Practice

Have children complete **Exercises 1–2** as you observe. Give children the opportunity to answer the Explain Your Thinking question. Then discuss their responses with the class.

277   CHAPTER 10   Lesson 1

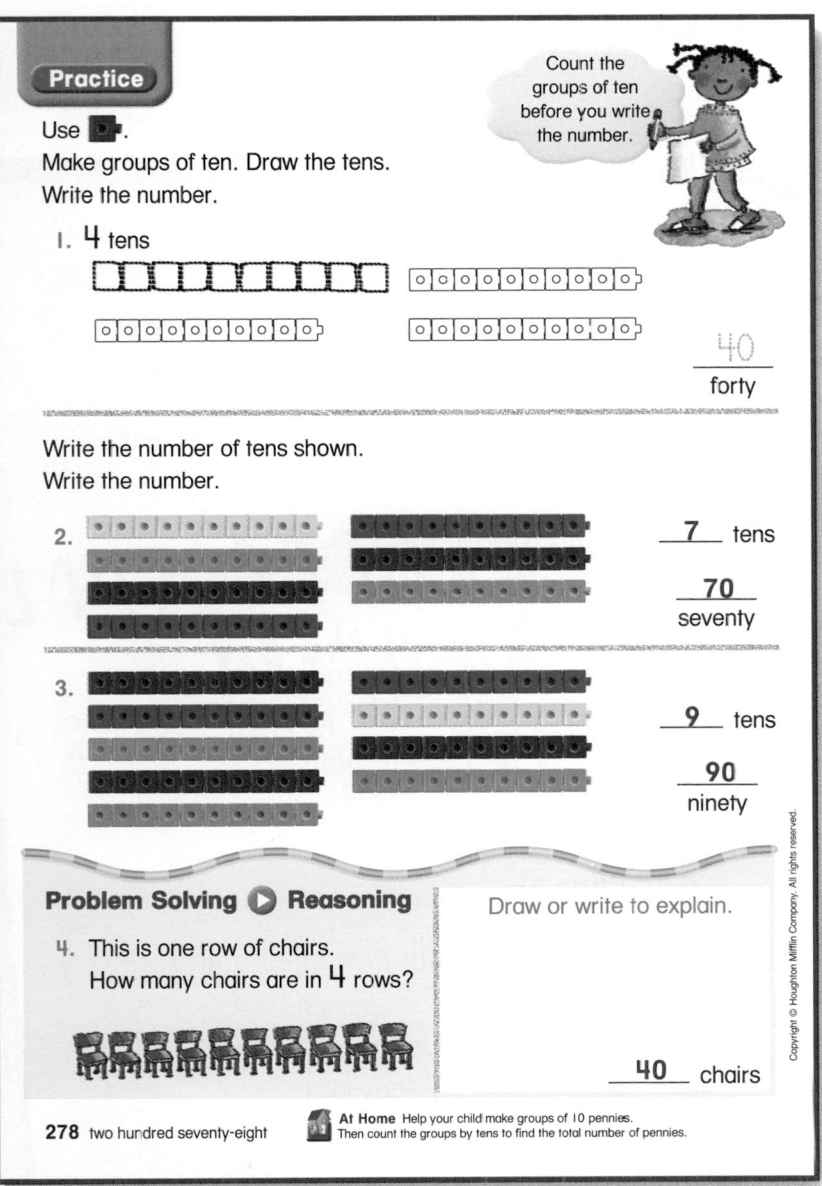

Practice

Use ▉.
Make groups of ten. Draw the tens.
Write the number.

> Count the groups of ten before you write the number.

1. 4 tens

<u>40</u>
forty

Write the number of tens shown.
Write the number.

2. <u>7</u> tens
<u>70</u> seventy

3. <u>9</u> tens
<u>90</u> ninety

Problem Solving ▶ Reasoning

4. This is one row of chairs.
How many chairs are in 4 rows?

Draw or write to explain.

<u>40</u> chairs

278 two hundred seventy-eight

At Home Help your child make groups of 10 pennies. Then count the groups by tens to find the total number of pennies.

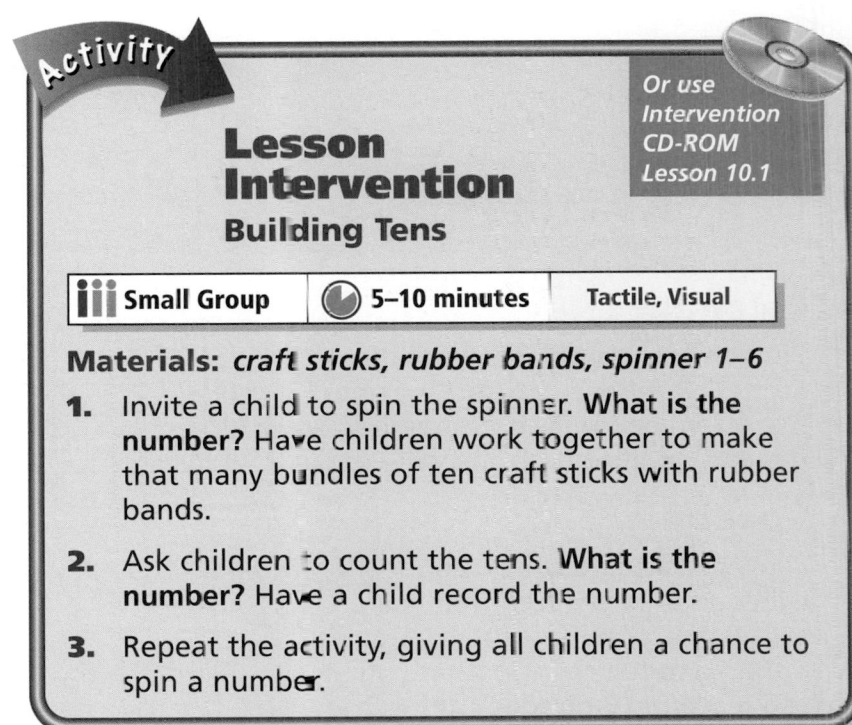

Activity

Or use Intervention CD-ROM Lesson 10.1

Lesson Intervention
Building Tens

| 👤👤👤 Small Group | ⏱ 5–10 minutes | Tactile, Visual |

Materials: *craft sticks, rubber bands, spinner 1–6*

1. Invite a child to spin the spinner. **What is the number?** Have children work together to make that many bundles of ten craft sticks with rubber bands.

2. Ask children to count the tens. **What is the number?** Have a child record the number.

3. Repeat the activity, giving all children a chance to spin a number.

---

3 Practice

Independent Practice

Children complete **Exercises 1–3** independently.

Problem Solving

After children complete **Exercise 4**, call on volunteers to share their answers. Discuss strategies children used to solve the problem.

Common Error

Omitting the Zero
Children may omit the zero when writing the numbers. Remind children to write 0 and reinforce tens. Have the child model the ones number and the tens number to see the difference.

4 Assess and Close

What do you notice about every number you wrote?
(There is a zero in the ones place.)

If there are 10 books on each shelf, how many books are on 3 shelves? (30)

 **Keeping a Journal**

Draw a picture of a garden. Show rows of ten plants. Write the number of rows. Then write the number of plants.

Hands On: Tens and Ones

PLANNING THE LESSON

MATHEMATICS OBJECTIVE
Regroup 10 ones as 1 ten and write the number.

Use Lesson Planner CD-ROM for Lesson 10.2.

Daily Routines

Calendar
Randomly choose dates from the 5th to 29th. Have children say how many tens and ones each number has and point to it on the calendar.

Sunday	Monday	Tuesday	Wednesday	Thursday	Friday	Saturday
				1	2	3	4
5	6	7	8	9	10	11
12	13	14	15	16	17	18
19	20	21	22	23	24	25
26	27	28	29	30	31	

Vocabulary
Show children 10 cubes. Count the cubes and tell children that there are 10 **ones**. Connect the cubes into a train and tell children that you can **regroup** 10 **ones** as 1 **ten**.

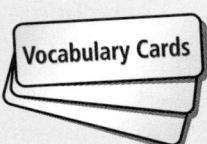

Vocabulary Cards

Meeting North Carolina's Standards

1.01 Develop number sense for whole numbers through 99.
- Connect the model, number word, and number using a variety of representations.

Lesson Transparency **10.2**

Problem of the Day
Pat wrote 2 tens 5 ones in a tens and ones chart. Arthur wrote the number 25. Who wrote the greater number? (Neither. 25 is equal to 2 tens 5 ones.)

Quick Review
Write how many.

(8)   (11)   (3)   (6)

Lesson Quiz
Write how many tens and ones.
Write the number.

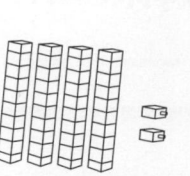

(4 tens 2 ones; 42)

LEVELED PRACTICE

RETEACH 10.2

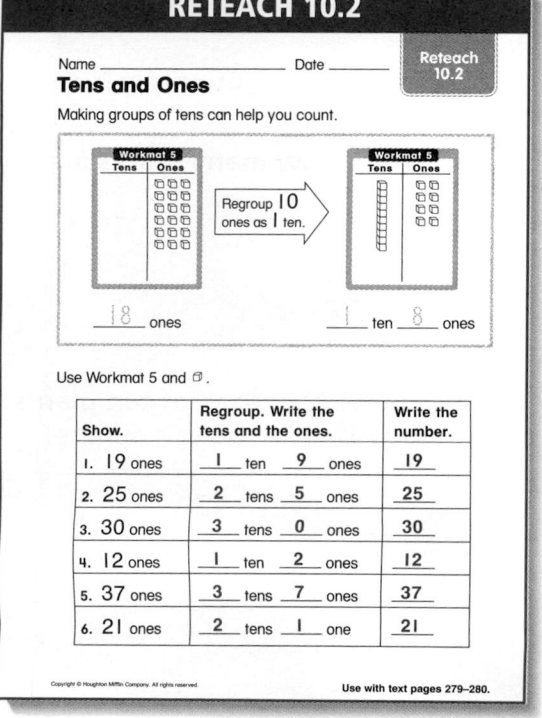

Name _____ Date _____   Reteach 10.2

Tens and Ones

Making groups of tens can help you count.

Use Workmat 5 and □.

Show.	Regroup. Write the tens and the ones.	Write the number.
1. 19 ones	1 ten 9 ones	19
2. 25 ones	2 tens 5 ones	25
3. 30 ones	3 tens 0 ones	30
4. 12 ones	1 ten 2 ones	12
5. 37 ones	3 tens 7 ones	37
6. 21 ones	2 tens 1 one	21

Copyright © Houghton Mifflin Company. All rights reserved.   Use with text pages 279–280.

PRACTICE 10.2

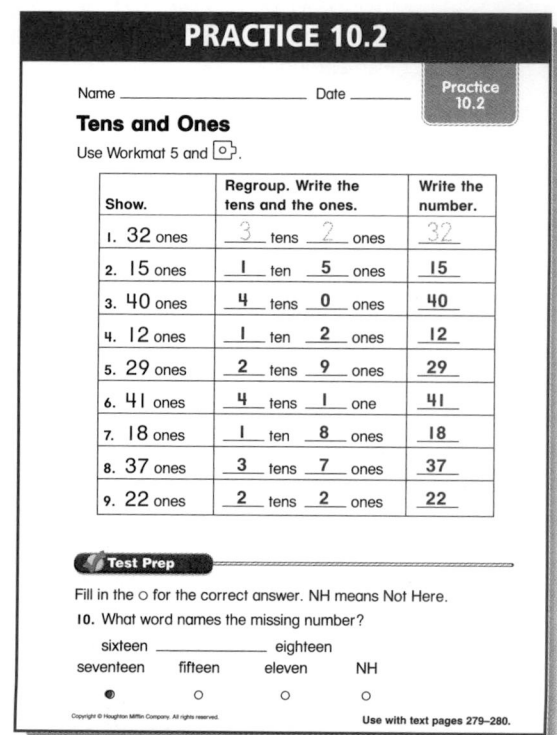

Name _____ Date _____   Practice 10.2

Tens and Ones

Use Workmat 5 and □.

Show.	Regroup. Write the tens and the ones.	Write the number.
1. 32 ones	3 tens 2 ones	32
2. 15 ones	1 ten 5 ones	15
3. 40 ones	4 tens 0 ones	40
4. 12 ones	1 ten 2 ones	12
5. 29 ones	2 tens 9 ones	29
6. 41 ones	4 tens 1 one	41
7. 18 ones	1 ten 8 ones	18
8. 37 ones	3 tens 7 ones	37
9. 22 ones	2 tens 2 ones	22

Test Prep

Fill in the ○ for the correct answer. NH means Not Here.

10. What word names the missing number?

sixteen _____ eighteen

seventeen   fifteen   eleven   NH
●   ○   ○   ○

Copyright © Houghton Mifflin Company. All rights reserved.   Use with text pages 279–280.

ENRICHMENT 10.2

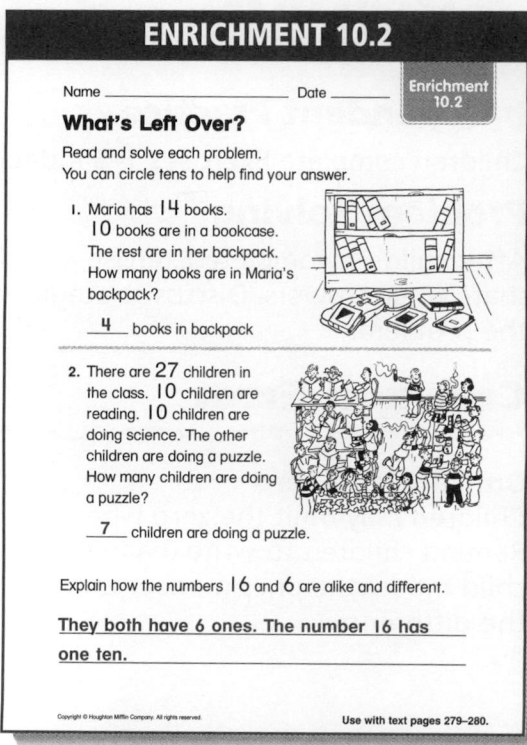

Name _____ Date _____   Enrichment 10.2

What's Left Over?

Read and solve each problem.
You can circle tens to help find your answer.

1. Maria has 14 books.
10 books are in a bookcase.
The rest are in her backpack.
How many books are in Maria's backpack?

___4___ books in backpack

2. There are 27 children in the class. 10 children are reading. 10 children are doing science. The other children are doing a puzzle. How many children are doing a puzzle?

___7___ children are doing a puzzle.

Explain how the numbers 16 and 6 are alike and different.

They both have 6 ones. The number 16 has one ten.

Copyright © Houghton Mifflin Company. All rights reserved.   Use with text pages 279–280.

Reaching All Learners

Differentiated Instruction

English Learners

English-language learners may not be familiar with prefixes in English. Use Worksheet 10.2 to teach children the prefix *re-* that they will encounter when they learn to regroup objects into tens and ones.

Special Needs
TACTILE, VISUAL

Materials: *straws, rubber bands, cups*

- Have the child count a group of straws and make groups of tens.
- Place the tens in one cup and the ones in another. Have the child write the number of tens and ones, read them, and say the number.

tens 2 ones 5

Gifted and Talented
AUDITORY, VISUAL

- Say a number riddle. Have children guess the correct number. **My number is between 10 and 40. It has 6 ones. It is greater than 19 and less than 29. What is the number?** (26)
- Have children make up number riddles for partners to solve.

TECHNOLOGY

Spiral Review

To reinforce skills on lessons taught earlier, create **customized** spiral review worksheets using the *Ways to Assess* CD-ROM.

Education Place

Encourage students to visit **Education Place** at **eduplace.com/kids/mw/** for more student activities.

Manipulatives

Interactive **Connecting Cubes** with several workmats are available on the *Ways to Success* CD-ROM.

Literature Connection

Refer to the Unit Literature selection, *100 Days of School* by Trudy Harris. Read the section about eating salty peanuts. Guide children to make 10 groups of 10 counters each. Have them count the groups by ten and write the number, 100.

MATH CENTER

Basic Skills Activity

Motivate children to build basic skills. Use this activity to address multiple learning styles using hands-on activities related to the skills of this lesson.

PROBLEM SOLVING 10.2

Name _____ Date _____

Problem Solving 10.2

Tens and Ones

Read. Think about tens and ones.
Use ▭▭▭▭▭ and ▫, if you wish.

Patty has 59 buttons to put in small boxes. Each box holds ten buttons. How many tens can she make? How many ones are left over?

Draw or write to explain.

_5_ tens _9_ ones

1. Don has 45 chairs to arrange. There are 10 chairs in each row. How many tens can he make? How many chairs are left over?

Draw or write to explain.

_4_ tens _5_ ones

2. Bette has 62 trading cards. How many tens can she trade? How many ones can she save?

_6_ tens _2_ ones

3. Nick wants to save twenty-three stickers. How many tens must he save? How many ones?

_2_ tens _3_ ones

Use with text pages 279–280.

HOMEWORK 10.2

Name _____ Date _____

Homework 10.2

Tens and Ones

Making groups of ten can help you count.	Regroup 12 ones as 1 ten and 2 ones.
Workmat 3 — Tens / Ones	Workmat 3 — Tens / Ones
12 ones	___ ten _2_ ones

Use small items such as coins or macaroni.
Regroup. Write the tens and the ones.
Then write the number.

1. 14 ones   _1_ ten _4_ ones   _14_
2. 23 ones   _2_ tens _3_ ones   _23_
3. 31 ones   _3_ tens _1_ one   _31_

4. Draw 25 marbles in the jar. Circle the groups of ten. How many groups of ten are there? How many ones are there?

_2_ tens _5_ ones

Use with text pages 279–280.

ENGLISH LEARNERS 10.2

Name _____ Date _____

English Learners 10.2

Tens and Ones

Re + build = rebuild.
Re means "do again."
Rebuild means to build again.

Complete the words.

1. If you **do** something again, you re_do_ it.
2. If you **read** a book again, you re_read_ it.
3. If you **tell** a story again, you re_tell_ it.
4. If you **draw** a picture again, you re_draw_ it.
5. If you **write** your name again, you re_write_ it.

Use with text pages 279–280.

Homework Workbook Page 64

TEACHING LESSON 10.2

LESSON ORGANIZER

Objective Regroup 10 ones as 1 ten and write the number.

Resources Reteach, Practice, Enrichment, Problem Solving, Homework, English Learners, Transparencies, Math Center

Materials Cubes, Tens and Ones Chart transparency, Workmat 5, paper clips, number cards (teacher-made)

Warm-Up Activity
Model Making Tens

iiii Whole Group	⏱ 5 minutes	Auditory, Tactile

Materials: *cubes*

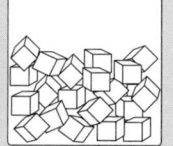

1. Give each child 21 cubes. **How can you find out if there is a group of 10 cubes in your pile of cubes?** (Count out 10 cubes.)

2. Model making a train of 10 cubes. **Can you make another group of 10?** (yes) **How?** (Possible response: Count 10 more.)

3. **Can you make another group of 10?** (no) **Why?** (There are not 10 cubes left.) **How many cubes are left over?** (1)

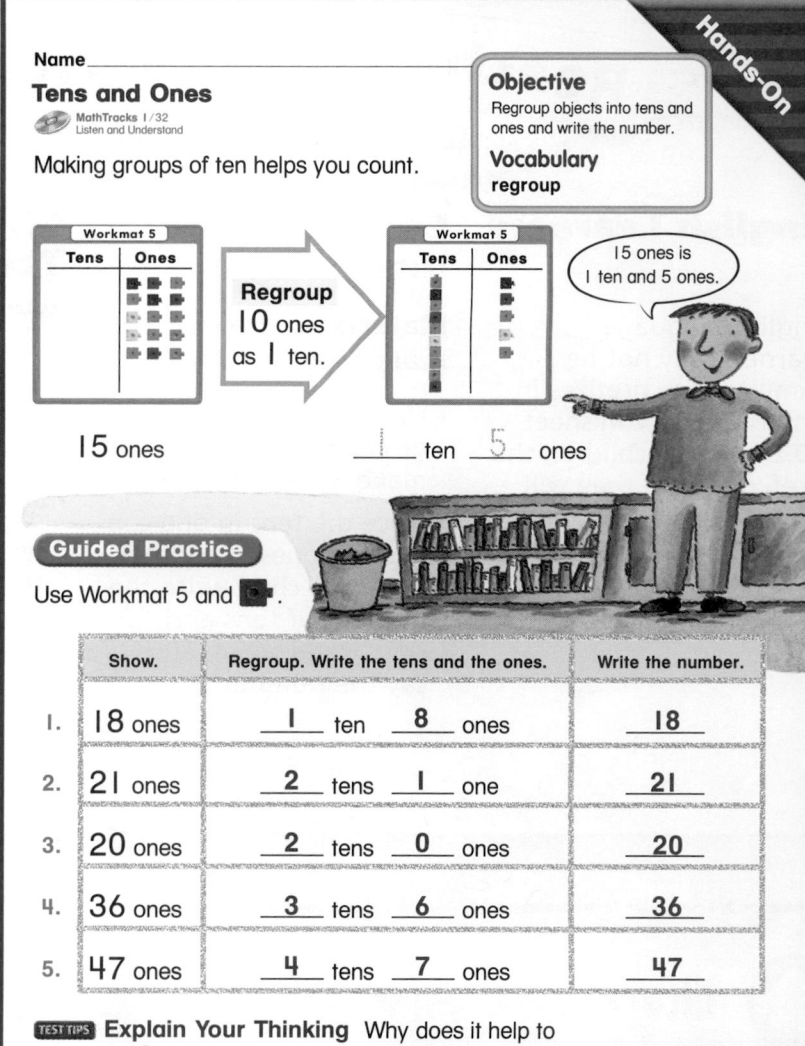

Name_____

Tens and Ones

MathTracks 1/32
Listen and Understand

Making groups of ten helps you count.

| Workmat 5 | | | Workmat 5 | |
| Tens | Ones | Regroup 10 ones as 1 ten. | Tens | Ones |

15 ones is 1 ten and 5 ones.

15 ones   1 ten 5 ones

Guided Practice

Use Workmat 5 and 🔲.

	Show.	Regroup. Write the tens and the ones.	Write the number.
1.	18 ones	1 ten 8 ones	18
2.	21 ones	2 tens 1 one	21
3.	20 ones	2 tens 0 ones	20
4.	36 ones	3 tens 6 ones	36
5.	47 ones	4 tens 7 ones	47

TEST TIPS Explain Your Thinking Why does it help to regroup 10 ones as 1 ten? **Possible answer: It is quicker and easier to count groups of ten.**

Chapter 10 Lesson 2   two hundred seventy-nine **279**

---

1 Introduce
Discuss Tens and Ones

iiii Whole Group	⏱ 10–15 minutes	Visual, Auditory

Materials: *cubes, Tens and Ones Chart transparency, Workmat 5*

1. *Model 2 tens 6 ones.* Place 26 cubes on the overhead and identify them as ones. **Let's count to see how many ones there are.** (26) **Can we make a group of 10?** (yes) Have a volunteer make a group of 10 ones on the overhead. **We can regroup 10 ones as 1 ten.** Make a train of 10 cubes.

2. **Can we make another group of ten?** (yes) Repeat the procedure and identify 2 tens. **Can we make another group of ten?** (no) **Why?** (We have only 6 ones left.)

3. Place the tens and ones on the transparency. **How many tens and ones in 26?** (2 tens 6 ones)

4. Repeat the procedure for 23, 29, and 24. Have children model along at their desks.

2 Develop

Guided Learning

Teaching Example Introduce the objective and vocabulary to the children. Guide them through the example to model how to regroup 15 ones as 1 ten 5 ones.

Guided Practice

Have children complete **Exercises 1–5** as you observe. Give children the opportunity to answer the Explain Your Thinking question. Then discuss their responses with the class.

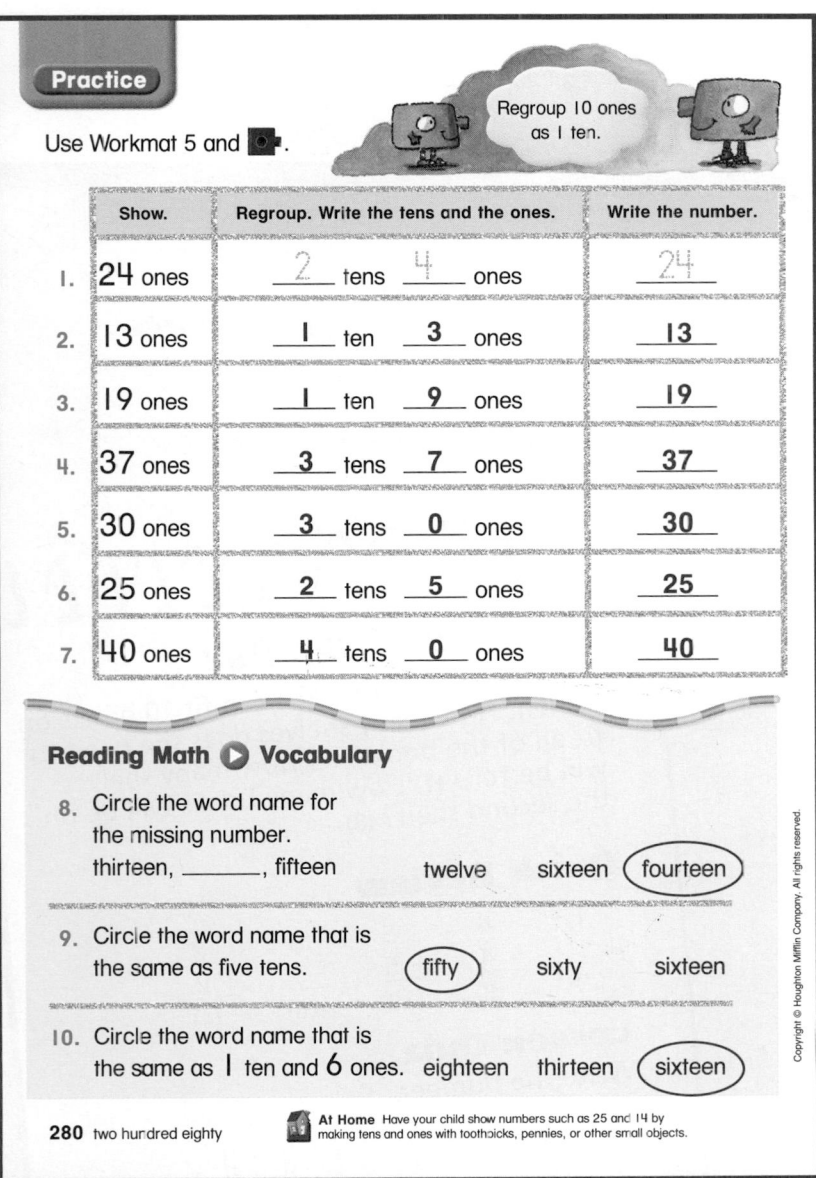

Practice

Use Workmat 5 and ▪️.

Regroup 10 ones as 1 ten.

	Show.	Regroup. Write the tens and the ones.	Write the number.
1.	24 ones	__2__ tens __4__ ones	24
2.	13 ones	__1__ ten __3__ ones	13
3.	19 ones	__1__ ten __9__ ones	19
4.	37 ones	__3__ tens __7__ ones	37
5.	30 ones	__3__ tens __0__ ones	30
6.	25 ones	__2__ tens __5__ ones	25
7.	40 ones	__4__ tens __0__ ones	40

Reading Math ▶ Vocabulary

8. Circle the word name for the missing number.

   thirteen, _____, fifteen   twelve   sixteen   (fourteen)

9. Circle the word name that is the same as five tens.   (fifty)   sixty   sixteen

10. Circle the word name that is the same as 1 ten and 6 ones.   eighteen   thirteen   (sixteen)

280 two hundred eighty

🏠 **At Home** Have your child show numbers such as 25 and 14 by making tens and ones with toothpicks, pennies, or other small objects.

Daily Test Prep

$$\begin{array}{r} 0 \\ + 9 \\ \hline \end{array}$$

8 ○   9 ●   10 ○   NH ○

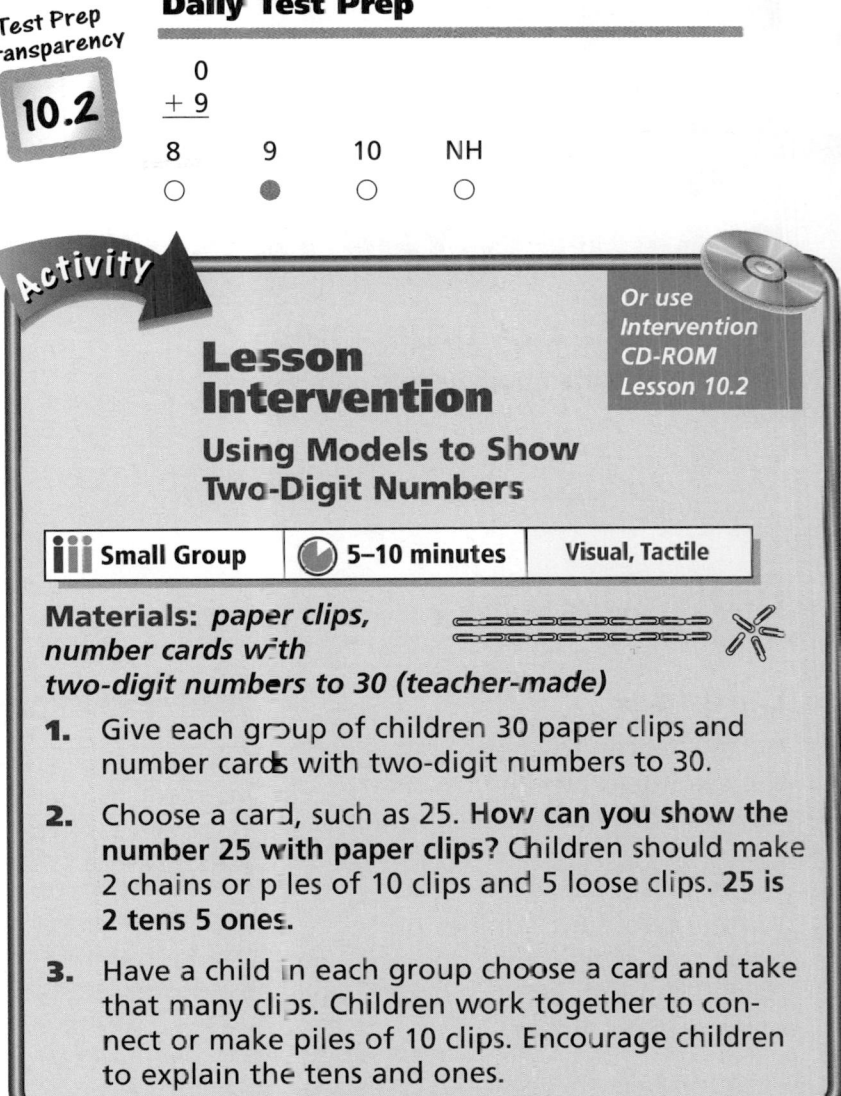

Activity

Lesson Intervention

Or use Intervention CD-ROM Lesson 10.2

Using Models to Show Two-Digit Numbers

👥 Small Group	⏱ 5–10 minutes	Visual, Tactile

Materials: *paper clips, number cards with two-digit numbers to 30 (teacher-made)*

1. Give each group of children 30 paper clips and number cards with two-digit numbers to 30.

2. Choose a card, such as 25. **How can you show the number 25 with paper clips?** Children should make 2 chains or piles of 10 clips and 5 loose clips. 25 is 2 tens 5 ones.

3. Have a child in each group choose a card and take that many clips. Children work together to connect or make piles of 10 clips. Encourage children to explain the tens and ones.

---

③ Practice

Independent Practice

Children complete **Exercises 1–7** independently.

Reading Math

After children complete **Exercises 8–10**, call on volunteers to share their answers.

Common Error

Writing an Incorrect Number in the Tens Place

Children may always write 1 in the tens place. Help them identify the number of tens as they make tens and ones using cubes.

④ Assess and Close

Write these numbers: 1 ten 6 ones; 2 tens 6 ones. (16; 26)

How are the numbers different? (16 has 1 ten; 26 has 2 tens)

What number has 4 tens 6 ones? (46)

Keeping a Journal

Write a number greater than 10. Draw a picture to show how many tens and how many ones there are.

Hands On: Numbers Through 50

Lesson 10.3

PLANNING THE LESSON

MATHEMATICS OBJECTIVE
Read and write numbers through 50.

Use Lesson Planner CD-ROM for Lesson 10.3.

Daily Routines

Calendar
Invite children to choose dates on the calendar and tell how many tens and ones are in each number.

Vocabulary
Write a two-digit number on the board and review **tens** and **ones** by having children identify how many of each in a number.

Vocabulary Cards

Meeting North Carolina's Standards
1.01 Develop number sense for whole numbers through 99.
• Connect the model, number word, and number using a variety of representations.

Lesson Transparency 10.3

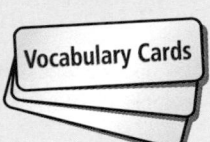

Problem of the Day
Janine has 18 books. She can fit 10 books on a shelf. How many shelves does she need to fit all of the books? (2) How many shelves will be full? (1) How many books will be on the second shelf? (8)

Quick Review

$$\begin{array}{c}1\\+1\\\hline(2)\end{array} \qquad \begin{array}{c}4\\+4\\\hline(8)\end{array} \qquad \begin{array}{c}5\\+5\\\hline(10)\end{array} \qquad \begin{array}{c}3\\+3\\\hline(6)\end{array} \qquad \begin{array}{c}2\\+2\\\hline(4)\end{array}$$

Lesson Quiz
Write the number.

1. ▯▯▯ (26)   2. ▯▯▯▯ (38)

LEVELED PRACTICE

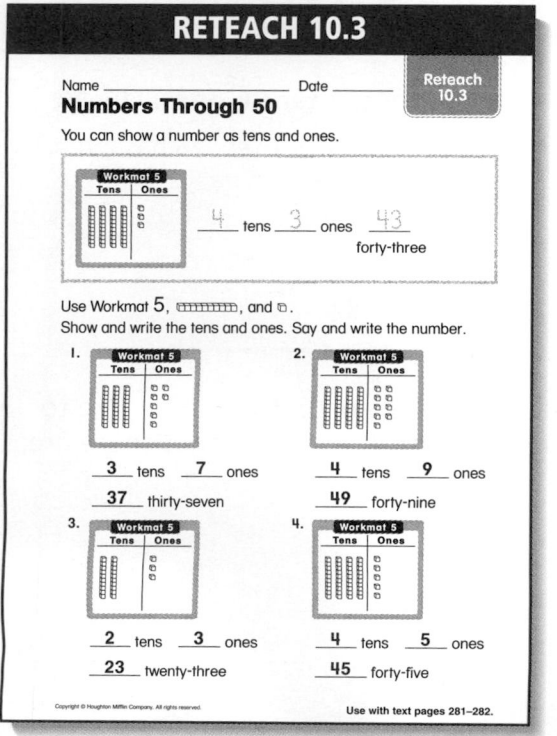

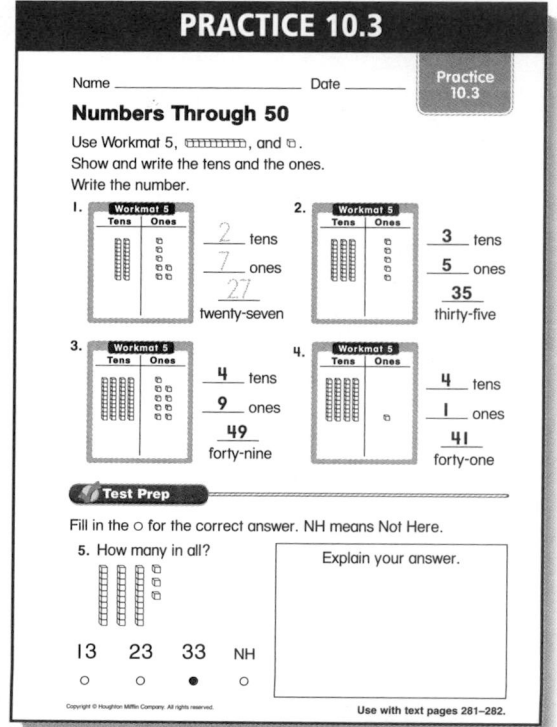

Practice Workbook Page 65

Reaching All Learners
Differentiated Instruction

English Learners

English-language learners may not be familiar with number words in English. Use Worksheet 10.3 to give children practice in associating number words with numbers.

Special Needs
VISUAL, TACTILE

Materials: *egg carton, beans*

- Cut an egg carton so it has 10 sections.
- Give the child up to 49 beans. Have the child use the carton to make 1 ten at a time.
- Then have the child count the tens and the ones. Write the number.

Early Finishers
TACTILE, VISUAL

- Have children make word and number cards for numbers 40 to 50. Tell them to mix the cards, and place them facedown in an array to play "concentration."
- Have children take turns until all cards have been matched.

TECHNOLOGY
Spiral Review

Help students remember skills they learned earlier by creating **customized** spiral review worksheets using the *Ways to Assess* CD-ROM.

Education Place

You can visit **Education Place** at eduplace.com/math/mw/ for teacher support materials.

Manipulatives

Interactive **Base Ten Blocks** with several workmats are available on the *Ways to Success* CD-ROM.

ScienceConnection

Tell children that there are about 19 different breeds of working dogs. Explain that these dogs are bred to do jobs. They might work as guard dogs, pull sleds, or rescue people who are in danger. Have children use cubes to show the number 19 in tens and ones.

MATH CENTER
Vocabulary Activity

This vocabulary-building activity helps children understand and remember new words. Encourage children to use the words in math discussion.

PROBLEM SOLVING 10.3

Name _____ Date _____ | Problem Solving 10.3

Numbers Through 50

Read and solve. Think about tens and ones.
Use ▭▭▭ and ▫, if you wish.

Draw or write to explain.

Paolo has 27 hats in his store. 10 hats fit on a shelf. How many shelves can Paola fill? How many hats are left over?

__2__ shelves __7__ hats left over

1. Alma has 42 party favors. 10 fit in each party bag. How many bags can she fill? How many party favors are left over?

Draw or write to explain.

__4__ bags __2__ favors left over

2. Dean has 35 pictures to put into an album. 10 pictures fit on each page. How many pages can he fill? How many pictures are left over?

__3__ pages __5__ pictures left over

Copyright © Houghton Mifflin Company. All rights reserved.
Use with text pages 281–282.

HOMEWORK 10.3

Name _____ Date _____ | Homework 10.3

Numbers Through 50

You can show a number as tens and ones.

Tens	Ones
ᗯᗯ	⦀⦀

__2__ tens __3__ ones __23__ twenty-three

Use small items such as buttons or coins.
Show the tens and ones.
Write the tens and the ones. Then write the number.

1.
Tens	Ones
ᗯᗯᗯ	⦀⦀⦀⦀

__3__ tens __4__ ones __34__ thirty-four

2.
Tens	Ones
ᗯᗯ	⦀⦀⦀⦀⦀⦀⦀

__2__ tens __7__ ones __27__ twenty-seven

3. Use paper clips. Show a number to a family member. Include at least one group of ten. Have the family member say the number you are showing. Take turns showing and telling.

Copyright © Houghton Mifflin Company. All rights reserved.
Use with text pages 281–282.

Homework Workbook Page 65

ENGLISH LEARNERS 10.3

Name _____ Date _____ | English Learners 10.3

Numbers Through 50

21 twenty-one	35 thirty-five	46 forty-six	54 fifty-four
67 sixty-seven	72 seventy-two	84 eighty-four	99 ninety-nine

Write the words for the numbers.

1. 31 __thirty-one__

2. 56 __fifty-six__

3. 62 __sixty-two__

4. 76 __seventy-six__

5. 95 __ninety-five__

6. 84 __eighty-four__

7. 42 __forty-two__

8. 24 __twenty-four__

9. 57 __fifty-seven__

To the Teacher: Use the examples at the top of the page to show children the relationship between number words and numbers. Then read each number and have children write the number word below it.

Copyright © Houghton Mifflin Company. All rights reserved.
Use with text pages 281–282.

TEACHING LESSON 10.3

LESSON ORGANIZER

Objective Model, read, and write numbers through 50.

Resources Reteach, Practice, Enrichment, Problem Solving, Homework, English Learners, Transparencies, Math Center

Materials Counters, paper bag, egg cartons, place-value blocks, Tens and Ones Chart transparency, overhead place-value blocks, Workmat 5

Activity

Warm-Up Activity
Modeling Tens

| 👤👤👤👤 Whole Group | ⏱ 10 minutes | Tactile, Auditory |

Materials: *counters, paper bag, 3 egg cartons with 2 sections cut out*

1. Place 30 counters in a paper bag. Have one child take a handful of counters from the bag. Have the child place 1 counter in each section of an egg carton, filling one carton before moving to the next.

2. When cartons are full, ask: **How many sections are in each of these egg cartons?** (10) **How many cartons are full?** (Answers may vary.)

3. Elicit that each full carton is 1 ten. Have children count each filled carton as 1 ten and then count the ones and say the numbers. Repeat the activity.

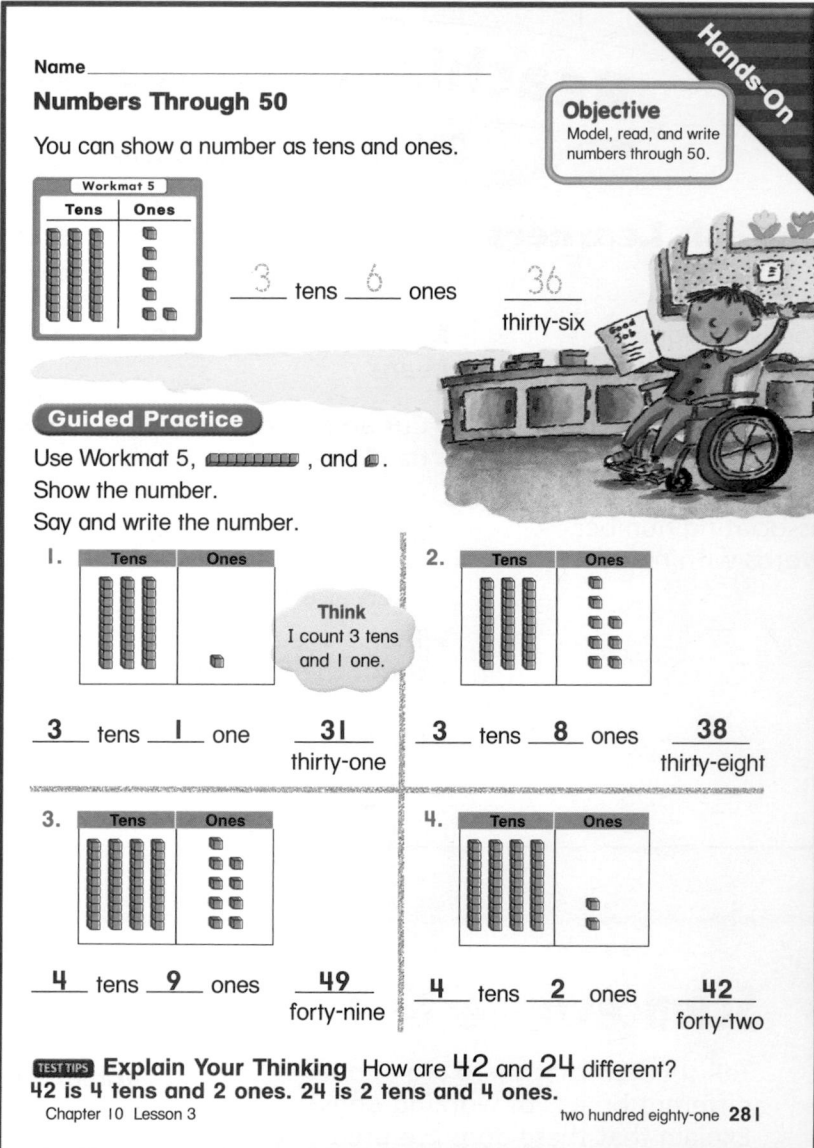

Name _____

Numbers Through 50

You can show a number as tens and ones.

Objective
Model, read, and write numbers through 50.

Workmat 5

| Tens | Ones |

___3___ tens ___6___ ones   ___36___
thirty-six

Guided Practice

Use Workmat 5, ▭▭▭▭▭ , and ▫.
Show the number.
Say and write the number.

1. Tens | Ones

Think
I count 3 tens and 1 one.

___3___ tens ___1___ one   ___31___
thirty-one

2. Tens | Ones

___3___ tens ___8___ ones   ___38___
thirty-eight

3. Tens | Ones

___4___ tens ___9___ ones   ___49___
forty-nine

4. Tens | Ones

___4___ tens ___2___ ones   ___42___
forty-two

TEST TIPS **Explain Your Thinking** How are 42 and 24 different? **42 is 4 tens and 2 ones. 24 is 2 tens and 4 ones.**

Chapter 10 Lesson 3   two hundred eighty-one **281**

---

1 Introduce
Model Numbers Through 50

| 👤👤👤👤 Whole Group | ⏱ 10–15 minutes | Visual, Tactile |

Materials: *overhead place-value blocks, Tens and Ones Chart transparency*

1. *Model 35.* Display 3 tens blocks and 5 ones blocks. Reinforce that the long rods have 10 ones and each is 1 ten. **On what side of the chart do we show tens?** (the left side, tens column) Have a volunteer place the tens on the left side of the chart.

2. **Where do we show the ones?** (on the right side of the chart)

3. **What number do the tens and ones show?** (35) Write 35 on the transparency. Now write the word name. **35 written in words is thirty-five.** Repeat the activity with other numbers.

2 Develop

Guided Learning

Teaching Example Introduce the objective to the children. Guide them through the example as they model 36 to show the number as tens and ones.

Guided Practice

Have children complete **Exercises 1–4** as you observe. Give children the opportunity to answer the Explain Your Thinking question. Model similar pairs of numbers to reinforce place value as you discuss their responses with the class.

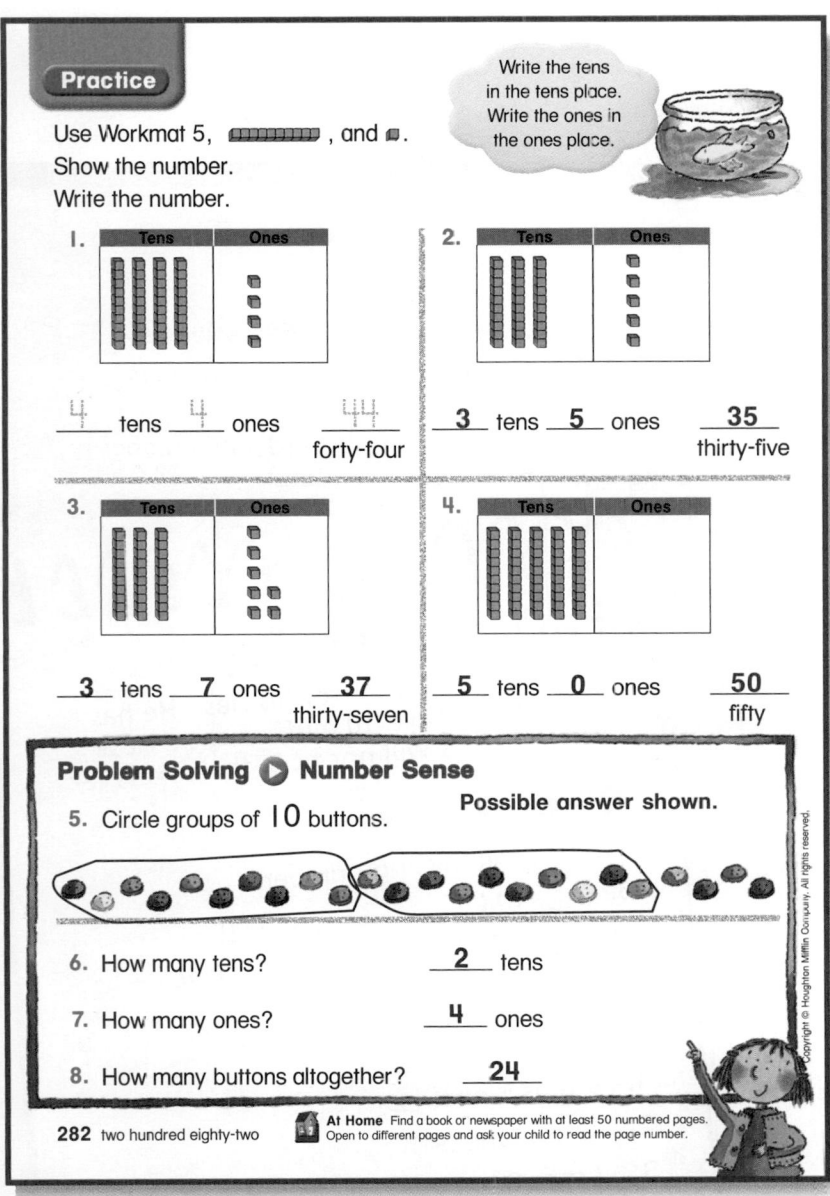

Practice

Use Workmat 5, ▭▭▭▭▭, and ▪.
Show the number.
Write the number.

Write the tens in the tens place. Write the ones in the ones place.

1.

Tens	Ones

__4__ tens __4__ ones __44__
forty-four

2.

Tens	Ones

__3__ tens __5__ ones __35__
thirty-five

3.

Tens	Ones

__3__ tens __7__ ones __37__
thirty-seven

4.

Tens	Ones

__5__ tens __0__ ones __50__
fifty

Problem Solving ▶ Number Sense

Possible answer shown.

5. Circle groups of 10 buttons.

6. How many tens? __2__ tens

7. How many ones? __4__ ones

8. How many buttons altogether? __24__

282 two hundred eighty-two

At Home Find a book or newspaper with at least 50 numbered pages. Open to different pages and ask your child to read the page number.

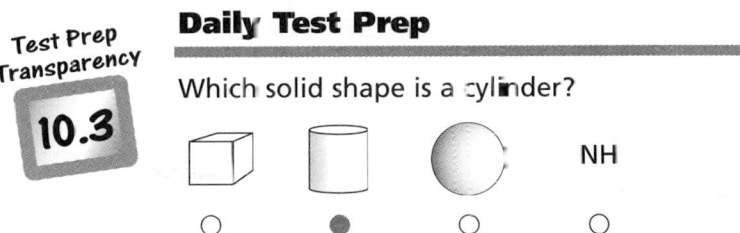

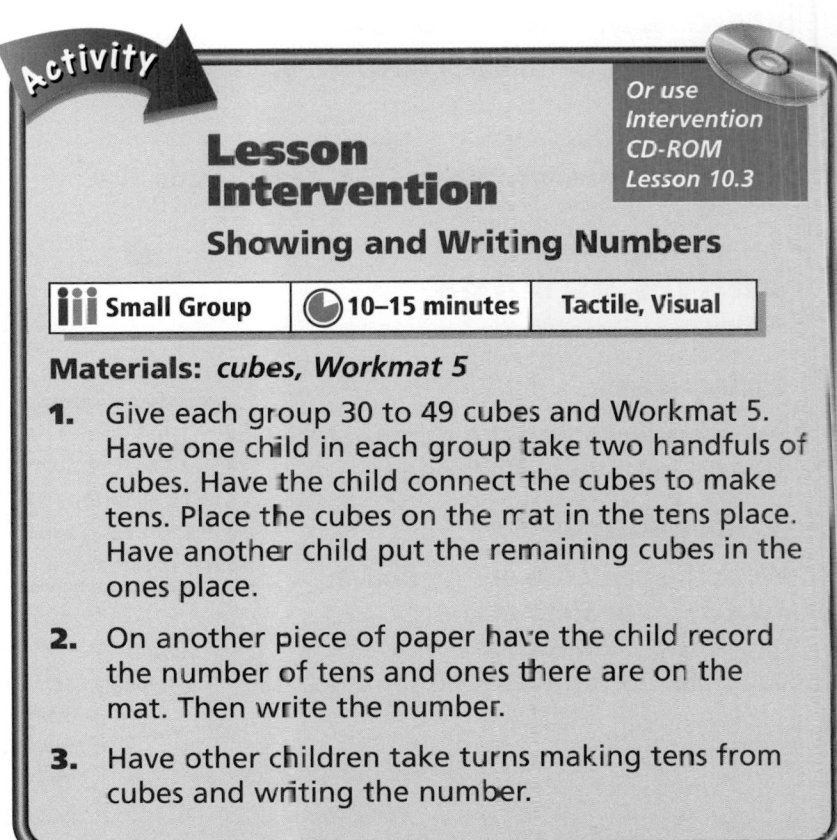

Test Prep Transparency **10.3**

Daily Test Prep

Which solid shape is a cylinder?

☐ ● ☐ NH ☐

Activity

Lesson Intervention

Or use Intervention CD-ROM Lesson 10.3

Showing and Writing Numbers

👤👤👤 Small Group	🕐 10–15 minutes	Tactile, Visual

Materials: *cubes, Workmat 5*

1. Give each group 30 to 49 cubes and Workmat 5. Have one child in each group take two handfuls of cubes. Have the child connect the cubes to make tens. Place the cubes on the mat in the tens place. Have another child put the remaining cubes in the ones place.

2. On another piece of paper have the child record the number of tens and ones there are on the mat. Then write the number.

3. Have other children take turns making tens from cubes and writing the number.

③ Practice

Independent Practice

Children complete **Exercises 1–4** independently.

Problem Solving

After children complete **Exercises 5–8**, call on volunteers to share their answers.

Common Error

Transposing Numbers
Children may write the tens and ones in the wrong place. Highlight the tens with a marker to help children focus on place value.

④ Assess and Close

How many ones are there in the number 38? (8)
How many tens are there in the number 41? (4)
What number do we say for 4 tens 9 ones? (49)

Keeping a Journal

Write a number between 21 and 49. Draw a picture to show the number of tens and ones. Write the number.

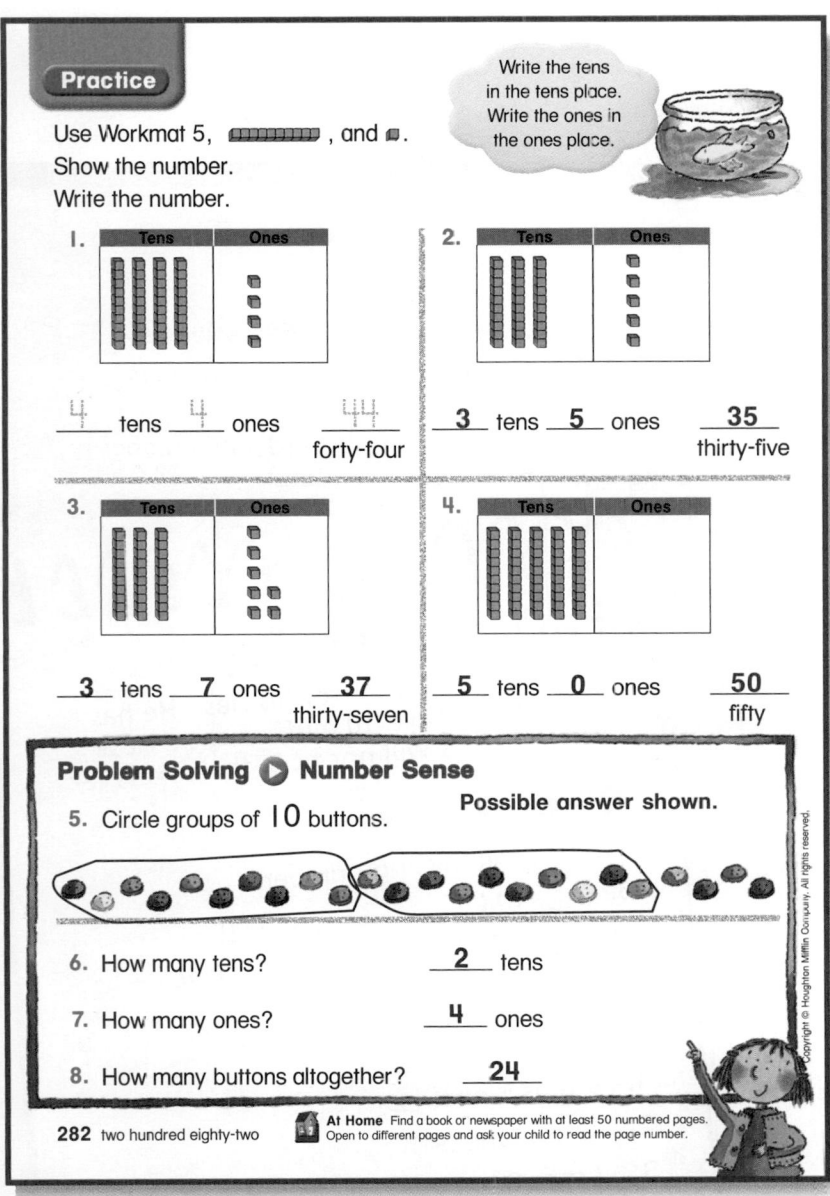

Numbers Through 99

PLANNING THE LESSON

MATHEMATICS OBJECTIVE
Read and write numbers through 99.

Use Lesson Planner CD-ROM for Lesson 10.4.

Daily Routines

Calendar
Ask children to find the date that is 10 days before or after today.

Sunday	Monday	Tuesday	Wednesday	Thursday	Friday	Saturday
			1	2	3	4
5	6	7	8	9	10	11
12	13	14	15	16	17	18
19	20	21	22	23	24	25
26	27	28	29	30	31	

Vocabulary
Write this sentence on the board. *I can regroup 30 to make ____tens ____ones* (3;0). Ask a volunteer to complete the sentence.

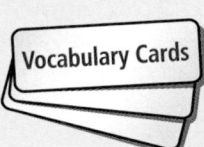

Vocabulary Cards

Meeting North Carolina's Standards
1.01 Develop number sense for whole numbers through 99.
• Connect the model, number word, and number using a variety of representations.

Lesson Transparency 10.4

Problem of the Day
Greg has 32 muffins for his class. He has 3 boxes that hold 10 muffins each. How many muffins will not fit in the boxes? (2)

Quick Review
What is the missing number?

8, ____, 10 (9)   3, ____, 5 (4)

18, ____, 20 (19)   13, ____, 15 (14)

Lesson Quiz
Write the number.
1. 6 tens 5 ones (65)
2. ninety-one (91)
3. 7 tens 8 ones (78)

LEVELED PRACTICE

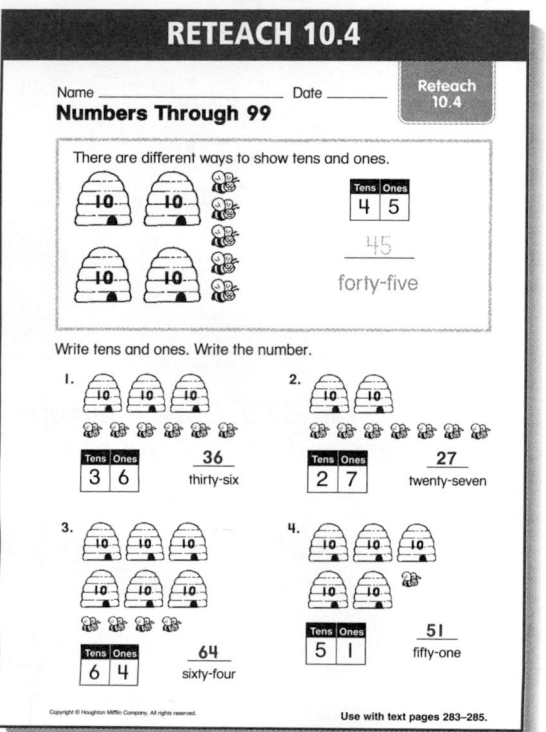

RETEACH 10.4

Name _____ Date _____

Reteach 10.4

Numbers Through 99

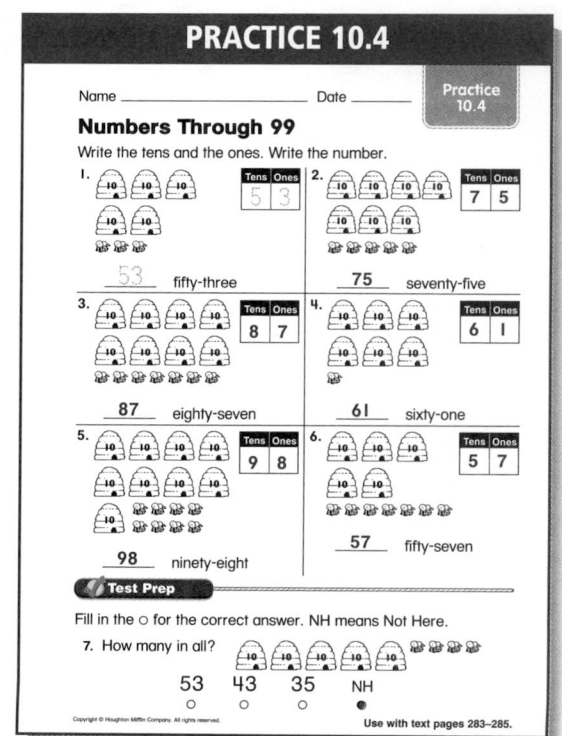

PRACTICE 10.4

Name _____ Date _____

Practice 10.4

Numbers Through 99

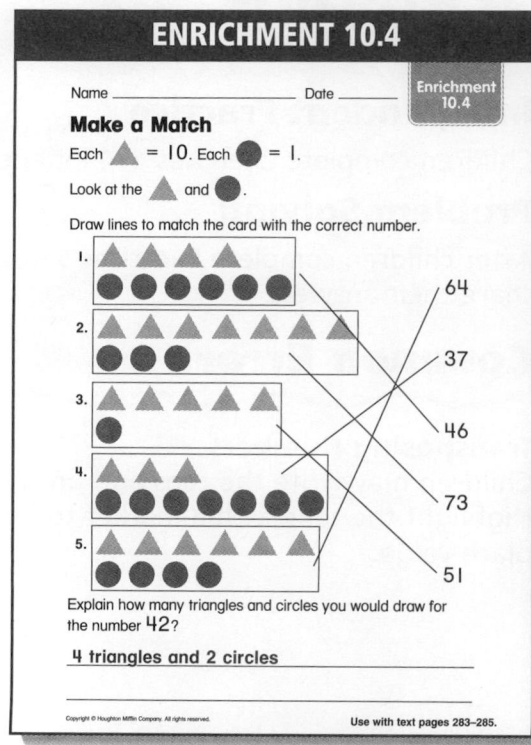

ENRICHMENT 10.4

Name _____ Date _____

Enrichment 10.4

Make a Match

Practice Workbook Page 66

Reaching All Learners

Differentiated Instruction

English Learners

The word *model* has several meanings in English. English-language learners will need to understand the meaning of the word in the context of mathematics in order to solve some problems involving numbers through 99.

Special Needs
VISUAL, TACTILE

Materials: *toothpicks, LT 6*

- Use toothpicks to model 63.
- Have the child count the groups of tens and ones. Write the number on LT 6. **There are 6 tens 3 ones. What is the number?** (63)

 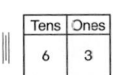

Tens	Ones
6	3

Gifted and Talented
VISUAL, TACTILE

Materials: *centimeter grid paper (LT 30)*

- Give children centimeter grid paper. Have children draw a "fence" around 96 squares.
- Suggest that children count 9 rows of ten squares and then count 6 single squares.
- Continue with different numbers.

Art Connection

Invite children to make "99 collages." Have 9 children each cut out 11 construction paper shapes. Then have children glue the shapes onto a large sheet of paper to create a collage.

MATH CENTER

Vocabulary Activity

This vocabulary-building activity helps children understand and remember new words. Encourage children to use the words in math discussion.

TECHNOLOGY

Spiral Review

You can prepare students for standardized tests with **customized** spiral review on key skills using the *Ways to Assess* CD-ROM.

eBook

eMathBook allows students to review lessons and do homework without carrying their textbooks home.

Games

Students can practice their math vocabulary using the Math Lingo game, available on the *Ways to Success* CD-ROM.

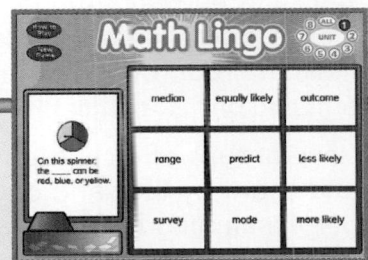

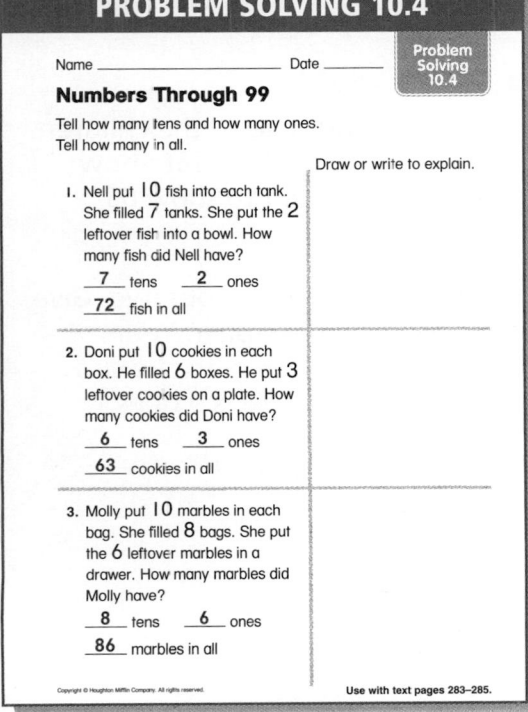

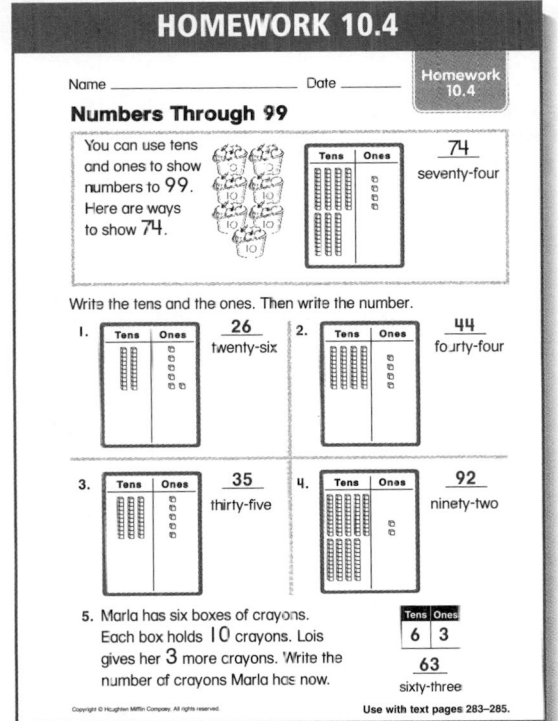

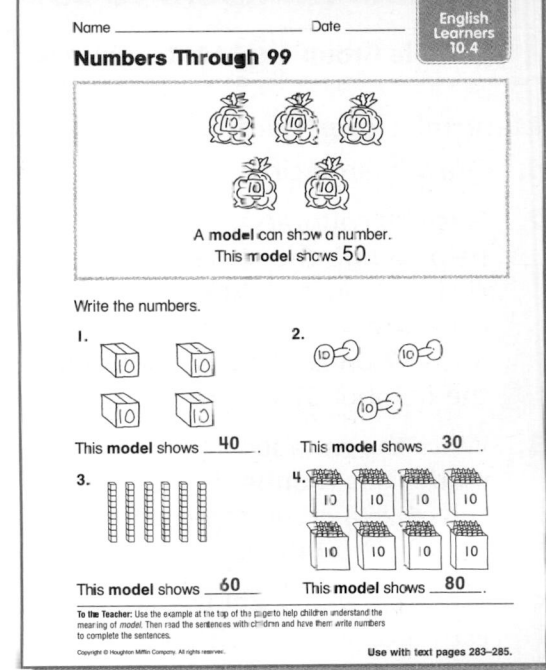

Homework Workbook Page 66

TEACHING LESSON 10.4

LESSON ORGANIZER

Objective Read and write numbers through 99.

Resources Reteach, Practice, Enrichment, Problem Solving, Homework, English Learners, Transparencies, Math Center

Materials Counters, paper cups, overhead counters, blank transparency, number cards (teacher-made)

Warm-Up Activity
Modeling Tens and Ones

| iiii Whole Group | ⏱ 10 minutes | Auditory, Tactile |

Materials: *counters, paper cups*

1. Review regrouping by giving each child 11 counters and a cup. **How can you regroup to show tens?** (Place 10 counters in a cup.) Have each child regroup to show ten.

2. Tell children that you want them to make 4 tens 4 ones. **You each have 1 ten 1 one. How can you make a group of 44?** (Four children can group their tens and ones together.)

3. Have groups of 4 children group their counters and count by tens and ones to confirm the number. Remaining children can group their counters and tell what number they have.

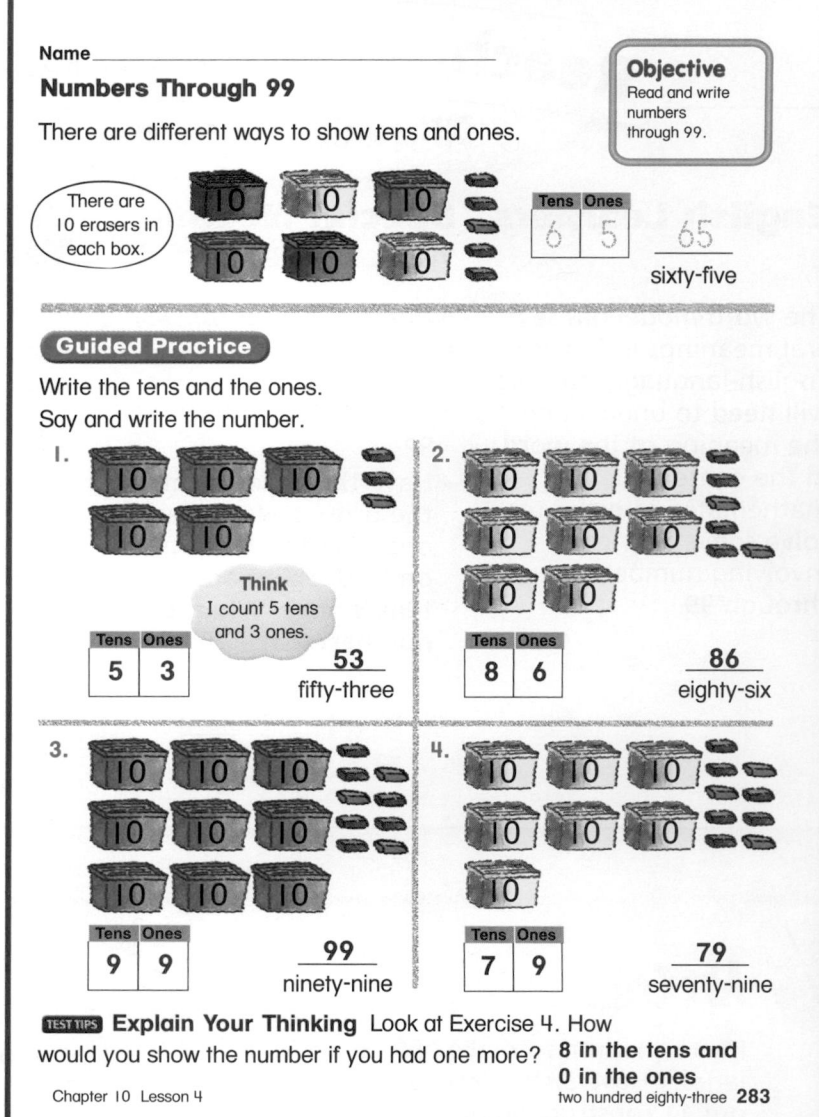

1 Introduce
Model Numbers to 99

| iiii Whole Group | ⏱ 10–15 minutes | Visual, Auditory |

Materials: *overhead counters, blank transparency*

1. Draw 9 large circles on a transparency.

2. Place 10 counters in one large circle. Have volunteers help you do the same for 4 of the other circles. **5 large circles show groups of 10.** Ask a volunteer to place 7 counters to the right of the transparency. **We show 5 tens 7 ones. What number do we show?** (57) Write the number 57 on the transparency.

3. Write the number 63 on the transparency. **How can we model this number?** (Put 10 counters on each of 6 circles and make a group of 3 counters to the side.) Ask volunteers to help you model the number.

4. **How can we model the number 99?** (Put 10 counters in each circle and make a group of 9 counters to the side.)

2 Develop

Guided Learning

Teaching Example Introduce the objective to the children. Guide them through the example to demonstrate how models, numbers, and words can be used to show 65.

Guided Practice

Have children complete **Exercises 1–4** as you observe. Give children the opportunity to answer the Explain Your Thinking question. Discuss their responses with the class. Point out that 8 tens is one more than 7 tens 9 ones.

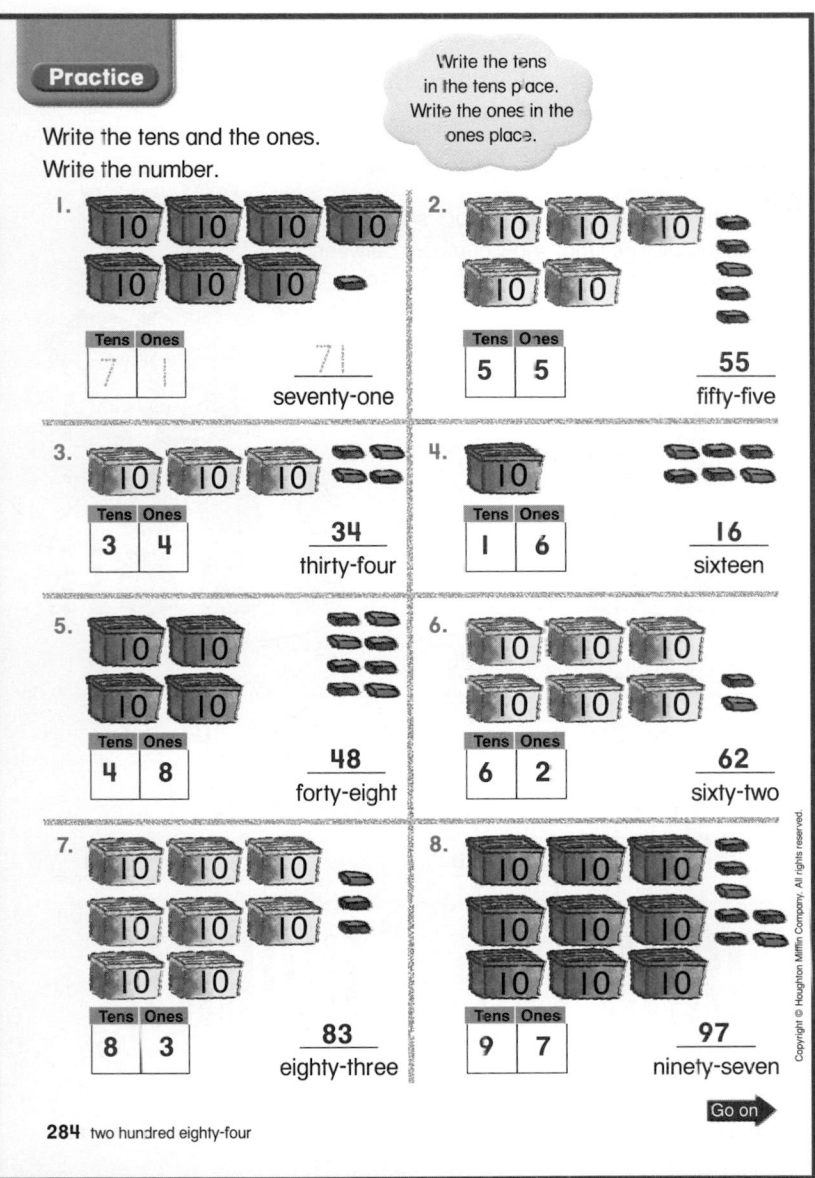

Practice

Write the tens and the ones.
Write the number.

Write the tens in the tens place. Write the ones in the ones place.

1.
Tens	Ones
7	1

71
seventy-one

2.
Tens	Ones
5	5

55
fifty-five

3.
Tens	Ones
3	4

34
thirty-four

4.
Tens	Ones
1	6

16
sixteen

5.
Tens	Ones
4	8

48
forty-eight

6.
Tens	Ones
6	2

62
sixty-two

7.
Tens	Ones
8	3

83
eighty-three

8.
Tens	Ones
9	7

97
ninety-seven

Go on

284 two hundred eighty-four

Connection

Refer back to the unit story, *100 Days of School* by Trudy Harris. Have children solve some of the following problems based on the passage that appears in the student book.

- If 5 children take off their shoes, how many toes are showing? (50)
- If 9 children take off their shoes, how many toes are showing? (90)
- If each child drops 10 papers, how many papers do 2 children drop? (20)
- If each child drops 10 papers, how many papers do 5 children drop? (50)

3 Practice

Independent Practice

Children complete **Exercises 1–8** independently.

Lesson continues

Daily Test Prep

What is the number?

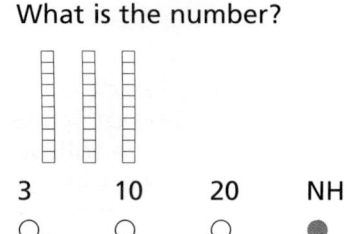

3   10   20   NH
○   ○   ○   ●

Activity

Lesson Intervention
Matching Numbers to Models

Or use Intervention CD-ROM Lesson 10.4

| 👥 Small Group | 🕐 5–10 minutes | Auditory, Visual |

Materials: *number cards 61–79 (teacher-made)*

1. Give each child a number card. Have children place the cards faceup in front of them.

2. Draw 6 large circles on the board and explain that each circle stands for groups of 10. Draw 8 small circles on the right and explain that they stand for ones.

3. **How many tens?** (6) **How many ones?** (8) **Who can show a card with this number?** The child with the matching number holds it up. Continue with other numbers.

Name _____

Problem Solving ▶ Number Sense

Write the number that each picture shows. Circle the pictures that show numbers between 40 and 70.

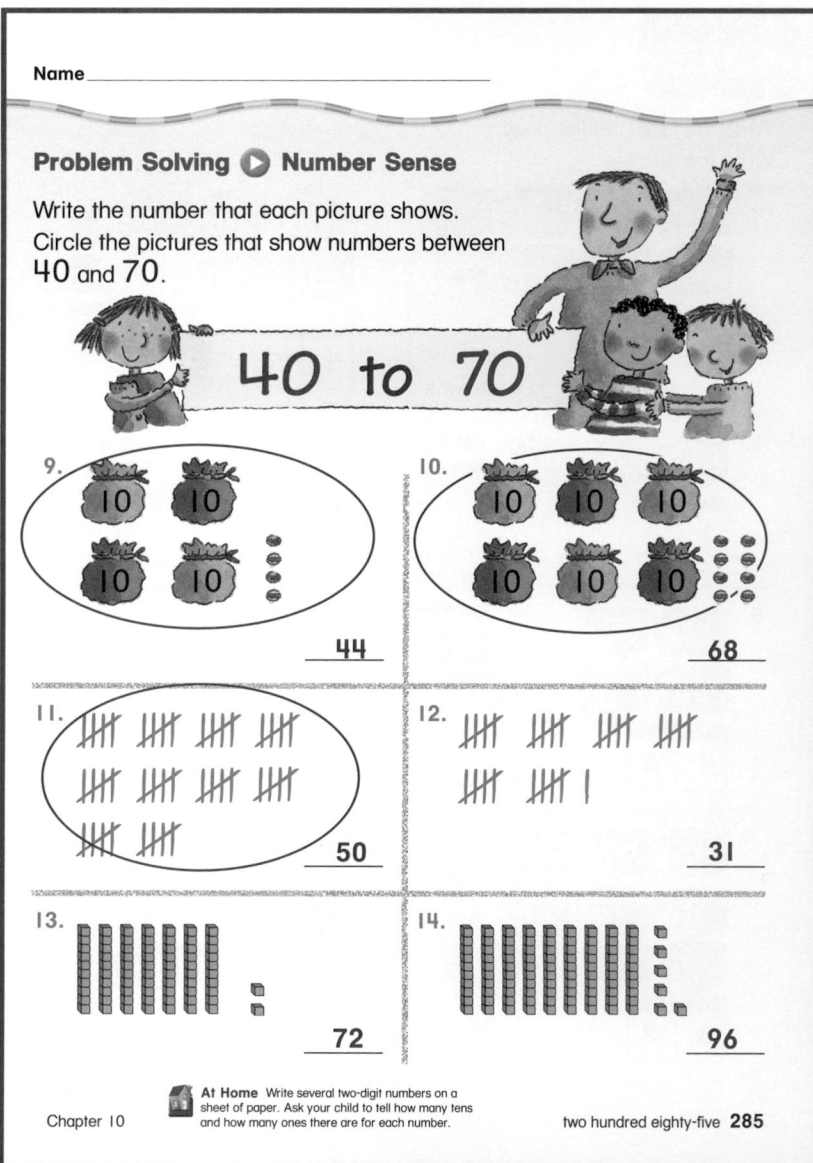

40 to 70

9. ____44____

10. ____68____

11. ____50____

12. ____31____

13. ____72____

14. ____96____

At Home Write several two-digit numbers on a sheet of paper. Ask your child to tell how many tens and how many ones there are for each number.

Chapter 10   two hundred eighty-five **285**

---

③ Practice

Problem Solving

After children complete **Exercises 9–14** on page 285, call on volunteers to share their solutions and say the numbers each model represents.

Common Error

Omitting the Ones
Children may forget to count and include the ones when they record the number. Suggest that they circle the ones and then count them.

④ Assess and Close

Sasha has 89 marbles. How many bags of 10 can she make? (8)

Nora has 9 bags with 10 marbles in each bag and 2 extra marbles. How many marbles does she have? (92)

 **Keeping a Journal**

Write a number between 51 and 99. Then draw a picture to show your number.

Quick Check

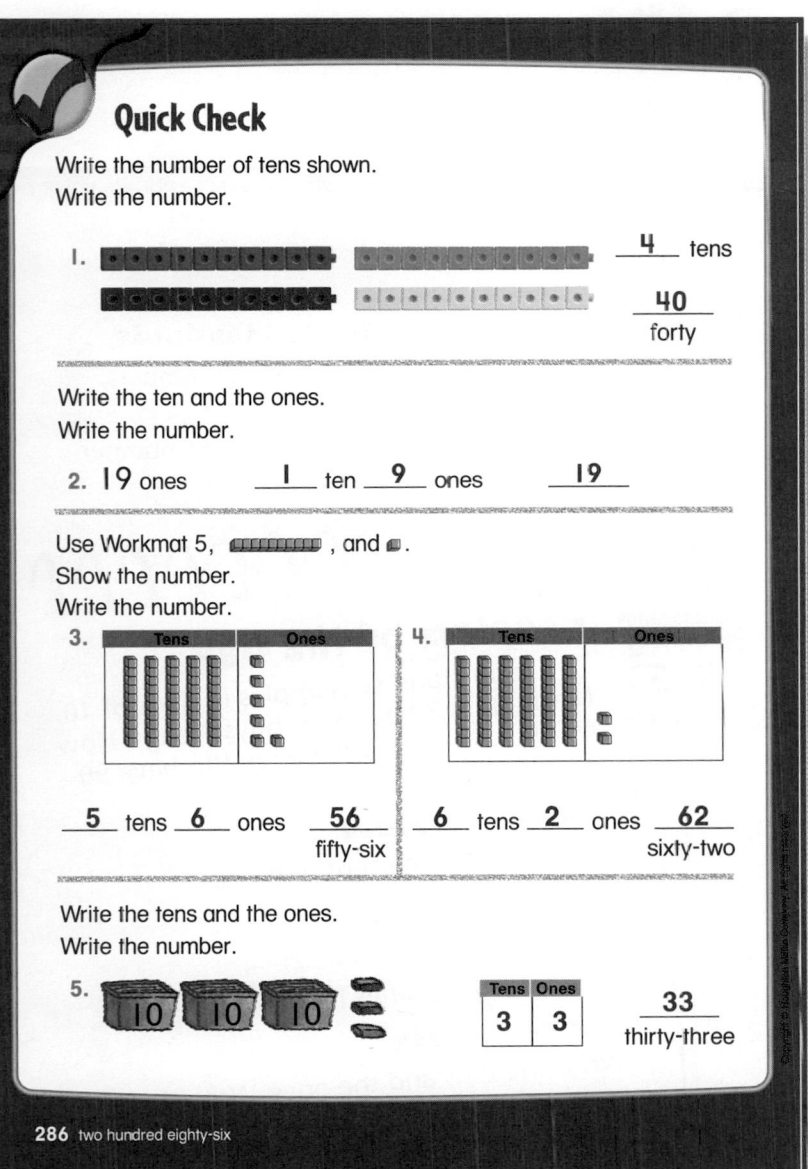

Write the number of tens shown.
Write the number.

1. ____4____ tens

   ___40___
   forty

Write the ten and the ones.
Write the number.

2. 19 ones ___1___ ten ___9___ ones ____19____

Use Workmat 5, ⬛⬛⬛⬛⬛, and ▪.
Show the number.
Write the number.

3.

Tens	Ones

   ___5___ tens ___6___ ones ___56___
   fifty-six

4.

Tens	Ones

   ___6___ tens ___2___ ones ___62___
   sixty-two

Write the tens and the ones.
Write the number.

5.

Tens	Ones
3	3

   ___33___
   thirty-three

Quick Check

Have children complete the Quick Check exercises independently to assess their understanding of the concepts and skills taught in **Lessons 1–4.**

Item	Lesson	Error Analysis	Intervention
1	10.1	Children may omit the zero when writing tens.	Reteach Resource 10.1 *Ways to Success* 10.1
2	10.2	Children may write an incorrect number in the tens place.	Reteach Resource 10.2 *Ways to Success* 10.2
3–4	10.3	Children may transpose the ones and tens digits when writing the numbers.	Reteach Resource 10.3 *Ways to Success* 10.3
5	10.4	Children may forget the ones digit when writing the numbers.	Reteach Resource 10.4 *Ways to Success* 10.4

Place Value Through 99

Lesson 10.5

PLANNING THE LESSON

MATHEMATICS OBJECTIVE
Identify the place value of numbers through 99.

Use Lesson Planner CD-ROM for Lesson 10.5.

Daily Routines

Calendar
Mark the first and last date of the month and have children count how many days are in between.

Sunday	Monday	Tuesday	Wednesday	Thursday	Friday	Saturday
				1	2	3	4
5	6	7	8	9	10	11
12	13	14	15	16	17	18
19	20	21	22	23	24	25
26	27	28	29	30	31	

Vocabulary
Ask children to describe the numbers 25, 70, and 99 in terms of **tens** and **ones**.

Vocabulary Cards

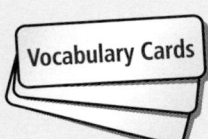

Meeting North Carolina's Standards
1.01 Develop number sense for whole numbers through 99.
- Connect the model, number word, and number using a variety of representations.

Lesson Transparency 10.5

Problem of the Day
The farm stand sells apples in bags of 10. Maria buys 3 bags. Ben buys 4 bags. How many more bags are needed to have 90 apples in all? (2 bags)

Quick Review
Write how many tens and ones.

14 ___ ten ___ ones (1; 4)

32 ___ tens ___ ones (3; 2)

49 ___ tens ___ ones (4; 9)

Lesson Quiz
Write the tens and the ones. Write the number.

1.   (7 tens; 2 ones; 72)   2.   (6 tens; 9 ones; 69)

LEVELED PRACTICE

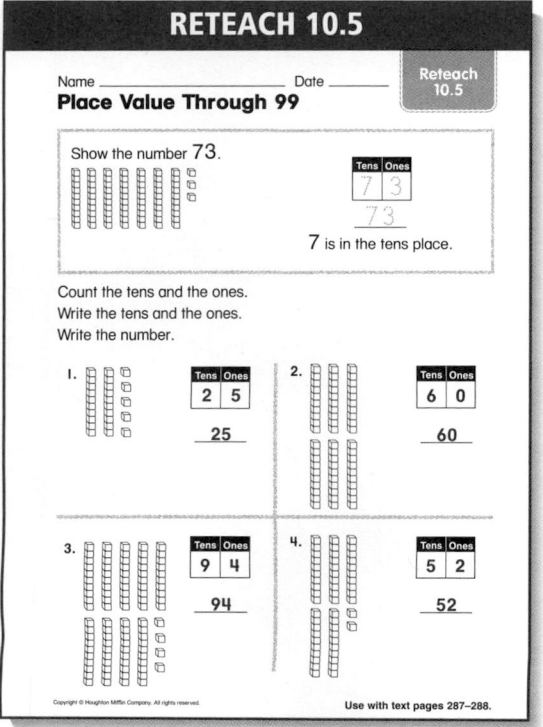

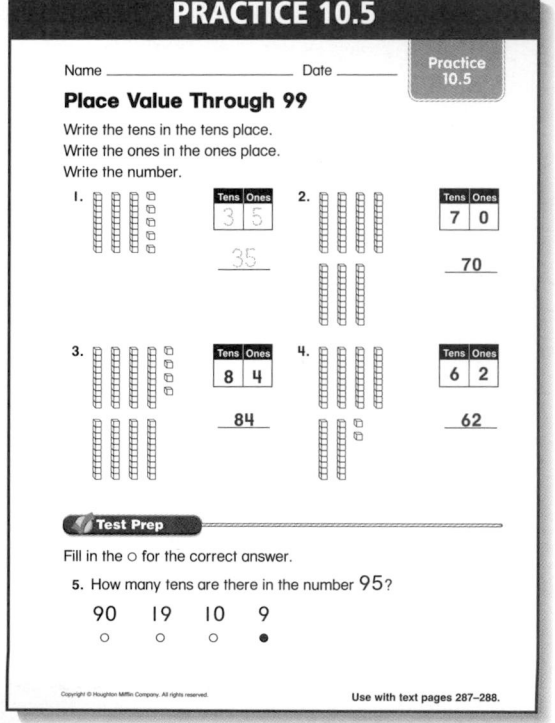

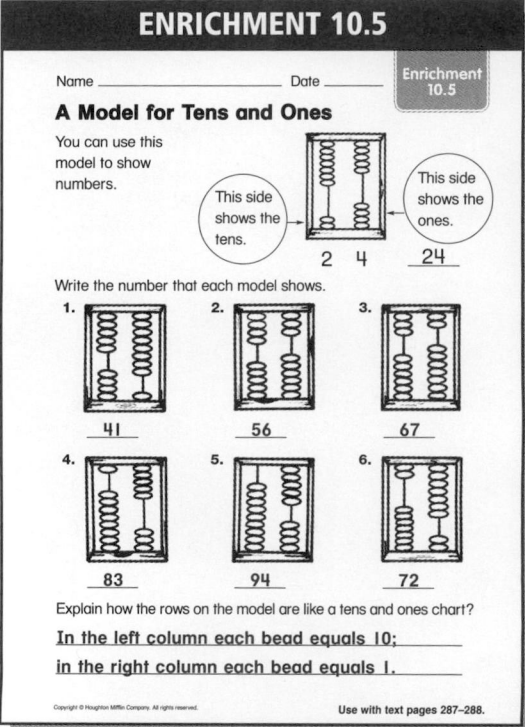

Practice Workbook Page 67

Reaching All Learners
Differentiated Instruction

English Learners

English-language learners will need to understand the word *digit* in order to complete the Talk About It problem. Use Worksheet 10.5 to teach children the meaning of this word.

Special Needs
AUDITORY, TACTILE

Materials: *place-value blocks*

- Write 2 tens 5 ones. Have the child show 2 tens 5 ones with place-value blocks.
- **What is another way to write 2 tens?** (20) Write 20 under *2 tens*.
- **What is another way to write 5 ones?** (5) Write 5 under *five ones*.
- **What is 20 and 5?** (25)

Early Finishers
AUDITORY, TACTILE

Materials: *hundred chart (LT 7), cards for 1–9 (LT 14)*

- Children use the chart as a game board and one child picks cards and calls the numbers as either *tens* or *ones*.
- If the caller picks 2 and says 2 tens, the players each cross out any one number with 2 tens.
- Play continues until one player has crossed off 5 numbers in a row.

TECHNOLOGY

Spiral Review

Create **customized** spiral review worksheets for individual students using the *Ways to Assess* CD-ROM.

Lesson Planner

You can customize your teaching plan or meet your curriculum requirements with the **Lesson Planner CD-ROM.**

Education Place

Recommend that parents visit **Education Place** at **eduplace.com/parents/mw/** for parent support activities.

Science Connection

Discuss magnets and their properties. Have children pass the magnet over a pile of paper clips to see how many they can pick up. Have them take the clips off the magnet, arrange them as tens and ones, and write the number.

MATH CENTER

Basic Skills Activity

Motivate children to build basic skills. Use this activity to address multiple learning styles using hands-on activities related to the skills of this lesson.

PROBLEM SOLVING 10.5

Name _____ Date _____

Problem Solving 10.5

Place Value Through 99

Read and solve.
Write the tens and the ones.

Draw or write to explain.

1. Jay has 93 pennies to put in wrappers. Each wrapper holds 10 pennies. How many wrappers for 10 pennies will he need? How many pennies will be left?

   __9__ wrappers __3__ pennies left

   __9__ tens __3__ ones

2. Abdullah has 76 seeds to plant. If he plants 10 seeds in each row, how many rows will he need? How many seeds will be left over?

   __7__ rows __6__ seeds left

   __7__ tens __6__ ones

3. Jane is making drinks for 50 children. She can put 10 drinks in a pitcher. How many pitchers will she need?

   __5__ pitchers __0__ drinks left over

   __5__ tens __0__ ones

Use with text pages 287–288.

HOMEWORK 10.5

Name _____ Date _____

Homework 10.5

Place Value Through 99

Rita looks at the cubes.
She writes 9 in the tens place.
She writes 3 in the ones place.
Then she writes the number.

Tens	Ones
9	3

93

ninety-three

Write the tens in the tens place.
Write the ones in the ones place.
Then write the number.

1.
Tens	Ones
8	6
86

2.
Tens	Ones
5	1
51

3.
Tens	Ones
7	0
70

4.
Tens	Ones
4	5
45

5. Manuel has 8 boxes of crayons. Each box has 10 crayons. Ruth gives him 3 more crayons. Write how many crayons he has now.

Tens	Ones
8	3

83 crayons

Use with text pages 287–288.

ENGLISH LEARNERS 10.5

Name _____ Date _____

English Learners 10.5

Place Value Through 99

27
There are two **digits** in this number.
They are 2 and 7.

Write the two digits in each of these numbers.

1. 92 __9__ __2__
2. 56 __5__ __6__
3. 63 __6__ __3__
4. 36 __3__ __6__

Write two numbers with each of these digits.

5. 2, 6 __26__ __62__
6. 8, 5 __85__ __58__
7. 7, 1 __71__ __17__
8. 4, 3 __43__ __34__

To the Teacher: Use the example at the top of the page to help children understand the meaning of the word *digit*. Then have them follow the directions to complete the page.

Use with text pages 287–288.

Homework Workbook Page 67

TEACHING LESSON 10.5

LESSON ORGANIZER

Objective Identify the place value of numbers through 99.

Resources Reteach, Practice, Enrichment, Problem Solving, Homework, English Learners, Transparencies, Math Center

Materials overhead place-value blocks, tens and ones chart transparency, place-value blocks, Workmat 5, two-color counters

Activity

Warm-Up Activity
Modeling Tens and Ones

Whole Group	5 minutes	Auditory, Tactile

Materials: *place-value blocks*

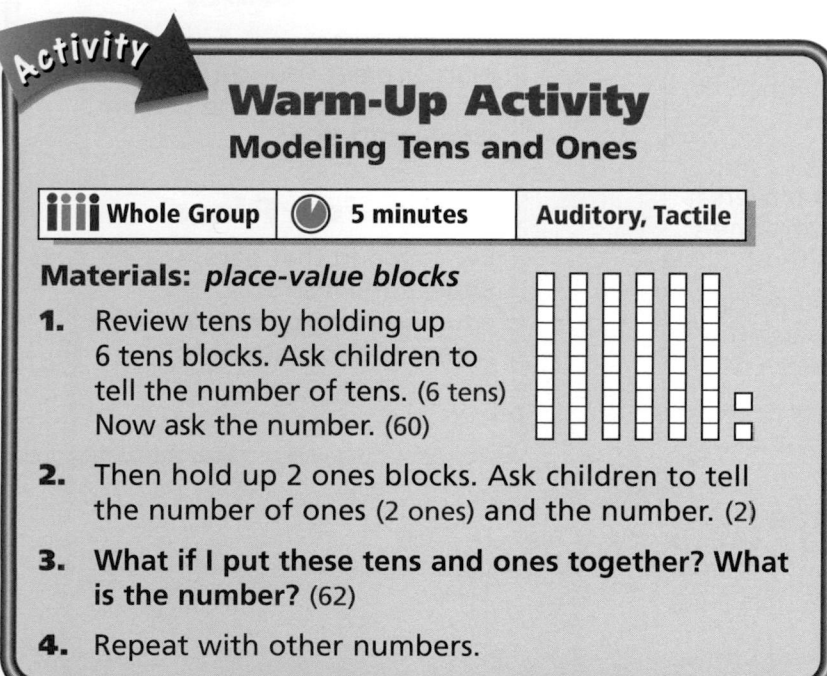

1. Review tens by holding up 6 tens blocks. Ask children to tell the number of tens. (6 tens) Now ask the number. (60)

2. Then hold up 2 ones blocks. Ask children to tell the number of ones (2 ones) and the number. (2)

3. What if I put these tens and ones together? What is the number? (62)

4. Repeat with other numbers.

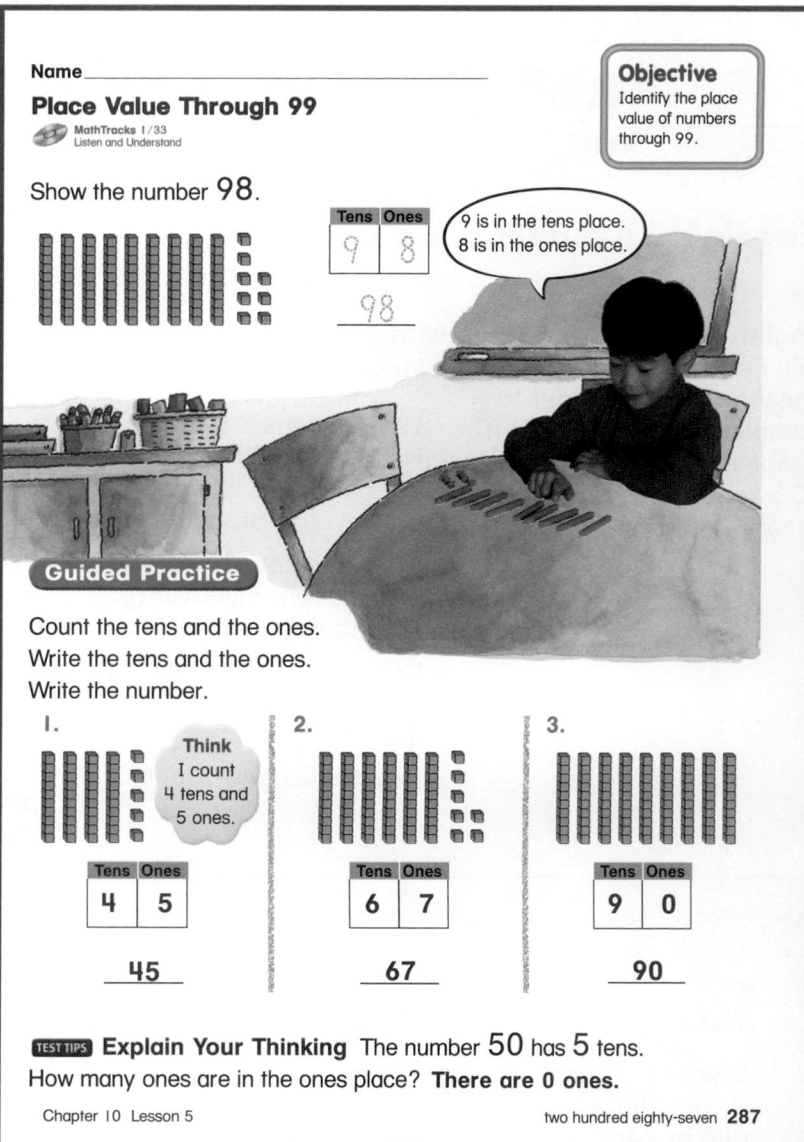

Place Value Through 99
MathTracks 1/33
Listen and Understand

Objective
Identify the place value of numbers through 99.

Show the number 98.

Tens	Ones
9	8

98

9 is in the tens place.
8 is in the ones place.

Guided Practice

Count the tens and the ones.
Write the tens and the ones.
Write the number.

1.

Think
I count
4 tens and
5 ones.

Tens	Ones
4	5

45

2.

Tens	Ones
6	7

67

3.

Tens	Ones
9	0

90

TEST TIPS **Explain Your Thinking** The number 50 has 5 tens. How many ones are in the ones place? **There are 0 ones.**

Chapter 10 Lesson 5   two hundred eighty-seven **287**

---

1 Introduce   Activity
Model Place Value

Whole Group	10–15 minutes	Visual, Auditory

Materials: *overhead place-value blocks, tens and ones chart transparency, place-value blocks, Workmat 5*

1. *Model 74.* Display 7 tens and 4 ones on the overhead as children do on their Workmats.

2. How many tens are there? (7) So I write a 7 in the tens place in the chart.

3. How many ones are there? (4) So I write a 4 in the ones place in the chart.

4. Point to the 7 and the 4 as you say: 7 in the tens place, 4 in the ones place. What is the number? (74) Write 74.

5. Repeat with other numbers, having children show the models.

2 Develop

Guided Learning

Teaching Example Introduce the objective to the children. Guide them through the example to help them understand that the tens and ones on the chart and the written number are both ways to show 9 tens 8 ones.

Guided Practice

Have children complete **Exercises 1–3** as you observe. Give children the opportunity to answer the Explain Your Thinking question. Then discuss their responses with the class. Emphasize the importance of the zero and the difference between 5 and 50.

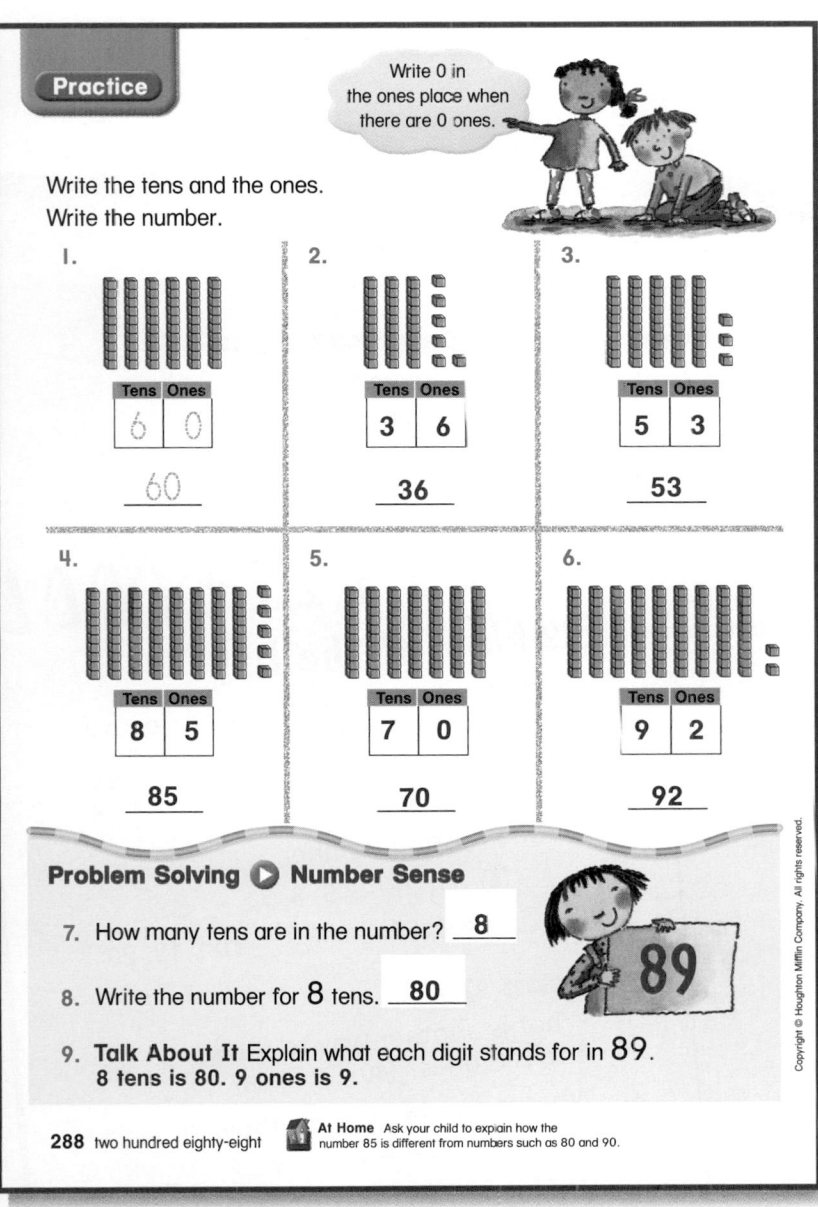

Practice

Write 0 in the ones place when there are 0 ones.

Write the tens and the ones.
Write the number.

1.

Tens	Ones
6	0

60

2.

Tens	Ones
3	6

36

3.

Tens	Ones
5	3

53

4.

Tens	Ones
8	5

85

5.

Tens	Ones
7	0

70

6.

Tens	Ones
9	2

92

Problem Solving ▶ Number Sense

7. How many tens are in the number? **8**

8. Write the number for 8 tens. **80**

89

9. **Talk About It** Explain what each digit stands for in 89.
8 tens is 80. 9 ones is 9.

At Home Ask your child to explain how the number 85 is different from numbers such as 80 and 90.

Test Prep Transparency 10.5

What shape comes next in this pattern?

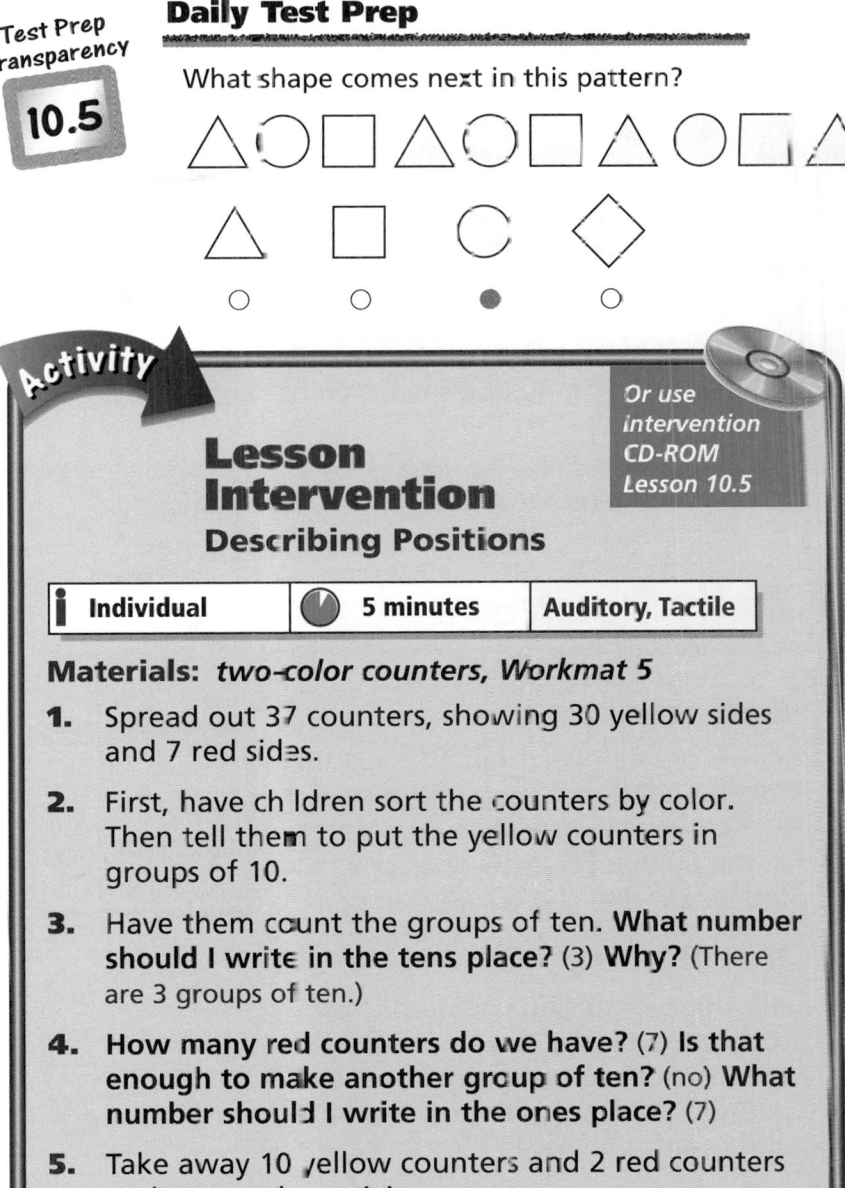

Activity

Lesson Intervention

Or use intervention CD-ROM Lesson 10.5

Describing Positions

ℹ Individual	⏱ 5 minutes	Auditory, Tactile

Materials: *two-color counters, Workmat 5*

1. Spread out 37 counters, showing 30 yellow sides and 7 red sides.

2. First, have children sort the counters by color. Then tell them to put the yellow counters in groups of 10.

3. Have them count the groups of ten. **What number should I write in the tens place?** (3) **Why?** (There are 3 groups of ten.)

4. **How many red counters do we have?** (7) **Is that enough to make another group of ten?** (no) **What number should I write in the ones place?** (7)

5. Take away 10 yellow counters and 2 red counters and repeat the activity.

---

3 Practice

Independent Practice

Children complete **Exercises 1–6** independently.

Problem Solving

After children complete **Exercises 7 and 8**, call on volunteers to share their answers. Use the Talk About It in **Exercise 9** to discuss how children describe what each digit stands for in the number.

Common Error

Confusing Tens and Ones

Children may write the number of ones in the tens place. Remind children to read the words *Tens* and *Ones* on the chart before they write the numbers each time.

4 Assess and Close

Display overhead place-value blocks as shown here.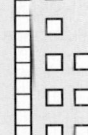

What number goes in the tens place? (1)

What number goes in the ones place? (8)

Keeping a Journal

Read the riddle

There is a <u>6</u> in my tens place. There is a <u>2</u> in my ones place. What number am I? I am 62.

Write your own number riddle. Write the answer.

Different Ways to Show Numbers

PLANNING THE LESSON

MATHEMATICS OBJECTIVE
Show two-digit numbers in different ways.

Use Lesson Planner CD-ROM for Lesson 10.6.

Daily Routines

Calendar

Point to a number from 10 to 31 on the calendar and ask children how many tens and how many ones are in the number. If applicable, use today's date as the target number.

Sunday	Monday	Tuesday	Wednesday	Thursday	Friday	Saturday
			1	2	3	4
5	6	7	8	9	10	11
12	13	14	15	16	17	18
19	20	21	22	23	24	25
26	27	28	29	30	31	

Vocabulary

Ask children to find common class-room objects that can be grouped in **tens**, such as crayons, pencils, and paper clips. Have them make groups and count how many tens there are.

Vocabulary Cards

Meeting North Carolina's Standards
1.01 Develop number sense for whole numbers through 99.
- Connect the model, number word, and number using a variety of representations.

Lesson Transparency **10.6**

Problem of the Day
How many more circles do you need to make 12 circles in all? (5)

```
O X O X
O O X X
X O O X
X O X X
```

Quick Review
Write the missing number.

15, ___ (16), 17, 18   9, 8, 7, ___ (6)

63, 64, ___ (65), 66   17, ___ (18), 19, 20

Lesson Quiz
1. What is another way to show 4 tens 8 ones? (40 + 8 or 48)
2. What is another way to show 20 + 5? (2 tens 5 ones or 25)
3. What is another way to show 93? (9 tens 3 ones or 90 + 3)

LEVELED PRACTICE

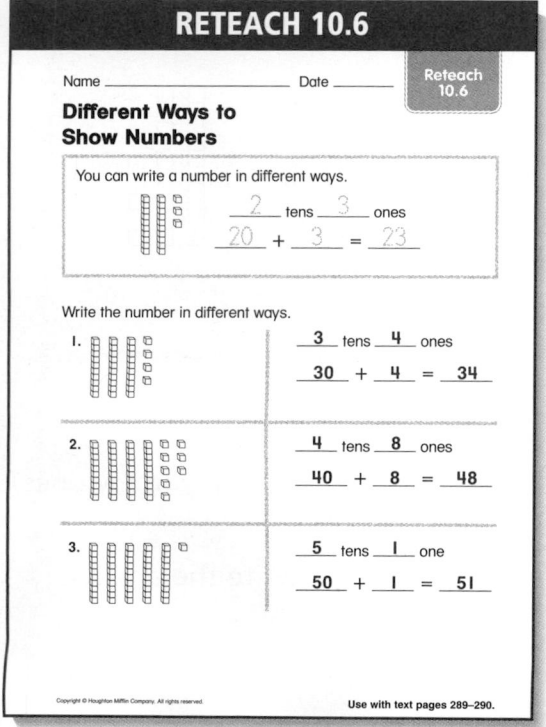

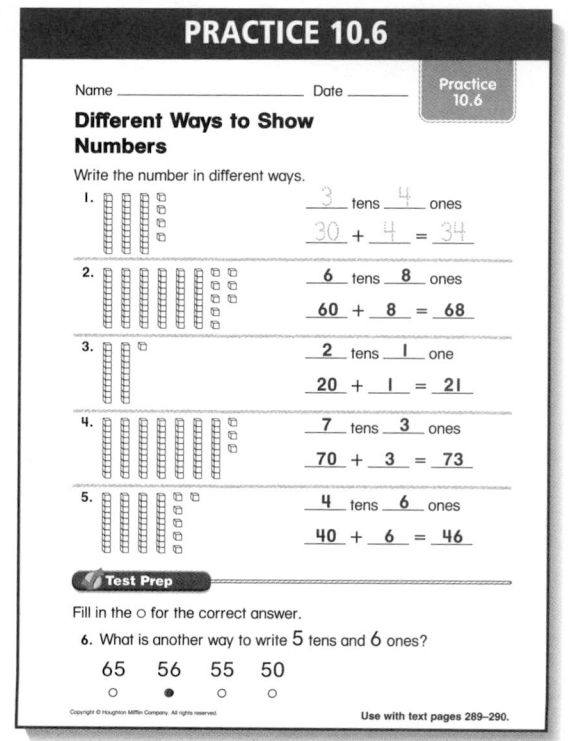

Practice Workbook Page 68

Reaching All Learners
Differentiated Instruction

English Learners

English-language learners may not have the language skills to explain the process behind their thinking. Use Worksheet 10.6 to provide children with sentence frames they can use to complete the Explain Your Thinking activity.

Special Needs
VISUAL, TACTILE

Materials: *cubes, index cards*

- Show the child 3 cube trains of 10 each.
- Have the child count by tens to find how many in all and write 30 on an index card.
- Give the child 4 ones and have the child write 4 on another card.
- Place the cards together with a plus sign and read 30 plus 4. Say the number, 34.

Early Finishers
VISUAL, TACTILE

- Invite children to draw a picture of a garden.
- Have them choose a two-digit number and draw that number of flowers. Then have them circle groups of ten flowers.
- Have children exchange pictures and write the number of flowers.

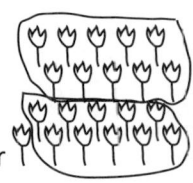

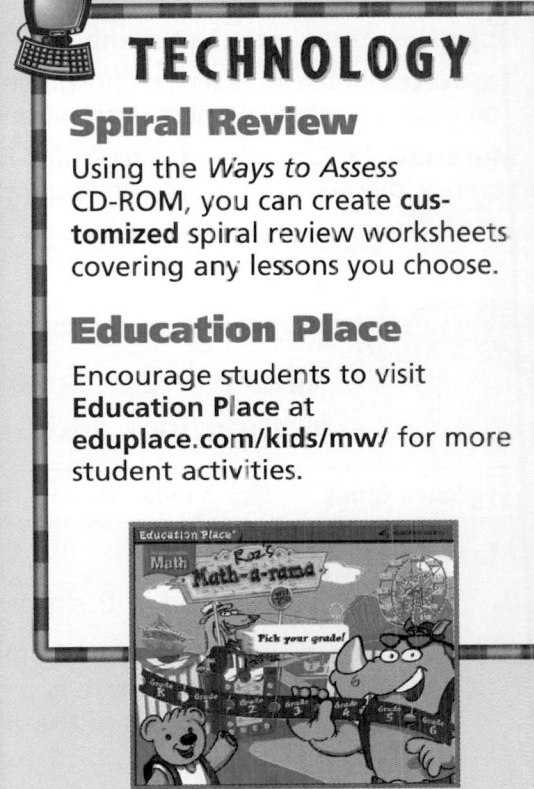

TECHNOLOGY

Spiral Review

Using the *Ways to Assess* CD-ROM, you can create **customized** spiral review worksheets covering any lessons you choose.

Education Place

Encourage students to visit **Education Place** at **eduplace.com/kids/mw/** for more student activities.

Social Studies Connection

Use a phone book to find the number of schools in your city or town, or other information about your area or state. Have children draw and write to show the numbers in different ways.

MATH CENTER

Real-Life Activity

Help children understand the usefulness of mathematics. This activity makes math come alive by connecting the lesson skills to a real-life situation.

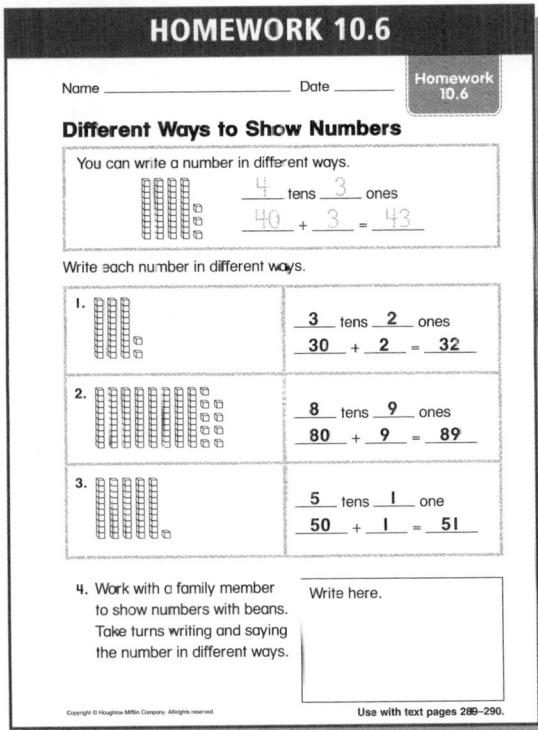

Homework Workbook Page 68

TEACHING LESSON 10.6

LESSON ORGANIZER

Objective Show two-digit numbers in different ways.

Resources Reteach, Practice, Enrichment, Problem Solving, Homework, English Learners, Transparencies, Math Center

Materials LT 6, overhead place-value blocks, blank transparency, place-value blocks, connecting cubes, counters

Activity

Warm-Up Activity
Writing Tens and Ones

iii Small Group	⏱ 5 minutes	Auditory, Tactile

Materials: *LT 6*

	Tens	Ones
	5	9

1. Give LT 6 to each child in the group.

2. Tell children number riddles. **I am thinking of a number. There is a 5 in the tens place and a 9 in the ones place.**

3. Have children write the digits in the correct place value in their charts.

4. **What is the number?** (59)

5. Repeat with other numbers.

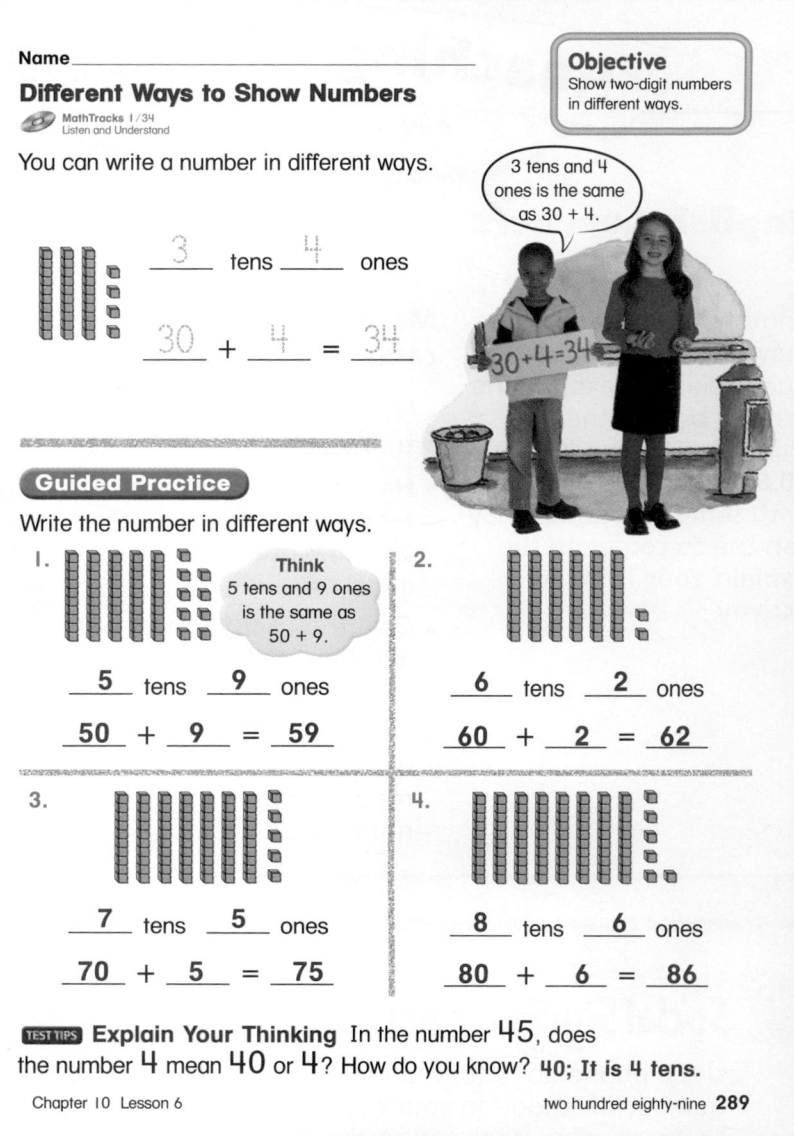

Objective
Show two-digit numbers in different ways.

Name_____

Different Ways to Show Numbers

MathTracks 1/34
Listen and Understand

You can write a number in different ways.

3 tens and 4 ones is the same as 30 + 4.

___3___ tens ___4___ ones

___30___ + ___4___ = ___34___

30+4=34

Guided Practice

Write the number in different ways.

1. Think 5 tens and 9 ones is the same as 50 + 9.

___5___ tens ___9___ ones

___50___ + ___9___ = ___59___

2. ___6___ tens ___2___ ones

___60___ + ___2___ = ___62___

3. ___7___ tens ___5___ ones

___70___ + ___5___ = ___75___

4. ___8___ tens ___6___ ones

___80___ + ___6___ = ___86___

TEST TIPS Explain Your Thinking In the number 45, does the number 4 mean 40 or 4? How do you know? 40; It is 4 tens.

Chapter 10 Lesson 6 two hundred eighty-nine **289**

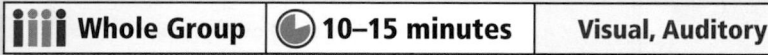

1 Introduce
Model Ways to Show Numbers

iiii Whole Group	⏱ 10–15 minutes	Visual, Auditory

Materials: *overhead place-value blocks, blank transparency*

1. Display 5 tens and 2 ones. **How many tens and ones do you see?** (5 tens 2 ones)

2. Write 5 tens 2 ones on the board. **I can write the number as 5 tens 2 ones.**

3. **What number stands for 5 tens?** (50) **What number stands for 2 ones?** (2) Write *50* under *5 tens* and *2* under *2 ones*.

4. Point to the corresponding words and numbers as you say: **Five tens is 50. Plus there are 2 ones. That's 2 more. 50 + 2 equals 52.**

5. Repeat with other numbers.

2 Develop

Guided Learning

Teaching Example Introduce the objective to the children. Guide them through the example to show how the place-value blocks, the words, and the numbers with symbols are all different ways to show 34.

Guided Practice

Have children complete **Exercises 1–4** as you observe. Give children the opportunity to answer the Explain Your Thinking question. Then discuss their responses with the class. Ask for the value of 5 in 45.

Practice

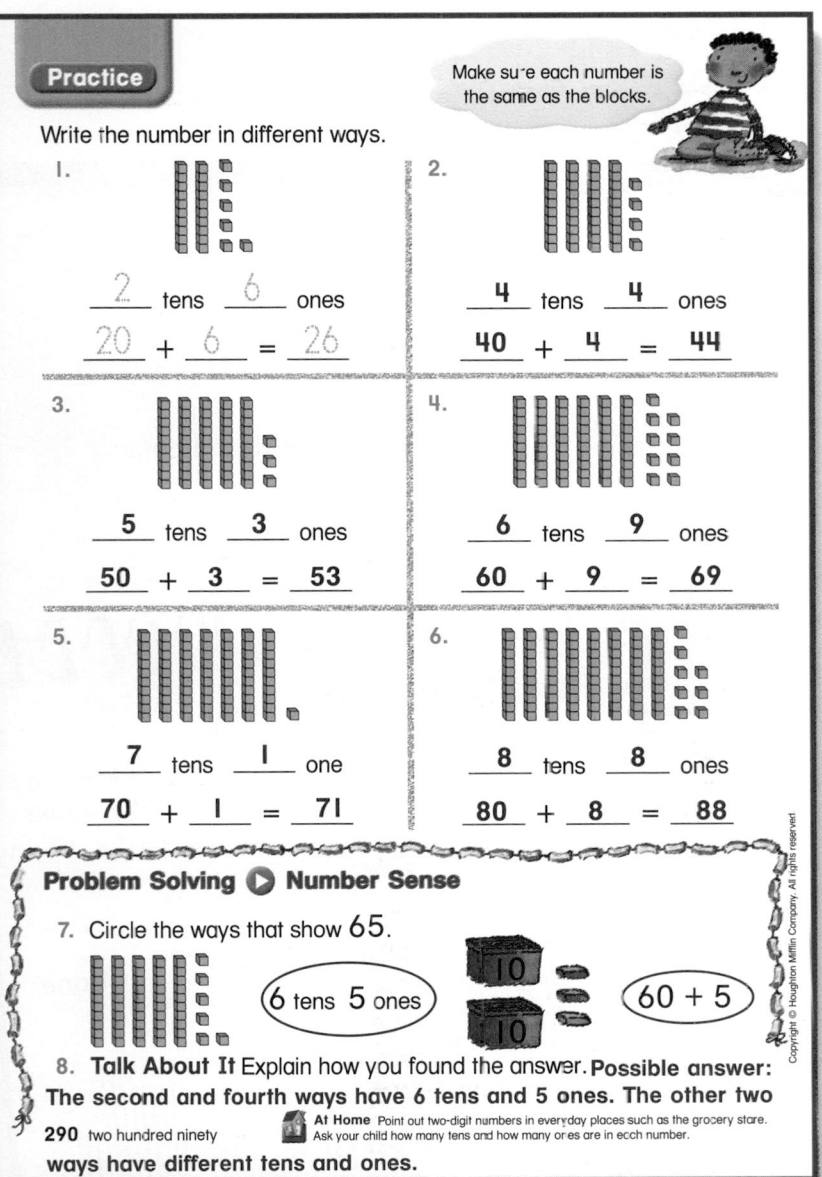

Make sure each number is the same as the blocks.

Write the number in different ways.

1.
___2___ tens ___6___ ones
___20___ + ___6___ = ___26___

2.
___4___ tens ___4___ ones
___40___ + ___4___ = ___44___

3.
___5___ tens ___3___ ones
___50___ + ___3___ = ___53___

4.
___6___ tens ___9___ ones
___60___ + ___9___ = ___69___

5.
___7___ tens ___I___ one
___70___ + ___I___ = ___71___

6.
___8___ tens ___8___ ones
___80___ + ___8___ = ___88___

Problem Solving ▶ Number Sense

7. Circle the ways that show 65.

(6 tens 5 ones)   (60 + 5)

8. **Talk About It** Explain how you found the answer. **Possible answer:**
The second and fourth ways have 6 tens and 5 ones. The other two
ways have different tens and ones.

290 two hundred ninety

At Home Point out two-digit numbers in everyday places such as the grocery store. Ask your child how many tens and how many ones are in each number.

Daily Test Prep

What number is 40 + 3?

7   43   70   403
○   ●   ○   ○

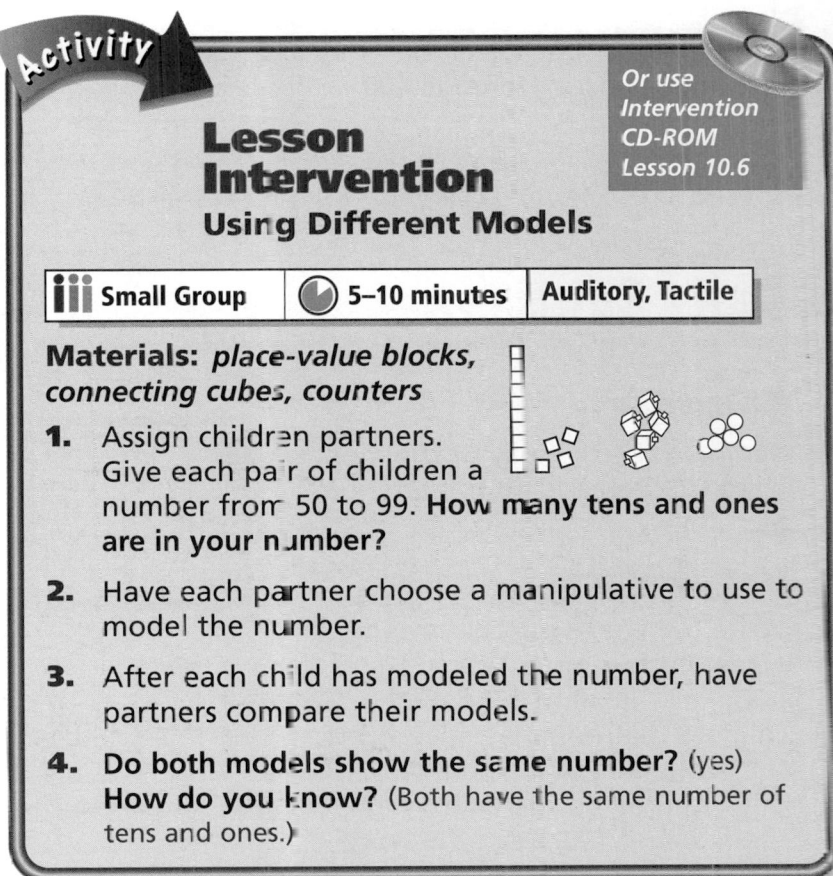

Activity

Or use Intervention CD-ROM Lesson 10.6

Lesson Intervention
Using Different Models

| 👤👤👤 Small Group | 🕐 5–10 minutes | Auditory, Tactile |

Materials: *place-value blocks, connecting cubes, counters*

1. Assign children partners. Give each pair of children a number from 50 to 99. **How many tens and ones are in your number?**

2. Have each partner choose a manipulative to use to model the number.

3. After each child has modeled the number, have partners compare their models.

4. **Do both models show the same number?** (yes) **How do you know?** (Both have the same number of tens and ones.)

---

3 Practice

Independent Practice

Children complete **Exercises 1–6** independently.

Problem Solving

After children complete **Exercise 7**, call on volunteers to share their answers. Use the Talk About It in **Exercise 8** to discuss how answers were found.

Common Error

Counting by Ones Rather Than Tens

Children may forget to count the tens blocks by tens. Have them point to each rod as they count aloud by tens.

4 Assess and Close

How can you show 2 tens 9 ones in two different ways? (20 + 9; 29)

How can you show 74 in two different ways? (7 tens 4 ones; 70 + 4)

Keeping a Journal

Draw a picture of tens and ones models. Then write the number shown in 3 different ways.

Numbers Through 100

PLANNING THE LESSON

MATHEMATICS OBJECTIVE
Identify numbers through 100.

Use Lesson Planner CD-ROM for Lesson 10.7.

Daily Routines

Calendar

Begin on the first day of the month. Have children add 10 to each number—11, 12, 13, and so on.

Sunday	Monday	Tuesday	Wednesday	Thursday	Friday	Saturday
			1	2	3	4
5	6	7	8	9	10	11
12	13	14	15	16	17	18
19	20	21	22	23	24	25
26	27	28	29	30	31	

Vocabulary

Write the words *one*, *two*, and *three* on the board next to the numerals 1, 2, and 3. Remind children that numbers have words that describe them. Then write **one hundred** on the board next to the numeral 100. Read the word aloud and explain that 100 is the number after 99.

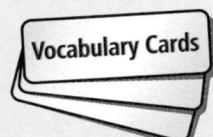
Vocabulary Cards

Meeting North Carolina's Standards

1.01 Develop number sense for whole numbers through 99.

• Connect the model, number word, and number using a variety of representations.

Lesson Transparency **10.7**

Problem of the Day
There are three piles of 10 books. There are six more piles of 10 books. How many books are there in all? (90)

Quick Review
Write the number.

7 tens 3 ones ____ (73)

4 tens 9 ones ____ (49)

1 ten 1 one ____ (11)

Lesson Quiz
1. How many tens? (5)
2. How many ones? (3)
3. How many tens are there in one hundred? (10)

LEVELED PRACTICE

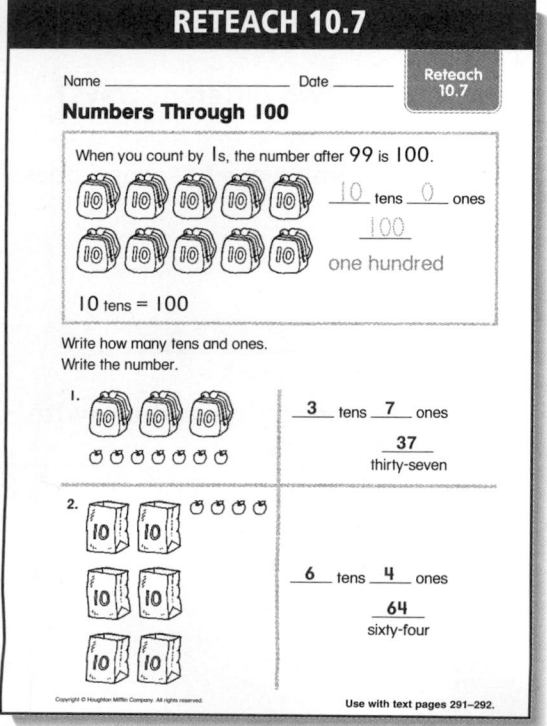

RETEACH 10.7

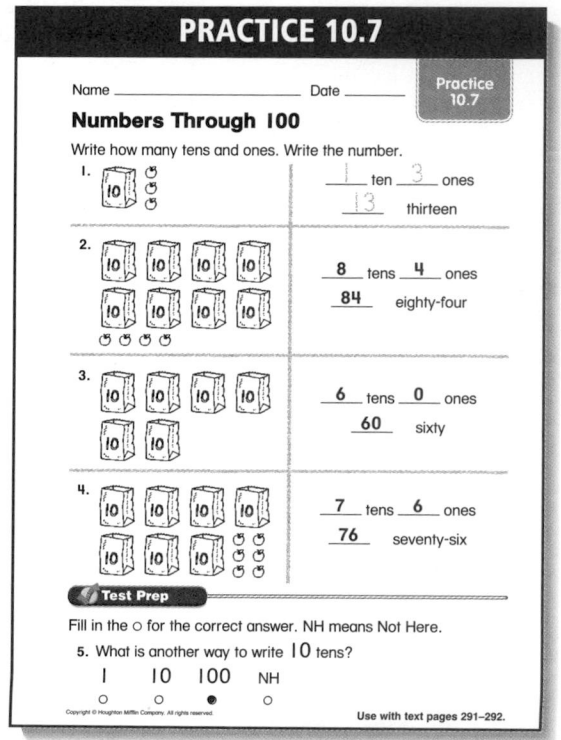

PRACTICE 10.7

ENRICHMENT 10.7

Practice Workbook Page 69

Reaching All Learners

Differentiated Instruction

English Learners

Use Worksheet 10.7 to teach children the meaning of the word *after*. Children will need to understand this word in order to understand that 100 is the number after 99.

Special Needs
VISUAL, TACTILE

Material: *hundred chart (LT 7)*

- Cut, tape, and copy a hundred chart as shown.
- Have the child circle the tens, then color each row a different color.

Early Finishers
VISUAL, TACTILE

Materials: *paper clips, paper cups*

- Give children paper cups of 30, 40, 50, 60, or 70 paper clips.
- Have them count the paper clips in their cups. Have them write the number.
- Then children show 100 clips by finding a partner and combining the clips.

TECHNOLOGY

Spiral Review

To reinforce skills on lessons taught earlier, create **customized** spiral review worksheets using the *Ways to Assess* CD-ROM.

Lesson Planner

Use the **Lesson Planner CD-ROM** to see how lesson objectives for this chapter are correlated to standards.

eBook

An electronic version of this lesson can be found in **eMathBook**, featuring an animated teaching model.

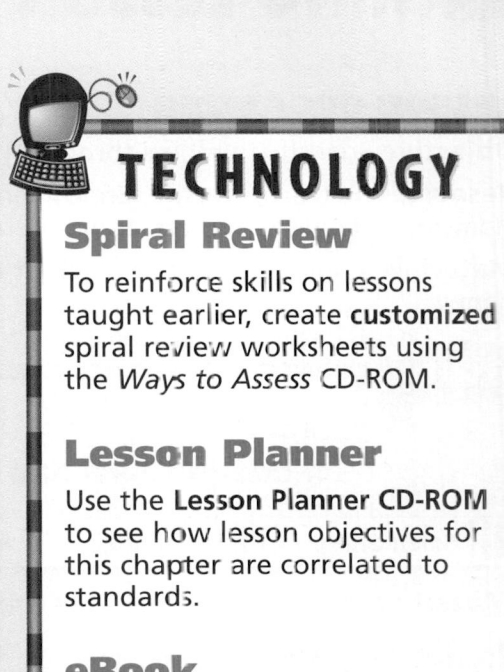

Houghton Mifflin **Math**

e **MathBook**

Social Studies Connection

Talk about the impact of recycling products made of paper, plastics, and glass. Ask children to bring in small empty cardboard boxes. Have children arrange the boxes in tens and ones until you have 10 tens. Then recycle the boxes.

MATH CENTER

Vocabulary Activity

This vocabulary-building activity helps children understand and remember new words. Encourage children to use the words in math discussion.

PROBLEM SOLVING 10.7

Name _____ Date _____ | Problem Solving 10.7

Numbers Through 100

Read and solve.

Draw or write to explain.

1. Ricardo has 10 boxes. Each box holds 10 model cars. How many model cars does Ricardo have?

   __100__ cars

2. Mattie packed 7 boxes for the clothing drive. There are 10 shirts in each box. How many shirts did she pack?

   __70__ shirts

3. Mr. Wu loaded 8 boxes in his truck. Each box held 10 cans of soup. How many cans of soup did he load?

   __80__ cans of soup

4. Ms. Ritz arranged 6 vases of flowers. There are 10 flowers in each vase. How many flowers did she have?

   __60__ flowers

Copyright © Houghton Mifflin Company. All rights reserved.

Use with text pages 291–292.

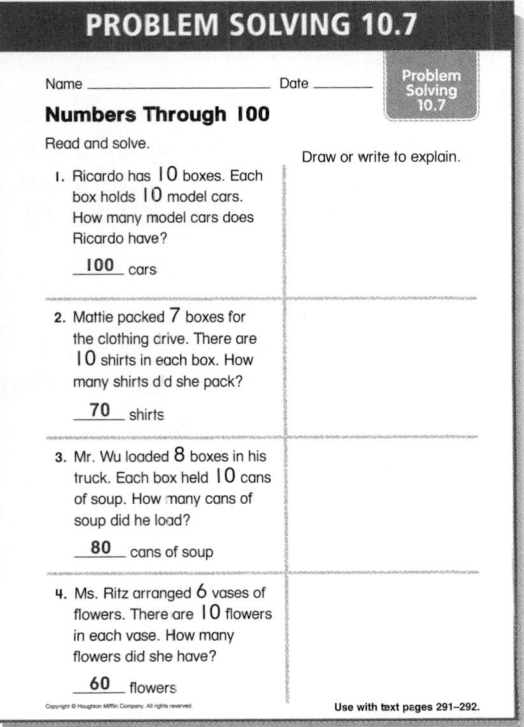

HOMEWORK 10.7

Name _____ Date _____ | Homework 10.7

Numbers Through 100

When you count by ones, the number after 99 is 100.

10 tens = 100

100 one hundred

Write how many tens and ones. Write the number.

1. __8__ tens __2__ ones
   __82__
   eighty-two

2. __2__ tens __9__ ones
   __29__
   twenty-nine

3. __9__ tens __9__ ones
   __99__
   ninety-nine

4. 10 friends pick up cans at the beach. Each friend picks up 10 cans. How many cans do they have in all?

   __100__ cans

   Draw or write to explain.

Copyright © Houghton Mifflin Company. All rights reserved.

Use with text pages 291–292.

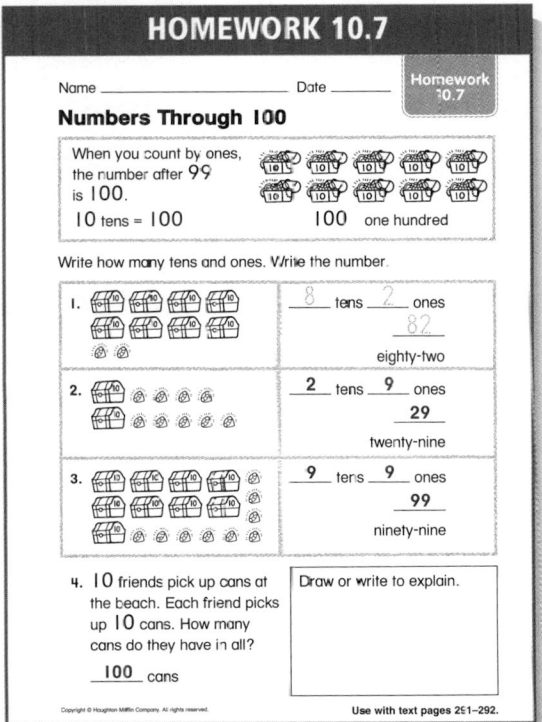

ENGLISH LEARNERS 10.7

Name _____ Date _____ | English Learners 10.7

Numbers Through 100

Jill Sam José Marta

Sam is **after** Jill. José is **after** Sam. Marta is **after** José.

Circle the animal after the cat.   Circle the animal after the dog.

1.   2.

Circle the animal after the cow.   Circle the animal after the hen.

3.   4.

To the Teacher: Use the illustration and sentences at the top of the page to demonstrate the meaning of the word *after*. Then have children circle the correct pictures.

Copyright © Houghton Mifflin Company. All rights reserved.

Use with text pages 291–292.

TEACHING LESSON 10.7

LESSON ORGANIZER

Objective Identify numbers through 100.

Resources Reteach, Practice, Enrichment, Problem Solving, Homework, English Learners, Transparencies, Math Center

Materials Cubes, tens and ones chart (LT 6), Workmat 6, penny

Warm-Up Activity
Modeling Tens and Ones

iii Small Group	⏱ 5 minutes	Auditory, Visual

Materials: *cubes, tens and ones chart*

1. Show 5 trains of 10 cubes and 4 single cubes. **How many tens are there?** (5 tens) **How many ones are there?** (4 ones)

2. Show a tens and ones chart. **How do you write the value of tens?** (Write 5 in the tens place.) **How do you write the value of ones?** (Write 4 in the ones place.)

3. Discuss the meaning of a 5 in the tens place and a 4 in the ones place. **Write the number.** (Children write 54.)

4. Repeat with other numbers.

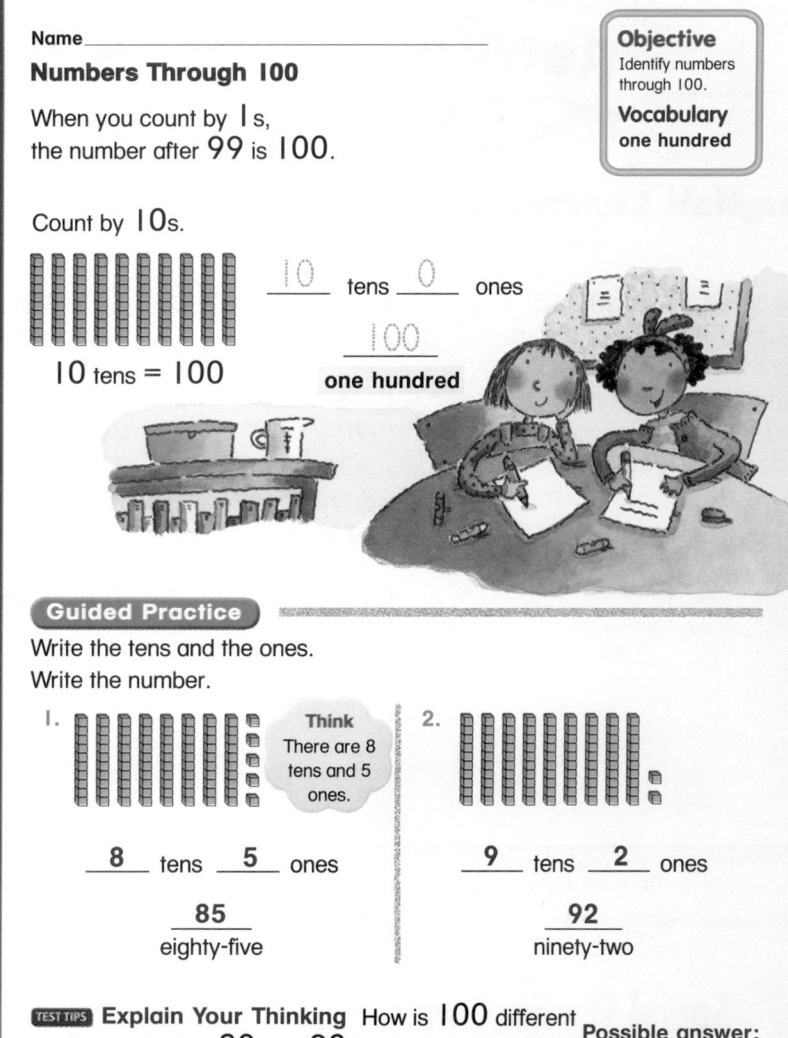

Name_____

Numbers Through 100

Objective Identify numbers through 100.

Vocabulary one hundred

When you count by 1s, the number after 99 is 100.

Count by 10s.

10 tens = 100

10 tens 0 ones

100 one hundred

Guided Practice

Write the tens and the ones.
Write the number.

1. Think There are 8 tens and 5 ones.

___8___ tens ___5___ ones

___85___ eighty-five

2. ___9___ tens ___2___ ones

___92___ ninety-two

TEST TIPS **Explain Your Thinking** How is 100 different from numbers like 80 and 90? **Possible answer: 100 is a three-digit number.**

Chapter 10 Lesson 7

two hundred ninety-one **291**

---

1 Introduce
Count by Tens to 100

iiii Whole Group	⏱ 10–15 minutes	Visual, Auditory

1. Draw 10 circles on the board and label each circle 10.

2. **Let's count by tens.** Point to each circle as you count aloud to 100.

3. Write 90 on the board. Circle the 9 and ask: **How many tens are in 90?** (9 tens) Circle the 0 and ask: **How many ones are in 90?** (0 ones)

4. Write 100 on the board. Circle the first 2 digits and ask: **How many tens are in 100?** (10 tens) Circle the 0 and ask: **How many ones are in 100?** (0 ones) Write 10 tens 0 ones and 100 next to the circles.

2 Develop

Guided Learning

Teaching Example Introduce the objective and vocabulary to the children. Guide them through the example to show that 10 groups of 10 are equal to 100 and that 100 has 10 tens 0 ones.

Guided Practice

Have children complete **Exercises 1–2** as you observe. Give children the opportunity to answer the Explain Your Thinking question. Then discuss their responses with the class.

Practice

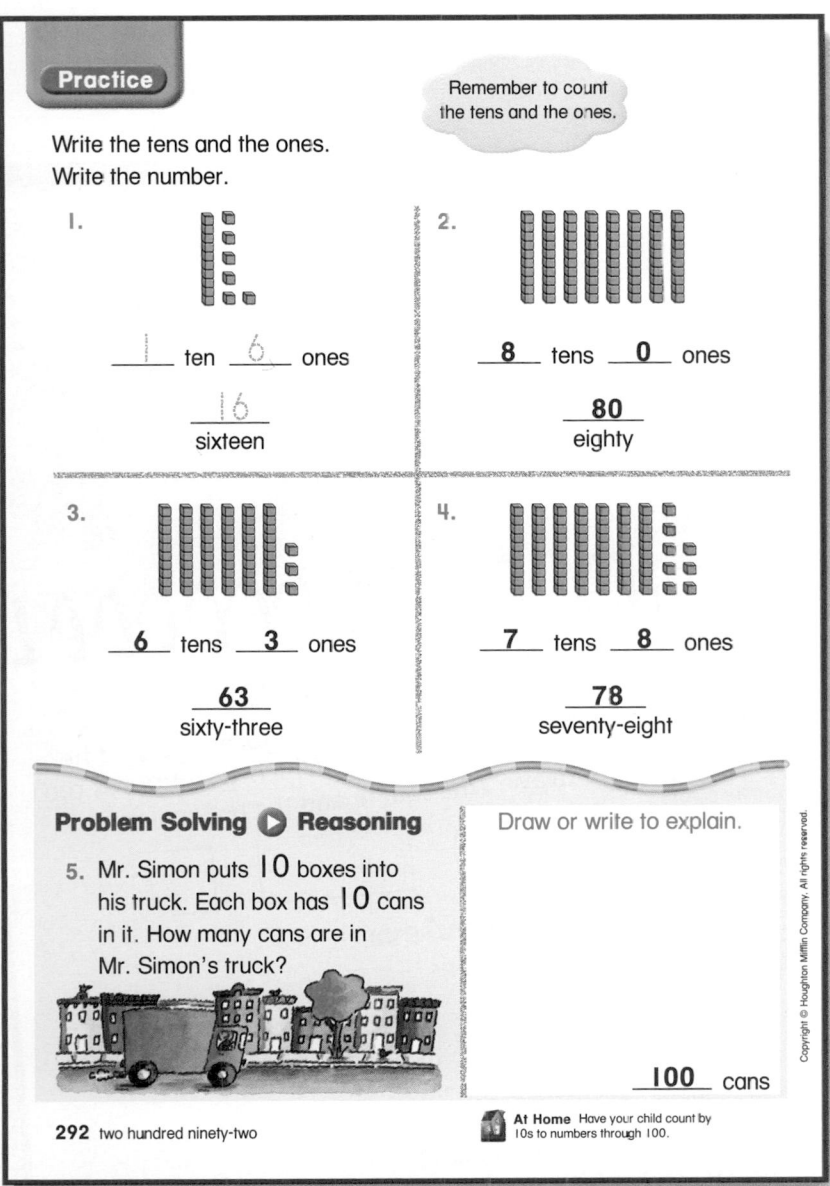

Remember to count the tens and the ones.

Write the tens and the ones.
Write the number.

1.

_1_ ten _6_ ones

_16_
sixteen

2.

_8_ tens _0_ ones

_80_
eighty

3.

_6_ tens _3_ ones

_63_
sixty-three

4.

_7_ tens _8_ ones

_78_
seventy-eight

Problem Solving ▶ Reasoning

5. Mr. Simon puts 10 boxes into his truck. Each box has 10 cans in it. How many cans are in Mr. Simon's truck?

Draw or write to explain.

_100_ cans

At Home Have your child count by 10s to numbers through 100.

292 two hundred ninety-two

Which shape is a cube?

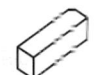
○　　●　　○　　○

Activity

Lesson Intervention

Or use Intervention CD-ROM Lesson 10.7

Identify Tens and Ones on a Hundred Chart

| 👤👤👤 Small Group | 🕐 5–10 minutes | Visual, Auditory |

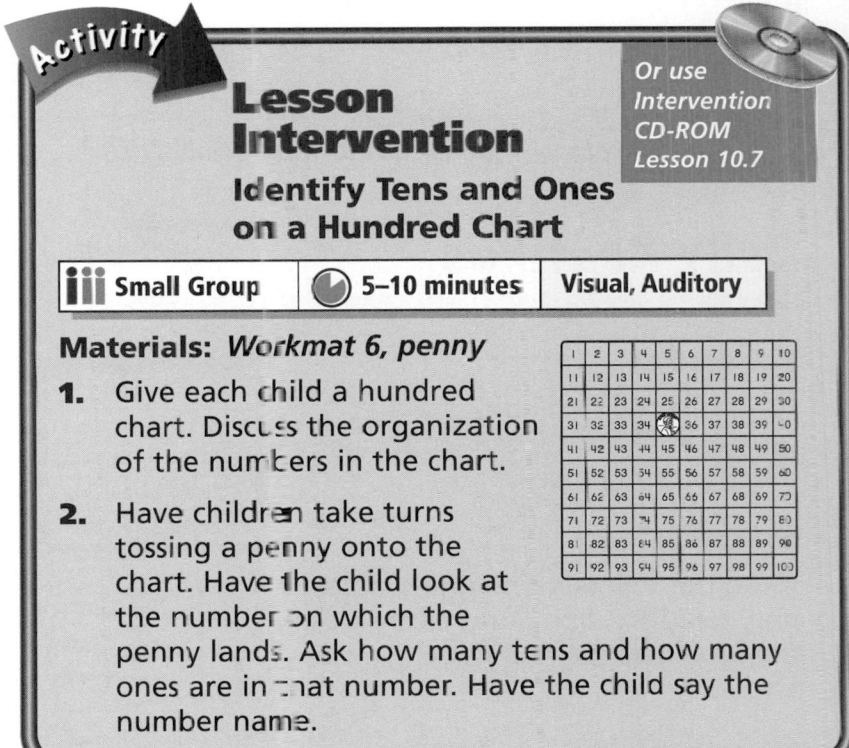

Materials: *Workmat 6, penny*

1. Give each child a hundred chart. Discuss the organization of the numbers in the chart.

2. Have children take turns tossing a penny onto the chart. Have the child look at the number on which the penny lands. Ask how many tens and how many ones are in that number. Have the child say the number name.

---

3 Practice

Independent Practice

Children complete **Exercises 1–4** independently.

Problem Solving

After children complete **Exercise 5**, call on volunteers to share their solutions.

Common Error

Not Recording Ones

Children may forget to record a 0 in the space provided for ones. Remind them that when there are no ones, they need to write a 0 on the line. In the case of 100, they would write two zeroes.

4 Assess and Close

How many tens in the number 47? (4 tens) **How many ones?** (7 ones) **What number has 10 tens 0 ones?** (100)

 ### Keeping a Journal

Write a list of things you own of which you have one hundred. For example: beads, baseball cards, or stickers.

Problem Solving: Act It Out With Models

PLANNING THE LESSON

MATHEMATICS OBJECTIVE
Use models and place value to solve problems.

Use Lesson Planner CD-ROM for Lesson 10.8.

Meeting North Carolina's Standards
1.01 Develop number sense for whole numbers through 99.

• Connect the model, number word, and number using a variety of representations.

Also 1.04

Daily Routines

Calendar
Have children find numbers that can be added or subtracted to find a sum or difference of 10.

Sunday	Monday	Tuesday	Wednesday	Thursday	Friday	Saturday
				1	2	3	4
5	6	7	8	9	10	11
12	13	14	15	16	17	18
19	20	21	22	23	24	25
26	27	28	29	30	31	

Vocabulary
Write the following number names: **one, ten, fifty, one hundred**. Ask children to write the numbers.

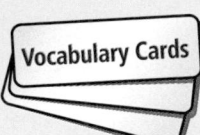
Vocabulary Cards

Lesson Transparency 10.8

Problem of the Day
José drew two of these figures. He said he drew 8 corners in all. Which two figures did he draw? (the square and the rectangle)

Quick Review
How many tens?

53 (5 tens)

66 (6 tens)

41 (4 tens)

Lesson Quiz
1. Channa puts 72 fish in fish bowls. Each bowl holds 10 fish. How many bowls does he use? (8 bowls)

LEVELED PRACTICE

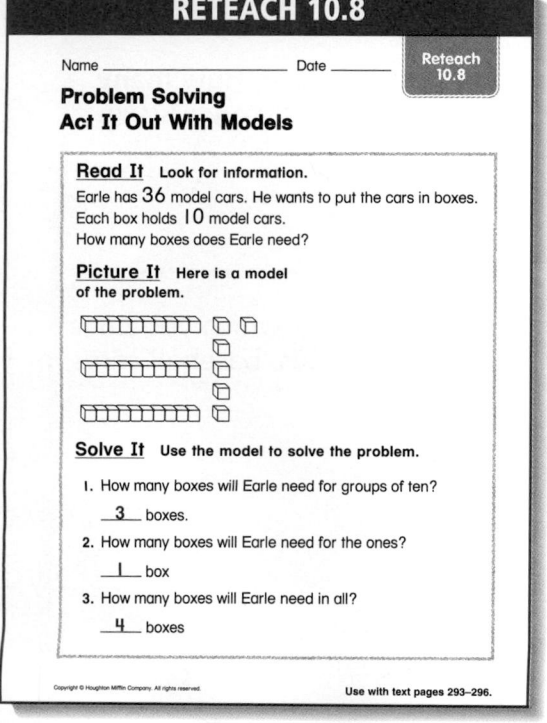

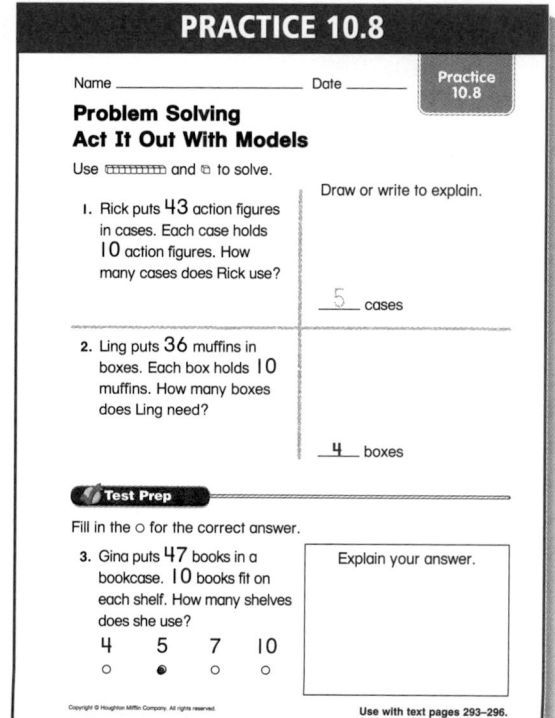

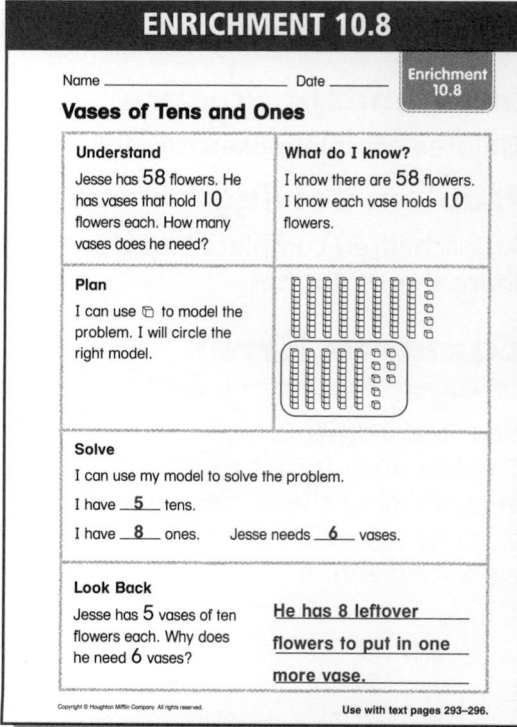

Practice Workbook Page 70

Reaching All Learners

Differentiated Instruction

English Learners

In order to solve some problems involving groups of tens, children will have to understand the meaning of the word *row*. Use Worksheet 10.8 to develop children's understanding of this word.

Inclusion
VISUAL, TACTILE

Materials: *counters*

- Present a problem for the child to act out. *25 children will go to the zoo in school vans. Each van holds 10 children. How many vans will go to the zoo?*

- Draw a van and have the child fill it with 10 counters. Repeat for another 10. Focus on the remaining 5 counters. Guide the child to see that a third van is needed.

Gifted and Talented
AUDITORY

- Present children with this problem:

  Jake is going to read a book with 62 pages. If he starts the book today and reads 10 pages every day, what day of the week will it be when he finishes the book?

- Have children compare their answers.

TECHNOLOGY

Spiral Review

Help students remember skills they learned earlier by creating **customized** spiral review worksheets using the *Ways to Assess* CD-ROM.

Education Place

Visit **Data Place** at **eduplace.com/dataplace/** to take a survey and see graphs of the results.

Intervention

Use the *Ways to Success* intervention software to support students who need more help in understanding the concepts and skills taught in this chapter.

Science Connection

Show children flower seeds. Ask children how many pots you would need in order to plant 33 seeds if you put 10 seeds in each pot. Model the problem with seeds and teach children how to care for the seeds and flowers.

MATH CENTER

Number of the Week Activity

Display the Number of the Week to motivate children to use their problem-solving skills. The exercises cover topics across all math strands.

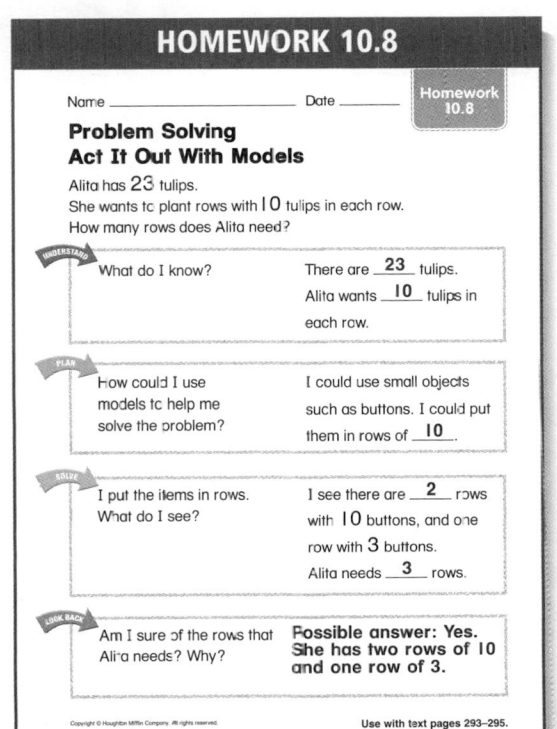

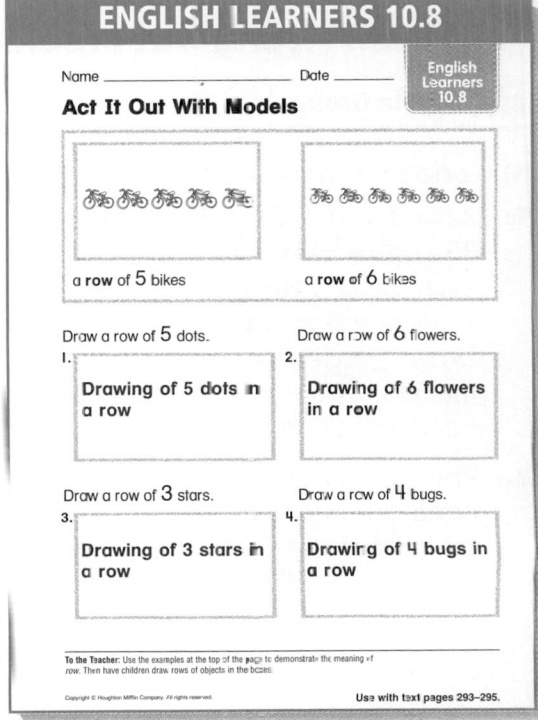

Homework Workbook Page 70

TEACHING LESSON 10.8

LESSON ORGANIZER

Objective Use models and place value to solve problems.

Resources Reteach, Practice, Enrichment, Problem Solving, Homework, English Learners, Transparencies, Math Center

Materials Counters, tens and ones chart (LT6), blank transparency, paper clips

Activity

Warm-Up Activity
Making Groups of Ten

👫👫👫 Small Group	🕐 5 minutes	Auditory, Visual

Materials: *counters, LT6*

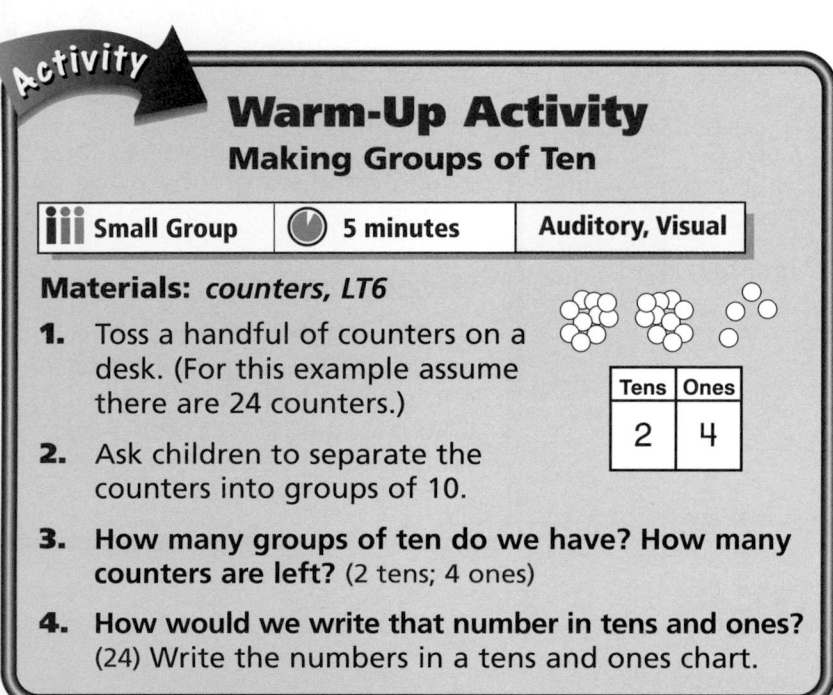

Tens	Ones
2	4

1. **Toss a handful of counters on a desk.** (For this example assume there are 24 counters.)

2. **Ask children to separate the counters into groups of 10.**

3. **How many groups of ten do we have? How many counters are left?** (2 tens; 4 ones)

4. **How would we write that number in tens and ones?** (24) Write the numbers in a tens and ones chart.

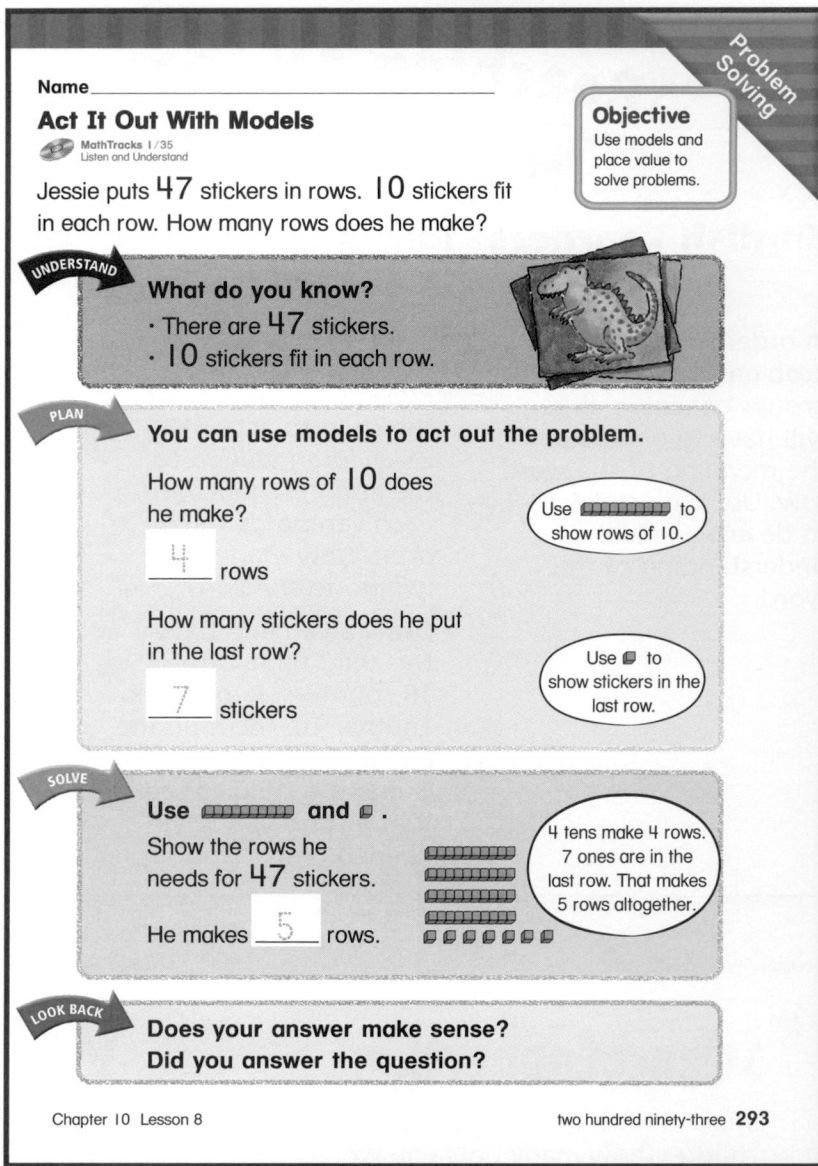

Name_____

Act It Out With Models

MathTracks 1/35
Listen and Understand

Objective Use models and place value to solve problems.

Jessie puts 47 stickers in rows. 10 stickers fit in each row. How many rows does he make?

UNDERSTAND

What do you know?
- There are 47 stickers.
- 10 stickers fit in each row.

PLAN

You can use models to act out the problem.

How many rows of 10 does he make?

4 rows

Use ▭▭▭ to show rows of 10.

How many stickers does he put in the last row?

7 stickers

Use ▫ to show stickers in the last row.

SOLVE

Use ▭▭▭ and ▫.
Show the rows he needs for 47 stickers.

He makes 5 rows.

4 tens make 4 rows. 7 ones are in the last row. That makes 5 rows altogether.

LOOK BACK

Does your answer make sense? Did you answer the question?

Chapter 10 Lesson 8   two hundred ninety-three **293**

---

1 Introduce

Model Acting Out Problems with Models

👫👫👫👫 Whole Group	🕐 10–15 minutes	Visual, Auditory

Materials: *counters, blank transparency*

1. *Act out a problem.* Present the problem: **Scott has 35 apples he wants to put in baskets. 10 apples fit in each basket. How many baskets will he need?** After you present the problem, act out the problem with counters. Draw 3 circles for baskets. Show children that Scott can make 3 groups of ten apples and explain that Scott will need 3 baskets for those apples.

2. Point out that there will be 5 apples left over, so he will need one more basket for those 5 apples. Draw another basket for the 5 left over apples. **How many baskets are there in all?** (4 baskets)

2 Develop

Guided Learning

Teaching Example Introduce the objective to the children. Then read the problem aloud.

UNDERSTAND What do you know? (There are 47 stickers in rows. 10 stickers fit in each row.)

PLAN How many rows of ten should you show? (4 rows) **Why?** (because there are 4 tens in 47) **How many ones blocks should you show in the last row?** (7)

SOLVE 4 tens make 4 rows. There are 7 ones in the last row. That makes 5 rows altogether. What is the answer to the question? (He needs to make 5 rows.)

LOOK BACK Does your answer make sense? (yes) **Did you answer the question?** (yes)

Guided Practice

Have children complete **Exercises 1–2** on page 294 as you observe. Remind students to fill up rows of 10 first. Then use leftovers to put in the last row.

Guided Practice

Use ▭▭▭▭▭ and ▯ to solve.

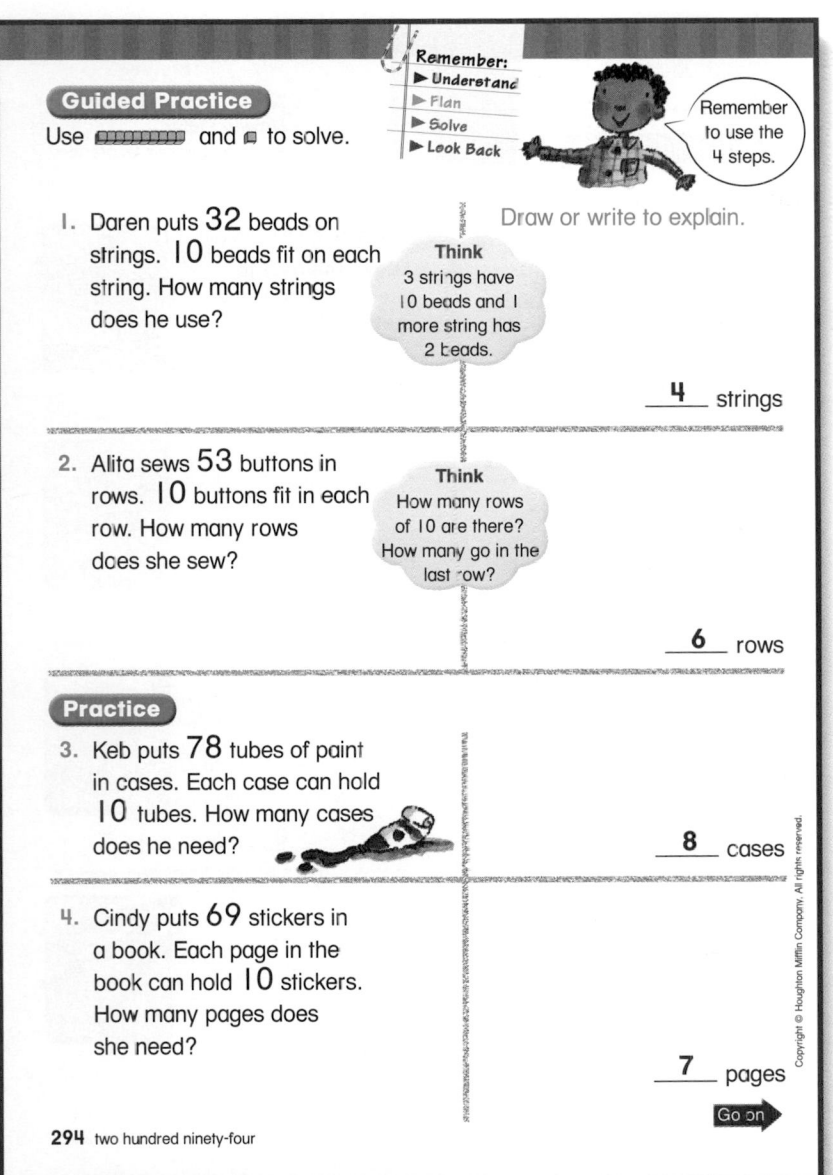

Draw or write to explain.

1. Daren puts 32 beads on strings. 10 beads fit on each string. How many strings does he use?

Think
3 strings have 10 beads and 1 more string has 2 beads.

____4____ strings

2. Alita sews 53 buttons in rows. 10 buttons fit in each row. How many rows does she sew?

Think
How many rows of 10 are there? How many go in the last row?

____6____ rows

Practice

3. Keb puts 78 tubes of paint in cases. Each case can hold 10 tubes. How many cases does he need?

____8____ cases

4. Cindy puts 69 stickers in a book. Each page in the book can hold 10 stickers. How many pages does she need?

____7____ pages

Go on ▸

294 two hundred ninety-four

Play "Turn Two-Digits"

Materials: number cards 0–9 (LT 14); one set for each pair

• Have children mix up cards and deal 2 cards facedown to each child.

• Children turn cards face up and arrange in any order to make a two-digit number.

• Children compare tens and the child with the greater number of tens gets a point.

• Replace cards, mix up, and repeat.

• Continue until one child gets 10 points.

Variation: Child with least number of tens gets the point.

 **Practice**

Independent Practice

Children complete **Exercises 3–4** on page 294 independently.

Lesson continues ➔

Daily Test Prep

Hong-Ju had 9 pages to read in a book. He read 4 pages. How many more pages does he have to read?

3   4   5   6
○   ○   ●   ○

Activity

Lesson Intervention

Or use Intervention CD-ROM Lesson 10.8

Modeling a Problem

| i Individual | ⏱ 5 minutes | Auditory, Tactile |

Materials: *paper clips*

1. Give each child 24 paper clips. Tell them this problem. **Jill has to arrange 24 chairs for her class. 10 chairs fit in each row. How many rows does she need to make?**

2. **How many chairs fit in 1 row?** (10 chairs) **How can we show that?** (Put 10 paper clips in a row.) **Is that enough chairs?** (no) **What should we do?** (Make another row of 10.)

3. **How many paper clips are in 2 rows of ten?** (20) **How many total chairs did Jill need?** (24) **What should we do now?** (Put 4 more paper clips in another row.) **How many rows is that altogether?** (3 rows) **How many rows of chairs did Jill need to make?** (3 rows)

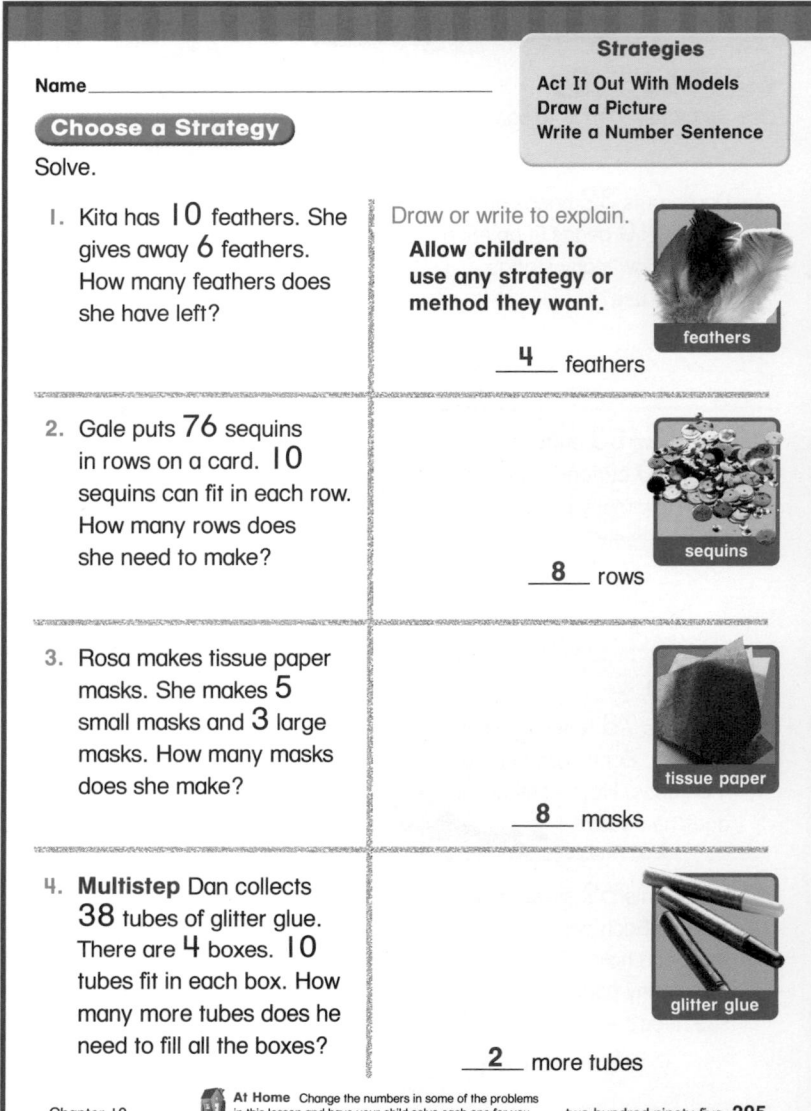

Name _____

Choose a Strategy

Strategies
Act It Out With Models
Draw a Picture
Write a Number Sentence

Solve.

1. Kita has 10 feathers. She gives away 6 feathers. How many feathers does she have left?

   Draw or write to explain.
   Allow children to use any strategy or method they want.

   __4__ feathers

   feathers

2. Gale puts 76 sequins in rows on a card. 10 sequins can fit in each row. How many rows does she need to make?

   __8__ rows

   sequins

3. Rosa makes tissue paper masks. She makes 5 small masks and 3 large masks. How many masks does she make?

   __8__ masks

   tissue paper

4. **Multistep** Dan collects 38 tubes of glitter glue. There are 4 boxes. 10 tubes fit in each box. How many more tubes does he need to fill all the boxes?

   __2__ more tubes

   glitter glue

Chapter 10

At Home Change the numbers in some of the problems in this lesson and have your child solve each one for you.

two hundred ninety-five **295**

3 Practice

Mixed Strategy Practice

Read the problem-solving strategies with children. Make sure children can read and comprehend the problems in Exercises 1–4 on page 295. If necessary, pair more proficient readers with less proficient readers. Encourage them to discuss the problems before solving.

Common Error

Forgetting to Count the Last Group

Children may forget to count the group that does not have ten objects. Remind them to count all the groups to find the answer.

4 Assess and Close

Mr. Garcia made 45 tacos for a party. 10 tacos fit on a plate. How many plates will Mr. Garcia need? (5 plates)

 **Keeping a Journal**

Write a problem about putting 43 objects in boxes. Each box can hold 10 objects. Draw a picture to solve the problem. Write the answer.

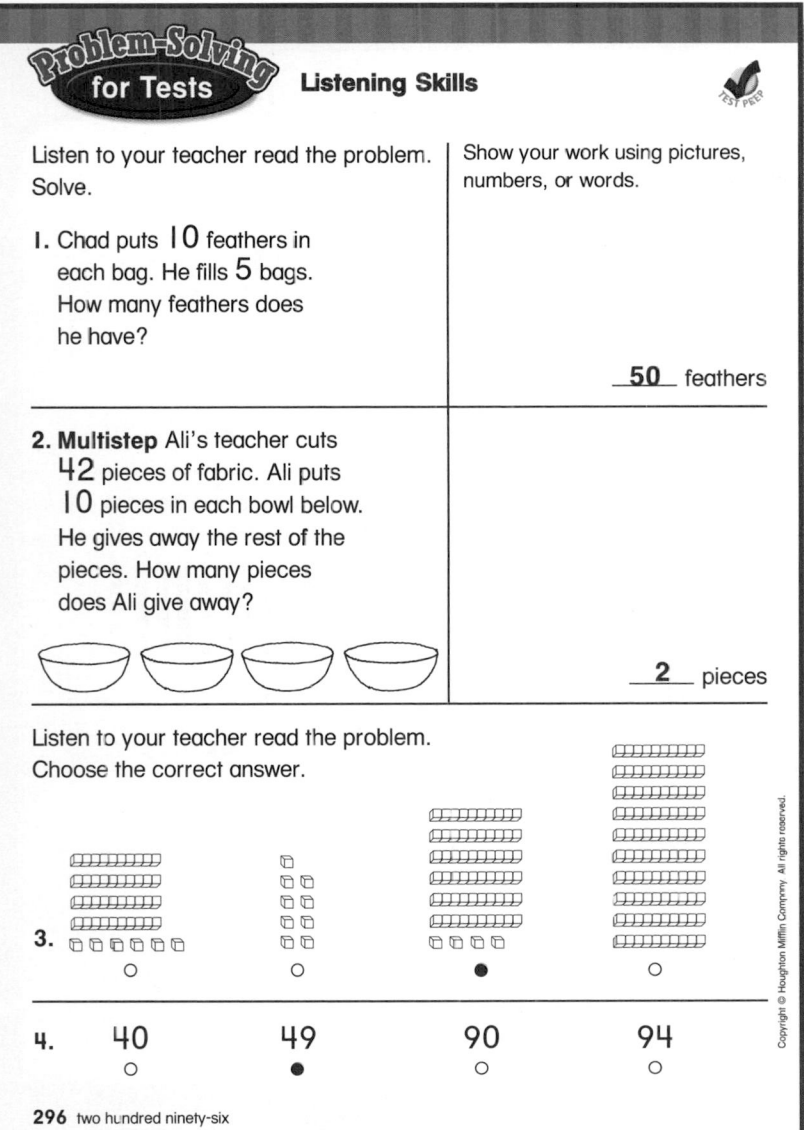

Problem-Solving for Tests   Listening Skills

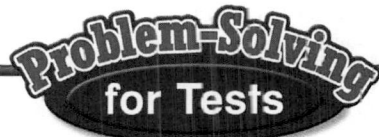

Listen to your teacher read the problem. Solve.

Show your work using pictures, numbers, or words.

1. Chad puts 10 feathers in each bag. He fills 5 bags. How many feathers does he have?

___50___ feathers

2. **Multistep** Ali's teacher cuts 42 pieces of fabric. Ali puts 10 pieces in each bowl below. He gives away the rest of the pieces. How many pieces does Ali give away?

___2___ pieces

Listen to your teacher read the problem. Choose the correct answer.

3. ○   ○   ●   ○

4.   40   49   90   94
     ○   ●   ○   ○

Problem-Solving for Tests

Listening Skills

This page provides children practice with the oral problem-solving format used in some standardized test items.

You may want to read each item only once to mimic the style of oral tests.

Use with Items 1 and 2

Listening Strategy: Read the problem silently as the teacher reads it aloud.

- *This problem is on the page. Read it to yourself while I read it aloud.*

- *Listen to the whole problem. Wait until I finish before you begin to write.*

Use with Item 3

Listening Strategy: Listen to the problem. Listen carefully for important facts and numbers.

- *Look at the pictures and listen as I read the problem.*

  Faris puts paint jars on a shelf. He puts the jars in rows of 10. He makes 6 full rows. Then he makes a row of 4. Which model shows how Faris puts away the paint jars?

- *See which model matches the words and numbers in the problem. Then mark your answer.*

Use with Item 4

Listening Strategy: Listen for important facts and numbers.

- *Listen for what the problem asks you to do.*

  Jane solves a problem and ends up with 4 tens and 9 ones blocks. Which number shows the answer to Jane's problem?

- *Use the information you heard to solve the problem.*

Quick Check

Have children complete the Quick Check exercises independently to assess their understanding of the concepts and skills taught in **Lessons 5–8.**

Item	Lesson	Error Analysis	Intervention
1, 2	10.5	Children may write the number of ones in the tens place.	Reteach Resource 10.5 *Ways to Success* 10.5
3	10.6	Children may forget to count the tens blocks by tens.	Reteach Resource 10.6 *Ways to Success* 10.6
4	10.7	Children may forget to record the ones.	Reteach Resource 10.7 *Ways to Success* 10.7
5	10.8	Children may forget to count the group that does not have ten objects.	Reteach Resource 10.8 *Ways to Success* 10.8

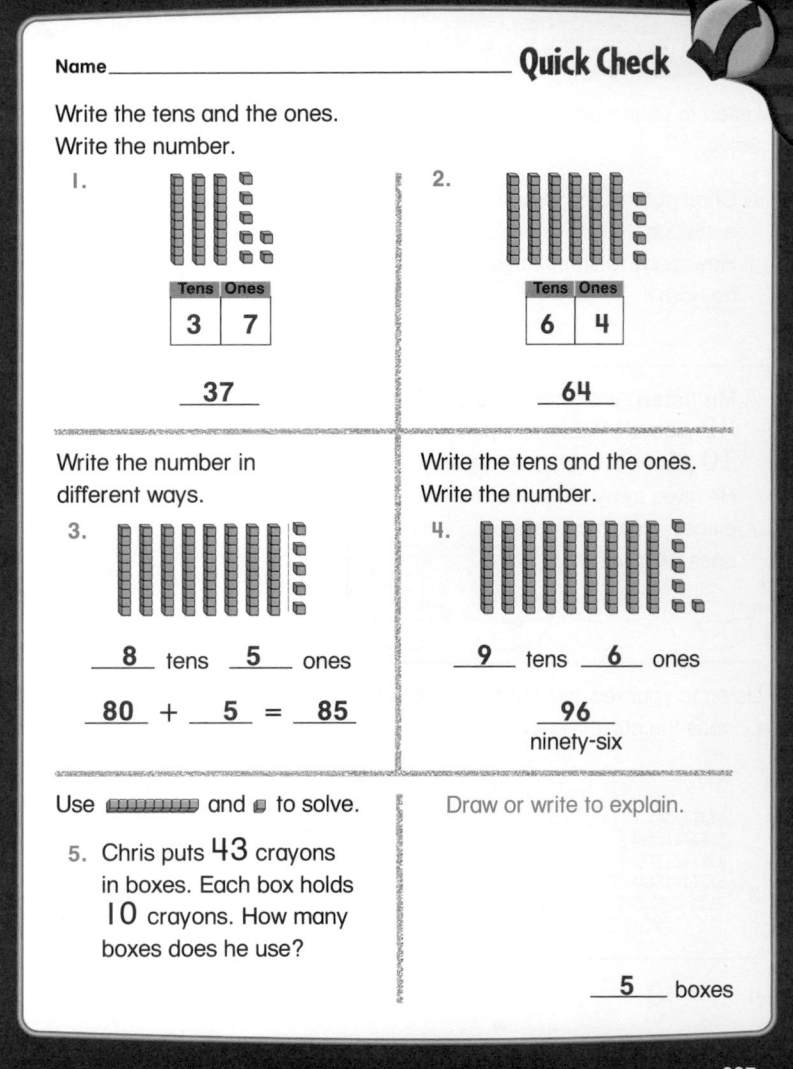

Name _____   **Quick Check**

Write the tens and the ones.
Write the number.

1.

Tens	Ones
3	7

___37___

2.

Tens	Ones
6	4

___64___

Write the number in different ways.

3.

___8___ tens ___5___ ones

___80___ + ___5___ = ___85___

Write the tens and the ones.
Write the number.

4.

___9___ tens ___6___ ones

___96___
ninety-six

Use ▭▭▭ and ▪ to solve.

5. Chris puts 43 crayons in boxes. Each box holds 10 crayons. How many boxes does he use?

Draw or write to explain.

___5___ boxes

Chapter 10 Lesson 8   two hundred ninety-seven **297**

Key Topic Review

Use shapes to copy the pattern.
Circle the one that comes next.

Math Challenge

Seeing Stars

There are objects in nature
that are star shaped.

This star is found in the ocean. ___sea star___

Five seeds make the star in
this fruit that grows on a tree. ___apple___

sea star   star fruit

blueberry   apple

298 two hundred ninety-eight

Key Topic Review

This assessment provides a review of skills and concepts taught n Chapter 8.

Check to make sure that children:

• recognize p ane shapes

• can identify shape, color, and size patterns

• can extend a pattern

Math Challenge

Seeing Stars

Discuss with children that we see many shapes in nature. Have children identify the 4 objects with stars. **Have you ever seen a sea star? Where? What do you know about a sea star?** Explain that the star fruit is found in some grocery stores. **Have you ever eaten one? Do you know where the star is n an apple?** If possible have an apple already cut to show that the seeds form a star. **Have you seen any other star shapes in nature?** Read the sentences and have children fill in the blanks.

 **Chapter Review/Test**

Purpose: This test provides an informal assessment of the Chapter 10 objectives.

Chapter 10 Test Items 1–15

To assign a numerical grade for this Chapter Test, use 6 points for each test item.

Check Understanding

Use children's work on word problems to informally assess progress on chapter content.

Customizing Your Instruction

For children who have not yet mastered these objectives, you can use the reteaching resources listed in the chart below.

 Assessment Options

A summary test for this chapter is also provided in the Unit Resource Folder.

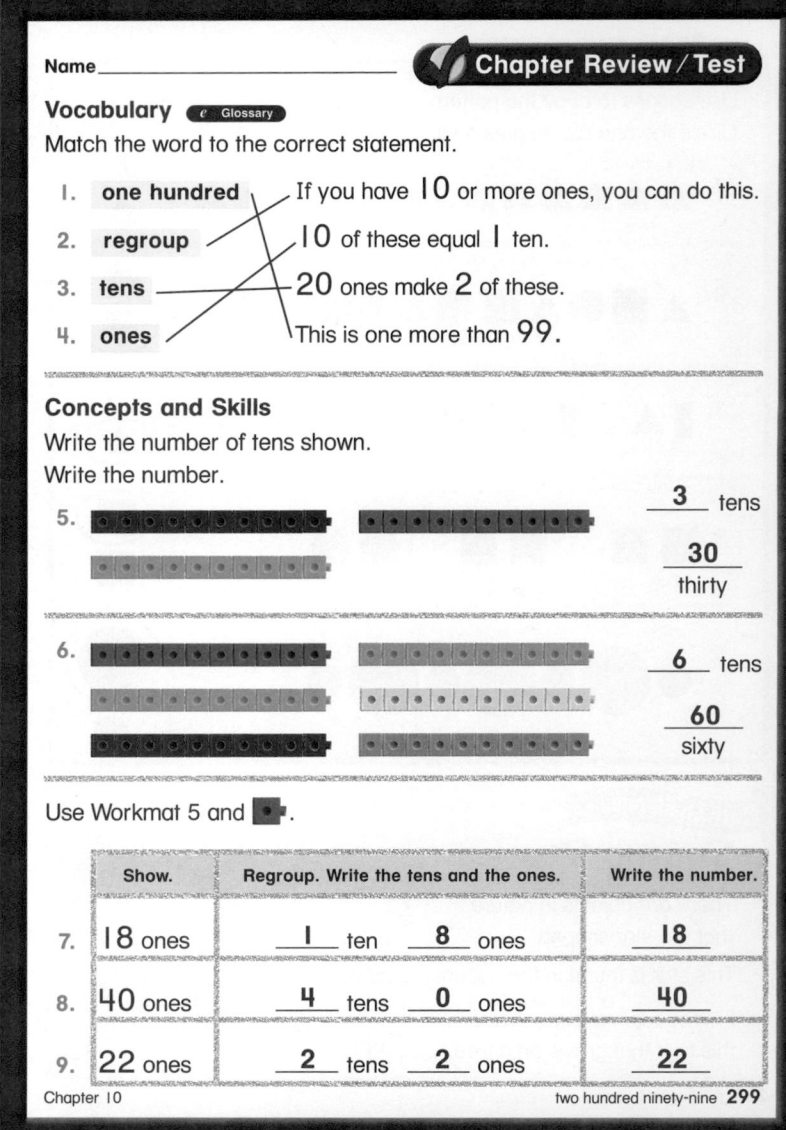

Name _____

Chapter Review/Test

Vocabulary *e Glossary*

Match the word to the correct statement.

1. **one hundred** — If you have 10 or more ones, you can do this.
2. **regroup** — 10 of these equal 1 ten.
3. **tens** — 20 ones make 2 of these.
4. **ones** — This is one more than 99.

Concepts and Skills

Write the number of tens shown.
Write the number.

5. ___3___ tens
   ___30___ thirty

6. ___6___ tens
   ___60___ sixty

Use Workmat 5 and ▪.

	Show.	Regroup. Write the tens and the ones.	Write the number.
7.	18 ones	__1__ ten __8__ ones	__18__
8.	40 ones	__4__ tens __0__ ones	__40__
9.	22 ones	__2__ tens __2__ ones	__22__

Chapter 10   two hundred ninety-nine **299**

Reteaching Support

Chapter Test Items	Summary Test Items	Chapter Objectives Tested	TE Pages	Use These Reteaching Resources
1–4	1–4	**10A** Develop and use math vocabulary relating to place value to 100.	277A–280, 291A–292	Reteach Resources and *Ways to Success* CD: 10.1, 10.2, 10.7 Skillsheet 69
5–6	5–6	**10B** Identify, model, read and write numbers through 100 including representing numbers in different ways.	277A–278, 281A–285	Reteach Resources and *Ways to Success* CD: 10.1, 10.3, 10.4 Skillsheets 70 and 71
7–14	7–8	**10C** Regroup objects into tens and ones, write, and identify the place value of numbers through 99.	279A–280, 287A–292	Reteach Resources and *Ways to Success* CD: 10.2, 10.5–10.7 Skillsheet 72
15	9–10	**10D** Use models and place value to solve problems.	293A–296	Reteach Resource and *Ways to Succes* CD: 10.8 Skillsheet 73

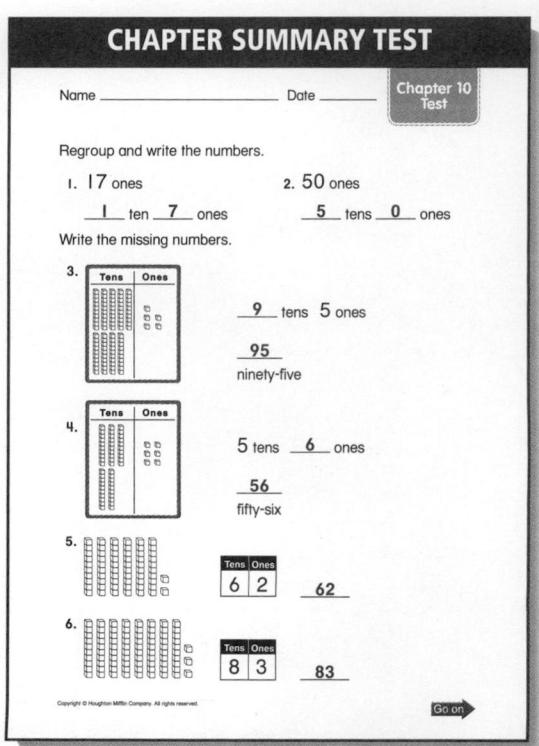

CHAPTER SUMMARY TEST

Name _____ Date _____ Chapter 10 Test

Regroup and write the numbers.

1. 17 ones
   __1__ ten __7__ ones

2. 50 ones
   __5__ tens __0__ ones

Write the missing numbers.

3. | Tens | Ones |
   __9__ tens 5 ones
   __95__
   ninety-five

4. | Tens | Ones |
   5 tens __6__ ones
   __56__
   fifty-six

5. | Tens | Ones |
   | 6 | 2 |
   __62__

6. | Tens | Ones |
   | 8 | 3 |
   __83__

Copyright © Houghton Mifflin Company. All rights reserved.

Go on ▶

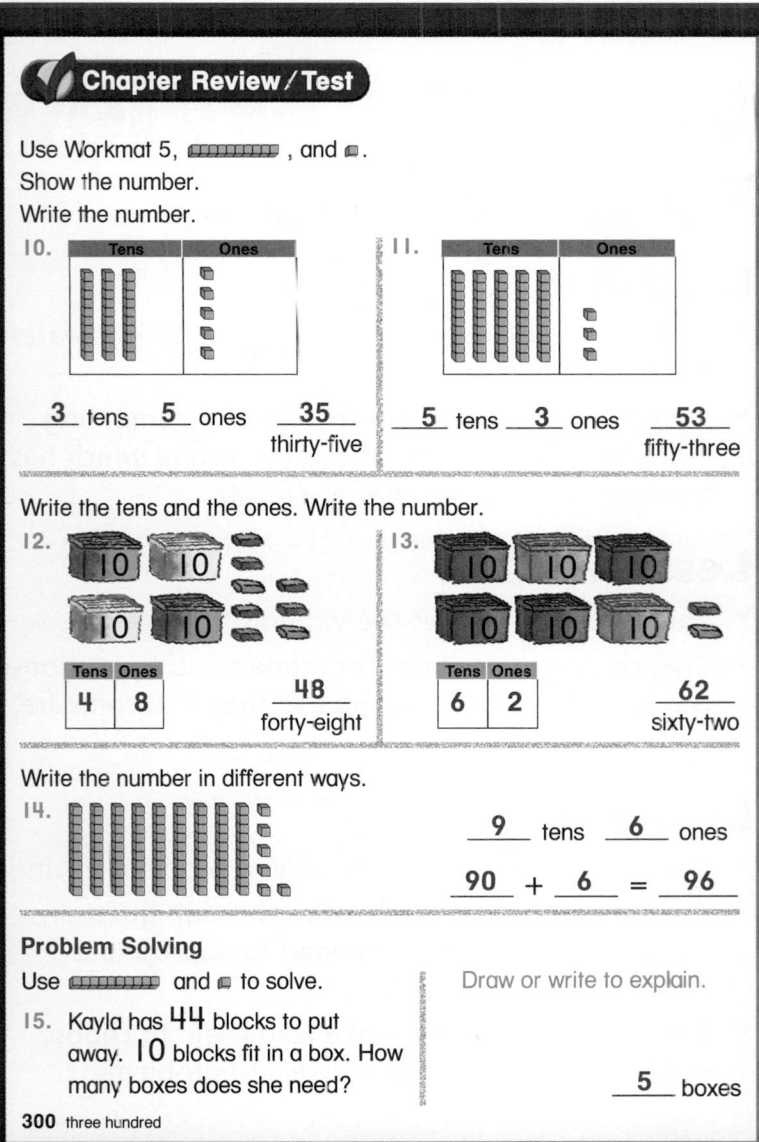

Chapter Review/Test

Use Workmat 5, ▭▭▭▭▭ , and ▪.
Show the number.
Write the number.

10.

Tens	Ones

__3__ tens __5__ ones __35__
thirty-five

11.

Tens	Ones

__5__ tens __3__ ones __53__
fifty-three

Write the tens and the ones. Write the number.

12.

Tens	Ones
4	8

__48__
forty-eight

13.

Tens	Ones
6	2

__62__
sixty-two

Write the number in different ways.

14.

__9__ tens __6__ ones

__90__ + __6__ = __96__

Problem Solving

Use ▭▭▭▭▭ and ▪ to solve.

Draw or write to explain.

15. Kayla has **44** blocks to put away. **10** blocks fit in a box. How many boxes does she need?

__5__ boxes

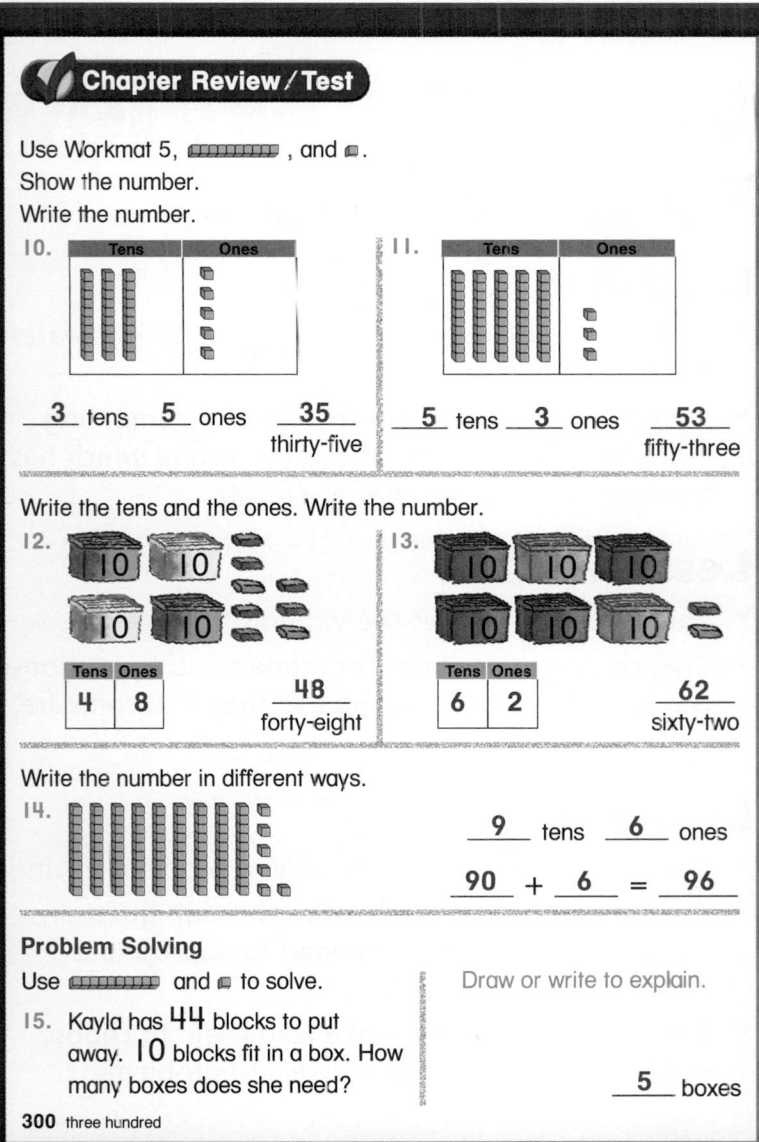

300 three hundred

CHAPTER SUMMARY TEST

Name _____ Date _____

Chapter 10 Test continued

7. 3 tens 4 ones __30__ + 4 = 34

8. 7 tens 6 ones 70 + 6 = __76__

Use the ▭▭▭▭▭ and ▪. Write the number.

9. Tani has **37** beads. She wants to put them in small boxes. Each box holds **10** beads. How many boxes does she need?

__4__ boxes

10. There are **65** children in Lee's school. The children are going in vans on a field trip. Each van holds **10** children. How many vans do they need?

__7__ vans

Use the End of Grade Test Prep Assessment Guide to help familiarize your children with the format of standardized tests.

Lesson by Lesson Overview
Order and Compare Numbers

Lesson 1

- In Chapter 1 children ordered numbers through 20. They now order numbers through 100.
- The use of a familiar format for ordering allows children to focus their attention on the numbers.

Lesson 2

- In this lesson, children learn ordinal numbers to tenth.
- They color objects in a row to identify ordinal position.
- Children also solve real-life problems that involve ordinal numbers.

Lesson 3

- This lesson has children estimate quantity by using 10 as a benchmark.
- Knowing what 10 looks like helps children determine the number of tens in a pictured group.
- A full page of problem solving has children compare data in a graph.

Lesson 4

- Children compare numbers using the terms *greater than* and *less than.*
- They also solve problems that involve comparing more than two groups of objects to find which has the fewest and which has the most.

Lesson 5

- This lesson introduces the symbols >, <, and =.
- Children write numbers for models and then choose the correct symbol to compare. They also compare without models.

Lesson 6

- Decision-making is a critical skill in problem solving.
- Children are taught basic steps through questions they ask themselves which lead to appropriate decisions.
- The decisions children make lead them to choose reasonable estimates as answers to problems.

SKILLS TRACE: ORDER AND COMPARE NUMBERS

Grade K	Grade 1	Grade 2
• compare to find 2 more, 2 less (ch. 8)	• **order numbers through 100**	• make a ten to estimate quantity, to 50 (ch. 1)
• order numbers to 31 (ch. 16)	• **identify ordinal numbers through tenth**	• compare 2-digit numbers using symbols (ch. 5)
• estimate quantity (ch. 8, 15)	• **make a ten to estimate quantity**	• order numbers to 100 (ch. 6)
• identify ordinal numbers to tenth (ch. 16)	• **compare numbers to 100**	• identify ordinal numbers to 100th (ch. 6)
	• **compare numbers with symbols**	

Chapter Planner

Lesson	Objective	Vocabulary	Materials	✓ NCTM Standards
11.1 **Order Numbers** p. 303A	Order numbers through 100.	before after between	number cards 10–20 (Learning Tools (LT) 14 and 15), counters, Workmat 6	Develop understanding of the relative position and magnitude of whole numbers and of ordinal and cardinal numbers and their connections.
11.2 **Ordinal Numbers** p. 305A	Identify ordinal numbers from first through tenth.		index cards, blank transparency, pattern blocks, number line (LT 8)	Develop understanding of the relative position and magnitude of whole numbers and of ordinal and cardinal numbers and their connections.
11.3 **Use Ten to Estimate** p. 307A	Estimate how many, using a group of ten.	estimate	counters, cubes, blank transparency	Develop a sense of whole numbers and represent and use them in flexible ways, including relating, composing, and decomposing numbers.
11.4 **Greater Than, Less Than** p. 311A	Compare two numbers, using *is greater than* and *is less than*.	greater than less than	place-value blocks, blank transparency, tens and ones chart transparency	Develop understanding of the relative position and magnitude of whole numbers and of ordinal and cardinal numbers and their connections.
11.5 **Use Symbols to Compare Numbers** p. 313A	Compare two-digit numbers, using >, <, and =.	equal to	number lines (LT 9), overhead place-value blocks, blank transparency	Develop understanding of the relative position and magnitude of whole numbers and of ordinal and cardinal numbers and their connections.
11.6 **Problem Solving:** **Reasonable Answers** p. 315A	Use estimation to find reasonable answers to problems.		cubes, clear container, counters, coins	Solve problems that arise in mathematics and in other contexts.

Resources For Reaching All Learners

LESSON RESOURCES: Reteach, Practice, Enrichment, Problem Solving, Homework, English Learners, Daily Routines, Transparencies, Math Center.

ADDITIONAL RESOURCES FROM HOUGHTON MIFFLIN: Chapter Challenges, Combination Classroom Planning Guide, Every Day Counts, Math to Learn (Student Handbook)

Every Day Counts
The *Calendar* activities in **Every Day Counts** support the math in this chapter.

Assessing Prior Knowledge

Before beginning the chapter, you can assess student understandings in order to assist you in differentiating instruction.

Complete Chapter Pretest in Unit Resource Folder

Use this test to assess both prerequisite skills (**Are You Ready?** — one page) and chapter content (**Check What You Know** — two pages).

Chapter 11 Prerequisite Skills Pretest

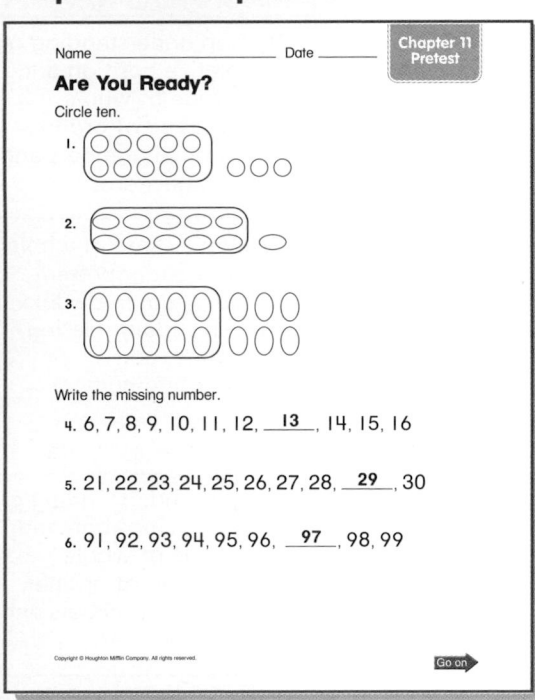

Chapter 11 New Content Pretest

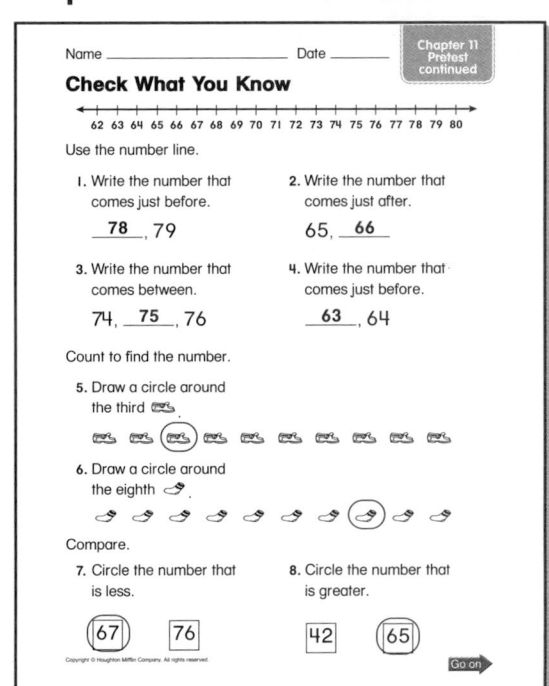

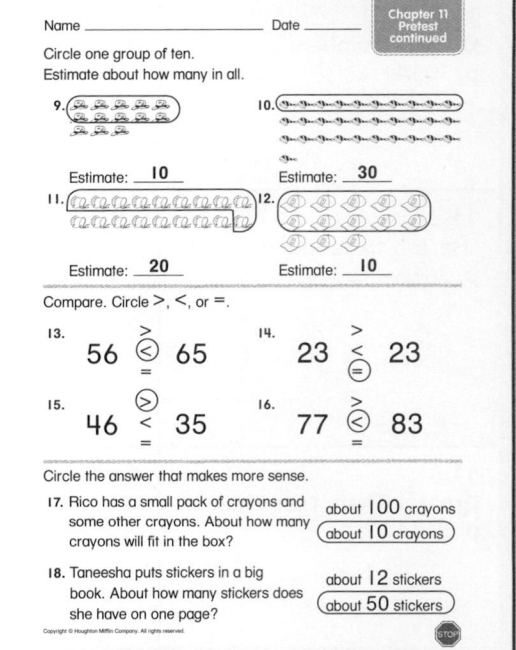

Chapter 11 New Content Pretest Items 1–18
To assign a numerical grade for this Pretest, use 5 points for each test item and then add 10.

Customizing Instruction

For Students Having Difficulty

Items	Prerequisites	*Ways to Success*
1–3	Understanding Groups of 10.	CD: 10.1 Skillsheet 74
4–6	Order numbers through 100.	CD: 1.4 Skillsheet 75

Ways to Success: Intervention for every concept and skill (CD-ROM or Chapter Intervention Skillsheets).

For Students Having Success

Items	Objectives	Resources
1–4	11A Use vocabulary relating to ordering and comparing numbers.	Enrichment 11.1, 11.5
13–16	11B Order and compare numbers to 100.	Enrichment 11.1
5–8	11C Identify ordinal numbers to 10th.	Enrichment 11.2
9–12	11D Estimate using 10 as a referent.	Enrichment 11.3
17–18	11E Find reasonable answers to problems.	

Other Pretest Options

Informal Pretest

The pretest assesses vocabulary and prerequisite skills needed for success in this chapter

Ways to Success CD-ROM

The *Ways to Success* chapter pretest has automatic assignment of appropriate review lessons.

Use **Chapter Challenges** with any students who have success with all new chapter content.

Chapter Resources

Assessing Prior Knowledge

Math Practice (count on, count back)

- Use lining up to going to an activity or to the bus as a time for math practice. For example, when children line up, give the first child a number card for a 2-digit number.
- After the child says the number out loud, children count on from that number.
- As a variation, you can have children count back from the number.

Activity

Ongoing Skill Activity

Calendar Counting (order numbers)

- As children read the calendar each day, use the dates to reinforce the concepts of *before, after,* and *between*.
- Invite a volunteer to read the date. Then have children tell which date comes *just before* and which comes *just after* today's date.
- Point out two dates and ask which date comes between them.

Activity

Connecting to the Unit Project

- Pair children for this activity.
- Provide each pair with rocks and cards with the signs for *greater than* (>) and *less than* (<).
- Tell each child to take a handful of rocks. Have children count the rocks and record the number on blank cards.
- Have children work together to compare the numbers, using the *greater than* and *less than* symbols.

Teacher Support

Professional Resources Handbook

Research, Mathematics Content, and Language Intervention

Research-Based Teaching

Research shows that several patterns emerge when children begin to count numbers higher than 12. First, they begin to notice something known as decade transition—that is, after the number with a 9, there is a new-sounding number (for example, "twenty-nine, thirty, forty-nine, fifty). Second, they know that after the number "12," each number ends in "teen" (e.g., thirteen, fourteen, fifteen . . .). See *Professional Resources Handbook, Grade 1,* Unit 4.

For more ideas relating to Unit 4, see the Teacher Support Handbook at the back of this Teacher's Edition.

Language Intervention

East Asian number names for the numbers greater than ten are based on ten and read in expanded notation. This counting sequence consistently reinforces the grouping-by-ten nature of our numeral system (National Research Council, 2001, pp. 163–168). For further explanation, see "Mathematical Language and Place Value" in the *Professional Resources Handbook Grade 1.*

 **Technology**

Time-Saving Technology Support
Ways to Assess Customized Spiral Review
   Test Generator CD
Lesson Planner CD-ROM
Ways to Success Intervention CD-ROM
MathTracks CD-ROM
Education Place: www.eduplace.com/math/mw
Houghton Mifflin Math eBook CD-ROM
eManipulatives
eGames

Starting Chapter 11
Order and Compare Numbers

CHAPTER OBJECTIVES

11A Develop and use math vocabulary relating to ordering and comparing numbers.

11B Order and compare numbers through 100 using words and symbols.

11C Identify ordinal numbers 1st through 10th.

11D Estimate, using a group of ten as a referent.

11E Find reasonable answers to problems.

Math Background

Order and Compare Numbers

Using a number line allows children to develop a sense of the order of numbers. Indicating the position of a number relative to another number, as *before*, *after*, or *between* enhances the development of vocabulary. Numbers such as first, second, third, and fourth are ordinal or positional numbers. Children need to identify ordinal positions as well as the words associated with the positions. At this grade level, ordinal numbers through tenth are discussed.

An important application of place value arises in the comparison of numbers. To compare 19 and 7, note that the first number has two digits and the second number has one digit. From this, conclude that 19 is greater than 7. This method is justified by the fact that for whole numbers the smallest two-digit number (10) is greater than the greatest one-digit number (9).

In comparing two whole numbers with the same number of digits, begin by comparing digits in each place value, starting at the left, until different digits appear. The number containing the greater of the different digits is the greater number.

Chapter 11

three hundred one **301**

Using The Investigation

- Ask volunteers to define *greater than* and *less than,* and use them in sentences.

- Draw the < and > symbols on the board. Point to the <. **What does this symbol mean?** (less than) Point to the >. **What does this symbol mean?** (greater than)

- Write the numbers 33 and 43 on the board. Have a volunteer tell which symbol makes the comparison true. (<)

- Read the question to children. **Are there more stars or music notes? Compare.** (more music notes)

Students should first find and count the number of stars and music notes, then compare the numbers.

 For more information about projects and investigations, visit Education Place. **eduplace.com/math/mw/**

Home Sweet Home

Find the way home.
Circle the number that is greater as you move up the path.

50 and (90)

26 and (29)

(50) and 40

75 and (85)

(83) and 38

10 and (100)

(65) and 25

(32) and 30

(71) and 17

47 and (67)

Start

302 three hundred two

For Mathematically Promising Students

The *Chapter Challenges* resource book provides blackline masters for activities that explore, extend, and connect the mathematics in every chapter. To support this independent work, see the Teacher Notes for each activity.

Explore: Fifty Squares, page 61, after Lesson 1
Extend: Calendar Days, page 63, after Lesson 3
Connect: Comparing Stamps, page 65, after Lesson 5

Using This Page

- Direct children to the picture of a path on page 302. **You are going to begin at Start, and follow the path that leads Home.**

- **As you reach each pair of numbers, compare them and circle the number that is greater.**

NSF Children's Math Worlds

Using *Children's Math Worlds* helps develop student communication skills because of the daily work with Math Talk, a teaching practice that can be used with all lessons. The emphasis on building a helping community will also enhance student participation in all classroom discussion.

Lesson 11.1

Order Numbers

PLANNING THE LESSON

MATHEMATICS OBJECTIVE
Order numbers through 100.

Use Lesson Planner CD-ROM for Lesson 11.1.

Daily Routines

Calendar
Point to today's date. Ask children to identify the date of the day before and the day after today. Repeat with other examples.

Vocabulary
Review the terms **before, after,** and **between** and give an example of each. Then use the vocabulary cards to help children differentiate the meaning of each term.

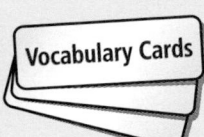
Vocabulary Cards

Meeting North Carolina's Standards

1.01 Develop number sense for whole numbers through 99.

• Compare and order sets and numbers.

Lesson Transparency 11.1

Problem of the Day
Rita has 3 packs of ten cards and Jin has 4 packs of ten. How many cards do they have altogether? (70 cards)

Quick Review

A B C D

What letter is between A and C? (B)

What letter is to the left of B? (A)

What letter is to the right of C? (D)

Lesson Quiz
Write the missing number.

1. 33, ___, 35 (34)   **2.** 69, ___, 71 (70)

3. 44, ___, 46 (45)   **4.** 88, ___, 90 (89)

LEVELED PRACTICE

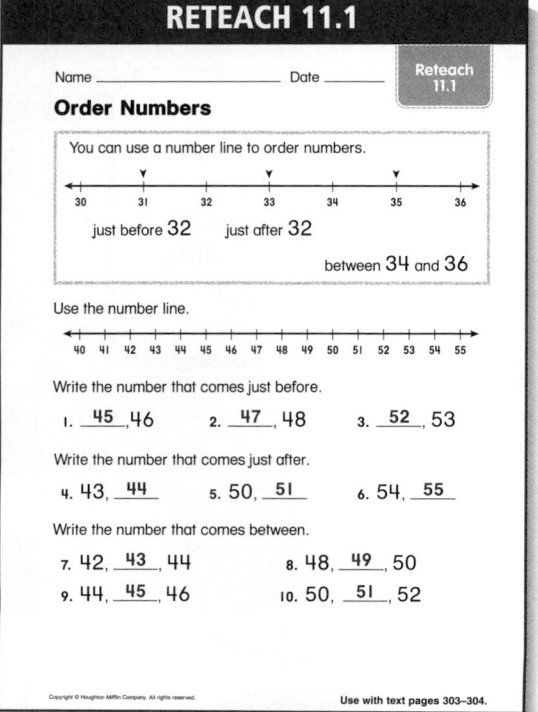

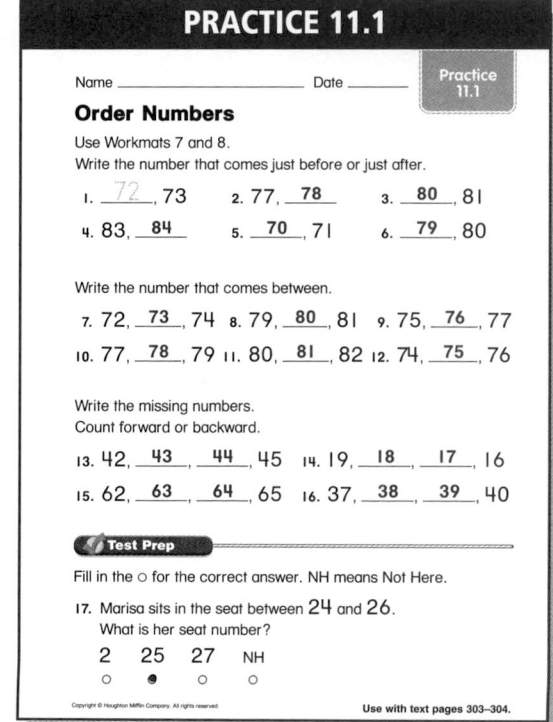

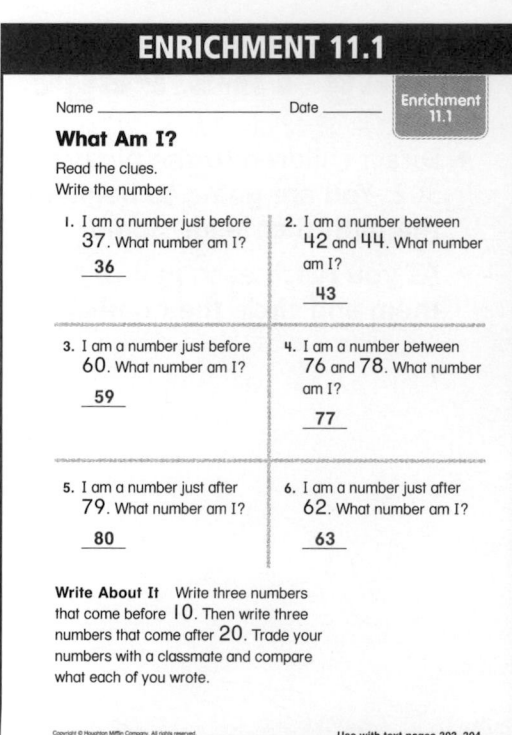

Reaching All Learners
Differentiated Instruction

English Learners

Children will need to understand the terms *just before* and *just after* in order to understand how numbers are ordered on a number line. Use Worksheet 11.1 to develop children's understanding of these terms.

Inclusion
VISUAL, TACTILE

- Draw a number line and circle a number on it.
- Have the child draw a box around the number that comes just before and a triangle around the number that comes just after the circled number.
- Tell the child that the circled number is between the other two.
- Repeat with other numbers.

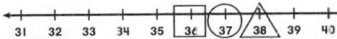

Gifted and Talented
VISUAL, TACTILE

- Challenge children to write number riddles that use the words *before, after,* and *between.* Guide children to give clues to the order of one number.
- Have children share the completed riddles with a partner. Have partners solve the riddles.

> What number am I?
> I am before 22.
> I am after 20.

TECHNOLOGY

Spiral Review

To reinforce skills on lessons taught earlier, create **customized** spiral review worksheets using the *Ways to Assess* CD-ROM.

eBook

An electronic version of this lesson can be found in **eMathBook.**

Lesson Planner

Use the **Lesson Planner CD-ROM** to see how lesson objectives for this chapter are correlated to standards.

Social Studies Connection

Have children count from 20–29. Point out that each number begins with the word *twenty*. Then ask bilingual children to count from 20–29 in another language. Do the numbers 20–29 begin the same way?

MATH CENTER

Real-Life Activity

Help children understand the usefulness of mathematics. This activity makes math come alive by connecting the lesson skills to a real-life situation.

PROBLEM SOLVING 11.1

Name _____ Date _____

Problem Solving 11.1

Order Numbers

Read and solve.

Draw or write to explain.

1. The Ryan family is going to the circus. Their seats are between rows 11 and 13. In what row are their seats?

   Row __12__

2. The Ryan family has 3 seats. Their seats are just after seat 41. What are their seat numbers?

   __42__, __43__, __44__

3. Jane is sitting in seat number 56. Linda is in the seat just before Jane's. What is Linda's seat number?

   __55__

4. Each clown wears a number. Jane likes the clown whose number is between 66 and 68. What number is the clown wearing?

   __67__

Use with text pages 303–304.

HOMEWORK 11.1

Name _____ Date _____

Homework 11.1

Order Numbers

Look at the number line.

90 91 92 93 94 95 96 (97) 98 99 100

96 comes before 97.
98 comes after 97.

Use the number line.
Write the number that comes before, after, or between.

85 86 87 88 89 90 91 92 93 94 95 96 97 98 99 100

1. 89, __90__   2. __86__, 87

3. 92, __93__   4. __99__, 100

5. 93, __94__, 95   6. 85, __86__, 87

7. Ben has to pick a number for his baseball shirt. He wants the number just after 14. What number does Ben want?

   __15__

Use with text pages 303–304.

Homework Workbook Page 71

ENGLISH LEARNERS 11.1

Name _____ Date _____

English Learners 11.1

Order Numbers

The fork and spoon are **before** the cup.
The spoon is **just before** the cup.

The spoon and cup are **after** the fork.
The spoon is **just after** the fork.

Draw a fork before the spoon.

1. Drawing of fork can be in box 1 or 2.

Draw a spoon just after the bowl.

2. Drawing of a spoon

Draw a bowl after the cup.

3. Drawing of bowl can be in box 2 or 3

Draw a cup just before the dish.

4. Drawing of a cup

To the Teacher: Use the examples at the top of the page to demonstrate the meaning of the terms *just before* and *just after*. Then read each sentence with children and have them draw pictures.

Use with text pages 303–304.

TEACHING LESSON 11.1

LESSON ORGANIZER

Objective Order numbers through 100.

Resources Reteach, Practice, Enrichment, Problem Solving, Homework, English Learners, Transparencies, Math Center

Materials Number cards 10–20 (Learning Tools (LT) 14 and 15), counters, workmat 6

Activity

Warm-Up Activity
Discuss Counting On

👤👤👤 Small Group	🕐 5 minutes	Auditory, Visual

1. Draw a number line for 15–30 on the board. Lead children in counting on and back by ones from various starting numbers. Refer to the number line as needed.

2. Encourage children to notice patterns in the counting sequence. **What number is to the right of the starting number?** (Answers may vary.) **What number is to the left of each starting number?** (Answers may vary.) Continue by having volunteers point to a starting number on the number line. Have classmates find the number to the right and to the left.

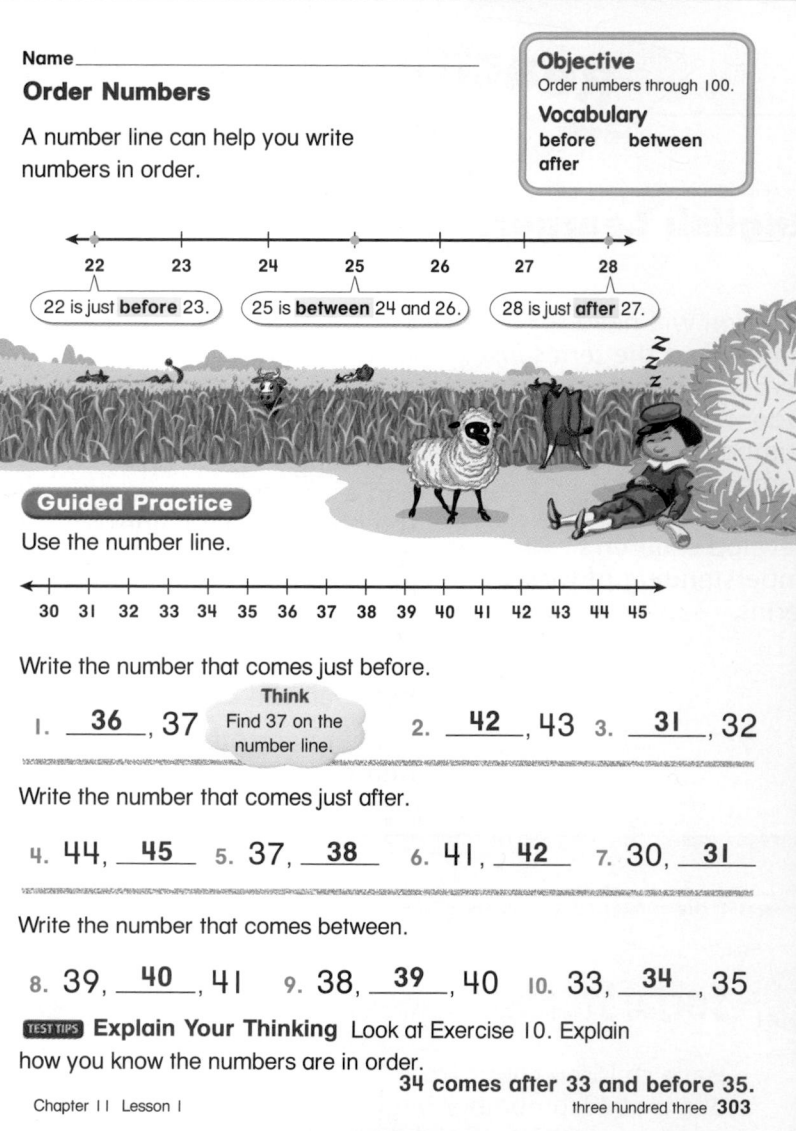

Name_____

Order Numbers

A number line can help you write numbers in order.

Objective
Order numbers through 100.

Vocabulary
before   between   after

22 is just **before** 23.   25 is **between** 24 and 26.   28 is just **after** 27.

Guided Practice

Use the number line.

30 31 32 33 34 35 36 37 38 39 40 41 42 43 44 45

Write the number that comes just before.

Think Find 37 on the number line.

1. __36__, 37   2. __42__, 43   3. __31__, 32

Write the number that comes just after.

4. 44, __45__   5. 37, __38__   6. 41, __42__   7. 30, __31__

Write the number that comes between.

8. 39, __40__, 41   9. 38, __39__, 40   10. 33, __34__, 35

TEST TIPS **Explain Your Thinking** Look at Exercise 10. Explain how you know the numbers are in order.

34 comes after 33 and before 35.

Chapter 11 Lesson 1

three hundred three **303**

① Introduce

Activity

Model Ordering Numbers

👤👤👤👤 Whole Group	🕐 10–15 minutes	Kinesthetic, Visual

Materials: *number cards 10–20 (LT 14 and LT 15)*

1. Give each child a number card. Say a number and have that child come to the front of the class. **Number 11, come to the front and hold up the number card.** Then ask: **What number comes after 11?** (12) Have the child with 12 stand next to the 11. **Where do you stand?** (after 11) **Are the numbers in the correct order?** (yes)

2. Continue with other numbers. Then repeat to show numbers that come before.

3. Finally, call for 2 numbers such as 12 and 14. **What number is between 12 and 14?** (13) Repeat with other examples.

② Develop

Guided Learning

Teaching Example Read the objective and vocabulary with children. Guide children through the example as you focus on the use of the vocabulary and discuss the numbers **before**, **between**, and **after** given numbers on the number line.

Guided Practice

Have children complete **Exercises 1–10** as you observe. Give children the opportunity to answer the Explain Your Thinking question. Allow children to discuss how they know the numbers are in order.

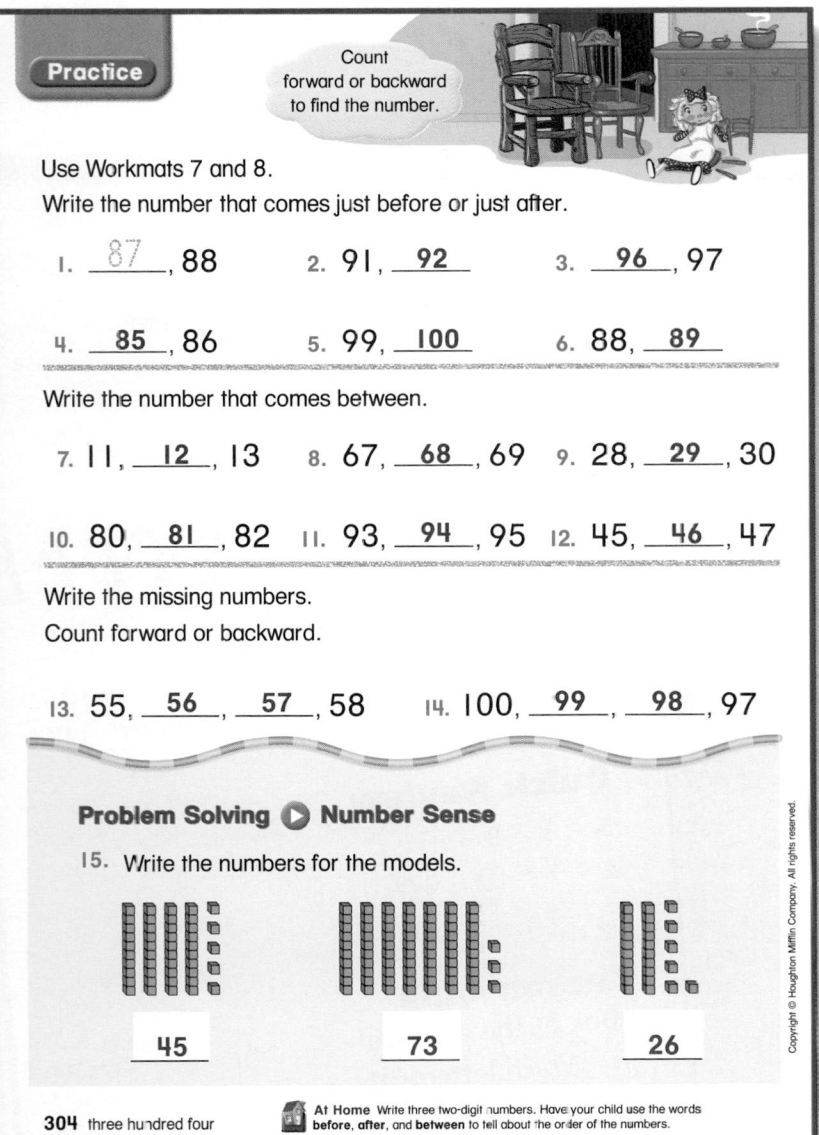

Practice

Count forward or backward to find the number.

Use Workmats 7 and 8.
Write the number that comes just before or just after.

1. _87_, 88   2. 91, _92_   3. _96_, 97

4. _85_, 86   5. 99, _100_   6. 88, _89_

Write the number that comes between.

7. 11, _12_, 13   8. 67, _68_, 69   9. 28, _29_, 30

10. 80, _81_, 82   11. 93, _94_, 95   12. 45, _46_, 47

Write the missing numbers.
Count forward or backward.

13. 55, _56_, _57_, 58   14. 100, _99_, _98_, 97

Problem Solving ▷ Number Sense

15. Write the numbers for the models.

| 45 | 73 | 26 |

304 three hundred four

At Home Write three two-digit numbers. Have your child use the words **before, after,** and **between** to tell about the order of the numbers.

Daily Test Prep

What number comes between 34 and 36?

33   35   37   43
○   ◑   ○   ○

Test Prep Transparency **11.1**

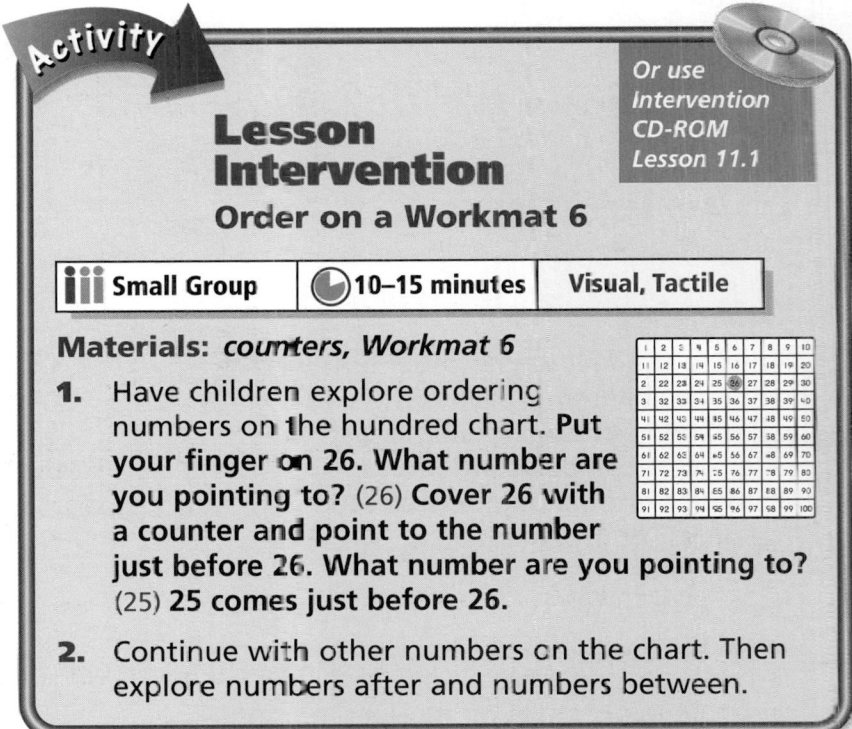

Activity

Lesson Intervention
Order on a Workmat 6

Or use Intervention CD-ROM Lesson 11.1

| Small Group | 10–15 minutes | Visual, Tactile |

Materials: *counters, Workmat 6*

1. Have children explore ordering numbers on the hundred chart. **Put your finger on 26. What number are you pointing to?** (26) Cover 26 with a counter and point to the number just before 26. **What number are you pointing to?** (25) **25 comes just before 26.**

2. Continue with other numbers on the chart. Then explore numbers after and numbers between.

---

3 Practice

Independent Practice

Children complete **Exercises 1–14** independently.

Problem Solving

After children complete **Exercise 15,** call on volunteers to share their answers. Write 45, 73, and 26 on the board, and discuss how to put them in order from least to greatest: (26, 45, 73)

Common Error

Confusing Terms

If children confuse the vocabulary **before** and **after,** demonstrate that you count backward on the number line to find the number before. Children may find it easier to connect the 2 words by remembering that they both begin with b.

4 Assess and Close

How can you count to find the numbers between 37 and 40? (Count forward: 38, 39.)

What number comes just before 50? (49) **Just after 50?** (51)

Keeping a Journal

Write the numbers from 20 to 29 in order.

Ordinal Numbers

PLANNING THE LESSON

MATHEMATICS OBJECTIVE
Identify ordinal numbers from first through tenth.

Use Lesson Planner CD-ROM for Lesson 11.2.

Daily Routines

Calendar

Point to the first day of the month and lead children in saying the date. Then ask what the date just after that is called. Continue to introduce ordinal numbers by reading dates on the calendar.

Sunday	Monday	Tuesday	Wednesday	Thursday	Friday	Saturday
			1	2	3	4
5	6	7	8	9	10	11
12	13	14	15	16	17	18
19	20	21	22	23	24	25
26	27	28	29	30	31	

Vocabulary

Use **ordinal numbers** to talk about the order of the nine innings in a baseball game, dates on a calendar, floor numbers, and so on. Then ask volunteers to use ordinal numbers in sentences.

Vocabulary Cards

Meeting North Carolina's Standards

Maintain Grade K Standard 1.01 Develop number sense for whole numbers through 30.

Lesson Transparency **11.2**

Problem of the Day
Allie's secret number is between 10 and 15. The number is before 13. The number is not 12. What is the number? (11)

Quick Review
$5 + 3 = 3 + \square$ (5)
$2 + 7 = \square + 2$ (7)
$6 + 0 = 0 + \square$ (6)

Lesson Quiz
Look at the alphabet.
1. Which letter is third? (C)
2. Which letter is fifth? (E)
3. Which letter is before the second letter? (A)

LEVELED PRACTICE

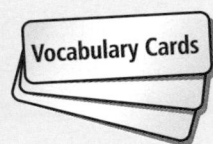

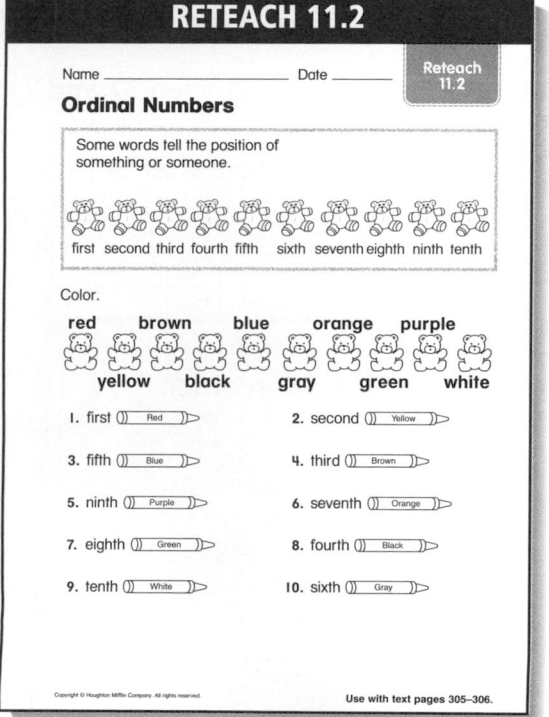

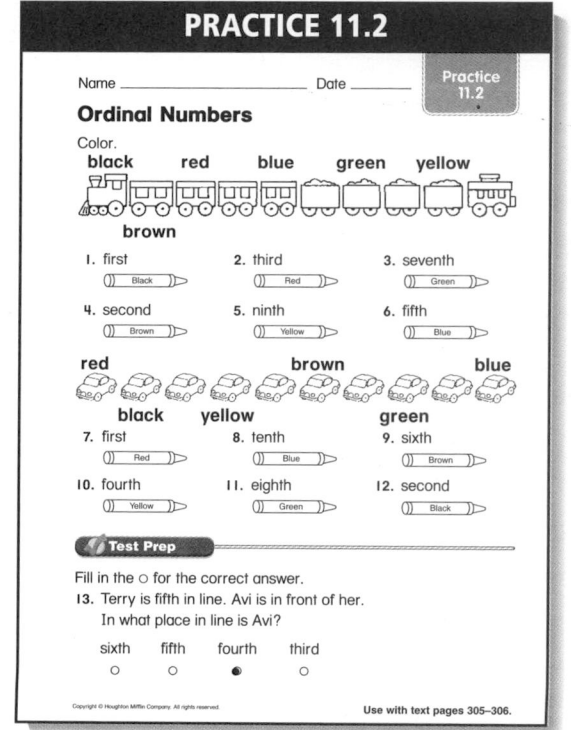

Practice Workbook Page 72

Reaching All Learners

Differentiated Instruction

English Learners

To solve some word problems involving ordinal numbers, children will need to understand the term *in line*. Use Worksheet 11.2 to help English-language learners understand the meaning of this term.

Special Needs
VISUAL, TACTILE

Materials: *cubes*

- Make a cube train with 5 cubes of different colors. Use this to model the ordinal numbers *first* through *fifth*.

- When the child is comfortable identifying these ordinal numbers, add to the cube train as you introduce the terms *sixth* through *tenth*.

Gifted and Talented
VISUAL, TACTILE

Materials: *cubes, index cards*

- Have children make 6 cube towers of different heights and arrange them in order from shortest to tallest.
- Then have children write *first, second, third*, etc. on index cards and place in front of the towers with the shortest stack first.

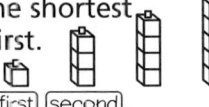

TECHNOLOGY

Spiral Review

Help students remember skills they learned earlier by creating **customized** spiral review worksheets using the *Ways to Assess* CD-ROM.

Lesson Planner

You can use the **Lesson Planner CD-Rom** to create a report of the lessons and standards you have taught.

eBook

eMathBook allows students to review lessons and do homework without carrying their textbooks home.

ScienceConnection

List the planets in order from the Sun: Mercury, Venus, Earth, Mars, Jupiter, Saturn, Uranus, Neptune, and Pluto. Have children use ordinal numbers to describe each planet's position.

MATH CENTER

Vocabulary Activity

This vocabulary-building activity helps children understand and remember new words. Encourage children to use the words in math discussion.

PROBLEM SOLVING 11.2

Name _____ Date _____   Problem Solving 11.2

Ordinal Numbers

Read and solve.

| first second third fourth fifth sixth seventh eighth ninth tenth |

Draw or write to explain.

1. There are 5 children in line. Dan is last in line. In which place is Dan?

   __fifth__

2. Maria puts 7 stuffed animals on a shelf. The teddy bear is in the middle. In which place is the teddy bear?

   __fourth__

3. Rafael lines up 9 model cars. The red car is last. The blue car is in front of the red car. In which place is the blue car?

   __eighth__

4. Tim is fifth in line. Karen is seventh in line. Kwame is between Tim and Karen. In which place is Kwame?

   __sixth__

Use with text pages 305–306.

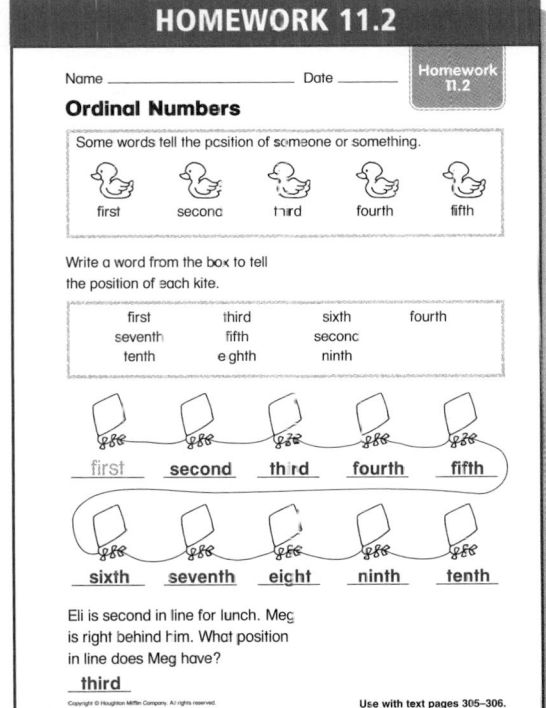

HOMEWORK 11.2

Name _____ Date _____   Homework 11.2

Ordinal Numbers

Some words tell the position of someone or something.

first   second   third   fourth   fifth

Write a word from the box to tell the position of each kite.

first	third	sixth	fourth
seventh	fifth	second	
tenth	eighth	ninth	

first   second   third   fourth   fifth

sixth   seventh   eight   ninth   tenth

Eli is second in line for lunch. Meg is right behind him. What position in line does Meg have?

__third__

Use with text pages 305–306.

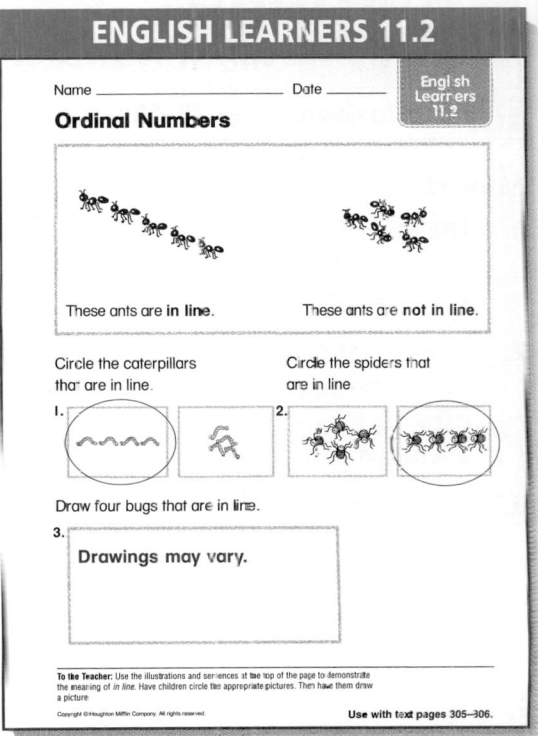

ENGLISH LEARNERS 11.2

Name _____ Date _____   English Learners 11.2

Ordinal Numbers

These ants are **in line**.   These ants are **not in line**.

Circle the caterpillars that are in line.

Circle the spiders that are in line

1.   2.

Draw four bugs that are in line.

3.

Drawings may vary.

To the Teacher: Use the illustrations and sentences at top of the page to demonstrate the meaning of *in line*. Have children circle the appropriate pictures. Then have them draw a picture.

Use with text pages 305–306.

TEACHING LESSON 11.2

LESSON ORGANIZER

Objective Identify ordinal numbers from first through tenth.

Resources Reteach, Practice, Enrichment, Problem Solving, Homework, English Learners, Transparencies, Math Center

Materials Index cards, number line (LT 8), blank transparency, pattern blocks

Activity
Warm-Up Activity
Counting in Order

iii Small Group	⏱ 5 minutes	Visual, Auditory

Materials: *number line (LT 8)*

1. Use the number line to review how to count in order from 0 to 10.

2. **Which direction do we move as we count?** (from left to right) Show the direction on the number line. Point out that this is the same direction we use when we read words in a sentence on a page.

Ordinal Numbers

MathTracks 1/36
Listen and Understand

Objective Identify ordinal numbers from first through tenth.

Some words tell the position of something or someone.

First Second Third Fourth Fifth Sixth Seventh Eighth Ninth Tenth

Guided Practice

Color.

blue   red   green   yellow brown

1. third

Think Count first, second, third.

2. fifth

3. eighth   4. first   5. seventh

yellow   purple   blue red   green orange

6. second   7. sixth   8. ninth

9. fourth   10. seventh   11. tenth

TEST TIPS **Explain Your Thinking** If you are fifth in line, how many people are in front of you? **4 people**

Chapter 11 Lesson 2   three hundred five **305**

---

1 Introduce
Activity
Model Ordinal Numbers

iiii Whole Group	⏱ 10–15 minutes	Kinesthetic, Visual

Materials: *index cards*

1. Make ordinal number cards. Ask 5 volunteers to line up in front of the class and face the class. Count 1 to 5 from left to right as you touch each child's shoulder.

2. Give each child the corresponding ordinal number card. Read the ordinal numbers to fifth, and have children repeat. Have class volunteers use one term at a time by asking questions such as: **Who is fifth in line?**

3. Then have 5 more children join the line and model sixth through tenth.

2 Develop

Guided Learning

Teaching Example Read the objective with children. Guide children through the example as you focus on the ordinal number words. Emphasize that these numbers tell the order of the ducks marching in a line.

Guided Practice

Have children complete **Exercises 1–11** as you observe. Give children the opportunity to answer the Explain Your Thinking question. Discuss their responses with the class.

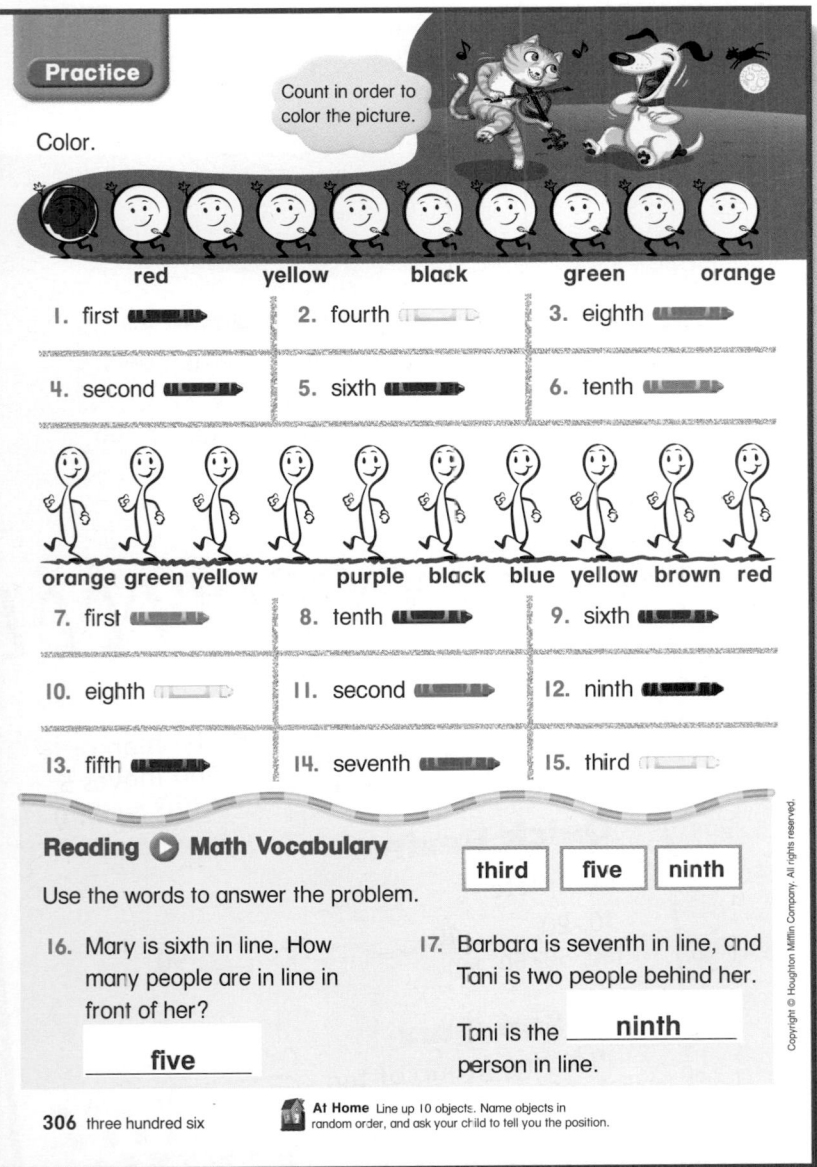

Practice

Count in order to color the picture.

Color.

red yellow black green orange

1. first
2. fourth
3. eighth
4. second
5. sixth
6. tenth

orange green yellow purple black blue yellow brown red

7. first
8. tenth
9. sixth
10. eighth
11. second
12. ninth
13. fifth
14. seventh
15. third

Reading ▶ Math Vocabulary

Use the words to answer the problem.

| third | five | ninth |

16. Mary is sixth in line. How many people are in line in front of her?

__five__

17. Barbara is seventh in line, and Tani is two people behind her.

Tani is the __ninth__ person in line.

306 three hundred six

At Home Line up 10 objects. Name objects in random order, and ask your child to tell you the position.

Daily Test Prep

Which letter is fourth?

A B C D E F G H I J

○ H   ○ E   ● D   ○ A

Activity

Lesson Intervention

Modeling Ordinal Numbers

Or use Intervention CD-ROM Lesson 11.2

| 👤👤👤 Small Group | 🕐 10–15 minutes | Tactile, Visual |

Materials: blank transparency, pattern blocks ■◆▲⬡▰

1. Make a row of 5 different shapes. Point to each shape from left to right and say its ordinal number.

2. Have volunteers come and identify shapes. **Point to the fourth shape. Show us how you counted to fourth.** (first, second, third, fourth) **What ordinal number could we use to describe the next shape?** (fifth)

3. Extend the row to model sixth through tenth. **What shape is ninth in the row?** (Answers will vary.)

---

③ Practice

Independent Practice

Children complete **Exercises 1–15** independently.

Reading Math

After children complete **Exercises 16–17**, call on volunteers to share their solutions. Draw stick figures on the board as you discuss each solution.

Common Error

Misunderstanding Ordinal Names

Children may confuse the names of some ordinal numbers. Review the relationship between the names of ordinal and cardinal numbers. Emphasize the order.

④ Assess and Close

If you are eighth in line, in what position is the person in front of you? (seventh)

Nine people are in line. You are exactly in the middle. What position are you in? (fifth)

 **Keeping a Journal**

Use an ordinal number to tell your grade level. Tell the grade you will be in next year.

Use Ten to Estimate

PLANNING THE LESSON

MATHEMATICS OBJECTIVE
Estimate how many, using a group of ten.

Use Lesson Planner CD-ROM for Lesson 11.3.

Meeting North Carolina's Standards
1.01 Develop number sense for whole numbers through 99.
• Estimate quantities fewer than or equal to 100.

Daily Routines

Calendar
Have children estimate about how many groups of 10 days are found in the current month's calendar. Then circle groups of 10 days to check.

Vocabulary
Give an example of when you **estimate** to find how many and when you count to find the exact number. You can estimate how many cars are in the parking lot. You need to know the exact number of children in class today.

Vocabulary Cards

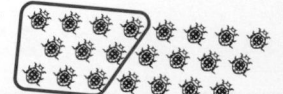

Lesson Transparency
11.3

Problem of the Day
Gia is playing a board game. Her marker is on the third space. She spins and moves 5. Now what space is the marker on? (eighth)

Quick Review
Complete.

10, 20, ___, 40, ___, ___, 70, ___, 90
(30, 50, 60, 80)

Lesson Quiz
Circle one group of ten. Estimate about how many in all. (about 20)
Count. How many ladybugs are there? (22)

LEVELED PRACTICE

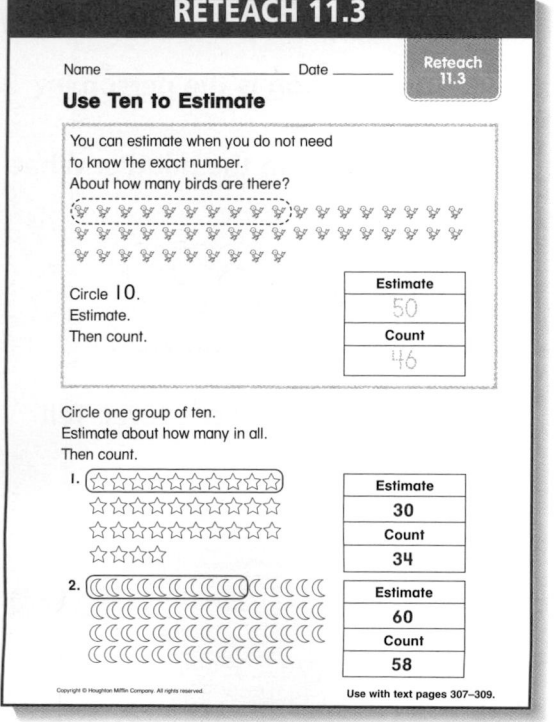

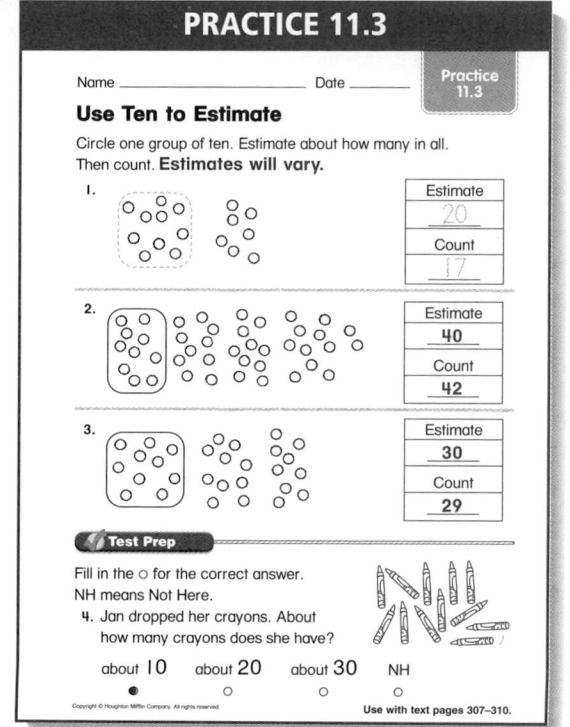

Practice Workbook Page 73

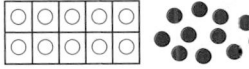

Reaching All Learners

Differentiated Instruction

English Learners

English-language learners will need to understand the word *about* in order to learn how to estimate. Use Worksheet 11.3 to help children understand this word and to estimate how many.

Inclusion
TACTILE, VISUAL

Materials: *ten-frame (Workmat 1), counters*

- Give the child a handful of counters. Have the child count out 10 counters. Use this benchmark of 10 to help the child estimate the total number of counters.
- Then help the child count to find how many counters in all.

Gifted and Talented
VISUAL, TACTILE

Materials: *egg carton, counters*

- Have children cut off two sections from the end of egg cartons. Have children draw a picture to show how to use 1 group of 10 to estimate how many eggs are in 5 cartons. Then have them use counters to model their drawings.

TECHNOLOGY

Spiral Review

You can prepare students for standardized tests with **customized** spiral review on key skills using the *Ways to Assess* CD-ROM.

Education Place

Encourage students to visit **Education Place** at eduplace.com/kids/mw/ for more student activities.

Games

Students can practice their computational skills using the **Rock Hopper** math game, available on the *Ways to Success* CD-ROM.

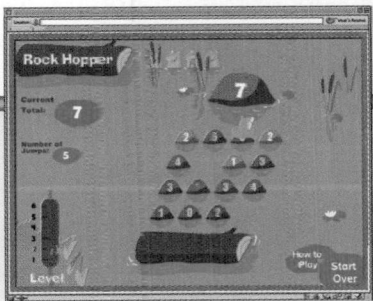

Literature Connection

Share parts of the book, *Take Off with Numbers*, by Sally Hewitt. Involve children in observing and counting the number of objects shown on different pages. Then ask children to estimate the number of stars shown on page 22.

MATH CENTER

Cross-Curricular Activity

As you use this activity to relate the mathematics of this lesson to another curriculum area, children will see how math can help them with other subjects.

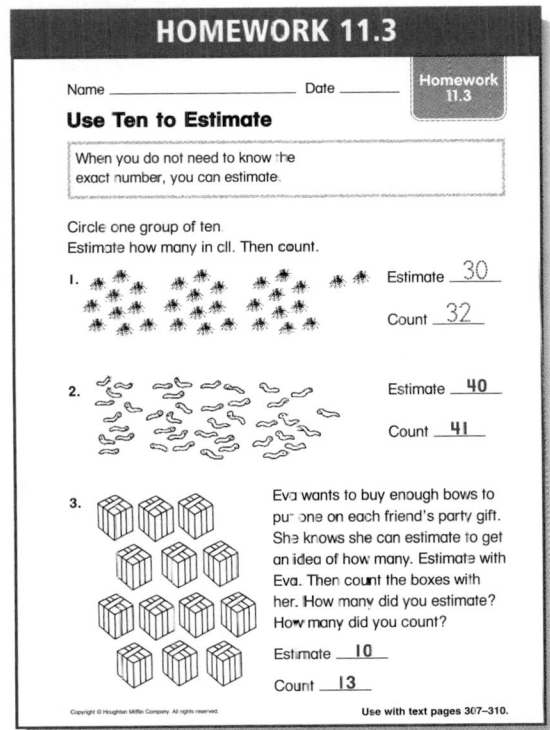

Homework Workbook Page 73

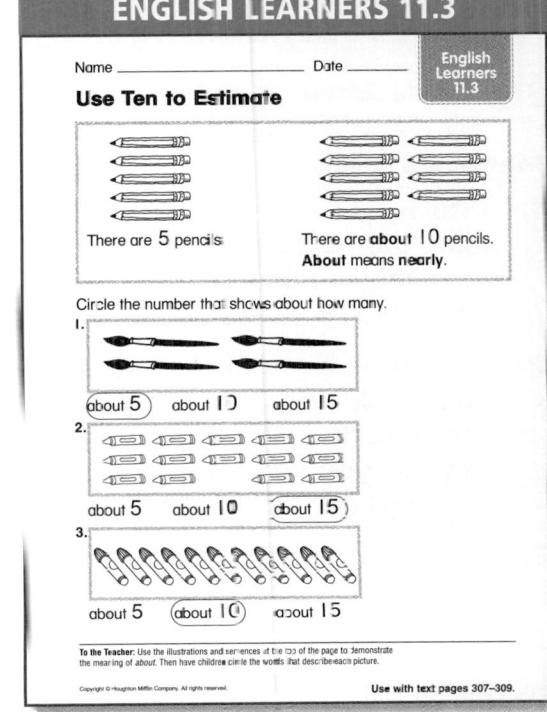

TEACHING LESSON 11.3

LESSON ORGANIZER

Objective Estimate how many, using a group of ten.

Resources Reteach, Practice, Enrichment, Problem Solving, Homework, English Learners, Transparencies, Math Center

Materials Counters, cubes, blank transparency

Activity

Warm-Up Activity
Counting by Tens

| Small Group | 5 minutes | Visual, Auditory |

Have 4 children come to the front of the class and hold up all their fingers. **How many fingers do you see in all?** (40) Discuss how children found the number. Did they count? Refer to the class hundred chart as you review oral counting by tens to 100.

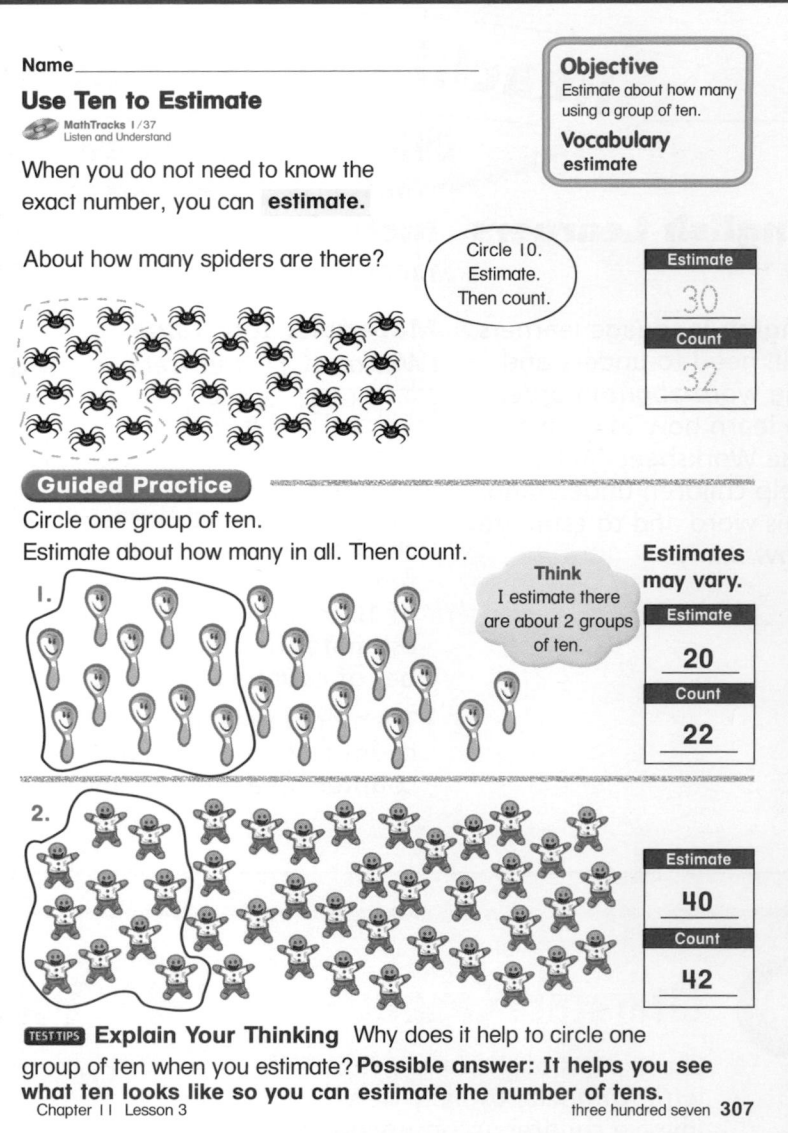

Name _____

Use Ten to Estimate

MathTracks 1/37
Listen and Understand

When you do not need to know the exact number, you can **estimate.**

About how many spiders are there?

Circle 10. Estimate. Then count.

| Estimate |
| 30 |
| Count |
| 32 |

Objective
Estimate about how many using a group of ten.

Vocabulary
estimate

Guided Practice

Circle one group of ten.
Estimate about how many in all. Then count.

Think
I estimate there are about 2 groups of ten.

Estimates may vary.

1.
| Estimate |
| 20 |
| Count |
| 22 |

2.
| Estimate |
| 40 |
| Count |
| 42 |

TEST TIPS **Explain Your Thinking** Why does it help to circle one group of ten when you estimate? **Possible answer: It helps you see what ten looks like so you can estimate the number of tens.**

Chapter 11 Lesson 3
three hundred seven **307**

1 Introduce
Activity
Model Estimating

| Whole Group | 10–15 minutes | Visual, Tactile |

Materials: *counters*

1. Display 33 counters on the overhead. **I want to estimate the number of counters. I do not need to know the exact number. About how many counters do I have?** (Accept all reasonable answers.)

2. **I can make a group of 10 to help estimate the total number.** Move 10 counters aside. **Do you think there are more than 10 counters remaining?** (Answers will vary.) **Do you want to change your estimate?** (Answers may vary.) Record the estimates.

3. Count on by tens and then by ones to count all the counters. **How many counters are there?** (33) Discuss how making a group of 10 helps estimate how many in all. Compare estimates to 33. **Which is the best estimate?** (30) Repeat with other amounts.

2 Develop

Guided Learning

Teaching Example Introduce the objective and vocabulary to children. Read the example and guide children to count and circle one group of 10 spiders. Then model how to use that group of 10 to estimate by deciding how many more groups of ten there are, without counting. Have children write the estimate and then count to find the total number of spiders. Remind children that estimates are not exact amounts, but are *about* how many.

Guided Practice

Have children complete **Exercises 1–2** as you observe. Give children the opportunity to share answers to the Explain Your Thinking question.

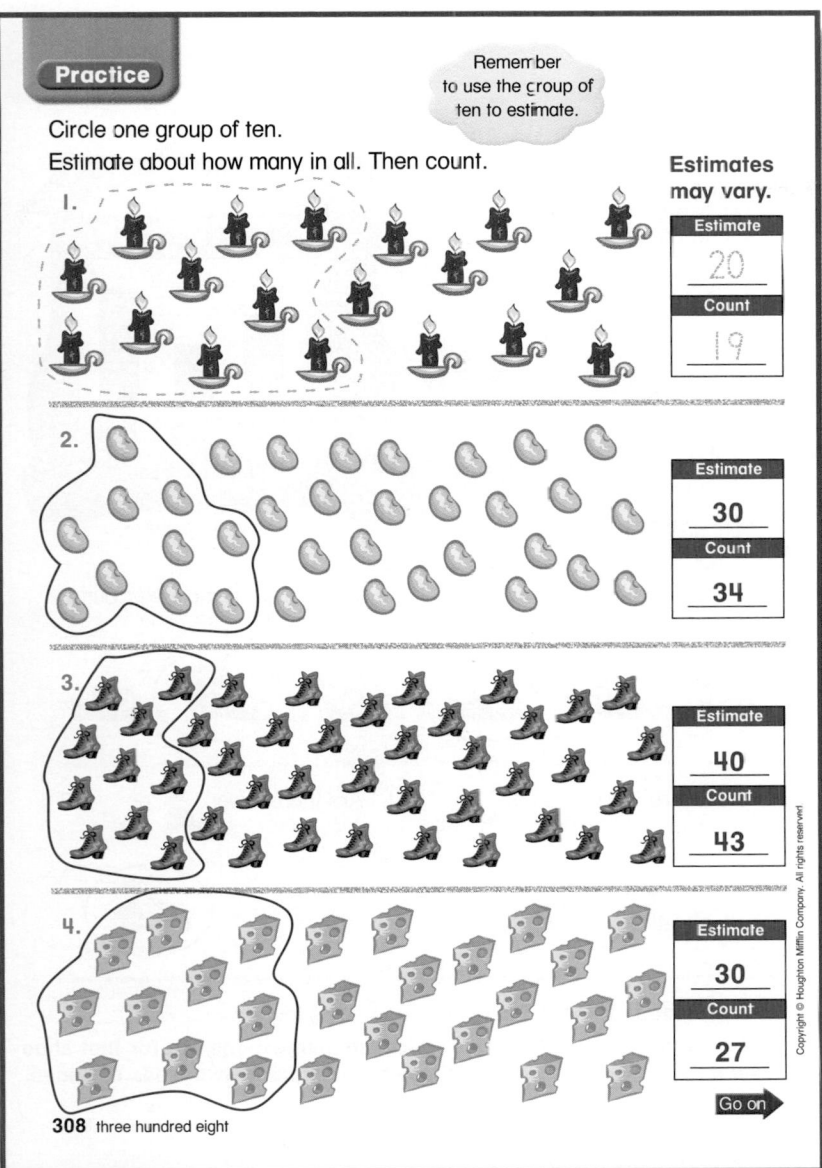

Practice

Remember to use the group of ten to estimate.

Circle one group of ten.
Estimate about how many in all. Then count.

Estimates may vary.

1.
| Estimate |
| 20 |
| Count |
| 19 |

2.
| Estimate |
| 30 |
| Count |
| 34 |

3.
| Estimate |
| 40 |
| Count |
| 43 |

4.
| Estimate |
| 30 |
| Count |
| 27 |

Go on

308 three hundred eight

TechnologyConnection
Use Technology to Represent Ordinal Numbers

Using the one-color counter virtual manipulatives found at eduplace.com/kids/mwl, students practice previously learned skills in working with ordinal numbers.

Show students how to place and arrange counters in the virtual manipulative. Then have them complete the activity.

• Tell students to use **Choose Counter** to pick counters, to use **Place** to stamp them, and to use **Move** to arrange them.

• Make a large chart. In the left column list ordinals from first to tenth, mixing up the order. In the right column draw pictures of counters found in the virtual manipulative. Have students arrange the counters in the order shown.

• Have students make their own chart and trade with a partner. Then have them arrange the counters in the order given on their partner's chart.

3 Practice

Independent Practice

Children complete **Exercises 1–4** on page 308 independently.

Common Error

Forgetting to Include the Circled Group of 10 in the Estimate

Remind children that they need to count a group of 10, then use it to think about how many other groups of 10 there are, and include it as they estimate. Suggest they count by 10s: 10, 20, 30, and so on.

Lesson continues

Daily Test Prep

Estimate. About how many?

☆☆☆☆☆
☆☆☆☆☆
☆☆☆☆☆
☆☆☆☆☆
☆☆☆☆☆

about 10   about 20   about 30   about 40
   ○   ●   ○   ○

Activity

Or use Intervention CD-ROM Lesson 11.3

Lesson Intervention
Modeling Using Ten to Estimate

| 👤👤👤 Small Group | 🕐 10–15 minutes | Tactile, Visual |

Materials: *cubes, blank transparency*

1. Place 42 cubes randomly on the transparency. Move 10 cubes aside. **This is 10. About how many more groups of 10 could I make from these cubes?** Model your thinking as you look at the 1 group of 10. Then ask children for estimates. **Estimate how many.** (40)

2. Explain that after estimating, you can count to check your estimate. Have volunteers help you make groups of 10 cubes. **Count: 10, 20, 30, 40, 41, 42. How many cubes did we count?** (42) **So, our estimate of 40 was a good estimate.**

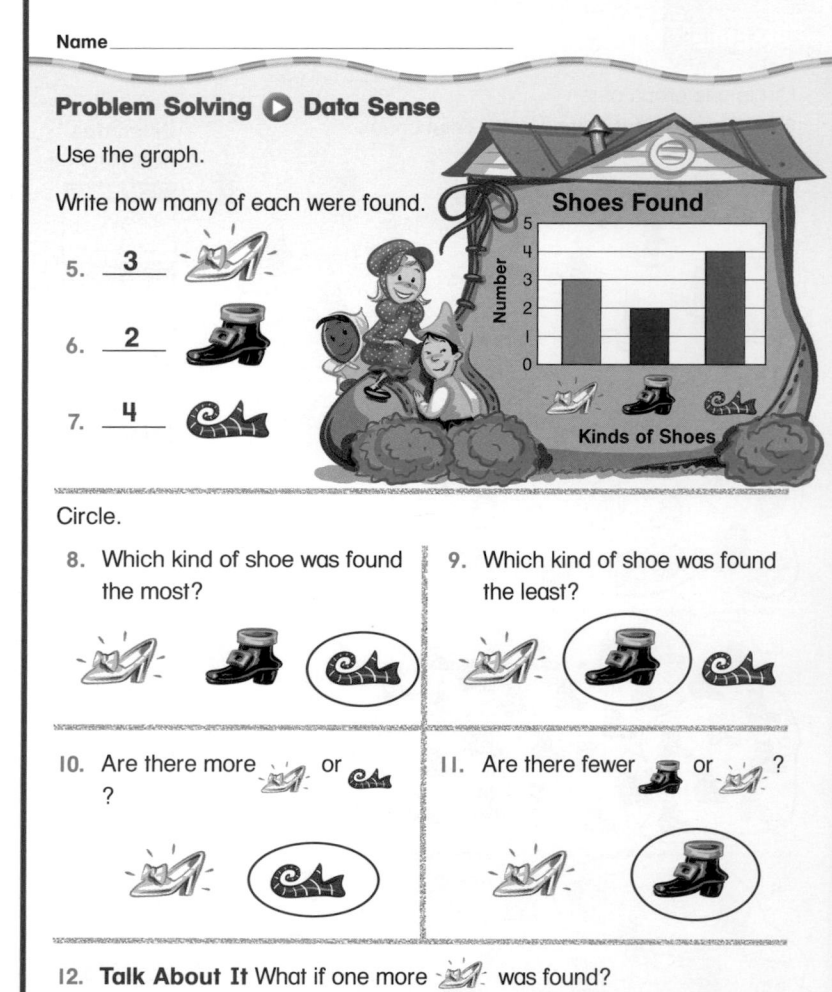

Name_____

Problem Solving ▶ Data Sense

Use the graph.

Write how many of each were found.

Shoes Found

5. __3__

6. __2__

7. __4__

Circle.

8. Which kind of shoe was found the most?

9. Which kind of shoe was found the least?

10. Are there more 👞 or 👟 ?

11. Are there fewer 👢 or 👠 ?

12. **Talk About It** What if one more 👠 was found? How would the graph change? **Possible answer: The bar for that shoe would go to 4. There would be the same number of two kinds of shoes.**

Chapter 11   **At Home** Place 30 to 50 of the same objects in a jar. Ask your child to estimate about how many. Then count the objects together.   three hundred nine **309**

---

3 Practice

Problem Solving

Introduce the graph on page 309. Observe as children complete **Exercises 5–11** independently. Have volunteers share their solutions and use the **Talk About It** question in Exercise 12 to discuss the data on the graph.

4 Assess and Close

How is estimating different than counting? (When you estimate, you find about how many. You count when you need to find the exact answer.)

Would it be better for us to estimate or count to find about how many children go to our school? Why? (Estimate. Children may point out that it is difficult to count such a large number.)

📝 Keeping a Journal

Draw a lot of little circles on your page. Have a classmate estimate how many you drew. Then count to find the exact number.

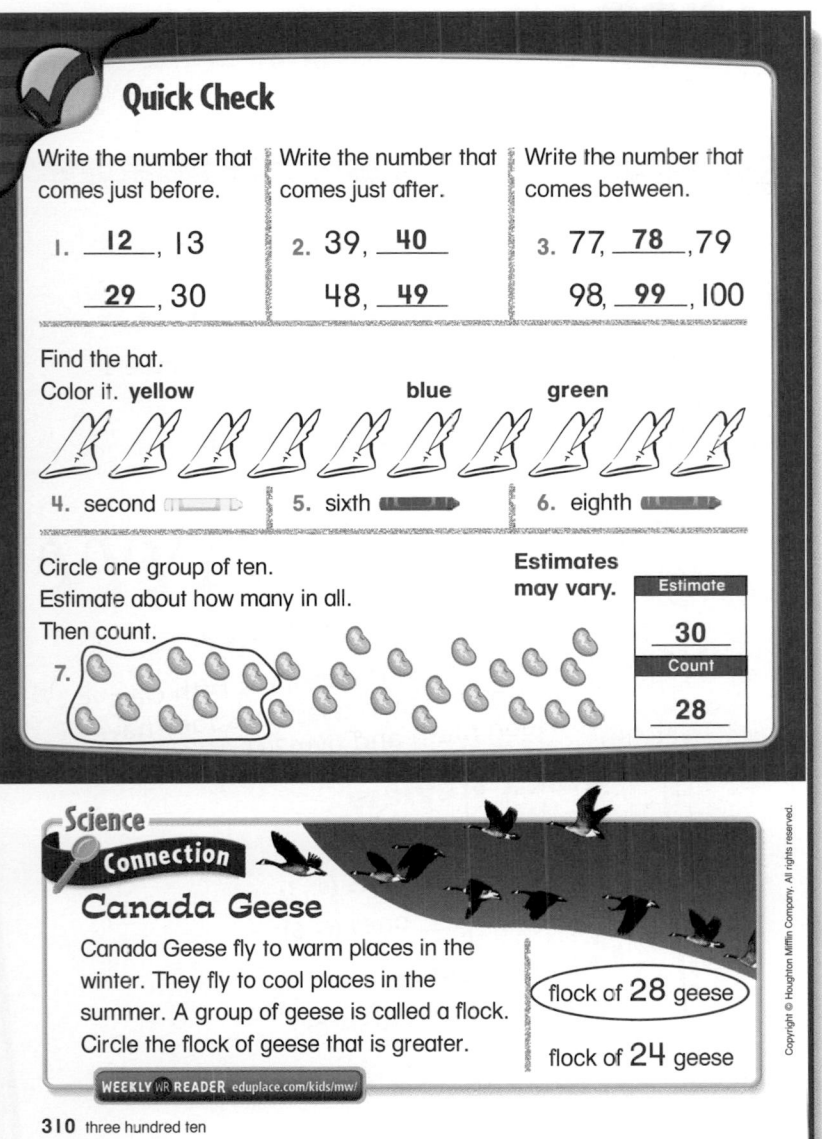

Quick Check

Write the number that comes just before.	Write the number that comes just after.	Write the number that comes between.
1. __12__, 13	2. 39, __40__	3. 77, __78__, 79
__29__, 30	48, __49__	98, __99__, 100

Find the hat.
Color it. **yellow**   **blue**   **green**

4. second   5. sixth   6. eighth

Circle one group of ten.
Estimate about how many in all.
Then count.

Estimates may vary.

7.

Estimate
30
Count
28

Science Connection

Canada Geese

Canada Geese fly to warm places in the winter. They fly to cool places in the summer. A group of geese is called a flock. Circle the flock of geese that is greater.

flock of 28 geese

flock of 24 geese

WEEKLY WR READER eduplace.com/kids/mw/

310 three hundred ten

Quick Check

Have children complete the Quick Check exercises independently to assess their understanding of concepts and skills taught in **Lessons 1–3**.

Item	Lesson	Error Analysis	Intervention
1–3	11.1	Children may confuse the vocabulary *before*, *after*, *between*.	Reteach Resource 11.1 *Ways to Success* 11.1
4–6	11.2	Children may confuse the names of some ordinal numbers.	Reteach Resource 11.2 *Ways to Success* 11.2
7	11.3	Children may forget to include the 10 they circled when they estimate.	Reteach Resource 11.3 *Ways to Success* 11.3

Science Connection

Read the text to children and have them compare the 2 flocks. Ask children if they have ever seen Canada Geese in their neighborhood. Point out that some Canada Geese do not migrate anymore. They just stay in parks and on farms all year round. Have children name other animals that are often seen in groups. Ask if they would count or estimate the number of animals in these groups and why.

Greater Than, Less Than

PLANNING THE LESSON

MATHEMATICS OBJECTIVE
Compare two numbers, using *is greater than* and *is less than.*

Use Lesson Planner CD-ROM for Lesson 11.4.

Daily Routines

Calendar
Compare the number of days in the current and previous months. Have children tell which month has a greater number of days.

Sunday	Monday	Tuesday	Wednesday	Thursday	Friday	Saturday
				1	2	3	4
5	6	7	8	9	10	11
12	13	14	15	16	17	18
19	20	21	22	23	24	25
26	27	28	29	30	31	

Vocabulary
Use the number of children in two classes or grades to introduce the language of **greater than** and **less than**. Have children say sentences that use these terms to **compare** the **number** of adults and children in their family or boys and girls in the class.

Vocabulary Cards

Meeting North Carolina's Standards
1.01 Develop number sense for whole numbers through 99.
• Compare and order sets and numbers.

Lesson Transparency 11.4

Problem of the Day
Joey's first class is math. His fifth class is gym. How many classes does Joey have between math and gym? (3 classes)

Quick Review
75 ___ tens ___ ones (7; 5)
43 ___ tens ___ ones (4; 3)
66 ___ tens ___ ones (6; 6)

Lesson Quiz
Which number is greater?
1. 72 69 (72)
2. 50 55 (55)
Which number is less?
3. 43 34 (34)
4. 39 90 (39)

LEVELED PRACTICE

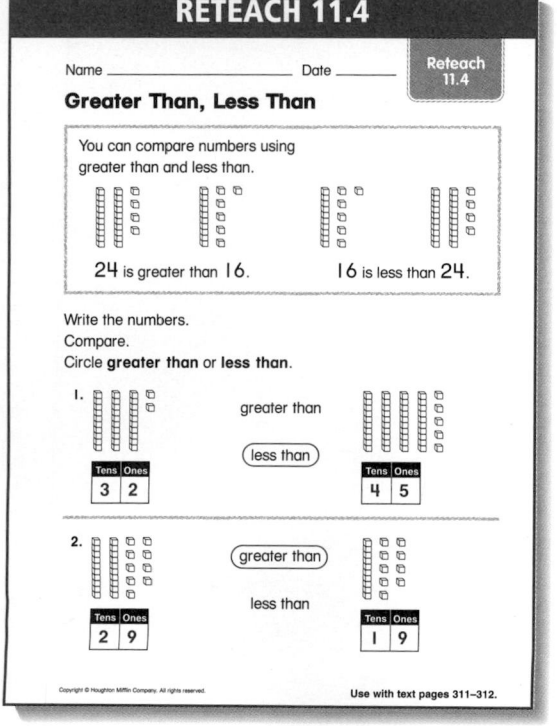

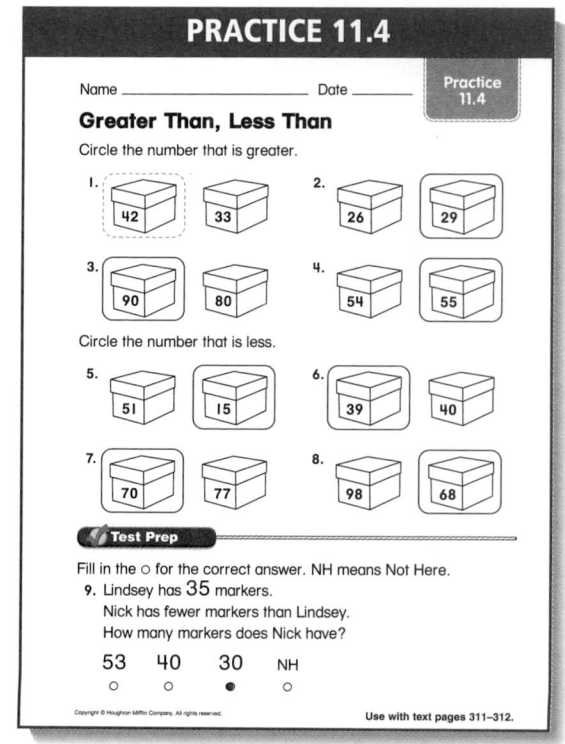

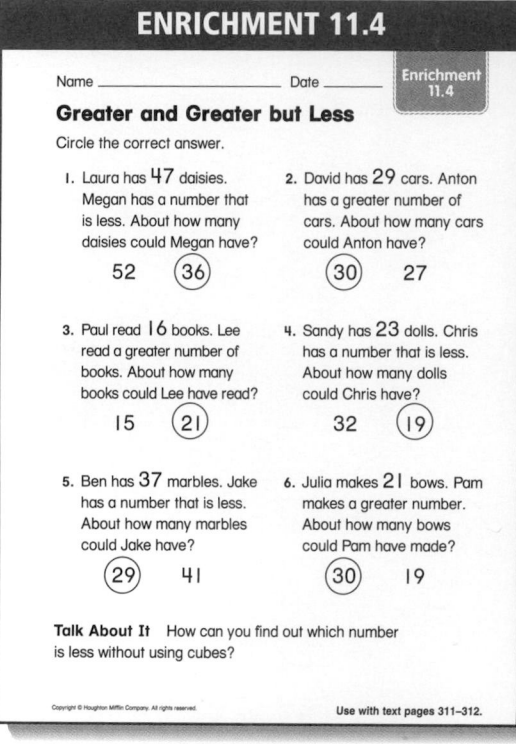

Reaching All Learners

Differentiated Instruction

English Learners

English-language learners may not have the language skills to explain the process behind their thinking. Use Worksheet 11.4 to provide children with sentence frames they can use to complete the Explain Your Thinking activity.

Inclusion
VISUAL, TACTILE

Materials: *place-value blocks, Workmat 5*

- Have the child show models for 37 and 29.
- Help the child match the tens 1 to 1 to find which number has more tens. Explain that this is the greater number.
- Repeat to compare 29 and 25. Explain that when the tens are the same, they need to compare the ones.

Early Finishers
VISUAL, TACTILE

Materials: *cubes*

- Display 15 red cubes, 13 blue cubes, and 18 yellow cubes.
- Have children write sentences to describe the groups of cubes, using the Reading Math activity from page 312 as a guide.

TECHNOLOGY

Spiral Review

Create **customized** spiral review worksheets for individual students using the *Ways to Assess* CD-ROM.

eBook

An electronic version of this lesson can be found in **eMathBook**.

Lesson Planner

Use the **Lesson Planner CD-ROM** to see how lesson objectives for this chapter are correlated to standards.

Houghton Mifflin
Math

e **MathBook**

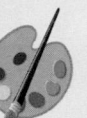

Art Connection

Tear small squares from 2 colors of paper. Show children samples of mosaic art. Have children make number mosaics. Use mosaics to compare numbers.

MATH CENTER

Vocabulary Activity

This vocabulary-building activity helps children understand and remember new words. Encourage children to use the words in math discussion.

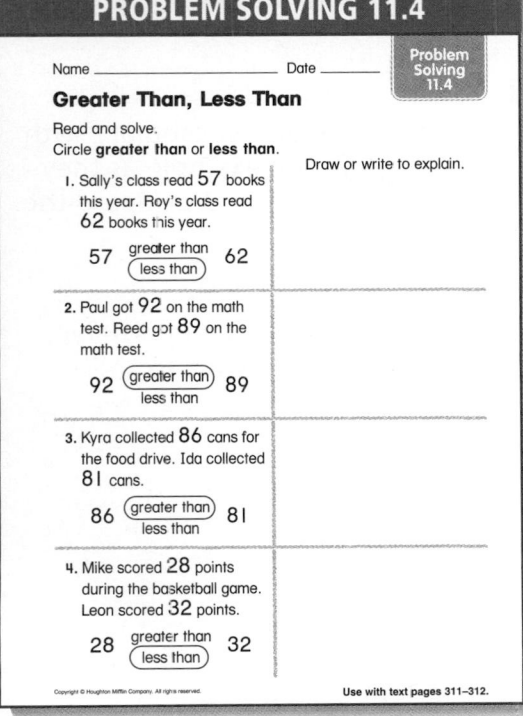

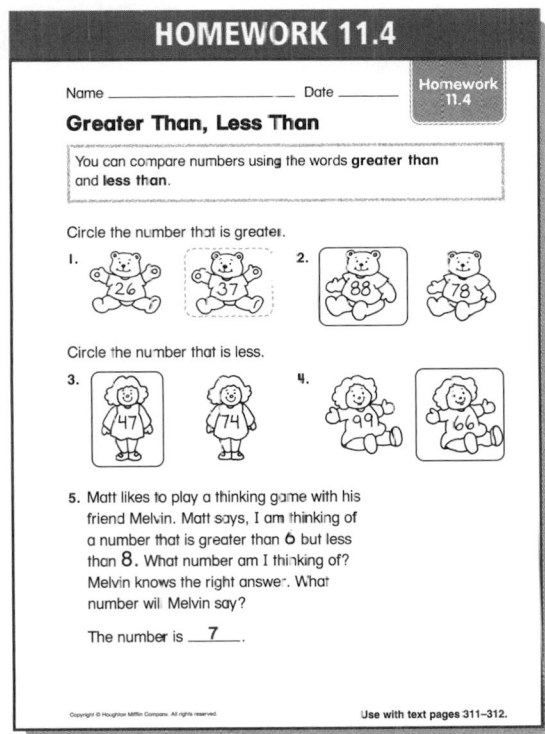

Homework Workbook Page 74

TEACHING LESSON 11.4

LESSON ORGANIZER

Objective Compare two numbers, using *greater than* and *less than*.

Resources Reteach, Practice, Enrichment, Problem Solving, Homework, English Learners, Transparencies, Math Center

Materials Place-value blocks, blank transparency, tens and ones chart transparency

Activity

Warm-Up Activity
Comparing Tens

⫪ Small Group	⏱ 5 minutes	Tactile, Visual

Materials: *place-value blocks (tens), blank transparency*

1. Have 2 volunteers each take a handful of place-value blocks. Ask: **Who has more blocks?**

2. Place the blocks on the overhead. Have each child write the number the blocks represent. Have the class decide which number is greater. Label the other number as less.

40   50

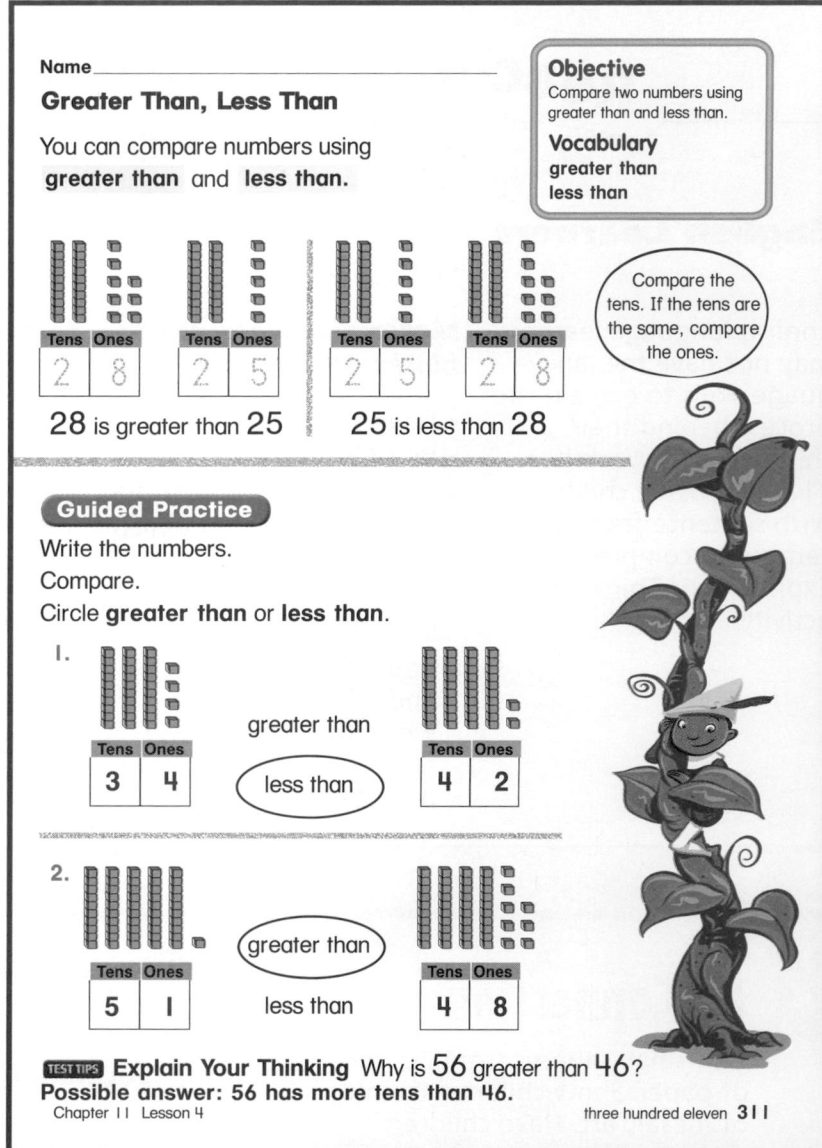

---

1 Introduce
Activity
Model Comparing Numbers

⫪ Whole Group	⏱ 10–15 minutes	Tactile, Visual

Materials: *place-value blocks*

1. Draw 2 tens and ones charts side-by-side on the board. Write 32 in one, 41 in another. **How can you tell which number is greater?** (Compare the numbers or show models for each and count.) Ask children to show both numbers with blocks.

2. Have children cover the ones in each number and focus on the tens. **How many tens are in 32?** (3 tens) **How many tens are in 41?** (4 tens) **41 has more tens, so it is the greater number. 41 is greater than 32. So, 32 is less than 41.**

3. Repeat with two numbers that have the same number of tens. Explain the rule that if the number of tens is the same, you compare ones.

2 Develop

Guided Learning

Teaching Example Read the objective and vocabulary with the children. Guide children through the example as they use place-value blocks to show 28 and 25 and compare the numbers.

Guided Practice

Have children complete **Exercises 1 and 2** as you observe. Give children the opportunity to share answers to the Explain Your Thinking question.

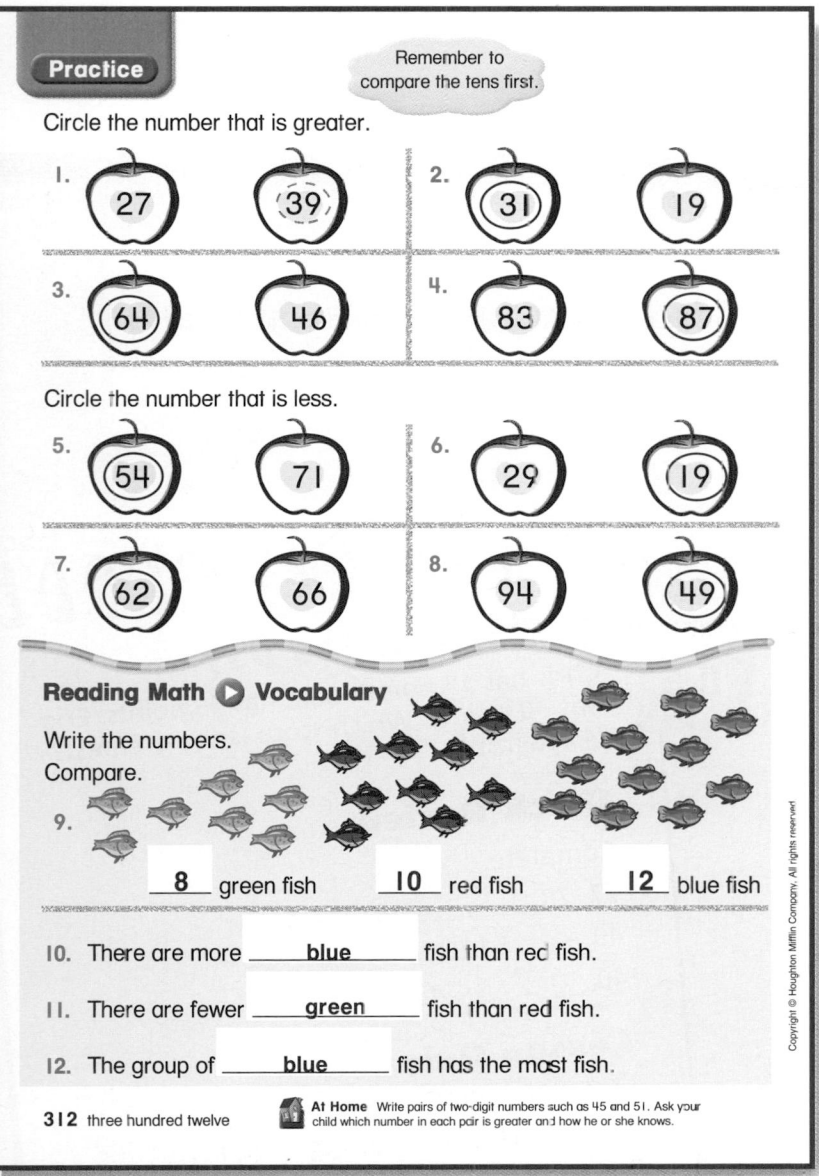

Practice

Remember to compare the tens first.

Circle the number that is greater.

1. 27   (39)   2. (31)   19

3. (64)   46   4. 83   (87)

Circle the number that is less.

5. (54)   71   6. (29)   19

7. (62)   66   8. 94   (49)

Reading Math ▷ Vocabulary

Write the numbers. Compare.

9. __8__ green fish   __10__ red fish   __12__ blue fish

10. There are more __blue__ fish than red fish.

11. There are fewer __green__ fish than red fish.

12. The group of __blue__ fish has the most fish.

312 three hundred twelve

🏠 **At Home** Write pairs of two-digit numbers such as 45 and 51. Ask your child which number in each pair is greater and how he or she knows.

Daily Test Prep

Which number is less than 41?

14   44   51   72
●   ○   ○   ○

Activity

Or use Intervention CD-ROM Lesson 11.4

Lesson Intervention
Modeling Ordinal Numbers

| 👤👤👤 Small Group | 🕐 10–15 minutes | Visual, Auditory |

Materials: *tens and ones chart transparency*

1. Display tens and ones for 2 different numbers on the top and bottom of a tens and ones chart. Draw a horizontal line between the two representations.

| Tens | Ones |

2. Model how to first compare tens by counting the tens in each number. If the tens are the same, repeat to compare the number of ones. Describe the steps. **First I look at the tens. Here I count 1, 2, 3, 4 tens. Below there are 1, 2, 3, 4 tens. Both numbers have the same number of tens. When that happens, we need to compare the ones.**

3. Continue until children agree on the greater number. Repeat with other numbers.

---

③ Practice

Independent Practice

Children complete **Exercises 1–8** independently.

Reading Math

After children complete **Exercises 9–12**, call on volunteers to share their sentences.

Common Error

Comparing Ones First
Remind children that you always compare the tens first. If the number of tens is the same, you compare the ones. Model this with place-value models.

④ Assess and Close

Is 25 less than or greater than 19? (greater than)

What is a number that is greater than 36 and less than 63? (Accept any number from 37 to 62.)

  **Keeping a Journal**

Draw a picture to show that 26 is less than 28.

Use Symbols to Compare Numbers

Lesson 11.5

PLANNING THE LESSON

MATHEMATICS OBJECTIVE
Compare two-digit numbers, using >, <, and =.

Use Lesson Planner CD-ROM for Lesson 11.5.

Daily Routines

Calendar

Point out that the number of days in January (31) is equal to the number of days in March (31). Make a list of the number of days in each month and have children find other pairs of months that have the same number of days.

Sunday	Monday	Tuesday	Wednesday	Thursday	Friday	Saturday
				1	2	3	4
5	6	7	8	9	10	11
12	13	14	15	16	17	18
19	20	21	22	23	24	25
26	27	28	29	30	31	

Vocabulary

Introduce the term **equal to** by using it in a question that compares the same number of objects in the room. Then have volunteers share similar examples. Is the number of cubbies equal to the number of children?

Vocabulary Cards

Meeting North Carolina's Standards

1.01 Develop number sense for whole numbers through 99.

• Compare and order sets and numbers.

Lesson Transparency 11.5

Problem of the Day

Chris has 15 points. Sam has 45 points. Eric has 30 points. Which score is the greatest? (45 points)

Quick Review

Complete.

77, 78, ___ , ___ , 81 (79, 80)

49, ___ , 51 (50)

40, ___ , ___ , 43 (41, 42)

Lesson Quiz

Complete with >, <, or =.

1. 18 ○ 20 (<) 2. 35 ○ 35 (=)
3. 42 ○ 24 (>) 4. 60 ○ 59 (>)

LEVELED PRACTICE

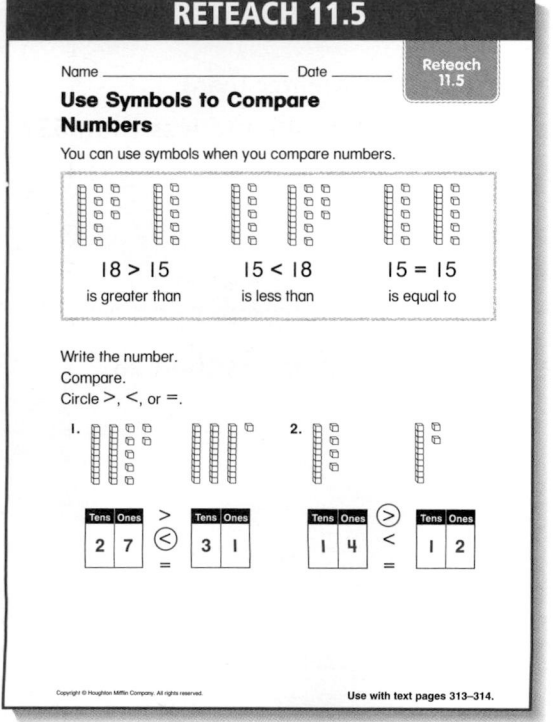

RETEACH 11.5

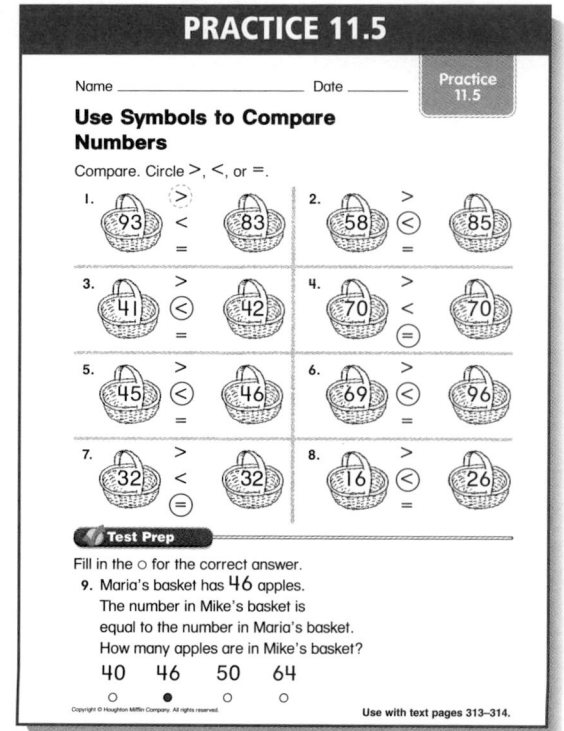

PRACTICE 11.5

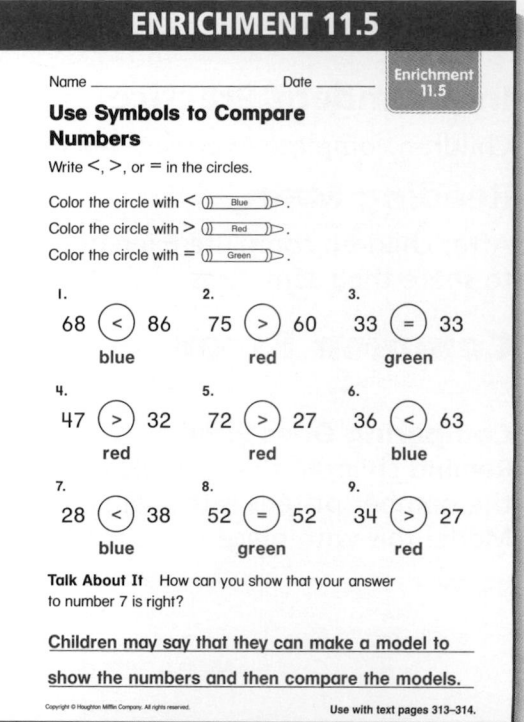

ENRICHMENT 11.5

Practice Workbook Page 75

Reaching All Learners
Differentiated Instruction

English Learners

English-language learners may not be familiar with the concept of symbols. Use Worksheet 11.5 to build familiarity with this concept.

Special Needs
VISUAL, TACTILE

Materials: *number cards (LT 14 and 15), number lines (LT 8)*

- Have the child pick 2 number cards and find and circle the numbers on the number line.
- Explain that the greater number comes after the lesser number. *Which number is greater? How do you know?*
- Repeat with other cards.

Early Finishers
VISUAL, TACTILE

Materials: *pennies, hundred chart (LT 7)*

- Have children toss 2 pennies on the hundred chart and then write a number sentence for the comparison using > or <.

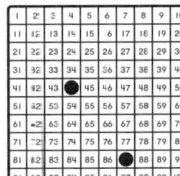

TECHNOLOGY

Spiral Review

Using the *Ways to Assess* CD-ROM, you can create **customized** spiral review worksheets covering any lessons you choose.

eBook

eMathBook, allows students to review lessons and do homework without carrying their textbooks home.

Education Place

You can visit **Education Place** at **eduplace.com/math/mw/** for teacher support activities.

Social Studies Connection

Display a map that uses symbols such as trees. Explain that a symbol is a picture that stands for something, just as > is a symbol for *is greater than*. Discuss map keys. Then have children choose symbols for a map of the classroom and create a map key.

MATH CENTER

Basic Skills Activity

Motivate children to build basic skills. Use this activity to address multiple learning styles using hands-on activities related to the skills of this lesson.

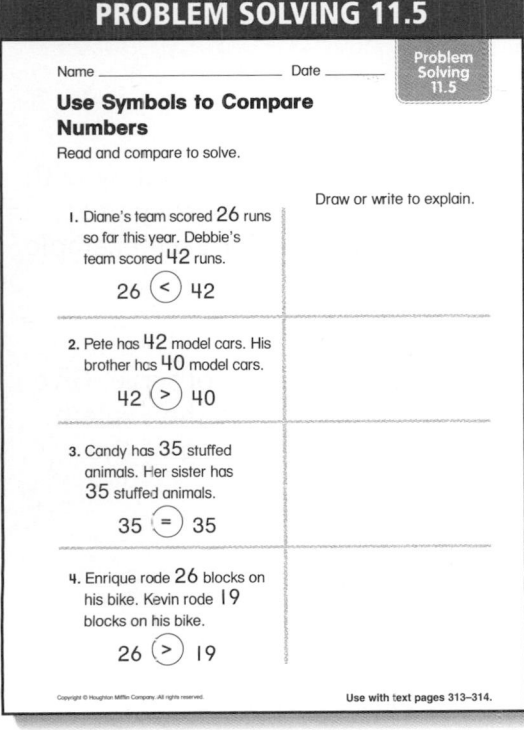

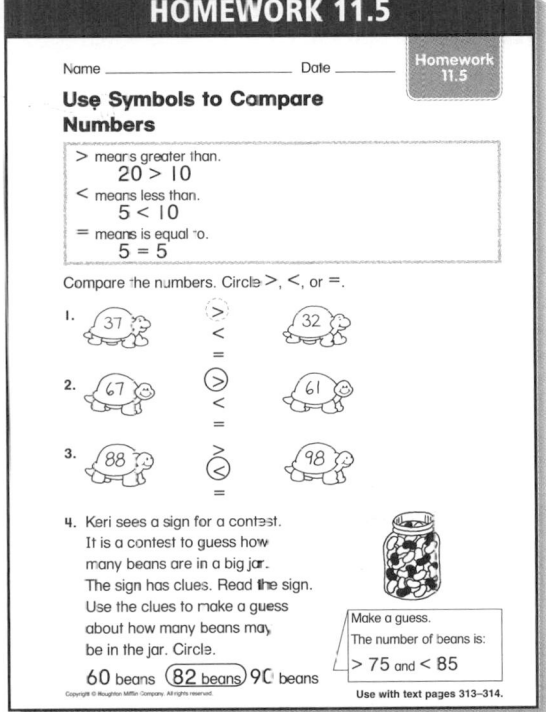

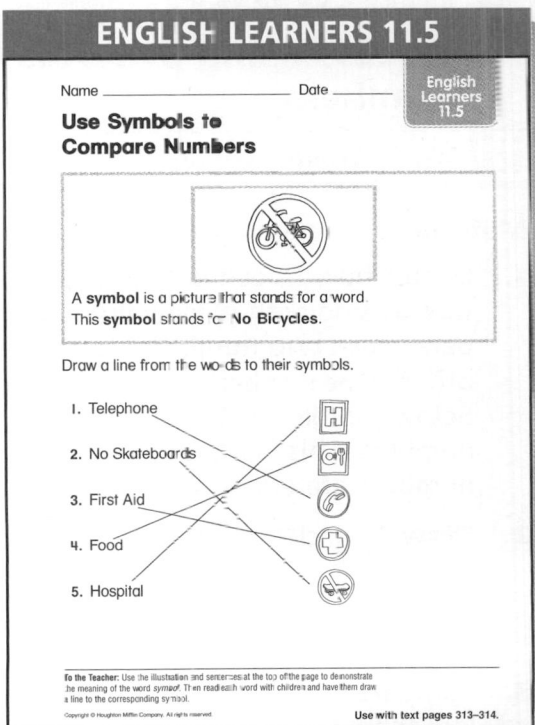

Homework Workbook Page 75

TEACHING LESSON 11.5

LESSON ORGANIZER

Objective Compare two-digit numbers, using >, <, and =.

Resources Reteach, Practice, Enrichment, Problem Solving, Homework, English Learners, Transparencies, Math Center

Materials Number line (LT 9), overhead place-value blocks, blank transparency

Warm-Up Activity
Comparing Numbers

| 👤👤👤 Small Group | 🕐 5 minutes | Visual, Auditory |

Materials: *number line (LT 9)*

1. Point to 86 and 89 on a number line. **Is 86 before or after 89?** (before) **Is 86 less than or greater than 89?** (less than) Discuss how children can tell, relating order to comparing.

2. Repeat with 85 and 83 to find the greater number.

83 84 85 86 87 88 89 90 91 92

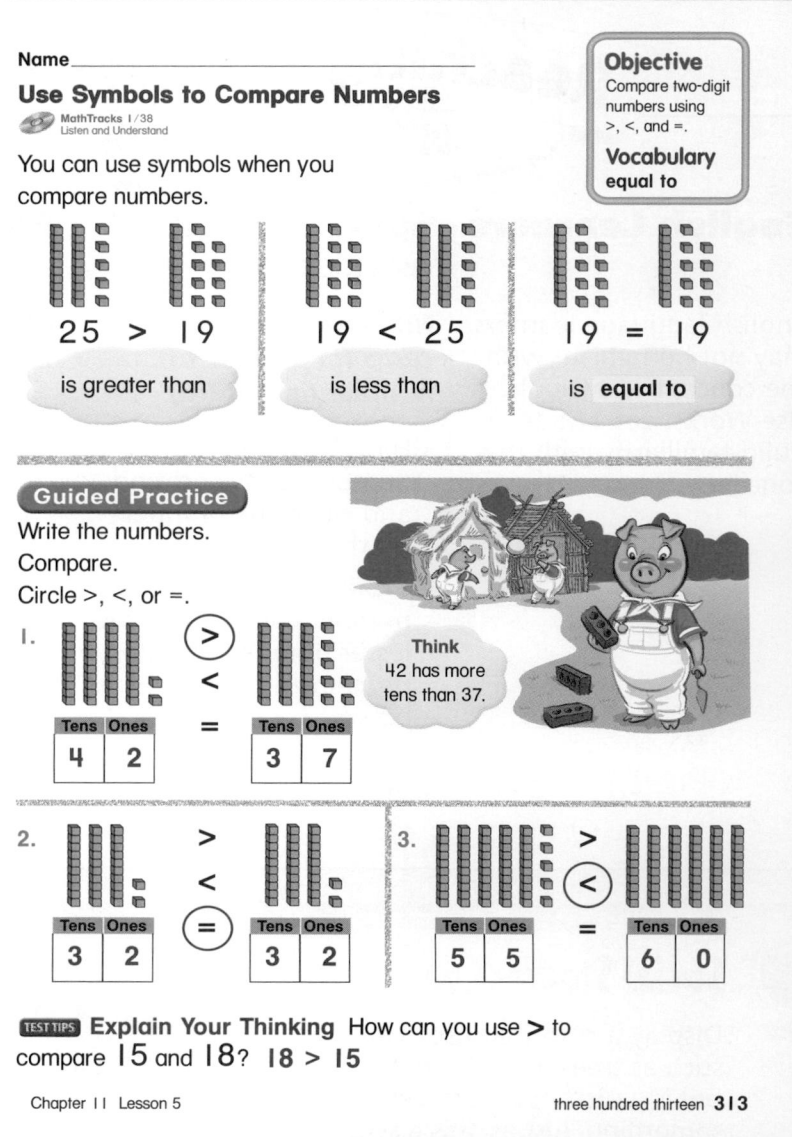

Name_____

Use Symbols to Compare Numbers

MathTracks 1/38
Listen and Understand

Objective Compare two-digit numbers using >, <, and =.

Vocabulary equal to

You can use symbols when you compare numbers.

25 > 19   19 < 25   19 = 19

is greater than   is less than   is **equal to**

Guided Practice

Write the numbers.
Compare.
Circle >, <, or =.

1. [blocks] > < = [blocks]

Think 42 has more tens than 37.

Tens	Ones
4	2

Tens	Ones
3	7

2. [blocks] > < = [blocks]

Tens	Ones
3	2

Tens	Ones
3	2

3. [blocks] > < = [blocks]

Tens	Ones
5	5

Tens	Ones
6	0

TEST TIPS Explain Your Thinking How can you use > to compare 15 and 18? 18 > 15

Chapter 11 Lesson 5   three hundred thirteen **313**

---

① Introduce

Discuss Using Symbols to Compare Numbers

| 👤👤👤👤 Whole Group | 🕐 10–15 minutes | Tactile, Visual |

Materials: *overhead place-value blocks, blank transparency*

1. Discuss how to compare 2 numbers. Show 24 and 24 side-by-side with place-value blocks. **How can we compare these two numbers? Is one greater or less than the other?** (The numbers are the same.) Write the numbers below the blocks. Write the equal sign between the two numbers. **This is a symbol we use to show that two numbers are equal. 24 is equal to 24.**

2. Show 34 and 26 with place-value blocks. **Which number is greater?** (34) Explain that there is also a symbol that means *greater than*. Write the symbol > between the two numbers. **34 is greater than 26.**

3. Compare 33 and 37 to introduce the symbol <. **33 is less than 37.**

② Develop

Guided Learning

Teaching Example Read the objective and vocabulary with children. Guide them through the example as they use place-value blocks to show the numbers. For each example, help children focus on the symbol.

Guided Practice

Have children complete **Exercises 1–3** as you observe. Give children the opportunity to share answers to the Explain Your Thinking question. Reinforce the meaning of the symbol.

313   **CHAPTER 11   Lesson 5**

Practice

Compare.
Circle >, <, or =.

> means is greater than,
< means is less than,
= means is equal to.

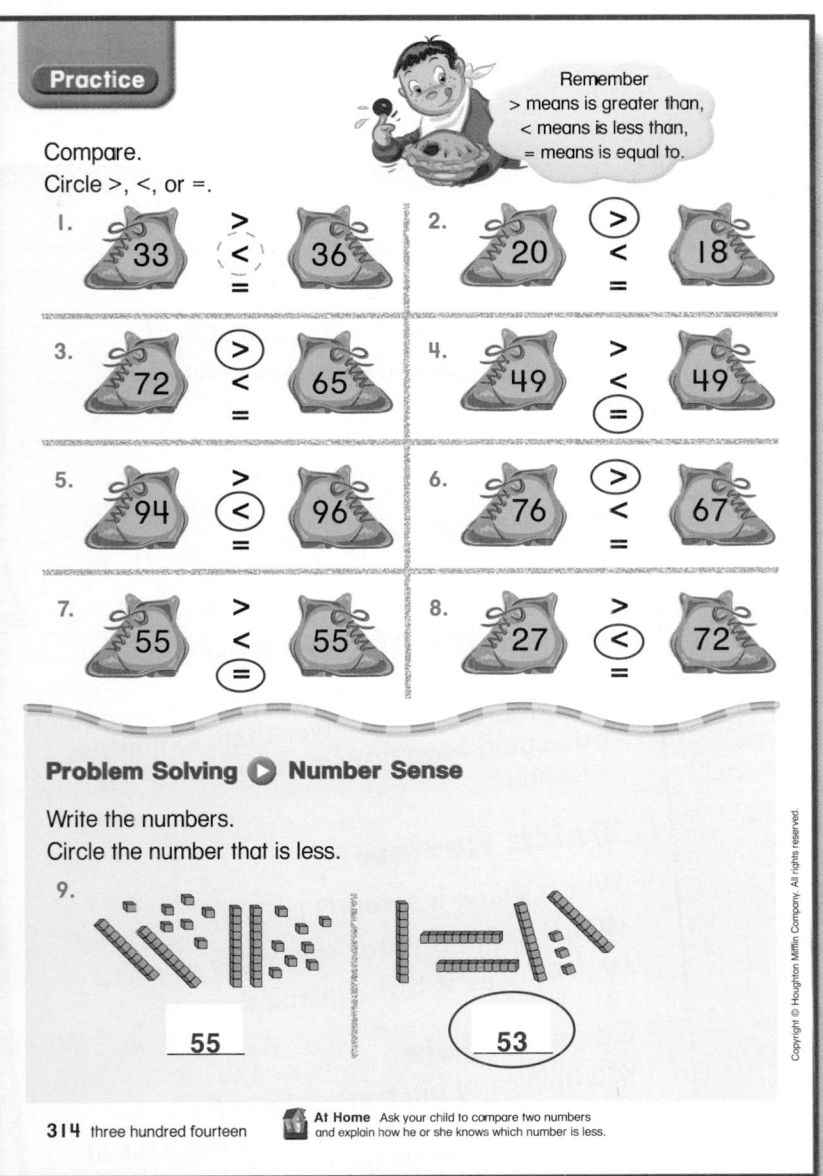

1. 33 > < = 36
2. 20 > < = 18
3. 72 > < = 65
4. 49 > < = 49
5. 94 > < = 96
6. 76 > < = 67
7. 55 > < = 55
8. 27 > < = 72

Problem Solving ▶ Number Sense

Write the numbers.
Circle the number that is less.

9.

55   53

314   three hundred fourteen

At Home Ask your child to compare two numbers
and explain how he or she knows which number is less.

Which is correct?

15 = 10	25 = 52	70 = 7	41 = 41
○	○	○	●

Activity

Lesson Intervention
Meaning of the Symbols

Or use
Intervention
CD-ROM
Lesson 11.5

👥 Small Group	🕐 10–15 minutes	Visual, Tactile

1. Reinforce the meaning of each symbol and create a helpful tool for children to use.

2. Draw the < and > symbols as mouths of an animal to which children can relate.

3. Write numbers on either side of each animal's head. **The hungry alligator always eats the greater number. The mouth is open this way so 43 is greater than 34. Here the mouth is open the other way so 34 is less than 43.**

43   34   34   43

---

3 Practice

Independent Practice

Children complete **Exercises 1–8** independently.

Problem Solving

After children complete **Exercise 9,** call on volunteers to share their answers. Discuss how they counted the blocks that show 55 and 53 and how they compared the numbers.

Common Error

Reversing Symbols

Tell children that the arrow always points to the lesser number and opens to the greater number. Allow children to use cards with the definitions of the symbols.

---

4 Assess and Close

Which is greater, 2 tens 5 ones or 40? (40) **How can you use symbols to compare these numbers?** (25 < 40 or 40 > 25)

When do you use the equal sign to compare numbers? (When the numbers are the same.)

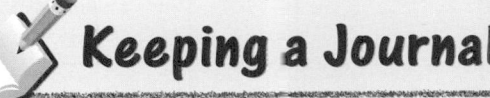 **Keeping a Journal**

Use a symbol to compare the numbers 30 and 50.

Problem Solving: Reasonable Answers

PLANNING THE LESSON

MATHEMATICS OBJECTIVE
Use estimation to find reasonable answers to problems.

Use Lesson Planner CD-ROM for Lesson 11.6.

Daily Routines

Calendar
Have children estimate about how many school days are in the month. Discuss children's ideas, and talk about whether they are reasonable. Then lead children in counting to find how many school days are in the current month.

Sunday	Monday	Tuesday	Wednesday	Thursday	Friday	Saturday
			1	2	3	4
5	6	7	8	9	10	11
12	13	14	15	16	17	18
19	20	21	22	23	24	25
26	27	28	29	30	31	

Vocabulary
Introduce the word **reasonable** as "making sense." Talk about examples of quantities that do and do not make sense: for example, *there are about 20 children in the class, there are about 100 children in the class.*

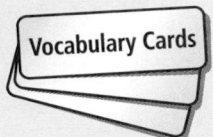
Vocabulary Cards

Meeting North Carolina's Standards
1.01 Develop number sense for whole numbers through 99.
- Connect the model, number word, and number using a variety of representations.

Lesson Transparency 11.6

Problem of the Day
Marc has 17 marbles. Bob has more marbles than Marc. He has fewer than 20 marbles. Bob could have how many marbles? (18 or 19 marbles)

Quick Review

Which shape is second? (square)
Which shape is third? (rectangle)
Which shape is fifth? (triangle)

Lesson Quiz
You help carry big bags of food from the grocery store. About how many big bags of food can you carry? (about 1 bag)

about 1 bag   about 10 bags

LEVELED PRACTICE

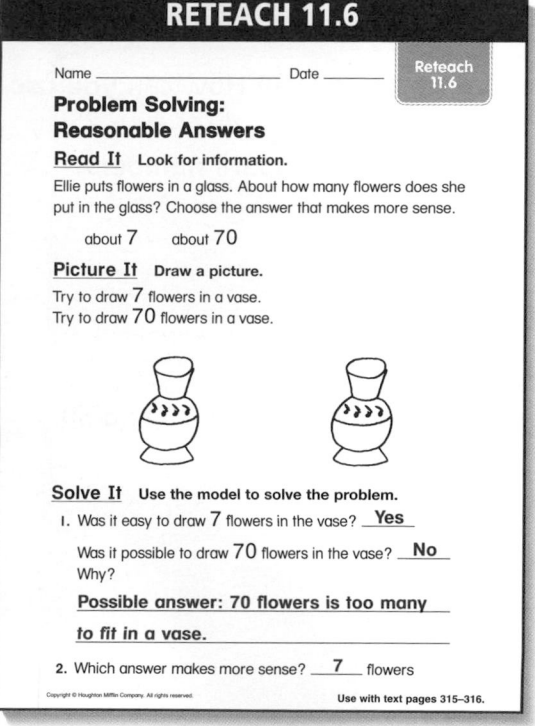

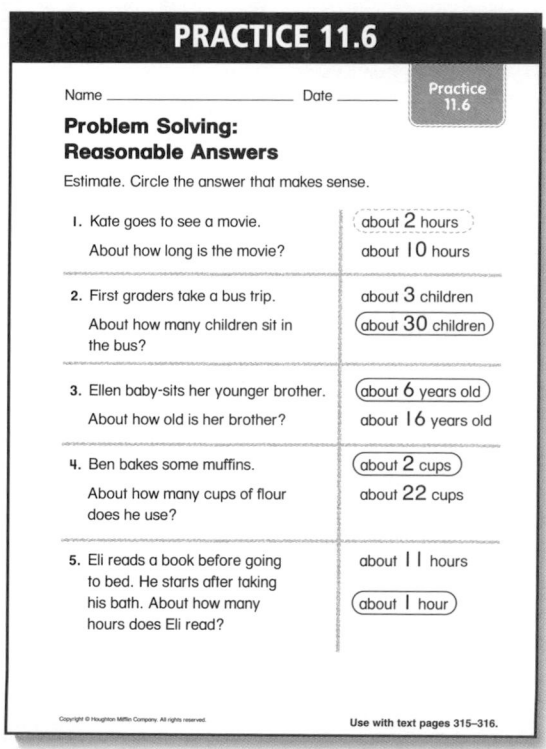

Practice Workbook Page 76

Reaching All Learners
Differentiated Instruction

English Learners

English-language learners may not be familiar with the expression *makes sense*. Use Worksheet 11.6 to build familiarity with this concept.

Inclusion
AUDITORY, TACTILE

Materials: *cubes*

- Have the child make a pile of 5 cubes, 15 cubes, and 30 cubes.
- **About how many cubes can you hold in one of your hands?**
- Have the child place one hand beside each stack. Guide the child to see that 5 is the most reasonable answer. Repeat with other numbers.

Gifted and Talented
VISUAL, TACTILE

Materials: *pattern blocks, 6-inch square (LT 28)*

- Have children estimate how many square pattern blocks will cover the 6-inch square.
- Then have the child cover the square with pattern blocks and count how many. **Was the estimate reasonable?**

TECHNOLOGY

Spiral Review

To reinforce skills on lessons taught earlier, create **customized** spiral review worksheets using the *Ways to Assess* CD-ROM.

Education Place

Recommend that parents visit **Education Place** at eduplace.com/parents/mw/ for parent support activities.

Intervention

Use the *Ways to Success* intervention software to support students who need more help in understanding the concepts and skills taught in this chapter.

 ## Literature Connection

Share the book, *What's a Pair? What's a Dozen?* by Stephen R. Swinburne. Create problems, such as: The girl has a box of donuts. How many do you think her mother will let her eat?

2 donuts   12 donuts

 MATH CENTER

Number of the Week Activity

Display the Number of the Week to motivate children to use their problem-solving skills. The exercises cover topics across all math strands.

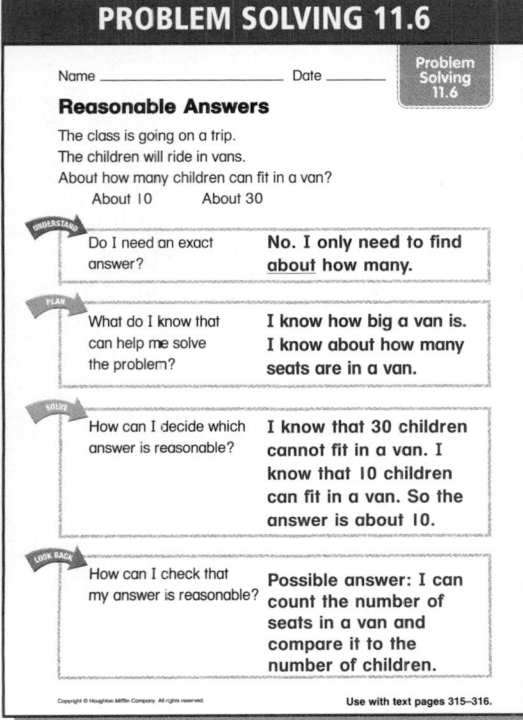

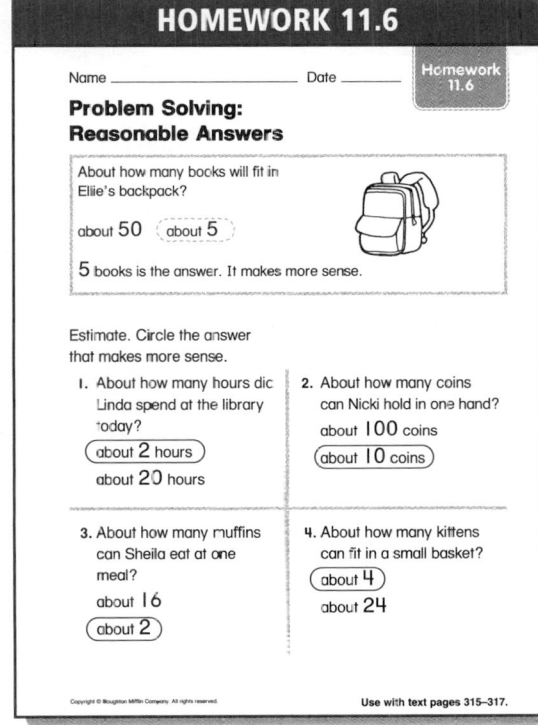

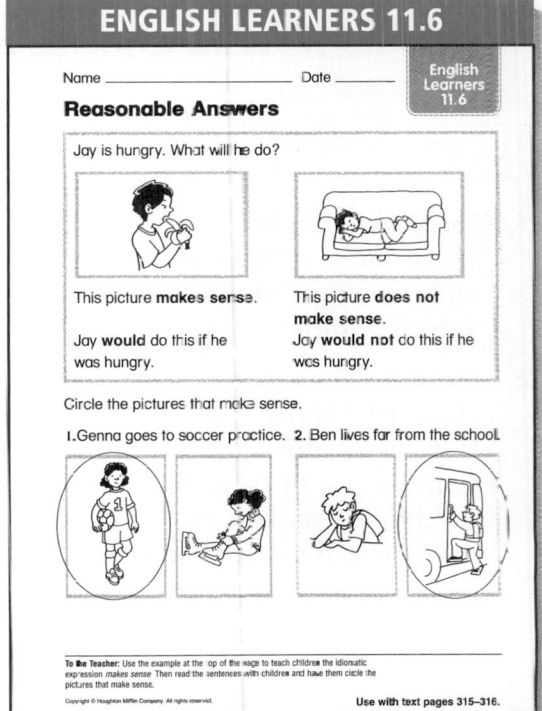

Homework Workbook Page 76

TEACHING LESSON 11.6

LESSON ORGANIZER

Objective Use estimation to find reasonable answers to problems.

Resources Reteach, Practice, Enrichment, Problem Solving, Homework, English Learners, Transparencies, Math Center

Materials Clear container, cubes, counters, coins

 **Activity**

Warm-Up Activity
Model Estimating

iiii Small Group	🕐 5 minutes	Visual, Auditory

Materials: *clear container, cubes*

1. Show a container of about 30 cubes. **About how many cubes are in the container?** Record children's estimates. Empty the contents and count about half the cubes. Ask the children if they want to change their estimates. Record the new estimates and complete the count. Compare it with the estimates. Remind children that one estimate can be better than another, but no reasonable estimate is wrong.

2. **Did I ask for an exact answer?** (no) **How do you know?** (You asked about how many.)

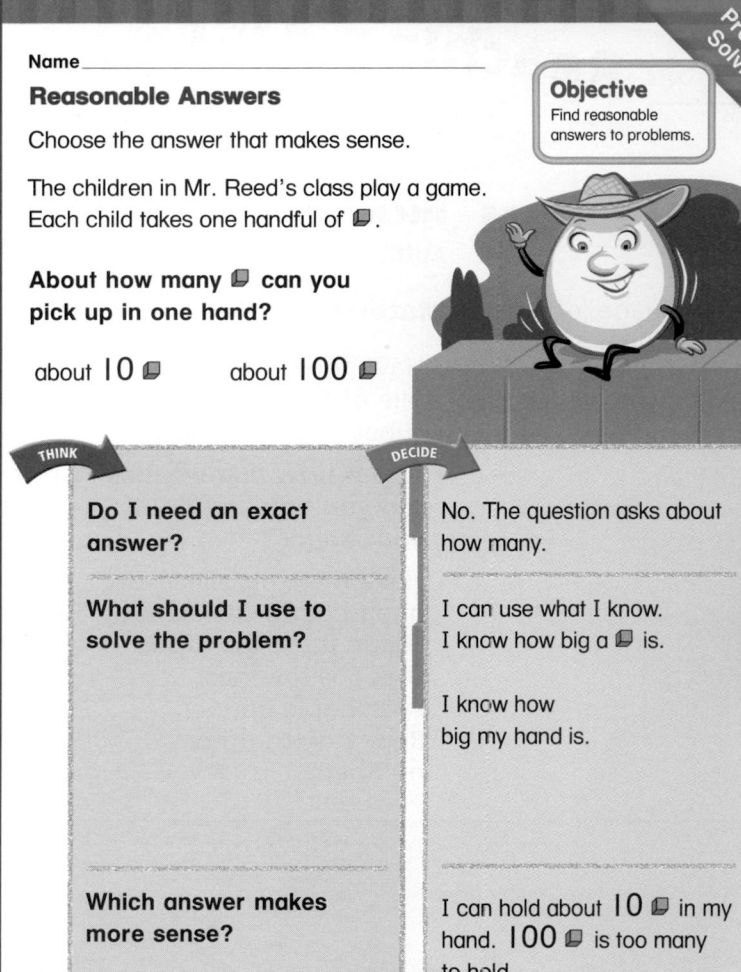

Name _____

Reasonable Answers

Choose the answer that makes sense.

The children in Mr. Reed's class play a game. Each child takes one handful of 🔲.

About how many 🔲 can you pick up in one hand?

about 10 🔲   about 100 🔲

THINK

Do I need an exact answer?

What should I use to solve the problem?

Which answer makes more sense?

DECIDE

No. The question asks about how many.

I can use what I know. I know how big a 🔲 is.

I know how big my hand is.

I can hold about 10 🔲 in my hand. 100 🔲 is too many to hold.

I can pick up about 10 🔲 in one hand.

Chapter 11 Lesson 6   three hundred fifteen **315**

Objective
Find reasonable answers to problems.

Problem Solving

---

❶ Introduce  Activity
Model How to Choose a Reasonable Answer

iiii Whole Group	🕐 10–15 minutes	Kinesthetic, Visual

1. Discuss the meaning of the word *reasonable* as making sense. **Does it make more sense that 100 children or 20 children could stand in our classroom library area? Which number is more reasonable?** (Answers may vary.)

2. Have children demonstrate which answer is reasonable. Have 10 children stand in that section of the classroom. **Is it reasonable that we can fit more children?** (yes) Continue until children can see which number is a reasonable answer to the question you posed. **What number is more reasonable, 100 or 20?** (20)

❷ Develop

Guided Learning

Teaching Example Introduce the objective to children. Guide them through the steps of the example problem focusing on the Think column and the Decide column. Emphasize that they are to choose the answer that makes more sense.

Guided Practice

Have children complete **Exercises 1–2** on page 316 as you observe. Remind them to use the hints that start with *Think*.

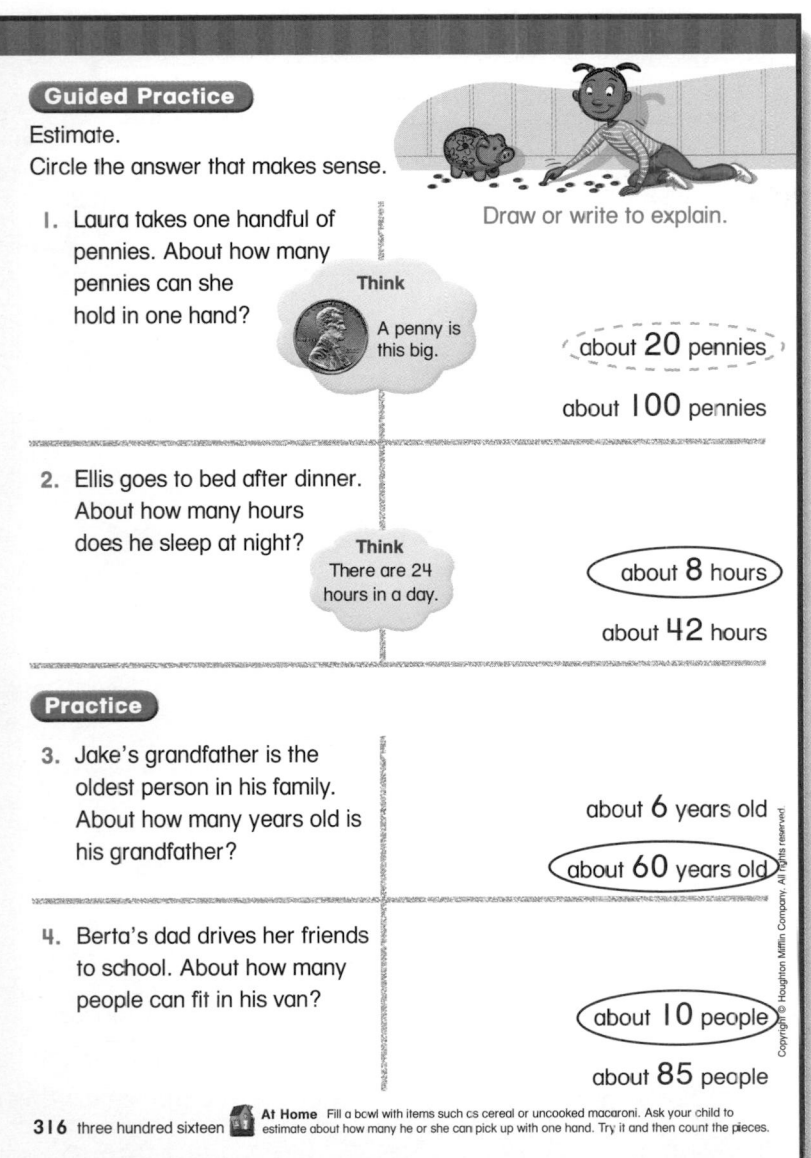

Guided Practice

Estimate.
Circle the answer that makes sense.

Draw or write to explain.

1. Laura takes one handful of pennies. About how many pennies can she hold in one hand?

   Think A penny is this big.

   (about 20 pennies)

   about 100 pennies

2. Ellis goes to bed after dinner. About how many hours does he sleep at night?

   Think There are 24 hours in a day.

   (about 8 hours)

   about 42 hours

Practice

3. Jake's grandfather is the oldest person in his family. About how many years old is his grandfather?

   about 6 years old

   (about 60 years old)

4. Berta's dad drives her friends to school. About how many people can fit in his van?

   (about 10 people)

   about 85 people

316 three hundred sixteen

At Home Fill a bowl with items such cs cereal or uncooked macaroni. Ask your child to estimate about how many he or she can pick up with one hand. Try it and then count the pieces.

Daily Test Prep

Elena is going apple picking. How many apples can she reasonably carry in both hands?

about 3 ●   about 10 ○   about 25 ○   about 30 ○

Activity

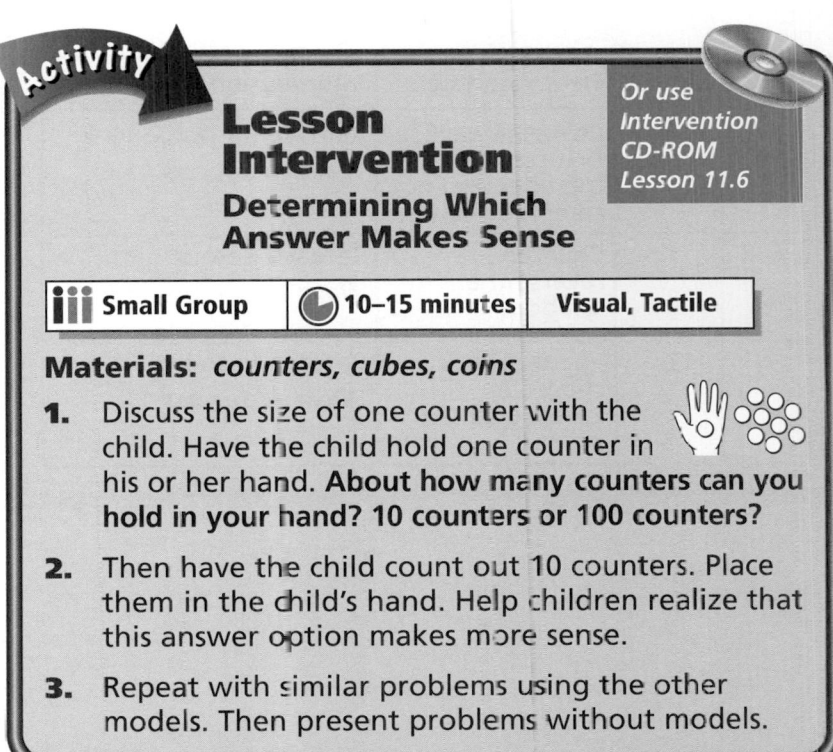

Lesson Intervention
Determining Which Answer Makes Sense

Or use Intervention CD-ROM Lesson 11.6

| 👤👤👤 Small Group | ⏱ 10–15 minutes | Visual, Tactile |

Materials: *counters, cubes, coins*

1. Discuss the size of one counter with the child. Have the child hold one counter in his or her hand. **About how many counters can you hold in your hand? 10 counters or 100 counters?**

2. Then have the child count out 10 counters. Place them in the child's hand. Help children realize that this answer option makes more sense.

3. Repeat with similar problems using the other models. Then present problems without models.

---

3 Practice

Independent Practice

Children complete **Exercises 3–4** independently.

Common Error

Choosing an Unreasonable Answer
Children may be unable to visualize the numbers of objects in the answer choices. Have children talk through problems as you provide hints about the size of the groups. Provide problems like those on the page, as well as problems that children can act out.

4 Assess and Close

Bert takes books out of the library. About how many books does he take at one time?

4 books   40 books

(4 books) **Why is this answer more reasonable?** (Possible answers: The library will not let you take out 40 books at one time; 40 books are too heavy to carry.)

 Keeping a Journal

Draw a picture of something that is not reasonable for you to carry in your arms. Now draw something that is reasonable.

Lesson continues →

Quick Check

Have children complete the Quick Check exercises independently to assess their understanding of concepts and skills taught in **Lessons 4–6.**

Item	Lesson	Error Analysis	Intervention
1–4	11.4	Children may first compare the ones and not compare the tens.	Reteach Resource 11.4 **Ways to Success** 11.4
5–8	11.5	Children may reverse the symbols.	Reteach Resource 11.5 **Ways to Success** 11.5
9	11.6	Children may choose an unreasonable answer.	Reteach Resource 11.6 **Ways to Success** 11.6

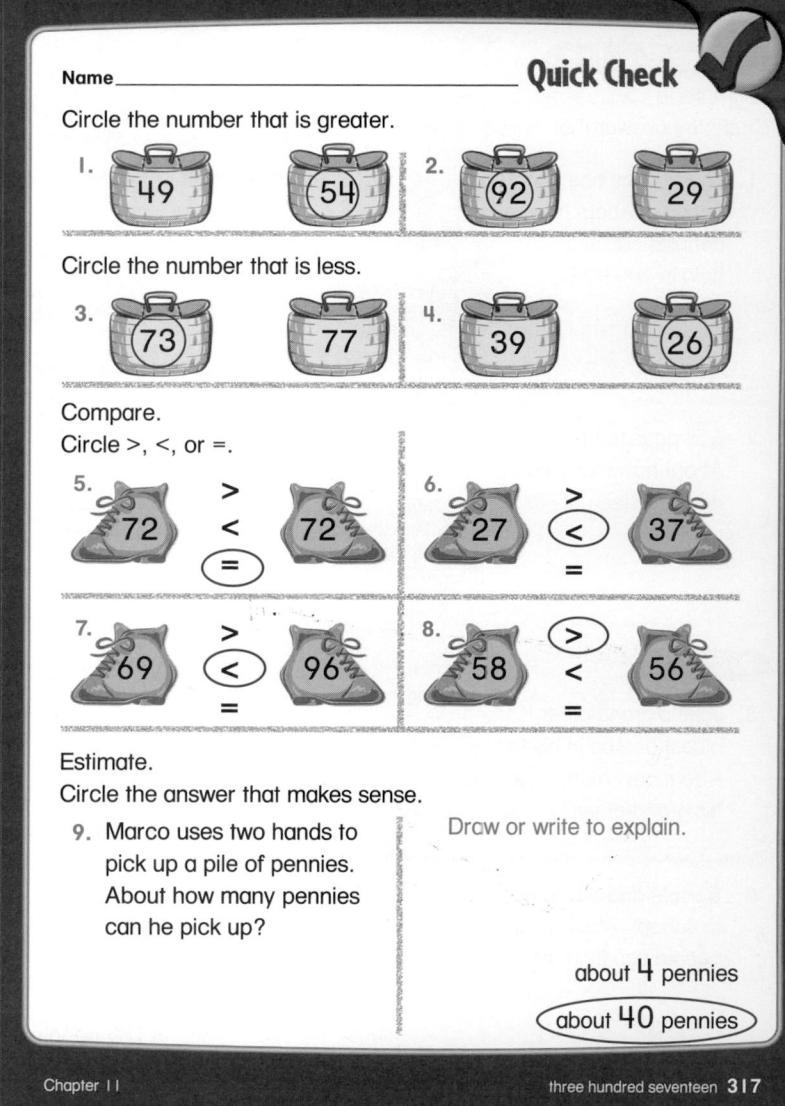

Name_____

Quick Check

Circle the number that is greater.

1. 49 (54) 2. (92) 29

Circle the number that is less.

3. (73) 77 4. (39) 26

Compare.
Circle >, <, or =.

5. 72 > (<) (=) 72

6. 27 > (<) = 37

7. 69 > (<) = 96

8. 58 (>) < = 56

Estimate.
Circle the answer that makes sense.

9. Marco uses two hands to pick up a pile of pennies. About how many pennies can he pick up?

Draw or write to explain.

about 4 pennies
(about 40 pennies)

Key Topic Review

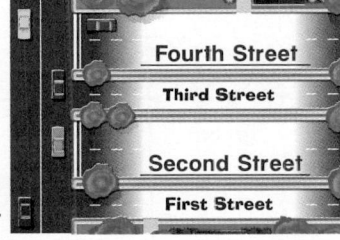

| cube | cone | cylinder | rectangular prism | pyramid | sphere |

Complete the table.

	Name of Solid	Number of Faces	Number of Edges	Number of Corners
1.	pyramid	5	8	5
2.	rectangular prism	6	12	8
3.	sphere	0	0	0

Find how each solid can move.
Write yes or no in the table.

		Slide	Stack	Roll
4.		yes	yes	no
5.		yes	yes	yes

Social Studies Connection

Number Streets

Some streets have number names. They are found in many cities. Look at the map. Write the missing street names on the map.

Fourth Street
Third Street

Second Street
First Street

Key Topic Review

This assessment provides a review of skills and concepts taught in Chapter 7.

Check to be sure that children:

• can identify each solid shape

• can describe the attributes of each shape

• can compare the attributes of the shapes

Social Studies Connection

Guide children as necessary to read the street names and fill in the missing ordinal numbers. **What streets could come after Fourth Street?** (Fifth, Sixth, Seventh, and so on)

If your city or town has such street names, ask children if they have ever been on First Street or Fifth Avenue. Discuss what can be found on those streets, such as stores, houses, and factories.

Monitoring Student Progress

Chapter Review/Test

Purpose: This test provides an informal assessment of the Chapter 11 objectives.

Chapter Test Items 1–20

To assign a numerical grade for this Chapter Test, use 5 points for each test item.

Check Understanding

Use children's work on word problems to informally assess progress on chapter content.

Customizing Your Instruction

For children who have not yet mastered these objectives, you can use the reteaching resources listed in the chart below.

 ## Assessment Options

A summary test for this chapter is also provided in the Unit Resource Folder.

Chapter Summary Test

To assign a numerical grade for this test, use 5 points for each test item and then add 10.

Name_____

Chapter Review/Test

Vocabulary *Glossary*
Complete the sentence.

| less than |
| equal to |
| after |

1. 60 is ____equal to____ 60.

2. 19 comes just ____after____ 18.

3. 37 is ____less than____ 47.

Concepts and Skills
Use Workmats 7 and 8.
Write the number that comes just before or just after.

4. __70__, 71   5. 62, __63__   6. __79__, 80

Write the number that comes between.

7. 13, __14__, 15   8. 31, __32__, 33   9. 64, __65__, 66

Color.

green   red   blue

10. fifth   11. tenth   12. third

Reteaching Support

Chapter Test Items	Summary Test Items	Chapter Objectives Tested	TE Pages	Use These Reteaching Resources
1–3	1–4	**11A** Develop and use math vocabulary relating to ordering and comparing numbers.	303A–304, 313A–314	Reteach Resources and *Ways to Success* CD: 11.1, 11.5 Skillsheet 76
4–9, 14–19	13–16	**11B** Order and compare numbers through 100 using words and symbols.	303A–304	Reteach Resource and *Ways to Success* CD: 11.1 Skillsheet 77
10–12	5–8	**11C** Identify ordinal numbers 1st through 10th.	305A–306	Reteach Resource and *Ways to Success* CD: 11.2 Skillsheet 78
13	9–12	**11D** Estimate using a group of ten as a referent.	307A–309	Reteach Resource and *Ways to Success* CD: 11.3 Skillsheet 79
20	17–18	**11E** Find reasonable answers to problems.	315A–316	Reteach Resource and *Ways to Success* CD: 11.6 Skillsheet 80

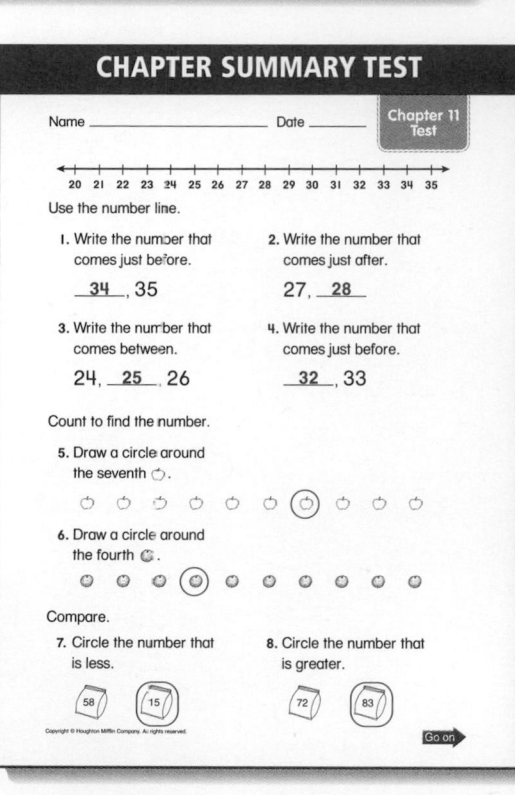

CHAPTER SUMMARY TEST

Name_____ Date_____ Chapter 11 Test

20 21 22 23 24 25 26 27 28 29 30 31 32 33 34 35
Use the number line.

1. Write the number that comes just before.
__34__, 35

2. Write the number that comes just after.
27, __28__

3. Write the number that comes between.
24, __25__ 26

4. Write the number that comes just before.
__32__, 33

Count to find the number.

5. Draw a circle around the seventh.

6. Draw a circle around the fourth.

Compare.

7. Circle the number that is less.
58   15

8. Circle the number that is greater.
72   83

Copyright © Houghton Mifflin Company. All rights reserved.

Go on

Circle one group of ten.
Estimate about how many in all. Then count.

Estimates may vary.

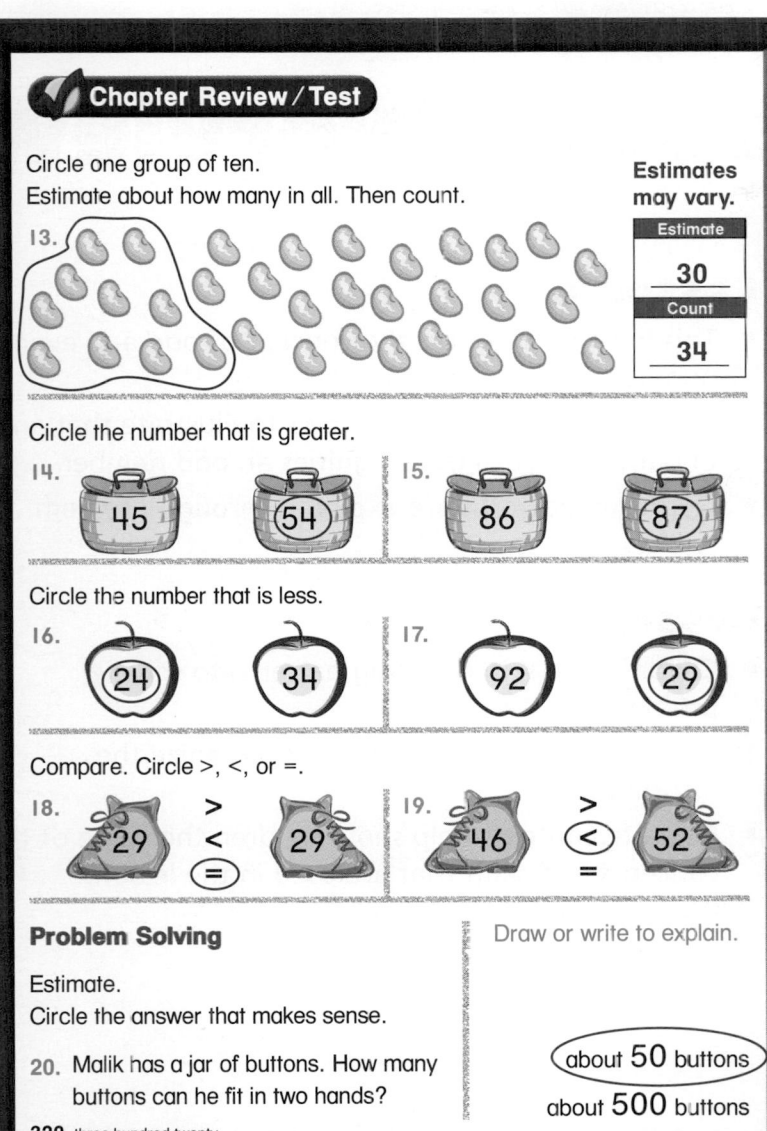

13.

Estimate
30
Count
34

Circle the number that is greater.

14. 45 54

15. 86 87

Circle the number that is less.

16. 24 34

17. 92 29

Compare. Circle >, <, or =.

18. 29 > < = 29

19. 46 > < = 52

Problem Solving

Draw or write to explain.

Estimate.
Circle the answer that makes sense.

20. Malik has a jar of buttons. How many buttons can he fit in two hands?

about 50 buttons

about 500 buttons

320 three hundred twenty

Adequate Yearly Progress

Use the End of Grade Test Prep Assessment Guide to help familiarize your children with the format of standardized tests.

CHAPTER SUMMARY TEST

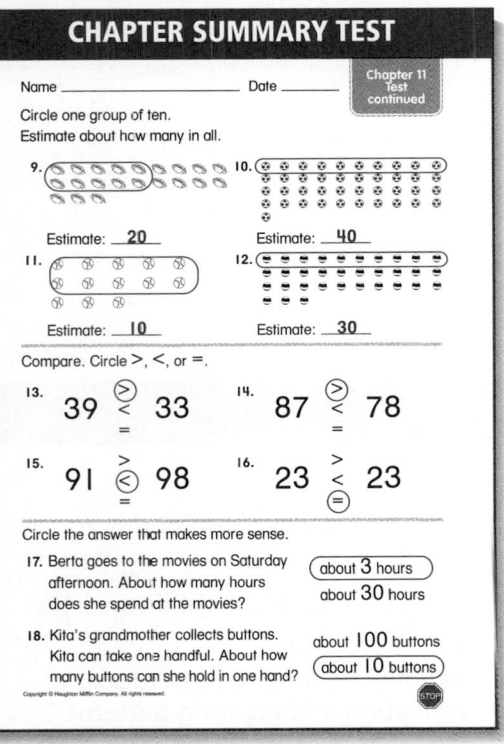

Name _____ Date _____

Chapter 11 Test continued

Circle one group of ten.
Estimate about how many in all.

9.

Estimate: __20__

10.

Estimate: __40__

11.

Estimate: __10__

12.

Estimate: __30__

Compare. Circle >, <, or =.

13. 39 > < = 33

14. 87 > < = 78

15. 91 > < = 98

16. 23 > < = 23

Circle the answer that makes more sense.

17. Berta goes to the movies on Saturday afternoon. About how many hours does she spend at the movies?

about 3 hours

about 30 hours

18. Kita's grandmother collects buttons. Kita can take one handful. About how many buttons can she hold in one hand?

about 100 buttons

about 10 buttons

Lesson by Lesson Overview
Number Patterns

Lesson 1

- The first number pattern in this chapter is counting by 2s.
- Children count pictured sets of distinct objects by 2s to find the totals.
- They also use a hundred chart to count on by 2s from various numbers.

Lesson 2

- In this lesson, children learn to skip count by 5s.
- Here the pictured sets of starfish present a different type of model. Children count by 5s to find the number of arms.
- This skill will later be applied to counting nickels.

Lesson 3

- This lesson teaches children how to use a hundred chart to find numbers that are 1 or 10 more and 1 or 10 less than given numbers.
- The horizontal 1s patterns and the vertical 10s patterns are supported by the format of the exercises.
- Children also use these patterns to fill in missing numbers on a fragment of a hundred chart.
- A game provides practice in skip counting by 5s and can be adapted to any number.

Lesson 4

- This lesson introduces the concept of *odd* and *even* numbers.
- Cubes are pictured in two rows to illustrate that an unpaired or extra cube signifies an odd number.
- Odd/even patterns are explored through problem solving.

Lesson 5

- Children use skip counting patterns to solve problems.
- Patterns are written in tables to organize the information.
- Real-life contexts help show children the value of the concepts and skills that are used in the lesson.

SKILLS TRACE: NUMBER PATTERNS

Grade K	Grade 1	Grade 2
• skip count by 2s, 5s, 10s (ch. 16) • find a number that is more or less (ch. 8) • build sets by 2s, 3s, and 5s (ch. 8)	• skip count by 2s to 100 • skip count by 5s to 100 • identify the number that is 1 or 10 more; 1 or 10 less • identify even and odd numbers	• identify even and odd numbers (ch. 5) • skip count by 2s, 3s, 4s, 5s, and 10s (ch. 5) • extend, describe, and create repeating and growing patterns (ch. 5)

Chapter Planner

Lesson	Objective	Vocabulary	Materials	✓ NCTM Standards
12.1 **Count by Twos** p. 323A	Skip count by twos to 100.	skip count	Workmat 6, hundred chart transparency strips of paper, hundred chart (Learning Tool (LT)7), counters	Recognize, describe, and extend patterns such as sequences of sounds and shapes or simple numeric patterns and translate from one representation to another.
12.2 **Count by Fives** p. 325A	Skip count by fives to 100.		Workmat 6, counters, hundred chart transparency	Recognize, describe, and extend patterns such as sequences of sounds and shapes or simple numeric patterns and translate from one representation to another.
12.3 **More Than, Less Than** p. 327A	Identify 1 more, 1 less, 10 more, and 10 less than a given number.	more than less than	cubes, hundred chart transparency, counters, sandwich bags, Workmat 6	Recognize, describe, and extend patterns such as sequences of sounds and shapes or simple numeric patterns and translate from one representation to another.
12.4 **Odd and Even Numbers** **(Hands-On)** p. 331A	Find a pattern in odd and even numbers.	odd even	cubes, paper bag, number cards 1-10 (LT 14)	Recognize, describe, and extend patterns such as sequences of sounds and shapes or simple numeric patterns and translate from one representation to another.
12.5 **Problem Solving: Find a Pattern** p. 333A	Use patterns to solve problems.		blank transparency, cubes	Analyze how both repeating and growing patterns are generated.

Resources For Reaching All Learners

LESSON RESOURCES: Reteach, Practice, Enrichment, Problem Solving, Homework, English Learners, Daily Routines, Transparencies, Math Center.

ADDITIONAL RESOURCES FROM HOUGHTON MIFFLIN: Chapter Challenges, Combination Classroom Planning Guide, Every Day Counts, Math to Learn (Student Handbook)

Every Day Counts
The *Calendar* and *Counting Tape* activities in Every Day Counts support the math in this chapter.

Assessing Prior Knowledge

Before beginning this chapter, you can assess student understandings in order to assist you in differentiating instruction.

Complete Chapter Pretest in Unit Resource Folder

Use this test to assess both prerequisite skills (**Are You Ready?** — one page) and chapter content (**Check What You Know** — two pages).

Chapter 12 Prerequisite Skills Pretest

Chapter 12 New Content Pretest

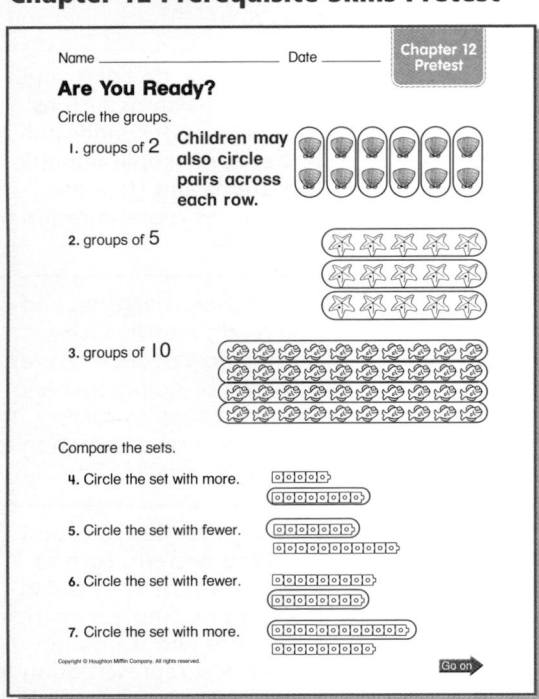

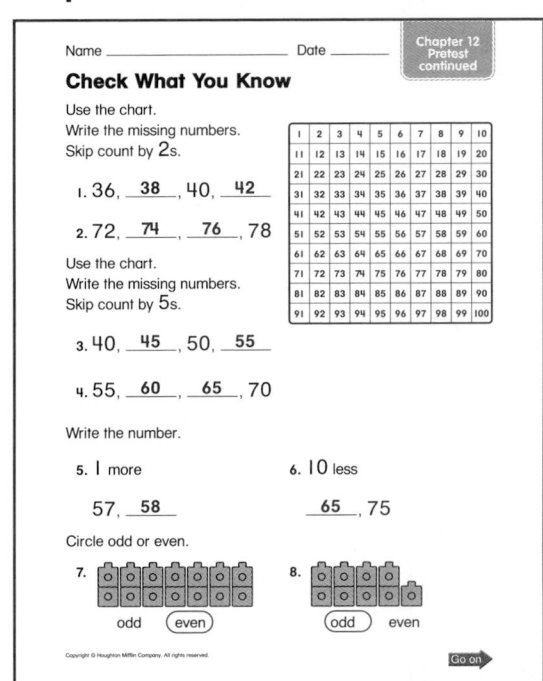

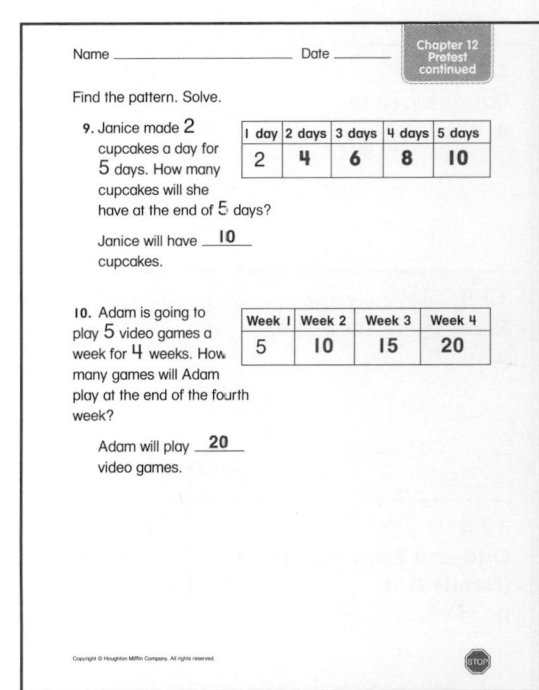

Customizing Instruction

For Students Having Difficulty

Items	Prerequisites	Ways to Success
1–3	Identify groups of 2, 5, and 10.	CD: 10.1 Skillsheet 81
4–7	Compare sets to find more or less.	CD: 1.1 Skillsheet 82

Ways to Success Intervention for every concept and skill (CD-ROM or Chapter Intervention Skillsheets).

For Students Having Success

Items	Objectives	Resources
1–4	12A Use vocabulary relating to number patterns.	Enrichment 12.1, 12.3, 12.4
1–4	12B Skip count by 2s and 5s to 100.	Enrichment 12.1, 12.2
5–8	12C Identify odd and even numbers and 1 more, 1 less, 10 more, 10 less.	Enrichment 12.3, 12.4
9–10	12D Use patterns to solve problems.	Enrichment 12.5

Use **Chapter Challenges** with any students who have success with all new chapter content.

Other Pretest Options

Informal Pretest

The pretest assesses vocabulary and prerequisite skills needed for success in this chapter.

Ways to Success **CD-ROM**

The *Ways to Success* chapter pretest has automatic assignment of appropriate review lessons.

Chapter Resources

Activity

Assessing Prior Knowledge

More Than 10 (more than, less than)

- Have available in the math center several sets of number cards 11–20. Invite pairs of children to work together for this activity.
- Children shuffle the cards and place them facedown in a pile. One child chooses a card, and reads the number. The other child uses tens and ones blocks to build the number.
- Then children determine how many more than 10 each number is.

Activity

Ongoing Skill Activity

Fair Sharing (odd and even numbers)

- Provide a container of counters and paper cups in the math center. Invite children to determine if a "scoop" of counters can be shared equally.
- Have pairs of children work together, alternating roles. One child takes a scoop of counters and the other child tries to share the counters equally.
- Children write an addition sentence for the activity. Encourage children to note a pattern of numbers that can be shared fairly. (even numbers)

Activity

Connecting to the Unit Project

- Give pairs of children 10 or 20 rocks.
- Have one child in each pair count the rocks by 2s. The other child can record the total number.
- Have children switch roles. This time, have one child count the rocks by 5s. Then the other children can record the number.
- Have children compare the numbers they record.

Teacher Support

Professional Resources Handbook

Research, Mathematics Content, and Language Intervention

Research-Based Teaching

Some studies have argued that the English language is not always conducive to pattern detection (Miller & Parades, 1996). Having children identify the tens and ones in numbers helps them better understand place value. Sisul (2002) suggests that children will naturally show their interest in the patterns and relationships found in a hundreds chart. See *Professional Resources Handbook, Grade 1,* Unit 4.

For more ideas relating to Unit 4, see the Teacher Support Handbook at the back of this Teacher's Edition.

Language Intervention

When students are working together on hands-on activities, encourage them to verbalize what they are doing and why. This will help them build their own understanding and math vocabulary. It will also benefit the other students in the group.

Technology

Time-Saving Technology Support
Ways to Assess Customized Spiral Review Test Generator CD
Lesson Planner CD-ROM
Ways to Success Intervention CD-ROM
MathTracks CD-ROM
Education Place: www.eduplace.com/math/mw
Houghton Mifflin Math eBook CD-ROM
eManipulatives
eGames

Starting Chapter 12
Number Patterns

CHAPTER OBJECTIVES

12A Develop and use math vocabulary relating to number patterns.

12B Skip count by 2s and 5s to 100.

12C Identify even and odd numbers and 1 more, 1 less, 10 more, 10 less than a given number.

12D Use patterns to solve problems.

Math Background

Number Patterns

Recognition of number patterns is an important mathematical skill for children to develop. Skip counting results in very simple number patterns, such as 2, 4, 6, 8, . . . , and 5, 10, 15, 20. In preparation for renaming skills required in computation, children also need to be able to recognize relationships between numbers, such as 1 more, 1 less, 10 more, and 10 less than a given number. Patterns of even and odd numbers build understanding of number relationships.

The hundred chart can be used in developing skills with number patterns and relationships. For example, by placing the counter on a number such as 26, and moving the counter forward one number to 27, children can see that the digit in the ones place increases while the digit in the tens place remains the same. By moving the counter forward ten spaces (down one row) from 26 to 36, children can see that the digit in the ones place remains the same while the digit in the tens place increases.

Number Patterns CHAPTER 12

INVESTIGATION

What patterns do you see?

Chapter 12   three hundred twenty-one 321

Using The Investigation

- Introduce the word *pattern* to children. Draw a shape pattern on the board. Ask a volunteer to describe it. Ask children to identify patterns they see around the classroom. Have them explain what makes their suggestion a pattern.

- Read the question to children. **Look at the picture. What patterns do you see?** (patterns on a fence, shells, roof, umbrella)

 For more information about projects and investigations, visit Education Place. **eduplace.com/math/mw/**

Painted Post

Skip count by 2s to find how many posts there are in the fence.

Use ▭▭▭▭▭ to color in every other post.

322 three hundred twenty-two

For Mathematically Promising Students

The *Chapter Challenges* resource book provides blackline masters for activities that explore, extend, and connect the mathematics in every chapter. To support this independent work, see the Teacher Notes for each activity.

Explore: Backward on the Calculator, page 67, after Lesson 1
Extend: Showing More and Less, page 69, after Lesson 3
Connect: Odd or Even?, page 71, after Lesson 5

Using This Page

- Direct children to the picture of a fence on page 322. Give each child a crayon.

- **Skip count by twos to find how many posts there are in the fence. Use your crayon to color in every other post.**

- When children have completed the exercise, have volunteers tell how many posts there are in the fence and describe the pattern they made. (14 posts) Make sure students only count the vertical posts on the fence.

- Have children draw a picture and create their own patterns to color, to show skip counting by fives.

NSF Children's Math Worlds

Children's Math Worlds focuses on the use of models to represent mathematical situations. Thus, using a *Children's Math Worlds* lesson helps students develop a general facility with drawing models to support their thinking that will transfer to all their mathematical work.

Count by Twos

PLANNING THE LESSON

MATHEMATICS OBJECTIVE
Skip count by twos to 100.

 Use Lesson Planner CD-ROM for Lesson 12.1.

Meeting North Carolina's Standards

1.02 Use groupings of 2's, 5's, and 10's with models and pictures to count collections of objects.

Also 5.03

Daily Routines

Calendar
Use the calendar to practice counting by 2s. Begin with 2, and point to every other date as children count to 30.

Vocabulary
Review **skip counting** by displaying a hundred chart and asking children to skip count by 2s to 100 with you. Discuss why the phrase skip counting makes sense.

Vocabulary Cards

Lesson Transparency **12.1**

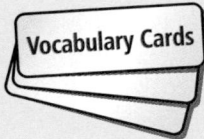

Problem of the Day
Allen has 10 pairs of socks. How many socks does he have? (20)

Quick Review
Name the number.

1 ten 1 one (11)   2 tens 6 ones (26)

5 tens 9 ones (59)   10 tens 0 ones (100)

Lesson Quiz
Skip count by 2s. Find the missing numbers.

1. 74, ___ (76), ___ (78), 80, 82

2. 16, 18, ___ (20), ___ (22), 24

3. 48, ___ (50), ___ (52), ___ (54), ___ (56)

LEVELED PRACTICE

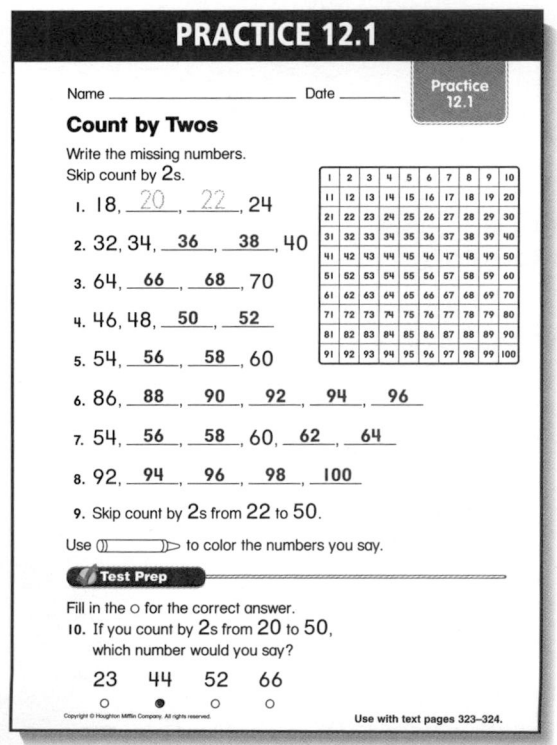

RETEACH 12.1

Name _____ Date _____   Reteach 12.1

Count By Twos

To skip count by 2s, count two at a time.

___12___ mittens

Find how many in all.
Skip count by 2s.

1.
2   4   6   8   10   10 puppies

2.
2   4   6   8
10   12   14   16   16 kittens

3.
2   4   6   8   10
12   14   16   18   20   20 rabbits

Use with text pages 323–324.

PRACTICE 12.1

Name _____ Date _____   Practice 12.1

Count by Twos

Write the missing numbers.
Skip count by 2s.

1. 18, _20_, _22_, 24

2. 32, 34, _36_, _38_, 40

3. 64, _66_, _68_, 70

4. 46, 48, _50_, _52_

5. 54, _56_, _58_, 60

6. 86, _88_, _90_, 92, _94_, 96

7. 54, _56_, _58_, 60, _62_, _64_

8. 92, _94_, _96_, _98_, 100

9. Skip count by 2s from 22 to 50.

Use (✏) to color the numbers you say.

Test Prep

Fill in the ○ for the correct answer.

10. If you count by 2s from 20 to 50, which number would you say?

23   44   52   66
○   ●   ○   ○

Use with text pages 323–324.

ENRICHMENT 12.1

Name _____ Date _____   Enrichment 12.1

Two by Two

Count by 2s.

Write the answer. **Answers will vary.**

1. How many ears do the boys in your class have in all?

2. How many ears do the girls in your class have in all?

3. How many eyes do the children in your class have in all?

4. How many pictures are hanging in your classroom?

5. How many children in your class have brown eyes?

6. How many children in your class have blue eyes?

7. How many children in your class are wearing blue today?

8. How many children in your class are wearing sneakers?

Write About It Why is it easier to count by 2s than 1s?

Children may say that it is faster than counting by 1s.

Use with text pages 323–324.

Practice Workbook Page 77

Reaching All Learners

Differentiated Instruction

English Learners

English-language learners may not be familiar with the word *skip*. Use Worksheet 12.1 to develop children's understanding of this word.

Special Needs
VISUAL, TACTILE

Materials: *counters*

- Have the child place counters in groups of two on a piece of paper.
- Together skip count by 2s as you write the number under each pair.
- Help the child see the pattern of counters increasing by 2 each time.

Early Finishers
TACTILE, VISUAL

Materials: *magazines*

- Have children find pictures in magazines showing items that come in pairs.
- They can skip count the pairs of items, labeling the skip-counting number of each pair to find the total number of items.

TECHNOLOGY

Spiral Review

Help students remember skills they learned earlier by creating **customized** spiral review worksheets using the *Ways to Assess* CD-ROM.

Lesson Planner

Use the **Lesson Planner CD-ROM** to see how lesson objectives for this chapter are correlated to standards.

Manipulatives

An interactive **Hundred Chart** is available on the *Ways to Success* CD.

Literature Connection

Read the story, *Missing Mittens* by Stuart J. Murphy. As you read, pause before turning each page to have children predict what animals Bill will visit next, and how many mittens they will need to stay warm. Point out that the number of mittens increases by 2 each time.

MATH CENTER

Basic Skills Activity

Motivate children to build basic skills. Use this activity to address multiple learning styles using hands-on activities related to the skills of this lesson.

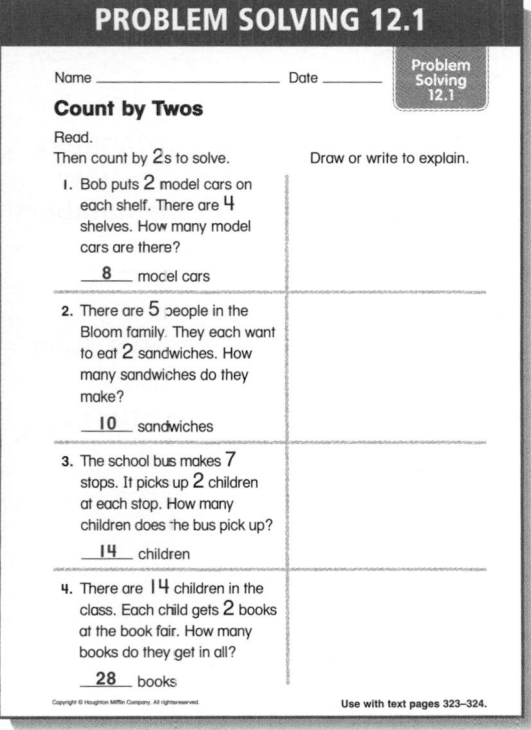

PROBLEM SOLVING 12.1

Name _____ Date _____   Problem Solving 12.1

Count by Twos

Read.
Then count by 2s to solve.   Draw or write to explain.

1. Bob puts 2 model cars on each shelf. There are 4 shelves. How many model cars are there?

   __8__ model cars

2. There are 5 people in the Bloom family. They each want to eat 2 sandwiches. How many sandwiches do they make?

   __10__ sandwiches

3. The school bus makes 7 stops. It picks up 2 children at each stop. How many children does the bus pick up?

   __14__ children

4. There are 14 children in the class. Each child gets 2 books at the book fair. How many books do they get in all?

   __28__ books

Use with text pages 323–324.

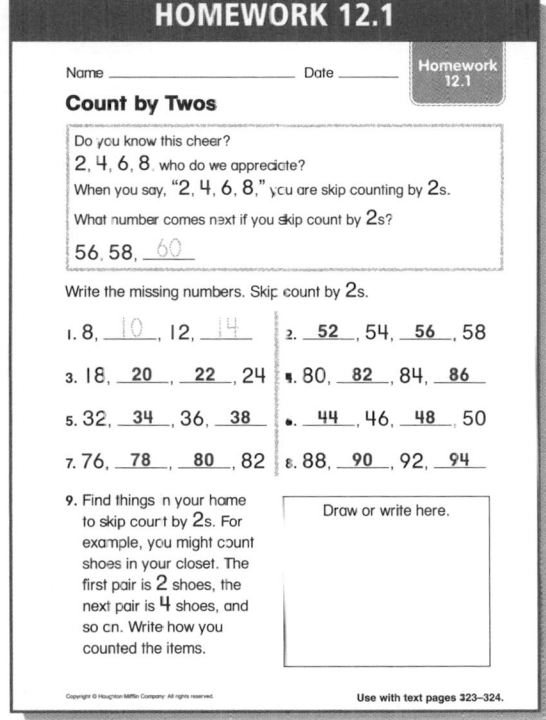

HOMEWORK 12.1

Name _____ Date _____   Homework 12.1

Count by Twos

Do you know this cheer?
2, 4, 6, 8, who do we appreciate?
When you say, "2, 4, 6, 8," you are skip counting by 2s.
What number comes next if you skip count by 2s?

56, 58, _60_

Write the missing numbers. Skip count by 2s.

1. 8, _10_, 12, _14_   2. _52_, 54, _56_, 58
3. 18, _20_, _22_, 24   4. 80, _82_, 84, _86_
5. 32, _34_, 36, _38_   6. _44_, 46, _48_, 50
7. 76, _78_, _80_, 82   8. 88, _90_, 92, _94_

9. Find things in your home to skip count by 2s. For example, you might count shoes in your closet. The first pair is 2 shoes, the next pair is 4 shoes, and so on. Write how you counted the items.

   Draw or write here.

Homework Workbook Page 77

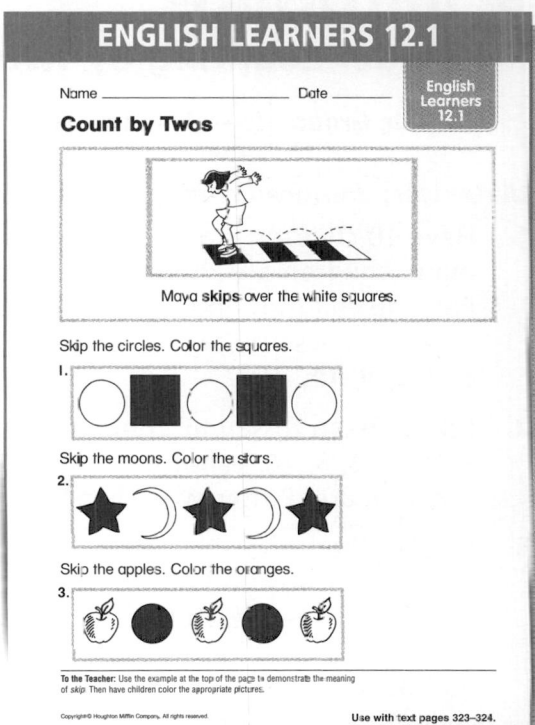

ENGLISH LEARNERS 12.1

Name _____ Date _____   English Learners 12.1

Count by Twos

Maya **skips** over the white squares.

Skip the circles. Color the squares.

1.

Skip the moons. Color the stars.

2.

Skip the apples. Color the oranges.

3.

To the Teacher: Use the example at the top of the page to demonstrate the meaning of skip. Then have children color the appropriate pictures.

Use with text pages 323–324.

TEACHING LESSON 12.1

LESSON ORGANIZER

Objective Skip count by twos to 100.

Resources Reteach, Practice, Enrichment, Problem Solving, Homework, English Learners, Transparencies, Math Center

Materials Workmat 6, hundred chart transparency, 5 strips of paper, hundred chart (LT7), counters

Activity

Warm-Up Activity
Model Counting to 100

| 👤👤👤 Small Group | ⏱ 5–10 minutes | Auditory, Visual |

Materials: *Workmat 6*

1. Display the hundred chart. **Why do you think this is called a hundred chart?** (It shows numbers 1 to 100.) **How many squares does it have?** (100)

2. Ask volunteers to read the rows of numbers in counting order from 1 to 100 as you point to each number.

3. Review with children that when you count, each number is 1 more than the number before it, or each number increases by 1.

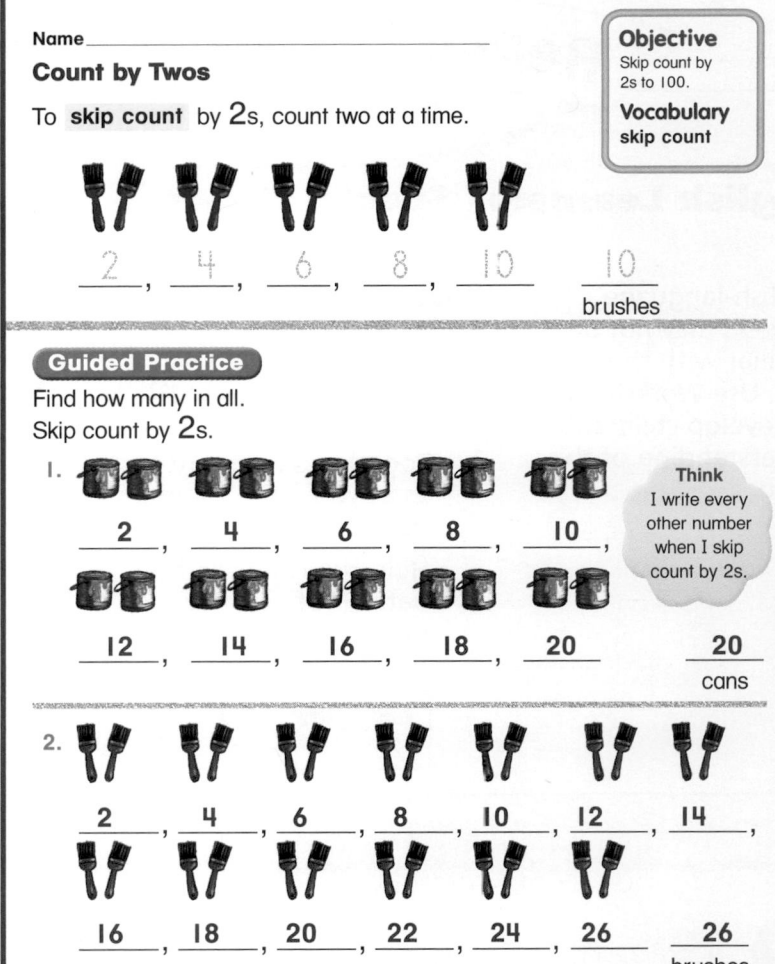

Name_____

Objective
Skip count by 2s to 100.

Vocabulary
skip count

Count by Twos

To **skip count** by 2s, count two at a time.

2, 4, 6, 8, 10   10
brushes

Guided Practice

Find how many in all.
Skip count by 2s.

1.
2, 4, 6, 8, 10
12, 14, 16, 18, 20   20
cans

Think I write every other number when I skip count by 2s.

2.
2, 4, 6, 8, 10, 12, 14,
16, 18, 20, 22, 24, 26   26
brushes

TEST TIPS **Explain Your Thinking** What pattern do you see when you skip count by 2s? **Possible answer: The number has a 0, 2, 4, 6, or 8 in the ones place.**

Chapter 12 Lesson 1   three hundred twenty-three **323**

① Introduce *Activity*
Model Counting by Twos

| 👤👤👤👤 Whole Group | ⏱ 10–15 minutes | Visual, Kinesthetic |

Materials: *hundred chart transparency, 5 strips of paper*

1. Have 10 children stand at the front of the board. **How many children are there? We can count them by 2s.** Pair the children and count them by whispering the odd numbers and saying the even numbers. *1*, **2**, *3*, **4**, *5*, **6**, *7*, **8**, *9*, **10**.

2. **I don't have to say all the numbers, I can just count by 2s: 2, 4, 6, 8, 10. What pattern do you hear?** (Each number is 2 more) **Either way that I count I get 10 children.**

3. Display the hundred chart on the overhead with paper strips covering the 1st, 3rd, 5th, 7th, and 9th columns. Have volunteers read the numbers they see in each row. (2, 4, 6, 8, 10, 12, 14, 16, etc.) **How did you count the numbers?** (by 2s) Conclude by counting by 2s aloud with children as you point to each number on the chart.

② Develop

Guided Learning

Teaching Example Introduce the objective and vocabulary to the children. Have children look at the example. **How many paint brushes do you see?** (10) **What do the numbers below the brushes stand for?** (skip counting by 2s)

Guided Practice

Have children complete **Exercises 1–2** as you observe. Give children the opportunity to answer the Explain Your Thinking question. Then discuss their responses with the class.

323   CHAPTER 12   Lesson 1

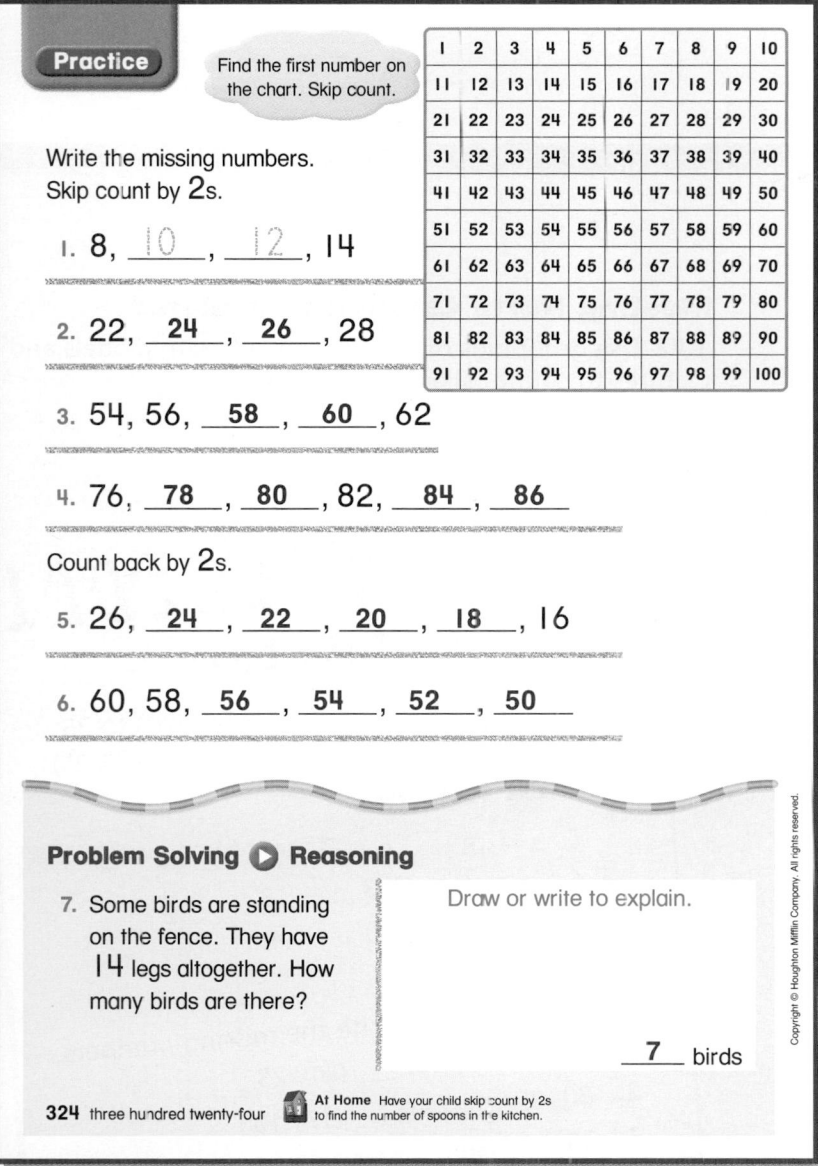

Practice

Find the first number on the chart. Skip count.

1	2	3	4	5	6	7	8	9	10
11	12	13	14	15	16	17	18	19	20
21	22	23	24	25	26	27	28	29	30
31	32	33	34	35	36	37	38	39	40
41	42	43	44	45	46	47	48	49	50
51	52	53	54	55	56	57	58	59	60
61	62	63	64	65	66	67	68	69	70
71	72	73	74	75	76	77	78	79	80
81	82	83	84	85	86	87	88	89	90
91	92	93	94	95	96	97	98	99	100

Write the missing numbers.
Skip count by 2s.

1. 8, __10__, __12__, 14

2. 22, __24__, __26__, 28

3. 54, 56, __58__, __60__, 62

4. 76, __78__, __80__, 82, __84__, __86__

Count back by 2s.

5. 26, __24__, __22__, __20__, __18__, 16

6. 60, 58, __56__, __54__, __52__, __50__

Problem Solving ▶ Reasoning

7. Some birds are standing on the fence. They have 14 legs altogether. How many birds are there?

Draw or write to explain.

___7___ birds

324 three hundred twenty-four

At Home Have your child skip count by 2s to find the number of spoons in the kitchen.

Daily Test Prep

What number is missing?

88, ___, 92, 94, 96

89   90   93   N-1
○   ●   ○   ○

Activity

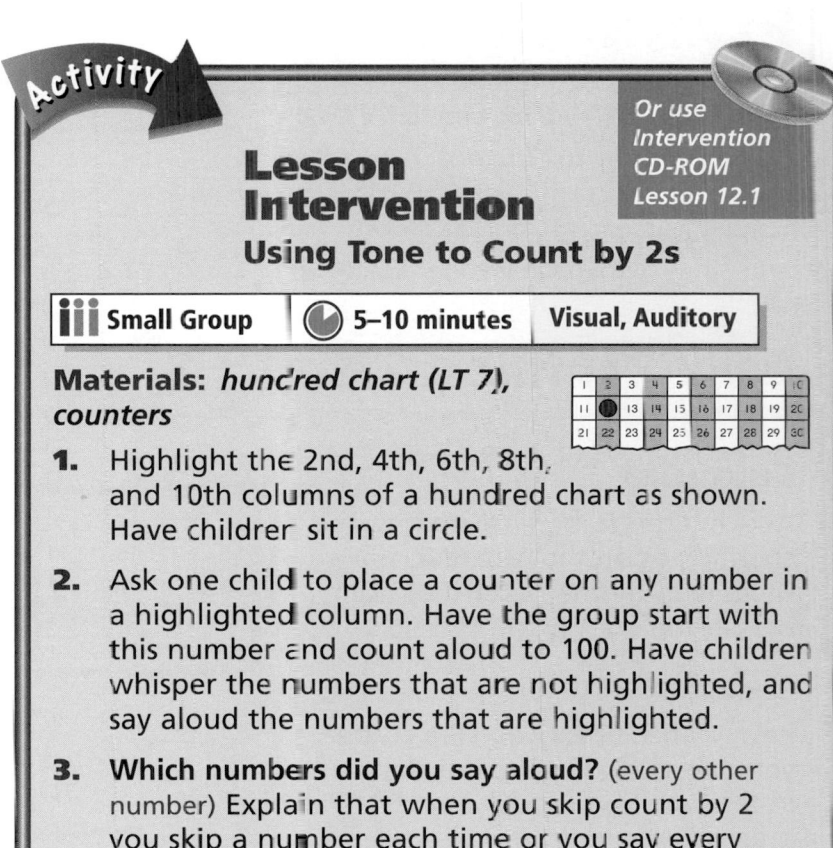

Or use Intervention CD-ROM Lesson 12.1

Lesson Intervention

Using Tone to Count by 2s

⬤⬤⬤ Small Group	🕐 5–10 minutes	Visual, Auditory

Materials: *hundred chart (LT 7), counters*

1. Highlight the 2nd, 4th, 6th, 8th, and 10th columns of a hundred chart as shown. Have children sit in a circle.

2. Ask one child to place a counter on any number in a highlighted column. Have the group start with this number and count aloud to 100. Have children whisper the numbers that are not highlighted, and say aloud the numbers that are highlighted.

3. **Which numbers did you say aloud?** (every other number) Explain that when you skip count by 2 you skip a number each time or you say every other number

   Continue with a different volunteer placing the counter on the chart.

---

③ Practice

Independent Practice

Children complete **Exercises 1–6** independently. Make sure children know that in Exercises 5 and 6 they need to count backwards on the hundred chart.

Problem Solving

After children complete **Exercise 7**, call on volunteers to share their solutions. **How does knowing that a bird has 2 legs help you solve the problem?** (You know you have to count 2 legs for each bird.)

Common Error

Losing Track When Skip Counting

Have children circle the first number in an exercise on the hundred chart in red. Then circle every other number in red to find the missing numbers.

④ Assess and Close

Name the missing number.

• 66, 68, ___ (70), 72, 74

• 78, ___ (80), 82, 84, 86

• 12, 14, ___ (16), 18, 20

✎ Keeping a Journal

Explain how using a hundred chart can help you count by 2s. Draw a chart to show counting by 2s to 30.

Lesson 12.2

Count by Fives

PLANNING THE LESSON

MATHEMATICS OBJECTIVE
Skip count by fives to 100.

Use Lesson Planner CD-ROM for Lesson 12.2.

Daily Routines

Calendar
Ask children to begin with five and count by 5s on the calendar. Have them identify the pattern of numbers in the ones place. (5,0,5,0,5,0)

Sunday	Monday	Tuesday	Wednesday	Thursday	Friday	Saturday
				1	2	3	4
5	6	7	8	9	10	11
12	13	14	15	16	17	18
19	20	21	22	23	24	25
26	27	28	29	30	31	

Vocabulary
Review that when you **skip count** you pass over or leave out numbers in the counting sequence. Have children tell you which numbers they skip or pass over when they skip count by 5s to 20.

Vocabulary Cards

Meeting North Carolina's Standards
1.02 Use groupings of 2's, 5's, and 10's with models and pictures to count collections of objects.
Also 5.03

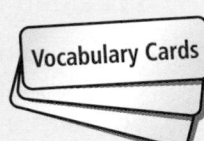

Lesson Transparency 12.2

Problem of the Day
Joe begins at 10 and counts by fives to 25. Which numbers does he say? (10, 15, 20, 25)

Quick Review

6	8	4	7	5
+ 2	− 2	+ 3	− 3	+ 5
(8)	(6)	(7)	(4)	(10)

Lesson Quiz
Skip count by 5s. Write the missing numbers.

1. 5, ___ (10), 15, ___ (20), 25
2. 80, 85, ___ (90), ___ (95), 100
3. 35, ___ (40), ___ (45), 50, 55

LEVELED PRACTICE

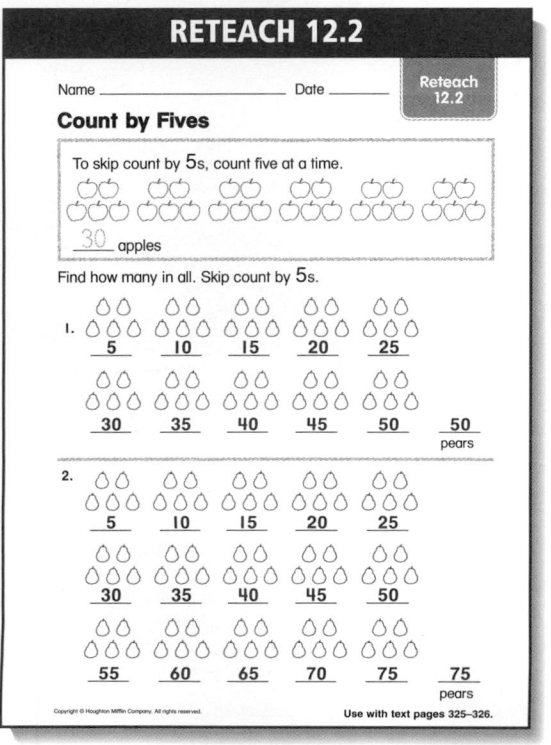

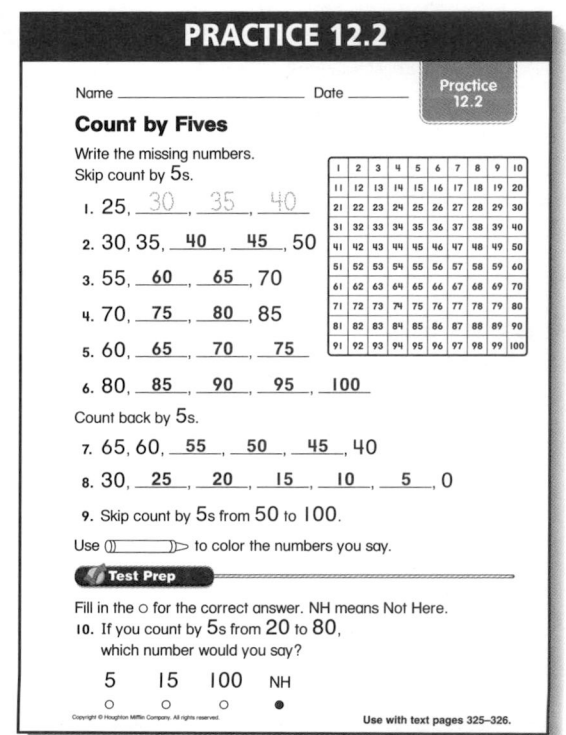

Reaching All Learners

Differentiated Instruction

English Learners

English-language learners may not be familiar with the word *missing*. Use Worksheet 12.2 to develop children's understanding of this word.

Special Needs
VISUAL, AUDITORY

Materials: *10 × 10 grid (LT 29)*

- Color the fives and tens columns on the grid yellow.
- Have the child count by 1s and write the number in every yellow box.
- Then have the child read the number to skip count by 5s.

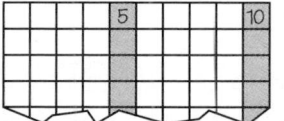

Gifted and Talented
AUDITORY, VISUAL

- Have children write and illustrate problems about counting by 5s. For example: *Jake had 5 pennies. His father gave him 5 more pennies. Then he found 5 pennies under the bed. How many pennies does he have in all?* (15)
- Have children exchange and solve each other's problems.

TECHNOLOGY

Spiral Review

You can prepare students for standardized tests with **customized** spiral review on key skills using the *Ways to Assess* CD-ROM.

Education Place

Encourage students to visit **Education Place** at **eduplace.com/kids/mw/** for more student activities.

Games

Students can practice their math vocabulary using the Math Lingo game, available on the *Ways to Success* CD-ROM.

 **Literature Connection**

Read the story, *Count on Pablo* by Barbara deRubertis, to children. As you read, pause to let volunteers act as Pablo and count aloud by 1s, 2s, 5s, and 10s.

 **MATH CENTER**

Cross-Curricular Activity

As you use this activity to relate the mathematics of this lesson to another curriculum area, children will see how math can help them with other subjects.

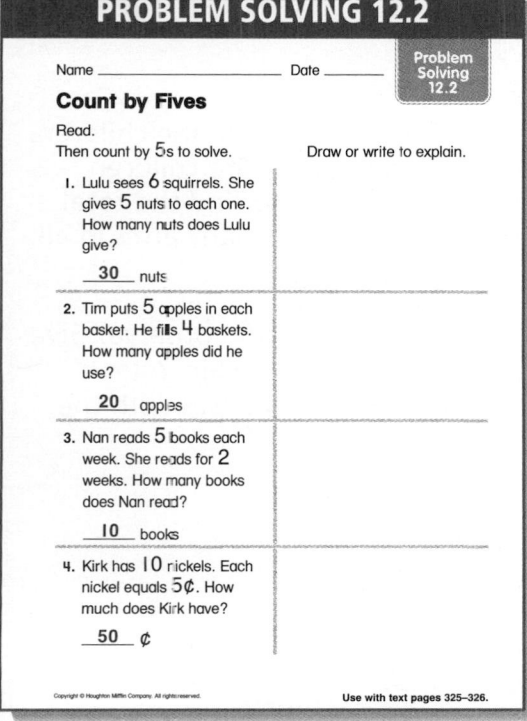

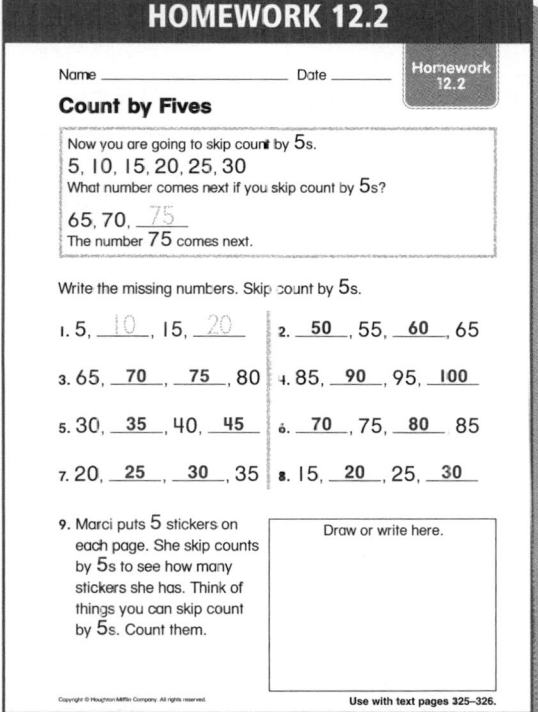

Homework Workbook Page 78

TEACHING LESSON 12.2

LESSON ORGANIZER

Objective Skip count by fives to 100.

Resources Reteach, Practice, Enrichment, Problem Solving, Homework, English Learners, Transparencies, Math Center

Materials Workmat 6, counters (such as pennies), hundred chart transparency

Warm-Up Activity
Model Counting Backwards

| iiii Small Group | ⏱ 5–10 minutes | Auditory, Visual |

Materials: *Workmat 6, counters*

1. Have children sit in a circle. Place the hundred chart in the center.

2. Ask one child to place a counter over one number on the chart. **Start with this number and count backwards.** Review that when you count backwards on the hundred chart, you read the numbers from right to left.

3. Continue by having a volunteer place a counter on a different number and then count backwards as a group from that number.

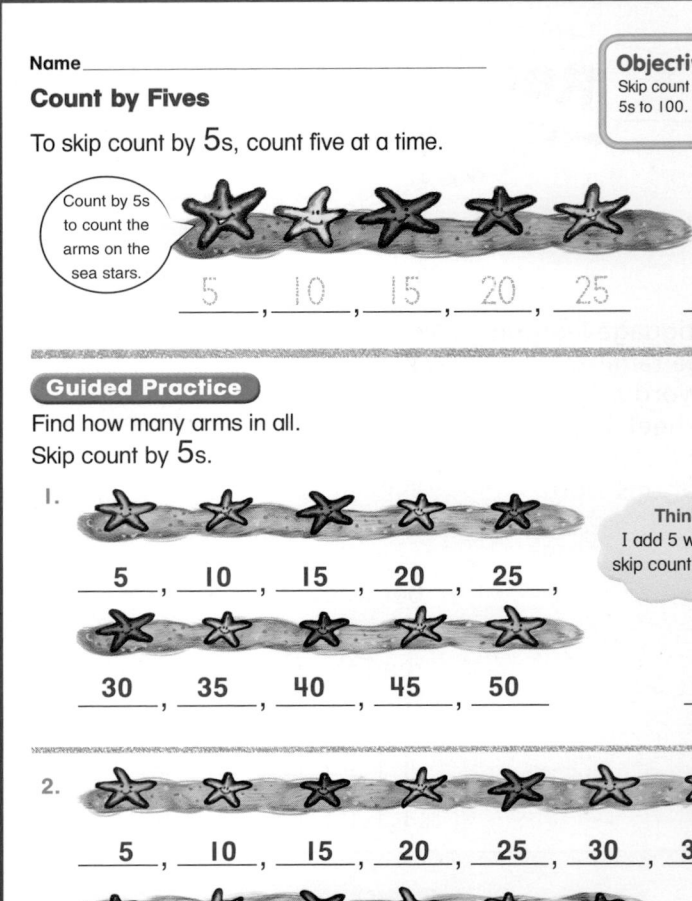

Name _____

Count by Fives

Objective Skip count by 5s to 100.

To skip count by 5s, count five at a time.

Count by 5s to count the arms on the sea stars.

5 , 10 , 15 , 20 , 25   25
arms

Guided Practice

Find how many arms in all.
Skip count by 5s.

1.

5 , 10 , 15 , 20 , 25 ,

30 , 35 , 40 , 45 , 50   50
arms

Think
I add 5 when I skip count by 5s.

2.

5 , 10 , 15 , 20 , 25 , 30 , 35 ,

40 , 45 , 50 , 55 , 60 , 65   65
arms

TEST TIPS **Explain Your Thinking** Why is it faster to skip count than to count by 1s? **Possible answer: You skip numbers so you say fewer numbers. That is faster.**

Chapter 12 Lesson 2   three hundred twenty-five **325**

1 Introduce
Discuss Counting by Fives

| iiii Whole Group | ⏱ 10–15 minutes | Visual, Kinesthetic |

Materials: *hundred chart transparency, counters*

1. Hold up a hand. **How many fingers do you see?** (5) Have 5 children stand at the front of the class and raise both hands. **How many fingers in all?** (50) Model counting fingers by 5s.

2. Next display the hundred chart on the overhead. Put a counter on number 5. Ask a volunteer to put a counter on the number that shows 5 more. **What number is the counter on?** (10) Continue. **How many 5s are in 10?** (2) Continue until there are counters on every fifth box.

3. Point out that the numbers have either a 5 or 0 in the ones place. Then count together by 5s to 100.

2 Develop

Guided Learning

Teaching Example Introduce the objective to the children. Guide them through the example. Make sure children understand that they are skip counting to find the total number of arms on the sea stars, or how many arms in all.

Guided Practice

Have children complete **Exercises 1–2** as you observe. Give children the opportunity to answer the Explain Your Thinking question. Then discuss their responses with the class.

Practice

Find the first number on the chart. Skip count.

1	2	3	4	5	6	7	8	9	10
11	12	13	14	15	16	17	18	19	20
21	22	23	24	25	26	27	28	29	30
31	32	33	34	35	36	37	38	39	40
41	42	43	44	45	46	47	48	49	50
51	52	53	54	55	56	57	58	59	60
61	62	63	64	65	66	67	68	69	70
71	72	73	74	75	76	77	78	79	80
81	82	83	84	85	86	87	88	89	90
91	92	93	94	95	96	97	98	99	100

Write the missing numbers.
Skip count by 5s.

1. 10, 15, __20__ , __25__

2. 25, 30, __35__ , __40__

3. 60, __65__ , __70__ , 75

4. 35, __40__ , __45__ , __50__ , __55__ , __60__

5. 75, __80__ , __85__ , 90, __95__ , __100__

Count back by 5s.

6. 25, 20, __15__ , __10__ , __5__ , 0

7. 50, 45, __40__ , __35__ , __30__ , __25__ , __20__

Problem Solving ▶ Logical Thinking

Write the mystery number.

Draw or write to explain.

8. It is greater than 80.
It is less than 90.
You say it when counting
by 5s. What number is it?

__85__

326 three hundred twenty-six

At Home Make groups of 5 pennies. Have your child skip count by 5s to find the number of pennies in all.

Test Prep Transparency 12.2

Daily Test Prep

What number is missing?
45, ___ , 55, 60, 65

46 ○   50 ●   54 ○   NH ○

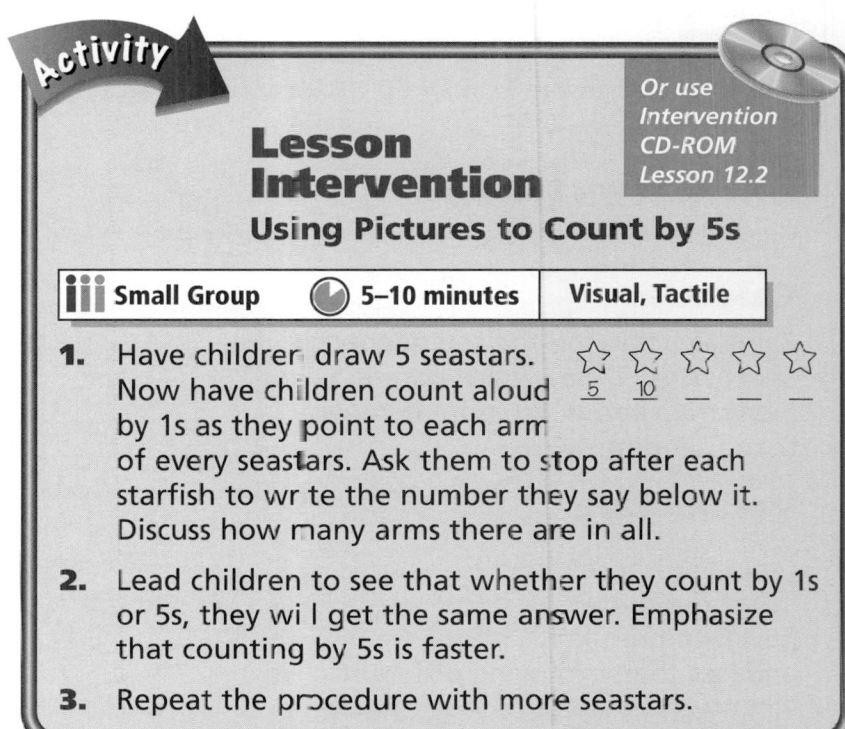

Activity

Lesson Intervention
Using Pictures to Count by 5s

Or use Intervention CD-ROM Lesson 12.2

| 👥 Small Group | 🕐 5–10 minutes | Visual, Tactile |

1. Have children draw 5 seastars. Now have children count aloud by 1s as they point to each arm of every seastars. Ask them to stop after each starfish to write the number they say below it. Discuss how many arms there are in all.

2. Lead children to see that whether they count by 1s or 5s, they will get the same answer. Emphasize that counting by 5s is faster.

3. Repeat the procedure with more seastars.

---

3 Practice

Independent Practice

Children complete **Exercises 1–7** independently. Make sure children know that in **Exercises 6** and **7** they need to count backwards on the hundred chart.

Problem Solving

After children complete **Exercise 8**, call on volunteers to share their solutions. Discuss how each number has either a 5 or 0 in the ones place when you count by 5s.

Common Error

Writing 5 Each Time Instead of Multiples of Five
Remind children that they are to count on by fives to find how many in all, not how many in each group.

4 Assess and Close

Which group of numbers shows counting by 5s? (35, 40, 45, 50)

- 5, 10, 25, 50
- 35, 40, 45, 50
- 20, 30, 40, 50

Keeping a Journal

Draw a number of 5-pointed stars.

Count by 5s to find how many points in all. Write the number.

More Than, Less Than

PLANNING THE LESSON

MATHEMATICS OBJECTIVE
Identify 1 more, 1 less, 10 more, and 10 less than a given number.

Use Lesson Planner CD-ROM for Lesson 12.3.

Daily Routines

Calendar
Point to a date on the calendar and ask children to say which date is 1 more than and which date is 1 less than that date.

Sunday	Monday	Tuesday	Wednesday	Thursday	Friday	Saturday
				1	2	3	4
5	6	7	8	9	10	11
12	13	14	15	16	17	18
19	20	21	22	23	24	25
26	27	28	29	30	31	

Vocabulary
Create sentence strips like those shown. Review **more than** and **less than** by having different volunteers complete the sentences orally with numbers that make sense.

_____ is more than _____.
_____ is less than _____.

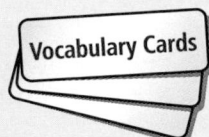
Vocabulary Cards

Meeting North Carolina's Standards
1.01 Develop number sense for whole numbers through 99.
• Connect the model, number word, and number using a variety of representations.

Lesson Transparency **12.3**

Problem of the Day
Kim has 17 cans. Fred has 19 cans. What could they do so that each has the same number of cans? (Fred could give one can to Kim so they each could have 18 cans.)

Quick Review
What number is between 29 and 31? (30)
What number is just before 50? (49)
What number is just after 99? (100)

Lesson Quiz
Use the hundred chart.
1. What number is 10 less than 45? (35)
2. What number is 1 more than 18? (19)
3. What number is 10 more than 89? (99)

LEVELED PRACTICE

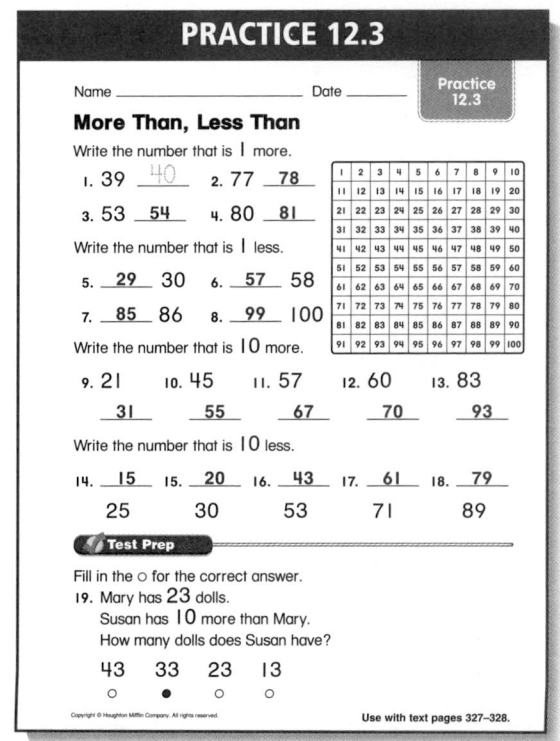

RETEACH 12.3

Name _____ Date _____   Reteach 12.3

More Than, Less Than

You can use the words more than and less than to tell about number patterns.

5 is less than 10.
20 is 5 more than 15.

31	32	33	34	35	36	37	38	39	40
41	42	43	44	45	46	47	48	49	50
51	52	53	54	55	56	57	58	59	60
61	62	63	64	65	66	67	68	69	70
71	72	73	74	75	76	77	78	79	80
81	82	83	84	85	86	87	88	89	90
91	92	93	94	95	96	97	98	99	100

Write the number that is 1 more.
1. 31 _32_ 2. 49 _50_ 3. 67 _68_ 4. 73 _74_

Write the number that is 1 less.
5. _42_ 43 6. _51_ 52 7. _65_ 66 8. _96_ 97

Write the number that is 10 more.
9. 30 _40_ 10. 35 _45_ 11. 66 _76_ 12. 73 _83_

Write the number that is 10 less.
13. _38_ 48 14. _45_ 55 15. _60_ 70 16. _90_ 100

Copyright © Houghton Mifflin Company. All rights reserved.   Use with text pages 327–328.

PRACTICE 12.3

Name _____ Date _____   Practice 12.3

More Than, Less Than

Write the number that is 1 more.
1. 39 _40_ 2. 77 _78_
3. 53 _54_ 4. 80 _81_

Write the number that is 1 less.
5. _29_ 30 6. _57_ 58
7. _85_ 86 8. _99_ 100

1	2	3	4	5	6	7	8	9	10
11	12	13	14	15	16	17	18	19	20
21	22	23	24	25	26	27	28	29	30
31	32	33	34	35	36	37	38	39	40
51	52	53	54	55	56	57	58	59	60
61	62	63	64	65	66	67	68	69	70
71	72	73	74	75	76	77	78	79	80
81	82	83	84	85	86	87	88	89	90
91	92	93	94	95	96	97	98	99	100

Write the number that is 10 more.
9. 21 10. 45 11. 57 12. 60 13. 83
   _31_   _55_   _67_   _70_   _93_

Write the number that is 10 less.
14. _15_ 15. _20_ 16. _43_ 17. _61_ 18. _79_
    25   30   53   71   89

Test Prep

Fill in the ○ for the correct answer.
19. Mary has 23 dolls.
    Susan has 10 more than Mary.
    How many dolls does Susan have?

    43   33   23   13
    ○   ●   ○   ○

Copyright © Houghton Mifflin Company. All rights reserved.   Use with text pages 327–328.

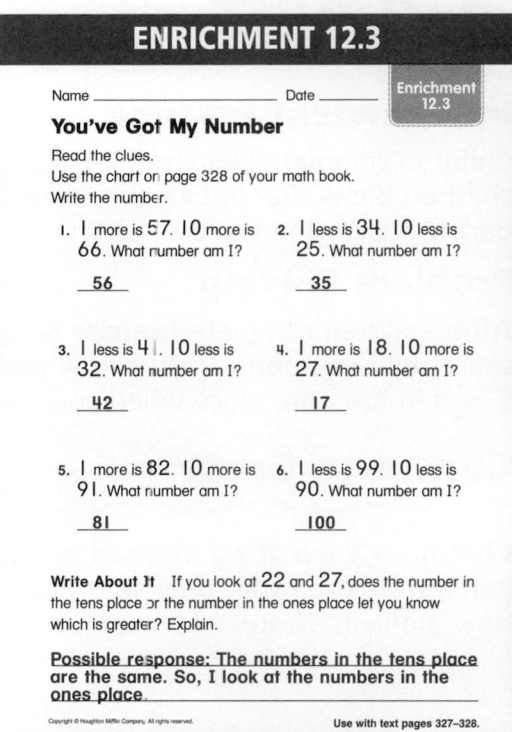

ENRICHMENT 12.3

Name _____ Date _____   Enrichment 12.3

You've Got My Number

Read the clues.
Use the chart on page 328 of your math book.
Write the number.

1. 1 more is 57. 10 more is 66. What number am I?
   _56_

2. 1 less is 34. 10 less is 25. What number am I?
   _35_

3. 1 less is 41. 10 less is 32. What number am I?
   _42_

4. 1 more is 18. 10 more is 27. What number am I?
   _17_

5. 1 more is 82. 10 more is 91. What number am I?
   _81_

6. 1 less is 99. 10 less is 90. What number am I?
   _100_

Write About It If you look at 22 and 27, does the number in the tens place or the number in the ones place let you know which is greater? Explain.

__Possible response: The numbers in the tens place are the same. So, I look at the numbers in the ones place.__

Copyright © Houghton Mifflin Company. All rights reserved.   Use with text pages 327–328.

Practice Workbook Page 79

Reaching All Learners
Differentiated Instruction

English Learners

English-language learners may not have the language skills to explain the process behind their thinking. Use Worksheet 12.3 to provide children with sentence frames they can use to complete the Explain Your Thinking activity.

Special Needs
VISUAL, TACTILE

Materials: *Workmat 6*

- Circle a number on the chart. Have the child say the number that is just before and just after. Explain that these numbers are 1 less and 1 more than the circled number.

- Continue with the numbers just above and just below to develop 10 less and 10 more.

Early Finishers
VISUAL, TACTILE

Materials: *number cards for 11–20 (LT 14 and LT 15), number cards for 21–89 (teacher-made) spinner*

Partners take turns. One child chooses a card and spins. The child follows the instructions on the spinner by writing the new number on the number card. The partner checks. Partners switch roles and continue.

TECHNOLOGY
Spiral Review

Create **customized** spiral review worksheets for individual students using the *Ways to Assess* CD-ROM.

Manipulatives

An interactive **Hundred Chart** is available on the *Ways to Success* CD-ROM.

Education Place

You can visit **Education Place** at eduplace.com/math/mw/ for teacher support materials.

Music Connection

Discuss how rhythms can be made by clapping, tapping, or making other sounds. Clap out a rhythm such as 2 short, 1 long. Then say 1 more or 1 less. The class then claps the new rhythm: 2 short, 2 long or 2 short.

MATH CENTER
Real-Life Activity

Help children understand the usefulness of mathematics. This activity makes math come alive by connecting the lesson skills to a real-life situation.

PROBLEM SOLVING 12.3

Name _____ Date _____
Problem Solving 12.3

More Than, Less Than

Read and solve.
Write the answer.   Draw or write to explain.

1. There are 32 children on the green bus. There are 22 children on the yellow bus. Is 22 more than or less than 32?

   22 is **less than** 32

2. At the zoo, 31 children want to see the lions. 41 want to see the elephants. Is 41 more than or less than 31?

   41 is **more than** 31

3. Dan counts 20 monkeys. Mark counts a number of monkeys that is 1 less than 20. How many monkeys did Mark count?

   __19__ monkeys

Copyright © Houghton Mifflin Company. All rights reserved.   Use with text pages 327–328.

HOMEWORK 12.3

Name _____ Date _____
Homework 12.3

More Than, Less Than

You know that 16 is more than 11.
16 is also less than 21.
You can use the words more than and less than when you talk about numbers.

Use this table to write the numbers.

5	6	7	8	9
10	11	12	13	14
15	16	17	18	19
20	21	22	23	24
25	26	27	28	29

1. This number is 1 more.
   28 _29_

2. This number is 1 less.
   _18_ 19

3. This number is 5 more.
   15 _20_

4. This number is 10 less.
   _12_ 22

5. How old are you? _____
   You were 1 less year last year. How old were you then? _____
   How old will you be 5 years from now? _____
   How old will you be in 10 more years? _____

   Draw or write here.

Copyright © Houghton Mifflin Company. All rights reserved.   Use with text pages 327–328.

ENGLISH LEARNERS 12.3

Name _____ Date _____
English Learners 12.3

More Than, Less Than

1	2	3	4	5	6	7	8	9	10
11	12	13	14	15	16	17	18	19	20
21	22	23	24	25	26	27	28	29	30
31	32	33	34	35	36	37	38	39	40
41	42	43	44	45	46	47	48	49	50
51	52	53	54	55	56	57	58	59	60
61	62	63	64	65	66	67	68	69	70
71	72	73	74	75	76	77	78	79	80
81	82	83	84	85	86	87	88	89	90
91	92	93	94	95	96	97	98	99	100

20 is 10 more 10.
10 is 10 less than 20.

Tell how you use the chart to find 10 less than 26.

First, I find __26__ on the chart.

Then I move up ____ row on the chart.

Now I am on __16__.

__16__ is 10 less than 26

To the Teacher: Use the illustration and sentences at the top of the page to explain how to use a hundred chart to find 10 less and 10 more than a number. Then read the sentences with children and have them complete each one.

Copyright © Houghton Mifflin Company. All rights reserved.   Use with text pages 327–328.

Homework Workbook Page 79

TEACHING LESSON 12.3

LESSON ORGANIZER

Objective Identify 1 more, 1 less, 10 more, and 10 less than a given number.

Resources Reteach, Practice, Enrichment, Problem Solving, Homework, English Learners, Transparencies, Math Center

Materials Cubes, hundred chart transparency, counter (such as a penny), sandwich bags, Workmat 6

 Activity

Warm-Up Activity
Modeling Counting and Comparing

Small Group	⏱ 5–10 minutes	Tactile, Visual

Materials: *cubes*

1. Display 19 blue cubes and 9 red cubes. **How many blue cubes?** (19) **How many red cubes?** (9) Model how to pair one blue cube to each red cube.

2. **Are there more red or blue cubes?** (more blue) **How do you know?** (There are not enough red cubes to make more pairs.) **How many more blue than red?** (10 more) **So, 19 is 10 more than 9. Are there fewer red or blue cubes?** (fewer red) **How many fewer?** (10 fewer) **9 is 10 less than 19.**

3. Repeat with 7 blue cubes and 8 red cubes to review 1 more than and 1 less than.

 **1** **Introduce**  Activity

Discuss More Than, Less Than

 Whole Group	⏱ 10–15 minutes	Visual, Auditory

Materials: *hundred chart transparency, counter*

1. Display the hundred chart and put a counter on the number 26. Have a child move the counter 1 space right. **Is this number greater or less?** (greater) **Does the number change in the ones place?** (yes) **Does the number change in the tens place?** (no) **How is the number different from 26?** (It is 1 more than 26.) Move the counter back to 26. Have a volunteer move the counter 1 space to the left of 26. Discuss 1 less.

2. Continue while introducing numbers that are 10 more and 10 less. Emphasize that the change occurs in the tens place of a number as you move 10 more or 10 less. Also point out that 10 more is directly below a number on the chart and 10 less is directly above. For practice, start at 100 and count backwards by 10s to 10. Repeat.

2 **Develop**

Guided Learning

Teaching Example Introduce the objective and vocabulary to the children. Guide them through the example to show how to use a hundred chart to find numbers that are 1 more, 1 less, 10 more, and 10 less than a number.

Guided Practice

Have children complete **Exercises 1–11** as you observe.

For additional support, allow children to move a counter on a hundred chart (Workmat 6) to help find the numbers.

Give children the opportunity to answer the Explain Your Thinking question. Then discuss their responses with the class.

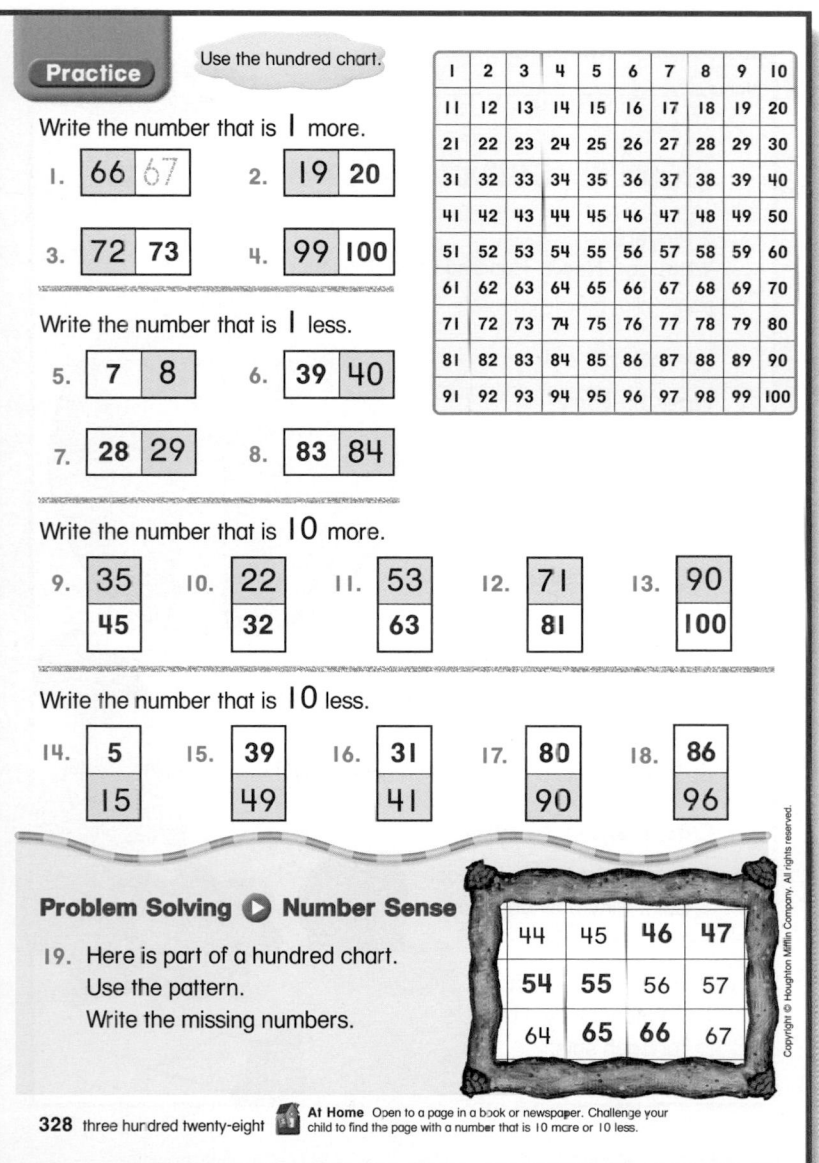

Practice Use the hundred chart.

Write the number that is 1 more.

1	2	3	4	5	6	7	8	9	10
11	12	13	14	15	16	17	18	19	20
21	22	23	24	25	26	27	28	29	30
31	32	33	34	35	36	37	38	39	40
41	42	43	44	45	46	47	48	49	50
51	52	53	54	55	56	57	58	59	60
61	62	63	64	65	66	67	68	69	70
71	72	73	74	75	76	77	78	79	80
81	82	83	84	85	86	87	88	89	90
91	92	93	94	95	96	97	98	99	100

1. 66 | 67   2. 19 | 20

3. 72 | 73   4. 99 | 100

Write the number that is 1 less.

5. 7 | 8   6. 39 | 40

7. 28 | 29   8. 83 | 84

Write the number that is 10 more.

9. 35 / 45   10. 22 / 32   11. 53 / 63   12. 71 / 81   13. 90 / 100

Write the number that is 10 less.

14. 5 / 15   15. 39 / 49   16. 31 / 41   17. 80 / 90   18. 86 / 96

Problem Solving ▶ Number Sense

19. Here is part of a hundred chart.
Use the pattern.
Write the missing numbers.

44	45	46	47
54	55	56	57
64	65	66	67

328 three hundred twenty-eight

At Home Open to a page in a book or newspaper. Challenge your child to find the page with a number that is 10 more or 10 less.

Daily Test Prep

Test Prep Transparency **12.3**

Mark under the number that is 10 more than 11.

11   12   21   NH
○   ○   ●   ○

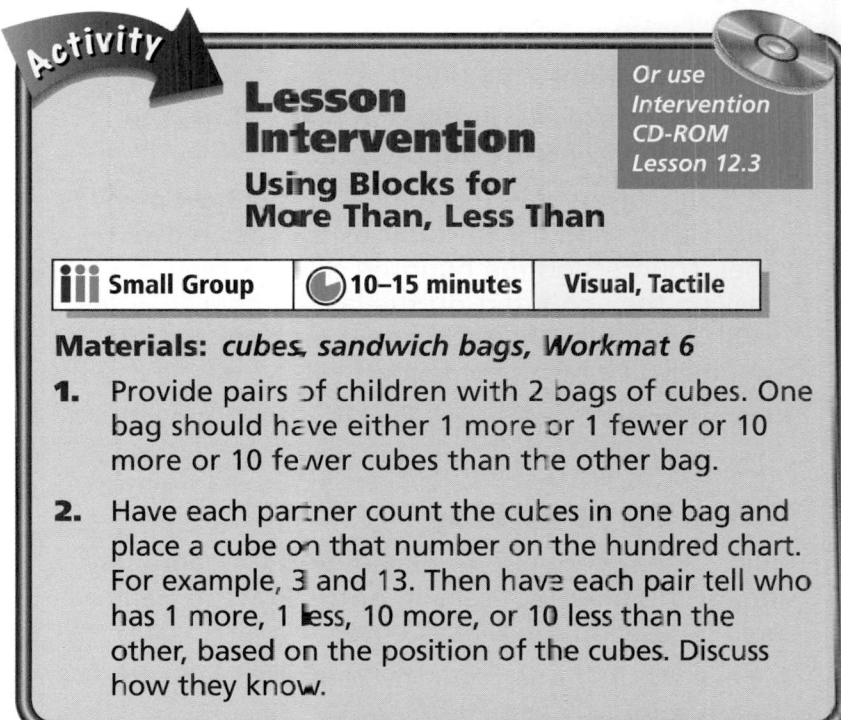

Activity

Lesson Intervention
Using Blocks for More Than, Less Than

Or use Intervention CD-ROM Lesson 12.3

| 👥 Small Group | 🕙 10–15 minutes | Visual, Tactile |

Materials: *cubes, sandwich bags, Workmat 6*

1. Provide pairs of children with 2 bags of cubes. One bag should have either 1 more or 1 fewer or 10 more or 10 fewer cubes than the other bag.

2. Have each partner count the cubes in one bag and place a cube on that number on the hundred chart. For example, 3 and 13. Then have each pair tell who has 1 more, 1 less, 10 more, or 10 less than the other, based on the position of the cubes. Discuss how they know.

---

③ Practice

Independent Practice

Children complete **Exercises 1–18** independently.

Problem Solving

After children complete **Exercise 19**, call on volunteers to share their answers. Discuss how the number directly above a missing number on a hundred chart will be 10 less than that number.

Common Error

Reversing Direction on the Hundred Chart
Emphasize that on the hundred chart numbers become greater as you move right and down on the chart and less as you move left and up on the chart.

④ Assess and Close

Display the hundred chart on the overhead.

- **What number is 1 more than 82?** (83)
- **10 more than 65?** (75)
- **10 less than 99?** (89)

Keeping a Journal

Write a number that is greater than 20. Then write the numbers that are 1 more, 1 less, 10 more, and 10 less.

Spin and Skip Count

Purpose: This game provides practice in skip counting by 5s.

Materials: *for each pair of children: Workmat 6, 2 two-color counters, pencil, paper clip*

How to Play

- Remind children how to use a pencil and paper clip to complete the spinner.
- Each child takes a counter and places it next to the number 5 on the hundred chart.
- In turn, players spin the spinner to see how many times they should skip count by 5s. They move their counters on the hundred chart as they count, leaving their counters on the last number they say. With each turn, they skip count on from the last number on which they landed.
- Encourage players to check each other's moves.
- Play continues until a player reaches 100.

Other Ways to Play

Children may continue to play during the same session, or this alternate version of the Practice Game could be used in the Math Center at a later date.

A Have children skip count by 2s instead of 5s for each spin.

B Have children begin at 100 and count back by 10s for each spin.

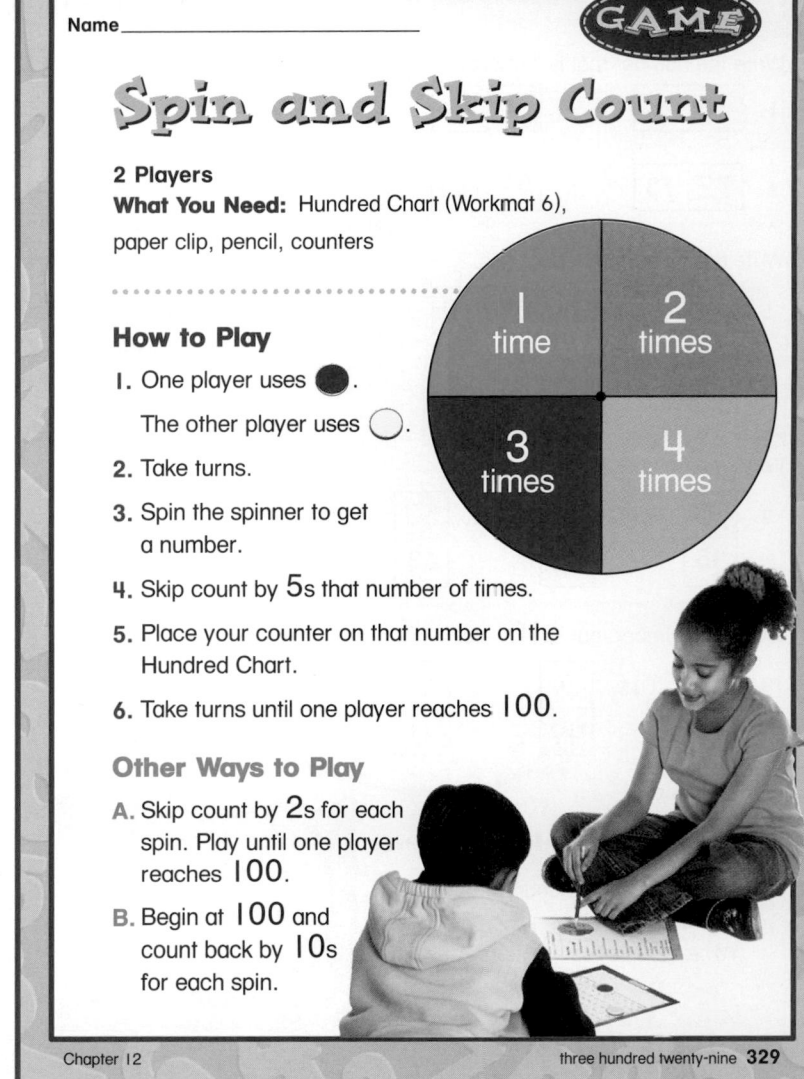

Name_____

Spin and Skip Count

2 Players
What You Need: Hundred Chart (Workmat 6), paper clip, pencil, counters

How to Play

1. One player uses ●.
   The other player uses ○.
2. Take turns.
3. Spin the spinner to get a number.
4. Skip count by 5s that number of times.
5. Place your counter on that number on the Hundred Chart.
6. Take turns until one player reaches 100.

Spinner:
| 1 time | 2 times |
| 3 times | 4 times |

Other Ways to Play

A. Skip count by 2s for each spin. Play until one player reaches 100.

B. Begin at 100 and count back by 10s for each spin.

Mathematical Proficiency

Developing Problem-Solving Approaches

Mathematical proficiency involves the ability to solve problems from real life. **Studies indicate that problem solving provides an important context in which children can learn about numbers and other mathematical concepts.**

In this lesson, children use patterns to solve problems. First, they learn the strategy of finding a pattern and understand how to use the strategy to solve a problem. Then they have the opportunity to **find patterns from given information and use the patterns to solve several problems on their own.**

When children are encouraged to solve problems themselves, as well as see how problems are solved, they are building mathematical proficiency.

Quick Check

Write the missing numbers.
Skip count by 2s.

1	2	3	4	5	6	7	8	9	10
11	12	13	14	15	16	17	18	19	20
21	22	23	24	25	26	27	28	29	30
31	32	33	34	35	36	37	38	39	40
41	42	43	44	45	46	47	48	49	50
51	52	53	54	55	56	57	58	59	60
61	62	63	64	65	66	67	68	69	70
71	72	73	74	75	76	77	78	79	80
81	82	83	84	85	86	87	88	89	90
91	92	93	94	95	96	97	98	99	100

1. 4, 6, __8__, __10__

2. 58, 60, __62__, __64__

Write the missing numbers.
Skip count by 5s.

3. 25, 30, __35__, __40__, __45__, __50__, __55__, __60__

4. 70, __75__, __80__, __85__, __90__, __95__, __100__

Write the number that is 1 more. | Write the number that is 1 less.

5. | 27 | 28 | 6. | 61 | 62 | 7. | 30 | 31 | 8. | 52 | 53 |

Write the number that is 10 more. | Write the number that is 10 less.

9. | 39 | 10. | 81 | 11. | 89 | 12. | 45 |
   | 49 | | 91 | | 99 | | 55 |

Quick Check

Have children complete the Quick Check exercises independently to assess their understanding of concepts and skills taught in **Lessons 1–3**.

Item	Lesson	Error Analysis	Intervention
1–2	12.1	Children may lose track when they skip count.	Reteach Resource 12.1 *Ways to Success* 12.1
3–4	12.2	Some children may write 5 each time rather than multiples of five.	Reteach Resource 12.2 *Ways to Success* 12.2
5–12	12.3	Children may reverse direction on the Hundred chart.	Reteach Resource 12.3 *Ways to Success* 12.3

Hands On: Even and Odd Numbers

Lesson 12.4

PLANNING THE LESSON

MATHEMATICS OBJECTIVE
Find a pattern in odd and even numbers.

Use Lesson Planner CD-ROM for Lesson 12.4.

Daily Routines

Calendar
Point to different dates on the calendar and ask children whether the number is odd or even.

Sunday	Monday	Tuesday	Wednesday	Thursday	Friday	Saturday
				1	2	3	4
5	6	7	8	9	10	11
12	13	14	15	16	17	18
19	20	21	22	23	24	25
26	27	28	29	30	31	

Vocabulary
Write **odd** and **even** on the board. Have 6 children stand in pairs. Explain that 6 is an even number because you can make pairs. Repeat with 5 children and identify 5 as an odd number because you cannot make pairs.

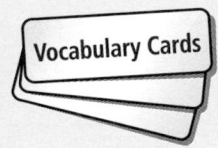 Vocabulary Cards

Meeting North Carolina's Standards
Prepare for Grade 2 Standard 1.06 Define and recognize odd and even numbers.

Lesson Transparency 12.4

Problem of the Day
Jason has 1 rock in each of his pant pockets. He has 6 pockets. Julie has 1 more rock than Jason. How many rocks does Julie have? (7)

Quick Review

$$\begin{array}{cccc} 6 & 3 & 9 & 9 \\ +3 & +6 & -3 & -6 \\ \hline (9) & (9) & (6) & (3) \end{array}$$

Lesson Quiz
Pair cubes to show the number. Is the number odd or even?
1. 20 (even)
2. 9 (odd)
3. 13 (odd)

LEVELED PRACTICE

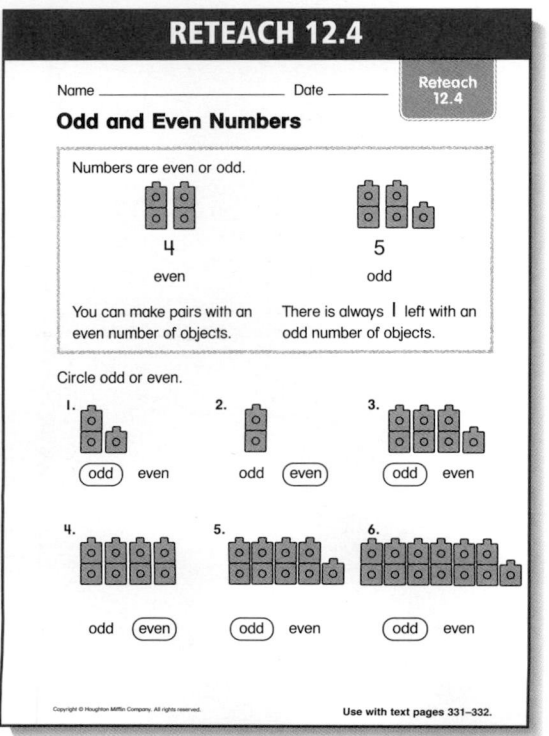

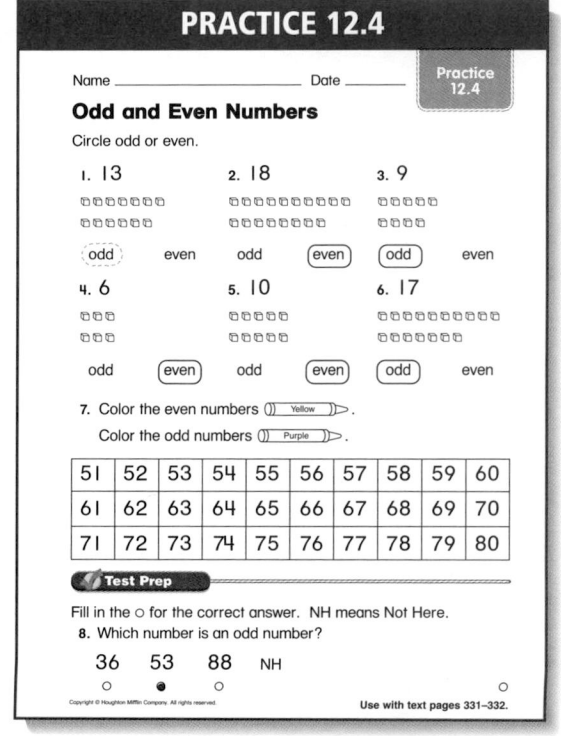

Practice Workbook Page 80

Reaching All Learners

Differentiated Instruction

English Learners

English-language learners may not be familiar with the meaning of the word *pair*. Use Worksheet 12.4 to develop children's understanding of this word.

Special Needs
VISUAL, TACTILE

Materials: *part-part-whole mat (Workmat 3), counters*

- Place 5 counters in the whole section of a part-part-whole mat. Have the child pair the counters in both parts
- Write 5 in the whole and label it *odd* because three is 1 extra counter than two.

5	odd
•••	••

- Repeat with 6, 7, and 8.

Gifted and Talented
TACTILE, AUDITORY

Materials: *cubes, doubles and doubles-plus-one fact cards (teacher-made)*

Have children work in pairs with cubes and cards placed facedown. Have one child turn over a card and predict whether the sum will be odd or even. Have the partner use cubes to check. Children switch roles and continue.

TECHNOLOGY

Spiral Review

Using the *Ways to Assess CD-ROM,* you can create **customized** spiral review worksheets covering any lessons you choose.

Lesson Planner

You can customize your teaching plan or meet your curriculum requirements with the **Lesson Planner CD-Rom.**

eBook

An electronic version of this lesson can be found in **eMathBook.**

Social Studies Connection

Explain that an American flag is the flag of the United States. Each star represents one state. Each state has its own flag. Show pictures of state flags and have children find odd and even numbers of stars or stripes.

MATH CENTER

Vocabulary Activity

This vocabulary-building activity helps children understand and remember new words. Encourage children to use the words in math discussion.

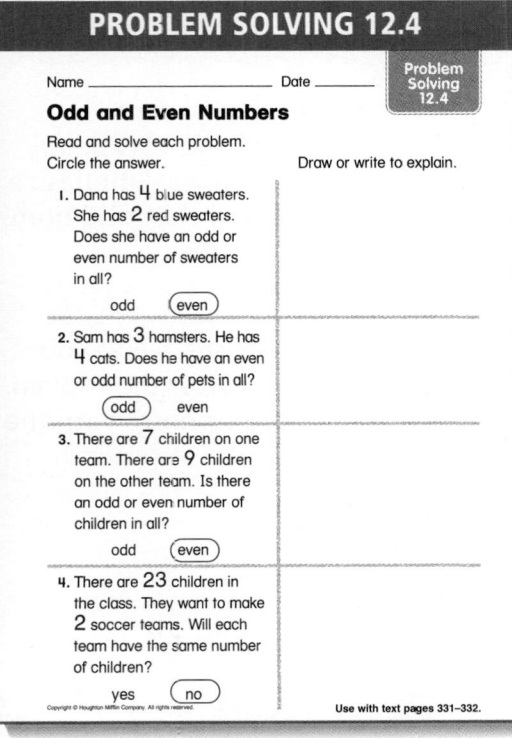

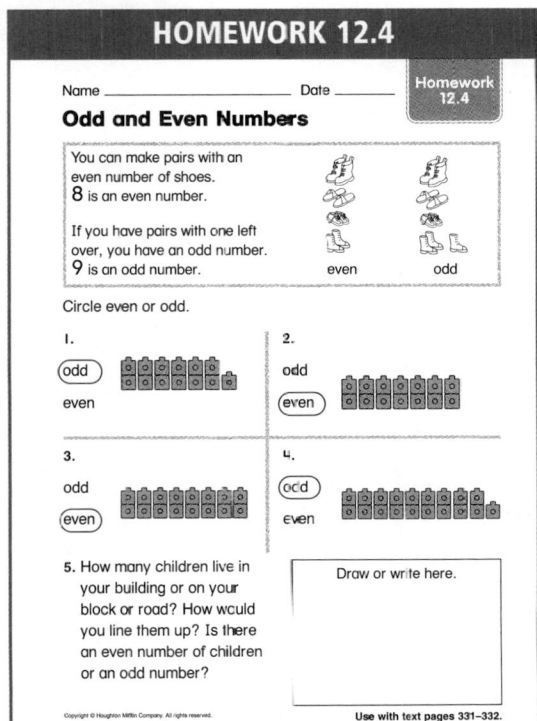

Homework Workbook Page 80

TEACHING LESSON 12.4

LESSON ORGANIZER

Objective Find a pattern in even and odd numbers.

Resources Reteach, Practice, Enrichment, Problem Solving, Homework, English Learners, Transparencies, Math Center

Materials Cubes, paper bag, number cards 1–10 (LT 14)

Activity

Warm-Up Activity
Model Making Pairs

iiii Small Group	🕐 5–10 minutes	Tactile, Visual

Materials: *2 cubes of each color, paper bag*

1. Have children sit in a circle.
   Place the cubes in a bag. Shake the bag and gently pour out the cubes onto the table.

2. Have the children pair the cubes by color. **How many cubes are in a pair?** (2) **Does every cube have a partner?** (yes) **Are there any cubes left over?** (no)

3. Now take out one cube and repeat.

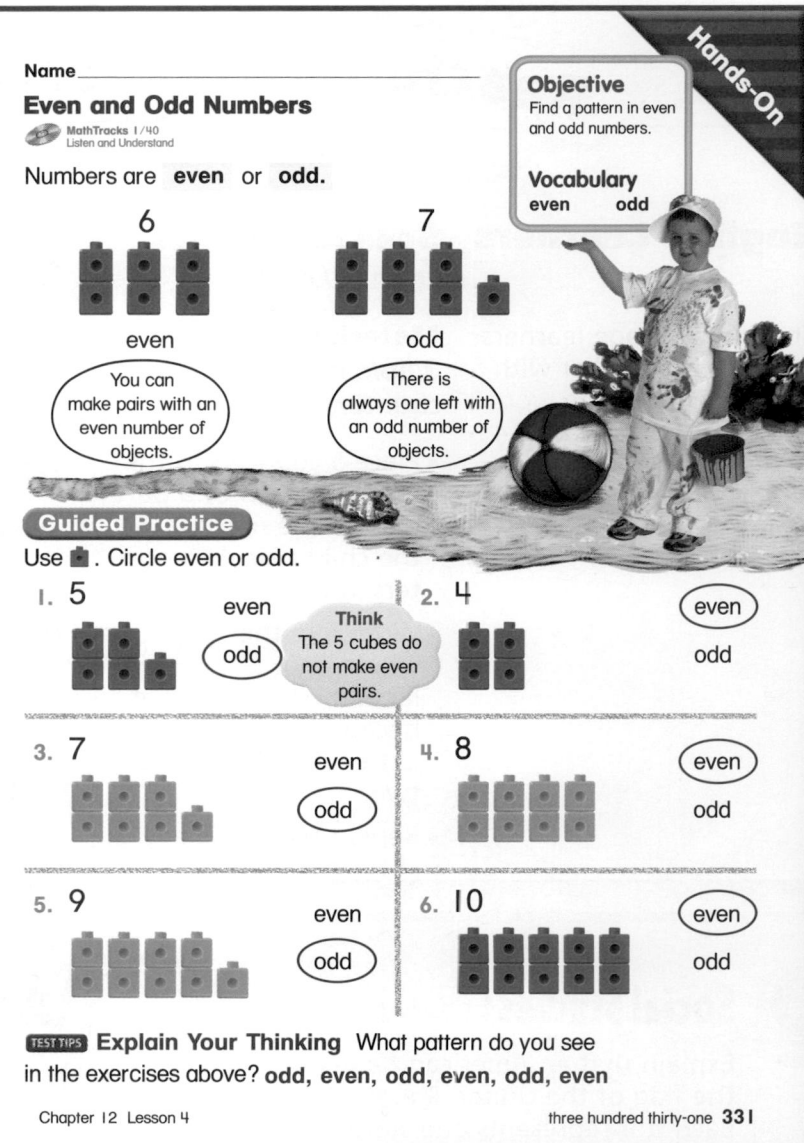

Name_____

Even and Odd Numbers

MathTracks 1/40
Listen and Understand

Objective Find a pattern in even and odd numbers.

Vocabulary even   odd

Numbers are **even** or **odd.**

6 — even
You can make pairs with an even number of objects.

7 — odd
There is always one left with an odd number of objects.

Guided Practice

Use 🔲. Circle even or odd.

1. 5 — even / **odd**   Think The 5 cubes do not make even pairs.

2. 4 — **even** / odd

3. 7 — even / **odd**

4. 8 — **even** / odd

5. 9 — even / **odd**

6. 10 — **even** / odd

TEST TIPS Explain Your Thinking What pattern do you see in the exercises above? **odd, even, odd, even, odd, even**

Chapter 12 Lesson 4   three hundred thirty-one **331**

1 Introduce
Discuss Odd and Even Numbers

iiii Whole Group	🕐 10–15 minutes	Visual, Tactile

Materials: *cubes*

1. Give each student 8 cubes. Write the numbers 1 through 10 in a row on the board. Show 8 cubes on the overhead. **How many cubes?** (8) Have children count as you point to each cube.

2. Ask a volunteer to put the cubes into pairs. **Does every cube have a partner?** (yes) **Are there any cubes left over?** (no) **There are an even number of cubes. 8 is an even number.** Circle the number 8.

2. Repeat with the number 5, emphasizing that the number is odd because there is 1 left over. Put a square around the number 5.

3. Continue until all the numbers have been outlined. **Do you see any pattern?** (Possible answer: Every other number is odd.)

2 Develop

Guided Learning

Teaching Example Introduce the objective and vocabulary to the children. Model each number with cubes. Emphasize that even numbers can be paired evenly and that odd numbers, when paired, always have a leftover cube.

Guided Practice

Have children use cubes and complete **Exercises 1–6** as you observe. Give children the opportunity to answer the Explain Your Thinking question. Then discuss their responses with the class.

331   CHAPTER 12   Lesson 4

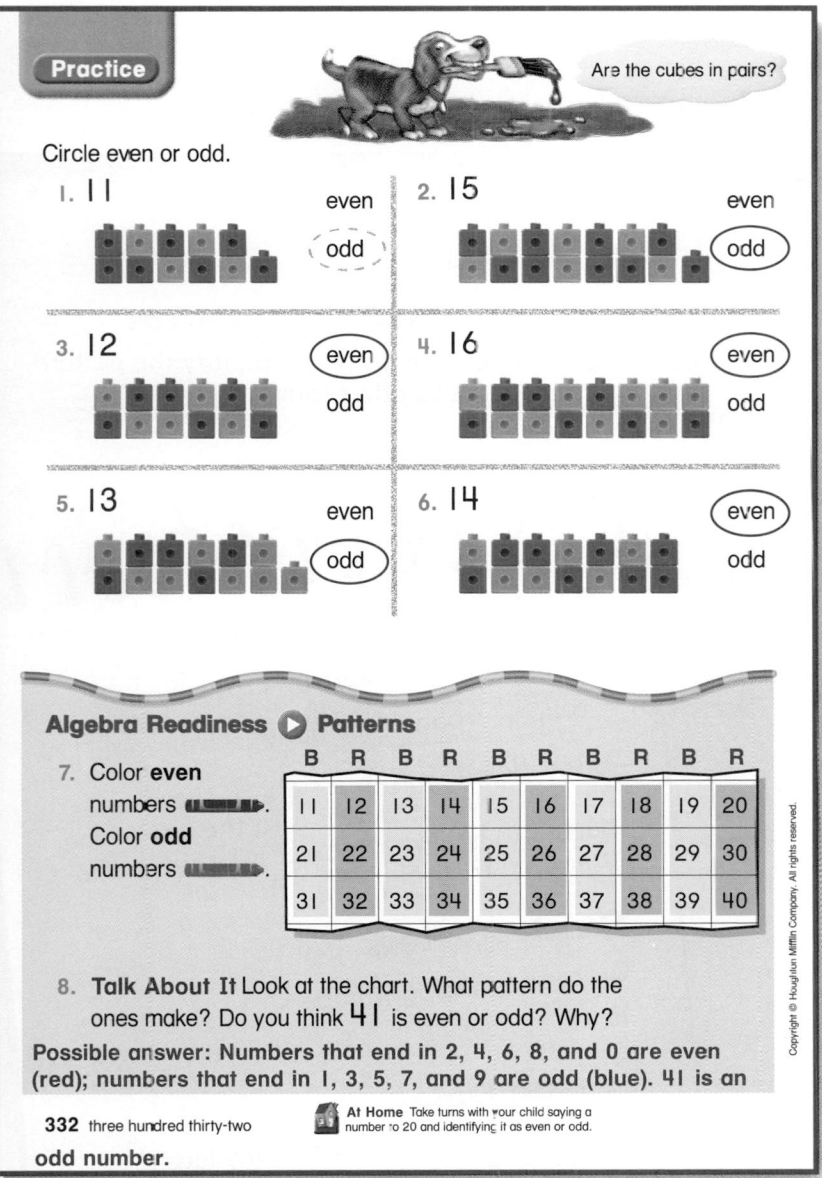

Practice

Are the cubes in pairs?

Circle even or odd.

1. 11   even / **odd**

2. 15   even / **odd**

3. 12   **even** / odd

4. 16   **even** / odd

5. 13   even / **odd**

6. 14   **even** / odd

Algebra Readiness ▶ Patterns

7. Color **even** numbers [blue].
   Color **odd** numbers [red].

B	R	B	R	B	R	B	R	B	R
11	12	13	14	15	16	17	18	19	20
21	22	23	24	25	26	27	28	29	30
31	32	33	34	35	36	37	38	39	40

8. **Talk About It** Look at the chart. What pattern do the ones make? Do you think 41 is even or odd? Why?

Possible answer: Numbers that end in 2, 4, 6, 8, and 0 are even (red); numbers that end in 1, 3, 5, 7, and 9 are odd (blue). 41 is an odd number.

332 three hundred thirty-two

At Home Take turns with your child saying a number to 20 and identifying it as even or odd.

Test Prep Transparency

12.4

Daily Test Prep

Which of these numbers is odd?

2   5   6   NH

○   ●   ○   ○

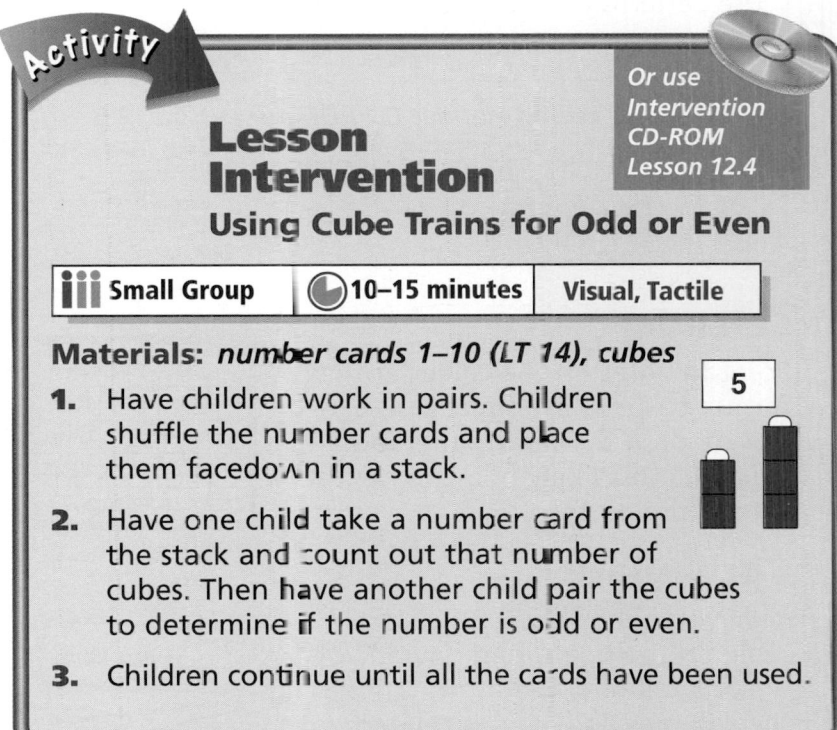

Activity

Or use Intervention CD-ROM Lesson 12.4

Lesson Intervention

Using Cube Trains for Odd or Even

ⅲ Small Group	⏱ 10–15 minutes	Visual, Tactile

Materials: *number cards 1–10 (LT 14), cubes*

1. Have children work in pairs. Children shuffle the number cards and place them facedown in a stack.

2. Have one child take a number card from the stack and count out that number of cubes. Then have another child pair the cubes to determine if the number is odd or even.

3. Children continue until all the cards have been used.

5

③ Practice

Independent Practice

Children complete **Exercises 1–6** independently.

Algebra Readiness

After children complete **Exercise 7**, invite volunteers to share their charts. Then use the **Talk About It** question in **Exercise 8** to discuss the patterns in the ones place of odd and even numbers.

Common Error

Children Don't See the Pairs

Some children may have difficulty seeing the pairs of cubes in the art. Allow children to show the number in actual cubes and then pair them together to determine if there is a leftover.

④ Assess and Close

- If a number can be shown as pairs with no leftover, is it odd or even? (even)

- If you have 3 mittens, do you have an odd or even number of mittens? (odd)

 **Keeping a Journal**

Write a rule to remember how to tell whether a number is even. Then draw a picture to show the rule.

Problem Solving: Find a Pattern

PLANNING THE LESSON

MATHEMATICS OBJECTIVE
Use patterns to solve problems.

Use Lesson Planner CD-ROM for Lesson 12.5.

Daily Routines

Calendar

Point to dates on the calendar that form a pattern. Example: 2, 4, 6, 8. Ask children to identify the date you will most likely point to next to extend the pattern.

Sunday	Monday	Tuesday	Wednesday	Thursday	Friday	Saturday
			1	2	3	4
5	6	7	8	9	10	11
12	13	14	15	16	17	18
19	20	21	22	23	24	25
26	27	28	29	30	31	

Vocabulary

Review **table** by drawing a simple table on the board and having volunteers tell how the information in the columns and rows is related.

Vocabulary Cards

Meeting North Carolina's Standards

5.03 Create and extend patterns, identify the pattern unit, and translate into other forms.
Also 1.02, 1.04

Lesson Transparency
12.5

Problem of the Day

Carol planted flowers in a row:

| tulip | pansy | daisy | marigold |

What flower is to the right of the daisy? (marigold) What flower is to the left of the pansy? (tulip) What flower is between the tulip and the daisy? (pansy)

Quick Review

Write the missing numbers.
10, 20, ___ (30), 40, ___ (50), 60, 70, 80, ___ (90), 100

Lesson Quiz

If a spider has 8 legs, how many legs do 2 spiders have? (16 legs)

LEVELED PRACTICE

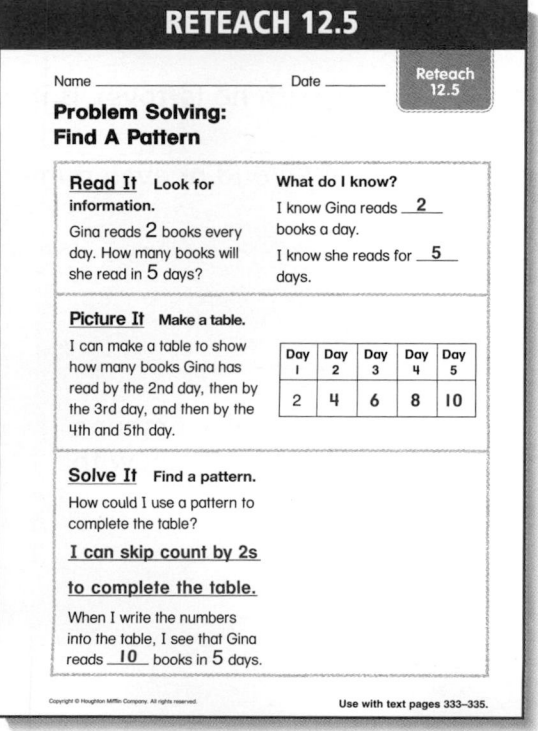

RETEACH 12.5

Name _____ Date _____

Reteach 12.5

Problem Solving: Find A Pattern

Read It Look for information.

Gina reads 2 books every day. How many books will she read in 5 days?

What do I know?
I know Gina reads __2__ books a day.
I know she reads for __5__ days.

Picture It Make a table.

I can make a table to show how many books Gina has read by the 2nd day, then by the 3rd day, and then by the 4th and 5th day.

Day 1	Day 2	Day 3	Day 4	Day 5
2	4	6	8	10

Solve It Find a pattern.

How could I use a pattern to complete the table?

I can skip count by 2s to complete the table.

When I write the numbers into the table, I see that Gina reads __10__ books in 5 days.

Copyright © Houghton Mifflin Company. All rights reserved.

Use with text pages 333–335.

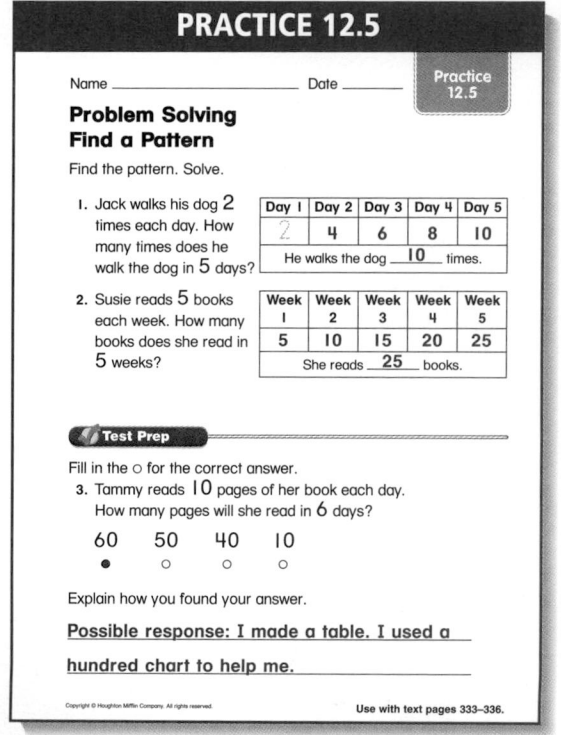

PRACTICE 12.5

Name _____ Date _____

Practice 12.5

Problem Solving Find a Pattern

Find the pattern. Solve.

1. Jack walks his dog 2 times each day. How many times does he walk the dog in 5 days?

Day 1	Day 2	Day 3	Day 4	Day 5
2	4	6	8	10

He walks the dog __10__ times.

2. Susie reads 5 books each week. How many books does she read in 5 weeks?

Week 1	Week 2	Week 3	Week 4	Week 5
5	10	15	20	25

She reads __25__ books.

Test Prep

Fill in the ○ for the correct answer.

3. Tammy reads 10 pages of her book each day. How many pages will she read in 6 days?

60 ●   50 ○   40 ○   10 ○

Explain how you found your answer.

Possible response: I made a table. I used a hundred chart to help me.

Copyright © Houghton Mifflin Company. All rights reserved.

Use with text pages 333–336.

ENRICHMENT 12.5

Name _____ Date _____

Enrichment 12.5

Day By Day Pay

1. **Read the problem.**
Susie walks the dog 1 time each day.
She gets 5¢ each time.
How much will she have after 7 days?

2. **Think about the problem.**
Is there a pattern? How can I show the pattern?

Monday	Tuesday	Wed.	Thursday	Friday	Saturday	Sunday
5¢	10¢	15¢	20¢	25¢	30¢	35¢

3. **Solve the problem.** Complete the table.
Write the answer.
Susie will have __35__ ¢.

Write a problem about Susie.	Problems and solutions will vary.
Solve the problem. Write the answer.	
Look back at the problem. Did you look for a pattern? What was it?	

Copyright © Houghton Mifflin Company. All rights reserved.

Use with text pages 333–335.

Practice Workbook Page 81

Reaching All Learners

Differentiated Instruction

English Learners

English-language learners may not be familiar with the names of the days of the week. Use Worksheet 12.5 to familiarize children with the names in English.

Special Needs
VISUAL, AUDITORY

- Draw a table as shown with 4 columns and 2 rows. Help the child sketch a picture of 4 people on a separate piece of paper. Point to 1 person and ask how many legs. Have the child write 2 in the first box. Continue to complete the table.

1 PERSON	2 PEOPLE	3 PEOPLE	4 PEOPLE
2 LEGS	4 LEGS	6 LEGS	8 LEGS

Early Finishers
TACTILE, VISUAL

- Draw a table and have children copy it.
- Children choose a favorite animal, draw a picture, and write the name. Then children fill in the information in the table. Ask children to share the pattern they used in counting how many in all.

Number of Legs			
1 giraffe	2 giraffes	3 giraffes	4 giraffes

TECHNOLOGY

Spiral Review

To reinforce skills on lessons taught earlier, create **customized** spiral review worksheets using the *Ways to Assess* CD-ROM.

Intervention

Use the *Ways to Success* intervention software to support students who need more help in understanding the concepts and skills taught in this chapter.

Lesson Planner

Use the **Lesson Planner CD-ROM** to see how lesson objectives for this chapter are correlated to standards.

ScienceConnection

Display pictures of various animals and ask children to write pattern questions, such as: How many eyes does 1 shark have? 2 sharks? If 2 geese have 4 legs, how many geese have 8 legs? Children can exchange papers and answer each other's questions.

MATH CENTER

Number of the Week Activity

Display the Number of the Week to motivate children to use their problem-solving skills. The exercises cover topics across all math strands.

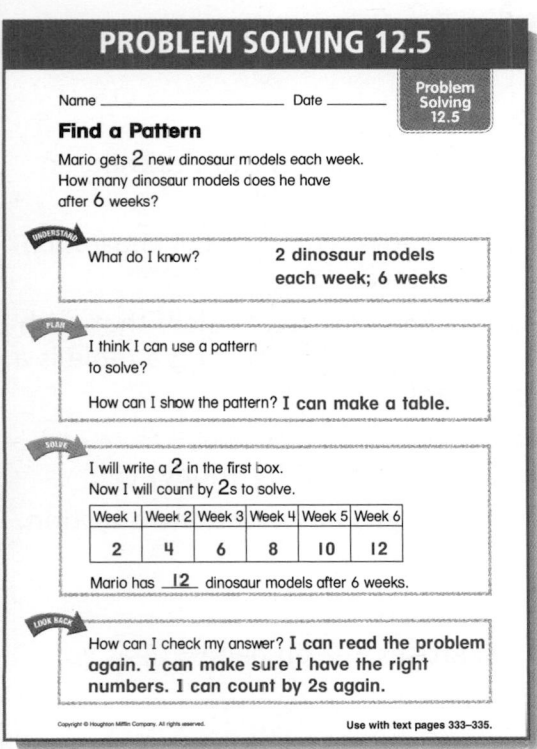

PROBLEM SOLVING 12.5

Name _____ Date _____   Problem Solving 12.5

Find a Pattern

Mario gets 2 new dinosaur models each week. How many dinosaur models does he have after 6 weeks?

UNDERSTAND

What do I know?   2 dinosaur models each week; 6 weeks

PLAN

I think I can use a pattern to solve.

How can I show the pattern? I can make a table.

SOLVE

I will write a 2 in the first box. Now I will count by 2s to solve.

Week 1	Week 2	Week 3	Week 4	Week 5	Week 6
2	4	6	8	10	12

Mario has __12__ dinosaur models after 6 weeks.

LOOK BACK

How can I check my answer? I can read the problem again. I can make sure I have the right numbers. I can count by 2s again.

Use with text pages 333–335.

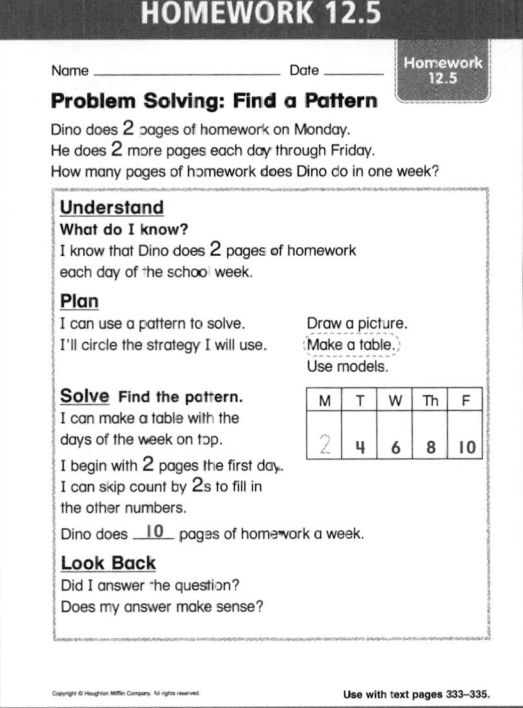

HOMEWORK 12.5

Name _____ Date _____   Homework 12.5

Problem Solving: Find a Pattern

Dino does 2 pages of homework on Monday. He does 2 more pages each day through Friday. How many pages of homework does Dino do in one week?

Understand
What do I know?
I know that Dino does 2 pages of homework each day of the school week.

Plan
I can use a pattern to solve.
I'll circle the strategy I will use.

Draw a picture.
Make a table.
Use models.

Solve Find the pattern.
I can make a table with the days of the week on top.

M	T	W	Th	F
2	4	6	8	10

I begin with 2 pages the first day. I can skip count by 2s to fill in the other numbers.

Dino does __10__ pages of homework a week.

Look Back
Did I answer the question?
Does my answer make sense?

Use with text pages 333–335.

ENGLISH LEARNERS 12.5

Name _____ Date _____   English Learners 12.5

Find a Pattern

Monday	Tuesday	Wednesday	Thursday	Friday

Draw a picture to show something you do on one day of the week.

A day of the week
Check children's drawings.

To the Teacher: Use the chart at the top of the page to teach children the names of the days of the week. Then have them choose a day of the week and draw a picture of something they do on each day of the week.

Use with text pages 333–335.

Homework Workbook Page 81

TEACHING LESSON 12.5

LESSON ORGANIZER

Objective Use patterns to solve problems.

Resources Reteach, Practice, Enrichment, Problem Solving, Homework, English Learners, Transparencies, Math Center

Materials Blank transparency, cubes

Activity
Warm-Up Activity
Modeling Skip Counting

👥 Small Group	⏱ 5 minutes	Kinesthetic, Auditory

1. Have children stand in a circle. **How many fingers are on 1 hand?** (5) **We can skip count by 5s to find how many fingers in all.** Point to each child as you count, having children put one hand in the circle as they are counted.

2. **How many arms does 1 person have?** (2) **We can skip count by 2s to find out how many arms in all.** Again point to each child as you count, having children put their arms in the circle as they are counted.

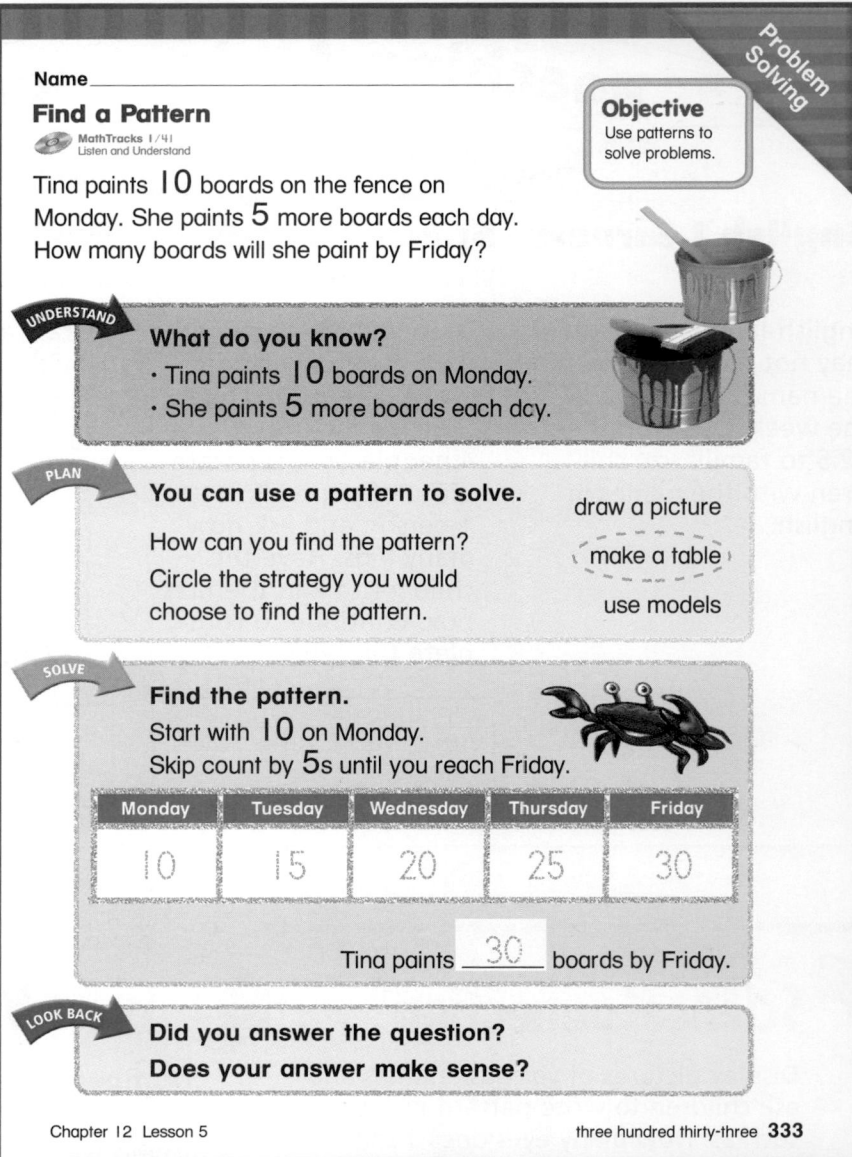

Name_____

Find a Pattern

🎵 MathTracks 1/41
Listen and Understand

Objective Use patterns to solve problems.

Tina paints 10 boards on the fence on Monday. She paints 5 more boards each day. How many boards will she paint by Friday?

UNDERSTAND

What do you know?
· Tina paints 10 boards on Monday.
· She paints 5 more boards each day.

PLAN

You can use a pattern to solve.

How can you find the pattern? Circle the strategy you would choose to find the pattern.

draw a picture
make a table
use models

SOLVE

Find the pattern.
Start with 10 on Monday.
Skip count by 5s until you reach Friday.

Monday	Tuesday	Wednesday	Thursday	Friday
10	15	20	25	30

Tina paints __30__ boards by Friday.

LOOK BACK

Did you answer the question?
Does your answer make sense?

Chapter 12 Lesson 5   three hundred thirty-three **333**

---

1 Introduce
Discuss Finding a Pattern

👥 Whole Group	⏱ 10–15 minutes	Visual, Auditory

Materials: *blank transparency*

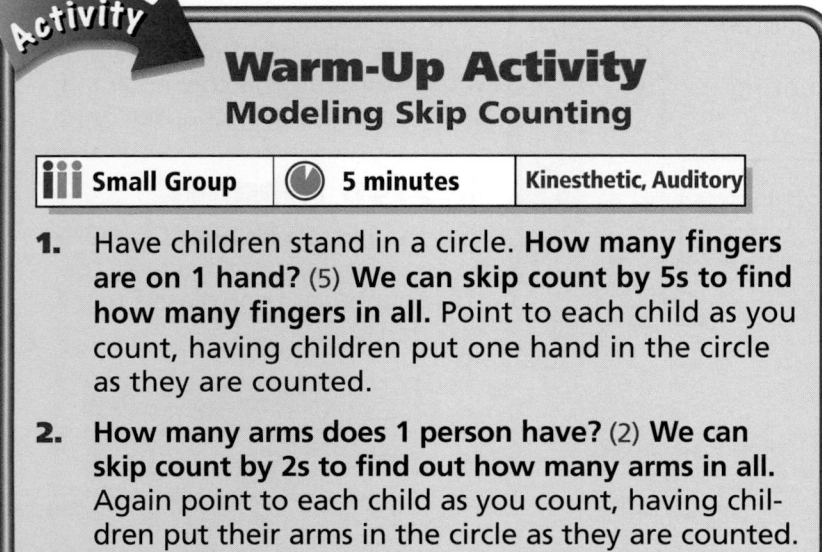

Number of Wheels		
1 bike	2 bikes	3 bikes

1. Draw a 2-row, 3-column table on a transparency with the title "Number of Wheels." Display the table. **How many wheels does one bike have?** (2) Write 2 in the first column. **Use a pattern to find out how many wheels are on 3 bikes.** Have volunteers help you fill in the table and describe the pattern.

2. Then make a similar chart for a car. **A car has how many wheels?** (4) Write 4 in the first column. Continue to fill in the chart and identify the pattern they use.

2 Develop

Guided Learning

Teaching Example Introduce the objective to the children. Then call on a volunteer to read the problem.

UNDERSTAND What do you know? (Tina paints 10 boards on Monday. She paints 5 more boards each day.)

PLAN Decide what strategy you will use. Explain that each strategy will work to find a pattern, but making a table is a good strategy for this problem.

SOLVE Do you see a pattern? (counting by 5s or 5 more each day) **How many boards does Tina paint by Friday?** (30)

LOOK BACK Check to see that you answered the question. Does 30 make sense?

Guided Practice

Have children complete **Exercises 1–2** on page 334 as you observe.

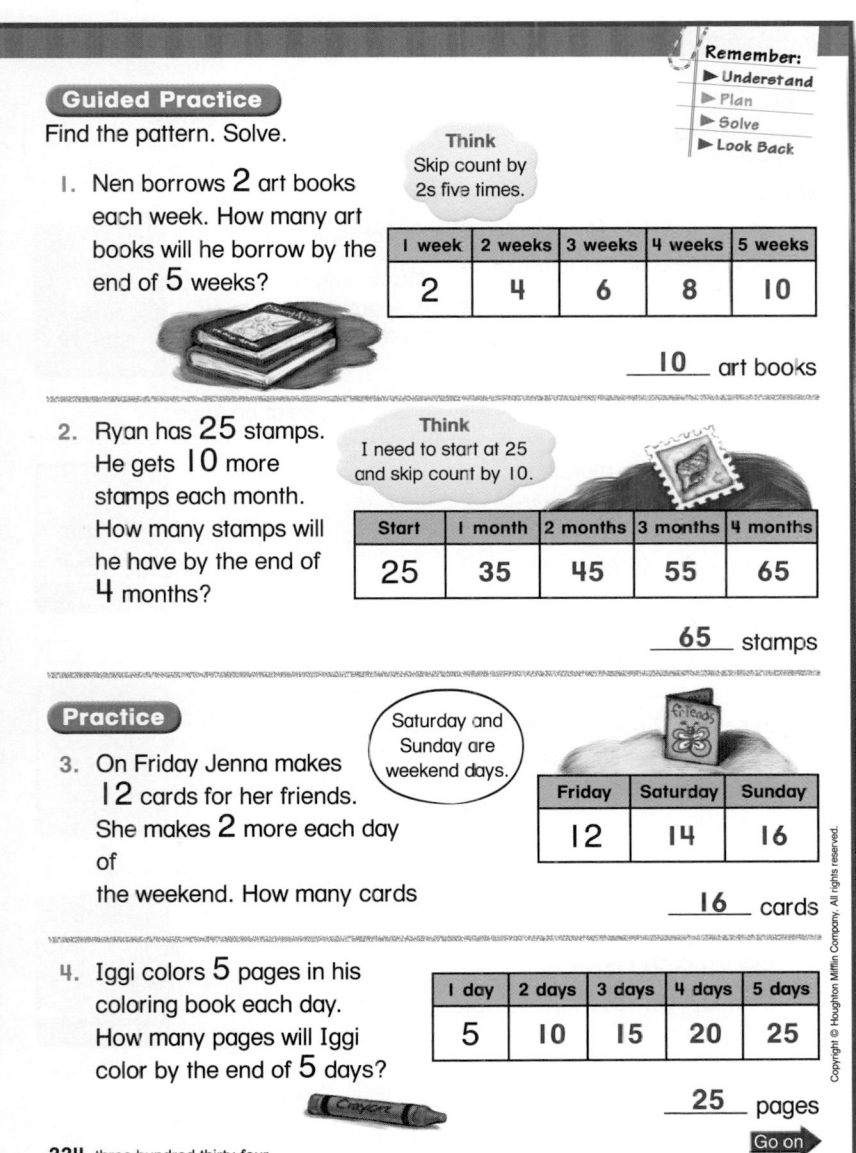

Guided Practice

Remember:
▶ Understand
▶ Plan
▶ Solve
▶ Look Back

Find the pattern. Solve.

1. Nen borrows 2 art books each week. How many art books will he borrow by the end of 5 weeks?

Think
Skip count by 2s five times.

1 week	2 weeks	3 weeks	4 weeks	5 weeks
2	4	6	8	10

_____10_____ art books

2. Ryan has 25 stamps. He gets 10 more stamps each month. How many stamps will he have by the end of 4 months?

Think
I need to start at 25 and skip count by 10.

Start	1 month	2 months	3 months	4 months
25	35	45	55	65

_____65_____ stamps

Practice

3. On Friday Jenna makes 12 cards for her friends. She makes 2 more each day of the weekend. How many cards

Saturday and Sunday are weekend days.

Friday	Saturday	Sunday
12	14	16

_____16_____ cards

4. Iggi colors 5 pages in his coloring book each day. How many pages will Iggi color by the end of 5 days?

1 day	2 days	3 days	4 days	5 days
5	10	15	20	25

_____25_____ pages

Go on ▶

334 three hundred thirty-four

KEEPING **SKILLS** SHARP

Play "Weekday Patterns"

Draw several blank tables on the board. Separate the class into two teams and decide which team goes first. Ask a pattern question; for example:

If a student eats 2 snacks each school day, how many snacks does he or she eat in one school week? (10)

A child from the first team makes a table and states the answer. If the table and answer are correct, the team gets 1 point. If not, the other team gets a chance to change the table and state the answer. Then ask another pattern question and have a child from the second team make a table and state the answer. Continue as time allows.

③ Practice

Independent Practice

Children complete **Exercises 3–4** on page 334 independently.

Lesson continues ▶

Daily Test Prep

Sara eats a package of crackers each school day. If there are 2 crackers in each package, how many crackers does she eat in a full school week?

2   10   14   NH
○   ●   ○   ○

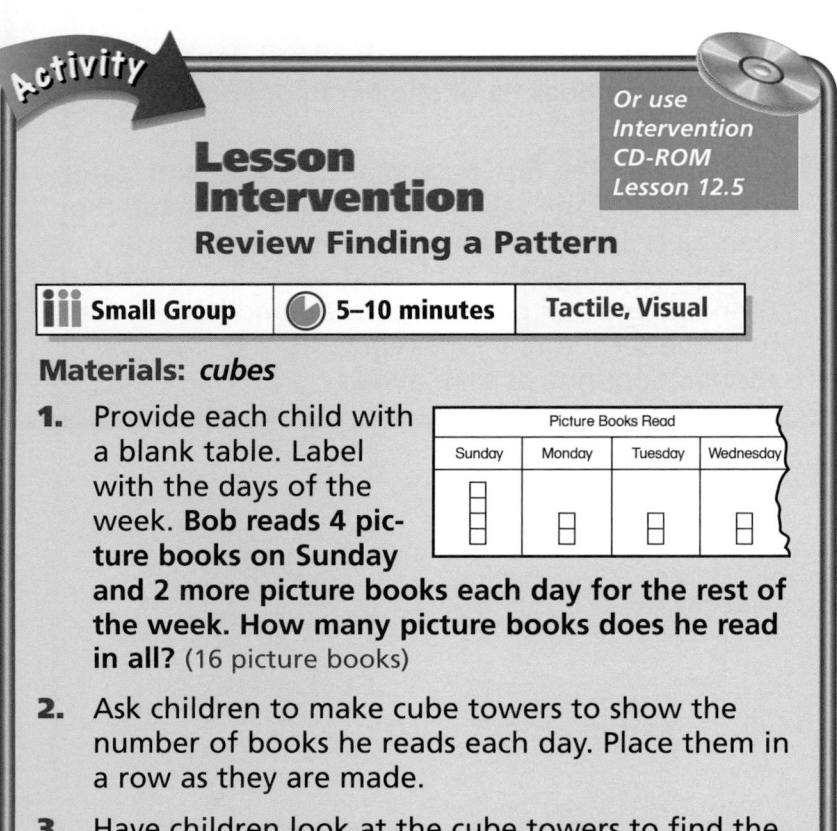

Activity

Or use
Intervention
CD-ROM
Lesson 12.5

Lesson Intervention

Review Finding a Pattern

👥 Small Group	🕐 5–10 minutes	Tactile, Visual

Materials: *cubes*

1. Provide each child with a blank table. Label with the days of the week. **Bob reads 4 picture books on Sunday and 2 more picture books each day for the rest of the week. How many picture books does he read in all?** (16 picture books)

Picture Books Read			
Sunday	Monday	Tuesday	Wednesday

2. Ask children to make cube towers to show the number of books he reads each day. Place them in a row as they are made.

3. Have children look at the cube towers to find the pattern of counting on by 2s from 4.

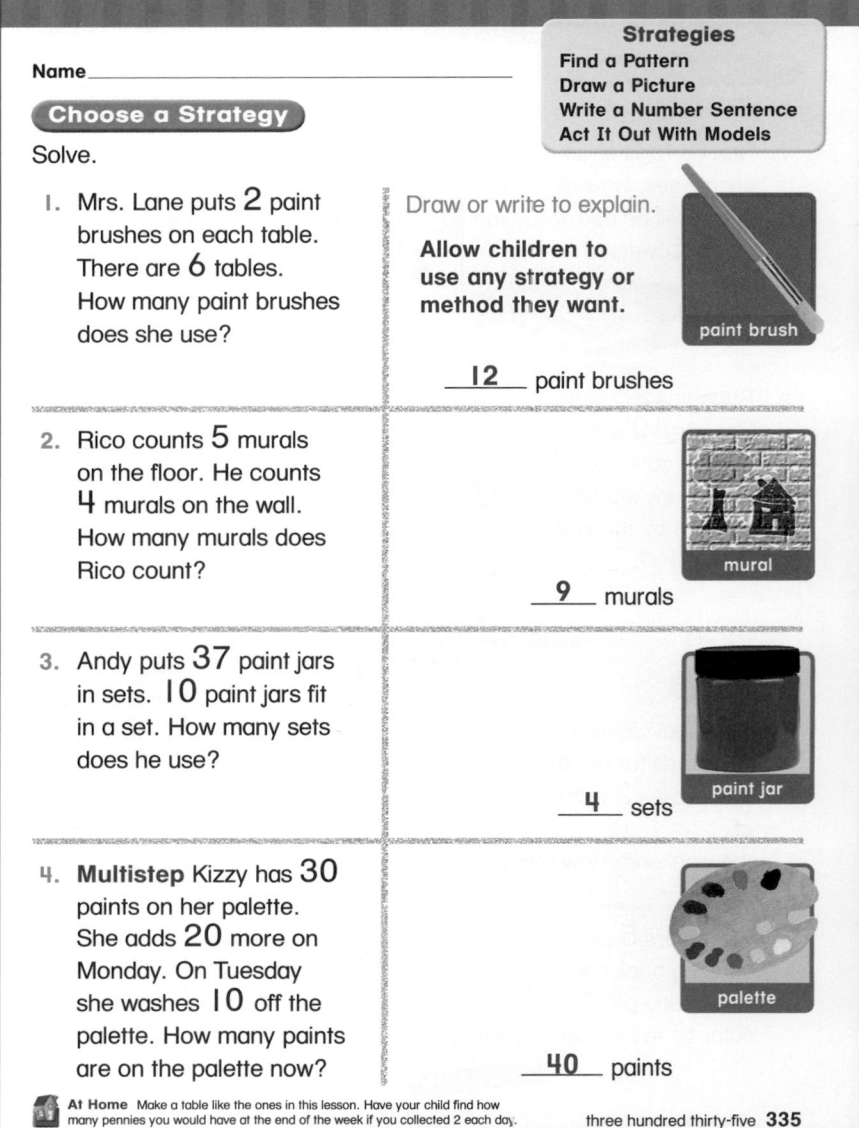

Name_____

Strategies
Find a Pattern
Draw a Picture
Write a Number Sentence
Act It Out With Models

Choose a Strategy

Solve.

1. Mrs. Lane puts 2 paint brushes on each table. There are 6 tables. How many paint brushes does she use?

   Draw or write to explain.
   Allow children to use any strategy or method they want.

   paint brush

   __12__ paint brushes

2. Rico counts 5 murals on the floor. He counts 4 murals on the wall. How many murals does Rico count?

   mural

   __9__ murals

3. Andy puts 37 paint jars in sets. 10 paint jars fit in a set. How many sets does he use?

   paint jar

   __4__ sets

4. **Multistep** Kizzy has 30 paints on her palette. She adds 20 more on Monday. On Tuesday she washes 10 off the palette. How many paints are on the palette now?

   palette

   __40__ paints

At Home Make a table like the ones in this lesson. Have your child find how many pennies you would have at the end of the week if you collected 2 each day.

three hundred thirty-five **335**

---

3 Practice

Mixed Strategy Practice

Read the problem-solving strategies with children. Make sure children can read and comprehend the problems in **Exercises 1–4** on page 335. If necessary, pair more proficient readers with less proficient readers. Encourage them to discuss the problems before solving.

Common Error

Counting by Ones Rather Than by the Pattern
Children may confuse counting by ones with counting by the amount of the pattern. Write + and the pattern number under each box in the exercise.

4 Assess and Close

Mary works at her computer 2 hours each day. What pattern can you use to find how many hours she works at her computer from Monday through Friday? (Count by 2s.) How many hours does she work in 5 days? (10 hours)

 **Keeping a Journal**

Write a pattern question that includes days of the week. Find the answer. Example:

If I brush my teeth 2 times each day, how many times do I brush my teeth in 7 days? (14 times)

 **Listening Skills**

Listen to your teacher read the problem.
Solve.

1. 10 paint brushes fit in 1 case.
20 paint brushes fit in 2 cases.
How many cases are needed for
40 paint brushes?

Show your work using pictures, numbers, or words.

_____4_____ cases

2. Maria makes necklaces with beads
and string. She has 47 beads.
Each string can hold 10 beads.
How many strings does she need?

_____5_____ strings

Listen to your teacher read the problem.
Choose the correct answer.

3. 50   52   60   70
   ○   ○   ○   ●

4. 4   8   12   16
   ○   ○   ●   ○

Listening Skills

This page provides children practice with the oral problem-solving format used in some standardized test items.

You may want to read each item only once to mimic the style of oral tests.

Use With Items 1 and 2

Listening Strategy: Read the problem silently while the teacher reads it aloud.

• *This problem is on the page. Read it to yourself while I read it aloud.*

• *Listen to the whole problem. Wait until I finish before you start writing.*

Use With Item 3

Listening Strategy: Listen for important facts and numbers.

• *Listen carefully as I read the problem. You can write down any details you think are important.*

Abby has 50 stickers in a box. She earns 10 stickers for feeding the dog and 10 stickers for feeding the cat. How many stickers does she have now?

• *Look at your notes. Then mark your answer.*

Use With Item 4

Listening Strategy: Listen for a pattern.

• *Listen carefully as I read the problem. You can make a table to continue the pattern and solve the problem.*

There are 4 wheels on 1 wagon. There are 8 wheels on 2 wagons. How many wheels are on 3 wagons?

• *Complete your table. Then mark your answer.*

Quick Check

Have children complete the Quick Check exercises independently to assess their understanding of concepts and skills taught in **Lessons 4–5.**

Item	Lesson	Error Analysis	Intervention
1–4	12.4	Some children may not see the pairs in the art.	Reteach Resource 12.4 *Ways to Success* 12.4
5–6	12.5	Children may count by ones rather than by the pattern.	Reteach Resource 12.5 *Ways to Success* 12.5

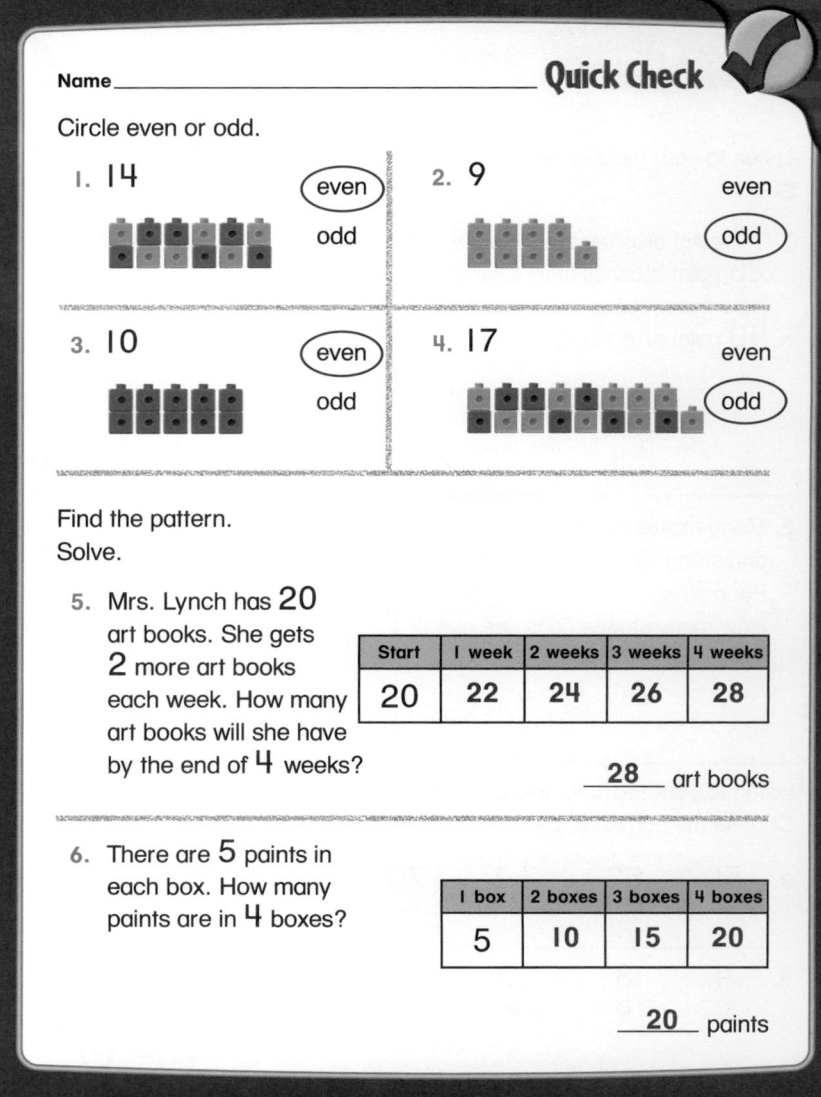

Name_____

Quick Check

Circle even or odd.

1. 14   (even)   odd

2. 9   even   (odd)

3. 10   (even)   odd

4. 17   even   (odd)

Find the pattern.
Solve.

5. Mrs. Lynch has 20 art books. She gets 2 more art books each week. How many art books will she have by the end of 4 weeks?

Start	1 week	2 weeks	3 weeks	4 weeks
20	22	24	26	28

___28___ art books

6. There are 5 paints in each box. How many paints are in 4 boxes?

1 box	2 boxes	3 boxes	4 boxes
5	10	15	20

___20___ paints

How Children Ride to School

Key: Each 𝓍 stands for 1 child

Use the pictograph.

1. How many children ride 🚌?

   ___6___ children

2. How many children ride 🚲?

   ___2___ children

3. Which way do fewer children ride?

   🚌 (🚗)

4. How do most children get to school?

   (🚌) 🚲 🚗

Music Connection

Counting Notes

This is one type of note. ♪

A note is a symbol used for writing music.
A beat is a way to count when singing music.
In some songs, 2 of these notes make 1 beat.
How many of these notes are in 8 beats?
Skip count by 2s.

♫   ♫   ♫   ♫   ♫   ♫   ♫   ♫

_2_ _4_ _6_ _8_ _10_ _12_ _14_ _16_

___16___ notes

WEEKLY WR READER eduplace.com/kids/mw

338 three hundred thirty-eight

Key Topic Review

This assessment provides a review of skills and concepts taught in Chapter 4.

Check to be sure that children:

• can read a pictograph

• understand comparison vocabulary: fewer, most

Music Connection

Counting Notes

Discuss how music and songs are written using different notes. Draw a whole note, a half note, and a quarter note on the board. Write how many beats each note receives.

• Clap each note with the children. (For example, a whole note gets 4 claps, a half note gets 2 claps, etc.)

• Ask volunteers to write 4 notes on the board. Clap the pattern with the children.

• Ask children if they notice a pattern when a row of half notes is clapped. (It is like counting by 2s.) **Have children complete the page.**

Monitoring Student Progress

Purpose: This test provides an informal assessment of the Chapter 12 objectives.

Chapter Test Items 1–20

To assign a numerical grade for this Chapter Test, use 5 points for each test item.

Check Understanding

Use children's work on word problems to informally assess progress on chapter content.

Customizing Your Instruction

For children who have not yet mastered these objectives, you can use the reteaching resources listed in the chart below.

 Assessment Options

A summary test for this unit test is also provided in the Unit Resource Folder.

Name_____

Chapter Review/Test

Vocabulary *e* Glossary

Complete the sentence.

skip count
odd
more than

1. 37 is ___more than___ 32.

2. If I cannot make equal groups,
   it is an ___odd___ number.

3. When I count by 2s I ___skip count___.

Concepts and Skills

Write the missing numbers.
Skip count by 2s.

4. 40, 42, _44_, 46, 48, _50_

5. 90, _92_, 94, _96_, _98_, 100

Write the missing numbers.
Skip count by 5s.

6. 20, 25, _30_, _35_, _40_

7. 80, _85_, _90_, _95_, _100_

Write the number that is 1 more or 1 less.

8. | 19 | 20 | 9. | 57 | 58 | 10. | 72 | 73 | 11. | 51 | 52 |

Chapter 12   three hundred thirty-nine **339**

Reteaching Support

Chapter Test Items	Summary Test Items	Chapter Objectives Tested	TE Pages	Use These Reteaching Resources
1–3	1–4	**12A** Develop and use math vocabulary relating to number patterns.	323A–324, 327A–328, 331A–332	Reteach Resources and *Ways to Success* CD: 12.1, 12.3, 12.4 Skillsheet 83
4–7	1–4	**12B** Skip count by 2s and 5s to 100.	323A–326	Reteach Resources and *Ways to Success* CD: 12.1, 12.2 Skillsheet 84
8–18	5–8	**12C** Identify odd and even numbers and 1 more, 1 less, 10 more, 10 less than a given number.	327A–328, 331A–332	Reteach Resources and *Ways to Success* CD: 12.3, 12.4 Skillsheets 85 and 86
19–20	9–10	**12D** Use patterns to solve problems.	333A–336	Reteach Resource and *Ways to Success* CD: 12.5 Skillsheet 87

CHAPTER SUMMARY TEST

Name_____ Date_____

Chapter 12 Test

Use the chart.
Write the missing numbers.
Skip count by 2s

1. 56, _58_, 60, _62_

2. 68, _70_, 72, 74

1	2	3	4	5	6	7	8	9	10
11	12	13	14	15	16	17	18	19	20
21	22	23	24	25	26	27	28	29	30
31	32	33	34	35	36	37	38	39	40
41	42	43	44	45	46	47	48	49	50
51	52	53	54	55	56	57	58	59	60
61	62	63	64	65	66	67	68	69	70
71	72	73	74	75	76	77	78	79	80
81	82	83	84	85	86	87	88	89	90
91	92	93	94	95	96	97	98	99	100

Use the chart.
Write the missing numbers.
Skip count by 5s.

3. 50, _55_, 60, _65_

4. 65, _70_, 75, _80_

Write the number.

5. 1 less   6. 10 more

   _72_, 73   65, _75_

Circle odd or even.

7.   8.
   (odd) even   odd (even)

Go on ▶

Write the number that is 10 more or 10 less.

12.	46
	56

13.	18
	28

14.	60
	70

15.	81
	91

Circle even or odd.

16. 13   even   (odd)

17. 12   (even)   odd

18. 10   (even)   odd

Problem Solving

Find the pattern.
Solve.

19. Katie writes 2 stories a week. How many stories will she write by the end of 5 weeks?

1 week	2 weeks	3 weeks	4 weeks	5 weeks
2	4	6	8	10

_10_ stories

20. Kyle has 5 patches. He earns 5 more patches a month. How many patches will he have by the end of 4 months?

Start	1 month	2 months	3 months	4 months
5	10	15	20	25

_25_ patches

340 three hundred forty

Use the End of Grade Test Prep Assessment Guide to help familiarize your children with the format of standardized tests.

CHAPTER SUMMARY TEST

Name _____ Date _____   Chapter 12 Test continued

Find the pattern. Solve.

9. Felix is going to buy 5 action toys each week for 5 weeks. How many action toys will Felix have by the end of the fifth week?

Week 1	Week 2	Week 3	Week 4	Week 5
5	10	15	20	25

Felix will have _25_ action toys.

10. Kiki will get 10 stars for each month she comes to school. She comes to school for 6 months. How many stars does she have at the end of the sixth month?

Kiki will have _60_ stars.

1 months	2 months	3 months	4 months	5 months	6 months
10	20	30	40	50	60

STOP

Facts Practice ....

Name_____

Add.
Write the sum.

1.
$\begin{array}{r} 7 \\ +1 \\ \hline 8 \end{array}$
$\begin{array}{r} 6 \\ +2 \\ \hline 8 \end{array}$
$\begin{array}{r} 7 \\ +0 \\ \hline 7 \end{array}$
$\begin{array}{r} 3 \\ +4 \\ \hline 7 \end{array}$
$\begin{array}{r} 0 \\ +5 \\ \hline 5 \end{array}$
$\begin{array}{r} 1 \\ +3 \\ \hline 4 \end{array}$
$\begin{array}{r} 6 \\ +3 \\ \hline 9 \end{array}$

2.
$\begin{array}{r} 2 \\ +2 \\ \hline 4 \end{array}$
$\begin{array}{r} 1 \\ +4 \\ \hline 5 \end{array}$
$\begin{array}{r} 4 \\ +4 \\ \hline 8 \end{array}$
$\begin{array}{r} 2 \\ +5 \\ \hline 7 \end{array}$
$\begin{array}{r} 3 \\ +3 \\ \hline 6 \end{array}$
$\begin{array}{r} 4 \\ +0 \\ \hline 4 \end{array}$
$\begin{array}{r} 5 \\ +3 \\ \hline 8 \end{array}$

3.
$\begin{array}{r} 1 \\ +5 \\ \hline 6 \end{array}$
$\begin{array}{r} 4 \\ +3 \\ \hline 7 \end{array}$
$\begin{array}{r} 3 \\ +2 \\ \hline 5 \end{array}$
$\begin{array}{r} 8 \\ +0 \\ \hline 8 \end{array}$
$\begin{array}{r} 3 \\ +5 \\ \hline 8 \end{array}$
$\begin{array}{r} 0 \\ +7 \\ \hline 7 \end{array}$
$\begin{array}{r} 9 \\ +1 \\ \hline 10 \end{array}$

4.
$\begin{array}{r} 8 \\ +1 \\ \hline 9 \end{array}$
$\begin{array}{r} 6 \\ +3 \\ \hline 9 \end{array}$
$\begin{array}{r} 7 \\ +3 \\ \hline 10 \end{array}$
$\begin{array}{r} 4 \\ +5 \\ \hline 9 \end{array}$
$\begin{array}{r} 0 \\ +9 \\ \hline 9 \end{array}$
$\begin{array}{r} 7 \\ +2 \\ \hline 9 \end{array}$
$\begin{array}{r} 6 \\ +4 \\ \hline 10 \end{array}$

5.
$\begin{array}{r} 0 \\ +4 \\ \hline 4 \end{array}$
$\begin{array}{r} 5 \\ +4 \\ \hline 9 \end{array}$
$\begin{array}{r} 3 \\ +6 \\ \hline 9 \end{array}$
$\begin{array}{r} 1 \\ +9 \\ \hline 10 \end{array}$
$\begin{array}{r} 1 \\ +8 \\ \hline 9 \end{array}$
$\begin{array}{r} 4 \\ +2 \\ \hline 6 \end{array}$
$\begin{array}{r} 4 \\ +1 \\ \hline 5 \end{array}$

6.
$\begin{array}{r} 5 \\ +5 \\ \hline 10 \end{array}$
$\begin{array}{r} 1 \\ +7 \\ \hline 8 \end{array}$
$\begin{array}{r} 5 \\ +2 \\ \hline 7 \end{array}$
$\begin{array}{r} 6 \\ +4 \\ \hline 10 \end{array}$
$\begin{array}{r} 0 \\ +8 \\ \hline 8 \end{array}$
$\begin{array}{r} 2 \\ +6 \\ \hline 8 \end{array}$
$\begin{array}{r} 6 \\ +1 \\ \hline 7 \end{array}$

7.
$\begin{array}{r} 5 \\ +1 \\ \hline 6 \end{array}$
$\begin{array}{r} 2 \\ +6 \\ \hline 8 \end{array}$
$\begin{array}{r} 0 \\ +7 \\ \hline 7 \end{array}$
$\begin{array}{r} 2 \\ +3 \\ \hline 5 \end{array}$
$\begin{array}{r} 5 \\ +0 \\ \hline 5 \end{array}$
$\begin{array}{r} 3 \\ +1 \\ \hline 4 \end{array}$
$\begin{array}{r} 9 \\ +0 \\ \hline 9 \end{array}$

Facts Practice

Subtract.
Write the difference.

1.
$$8 - 1 = 7 \qquad 8 - 6 = 2 \qquad 7 - 0 = 7 \qquad 7 - 3 = 4 \qquad 5 - 0 = 5 \qquad 4 - = 3 \qquad 9 - 6 = 3$$

2.
$$4 - 2 = 2 \qquad 5 - 1 = 4 \qquad 8 - 4 = 4 \qquad 7 - 2 = 5 \qquad 6 - 3 = 3 \qquad 4 - 0 = 4 \qquad 8 - 5 = 3$$

3.
$$6 - 1 = 5 \qquad 7 - 4 = 3 \qquad 5 - 3 = 2 \qquad 8 - 0 = 8 \qquad 8 - 3 = 5 \qquad 6 - 0 = 6 \qquad 10 - 1 = 9$$

4.
$$9 - 1 = 8 \qquad 9 - 3 = 6 \qquad 10 - 3 = 7 \qquad 9 - 4 = 5 \qquad 9 - 0 = 9 \qquad 9 - 2 = 7 \qquad 10 - 6 = 4$$

5.
$$3 - 0 = 3 \qquad 9 - 5 = 4 \qquad 9 - 6 = 3 \qquad 10 - 1 = 9 \qquad 9 - 1 = 8 \qquad 6 - 4 = 2 \qquad 5 - 4 = 1$$

6.
$$10 - 5 = 5 \qquad 8 - 1 = 7 \qquad 5 - 2 = 3 \qquad 10 - 4 = 6 \qquad 2 - 0 = 2 \qquad 8 - 2 = 6 \qquad 7 - 6 = 1$$

7.
$$6 - 1 = 5 \qquad 8 - 4 = 4 \qquad 7 - 3 = 4 \qquad 5 - 2 = 3 \qquad 1 - 0 = 1 \qquad 4 - 1 = 3 \qquad 10 - 2 = 8$$

Science Connection

PURPOSE

To compare and order numbers to 100.

Animal Speeds

WEEKLY **WR** READER®
Science Connection

Animals are all different shapes and sizes. They run at different speeds. Some animals can run as fast as a car. One of these is the cheetah. The cheetah is the fastest animal that lives on the ground. It can run at a speed of **70** miles an hour!

Animals That Run	Speed (miles an hour)
Cheetah	70
Lion	50
Rabbit	35
Elephant	25
Pig	11

The Fort Worth Zoo in Texas is home to a group of cheetahs.

The chart shows how fast some animals move on the ground.

Draw or write to explain.

1. The lion can run **50** miles an hour. Write the number that comes just before **50**.

   __49__ , 50

2. Which number in the chart has **2** tens?

   __25__

3. Is the speed of the rabbit greater than or less than the speed of the pig? Write < or >.

   35 ⊗ 11

4. Which animals run faster than the rabbit?

   __lion__   __cheetah__

Using These Pages
Discussion Topics

- Explain to children that each animal can run the speed listed for only a very short distance. They would not be able to keep up that speed for a full hour.

- Tell children that an Olympic record-setting runner runs about 27 miles an hour. **Is that greater than or less than the speed of a rabbit?** (less than)

- **Which animal's speed is closest to 27 miles an hour?** (elephant)

- Refer children to the chart on page 344, that shows the speeds of the sailfish, blue shark, and blue whale. **Order the speeds of the animals that swim from slowest to fastest.** (30, 43, 68)

Fish and birds also move at different speeds. The charts show how fast some of these animals move.

Animals That Fly	Speed (miles an hour)
Falcon	100
Hummingbird	60
Eagle	30

Animals That Swim	Speed (miles an hour)
Sailfish	68
Blue shark	43
Blue whale	30

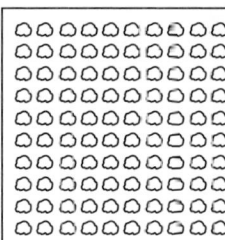

Use the charts to solve.

Draw or write to explain.

1. A sailfish can swim **68** miles an hour. Is this greater than or less than how fast a blue shark can swim an hour?

_____ greater than _____

2. Order the speeds of the animals that fly from slowest to fastest.

_30_ _60_ _100_

3. Which animals have a speed that is equal to **3** tens?

_____ eagle _____ _____ blue whale _____

 Technology
Visit *Education Place* at **eduplace.com/kids/mw/** to learn more about this topic.

344 three hundred forty-four

Wrap Up the Unit Project

7

"7 tens"
"70"

- As children complete a row on the grid, have them count the number of rocks thus far.

- Ask questions such as, **What is 10 more than 40? What is 10 more than 70?** (50; 80)

- When the grid is complete, give each child a number card 1–10. Ask them to count that many rows on the grid, tell how many tens, and how many in all.

- Invite children to take a handful of rocks, count them, and glue them onto cardboard as a mosaic. You might want to have pictures of simple mosaic designs available for children to look at for ideas.

Unit 4 Test

PURPOSE

This test provides an informal assessment of the Unit 4 objectives.

Unit Test Items 1–20

To assign a numerical grade for this Unit Test, use 5 points for each test item

Customizing Your Instruction

For Children who have not yet mastered these objectives, you can use the **Reteaching Resources** listed in the chart below. *Ways to Success* is Houghton Mifflin's Intervention program available in CD-ROM and blackline master formats.

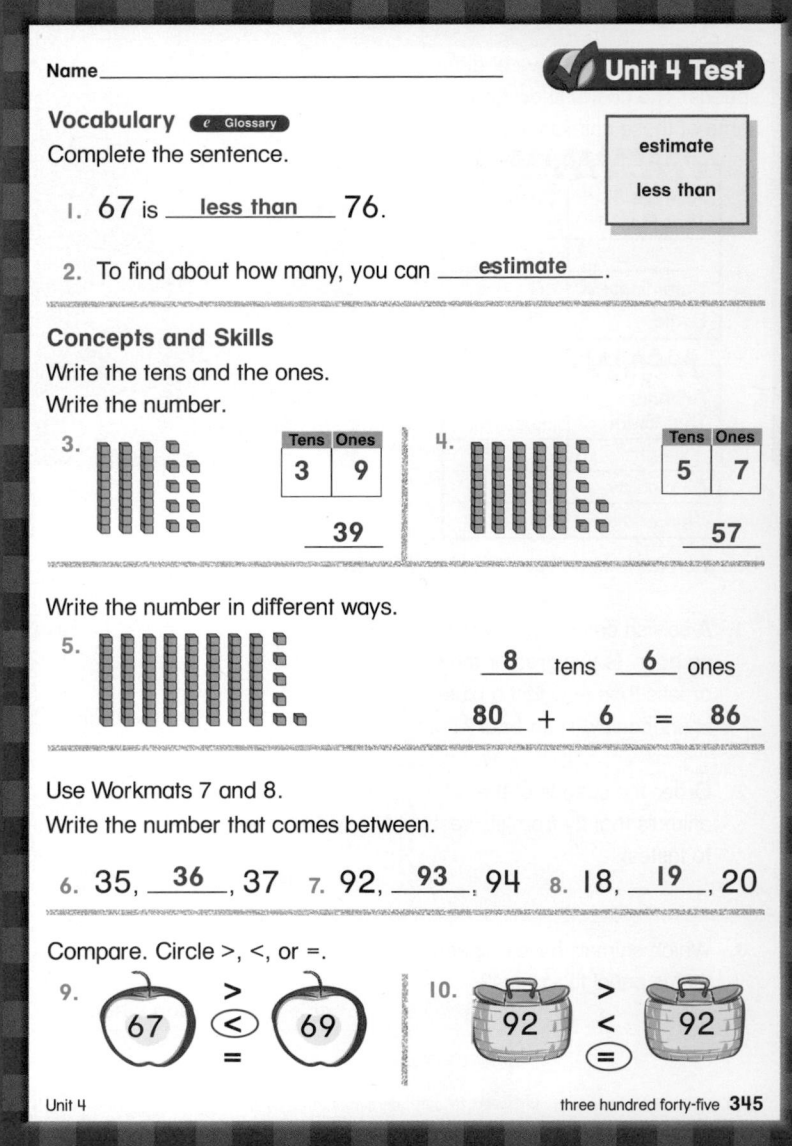

Reteaching Support

Unit Test Item		Unit Objectives Tested		TE Pages	Use These Reteaching Resources
p. 345–346 1–2, 6–10	Tests A & B 9–10, 15–16	4A	Identify, read, write, order, and compare numbers through 100.	311A–312, 313A–314	Reteach Resources and *Ways to Success*, 11.1, 11.4, 11.5
3–4	1–2	4B	Count and regroup tens and ones.	277A–285	Reteach Resources and *Ways to Success*, 10.1–10.4
5	3–8	4C	Identify place value through 99.	303A–304	Reteach Resources and *Ways to Success*, 10.3–10.5
11–13	11–14	4D	Identify ordinal numbers 1st through 10th.	305A–306	Reteach Resource and *Ways to Success*, 11.2
14–17	17–20	4E	Use a hundred chart to skip count by 2s and 5s to 100.	323A–326	Reteach Resources and *Ways to Success*, 12.1, 12.2
18–19	21–23	4F	Identify odd and even numbers.	331A–332	Reteach Resource and *Ways to Success*, 11.4
20	24–25	4G	Apply skills and strategies to solve problems.	293A–296, 333A–336	Reteach Resources and *Ways to Success*, 10.8, 12.5

Unit 4 Test

Color.

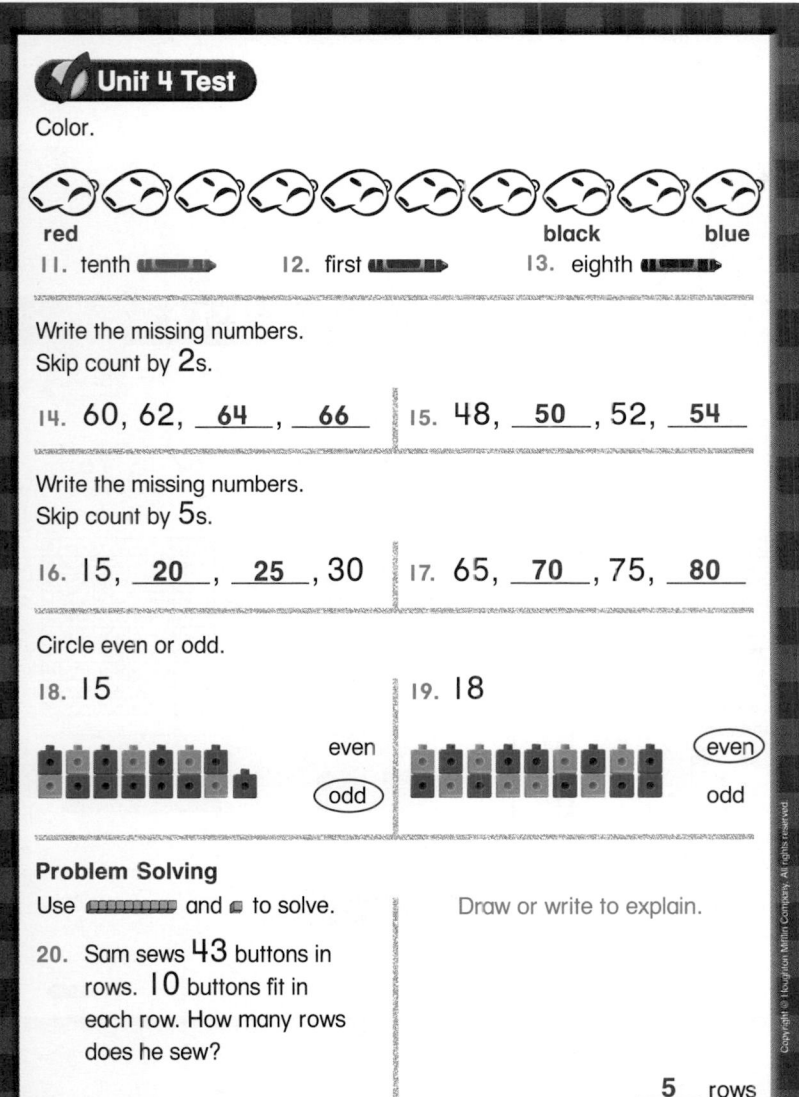

red black blue

11. tenth   12. first 13. eighth

Write the missing numbers.
Skip count by 2s.

14. 60, 62, __64__, __66__ | 15. 48, __50__, 52, __54__

Write the missing numbers.
Skip count by 5s.

16. 15, __20__, __25__, 30 | 17. 65, __70__, 75, __80__

Circle even or odd.

18. 15   even (odd)

19. 18   (even) odd

Problem Solving

Use ▭▭▭ and ▫ to solve.

Draw or write to explain.

20. Sam sews 43 buttons in rows. 10 buttons fit in each row. How many rows does he sew?

__5__ rows

346 three hundred forty-six

Assessment Options

Formal Tests for this unit are also provided in the Unit Resource Folder.

- Unit 4 Test A (Open Response)
- Unit 4 Test B (Multiple Choice)

Performance Assessment

You may want to use the Performance Assessment instead of, or in addition to, the Unit Test. Three Performance Assessment tasks can be found on Student Book pages 347–348.

Adequate Yearly Progress

Use the *End of Grade Test Prep Assessment Guide* to help familiarize your children with the format of standardized tests.

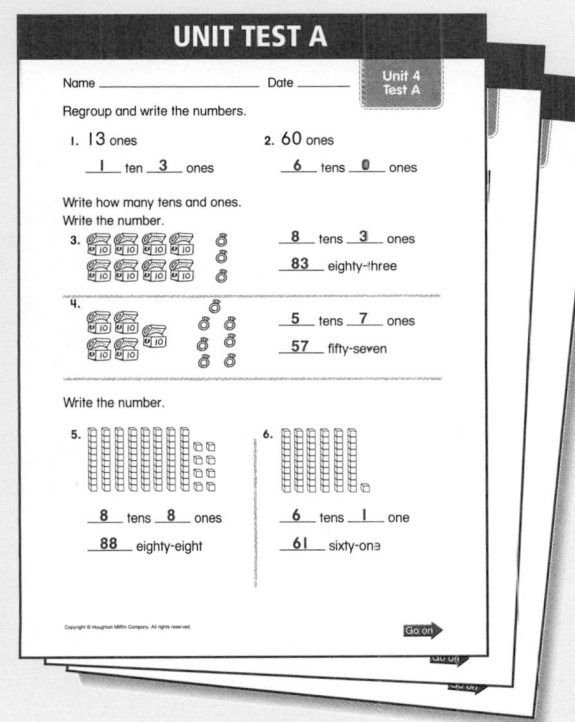

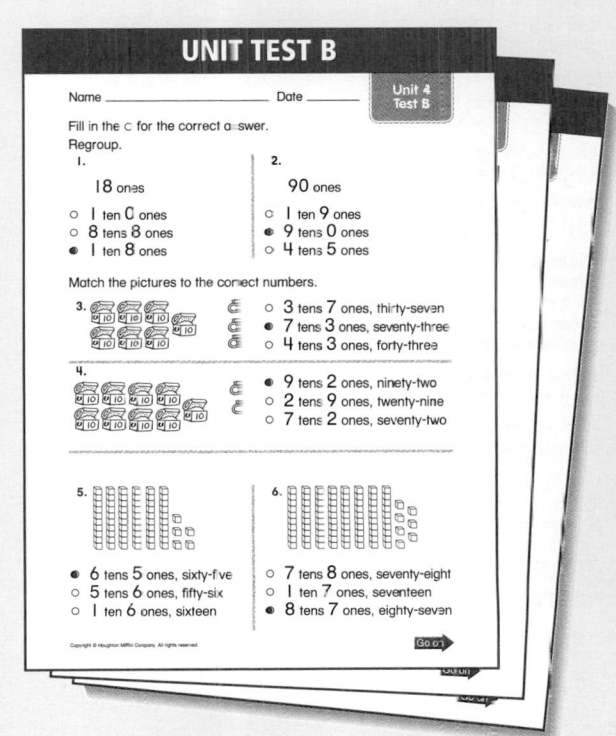

Unit 4 Tests
See pages 347A–347B for answers.

Unit Test Answers: Form A

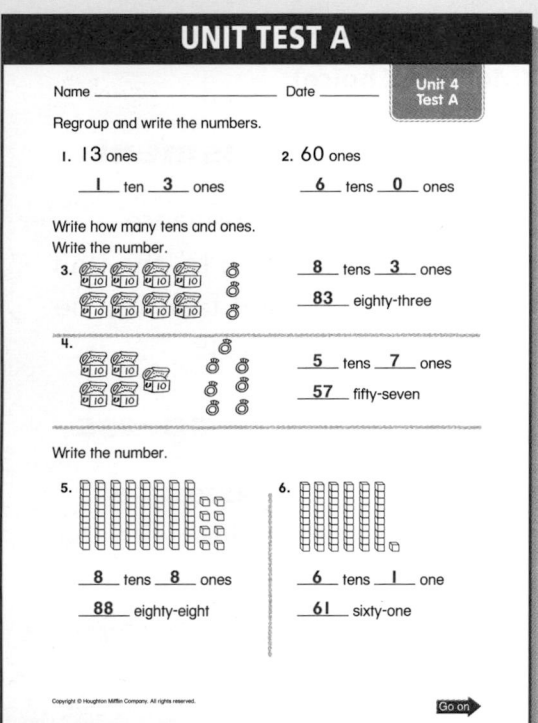

UNIT TEST A

Name _____ Date _____ | Unit 4 Test A

Regroup and write the numbers.

1. 13 ones

   _1_ ten _3_ ones

2. 60 ones

   _6_ tens _0_ ones

Write how many tens and ones.
Write the number.

3. _8_ tens _3_ ones

   _83_ eighty-three

4. _5_ tens _7_ ones

   _57_ fifty-seven

Write the number.

5. _8_ tens _8_ ones

   _88_ eighty-eight

6. _6_ tens _1_ one

   _61_ sixty-one

Go on

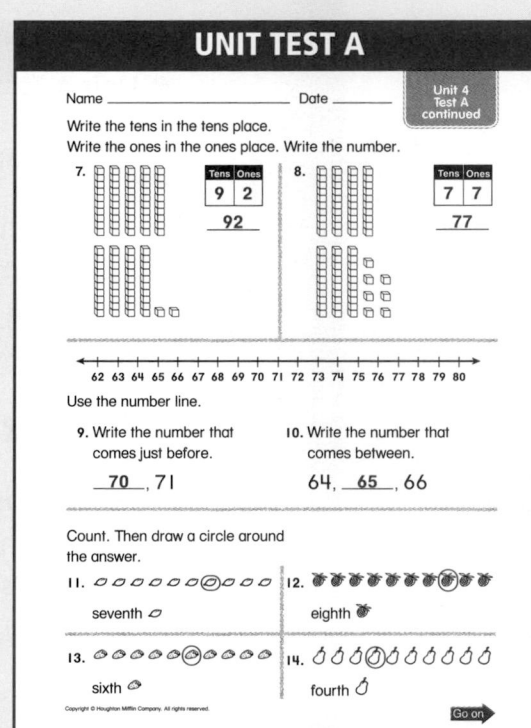

UNIT TEST A

Name _____ Date _____ | Unit 4 Test A continued

Write the tens in the tens place.
Write the ones in the ones place. Write the number.

7. | Tens | Ones |
   | 9 | 2 |
   _92_

8. | Tens | Ones |
   | 7 | 7 |
   _77_

Use the number line.

62 63 64 65 66 67 68 69 70 71 72 73 74 75 76 77 78 79 80

9. Write the number that comes just before.

   _70_, 71

10. Write the number that comes between.

    64, _65_, 66

Count. Then draw a circle around the answer.

11. seventh ⬠

12. eighth 🐢

13. sixth ⬠

14. fourth ⬠

Go on

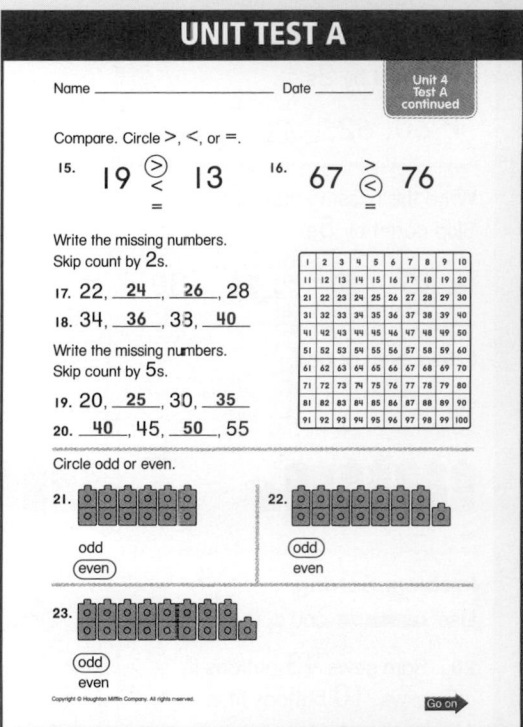

UNIT TEST A

Name _____ Date _____ | Unit 4 Test A continued

Compare. Circle >, <, or =.

15. 19 (>) 13

16. 67 (<) 76

Write the missing numbers.
Skip count by 2s.

17. 22, _24_, _26_, 28

18. 34, _36_, 33, _40_

Write the missing numbers.
Skip count by 5s.

19. 20, _25_, 30, _35_

20. _40_, 45, _50_, 55

Circle odd or even.

21. odd (even)

22. (odd) even

23. (odd) even

Go on

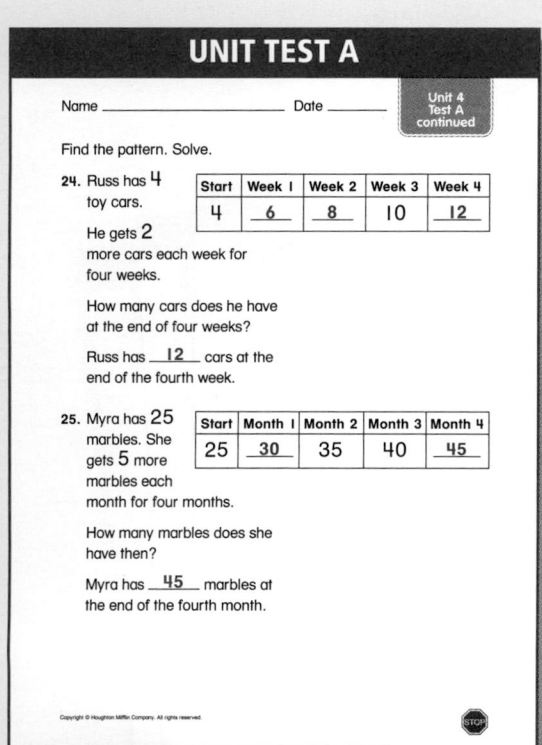

UNIT TEST A

Name _____ Date _____ | Unit 4 Test A continued

Find the pattern. Solve.

24. Russ has 4 toy cars.

    | Start | Week 1 | Week 2 | Week 3 | Week 4 |
    | 4 | _6_ | _8_ | 10 | _12_ |

    He gets 2 more cars each week for four weeks.

    How many cars does he have at the end of four weeks?

    Russ has _12_ cars at the end of the fourth week.

25. Myra has 25 marbles. She gets 5 more marbles each month for four months.

    | Start | Month 1 | Month 2 | Month 3 | Month 4 |
    | 25 | _30_ | 35 | 40 | _45_ |

    How many marbles does she have then?

    Myra has _45_ marbles at the end of the fourth month.

STOP

Unit Test Answers: Form B

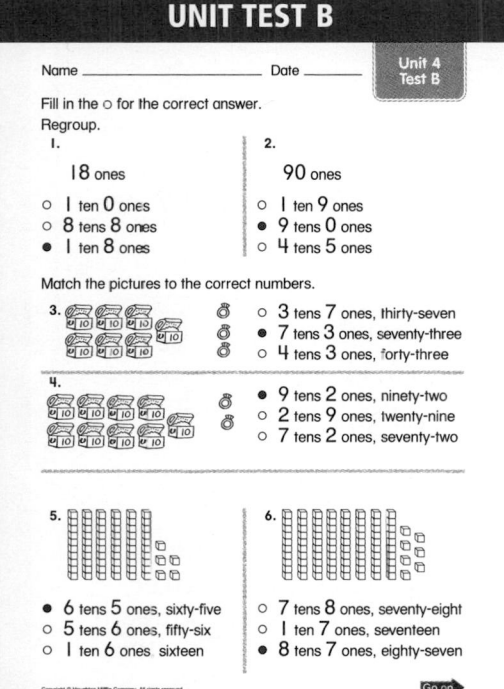

UNIT TEST B

Name _____ Date _____ **Unit 4 Test B**

Fill in the ○ for the correct answer.
Regroup.

1.
18 ones
- ○ 1 ten 0 ones
- ○ 8 tens 8 ones
- ● 1 ten 8 ones

2.
90 ones
- ○ 1 ten 9 ones
- ● 9 tens 0 ones
- ○ 4 tens 5 ones

Match the pictures to the correct numbers.

3.
- ○ 3 tens 7 ones, thirty-seven
- ● 7 tens 3 ones, seventy-three
- ○ 4 tens 3 ones, forty-three

4.
- ● 9 tens 2 ones, ninety-two
- ○ 2 tens 9 ones, twenty-nine
- ○ 7 tens 2 ones, seventy-two

5.
- ● 6 tens 5 ones, sixty-five
- ○ 5 tens 6 ones, fifty-six
- ○ 1 ten 6 ones, sixteen

6.
- ○ 7 tens 8 ones, seventy-eight
- ○ 1 ten 7 ones, seventeen
- ● 8 tens 7 ones, eighty-seven

Copyright © Houghton Mifflin Company. All rights reserved.   Go on →

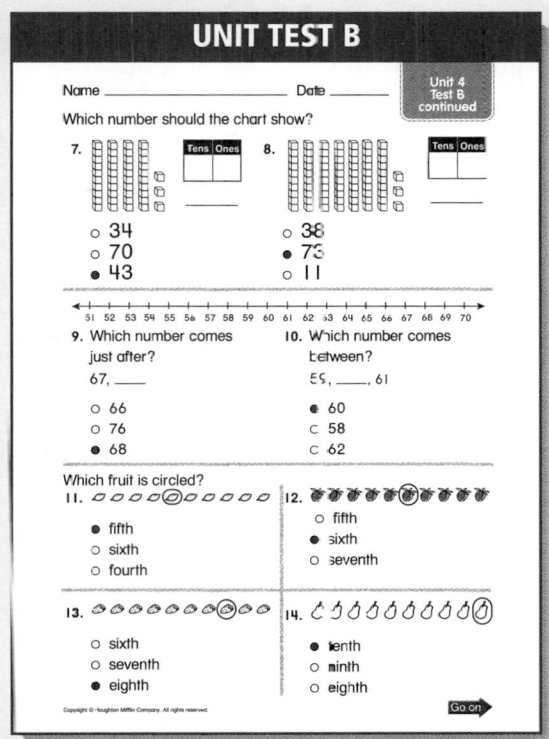

UNIT TEST B

Name _____ Date _____ **Unit 4 Test B continued**

Which number should the chart show?

7.
Tens | Ones
- ○ 34
- ○ 70
- ● 43

8.
Tens | Ones
- ○ 38
- ● 73
- ○ 11

51 52 53 54 55 56 57 58 59 60 61 62 63 64 65 66 67 68 69 70

9. Which number comes just after?
67, ___
- ○ 66
- ○ 76
- ● 68

10. Which number comes between?
59, ___, 61
- ● 60
- ○ 58
- ○ 62

Which fruit is circled?

11.
- ● fifth
- ○ sixth
- ○ fourth

12.
- ○ fifth
- ● sixth
- ○ seventh

13.
- ○ sixth
- ○ seventh
- ● eighth

14.
- ● tenth
- ○ ninth
- ○ eighth

Copyright © Houghton Mifflin Company. All rights reserved.   Go on →

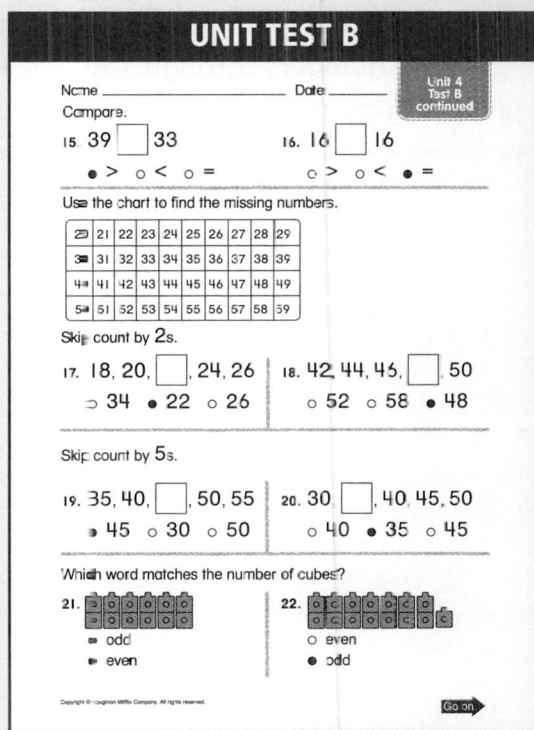

UNIT TEST B

Name _____ Date _____ **Unit 4 Test B continued**

Compare.

15. 39 ☐ 33
● > ○ < ○ =

16. 16 ☐ 16
○ > ○ < ● =

Use the chart to find the missing numbers.

20	21	22	23	24	25	26	27	28	29
30	31	32	33	34	35	36	37	38	39
40	41	42	43	44	45	46	47	48	49
50	51	52	53	54	55	56	57	58	59

Skip count by 2s.

17. 18, 20, ☐, 24, 26
- ○ 34
- ● 22
- ○ 26

18. 42, 44, 46, ☐, 50
- ○ 52
- ○ 58
- ● 48

Skip count by 5s.

19. 35, 40, ☐, 50, 55
- ● 45
- ○ 30
- ○ 50

20. 30, ☐, 40, 45, 50
- ○ 40
- ● 35
- ○ 45

Which word matches the number of cubes?

21.
- ● odd
- ○ even

22.
- ○ even
- ● odd

Copyright © Houghton Mifflin Company. All rights reserved.   Go on →

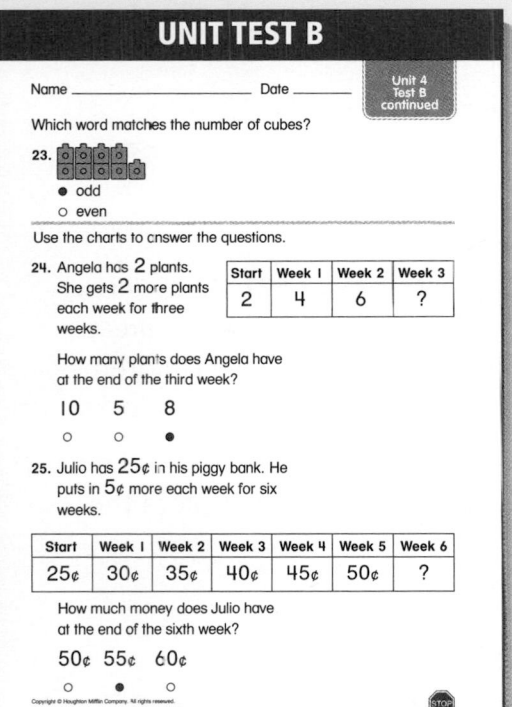

UNIT TEST B

Name _____ Date _____ **Unit 4 Test B continued**

Which word matches the number of cubes?

23.
- ● odd
- ○ even

Use the charts to answer the questions.

24. Angela has 2 plants. She gets 2 more plants each week for three weeks.

| Start | Week 1 | Week 2 | Week 3 |
| 2 | 4 | 6 | ? |

How many plants does Angela have at the end of the third week?

10   5   8
○   ○   ●

25. Julio has 25¢ in his piggy bank. He puts in 5¢ more each week for six weeks.

| Start | Week 1 | Week 2 | Week 3 | Week 4 | Week 5 | Week 6 |
| 25¢ | 30¢ | 35¢ | 40¢ | 45¢ | 50¢ | ? |

How much money does Julio have at the end of the sixth week?

50¢   55¢   60¢
○   ●   ○

Copyright © Houghton Mifflin Company. All rights reserved.   STOP

Performance Assessment

PURPOSE

This assessment focuses on number concepts. Children should be able to read, write, build, and compare numbers through 100. They should be able to apply skills and strategies to solve problems.

Performance Assessment

Name_____

Show the number.
Write the number.

1. | Tens | Ones |
   |------|------|
   | 6 | 7 |

Show your work using pictures, numbers, or words.

Possible answer shown.

6 tens and 7 ones

_____67

2. Which number is greater: **28** or **34**?

Show your work using pictures, numbers, or words.

Possible answer shown.

34 is greater because it has more tens.

___34___ is greater

Using These Pages

- Display 4 tens blocks and 5 ones blocks. **What is the number that these blocks show?** (45) **How do you know?** (Children should be able to explain that 4 tens = 40, and 5 ones = 5, and show the numbers in a tens and ones chart.)

- Display 4 tens blocks and 12 ones blocks. **What is the number that these blocks show?** (52) Have a volunteer write the number on the board. **Explain how you know the number is 52.** (Children should be able to explain that ten ones is the same as 1 ten, so the regrouped number is 5 tens 2 ones.)

- **Which number is greater: 45 or 52?** (52; Children should recognize the greater number has the greater number of tens.) You may wish to have children work in small groups with tens and ones blocks to compare the numbers they build.

- Observe children as they work to complete the tasks.

Exercise One

In Exercise 1, children should be able to draw shapes or blocks in groups of tens and ones to represent the given number. (67)

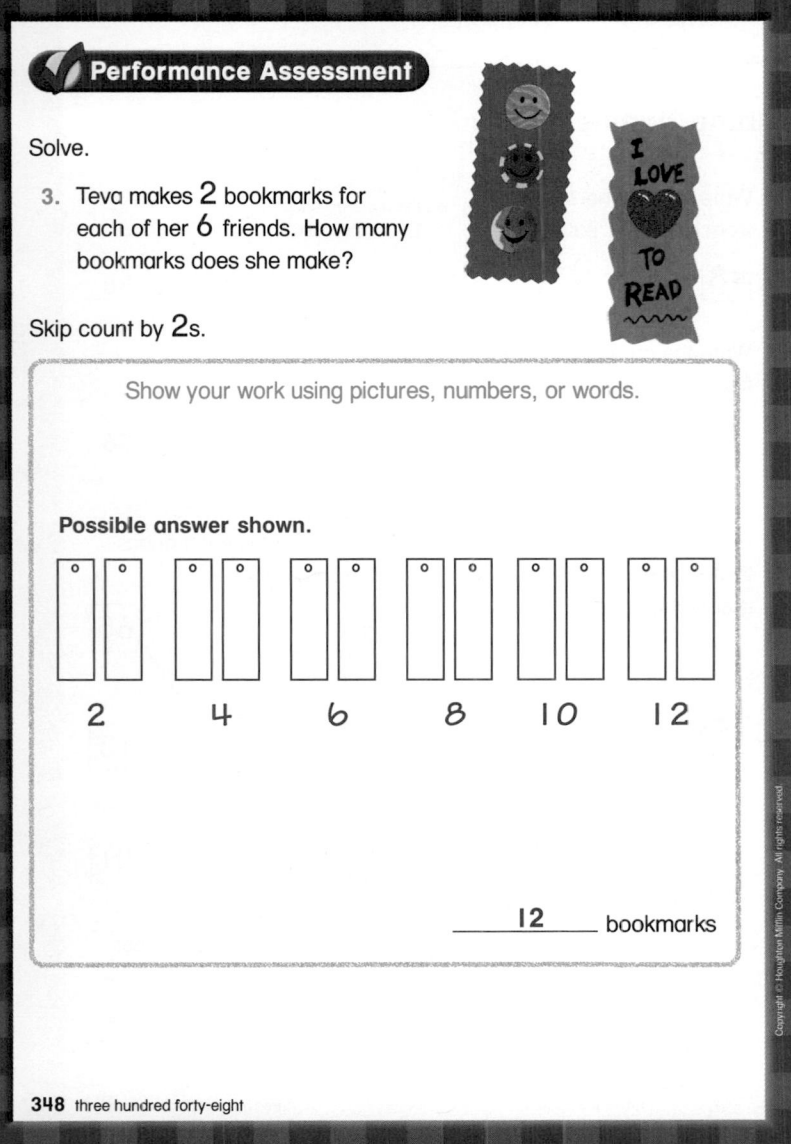

Performance Assessment

Solve.

3. Teva makes **2** bookmarks for each of her **6** friends. How many bookmarks does she make?

Skip count by **2**s.

Show your work using pictures, numbers, or words.

Possible answer shown.

2   4   6   8   10   12

_____12_____ bookmarks

348 three hundred forty-eight

Assessing Student Work

Use the **Scoring Rubric** to evaluate children's performance on these three tasks.

Scoring Rubric

4 EXEMPLARY

Represents, writes, and compares given numbers through 100 correctly and applies skills and strategies to solve problems correctly.

3 PROFICIENT

Represents, writes, and compares given numbers through 100 correctly. Solution to problems demonstrates mathematical reasoning, although the reasoning is faulty.

2 ACCEPTABLE

Represents, writes, and compares given numbers through 100 correctly. Solution to problems is incomplete.

1 LIMITED

Represents, writes, or compares given numbers through 100 incorrectly. Solution to problems shows no mathematical reasoning.

Exercise Two

In Exercise 2, children should be able to represent the given numbers and show that the greater number has the greater number of tens. (34 is greater)

Exercise Three

In Exercise 3 children should be able to model the problem by drawing pictures in 6 groups of 2, or show the counting numbers marked with skip counts of 2. (12)

UNIT 4

Enrichment

▶ Putting Numbers in Order

PURPOSE

This page provides an opportunity for children to apply their understanding of numbers through 100 by ordering non-consecutive numbers.

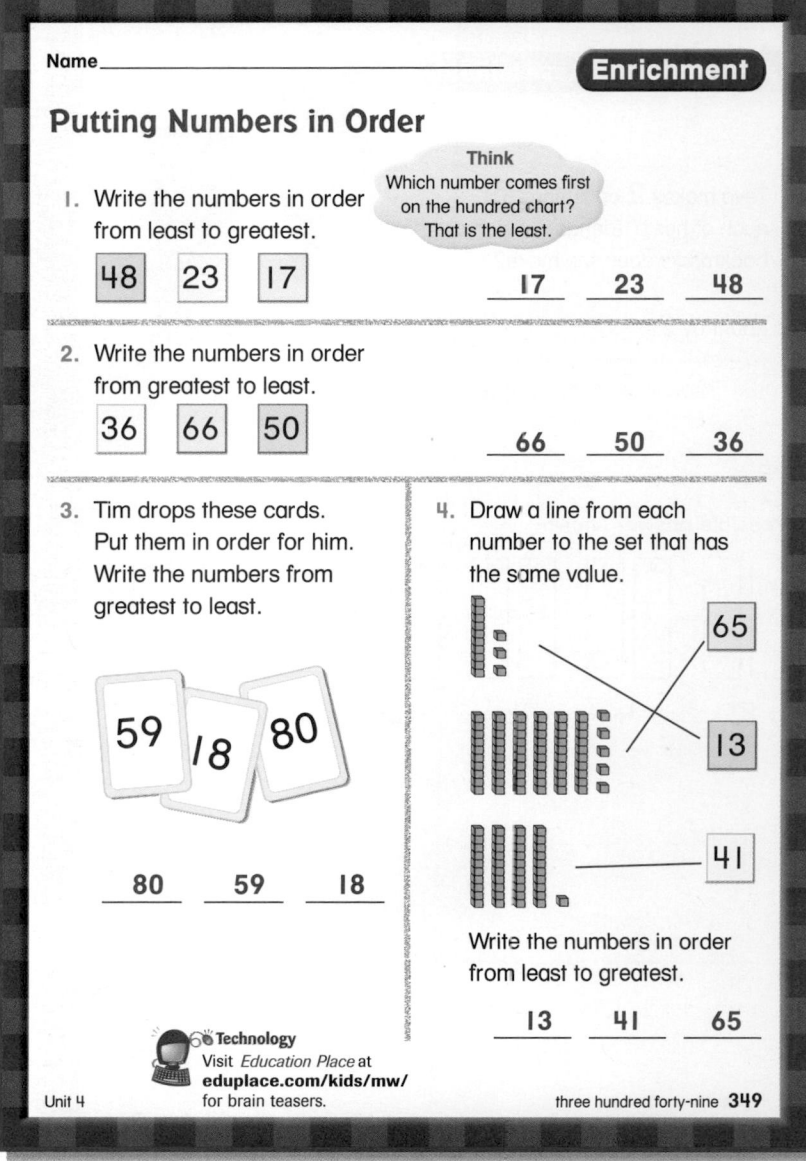

Using This Page

Discussion Topics

- This page extends Chapter 11, Lesson 1, by having children order non-consecutive numbers.

- You may want to review the definitions of **before**, **after**, and **between** with children. Instead of using number examples, use events in their day.

- For Exercises 1 and 2, remind children that greatest means largest and least means smallest.

- For Exercise 3, remind children to begin with the greatest number. For Exercise 4, children begin with the number that is least. Students may see on some standardized tests the terms largest to smallest or greatest to least.

- Have children work individually or in pairs to complete the page. In pairs, children take turns solving the exercises and then check each other's work.

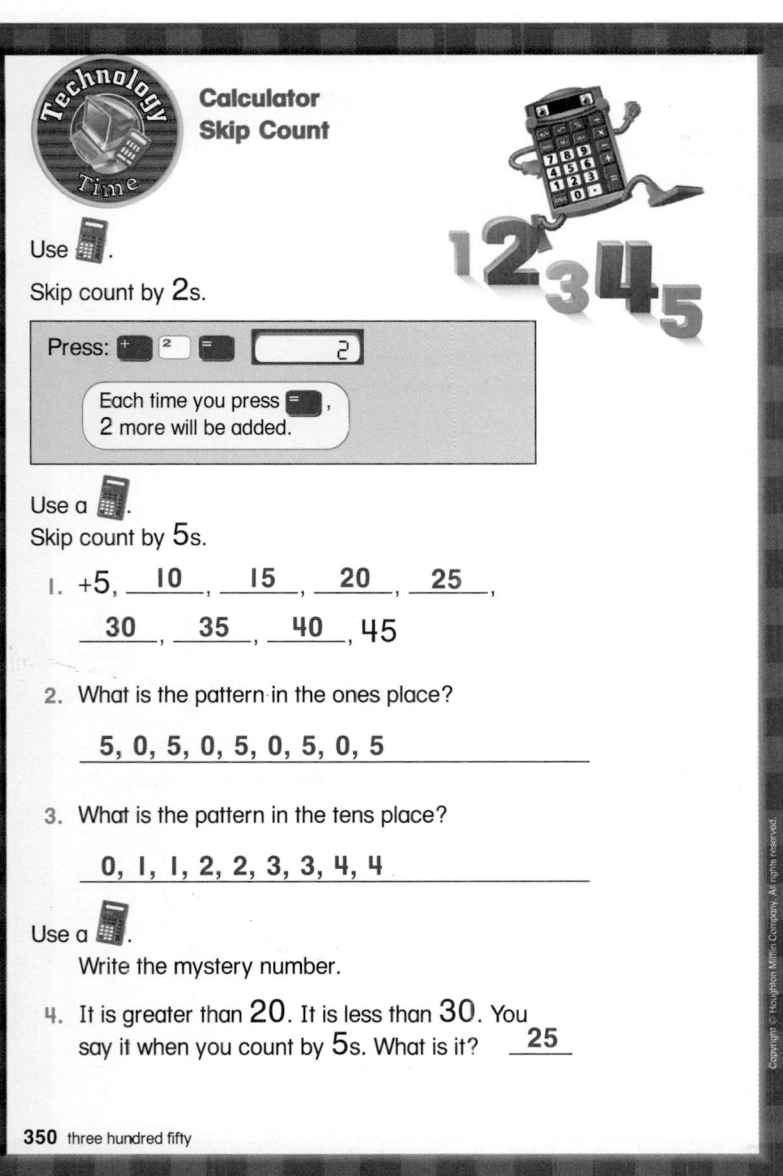

Calculator Skip Count

Use 🖩.

Skip count by 2s.

Press: [+] [2] [=] [2]

Each time you press [=],
2 more will be added.

Use a 🖩.
Skip count by 5s.

1. +5, __10__, __15__, __20__, __25__,
   __30__, __35__, __40__, 45

2. What is the pattern in the ones place?

   __5, 0, 5, 0, 5, 0, 5, 0, 5__

3. What is the pattern in the tens place?

   __0, 1, 1, 2, 2, 3, 3, 4, 4__

Use a 🖩.
Write the mystery number.

4. It is greater than 20. It is less than 30. You
   say it when you count by 5s. What is it? __25__

350 three hundred fifty

SKIP COUNTING

PURPOSE

To provide an opportunity for children to use a
calculator to skip count.

Using This Page

Discussion Topics

- This is another way for the children to practice
  skip counting.

- You may want to review how to enter numbers
  and use the = sign on the calculator.

- Work through the example with the children.
  Remind children that each time they press the
  = key they are skip counting by 2s since they had
  entered the 2 at the beginning of the example.

- Read the remaining exercises and allow time for
  the children to complete them. When the page is
  completed, have children share their answers
  with a partner. Then make up another mystery
  number for children to find.

Cumulative Test Prep

PURPOSE

This page will familiarize children with the multiple-choice and open-response formats of many standardized state tests. Children can mark their responses directly on these pages. You may wish to read each multiple-choice test item and the answer choices aloud to the children.

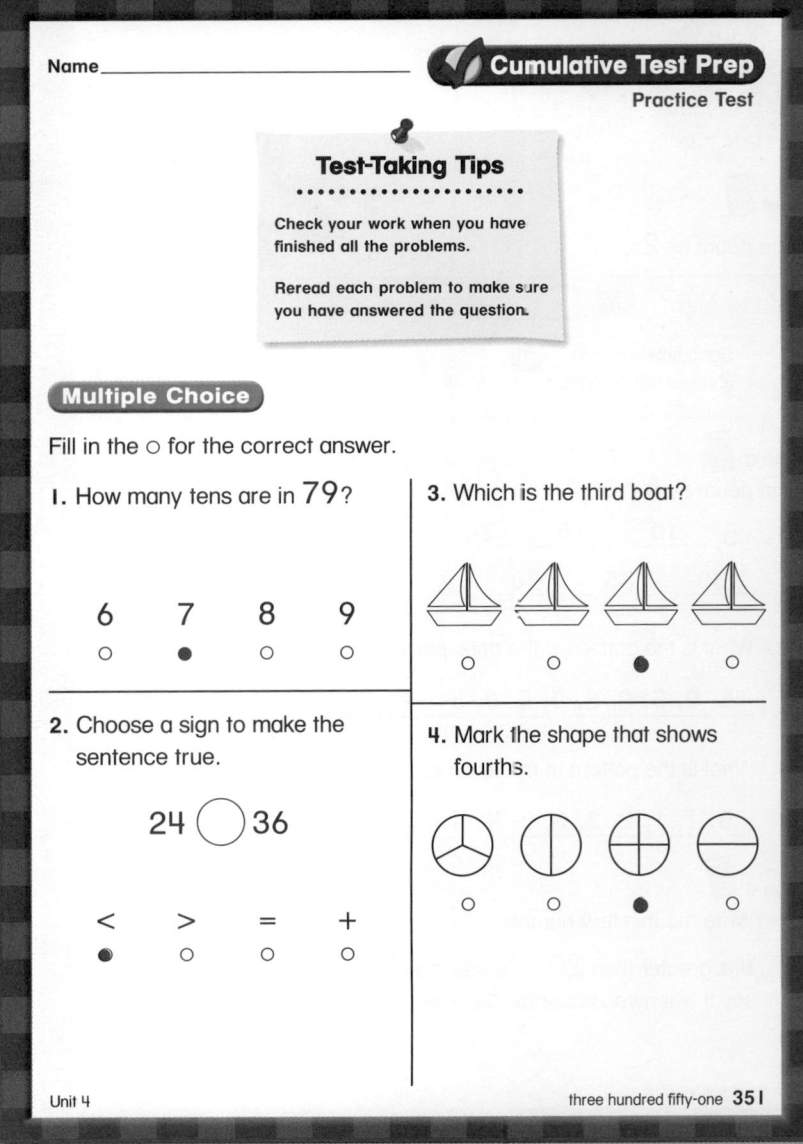

Test-Taking TIPS

Review the test-taking tips with children before they begin the test. Remind children to reread each problem to be sure they answered the question.

- Remind children to fill in only one answer for each question.
- Tell children that, as they are checking their work, they should ask themselves: *Does my answer make sense?*

- Discuss with children some of the ways they can check their work.
- Remind children that if they have made a mistake, they must erase the mark completely.

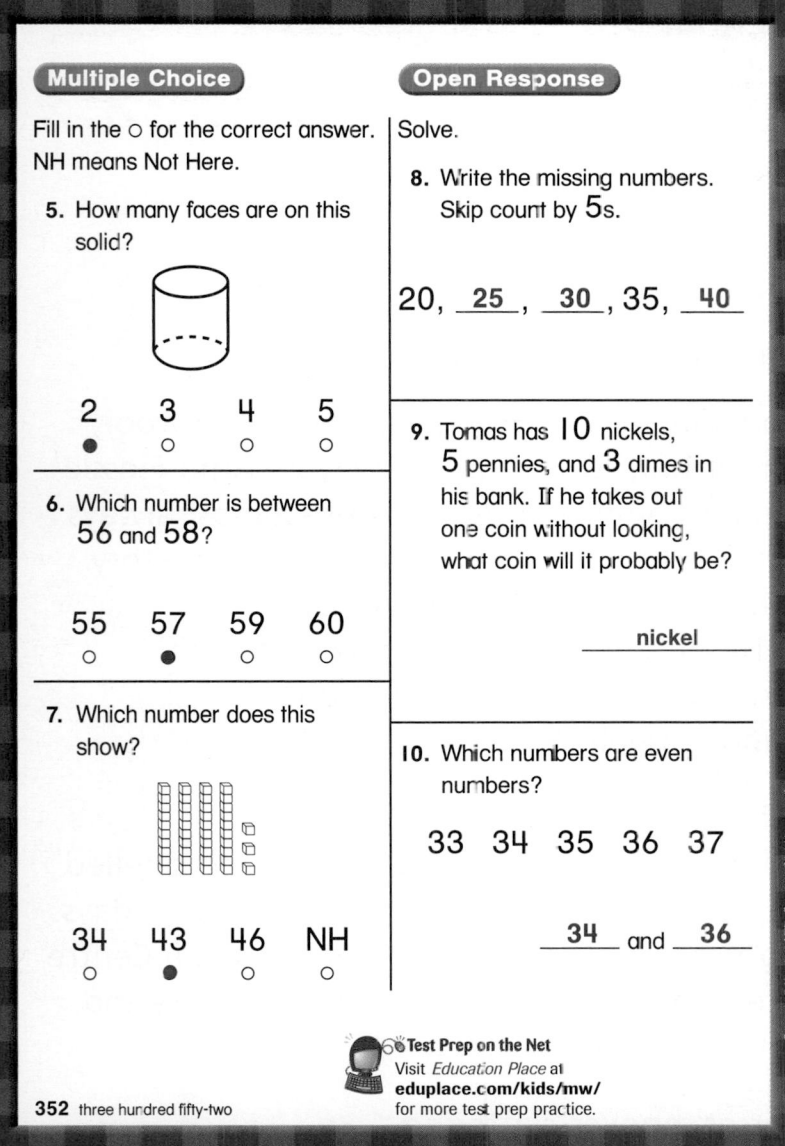

Fill in the ○ for the correct answer. NH means Not Here.

5. How many faces are on this solid?

2	3	4	5
●	○	○	○

6. Which number is between 56 and 58?

55	57	59	60
○	●	○	○

7. Which number does this show?

34	43	46	NH
○	●	○	○

Solve.

8. Write the missing numbers. Skip count by 5s.

20, __25__, __30__, 35, __40__

9. Tomas has 10 nickels, 5 pennies, and 3 dimes in his bank. If he takes out one coin without looking, what coin will it probably be?

_____nickel_____

10. Which numbers are even numbers?

33 34 35 36 37

__34__ and __36__

Test Prep on the Net
Visit *Education Place* at
eduplace.com/kids/mw/
for more test prep practice.

352 three hundred fifty-two

Test-Taking Vocabulary

- Have a volunteer define greater than and less than and use the terms in number comparisons. Ask children to name a number between 45 and 53.
- Write the number 67 on the board. Have volunteers tell how many ones and how many tens.
- Have children skip count from 1 to 20 using only even numbers. Have them skip count to 30 using only odd numbers.

National and state tests may use these words when talking about patterns:

- *complete*
- *follow*

UNIT 1

AUNT FLOSSIE'S HATS (and Crab Cakes Later)

By Elizabeth Fitzgerald Howard

On Sunday afternoons, Sarah and I go to see
Great-great-aunt Flossie. Sarah and I love
Aunt Flossie's house. It is crowded full of
stuff and things. Books and pictures and
lamps and pillows . . .

Plates and trays and old dried flowers . . .
And boxes
and boxes
and boxes
of HATS!

On Sunday afternoons when Sarah and I
go to see Aunt Flossie, she says,
"Come in, Susan. Come in, Sarah.
Have some tea. Have some cookies.
Later we can get some crab cakes!"

We sip our tea and eat our cookies, and then
Aunt Flossie lets us look in her hatboxes.

We pick out hats and try them on.
Aunt Flossie says they are her
memories, and each hat has its story.

Hats, hats, hats, hats!
A stiff black one with bright red ribbons. A
soft brown one with silver buttons. Thin
floppy hats that hide our eyes. Green or blue
or pink or purple. Some have fur and some
have feathers. Look! This hat is just one
smooth soft rose, but here's one with a trillion
flowers! Aunt Flossie has so many hats!

One Sunday afternoon, I picked out a wooly
winter hat, sort of green, maybe. Aunt Flossie
thought a minute. Aunt Flossie almost always
thinks a minute before she starts a hat story.
Then she sniffed the wooly hat.
"Just a little smoky smell now," she said.
Sarah and I sniffed the hat, too.
"Smoky smell, Aunt Flossie?"

"The big fire," Aunt Flossie said.
"The big fire in Baltimore. Everything smelled
of smoke for miles around. For days and days.
Big fire. Didn't come near our house on Centre
Street, but we could hear fire engines racing
down St. Paul.

Horses' hooves clattering.
Bells! Whistles!
Your great-grandma and I couldn't sleep. We
grabbed our coats and hats and ran outside.
Worried about Uncle Jimmy's grocery store,
worried about the terrapins and crabs. Big fire
in Baltimore."

Aunt Flossie closed her eyes. I think she was
seeing long ago. I wondered about crab cakes.
Did they have crab cakes way back then?

Then Sarah sniffed Aunt Flossie's hat.
"No more smoky smell," she said. But I
thought I could smell some, just a little.

Then Sarah tried a different hat. Dark, dark
blue, with a red feather.
"This one, Aunt Flossie! This one!"
Aunt Flossie closed her eyes and thought a
minute.

AUNT FLOSSIE'S HATS (and Crab Cakes Later) *continued*

"Oh my, yes, my, my. What an exciting day!"

We waited, Sarah and I.
"What happened, Aunt Flossie?" I asked.

"Big parade in Baltimore."

"Ooh! Parade!" said Sarah. "We love parades."

"I made that hat," Aunt Flossie said,
"to wear to watch that big parade.
Buglers bugling. Drummers drumming.

Flags flying everywhere. The boys—
soldiers, you know—back from France.
Marching up Charles Street. Proud.
Everyone cheering, everyone shouting!
The Great War was over!
The Great War was over!"

"Let's have a parade!" I said. Sarah put on the dark blue hat. I found a red one with a furry pompom. We marched around Aunt Flossie's house.

"March with us, Aunt Flossie!" I called.
But she was closing her eyes. She was seeing long ago.
"Maybe she's dreaming about crab cakes," Sarah said.

Then we looked in the very special box.
"Look, Aunt Flossie! Here's your special hat."
It was the big straw hat with the pink and yellow flowers and green velvet ribbon. Aunt Flossie's favorite best Sunday hat! It's our favorite story, because we are in the story, and we can help Aunt Flossie tell it!

Aunt Flossie smiled.
"One Sunday afternoon," she said,
"we were going out for crab cakes. Sarah and Susan . . ."
"And Mommy and Daddy," I said.
"And Aunt Flossie," said Sarah.
Aunt Flossie nodded.
"We were walking by the water. And the wind came."

"Let me tell it," I said. "The wind came and blew away your favorite best Sunday hat!"
"My favorite best Sunday hat," said Aunt Flossie.
"It landed in the water."
"It was funny," said Sarah.
"I didn't think so," said Aunt Flossie.

"And Daddy tried to reach it," I said,
"but he slid down in the mud. Daddy looked really surprised, and everybody laughed."
"He couldn't rescue my favorite, favorite best Sunday hat," said Aunt Flossie.

"And Mommy got a stick and leaned far out. She almost fell in, but she couldn't reach it either. The water rippled, and your favorite best Sunday hat just floated by like a boat!"

"Now comes the best part, and I'll tell it!" said Sarah. "A big brown dog came. It was walking with a boy.
'May we help you?' the boy asked.
'My dog Gretchen can get it.'
The boy threw a small, small stone.
It landed in Aunt Flossie's hat!
'Fetch, Gretchen, fetch!
Fetch, Gretchen, fetch!'

AUNT FLOSSIE'S HATS (and Crab Cakes Later) *continued*

Gretchen jumped into the water and she
swam. She swam and she got it!
Gretchen got Aunt Flossie's hat!
'Hurray for Gretchen!'
We all jumped up and down.
'Hurray for Aunt Flossie's hat!'"

"It was very wet," said Aunt Flossie,
"but it dried just fine . . . almost like new.
My favorite, favorite best Sunday hat."

"I like that story," I said.
"So do I," said Sarah.
"And I like what happened next! We went to
get crab cakes!"

"Crab cakes!" said Aunt Flossie.
"What a wonderful idea! Sarah, Susan,
telephone your parents. We'll go get some
crab cakes right now!"

I think Sarah and I will always agree about
one thing: Nothing in the whole wide world
tastes as good as crab cakes.

But crab cakes taste best after stories . . .
stories about Aunt Flossie's hats!

Literature Selections

UNIT 2

BUG FUN!

by Sarah Curran

It is night, there is no sun.
The time has come to have some fun.
I'll get the others as I fly.
How many bugs do you spy?

____ bugs

3 little ants soon strike out.
The others give a great big shout.
Now 4 ants wait to hit the ball.
How many ants are there in all?

$3 + 4 =$ ___ ants

One little spider sings a song.
2 more spiders play along.
They'll sing and play their songs tonight.
How many spiders in the bright moonlight?

$1 + 2 =$ ___ spiders

8 little ladybugs like to chat,
Telling stories about this and that.
Then 5 little ladybugs fly away.
How many ladybugs are left to play?

$8 - 5 =$ ___ ladybugs

All the grasshoppers take a dip.

They are careful not to slip.
Then 2 grasshoppers hop away.
How many grasshoppers stay to play?

$6 - 2 =$ ___ grasshoppers

Oh, now look at the great big sun.
This is the end of our night of fun.
7 fireflies look around.
5 fly off without a sound.
How many fireflies are on the ground?

$7 - 5 =$ ___ fireflies

UNIT 4

100 DAYS OF SCHOOL

by Trudy Harris

If you go to school for 95 days, and then go 5 more days, what do you get?
Smarter and smarter. And…
(how cool)
100 DAYS OF SCHOOL!

If 10 tired children all take off their shoes, what do you get?
Lots of bare feet! And…
(I suppose)
100 toes!

If you find a tiny bug with 50 legs on one side and 50 on the other, what do you get?
100 legs. And…
(yes, indeed)
a centipede.

If 20 children each drop 5 papers on the floor, what do you get?
100 papers. And…
(I would guess)
an awful mess.

If you eat 10 salty peanuts every minute for 10 minutes, what do you get?
100 peanuts. And…
(big mistake)
a tummy ache!

If 99 dots are on a clown's suit, what do you get?
100 polka dots. Those…
(on his clothes)
plus 1 on his nose.

If 25 bees fly out of a hive, then 25 more and 25 more and 25 MORE, what do you get?
100 bees. And…
(no surprise)
some exercise!

If you put 10 candles on a birthday cake, and then add 90 more, what do you get?
100 candles. And…
(with ALL those)
a fire hose!

If every day you save 1 penny for 100 days, what do you get?
100 pennies! Or…
(better still)
1 dollar bill!

If you pick 75 blackberries, and your mom picks 25 more, what do you get?
100 berries. And…
(Oh, my)
blackberry pie!

If a train goes by with 99 cars and then 1 red caboose, what do you get?
100 cars. And…
(my friend)
the end!

Literature Selections

UNIT 5

MY BIG NIGHT

by Harold Mitchell

Tonight at 7 o'clock
I'll be acting in a a play.
But it's only ____ o'clock.
It's still 6 hours away.

Tonight at 7 o'clock
I'll be singing in play.
But it's only ___ o'clock.
It's still 5 hours away.

Tonight at 7 o'clock
I'll be dancing in a play.
But it's only ___ o'clock.
It's still 4 hours away.

Tonight at 7 o'clock
I'll be roaring in a play.
But it's only ___ o'clock.
It's still 2 hours away.

It's Saturday at ___ o'clock.
It's time to start the play.
I've got butterflies in my stomach.
I wish they'd go away!

It's Saturday at ___ o'clock
I just completed the play.
I smile so wide and take a bow,
While the crowd shouts out, "Hooray!"

Literature Selections

UNIT 6

TWENTY IS TOO MANY

by Kate Duke

Twenty guinea pigs can be too many.
Twenty guinea pigs can start to sink.
But twenty sinking guinea pigs
minus ten diving guinea pigs
leaves ten
floating guinea pigs.   **20 − 10 = 10**

Ten floating guinea pigs
minus one ballooning guinea pig
leaves nine
waving guinea pigs.   **10 − 1 = 9**

Nine waving guinea pigs
minus one swinging guinea pig
leaves eight
seasick guinea pigs.   **9 − 1 = 8**

Eight seasick guinea pigs
minus one exploring guinea pig
leaves seven
excited guinea pigs.   **8 − 1 = 7**

Seven excited guinea pigs
minus one sneaky guinea pig
leaves six
yelling guinea pigs.   **7 − 1 = 6**

Six yelling guinea pigs
minus one fishing guinea pig
leaves five
flabbergasted guinea pigs. **6 − 1 = 5**

Five flabbergasted guinea pigs
minus one surfing guinea pig
leaves four
copycatting guinea pigs.   **5 − 1 = 4**

Four copycatting guinea pigs
minus one belly-flopping guinea pig
leaves three
wet guinea pigs.   **4 − 1 = 3**

Three wet guinea pigs
minus one greedy guinea pig
leaves two
thirsty guinea pigs.   **3 − 1 = 2**

Two thirsty guinea pigs
minus one sleepy guinea pig
leaves just one guinea pig.
And one . . .   **2 − 1 = 1**
can be fun.

Literature Selections

UNIT 8

ONE WATERMELON SEED
by Celia Barker Lottridge

Max and Josephine planted a garden.

1 They planted one watermelon seed . . .
and it grew.
They planted two pumpkin seeds . . .
and they grew. **2**

3 Max planted three eggplants . . .
and they grew.
Josephine planted four pepper seeds . . .
and they grew. **4**

5 Then she planted five tomato plants . . .
and they grew.
Max planted six blueberry bushes . . .
and they grew. **6**

7 And seven strawberry plants . . .
and they grew.
Josephine planted eight bean seeds . . .
and they grew. **8**

9 And nine seed potatoes . . .
and they grew.
They planted ten corn seeds . . .
and they grew. **10**

The rain fell and the sun shone. The seeds and the leaves, the stalks and the vines grew and grew and grew.

Max and Josephine weeded and watered and waited. One day they looked at their garden and saw there was plenty to pick. So . . .

10 They picked ten watermelons, big and green.
And twenty pumpkins, glowing orange. **20**

30 Max picked thirty eggplants, dark and purple,
and forty peppers, shiny yellow. **40**

50 They both picked fifty tomatoes, plump and juicy
and sixty blueberries, small and round. **60**

70 Josephine picked seventy strawberries, sweet and red.
Max picked eighty stringbeans, thin and crisp. **80**

90 Josephine dug ninety potatoes, nobby and brown.
And they picked one hundred ears of corn.
100

It was not ordinary corn. Max and Josephine saved it for cold winter nights, when the garden was covered with snow. Then they turned it into hundreds and thousands of big white crunchy puffs because that corn was
POPCORN!

Glossary

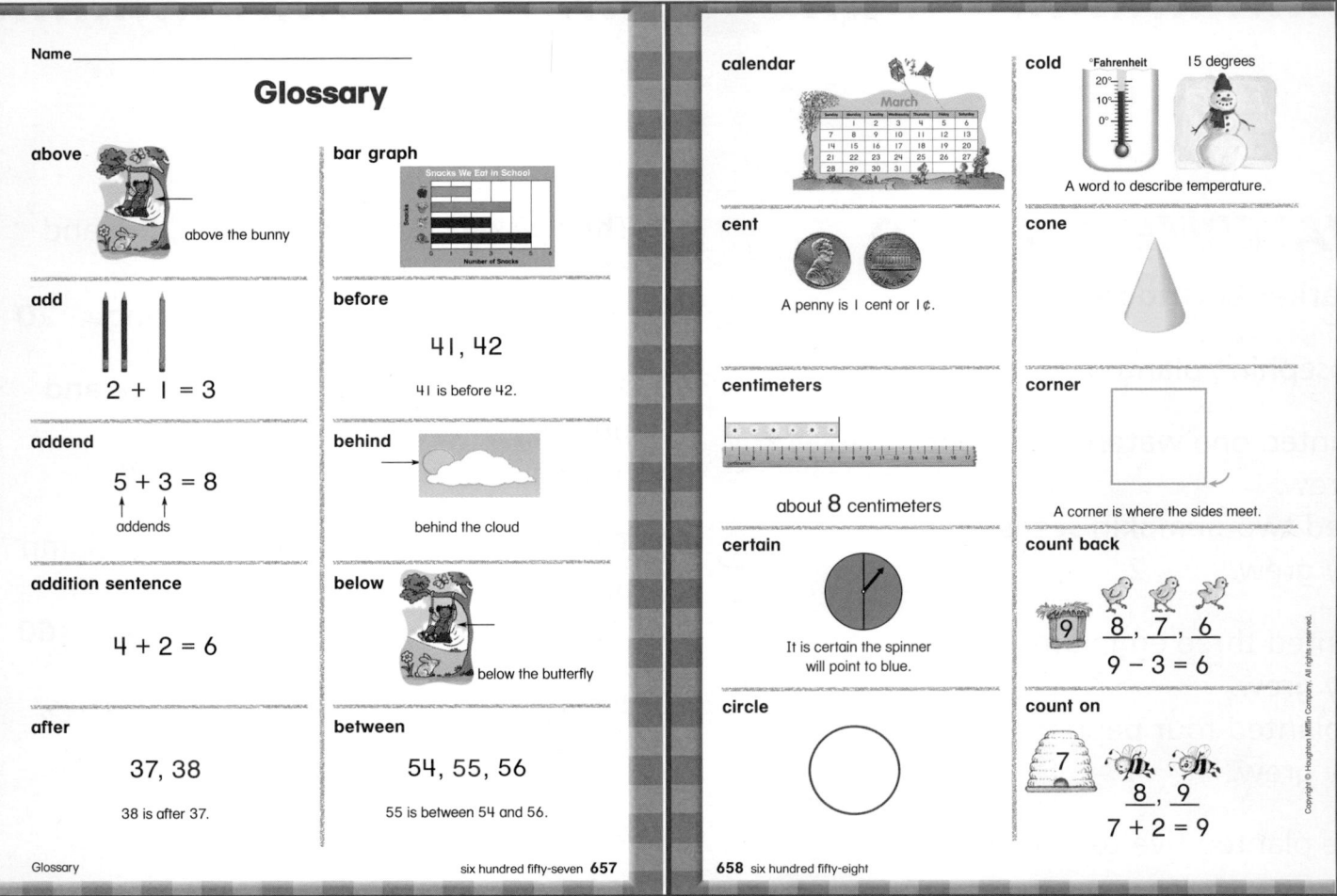

Name_____

Glossary

above

above the bunny

add

$2 + 1 = 3$

addend

$5 + 3 = 8$
↑ ↑
addends

addition sentence

$4 + 2 = 6$

after

37, 38

38 is after 37.

bar graph

Snacks We Eat in School

Number of Snacks

before

41, 42

41 is before 42.

behind

behind the cloud

below

below the butterfly

between

54, 55, 56

55 is between 54 and 56.

Glossary

six hundred fifty-seven **657**

calendar

March

cent

A penny is 1 cent or 1¢.

centimeters

about 8 centimeters

certain

It is certain the spinner
will point to blue.

circle

cold

°Fahrenheit   15 degrees

A word to describe temperature.

cone

corner

A corner is where the sides meet.

count back

9   8, 7, 6

$9 - 3 = 6$

count on

7   8, 9

$7 + 2 = 9$

658 six hundred fifty-eight

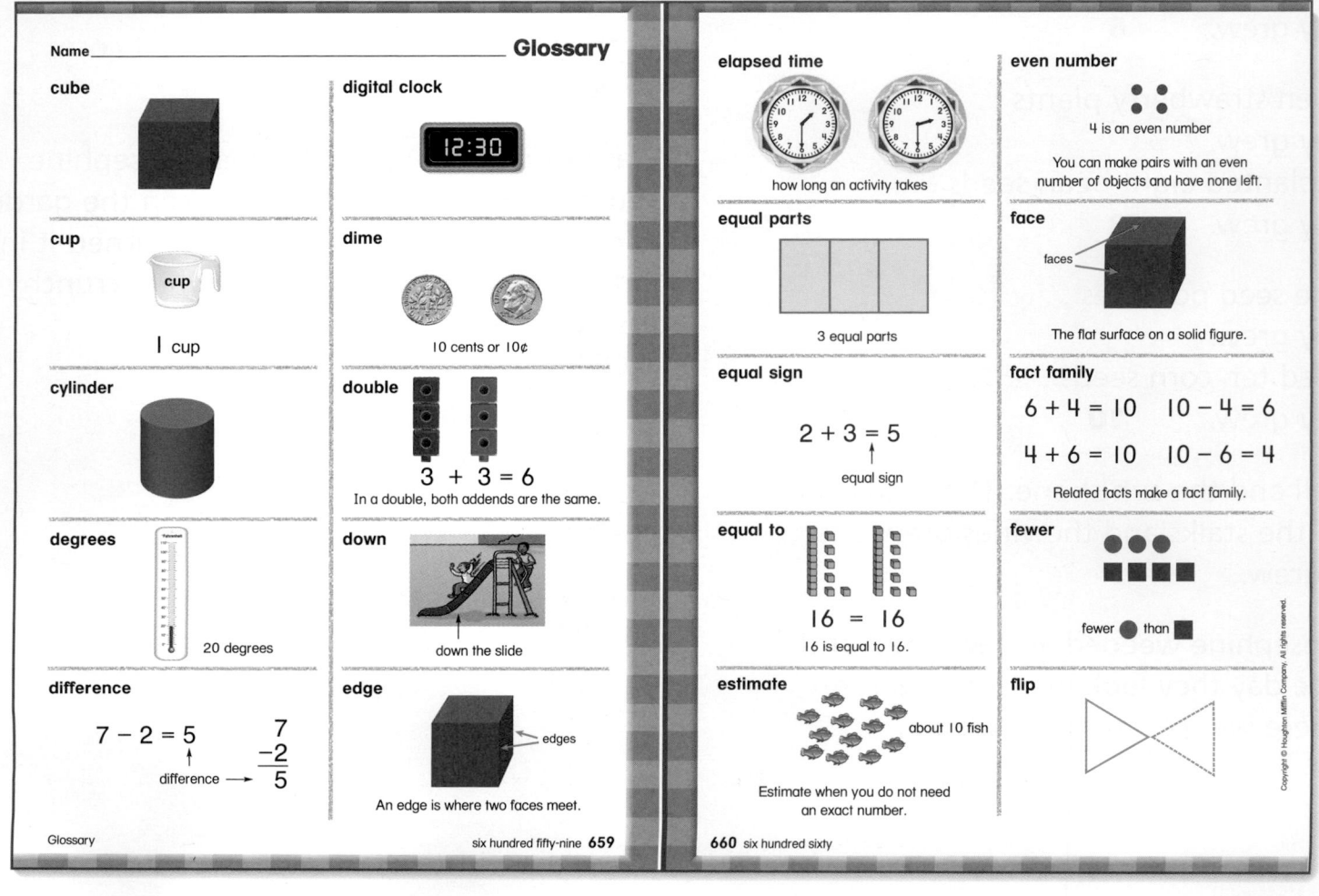

Name_____   **Glossary**

cube

cup

cup

1 cup

cylinder

degrees

20 degrees

difference

$7 - 2 = 5$ $\begin{array}{r} 7 \\ -2 \\ \hline 5 \end{array}$

↑
difference

digital clock

12:30

dime

10 cents or 10¢

double

$3 + 3 = 6$

In a double, both addends are the same.

down

down the slide

edge

edges

An edge is where two faces meet.

Glossary

six hundred fifty-nine **659**

elapsed time

how long an activity takes

equal parts

3 equal parts

equal sign

$2 + 3 = 5$
↑
equal sign

equal to

$16 = 16$

16 is equal to 16.

estimate

about 10 fish

Estimate when you do not need
an exact number.

even number

4 is an even number

You can make pairs with an even
number of objects and have none left.

face

faces

The flat surface on a solid figure.

fact family

$6 + 4 = 10$ $10 - 4 = 6$

$4 + 6 = 10$ $10 - 6 = 4$

Related facts make a fact family.

fewer

fewer ● than ■

flip

660 six hundred sixty

Glossary

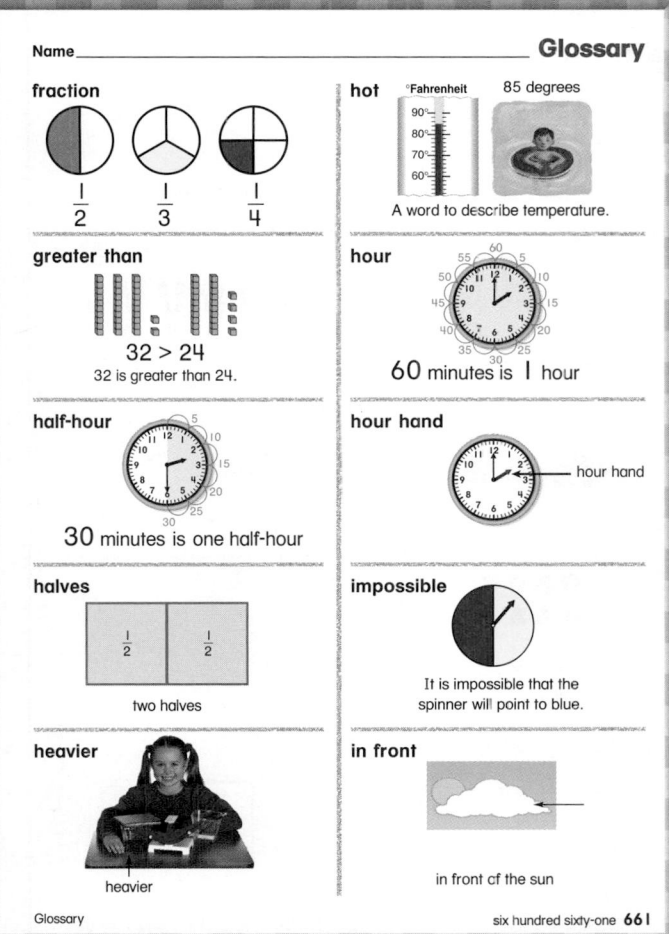

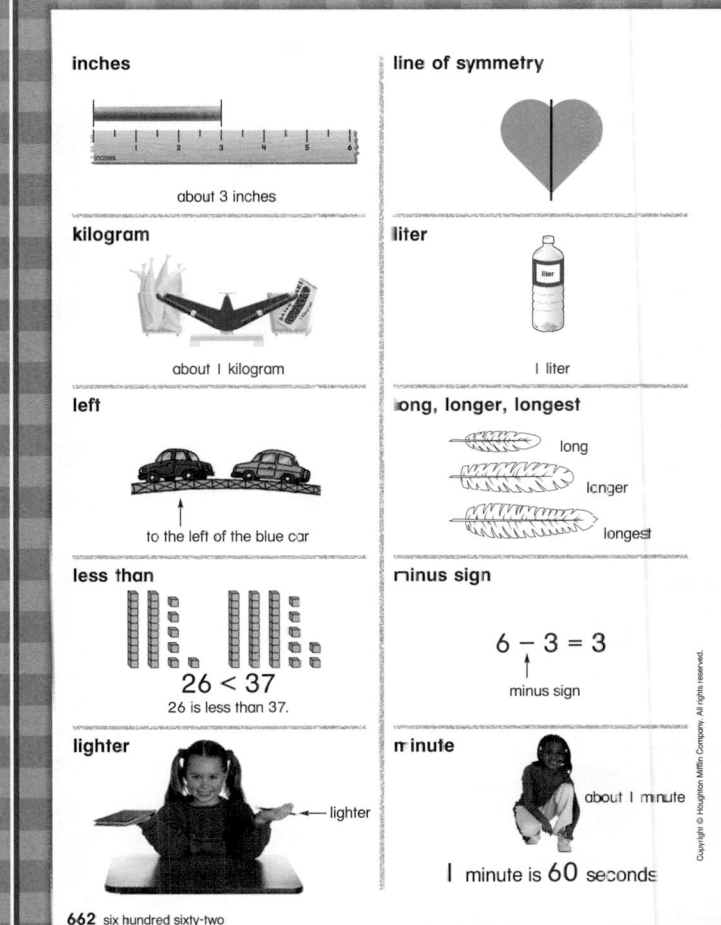

Name _____ **Glossary**

fraction

$\frac{1}{2}$ $\frac{1}{3}$ $\frac{1}{4}$

greater than

32 > 24

32 is greater than 24.

half-hour

30 minutes is one half-hour

halves

$\frac{1}{2}$ $\frac{1}{2}$

two halves

heavier

heavier

hot

Fahrenheit   85 degrees

A word to describe temperature.

hour

60 minutes is 1 hour

hour hand

hour hand

impossible

It is impossible that the spinner will point to blue.

in front

in front of the sun

Glossary   six hundred sixty-one **661**

inches

about 3 inches

kilogram

about 1 kilogram

left

to the left of the blue car

less than

26 < 37

26 is less than 37.

lighter

lighter

line of symmetry

liter

1 liter

long, longer, longest

long
longer
longest

minus sign

6 − 3 = 3

minus sign

minute

about 1 minute

1 minute is 60 seconds

662 six hundred sixty-two

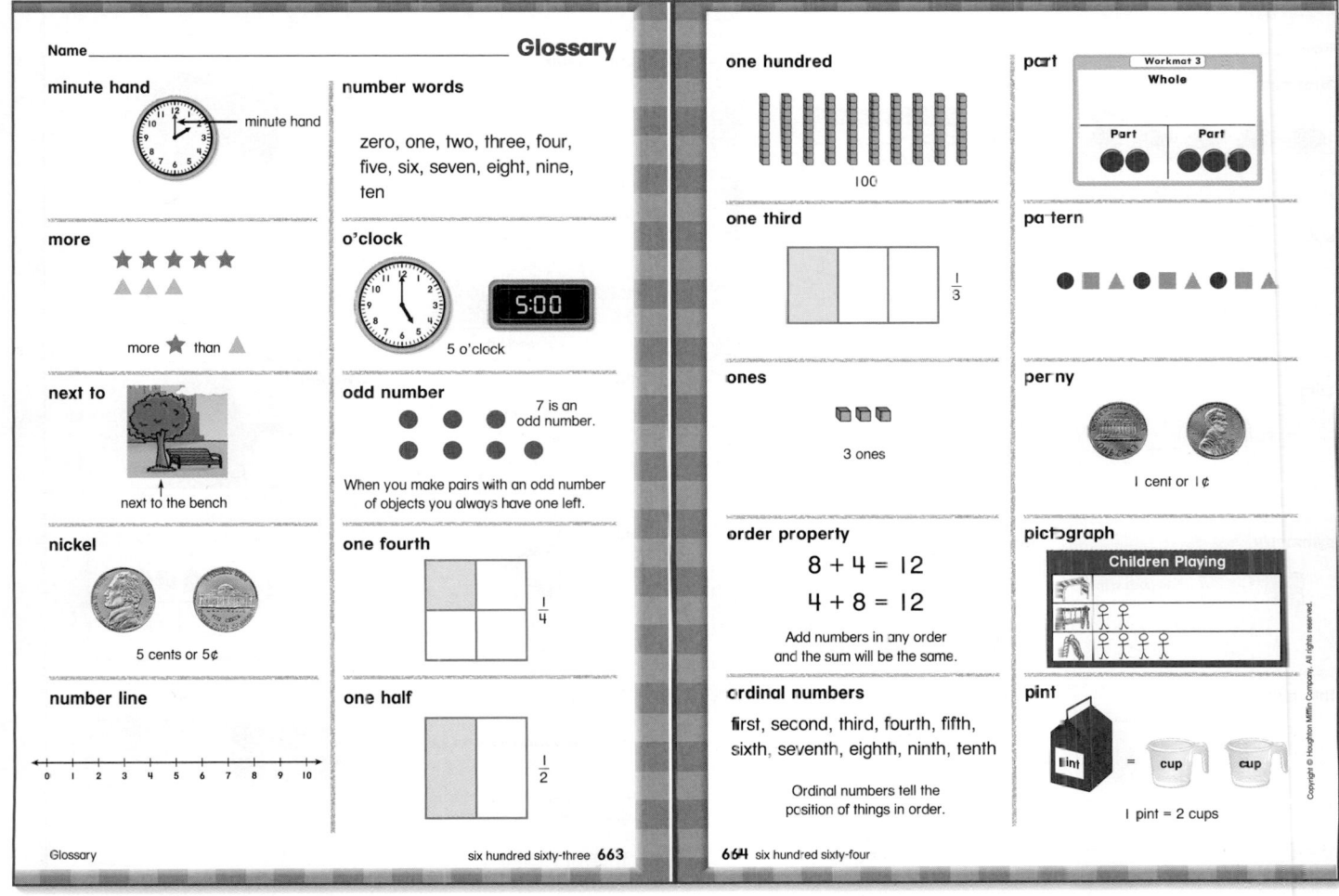

Name _____ **Glossary**

minute hand

minute hand

more

★ ★ ★ ★ ★
▲ ▲ ▲

more ★ than ▲

next to

next to the bench

nickel

5 cents or 5¢

number line

0 1 2 3 4 5 6 7 8 9 10

number words

zero, one, two, three, four, five, six, seven, eight, nine, ten

o'clock

5:00

5 o'clock

odd number

7 is an odd number.

When you make pairs with an odd number of objects you always have one left.

one fourth

$\frac{1}{4}$

one half

$\frac{1}{2}$

Glossary   six hundred sixty-three **663**

one hundred

100

one third

$\frac{1}{3}$

ones

3 ones

order property

8 + 4 = 12

4 + 8 = 12

Add numbers in any order and the sum will be the same.

ordinal numbers

first, second, third, fourth, fifth, sixth, seventh, eighth, ninth, tenth

Ordinal numbers tell the position of things in order.

part

Workmat 3
Whole
Part   Part

pattern

● ■ ▲ ● ■ ▲ ● ■ ▲

penny

1 cent or 1¢

pictograph

Children Playing

pint

pint = cup cup

1 pint = 2 cups

664 six hundred sixty-four

Glossary ....

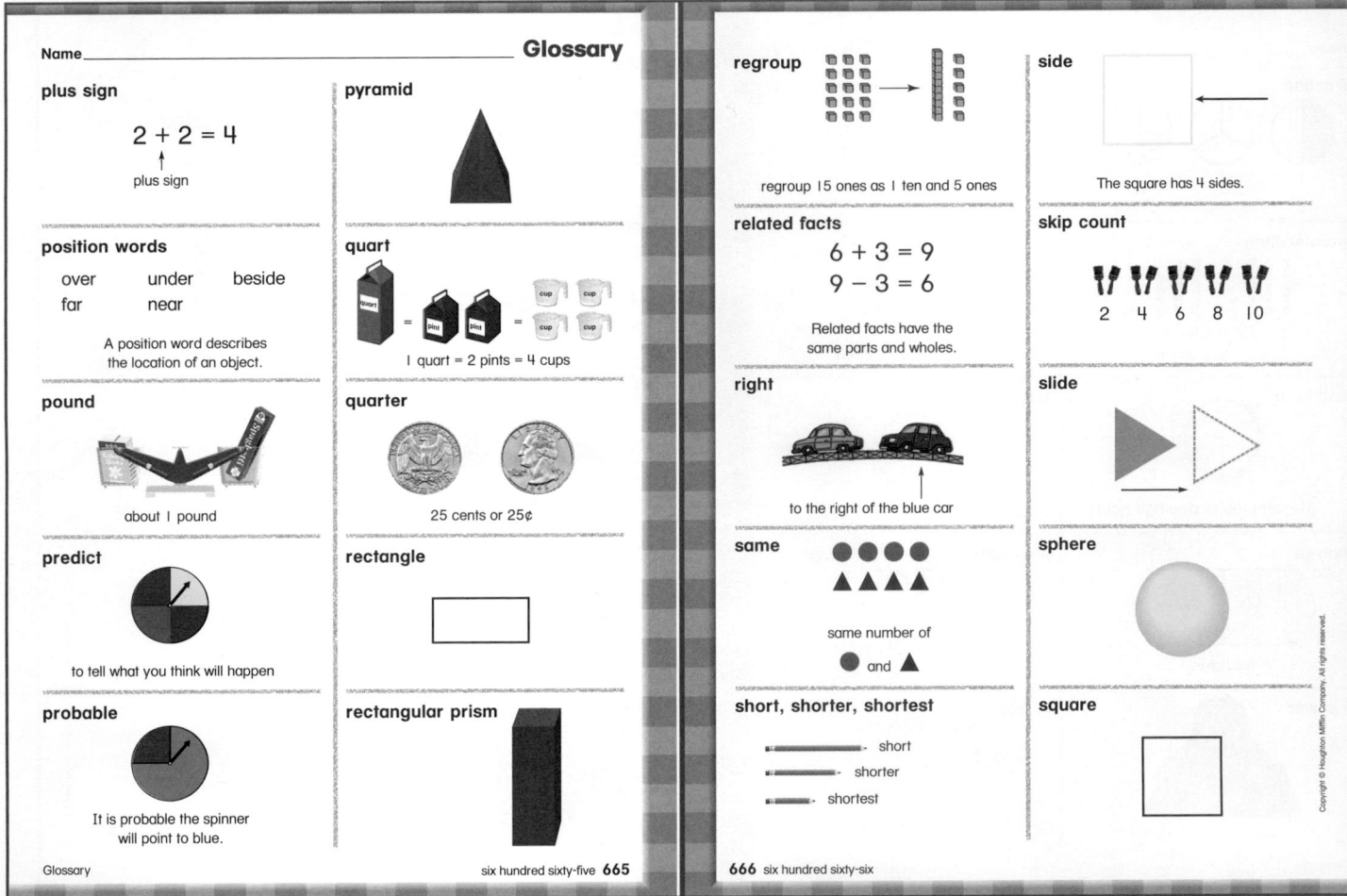

Name _____ **Glossary**

plus sign

$$2 + 2 = 4$$
↑
plus sign

pyramid

position words

| over | under | beside |
| far | near | |

A position word describes the location of an object.

quart

1 quart = 2 pints = 4 cups

pound

about 1 pound

quarter

25 cents or 25¢

predict

to tell what you think will happen

rectangle

probable

It is probable the spinner will point to blue.

rectangular prism

Glossary   six hundred sixty-five **665**

---

regroup

regroup 15 ones as 1 ten and 5 ones

side

The square has 4 sides.

related facts

$$6 + 3 = 9$$
$$9 - 3 = 6$$

Related facts have the same parts and wholes.

skip count

2 4 6 8 10

right

to the right of the blue car

slide

same

same number of
● and ▲

sphere

short, shorter, shortest

- short
- shorter
- shortest

square

666 six hundred sixty-six

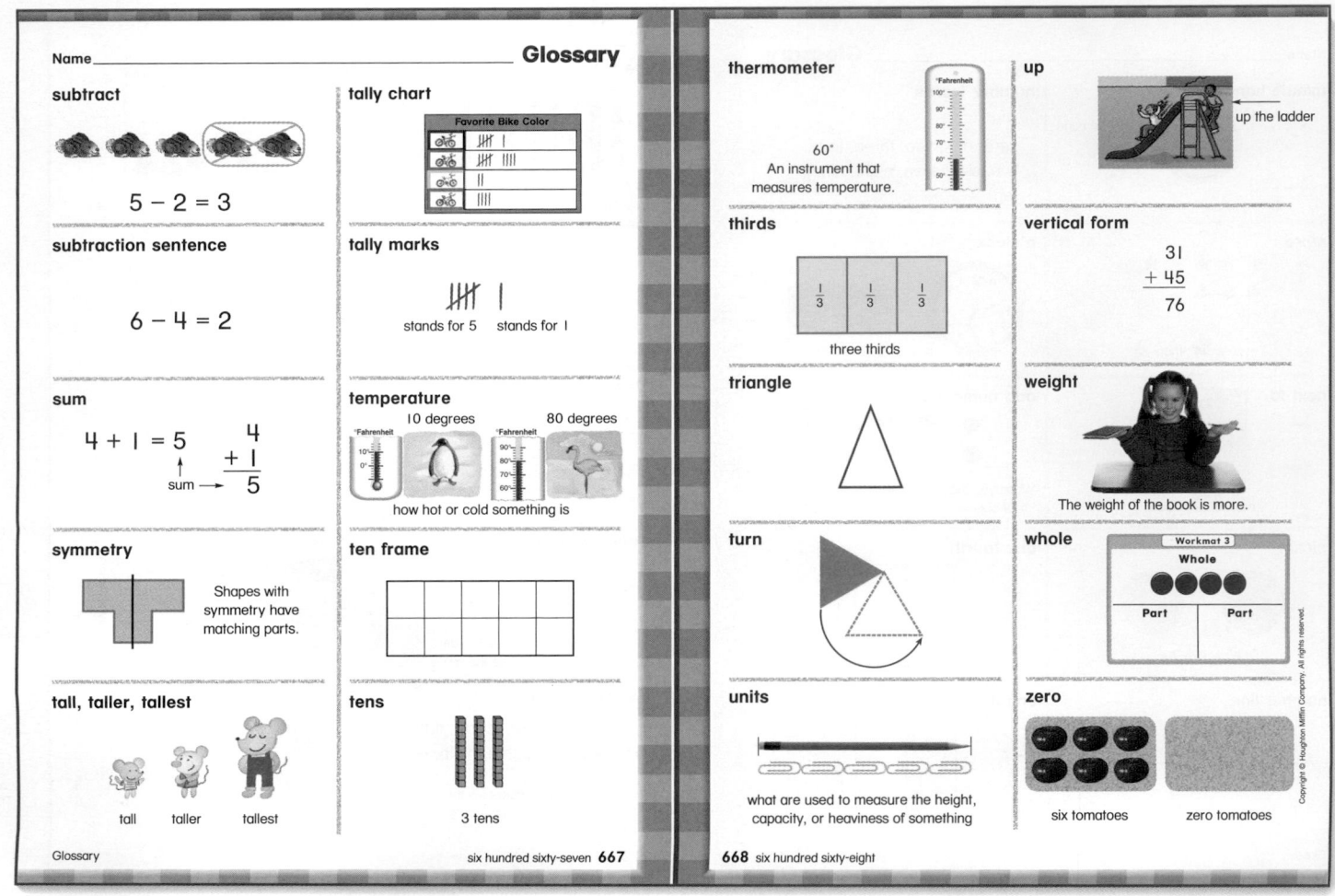

Name _____ **Glossary**

subtract

$$5 - 2 = 3$$

tally chart

Favorite Bike Color	
🚲	JHT I
🚲	JHT IIII
🚲	II
🚲	IIII

subtraction sentence

$$6 - 4 = 2$$

tally marks

JHHT I
stands for 5   stands for 1

sum

$$4 + 1 = 5 \qquad \begin{array}{r} 4 \\ + 1 \\ \hline 5 \end{array}$$
↑
sum   sum →

temperature

10 degrees   80 degrees

how hot or cold something is

symmetry

Shapes with symmetry have matching parts.

ten frame

tall, taller, tallest

tall   taller   tallest

tens

3 tens

Glossary   six hundred sixty-seven **667**

---

thermometer

60°
An instrument that measures temperature.

up

up the ladder

thirds

| $\frac{1}{3}$ | $\frac{1}{3}$ | $\frac{1}{3}$ |

three thirds

vertical form

$$\begin{array}{r} 31 \\ + 45 \\ \hline 76 \end{array}$$

triangle

weight

The weight of the book is more.

turn

whole

Workmat 3	
Whole	
●●●●	
Part	Part

units

what are used to measure the height, capacity, or heaviness of something

zero

six tomatoes   zero tomatoes

668 six hundred sixty-eight

Houghton Mifflin Math and *Weekly Reader* have worked together to provide you with enriching real-world activities and internet connections for your students. The *Weekly Reader Activity Almanac* includes a map activity designed to link math and map skills along with data-related information and activities for each unit.

The Weekly Reader Activity Almanac presents intriguing information about North Carolina and provides Data Hunt activities that encourage learning about historic sites, national and state parks, plants and animals, and other fascinating topics related to North Carolina. The Weekly Reader Web Connections found throughout the student book provide safe access to more information about many cross-curricular connections and math topics on Houghton Mifflin's Education Place Web site: **www.eduplace.com/kids/mw/**.

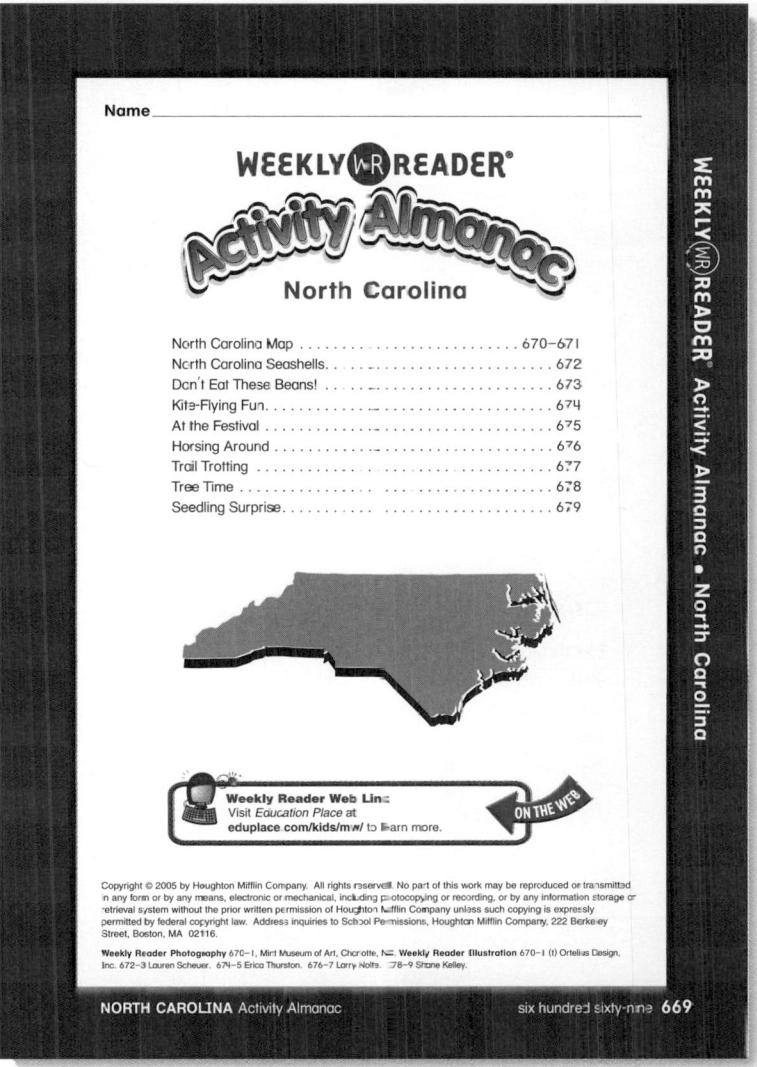

Name _____

WEEKLY WR READER®
Activity Almanac
North Carolina

Weekly Reader Web Link
Visit *Education Place* at
eduplace.com/kids/mw/ to learn more.

ON THE WEB

NORTH CAROLINA Activity Almanac   six hundred sixty-nine **669**

Activity Almanac

WEEKLY WR READER

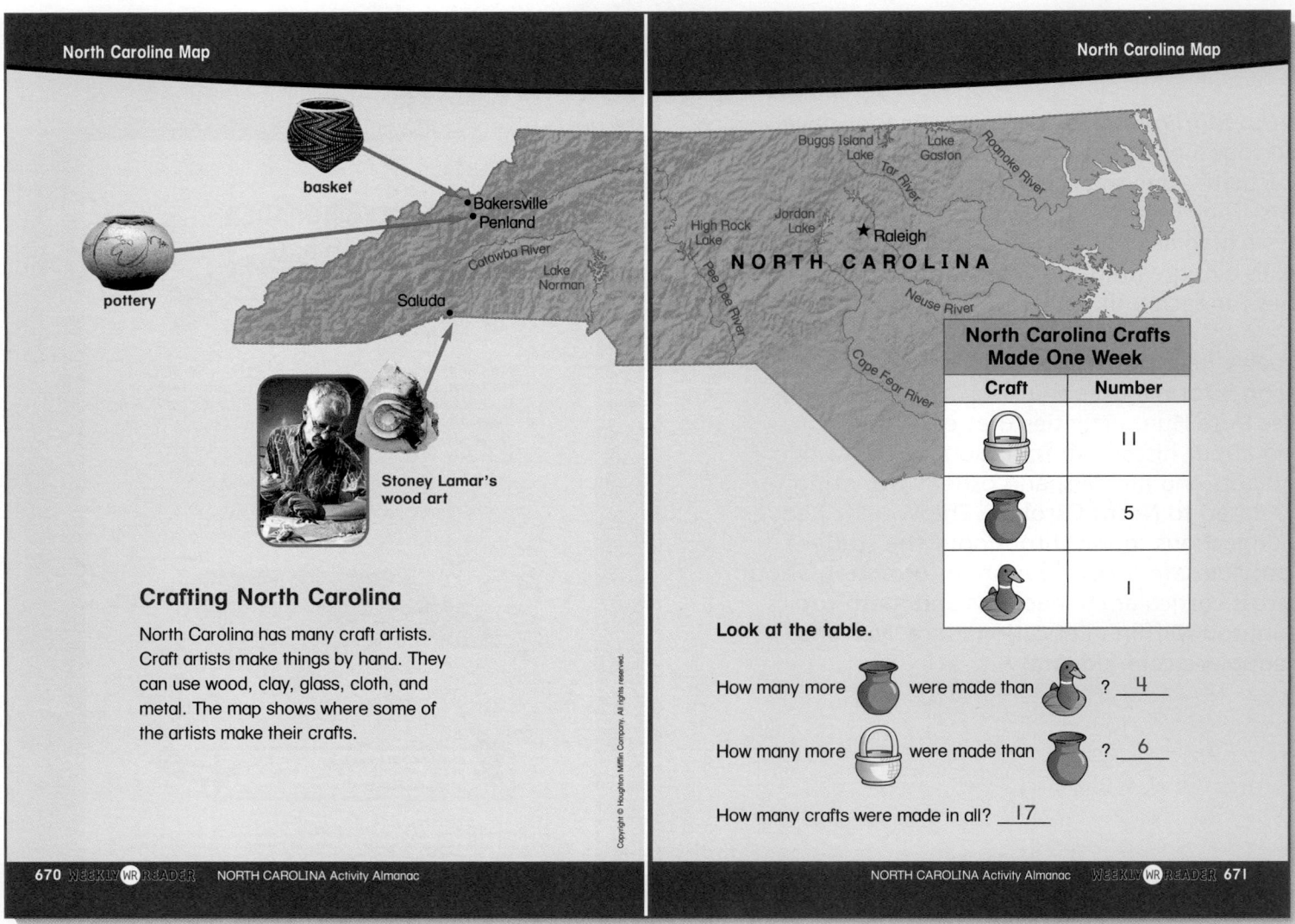

North Carolina Map

Teacher's Notes

Pottery can be objects such as vases, pots, bowls, or plates shaped from moist clay and hardened by heat. Sometimes a potter's wheel is used to help shape the clay by hand. Baskets are typically weaved from materials such as plant stems or twigs. Pottery and baskets can be decorative or used as containers to carry items such as water and food.

Stoney Lamar is an artist who uses objects such as wood and metal to create sculptures. Wet wood works best for his sculpture. He works on five to six pieces at a time and allows them to dry in stages prior to finishing them. His work has been shown in many museums in Atlanta, New York, Los Angeles, and Washington, DC.

Children should be able to read the information in the table, then use addition and subtraction to answer the questions.

WEEKLY (WR) READER   Activity Almanac

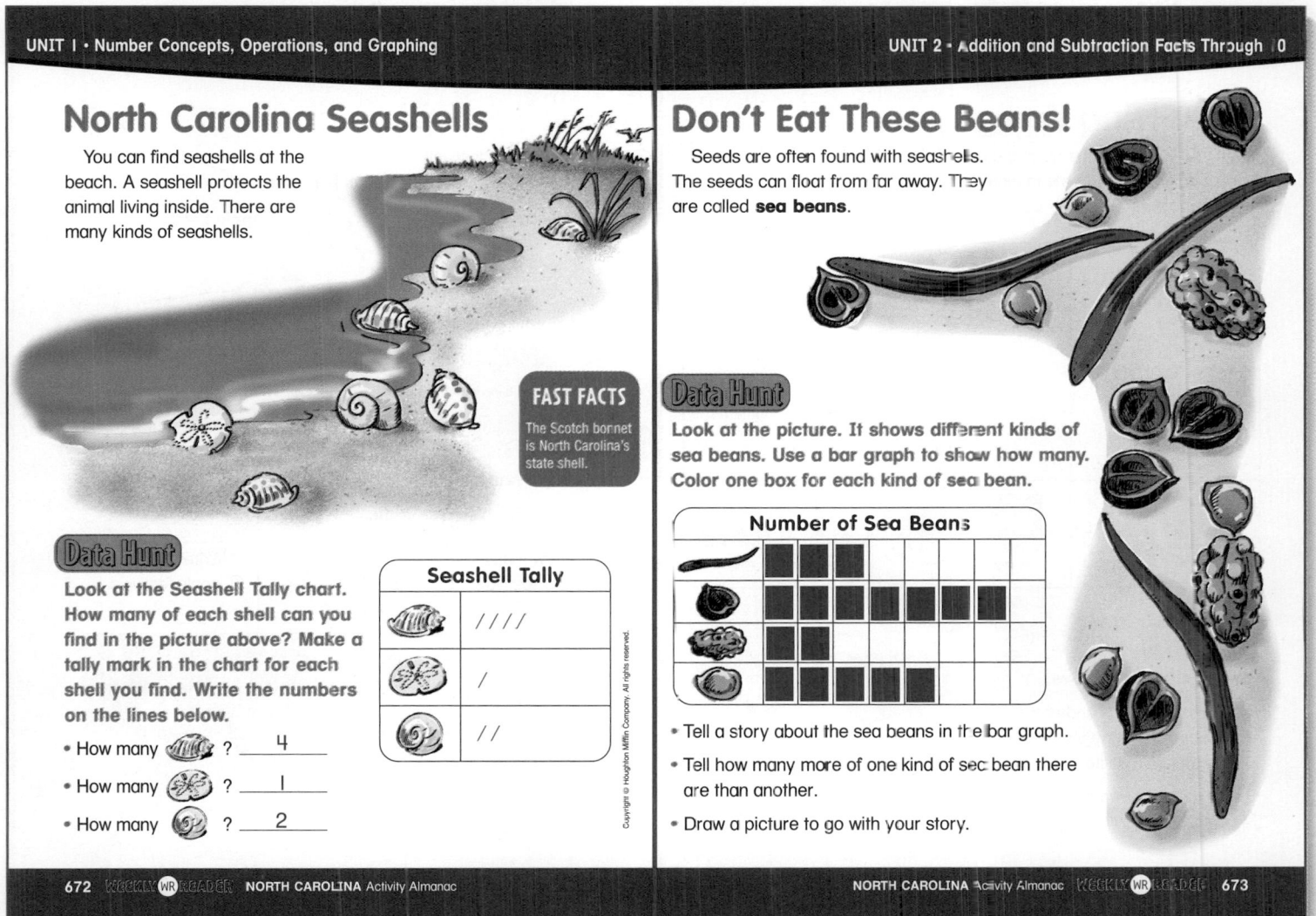

North Carolina Seashells

You can find seashells at the beach. A seashell protects the animal living inside. There are many kinds of seashells.

FAST FACTS
The Scotch bonnet is North Carolina's state shell.

Data Hunt

Look at the Seashell Tally chart. How many of each shell can you find in the picture above? Make a tally mark in the chart for each shell you find. Write the numbers on the lines below.

- How many 🐚 ? ___4___
- How many 🐚 ? ___1___
- How many 🐚 ? ___2___

Seashell Tally

🐚	////
🐚	/
🐚	//

Don't Eat These Beans!

Seeds are often found with seashells. The seeds can float from far away. They are called **sea beans**.

Data Hunt

Look at the picture. It shows different kinds of sea beans. Use a bar graph to show how many. Color one box for each kind of sea bean.

Number of Sea Beans

- Tell a story about the sea beans in the bar graph.
- Tell how many more of one kind of sea bean there are than another.
- Draw a picture to go with your story.

Unit 1   # Unit 2

Teacher's Notes

The tally chart shows three shells. The first is the scotch bonnet, the second is the sand dollar, and the third is the moon shell. The scotch bonnet and moon shell are used as homes to many types of snails. The sand dollar is also known as a keyhole urchin. These three shells can be found all along the East Coast.

Teacher's Notes

The illustration shows four different types of sea beans found in North Carolina.

The coin plant looks like a misshapen coin. The red mangrove has a long tube shape. The blister pod has bumps that look like blisters. The black walnut looks like a walnut.

Check children's stories and drawings.

UNIT 3 · Geometry and Fractions

UNIT 4 · Numbers Through 100

Kite-Flying Fun

Kites fly high up in the air at the Rogallo Kite Festival in North Carolina. Kites come in many shapes. Some kites can do tricks in the sky.

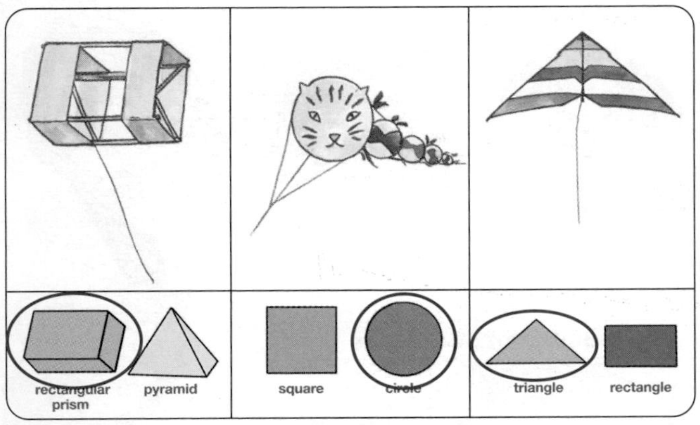

rectangular prism   pyramid   square   circle   triangle   rectangle

Data Hunt

Look at the kites above.

- Look at the shapes under each kite. Circle the shape that matches the kite.
- Draw a kite you would like to fly.
- Tell what shapes you see in your kite.

JOCKEY'S RIDGE STATE PARK, NAGS HEAD, NORTH CAROLINA

At the Festival

Everyone loves a festival! Festivals have parades and rides. North Carolina has many festivals that happen once a year.

Strawberry Festival

This festival has happened 73 times.

Apple Festival

This festival has happened 59 times.

Data Hunt

Compare the numbers.

Circle **greater than** or **less than.**

Write how many strawberry festivals.	greater than	Write how many apple festivals.
73	less than	59

Use **>** or **<** to compare the numbers.

73 (**>**) 59

Plan your own festival.

- Write the name of your festival.
- Tell what people can do there.
- Draw a picture of the festival.

Unit 3

Unit 4

Teacher's Notes

The Rogallo Kite Festival takes place annually at Jockey's Ridge State Park in Nags Head, North Carolina — the site of the highest sand dune on the East Coast. Kites of all shapes and sizes are entered in the festival. There are events for different kinds of kites. Sport kites perform tricks. There is music, food, contests, and kite-flying lessons.

Teacher's Notes

The number of times the North Carolina Apple and Strawberry Festivals have happened is up-to-date as of 2003.

You may wish to explain to children what a festival is. Ask children if they have ever been to a festival. Discuss the type of attractions they might see. They might see a parade, animals in animal shows, contests, food, music groups, and dancing.

Activity Almanac

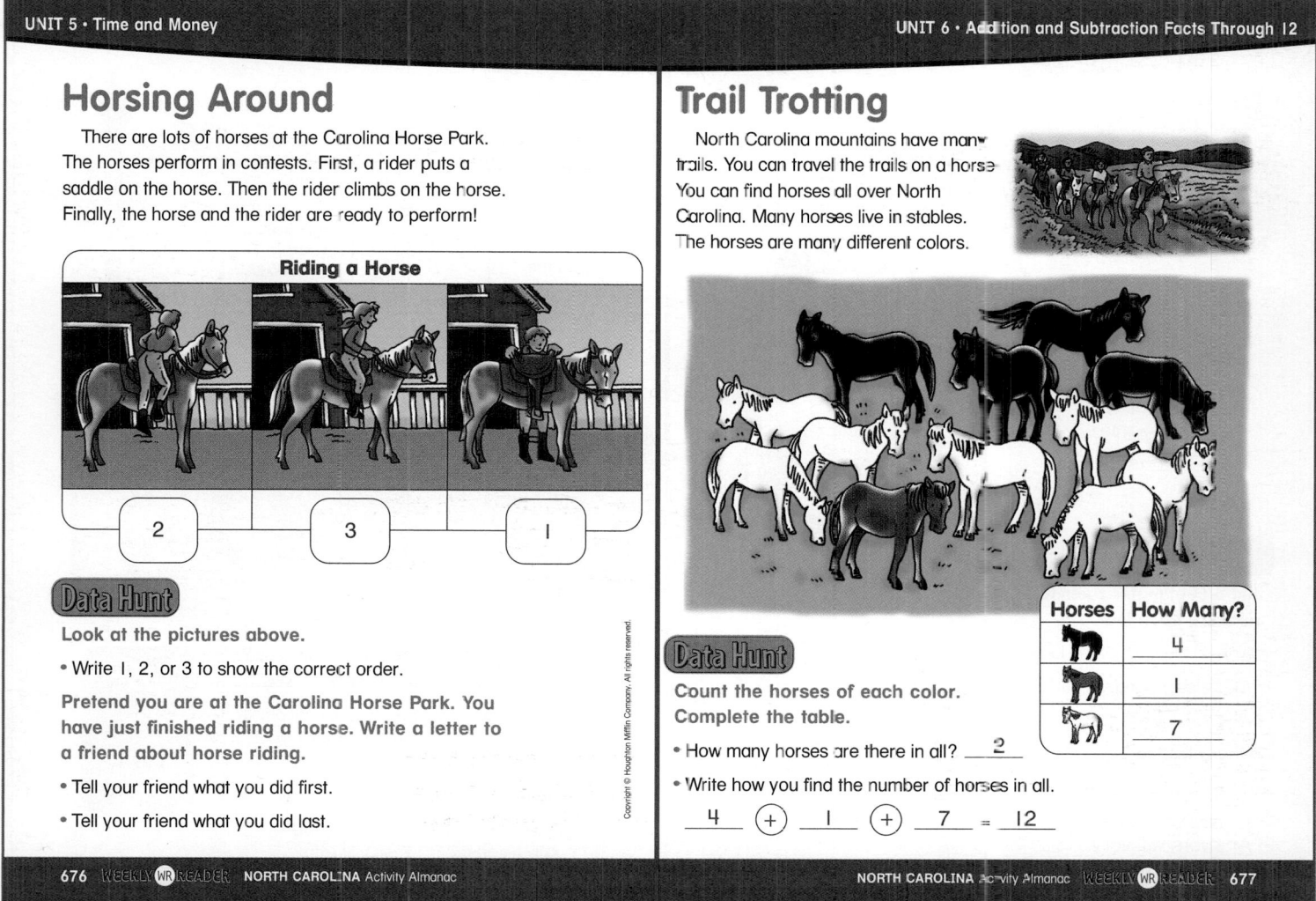

Horsing Around

There are lots of horses at the Carolina Horse Park. The horses perform in contests. First, a rider puts a saddle on the horse. Then the rider climbs on the horse. Finally, the horse and the rider are ready to perform!

Riding a Horse

2   3   1

Data Hunt

Look at the pictures above.

• Write 1, 2, or 3 to show the correct order.

Pretend you are at the Carolina Horse Park. You have just finished riding a horse. Write a letter to a friend about horse riding.

• Tell your friend what you did first.

• Tell your friend what you did last.

Trail Trotting

North Carolina mountains have many trails. You can travel the trails on a horse. You can find horses all over North Carolina. Many horses live in stables. The horses are many different colors.

Horses	How Many?
	4
	1
	7

Data Hunt

Count the horses of each color. Complete the table.

• How many horses are there in all? __2__

• Write how you find the number of horses in all.

__4__ (+) __1__ (+) __7__ = __12__

Unit 5

Unit 6

Teacher's Notes

This lesson explains the order of events for riding a horse. You may wish to explain what a saddle is to the children. Tell them that a saddle is used to ride horses. Riders usually sit on the saddle when they are on the horse.

Teacher's Notes

This lesson shows the different colors of horses found at a North Carolina stable. Explain to children that a stable is a shelter where animals live. You may wish to tell children that most horses come in various shades of brown, black, grey, and white.

UNIT 7 • Measurement

Tree Time

Trees grow lots of leaves. Different kinds of trees have different leaves. The leaves are different sizes and shapes. North Carolina has many trees with many leaves.

North Carolina Leaves

American Beech

_5_ centimeters

Sweet Birch

_8_ centimeters

American Holly

_10_ centimeters

Data Hunt

Use a centimeter ruler to measure each leaf.

• Write the lengths of the leaves.

• Which leaf is longest?   American Holly

• Which leaf is shortest?   American Beech

Bring a leaf to class. Measure your leaf.

• Is your leaf longer or shorter than the American holly leaf?

• Tell how your leaf is different from the leaves on this page.
  Answers will vary.

UNIT 8 • Two-Digit Addition and Subtraction

Seedling Surprise

Where do pine trees come from? They come from seedlings! Seedlings are planted in the ground. They grow to become large pine trees.

Seedlings are sold in packs. The seedlings in the chart come from North Carolina.

Pine Tree Seedling

Name of Pine Tree	Number of Seedlings in a Pack
Loblolly pine	25
White pine	25
Longleaf pine	10
Shortleaf pine	5

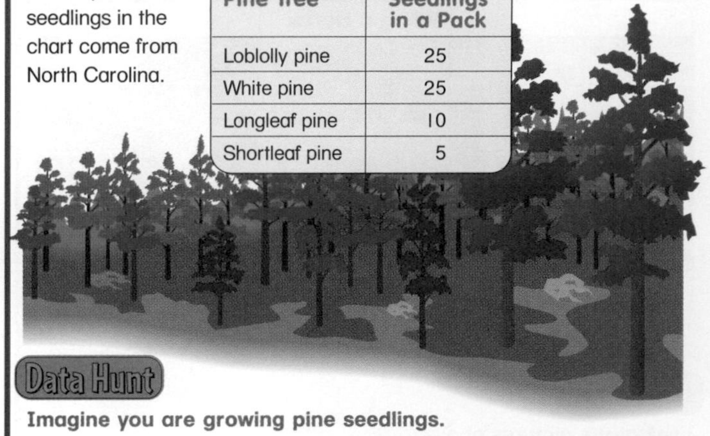

Data Hunt

Imagine you are growing pine seedlings.

• How many seedlings are in one pack of white and one pack of shortleaf pines altogether?   _30_

• How many more seedlings are in a pack of Loblolly seedlings than in a pack of Longleaf seedlings?
  _15_

• Draw what your pine tree garden will look like and color it.   Check children's drawings.

FAST FACTS

Many pine trees grow in North Carolina. In fact, the state tree of North Carolina is the pine tree.

Unit 7

Unit 8

Teacher's Notes

American Hollies have bright, round, red berries. They grow in the autumn and stay on all winter. American Beeches grow best in mountain coves. The leaves are found towards the ends of branches. Sweet Birches make scaly, oval-shaped fruit. The stems of their leaves are hairy.

Teacher's Notes

Seedlings can be purchased from the North Carolina Tree Seedling Nursery Program. They are sold to agencies and landowners that support the planting of trees in North Carolina.

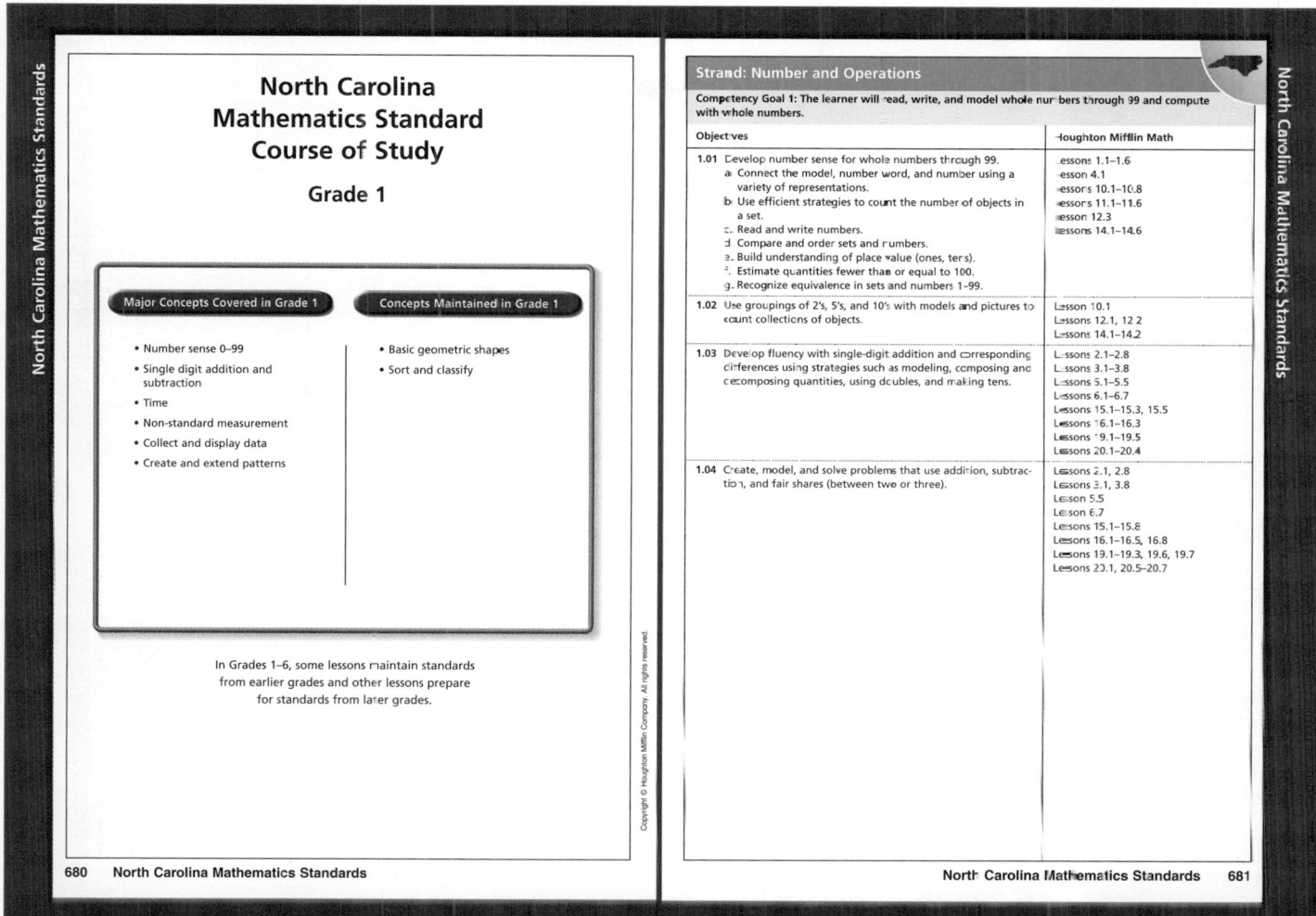

Strand: Number and Operations

Competency Goal 1: The learner will read, write, and model whole numbers through 99 and compute with whole numbers.

Objectives	Houghton Mifflin Math
1.01 Develop number sense for whole numbers through 99. a. Connect the model, number word, and number using a variety of representations. b. Use efficient strategies to count the number of objects in a set. c. Read and write numbers. d. Compare and order sets and numbers. e. Build understanding of place value (ones, tens). f. Estimate quantities fewer than or equal to 100. g. Recognize equivalence in sets and numbers 1–99.	Lessons 1.1–1.6 Lesson 4.1 Lessons 10.1–10.8 Lessons 11.1–11.6 Lesson 12.3 Lessons 14.1–14.6
1.02 Use groupings of 2's, 5's, and 10's with models and pictures to count collections of objects.	Lesson 10.1 Lessons 12.1, 12.2 Lessons 14.1–14.2
1.03 Develop fluency with single-digit addition and corresponding differences using strategies such as modeling, composing and decomposing quantities, using doubles, and making tens.	Lessons 2.1–2.8 Lessons 3.1–3.8 Lessons 5.1–5.5 Lessons 6.1–6.7 Lessons 15.1–15.3, 15.5 Lessons 16.1–16.3 Lessons 19.1–19.5 Lessons 20.1–20.4
1.04 Create, model, and solve problems that use addition, subtraction, and fair shares (between two or three).	Lessons 2.1, 2.8 Lessons 3.1, 3.8 Lesson 5.5 Lesson 6.7 Lessons 15.1–15.8 Lessons 16.1–16.5, 16.8 Lessons 19.1–19.3, 19.6, 19.7 Lessons 20.1, 20.5–20.7

North Carolina Mathematics Standard Course of Study

Grade 1

Major Concepts Covered in Grade 1	Concepts Maintained in Grade 1
• Number sense 0–99 • Single digit addition and subtraction • Time • Non-standard measurement • Collect and display data • Create and extend patterns	• Basic geometric shapes • Sort and classify

In Grades 1–6, some lessons maintain standards from earlier grades and other lessons prepare for standards from later grades.

Meeting the Standards

The North Carolina Department of Education has developed the Mathematics Standard Course of Study for the teaching of mathematics across all grade levels. These standards reflect an approach for teaching mathematics that will prepare today's students for living and working in tomorrow's world.

These pages in the Student Book will help you show parents how your classroom teaching reflects the Strands and Competency Goals of the Standard Course of Study. This should help both parents and students understand how a particular lesson contributes to a student's overall achievement of the Competency Goals for Mathematics.

Strand: Measurement

Competency Goal 2: The learner will use non-standard units of measure and tell time.

Objectives	Houghton Mifflin Math
2.01 For given objects: a. Select an attribute (length, capacity, mass) to measure (use non-standard units). b. Develop strategies to estimate size. c. Compare, using appropriate language, with respect to the attribute selected.	Lessons 17.1, 17.2, 17.5, 17.8 Lesson 18.1
2.02 Develop an understanding of the concept of time. a. Tell time at the hour and half-hour. b. Solve problems involving applications of time (clock and calendar).	Lessons 13.1–13.9

Strand : Geometry

Competency Goal 3: The learner will identify, describe, draw, and build basic geometric figures.

Objectives	Houghton Mifflin Math
3.01 Identify, build, draw and name parallelograms, squares, trapezoids, and hexagons.	Lessons 7.2, 7.3 Lesson 8.4
3.02 Identify, build, and name cylinders, cones, and rectangular prisms.	Lessons 7.4–7.6
3.03 Compare and contrast geometric figures.	Lessons 7.2–7.6
3.04 Solve problems involving spatial visualization.	Lesson 7.7 Lessons 8.1–8.4, 8.7

Strand: Data Analysis and Probability

Competency Goal 4: The learner will understand and use data and simple probability concepts.

Objectives	Houghton Mifflin Math
4.01 Collect, organize, describe and display data using line plots and tallies.	Lesson 4.1 Lesson 9.5
4.02 Describe events as certain, impossible, more likely, or less likely to occur.	Lessons 9.5–9.6

Strand: Algebra

Competency Goal 5: The learner will demonstrate an understanding of classification and patterning.

Objectives	Houghton Mifflin Math
5.01 Sort and classify objects by two attributes.	Lesson 7.3
5.02 Use Venn diagrams to illustrate similarities and differences in two sets.	Lesson 7.5
5.03 Create and extend patterns, identify the pattern unit, and translate into other forms.	Lessons 8.5, 8.6, 8.8 Lesson 9.6 Lessons 12.1, 12.2, 12.5 Lesson 16.7

Workmats ....

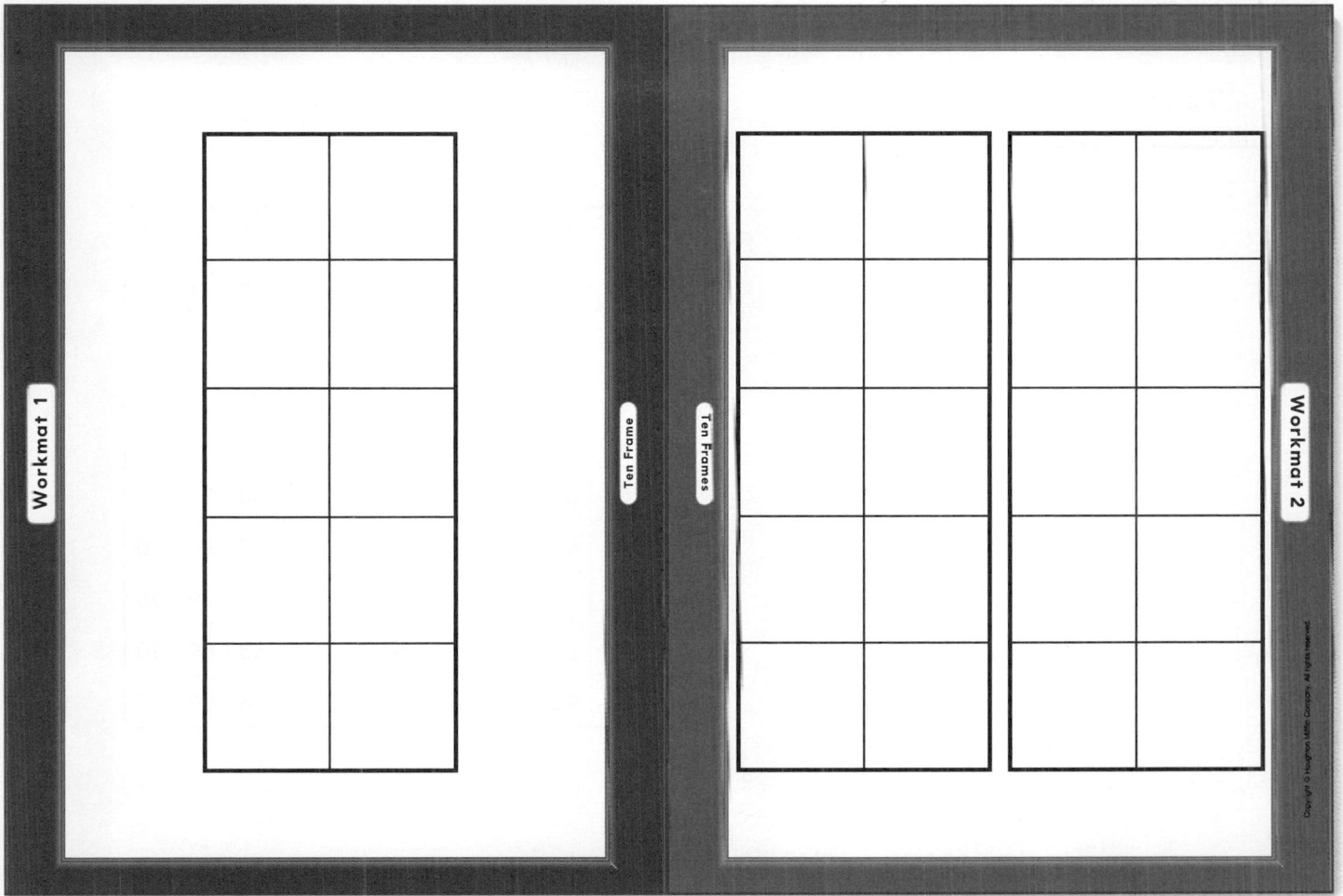

Workmat 1

Ten Frame

Ten Frames

Workmat 2

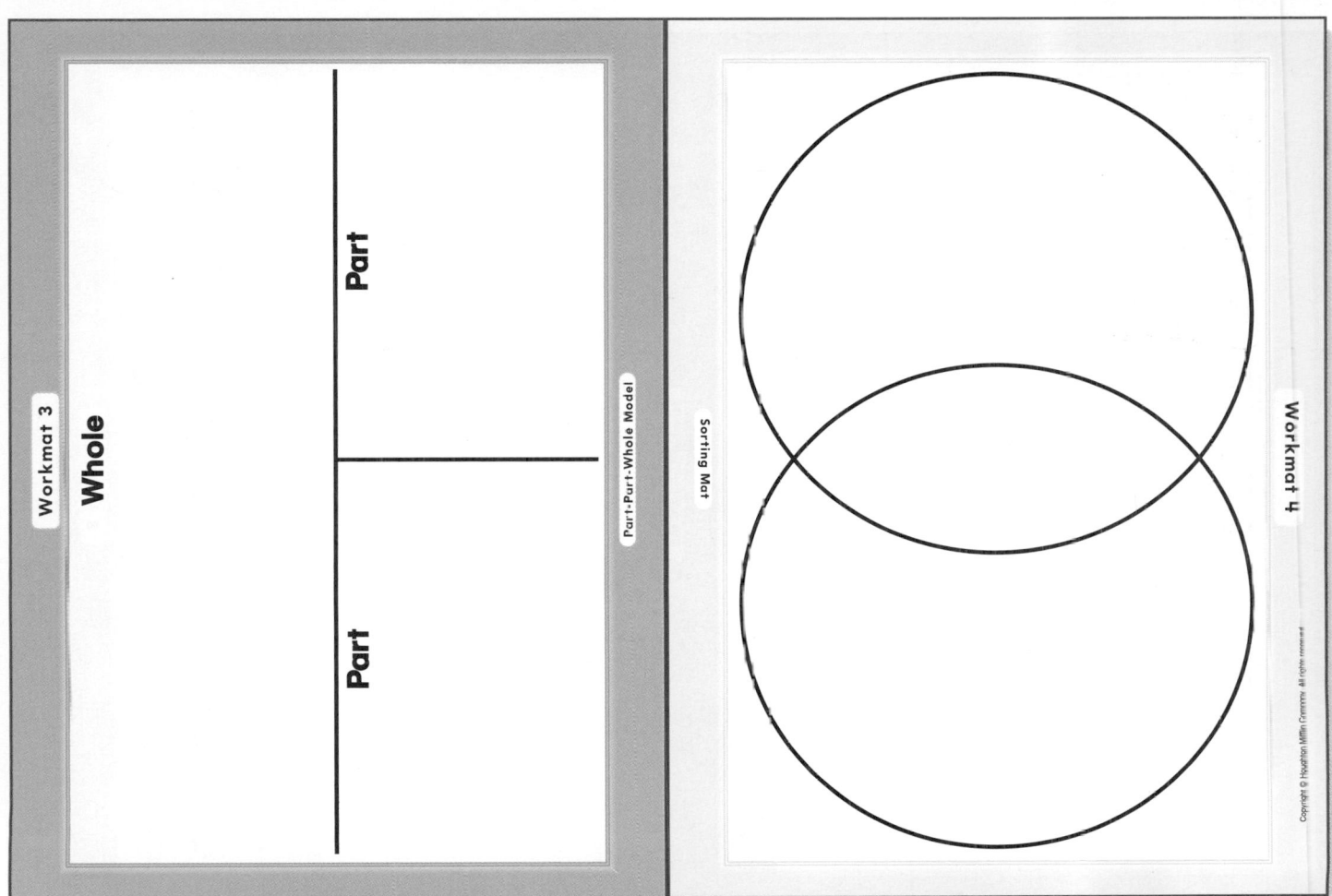

Workmat 3

Whole

Part

Part

Part-Part-Whole Model

Sorting Mat

Workmat 4

Workmats ································

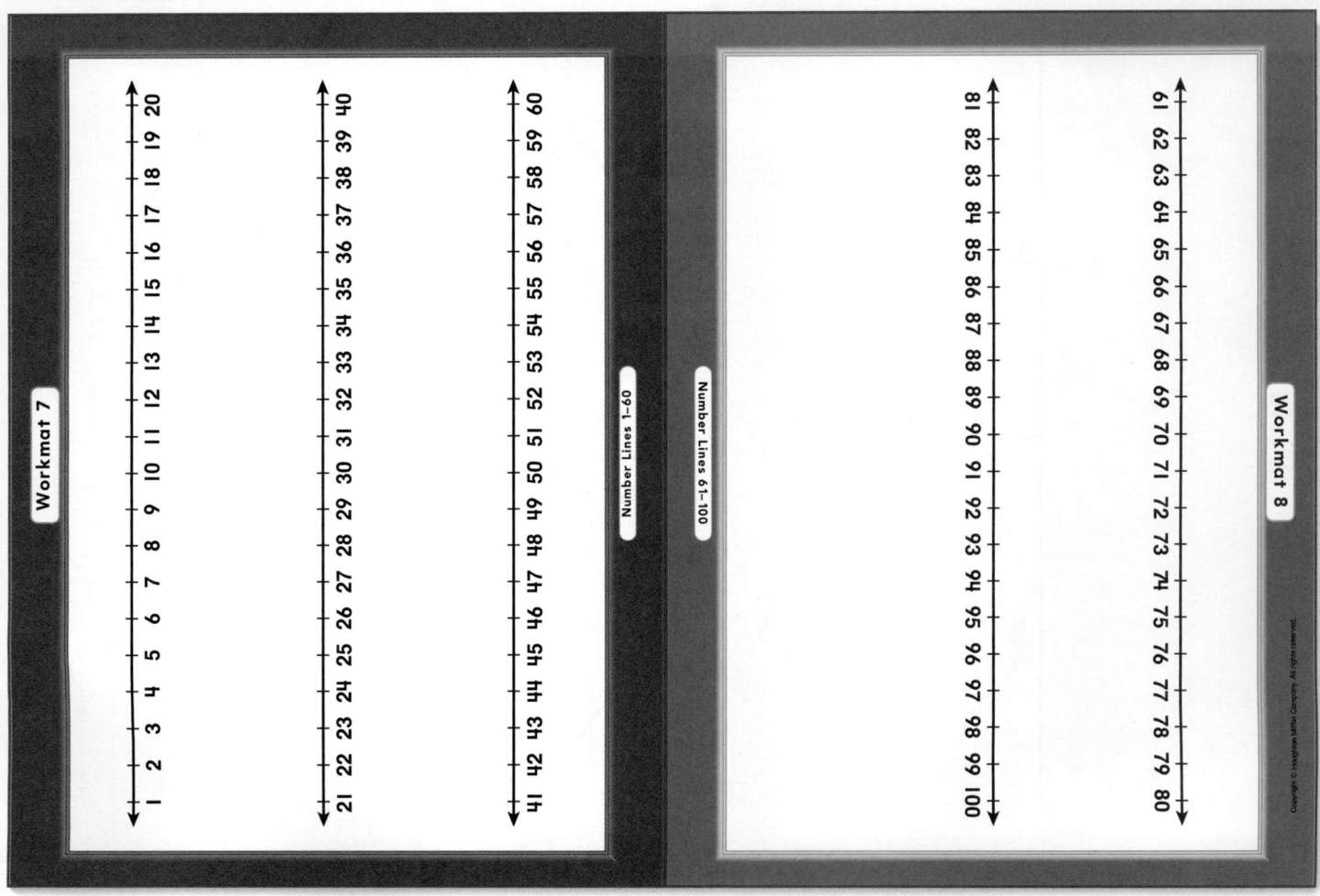

Workmat 5

Tens	Ones

Tens and Ones Chart

Workmat 6

1	2	3	4	5	6	7	8	9	10
11	12	13	14	15	16	17	18	19	20
21	22	23	24	25	26	27	28	29	30
31	32	33	34	35	36	37	38	39	40
41	42	43	44	45	46	47	48	49	50
51	52	53	54	55	56	57	58	59	60
61	62	63	64	65	66	67	68	69	70
71	72	73	74	75	76	77	78	79	80
81	82	83	84	85	86	87	88	89	90
91	92	93	94	95	96	97	98	99	100

Hundred Chart

Workmat 7

Number Lines 1–60

1 2 3 4 5 6 7 8 9 10 11 12 13 14 15 16 17 18 19 20

21 22 23 24 25 26 27 28 29 30 31 32 33 34 35 36 37 38 39 40

41 42 43 44 45 46 47 48 49 50 51 52 53 54 55 56 57 58 59 60

Workmat 8

Number Lines 61–100

61 62 63 64 65 66 67 68 69 70 71 72 73 74 75 76 77 78 79 80

81 82 83 84 85 86 87 88 89 90 91 92 93 94 95 96 97 98 99 100

Teacher Support Handbook

References for a number of professional resources are presented in this section of your Teacher's Edition. These materials reflect the needs expressed by classroom teachers around the country for additional resources to help them enrich their teaching or enhance their understanding of mathematics.

Math and Literature Bibliography

Addition Annie
by David Gisler
Children's Press, 2002
Annie counts everything around her, from trees to knees to peas.

Aunt Flossie's Hats (and Crab Cakes Later)
by Elizabeth Fitzgerald Howard
Clarion, 1991
A picture book about two African-American girls that can be connected to numbers, sorting, and graphing.

*A Bag Full of Pups
by Dick Gackenbach
Houghton Mifflin, 1983
Most of Mr. Mullin's pups go to people who want a dog to do tasks for them, but one little boy just wants a pet to love.

The Best Vacation Ever
by Stuart J. Murphy
HarperCollins, 1997
As a family decides where to go on vacation, the narrator gathers all of their ideas in a chart.

Can You Count Ten Toes?
by Lezlie Evans
Houghton Mifflin, 1999
You can learn to count in ten different languages in this counting book.

*Cat Up a Tree
by John and Ann Hassett
Houghton Mifflin, 2003
Nana Quimby has too many cats stuck in her tree, but the people she asks for help will not help rescue the cats.

A Collection for Kate
by Barbara deRubertis
Econo-Clad Books, 2000
It's Collection Week at Kate's school and she doesn't have a collection. What can she do?

Count on Pablo
by Barbara deRubertis
Econo-Clad Books, 1999
Pablo shows how good he is at counting when he helps his grandmother, his "abuela," sell vegetables.

Counting Cranes
by Mary Beth Owens
Little, Brown & Company, 1993
A counting book that describes the characteristics and behaviors of a whooping crane.

*Dim Sum for Everyone!
by Grace Lin
Random House Children's Books, 2001
On a visit to a Chinatown restaurant with her family, a child describes all the different dishes of dim sum.

Dinner at the Panda Palace
by Stephanie Calmenson
Bt Bound, 1999
Mr. Panda greets a growing list of guests arriving at his restaurant in this counting rhyme.

The Doorbell Rang
by Pat Hutchins
Greenwillow, 1986
Every time the doorbell rings, more friends arrive to share the cookies that Ma has made.

Each Orange Had 8 Slices: A Counting Book
by Paul Giganti, Jr.
Pearson Learning, 1992
Have fun counting, adding, or multiplying your way through the math hiding in the world around you.

Eating Fractions
by Bruce McMillan
Scholastic, 1991
A boy and a girl discover halves, thirds, and fourths as they divide bananas, pizza, and strawberry pie.

The Eentsy, Weentsy Spider: Fingerplays and Action Rhymes
by Joanna Cole and Stephanie Calmenson
Econo-Clad Books, 1991
Say, sing, and act out this collection of favorite fingerplays and action rhymes.

*Feast for 10
by Cathryn Falwell
Houghton Mifflin Company, 1995
A counting book that features a family shopping for, and preparing, a meal.

Fish Eyes: A Book You Can Count On
by Lois Ehlert
Harcourt, 2001
Brightly colored fish introduce children to counting.

Gator Pie
by Louise Mathews
Sundance, 1995
A group of alligators divide a pie into smaller and smaller fractional parts.

The Grapes of Math: Mind-Stretching Math Riddles
by Greg Tang
Scholastic, 2001
Use visual clues to solve a variety of math riddles.

How Long?
by Elizabeth Dale
Orchard Books, 1998
Caroline the dormouse wants to find out how long a minute is so she paints a line. She continues playing to find out how long 10 minutes and 15 minutes are.

How Many Feet In the Bed?
by Dianne Johnston Hamm
Simon & Schuster, 1994
Count feet as five family members tumble in and out of bed.

Inch by Inch
by Leo Lionni
Bt Bound, 1999
An inchworm is proud of his ability to measure everything under the sun.

*Just a Little Bit
by Ann Tompert
Houghton Mifflin, 1993
Mouse and Elephant are playing on a seesaw and need help from lots of animal friends to balance the scales.

Just Enough Carrots
by Stuart J. Murphy
Scott Foresman, 1997
Count and compare food in shopping carts while a bunny and his mother shop.

Just One More
by Michelle Koch
Greenwillow Books, 1991
A counting book from one to fifteen that also explores the concept of "one more."

Lemonade for Sale
by Stuart J. Murphy
HarperCollins, 1997
The Elm Street Kids' Club wants to fix up their clubhouse, so they decide to sell lemonade and use a graph to track their sales.

Let's Fly a Kite
by Stuart J. Murphy
HarperCollins, 2000
Bob and Hannah learn about symmetry as they build and fly a kite.

Lights Out!
by Lucille Recht Penner
Econo-Clad Books, 2000
A young girl counts the lights as each is turned out in the apartment building across from hers.

*Look Inside
by Lilly Ernesto
DC Heath, 1989
Take a look inside different buildings and find out who is there.

Lulu's Lemonade
by Barbara deRubertis
Econo-Clad Books, 2000
Three children make special lemonade on a hot day and squabble over which ingredients and what quantities to use.

Me Counting Time
by Joan Sweeney
Crown Books for Young Readers, 2000
Describes the relationship between various measurements of time.

*Also available in the Math Trade Book Literature Library

Math and Literature Bibliography

Measuring Penny
by Loreen Leedy
Econo-Clad Books, 2000
For homework, Lisa decides to measure her dog, Penny. She uses all sorts of units, including pounds, inches, dog biscuits, and cotton swabs.

Missing Mittens
by Stuart J. Murphy
Econo-Clad Books, 2001
Children are introduced to odd and even numbers as they unravel the mitten mystery on Farmer Bill's farm.

***The Mitten**
adapted and illustrated
by Jan Brett
Putnam, 1996
Nicki accidentally drops his mitten in the snow and several animals sleep inside it.

Musical Chairs and Dancing Bears
by Joanne Rocklin
Holt, 1993
Bears play musical chairs to demonstrate simple subtraction.

Numbers (Math Counts)
by Henry Arthur Pluckrose
Scholastic Library Publishing, 1995
Using the Math Counts series, children can become mathematical problem solvers.

100 Days of School
by Trudy Harris
Millbrook Press, 1999
Children celebrate 100 days of school. Using fun examples, kids will learn many of the ways to reach 100 through groupings.

One Hundred is a Family
by Pam Muñoz Ryan
Hyperion, 1994
Groups making up different types of families introduce numbers from one to ten, and then by tens to one hundred.

one less fish
by Kim Michelle Toft
Charlesbridge, 1998
Learn about threatened tropical fish in the Great Barrier Reef as you count down from twelve to zero.

One More Bunny
by Rick Walton
HarperCollins, 2001
Bunnies introduce the numbers one through ten as they play.

1 + 1 Take Away Two!
by Michael Berenstain
Golden Books, 1991
Single-digit addition and subtraction equations are modeled with jungle animal illustrations.

One Watermelon Seed
by Celia Barker Lottridge
Oxford University Press, 1988
Two children plant a garden and then harvest the fruits and vegetables they have grown. Practice counting up to ten and then by tens up to one hundred.

Over in the Meadow, a Rhyme
illustrated
by Ezra Jack Keats
Penguin Group, 1999
Animal mothers and their babies introduce the numbers one through ten in this favorite counting rhyme.

***The Pig Is in the Pantry, the Cat Is on the Shelf**
by Shirley Mozelle
Houghton Mifflin, 2000
When Mr. McDuffel goes shopping and forgets to lock his house, eight farm animals take it over and cause chaos.

Probably Pistachio
by Stuart J. Murphy
HarperCollins, 2000
Everything is going wrong for Jack today, and during the course of the day he learns all about probability.

The Purse
by Kathy Caple
Houghton Mifflin, 1986
Kathy spends all of her money to buy a purse, but then must earn the money to put in it.

A Quarter From the Tooth Fairy
by Caren Holtzman
Econo-Clad Books, 1995
A young boy gets a quarter from the Tooth Fairy and has trouble deciding how to spend it.

The Right Number of Elephants
by Jeff Sheppard
HarperCollins, 1992
A girl decides how many elephants are needed for several projects.

Sea Sums
by Joy N. Hulme
Hyperion, 1996
Changing numbers of sea creatures are added and subtracted as they swim in the shallows of a coral reef.

Shape (Math Counts)
by Henry Arthur Pluckrose
Scholastic, 1995
Using the Math Counts series, children can become mathematical problem solvers.

So Many Cats!
by Beatrice Schenk de Regniers
Houghton Mifflin, 1991
One lonely cat turns into twelve in this counting story.

Take Off with Numbers
by Sally Hewitt
Raintree Publishers, 1996
Use everyday objects and situations to explore the world of numbers.

Ten Little Mice
by Joyce Dunbar
Harcourt, 1990
Ten mischievous mice play happily outside and then scurry home, one by one.

12 Ways to Get to 11
by Eve Merriam
Simon & Schuster, 1993
Various combinations of items are added together to reach the number eleven.

Twenty Is Too Many
by Kate Duke
Penguin Putnam, 2000
One by one twenty guinea pigs jump ship in this book about subtraction.

Two of Everything
by Lily Toy Hong
Whitman, 1993
Mr. and Mrs. Haktak become rich after discovering a brass pot that doubles everything that's put into it.

What's a Pair? What's a Dozen?
by Stephen R. Swinburne
Boyds Mills Press, 2000
Introduce children to number-related words. Using lively photos children are then asked to identify what they've learned.

What Time Is It, Mr. Wolf?
by Bob Beeson
Hambleton-Hill Publishing, Inc., 1994
Children will learn about time on the hour, using analog and digital clocks.

Where the Sidewalk Ends
by Shel Silverstein
HarperCollins Children's Books
A collection of humorous poetry, including One Inch Tall.

Where's That Bone
by Lucille Recht Penner
The Kane Press, 2000
When Jill's dog Bingo buries his bones to hide them from Hulk the cat, Jill keeps track of where they are with a map.

Also available for purchase
Math Trade Book Literature Library

Professional Resources Bibliography

Bresser, R., and C. Holtzman. *Developing Number Sense –Grades 3-6.* Math Solutions Publications, 1999.

Brodie, J. P. *Constructing Ideas About Large Numbers.* Creative Publications, 1995.

Burns, Marilyn. *About Teaching Mathematics: A K–8 Resource,* 2nd Ed. Sausalito, CA: Math Solutions Publications, 2000.

Butterworth, B. *The Mathematical Brain.* Macmillan, 1999.

Carpenter, Thomas P., Elizabeth Fennema, Megan Loef Franke, Linda Levi, and Susan P. Empson. *Children's Mathematics: Cognitively Guided Instruction.* Portsmouth, NH: Heinemann, 1999.

Cathcart. W., Y. Pothier, J. Vance, and N. Bezuk. *Learning Mathematics in Elementary and Middle Schools.* Merrill: Prentice-Hall, Inc., 2000.

Childs, L., and L Choate. *Nimble with Numbers.* Dale Seymour Publications, 1999.

Clapham, C. *Concise Dictionary of Mathematics.* Oxford University Press, 1996.

Coates, G., and J. Stenmark. *Family Math for Young Children.* Lawrence Hall of Science, 1997.

Cowan, T., and J. Maguire. *Timelines of African-American History: 500 Years of Black Achievement.* Berkley Publishing Group, 1994.

Crawford, M., and M. Witte. *"Strategies for Mathematics: Teaching in Context."* Educational Leadership, Vol. 57, ASCD, November 1999.

Eby, J., and E. Kujawa. *Reflective Planning, Teaching and Evaluation: K-12.* Merrill: Macmillan Publishing Company, 1994.

Flournoy, V., et al. *The Patchwork Quilt.* Scholastic, 1996.

Franco, B., et al. *Understanding Geometry.* Great Source Education Group, 1998.

Garland, T. Fibonacci *Fun: Fascinating Activities with Intriguing Numbers.* Dale Seymour Publications, 1998.

Geary, D. C. *Children's Mathematical Development: Research and Practical Applications.* Washington, D.C., 1994.

Gelfand, I., and A. Shen. *Algebra.* Birkhauser, 1993.

Ginsburg, H.P., Greenes, C., and Balfanz, R. *Big Math for Little Kids.* Dale Seymour Publications, 2003

Ginsburg, H. P., Greenes, C., Balfanz, R., Glassman, B., ed. *Macmillan Visual Almanac.* Blackbirch Press, 1996.

Greenes, C., and G. Immerzeel. *Problem Solving Focus: Time and Money.* Dale Seymour Publications, 1993.

Hiebert, J., T. Carpenter, E. Fennema, K. Fuson, D. Wearne, H. Murray, A. Olivier, and P. Humam. *Making Sense: Teaching and Learning Mathematics with Understanding.* Heinemann, 1997.

Hoffman, P. *The Man Who Loved Only Numbers: The Story of Paul Erdos and the Search for Mathematical Truth.* Hyperion, 1998.

Karp, Karen, E. Todd Brown, Linda Allen, and Candy Allen. *Feisty Females: Inspiring Girls to Think Mathematically.* Portsmouth, NH: Heinemann, 1998.

Kovalik, Susan J., and Karen D. Olsen. *Exceeding Expectations: A User's Guide to Implementing Brain Research in the Classroom,* 2nd Ed. Covington, WA: Books for Educators, Inc., 2001.

Lamon. Susan J. *Teaching Fractions and Ratios for Understanding.* Mahwah, NJ: Lawrence Erlbaum Associates, 1999.

Lee, M., and M. Miller. *Great Graphing.* Scholastic Professional Books, 1993.

Ma, Liping. *Knowing and Teaching Elementary Mathematics.* Lawrence Erlbaum Associates, 1999.

Mamchur, C. *A Teacher's Guide to Cognitive Type Theory and Learning Style.* ASCD, 1996.

The Math Learning Center. *"Fractions on a Geoboard," in Opening Eyes to Mathematics,* Volume 3. 1995.

McIntosh, A., B. Reys, R. Reys, and J. Hope. *Number SENSE: Simple Effective Number Sense Experiences, Grades 4-6.* Dale Seymour Publications, 1997.

Means, B., C. Chelener, and M. Knapp. *Teaching Advanced Skills to At-Risk Students.* Jossey-Bass Inc., 1991.

Mendlesohn, E. *Teaching Primary Math with Music.* Dale Seymour Publications, 1990.

Miller, D., and A. McKinnon. *The Beginning School Mathematics Project.* ASCD, 1995.

Miller, E. *Read It! Draw It! Solve It! Problem Solving for Primary Grades.* Dale Seymour Publications, 1997.

Myren, C. *Posing Open-Ended Questions in the Primary Classroom.* Teaching Resource Center, 1997.

Professional Resources Bibliography

National Council of Teachers of Mathematics. Principles and Standards for School Mathematics (2000)
See also these NCTM products:
Addenda Series
Navigations Series
Yearbook

National Research Council. *Adding It Up: Helping Children Learn Mathematics.* Washington, DC, National Academy Press, 2001.

Newman, V. *Math Journals, Grades K-5.* Teaching Resource Center, 1994.

Norton-Wolf, S. *Base-Ten Block Activities.* Learning Resources, 1990.

Ohanian, S. *Garbage, Pizza, Patchwork Quilts, and Math Magic.* W. H. Freeman and Co., 1992.

Pappas, T. *The Magic of Mathematics – Discovering the Spell of Mathematics.* Wide World Publishing/Tetra, 1994.

Parker, M., ed. *She Does Math! – Real-Life Problems from Women on the Job.* The Mathematical Association of America, 1995.

Piccirilli, R. *Mental Math: Computation Activities for Anytime.* Scholastic Professional Books, 1996.

Rich, D. *MegaSkills.* Houghton Mifflin Company, 1992.

Salvin, R. E., N. L. Karweit, and B. A. Wasik, eds. *Preventing Early School Failure: Research, Policy, and Practice.* Boston: Allyn and Bacon. 1994.

Satariano, P. *Storytime, Mathtime: Math Explorations in Children's Literature.* Dale Seymour Publications, 1997.

Schechter, B. *My Brain Is Open: The Mathematical Journeys of Paul Erdos.* Simon & Schuster, 1998.

Schoenfeld, A. *"When Good Teaching Leads to Bad Results: The Disasters of Well-Taught Mathematics Courses,"* Educational Psychologist, Vol. 23, 145-66. 1998.

Schullman, D., and E. Rebeka. *Growing Mathematical Ideas in Kindergarten.* Math Solutions Publications, 1999.

Sheffield, Linda Jensen. *Extending the Challenge in Mathematics: Developing Mathematical Promise in K–8 Students.* Thousand Oaks, CA: Corwin Press, Inc., 2002.

Singer, Margie, et al. *Between Never and Always.* Dale Seymour Publications, 1997.

Skinner, P. *It All Adds Up! Math Solutions Publications* (Adapted by Permission of Addison-Wesley Longman, Australia), 1999.

Sparrow, Len, and Paul Swan. *Learning Math with Calculators: Activities for Grades 3–8.* Sausalito, CA: Math Solutions Publications, 2001.

Sternberg, R., and W. Williams. *How to Develop Student Creativity.* ASCD. 1996

Stewart, K., and K. Walker. *20 Thinking Questions for Base-Ten Blocks, Grades 3-6.* Creative Publications, 1995.

Tomlinson, Carol Ann. *How to Differentiate Instruction in Mixed-Ability Classrooms.* ASCD, 1995.

Trafton, P., and D. Thiesen. *Learning Through Problems: Number Sense and Computational Strategies/A Resource for Teachers.* Heinemann, 1999.

Van De Walle, J. *Elementary and Middle School Mathematics: Teaching Developmentally,* Fourth Edition. Dale Seymour Publications, 2000.

Wahl, Mark. *Math for Humans: Teaching Math Through 8 Intelligences,* 2nd Ed. Vernon Hills, IL: LivnLern Press, 1999.

Webb, N., and T. Romberg. *Peforming Mathematics Education in America's Cities: The Urban Mathematics Collaborative Project.* Teachers College Press, 1994.

Zaslavsky, C. *Fear of Math – How to Get Over It and Get On with Your Life.* Rutgers University Press, 1994.

Zemelman, S., H. Daniels, and A. Hyde. *Best Practice: New Standards for Teaching and Learning in America's Schools.* Heinemann, 1998.

Research Support* for Unit 1

TO: **First Grade Teachers**

SUBJECT: **Basic Facts Are Still Fundamental**

The mastery of lower-order skills instills confidence for higher-order mathematics. According to Chinese teaching tradition, how teachers help students learn basic facts is most important. One reason that Chinese children appear to master basic facts well is the difference in the way numbers are written and spoken in Chinese versus English.

Chinese numeration highlights grouping by ten, and encourages children to view two-digit numbers as "tens" and "ones." This, in turn, promotes "ten" as a "bridge" when performing addition and subtraction.

In America, addition is taught by "adding on." Chinese children are taught to "make ten."

Example: 9 + 4 = ?

Chinese teaching: 9 + ? = 10

$9 + 1 = 10$ Make a ten using 1.

$4 = 1 + 3$ See how many more need to be added.

$10 + 3 = 13$ Add 3 to the 10 made from 9 and 1.

So, 9 + 4 is the same as 10 + + 3, or 13.

By using ten as a bridge in both addition and subtraction, children are encouraged to rely on understanding about facts that they have used repeatedly.

TRY IT OUT!

The creative teacher can employ an "adding-on" strategy in the introduction of addition, or a "take-away" strategy with subtraction. Later, with two-digit numbers, the Chinese approach of "making or removing ten" can be used to advantage.

CHECK IT OUT!

Horvath, Tara (2005). Number concepts, operations, and graphing. *Professional Resources Handbook—Grade 1*. Boston: Houghton-Mifflin.

Howard, K. (1979). *I can count to 100…can you?* New York: Random House.

Ma, L. (1999). *Knowing and teaching elementary mathematics*. Mahwah, NJ: Lawrence Erlbaum.

* For more information about the research base for this unit of *Houghton Mifflin Math*, see *Professional Resources Handbook, Grade 1*.

Research Support* for Unit 2

TO: First Grade Teachers

SUBJECT: Working Out Facts You Don't Remember

The use of counting materials such as bottle caps, sticks, rods, and other manipulatives is essential in laying the cognitive foundations for addition and subtraction of whole numbers through 10. While children should be encouraged to "work out" a basic fact by "combining" or "taking away" collections of counters, most teachers expect children eventually to memorize basic facts. Many children, however, cannot recall every basic fact reliably.

Children should be taught to "work out" facts, not just with manipulatives but with various fact generation strategies based upon fundamental properties of arithmetic. For example, "7" facts are notoriously difficult for some children.

The fact for $7 + 5 = 12$ is especially troublesome; however, if 7 is rewritten as $2 + 5$, then the fact becomes $2 + 5 + 5 = 12$ and is more easily remembered by making 10.

Some of the most useful "fact generation" strategies include:

1) The order property of addition

2) The grouping property of addition

3) The "one more" or "one less" strategies.

For example, if the fact $8 + 3$ is remembered, then $3 + 8$ can be "generated" using the order property. Similarly, if $8 + 3 = 11$ is recalled, then $8 + 4 = 12$ can be "generated" since 4 is one more than 3.

TRY IT OUT!

Play the "related facts" game—it's almost like bingo! Distribute blank addition tables to your class. Each table should have rows and columns from 0 through 10.

Place one entry on an overhead copy of the grid. For example, you might write 11 in the intersection of the 5 row and 6 column.

Children must begin with this entry. To make another entry, they must use a "generation strategy"; for example, the grid square to the left of 11 can be filled with "10" since $5 + 5$ is one less than $5 + 6$. What strategy could be used to fill the shaded square? [$6 + 7 = 5 + 1 + 6 + 1 = 5 + 6 + 2$]

The first child to complete an entire row, column or diagonal calls "bingo" and explains how they found the entries by beginning only with 11.

Go to the next grid and enter another sum to repeat the game.

Ask where a sum could be entered to make it very easy or very hard to call "bingo."

CHECK IT OUT!

Bergeron, J. C., & Herscovice, N. (1990). Kindergartners' knowledge of the precepts of number. In L. P. Steff & T. Wood (Eds.), *Transforming children's mathematics education: International perspectives* (pp. 125-134). Hillsdale, NJ: Erlbaum.

Han, Annie Yi and Peskoff, Fred (2005). Addition and subtraction facts through ten. *Professional Resources Handbook—Grade 1*. Boston: Houghton-Mifflin.

Moser, J. (1992). Arithmetic operations on whole numbers: Addition and subtraction. In T. Post (Ed.), *Teaching mathematics in grades K-8* (pp. 123-155). Needham Heights, MA: Allyn & Bacon.

* For more information about the research base for this unit of *Houghton Mifflin Math*, see *Professional Resources Handbook, Grade 1*.

Research Support* for Unit 3

TO: **First Grade Teachers**

SUBJECT: **Developing Spatial Skills**

Froebel (1782-1852) was among the first to emphasize that experience with everyday objects was an integral part of children's intellectual development. Froebel's teaching materials or "gifts" were geometric solids—spheres, cubes, cylinders—that were part of the real world of the child. Piaget and Inhelder (1967) underscored Froebel's belief in concrete geometric experiences; however, they believed that children's concepts of space develop sequentially from the most general (closed, connected) to the most specific (congruent, similar).

In the first grade, teachers should build upon the child's out-of-school geometric knowledge by emphasizing play and experimentation with actual objects rather than focusing exclusively upon memorizing terms and definitions.

Geometric play and experimentation are especially important for girls since some assessments show that girls may have less well-developed special skills than boys. Activities with blocks or with computer or video games may help build special skills; for example, geometric puzzles that require children to "visualize" the number of blocks in various configurations are useful to promote visual thinking.

TRY IT OUT!

Construct a "Puzzle of the Day" from wood or plastic cubes. Leave holes and cavities that are not hidden from external view. Then ask children how they solved the puzzle.

CHECK IT OUT!

Nickson, M. (2000). *Teaching and learning mathematics: A teacher's guide to recent research*. London: Cassell.

Sisul, J. (2002). Fostering flexibility with number in the primary grades. *Teaching Children Mathematics*, 9(4), 212-217.

Walker, Erica (2005). Geometry and fractions. *Professional Resources Handbook—Grade 1*. Boston: Houghton-Mifflin.

* For more information about the research base for this unit of *Houghton Mifflin Math*, see *Professional Resources Handbook, Grade 1*.

Research Support* for Unit 4

TO: **First Grade Teachers**

SUBJECT: **Fun with Place Value Cards**

"Numeration" is the process of associating some symbolic representation with a collection of objects. Ordinarily "standard" numerals such as 1, 7 or 12 are used. Other "names" for standard numerals are often used too; for example, 5 + 2 is another name for 7. Expressions such as 5 + 2 are not readily accepted by children as just another name for 7.

This close association can be emphasized by using not only the standard numeral for numbers greater than 10, but also the expanded form. For example:

$$10 + 8 \text{ for } 18$$
$$70 + 3 \text{ for } 73$$

When the expanded form is used in conjunction with sticks bundled by tens or place-value pockets, the importance of the position of a digit within a standard numeral is clarified.

Using collections of counters and their basic counting skills, children can count without knowledge of place value. For very large collections, confusion in keeping track of the association between the words and the objects being counted forces the use of some form of grouping—into tens, hundreds, etc. A number of commercial teaching aids may be helpful in teaching place value numeration, but simple teacher-made material can serve equally well.

TRY IT OUT!

Make a set of place-value numeration cards—for 11 – 20, twenty cards are required: 10, 11, 12, 13, 14, 15, 16, 17, 18, 19, 20, 10 + 0, 10 + 1, 10 + 2, 10 + 3, 10 + 4, 10 + 5, 10 + 6, 10 + 7, 10 + 8, 10 + 9. Each number has two cards, such as 12 and 10 + 2.

Shuffle and deal one card to each student. The first player writes his numeral(s) on the chalkboard and asks who has the same number. Ask the children to make cards for 20 – 30, 30 – 40, 40 – 50, etc. To avoid the expense of 3 × 5 cards, cut paper into strips, and then cut each strip into three cards.

CHECK IT OUT!

Howard, K. (1979). *I can count to 100...can you?* New York; Random House.

Ness, Daniel (2005). Numbers through 100. *Professional Resources Handbook—Grade 1*. Boston: Houghton-Mifflin.

Sztajn, P. (2002). Celebrating 100 with number sense. *Teaching Children Mathematics*, 9(4), 212-217.

* For more information about the research base for this unit of *Houghton Mifflin Math*, see *Professional Resources Handbook, Grade 1.*

Research Support* for Unit 5

TO: **First Grade Teachers**

SUBJECT: **How Big Is a Nickel?**

Time and money are two of the most relevant topics in the primary curricula. Children arrive in first grade with informal out-of-school experience with both time and money, but usually this experience is quite incomplete.

Telling time or reading a clock is not the same as understanding time, its sequence, its duration, and its relativity (Mock, 1999). Children should learn to associate concrete events with the passing of time. Egg timers or hourglasses can be used to "time" games, songs or other classroom activities.

One difficulty associated with teaching about money is the lack of a relationship between the size of coins and their value (Botula, 1999). Thus coins are abstract models when used to teach values rather than concrete ones. Some educators suggest the use of proportionally-sized models of coins. For example, a cut-out dime would be about ten times the area of a cut-out penny. Other coins would also be proportional to the size of the model penny.

TRY IT OUT!

Introduce coin names by using proportional coins. Cut out a model penny about 1 inch in diameter from copper-colored construction paper. Cut out nickel and dime models that are about 2 inches and 3 inches in diameter, respectively, and label them "Nickel 5¢" and "Dime 10¢." A proportional model quarter would be about 5 inches in diameter. Use the proportional models in buying and making change activities to establish understanding of the relative values of the coins.

CHECK IT OUT!

Baroody, A. J., & Wilkins, J. L. (1999). The development of informal counting, number, and arithmetic skills and concepts. In J. V. Copley (Ed.), *Mathematics in the early years* (pp. 48-65). Reston, VA: National Council of Teachers of Mathematics.

Esposito, Linda (2005). Time and money. *Professional Resources Handbook—Grade 1.* Boston: Houghton-Mifflin.

Friederwitzer, F. J., & Berman, B. (1999). The language of time. *Teaching Children Mathematics, 6*(4), 254-259.

*   **For more information about the research base for this unit of *Houghton Mifflin Math*, see *Professional Resources Handbook, Grade 1.***

Research Support* for Unit 6

TO: **First Grade Teachers**

SUBJECT: **Planning a "Double Facts" Day!**

Much early research on the teaching of arithmetic concentrated upon which basic addition and subtraction facts were the most difficult for children and how much repetition was needed for memorization (Brownell, 1941). More recent research indicates that "doubles facts," "make ten," and "ten combination" facts are among the easiest for children to master (Baroody, 1984). Repetition does not insure mastery unless a rationale for the fact is present.

These research results are especially useful for facts involving 11 and 12. The doubles fact $6 + 6 = 12$ and the related subtraction fact $12 - 6 = 6$ are easily remembered when the "doubles" rationale is stressed. Similarly, the "ten combinations" $10 + 1 = 11$ and $10 + 2 = 12$ together with the subtraction facts $11 - 1 = 10$ and $12 - 2 = 10$ lead directly to a "make ten" rationale for extended facts; for example, $12 + 7 = 10 + 2 + 7 = 10 + 9 = 19$. This strategy emphasizes the use of 10 as a base. While these strategies require application of the grouping (associative) property, at the first grade level this important property need not be made explicit.

TRY IT OUT!

Plan a "double facts" day! Make index cards for each "doubles fact" through 12. Put the related subtraction fact on the back of each card. For example, $7 + 7 = 14$ on one side of a card and $14 - 7 = 7$ on the other side of the card.

Distribute each of the twelve cards to groups of two or three children. Each group then makes up two story problems—one for their "addition doubles fact" and one for the related subtraction fact.

CHECK IT OUT!

Ginsburg, H. P. (1989). *Children's arithmetic: How they learn it and how you teach it.* Austin, TX: Pro-Ed.

Lin, Chia-ling (2005). Addition and subtraction facts through 12. *Professional Resources Handbook—Grade 1.* Boston: Houghton-Mifflin.

Steffe, L. P., & Cobb, P. (1988). *Construction of arithmetical meanings and strategies.* New York: Springer-Verlag.

* **For more information about the research base for this unit of *Houghton Mifflin Math*, see *Professional Resources Handbook, Grade 1*.**

Research Support* for Unit 7

TO: **First Grade Teachers**

SUBJECT: **Use Your Math Books to Measure Length**

Children's ability to measure is dependent upon their understanding of the concept of a unit of measure. Activities with non-standard units are important prerequisites for measurement with standard units. Often children will compare lengths measured with different non-standard units by counting the units in each case, but will not recognize that the numbers alone provide little information about the relative size of the objects measured.

Children need to understand that useful measurements require the use of identical units when comparisons are to be made. Activities with multiple non-standard units are helpful in overcoming the reluctance of children to consider a unit only of a single entity.

TRY IT OUT!

Put two equal 8–10 ft pieces of masking tape on the floor in different parts of the classroom. Partition the class into two groups, say, boys and girls. Have one group "measure" the length of the tape by placing their mathematics books side-by-side along the tape, and have the other group measure the second tape by placing their books end-to-end as shown.

Count the books in each case. Which tape is longer in the sense that the book count is larger? Why is that not a good way to compare the lengths of the two tapes?

Now let's try to use the books to measure the width (length) of the classroom. There are not enough books! Try it by opening each book.

How many "books"-wide is the classroom? Each "unit" here is really as wide as two unopened books.

CHECK IT OUT!

Cloherty, Helen (2005). Measurement. *Professional Resources Handbook—Grade 1*. Boston: Houghton-Mifflin.

Kamii, C., Lewis, B., & Livingston, S. (1993). Primary arithmetic: Children inventing their own procedures. *Arithmetic Teacher*, 41, 200-203.

Lindquist, M., & Kuvba, V. (1989). Measurement. In M. M. Lindquist (Ed.), *Results from the Fourth Mathematics Assessment of the National Assessment of Educational Progress* (pp. 35-43). Reston, VA: National Council of Teachers of Mathematics.

* For more information about the research base for this unit of *Houghton Mifflin Math*, see *Professional Resources Handbook, Grade 1*.

Research Support* for Unit 8

TO: First Grade Teachers

SUBJECT: Making 10's and 20's

Research indicates that many children have difficulty applying algorithms for multi-digit addition and subtraction, especially when regrouping is required. Many children rely instead on various thinking strategies. The number sense promoted by these strategies is an important asset in applying mathematics in the world outside the classroom.

A common theme in these strategies is the decomposition of one or more of the given numbers to reduce the problem by one requiring basic facts the child knows; for example, the use of expanded form alters the problem $15 + 12$ to $10 + 5 + 10 + 2$. The child thinks of the addends in a different way.

$$15 + 12 \text{ to } 10 + 5 + 10 + 2$$

The child then rearranges the problem to add tens and then add units:

$$15 + 12 = 10 + 5 + 10 + 2 = 10 + 10 + 5 + 2 = 20 + 7 = 27$$

This use of expanded form is the basis of the standard algorithm, however, the same decomposition thinking strategy can be used in other ways. For example:

$$15 + 12 = 15 + 5 + 7 = 20 + 7 = 27$$

Here, a "make 20" strategy avoids use of expanded form as well as the formal algorithm.

TRY IT OUT!

Use a "make 20" strategy to add:

$$17 + 9 = ? \qquad 13 + 18 = ?$$

Use a "make 30" strategy to add:

$$28 + 8 = ? \qquad 17 + 15 = ?$$

CHECK IT OUT!

Evered, Lisa (2005). Two-digit addition and subtraction. *Professional Resources Handbook—Grade 1*. Boston: Houghton-Mifflin.

Isaacs, A. C., & Carroll, W. M. (1999). Strategies for basic-facts instruction. *Teaching Children Mathematics, 5*, 508-515.

Leutzinger, L. P. (1999). Developing thinking strategies for addition facts. *Teaching Children Mathematics, 6*, 14-18.

* For more information about the research base for this unit of *Houghton Mifflin Math*, see *Professional Resources Handbook, Grade 1.*

Grade 1 Index

Grade 1 Credits ....